RAND McNALLY
GOODE'S WORLD ATLAS
17th EDITION

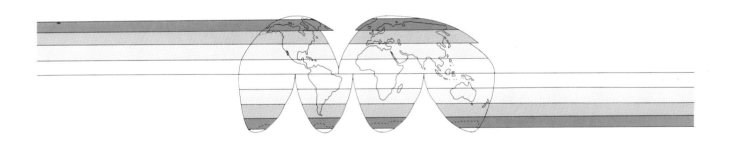

EDWARD B. ESPENSHADE, JR., *Editor*
Professor Emeritus of Geography
Northwestern University

JOEL L. MORRISON, *Senior Consultant*
United States Geological Survey

RAND McNALLY & COMPANY / *Chicago • New York • San Francisco*

Photo credits:
Figures 22, 23 - United States Geological Survey;
Figures 1, 2, 18, 19, 20 - National Aeronautics & Space Administration

contents

Introduction: Maps and Imagery

vii	Cartographic Communication: Mapmakers, Maps, and the Reader
vii	Map Data
ix	Map Scale
x	Map Projections
xiii	Remotely Sensed Imagery
xiv	Landsat
xv	High–Altitude Imagery
xvi	Earth–Sun Relations and World Time Zones

World Thematic Maps

1	Introduction
2	Political
4	Physical
6	Landforms
8	Climatic Regions
10	Surface Temperature Regions / January Normal Temperature
11	Normal Annual Range in Temperature / July Normal Temperature
12	January Pressure and Predominant Winds / Precipitation November 1 to April 30
13	July Pressure and Predominant Winds / Precipitation May 1 to October 31
14	Annual Precipitation and Ocean Currents *Insets: Variability of Annual Precipitation / Zones of Precipitation*
16	Natural Vegetation
18	Soils
20	Population Density
22	Birth Rate / Death Rate
23	Natural Increase / Urbanization
24	Gross National Product / Literacy
25	Languages / Religions
26	Nutrition: Calorie Supply / Protein Consumption
27	Health: Population per Physician / Life Expectancy
28	Predominant Economies
30	Major Agricultural Regions
32	Wheat / Tea, Rye
33	Maize (Corn) / Coffee, Oats
34	Barley, Cacao / Rice, Millet and Grain Sorghum
35	Cane Sugar, Beet Sugar / Rubber, Grapes
36	Fruits / Tobacco, Fisheries
37	Vegetable Oils
38	Natural Fibers / Man Made Fibers
39	Cattle / Swine
40	Sheep / Forest Regions
41	Copper / Tin, Bauxite
42	Iron Ore and Ferroalloys
44	Lead / Zinc
45	Mineral Fertilizers / Water Power
46	Mineral Fuels
48	Energy Production / Energy Consumption
49	Manufacturing / Steel
50	Land and Ocean Transportation
52	Exports / Imports

Major Cities Maps *Scale 1:300,000*

53	Introduction and Legend
54	Montréal / Toronto / Boston
55	New York
56	Baltimore / Washington / Philadelphia / Cleveland
57	Buffalo / Pittsburgh / Detroit
58	San Francisco / Chicago
59	Los Angeles
60	Mexico City / Havana / Lima / Buenos Aires
61	Caracas / Santiago / Rio de Janeiro / São Paulo
62	London
63	Ruhr Area
64	Liverpool / Manchester / Paris
65	Berlin / Madrid / Milan / Lisbon / Barcelona
66	Leningrad / Moscow / Rome / Athens / Vienna / İstanbul / Budapest
67	Calcutta / Delhi / Bombay / Singapore / Peking
68	Shanghai / Seoul / Victoria / T'aipei / Kyōto / Bangkok / Manila / Tehrān / Jakarta / Ho Chi Minh City (Saigon)
69	Tōkyō-Yokohama / Ōsaka-Kōbe
70	Sydney / Melbourne
71	Lagos / Kinshasa and Brazzaville / Cairo / Johannesburg

Regional Section

Regional Thematic Maps / Environment Maps /

Physical-Political Reference Maps

72	Introduction and Legends

North America

74	North America • Energy / Water Resources / Natural Hazards / Landforms
75	North America • Annual Rainfall / Vegetation / Population / Economic, Minerals

76 North America • Environments *Scale 1:24,000,000*

78 United States and Canada • Environments *Scale 1:12,000,000*

80 United States and Canada • Physiography *Scale 1:12,000,000*

82 United States and Canada • Precipitation / Glaciation

83 United States and Canada • Climatic Elements

84 United States and Canada • Natural Vegetation

86 United States • Water Resources

87 United States and Canada • Minerals

88 United States and Canada • Population

89 United States • Demographic

90 United States and Canada • Types of Farming / Manufacturing

91 United States and Canada • Transportation

92 United States • Labor Structure / Westward Expansion

93 Northern Lands and Seas *Scale 1:60,000,000*

94 North America *Scale 1:40,000,000*

95 Canada • Cities and Environs *Scale 1:1,000,000*
Montréal / Québec / Toronto / Ottawa / Calgary / Winnipeg /
Edmonton

96 Canada *Scale 1:12,000,000*
Inset: Newfoundland *Same scale*

98 Southwestern Canada *Scale 1:4,000,000*

100 South-Central Canada *Scale 1:4,000,000*

102 Southeastern Canada *Scale 1:4,000,000*

104 Northern New England, Eastern Gateway of Canada and
Newfoundland *Scale 1:4,000,000*
Inset: Boston and Environs *Scale 1:1,000,000*

106 Hawaii • Annual Precipitation / Vegetation / Population /
Land Use

107 Alaska *Scale 1:12,000,000*

108 United States of America *Scale 1:12,000,000*
Inset: Hawaii *Same scale* / Alaska *Scale 1:36,000,000*

110 Northeastern U.S.A. *Scale 1:4,000,000*

112 United States • Cities and Environs *Scale 1:1,000,000*
*New York / Providence / Atlanta / New Orleans / Baltimore-
Washington / Philadelphia / Norfolk / Birmingham / Milwaukee-
Chicago / Detroit / Buffalo / Cleveland / Pittsburgh / Cincinnati /
Indianapolis / Louisville*

114 Northern Interior U.S.A. *Scale 1:4,000,000*

116 Northwestern U.S.A. *Scale 1:4,000,000*

118 United States and Canada • Cities and Environs
Scale 1:1,000,000
*Victoria-Seattle-Tacoma / San Francisco-Oakland /
Portland / Vancouver / Los Angeles / Salt Lake City / Dallas-
Ft. Worth / San Antonio / St. Louis / Kansas City / Duluth /
Sault Ste. Marie / Minneapolis-St. Paul*

120 Southwestern U.S.A. *Scale 1:4,000,000*
Inset: San Diego *Scale 1:1,000,000*

122 Central U.S.A. *Scale 1:4,000,000*

124 Western Gulf Region of U.S.A. and Part of Mexico
Scale 1:4,000,000
Inset: Houston-Galveston *Scale 1:1,000,000*

126 Southeastern U.S.A. *Scale 1:4,000,000*

128 Gulf and Caribbean Lands *Scale 1:16,000,000*
Insets: Panama Canal *Scale 1:1,000,000*
Puerto Rico and Virgin Islands *Scale 1:4,000,000*
St. Thomas *Scale 1:500,000*

130 Mexico • Central *Scale 1:4,000,000*
Inset: Mexico City *Scale 1:1,000,000*

132 Central America *Scale 1:4,000,000*
Insets: Yucatan Peninsula / Leeward and Windward Islands
Same scale

134 West Indies • Western *Scale 1:4,000,000*
Cuba, Bahamas, Jamaica, Hispaniola
Inset: Havana *Scale 1:1,000,000*

South America

136 South America • Energy / Peoples / Natural Hazards /
Landforms

137 South America • Annual Rainfall / Vegetation / Population /
Economic, Minerals

138 South America • Environments *Scale 1:24,000,000*

140 South America *Scale 1:40,000,000*

141 South America • Cities and Environs *Scale 1:4,000,000*
São Paulo-Rio de Janeiro / Santiago / Buenos Aires-
Montevideo

142 South America • Northern *Scale 1:16,000,000*
Insets: Caracas / Medellín-Bogotá-Cali *Scale 1:4,000,000*

144 South America • Southern *Scale 1:16,000,000*
Insets: Buenos Aires / Rio de Janeiro *Scale 1:1,000,000*

Europe

145 Europe • Energy / Natural Hazards

146 Europe • Annual Rainfall / Vegetation

147 Europe • Population / Minerals

148 Europe • Environments *Scale 1:16,000,000*

150 Europe • Physiography *Scale 1:16,000,000*
Insets: Physiographic Provinces / Europe During the Ice Age

152 Europe • Languages *Scale 1:16,500,000*

154 Europe and Western Asia *Scale 1:16,000,000*

156 England • Central Manufacturing Region / London
Scale 1:1,000,000

157 Europe • Cities and Environs *Scale 1:1,000,000*
Amsterdam-The Hague-Rotterdam-Antwerp-Brussels / Berlin /
Hamburg / Vienna / Munich

158 Western Europe *Scale 1:10,000,000*

160 Mediterranean Lands *Scale 1:10,000,000*

162 British Isles and North Sea Lands *Scale 1:4,000,000*
Inset: Shetland Islands, Orkney Islands *Same scale*

164 Southern Scandinavia and the East Baltic Republics
Scale 1:4,000,000

166 Central Europe *Scale 1:4,000,000*

168 France *Scale 1:4,000,000*
Insets: Marseille / Paris / Ruhr *Scale 1:1,000,000*

170 Spain and Portugal *Scale 1:4,000,000*
Insets: Madrid / Lisbon / Naples / Rome *Scale 1:1,000,000*

172 Italy, Yugoslavia, Bulgaria and Greece *Scale 1:4,000,000*
Inset: Crete *Same scale*

174 Southwestern Soviet Union *Scale 1:4,000,000*

176 Soviet Union *Scale 1:20,000,000*

178 Soviet Union in Europe (Eastern Europe and Asia Minor)
Scale 1:10,000,000

180 Soviet Union in Asia / Siberia *Scale 1:16,000,000*

182 Soviet Union • Ural Industrial Area *Scale 1:4,000,000*
   Insets: Moscow / Leningrad *Scale 1:1,000,000*

Asia

183 Asia • Energy / Natural Hazards

184 Asia • Annual Rainfall / Population

185 Asia • Vegetation / Economic, Minerals

186 Asia, Northern • Environments *Scale 1:24,000,000*

188 Asia, Southern • Environments *Scale 1:24,000,000*

190 Asia *Scale 1:40,000,000*
   Insets: Lebanon, Israel, West Jordan / The Singapore
   Region *Scale 1:4,000,000*

192 Asia • Southwestern *Scale 1:16,000,000*
   Inset: Khyber Pass *Scale 1:4,000,000*
   Inset: Sri Lanka (Ceylon) *Scale 1:16,000,000*
   Inset: India-Political *Scale 1:40,000,000*

194 Middle East *Scale 1:12,000,000*

196 India *Scale 1:10,000,000*
   Insets: Calcutta / Bombay *Scale 1:1,000,000*
   Major Languages / Economic and Land Use

198 China and Japan *Scale 1:16,000,000*

200 Part of Eastern China *Scale 1:4,000,000*

201 China • Economic, Minerals / Population
   Insets: Canton / Shanghai *Scale 1:1,000,000*

202 China • Eastern *Scale 1:10,000,000*
   Inset: Peking *Scale 1:1,000,000*

204 Korea and Japan *Scale 1:10,000,000*

205 Southern Japan *Scale 1:4,000,000*
   Insets: Ōsaka-Kōbe-Kyōto / Tōkyō-Yokohama
   Scale 1:1,000,000

206 Indonesia and the Philippines *Scale 1:16,000,000*
   Inset: Northern Philippines *Scale 1:4,000,000*

208 Pacific Ocean *Scale 1:50,000,000*

Australia

210 Australia and New Zealand • Energy / Natural Hazards

211 Australia • Annual Rainfall / Vegetation / Population /
   Economic, Minerals
   Insets: Melbourne / Sydney *Scale 1:1,000,000*

212 Australia and New Zealand • Environments
   Scale 1:24,000,000

214 Australia and New Zealand *Scale 1:16,000,000*

216 Australia • Southeastern *Scale 1:8,000,000*

217 New Zealand *Scale 1:6,000,000*
   Insets: Land Use *Scale 1:12,000,000*
   Auckland / Wellington *Scale 1:1,000,000*

Africa

218 Africa • Political Change / Peoples / Natural
   Hazards / Landforms

219 Africa • Annual Rainfall / Vegetation / Population /
   Economic, Minerals

220 Africa • Environments *Scale 1:24,000,000*

222 Africa *Scale 1:40,000,000*

223 Africa • Regional
   Somalia *Scale 1:16,000,000*
   Lower Nile Valley *Scale 1:4,000,000*

   Suez Canal *Scale 1:1,000,000*
   Northeastern South Africa *Scale 1:4,000,000*

224 Africa • Northern *Scale 1:16,000,000*
   Insets: Azores, Cape Verde *Same scale*

226 Africa • Southern *Scale 1:16,000,000*
   Insets: Cape Town / Johannesburg-Pretoria *Scale 1:1,000,000*
   Southeastern South Africa *Scale 1:4,000,000*

228 Africa • Western *Scale 1:10,000,000*

230 Africa • Central *Scale 1:10,000,000*

232 Southern Lands and Seas *Scale 1:60,000,000*

Plate Tectonics and Ocean Floor Maps

233 Earth Plate Tectonics

234 Continental Drift / Ocean Floor Maps

235 Arctic Ocean Floor / South Polar Ocean Floor
   Scale 1:60,000,000

236 Atlantic Ocean Floor *Scale 1:44,000,000*

238 Pacific Ocean Floor *Scale 1:58,000,000*

240 Indian Ocean Floor *Scale 1:46,000,000*

Geographical Tables and Indexes

241 World Political Information Table

246 World Comparisons

247 Principal Cities of the World

248 Glossary of Foreign Geographical Terms

249 Abbreviations of Geographical Names and Terms

249 Pronunciation of Geographical Names

250 Pronouncing Index

acknowledgments

This is the seventeenth edition of the Rand McNally *Goode's World Atlas* which was first published over sixty years ago. The name of Dr. J. Paul Goode, the original editor and distinguished cartographer who designed the early editions, has been retained to affirm the high standards which all those who have participated in the preparation of the book during these years have sought to attain.

Through the years, general-reference maps coverage has been expanded; the number of thematic maps has been increased and their kinds extended; and systematic improvements in symbolism, cartographic presentation, and map production and printing have been incorporated.

This seventeenth edition has been expanded to include United States thematic maps on water resources, minorities, income, education, life expectancy, population change, labor structure, and westward expansion. We have thus added to the sixteenth edition's seven world maps on nutrition and health, and eighteen continent maps covering energy resources, water resources, natural hazards, landform regions, ethnic groups, and political change. In line with our policy of periodic revision, most of the thematic maps and graphs have been revised. A new reference map of the Middle East (scale of 1:12,000,000) supplements the map coverage of that strategic region. To the ocean-floor section, we have added material on the theory of plate tectonics and continental drift. The World Political Information Table, added in the sixteenth edition, has been revised, as have the World Comparisons and Principal Cities of the World tables. For this edition, the Major Cities Map Index has been combined with the main Pronouncing Index. Thus one universal index serves the user as a reference for places on all the maps. These additions and the other revisions to the atlas reflect the editors' and publisher's commitment to maintaining the Rand McNally *Goode's World Atlas* as a standard of world atlases.

Sources

Every effort was made to assemble the latest and most authentic source materials to use in this edition. In the general physical-political maps, data from national and state surveys, recent military maps, and hydrographic charts were utilized. Source materials for the specialized maps were even more varied. They included both published and unpublished items in the form of maps, descriptions in articles and books, statistics, and correspondence with geographers and others. To the various agencies and organizations, official and unofficial, that cooperated, appreciation and thanks are expressed. Noteworthy among these organizations and agencies were: The United Nations (for demographic and trade statistics); the Food and Agriculture Organization of The United Nations (for production statistics on livestock, crops, and forest products and for statistics on world trade); the Population Reference Bureau (for population data); the Office of the Geographer, Department of State (for the map "Surface Transport Facilities" and other items); the office of Foreign Agricultural Relations, Department of Agriculture (for information on crop and livestock production and distribution); the Bureau of Mines, Department of the Interior (for information on mineral production); various branches of the national military establishment and the Weather Bureau, Department of Commerce (for information on temperature, wind, pressure, and ocean currents); the Maritime Commission and the Department of Commerce (for statistics on ocean trade); the American Geographical Society (for use of its library and permission to use the Miller cylindrical projection); the University of Chicago Press, owners of the copyright (for permission to use Goode's Homolosine equal-area projection); the McGraw-Hill Book Company (for cooperation in permitting the use of Glenn Trewartha's map of climatic regions and Petterssen's diagram of zones of precipitation); the Association of American Geographers (for permission to use Richard Murphy's map of landforms); and publications of the World Bank (for nutrition, health, and economic information).

Some additional sources of specific data and information are as follows: *World Oil* (for oil and gas data); International Labour Organisation (for labor statistics); International Road Federation (for transportation data); Miller Freeman Publications, Inc. (for data on coal, copper, tin, and iron ore); Organisation for Economic Co-operation and Development (for data on ocean transportation and uranium); and Textile Economics Bureau, Inc. (for data on fibers).

Other Acknowledgments

The variety and complexity of the problems involved in the preparation of a world atlas make highly desirable the participation of specialists in the fields concerned. In the preparation of the new edition of the Rand McNally *Goode's World Atlas*, the editors have been ably assisted by several such experts. They express their deep appreciation and thanks to all of them.

They are particularly indebted to the following experts who have cooperated over the years: A. W. Kuchler, Department of Geography, University of Kansas; Richard E. Murphy, late professor of geography, University of New Mexico; Erwin Raisz, late cartographer, Cambridge, Massachusetts; Glenn T. Trewartha, late professor of geography, University of Wisconsin; Derwent Whittlesey, late professor of geography, Harvard University; and Bogdan Zaborski, professor emeritus of geography, University of Ottawa.

The editors thank the entire Cartographic and Design staff of Rand McNally & Company for their continued outstanding contributions.

EDWARD B. ESPENSHADE, JR.
JOEL L. MORRISON

introduction: maps and imagery

The map is a unique means of recording and communicating geographic information. By reducing the world to a smaller scale, it enables us to see regions of the earth well beyond our ordinary range of vision. Thus, a map represents one of the most convenient, accurate, and effective ways to learn about size, distance, direction, and the geographic features of our planet.

An atlas is a collection of general reference maps and thematic maps (maps that depict specialized information) along with related graphic and statistical data. Whether readers are interested in the political boundaries of the Middle East or in the distribution of oil reserves, an atlas is an indispensable aid to understanding the many facets of our complex earth and the general course of world events.

The maps in *Goode's World Atlas* are grouped into four sections, beginning with World Thematic Maps, portraying the distribution of climatic regions, raw materials, landforms, and other major worldwide features. The second section, Major Cities Maps, focuses on individual cities and their environs. The main body of the atlas is the Regional Section, providing detailed physical-political reference maps for all inhabited land areas. Finally, the section Plate Tectonics / Ocean Floor Maps discusses the theory of plate tectonics and continental drift while maps vividly depict the terrain beneath the world's seas.

Geographical tables and indexes complete the atlas, providing comparative data, a glossary of foreign geographical terms, and a universal pronouncing index for place-names on the general reference maps. Each of the four map sections contains a separate introduction and appropriate legends to help readers understand and interpret the material.

CARTOGRAPHIC COMMUNICATION:
Mapmakers, Maps, and the Reader

To communicate information through a map, cartographers must assemble the geographic data, use their personal perception of the world to select the relevant information, and apply graphic techniques to produce the map. Readers must then be able to interpret the mapped data and relate it to their own experience and need for information. Thus, the success of any map depends on both the cartographer's and the map reader's knowledge and perception of the world and on their common understanding of a map's purpose and limitations.

Maps can present an almost infinite variety of information about our world. However, when reduced to fundamentals, the map shows only existence, associative existence, and spatially associated existence. *Existence* refers simply to the notation on a map that a point or area exists. *Associative existence* implies adding an absolute or relative quantity to the identified point or area (e.g., its elevation or annual rainfall). *Spatially associated existence* indicates spatial relationships between points or areas (e.g., distances and directions between cities)

Technological advances in gathering geographic information through satellites and high-altitude photography have greatly expanded the cartographer's ability to collect data and create accurate maps. These pictures and images enable us to see the world through infrared, radar, and other spectral wavelengths. The images created can be used as background for maps or manipulated to show us totally new ways of viewing natural and human patterns and landforms on the earth's surface.

The ability to understand maps and related imagery depends first on the reader's skill at recognizing how a curved, three-dimensional world is symbolized on a flat, two-dimensional map. Normally, we view the world horizontally (that is, our line of vision parallels the horizon), at an eye level about five and one-half to six feet above the ground. Images appear directly in front and to either side of us, with our eyes encompassing all details as nonselectively as a camera. Less frequently, when we are atop a high platform or in an airplane, we view the world obliquely, as shown in Figure 1, in which both vertical and horizontal facets of objects can be seen. And only those persons at very high altitudes will view the world at a vertical angle (Figure 2). Yet maps are based on our ability to visualize the world from an overhead, or vertical, perspective.

A map differs from a purely vertical photograph in two important respects. First, in contrast to the single focal point of a photograph, a map is created as if the viewer were directly overhead at all points (see Figure 3). Second, just as our brains select from the myriad items in our field of vision those objects of interest or importance to us, so each map presents only those details necessary for a particular purpose—a map is not an inventory of all that is visible. Selectivity is one of a map's most important and useful characteristics.

Imagery gained from high altitudes and satellites can have properties of both photographs and maps, for it can show complex detail or selected features; but its focal point may be that of neither a photograph nor a map. Because these remotely sensed images often look odd or unfamiliar, map readers need more-detailed explanations to help them interpret the information.

Skill in reading maps is basically a matter of practice, but a fundamental grasp of cartographic principles and the symbols, scales, and projections commonly employed in creating maps is essential to comprehensive map use.

Map Data

When creating a map, the cartographer must select the objects and information to be shown, evaluate their relative importance, and find some way to simplify their form. The combined process is called *cartographic generalization*. In attempting to generalize data, the cartographer is limited by the purpose of the map, its scale, the technical methods used to produce it, and the accuracy and reliability of the data. Because a well-drawn map creates an aura of truth and exactness, the cartographer should caution the reader against interpreting the generalized data too literally.

Figure 1. Oblique aerial photograph of New York City.

Figure 2. High-altitude vertical photograph of New York City area.

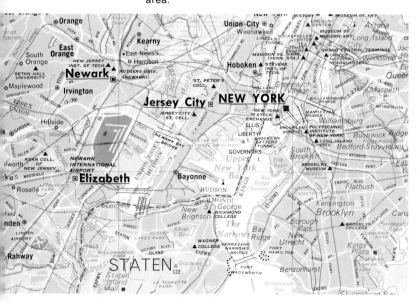

Figure 3. Map of New York City and environs.

Cartographic generalization consists of simplification, classification, symbolization, and induction.

Simplification involves omitting details that will clutter the map and confuse the reader. The degree of simplification depends on the purpose and scale of the map. If the cartographer is creating a detailed map of Canada and merely wants to show the location of the United States, he or she can draw a simplified outline of the country. However, if the map requires a precise identification of the states in New England and the Great Lakes region, the mapmaker will have to draw a more detailed outline, still being careful not to distract the reader from the main features of the Canadian map.

Classification of data is a way of reducing the information to a form that can be easily presented on a map. For example, portraying precise urban populations in the United States would require using as many different symbols as there are cities. Instead, the cartographer groups cities into population categories and assigns a distinct symbol to each one. With the help of a legend, the reader can easily decode the classifications (for an example, see page 51).

Symbolization of information depends largely on the nature of the original data. Information can be *nominal* (showing differences in kind, such as land versus water, grassland versus forest); or *ordinal* (showing relative differences in quantities as well as kind, such as *major* versus *minor* ore deposits); or *interval* (degrees of temperature, inches of rainfall) or *ratio* (population densities), both expressing quantitative details about the data being mapped.

Cartographers use various shapes, colors, or patterns to symbolize these categories of data, and the particular nature of the information being communicated often determines how it is symbolized. Population density, for example, can be shown by the use of small dots or different intensities of color. However, if nominal data is being portrayed—for instance, the desert and fertile areas of Egypt—the mapmaker may want to use a different method of symbolizing the data, perhaps pattern symbols. The color, size, and style of type used for the different elements on a map are also important to symbolization.

Induction is the term cartographers use to describe the process whereby more information is represented on a map than is actually supplied by the original data. For instance, in creating a rainfall map, a cartographer may start with precise rainfall records for relatively few points on the map. After deciding the interval categories into which the data will be divided (e.g., thirty inches or more, fifteen to thirty inches, under fifteen inches), the mapmaker infers from the particular data points that nearby places receive the same or nearly the same amount of rainfall and draws the lines that distinguish the various rainfall regions accordingly. Obviously, generalizations arrived at through induction can never be as precise as the real-world patterns they represent. The map will only tell the reader that all the cities in a given area received about the same amount of rainfall; it will not tell exactly how much rain fell in any particular city in any particular time period.

Cartographers must also be aware of the map reader's perceptual limitations and preferences. During the past two decades, numerous experiments have helped determine how much information readers actually glean from a map and how symbols, colors, and shapes are recognized and interpreted. As a result, cartographers now have a better idea of what kind of rectangle to use; what type of layout or lettering suggests qualities such as power, stability, movement; and what colors are most appropriate.

Map Scale

Since part or all of the earth's surface may be portrayed on a single page of an atlas, the reader's first question should be: What is the relation of map size to the area represented? This proportional relationship is known as the *scale* of a map.

Scale is expressed as a ratio between the distance or area on the map and the same distance or area on the earth. The map scale is commonly represented in three ways: (1) as a simple fraction or ratio called the representative fraction, or RF; (2) as a written statement of map distance in relation to earth distance; and (3) as a graphic representation or a bar scale. All three forms of scale for distances are expressed on Maps A–D.

The RF is usually written as 1:62,500 (as in Map A), where 1 always refers to a unit of distance on the map. The ratio means that 1 centimeter or 1 millimeter or 1 foot on the map represents 62,500 centimeters or millimeters or feet on the earth's surface. The units of measure on both sides of the ratio must always be the same.

Maps may also include a *written statement* expressing distances in terms more familiar to the reader. In Map A the scale 1:62,500 is expressed as being (approximately) 1 inch to 1 mile; that is, 1 inch on the map represents roughly 1 mile on the earth's surface.

The *graphic scale* for distances is usually a bar scale, as shown in Maps A–D. A bar scale is normally subdivided, enabling the reader to measure distance directly on the map.

An *area scale* can also be used, in which one unit of area (square inches, square centimeters) is proportional to the same square units on the earth. The scale may be expressed as either $1:62,500^2$ or 1 to the square of 62,500. Area scales are used when the transformation of the globe to the flat map has been made so that areas are represented in true relation to their respective area on the earth.

When comparing map scales, it is helpful to remember that the *larger* the scale (see Map A) the smaller the area represented and the greater the amount of detail that a map can include. The *smaller* the scale (see Maps B, C, D) the larger the area covered and the less detail that can be presented.

Large-scale maps are useful when readers need such detailed information as the location of roadways, major buildings, city plans, and the like. On a smaller scale, the reader is able to place cities in relation to one another and recognize other prominent features of the region. At the smallest scale, the reader can get a broad view of several states and an idea of the total area. Finer details cannot be shown.

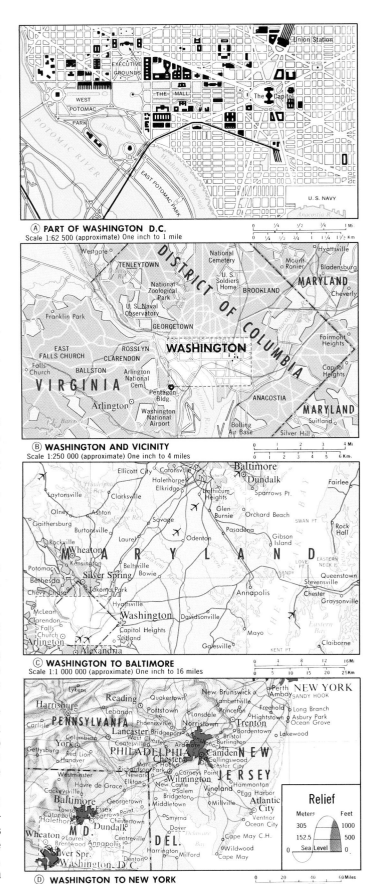

Ⓐ **PART OF WASHINGTON D.C.**
Scale 1:62 500 (approximate) One inch to 1 mile

Ⓑ **WASHINGTON AND VICINITY**
Scale 1:250 000 (approximate) One inch to 4 miles

Ⓒ **WASHINGTON TO BALTIMORE**
Scale 1:1 000 000 (approximate) One inch to 16 miles

Ⓓ **WASHINGTON TO NEW YORK**
Scale 1:4 000 000 one inch to 64 miles. Conic Projection

Map Projections

Every cartographer is faced with the problem of transforming the curved surface of the earth onto a flat plane with a minimum of distortion. The systematic transformation of locations on the earth (spherical surface) to locations on a map (flat surface) is called projection.

It is not possible to represent on a flat map the spatial relationships of angle, distance, direction, and area that only a globe can show faithfully. As a result, projection systems inevitably involve some distortion. On large-scale maps representing a few square miles, the distortion is generally negligible. But on maps depicting large countries, continents, or the entire world, the amount of distortion can be significant. Some maps of the Western Hemisphere, because of their projection, incorrectly portray Canada and Alaska as larger than the United States and Mexico, while South America looks considerably smaller than its northern neighbors.

One of the more practical ways map readers can become aware of projection distortions and learn how to make allowances for them is to compare the projection grid of a flat map with the grid of a globe. Some important characteristics of the globe grid are found listed on page xii.

There are an infinite number of possible map projections, all of which distort one or more of the characteristics of the globe in varying degrees. The projection system that a cartographer chooses depends on the size and location of the area being projected and the purpose of the map. In this atlas, most of the maps are drawn on projections that give a consistent area scale; good land and ocean shape; parallels that are parallel; and as consistent a linear scale as possible throughout the projection.

The transformation process is actually a mathematical one, but to aid in visualizing this process, it is helpful to consider the earth reduced to the scale of the intended map and then projected onto a simple geometric shape—a cylinder, cone, or plane. These geometric forms are then flattened to two dimensions to produce cylindrical, conic, and plane projections (see Figures 4, 5, and 6). Some of the projection systems used in this atlas are described on the following pages. By comparing these systems with the characteristics of a globe grid, readers can gain a clearer understanding of map distortion.

Mercator: This transformation—bearing the name of a famous sixteenth century cartographer—is conformal; that is, land masses are represented in their true shapes. Thus, for every point on the map, the angles shown are correct in every direction within a limited area. To achieve this, the projection increases latitudinal and longitudinal distances away from the equator. As a result, land *shapes* are correct, but their *areas* are distorted. The farther away from the equator, the greater the area distortion. For example, on a Mercator map, Alaska appears far larger than Mexico, whereas in fact Mexico's land area is greater. The Mercator projection is used in nautical navigation, because a line connecting any two points gives the compass direction between them. (See Figure 4.)

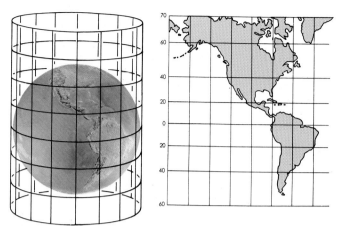

Figure 4. Mercator Projection (right), based upon the projection of the globe onto a cylinder.

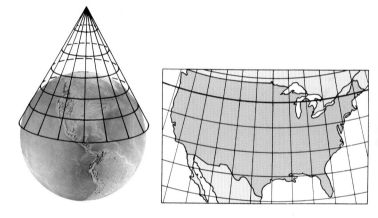

Figure 5. Projection of the globe onto a cone and a resultant Conic Projection.

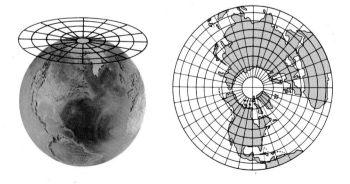

Figure 6. Lambert Equal-Area Projection (right), which assumes the projection of the globe onto a plane surface.

Conic: In this transformation—a globe projected onto a tangent cone—meridians of longitude appear as straight lines, and lines of latitude appear as parallel arcs. The parallel of tangency (that is, where the cone is presumed to touch the globe) is called a standard parallel. In this projection, distortion increases in bands away from the standard parallel. Conic projections are helpful in depicting middle-latitude areas of east-west extension. (See Figure 5.)

Lambert Equal Area *(polar case):* This projection assumes a plane touching the globe at a single point. It shows true distances close to the center (the tangent point) but increasingly distorted ones away from it. The equal-area quality (showing land areas in their correct proportion) is maintained throughout; but in regions away from the center, distortion of shape increases. (See Figure 6.)

Miller Cylindrical: O. M. Miller suggested a modification to the Mercator projection to lessen the severe area distortion in the higher latitudes. The Miller projection is neither conformal nor equal-area. Thus, while shapes are less accurate than on the Mercator, the exaggeration of *size* of areas has been somewhat decreased. The Miller cylindrical is useful for showing the entire world in a rectangular format. (See Figure 7.)

Mollweide Homolographic: The Mollweide is an equal-area projection; the least distorted areas are ovals centered just above and below the center of the projection. Distance distortions increase toward the edges of the map. The Mollweide is used for world-distribution maps where a pleasing oval look is desired along with the equal-area quality. It is one of the bases used in the Goode's Interrupted Homolosine projection. (See Figure 8.)

Sinusoidal, or Sanson-Flamsteed: In this equal-area projection the scale is the same along all parallels and the central meridian. Distortion of shapes is less along the two main axes of the projection but increases markedly toward the edges. Maps depicting areas such as South America or Africa can make good use of the Sinusoidal's favorable characteristics by situating the land masses along the central meridian, where the shapes will be virtually undistorted. The Sinusoidal is also one of the bases used in the Goode's Interrupted Homolosine. (See Figure 9.)

Goode's Interrupted Homolosine: An equal-area projection, Goode's is composed of the Sinusoidal grid from the equator to about 40° N and 40° S latitudes; beyond these latitudes, the Mollweide is used. This grid is interrupted so that land masses can be projected with a minimum of shape distortion by positioning each section on a separate central meridian. Thus, the shapes as well as the sizes of land masses are represented with a high degree of fidelity. Oceans can also be positioned in this manner. (See Figure 10.)

Robinson: This recently devised transformation is a projection that serves as a compromise of all the distortions that can occur on a world map. Though no single attribute is maintained, the projection minimizes visually disturbing distortions. As a result, the continental outlines "look" appropriate.

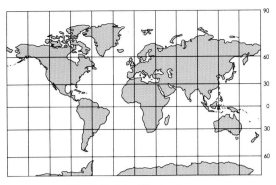

Figure 7. Miller Cylindrical Projection.

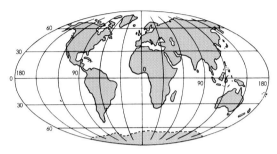

Figure 8. Mollweide Homolographic Projection.

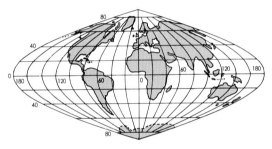

Figure 9. Sinusoidal Projection.

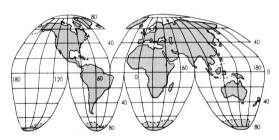

Figure 10. Goode's Interrupted Homolosine Projection.

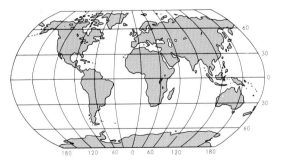

Figure 11. Robinson Projection.

Bonne: This equal-area transformation is mathematically related to the Sinusoidal. Distances are true along all parallels and the central meridian. Farther out from the central meridian, however, the increasing obliqueness of the grid's angles distorts shape and distance. This limits the area that can be usefully projected. Bonne projections, like conics, are best employed for relatively small areas in middle latitudes. (See Figure 12.)

Conic with Two Standard Parallels: The linear scale of this projection is consistent along two standard parallels instead of only one as in the simple conic. Since the spacing of the other parallels is reduced somewhat between the standard parallels and progressively enlarged beyond them, the projection does not exhibit the equal-area property. Careful selection of the standard parallels, however, provides good representation of limited areas. Like the Bonne projection, this system is widely used for areas in middle latitudes. (See Figure 13.)

Polyconic: In this system, the globe is projected onto a series of strips taken from tangent cones. Parallels are nonconcentric circles, and each is divided equally by the meridians, as on the globe. While distances along the straight central meridian are true, they are increasingly exaggerated along the curving meridians. Likewise, general representation of areas and shapes is good near the central meridian but progressively distorted away from it. Polyconic projections are used for middle-latitude areas to minimize all distortions and were employed for large-scale topographic maps. (See Figure 14.)

Lambert Conformal Conic: This conformal transformation system usually employs two standard parallels. Distortion increases away from the standard parallels, being greatest at the edges of the map. It is useful for projecting elongated east-west areas in the middle latitudes and is ideal for depicting the forty-eight contiguous states. It is also widely used for aeronautical and meteorological charts. (See Figure 15.)

Lambert Equal Area *(oblique and polar cases):* This equal-area projection can be centered at any point on the earth's surface, perpendicular to a line drawn through the globe. It maintains correct angles to all points on the map from its center (point of tangency), but distances become progressively distorted toward the edges. It is most useful for roughly circular areas or areas whose dimensions are nearly equal in two perpendicular directions.

The two most common forms of the Lambert projection are the oblique and the polar, shown in Figures 6 and 16. Although the meridians and parallels for the forms are different, the distortion characteristics are the same.

Important characteristics of the globe grid

1. All meridians of longitude are equal in length and meet at the Poles.
2. All lines of latitude are parallel and equally spaced on meridians.
3. The length, or circumference, of the parallels of latitude decreases as one moves from the equator to the Poles. For instance, the circumference of the parallel at 60° latitude is one-half the circumference of the equator.
4. Meridians of longitude are equally spaced on each parallel, but the distance between them decreases toward the Poles.
5. All parallels and meridians meet at right angles.

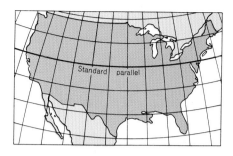

Figure 12.
Bonne Projection.

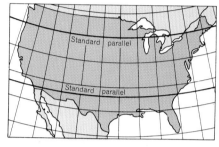

Figure 13.
Conic Projection with Two Standard Parallels.

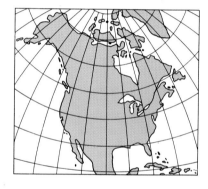

Figure 14.
Polyconic Projection.

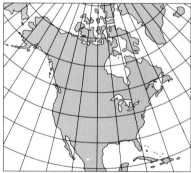

Figure 15.
Lambert Conformal Conic Projection.

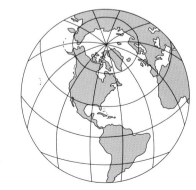

Figure 16.
Lambert Equal-Area Projection (oblique case).

REMOTELY SENSED IMAGERY

Recent technological advances have greatly expanded our ability to "see" surface features on the earth. *Remote sensing* can be defined as gathering and recording from a distance information about many types of geographic features. Human beings have been using a form of remote sensing for thousands of years. To gather information about terrain, people have climbed trees or hilltops and used their eyes, ears, and even their sense of smell to detect what lay in the distance. Now, with highly sophisticated cameras and electronic sensing equipment as our remote sensors, we can learn a great deal more about our world than we have been able to gather with our physical senses.

Remote sensing is based on two fundamental principles. First, each type of surface material (rock, soil, vegetation) absorbs and reflects solar energy in a characteristic manner. In addition, a certain amount of internal energy is emitted by each surface. Remote-sensing instruments can detect this absorbed, reflected, and emitted energy and produce photographs or images.

Second, while the human eye is sensitive to only a small portion of the electromagnetic spectrum (shown as A in the top illustration of Figure 17), remote-sensing instruments can work in longer and shorter wavelengths, generally in the infrared and radar, or microwave, regions. These areas of the spectrum are often referred to as bands.

In remote-sensing photography, the most commonly used bands, in addition to those in the visible spectrum, are the near-infrared bands of 0.7 to 0.8μ (micrometers) and 0.8 to 1.1μ. Infrared photography has proved invaluable in studying agricultural areas. Since healthy plants reflect a considerable amount of near-infrared light, high-altitude photographs using this band of the spectrum can detect diseased vegetation before the problem is visible to the naked eye.

Multispectral photographic techniques are also being used. In this type of remote sensing, reflected energy from a surface is isolated into a number of given wavelength bands (shown in the bottom illustration of Figure 17). Each band can be separately recorded on film, or bands can be recorded simultaneously. These restricted wavelengths include a blue band of 0.4 to 0.5μ, a green band of 0.5 to 0.6μ, and a red band of 0.6 to 0.7μ. Scientists can select various band widths in order to highlight certain features within an area. The photographs in Figure 18 demonstrate the different effects that multispectral photography can produce and the types of information that can be revealed.

Thermal infrared (shown as B in the top illustration in Figure 17) and radar, or microwave, (shown as C) have also been important for gathering geographical data. Thermal imagery records the temperatures of surface features and is collected through electronic sensing instruments, not by cameras. These images show "hot spots" in lakes, rivers, and coastal areas where waste discharges are affecting the water temperature. Thermal-infrared sensing can also pick up animal populations that may be camouflaged to the naked eye. Heat loss from buildings can also be measured.

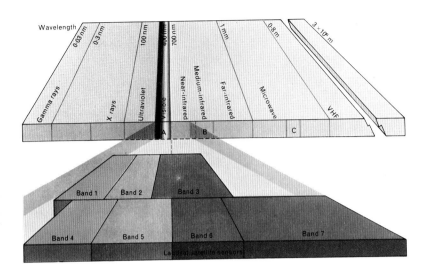

Figure 17. Top: The electromagnetic spectrum.

Bottom: Visible portion of the spectrum.

0.7 to 0.8μ band: Black-and-white, infrared.

0.8 to 0.9μ band: Black-and-white, infrared.

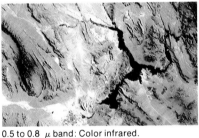
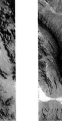

0.5 to 0.8 μ band: Color infrared.

0.4 to 0.7μ band: Color.

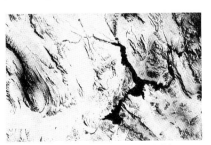

0.6 to 0.7μ band: Black-and-white, visible.

0.5 to 0.6μ band: Black-and-white, visible.

Figure 18. Images taken over Lake Mead, Nevada, by a multispectral camera. Each of the images has been derived from a different wavelength band of the spectrum.

Figure 19. Landsat (satellite) image of southeastern Colorado.

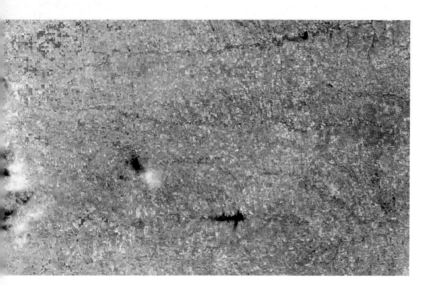

Figure 20. Landsat (satellite) image of western Kansas.

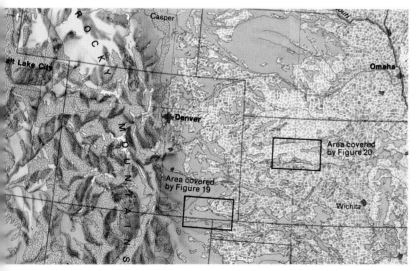

Figure 21. Land use (environment) map derived by using information from the satellite images in Figures 19 and 20.

Radar differs from other sensing methods in that a signal is sent out by the sensor, and the intensity of the reflected "echo" is recorded electronically. (The images may then be printed as a photograph.) Radar has the advantage of being unaffected by weather conditions, and in areas with persistent cloud cover it has proved to be the most reliable instrument available. This type of remote sensing can record surface relief features with remarkable accuracy. It is also useful in searching for mineral deposits and in detecting the types and extent of land ice, sea ice, and groundwater.

Landsat

Perhaps the most well-known examples of remotely sensed imagery are the pictures gathered by the Landsat satellites. Originally known as ERTS (Earth Resource Technology Satellite), Landsat 1 was launched in 1972 and functioned until 1979. Landsat 2 and Landsat 3—launched in 1975 and 1978, respectively—are still collecting data.

These satellites carry a system that views the earth in two visible and two near-infrared bands. The images are gathered electronically by sensors that scan the terrain directly beneath the satellite and record energy from individual areas on the ground. The size of these areas is determined by the spot size, or resolution capacity, of the optical scanner on board the satellite.

The smallest individual area distinguished by the scanner is called a picture element, or *pixel*. Each Landsat pixel covers about an acre of the earth's surface, with approximately 7,800,000 pixels composing each image (an image covers 115 x 115 mi or 185 x 185 km). The pixels are recorded as digits and transmitted to a ground receiving station. The digits represent brightness values and are stored in a computer as four separate arrays, one for each band of the visible and near-infrared light used. The digits can be electronically manipulated to produce false-color pictures like those shown in Figure 19 and Figure 20. A single Landsat satellite can gather some thirty million bits of data for each frame in about twenty-five seconds.

This form of data gathering has a number of advantages over conventional photography. Chiefly, the digits can be computer enhanced to bring out specific features more clearly and reveal subtle changes that may not appear on a conventional photograph of the same area.

Scientists are still discovering new uses for Landsat images. The uniform orbits of the Landsat satellites allow for coverage of the same terrain every eighteen days. As a result, the scanners can detect changes in crops, vegetation, and farming patterns; damage resulting from earthquakes, hurricanes, floods, and fires; and movements of desert sands, erosion patterns, and levels of some pollutants discharged into waterways.

Landsat images are particularly helpful to cartographers in correcting existing maps or creating new ones, as the striking resemblance between the environmental map (Figure 21) and the two pictures above it shows.

High-Altitude Imagery

Cartographers also benefit from the increased use of high-altitude photography. Figure 22 is a good example of an infrared photograph taken with a high-altitude camera mounted in an aircraft. The imagery gathered is limited by the sensitivity of the film, which can record only in the 0.3 to 1.1μ range of the spectrum. Even within this range, and using only black-and-white film, the data collected can be used to generate highly accurate 1:24,000 topographic maps, such as the one shown in Figure 23. Side benefits of this form of photography can be the production of orthophotomaps and digital elevation models (DEM). A DEM is composed of a set of equally spaced surface elevations for an area of the earth.

High-altitude photographs, like satellite pictures, can be used to monitor changes. Often these pictures will record shifts in land use, transportation lines, erosion, drainage patterns, soil characteristics, and surface structures.

Although *Goode's World Atlas* does not employ topographic maps, they are used as a reference source for the volume. High-altitude photography makes it possible to update such features as highway networks, metropolitan areas, the shape and flow of rivers and lakes, ocean currents, and ice formations.

Recent and future technological advances in collecting geographic information promise to make the cartographer's job somewhat easier. More important, these advances will allow us to give the atlas user more-detailed and up-to-date knowledge about our world and the impact of human activity around the globe.

Joel L. Morrison

Edward B. Espenshade, Jr.

Figure 22. High-altitude infrared image of the Goodland, Kansas, area.

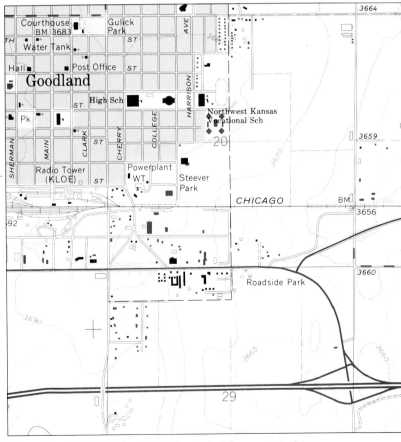

Figure 23. 1:24,000 United States Geological Survey map of the Goodland, Kansas, area.

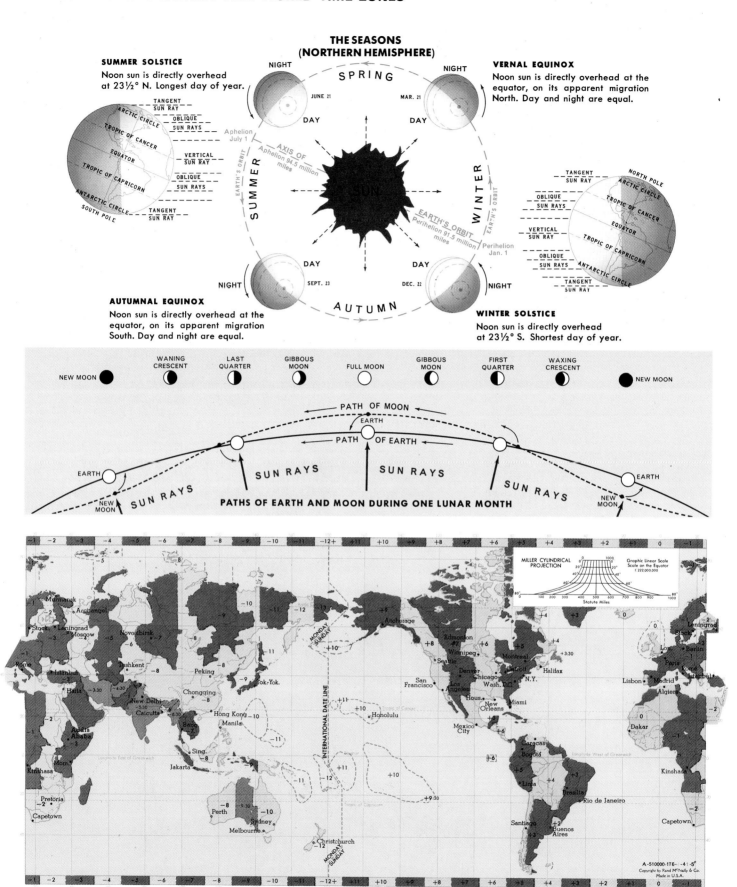

THE SEASONS
(NORTHERN HEMISPHERE)

SUMMER SOLSTICE
Noon sun is directly overhead at 23½° N. Longest day of year.

VERNAL EQUINOX
Noon sun is directly overhead at the equator, on its apparent migration North. Day and night are equal.

AUTUMNAL EQUINOX
Noon sun is directly overhead at the equator, on its apparent migration South. Day and night are equal.

WINTER SOLSTICE
Noon sun is directly overhead at 23½° S. Shortest day of year.

SPRING — SUMMER — WINTER — AUTUMN

SUN

Aphelion July 1
AXIS OF Aphelion 94.5 million miles
EARTH'S ORBIT
Perihelion 91.5 million miles
Perihelion Jan. 1

JUNE 21 — MAR. 21 — SEPT. 23 — DEC. 22

NEW MOON — WANING CRESCENT — LAST QUARTER — GIBBOUS MOON — FULL MOON — GIBBOUS MOON — FIRST QUARTER — WAXING CRESCENT — NEW MOON

PATH OF MOON
EARTH
PATH OF EARTH
SUN RAYS — SUN RAYS — SUN RAYS
NEW MOON

PATHS OF EARTH AND MOON DURING ONE LUNAR MONTH

MILLER CYLINDRICAL PROJECTION
Graphic Linear Scale Scale on the Equator
1:222,000,000
Statute Miles

A.-510000-1T6-.-41-5°
Copyright by Rand McNally & Co.
Made in U.S.A.

Time Zones

The surface of the earth is divided into 24 time zones. Each zone represents 15° of longitude or one hour of time. The time of the initial, or zero, zone is based on the central meridian of Greenwich and is adopted eastward and westward for a distance of 7½° of longitude. Each of the zones in turn is designated by a number representing the hours (+ or −) by which its standard time differs from Greenwich mean time. These standard time zones are indicated by bands of orange and yellow. Areas which have a fractional deviation from standard time are shown in an intermediate color. The irregularities in the zones and the fractional deviations are due to political and economic factors.
(Revised to 1980. After U.S. Defense Mapping Agency)

world thematic maps

This section of the atlas consists of more than sixty thematic maps presenting world patterns and distributions. Together with accompanying graphs, these maps communicate basic information on mineral resources, agricultural products, trade, transportation, and other selected aspects of the natural and cultural geographical environment.

A thematic map uses symbols to show certain characteristics of, generally, one class of geographical information. This "theme" of a thematic map is presented upon a background of basic locational information—coastline, country boundaries, major drainage, etc. The map's primary concern is to communicate visually basic impressions of the distribution of the theme. For instance, on page 39 the distribution of cattle shown by point symbols impresses the reader with relative densities—the distribution of cattle is much more uniform throughout the United States than it is in China, and cattle are more numerous in the United States than in China.

Although it is possible to use a thematic map to obtain exact values of a quantity or commodity, it is not the purpose intended, any more than a thematic map is intended to be used to give precise distances from New York to Moscow. If one seeks precise statistics for each country, he may consult the bar graph on the map or a statistical table.

The map on this page is an example of a special class of thematic maps called cartograms. The cartogram assigns to a named earth region an area based on some value other than land surface area. In the cartogram below the areas assigned are proportional to their countries' populations and tinted according to their rate of natural increase. The result of mapping on this base is a meaningful way of portraying this distribution since natural increase is causally related to existing size of population. On the other hand, natural increase is not causally related to earth area. In the other thematic maps in this atlas, relative earth sizes have been considered when presenting the distributions.

Real and hypothetical geographical distributions of interest to man are practically limitless but can be classed into point, line, area, or volume information relative to a specific location or area in the world. The thematic map, in communicating these fundamental classes of information, utilizes point, line, and area symbols. The symbols may be employed to show *qualitative* differences (differences in *kind*) of a certain category of information and may also show *quantitative* differences in the information (differences in *amount*). For example, the natural-vegetation map (page 16) was based upon information gathered by many observations over a period of time. It utilizes area symbols (color and pattern) to show the difference in the *kind* of vegetation as well as the extent. Quantitative factual information was shown on the annual-precipitation map, page 14, by means of isohyets (lines connecting points of equal rainfall). Also, area symbols were employed to show the intervals between the lines. In each of these thematic maps, there is one primary theme, or subject; the map communicates the information far better than volumes of words and tables could.

One of the most important aspects of the thematic-map section is use of the different maps to show comparisons and relationships among the distributions of various types of geographical information. For example, the relationship of dense population (page 20) to areas of intensive subsistence agriculture (page 30) and to manufacturing and commerce (page 28) is an important geographic concept.

The statistics communicated by the maps and graphs in this section are intended to give an idea of the relative importance of countries in the distributions mapped. The maps are not intended to take the place of statistical reference works. No single year affords a realistic base for production, trade, and certain economic and demographic statistics. Therefore, averages of data for three or four years have been used. Together with the maps, the averages and percentages provide the student with a realistic idea of the importance of specific areas.

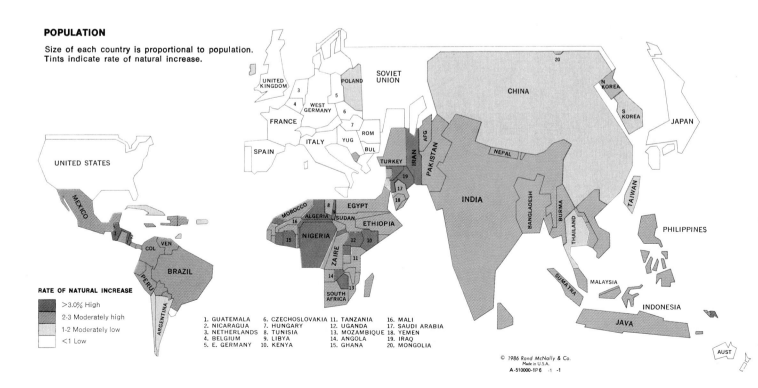

POPULATION

Size of each country is proportional to population.
Tints indicate rate of natural increase.

RATE OF NATURAL INCREASE

- >3.0% High
- 2-3 Moderately high
- 1-2 Moderately low
- <1 Low

1. GUATEMALA	6. CZECHOSLOVAKIA	11. TANZANIA	16. MALI
2. NICARAGUA	7. HUNGARY	12. UGANDA	17. SAUDI ARABIA
3. NETHERLANDS	8. TUNISIA	13. MOZAMBIQUE	18. YEMEN
4. BELGIUM	9. LIBYA	14. ANGOLA	19. IRAQ
5. E. GERMANY	10. KENYA	15. GHANA	20. MONGOLIA

© 1986 Rand McNally & Co.
Made in U.S.A.
A-510000-1P6 -1 -1

2

POLITICAL

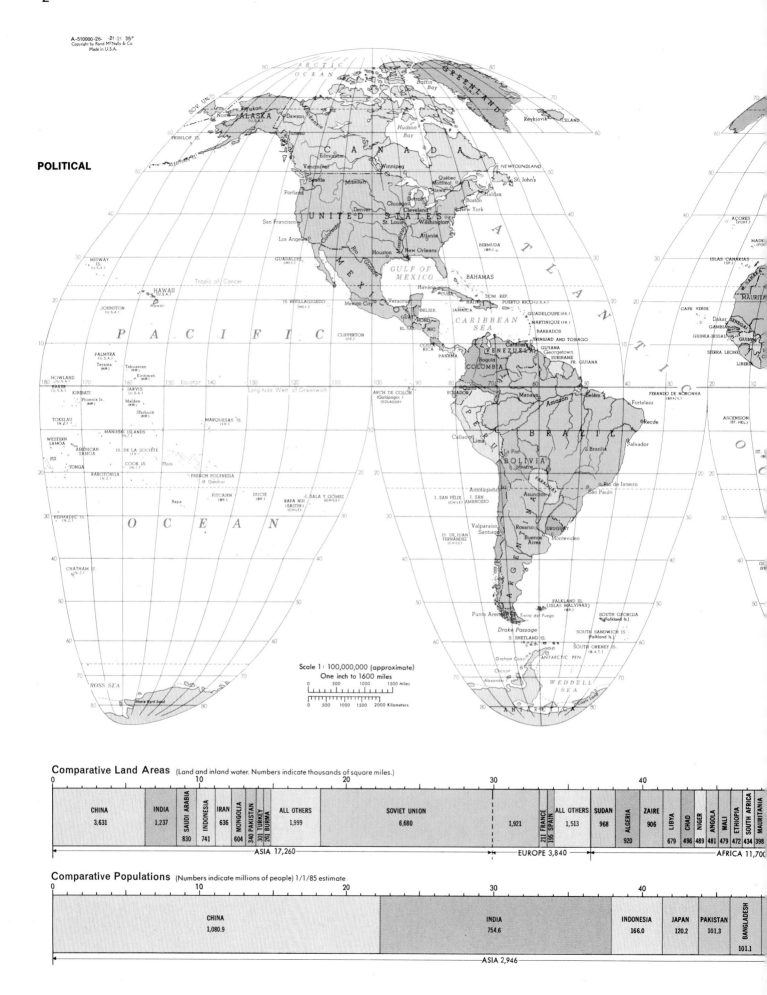

Scale 1: 100,000,000 (approximate)
One inch to 1600 miles

0   500   1000   1500 Miles

0   500   1000   1500   2000 Kilometers

Comparative Land Areas (Land and inland water. Numbers indicate thousands of square miles.)

0	10	20	30	40

| CHINA 3,631 | INDIA 1,237 | SAUDI ARABIA 830 | INDONESIA 741 | IRAN 636 | MONGOLIA 604 | PAKISTAN 340 | TURKEY 301 | BURMA 261 | ALL OTHERS 1,999 | SOVIET UNION 6,680 | 1,921 | FRANCE 211 | SPAIN 195 | ALL OTHERS 1,513 | SUDAN 968 | ALGERIA 920 | ZAIRE 906 | LIBYA 679 | CHAD 496 | NIGER 489 | ANGOLA 481 | MALI 479 | ETHIOPIA 472 | SOUTH AFRICA 434 | MAURITANIA 398 |

←——————————— ASIA 17,260 ———————————→ ←—— EUROPE 3,840 ——→ AFRICA 11,700

Comparative Populations (Numbers indicate millions of people) 1/1/85 estimate

0	10	20	30	40

| CHINA 1,080.9 | INDIA 754.6 | INDONESIA 166.0 | JAPAN 120.2 | PAKISTAN 101.3 | BANGLADESH 101.1 |

←——————————— ASIA 2,946 ———————————→

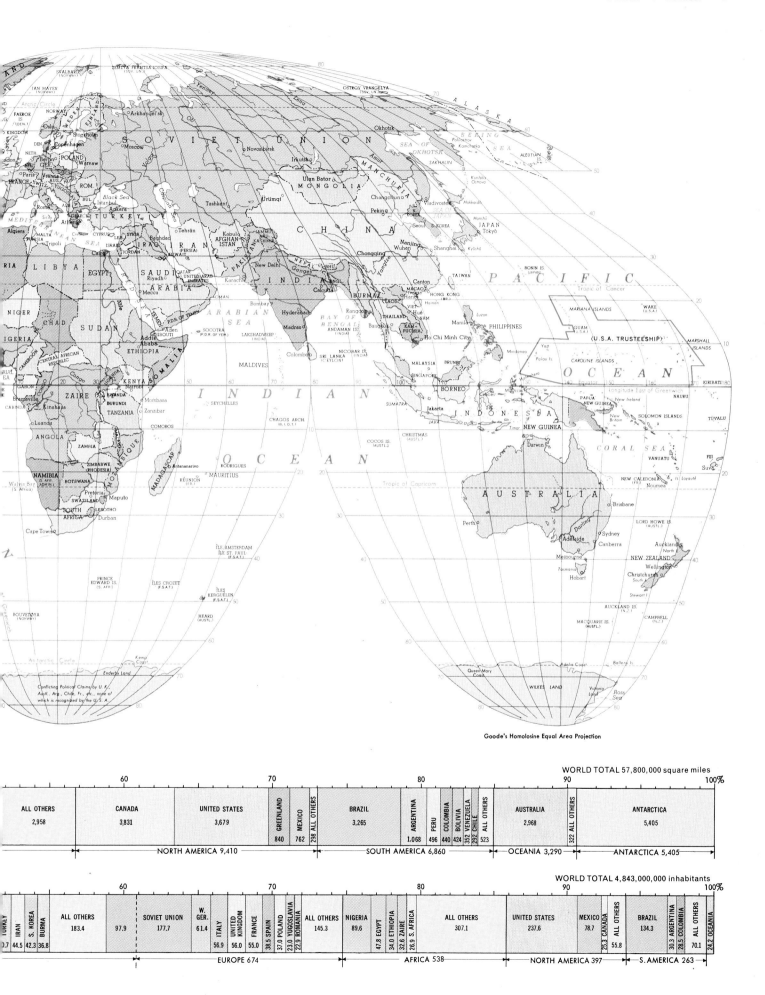

Goode's Homolosine Equal Area Projection

WORLD TOTAL 57,800,000 square miles

	60		70				80						90		100%
ALL OTHERS 2,958	CANADA 3,831	UNITED STATES 3,679	GREENLAND 840	MEXICO 762	ALL OTHERS 298	BRAZIL 3,265	ARGENTINA 1,068	PERU 496	COLOMBIA 440	BOLIVIA 424	VENEZUELA 352	CHILE 292	ALL OTHERS 523	AUSTRALIA 2,968	ALL OTHERS 322	ANTARCTICA 5,405

NORTH AMERICA 9,410 — SOUTH AMERICA 6,860 — OCEANIA 3,290 — ANTARCTICA 5,405

WORLD TOTAL 4,843,000,000 inhabitants

	60			70							80					90			100%
TURKEY 7	IRAN 44.5	S. KOREA 42.3	BURMA 36.8	ALL OTHERS 183.4	97.9	SOVIET UNION 177.7	W. GER. 61.4	ITALY 56.9	UNITED KINGDOM 56.0	FRANCE 55.0	SPAIN 38.5	POLAND 37.0	YUGOSLAVIA 23.0	ROMANIA 22.9	ALL OTHERS 145.3	NIGERIA 89.6	EGYPT 47.8	ETHIOPIA 34.0	ZAIRE 32.6	S. AFRICA 26.9	ALL OTHERS 307.1	UNITED STATES 237.6	MEXICO 78.7	CANADA 25.3	ALL OTHERS 55.8	BRAZIL 134.3	ARGENTINA 30.3	COLOMBIA 28.5	ALL OTHERS 70.1	OCEANIA 24.2

EUROPE 674 — AFRICA 538 — NORTH AMERICA 397 — S. AMERICA 263

PHYSICAL

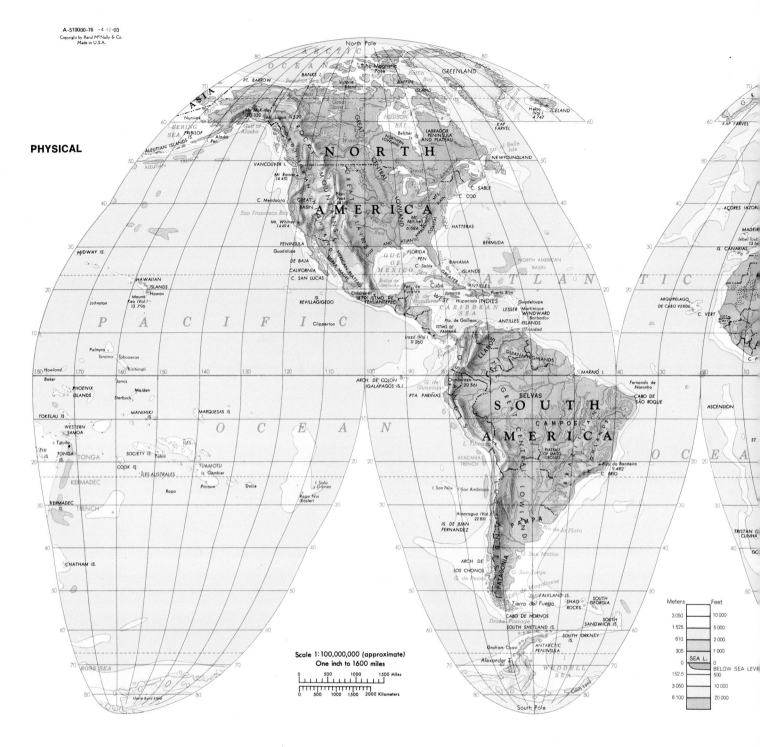

Scale 1:100,000,000 (approximate)
One inch to 1600 miles

0   500   1000   1500 Miles

0   500   1000   1500   2000 Kilometers

Meters		Feet
3 050		10 000
1 525		5 000
610		2 000
305		1 000
0	SEA L.	
		BELOW SEA LEVEL
152.5		500
3 050		10 000
6 100		20 000

Land Elevations in Profile

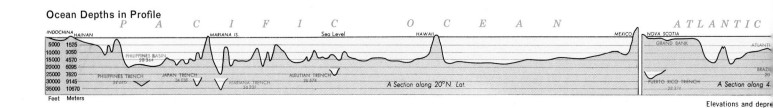

Ocean Depths in Profile

Elevations and depr

For Glossary of Foreign Geographical Terms see page 248

Goode's Homolosine Equal Area Projection

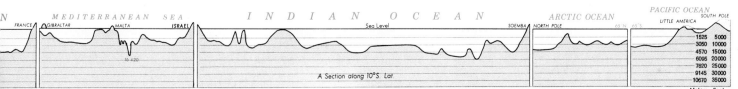

A Section along 10°S. Lat.

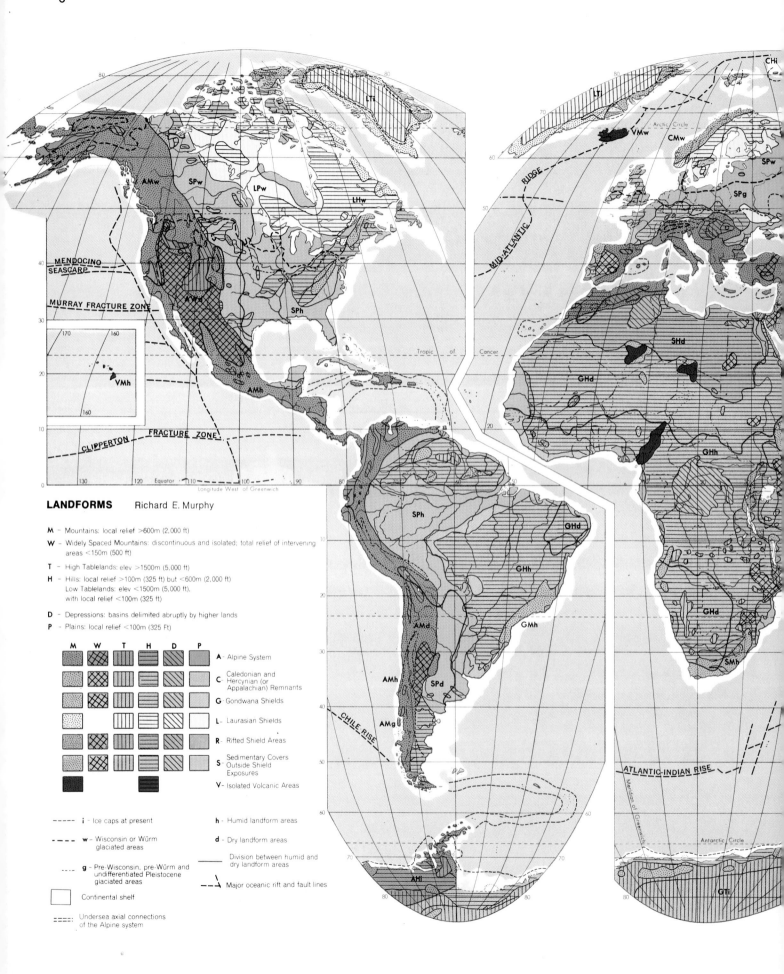

6

LANDFORMS   Richard E. Murphy

M – Mountains: local relief >600m (2,000 ft)

W – Widely Spaced Mountains: discontinuous and isolated; total relief of intervening areas <150m (500 ft)

T – High Tablelands: elev >1500m (5,000 ft)

H – Hills: local relief >100m (325 ft) but <600m (2,000 ft)
Low Tablelands: elev <1500m (5,000 ft), with local relief <100m (325 ft)

D – Depressions: basins delimited abruptly by higher lands

P – Plains: local relief <100m (325 Ft)

M W T H D P

A – Alpine System

C – Caledonian and Hercynian (or Appalachian) Remnants

G – Gondwana Shields

L – Laurasian Shields

R – Rifted Shield Areas

S – Sedimentary Covers Outside Shield Exposures

V – Isolated Volcanic Areas

----- **i** – Ice caps at present

- - - - **w** – Wisconsin or Würm glaciated areas

······ **g** – Pre-Wisconsin, pre-Würm and undifferentiated Pleistocene glaciated areas

Continental shelf

----- Undersea axial connections of the Alpine system

h – Humid landform areas

d – Dry landform areas

Division between humid and dry landform areas

Major oceanic rift and fault lines

SPg

SHh

AMg

SPh

SPd

ADd

AMh

SHd

GHh

AMh

OWEN FRACTURE ZONE

CARLSBURG RIDGE

Longitude East of Greenwich

MID-INDIAN RIDGE

GMh

WEST INDIAN RIDGE

Tropic of Cancer

Equator

Tropic of Capricorn

GHd

SPd

CHh

AMh

AMg

AUSTRALIAN-ANTARCTIC RISE

GTi

Scale 1 : 75 000 000 (approximate)
One inch to 1 200 miles

0   500   1000   1500 Miles

0   500   1000   1500   2000 Kilometers

Goode's Homolosine Equal Area Projection (Condensed)

8

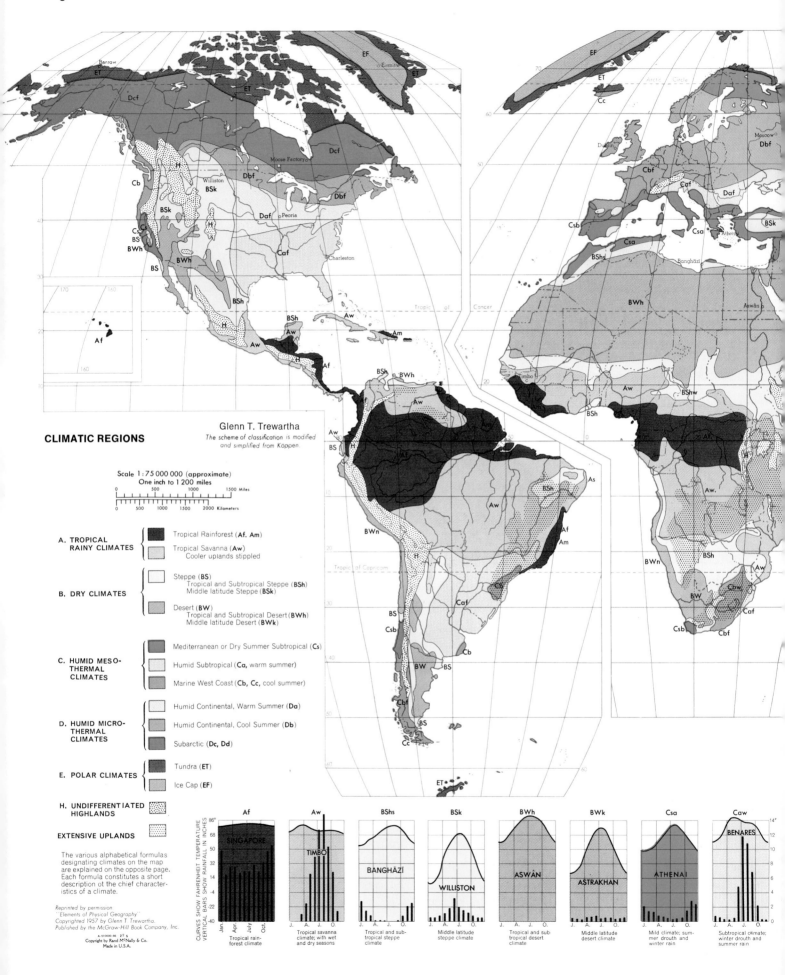

CLIMATIC REGIONS

Glenn T. Trewartha

The scheme of classification is modified and simplified from Köppen

Scale 1:75 000 000 (approximate)
One inch to 1 200 miles

A. TROPICAL RAINY CLIMATES
- Tropical Rainforest (**Af, Am**)
- Tropical Savanna (**Aw**)
  Cooler uplands stippled

B. DRY CLIMATES
- Steppe (**BS**)
  Tropical and Subtropical Steppe (**BSh**)
  Middle latitude Steppe (**BSk**)
- Desert (**BW**)
  Tropical and Subtropical Desert (**BWh**)
  Middle latitude Desert (**BWk**)

C. HUMID MESO-THERMAL CLIMATES
- Mediterranean or Dry Summer Subtropical (**Cs**)
- Humid Subtropical (**Ca**, warm summer)
- Marine West Coast (**Cb, Cc**, cool summer)

D. HUMID MICRO-THERMAL CLIMATES
- Humid Continental, Warm Summer (**Da**)
- Humid Continental, Cool Summer (**Db**)
- Subarctic (**Dc, Dd**)

E. POLAR CLIMATES
- Tundra (**ET**)
- Ice Cap (**EF**)

H. UNDIFFERENTIATED HIGHLANDS

EXTENSIVE UPLANDS

The various alphabetical formulas designating climates on the map are explained on the opposite page. Each formula constitutes a short description ot the chief character-istics of a climate.

CURVES SHOW FAHRENHEIT TEMPERATURE
VERTICAL BARS SHOW RAINFALL IN INCHES

Af	Aw	BShs	BSk	BWh	BWk	Csa	Caw
SINGAPORE	TIMBO	BANGHĀZĪ	WILLISTON	ASWĀN	ASTRAKHAN	ATHENAI	BENARES
Tropical rain-forest climate	Tropical savanna climate; with wet and dry seasons	Tropical and sub-tropical steppe climate	Middle latitude steppe climate	Tropical and sub-tropical desert climate	Middle latitude desert climate	Mild climate; sum-mer drouth and winter rain	Subtropical climate; winter drouth and summer rain

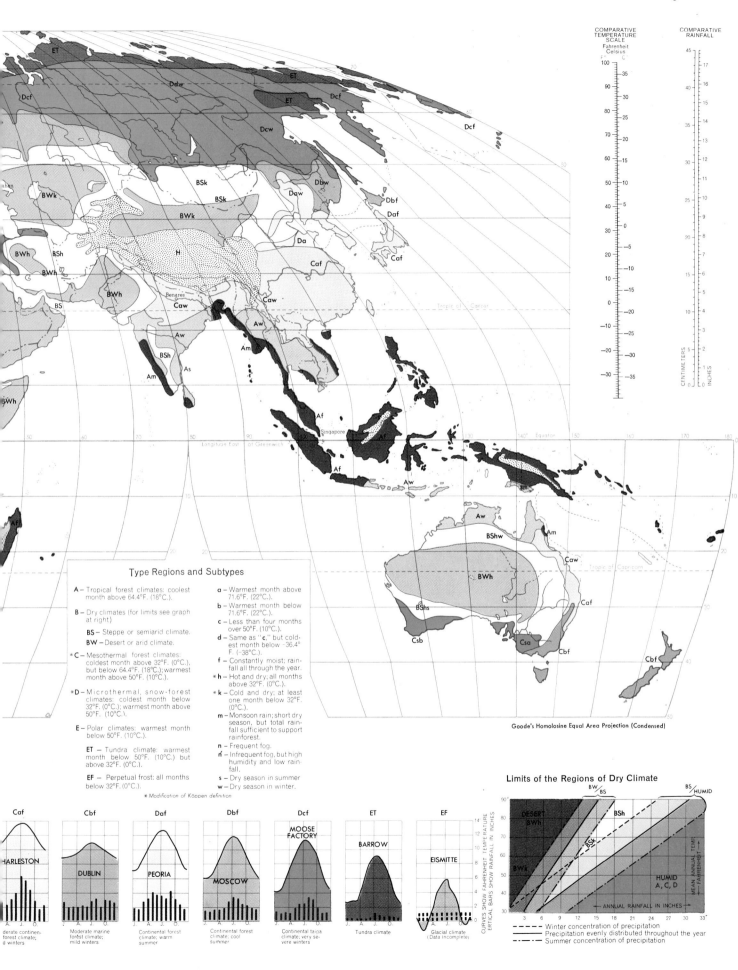

COMPARATIVE
TEMPERATURE
SCALE
Fahrenheit
Celsius

COMPARATIVE
RAINFALL

Goode's Homolosine Equal Area Projection (Condensed)

Type Regions and Subtypes

A – Tropical forest climates: coolest month above 64.4°F. (18°C.).

B – Dry climates (for limits see graph at right).

　BS – Steppe or semiarid climate.

　BW – Desert or arid climate.

*C – Mesothermal forest climates: coldest month above 32°F. (0°C.), but below 64.4°F. (18°C.); warmest month above 50°F. (10°C.).

*D – Microthermal, snow-forest climates: coldest month below 32°F. (0°C.); warmest month above 50°F. (10°C.).

E – Polar climates: warmest month below 50°F. (10°C.).

　ET – Tundra climate: warmest month below 50°F. (10°C.) but above 32°F. (0°C.).

　EF – Perpetual frost: all months below 32°F. (0°C.).

a – Warmest month above 71.6°F. (22°C.).

b – Warmest month below 71.6°F. (22°C.).

c – Less than four months over 50°F. (10°C.).

d – Same as "c," but coldest month below –36.4°F. (–38°C.).

f – Constantly moist; rainfall all through the year.

*h – Hot and dry; all months above 32°F. (0°C.).

*k – Cold and dry; at least one month below 32°F. (0°C.).

m – Monsoon rain; short dry season, but total rainfall sufficient to support rainforest.

n – Frequent fog.

ń – Infrequent fog, but high humidity and low rainfall.

s – Dry season in summer.

w – Dry season in winter.

* Modification of Köppen definition

Limits of the Regions of Dry Climate

CURVES SHOW FAHRENHEIT TEMPERATURE
VERTICAL BARS SHOW RAINFALL IN INCHES

MEAN ANNUAL TEMPERATURE °FAHRENHEIT

ANNUAL RAINFALL IN INCHES

DESERT BWh
BWk
BSk
BSh
HUMID A, C, D

- - - - Winter concentration of precipitation
———— Precipitation evenly distributed throughout the year
–·–·– Summer concentration of precipitation

Caf — CHARLESTON — Moderate continental-forest climate; mild winters

Cbf — DUBLIN — Moderate marine forest climate; mild winters

Daf — PEORIA — Continental forest climate; warm summer

Dbf — MOSCOW — Continental forest climate; cool summer

Dcf — MOOSE FACTORY — Continental taiga climate; very severe winters

ET — BARROW — Tundra climate

EF — EISMITTE — Glacial climate (Data Incomplete)

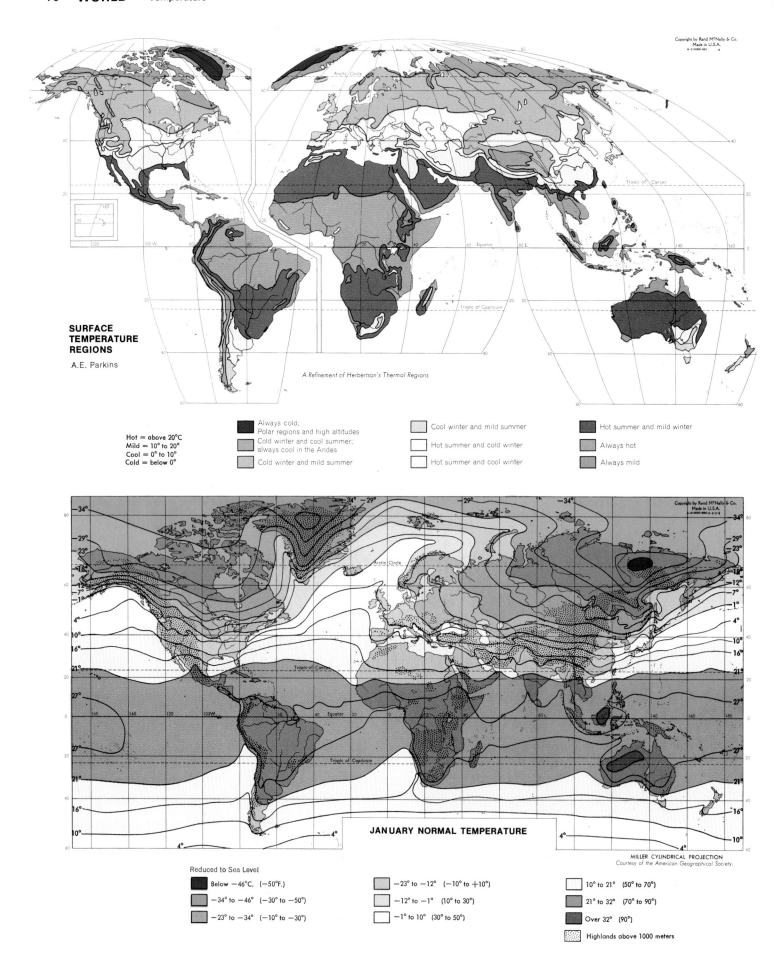

SURFACE
TEMPERATURE
REGIONS

A.E. Parkins

A Refinement of Herbertson's Thermal Regions

Copyright by Rand McNally & Co.
Made in U.S.A.

Hot = above 20°C
Mild = 10° to 20°
Cool = 0° to 10°
Cold = below 0°

Always cold;
Polar regions and high altitudes

Cold winter and cool summer;
always cool in the Andes

Cold winter and mild summer

Cool winter and mild summer

Hot summer and cold winter

Hot summer and cool winter

Hot summer and mild winter

Always hot

Always mild

JANUARY NORMAL TEMPERATURE

MILLER CYLINDRICAL PROJECTION
Courtesy of the American Geographical Society.

Reduced to Sea Level

Below −46°C. (−50°F.)

−34° to −46° (−30° to −50°)

−23° to −34° (−10° to −30°)

−23° to −12° (−10° to +10°)

−12° to −1° (10° to 30°)

−1° to 10° (30° to 50°)

10° to 21° (50° to 70°)

21° to 32° (70° to 90°)

Over 32° (90°)

Highlands above 1000 meters

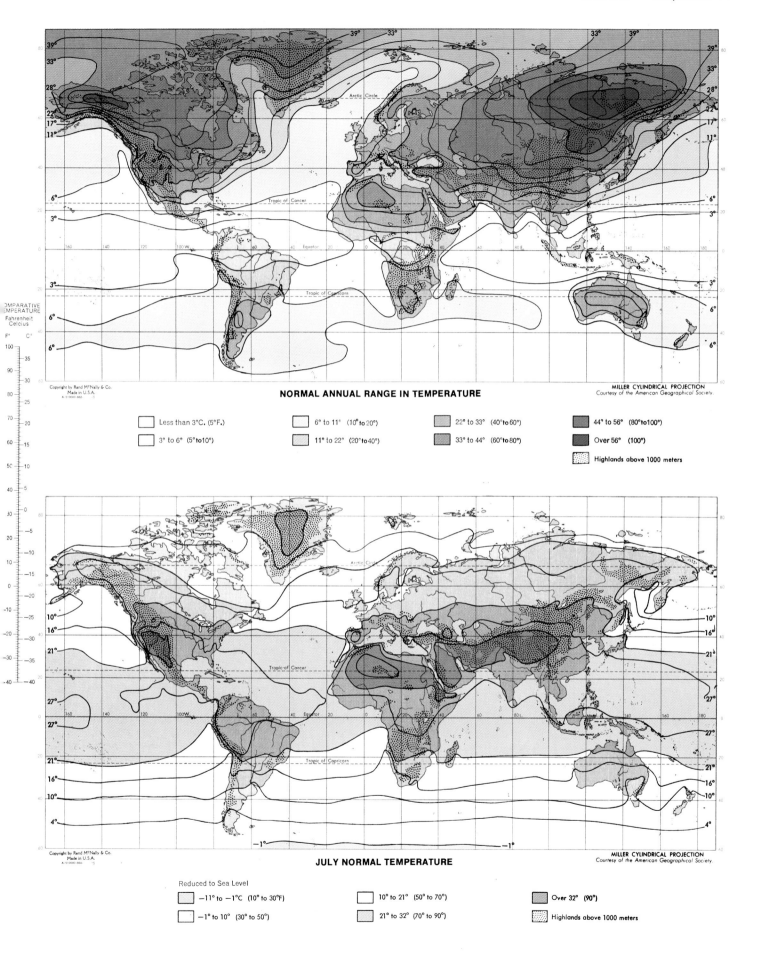

NORMAL ANNUAL RANGE IN TEMPERATURE

MILLER CYLINDRICAL PROJECTION
Courtesy of the American Geographical Society.

Copyright by Rand McNally & Co.
Made in U.S.A.

- Less than 3°C. (5°F.)
- 3° to 6° (5° to 10°)
- 6° to 11° (10° to 20°)
- 11° to 22° (20° to 40°)
- 22° to 33° (40° to 60°)
- 33° to 44° (60° to 80°)
- 44° to 56° (80° to 100°)
- Over 56° (100°)
- Highlands above 1000 meters

JULY NORMAL TEMPERATURE

MILLER CYLINDRICAL PROJECTION
Courtesy of the American Geographical Society.

Copyright by Rand McNally & Co.
Made in U.S.A.

Reduced to Sea Level

- −11° to −1°C (10° to 30°F)
- −1° to 10° (30° to 50°)
- 10° to 21° (50° to 70°)
- 21° to 32° (70° to 90°)
- Over 32° (90°)
- Highlands above 1000 meters

COMPARATIVE TEMPERATURE
Fahrenheit Celsius

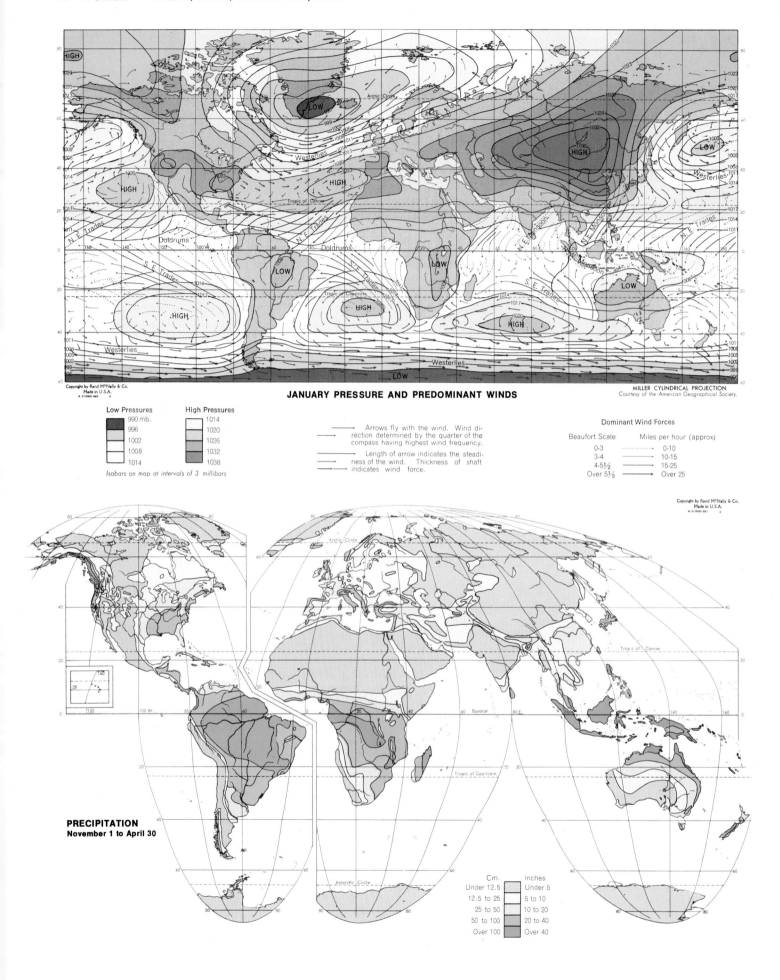

JANUARY PRESSURE AND PREDOMINANT WINDS

MILLER CYLINDRICAL PROJECTION
Courtesy of the American Geographical Society.

Copyright by Rand McNally & Co.
Made in U.S.A.
A-51000-883   4

Low Pressures
990 mb.
996
1002
1008
1014

High Pressures
1014
1020
1026
1032
1038

Isobars on map at intervals of 3 millibars

Arrows fly with the wind. Wind direction determined by the quarter of the compass having highest wind frequency.

Length of arrow indicates the steadiness of the wind. Thickness of shaft indicates wind force.

Dominant Wind Forces

Beaufort Scale	Miles per hour (approx)
0-3	0-10
3-4	10-15
4-5½	15-25
Over 5½	Over 25

Copyright by Rand McNally & Co.
Made in U.S.A.
A-51000-667   4

PRECIPITATION
November 1 to April 30

Cm.	Inches
Under 12.5	Under 5
12.5 to 25	5 to 10
25 to 50	10 to 20
50 to 100	20 to 40
Over 100	Over 40

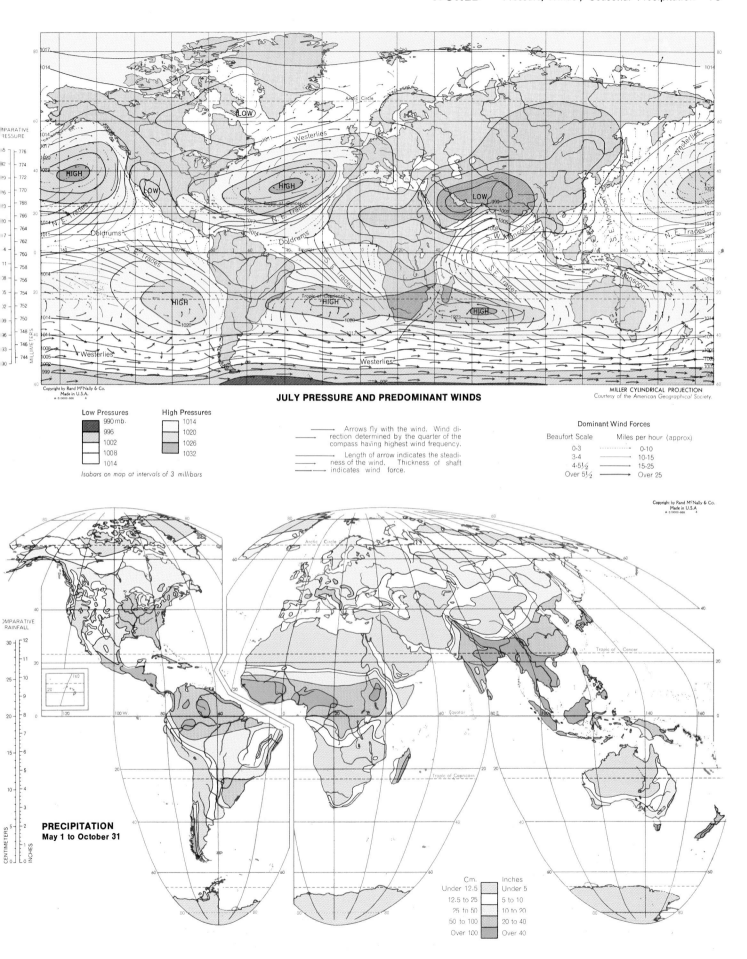

JULY PRESSURE AND PREDOMINANT WINDS

MILLER CYLINDRICAL PROJECTION
Courtesy of the American Geographical Society.

Copyright by Rand McNally & Co.
Made in U.S.A.
A-510000-666   4

Low Pressures
990 mb.
996
1002
1008
1014

High Pressures
1014
1020
1026
1032

Isobars on map at intervals of 3 millibars

Arrows fly with the wind. Wind direction determined by the quarter of the compass having highest wind frequency.

Length of arrow indicates the steadiness of the wind. Thickness of shaft indicates wind force.

Dominant Wind Forces

Beaufort Scale	Miles per hour (approx)
0-3	0-10
3-4	10-15
4-5½	15-25
Over 5½	Over 25

PRECIPITATION
May 1 to October 31

Cm.	Inches
Under 12.5	Under 5
12.5 to 25	5 to 10
25 to 50	10 to 20
50 to 100	20 to 40
Over 100	Over 40

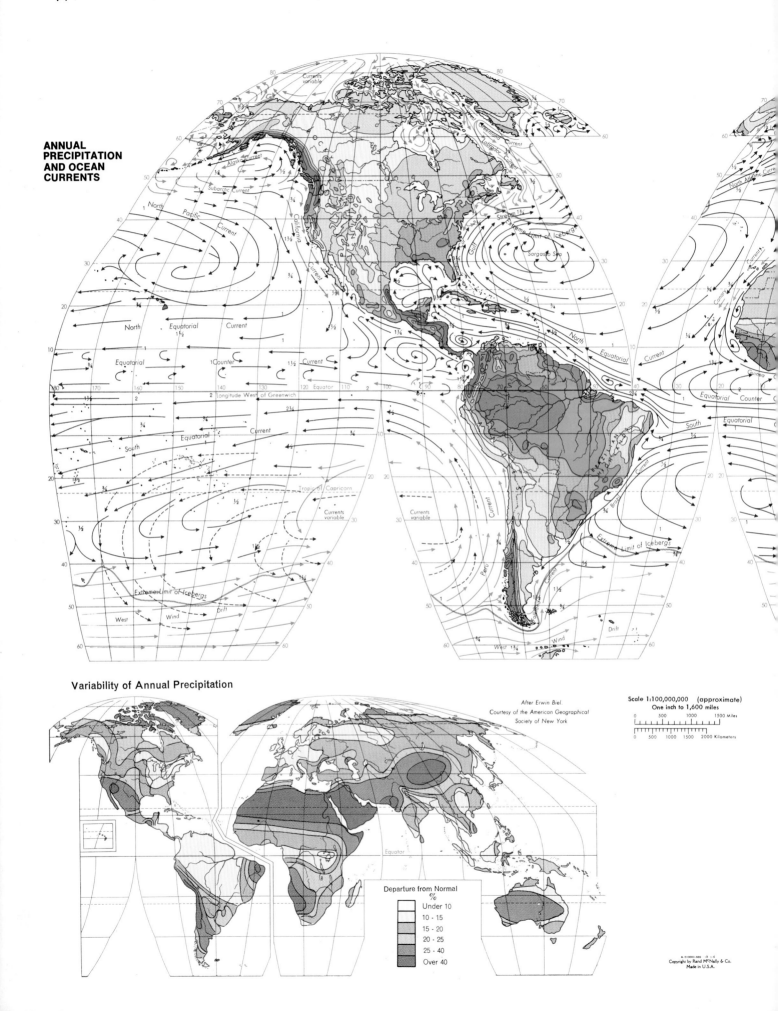

ANNUAL
PRECIPITATION
AND OCEAN
CURRENTS

Variability of Annual Precipitation

After Erwin Biel.
Courtesy of the American Geographical
Society of New York

Scale 1:100,000,000 (approximate)
One inch to 1,600 miles

Departure from Normal
%
Under 10
10 - 15
15 - 20
20 - 25
25 - 40
Over 40

Copyright by Rand McNally & Co.
Made in U.S.A.

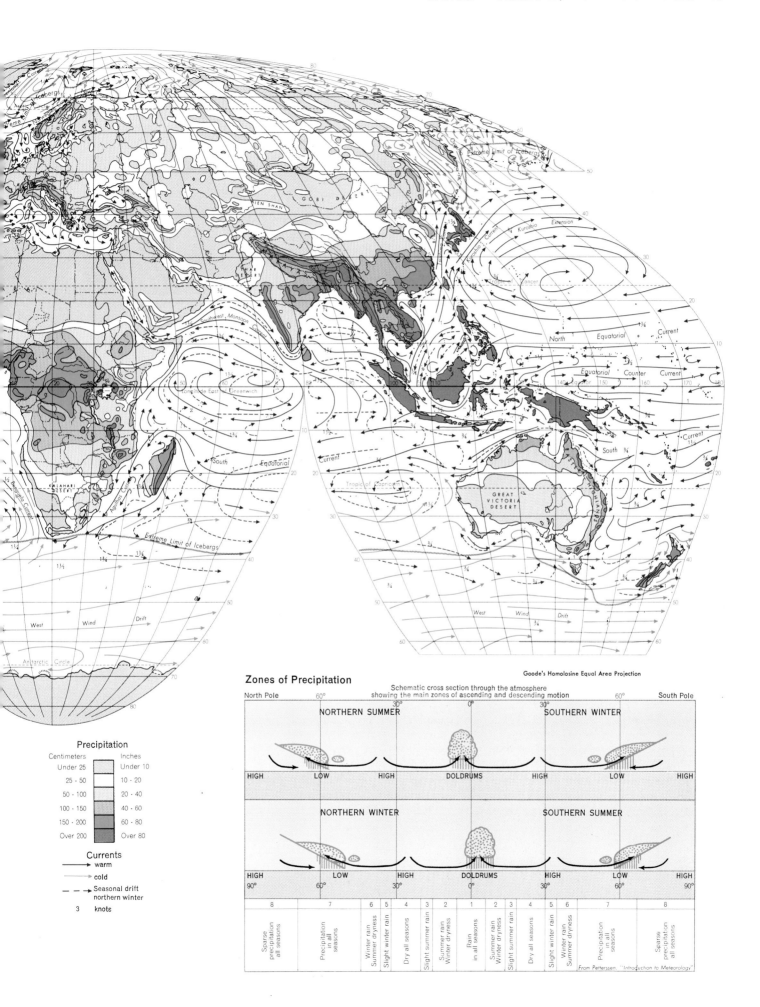

Goode's Homolosine Equal Area Projection

Precipitation

Centimeters	Inches
Under 25	Under 10
25 - 50	10 - 20
50 - 100	20 - 40
100 - 150	40 - 60
150 - 200	60 - 80
Over 200	Over 80

Currents

→ warm

→ cold

- - → Seasonal drift northern winter

3   knots

Zones of Precipitation

Schematic cross section through the atmosphere showing the main zones of ascending and descending motion

| North Pole | 60° | 30° | 0° | 30° | 60° | South Pole |

NORTHERN SUMMER   SOUTHERN WINTER

| HIGH | LOW | HIGH | DOLDRUMS | HIGH | LOW | HIGH |

NORTHERN WINTER   SOUTHERN SUMMER

| HIGH | LOW | HIGH | DOLDRUMS | HIGH | LOW | HIGH |
| 90° | 60° | 30° | 0° | 30° | 60° | 90° |

8	7	6	5	4	3	2	1	2	3	4	5	6	7	8
Sparse precipitation all seasons	Precipitation in all seasons	Winter rain Summer dryness	Slight winter rain	Dry all seasons	Slight summer rain	Summer rain Winter dryness	Rain in all seasons	Summer rain Winter dryness	Slight summer rain	Dry all seasons	Slight winter rain	Winter rain Summer dryness	Precipitation in all seasons	Sparse precipitation all seasons

From Petterssen, "Introduction to Meteorology"

16

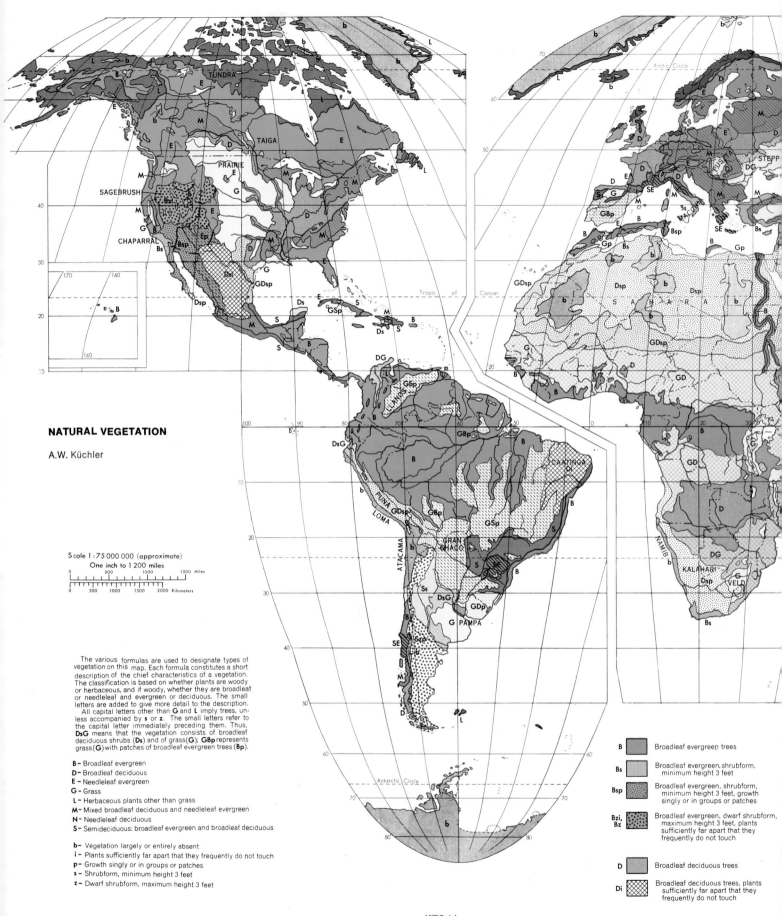

NATURAL VEGETATION

A.W. Küchler

Scale 1:75 000 000 (approximate)
One inch to 1 200 miles

0   500   1000   1500 Miles

0   500   1000   1500   2000 Kilometers

The various formulas are used to designate types of
vegetation on this map. Each formula constitutes a short
description of the chief characteristics of a vegetation.
The classification is based on whether plants are woody
or herbaceous, and if woody, whether they are broadleaf
or needleleaf and evergreen or deciduous. The small
letters are added to give more detail to the description.
All capital letters other than G and L imply trees, unless accompanied by s or z. The small letters refer to
the capital letter immediately preceding them. Thus,
DsG means that the vegetation consists of broadleaf
deciduous shrubs (**Ds**) and of grass (**G**); **GBp** represents
grass (**G**) with patches of broadleaf evergreen trees (**Bp**).

B – Broadleaf evergreen
D – Broadleaf deciduous
E – Needleleaf evergreen
G – Grass
L – Herbaceous plants other than grass
M – Mixed broadleaf deciduous and needleleaf evergreen
N – Needleleaf deciduous
S – Semideciduous: broadleaf evergreen and broadleaf deciduous

b – Vegetation largely or entirely absent
i – Plants sufficiently far apart that they frequently do not touch
p – Growth singly or in groups or patches
s – Shrubform, minimum height 3 feet
z – Dwarf shrubform, maximum height 3 feet

B	Broadleaf evergreen trees
Bs	Broadleaf evergreen, shrubform, minimum height 3 feet
Bsp	Broadleaf evergreen, shrubform, minimum height 3 feet, growth singly or in groups or patches
Bzi, Bz	Broadleaf evergreen, dwarf shrubform, maximum height 3 feet, plants sufficiently far apart that they frequently do not touch
D	Broadleaf deciduous trees
Di	Broadleaf deciduous trees, plants sufficiently far apart that they frequently do not touch

Goode's Homolosine
Equal Area Projection
(Condensed)

		Broadleaf deciduous, shrubform, minimum height 3 feet
	E	Needleleaf evergreen trees
		Broadleaf deciduous, shrubform, minimum height 3 feet, plants sufficiently far apart that they frequently do not touch
	Ep	Needleleaf evergreen trees, growth singly or in groups or patches
		Broadleaf deciduous, shrubform, minimum height 3 feet, growth singly or in groups or patches
	G	Grass and other herbaceous plants
		Broadleaf deciduous, dwarf shrubform, maximum height 3 feet, growth singly or in groups or patches
	Gp	Grass and other herbaceous plants, growth singly or in groups or patches
		Broadleaf deciduous, shrubform, minimum height 3 feet / Grass and other herbaceous plants
	GBp	Grass and other herbaceous plants / Broadleaf evergreen trees, growth singly or in groups or patches
		Broadleaf deciduous trees / Grass and other herbaceous plants
	GD	Grass and other herbaceous plants / Broadleaf deciduous trees
		Broadleaf deciduous trees / Broadleaf evergreen, shrubform, minimum height 3 feet
	GDp	Grass and other herbaceous plants / Broadleaf deciduous trees, growth singly or in groups or patches
GDsp	Grass and other herbaceous plants / Broadleaf deciduous, shrubform, minimum height 3 feet, growth singly or in groups or patches	
GSp	Grass and other herbaceous plants / Semideciduous: broadleaf evergreen and broadleaf deciduous trees, growth singly or in groups or patches	
L	Herbaceous plants other than grass	
M	Mixed: broadleaf deciduous and needleleaf evergreen trees	
N	Needleleaf deciduous trees	
ND	Needleleaf deciduous trees / Broadleaf deciduous trees	
S	Semideciduous: broadleaf evergreen and broadleaf deciduous trees	
Ss	Semideciduous: broadleaf evergreen and broadleaf deciduous, shrubform, minimum height 3 feet	
SsG	Semideciduous: broadleaf evergreen and broadleaf deciduous, shrubform, minimum height 3 feet / Grass and other herbaceous plants	
Szp	Semideciduous: broadleaf evergreen and broadleaf deciduous, dwarf shrubform, maximum height 3 feet, growth singly or in groups or patches	
SE	Semideciduous: broadleaf evergreen and broadleaf deciduous trees / Needleleaf evergreen trees	
b	Vegetation largely or entirely absent	

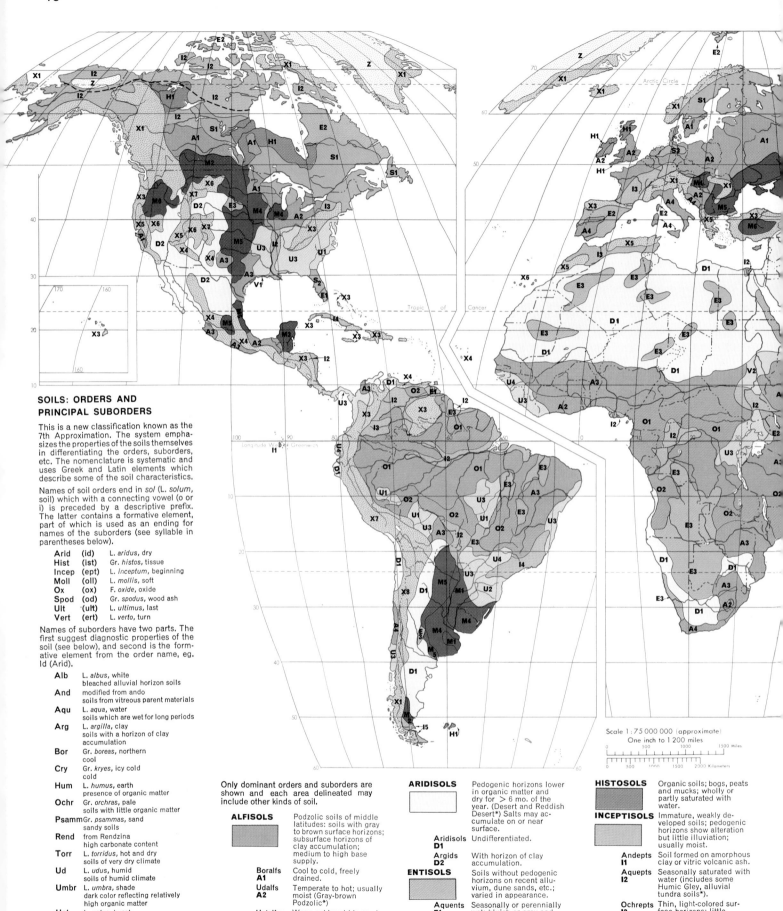

SOILS: ORDERS AND PRINCIPAL SUBORDERS

This is a new classification known as the 7th Approximation. The system emphasizes the properties of the soils themselves in differentiating the orders, suborders, etc. The nomenclature is systematic and uses Greek and Latin elements which describe some of the soil characteristics.

Names of soil orders end in *sol* (L. *solum*, soil) which with a connecting vowel (o or i) is preceded by a descriptive prefix. The latter contains a formative element, part of which is used as an ending for names of the suborders (see syllable in parentheses below).

Arid	(id)	L. *aridus*, dry
Hist	(ist)	Gr. *histos*, tissue
Incep	(ept)	L. *inceptum*, beginning
Moll	(oll)	L. *mollis*, soft
Ox	(ox)	F. *oxide*, oxide
Spod	(od)	Gr. *spodus*, wood ash
Ult	(ult)	L. *ultimus*, last
Vert	(ert)	L. *verto*, turn

Names of suborders have two parts. The first suggest diagnostic properties of the soil (see below), and second is the formative element from the order name, eg. Id (Arid).

Alb		L. *albus*, white bleached alluvial horizon soils
And		modified from ando soils from vitreous parent materials
Aqu		L. *aqua*, water soils which are wet for long periods
Arg		L. *argilla*, clay soils with a horizon of clay accumulation
Bor		Gr. *boreas*, northern cool
Cry		Gr. *kryes*, icy cold cold
Hum		L. *humus*, earth presence of organic matter
Ochr		Gr. *orchras*, pale soils with little organic matter
Psamm		Gr. *psammas*, sand sandy soils
Rend		from Rendzina high carbonate content
Torr		L. *torridus*, hot and dry soils of very dry climate
Ud		L. *udus*, humid soils of humid climate
Umbr		L. *umbra*, shade dark color reflecting relatively high organic matter
Ust		L. *ustus*, burnt soils of dry climates with summer rains
Xer		Gr. *xeros*, dry soils of dry climates with winter rains

Only dominant orders and suborders are shown and each area delineated may include other kinds of soil.

ALFISOLS

Podzolic soils of middle latitudes: soils with gray to brown surface horizons; subsurface horizons of clay accumulation; medium to high base supply.

Boralfs **A1**	Cool to cold, freely drained.
Udalfs **A2**	Temperate to hot; usually moist (Gray-brown Podzolic*).
Ustalfs **A3**	Warm subhumid to semi-arid; dry > 90 days (some Reddish Chestnut and Red & Yellow Podzolic soils*).
Xeralfs **A4**	Warm, dry in summer; moist in winter.

ARIDISOLS

Pedogenic horizons lower in organic matter and dry for > 6 mo. of the year. (Desert and Reddish Desert*) Salts may accumulate on or near surface.

Aridisols **D1**	Undifferentiated.
Argids **D2**	With horizon of clay accumulation.

ENTISOLS

Soils without pedogenic horizons on recent alluvium, dune sands, etc.; varied in appearance.

Aquents **E1**	Seasonally or perennially wet; bluish or gray and mottled.
Orthents **E2**	Shallow; or recent erosional surfaces (Lithosols*). A few on recent loams.
Psaments **E3**	Sandy soils on shifting and stabilized sands.

HISTOSOLS

Organic soils; bogs, peats and mucks; wholly or partly saturated with water.

INCEPTISOLS

Immature, weakly developed soils; pedogenic horizons show alteration but little illuviation; usually moist.

Andepts **I1**	Soil formed on amorphous clay or vitric volcanic ash.
Aquepts **I2**	Seasonally saturated with water (includes some Humic Gley, alluvial tundra soils*).
Ochrepts **I3**	Thin, light-colored surface horizons; little organic matter.
Tropepts **I4**	Continuously warm to hot; brownish to reddish.
Umbrepts **I5**	Dark colored surface horizons; rich in organic matter; medium to low base supply.

Scale 1 : 75 000 000 (approximate)
One inch to 1 200 miles

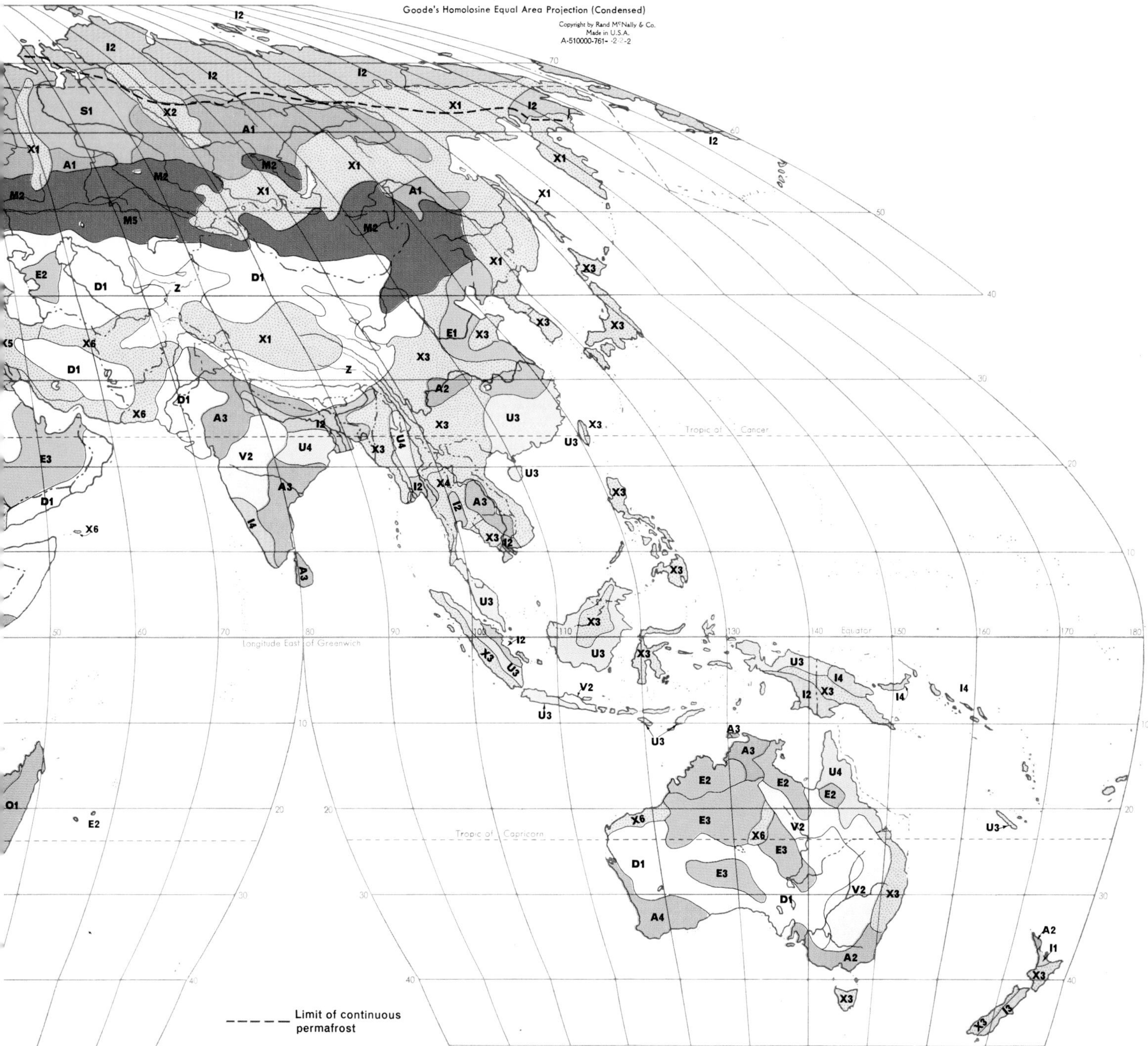

Goode's Homolosine Equal Area Projection (Condensed)
Copyright by Rand McNally & Co.
Made in U.S.A.
A-510000-761- -2 -2
Tropic of Cancer
Equator
Tropic of Capricorn
Longitude East of Greenwich
Limit of continuous permafrost

*Terms refer to Great Soils Group terminology.

MOLLISOLS Soils of the steppe (incl. Chernozem and Chestnut soils*). Thick, black organic rich surface horizons and high base supply.

- **Albolls M1** Seasonally saturated with water; light gray subsurface horizon.
- **Borolls M2** Cool or cold (incl. some Chernozem, Chestnut and Brown soils*).
- **Rendolls M3** Formed on highly calcareous parent materials (Rendzina*).
- **Udolls M4** Temperate to warm; usually moist (Prairie soils*).
- **Ustolls M5** Temperate to hot; dry for > 90 days (incl. some Chestnut and Brown soils*).
- **Xerolls M6** Cool to warm; dry in summer; moist in winter.

OXISOLS Deeply weathered tropical and subtropical soils (Laterites*); rich in sesquioxides of iron and aluminum; low in nutrients; limited productivity without fertilizer.

- **Orthox O1** Hot and nearly always moist.
- **Ustox O2** Warm or hot; dry for long periods but moist > 90 consecutive days.

SPODOSOLS Soils with a subsurface accumulation of amorphous materials overlaid by a light colored, leached sandy horizon.

- **Spodosols S1** Undifferentiated (mostly high latitudes).
- **Aquods S2** Seasonally saturated with water; sandy parent materials.
- **Humods S3** Considerable accumulations of organic matter in subsurface horizon.
- **Orthods S4** With subsurface accumulations of iron, aluminum and organic matter (Podzols*).

ULTISOLS Soils with some subsurface clay accumulation; low base supply; usually moist and low inorganic matter; usually moist and low in organic matter; can be productive with fertilization.

- **Aquults U1** Seasonally saturated with water; subsurface gray or mottled horizon.
- **Humults U2** High in organic matter; dark colored; moist, warm to temperate all year.
- **Udults U3** Low in organic matter; moist, temperate to hot (Red-Yellow Podzolic; some Reddish-Brown Lateritic soils*).
- **Ustults U4** Warm to hot; dry > 90 days.

VERTISOLS Soils with high content of swelling clays; deep, wide cracks in dry periods dark colored.

- **Uderts V1** Usually moist; cracks open < 90 days.
- **Usterts V2** Cracks open > 90 days; difficult to till (Black tropical soils*).

MOUNTAIN SOILS Soils with various moisture and temperature regimes; steep slopes and variable relief and elevation; soils vary greatly within short distance.

- **X1** Cryic great groups of Entisols, Inceptisols and Spodosols.
- **X2** Boralfs and Cryic groups of Entisols and Inceptisols.
- **X3** Udic great groups of Alfisols, Entisols and Ultisols; Inceptisols.
- **X4** Ustic great groups of Alfisols, Entisols, Inceptisols, Mollisols and Ultisols.
- **X5** Xeric great groups of Alfisols, Entisols, Inceptisols, Mollisols and Ultisols.
- **X6** Torric great groups of Entisols; Aridisols.
- **X7** Ustic and cryic great groups of Alfisols, Entisols; Inceptisols and Mollisols; ustic great groups of Ultisols; cryic great groups of Spodosols.
- **X8** Aridisols; torric and cryic great groups of Entisols, and cryic great groups of Spodosols and Inceptisols.

Z **Areas with little or no soil**; icefields, and rugged mountain.

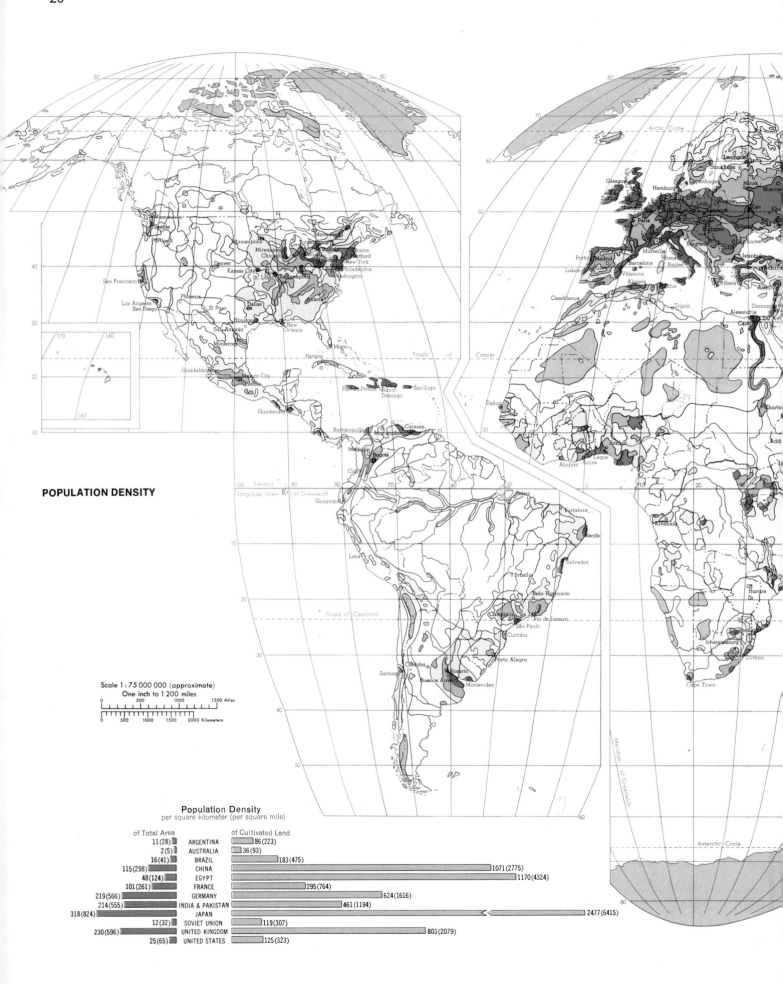

POPULATION DENSITY

Scale 1 : 75 000 000 (approximate)
One inch to 1 200 miles

Population Density
per square kilometer (per square mile)

of Total Area		of Cultivated Land
11 (28)	ARGENTINA	86 (223)
2 (5)	AUSTRALIA	36 (93)
16 (41)	BRAZIL	183 (475)
115 (298)	CHINA	1071 (2775)
48 (124)	EGYPT	1170 (4324)
101 (261)	FRANCE	295 (764)
219 (566)	GERMANY	624 (1616)
214 (555)	INDIA & PAKISTAN	461 (1194)
318 (824)	JAPAN	2477 (6415)
12 (32)	SOVIET UNION	119 (307)
230 (596)	UNITED KINGDOM	803 (2079)
25 (65)	UNITED STATES	125 (323)

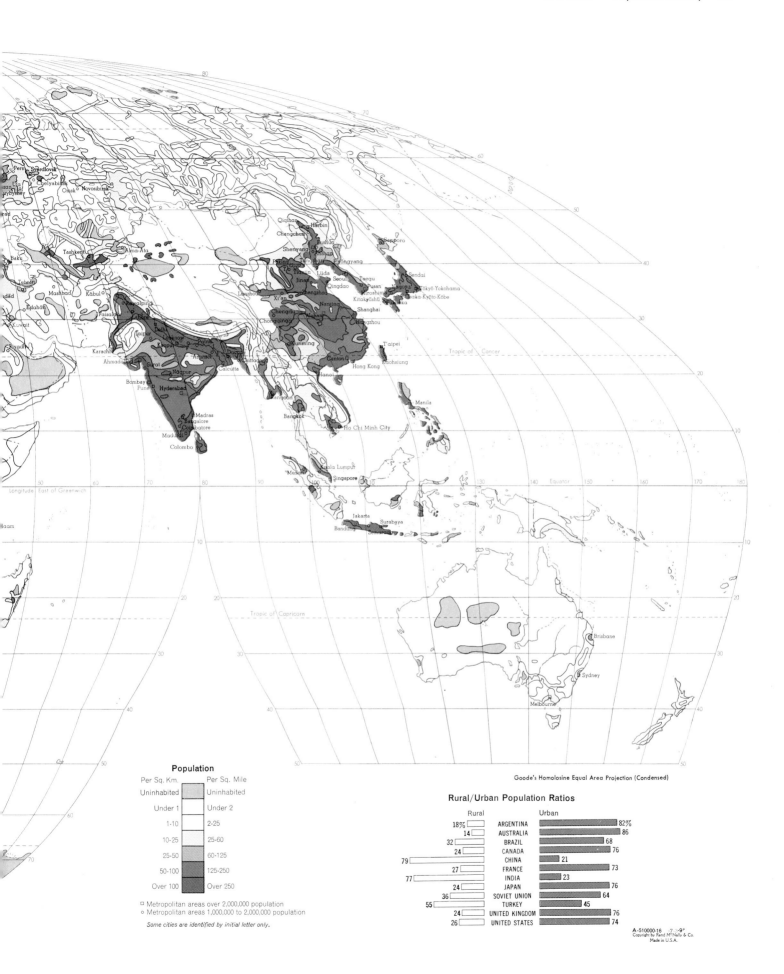

Population

Per Sq. Km.	Per Sq. Mile
Uninhabited	Uninhabited
Under 1	Under 2
1-10	2-25
10-25	25-60
25-50	60-125
50-100	125-250
Over 100	Over 250

□ Metropolitan areas over 2,000,000 population
○ Metropolitan areas 1,000,000 to 2,000,000 population

Some cities are identified by initial letter only.

Goode's Homolosine Equal Area Projection (Condensed)

Rural/Urban Population Ratios

Rural		Urban
18%	ARGENTINA	82%
14	AUSTRALIA	86
32	BRAZIL	68
24	CANADA	76
79	CHINA	21
27	FRANCE	73
77	INDIA	23
24	JAPAN	76
36	SOVIET UNION	64
55	TURKEY	45
24	UNITED KINGDOM	76
26	UNITED STATES	74

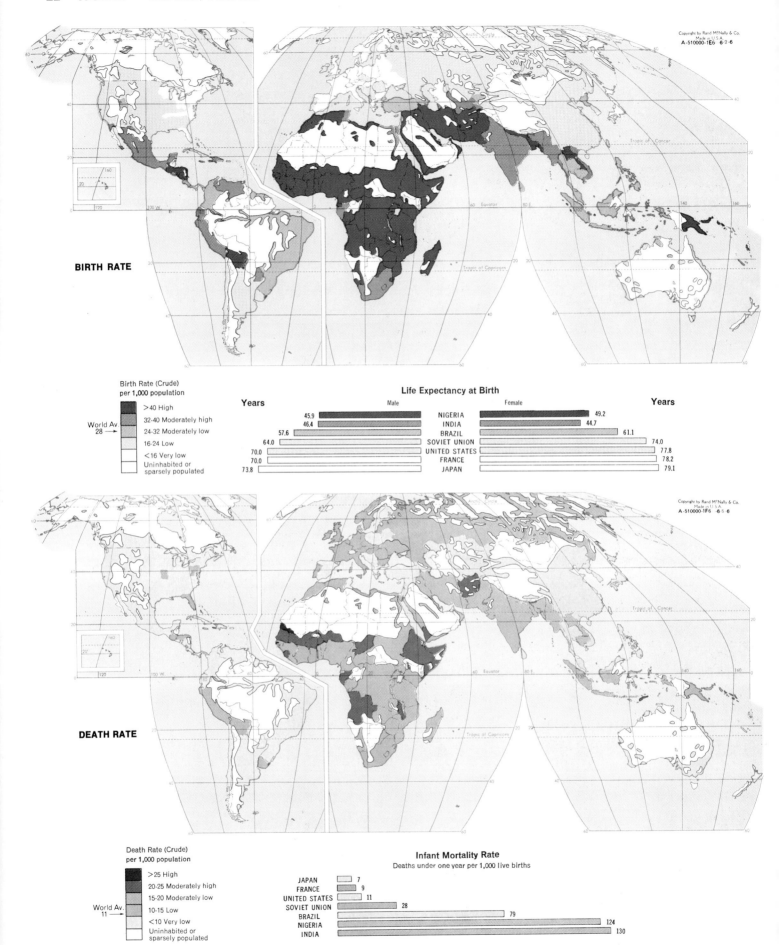

BIRTH RATE

Birth Rate (Crude)
per 1,000 population

>40 High
32-40 Moderately high
World Av. 24-32 Moderately low
28 → 16-24 Low
<16 Very low
Uninhabited or
sparsely populated

Life Expectancy at Birth

Years		Male		Female		Years
45.9		NIGERIA			49.2	
46.4		INDIA		44.7		
57.6		BRAZIL			61.1	
64.0		SOVIET UNION			74.0	
70.0		UNITED STATES			77.8	
70.0		FRANCE			78.2	
73.8		JAPAN			79.1	

DEATH RATE

Death Rate (Crude)
per 1,000 population

>25 High
20-25 Moderately high
15-20 Moderately low
World Av. 10-15 Low
11 → <10 Very low
Uninhabited or
sparsely populated

Infant Mortality Rate
Deaths under one year per 1,000 live births

JAPAN	7
FRANCE	9
UNITED STATES	11
SOVIET UNION	28
BRAZIL	79
NIGERIA	124
INDIA	130

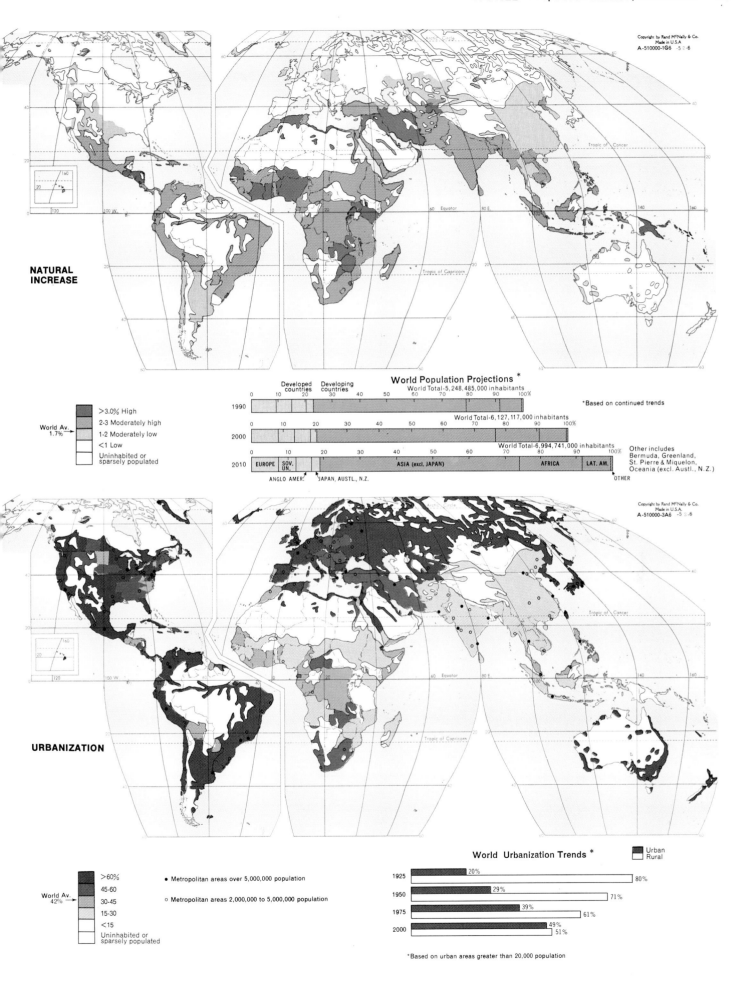

Copyright by Rand McNally & Co.
Made in U.S.A
A-510000-1G6 -5 2 -6

**NATURAL
INCREASE**

World Av.
1.7%

- >3.0% High
- 2-3 Moderately high
- 1-2 Moderately low
- <1 Low
- Uninhabited or sparsely populated

World Population Projections *

*Based on continued trends

Developed countries   Developing countries

1990 World Total-5,248,485,000 inhabitants
0 10 20 30 40 50 60 70 80 90 100%

2000 World Total-6,127,117,000 inhabitants
0 10 20 30 40 50 60 70 80 90 100%

2010 World Total-6,994,741,000 inhabitants
0 10 20 30 40 50 60 70 80 90 100%

| EUROPE | SOV. UN. | ASIA (excl. JAPAN) | AFRICA | LAT. AM. |

ANGLO AMER.   JAPAN, AUSTL., N.Z.   OTHER

Other includes Bermuda, Greenland, St. Pierre & Miquelon, Oceania (excl. Austl., N.Z.)

Copyright by Rand McNally & Co.
Made in U.S.A.
A-510000-3A6 -5 2 -6

URBANIZATION

World Av.
42%

- >60%
- 45-60
- 30-45
- 15-30
- <15
- Uninhabited or sparsely populated

● Metropolitan areas over 5,000,000 population

○ Metropolitan areas 2,000,000 to 5,000,000 population

World Urbanization Trends *

Urban
Rural

1925 20% 80%
1950 29% 71%
1975 39% 61%
2000 49% 51%

*Based on urban areas greater than 20,000 population

Arctic Circle
Tropic of Cancer
Equator
Tropic of Capricorn

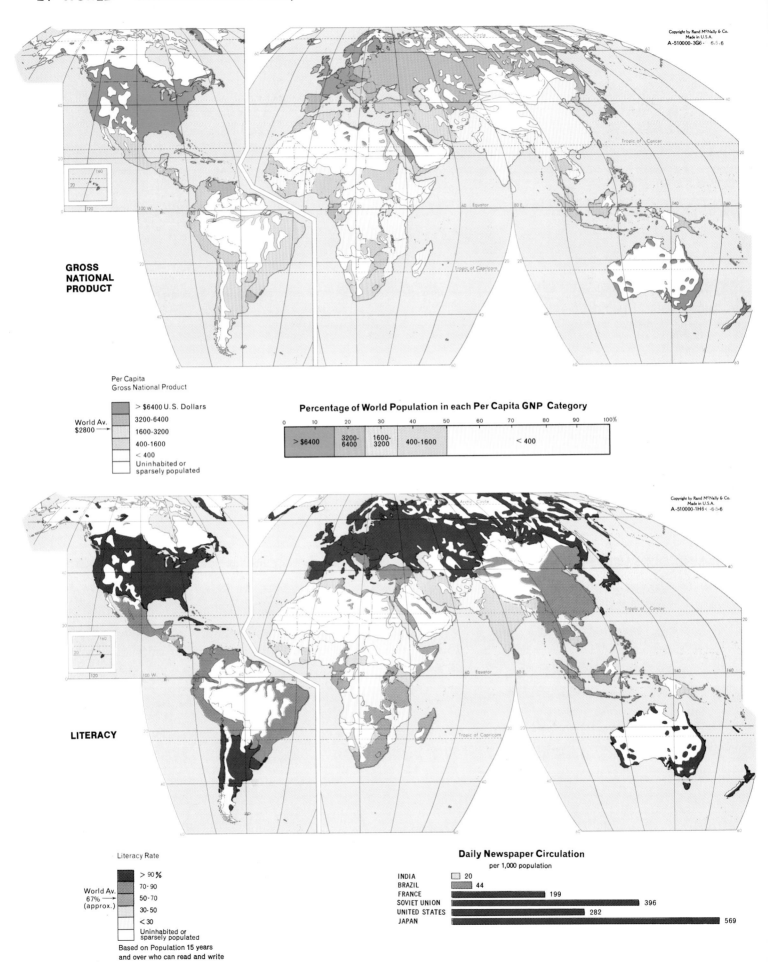

Copyright by Rand M⁣Nally & Co.
Made in U.S.A.
A-510000-3G6 · 6.5 · 6

**GROSS
NATIONAL
PRODUCT**

Per Capita
Gross National Product

> $6400 U.S. Dollars
3200-6400
1600-3200
400-1600
< 400
Uninhabited or
sparsely populated

World Av.
$2800 →

Percentage of World Population in each Per Capita GNP Category

| 0 | 10 | 20 | 30 | 40 | 50 | 60 | 70 | 80 | 90 | 100% |

| > $6400 | 3200-6400 | 1600-3200 | 400-1600 | < 400 |

Copyright by Rand M⁣Nally & Co.
Made in U.S.A.
A-510000-1H6 · ·6.5 · 6

LITERACY

Literacy Rate

> 90 %
70-90
50-70
30-50
< 30
Uninhabited or
sparsely populated

World Av.
67% →
(approx.)

Based on Population 15 years
and over who can read and write

Daily Newspaper Circulation

per 1,000 population

INDIA	20
BRAZIL	44
FRANCE	199
SOVIET UNION	396
UNITED STATES	282
JAPAN	569

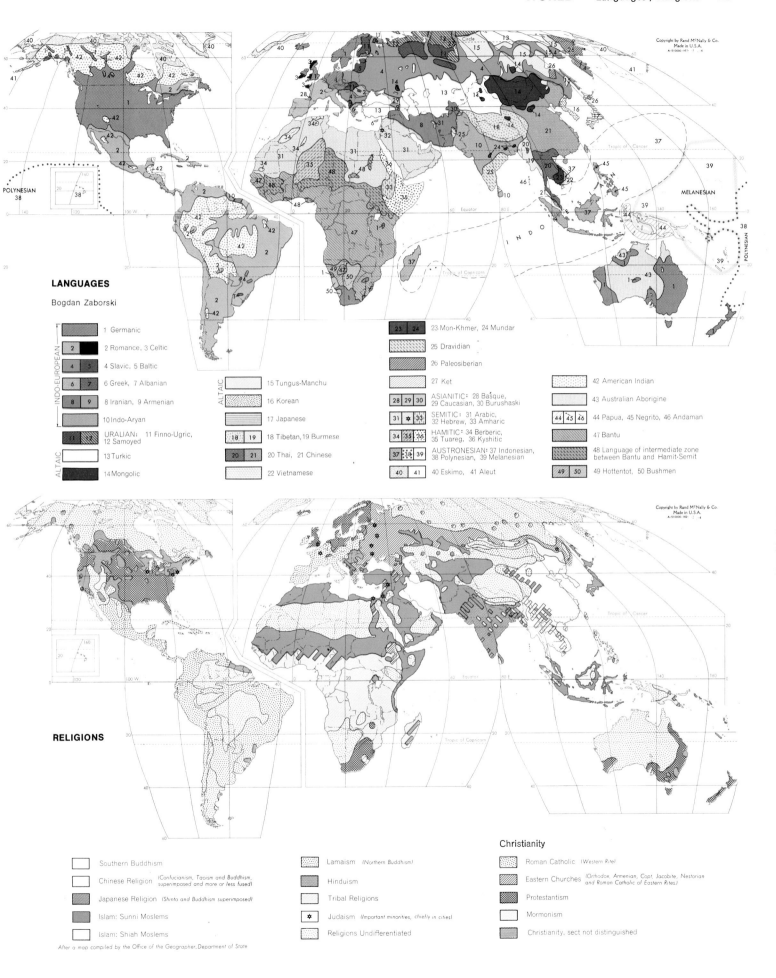

LANGUAGES

Bogdan Zaborski

INDO-EUROPEAN
- 1 Germanic
- 2 Romance, 3 Celtic
- 4 Slavic, 5 Baltic
- 6 Greek, 7 Albanian
- 8 Iranian, 9 Armenian
- 10 Indo-Aryan

URALIAN: 11 Finno-Ugric, 12 Samoyed

ALTAIC
- 13 Turkic
- 14 Mongolic
- 15 Tungus-Manchu
- 16 Korean
- 17 Japanese
- 18 Tibetan, 19 Burmese
- 20 Thai, 21 Chinese
- 22 Vietnamese

- 23 Mon-Khmer, 24 Mundar
- 25 Dravidian
- 26 Paleosiberian
- 27 Ket
- ASIANITIC: 28 Basque, 29 Caucasian, 30 Burushaski
- SEMITIC: 31 Arabic, 32 Hebrew, 33 Amharic
- HAMITIC: 34 Berberic, 35 Tuareg, 36 Kyshitic
- AUSTRONESIAN: 37 Indonesian, 38 Polynesian, 39 Melanesian
- 40 Eskimo, 41 Aleut

- 42 American Indian
- 43 Australian Aborigine
- 44 Papua, 45 Negrito, 46 Andaman
- 47 Bantu
- 48 Language of intermediate zone between Bantu and Hamit-Semit
- 49 Hottentot, 50 Bushmen

RELIGIONS

- Southern Buddhism
- Chinese Religion (Confucianism, Taoism and Buddhism, superimposed and more or less fused)
- Japanese Religion (Shinto and Buddhism superimposed)
- Islam: Sunni Moslems
- Islam: Shiah Moslems
- Lamaism (Northern Buddhism)
- Hinduism
- Tribal Religions
- Judaism (Important minorities, chiefly in cities)
- Religions Undifferentiated

Christianity
- Roman Catholic (Western Rite)
- Eastern Churches (Orthodox, Armenian, Copt, Jacobite, Nestorian and Roman Catholic of Eastern Rites)
- Protestantism
- Mormonism
- Christianity, sect not distinguished

After a map compiled by the Office of the Geographer, Department of State

CALORIE SUPPLY

Note: Size of each country is proportional to population

Calorie supply per capita
(percentage of requirements*)

≥120% Well above requirements
110 to 120 Above requirements
100 to 110 Adequate nutrition
90 to 100 Some malnutrition
<90 Serious malnutrition and/or hunger
n.a. Data not available

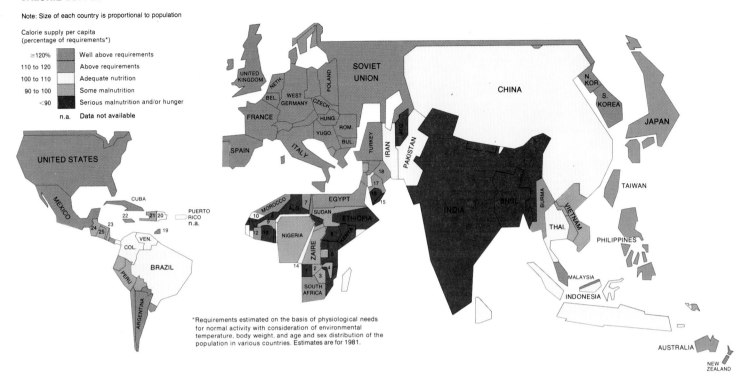

*Requirements estimated on the basis of physiological needs for normal activity with consideration of environmental temperature, body weight, and age and sex distribution of the population in various countries. Estimates are for 1981.

1. ANGOLA
2. ZAMBIA
3. ZIMBABWE
4. MALAWI
5. TANZANIA
6. UGANDA
7. TUNISIA
8. MALI
9. BURKINA FASO
10. SENEGAL
11. GUINEA
12. IVORY COAST
13. GHANA
14. CAMEROON
15. P.D.R. YEMEN
16. YEMEN
17. SAUDI ARABIA
18. IRAQ
19. TRIN. & TOBAGO
20. DOM. REPUBLIC
21. HAITI
22. JAMAICA
23. HONDURAS
24. GUATEMALA
25. EL SALVADOR

© 1986 Rand McNally & Co.
Made in U.S.A.
A-510000-1V 6   -2-3-2

PROTEIN CONSUMPTION

Note: size of each country is proportional to population

n.a. Data not available

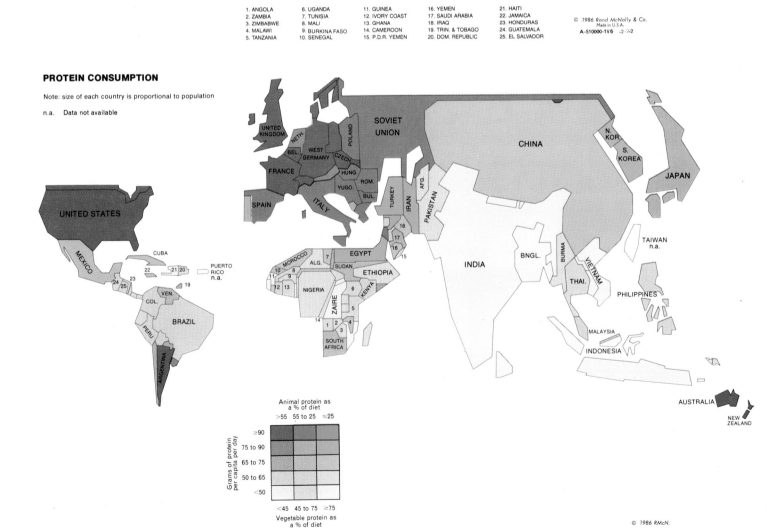

Animal protein as a % of diet
>55 55 to 25 ≤25

Grams of protein per capita per day
≥90
75 to 90
65 to 75
50 to 65
<50

<45 45 to 75 ≥75
Vegetable protein as a % of diet

© 1986 RMcN.

PHYSICIANS

Note: Size of each country is proportional to population

Population per physician

- <1000
- 1000 to 6000
- 6000 to 18000
- ≥18000

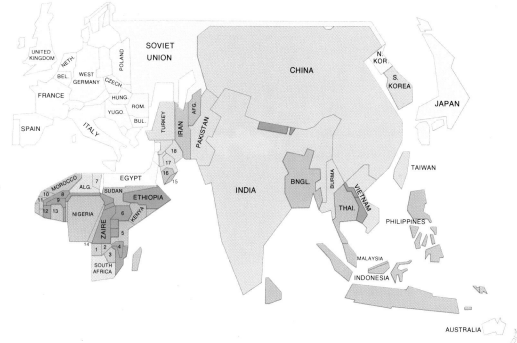

1. ANGOLA	6. UGANDA	11. GUINEA	16. YEMEN	21. HAITI
2. ZAMBIA	7. TUNISIA	12. IVORY COAST	17. SAUDI ARABIA	22. JAMAICA
3. ZIMBABWE	8. MALI	13. GHANA	18. IRAQ	23. HONDURAS
4. MALAWI	9. BURKINA FASO	14. CAMEROON	19. TRIN. & TOBAGO	24. GUATEMALA
5. TANZANIA	10. SENEGAL	15. P.D.R. YEMEN	20. DOM. REPUBLIC	25. EL SALVADOR

© 1986 Rand McNally & Co.
Made in U.S.A.
A-510000-1L6 -2-☆-2

LIFE EXPECTANCY

Note: Size of each country is proportional to population

Life expectancy at birth

- ≥70 years
- 60 to 70
- 50 to 60
- <50

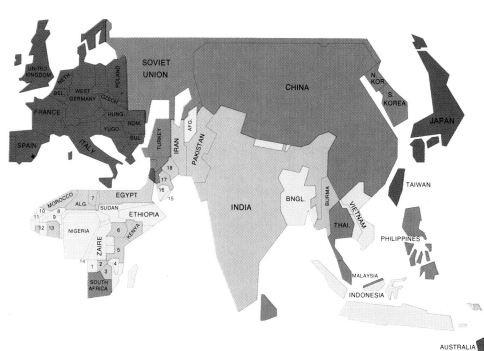

Deaths by Age Group as a % of Total Deaths

DEVELOPING COUNTRIES: Low Income (excluding China and India)*

INDUSTRIAL MARKET COUNTRIES*

Life Expectancy at Birth

DEVELOPING: Low Income*	56.1 years
DEVELOPING: Middle Income*	59.0
OIL EXPORTING*	57.3
EAST EUROPEAN NONMARKET*	69.6
INDUSTRIAL MARKET*	74.1

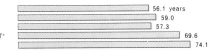

*as defined by the World Bank

© 1986 RMcN

28

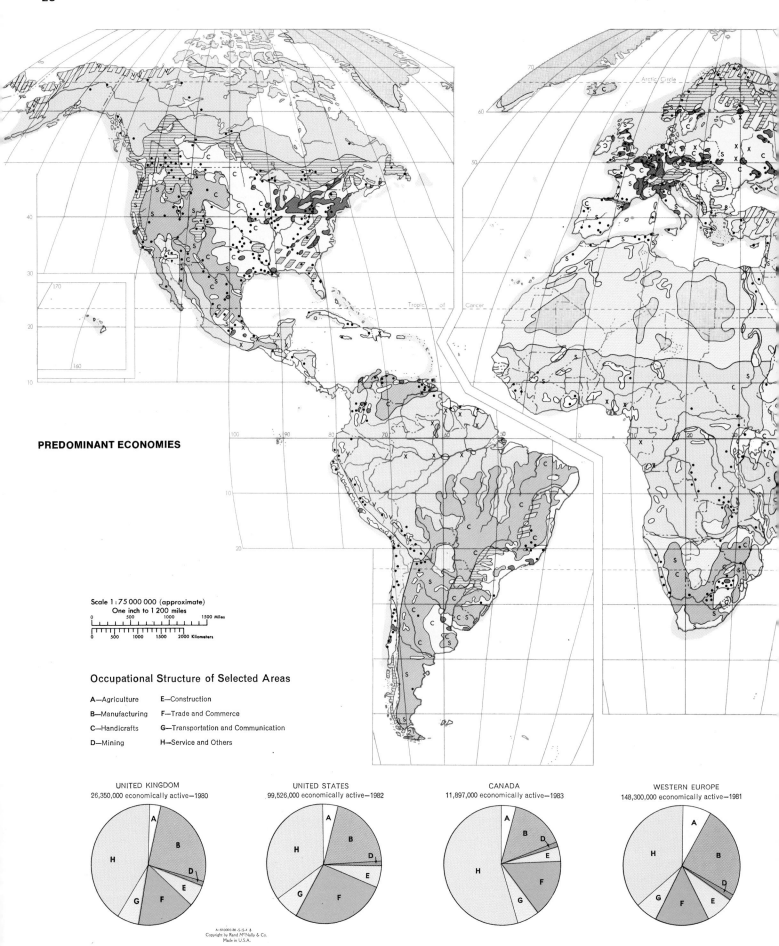

PREDOMINANT ECONOMIES

Scale 1 : 75 000 000 (approximate)
One inch to 1 200 miles
0   500   1000   1500 Miles
0   500   1000   1500   2000 Kilometers

Occupational Structure of Selected Areas

A—Agriculture   E—Construction

B—Manufacturing   F—Trade and Commerce

C—Handicrafts   G—Transportation and Communication

D—Mining   H—Service and Others

UNITED KINGDOM
26,350,000 economically active—1980

UNITED STATES
99,526,000 economically active—1982

CANADA
11,897,000 economically active—1983

WESTERN EUROPE
148,300,000 economically active—1981

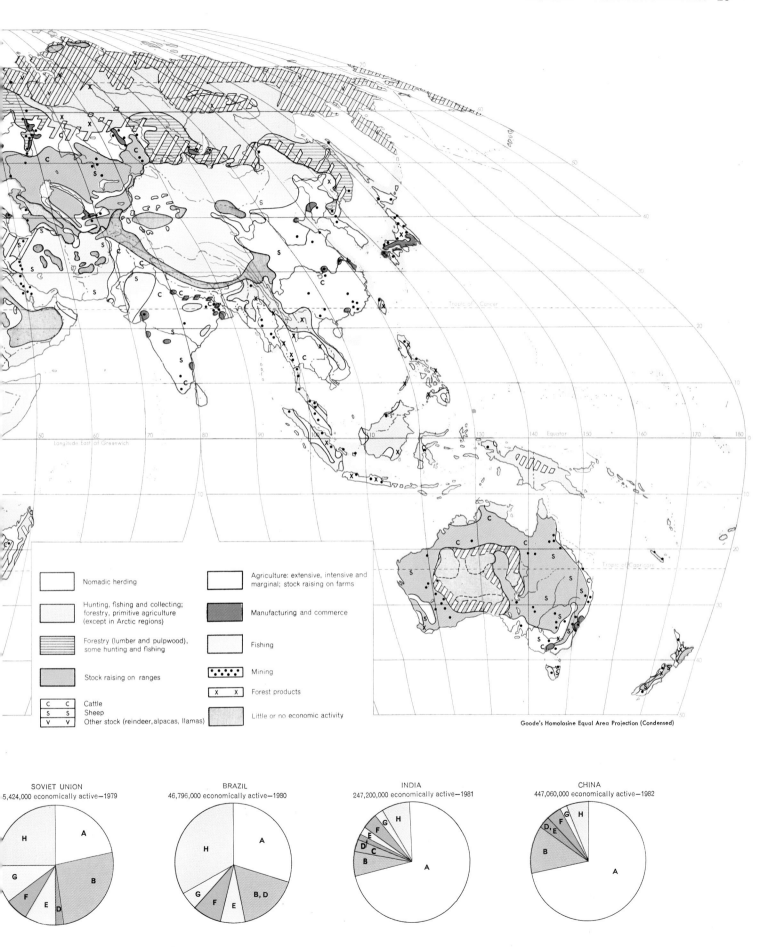

Nomadic herding

Hunting, fishing and collecting;
forestry, primitive agriculture
(except in Arctic regions)

Forestry (lumber and pulpwood),
some hunting and fishing

Stock raising on ranges

C	C	Cattle
S	S	Sheep
V	V	Other stock (reindeer, alpacas, llamas)

Agriculture: extensive, intensive and
marginal; stock raising on farms

Manufacturing and commerce

Fishing

Mining

Forest products

Little or no economic activity

Goode's Homolosine Equal Area Projection (Condensed)

SOVIET UNION
5,424,000 economically active—1979

BRAZIL
46,796,000 economically active—1980

INDIA
247,200,000 economically active—1981

CHINA
447,060,000 economically active—1982

30

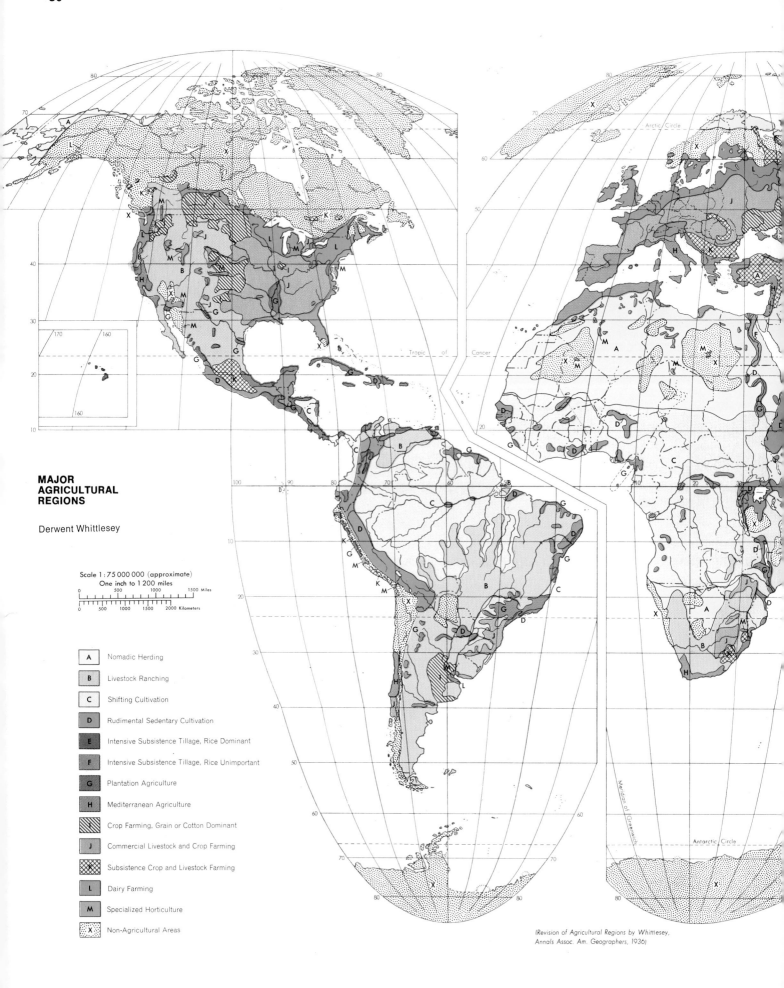

MAJOR AGRICULTURAL REGIONS

Derwent Whittlesey

Scale 1:75 000 000 (approximate)
One inch to 1 200 miles

0   500   1000   1500 Miles

0   500   1000   1500   2000 Kilometers

A	Nomadic Herding
B	Livestock Ranching
C	Shifting Cultivation
D	Rudimental Sedentary Cultivation
E	Intensive Subsistence Tillage, Rice Dominant
F	Intensive Subsistence Tillage, Rice Unimportant
G	Plantation Agriculture
H	Mediterranean Agriculture
	Crop Farming, Grain or Cotton Dominant
J	Commercial Livestock and Crop Farming
X	Subsistence Crop and Livestock Farming
L	Dairy Farming
M	Specialized Horticulture
X	Non-Agricultural Areas

(Revision of Agricultural Regions by Whittlesey, Annals Assoc. Am. Geographers, 1936)

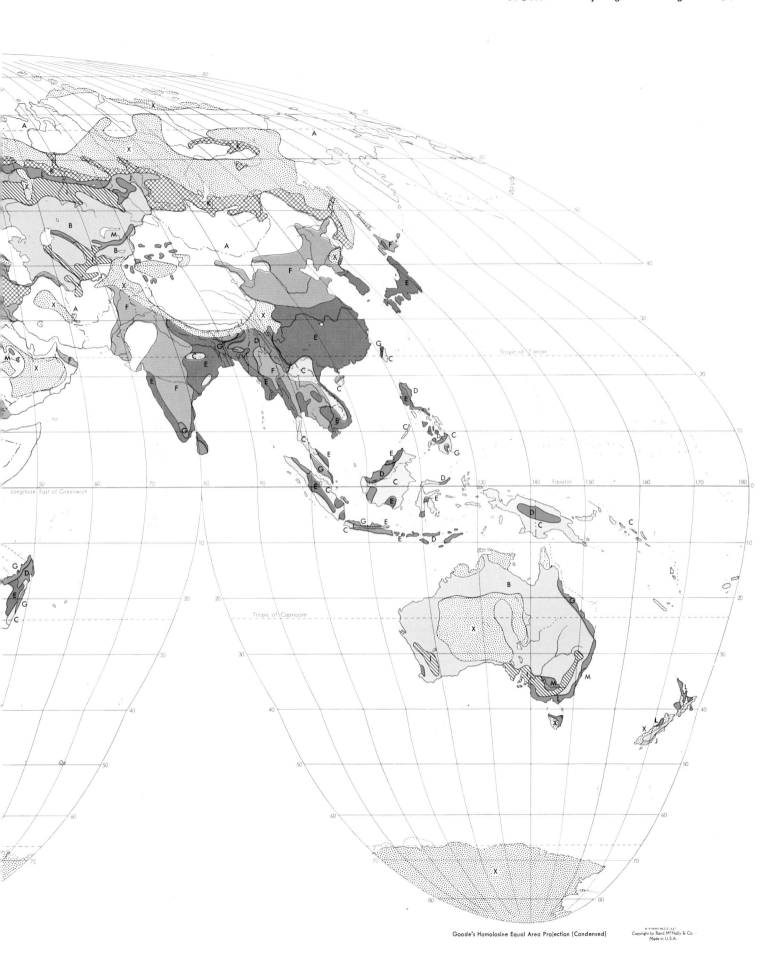

Goode's Homolosine Equal Area Projection (Condensed)

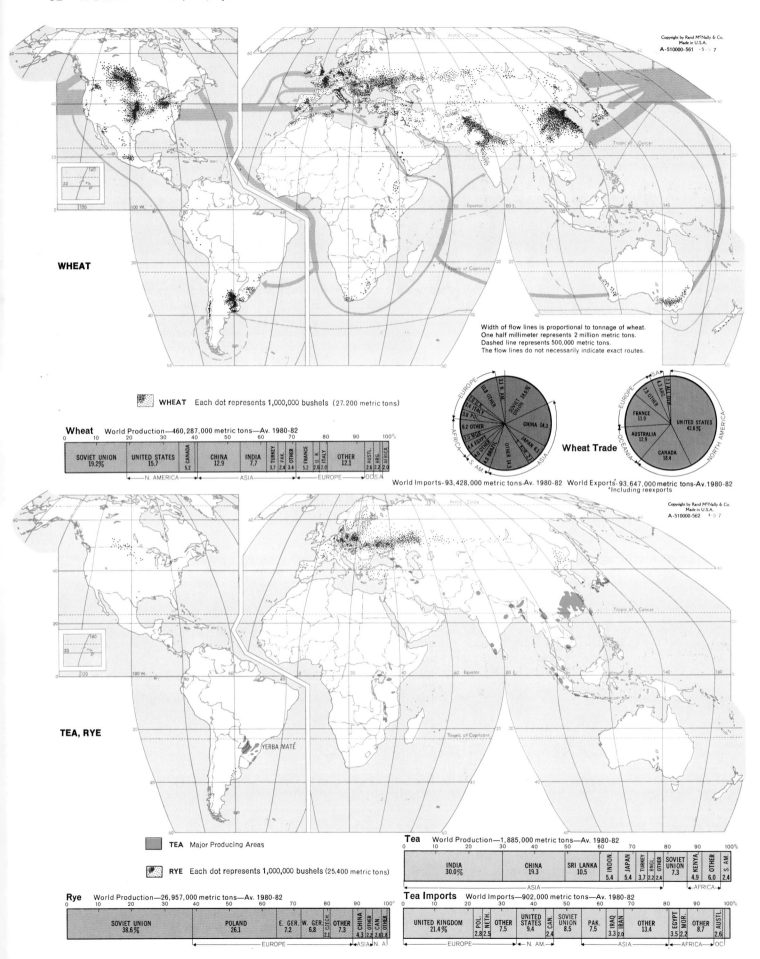

WHEAT

WHEAT

Width of flow lines is proportional to tonnage of wheat.
One half millimeter represents 2 million metric tons.
Dashed line represents 500,000 metric tons.
The flow lines do not necessarily indicate exact routes.

WHEAT Each dot represents 1,000,000 bushels (27,200 metric tons)

Wheat World Production—460,287,000 metric tons—Av. 1980-82

| SOVIET UNION 19.2% | UNITED STATES 15.7 | CANADA 5.2 | CHINA 12.9 | INDIA 7.7 | TURKEY 3.7 | PAK. 2.4 | OTHER 3.4 | FRANCE 5.2 | U.K. 2.0 | ITALY 2.0 | OTHER 12.1 | AUSTL. 2.6 | ARG. 2.2 | AFRICA 2.0 |

N. AMERICA — ASIA — EUROPE — OC. S.A.

Wheat Trade

World Imports-93,428,000 metric tons-Av. 1980-82   World Exports-93,647,000 metric tons-Av. 1980-82
*Including reexports

TEA, RYE

YERBA MATÉ

TEA Major Producing Areas

RYE Each dot represents 1,000,000 bushels (25,400 metric tons)

Tea World Production—1,885,000 metric tons—Av. 1980-82

| INDIA 30.0% | CHINA 19.3 | SRI LANKA 10.5 | INDON. 5.4 | JAPAN 5.4 | TURKEY 3.7 | BNGL. 2.2 | OTHER 2.4 | SOVIET UNION 7.3 | KENYA 4.9 | OTHER 6.0 | S. AM. 2.4 |

ASIA — AFRICA

Rye World Production—26,957,000 metric tons—Av. 1980-82

| SOVIET UNION 38.6% | POLAND 26.1 | E. GER. 7.2 | W. GER. 6.8 | CZECH. 2.1 | OTHER 7.3 | CHINA 4.3 | OTHER 2.2 | CAN. 1.8 | OTHER 1.8 |

EUROPE — ASIA N. A.

Tea Imports World Imports—902,000 metric tons—Av. 1980-82

| UNITED KINGDOM 21.4% | POL. 2.8 | NETH. 2.5 | OTHER 7.5 | UNITED STATES 9.4 | CAN. 2.4 | SOVIET UNION 8.5 | PAK. 7.5 | IRAQ 3.3 | IRAN 2.0 | OTHER 13.4 | EGYPT 3.5 | MOR. 2.2 | OTHER 8.7 | AUSTL. 2.6 |

EUROPE — N. AM. — ASIA — AFRICA — OC.

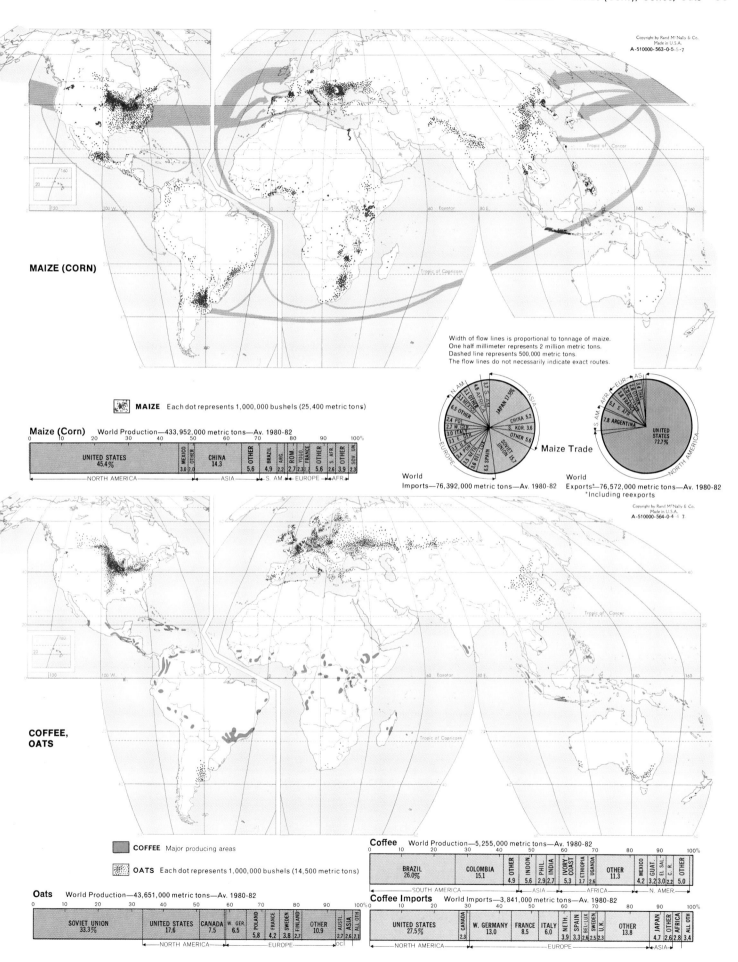

MAIZE (CORN)

Width of flow lines is proportional to tonnage of maize.
One half millimeter represents 2 million metric tons.
Dashed line represents 500,000 metric tons.
The flow lines do not necessarily indicate exact routes.

MAIZE Each dot represents 1,000,000 bushels (25,400 metric tons)

Maize (Corn) World Production—433,952,000 metric tons—Av. 1980-82

UNITED STATES 45.4%	MEXICO 3.0	OTHER 2.0	CHINA 14.3	OTHER 5.6	BRAZIL 4.9	ARG. 2.9	ROM. 2.7	YUGO 2.3	FRANCE 2.2	OTHER 5.6	S. AFR. 2.6	OTHER 3.9	SOV. UN. 2.3

NORTH AMERICA — ASIA — S. AM. — EUROPE — AFR.

Maize Trade

World Imports—76,392,000 metric tons—Av. 1980-82

World Exports*—76,572,000 metric tons—Av. 1980-82
*Including reexports

Pie chart (Imports): N AM 1, 4.6 AFRICA, 3.3 OTH, JAPAN 17.9%, CHINA 5.2, S. KOR. 3.6, OTHER 5.6, SOVIET UNION 14.7, 6.5 SPAIN, 3.6 BEL-LUX, 2.4 NETH., 2.4 PORT., 3.1 U.K., 3.1 E. GER., 3.0 ITALY, 2.4 W. GER., 2.7 POL., 6.5 OTHER

Pie chart (Exports): AFR., EUR., 3.4 OTH, 2.9 THAI., 2.4 FRANCE, 5.1 S. AFR., 7.8 ARGENTINA, UNITED STATES 72.7%

COFFEE, OATS

COFFEE Major producing areas

OATS Each dot represents 1,000,000 bushels (14,500 metric tons)

Coffee World Production—5,255,000 metric tons—Av. 1980-82

BRAZIL 26.0%	COLOMBIA 15.1	OTHER 4.9	INDON. 5.6	PHIL. 2.9	INDIA 2.7	IVORY COAST 5.3	ETHIOPIA	UGANDA	OTHER 11.3	MEXICO 4.2	GUAT. 3.2 EL SAL. 3.0 C. R. 2.2	OTHER 5.0

SOUTH AMERICA — ASIA — AFRICA — N. AMER.

Oats World Production—43,651,000 metric tons—Av. 1980-82

SOVIET UNION 33.3%	UNITED STATES 17.6	CANADA 7.5	W. GER. 6.5	POLAND 5.8	FRANCE 4.2	SWEDEN 3.8	FINLAND 2.7	OTHER 10.9	AUSTL. 2.7 ASIA 2.6 ALL OTH. 2.1	

NORTH AMERICA — EUROPE — OCI

Coffee Imports World Imports—3,841,000 metric tons—Av. 1980-82

UNITED STATES 27.5%	CANADA 2.3	W. GERMANY 13.0	FRANCE 8.5	ITALY 6.0	NETH. 3.9	SPAIN 3.3	BEL-LUX 2.6	SWEDEN 2.5	U.K. 2.3	OTHER 13.8	JAPAN 4.7	AFRICA 2.6 ALL OTH 3.4

NORTH AMERICA — EUROPE — ASIA

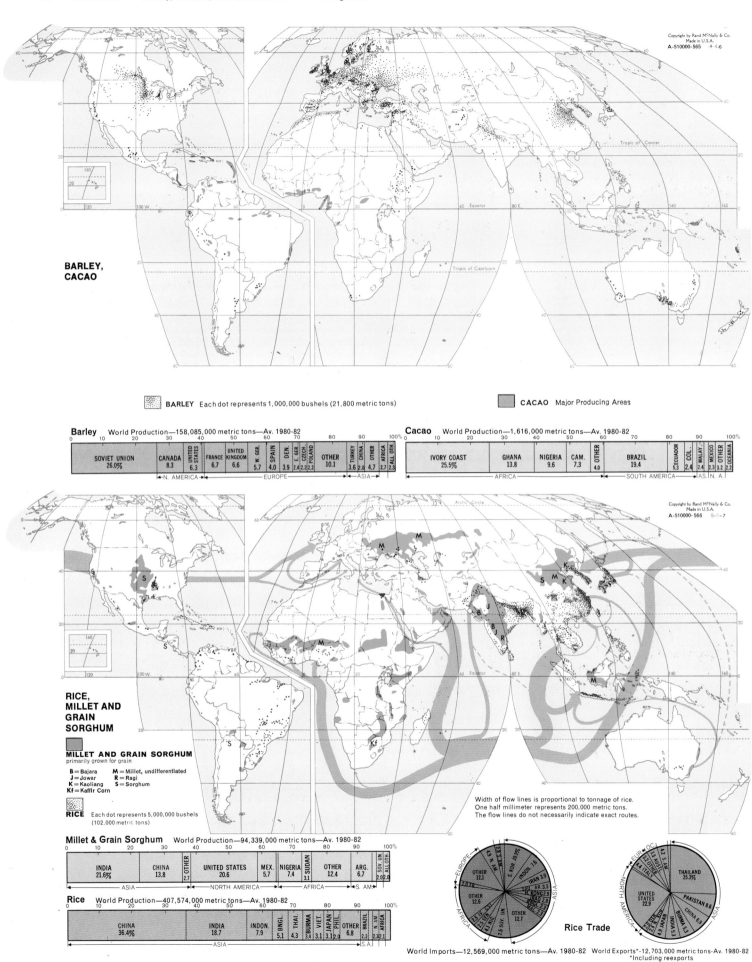

**BARLEY,
CACAO**

BARLEY Each dot represents 1,000,000 bushels (21,800 metric tons)

CACAO Major Producing Areas

Barley World Production—158,085,000 metric tons—Av. 1980-82

	0	10	20	30	40	50	60	70	80	90	100%

| SOVIET UNION 26.0% | CANADA 8.3 | UNITED STATES 6.3 | FRANCE 6.7 | UNITED KINGDOM 6.6 | W. GER. 5.7 | SPAIN 4.0 | DEN. 3.9 | E. GER. 2.2 | CZECH. 2.2 | POLAND 2.2 | OTHER 10.1 | TURKEY 3.6 | CHINA 2.0 | OTHER 4.7 | AFRICA 2.7 | ALL OTH. 2.3 |

◄─N. AMERICA─► ◄────────EUROPE──────► ◄──ASIA──►

Cacao World Production—1,616,000 metric tons—Av. 1980-82

	0	10	20	30	40	50	60	70	80	90	100%

| IVORY COAST 25.5% | GHANA 13.8 | NIGERIA 9.6 | CAM. 7.3 | OTHER 4.0 | BRAZIL 19.4 | ECUADOR 5.3 | COL. 2.4 | MALAY. 2.4 | MEXICO 3.2 | OTHER 3.2 | OCEANIA 2.2 |

◄────────────AFRICA────────────► ◄────SOUTH AMERICA────► ◄AS.IN. A.►

**RICE,
MILLET AND
GRAIN
SORGHUM**

MILLET AND GRAIN SORGHUM
primarily grown for grain

B = Bajara   M = Millet, undifferentiated
J = Jowar   R = Ragi
K = Kaoliang S = Sorghum
Kf = Kaffir Corn

RICE Each dot represents 5,000,000 bushels
(102,000 metric tons)

Width of flow lines is proportional to tonnage of rice.
One half millimeter represents 200,000 metric tons.
The flow lines do not necessarily indicate exact routes.

Millet & Grain Sorghum World Production—94,339,000 metric tons—Av. 1980-82

	0	10	20	30	40	50	60	70	80	90	100%

| INDIA 21.6% | CHINA 13.8 | OTHER 2.7 | UNITED STATES 20.6 | MEX. 5.7 | NIGERIA 7.4 | SUDAN 3.1 | OTHER 12.4 | ARG. 6.7 | SOV. UN 2.0 | ALL OTH 2.0 |

◄────────ASIA────────► ◄───NORTH AMERICA───► ◄──────AFRICA──────► ◄─S. AM.─►

Rice World Production—407,574,000 metric tons—Av. 1980-82

	0	10	20	30	40	50	60	70	80	90	100%

| CHINA 36.4% | INDIA 18.7 | INDON. 7.9 | BNGL. 5.1 | THAI. 4.3 | BURMA 3.4 | VIET. 3.1 | JAPAN 3.1 | PHIL. 2.0 | OTHER 6.8 | BRAZIL 2.3 | N. AM. 2.3 | AFRICA 2.1 |

◄────────────────────────ASIA──────────────────────► ◄S.A.►

Rice Trade

World Imports—12,569,000 metric tons—Av. 1980-82   World Exports*—12,703,000 metric tons-Av. 1980-82
*Including reexports

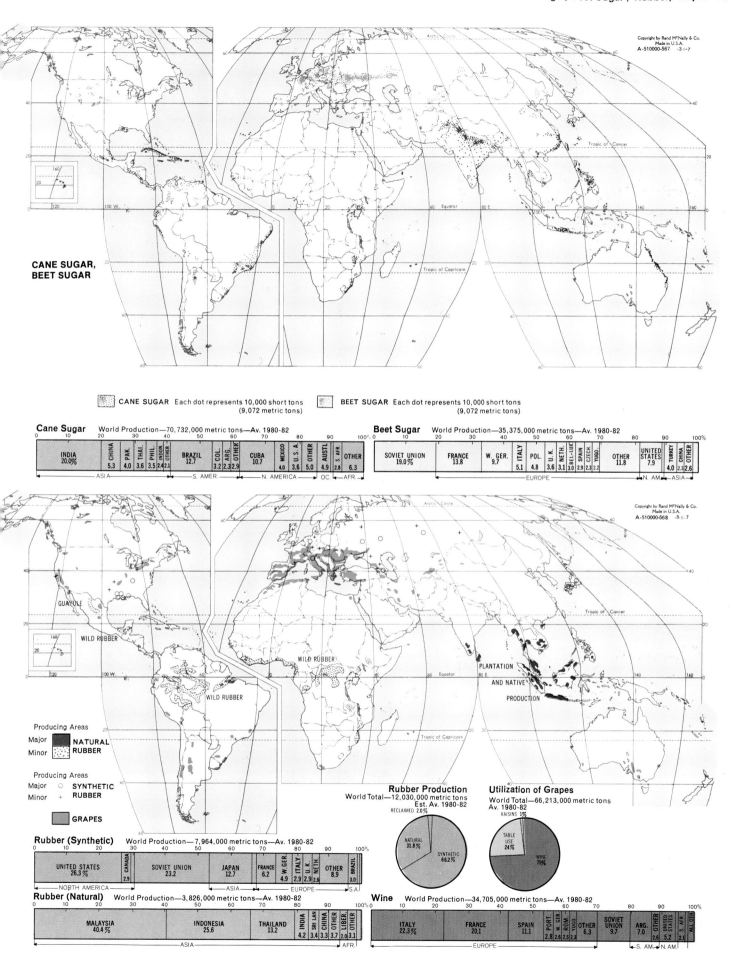

**CANE SUGAR,
BEET SUGAR**

CANE SUGAR Each dot represents 10,000 short tons (9,072 metric tons)

BEET SUGAR Each dot represents 10,000 short tons (9,072 metric tons)

Cane Sugar World Production—70,732,000 metric tons—Av. 1980-82

INDIA 20.0%	CHINA 5.3	PAK. 4.0	THAI. 3.6	PHIL. 3.5	INDON. 2.4	OTHER 2.1	BRAZIL 12.7	COL. 3.2	ARG. 2.3	OTHER 2.9	CUBA 10.7	MEXICO 4.0	U.S.A. 3.6	OTHER 5.0	AUSTL 4.9	S. AFR 2.8	OTHER 6.3

— ASIA — — S. AMER. — — N. AMERICA — OC. AFR.

Beet Sugar World Production—35,375,000 metric tons—Av. 1980-82

SOVIET UNION 19.0%	FRANCE 13.8	W. GER. 9.7	ITALY 5.1	POL. 4.8	U.K. 3.6	NETH. 3.1	BEL-LUX 3.0	SPAIN 2.9	CZECH. 2.3	YUGO. 2.2	OTHER 11.8	UNITED STATES 7.9	TURKEY 4.0	CHINA 2.3	OTHER 2.6

— EUROPE — N. AM. — ASIA —

GUAYULE

WILD RUBBER

WILD RUBBER

WILD RUBBER

PLANTATION
AND NATIVE
PRODUCTION

Producing Areas
Major — NATURAL
Minor — RUBBER

Producing Areas
Major ○ SYNTHETIC
Minor + RUBBER

GRAPES

Rubber Production
World Total—12,030,000 metric tons
Est. Av. 1980-82
RECLAIMED 2.0%
NATURAL 31.8%
SYNTHETIC 66.2%

Utilization of Grapes
World Total—66,213,000 metric tons
Av. 1980-82
RAISINS 1%
TABLE USE 24%
WINE 75%

Rubber (Synthetic) World Production—7,964,000 metric tons—Av. 1980-82

UNITED STATES 26.3%	CANADA 2.9	SOVIET UNION 23.2	JAPAN 12.7	FRANCE 6.2	W GER 4.9	ITALY 2.9	U.K. 2.9	NETH. 2.6	OTHER 8.9	BRAZIL 3.0

— NORTH AMERICA — — ASIA — — EUROPE — S.A.

Rubber (Natural) World Production—3,826,000 metric tons—Av. 1980-82

MALAYSIA 40.4%	INDONESIA 25.6	THAILAND 13.2	INDIA 4.2	SRI LAN 3.4	CHINA 3.3	OTHER 3.7	LIBER. 2.0	OTHER 3.1

— ASIA — AFR.

Wine World Production—34,705,000 metric tons—Av. 1980-82

ITALY 22.3%	FRANCE 20.1	SPAIN 11.1	PORT. 2.8	W GER 2.6	ROM. 2.5	YUGO 2.2	OTHER 6.3	SOVIET UNION 9.7	ARG. 7.0	OTHER 2.6	UNITED STATES 5.2	S. AFR 2.1	ALL OTH

— EUROPE — S. AM. N. AM.

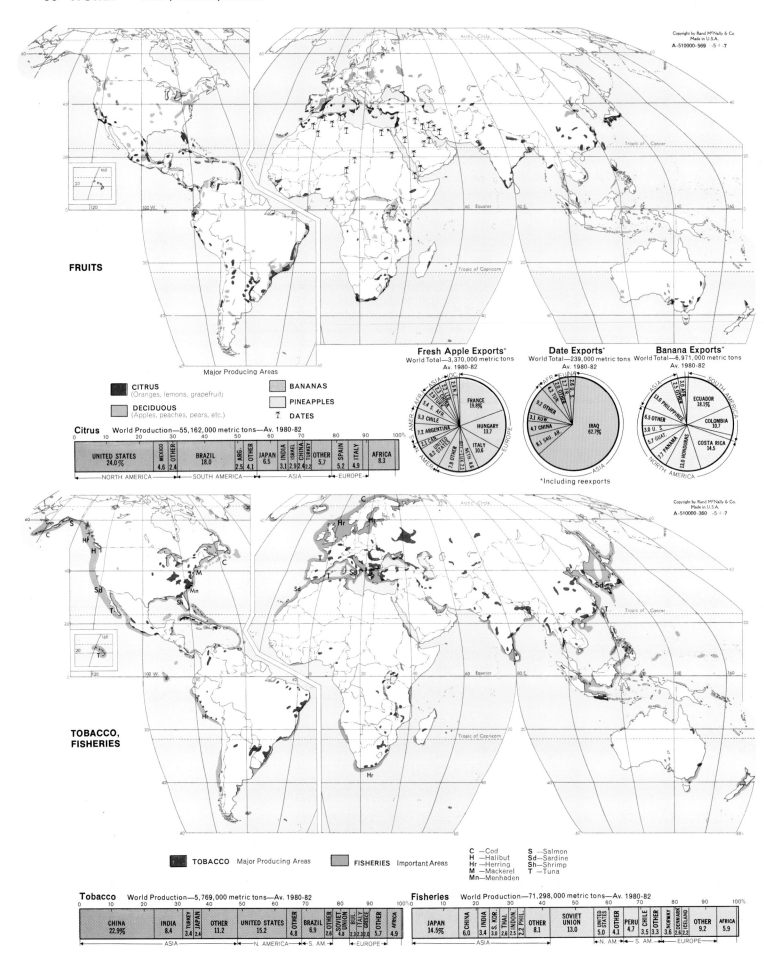

Copyright by Rand McNally & Co.
Made in U.S.A.
A-510000-569 -5-4-7

FRUITS

Major Producing Areas

CITRUS (Oranges, lemons, grapefruit)

DECIDUOUS (Apples, peaches, pears, etc.)

BANANAS

PINEAPPLES

DATES

Fresh Apple Exports*
World Total—3,370,000 metric tons
Av. 1980-82

FRANCE 19.8%
HUNGARY 13.7
ITALY 10.6
NETH. 4.6
7.8 OTHER
8.2 OTHER
2.1 CAN.
7.2 ARGENTINA
5.3 CHILE
5.4 S. AFR.
2.3 OTHER
2.6 CHINA
3.9 N.Z.

Date Exports*
World Total—239,000 metric tons
Av. 1980-82

IRAQ 62.7%
8.1 SAU. AR.
4.7 CHINA
3.1 KUW.
9.2 OTHER
2.0 OTHER
2.7 FR.
2.6 U.S.

Banana Exports*
World Total—6,971,000 metric tons
Av. 1980-82

ECUADOR 18.1%
COLOMBIA 10.7
COSTA RICA 14.5
13.0 HONDURAS
7.7 PANAMA
5.7 GUAT.
3.0 U. S.
6.5 OTHER
13.0 PHILIPPINES
2.2 OTHER

*Including reexports

Citrus World Production—55,162,000 metric tons—Av. 1980-82

UNITED STATES 24.0%	MEXICO 4.6	OTHER 2.4	BRAZIL 18.0	ARG. 2.5	OTHER 4.1	JAPAN 6.5	INDIA 3.1	ISRAEL 2.9	CHINA 2.4	TURKEY 2.2	OTHER 5.7	SPAIN 5.2	ITALY 4.9	AFRICA 8.3

NORTH AMERICA — SOUTH AMERICA — ASIA — EUROPE

TOBACCO, FISHERIES

Copyright by Rand McNally & Co.
Made in U.S.A.
A-510000-360 -5-4-7

TOBACCO Major Producing Areas

FISHERIES Important Areas

C —Cod
H —Halibut
Hr —Herring
M —Mackerel
Mn—Menhaden

S —Salmon
Sd —Sardine
Sh —Shrimp
T —Tuna

Tobacco World Production—5,769,000 metric tons—Av. 1980-82

CHINA 22.9%	INDIA 8.4	TURKEY 3.4	JAPAN 2.4	OTHER 11.2	UNITED STATES 15.2	OTHER 4.8	BRAZIL 6.9	SOVIET UNION 4.8	BUL. 2.3	ITALY 2.3	GREECE 2.0	OTHER 5.7	AFRICA 4.9

ASIA — N. AMERICA — S. AM. — EUROPE

Fisheries World Production—71,298,000 metric tons—Av. 1980-82

JAPAN 14.5%	CHINA 6.0	INDIA 3.4	S. KOR. 3.0	THAI. 2.6	INDON. 2.5	PHIL. 2.2	OTHER 8.1	SOVIET UNION 13.0	UNITED STATES 5.0	OTHER 4.1	PERU 4.7	CHILE 3.5	OTHER 3.3	NORWAY 3.6	DENMARK	ICELAND	OTHER 9.2	AFRICA 5.9

ASIA — N. AM. — S. AM. — EUROPE

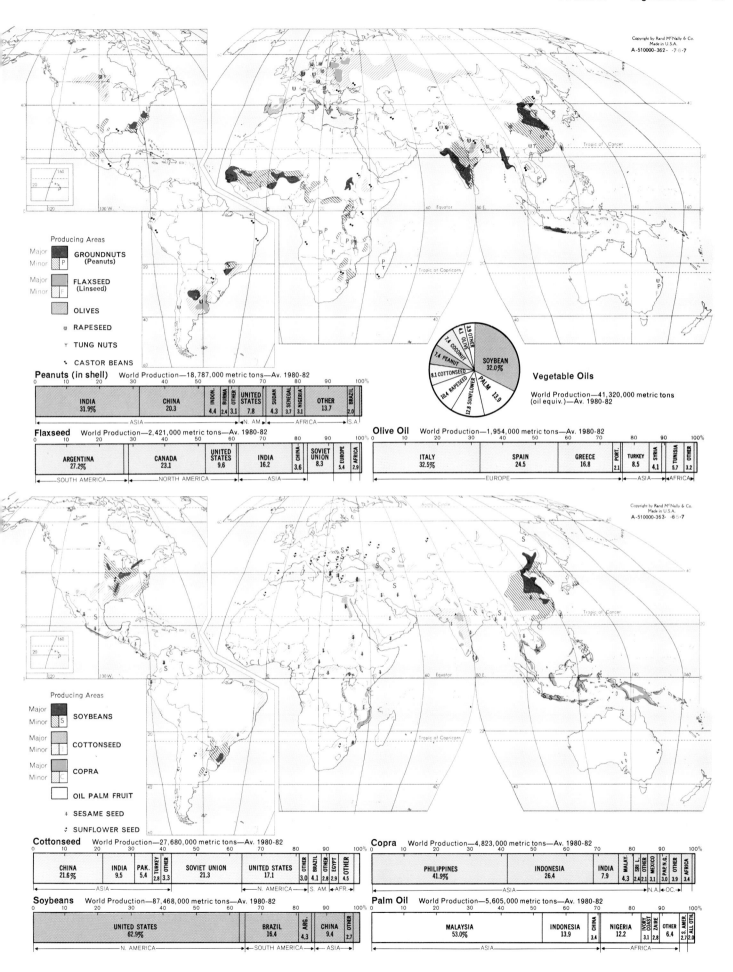

Producing Areas

Major / Minor ▪ P	**GROUNDNUTS** (Peanuts)
Major / Minor	**FLAXSEED** (Linseed)
	OLIVES
ω	**RAPESEED**
τ	**TUNG NUTS**
،	**CASTOR BEANS**

Vegetable Oils

World Production—41,320,000 metric tons
(oil equiv.)—Av. 1980-82

Pie chart: SOYBEAN 32.0%, PALM 13.9, 12.8 SUNFLOWER, 10.4 RAPESEED, 8.1 COTTONSEED, 7.4 PEANUT, 7.4 COCONUT, 4.1 OLIVE, 3.9 OTHER

Peanuts (in shell) World Production—18,787,000 metric tons—Av. 1980-82

INDIA 31.9%	CHINA 20.3	INDON. 4.4	BURMA 2.4	OTHER 3.1	UNITED STATES 7.8	SUDAN 4.3	SENEGAL 3.7	NIGERIA 3.1	OTHER 13.7	BRAZIL 2.0

← ASIA → ← N. AM → ← AFRICA → ← S.A →

Flaxseed World Production—2,421,000 metric tons—Av. 1980-82

ARGENTINA 27.2%	CANADA 23.1	UNITED STATES 9.6	INDIA 16.2	CHINA 3.6	SOVIET UNION 8.3	EUROPE 5.4	AFRICA 2.9

← SOUTH AMERICA → ← NORTH AMERICA → ← ASIA →

Olive Oil World Production—1,954,000 metric tons—Av. 1980-82

ITALY 32.5%	SPAIN 24.5	GREECE 16.8	PORT. 2.1	TURKEY 8.5	SYRIA 4.1	TUNISIA 5.7	OTHER 3.2

← EUROPE → ← ASIA → ← AFRICA →

Producing Areas

Major / Minor S	**SOYBEANS**
Major / Minor	**COTTONSEED**
Major / Minor	**COPRA**
	OIL PALM FRUIT
‡	**SESAME SEED**
،	**SUNFLOWER SEED**

Cottonseed World Production—27,680,000 metric tons—Av. 1980-82

CHINA 21.6%	INDIA 9.5	PAK. 5.4	TURKEY 2.8	OTHER 3.3	SOVIET UNION 21.3	UNITED STATES 17.1	OTHER 3.0	BRAZIL 4.1	EGYPT 2.8	OTHER 2.9	OTHER 4.5

← ASIA → ← N. AMERICA → ← S. AM. → ← AFR. →

Copra World Production—4,823,000 metric tons—Av. 1980-82

PHILIPPINES 41.9%	INDONESIA 26.4	INDIA 7.9	MALAY. 4.3	SRI L.	OTHER	MEXICO	PAP. N.G.	OTHER 3.9	AFRICA 3.4

← ASIA → ← N.A. → ← OC. →

Soybeans World Production—87,468,000 metric tons—Av. 1980-82

UNITED STATES 62.9%	BRAZIL 16.4	ARG. 4.3	CHINA 9.4	OTHER 2.7

← N. AMERICA → ← SOUTH AMERICA → ← ASIA →

Palm Oil World Production—5,605,000 metric tons—Av. 1980-82

MALAYSIA 53.0%	INDONESIA 13.9	CHINA 3.4	NIGERIA 12.2	IVORY COAST 3.1	ZAIRE 2.8	OTHER 6.4	S. AMER. 2.7	ALL OTH. 2.0

← ASIA → ← AFRICA →

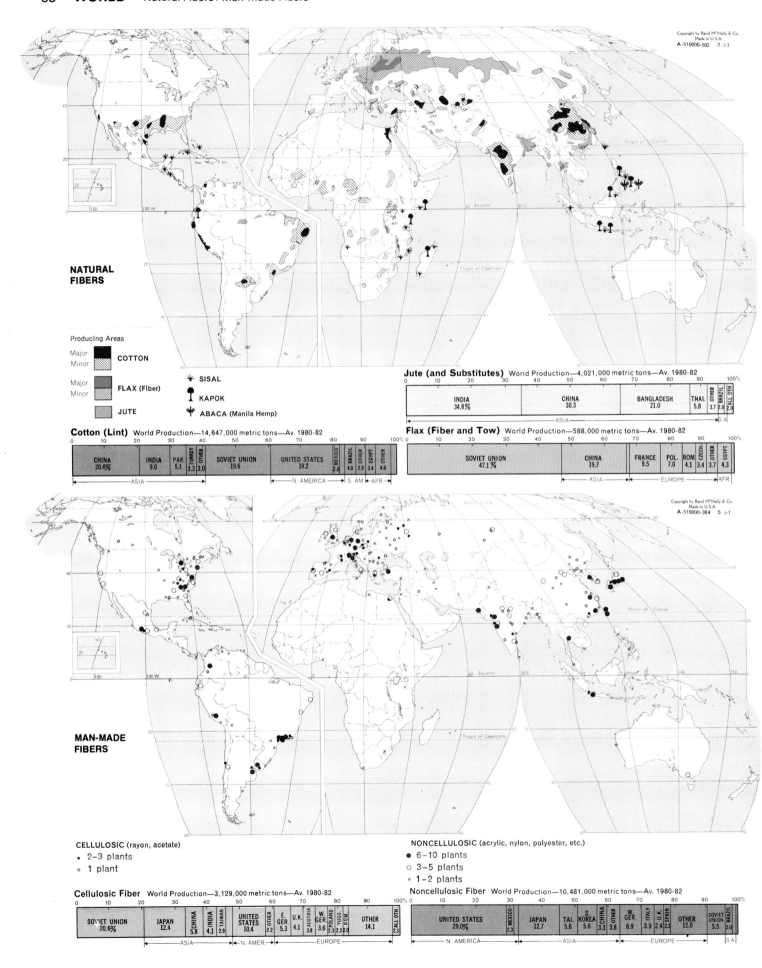

Copyright by Rand M°Nally & Co.
Made in U.S.A.
A-510000-560 -7-7-7

**NATURAL
FIBERS**

Producing Areas

Major
Minor ◼️ COTTON

Major
Minor ▨ FLAX (Fiber)

▨ JUTE

⚘ SISAL

🌴 KAPOK

⚘ ABACA (Manila Hemp)

Jute (and Substitutes) World Production—4,021,000 metric tons—Av. 1980-82

0	10	20	30	40	50	60	70	80	90	100%

INDIA 34.8%	CHINA 30.3	BANGLADESH 21.0	THAI. 5.8	OTHER 3.7	BRAZIL 2.0	ALL OTH 2.0

—————————————ASIA—————————————————— S.A.

Cotton (Lint) World Production—14,647,000 metric tons—Av. 1980-82

0	10	20	30	40	50	60	70	80	90	100%

| CHINA 20.4% | INDIA 9.0 | PAK. 5.1 | TURKEY 3.3 | OTHER 3.0 | SOVIET UNION 19.6 | UNITED STATES 19.2 | MEXICO 2.0 | BRAZIL 4.0 | OTHER 2.9 | EGYPT 3.4 | OTHER 4.8 |

——————ASIA—————— ———N. AMERICA——— S. AM. AFR.

Flax (Fiber and Tow) World Production—588,000 metric tons—Av. 1980-82

0	10	20	30	40	50	60	70	80	90	100%

| SOVIET UNION 47.1% | CHINA 19.7 | FRANCE 9.5 | POL. 7.0 | ROM 4.1 | CZECH. 3.4 | OTHER 3.7 | EGYPT 4.3 |

———ASIA——— ————EUROPE———— AFR

Copyright by Rand M°Nally & Co.
Made in U.S.A.
A-510000-364 -5 (-7

**MAN-MADE
FIBERS**

CELLULOSIC (rayon, acetate)
• 2-3 plants
○ 1 plant

NONCELLULOSIC (acrylic, nylon, polyester, etc.)
● 6-10 plants
○ 3-5 plants
× 1-2 plants

Cellulosic Fiber World Production—3,129,000 metric tons—Av. 1980-82

0	10	20	30	40	50	60	70	80	90	100%

| SOVIET UNION 20.6% | JAPAN 12.4 | CHINA 5.8 | INDIA 4.1 | TAIWAN 2.9 | UNITED STATES 10.4 | OTHER 2.2 | E. GER. 5.3 | U.K. 4.1 | AUSTRIA 3.8 | W. GER. 3.6 | POLAND 2.3 | YUGO 2.3 | ROM. 2.0 | OTHER 14.1 | ALL OTH 2.3 |

—————ASIA————— —N. AMER.— —————EUROPE—————

Noncellulosic Fiber World Production—10,481,000 metric tons—Av. 1980-82

0	10	20	30	40	50	60	70	80	90	100%

| UNITED STATES 29.0% | MEXICO 2.3 | JAPAN 12.7 | TAI. 5.6 | S. KOREA 5.6 | CHINA 3.1 | OTHER 3.8 | W. GER. 6.9 | ITALY 3.9 | U.K. 2.4 | SPAIN 2.0 | OTHER 12.0 | SOVIET UNION 5.5 | BRAZIL 2.0 |

————N. AMERICA———— —————ASIA————— —————EUROPE————— S.A.

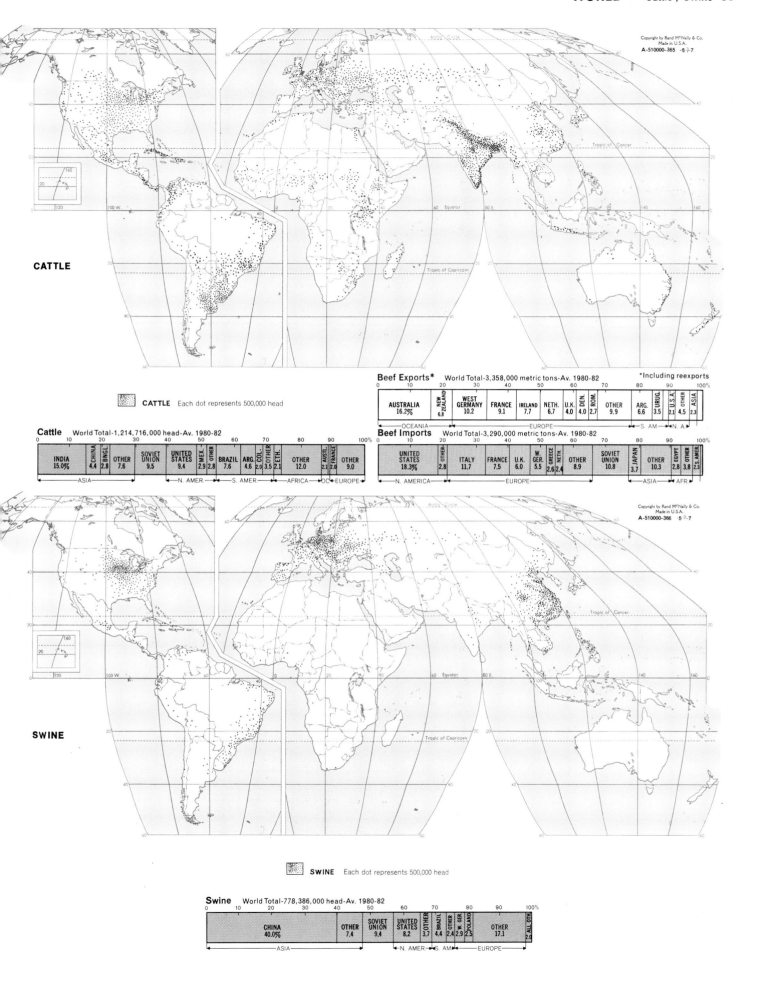

Copyright by Rand McNally & Co.
Made in U.S.A.
A-510000-365 -5-7

CATTLE

CATTLE — Each dot represents 500,000 head

Cattle World Total-1,214,716,000 head-Av. 1980-82

INDIA 15.0%	CHINA 4.4	BNGL. 2.8	OTHER 7.6	SOVIET UNION 9.5	UNITED STATES 9.4	MEX. 2.9	OTHER 2.8	BRAZIL 7.6	ARG. 4.6	COL. 2.0	OTHER 3.5	ETH. 2.1	OTHER 12.0	AUSTL. 2.1	FRANCE 2.0	OTHER 9.0
ASIA				N. AMER.				S. AMER.				AFRICA		OC	EUROPE	

Beef Exports* World Total-3,358,000 metric tons-Av. 1980-82   *Including reexports

AUSTRALIA 16.2%	NEW ZEALAND 6.8	WEST GERMANY 10.2	FRANCE 9.1	IRELAND 7.7	NETH. 6.7	U.K. 4.0	DEN. 4.0	ROM. 2.7	OTHER 9.9	ARG. 6.6	URUG. 3.5	U.S.A. 2.1	OTHER 4.5	ASIA 2.3
OCEANIA		EUROPE								S. AM.		N. A.		

Beef Imports World Total-3,290,000 metric tons-Av. 1980-82

UNITED STATES 18.3%	OTHER 2.8	ITALY 11.7	FRANCE 7.5	U.K. 6.0	W. GER. 5.5	GREECE 2.6	NETH. 2.4	OTHER 8.9	SOVIET UNION 10.8	JAPAN 3.7	OTHER 10.3	EGYPT 2.8	OTHER 3.8 S. AMER. 2.3
N. AMERICA		EUROPE								ASIA		AFR	

Copyright by Rand McNally & Co.
Made in U.S.A.
A-510000-366 -5-2-7

SWINE

SWINE — Each dot represents 500,000 head

Swine World Total-778,386,000 head-Av. 1980-82

CHINA 40.0%	OTHER 7.4	SOVIET UNION 9.4	UNITED STATES 8.2	BRAZIL 3.7	OTHER 4.4	W. GER 2.9	POLAND 2.5	OTHER 17.1 ALL OTH 2.0
ASIA			N. AMER.	S. AM.	EUROPE			

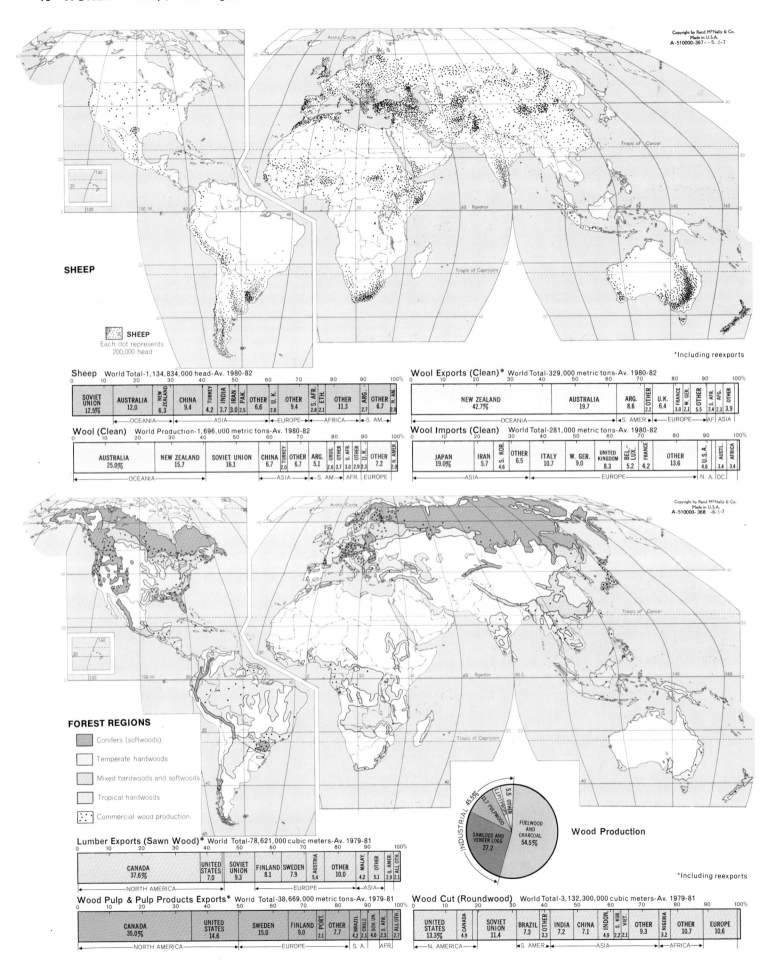

Copyright by Rand McNally & Co.
Made in U.S.A.
A-510000-367- -5-2-7

SHEEP

SHEEP
Each dot represents
200,000 head

*Including reexports

Sheep   World Total-1,134,834,000 head-Av. 1980-82

SOVIET UNION 12.5%	AUSTRALIA 12.0	NEW ZEALAND 6.3	CHINA 9.4	TURKEY 4.2	INDIA 3.7	IRAN 3.0	PAK. 2.5	OTHER 6.6	U.K. 2.8	OTHER 9.4	S. AFR. 2.8	ETH. 2.1	OTHER 11.3	ARG. 2.7	OTHER 6.7	N. AM.

← OCEANIA → ← ASIA → ← EUROPE → ← AFRICA → ← S. AM. →

Wool (Clean)   World Production-1,696,000 metric tons-Av. 1980-82

AUSTRALIA 25.0%	NEW ZEALAND 15.7	SOVIET UNION 16.1	CHINA 6.7	TURKEY 2.6	OTHER 6.7	ARG. 5.1	URUG. 2.6	OTHER 2.9	S. AFR. 3.0	OTHER 2.9	U.K. 2.9	OTHER 7.2	N. AMER.

← OCEANIA → ← ASIA → ← S. AM. → ← AFR. → ← EUROPE →

Wool Exports (Clean)* World Total-329,000 metric tons-Av. 1980-82

NEW ZEALAND 42.7%	AUSTRALIA 19.7	ARG. 8.6	OTHER 2.2	U.K. 6.4	FRANCE 3.0	W. GER. 2.4	OTHER 5.5	S. AFR. 2.3	AFG. 2.3	OTHER 3.9

← OCEANIA → ← S. AMER. → ← EUROPE → ← AF → ← ASIA →

Wool Imports (Clean)   World Total-281,000 metric tons-Av. 1980-82

JAPAN 19.0%	IRAN 5.7	S. KOR. 4.6	OTHER 6.5	ITALY 10.7	W. GER. 9.0	UNITED KINGDOM 8.3	BEL. LUX. 5.2	FRANCE 4.2	OTHER 13.6	U.S.A. 4.6	AUSTL. 3.4	AFRICA 3.4

← ASIA → ← EUROPE → ← N. A. → ← OC. →

Copyright by Rand McNally & Co.
Made in U.S.A.
A-510000-368 -6-5-7

FOREST REGIONS

Conifers (softwoods)

Temperate hardwoods

Mixed hardwoods and softwoods

Tropical hardwoods

Commercial wood production

Wood Production

INDUSTRIAL 45.5%

OTHER 5.5%
PITPROPS 4.1
PULPWOOD 9.7
SAWLOGS AND VENEER LOGS 27.2
FUELWOOD AND CHARCOAL 54.5%

*Including reexports

Lumber Exports (Sawn Wood)* World Total-78,621,000 cubic meters-Av. 1979-81

CANADA 37.6%	UNITED STATES 7.0	SOVIET UNION 9.3	FINLAND 8.1	SWEDEN 7.9	AUSTRIA 4.2	OTHER 10.0	MALAY. 4.2	OTHER 2.9	ALL OTH. 2.1

← NORTH AMERICA → ← EUROPE → ← ASIA → ← S. AMER. →

Wood Pulp & Pulp Products Exports* World Total-38,669,000 metric tons-Av. 1979-81

CANADA 35.0%	UNITED STATES 14.6	SWEDEN 15.0	FINLAND 9.0	PORT. 2.1	OTHER 7.7	BRAZIL 4.2	CHILE 4.0	SOV. UN. 2.3	S. AFR. 2.3	ALL OTH. 2.7

← NORTH AMERICA → ← EUROPE → ← S. A. → ← AFR. →

Wood Cut (Roundwood)   World Total-3,132,300,000 cubic meters-Av. 1979-81

UNITED STATES 13.3%	CANADA 4.9	SOVIET UNION 11.4	BRAZIL 7.3	OTHER 3.3	INDIA 7.2	CHINA 7.1	INDON. 4.9	S. KOR. 2.2	VIET. 2.1	OTHER 9.3	NIGERIA 3.2	OTHER 10.7	OTHER 10.6	EUROPE

← N. AMERICA → ← S. AMER. → ← ASIA → ← AFRICA →

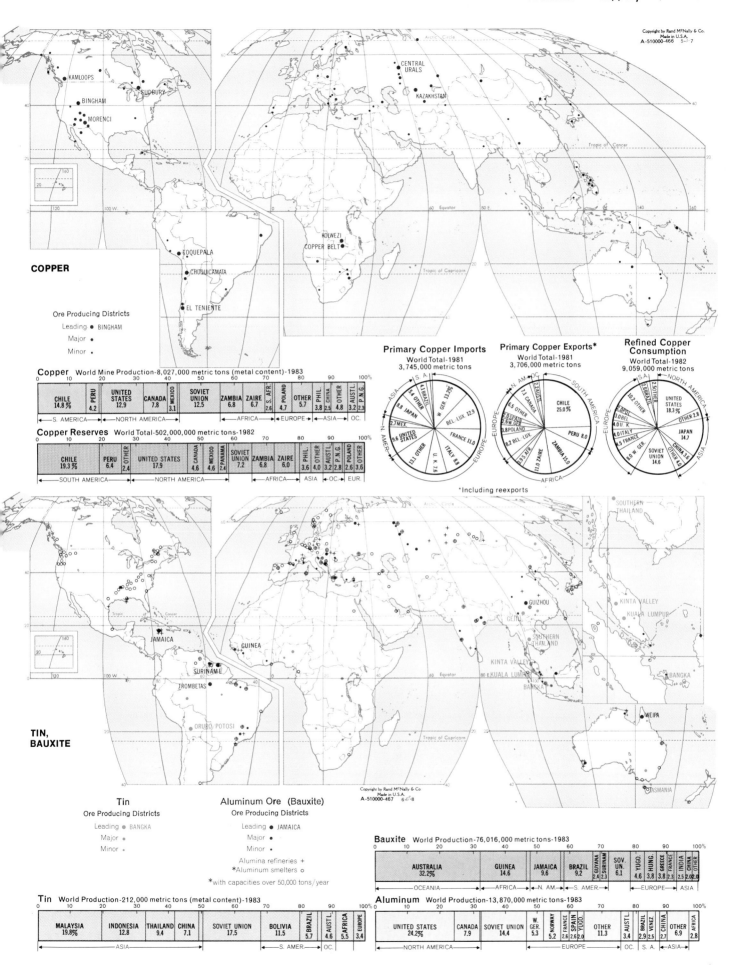

COPPER

Ore Producing Districts

Leading ● BINGHAM
Major ●
Minor ·

Copper World Mine Production-8,027,000 metric tons (metal content)-1983

CHILE 14.8%	PERU 4.2	UNITED STATES 12.9	CANADA 7.8	MEXICO 3.1	SOVIET UNION 12.5	ZAMBIA 6.8	ZAIRE 6.7	S. AFR. 2.6	POLAND 4.7	OTHER 5.7	PHIL. 3.8	CHINA 2.5	OTHER 4.8	AUSTL. 3.2	P.N.G. 2.3

S. AMERICA — NORTH AMERICA — AFRICA — EUROPE — ASIA — OC.

Copper Reserves World Total-502,000,000 metric tons-1982

CHILE 19.3%	PERU 6.4	OTHER 2.4	UNITED STATES 17.9	CANADA 4.6	MEXICO 4.6	PANAMA 2.4	SOVIET UNION 7.2	ZAMBIA 6.8	ZAIRE 6.0	PHIL. 3.6	OTHER 4.0	AUSTL. 3.2	P.N.G. 2.8	POLAND 2.6	OTHER 3.6

SOUTH AMERICA — NORTH AMERICA — AFRICA — ASIA — OC. — EUR.

Primary Copper Imports
World Total-1981
3,745,000 metric tons

CHILE 25.0%

Primary Copper Exports*
World Total-1981
3,706,000 metric tons

Refined Copper Consumption
World Total-1982
9,059,000 metric tons

UNITED STATES 18.3%
JAPAN 14.7
SOVIET UNION 14.6

*Including reexports

TIN, BAUXITE

Tin
Ore Producing Districts

Leading ● BANGKA
Major ●
Minor ·

Aluminum Ore (Bauxite)
Ore Producing Districts

Leading ◆ JAMAICA
Major ◆
Minor ·
Alumina refineries +
*Aluminum smelters ○

*with capacities over 50,000 tons/year

Bauxite World Production-76,016,000 metric tons-1983

AUSTRALIA 32.2%	GUINEA 14.6	JAMAICA 9.6	BRAZIL 9.2	GUYANA 2.4	SURINAM 2.3	SOV. UN. 6.1	YUGO. 4.6	HUNG. 3.8	GREECE 3.8	FRANCE 2.3	INDIA 2.5	CHINA 2.0	OTHER 2.0

OCEANIA — AFRICA — N. AM. — S. AMER. — EUROPE — ASIA

Tin World Production-212,000 metric tons (metal content)-1983

MALAYSIA 19.8%	INDONESIA 12.8	THAILAND 9.4	CHINA 7.1	SOVIET UNION 17.5	BOLIVIA 11.5	BRAZIL 5.7	AUSTL. 4.6	AFRICA 5.5	EUROPE 3.4

ASIA — S. AMER. — OC.

Aluminum World Production-13,870,000 metric tons-1983

UNITED STATES 24.2%	CANADA 7.9	SOVIET UNION 14.4	W. GER. 5.3	NORWAY 5.2	FRANCE 2.6	SPAIN 2.6	YUGO. 2.0	OTHER 11.3	AUSTL. 3.4	BRAZIL 2.9	VENEZ. 2.5	CHINA 2.7	OTHER 6.9	AFRICA 2.8

NORTH AMERICA — EUROPE — OC. — S. A. — ASIA

42

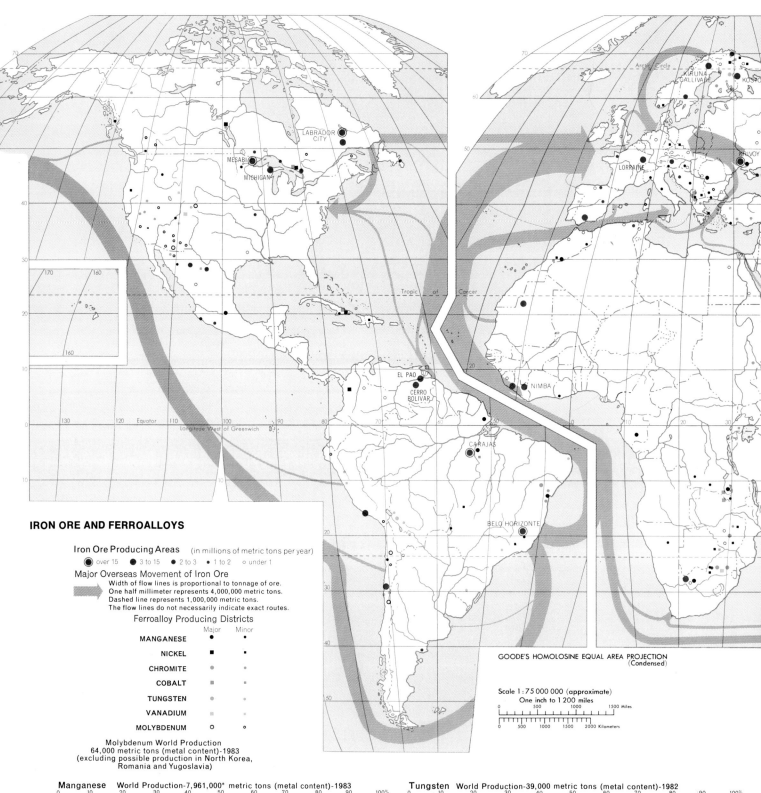

IRON ORE AND FERROALLOYS

Iron Ore Producing Areas (in millions of metric tons per year)
◉ over 15　● 3 to 15　● 2 to 3　• 1 to 2　○ under 1

Major Overseas Movement of Iron Ore
Width of flow lines is proportional to tonnage of ore.
One half millimeter represents 4,000,000 metric tons.
Dashed line represents 1,000,000 metric tons.
The flow lines do not necessarily indicate exact routes.

Ferroalloy Producing Districts

	Major	Minor
MANGANESE	●	•
NICKEL	■	▪
CHROMITE	●	•
COBALT	▪	▪
TUNGSTEN	●	•
VANADIUM	▪	▪
MOLYBDENUM	○	○

Molybdenum World Production
64,000 metric tons (metal content)-1983
(excluding possible production in North Korea,
Romania and Yugoslavia)

GOODE'S HOMOLOSINE EQUAL AREA PROJECTION
(Condensed)

Scale 1:75 000 000 (approximate)
One inch to 1 200 miles

Manganese World Production-7,961,000* metric tons (metal content)-1983

SOVIET UNION 40.6%	SOUTH AFRICA 14.1	GABON 11.9	BRAZIL 11.5	AUSTL. 7.6	INDIA 5.3	CHINA 4.0	ALL OTH. 2.9

←————AFRICA————→ ←S. AMER.→ ←OC.→ ←ASIA→

*Excluding possible production in Cuba and Namibia

Nickel World Production-689,000 metric tons (metal content)-1983

SOVIET UNION 24.6%	CANADA 17.7	CUBA 5.4	DOM. REP. 2.9	AUSTRALIA 13.1	NEW CALEDONIA 9.1	INDON. 6.8	PHIL. 2.8	S. AFR. 3.0	BOTS. 2.5	GREECE 2.2	OTHER 4.1	COL. 2.0

←NORTH AMERICA→ ←OCEANIA→ ←ASIA→ AFR. EUR. S.A

Tungsten World Production-39,000 metric tons (metal content)-1982

CHINA 32.1%	SOUTH KOREA 5.9	BURMA 2.4	OTHER 4.6	SOVIET UNION 23.4	BOLIVIA 6.2	BRAZIL 3.1	AUSTL. 5.3	PORT. 3.5	AUS. 2.9	OTHER 4.1	U.S.A. 2.5

←————————ASIA————————→ ←S. AMER.→ ←OC.→ ←EUR.→ N.A.

Vanadium World Mine Production-29,000 metric tons (metal content)-1983

SOVIET UNION 33.1%	SOUTH AFRICA 28.0	CHINA 15.8	JAPAN 2.4	FINLAND 11.1	UNITED STATES 9.7

←————AFRICA————→ ←—ASIA—→ ←EUROPE→ N. AMER.

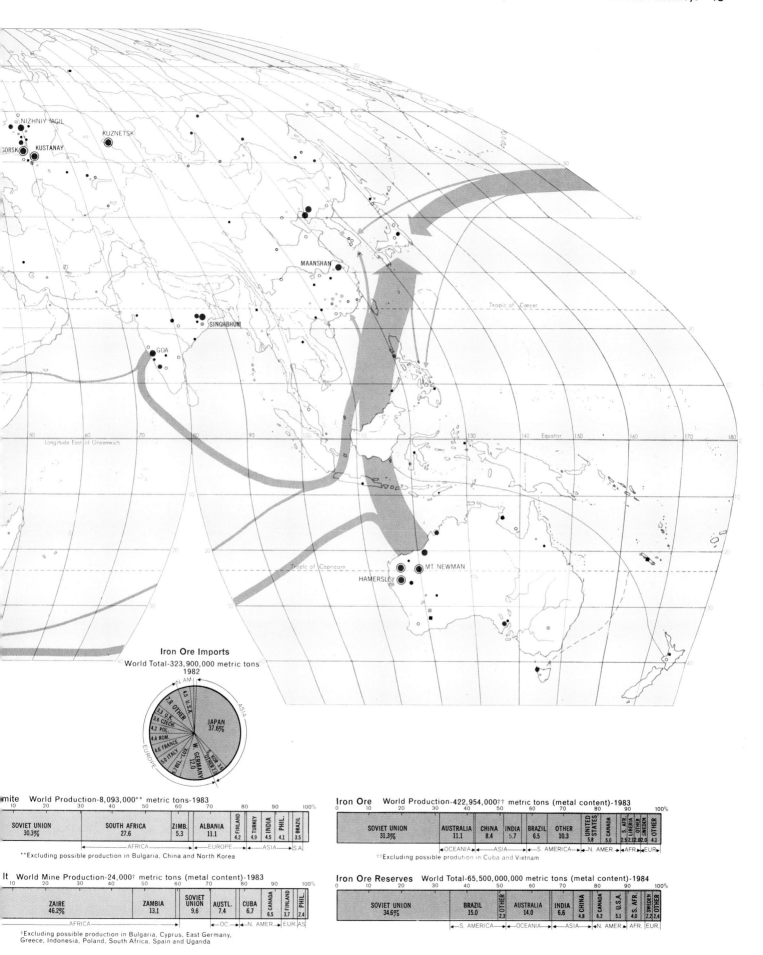

NIZHNIY TAGIL

KUZNETSK

GORSK KUSTANAY

KUZNETSK

MAANSHAN

Tropic of Cancer

SINGHBHUM

GOA

Longitude East of Greenwich

Equator

Tropic of Capricorn

MT. NEWMAN

HAMERSLEY

Iron Ore Imports
World Total-323,900,000 metric tons
1982

7.8 OTHER   4.5 U.S.A.
3.3 U.K.
3.6 CZECH.
4.2 POL.   JAPAN
4.4 ROM.   37.6%
4.6 FRANCE
5.0 ITALY
BEL.-LUX.   W. GERMANY KOR. 3.3
7.0   12.0   OTHER 2.

mite   World Production-8,093,000** metric tons-1983

10 20 30	40 50 60	70	80		90			100%
SOVIET UNION 30.3%	SOUTH AFRICA 27.6	ZIMB. 5.3	ALBANIA 11.1	FINLAND 4.2	TURKEY 4.9	INDIA 4.5	PHIL. 4.1	BRAZIL 3.5
	←————AFRICA————→		←——EUROPE——→		←——ASIA——→			S.A.

**Excluding possible production in Bulgaria, China and North Korea

Iron Ore   World Production-422,954,000†† metric tons (metal content)-1983

10 20 30	40	50	60	70	80	90		100%
SOVIET UNION 31.3%	AUSTRALIA 11.1	CHINA 8.4	INDIA 5.7	BRAZIL 6.5	OTHER 10.3	UNITED STATES 5.8	CANADA 5.0	S. AFR. 2.5 LIBERIA 2.1 OTHER 2.0 SWEDEN 2.0 OTHER 4.1
	←OCEANIA→	←——ASIA——→		←S. AMERICA→		←—N. AMER.—→		AFR. EUR.

††Excluding possible production in Cuba and Vietnam

It   World Mine Production-24,000† metric tons (metal content)-1983

10 20 30 40 50	60	70	80		90		100%
ZAIRE 46.2%	ZAMBIA 13.1	SOVIET UNION 9.6	AUSTL. 7.4	CUBA 6.7	CANADA 6.5	FINLAND 3.7	PHIL. 2.4
	←————AFRICA————→			OC.	←N. AMER.→	EUR. AS

†Excluding possible production in Bulgaria, Cyprus, East Germany,
Greece, Indonesia, Poland, South Africa, Spain and Uganda

Iron Ore Reserves   World Total-65,500,000,000 metric tons (metal content)-1984

10 20 30	40	50	60	70	80	90	100%
SOVIET UNION 34.6%	BRAZIL 15.0	OTHER 2.3	AUSTRALIA 14.0	INDIA 6.6	CHINA 4.8	CANADA 6.2	U.S.A. 5.1 S. AFR. 4.0 SWEDEN 2.2 OTHER 2.4
	←S. AMERICA→	←OCEANIA→		←—ASIA—→		←N. AMER.→	AFR. EUR.

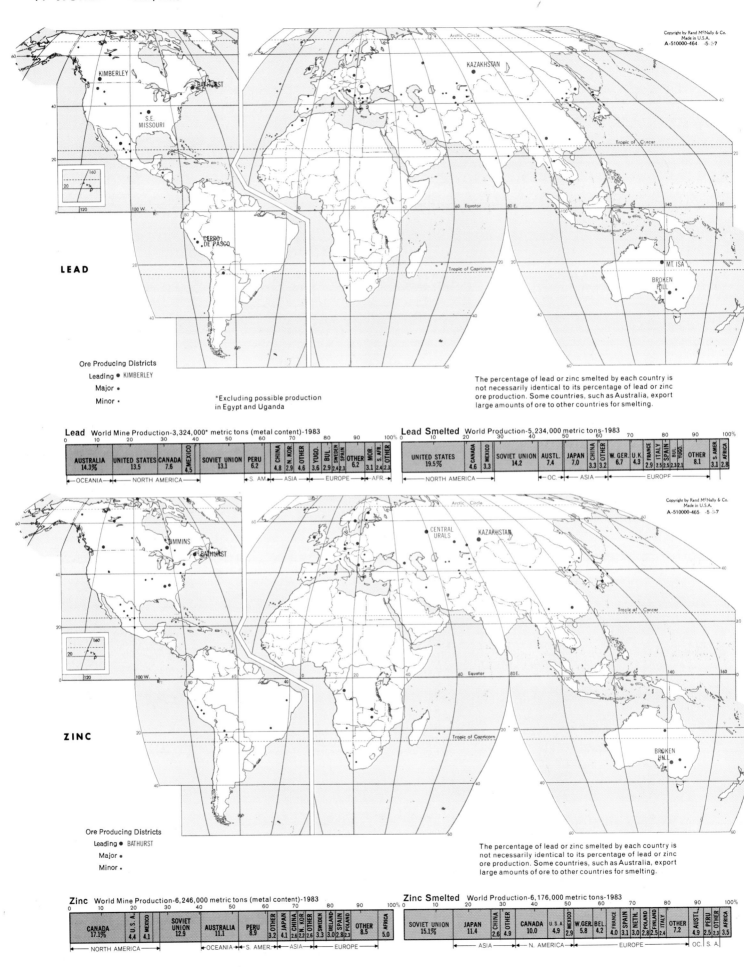

Copyright by Rand McNally & Co.
Made in U.S.A.
A-510000-464 -5-2-7

KAZAKHSTAN
KIMBERLEY
BATHURST
S.E. MISSOURI
CERRO DE PASCO
MT ISA
BROKEN HILL

LEAD

Ore Producing Districts

Leading ● KIMBERLEY

Major ●

Minor ·

*Excluding possible production in Egypt and Uganda

The percentage of lead or zinc smelted by each country is not necessarily identical to its percentage of lead or zinc ore production. Some countries, such as Australia, export large amounts of ore to other countries for smelting.

Lead World Mine Production-3,324,000* metric tons (metal content)-1983

| AUSTRALIA 14.3% | UNITED STATES 13.5 | CANADA 7.6 | MEXICO 4.5 | SOVIET UNION 13.1 | PERU 6.2 | CHINA 4.8 | JAPAN 2.9 | N. KOR. 4.6 | OTHER 3.6 | YUGO. 2.9 | SWEDEN 2.4 | SPAIN 2.3 | OTHER 6.2 | MOR. 3.1 | S. AFR. 2.4 | OTHER 2.3 |

OCEANIA — NORTH AMERICA — S. AM. — ASIA — EUROPE — AFR.

Lead Smelted World Production-5,234,000 metric tons-1983

| UNITED STATES 19.5% | CANADA 4.6 | MEXICO 3.3 | SOVIET UNION 14.2 | AUSTL. 7.4 | JAPAN 7.0 | CHINA 3.3 | OTHER 3.2 | W. GER. 6.7 | U.K. 4.3 | FRANCE 2.9 | ITALY 2.5 | SPAIN 2.3 | BUL. YUGO. 2.1 | OTHER 8.1 | S. AMER. 3.1 | AFRICA 2.8 |

NORTH AMERICA — OC. — ASIA — EUROPE

Copyright by Rand McNally & Co.
Made in U.S.A.
A-510000-465 -5-2-7

CENTRAL URALS
KAZAKHSTAN
TIMMINS
BATHURST
BROKEN HILL

ZINC

Ore Producing Districts

Leading ● BATHURST

Major ●

Minor ·

The percentage of lead or zinc smelted by each country is not necessarily identical to its percentage of lead or zinc ore production. Some countries, such as Australia, export large amounts of ore to other countries for smelting.

Zinc World Mine Production-6,246,000 metric tons (metal content)-1983

| CANADA 17.1% | U.S.A. 4.4 | MEXICO 4.1 | SOVIET UNION 12.9 | AUSTRALIA 11.1 | PERU 8.9 | OTHER 3.2 | JAPAN 4.1 | CHINA 2.6 | N. KOR. 2.6 | SWEDEN 3.3 | IRELAND 2.8 | SPAIN 2.8 | POLAND 2.3 | OTHER 8.5 | AFRICA 5.0 |

NORTH AMERICA — OCEANIA — S. AMER. — ASIA — EUROPE

Zinc Smelted World Production-6,176,000 metric tons-1983

| SOVIET UNION 15.1% | JAPAN 11.4 | CHINA 2.6 | OTHER 4.9 | CANADA 10.0 | U.S.A. 4.9 | MEXICO 2.9 | W.GER. 5.8 | BEL. 4.2 | FRANCE 4.0 | SPAIN 3.1 | NETH. 3.0 | POLAND 2.8 | FINLAND 2.4 | ITALY 2.4 | OTHER 7.2 | AUSTL. 4.9 | PERU 2.5 | OTHER 2.3 | AFRICA 3.5 |

ASIA — N. AMERICA — EUROPE — OC. — S. A.

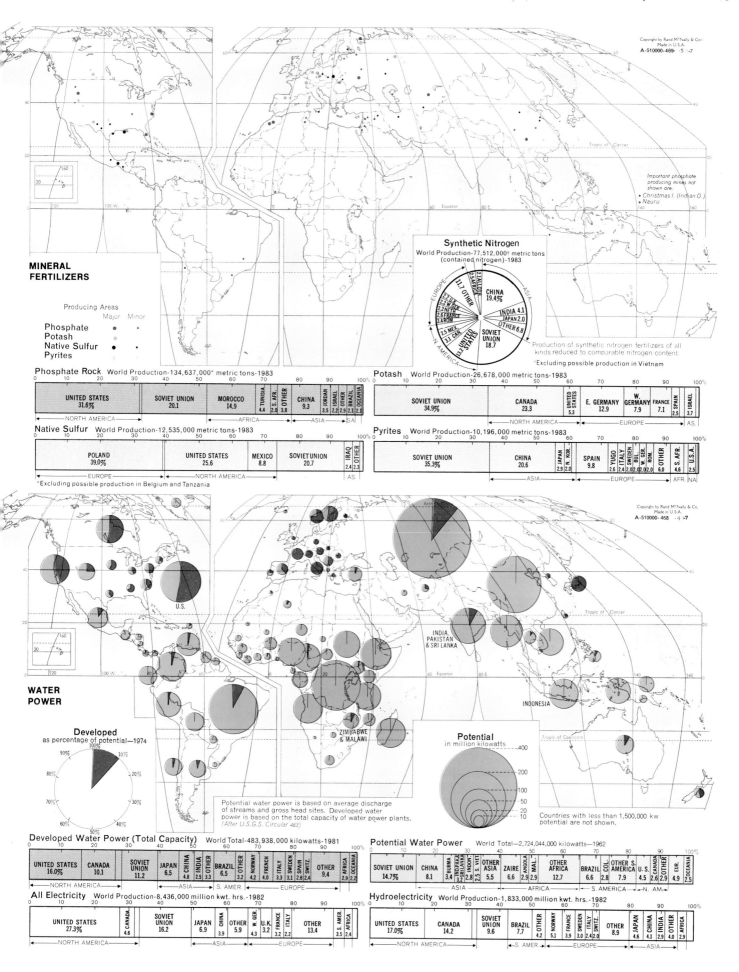

Copyright by Rand McNally & Co.
Made in U.S.A.
A-510000-469- -5 -7

Important phosphate
producing mines not
shown are:
• Christmas I. (Indian O.)
• Nauru

MINERAL FERTILIZERS

Producing Areas

	Major	Minor
Phosphate	●	●
Potash		
Native Sulfur	●	●
Pyrites		

Synthetic Nitrogen
World Production-77,512,000† metric tons
(contained nitrogen)-1983

Production of synthetic nitrogen fertilizers of all
kinds reduced to comparable nitrogen content.
†Excluding possible production in Vietnam

Phosphate Rock   World Production-134,637,000* metric tons-1983

UNITED STATES 31.6%	SOVIET UNION 20.1	MOROCCO 14.9	TUNISIA 4.4	S. AFR. 2.0	OTHER 3.8	CHINA 9.3	JORDAN 3.5	ISRAEL 2.2	OTHER 2.9	BRAZIL 2.1	OCEANIA 2.1

NORTH AMERICA | AFRICA | ASIA | SA.

Potash   World Production-26,678,000 metric tons-1983

SOVIET UNION 34.9%	CANADA 23.3	UNITED STATES 5.3	E. GERMANY 12.9	W. GERMANY 7.9	FRANCE 7.1	SPAIN 2.5	ISRAEL 3.7

NORTH AMERICA | EUROPE | AS.

Native Sulfur   World Production-12,535,000 metric tons-1983

POLAND 39.0%	UNITED STATES 25.6	MEXICO 8.8	SOVIET UNION 20.7	IRAQ 2.4	OTHER 2.3

EUROPE | NORTH AMERICA | AS.
*Excluding possible production in Belgium and Tanzania

Pyrites   World Production-10,196,000 metric tons-1983

SOVIET UNION 35.3%	CHINA 20.6	JAPAN 2.5	N. KOR. 2.0	SPAIN 9.8	YUGO 2.6	ITALY 2.4	SWEDEN 2.0	BUL. 2.0	W. GER. 2.0	ROM. 2.0	OTHER 6.0	S. AFR. 4.6	U.S.A. 2.5

ASIA | EUROPE | AFR. | NA

Copyright by Rand McNally & Co.
Made in U.S.A.
A-510000-468 -4 -7

WATER POWER

Developed
as percentage of potential—1974

Potential
in million kilowatts

Potential water power is based on average discharge
of streams and gross head sites. Developed water
power is based on the total capacity of water power plants.
(After U.S.G.S. Circular 483)

Countries with less than 1,500,000 kw
potential are not shown.

Developed Water Power (Total Capacity)   World Total-483,938,000 kilowatts-1981

UNITED STATES 16.0%	CANADA 10.1	SOVIET UNION 11.2	JAPAN 6.5	CHINA 4.8	INDIA 2.5	OTHER 3.3	BRAZIL 6.5	OTHER 3.2	NORWAY 4.2	FRENCH 4.1	ITALY 3.3	SPAIN 3.1	SWITZ. 2.4	OTHER 9.4	AFRICA 2.9	OCEANIA 2.3

NORTH AMERICA | ASIA | S. AMER. | EUROPE

Potential Water Power   World Total-2,724,044,000 kilowatts—1962

SOVIET UNION 14.7%	CHINA 8.1	BURMA 3.4	INDIA/PAK. 3.2	S. KOR/LANKA 3.1	INDON. 2.8	VIET. 2.5	OTHER ASIA 5.5	ZAIRE 6.6	ANGOLA 2.9	MAL. 2.9	OTHER AFRICA 12.7	BRAZIL 6.6	COL. 2.8	OTHER S. AMERICA 7.9	U.S. 4.5	CANADA 2.6	OTHER 2.9	EUR. 4.9	OCEANIA

ASIA | AFRICA | S. AMERICA | N. AM.

All Electricity   World Production-8,436,000 million kwt. hrs.-1982

UNITED STATES 27.3%	CANADA 4.6	SOVIET UNION 16.2	JAPAN 6.9	CHINA 3.9	OTHER 5.9	W. GER. 4.3	U.K. 3.2	FRANCE 3.2	ITALY 2.2	OTHER 13.4	S. AMER. 3.5	AFRICA 2.4

NORTH AMERICA | ASIA | EUROPE

Hydroelectricity   World Production-1,833,000 million kwt. hrs.-1982

UNITED STATES 17.0%	CANADA 14.2	SOVIET UNION 9.6	BRAZIL 7.7	OTHER 4.2	NORWAY 5.1	FRANCE 3.2	SWEDEN 3.0	ITALY 2.4	SWITZ. 2.0	OTHER 8.9	JAPAN 4.6	CHINA 4.1	INDIA 2.9	OTHER 4.0	AFRICA 4.9

NORTH AMERICA | S. AMER. | EUROPE | ASIA

46

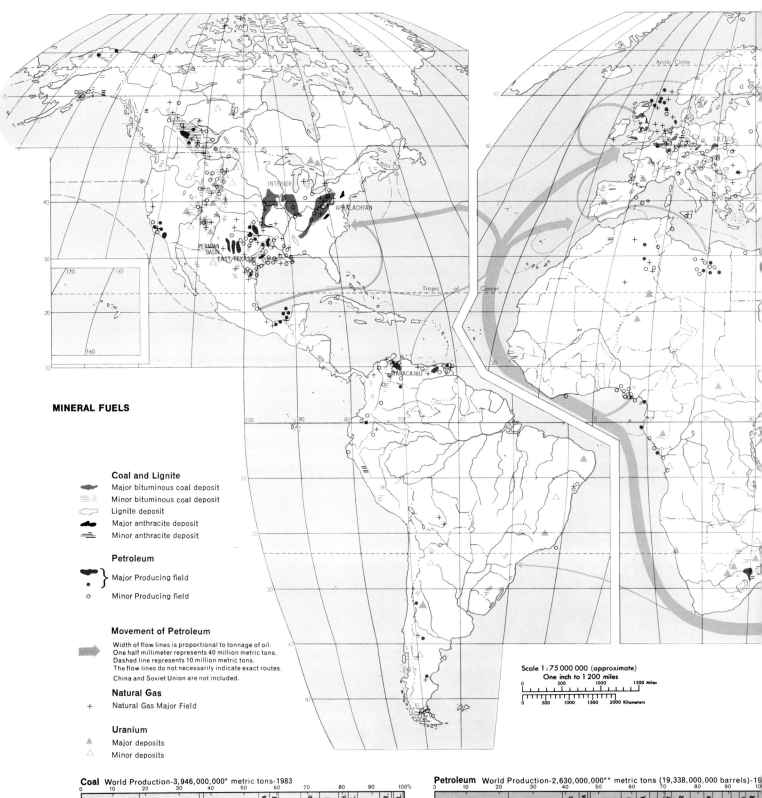

MINERAL FUELS

Coal and Lignite

Major bituminous coal deposit

Minor bituminous coal deposit

Lignite deposit

Major anthracite deposit

Minor anthracite deposit

Petroleum

} Major Producing field

o Minor Producing field

Movement of Petroleum

Width of flow lines is proportional to tonnage of oil.
One half millimeter represents 40 million metric tons.
Dashed line represents 10 million metric tons.
The flow lines do not necessarily indicate exact routes.
China and Soviet Union are not included.

Natural Gas

+ Natural Gas Major Field

Uranium

▲ Major deposits

△ Minor deposits

Coal World Production-3,946,000,000* metric tons-1983

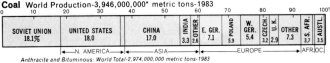

SOVIET UNION 18.1%	UNITED STATES 18.0	CHINA 17.0	INDIA 3.3	OTHER 2.6	E. GER. 7.1	POLAND 5.9	W. GER. 5.4	CZECH. 3.2	U.K. 2.9	OTHER 7.3	S. AFR. 3.7	AUSTL. 3.5

←— N. AMERICA —→ ←——— ASIA ———→ ←——————— EUROPE ———————→ AFR. OC.

Anthracite and Bituminous: World Total-2,974,000,000 metric tons-1983

Coal Reserves World Total-894,974,000,000* metric tons-1981

UNITED STATES 28.7%	SOVIET UNION 26.8	CHINA 11.0	AUSTL. 7.3	W. GER. 7.3	POLAND 4.4	SOUTH AFRICA 5.8

←———— NORTH AMERICA ————→ ←——— ASIA ———→ OC. ←— EUROPE —→ AFR.

Copyright by Rand Mᶜ Nally & Co.
Made in U.S.A.
A-510000-462 -7-6-8⁰

Anthracite and Bituminous: World Total-657,180,000,000 metric tons-1981
*Includes anthracite, subanthracite, bituminous, subbituminous, lignite and brown coal

Petroleum World Production-2,630,000,000** metric tons (19,338,000,000 barrels)-19

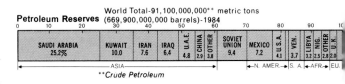

SOVIET UNION 22.7%	UNITED STATES 16.4	MEXICO 5.1	CANADA 2.7	SAUDI ARABIA 9.6	IRAN 4.6	CHINA 4.0	INDON. 2.6	U.A.E. 2.2	KUWAIT 2.0	OTHER 5.4	U.K. 4.3	OTHER 2.8	VEN. 3.8	OTHER 2.8	NIG. 2.3	LIBYA 2.0	OTHER 4.1

←——— NORTH AMERICA ———→ ←——————— ASIA ———————→ ←— EUR. —→ S. A. ←— AFR. —→

Petroleum Reserves World Total-91,100,000,000** metric tons (669,900,000,000 barrels)-1984

SAUDI ARABIA 25.2%	KUWAIT 10.0	IRAN 7.6	IRAQ 6.4	U.A.E. 4.8	CHINA 2.9	OTHER 3.8	SOVIET UNION 9.4	MEXICO 7.2	U.S.A. 4.1	VEN. 3.7	LIBYA 3.2	NIG. 2.5	OTHER 2.0	U.K.

←——————————————— ASIA ———————————————→ ←— N. AMER. —→ S. A. ←— AFR. —→

**Crude Petroleum

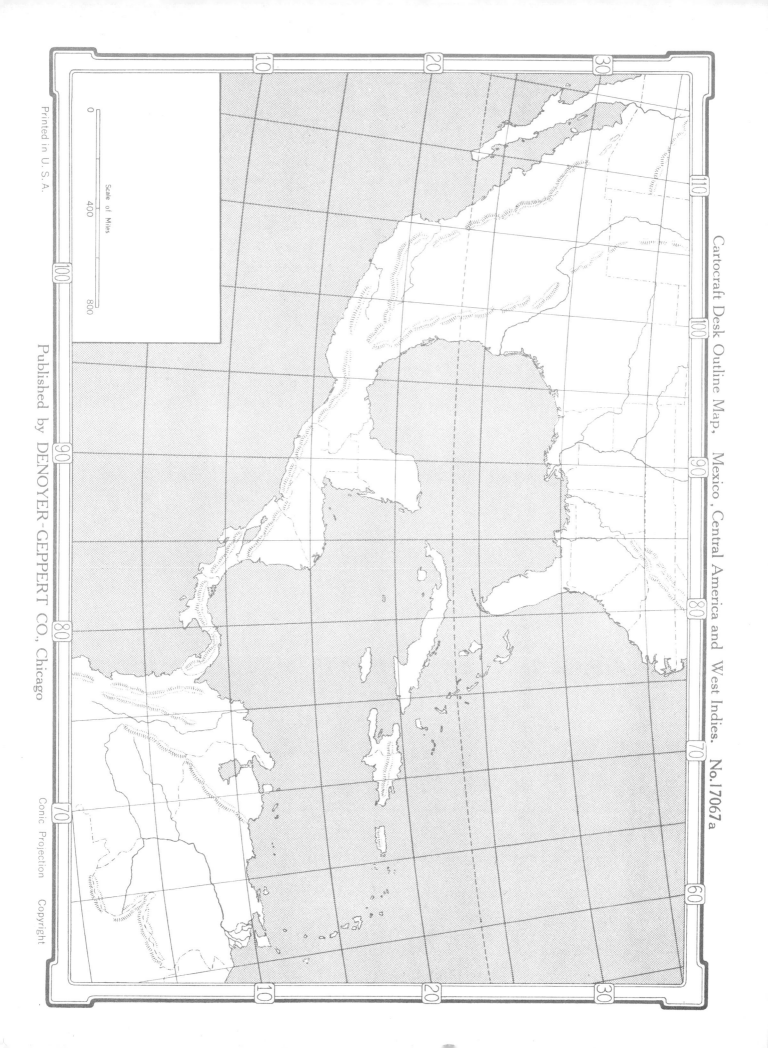

Cartocraft Desk Outline Map, Mexico, Central America and West Indies. No.17067a

Printed in U.S.A.

Published by DENOYER-GEPPERT CO., Chicago

Conic Projection   Copyright

Scale of Miles

0   400   800

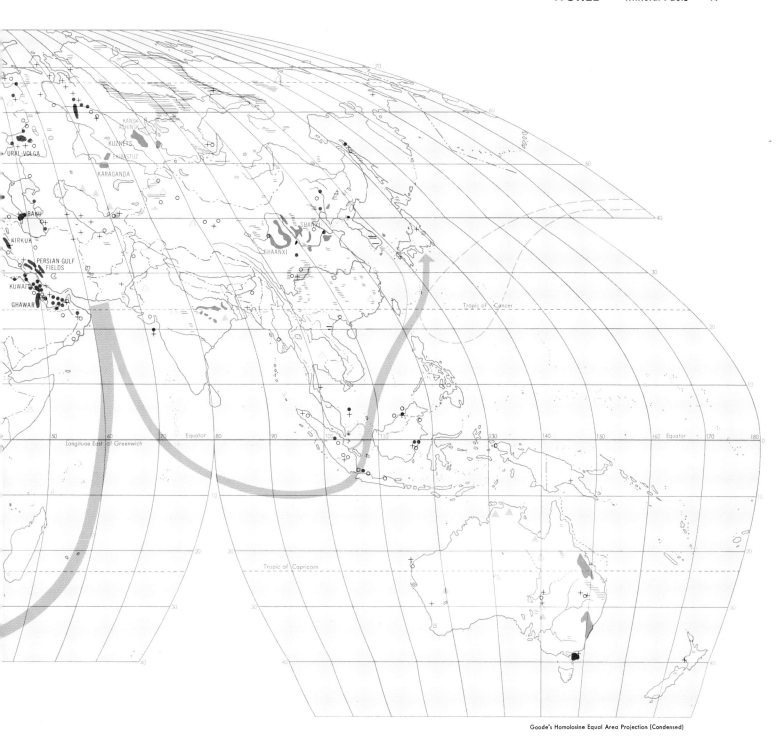

Goode's Homolosine Equal Area Projection (Condensed)

URAL-VOLGA

KANSK-
ACHINSK

KUZNETS

EKIBASTUZ

KARAGANDA

BAKU

KIRKUK

PERSIAN GULF
FIELDS

KUWAIT

GHAWAR

SHANXI

SHAANXI

Tropic of Cancer

Longitude East of Greenwich   Equator

Tropic of Capricorn

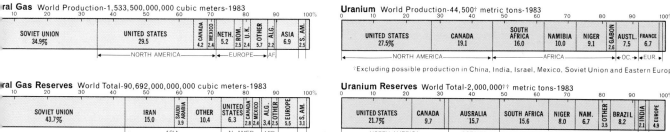

ral Gas World Production-1,533,500,000,000 cubic meters-1983

0	10	20	30	40	50	60	70	80	90	100%

SOVIET UNION 34.9%	UNITED STATES 29.5	CANADA 4.2	MEXICO 2.4	NETH. 5.2	ROM. 2.5	U.K. 2.4	OTHER 5.7	ALG. 2.2	ASIA 6.9	S. AM. 2.5

←———— NORTH AMERICA ————→ ←———— EUROPE ————→ ←AF.→

ral Gas Reserves World Total-90,692,000,000,000 cubic meters-1983

0	10	20	30	40	50	60	70	80	90	100%

SOVIET UNION 43.7%	IRAN 15.0	SAUDI ARABIA 3.9	OTHER 10.4	UNITED STATES 6.3	CANADA 2.8	MEXICO 2.4	ALG. 3.4	OTHER 5.5	EUROPE	S. AM. 3.1

←———————— ASIA ————————→ ←— N. AMER. —→ ←AFR.→

Uranium World Production-44,500† metric tons-1983

0	10	20	30	40	50	60	70	80	90	100%

UNITED STATES 27.5%	CANADA 19.1	SOUTH AFRICA 16.0	NAMIBIA 10.0	NIGER 9.1	GABON 2.6	AUSTL. 7.5	FRANCE 6.7

←—— NORTH AMERICA ——→ ←———————— AFRICA ————————→ ←OC.→ ←EUR.→

†Excluding possible production in China, India, Israel, Mexico, Soviet Union and Eastern Europe

Uranium Reserves World Total-2,000,000†† metric tons-1983

0	10	20	30	40	50	60	70	80	90	100%

UNITED STATES 21.7%	CANADA 9.7	AUSRALIA 15.7	SOUTH AFRICA 15.6	NIGER 8.0	NAM. 6.7	OTHER 3.5	BRAZIL 8.2	INDIA 2.1	EUROPE 4.9

←———— NORTH AMERICA ————→ ←— OCEANIA —→ ←———— AFRICA ————→ ←S. AM.→ ←AS.→

††Excluding possible reserves in China, Egypt, Israel, Libya, Soviet Union and Eastern Europe

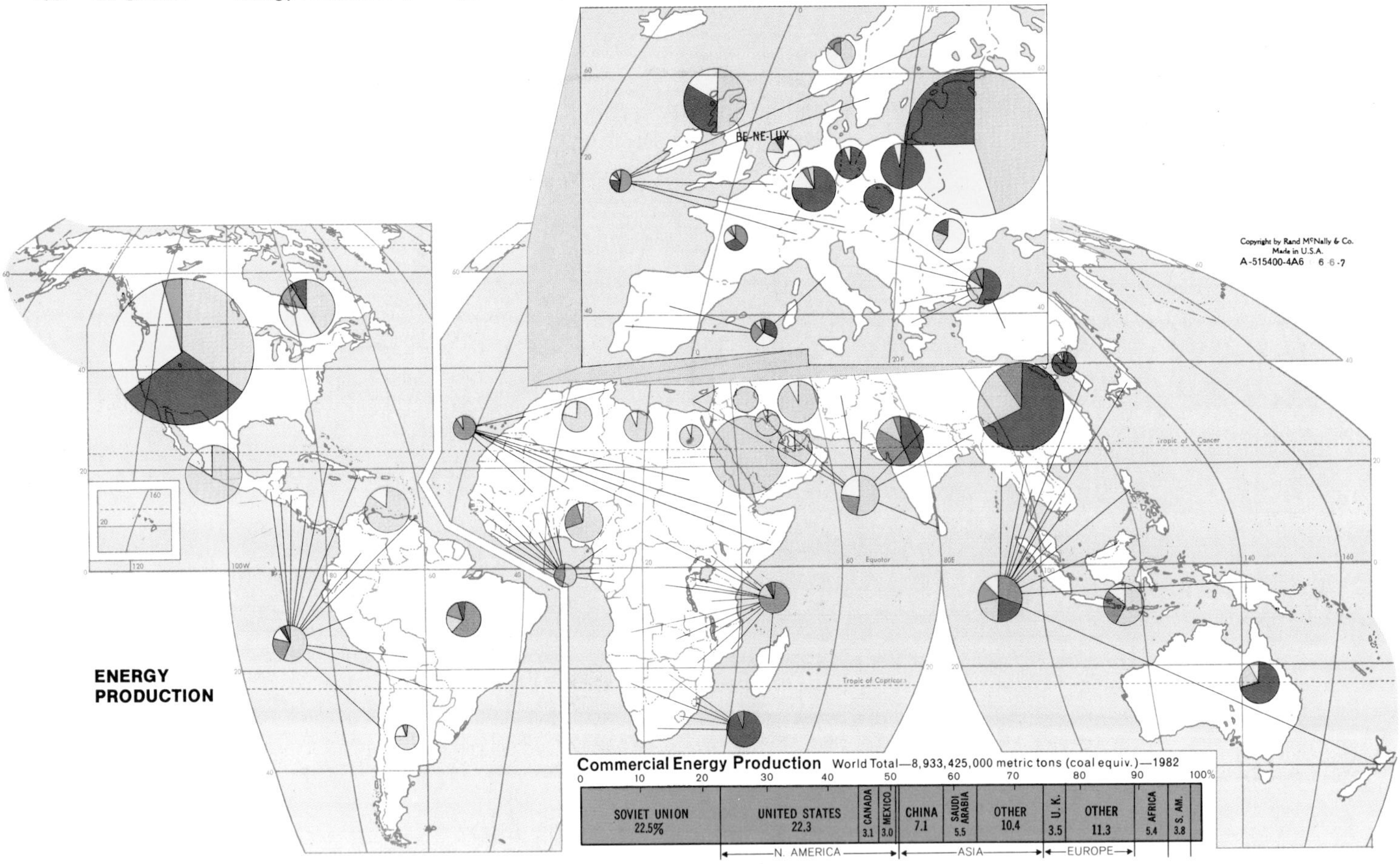
ENERGY PRODUCTION
BE-NE-LUX
Equator
Tropic of Cancer
Tropic of Capricorn
Commercial Energy Production World Total—8,933,425,000 metric tons (coal equiv.)—1982
0 10 20 30 40 50 60 70 80 90 100%
SOVIET UNION 22.5%
UNITED STATES 22.3
CANADA 3.1
MEXICO 3.0
CHINA 7.1
SAUDI ARABIA 5.5
OTHER 10.4
U. K. 3.5
OTHER 11.3
AFRICA 5.4
S. AM. 3.8
N. AMERICA
ASIA
EUROPE

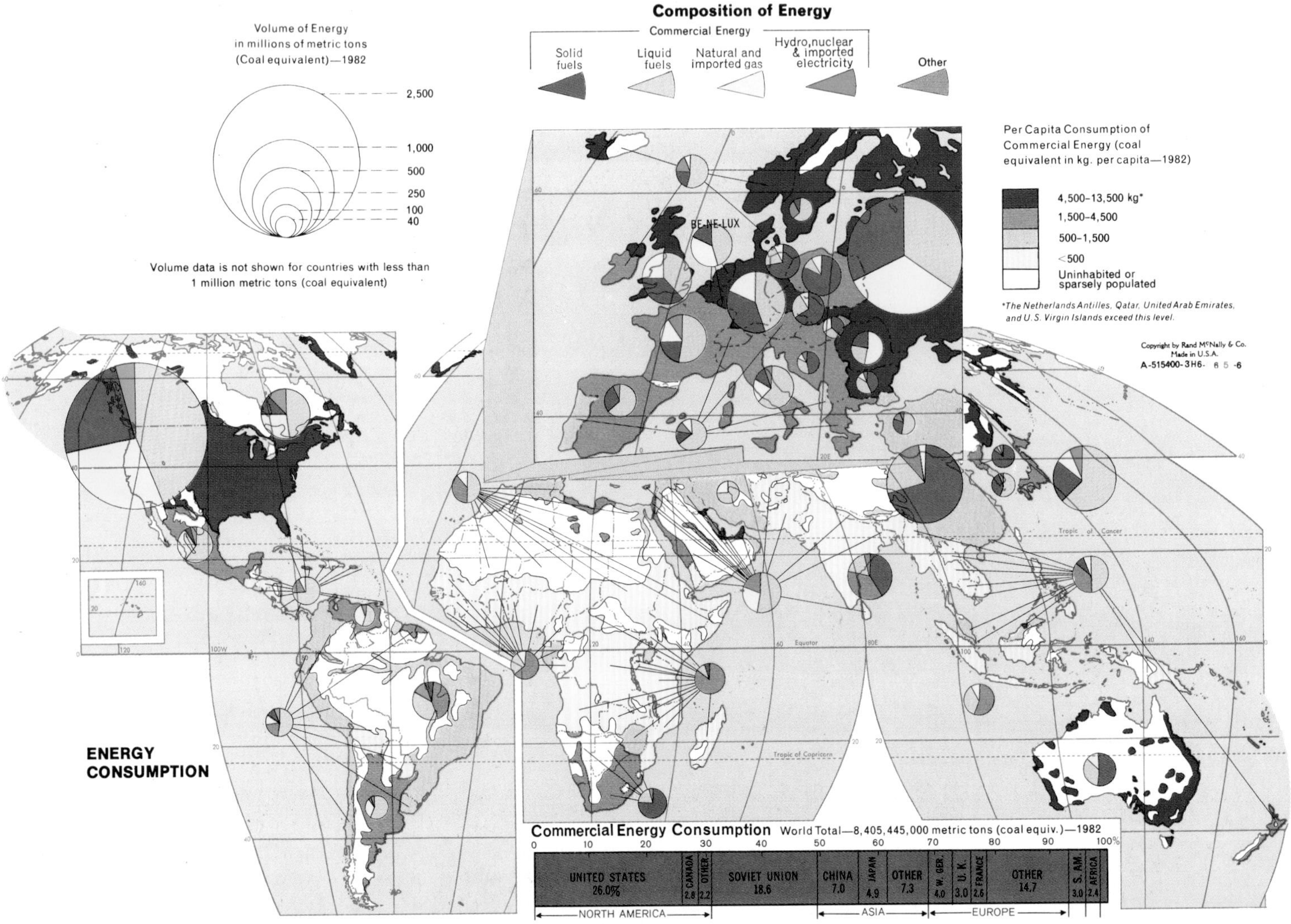
Composition of Energy
Commercial Energy
Solid fuels
Liquid fuels
Natural and imported gas
Hydro,nuclear & imported electricity
Other
Volume of Energy in millions of metric tons (Coal equivalent)—1982
2,500
1,000
500
250
100
40
Volume data is not shown for countries with less than 1 million metric tons (coal equivalent)
Per Capita Consumption of Commercial Energy (coal equivalent in kg. per capita—1982)
4,500–13,500 kg*
1,500–4,500
500–1,500
<500
Uninhabited or sparsely populated
*The Netherlands Antilles, Qatar, United Arab Emirates, and U.S. Virgin Islands exceed this level.

ENERGY CONSUMPTION
BE-NE-LUX
Equator
Tropic of Cancer
Tropic of Capricorn
Commercial Energy Consumption World Total—8,405,445,000 metric tons (coal equiv.)—1982
0 10 20 30 40 50 60 70 80 90 100%
UNITED STATES 26.0%
CANADA 2.8
OTHER 2.2
SOVIET UNION 18.6
CHINA 7.0
JAPAN 4.9
OTHER 7.3
W. GER. 4.0
U. K. 3.0
FRANCE 2.6
OTHER 14.7
S. AM. 3.0
AFRICA 2.4
NORTH AMERICA
ASIA
EUROPE

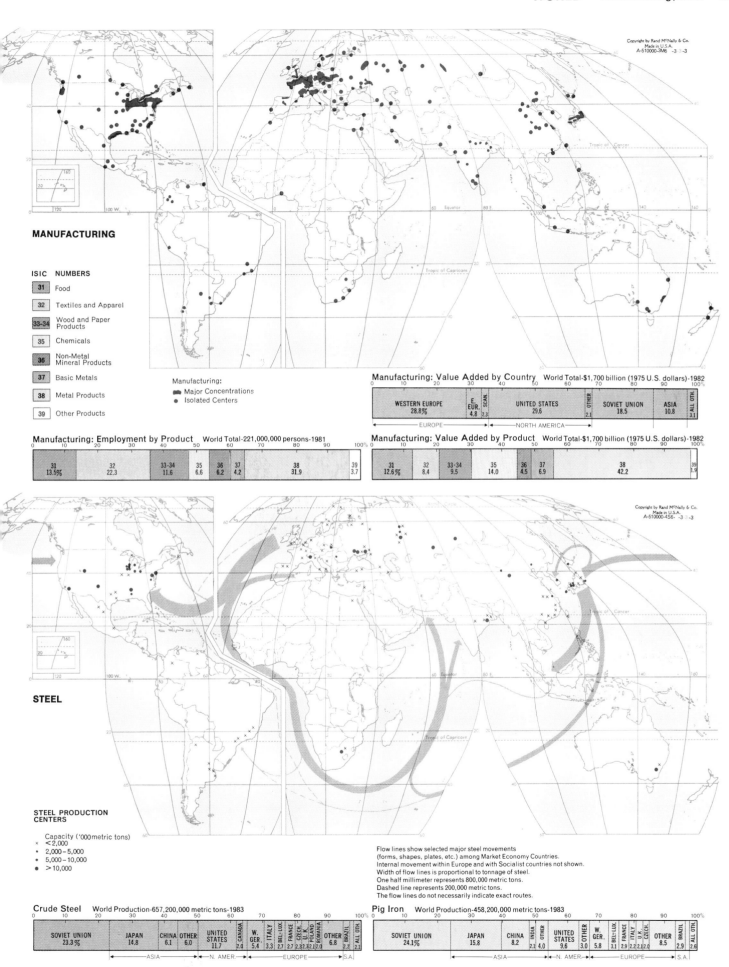

MANUFACTURING

ISIC NUMBERS

31	Food
32	Textiles and Apparel
33-34	Wood and Paper Products
35	Chemicals
36	Non-Metal Mineral Products
37	Basic Metals
38	Metal Products
39	Other Products

Manufacturing:
■ Major Concentrations
● Isolated Centers

Manufacturing: Value Added by Country   World Total-$1,700 billion (1975 U.S. dollars)-1982

	0	10	20	30	40	50	60	70	80	90	100%

| WESTERN EUROPE 28.8% | E. EUR. 4.8 | SCAN. 2.3 | UNITED STATES 29.6 | OTHER 2.1 | SOVIET UNION 18.5 | ASIA 10.8 | ALL OTH. 3.1 |

←——— EUROPE ———→ ←——NORTH AMERICA——→

Manufacturing: Employment by Product   World Total-221,000,000 persons-1981

| 31 13.5% | 32 22.3 | 33-34 11.6 | 35 6.6 | 36 6.2 | 37 4.2 | 38 31.9 | 39 3.7 |

Manufacturing: Value Added by Product   World Total-$1,700 billion (1975 U.S. dollars)-1982

| 31 12.6% | 32 8.4 | 33-34 9.5 | 35 14.0 | 36 4.5 | 37 6.9 | 38 42.2 | 39 1.9 |

STEEL

STEEL PRODUCTION CENTERS

Capacity ('000 metric tons)
× <2,000
● 2,000-5,000
● 5,000-10,000
● >10,000

Flow lines show selected major steel movements
(forms, shapes, plates, etc.) among Market Economy Countries.
Internal movement within Europe and with Socialist countries not shown.
Width of flow lines is proportional to tonnage of steel.
One half millimeter represents 800,000 metric tons.
Dashed line represents 200,000 metric tons.
The flow lines do not necessarily indicate exact routes.

Crude Steel   World Production-657,200,000 metric tons-1983

| SOVIET UNION 23.3% | JAPAN 14.8 | CHINA 6.1 | OTHER 6.0 | UNITED STATES 11.7 | CANADA 2.0 | W. GER. 5.4 | ITALY 3.3 | BEL.-LUX. 2.7 | FRANCE 2.7 | CZECH. 2.3 | U.K. 2.3 | POLAND 2.1 | ROMANIA 2.0 | OTHER 6.8 | BRAZIL 2.2 | ALL OTH. 2.1 |

←————ASIA————→ ←N. AMER.→ ←————EUROPE————→ S.A.

Pig Iron   World Production-458,200,000 metric tons-1983

| SOVIET UNION 24.1% | JAPAN 15.8 | CHINA 8.2 | INDIA 2.1 | OTHER 4.0 | UNITED STATES 9.6 | OTHER 3.0 | W. GER. 5.8 | BEL.-LUX. 3.1 | FRANCE 2.9 | ITALY 2.2 | U.K. 2.1 | CZECH. 2.0 | OTHER 8.5 | BRAZIL 2.9 | ALL OTH. 2.6 |

←————ASIA————→ ←N. AMER.→ ←————EUROPE————→ S.A.

Copyright by Rand McNally & Co.
Made in U.S.A.
A-510000-4C6 -6-4-6

LAND AND OCEAN TRANSPORTATION

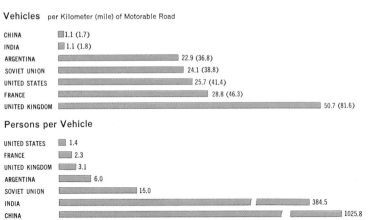

Vehicles per Kilometer (mile) of Motorable Road

CHINA	1.1 (1.7)
INDIA	1.1 (1.8)
ARGENTINA	22.9 (36.8)
SOVIET UNION	24.1 (38.8)
UNITED STATES	25.7 (41.4)
FRANCE	28.8 (46.3)
UNITED KINGDOM	50.7 (81.6)

Persons per Vehicle

UNITED STATES	1.4
FRANCE	2.3
UNITED KINGDOM	3.1
ARGENTINA	6.0
SOVIET UNION	15.0
INDIA	384.5
CHINA	1025.8

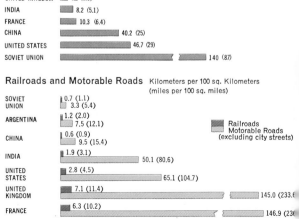

Inland Waterways Thousands of Kilometers (miles)

ARGENTINA	3.2 (2)
UNITED KINGDOM	4.2 (2.6)
INDIA	8.2 (5.1)
FRANCE	10.3 (6.4)
CHINA	40.2 (25)
UNITED STATES	46.7 (29)
SOVIET UNION	140 (87)

Railroads and Motorable Roads Kilometers per 100 sq. Kilometers (miles per 100 sq. miles)

Railroads
Motorable Roads (excluding city streets)

	Railroads	Motorable Roads
SOVIET UNION	0.7 (1.1)	3.3 (5.4)
ARGENTINA	1.2 (2.0)	7.5 (12.1)
CHINA	0.6 (0.9)	9.5 (15.4)
INDIA	1.9 (3.1)	50.1 (80.6)
UNITED STATES	2.8 (4.5)	65.1 (104.7)
UNITED KINGDOM	7.1 (11.4)	145.0 (233.6)
FRANCE	6.3 (10.2)	146.9 (236)

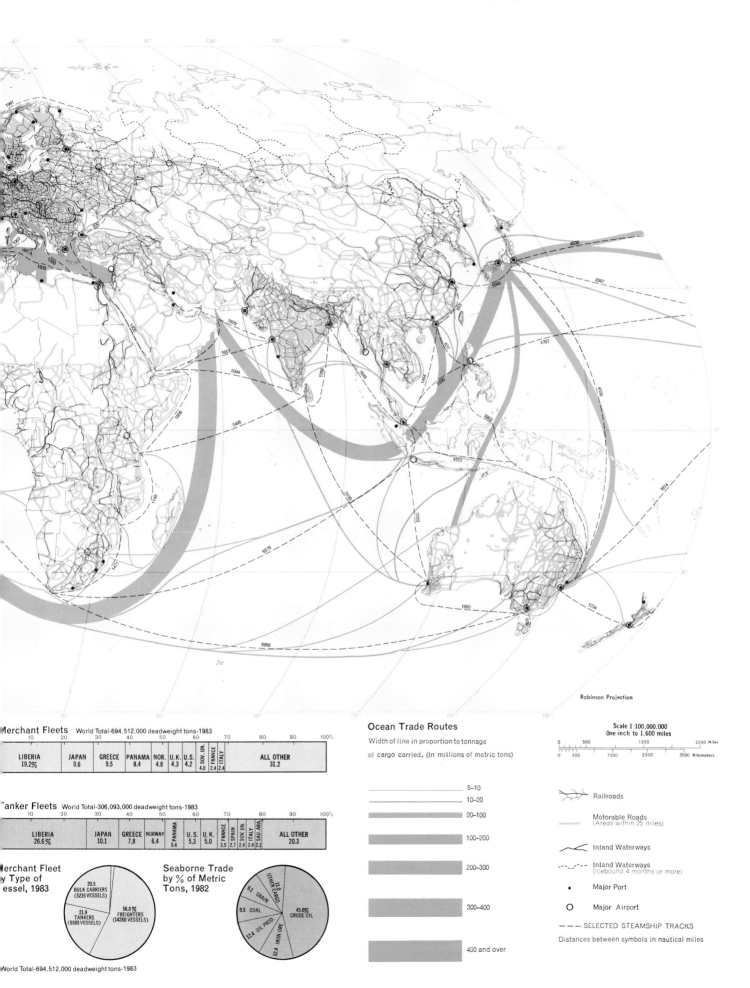

Robinson Projection

Merchant Fleets   World Total-694,512,000 deadweight tons-1983

	10	20	30	40	50	60	70	80	90	100%

| LIBERIA 19.2% | JAPAN 9.6 | GREECE 9.5 | PANAMA 8.4 | NOR. 4.8 | U.K. 4.3 | U.S. 4.2 | SOV. UN. 4.0 | FRANCE 2.4 | ITALY 2.4 | ALL OTHER 31.2 |

Tanker Fleets   World Total-306,093,000 deadweight tons-1983

	10	20	30	40	50	60	70	80	90	100%

| LIBERIA 26.6% | JAPAN 10.1 | GREECE 7.8 | NORWAY 6.4 | PANAMA 5.4 | U.S. 5.3 | U.K. 5.0 | FRANCE 3.5 | SPAIN 2.7 | SOV. UN. 2.4 | ITALY 2.4 | SAU. ARA. 2.1 | ALL OTHER 20.3 |

Merchant Fleet by Type of Vessel, 1983

20.5 BULK CARRIERS (5215 VESSELS)

21.9 TANKERS (5583 VESSELS)

56.0% FREIGHTERS (14280 VESSELS)

World Total-694,512,000 deadweight tons-1983

Seaborne Trade by % of Metric Tons, 1982

11.0 OTHER CARGO

9.1 GRAIN

9.5 COAL

12.4 OIL PROD

12.4 IRON ORE

45.6% CRUDE OIL

Ocean Trade Routes

Width of line in proportion to tonnage of cargo carried. (In millions of metric tons)

5–10
10–20
20–100
100–200
200–300
300–400
400 and over

Scale 1:100,000,000
One inch to 1,600 miles

0 500 1500 2500 Miles
0 500 1500 3500 Kilometers

Railroads

Motorable Roads (Areas within 25 miles)

Inland Waterways

Inland Waterways (Icebound 4 months or more)

• Major Port

O Major Airport

– – – SELECTED STEAMSHIP TRACKS

Distances between symbols in nautical miles

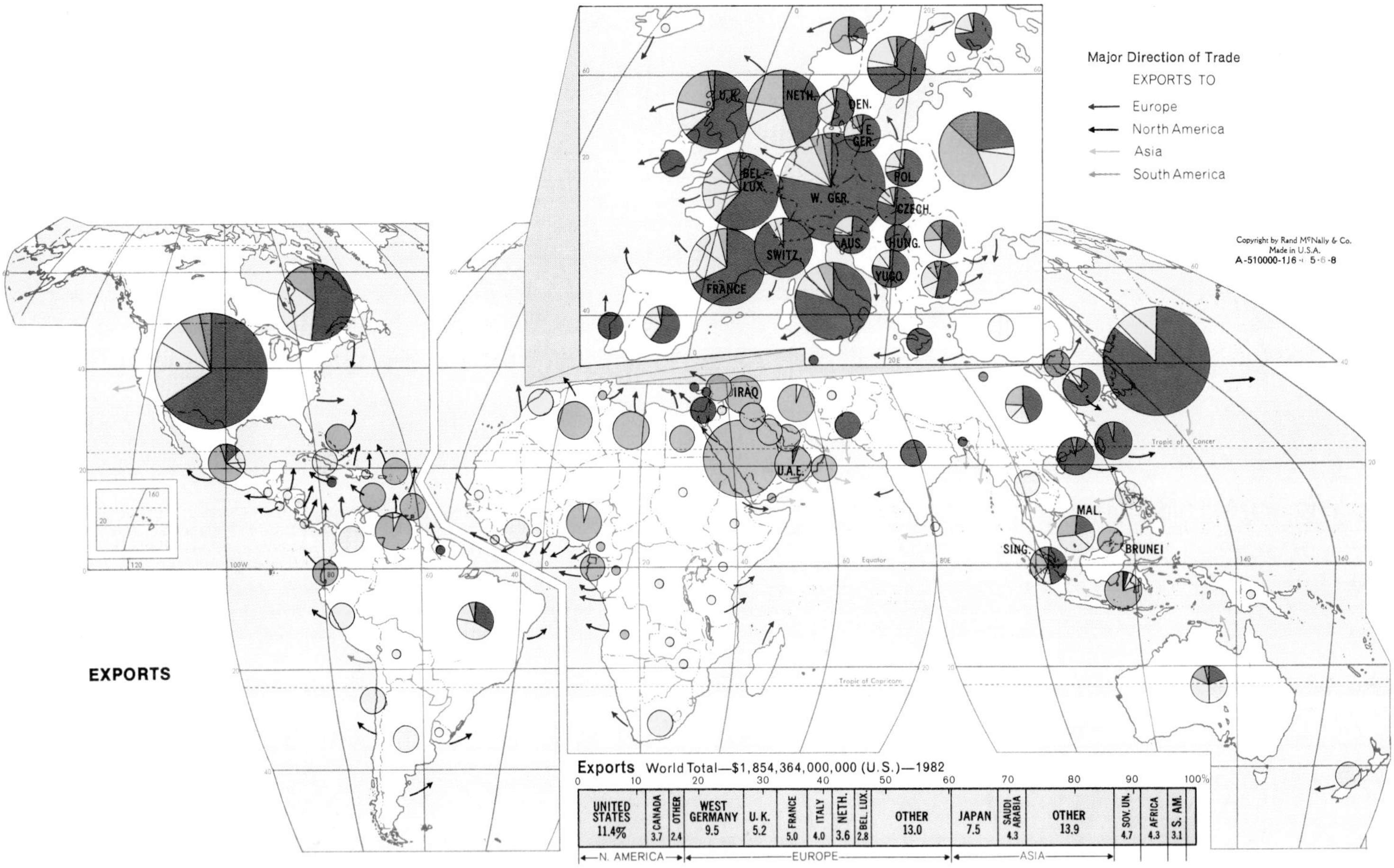

Major Direction of Trade
EXPORTS TO

← Europe
← North America
← Asia
← South America

IRAQ
U.A.E.
MAL
SING.
BRUNEI

EXPORTS

Exports World Total—$1,854,364,000,000 (U.S.)—1982

UNITED STATES 11.4%	CANADA 3.7	OTHER 2.4	WEST GERMANY 9.5	U.K. 5.2	FRANCE 5.0	ITALY 4.0	NETH. 3.6	BEL. LUX. 2.8	OTHER 13.0	JAPAN 7.5	SAUDI ARABIA 4.3	OTHER 13.9	SOV. UN. 4.7	AFRICA 4.3	S. AM. 3.1
←— N. AMERICA —→			←———————— EUROPE ————————→							←——————— ASIA ———————→					

Composition of Trade

Manufactured Articles	Food, bev. & tobacco	Raw Materials	Fuel & Related Prod.	All other or undifferentiated

Volume of Trade
(in millions of U.S. dollars, 1982)

— 100,000-200,000
— 50,000-100,000
— 25,000-50,000
— 10,000-25,000
— 2,000-10,000
— 0-2,000

United States: Exports-212,000; Imports-255,000
If volume of trade is less than 10 billion dollars, color indicates major class only. If no symbol is shown, volume of trade is less than 400 million dollars.

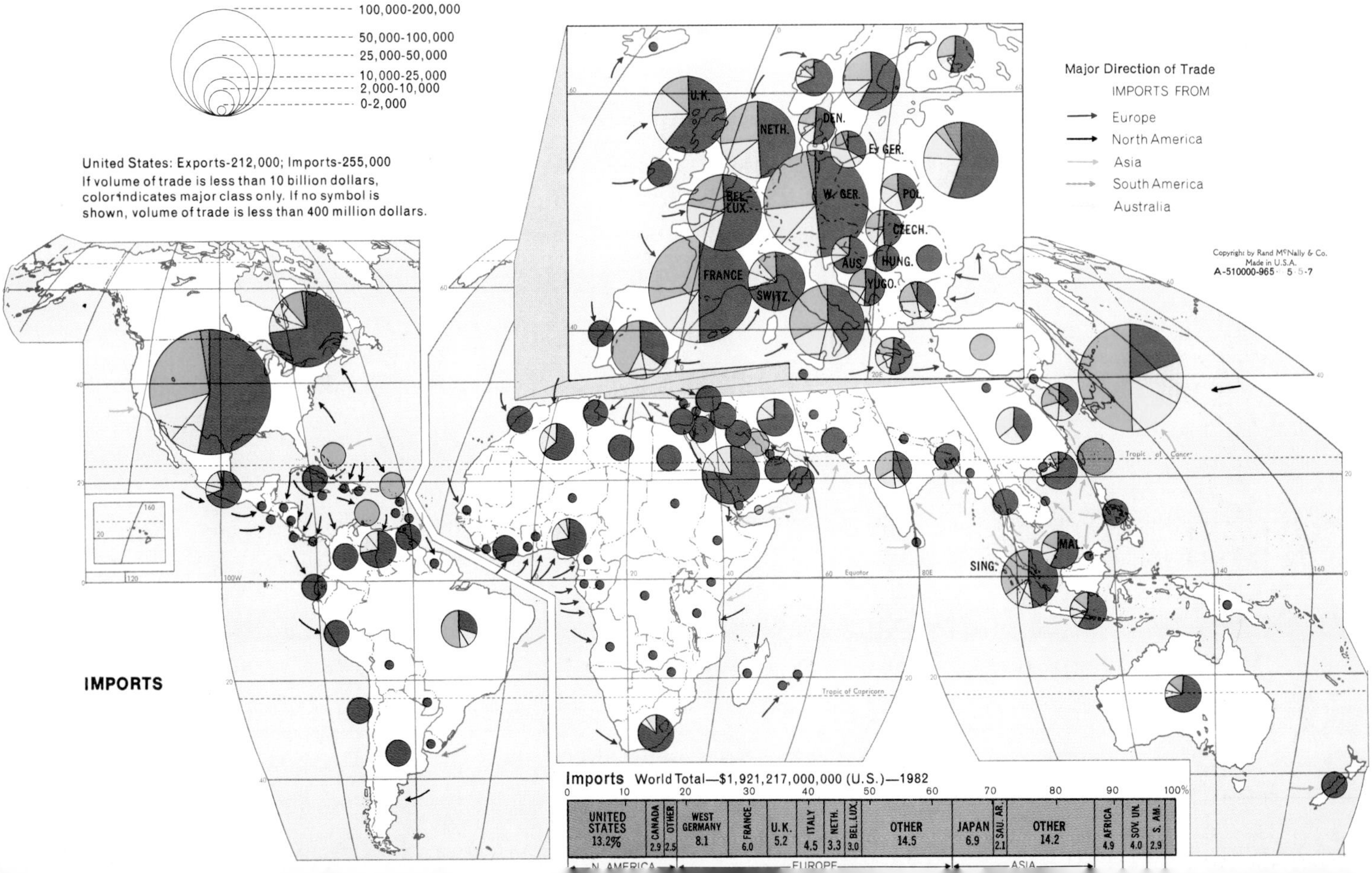

Major Direction of Trade
IMPORTS FROM

→ Europe
→ North America
→ Asia
→ South America
→ Australia

U.K.
NETH.
DEN.
E. GER.
BEL.-LUX.
W. GER.
POL.
CZECH.
FRANCE
AUS.
HUNG.
SWITZ.
YUGO.
SING.
MAL

IMPORTS

Imports World Total—$1,921,217,000,000 (U.S.)—1982

UNITED STATES 13.2%	CANADA 2.9	OTHER 2.5	WEST GERMANY 8.1	FRANCE 6.0	U.K. 5.2	ITALY 4.5	NETH. 3.3	BEL. LUX. 3.0	OTHER 14.5	JAPAN 6.9	SAU. AR. 2.1	OTHER 14.2	AFRICA 4.9	SOV. UN. 4.0	S. AM. 2.9
←— N. AMERICA —→			←———————— EUROPE ————————→							←——————— ASIA ———————→					

major cities maps

This section consists of 62 maps of the world's most populous metropolitan areas. In order to make comparison easier, all the metropolitan areas are shown at the same scale, 1:300,000.

Detailed urban maps are an important reference requirement for a world atlas. The names of many large settlements, towns, suburbs, and neighborhoods can be located on these large-scale maps. From a thematic standpoint the maps show generalized land-use patterns. Included were the total urban extent, major industrial areas, parks, public land, wooded areas, airports, shopping centers, streets, and railroads. A special effort was made to portray the various metropolitan areas in a manner as standard and comparable as possible. (For the symbols used, see the legend below.)

Notable differences occur in the forms of cities. In most of North America these forms were conditioned by a rectangular pattern of streets; land-use zones (residential, commercial, industrial) are well defined. The basic structure of most European cities is noticeably different and more complex; street patterns are irregular and zones are less well defined. In Asia, Africa, and South America the form tends to be even more irregular and complex. Widespread dispersion of craft and trade activities has lessened zonation, there may be cities with no identifiable city centers, and sometimes there may be dual centers (old and modern). Higher population densities result in more limited, compact urban places in these areas of the world.

Inhabited Localities

The symbol represents the number of inhabitants within the locality

- · 0—10,000
- ○ 10,000—25,000
- ◉ 25,000—100,000
- ▣ 100,000—250,000
- ▩ 250,000—1,000,000
- ■ >1,000,000

The size of type indicates the relative economic and political importance of the locality

Écommoy

Trouville

Lisieux

St.-Denis

PARIS

Hollywood   Section of a City,

Westminster   Neighborhood

Northland ■   Major Shopping Center

Center

Urban Area (area of continuous industrial, commercial, and residential development)

Major Industrial Area

Wooded Area

Political Boundaries

International (First-order political unit)

— · — · — Demarcated, Undemarcated, and Administrative

— — — — Demarcation Line

Internal

State, Province, etc. (Second-order political unit)

County, Oblast, etc. (Third-order political unit)

Okrug, Kreis, etc. (Fourth-order political unit)

- - - - - - - City or Municipality (may appear in combination with another boundary symbol)

Capitals of Political Units

BUDAPEST   Independent Nation

Recife   State, Province, etc.

White Plains County, Oblast, etc.

Iserlohn   Okrug, Kreis, etc.

Transportation

Road

PASSAIC EXPWY.   (I-80)   Primary

BERLINER RING   Secondary

Tertiary

Railway

CANADIAN NATIONAL   Primary

Secondary

Rapid Transit

Airport

LONDON (HEATHROW) AIRPORT

Rail or Air Terminal

■ SÜD BAHNHOF

REICHS-BRÜCKE   Bridge

GREAT ST. BERNARD TUNNEL   Tunnel

Houston Ship Channel   Shipping Channel

Canal du Midi   Navigable Canal

TO MALMO   Ferry

Hydrographic Features

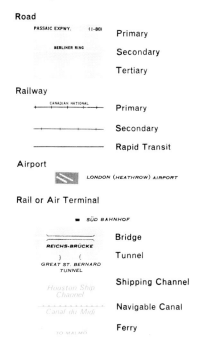

Shoreline

Undefined or Fluctuating Shoreline

River, Stream

Intermittent Stream

Rapids, Falls

Navigable Canal

Irrigation or Drainage Canal

Aqueduct

Pier, Breakwater

Reef

Lake, Reservoir

Intermittent Lake

Swamp

Amur

SALTO ANGEL

Canal du Midi

Los Angeles Aqueduct

GREAT BARRIER REEF

L. Victoria

The Everglades

Miscellaneous Cultural Features

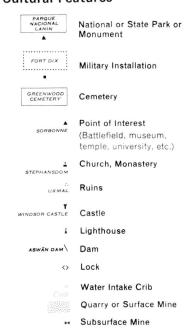

PARQUE NACIONAL LANIN   National or State Park or Monument

FORT DIX   Military Installation

GREENWOOD CEMETERY   Cemetery

SORBONNE   Point of Interest (Battlefield, museum, temple, university, etc.)

STEPHANSDOM   Church, Monastery

UXMAL   Ruins

WINDSOR CASTLE   Castle

Lighthouse

ASWĀN DAM\   Dam

<>   Lock

Water Intake Crib

Crib   Quarry or Surface Mine

Subsurface Mine

Topographic Features

Mt. Kenya 5199 △   Elevation Above Sea Level

Elevations are given in meters

⋆   Rock

A N D E S   Mountain Range, Plateau,

KUNLUNSHANMAI   Valley, etc.

BAFFIN ISLAND   Island

POLUOSTROV KAMČATKA   Peninsula, Cape, Point, etc.

CABO DE HORNOS

a

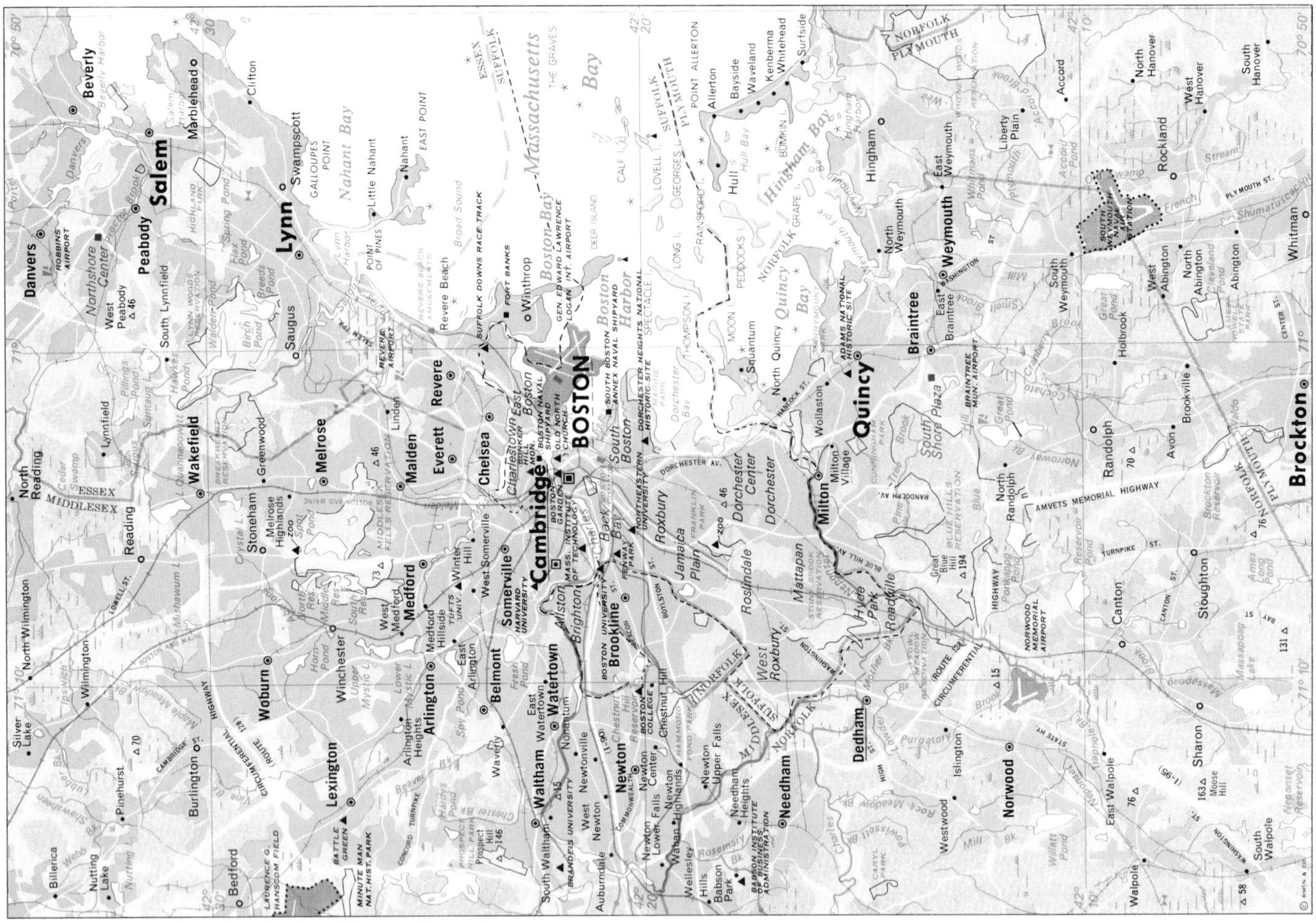

b

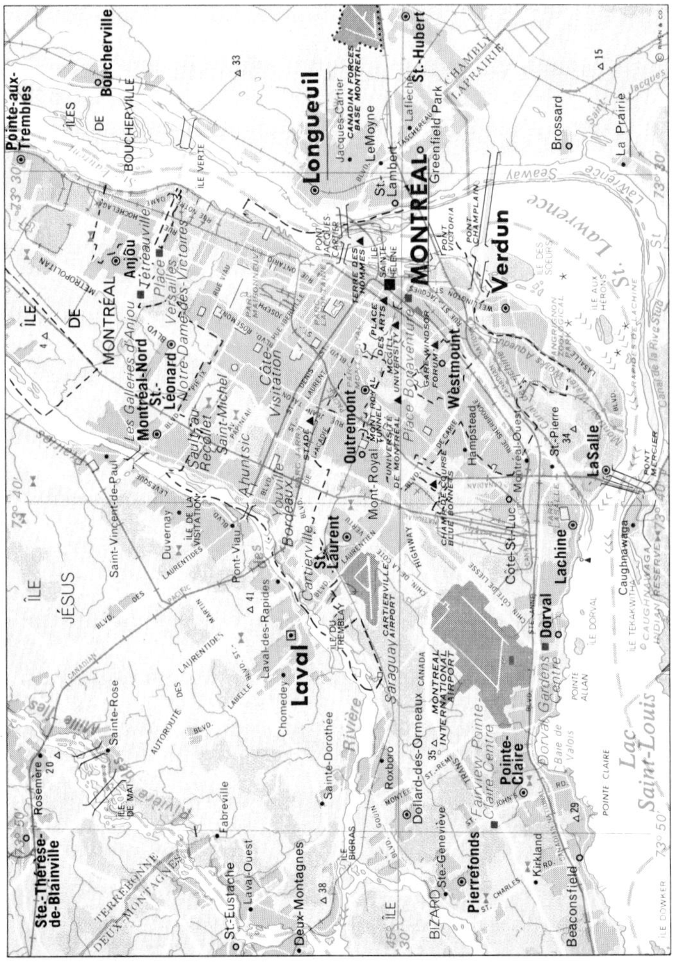

c

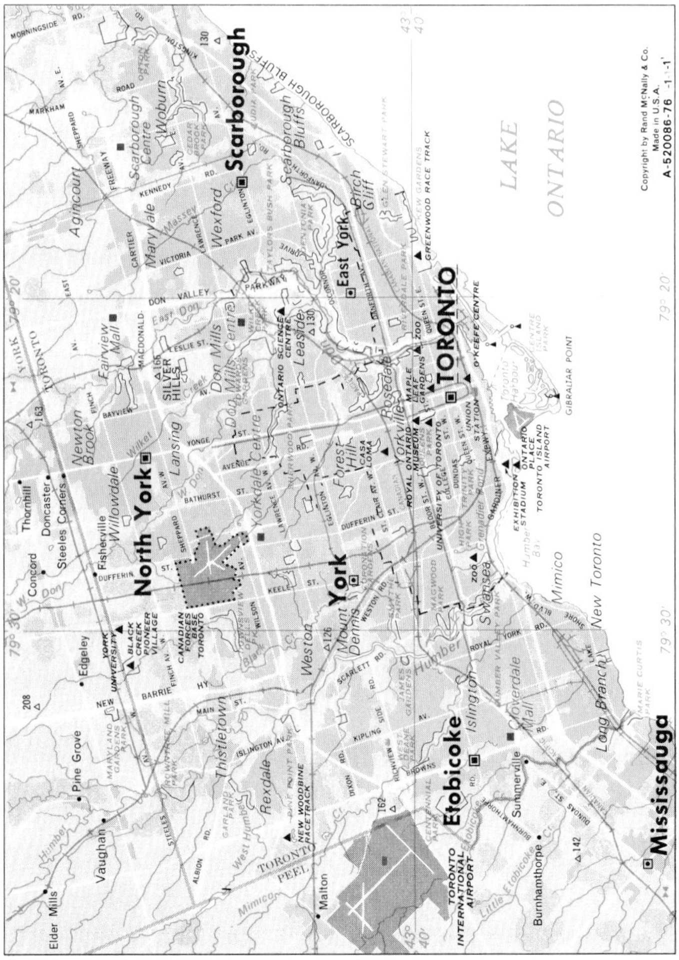

MONTRÉAL

TORONTO

BOSTON

Cambridge

Quincy

Brockton

Longueuil

Verdun

Laval

Scarborough

North York

York

East York

Etobicoke

Mississauga

LAKE ONTARIO

Lac Saint-Louis

Massachusetts Bay

Nahant Bay

Quincy Bay

Hingham Bay

Scale 1:300,000; one inch to 4.7 miles.

10 Miles

10 Kilometers

Scale 1:1,300,000; one inch to 4.7 miles.

10 Miles

10 Kilometers

CONN.
NEW YORK

LONG ISLAND

ATLANTIC OCEAN

Long Island Sound

NEW JERSEY
NEW YORK

Pompton Plains · Wayne · Paterson · Passaic · Paramus · Ridgewood · Fair Lawn · Clifton · Hackensack · Teaneck · Englewood · Fort Lee · Bergenfield · Garfield · Lodi · North Bergen · Union City · Hoboken · West New York · Weehawken

Yonkers · Mount Vernon · New Rochelle · Scarsdale · Harrison · Mamaroneck · Rye · Larchmont · Eastchester · Bronxville · Tuckahoe

BRONX · WESTCHESTER · NASSAU

Glen Cove · Sea Cliff · Glen Head · Port Washington · Manhasset · Great Neck · Roslyn · Plandome · Hicksville · Plainview · Syosset · Woodbury · Bethpage · Levittown · East Meadow · Hempstead · West Hempstead · Garden City · New Hyde Park · Floral Park · Franklin Square · Elmont · Valley Stream · Lynbrook · Rockville Centre · Freeport · Baldwin · Oceanside · Long Beach · Merrick · Massapequa · Seaford · Wantagh

Flushing · College Point · Whitestone · Astoria · QUEENS · Jamaica · JOHN F. KENNEDY INTERNATIONAL AIRPORT · Rockaway Park · Far Rockaway

Bronx · Manhattan · NEW YORK · BROOKLYN · Brownsville · Flatbush · Bensonhurst · Coney Island

STATEN ISLAND · RICHMOND · Bayonne · Elizabeth · Newark · NEWARK INTERNATIONAL AIRPORT · Jersey City · Kearny · Harrison · East Orange · Orange · West Orange · South Orange · Maplewood · Irvington · Hillside · Union · Roselle · Linden · Rahway · Cranford · Westfield · Woodbridge · Perth Amboy · Carteret

Montclair · Bloomfield · Nutley · Belleville · Livingston · Millburn · West Caldwell · Caldwell · Verona · Cedar Grove · Glen Ridge

BERGEN · PASSAIC · ESSEX · UNION · MORRIS · MIDDLESEX · HUDSON

WATCHUNG MOUNTAIN · FIRST MOUNTAIN · SECOND MOUNTAIN

a

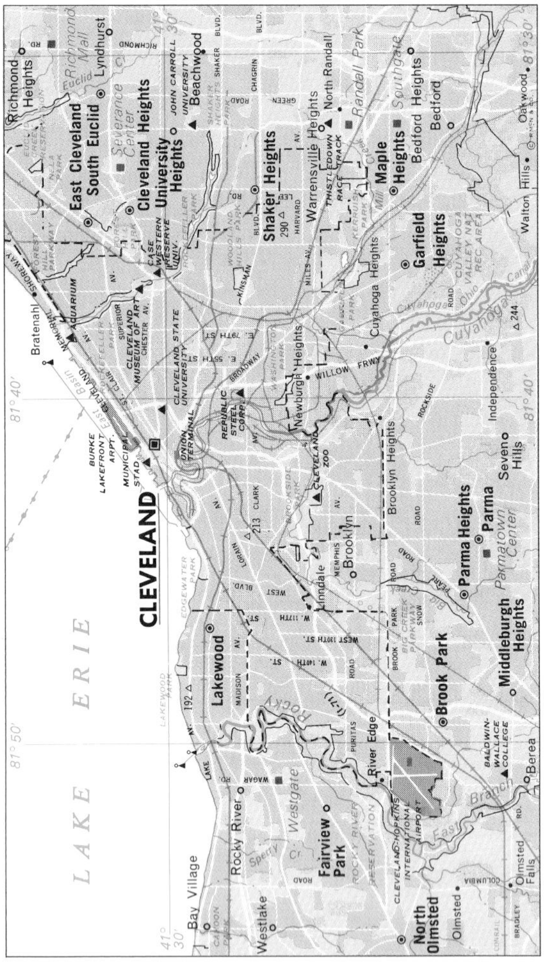

b

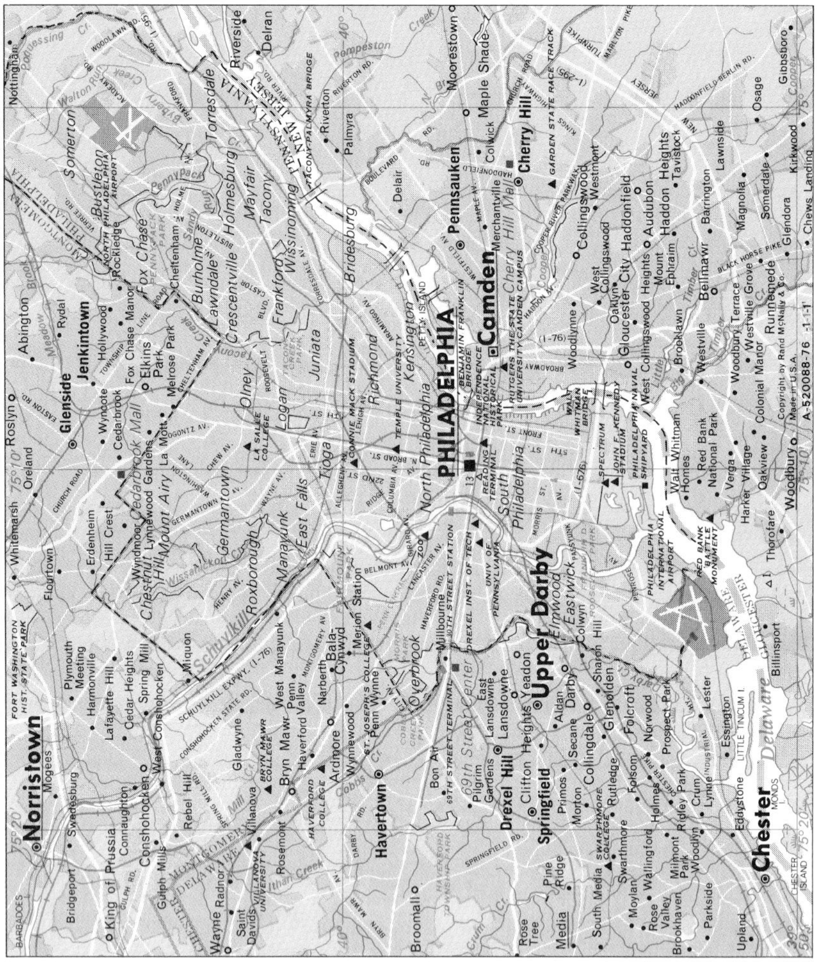

c

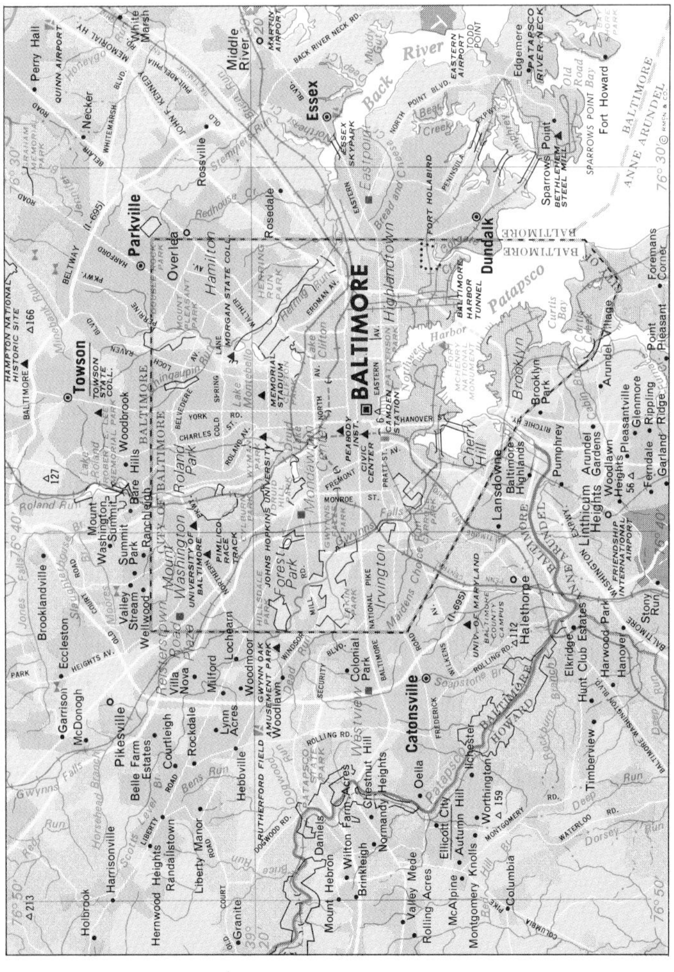

d

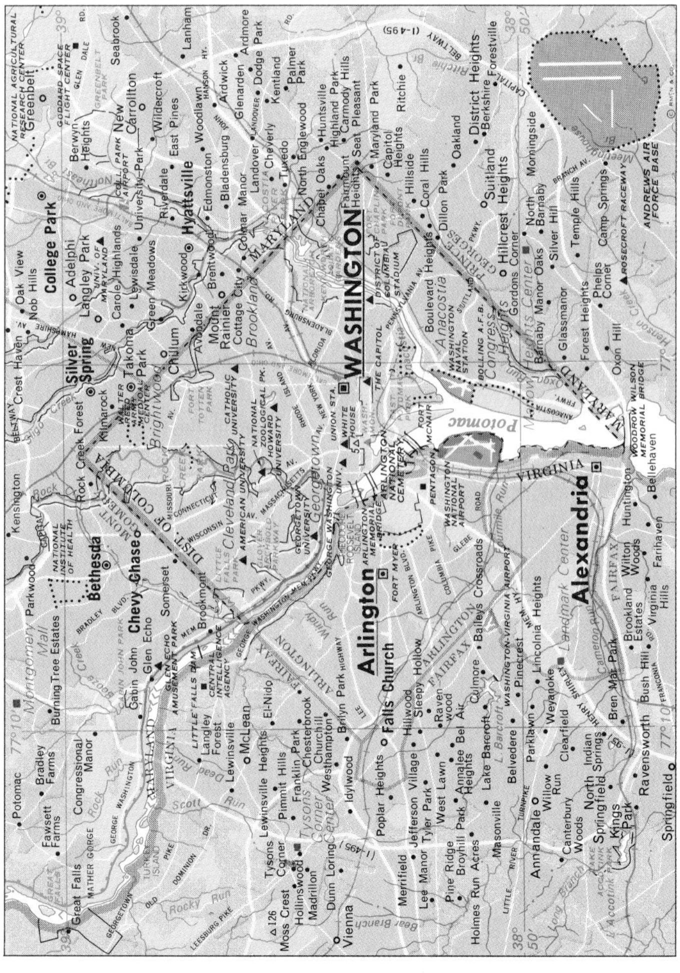

0 5 10 Miles
0 5 10 Kilometers
Scale 1:300,000; one inch to 4.7 miles.

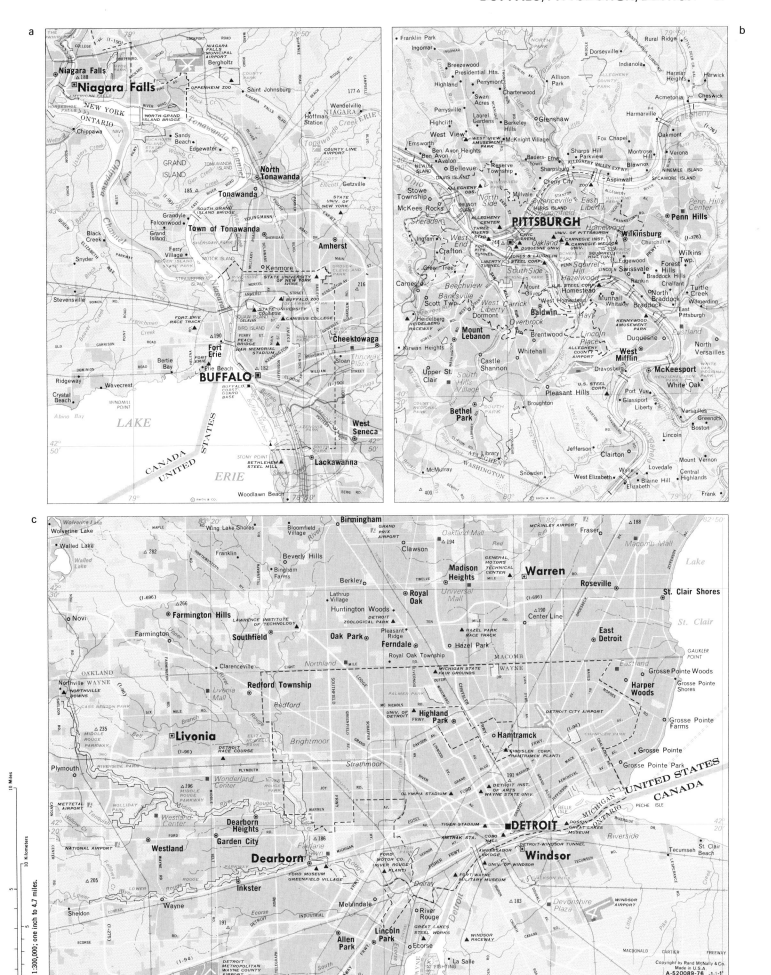

a

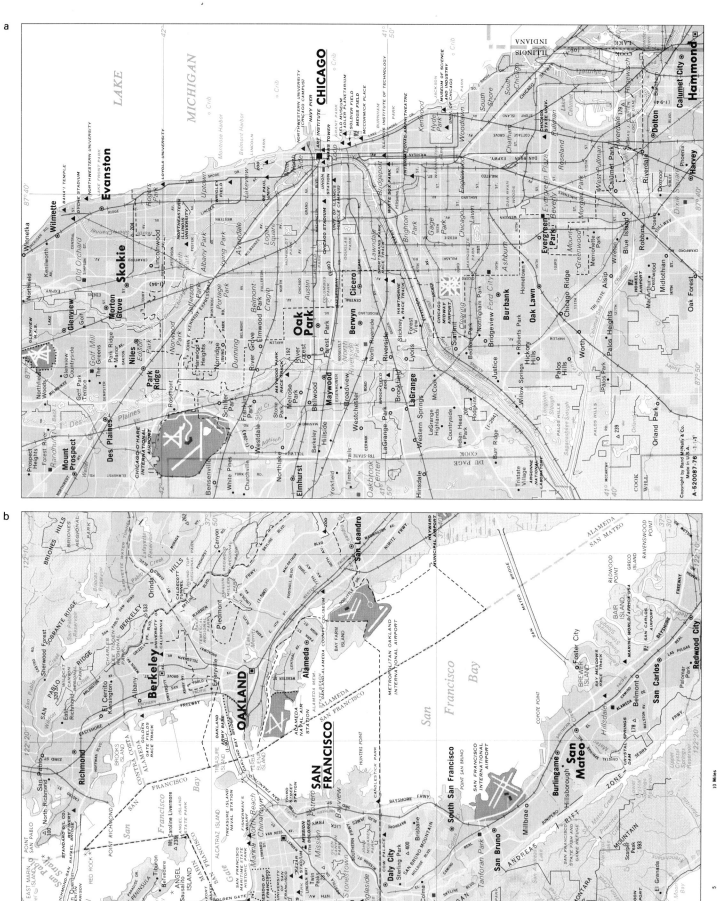

b

Scale 1:300,000; one inch to 4.7 miles.

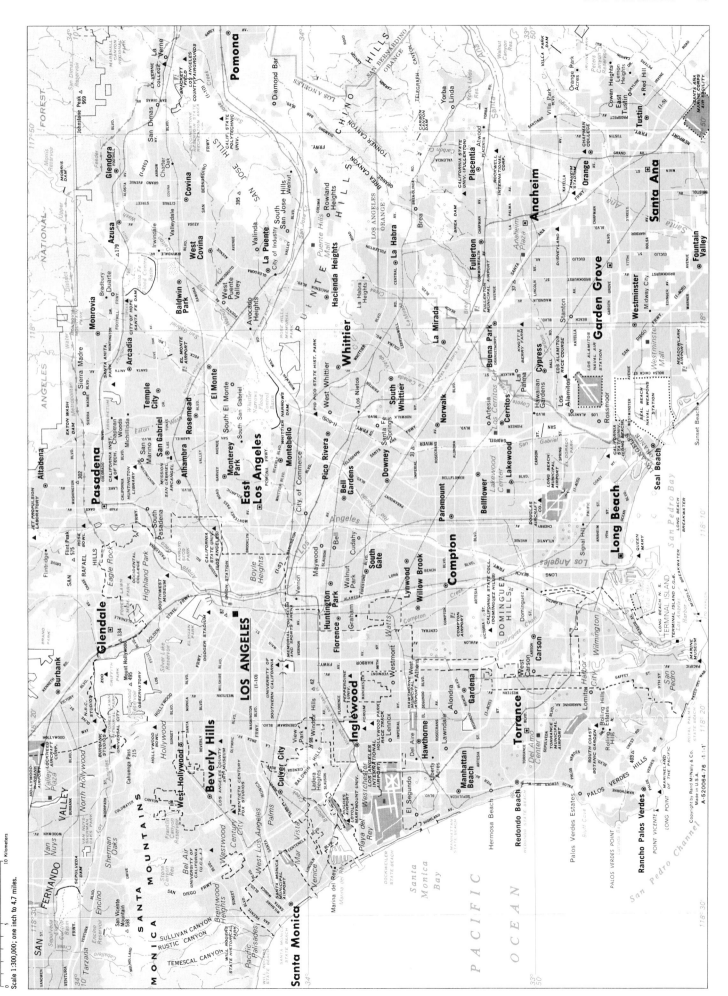

Scale 1:300,000; one inch to 4.7 miles.

a
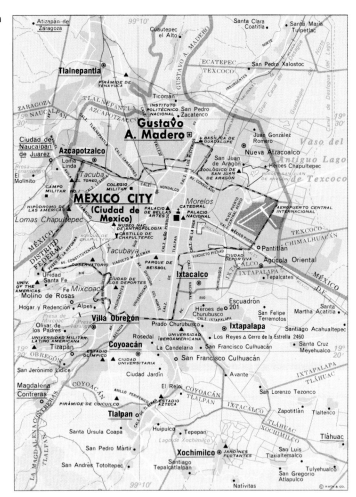

b
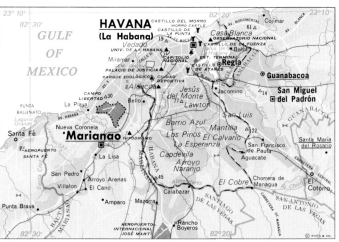

c
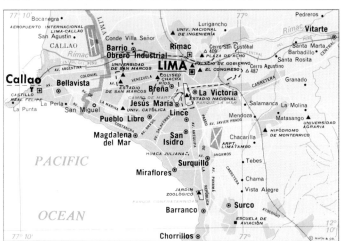

d
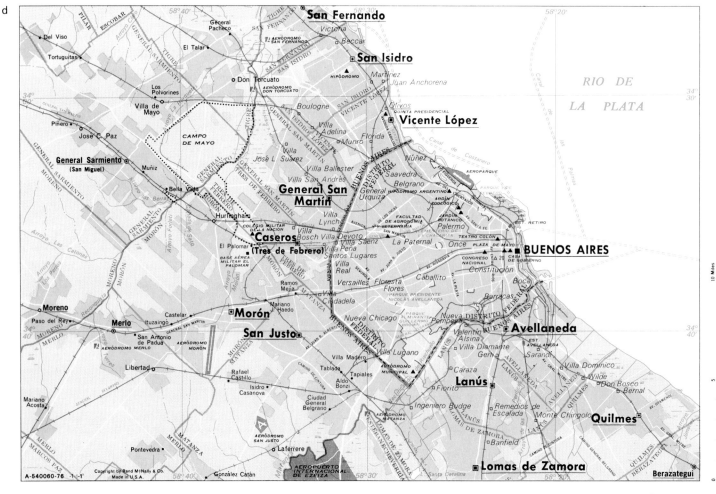

Scale 1:300,000; one inch to 4.7 miles.

a
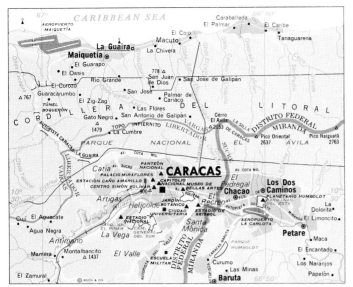

b

c
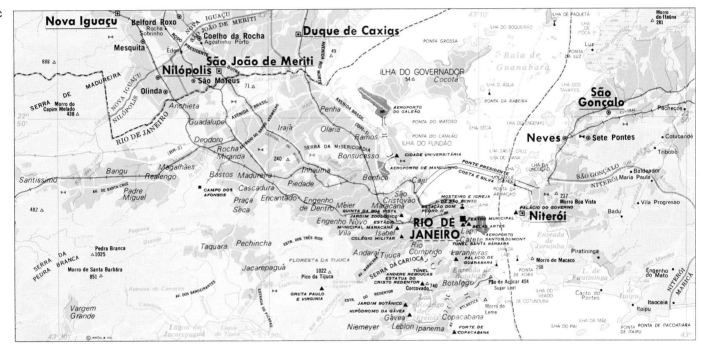

d
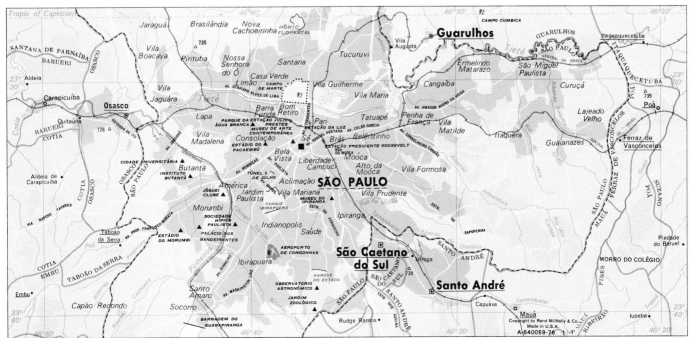

Scale 1:300,000; one inch to 4.7 miles.

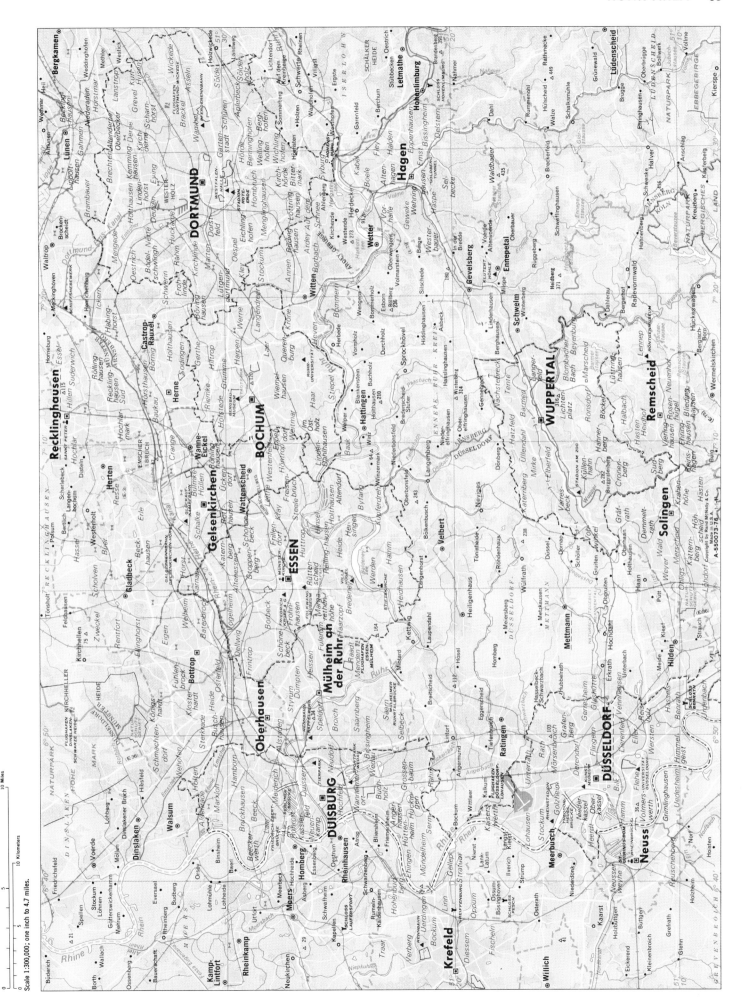

Scale 1:300,000; one inch to 4.7 miles.

Scale 1:300,000; one inch to 4.7 miles.

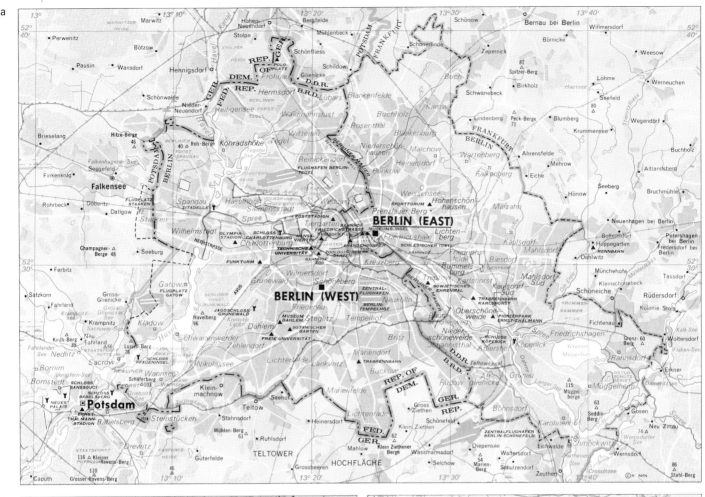

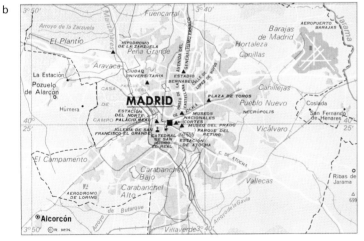

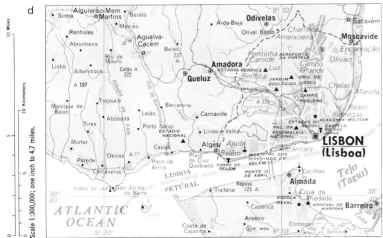

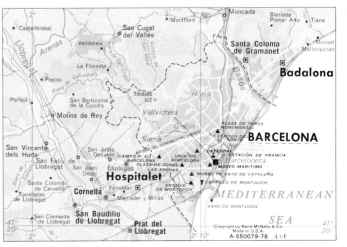

a LENINGRAD

b MOSCOW (Moskvá) — Chimki (Khimki), Mytishchi, Reutov

c ROME (Roma) — VATICAN CITY / CITTA DEL VATICANO

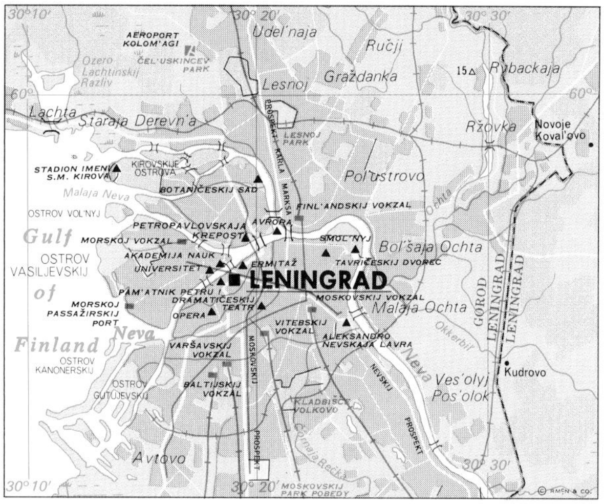

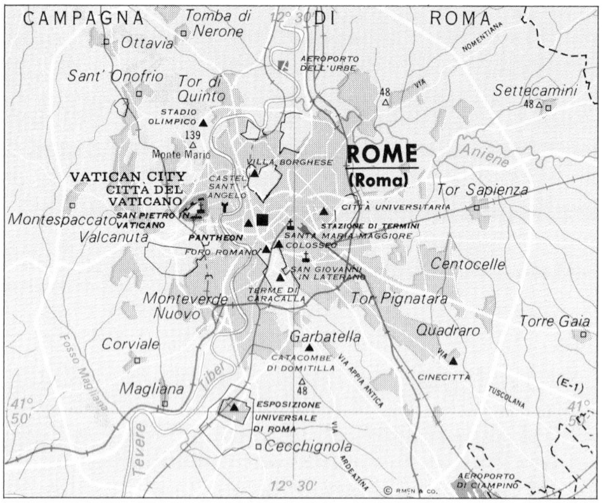

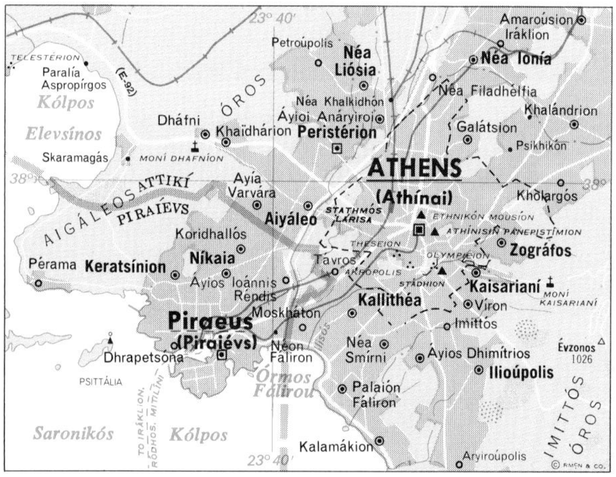

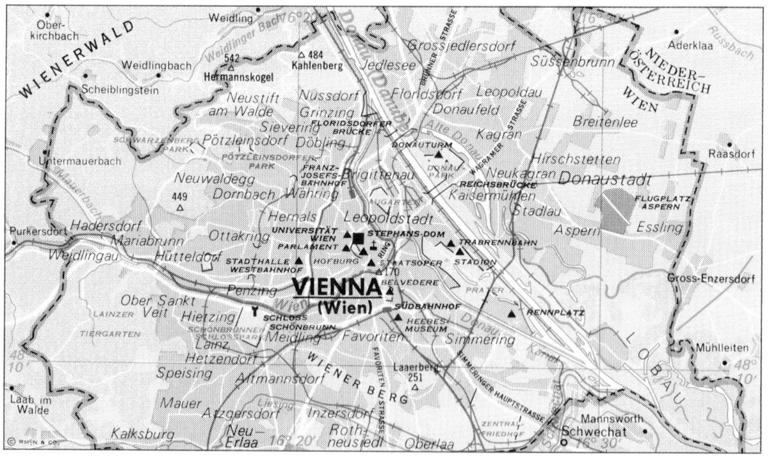

d ATHENS (Athínai) — Piraeus (Piraiévs)

e VIENNA (Wien)

f İSTANBUL

g BUDAPEST — Buda, Pest

Scale 1:300,000; one inch to 4.7 miles.

10 Miles
10 Kilometers

Copyright by Rand McNally & Co.
Made in U.S.A.

A-550080-76 -1-1-11

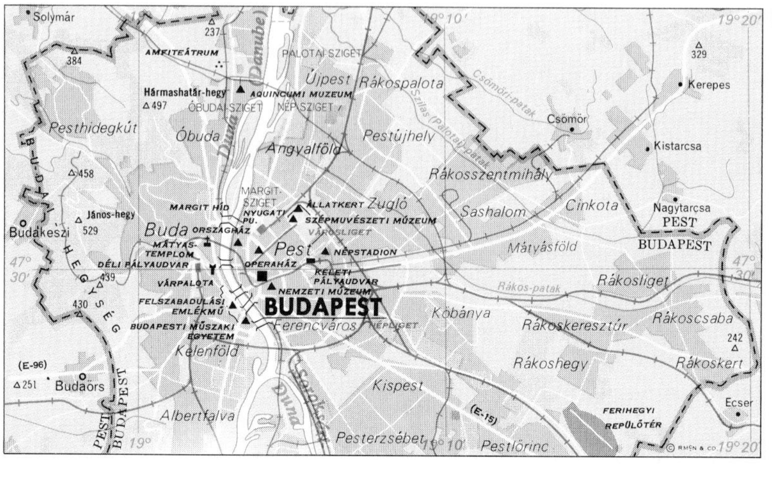

a

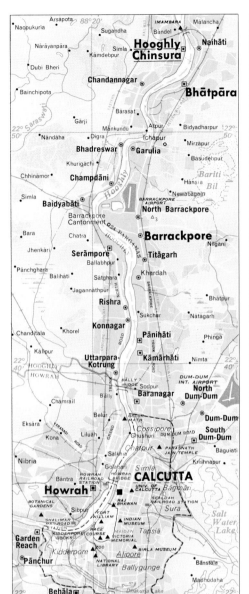

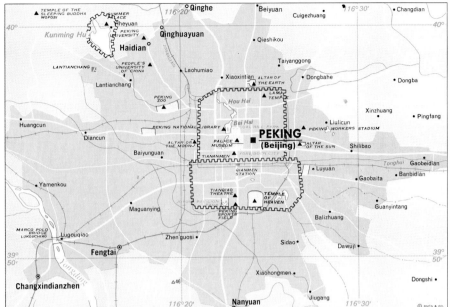
b

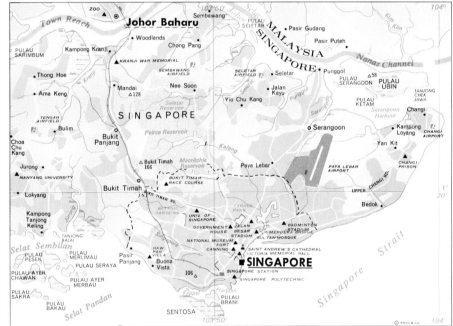
c

d
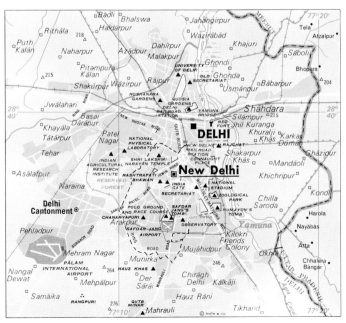

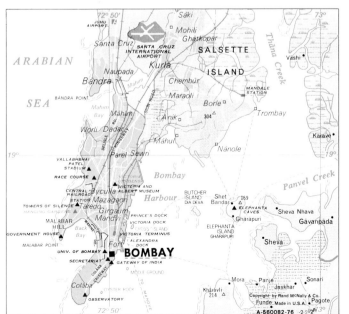
e

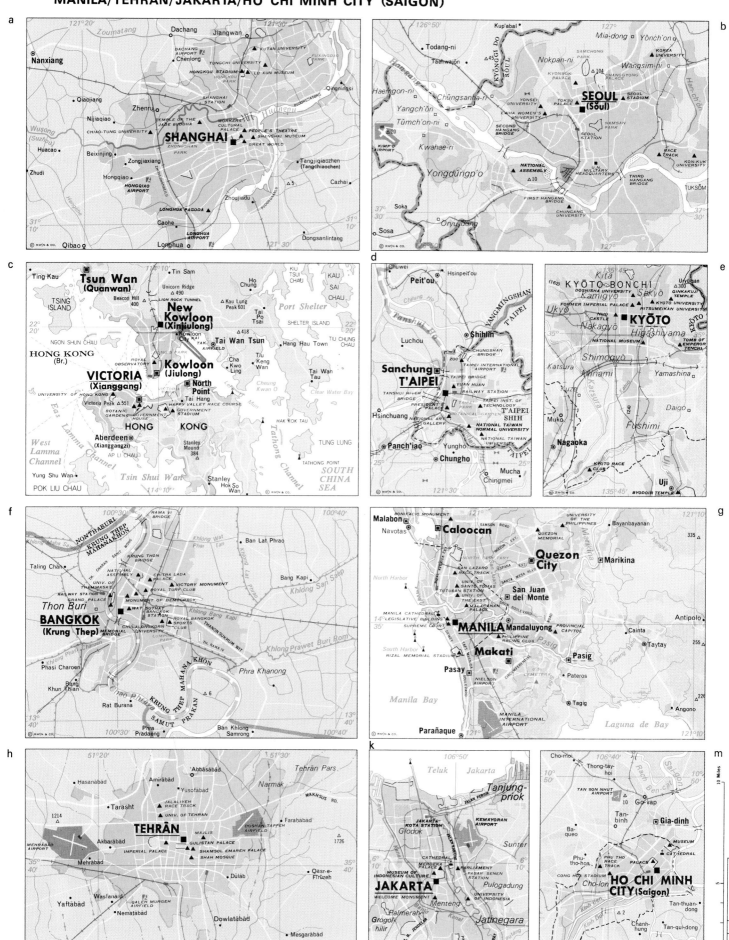

a

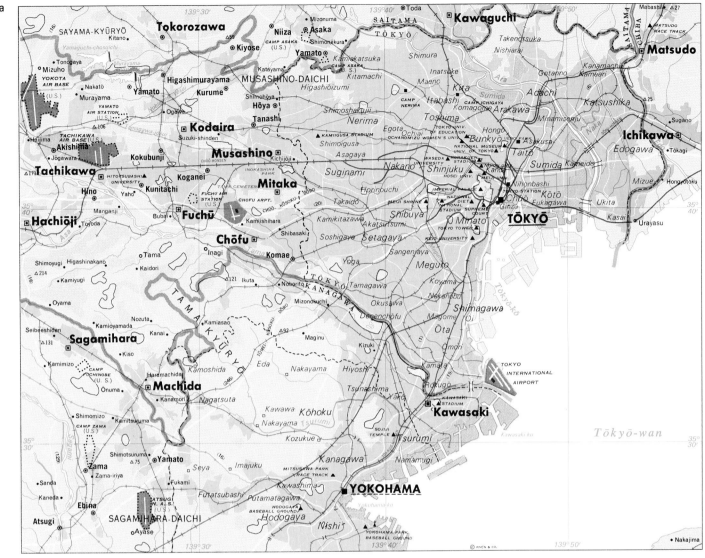

b

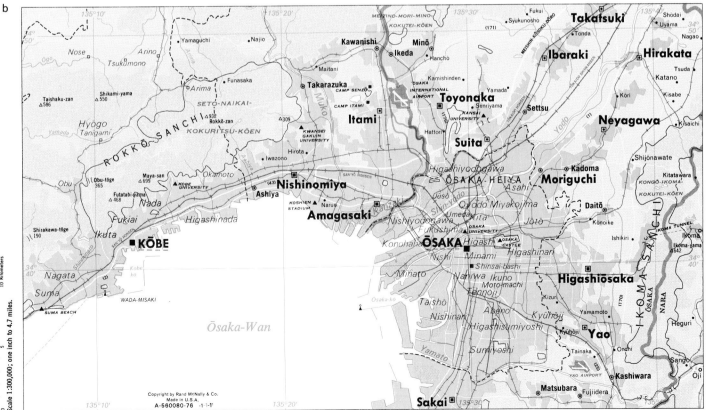

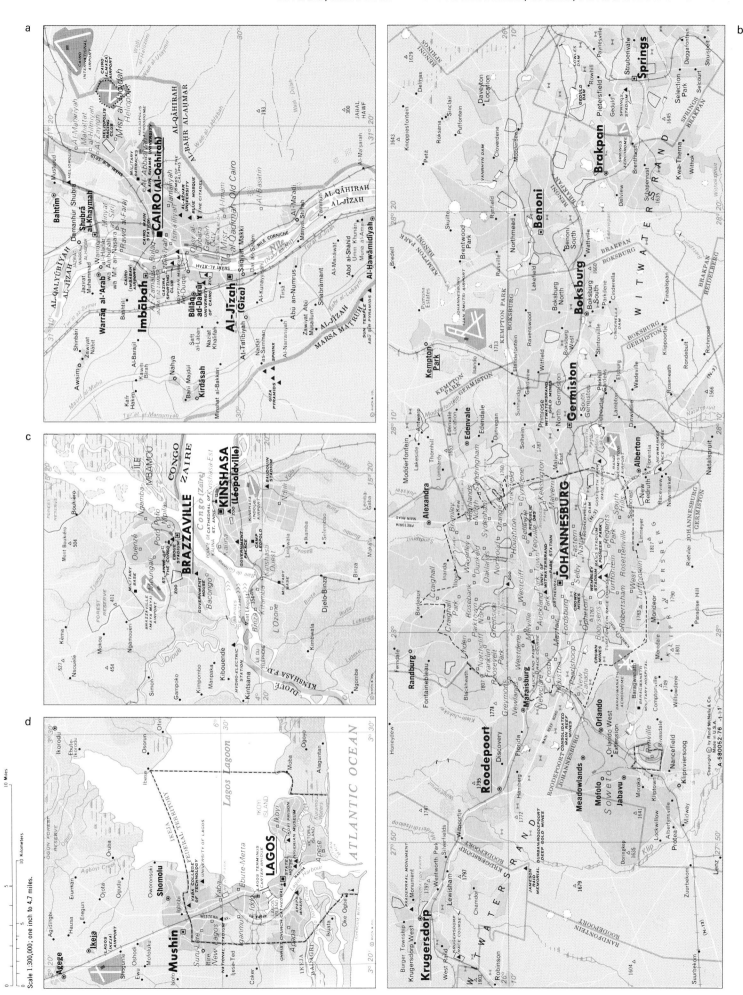

a

CAIRO (Al-Qāhirah)

Baḥtīm
Shubrā al-Khaymah
Damanhūr Shubrā
AL-QALYŪBĪYAH
AL-JĪZAH
Warrāq al-'Arab
Imbābah
Būlāq ad-Dakrūr
Al-Jīzah (Giza)
AL-QĀHIRAH
AL-JĪZAH
Kirdāsah
AL-BAḤR AL-AḤMAR
Al-Hawāmidīyah
MARṢĀ MAṬRŪḤ
GIZA PYRAMIDS
SPHINX
SUN TEMPLE ABŪ ṢĪR PYRAMIDS

b

Springs
Brakpan
Benoni
Boksburg
Germiston
Kempton Park
Edenvale
Alberton
WITWATERSRAND
Alexandra
JOHANNESBURG
Randburg
Maraisburg
Roodepoort
Orlando
Soweto
Mofolo
Jabavu
Meadowlands
KRUGERSDORP
Krugersdorp
WATERSRAND

c

CONGO
ZAIRE
ILE MBAMOU
BRAZZAVILLE
KINSHASA (Léopoldville)
Congo (Zaïre)
KINSHASA F.D.

d

ATLANTIC OCEAN
Lagos Lagoon
Ikeja
Shomolu
Mushin
LAGOS
Agege
Ikeja
IKOYI ISLAND
VICTORIA ISLAND

Copyright © by Rand McNally & Co.
Made in U.S.A.
A-580052-76

regional section

physical-political reference maps

Basic continental and regional coverage of the world's land areas is provided by the following section of physical-political reference maps. The section falls into a continental arrangement: North America, South America, Europe, Asia, Australia, and Africa. (Introducing each regional reference-map section are basic thematic maps and the environment maps.)

To aid the student in acquiring concepts of the relative sizes of continents and of some of the countries and regions, uniform scales for comparable areas were used so far as possible. Continental maps are at a uniform scale of 1:40,000,000. In addition, most of the world is covered by a series of regional maps at scales of 1:16,000,000 and 1:12,000,000.

Maps at 1:10,000,000 provide even greater detail for parts of Europe, Africa, and Southeast Asia. The United States, parts of Canada, and much of Europe and the Soviet Union are mapped at 1:4,000,000. Seventy-six urbanized areas are shown at 1:1,000,000. The new, separate metropolitan-area section contains larger-scale maps of selected urban areas.

Many of the symbols used are self-explanatory. A complete legend below provides a key to the symbols on the reference maps in this atlas.

General elevation above sea level is shown by layer tints for altitudinal zones, each of which has a different hue and is defined by a generalized contour line. A legend is given on each map, reflecting this color gradation.

The surface configuration is represented by hill-shading, which gives the three-dimensional impression of landforms. This terrain representation is superimposed on the layer tints to convey a realistic and readily visualized impression of the surface. The combination of altitudinal tints and hill-shading best shows elevation, relief, steepness of slope, and ruggedness of terrain.

If the world used one alphabet and one language, no particular difficulty would arise in understanding place-names. However, some of the people of the world, the Chinese and the Japanese, for example, use nonalphabetic languages. Their symbols are transliterated into the Roman alphabet. In this atlas a "local-name" policy generally was used for naming cities and towns and all local topographic and water features. However, for a few major cities the Anglicized name was preferred and the local name given in parentheses, for instance, Moscow (*Moskva*), Vienna (*Wien*), Cologne (*Köln*). In countries where more than one official language is used, a name is in the dominant local language. The generic parts of local names for topographic and water features are self-explanatory in many cases because of the associated map symbols or type styles. A complete list of foreign generic names is given in the Glossary, on page 248.

Place-names on the reference maps are listed in the Pronouncing Index, which is a distinctive feature of *Goode's World Atlas*.

Physical-Political Reference Map Legend

Cultural Features

Political Boundaries

International (Demarcated, Undemarcated, and Administrative) (over water)

Disputed de facto

Claim Boundary

Indefinite or Undefined

Secondary, State, Provincial, etc. (over water)

Parks, Indian Reservations

City Limits · Urbanized Areas

Neighborhoods, Sections of City

Populated Places

⊙ 1,000,000 and over

◎ 250,000 to 1,000,000

⊙ 100,000 to 250,000

• 25,000 to 100,000

○ 0 to 25,000

TŌKYŌ National Capitals

Boise Secondary Capitals

Note: On maps at 1:20,000,000 and smaller the town symbols do not follow the specific population classification shown above. On all maps, type size indicates the relative importance of the city.

Transportation

Railroads

Railroads On 1:1,000,000 scale maps

Railroad Ferries

Roads

Major / Other On 1:1,000,000 scale maps

Major / Other On 1:4,000,000 scale maps

On other scale maps

Caravan Routes

✈ Airports

Other Cultural Features

Dams

Pipelines

▲ Points of Interest

Ruins

Land Features

△ Peaks, Spot Heights

= Passes

Sand

Contours

Water Features

Lakes and Reservoirs

Fresh Water

Fresh Water: Intermittent

Salt Water

Salt Water: Intermittent

Other Water Features

Salt Basins, Flats

Swamps

Ice Caps and Glaciers

Rivers

Intermittent Rivers

Aqueducts and Canals

Ship Channels

Falls

Rapids

Springs

△ Water Depths

Fishing Banks

Sand Bars

Reefs

environment maps

The environment-map series shows the general nature of the environment, whether natural or modified by man. The appearance and/or general activity which characterize an area were the conditions for its being classified in one of the map categories. Inclusion in a category was determined largely by the percent of the area covered by urban development, crops (including pasture), trees, or grass. On these small-scale maps, no attempt was made to depict specific crops or the productivity of the area.

Ten major environments were depicted and the categories identified and described in the legend below. The colors and patterns for each category were chosen to illustrate the results of man's activity. Hill shading was used to show land configuration. Together, these design elements create a visual impression of the surface environment.

Naturally, when mapping any distribution it is necessary to limit the number of categories. Therefore, some gradations of meaning exist within the limits of the chosen categories. For example, the grassland, grazing-land category identifies the lush pampas of Argentina and the savanna of Africa as well as the steppes of the Soviet Union. Furthermore, in areas of cropland certain enclaves which might not be defined as cropland are included within the boundary. Tracts such as these, through the process of generalization were included within the boundary of the dominant environment surrounding them. Finally, it should be pointed out that boundaries on these maps, as on all maps, are never absolute but mark the center of transitional zones between categories.

Actual urban shapes were shown where metropolitan areas are of a large areal extent. A red dot indicates concentrated urbanized development where actual shapes would be indistinguishable at the map scale. Black dots were used to locate selected places important as locational reference points.

From these maps one may make comprehensive observations about the extent and distribution of the major world environments. For example, the urban areas of the world are limited in extent, although over 40 percent of the world's population lives in these areas. Together, the categories of cropland and cropland associated with woodland or grazing land apply to relatively small portions of the earth's surface. Conversely, vast areas of each continent show man's limited influence on the natural environment. The barren lands, wasteland, and tundra, the sparse grass and steppe land, and the tropical rain forests are notable in this respect.

Use of the environment-series maps with the world and continental thematic maps of population, landforms, transportation, and gross national product, for instance, allows further insights into the nature of the world's major environments.

Environment Map Legend

 URBAN
Major areas of contiguous residential, commercial, and industrial development.

 FOREST, WOODLAND
Extensive wooded areas with little or no cropland.

 CROPLAND
Cultivated land predominates (includes pasture, irrigated land, and land in crop rotation).

 SWAMP, MARSHLAND
Extensive wetland areas (includes mangroves).

 CROPLAND AND WOODLAND
Cultivated land interrupted by small wooded areas.

 TUNDRA
Areas of lichen, shrubs, small trees, and wetland.

 CROPLAND AND GRAZING LAND
Cultivated land with grassland and rangeland.

 SHRUB, SPARSE GRASS;
WASTELAND
Desert shrub and short grass, growing singly or in patches. Wasteland includes sand, salt flats, etc. (Extensive wastelands shown by pattern).

 GRASSLAND, GRAZING LAND
Extensive grassland and rangeland with little or no cropland.

 BARREN LAND
Icefields, glaciers, permanent snow, with exposed rock.

OASIS
Important small areas of cultivation within grassland or wasteland.

• Selected cities as points of reference.

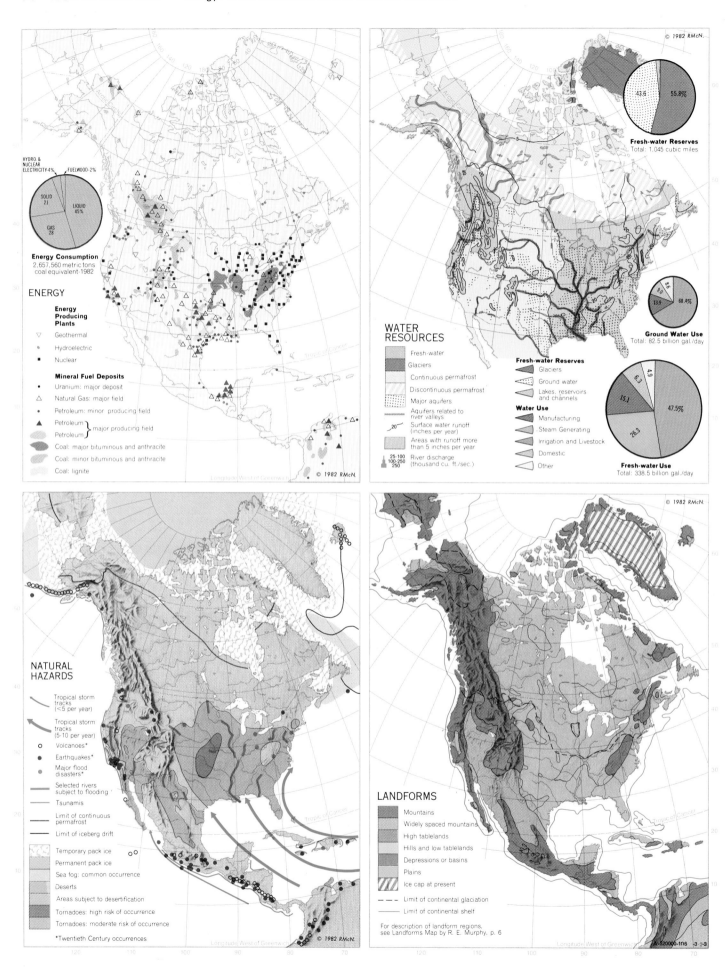

ENERGY

Energy Consumption
2,657,560 metric tons
coal equivalent-1982

HYDRO. &
NUCLEAR
ELECTRICITY-4%   FUELWOOD-2%

SOLID
21

LIQUID
45%

GAS
28

**Energy
Producing
Plants**

▽ Geothermal

• Hydroelectric

■ Nuclear

Mineral Fuel Deposits

• Uranium: major deposit

△ Natural Gas: major field

• Petroleum: minor producing field

▲ Petroleum } major producing field
   Petroleum

Coal: major bituminous and anthracite

Coal: minor bituminous and anthracite

Coal: lignite

© 1982 RMcN.

WATER RESOURCES

Fresh-water

Glaciers

Continuous permafrost

Discontinuous permafrost

Major aquifers

Aquifers related to
river valleys

—20— Surface water runoff
(inches per year)

Areas with runoff more
than 5 inches per year

25-100
100-250
250   River discharge
(thousand cu. ft./sec.)

Fresh-water Reserves

◣ Glaciers

◁ Ground water

◁ Lakes, reservoirs
and channels

Water Use

◣ Manufacturing

◁ Steam Generating

◁ Irrigation and Livestock

◁ Domestic

◁ Other

Fresh-water Reserves
Total: 1,045 cubic miles

43.6   55.8%

Ground Water Use
Total: 82.5 billion gal./day

8.6
9.0
13.9   68.4%

Fresh-water Use
Total: 338.5 billion gal./day

4.9
6.3
15.1   47.5%
26.3

© 1982 RMcN.

NATURAL HAZARDS

Tropical storm
tracks
(<5 per year)

Tropical storm
tracks
(5-10 per year)

○ Volcanoes*

● Earthquakes*

● Major flood
disasters*

Selected rivers
subject to flooding

Tsunamis

Limit of continuous
permafrost

Limit of iceberg drift

Temporary pack ice

Permanent pack ice

Sea fog: common occurrence

Deserts

Areas subject to desertification

Tornadoes: high risk of occurrence

Tornadoes: moderate risk of occurrence

*Twentieth Century occurrences

© 1982 RMcN.

LANDFORMS

Mountains

Widely spaced mountains

High tablelands

Hills and low tablelands

Depressions or basins

Plains

Ice cap at present

— — — Limit of continental glaciation

——— Limit of continental shelf

For description of landform regions,
see Landforms Map by R. E. Murphy, p. 6

© 1982 RMcN.

A-520000-1N6   -3-2-3

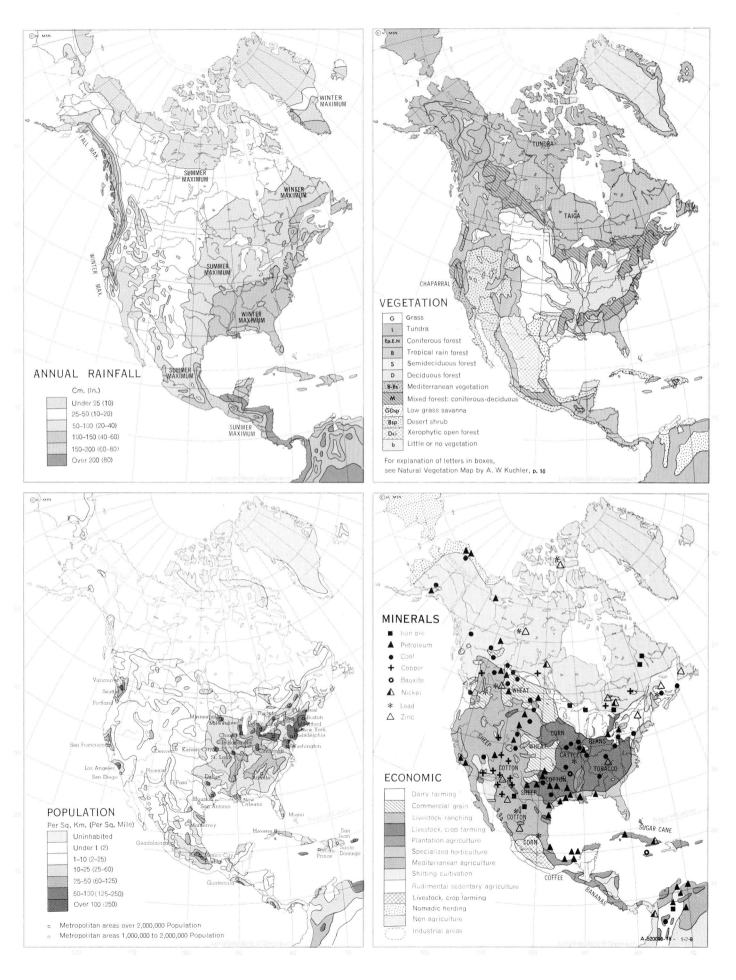

ANNUAL RAINFALL

Cm. (In.)

- Under 25 (10)
- 25–50 (10–20)
- 50–100 (20–40)
- 100–150 (40–60)
- 150–200 (60–80)
- Over 200 (80)

Labels on map: WINTER MAXIMUM, FALL MAX., WINTER MAX., SUMMER MAXIMUM, WINTER MAXIMUM, SUMMER MAXIMUM, WINTER MAXIMUM, SUMMER MAXIMUM, SUMMER MAXIMUM

VEGETATION

G	Grass
L	Tundra
Ep.E.N	Coniferous forest
B	Tropical rain forest
S	Semideciduous forest
D	Deciduous forest
B-Bs	Mediterranean vegetation
M	Mixed forest: coniferous-deciduous
GDsp	Low grass savanna
Bsp.	Desert shrub
Dxi	Xerophytic open forest
b	Little or no vegetation

For explanation of letters in boxes,
see Natural Vegetation Map by A. W Kuchler, p. 16

Labels on map: TUNDRA, TAIGA, CHAPARRAL

POPULATION

Per Sq. Km. (Per Sq. Mile)

- Uninhabited
- Under 1 (2)
- 1–10 (2–25)
- 10–25 (25–60)
- 25–50 (60–125)
- 50–100 (125–250)
- Over 100 (250)

□ Metropolitan areas over 2,000,000 Population
○ Metropolitan areas 1,000,000 to 2,000,000 Population

City labels: Vancouver, Seattle, Portland, San Francisco, Los Angeles, San Diego, Phoenix, El Paso, Denver, Kansas City, St. Louis, Dallas, San Antonio, Houston, New Orleans, Monterrey, Guadalajara, Mexico City, Puebla, Guatemala, Minneapolis, Milwaukee, Chicago, Indianapolis, Cincinnati, Detroit, Toronto, Buffalo, Montreal, Boston, Hartford, New York, Philadelphia, Washington, Atlanta, Miami, Havana, Port-au-Prince, Santo Domingo, San Juan

MINERALS

- ■ Iron ore
- ▲ Petroleum
- ● Coal
- + Copper
- ⊙ Bauxite
- ▲ Nickel
- ＊ Lead
- △ Zinc

ECONOMIC

- Dairy farming
- Commercial grain
- Livestock ranching
- Livestock, crop farming
- Plantation agriculture
- Specialized horticulture
- Mediterranean agriculture
- Shifting cultivation
- Rudimental sedentary agriculture
- Livestock, crop farming
- Nomadic herding
- Non agriculture
- Industrial areas

Labels on map: WHEAT, SHEEP, WHEAT, CORN, BEANS, CATTLE, TOBACCO, COTTON, COTTON, COTTON, SHEEP, CORN, SUGAR CANE, COFFEE, BANANAS

A-520000-46 - 1-2-9

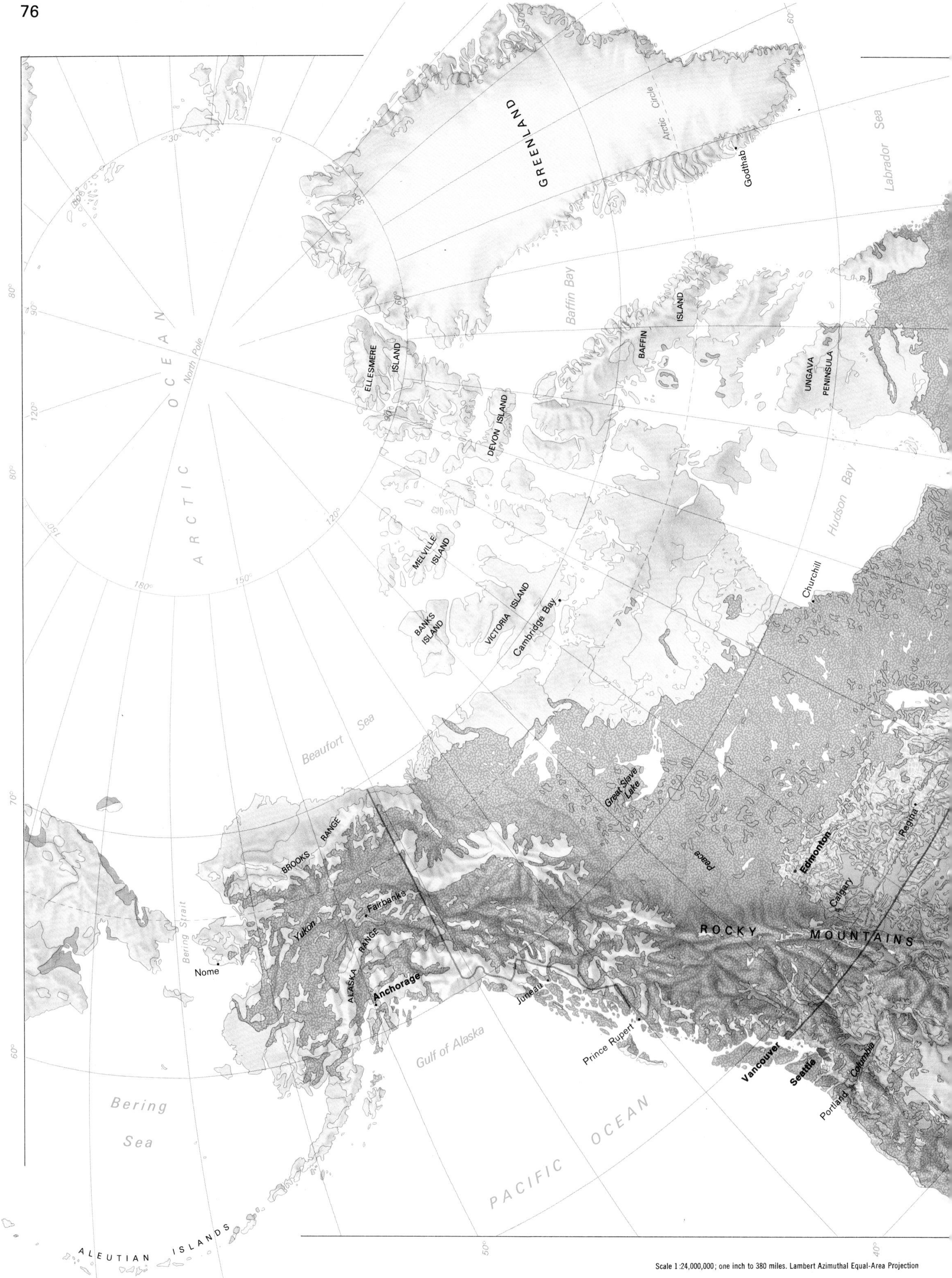

GREENLAND

Godthab

Arctic Circle

Labrador Sea

Baffin Bay

ELLESMERE ISLAND

BAFFIN ISLAND

DEVON ISLAND

UNGAVA PENINSULA

A R C T I C   O C E A N

North Pole

Hudson Bay

MELVILLE ISLAND

VICTORIA ISLAND

Cambridge Bay

BANKS ISLAND

Churchill

Beaufort Sea

Great Slave Lake

Regina

BROOKS RANGE

Edmonton

Peace

Fairbanks

Calgary

Yukon

ROCKY   MOUNTAINS

ALASKA RANGE

Nome

Bering Strait

Anchorage

Juneau

Prince Rupert

Vancouver Seattle

Gulf of Alaska

Columbia

Portland

Bering

Sea

P A C I F I C   O C E A N

A L E U T I A N   I S L A N D S

Scale 1:24,000,000; one inch to 380 miles. Lambert Azimuthal Equal-Area Projection

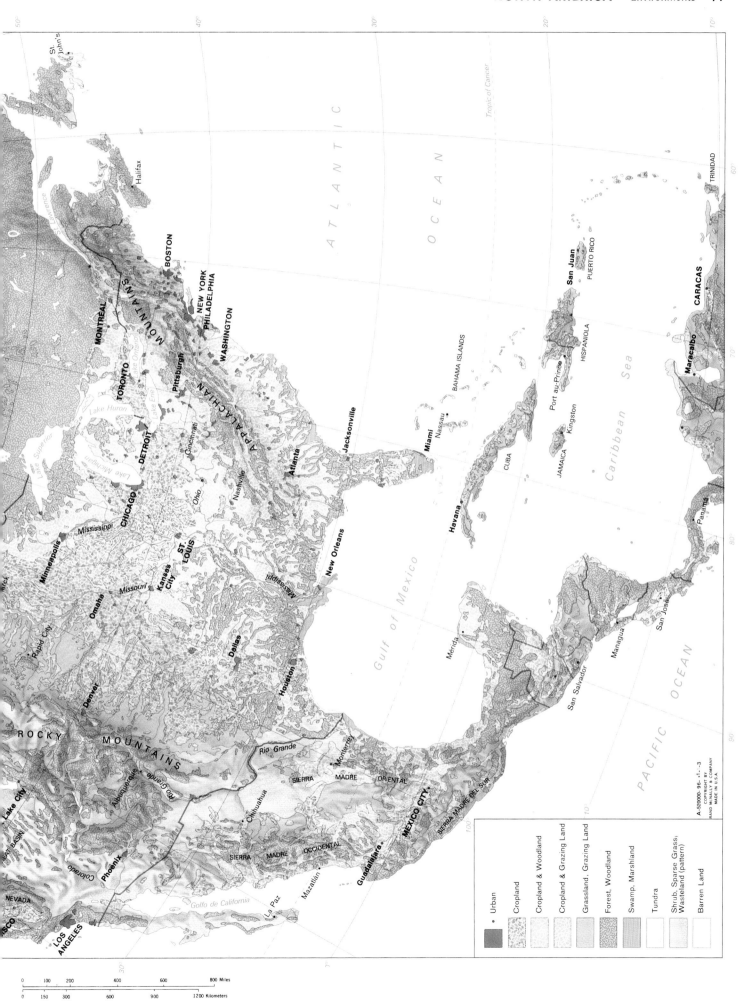

St. John's

Halifax

BOSTON
NEW YORK
PHILADELPHIA
WASHINGTON

MONTREAL
TORONTO
Pittsburgh
Lake Ontario
Lake Erie
Lake Huron
Lake Superior
Lake Michigan
DETROIT

APPALACHIAN MOUNTAINS

Cincinnati
Ohio
Nashville

CHICAGO

Mississippi

MINNEAPOLIS

ST. LOUIS

Atlanta

Jacksonville

Kansas City
Missouri

Omaha

Rapid City

Denver

Dallas

Houston

New Orleans

Gulf of Mexico

Miami
Nassau

Havana

CUBA

BAHAMA ISLANDS

Port au-Prince
Kingston
JAMAICA

HISPANIOLA

San Juan
PUERTO RICO

TRINIDAD

CARACAS

Maracaibo

Caribbean Sea

Panamá

San José

Managua

San Salvador

Mérida

Tropic of Cancer

ATLANTIC OCEAN

PACIFIC OCEAN

ROCKY MOUNTAINS

Rio Grande

Albuquerque
Rio Grande

SIERRA MADRE ORIENTAL

Monterrey

Chihuahua

SIERRA MADRE OCCIDENTAL

MEXICO CITY

SIERRA MADRE DEL SUR

Guadalajara

Mazatlán

La Paz

Golfo de California

Colorado

Phoenix

NEVADA

Lake City

LOS ANGELES

A-500000-96-·1-.-3
COPYRIGHT BY
RAND MCNALLY & COMPANY
MADE IN U.S.A.

Urban
Cropland
Cropland & Woodland
Cropland & Grazing Land
Grassland, Grazing Land
Forest, Woodland
Swamp, Marshland
Tundra
Shrub, Sparse Grass,
Wasteland (pattern)
Barren Land

0   100   200   400   600   800 Miles
0   150   300   600   900   1200 Kilometers

78

Moosonee

James Bay

Gulf of St. Lawrence

Thunder Bay

Lake Superior

Sudbury

Quebec

Halifax

MONTREAL

Bangor

Duluth

Lake Huron

Lake Michigan

apolis

Mississippi

Milwaukee

TORONTO

Lake Ontario

BOSTON

DETROIT

Buffalo

CHICAGO

Lake Erie

Cleveland

NEW YORK

Pittsburgh

PHILADELPHIA

Indianapolis

Cincinnati

WASHINGTON

ansas City

Missouri

Ohio

Norfolk

ST. LOUIS

Roanoke

PLATEAU

Nashville

Charlotte

OZARK

Arkansas

Memphis

Little Rock

ATLANTIC OCEAN

Mississippi

Atlanta

Birmingham

Charleston

Red

Jacksonville

Tallahassee

New Orleans

ton

Tampa

Gulf of Mexico

Nassau

Miami

APPALACHIAN MOUNTAINS

■	Urban
	Cropland
	Cropland & Woodland
	Cropland & Grazing Land
	Grassland, Grazing Land
	Forest, Woodland
	Swamp, Marshland
	Shrub, Sparse Grass, Wasteland (pattern)
	Barren Land

Scale 1:12,000,000; one inch to 190 miles. Polyconic Projection

0   50   100   200   300   400 Miles

0   75   150   300   450   600 Kilometers

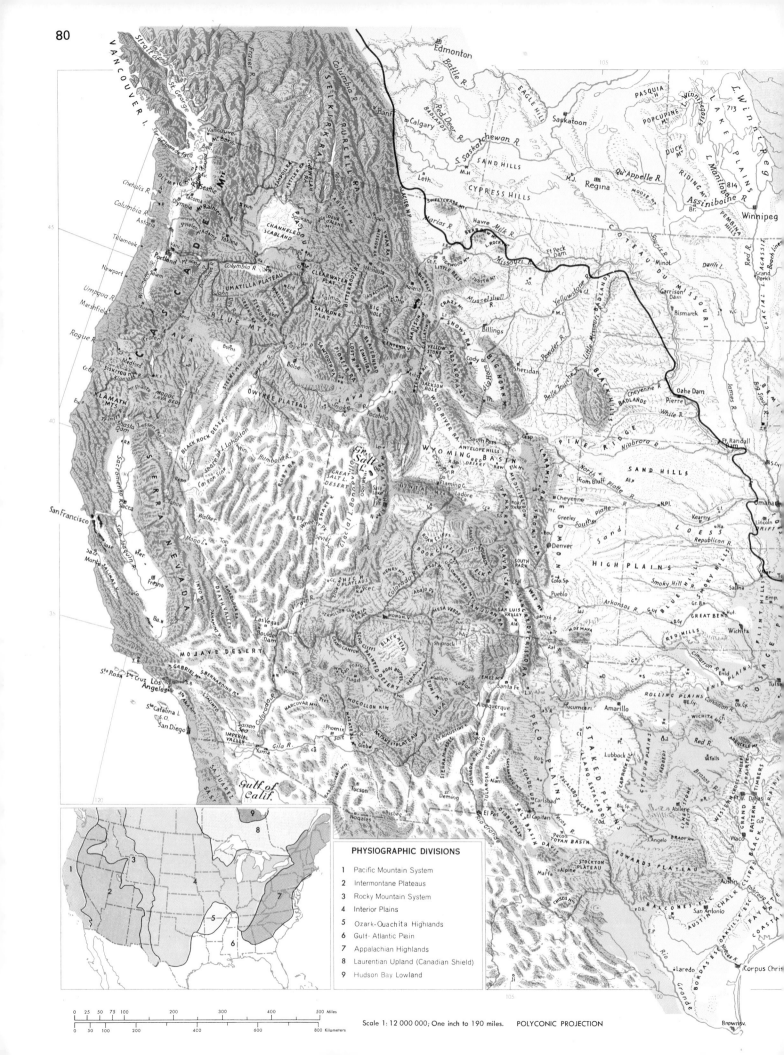

PHYSIOGRAPHY
BY
ERWIN RAISZ

LITHOLOGY AND STRUCTURE

Unconsolidated deposits: alluvium, sands, playa deposits, etc.

Essentially horizontal sedimentary rocks; many partially unconsolidated.

Slightly to moderately tilted, older sedimentary rocks.

Steeply folded or faulted, sedimentary rocks

Volcanics; largely lava flows.

Metamorphic and intrusive igneous rocks; structure complex.

Limits of continental glaciation.

LANDFORMS

PLATEAUS	BASIN RANGES
HILLS	VOLCANO AND LAVA
MOUNTAINS	SAND
MESAS	SINKS
CUESTAS	MORAINES
FOLDED MOUNTAINS	DRUMLINS

A-520500-762 -3 -5¹
Copyright by Rand McNally & Co.
Made in U.S.A.

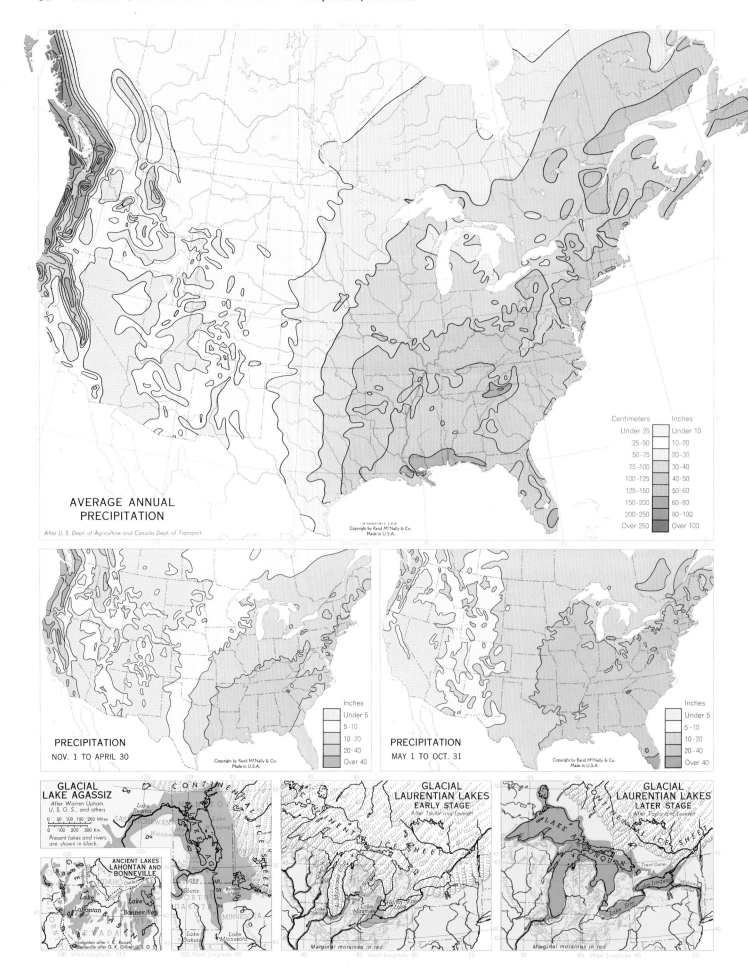

AVERAGE ANNUAL PRECIPITATION

After U. S. Dept. of Agriculture and Canada Dept. of Transport

A-520500-961 1-2-2 3°
Copyright by Rand M°Nally & Co.
Made in U.S.A.

Centimeters	Inches
Under 25	Under 10
25–50	10–20
50–75	20–30
75–100	30–40
100–125	40–50
125–150	50–60
150–200	60–80
200–250	80–100
Over 250	Over 100

PRECIPITATION

NOV. 1 TO APRIL 30

Copyright by Rand M°Nally & Co.
Made in U.S.A.

Inches
Under 5
5–10
10–20
20–40
Over 40

PRECIPITATION

MAY 1 TO OCT. 31

Copyright by Rand M°Nally & Co.
Made in U.S.A.

Inches
Under 5
5–10
10–20
20–40
Over 40

GLACIAL LAKE AGASSIZ

After Warren Upham,
U. S. G. S., and others

0 50 100 150 200 Miles
0 100 200 300 Km.

Present lakes and rivers
are shown in black.

ANCIENT LAKES LAHONTAN AND BONNEVILLE

Lahontan after I. C. Russell
Bonneville after G. K. Gilbert, U. S. G. S.

GLACIAL LAURENTIAN LAKES EARLY STAGE

After Taylor and Leverett

Marginal moraines in red

GLACIAL LAURENTIAN LAKES LATER STAGE

After Taylor and Leverett

Marginal moraines in red

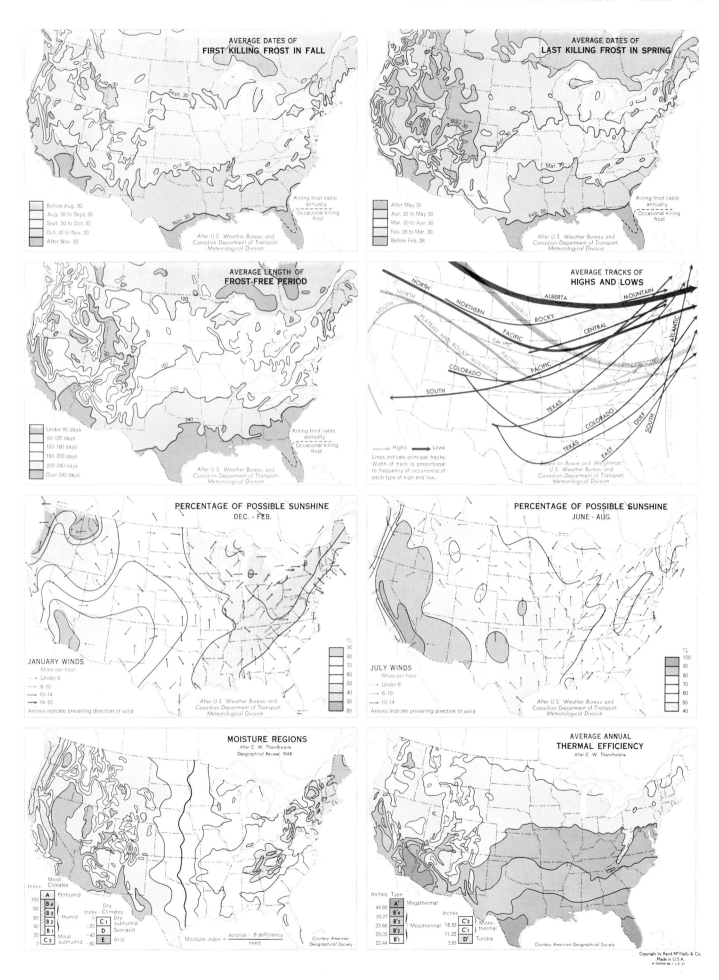

AVERAGE DATES OF
FIRST KILLING FROST IN FALL

Before Aug. 30
Aug. 30 to Sept. 30
Sept. 30 to Oct. 30
Oct. 30 to Nov. 30
After Nov. 30

Killing frost liable
annually
Occasional killing
frost

After U.S. Weather Bureau and
Canadian Department of Transport,
Meteorological Division

AVERAGE DATES OF
LAST KILLING FROST IN SPRING

After May 30
Apr. 30 to May 30
Mar. 30 to Apr. 30
Feb. 28 to Mar. 30
Before Feb. 28

Killing frost liable
annually
Occasional killing
frost

After U.S. Weather Bureau and
Canadian Department of Transport,
Meteorological Division

AVERAGE LENGTH OF
FROST-FREE PERIOD

Under 80 days
80-120 days
120-160 days
160-200 days
200-240 days
Over 240 days

Killing frost liable
annually
Occasional killing
frost

After U.S. Weather Bureau and
Canadian Department of Transport,
Meteorological Division

AVERAGE TRACKS OF
HIGHS AND LOWS

Highs   Lows
Lines indicate principal tracks.
Width of track is proportional
to frequency of occurrence of
each type of high and low.

Based on Bowie and Weightman,
U.S. Weather Bureau and
Canadian Department of Transport,
Meteorological Division

PERCENTAGE OF POSSIBLE SUNSHINE
DEC. - FEB.

JANUARY WINDS
Miles per hour
Under 6
6-10
10-14
14-20
Arrows indicate prevailing direction of wind

%
90
80
70
60
50
40
30
20

After U.S. Weather Bureau and
Canadian Department of Transport,
Meteorological Division

PERCENTAGE OF POSSIBLE SUNSHINE
JUNE - AUG.

JULY WINDS
Miles per hour
Under 6
6-10
10-14
Arrows indicate prevailing direction of wind

%
100
90
80
70
60
50
40

After U.S. Weather Bureau and
Canadian Department of Transport,
Meteorological Division

MOISTURE REGIONS
After C. W. Thornthwaite
Geographical Review, 1948

Index   Moist
        Climates
100   A   Perhumid
80   B4
60   B3   Humid
40   B2
20   B1
        C2 Moist
0   subhumid

        Dry Climates
Index
0   C1 Dry
-20   D   subhumid
-40   Semiarid
-60   E   Arid

Moisture index = $\dfrac{surplus - .6\ deficiency}{need}$

Courtesy American
Geographical Society

AVERAGE ANNUAL
THERMAL EFFICIENCY
After C. W. Thornthwaite

Inches Type
44.88   A'   Megathermal
39.27   B'4
33.66   B'3   Mesothermal
28.05   B'2
22.44   B'1

Inches
16.83   C'2 Micro-
11.22   C'1   thermal
5.61   D'   Tundra

Courtesy American Geographical Society

Copyright by Rand McNally & Co.
Made in U.S.A.
A-520500-86-1-12-3'

84

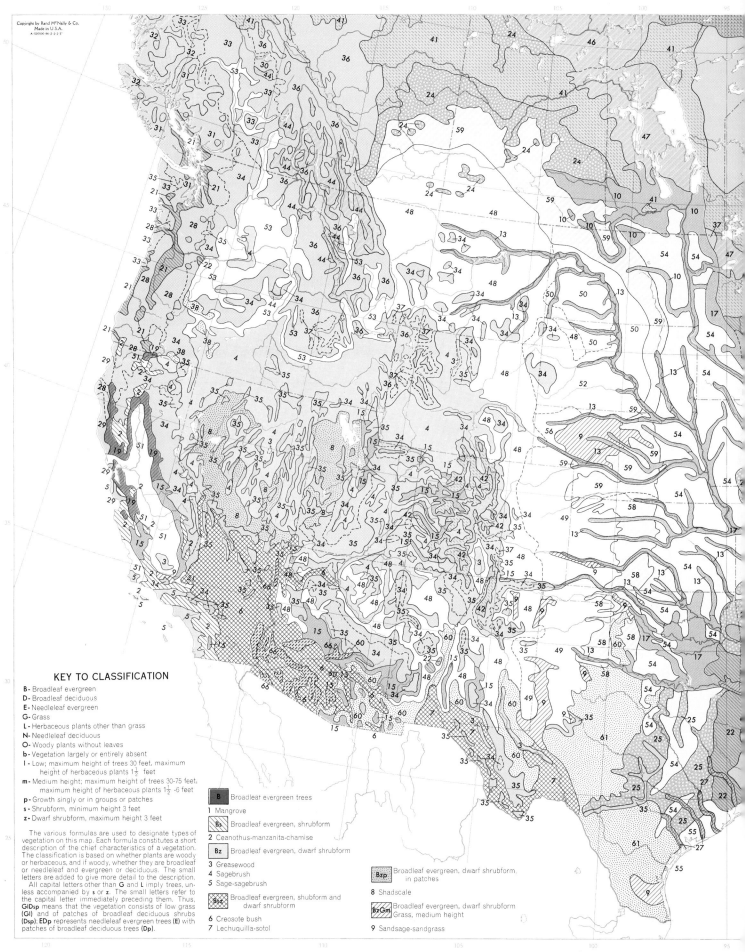

KEY TO CLASSIFICATION

B- Broadleaf evergreen
D- Broadleaf deciduous
E- Needleleaf evergreen
G- Grass
L- Herbaceous plants other than grass
N- Needleleaf deciduous
O- Woody plants without leaves
b- Vegetation largely or entirely absent
l - Low; maximum height of trees 30 feet, maximum height of herbaceous plants 1½ feet
m- Medium height; maximum height of trees 30-75 feet, maximum height of herbaceous plants 1½ -6 feet
p- Growth singly or in groups or patches
s - Shrubform, minimum height 3 feet
z- Dwarf shrubform, maximum height 3 feet

The various formulas are used to designate types of vegetation on this map. Each formula constitutes a short description of the chief characteristics of a vegetation. The classification is based on whether plants are woody or herbaceous, and if woody, whether they are broadleaf or needleleaf and evergreen or deciduous. The small letters are added to give more detail to the description.

All capital letters other than G and L imply trees, unless accompanied by s or z. The small letters refer to the capital letter immediately preceding them. Thus, **Glsp** means that the vegetation consists of low grass (**Gl**) and of patches of broadleaf deciduous shrubs (**Dsp**); **EDp** represents needleleaf evergreen trees (**E**) with patches of broadleaf deciduous trees (**Dp**).

B Broadleaf evergreen trees
1 Mangrove
Bs Broadleaf evergreen, shrubform
2 Ceanothus-manzanita-chamise
Bz Broadleaf evergreen, dwarf shrubform
3 Greasewood
4 Sagebrush
5 Sage-sagebrush
Bsz Broadleaf evergreen, shubform and dwarf shrubform
6 Creosote bush
7 Lechuquilla-sotol

Bzp Broadleaf evergreen, dwarf shrubform in patches
8 Shadscale
BzGm Broadleaf evergreen, dwarf shrubform Grass, medium height
9 Sandsage-sandgrass

0 25 50 75 100   200   300   400   500 Miles

0 50 100   200   400   600   800 Kilometers

Scale 1: 14 000 000;   One inch to 220 miles

NATURAL VEGETATION

BY A. W. KÜCHLER

Based on "A Physiognomic Classification of Vegetation"
Annals of the Assoc. of American Geographers, Vol. 39, September, 1949

D Broadleaf deciduous trees

10 Aspen-oak
11 Beech-maple
12 Beech-tulip tree-maple-basswood
13 Cottonwood-willow
14 Maple-basswood
15 Oak
16 Oak-ash-maple
17 Oak-hickory
18 Oak-tulip tree

DB Broadleaf deciduous trees
Broadleaf evergreen trees

19 Oak-madrone

DE Broadleaf deciduous trees
Needleleaf evergreen trees

20 Maple-yellow birch-hemlock-pine
21 Oak-Douglas fir
22 Oak-pine
23 Maple-beech-hemlock

D
Gmp Broadleaf deciduous trees
Grass, medium height, in patches

24 Aspen-needle grass-wheat grass
25 Oak-hickory-bluestem

DN Broadleaf deciduous trees
Needleleaf deciduous trees

26 Bay trees-bald cypress
27 Tupelo-gum-bald cypress

E Needleleaf evergreen trees

28 Douglas fir
29 Douglas fir-redwood
30 Hemlock-arbor vitae
31 Hemlock-arbor vitae-Douglas fir
32 Hemlock-arbor vitae-fir
33 Hemlock-spruce
34 Pine
35 Pine-juniper
36 Pine-spruce
37 Spruce-fir

Esp Needleleaf evergreen, shrubform,
in patches

38 Juniper

EDp Needleleaf evergreen trees
Broadleaf deciduous trees, in patches

39 Douglas fir-pine-aspen
40 Pine-spruce-birch
41 Spruce-aspen
42 Spruce-fir-aspen
43 Spruce-poplar-birch

EN Needleleaf evergreen trees
Needleleaf deciduous trees

44 Hemlock-arbor vitae-Douglas fir-larch
45 Pine-bald cypress
46 Pine-spruce-larch
47 Spruce-larch

Gl Grass, low

48 Grama grass
49 Grama grass-buffalo grass
50 Grama grass-needle grass
51 Needle grass-blue grass
52 Wheat grass
53 Wheat grass-blue grass

Gm Grass, medium height

54 Bluestem
55 Broom grass-water grass
56 Marsh grass
57 Saw grass

Gml Grass, medium and low height

58 Bluestem-bunch grass
59 Needle grass-wheat grass

Gl
Dsp Grass, low
Broadleaf deciduous, shrubform, in patches

60 Bunch grass-oak

Gm
Dsp Grass, medium height
Broadleaf deciduous, shrubform, in patches

61 Mesquite grass-mesquite

L Herbaceous plants other than grass

62 Lichens, etc.

LEp Herbaceous plants other than grass
Needleleaf evergreen trees, in patches

63 Lichens-spruce

LEp
Np Herbaceous plants other than grass
Needleleaf evergreen trees, in patches
Needleleaf deciduous trees, in patches

64 Lichens-spruce-larch

N Needleleaf deciduous trees

65 Bald cypress

OPp Woody plants without leaves, in patches

66 Palo verde-cacti-ocotillo

b Vegetation largely or entirely absent

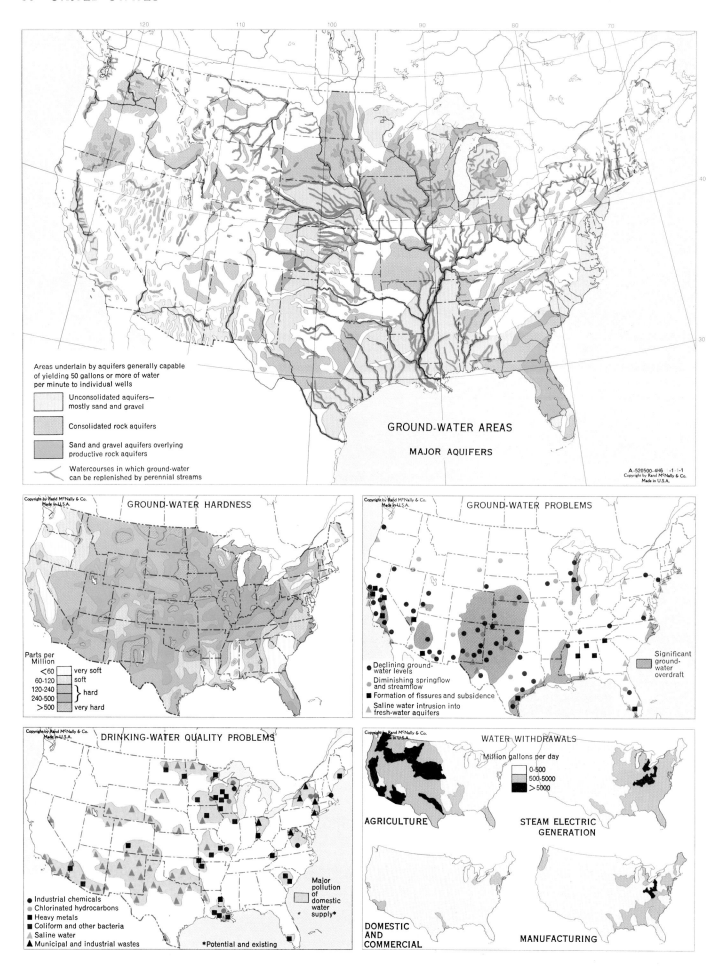

GROUND-WATER AREAS

MAJOR AQUIFERS

Areas underlain by aquifers generally capable
of yielding 50 gallons or more of water
per minute to individual wells

Unconsolidated aquifers—
mostly sand and gravel

Consolidated rock aquifers

Sand and gravel aquifers overlying
productive rock aquifers

Watercourses in which ground-water
can be replenished by perennial streams

A-520500-4H6 -1-|-1
Copyright by Rand M&Nally & Co.
Made in U.S.A.

GROUND-WATER HARDNESS

Parts per
Million

<60	very soft
60-120	soft
120-240	hard
240-500	hard
>500	very hard

GROUND-WATER PROBLEMS

● Declining ground-
water levels
● Diminishing springflow
and streamflow
■ Formation of fissures and subsidence
▲ Saline water intrusion into
fresh-water aquifers

Significant
ground-
water
overdraft

DRINKING-WATER QUALITY PROBLEMS

● Industrial chemicals
● Chlorinated hydrocarbons
■ Heavy metals
● Coliform and other bacteria
▲ Saline water
▲ Municipal and industrial wastes

Major
pollution
of
domestic
water
supply*

*Potential and existing

WATER WITHDRAWALS

Million gallons per day

	0-500
	500-5000
	>5000

AGRICULTURE

STEAM ELECTRIC
GENERATION

DOMESTIC
AND
COMMERCIAL

MANUFACTURING

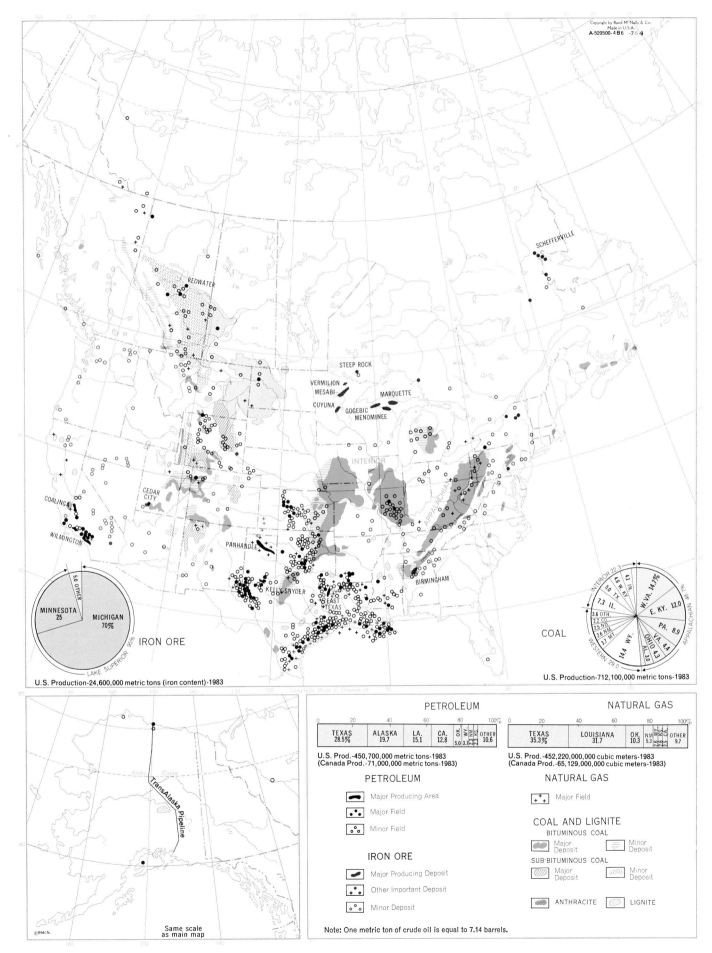

Copyright by Rand McNally & Co.
Made in U.S.A.
A-520500-4B6 -7-6-9

SCHEFFERVILLE

REDWATER

STEEP ROCK

VERMILION
MESABI
CUYUNA
GOGEBIC
MENOMINEE
MARQUETTE

INTERIOR

APPALACHIAN

COALINGA

CEDAR
CITY

WILMINGTON

PANHANDLE

KELLY SNYDER

EAST
TEXAS

BIRMINGHAM

IRON ORE

MINNESOTA
25

MICHIGAN
70%

5.0 OTHER

LAKE SUPERIOR 95%

U.S. Production-24,600,000 metric tons (iron content)-1983

COAL

INTERIOR 22.3 | 41 IN. | 4.6 W. KY. | W. VA. 14.1%
5.0 TX. | E. KY. 12.0
7.3 IL. | PA. 8.9
3.6 OTH. | VA. 4.4
2.2 CO. | OHIO 4.3
2.5 ND. | AL 3.0
2.6 NM. |
3.7 MT. |
14.4 WY. |
WESTERN 29.0 | APPALACHIAN 46

U.S. Production-712,100,000 metric tons-1983

TransAlaska Pipeline

Arctic Circle

© RMCN.

Same scale
as main map

PETROLEUM

	20	40	60	80	100%
TEXAS 28.5%	ALASKA 19.7	LA. 15.1	CA. 12.8	OK. 5.0 WY. 3.7 KS. 2.3	OTHER 10.6

U.S. Prod.-450,700,000 metric tons-1983
(Canada Prod.-71,000,000 metric tons-1983)

NATURAL GAS

0	20	40	60	80	100%
TEXAS 35.3%	LOUISIANA 31.7	OK. 10.3	NM 5.3 KS 2.6 CA. 2.5	OTHER 9.7

U.S. Prod.-452,220,000 cubic meters-1983
(Canada Prod.-65,129,000,000 cubic meters-1983)

PETROLEUM

Major Producing Area

Major Field

Minor Field

IRON ORE

Major Producing Deposit

Other Important Deposit

Minor Deposit

NATURAL GAS

Major Field

COAL AND LIGNITE

BITUMINOUS COAL

Major Deposit | Minor Deposit

SUB-BITUMINOUS COAL

Major Deposit | Minor Deposit

ANTHRACITE | LIGNITE

Note: One metric ton of crude oil is equal to 7.14 barrels.

Scale 1: 32 000 000; One inch to 500 miles.   LAMBERT CONFORMAL CONIC PROJECTION

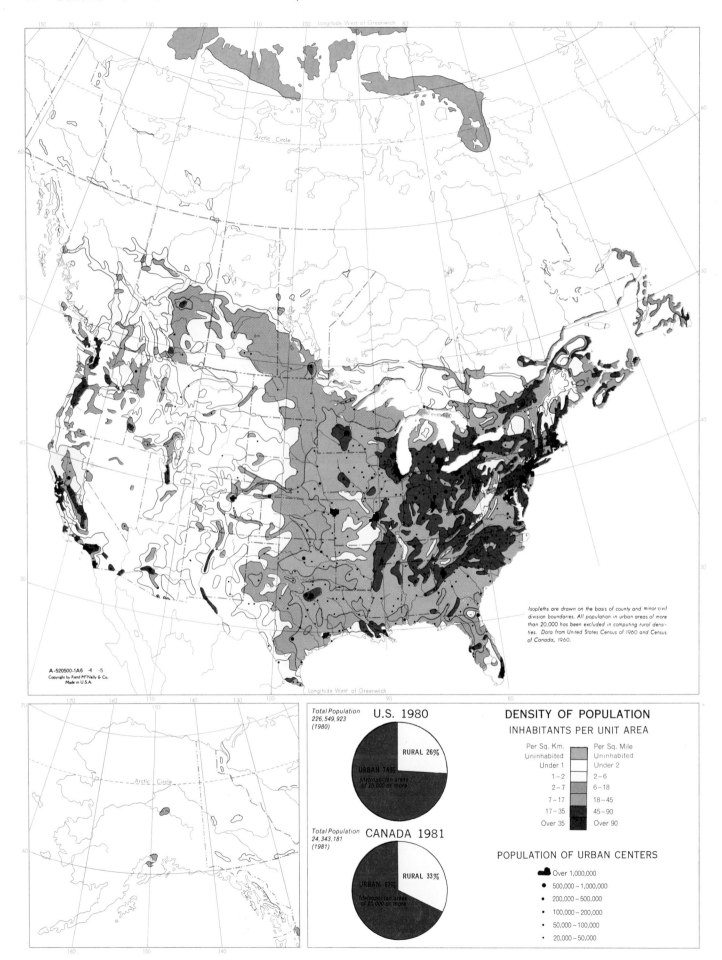

Isopleths are drawn on the basis of county and minor civil division boundaries. All population in urban areas of more than 20,000 has been excluded in computing rural densities. Data from United States Census of 1960 and Census of Canada, 1960.

A-520500-1A6 -4 -5
Copyright by Rand McNally & Co.
Made in U.S.A.

U.S. 1980

Total Population
226,549,923
(1980)

RURAL 26%

URBAN 74%

Metropolitan areas
of 20,000 or more

CANADA 1981

Total Population
24,343,181
(1981)

RURAL 33%

URBAN 67%

Metropolitan areas
of 20,000 or more

DENSITY OF POPULATION

INHABITANTS PER UNIT AREA

Per Sq. Km.	Per Sq. Mile
Uninhabited	Uninhabited
Under 1	Under 2
1 – 2	2 – 6
2 – 7	6 – 18
7 – 17	18 – 45
17 – 35	45 – 90
Over 35	Over 90

POPULATION OF URBAN CENTERS

Over 1,000,000
● 500,000 – 1,000,000
● 200,000 – 500,000
· 100,000 – 200,000
· 50,000 – 100,000
· 20,000 – 50,000

Scale 1: 32 000 000; One inch to 500 miles.   LAMBERT CONFORMAL CONIC PROJECTION

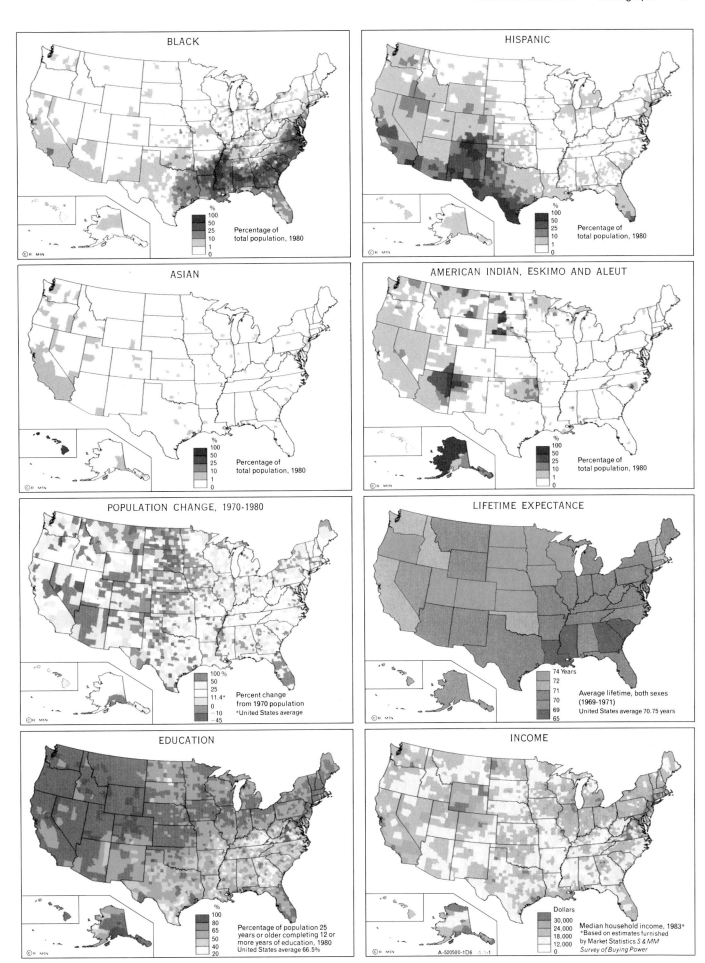

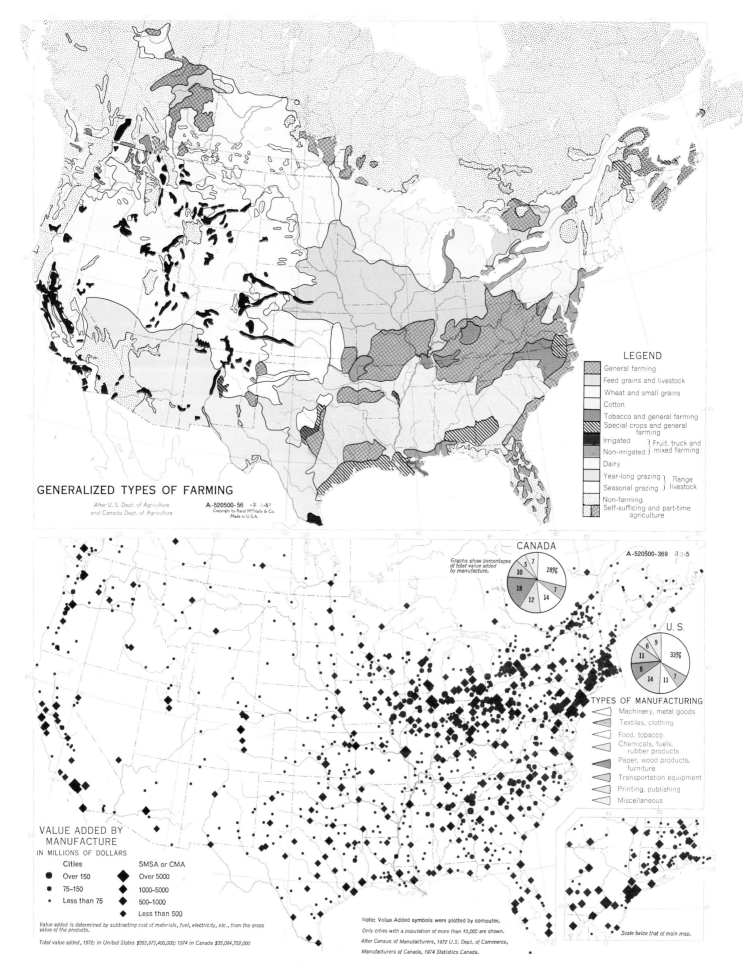

GENERALIZED TYPES OF FARMING

After U. S. Dept. of Agriculture
and Canada Dept. of Agriculture

A-520500-56 -3- 3-5²
Copyright by Rand McNally & Co.
Made in U.S.A.

LEGEND

General farming
Feed grains and livestock
Wheat and small grains
Cotton
Tobacco and general farming
Special crops and general farming
Irrigated } Fruit, truck and
Non-irrigated } mixed farming
Dairy
Year-long grazing } Range
Seasonal grazing } livestock
Non-farming
Self-sufficing and part-time agriculture

CANADA

Graphs show percentages
of total value added
by manufacture.

5 7
10   28%
18
12 14 7

A-520500-369 -3-3-5

U.S.

6 9
11   33%
8
14 11 7

TYPES OF MANUFACTURING

Machinery, metal goods
Textiles, clothing
Food, tobacco
Chemicals, fuels, rubber products
Paper, wood products, furniture
Transportation equipment
Printing, publishing
Miscellaneous

VALUE ADDED BY MANUFACTURE

IN MILLIONS OF DOLLARS

Cities	SMSA or CMA
Over 150	Over 5000
75–150	1000–5000
Less than 75	500–1000
	Less than 500

Value added is determined by subtracting cost of materials, fuel, electricity, etc., from the gross value of the products.

Total value added, 1972: in United States $353,973,400,000; 1974 in Canada $35,084,752,000

Note: Value Added symbols were plotted by computer.

Only cities with a population of more than 10,000 are shown.

After Census of Manufacturers, 1972 U.S. Dept. of Commerce,
Manufacturers of Canada, 1974 Statistics Canada.

Scale twice that of main map.

Scale 1: 28 000 000; One inch to 440 miles.   LAMBERT CONFORMAL CONIC PROJECTION

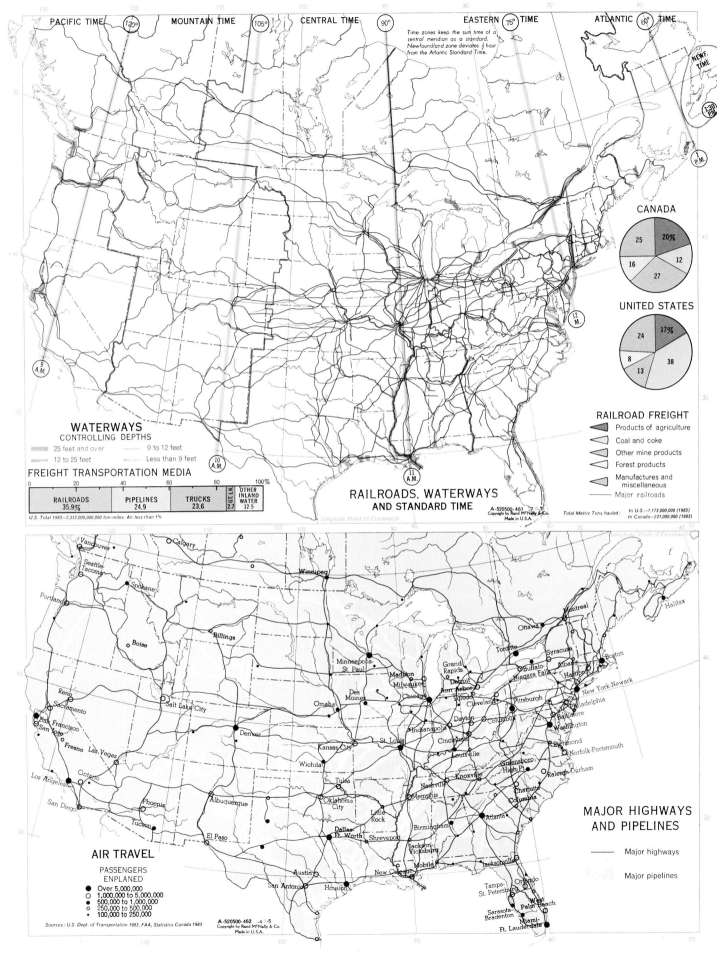

PACIFIC TIME MOUNTAIN TIME CENTRAL TIME EASTERN TIME ATLANTIC TIME

Time zones keep the sun time of a
central meridian as a standard.
Newfoundland zone deviates ½ hour
from the Atlantic Standard Time.

NEWF.
TIME

CANADA

20%
25
12
16
27

UNITED STATES

17%
24
38
8
13

RAILROAD FREIGHT
Products of agriculture
Coal and coke
Other mine products
Forest products
Manufactures and
miscellaneous
Major railroads

WATERWAYS
CONTROLLING DEPTHS
25 feet and over   9 to 12 feet
12 to 25 feet   Less than 9 feet

FREIGHT TRANSPORTATION MEDIA
0   20   40   60   80   100%
RAILROADS PIPELINES TRUCKS G.L.LK OTHER
35.9%   24.9   23.6   2.7   INLAND
                                      WATER
                                      12.5
U.S. Total 1983—2,333,000,000,000 ton-miles. Air less than 1%

RAILROADS, WATERWAYS
AND STANDARD TIME

A-520500-461
Copyright by Rand McNally & Co.
Made in U.S.A.

Total Metric Tons hauled:
In U.S.—1,173,000,000 (1983)
In Canada—221,000,000 (1983)

Longitude West of Greenwich

Vancouver
Calgary
Seattle
Tacoma
Spokane
Portland
Winnipeg
Billings
Boise
Minneapolis-
St. Paul
Madison
Grand
Rapids
Toronto
Montreal
Ottawa
Halifax
Reno
Sacramento
Salt Lake City
Omaha
Des
Moines
Milwaukee
Detroit
Ann Arbor
Chicago
Toledo
Cleveland
Buffalo
Niagara Falls
Syracuse
Albany
Hartford
Boston
San Francisco
San Jose
Fresno
Las Vegas
Denver
St. Louis
Pittsburgh
New York-Newark
Philadelphia
Baltimore
Washington
Ontario
Los Angeles
Kansas City
Cincinnati
Dayton
Columbus
Indianapolis
Louisville
Richmond
Norfolk-Portsmouth
San Diego
Phoenix
Wichita
Greensboro-
High Pt.
Raleigh-Durham
Tucson
Albuquerque
Tulsa
Oklahoma
City
Little
Rock
Nashville
Knoxville
Memphis
Charlotte
Columbia
El Paso
Dallas-
Ft. Worth
Shreveport
Birmingham
Atlanta
Jackson-
Vicksburg
Mobile
Jacksonville

MAJOR HIGHWAYS
AND PIPELINES
Major highways
Major pipelines

AIR TRAVEL
PASSENGERS
ENPLANED
Over 5,000,000
1,000,000 to 5,000,000
500,000 to 1,000,000
250,000 to 500,000
100,000 to 250,000

Austin
San Antonio
Houston
New Orleans
Tampa-
St. Petersburg
Orlando
West
Palm Beach
Sarasota-
Bradenton
Miami-
Ft. Lauderdale

Sources: U.S. Dept. of Transportation 1983, FAA, Statistics Canada 1983

A-520500-462
Copyright by Rand McNally & Co.
Made in U.S.A.

Scale 1: 28 000 000; One inch to 440 miles.   LAMBERT CONFORMAL CONIC PROJECTION

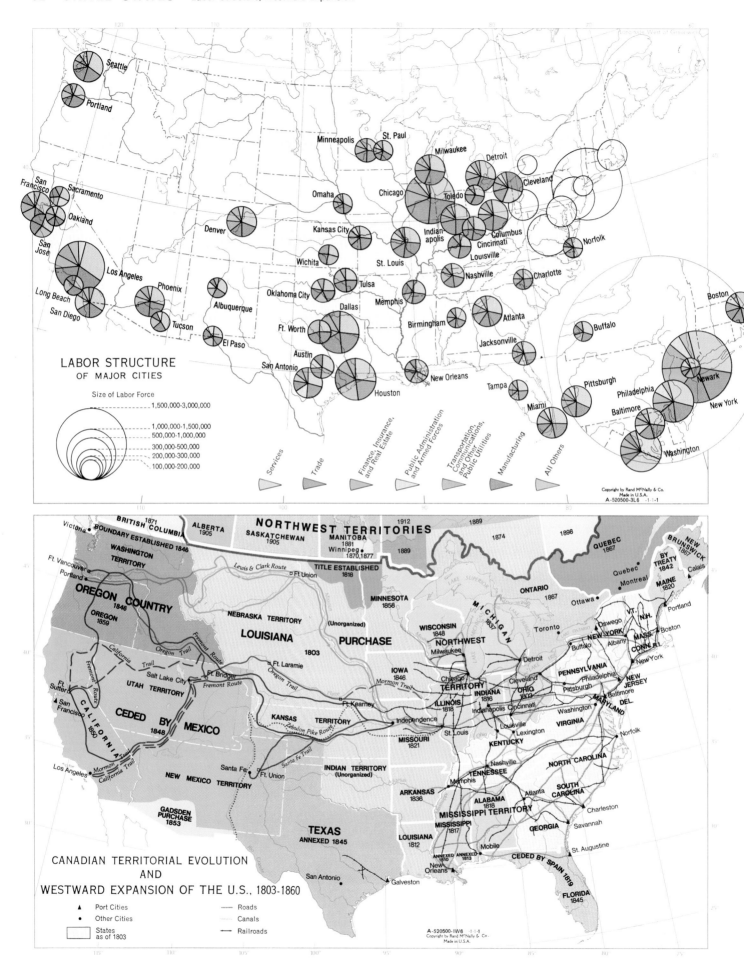

LABOR STRUCTURE OF MAJOR CITIES

CANADIAN TERRITORIAL EVOLUTION AND WESTWARD EXPANSION OF THE U.S., 1803-1860

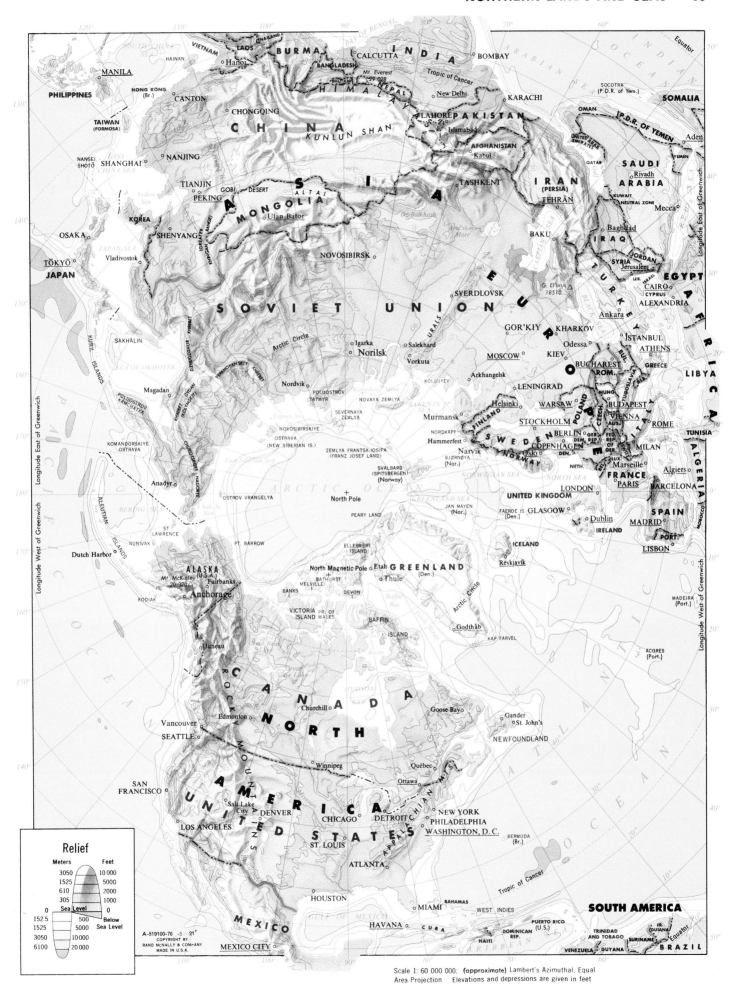

PHILIPPINES

MANILA

HONG KONG (Br.)

CANTON

TAIWAN (FORMOSA)

NANSEI SHOTŌ

SHANGHAI

NANJING

CHONGQING

CHINA

KUNLUN SHAN

TIANJIN

GOBI DESERT

PEKING

ALTAI

KOREA

MONGOLIA

SHENYANG

Ulan Bator

OSAKA

TŌKYŌ

JAPAN

Vladivostok

NOVOSIBIRSK

SOVIET UNION

SAKHALIN

SEA OF OKHOTSK

Magadan

KURIL ISLANDS

POLUOSTROV KAMCHATKA

VERKHOYANSKIY KHREBET

Arctic Circle

Igarka

Norilsk

Salekhard

Vorkuta

URALS

Nordvik

POLUOSTROV TAYMYR

NOVAYA ZEMLYA

SEVERNAYA ZEMLYA

KOMANDORSKIYE OSTRAVA

NOVOSIBIRSKIYE OSTRAVA (NEW SIBERIAN IS.)

ZEMLYA FRANTSA-IOSIFA (FRANZ JOSEF LAND)

OSTROV VRANGELYA

North Pole

SVÁLBARD (SPITSBERGEN) (Norway)

Anadyr

CHUKOTSKOYE NAGORYE

ARCTIC OCEAN

BERING SEA

PEARY LAND

ST LAWRENCE

NUNIVAK

PT. BARROW

Dutch Harbor

ALEUTIAN ISLANDS

PACIFIC OCEAN

KODIAK

ALASKA (U.S.A.)

Mt. McKinley 20 320

Fairbanks

Anchorage

ELLESMERE ISLAND

North Magnetic Pole

Etah

GREENLAND (Den.)

Thule

BATHURST

MELVILLE

BANKS

DEVON

Juneau

VICTORIA ISLAND

PR. OF WALES

Baffin Bay

Arctic Circle

Godthåb

KAP FARVEL

Vancouver

SEATTLE

CANADA

NORTH

Edmonton

ROCKY MOUNTAINS

Churchill

Goose Bay

Gander

St. John's

NEWFOUNDLAND

SAN FRANCISCO

AMERICA

UNITED

Salt Lake City

Winnipeg

Québec

Ottawa

APPALACHIAN MTS.

DENVER

CHICAGO

DETROIT

NEW YORK

PHILADELPHIA

WASHINGTON, D.C.

LOS ANGELES

STATES

ST. LOUIS

BERMUDA (Br.)

ATLANTA

HOUSTON

MEXICO

MIAMI

BAHAMAS

WEST INDIES

Tropic of Cancer

MEXICO CITY

HAVANA

CUBA

HAITI

DOMINICAN REP.

PUERTO RICO (U.S.)

SOUTH AMERICA

TRINIDAD AND TOBAGO

VENEZUELA

GUYANA

FR. GUIANA

SURINAM

BRAZIL

Equator

VIETNAM

LAOS

THAILAND

BURMA

Hanoi

HAINAN

BANGLADESH

CALCUTTA

INDIA

BOMBAY

BAY OF BENGAL

Mt. Everest 29 028

HIMALAY

NEPAL

BHUTAN

Tropic of Cancer

New Delhi

KARACHI

LAHORE

PAKISTAN

Islamabad

ARABIAN SEA

SOCOTRA (P.D.R. of Yem.)

SOMALIA

AFGHANISTAN

Kabul

OMAN

P.D.R. OF YEMEN

Aden

TASHKENT

IRAN (PERSIA)

TEHRĀN

UNITED ARAB EMIRATES

QATAR

YEMEN

SAUDI ARABIA

Riyadh

Mecca

KUWAIT

NEUTRAL ZONE

Oz.Balkhash

Baghdad

IRAQ

BAKU

Aral'skoye More

CASPIAN SEA

JORDAN

SYRIA

Jerusalem

ISRAEL

LEB.

EGYPT

CAIRO

CYPRUS

ALEXANDRIA

AFRICA

EUROPE

G. El'brus 18510

SVERDLOVSK

TURKEY

Ankara

İSTANBUL

ATHENS

GREECE

LIBYA

GOR'KIY

KHARKOV

Odessa

BLACK SEA

MOSCOW

KIEV

BUCHAREST

ROM.

BUL.

YUGOSLAVIA

ITALY

Arctic Circle

Murmansk

Arkhangelsk

LENINGRAD

KOLGUYEV

BARENTS SEA

Kanin Nos More

WARSAW

POLAND

BUDAPEST

HUNG.

VIENNA

AUS.

CZECH.

ROME

Helsinki

FINLAND

STOCKHOLM

BERLIN

DEM. REP.

FED. REP. OF GER.

GER.

MILAN

NORDKAPP

SWEDEN

COPENHAGEN

DEN.

Marseille

Hammerfest

NORWAY

Oslo

LUX.

NETH.

FRANCE

Algiers

ALGERIA

Narvik

BJØRNØYA (Nor.)

NORWEGIAN SEA

NORTH SEA

Barcelona

TUNISIA

UNITED KINGDOM

LONDON

PARIS

JAN MAYEN (Nor.)

FAEROE IS. (Den.)

GLASGOW

SPAIN

GREENLAND SEA

ICELAND

Reykjavík

Dublin

IRELAND

MADRID

MADEIRA (Port.)

PORT.

LISBON

ACORES (Port.)

ATLANTIC OCEAN

Tropic of Cancer

Equator

CARIBBEAN SEA

GULF OF MEXICO

SOUTH CHINA SEA

EAST CHINA SEA

Yellow Sea

JAPAN SEA

120° 110° 100° 90° 80° 70° 60°

130°

140°

150°

160°

170°

180°

170°

160°

150°

140°

130°

Longitude East of Greenwich

Longitude West of Greenwich

Longitude East of Greenwich

Longitude West of Greenwich

30°

40°

50°

50°

40°

30°

20°

Relief		
Meters		Feet
3050		10 000
1525		5000
610		2000
305		1000
0 Sea Level		0
152.5	500	Below Sea Level
1525		5000
3050		10 000
6100		20 000

A-519100-76 -5 -21
COPYRIGHT BY
RAND McNALLY & COMPANY
MADE IN U.S.A.

Scale 1: 60 000 000; (approximate) Lambert's Azimuthal, Equal Area Projection Elevations and depressions are given in feet

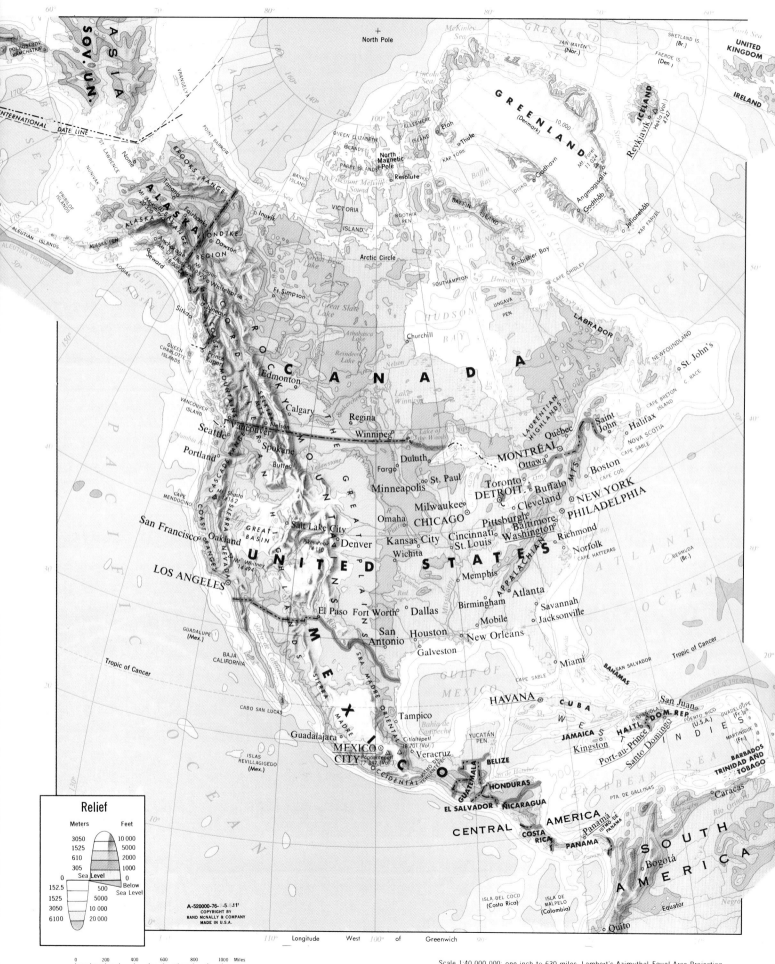

ASIA SOV. UN.

INTERNATIONAL DATE LINE

North Pole

GREENLAND
(Denmark)

10,000

Mt. Forel
11,024

Helge (Vol.)
4147

SHETLAND IS.
(Br.)

FAEROE IS.
(Den.)

UNITED KINGDOM

IRELAND

POLUOSTROV KAMCHATKA

McKinley Mts.

JAN MAYEN
(Nor.)

North Sea

Reykjavík ICELAND

ST. LAWRENCE

NUNIVAK

Nome

PRIBILOF ISLANDS

ALEUTIAN ISLANDS

ALEUTIAN TROUGH

KODIAK

POINT BARROW

BROOKS RANGE

ALASKA

ALASKA RANGE

Tanana

Fairbanks

Mt. McKINLEY
20,320

Mt. St. Elias
18,008

ANCHORAGE

Seward

Whitehorse

Juneau

Sitka

PRINCE RUPERT

QUEEN CHARLOTTE ISLANDS

Inuvik

Dawson

KLONDIKE REGION

Mt. Logan
19,850

Ft. Simpson

Great Bear Lake

Arctic Circle

Great Slave Lake

Athabasca Lake

Reindeer Lake

Churchill

QUEEN ELIZABETH ISLANDS

PARRY ISLANDS

BANKS ISLAND

Viscount Melville Sound

VICTORIA ISLAND

BOOTHIA PEN.

Resolute

North Magnetic Pole

Etah

Thule

KAP YORK

ELLESMERE ISLAND

Godhavn

DISKO

Angmagssalik

Godthåb

Julianehåb

KAP FARVEL

Lincoln Sea

Beaufort Sea

ARCTIC OCEAN

SOUTHAMPTON

Frobisher Bay

CAPE CHIDLEY

UNGAVA PEN.

Baffin Bay

BAFFIN ISLAND

Davis Strait

Denmark Strait

HUDSON BAY

HUDSON STR.

LABRADOR

CANADA

Edmonton

Calgary

Regina

Winnipeg

Lake Winnipeg

Nelson

Lake of the Woods

LAURENTIAN HIGHLANDS

Québec

Ottawa

MONTRÉAL

Saint John

Halifax

NOVA SCOTIA

CAPE BRETON ISLAND

NEWFOUNDLAND

St. John's

C. RACE

VANCOUVER ISLAND

Vancouver

Seattle

Spokane

Portland

Butte

Nelson

Columbia R.

Yellowstone

CAPE MENDOCINO

Mt. Shasta
4162

San Francisco

Oakland

LOS ANGELES

COAST RANGES

SIERRA NEVADA

Mt. Whitney
14,494

GREAT BASIN

Salt Lake City

Pikes Peak
14,110

Denver

UNITED STATES

Fargo

Duluth

Minneapolis

St. Paul

Milwaukee

Omaha

CHICAGO

Kansas City

Wichita

St. Louis

Cincinnati

Memphis

GREAT PLAINS

Red R.

Toronto

DETROIT

Cleveland

Buffalo

Pittsburgh

Boston

CAPE COD

NEW YORK

PHILADELPHIA

Baltimore

Washington

Richmond

Norfolk

CAPE HATTERAS

APPALACHIAN MTS.

Birmingham

Atlanta

Savannah

Mobile

Jacksonville

BERMUDA
(Br.)

ATLANTIC OCEAN

PACIFIC OCEAN

GUADALUPE
(Mex.)

BAJA CALIFORNIA

Tropic of Cancer

CABO SAN LUCAS

Golfo de California

El Paso

Fort Worth

Dallas

San Antonio

Houston

Galveston

New Orleans

SIERRA MADRE ORIENTAL

SIERRA MADRE OCCIDENTAL

MEXICO

Guadalajara

ISLAS REVILLAGIGEDO
(Mex.)

MEXICO CITY

Popocatépetl
17,887 (Vol.)

Citlaltépetl
18,701 (Vol.)

Tampico

Bahía de Campeche

Veracruz

YUCATÁN PEN.

GULF OF MEXICO

CAPE SABLE

Miami

BAHAMAS

HAVANA

CUBA

SAN SALVADOR

Tropic of Cancer

Yucatan Channel

BELIZE

GUATEMALA

HONDURAS

EL SALVADOR

NICARAGUA

COSTA RICA

CENTRAL AMERICA

PANAMA

ISTMO DE TEHUANTEPEC

Golfo de Honduras

JAMAICA

Kingston

HISPANIOLA

HAITI

Port-au-Prince

DOM. REP.

Santo Domingo

San Juan

PUERTO RICO
(U.S.A.)

GUADELOUPE
(Fr.)

MARTINIQUE
(Fr.)

BARBADOS

TRINIDAD AND TOBAGO

WEST INDIES

CARIBBEAN SEA

PTA. DE GALLINAS

PUERTO RICO TRENCH

Caracas

Rio Orinoco

Bogotá

SOUTH AMERICA

ISTMO DE PANAMÁ

ISLA DEL COCO
(Costa Rica)

ISLA DE MALPELO
(Colombia)

Equator

Quito

Rio Negro

Longitude West of Greenwich

Relief

Meters		Feet
3050		10 000
1525		5000
610		2000
305		1000
0	Sea Level	0
		Below Sea Level
152.5		500
1525		5000
3050		10 000
6100		20 000

A-520000-76-5-11
COPYRIGHT BY
RAND McNALLY & COMPANY
MADE IN U.S.A.

| 0 | 200 | 400 | 600 | 800 | 1000 Miles |
| 0 | 400 | 800 | 1200 | 1600 Kilometers |

Scale 1:40 000 000; one inch to 630 miles. Lambert's Azimuthal Equal Area Projection
Elevations and depressions are given in feet

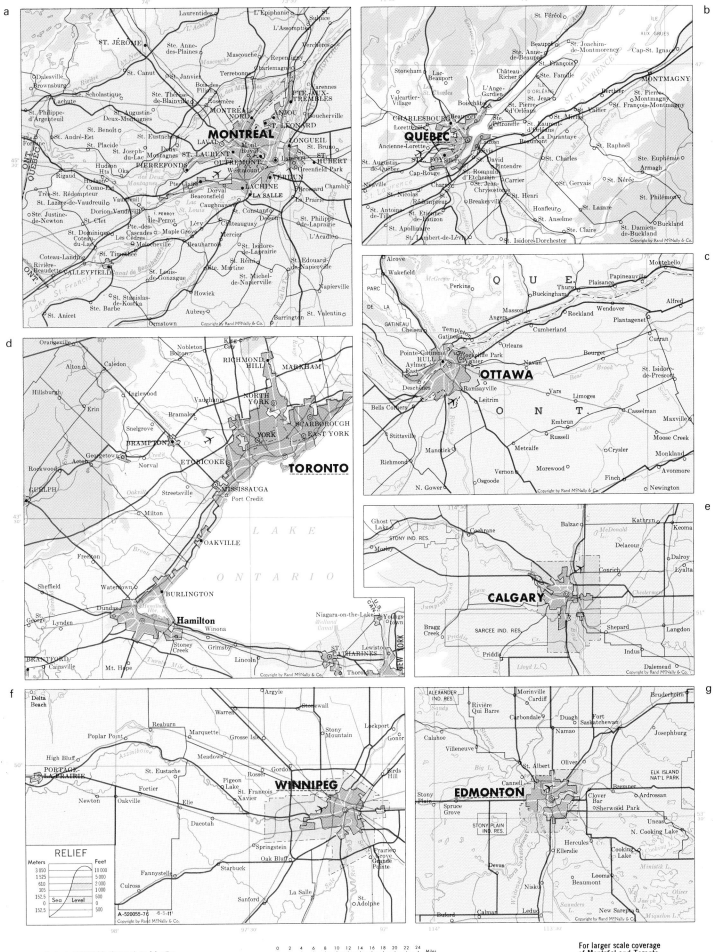

a

MONTRÉAL

b

QUÉBEC

c

OTTAWA

d

TORONTO

LAKE ONTARIO

Hamilton

e

CALGARY

f

WINNIPEG

RELIEF

Meters		Feet
3 050		10 000
1 525		5 000
610		2 000
305		1 000
0	Sea Level	500
152.5		0
152.5		500

A-520055-76   -6-5-11'
Copyright by Rand McNally & Co.

g

EDMONTON

Scale 1:1 000 000; One inch to 16 miles.
Elevations and depressions are given in feet.

0 2 4 6 8 10 12 14 16 18 20 22 24 Miles
0 4 8 12 16 20 24 28 32 36 40 Kilometers

For larger scale coverage
of Montréal and Toronto
see page 54.

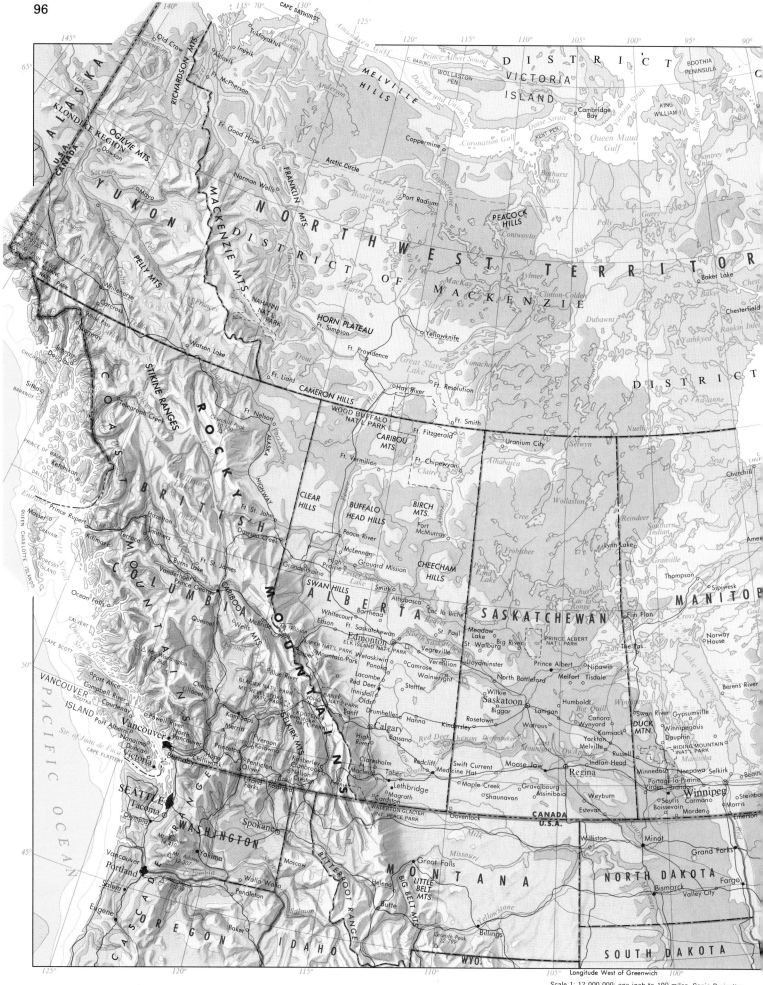

Scale 1: 12 000 000; one inch to 190 miles. Conic Projection

Elevations and depressions are given in feet

Longitude West of Greenwich

134°   132°   130°   128°   126°   124°

PRINCE OF WALES ISLAND

Klawock

Mt. Reid 4592 △

REVILLAGIGEDO ISLAND

Hydaburg

Copper Mtn 3916 △

Ketchikan

Metlakatla

ANNETTE ISLAND

DALL ISLAND

Revillagigedo Channel

UNITED STATES
CANADA

Dixon Entrance

CAPE KNOX

DUNDAS ISLAND

Chatham Sound

SKEENA MOUNTAINS

Shedin Pk 8750 △

OMINECA MOUNTAINS

Williston Lake

Alice Arm

Mt. Thomlinson △8050

Takla Lake

McLeod

HAZELTON MOUNTAINS

Hazelton

Smithers

BULKLEY MOUNTAINS RANGES

Tchentlo Lake

Babine Lake

Stuart Lake

Fort St. James

Johnson

NECHAKO

54°

Masset

QUEEN CHARLOTTE ISLANDS

QUEEN CHARLOTTE RANGES

Masset Inlet

GRAHAM ISLAND

Skidegate Inlet

MORESBY ISLAND

Mount Kermode △3550

Hecate Strait

PORCHER ISLAND

Prince Rupert

KITIMAT

Terrace

Skeena

Kitimat

COAST

B R I T I S H

Howson Pk 9050

Morice Lake

Burns Lake

Endako

Ootsa Lake

Nanika Lake

Tahtsa Lake

Michel Pk △7396

Nechako Reservoir

KENNEY DAM

Whitesail Lake

Eutsuk Lake

NECHAKO RANGE

Vanderhoof

Nechako

PLATEAU

BANKS ISLAND

PITT ISLAND

Hartley Bay

ESTEVAN GROUP

PRINCESS ROYAL ISLAND

Mt. Parry △3450

RODERICK ISLAND

PRINCE RUPERT

DOLPHIN ISLAND

SWINDLE ISLAND

ARISTAZABAL ISLAND

M O U N T A I N S

Tetachuck Lake

West Road

West

CAPE ST. JAMES

Ocean Falls

Namu

Bella Bella

Bella Coola

Monarch Mtn △11590

C O L U M

Charlotte Lake

Redstone

Chilcotin

FRASER

52°

Queen

Charlotte

Sound

CALVERT ISLAND

CAPE CAUTION

Bull Harbour

CAPE SCOTT

Port Hardy

Port Alice

Quatsino Sound

CAPE COOK

VANCOUVER ISLAND

Nootka Sound

NOOTKA ISLAND

Tofino

PACIFIC RIM NATIONAL PARK

Barkley Sound

CAPE BEALE

Rivers Inlet

Silverthrone Mtn △9700

Razorback Mtn 10432 △

Mt. Waddington △13260

Queen Bess △10791

Good Hope Mtn 10315 △

P A C I F I C

Smoot Sound

Kelsey Bay

Victoria Pk 7095 △

Bloedel

Golden Hinde △7291

Courtenay

Comox

Port Alberni

Mt. Whymper 5056 △

Mt. Tatlow △10058

Chilko Lake

Mt. Gilbert △3109

Monmouth Mtn △10480

R A N G E S

Campbell River

Powell Lake

Powell River

VANCOUVER ISLAND RANGES

Nanaimo

Ladysmith

Lake Cowichan

Duncan

Cowichan Lake

Squamish

Mt. Garibaldi △8755

North Vancouver

Vancouver
Burna

New Westm

Strait of Juan de Fuca

CAPE FLATTERY

Esquimalt

Victo

OLYMPIC NATIONAL PARK

Port Angeles

50°

P A C I F I C

O C E A N

48°

Continued on pages 116-117

130°   128°   Longitude West of Greenwich   126°   124°

132°

Relief

Meters		Feet
3050		10 000
1525		5000
610		2000
305		1000
152.5		500
0	Sea Level	0
152.5		500
1525		5000

A-520220-76- 6-5-71
COPYRIGHT BY
RAND McNALLY & COMPANY
MADE IN U.S.A.

Scale 1:4 000 000; one inch to 64 miles. Conic Projection

Elevations and depressions are given in feet.

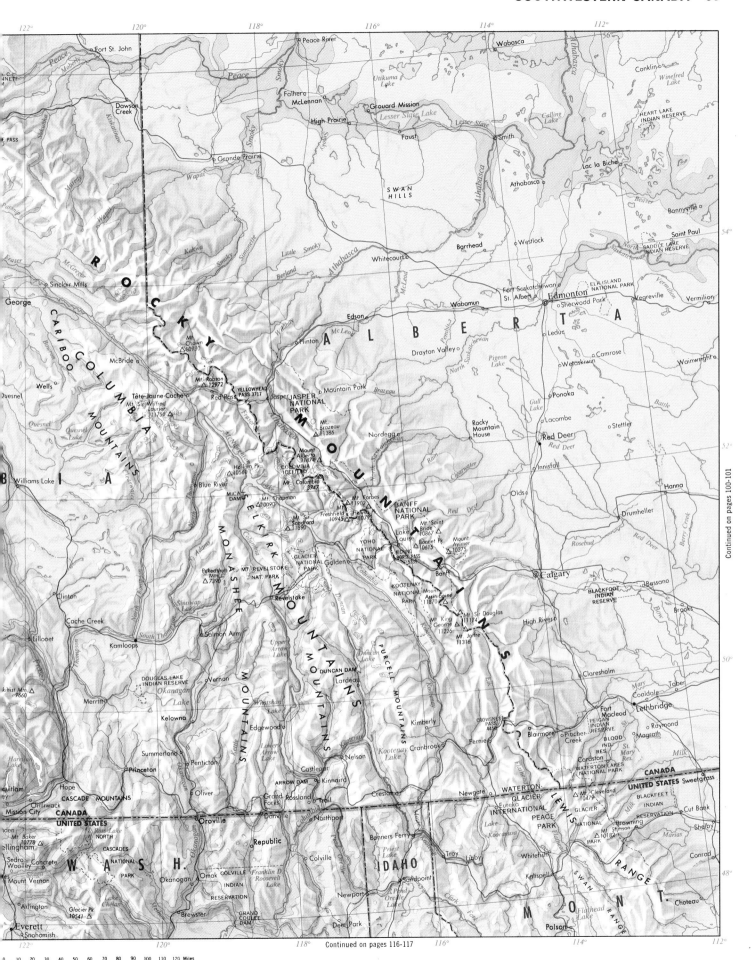

Continued on pages 100-101

Continued on pages 116-117

0 10 20 30 40 50 60 70 80 90 100 110 120 Miles

0   20   40   60   80   100   120   140   160   180   200 Kilometers

Continued on pages 98-99

Continued on pages 116-117

Longitude West of Greenwich

Scale 1:4 000 000; one inch to 64 miles. Conic Projection
Elevations and depressions are given in feet.

A-520218-76 5-4-6²
COPYRIGHT BY
RAND McNALLY & COMPANY
MADE IN U.S.A.

Relief

Meters		Feet
1525		5000
610		2000
305		1000
152.5		500
0	Sea Level	0

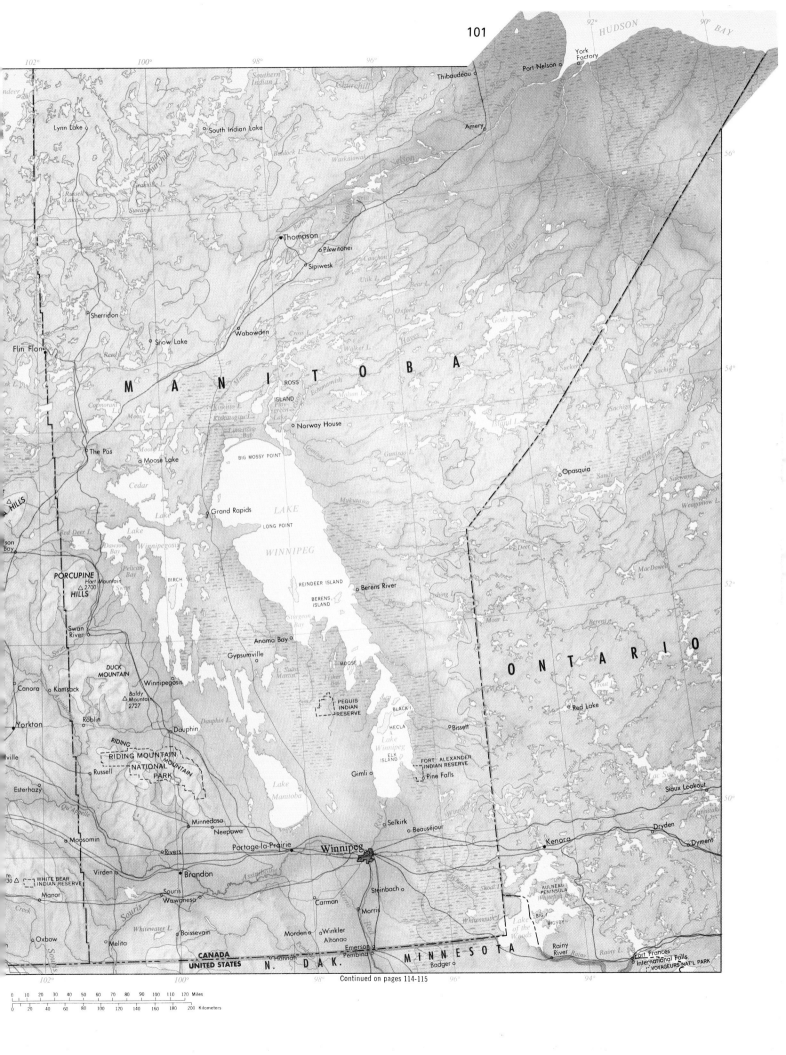

HUDSON   BAY

92°   90°

York
Factory

Port Nelson

Thibaudeau

Amery

56°

Lynn Lake   South Indian Lake

Southern
Indian L.

Churchill

Russell
Lake

Baldock L.

Waskaiowaka

Sherridon

Thompson   Pikwitonei

Sipiwesk

Utik L.

Bear L.

M   A   N   I   T   O   B   A

Snow Lake   Wabowden

54°

Flin Flon

Reed L.

Cross L.

Walker L.

Gods L.

Echimamish

Molson L.

Red Sucker

Île Sachigo

Cormorant
L.

ROSS
ISLAND

Play
Green
Lake

Oxford

Moose L.

Norway House

Guinsao L.

The Pas   Moose Lake

Big Mossy Point

Opasquia

Sandy

Severn

Cedar

Lake

Mukutawa

LAKE

Grand Rapids   LONG POINT

WINNIPEG

52°

MacDowell
L.

PORCUPINE
Hart Mountain
2700
HILLS

Pelican
Bay

Swan
L.

BIRCH
I.

REINDEER ISLAND

BERENS
ISLAND

Berens River

Weagamow L.

Dawson
Bay

Dauphin L.

Swan
River

Sturgeon
Bay

DUCK
MOUNTAIN

Anama Bay

Gypsumville

MOOSE I.

O   N   T   A   R   I   O

Canora   Kamsack

Baldy
Mountain
2727

Winnipegosis

L. St.
Martin

Fisher
Bay

Trout
L.

Yorkton

Roblin

Dauphin

PEGUIS
INDIAN
RESERVE

BLACK I.

Red Lake

RIDING

RIDING MOUNTAIN   MOUNTAIN

NATIONAL   PARK

Russell

HECLA
Lake
Winnipeg

Bissett

Esterhazy

Lake
Manitoba

ELK
ISLAND

FORT ALEXANDER
INDIAN RESERVE

Sioux Lookout

50°

Minnedosa
Neepawa

Gimli

Pine Falls

Moosomin

Rivers   Portage-la-Prairie

Selkirk

Beauséjour

Kenora   Dryden

Dyment

m.
30   WHITE BEAR
INDIAN RESERVE

Virden   Brandon

Assiniboine

Winnipeg

AULNEAU
PENINSULA

Whitefish

Manor   Souris
Wawanesa

Carman

Steinbach

BIG
BIGSBY

Oxbow   Melita

Whitewater L.   Boissevain

Morden   Winkler
Altonao

Morris

Lake
of the
Woods

Rainy
River

Fort Frances

Souris   Creek

CANADA
UNITED STATES

Hannah

Emerson
Pembina

N. DAK.

Badger

MINNESOTA

Rainy L.

International Falls
VOYAGEURS NAT'L PARK

Continued on pages 114-115

102°   100°   98°   96°   94°

0   10 20 30 40 50 60 70 80 90 100 110 120 Miles

0   20   40   60   80   100   120   140   160   180   200 Kilometers

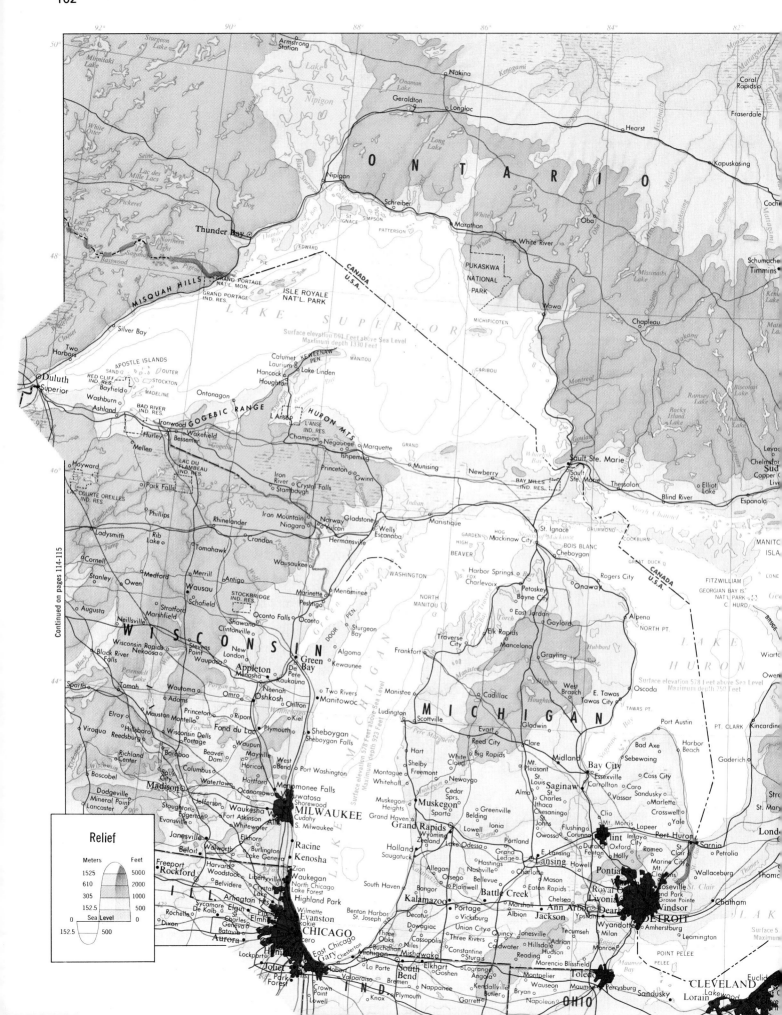

Continued on pages 114-115

Relief

Meters		Feet
1525		5000
610		2000
305		1000
152.5		500
0	Sea Level	0
152.5		500

O N T A R I O

WISCONSIN

MICHIGAN

LAKE SUPERIOR
Surface elevation 601 Feet above Sea Level
Maximum depth 1330 Feet

LAKE MICHIGAN
Surface elevation 578 Feet above Sea Level
Maximum depth 923 Feet

LAKE HURON
Surface elevation 578 Feet above Sea Level
Maximum depth 750 Feet

CANADA
U.S.A.

ILL.

IND.

OHIO

CLEVELAND

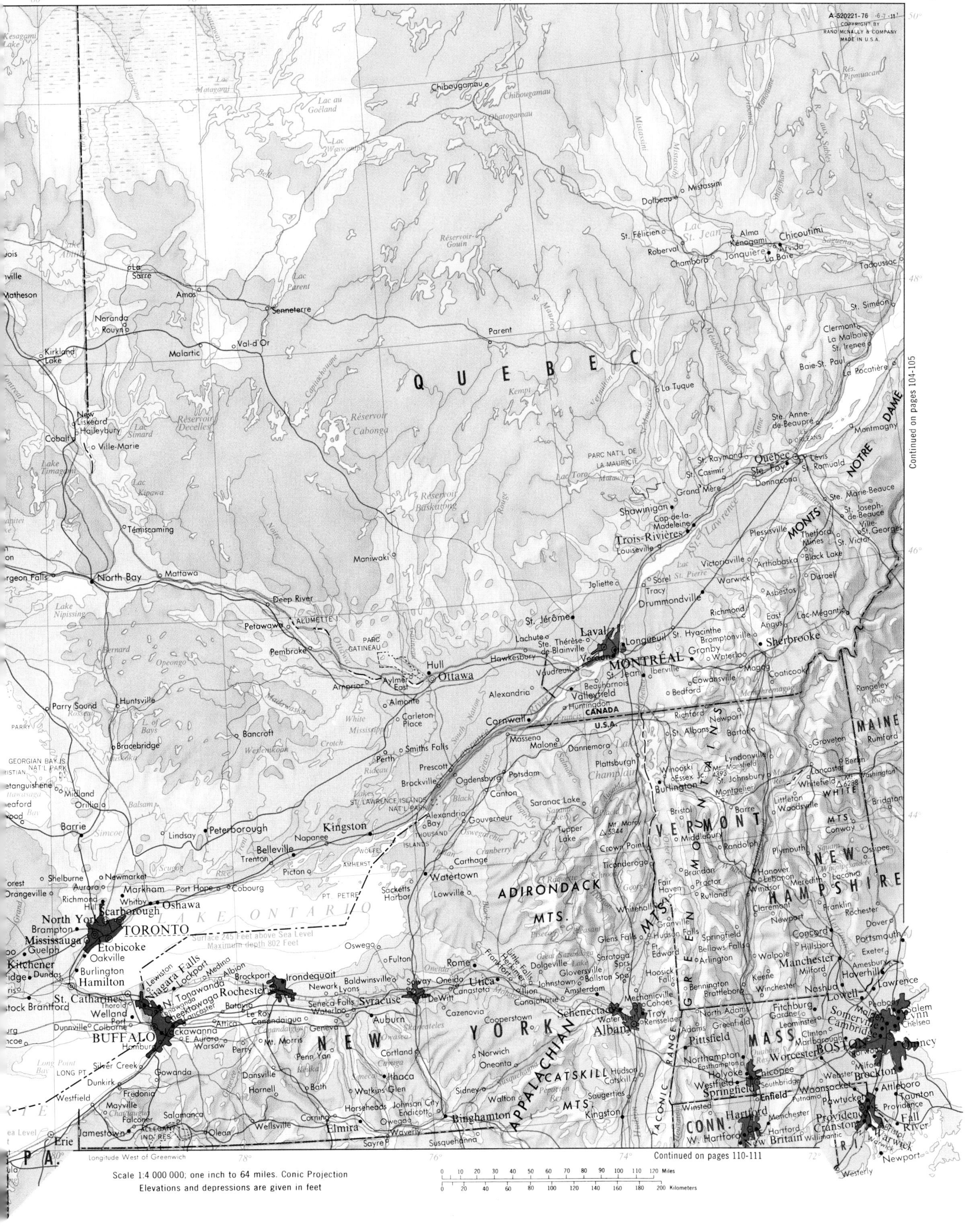

A-520221-76 -6-7 -11
COPYRIGHT BY
RAND McNALLY & COMPANY
MADE IN U.S.A.

Continued on pages 104-105

Q U E B E C

Chibougamau
Chibougamau
Obatogamau
Mistassini
Dolbeau
Lac au Goëland
Lac Waswanipi
St. Félicien   St. Jean   Alma   Chicoutimi
Roberval Kénogami Arvida
Chambord Jonquière La Baie
Tadoussac
St. Siméon
Clermont
La Malbaie
St. Irénée
Baie-St. Paul
Pocatière
Lac Matagami
Amos
Noranda
Rouyn
Senneterre
Val-d'Or
Malartic
Parent
La Tuque
PARC NAT'L DE LA MAURICIE
St. Raymond Québec Lévis
Ste. Foy St. Romuald
Donnacona
Ste. Marie-Beauce
St. Casimir
Grand Mère   St. Joseph-de-Beauce
Ville-St. Georges
St. Victor
Shawinigan
Cap-de-la-Madeleine
Trois-Rivières Plessisville Thetford Mines Black Lake
Louiseville Victoriaville Arthabaska Disraeli
Sorel St. Pierre Warwick Asbestos
Tracy Richmond East Angus Lac-Mégantic
Joliette Drummondville Rangeley
St. Jérôme St. Hyacinthe Sherbrooke
Lachute St. Thérèse Longueuil St. Hyacinthe Bromptonville
Ste-Blainville Granby Waterloo
MONTRÉAL Iberville Cowansville Coaticook
St. Jean Bedford Magog
Vaudreuil Beauharnois
Valleyfield Huntingdon
CANADA
U.S.A.
Rigaud Newport
Cornwall St. Albans Bartonville
Massena Malone
Dannemora
Plattsburgh Winooski Lyndonville Lancaster
Ogdensburg Potsdam Essex JC Mt. Mansfield St. Johnsbury Berlin
Canton Burlington Montgelier Littleton Whitefield
St. LAWRENCE ISLANDS NAT'L PARK Saranac Lake MAINE
Alexandria Gouverneur Tupper Lake Bristol Barre Conway
Bay Lake Mt. Marcy Middlebury Randolph WHITE
THOUSAND ISLANDS Carthage Crown Point Brandon Plymouth Ossipee
Watertown Ticonderoga Proctor Hanover Meredith Laconia
Cranberry Lake Fair Haven Rutland Lebanon Franklin
Lowville ADIRONDACK Whitehall Claremont Rochester
MTS. George Granville Newport Dover
Glens Falls Hudson Falls Springfield Concord
Saratoga Spgs. Bellows Falls Portsmouth
Rome Little Falls Gloversville Arlington Keene Manchester Milford
Utica Herkimer Johnstown Ballston Spa Bennington Brattleboro Winchester Nashua Lawrence
Oneida Amsterdam Hoosick Falls North Adams Fitchburg Lowell
Solvay DeWitt Canastota Conajoharie Mechanicville Greenfield Leominster Haverhill
Syracuse Cohoes Pittsfield MASS. Gardner Peabody
Cazenovia Schenectady Troy Northampton Clinton Salem Lynn
NEW YORK Water Rensselaer North Adams Marlborough Cambridge
Cooperstown Albany Easthampton Worcester BOSTON Quincy
Norwich Holyoke Chicopee Southbridge Webster Brockton
Oneonta Westfield Springfield Woonsocket Milford
Hudson Enfield Pawtucket Attleboro Taunton
Catskill Winsted Hartford Manchester Providence Fall River
APPALACHIAN CATSKILL CONN. W. Hartford Cranston Warwick
Saugerties New Britain Willimantic R.I.
Kingston New Haven Westerly Newport

New Liskeard
Haileybury
Ville-Marie
Cobalt
Kirkland Lake
Matheson
Noranda Rouyn
Témiscaming
North Bay Mattawa
Deep River
Petawawa ALUMETTE I.
Pembroke
PARC GATINEAU
Huntsville Amprior Aylmer East Hull Ottawa
Parry Sound Almonte Hawkesbury Alexandria
Bancroft Carleton Place
Bracebridge Smiths Falls
Perth Prescott
Midland Brockville Ogdensburg
Orillia Smiths Falls
Barrie Kingston
Lindsay Peterborough Napanee
Belleville Trenton Picton
Shelburne Newmarket Cobourg
Aurora Markham Port Hope
Richmond Hill Whitby Oshawa
North York Scarborough PT. PETRE
TORONTO
Brampton
Mississauga Etobicoke
Guelph Oakville Oswego
Kitchener Burlington
Dundas Hamilton
St. Catharines Lewiston Niagara Falls Lockport Medina
Welland Thorold N. Tonawanda Albion Brockport
Dunnville Port Colborne Rochester Batavia Le Roy Newark Lyons
BUFFALO Lancaster Attica Canandaigua Geneva Seneca Falls Waterloo
E. Aurora Warsaw Perry Mt. Morris Cazenovia
Silver Creek Gowanda Dansville Penn Yan Auburn
Dunkirk Fredonia Salamanca Hornell Bath Watkins Glen
Westfield Falconer Wellsville Corning Horseheads Johnson City Endicott
Jamestown Olean Elmira Owego Waverly Binghamton
Erie ALLEGANY IND. RES. Sayre Susquehanna

P A.

GEORGIAN BAY IS. NAT'L PARK
PARRY
Parry Sound
Huntsville
Midland
Orillia
Barrie

LAKE ONTARIO
Surface 245 Feet above Sea Level
Maximum depth 802 Feet

NOTRE DAME
MONTS
VERMONT
GREEN MTS.
TACONIC RANGE
NEW HAMPSHIRE
WHITE MTS.
APPALACHIAN MTS.
CATSKILL MTS.

Longitude West of Greenwich

Scale 1:4 000 000; one inch to 64 miles. Conic Projection
Elevations and depressions are given in feet

Continued on pages 110-111

0 10 20 30 40 50 60 70 80 90 100 110 120 Miles
0 20 40 60 80 100 120 140 160 180 200 Kilometers

104

Continued on pages 110-111

Scale 1:4 000 000; one inch to 64 miles. Conic Project
Elevations and depressions are given in feet.

Longitude West of Greenwich

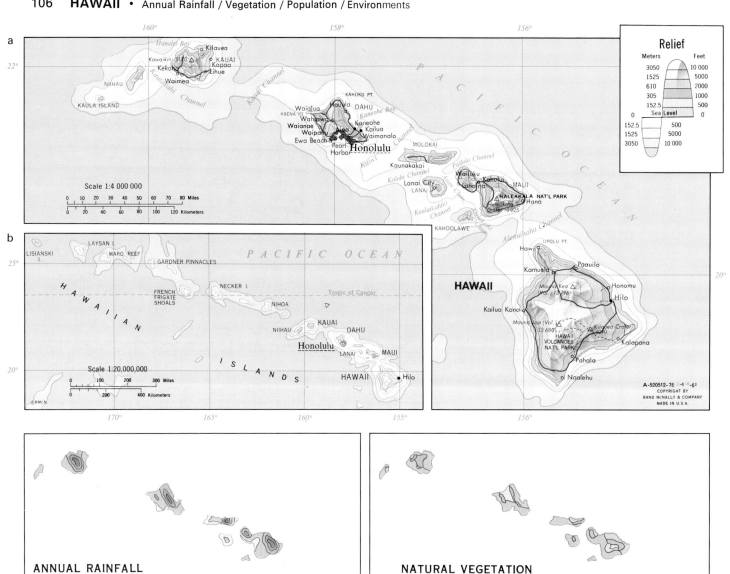

a

Relief		
Meters		Feet
3050		10 000
1525		5000
610		2000
305		1000
152.5		500
0	Sea Level	0
152.5		500
1525		5000
3050		10 000

Scale 1:4 000 000

0 10 20 30 40 50 60 70 80 Miles
0 20 40 60 80 100 120 Kilometers

b

PACIFIC OCEAN

LAYSAN I.
LISIANSKI I.
MARO REEF
GARDNER PINNACLES

H A W A I I A N

FRENCH
FRIGATE
SHOALS

NECKER I.

Tropic of Cancer

NIHOA

NIIHAU   KAUAI
          OAHU
Honolulu
          LANAI   MAUI
I S L A N D S
                  HAWAII   • Hilo

Scale 1:20,000,000

0   100   200   300 Miles
0   200   400 Kilometers

©RMCN.

HAWAII

A-520512-76 -4 -4 -5²
COPYRIGHT BY
RAND McNALLY & COMPANY
MADE IN U.S.A.

ANNUAL RAINFALL

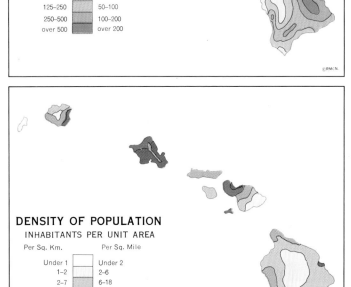

Centimeters	Inches
0–50	0–20
50–125	20–50
125–250	50–100
250–500	100–200
over 500	over 200

NATURAL VEGETATION

Tropical forest, shrubland and grassland
Guava mixed forest
Ohia lehua forest
Lama-manele forest
Koa forest
Koa-mamami parkland
Grassland, desert shrubland and barren

DENSITY OF POPULATION
INHABITANTS PER UNIT AREA

Per Sq. Km.	Per Sq. Mile
Under 1	Under 2
1–2	2–6
2–7	6–18
7–17	18–45
17–35	45–90
over 35	over 90

ENVIRONMENT

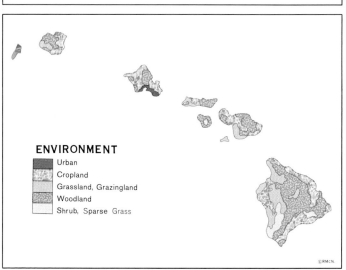

Urban
Cropland
Grassland, Grazingland
Woodland
Shrub, Sparse Grass

©RMCN.

Relief

Meters		Feet
3050		10 000
1525		5000
610		2000
305		1000
152.5		500
0	Sea Level	0
152.5		500
1525		5000
3050		10 000
6100		20 000

A-520502-76- -5 8'
COPYRIGHT BY
RAND McNALLY & COMPANY
MADE IN U.S.A.

Longitude West of Greenwich

a

©RMCN

Longitude East of Greenwich   Longitude West of Greenwich

Same scale as main map

Scale 1: 12 000 000; one inch to 190 miles.   Conic Projection

Elevations and depressions are given in feet

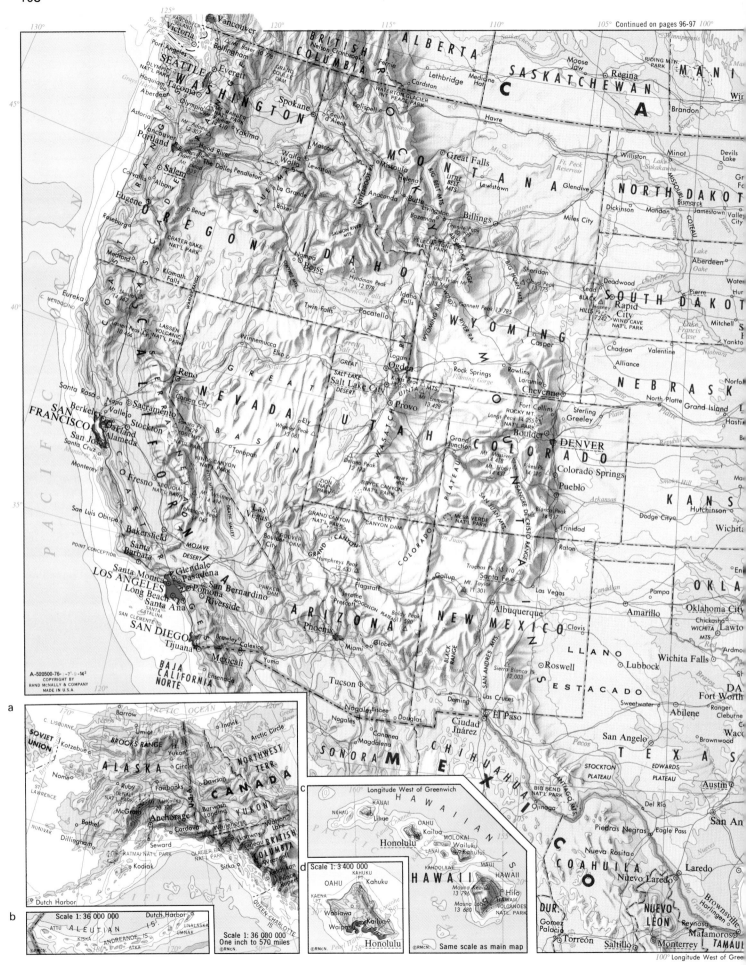

108

Continued on pages 96-97

Scale 1:12 000 000; one inch to 190 miles. Polyconic Proje

Elevations and depressions are given in feet

a

b

Scale 1:36 000 000

Dutch Harbor

Scale 1:36 000 000
One inch to 570 miles

c Longitude West of Greenwich

Scale 1:3 400 000

d

Same scale as main map

A-520500-76- -7'-9-14²
COPYRIGHT BY
RAND McNALLY & COMPANY
MADE IN U.S.A.

Continued on pages 114-115

Continued on pages 126-127

Cities and Towns	0 to 50,000	500,000 to 1,000,000
	50,000 to 500,000	1,000,000 and over

Longitude West of Greenwich

Scale 1:4 000 000; one inch to 64 miles. Conic Projection
Elevations and depressions are given in feet

Continued on pages 102-103

Relief

Meters		Feet
1525		5000
610		2000
305		1000
152.5		500
Sea Level		0
152.5		500
1525		5000
3050		10 000

A-520596-76 -5⅝-11²
COPYRIGHT BY
RAND McNALLY & COMPANY
MADE IN U.S.A.

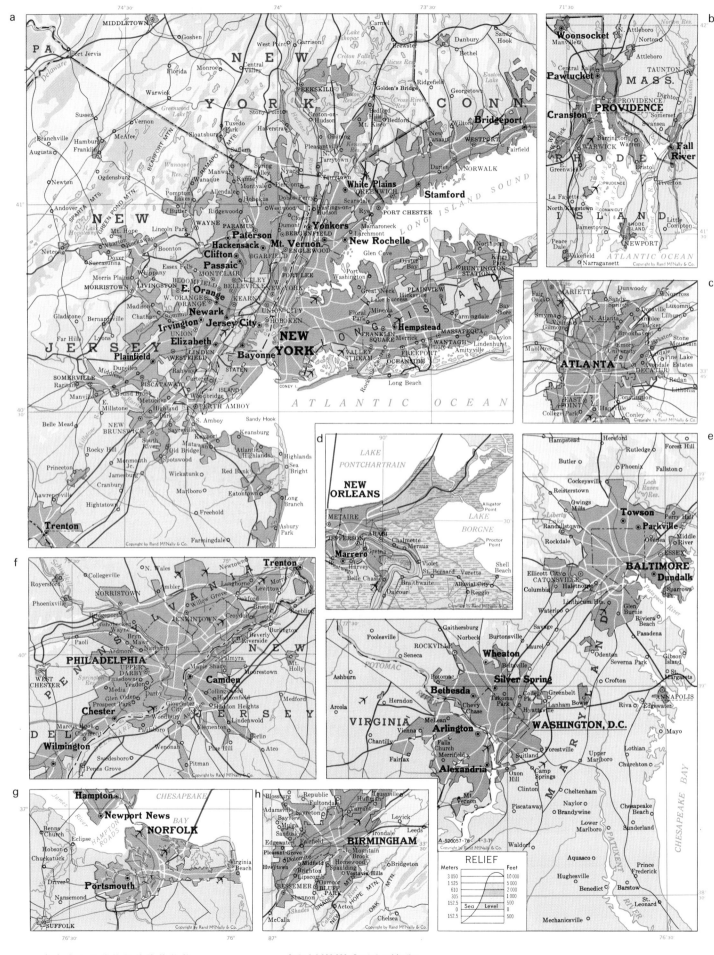

Scale 1:1 000 000; One inch to 16 miles.
Elevations and depressions are given in feet.

For larger scale coverage of New York, Baltimore, Washington, D. C. and Philadelphia see pages 55 and 56.

RELIEF

Meters		Feet
3 050		10 000
1 525		5 000
610		2 000
305		1 000
152.5		500
	Sea Level	0
152.5		500

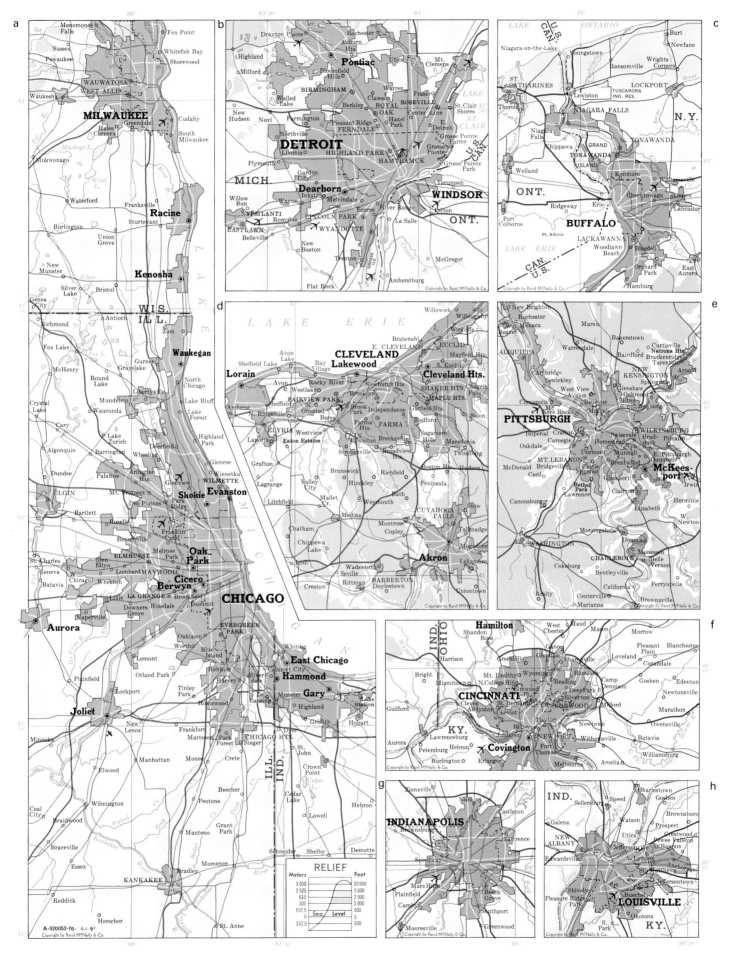

RELIEF

Meters		Feet
3 050		10 000
1 525		5 000
610		2 000
305		1 000
152.5		500
0	Sea Level	0
152.5		500

0 2 4 6 8 10 12 14 16 18 20 22 24 Miles
0 4 8 12 16 20 24 28 32 36 40 Kilometers

Scale 1:1 000 000; One inch to 16 miles.
Elevations and depressions are given in feet.

For larger scale coverage
of Chicago see page 58.

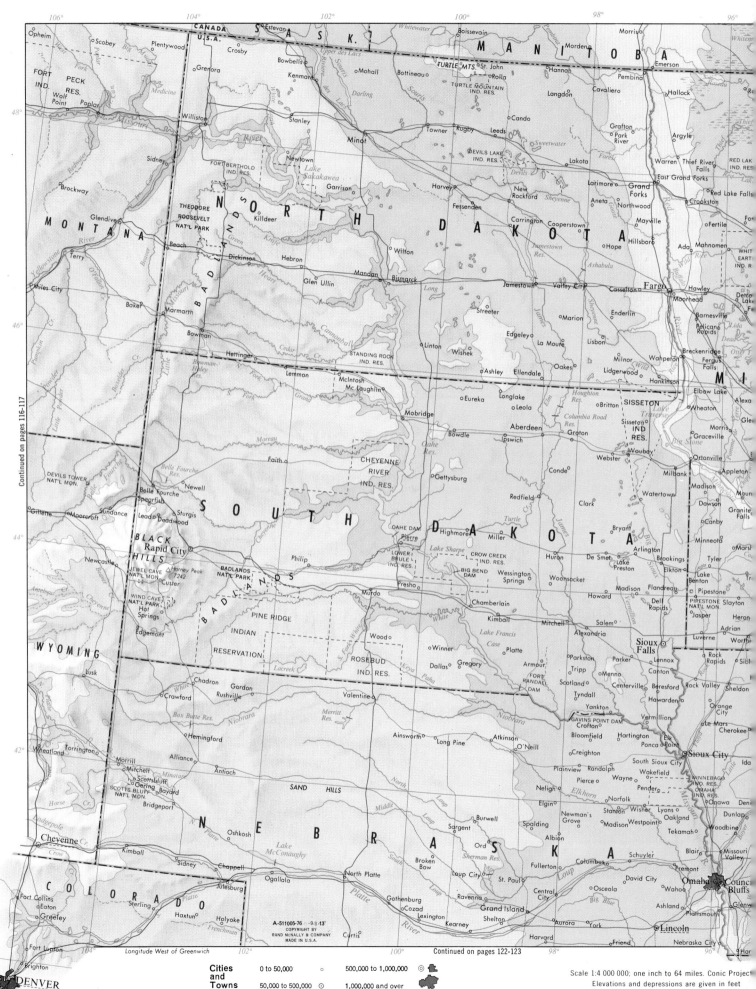

114

Continued on pages 116-117

Continued on pages 122-123

Cities
and
Towns

0 to 50,000 ○
50,000 to 500,000 ⊙
500,000 to 1,000,000 ◎
1,000,000 and over

Scale 1:4 000 000; one inch to 64 miles. Conic Project
Elevations and depressions are given in feet

A-511005-76 · 9-8-13'
COPYRIGHT BY
RAND MCNALLY & COMPANY
MADE IN U.S.A.

Longitude West of Greenwich

Continued on pages 110-111

Continued on pages 122-123

Relief

Meters	Feet
1525	5000
610	2000
305	1000
152.5	500
0 Sea Level	0
152.5	500

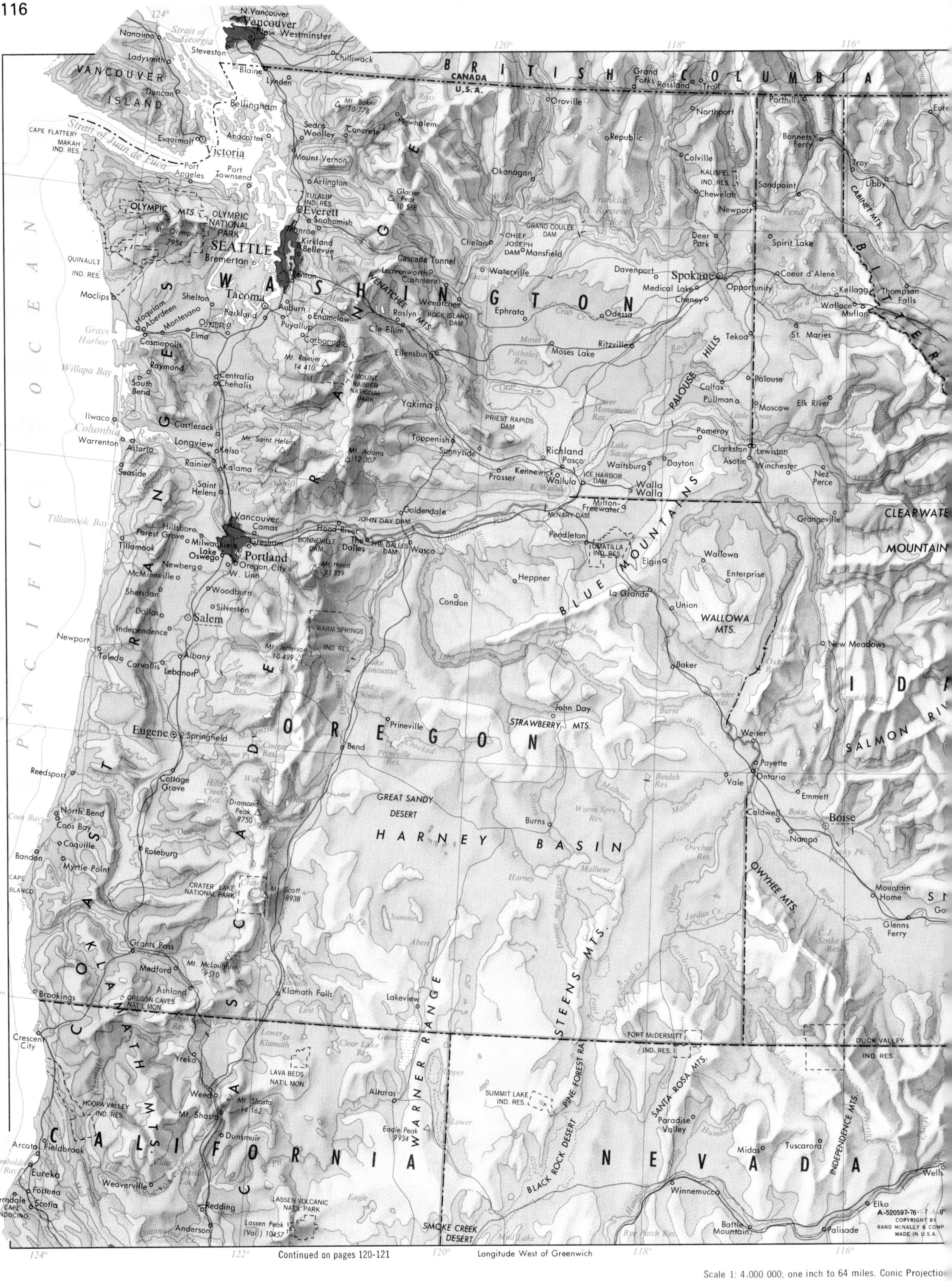

116

BRITISH COLUMBIA
CANADA
U.S.A.

VANCOUVER ISLAND
N. Vancouver
Vancouver
New Westminster
Steveston
Nanaimo
Ladysmith
Duncan
Chilliwack
Grand Forks
Rossland
Trail
Northport
Porthill
Troy
Libby
CABINET MTS.

Esquimalt
Victoria
Blaine
Lynden
Bellingham
Anacortes
Sedro Woolley
Concrete
Newhalem
Mt. Baker 10,778
Oroville
Republic
Colville
Chewelah
KALISPEL IND. RES.
Sandpoint
Newport
Bonners Ferry
Elk

CAPE FLATTERY
MAKAH IND. RES.
Port Angeles
Port Townsend
Mount Vernon
Arlington
Glacier Peak 10,568
Okanogan
Davenport
Spokane
Deer Park
Spirit Lake
Coeur d'Alene
Kellogg
Wallace
Mullan
Thompson Falls

OLYMPIC MTS.
OLYMPIC NATIONAL PARK
Mt. Olympus 7954
Everett
Snohomish
Monroe
Kirkland
Bellevue
Chelan
CHIEF JOSEPH DAM
GRAND COULEE DAM
Mansfield
Waterville
Medical Lake
Cheney
Opportunity
St. Maries

QUINAULT IND. RES.
SEATTLE
WASHINGTON
Bremerton
Tacoma
Renton
Auburn
Cascade Tunnel
Leavenworth
Cashmere
Wenatchee
ROCK ISLAND DAM
Ephrata
Odessa
Ritzville
Tekoa
Palouse
Colfax

Moclips
Shelton
Olympia
Parkland
Puyallup
Enumclaw
Carbonado
Cle Elum
Roslyn
ROSLYN MTS.
Ellensburg
Moses Lake
PALOUSE HILLS
Pullman
Moscow
Elk River

Hoquiam
Aberdeen
Montesano
Elma
Mt. Rainier 14,410
MOUNT RAINIER NATIONAL PARK
Yakima
PRIEST RAPIDS DAM
Pomeroy
Clarkston
Lewiston
Winchester
Nez Perce

Raymond
South Bend
Centralia
Chehalis
Mt. Saint Helens
Mt. Adams 12,307
Toppenish
Sunnyside
Richland
Pasco
Kennewick
Waitsburg
Dayton
Asotin
Grangeville
CLEARWATER MOUNTAIN

Ilwaco
Warrenton
Astoria
Castlerock
Longview
Kelso
Rainier
Kalama
Saint Helens
Goldendale
JOHN DAY DAM
Prosser
Wallula
ICE HARBOR DAM
Walla Walla
McNARY DAM
Milton-Freewater
Pendleton

Seaside
Hillsboro
Forest Grove
Tillamook
Vancouver
Camas
Gresham
Portland
Oregon City
W. Linn
Hood River
The Dalles
THE DALLES DAM
Wasco
BONNEVILLE DAM
Mt. Hood 11,239
UMATILLA IND. RES.
Elgin
Wallowa
Enterprise

McMinnville
Newberg
Sheridan
Dallas
Milwaukie
Lake Oswego
Woodburn
Silverton
Salem
Heppner
Condon
La Grande
Union
WALLOWA MTS.
Baker
New Meadows

Independence
Albany
Corvallis
Lebanon
Mt. Jefferson 10,499
WARM SPRINGS IND. RES.
Lake Billy Chinook
BLUE MOUNTAINS
John Day
STRAWBERRY MTS.
Weiser

Newport
Toledo
Eugene
Springfield
OREGON
Prineville
Bend
Payette
Ontario
Vale
Emmett
SALMON RIVER

Reedsport
Cottage Grove
Diamond Peak 8750
GREAT SANDY DESERT
Burns
HARNEY BASIN
Caldwell
Boise
Nampa
Mountain Home
Glenns Ferry

North Bend
Coos Bay
Coquille
Bandon
Myrtle Point
Roseburg
CRATER LAKE NATIONAL PARK
Mt. Scott 8938
Malheur
OWYHEE MTS.

CAPE BLANCO
Grants Pass
Medford
Mt. McLoughlin 9510
Ashland
Klamath Falls
Lakeview
STEENS MTS.
FORT McDERMITT IND. RES.
DUCK VALLEY IND. RES.

Brookings
OREGON CAVES NAT'L MON.
KLAMATH MTS.
WARNER RANGE
PINE FOREST RA.
Santa Rosa MTS.
INDEPENDENCE MTS.

Crescent City
Lower Klamath
Clear Lake
SUMMIT LAKE IND. RES.
Paradise Valley
Wells

Yreka
LAVA BEDS NAT'L MON.
Alturas
Eagle Peak 9934
BLACK ROCK DESERT
Midas
Tuscarora

HOOPA VALLEY IND. RES.
Weed
Mt. Shasta 14,162
Dunsmuir
CALIFORNIA
NEVADA

Arcata
Fieldbrook
Eureka
Fortuna
Ferndale
Scotia
CAPE MENDOCINO
Weaverville
Redding
Anderson
LASSEN VOLCANIC NAT'L PARK
Lassen Peak (Vol.) 10,457
SMOKE CREEK DESERT
Winnemucca
Battle Mountain
Palisade
Elko

PACIFIC OCEAN

Continued on pages 120-121
Longitude West of Greenwich

Scale 1: 4,000,000; one inch to 64 miles. Conic Projection
Elevations and depressions are given in feet

A-520597-76
COPYRIGHT BY
RAND McNALLY & COMP
MADE IN U.S.A.

Continued on pages 114-115

Continued on pages 120-121

Relief

Meters	Feet
3050	10000
1525	5000
610	2000
305	1000
152.5	500
Sea Level	0
1525	500

Cities and Towns

0 to 50,000	500,000 to 1,000,000
50,000 to 500,000	1,000,000 and over

20 40 60 80 100 120 Miles
20 40 60 80 100 120 140 160 180 200 Kilometers

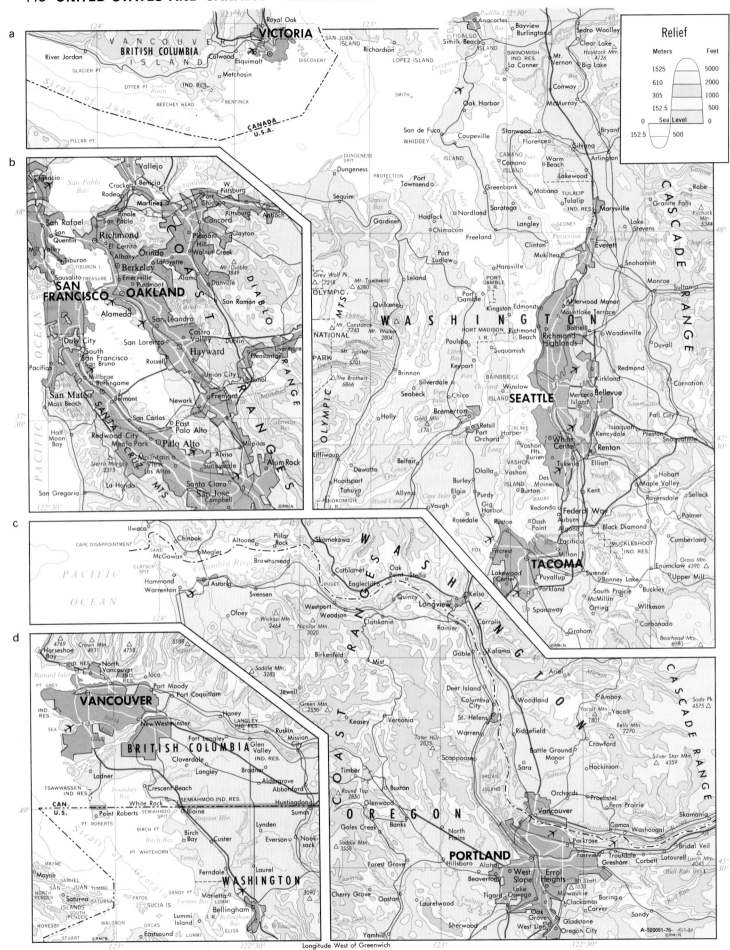

a

VANCOUVER
BRITISH COLUMBIA
ISLAND

River Jordan

GLACIER PT.

OTTER PT.
Sooke Basin

PILLAR PT.

Strait of Juan de Fuca

Royal Oak
VICTORIA
Colwood
Esquimalt
Metchosin

IND. RES.

BEECHEY HEAD
BENTINCK

SAN JUAN ISLAND

Richardson

DISCOVERY

LOPEZ ISLAND

SMITH

Padilla 122°30'
Anacortes
Bayview
Simlik Beach
FIDALGO
ISLAND

Sedro Woolley
Burlington
Clear Lake
Haystack Mtn.

SWINOMISH
IND. RES.
La Conner

Mt.
Vernon
Big Lake

Conway
McMurray

Bryant

Relief

Meters		Feet
1525		5000
610		2000
305		1000
152.5		500
0	Sea Level	0
152.5		500

b

San Pablo Bay
Ignacio
Vallejo
Crockett
Benicia
Rodeo
Martinez
Port Chicago
W. Pittsburg
Pinole
Pittsburg
Antioch
San Pablo
San Rafael
Richmond
El Cerrito
Concord
Clayton
San Quentin
Albany
Orinda
Pleasant Hill
Walnut Creek
Mill Valley
Berkeley
Lafayette
Tiburon
TIBURON I.
Emeryville
Mt. Diablo 3849
TREASURE I.
Piedmont
Sausalito
SAN FRANCISCO
OAKLAND
Alameda
Alamo
Danville
Daly City
San Leandro
San Ramon
South San Francisco
San Lorenzo
Castro Valley
Dublin
San Bruno
Hayward
Pleasanton
Livermore
Pacifica
Russell
Millbrae
Burlingame
Union City
Bunol
San Mateo
Belmont
Newark
Fremont
Moss Beach
San Carlos
East Palo Alto
Half Moon Bay
Redwood City
Palo Alto
Alviso
Alum Rock
Menlo Park
Milpitas
Sierra Morena 2315
Mountain View
Los Altos
Sunnyvale
San Gregoria
La Honda
Santa Clara
San Jose
Campbell

COAST
DIABLO
RANGE
SANTA CRUZ MTS.

Grey Wolf Pk. 7218
Mt. Townsend 6280
OLYMPIC
Mt. Constance 7743
Mt. Walker 2804
NATIONAL
Mt. Jupiter 5701
PARK
The Brothers 6866

OLYMPIC MTS.

Gardiner
Quilcene
Leland
Brinnon
Seabeck
Silverdale
Chico
Holly
Gold Mtn. 1761
Littlewaup
Hoodsport
Tahuya
SKOKOMISH IND. RES.

Dungeness Spit
Sequim
Dungeness
PROTECTION
Port Townsend
Hadlock
Nordland
Port Ludlow
Hansville
PORT GAMBLE I.R.
Kingston
Edmonds
Port Madison
Richmond Beach
Poulsbo
Suquamish
Keyport
BAINBRIDGE
Winslow
ISLAND
Dyes Inlet
Bremerton
Retsil
Port Orchard
Harper
BLAKE ISLAND
Belfair
Olalla
Dewatto
Allyn
Burley
Elgin
Purdy
Vaughn
Gig Harbor
Rosedale

WHIDBEY ISLAND
San de Fuca
Coupeville
Oak Harbor
Stanwood
Florenceo
CAMANO
ISLAND
Camano
Greenbank
Mabana
Freeland
Clinton
Langley
GEDNEY
Mukilteo
Possession Sound

Warm Beach
Silvana
Arlington
Lakewood
TULALIP
IND. RES.
Tulalip
Marysville
Lake Stevens
Everett
Snohomish
Monroe

Granite Falls
Robe
Pilchuck Mtn. 5344
CASCADE
RANGE
Canyon
Chaplain
Roesiger
Sultan
Startup

Richmond Highlands
Bothell
Mountlake Terrace
Woodinville
Duvall
Alderwood Manor
Kirkland
Redmond
Carnation
Mercer Island
SEATTLE
Bellevue
Fall City
Issaquah
Sammamish
White Center
Burien
Kennydale
Preston
Renton
Snoqualmie
Tukwila
Elliott
VASHON
Des Moines
Hobart
Vashon Hts.
Vashon
Burton
Kent
Maple Valley
MAURY ISLAND
Redondo
Federal Way
Ravensdale
Selleck
Dash Point
Auburn
Algona
Palmer
Ruston
Pacific
Black Diamond
Milton
MUCKLESHOOT IND. RES.
Cumberland

c

Ilwaco
CAPE DISAPPOINTMENT
Chinook
SAND
McGowan
Megler
Altoona
Pillar Rock
Brownsmead
Skamokawa
Cathlamet
Eaglecliff
Oak Point
Stella
Columbia River
CLATSOP SPIT
Hammond
Astoria
Svensen
Warrenton
Olney
Westport
Woodson
Clatskanie
Wickup Mtn. 2464
Nicolai Mtn. 3020

PACIFIC
OCEAN

WASHINGTON
COAST RANGE
PUGET
FOX

Quincy
Longview
Rainier
Carrolls
Kelso

Fircrest
Lakewood Center
TACOMA
Puyallup
Parkland
Sumner
McMillin
Spanaway
Orting
Graham
Bonney Lake
South Prairie
Buckley
Wilkeson
Carbonado
Enumclaw 4390
Upper Mill
Grass Mtn.
Bearhead Mtn. 6080

d

4769
Crown Mtn. 4931
4758
5188
Horseshoe Bay
North Vancouver
IND. RES.
Ioco
Port Moody
Port Coquitlam
VANCOUVER
IND. RES.
Haney
SEA
LULU
New Westminster
LANGLEY IND. RES.
Ruskin
Fort Langley
Mission City
Glen Valley
IND. RES.
BRITISH COLUMBIA
Cloverdale
Bradner
Langley
Aldergrove
Crescent Beach
Abbotsford
TSAWWASSEN IND. RES.
Ladner
Boundary Bay
White Rock
SEMIAHMOO IND. RES.
Huntingdon
CAN.
Point Roberts
Blaine
Sumas
U.S.
PT. ROBERTS
Birch Pt.
Drayton Hbr.
Lynden
Birch Bay
BIRCH BAY
Custer
Everson
Nooksack
PT. WHITEHORN
Saddle Mtn. 3550
Ferndale
Laurel
Strait of Georgia
MAYNE
Mayne
SAMUEL
SAN JUAN
TUMBO
Saturna
SATURNA
NORTH PENDER
Sandy Pt.
Marietta
ISLANDS
SUCIA IS.
PATOS
3090
WASHINGTON
MORESBY
SOUTH PENDER
STUART
WALDRON
ORCAS
PATOS
Lummi Island
LUMMI I.R.
Bellingham
Eastsound
ELISA
LUMMI
Whatcom Bay

Robe
South
Granite Falls
Pilchuck Mtn. 5344
CASCADE RANGE
Skykomish
Sultan
Startup

Ariel
Amboy
Yacolt
Yacolt Mtn. 1801
Soda Pk. 4575
Bells Mtn. 2270
Woodland
Crawford
Battle Ground
Ridgefield
Hockinson
Silver Star Mtn. 4359
Manor
Sara
Orchards
Proebstel
Fern Prairie
Vancouver
Skamania
Parkrose
Camas
Washougal
Fairview
Troutdale
Corbett
Latourell
Bridal Veil
PORTLAND
Gresham
Larch Mtn. 4045
Hillsboro
Aloha
West Slope
Errol Heights
Mt. Scott 1033
Beaverton
Tigard
Oak Grove
Milwaukie
Boring
Lake Oswego
Carver
Laurelwood
Clackamas
Cherry Grove
Gaston
West Linn
Gladstone
Sandy
Sherwood
Yamhill
Oregon City
Forest Grove
North Plains
Banks
Buxton
Glenwood
Gales Creek
Timber
Round Top 2850
Tater Hill 2633
St. Helens
Warren
Scappoose
Deer Island
Columbia City
Goble
Kalama
Mist
Birkenfeld
Saddle Mtn. 3283
Jewell
Green Mtn. 2550
Keasey
Vernonia
SAUVIE ISLAND
OREGON

COAST RANGE
WASHINGTON
46

CAN. U.S.
49

Longitude West of Greenwich

Scale 1:1 000 000; one inch to 16 miles.
Elevations and depressions are given in feet.

A-520051-76

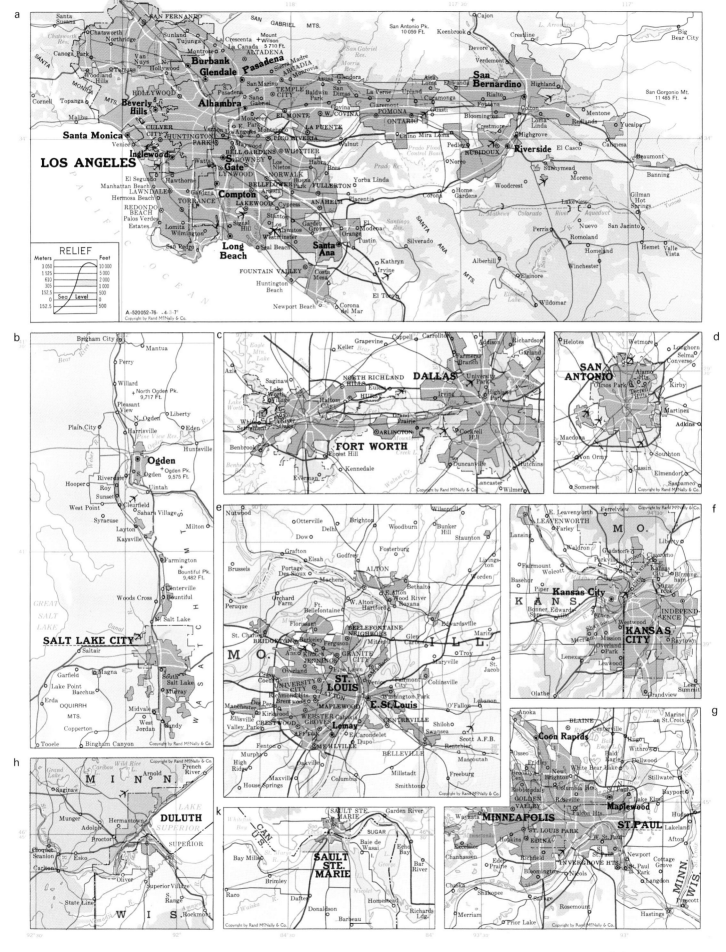

Scale 1:1 000 000; One inch to 16 miles.
Elevations and depressions are given in feet.

For larger scale coverage
of Los Angeles see page 59.

Cities and Towns

0 to 50,000   500,000 to 1,000,000
50,000 to 500,000   1,000,000 and over

Continued on pages 116-117

Relief

Meters	Feet
3050	10000
1525	5000
610	2000
305	1000
152.5	500
0 Sea Level	0
152.5	Below Sea Level 500
1525	5000
3050	10000

Anderson Lassen Peak (Vol.) 10,457 LASSEN VOLCANIC NATL. PARK Susanville SMOKE CREEK DESERT Mud Battle Mountain Palisade Franklin RUBY MTS. Ruby

Red Bluff Westwood PYRAMID Lovelock HUMBOLDT RA. Spring Cr. Pine Cr.

Chico Pyramid LAKE Winnemucca Humboldt STILLWATER RA. Humboldt Salt Marsh

Willows Oroville Res. Downieville INDIAN RESERVATION Sparks Wadsworth Fallon Carson Sink Austin Eureka

Gridley Oroville Reno Ruth Ely

Colusa Yuba City Nevada City Truckee Virginia City TOIYABE RANGE Duckwater Pk. 11,493

Ukiah Marysville Grass Valley Carson City Yerington WASSUK RANGE Arc Dome 11,775

POINT ARENA Lakeport Lincoln Auburn Placerville American Walker River Ind. Res. Hawthorne Goldfield

Cloverdale Woodland Roseville Folsom Walker Lake Sonora Pk. 11,429 Boundary Peak 13,145 Coaldale Tonopah

Healdsburg Santa Rosa Sacramento Folsom City Benton White Mt. Peak 14,246 Alamo

Sebastopol Napa Jackson YOSEMITE Dana Mtn. 13,053 Mono

Petaluma POINT REYES San Rafael Pittsburg San Andreas Angels Camp Sonora NATIONAL Mt. Lyell 13,095 DEVILS POSTPILE N.M. Bishop MOAPA RIV. IND. RES.

MUIR WOODS NATL. MON. Richmond Stockton Oakdale PARK DEATH VALLEY Beatty FRENCHMAN FLAT

Sausalito Oakland Alameda Livermore Modesto Turlock Kings Canyon Natl. Park Lone Pine Death Valley Las V

San Francisco Daly City Tracy Merced Fresno Reedley Mt. Whitney 14,494 Telescope Peak 11,045 Henderson HOOVER DAM

Burlingame San Mateo Redwood City Palo Alto Santa Clara San Jose Los Gatos Madera Sanger Selma Dinuba SEQUOIA NATL. PARK Owens Death Valley Jct. SPRING MTS. Boulder Cit

Santa Cruz Gilroy Hollister Fresno Visalia Exeter NATL. MON.

Watsonville Salinas Hanford Tulare TULE RIVER IND. RES.

Monterey Bay Pacific Grove Monterey PINNACLES NATL. MON. Coalinga Porterville Delano Tronac Searles Inyokern

King City Tulare Basin Bakersfield MOJAVE

Paso Robles Buena Vista Lake Reservoir Taft Mojave Barstow FORT MO

Atascadero San Luis Obispo Santa Maria Lompoc POINT ARGUELLO POINT CONCEPTION TEHACHAPI MTS. Daggett Goffs

Santa Barbara Ventura Oxnard Santa Paula Santa Clara Burbank Glendale Pasadena Monrovia San Bernardino JOSHUA TREE NATL. MON. Aqueducts Cadiz

SANTA BARBARA ISLANDS LOS ANGELES Alhambra Arlington Pomona Redlands Palm Springs MORONGO IND. RES.

Santa Monica Inglewood Compton Riverside Orange Elsinore AGUA CALIENTE IND. RES.

Redondo Beach San Pedro Long Beach Huntington Beach Santa Ana Newport Beach SANTA ROSA IND. RES. Salton Sea Calipatria IMPERIAL VALLEY

SANTA BARBARA CHANNEL ISLANDS NAT'L PARK SANTA CATALINA Avalon TORRES MARTINEZ IND. RES. Brawley Holtville FT IN

SAN NICOLAS Oceanside Escondido SANTA YSABEL IND. RES. INAJA IND. RES. El Centro Calexico

SAN CLEMENTE Gulf of LA JOLLA IND. RES. CAMP IND. RES. Mexicali Sea

Santa Catalina SAN DIEGO Coronado National City Chula Vista GUYAPAIPE IND. RES. Laguna Salada

Tijuana BAJA CALIFORNIA NORTE

PACIFIC   OCEAN

COAST RANGES SIERRA NEVADA CALIFORNIA NEVADA COAST RANGE SAN JOAQUIN VALLEY INYO MTS. PANAMINT RA. PANAMINT RANGE MOJAVE DESERT SPRING MTS.

a

Del Mar La Jolla Lakeside Santee El Cajon La Mesa CALIFORNIA

SAN DIEGO CABRILLO NATL. MON. Coronado National City Spring Valley Lemon Grove Otay Chula Vista Sweetwater Reservoir Lower Otay Reservoir

PACIFIC OCEAN Imperial Beach Tijuana USA MEXICO BAJA CALIFORNIA NORTE

Scale 1:1 000 000
0   10 Miles
0 4 8 12 16 Kilometers
©RMcN.

A-520599-76 -7.7-111 COPYRIGHT BY RAND McNALLY & COMPANY MADE IN U.S.A.

Longitude West of Greenwich

Scale 1:4 000 000; one inch to 64 miles. Conic Projection
Elevations and depressions are given in feet

0   20   40   60   80   100   120 Miles
0 20 40 60 80 100 120 140 160 180 200 Kilometers

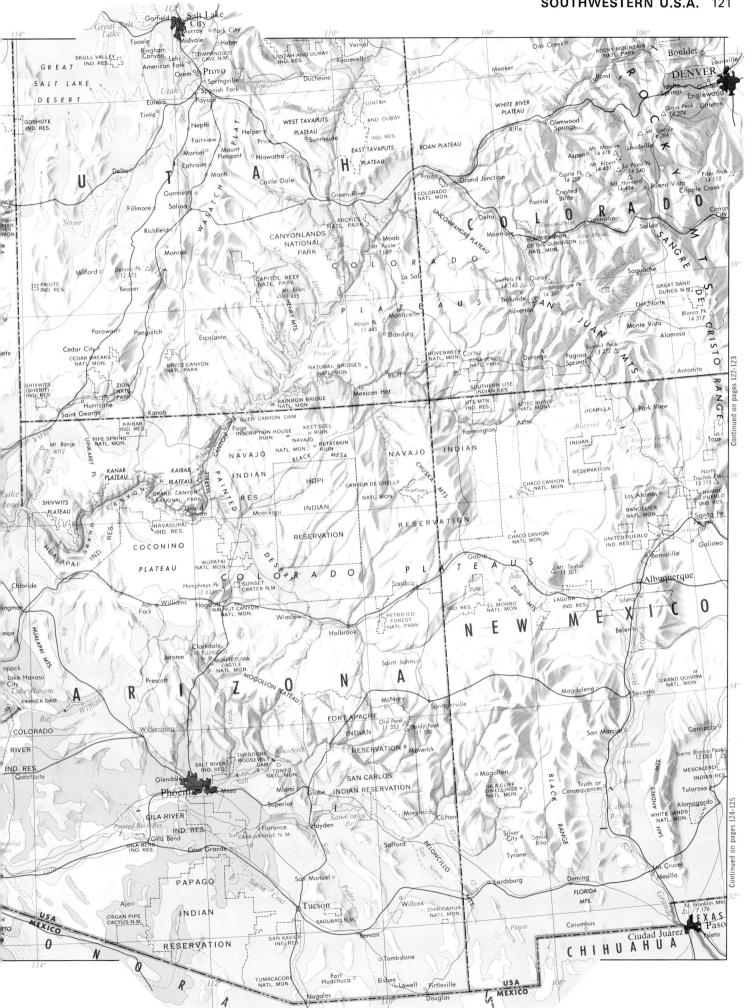

Continued on pages 122-123

Continued on pages 124-125

122

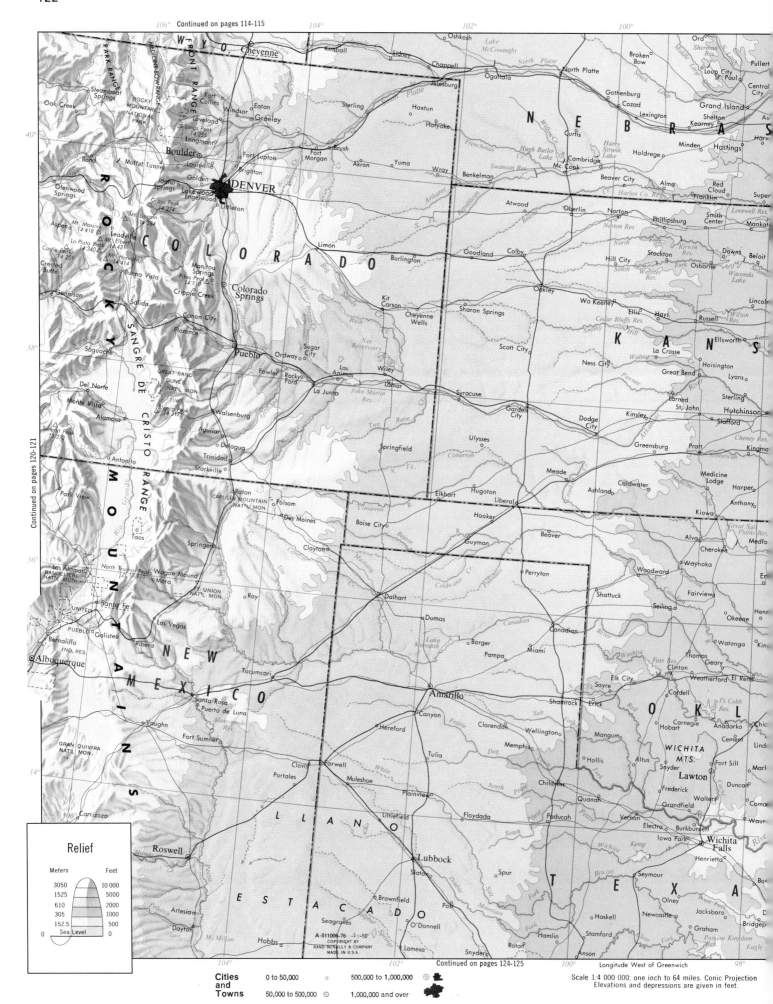

Continued on pages 114-115

106°   104°   102°   100°

Continued on pages 120-121

WYO.
Cheyenne
Kimball
Sidney
Oshkosh   Lake McConaughy   Broken Bow   Ord   Middle Loup   Fullert
Loup City   St. Paul

FRONT RANGE
PARK RANGE
MEDICINE-BOW RANGE
North Platte
Chappell   Ogallala   North Platte   Gothenburg   Cozad   Lexington   Grand Island   Central Ci
Au

Steamboat Springs
Oak Creek
Fort Collins   Windsor   Eaton   Greeley   Sterling   Julesburg   Platte   Haxtun   Curtis   Shelton   Kearney   Hastings   Harv

ROCKY MOUNTAIN NATIONAL PARK
Loveland   Longmont   Holyoke   Frenchman   Hugh Butler Lake   Cambridge   McCook   Holdrege   Minden   NEBRAS

Longs Peak 14 255
Boulder
Fort Lupton   Brush   Fort Morgan   Akron   Yuma   Wray   Benkelman   Swanson Res.   Beaver City   Alma   Red Cloud   Super
Moffat Tunnel   Louisville   Brighton   Harlan Co. Res.   Franklin

Glenwood Springs
Idaho Springs   Golden   DENVER   Lakewood   Engelwood   Littleton

Grays Peak 14 274

40°

Aspen   Mt. Massive 14 418   Leadville   Mt. Lincoln 14 284   Limon   Burlington   Goodland   Colby   Atwood   Oberlin   Norton   Phillipsburg   Smith Center   Mankat
Mt. Elbert 14 431   COLORADO   Oakley   Hill City   Stockton   Downs   Beloit
La Plata Peak 14 340   Mt. Harvard 14 414

Castle Peak 14 259
Crested Butte   Buena Vista   Manitou Springs   Pikes Peak 14 110   Colorado Springs   Kit Carson   Cheyenne Wells   Sharon Springs   Scott City   Wa Keeney   Ellis   Hays   Russell   Ellsworth   KANS   Lincoln   Wilson Res.

Gunnison   Cripple Creek   ROCKY   Ness City   Great Bend   La Crosse   Hoisington   Lyons   Sterling

38°
Saguache   Salida   Canon City   Ordway   Wiley   Syracuse   Garden City   Kinsley   Larned   St. John   Hutchinson
Del Norte   Florence   Pueblo   Sugar City   Las Animas   Lamar   Dodge City   Pratt   Stafford   Kingm
Monte Vista   GREAT SAND DUNES NAT'L MON.   Fowler   Rocky Ford   La Junta   John Martin Res.   Dodge City   Greensburg   Pratt   Cheney Res.
Alamosa   Blanca Peak 14 317   Walsenburg   Meade   Medicine Lodge   Harper   Anthony
Summit Peak 13 272   Aguilar   Springfield   Ulysses   Ashland   Coldwater   Kiowa   Great Salt Plains Res.
Delagua   Trinidad   Elkhart   Hugoton   Liberal   Alva   Cherokee   Medfo
Park View   Starkville   Raton   CAPULIN MOUNTAIN NAT'L MON.   Folsom   Boise City   Hooker   Beaver   Guymon   Waynoka
Taos   Des Moines   Clayton   Woodward   Fairview   Okeene   Hen
36°   North Truchas Peak 13 110   Springer   UNION NAT'L MON.   Roy   Dalhart   Perryton   Shattuck   Seiling   Watonga   Kin
Los Alamos   BANDELIER NAT'L MON.   Mora   Wagon Mound   Dumas   Borger   Miami   Pampa   Clinton   Thomas   Geary   Weatherford   El Reno
Santa Fe   Las Vegas   Lake Meredith   Canadian   Elk City   OKL
PUEBLO   Galisteo   Ribera   NEW   Tucumcari   Amarillo   Shamrock   Erick   Sayre   Cordell   Ft. Cobb Res.
Bernalillo   IND. RES.   Canyon   Clarendon   Wellington   Mangum   Hobart   Carnegie   Anadarko   Chic
Albuquerque   MEXICO   Santa Rosa   Hereford   Memphis   Hollis   Altus   Snyder   Fort Sill   Lawton   Frederick   Duncan   Marl
Puerto de Luna   Tulia   Quanah   Grandfield   Walters
Vaughn   Clovis   Farwell   Muleshoe   Plainview   Childress   Vernon   Electra   Burkburnett   Iowa Park   Wichita Falls
Fort Sumner   Portales   Floydada   Paducah   Henrietta
34°   Littlefield   Spur   Seymour   Olney   Bo
Roswell   Lubbock   Slaton   TEXA
Brownfield   Post   Hamlin   Stamford   Anson
Artesia   Seagraves   O'Donnell   Lamesa   Rotan   Snyder   Graham   Bridgep
Dayton   Hobbs   McMillan   Eagle   Possum Kingdom Res.

ROCKY MOUNTAINS
SANGRE DE CRISTO RANGE
NEW MEXICO
LLANO ESTACADO

Carrizozo
GRAN QUIVIRA NAT'L MON.

104°   102°   100°   98°

Continued on pages 124-125

Longitude West of Greenwich

Relief

Meters		Feet
3050		10 000
1525		5000
610		2000
305		1000
152.5		500
0	Sea Level	0

A-511006-76 -7-10'
COPYRIGHT BY
RAND MCNALLY & COMPANY
MADE IN U.S.A.

Cities and Towns

| | 0 to 50,000 | o | 500,000 to 1,000,000 | ◎ |
| | 50,000 to 500,000 | ⊙ | 1,000,000 and over | ■ |

Scale 1:4 000 000; one inch to 64 miles. Conic Projection
Elevations and depressions are given in feet.

Continued on pages 114-115

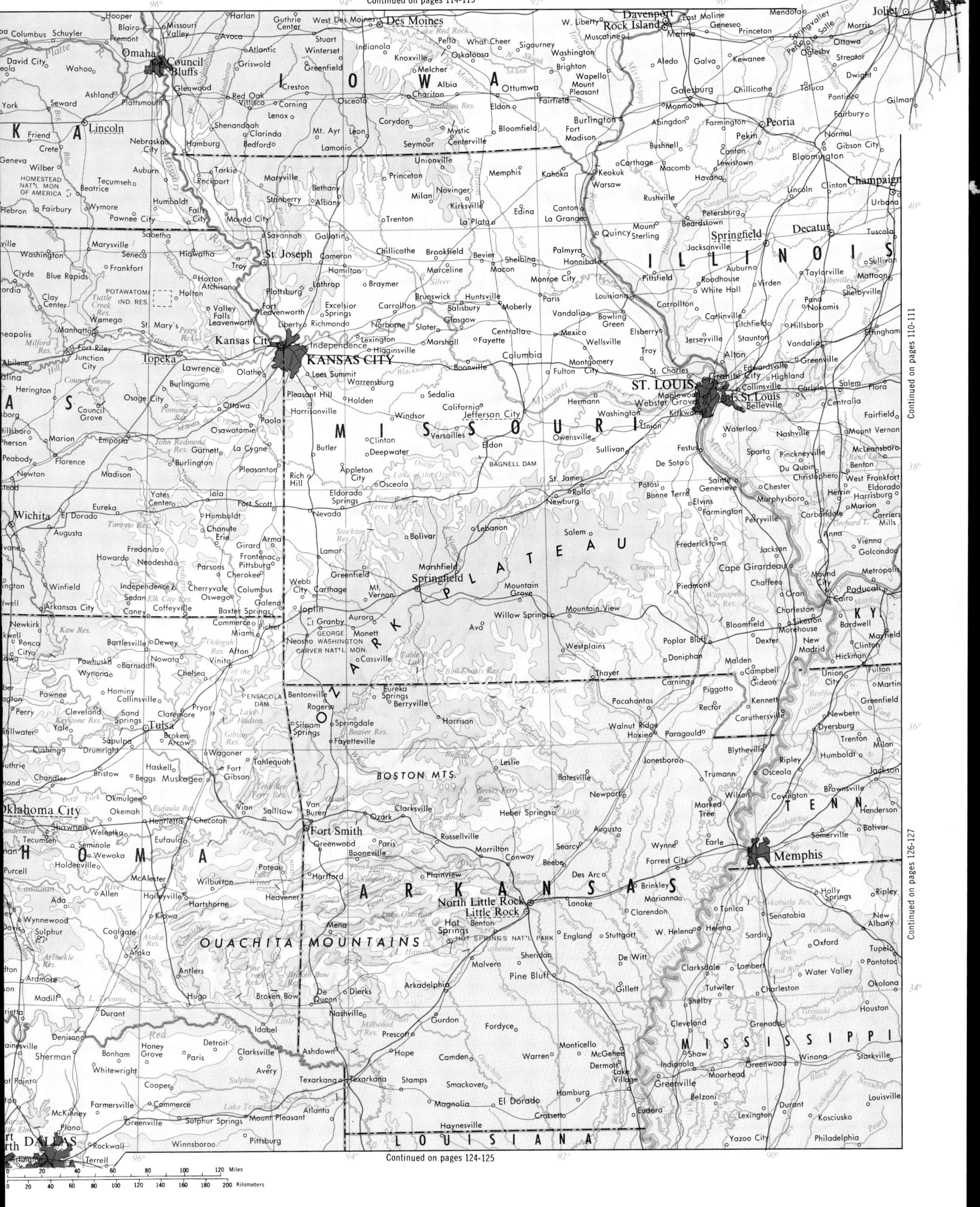

Continued on pages 110-111

Continued on pages 126-127

Continued on pages 124-125

Aurora
CHICAGO
Joliet

IOWA

ILLINOIS

MISSOURI

KANSAS

OKLAHOMA

ARKANSAS

TENN.

MISSISSIPPI

KY.

LOUISIANA

OZARK PLATEAU

BOSTON MTS.

OUACHITA MOUNTAINS

GEORGE WASHINGTON CARVER NAT'L MON.

HOMESTEAD NAT'L MON. OF AMERICA

POTAWATOMI IND. RES.

BAGNELL DAM

PENSACOLA DAM

HOT SPRINGS NAT'L PARK

Lake of the Ozarks

Omaha
Council Bluffs
Lincoln
Des Moines
Davenport
Rock Island
Peoria
Champaign
Decatur
Springfield
St. Joseph
Kansas City
KANSAS CITY
Topeka
Wichita
Tulsa
Oklahoma City
Fort Smith
Little Rock
North Little Rock
Hot Springs
Memphis
ST. LOUIS
St. Louis
Dallas
Texarkana
El Dorado

Missouri River
Mississippi River
Arkansas River
Red River
Platte River

0 20 40 60 80 100 120 Miles
0 20 40 60 80 100 140 160 180 200 Kilometers

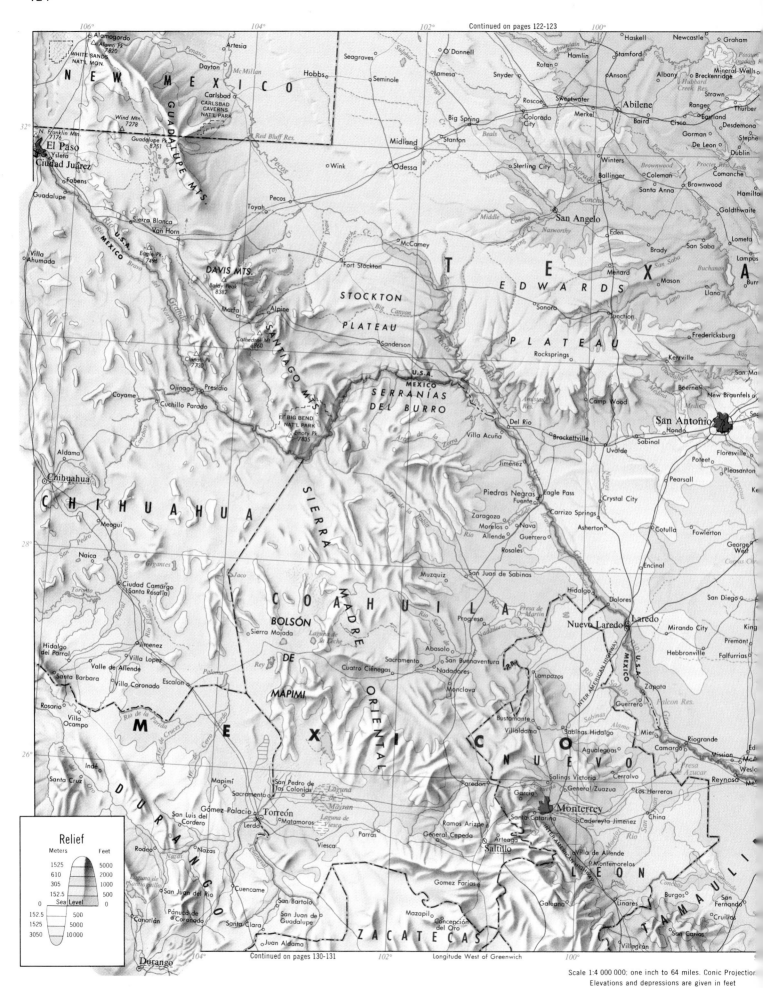

124

Continued on pages 122-123

NEW MEXICO

WHITE SANDS NAT'L MON.

Alamogordo
Alamo Pk. 7820

Penasco

Artesia

Dayton

McMillan

O'Donnell

Seagraves

Seminole

Haskell
Newcastle
Graham

Double Mountain
Fork

Rotan
Hamlin
Stamford

Snyder

Roscoe
Sweetwater
Merkel

Anson
Albany

Breckenridge
Hubbard Creek Res.

Mineral Wells

Possum Kingdom

Carlsbad
CARLSBAD CAVERNS NAT'L PARK

Hobbs

32°

Wind Mtn. 7278

Guadalupe Pk. 8751

N. Franklin Mtn. 7176

El Paso
Ysleta
Ciudad Juárez

Fabens

Guadalupe

Villa Ahumada

Sierra Blanca

Van Horn

Eagle Pk. 7496

Coyame

Ojinaga
Presidio

Cuchillo Parado

Aldama

Chihuahua

CHIHUAHUA

Meogui

Naica

San Pedro

Gigantes

Ciudad Camargo
Santa Rosalia

Jimenez
Villa Lopez

Hidalgo del Parral

Santa Barbara

Rosario

Villa Ocampo

Indé

Santa Cruz

DURANGO

Rodeo

Nazas

San Juan del Rio

Pánuco de Coronado

Canatlán

Durango

Red Bluff Res.

DAVIS MTS.
Baldy Peak 8382

Chinati Pk. 7730

Marfa
Alpine

Cathedral Mt. 6860

SANTIAGO MTS.

BIG BEND NAT'L PARK
Emory Pk. 7835

Pecos

Toyah

Pecos

Wink

Toyah Cr.

STOCKTON PLATEAU

Fort Stockton

Big Canyon

Sanderson

Comanche Draw

Coyanosa Draw

Comanche Cr.

McCamey

U.S.A.
MEXICO
SERRANÍAS DEL BURRO

SIERRA

MADRE

ORIENTAL

DE

BOLSÓN

Sierra Mojada

Laguna de la Leche

MAPIMÍ

Jimenez

Valle de Allende

Escalón

Villa Coronado

Villa Lopez

Rio de la Parida

Palomas

Rio Florido

Rey

Mapimí

San Pedro de las Colonias

Sacramento

Gómez Palacio
Lerdo

Torreón
Matamoros

San Luis del Cordero

San Juan de Guadalupe

San Bartolo

Cuencamé

Santa Clara

Laguna de Santiaguillo

Laguna de Mayran

Laguna de Viesca

Viesca

Parras

ZACATECAS

Mazapil

Concepción del Oro

Juan Aldama

Midland

Odessa

Stanton

Big Spring

Colorado City

Sterling City

San Angelo

Middle Concho

Nasworthy

Eden

Sonora

Junction

ROCKSprings

EDWARDS

PLATEAU

Ramos Arizpe

General Cepeda

Saltillo

Arteaga

Montemorelos

Gomez Farias

Galeana

Linares

TAMAULI

Durango

Colorado

Beals Cr.

Stanton

Winters

Ballinger

Coleman

Santa Anna

Brownwood

Brady

San Saba

Llano

Menard

Mason

Burr

Lometa

Lampas

Buchanan

Fredericksburg

Kerrville

Boerne

San Ma

New Braunfels

San Antonio

Hondo

Floresville

Poteet

Pleasanton

Pearsall

Crystal City

Cotulla

Fowlerton

George West

Encinal

San Diego

King

Mirando City

Premont

Hebbronville

Falfurrias

TEXAS

Roscoe

Baird
Cisco
Eastland

Gorman

De Leon

Ranger

Thurber

Strawn

Comanche

Hamilto

Goldthwaite

Abilene

Stephe
Dublin

Del Rio

Villa Acuña

Jiménez

Piedras Negras
Fuente

Zaragoza

Morelos

Nava

Allende

Guerrero

Rosales

Muzquiz

San Juan de Sabinas

Progreso

Abasolo

San Buenaventura

Nadadores

Sacramento

Cuatro Ciénegas

Monclova

Bustamante

Villaldama

Sabinas Hidalgo

Lampazos

Salinas Victoria

García

Santa Catarina

Monterrey

Cadereyta Jimenez

China

Villa de Allende

Eagle Pass

Carrizo Springs

Asherton

Uvalde
Sabinal

Brackettville

Camp Wood

Amistad Res.

Presa de Martin

Hidalgo

Dolores

Nuevo Laredo

Laredo

NUEVO

LEÓN

INTER-AMERICAN HIGHWAY

Aguagueguas

Sabinas

Alamo

Mier

Guerrero

Camargo

Riogrande

Zapata

Falcon Res.

Presa de Azucar

Paredon

General Zuazua

Los Herreros

Cerralvo

Reynosa

Mission

Weslo

Ed

MCA

Me

Burgos

San Fernando

San Carlos

Villagrán

Cruillas

Rio Grande

COAHUILA

MEXICO

U.S.A.
MEXICO

Continued on pages 130-131

Longitude West of Greenwich

106°   104°   102°   100°

28°

26°

32°

Relief

Meters	Feet
1525	5000
610	2000
305	1000
152.5	500
0	Sea Level	0
152.5	500
1525	5000
3050	10000

Scale 1:4 000 000; one inch to 64 miles. Conic Projection
Elevations and depressions are given in feet

Continued on pages 122-123

Continued on pages 126-127

A R K.

McKinney Farmersville Greenville Sulphur Springs Mount Pleasant Atlanta Haynesville Lake Providence Yazoo City Canton
Denton Plano Rockwall Winnsboro Pittsburg Vivian Homer Bastrop Pearl
Fort Garland City Jefferson Bayou Minden Arcadia Royville Delhi Ross Barnette Res. Forest
Worth DALLAS Lake O' the Pines Bossier City Rustono Monroe Vicksburg Jackson Pelahatchie
Arlington Terrell Mineola Gilmer Marshall Shreveport Eros Jonesboro Alto Tallulah Crystal Springs Hazlehurst
Waxahachie Kaufman Wills Point Longview Kilgore Carthage Winnsboro Winnfield Port Gibson Fayette MISSISSIPPI Collins
Cleburne Ennis Tyler Henderson Jonesville Vidalia Natchez Gloster Magnolia Sumrall
Itasca Italy Corsicana Athens Jacksonville Timpson Center Natchitoches Colfax Woodville McComb Lumberton
Hillsboro Mexia Teague Palestine Rusk Nacogdoches San Augustine Fisher Pineville Alexandria Marksville Tylertown
Meridian Hubbard Wortham Elkhart Lufkin Hemphill Peason Leesville Lecompte McNary Bunkie Kentwood Poplarville
Clifton Waco Groesbeck Oakwood Ratcliff Crockett Wiergate Fullerton Glenmora Oakdale Jackson Amite Bogalusa
McGregor Mart Buffalo Jasper Newton De Ridder Elizabeth Ville Platte LOUISIANA Covington Picayune
Moody Marquez Madisonville Trinity Groveton Woodville Merryville Melville New Roads Hammond Slidell
Temple Calvert Hearne Huntsville Kirbyville Longville Kinder Eunice Opelousas Baton Rouge Madisonville Bay St. Louis
Cameron Bryan Willis Conroe Silsbee De Quincy Jennings Lafayette Plaquemine White Castle Lake Pontchartrain
Bartlett Rockdale Navasota Cleveland Saratoga Vinton Lake Crowley St. Martinville Donaldsonville Lutcher New Orleans
Taylor Caldwell Brenham Dayton Sourlake Orange Charles Rayne Abbeville New Iberia Napoleonville Metairie Gretna
Round Rock Elgin Somerville Hempstead Liberty Beaumont Ged Lake Arthur Jeanerette Thibodaux Houma
Bastrop Giddings HOUSTON Port Neches Gueydan Franklin Morgan City
Smithville Bellville Humble Port Arthur Sabine Patterson Port Sulphur
Lockhart Columbus Sealy Baytown High Island White
Luling Eagle Richmond Galveston BOLIVAR PEN. MARSH
Gonzales Lake Alvin Texas City
Hallettsville Wharton Port Bolivar
Yoakum El Campo West Columbia Angleton Galveston
Cuero Edna Bay City Freeport
Victoria Palacios
Goliad Port Lavaca

G U L F   O F   M E X I C O

Refugio Rockport ST. JOSEPH MATAGORDA
Skidmore Aransas Pass MUSTANG
Sinton Portland
Corpus Christi PADRE
Baffin Bay ISLAND
Brownsville San Benito
Matamoros

(Houston inset map)

a

HOUSTON Crosby Sheldon Mont Belvieu Wallisville Hankamer
Highlands Anahuac
Jacinto City Channelview Turtle Bay
West University Galena Pk. Baytown
Place Pasadena
Bellaire La Porte
Missouri South GALVESTON
City Houston High Island
Genoa Seabrook BAY Smith Point
Pearland Kemah
Clear EAST BAY
Arcola Friendswood League City
Manvel Dickinson
Alvin Algoa Texas City BOLIVAR PENINSULA
Sandy Point Alta Loma La Marque Port Bolivar
Hitchcock
Liverpool Galveston GULF
Danbury OF MEXICO
GALVESTON
Angleton ISLAND

Scale 1:1 000 000
0   5   10 Miles
0   4   8   12   16 Kilometers

0   20   40   60   80   100   120 Miles
0 20 40 60 80 100 120 140 160 180 200 Kilometers

Cities and Towns

0 to 50,000	○	500,000 to 1,000,000
50,000 to 500,000	⊙	1,000,000 and over

Continued on pages 110-111

Continued on pages 122-123

Continued on pages 124-125

Scale 1:4 000 000; one inch to 64 miles. Conic Projection
Elevations and depressions are given in feet

Longitude West of Greenwich

A-520598-76-
COPYRIGHT BY
RAND McNALLY & COMPANY
MADE IN U.S.A.

Relief

Meters		Feet
1525		5000
610		2000
305		1000
152.5		500
0	Sea Level	0
152.5		500
1525		5000

Jacksonville   Same scale as main map

Cities and Towns

0 to 50,000	∘	500,000 to 1,000,000	◉
50,000 to 500,000	⊙	1,000,000 and over	

0 10 20 30 40 50 60 70 80 90 100 110 120 Miles
0 20 40 60 80 100 120 140 160 180 200 Kilometers

Scale 1:16 000 000; one inch to 250 miles. Polyconic Projection
Elevations and depressions are given in feet

A-530000 76- -9 -21'
COPYRIGHT BY
RAND McNALLY & COMPANY

b

ATLANTIC OCEAN

Arecibo • San Juan
• Aguadilla • Bayamón CABEZAS DE ST. THOMAS TORTOLA
PTA. HIGUERO Utuado SAN JUAN (Br.) I
PUERTO RICO Caguas • Fajardo Charlotte ST. JOHN
(U.S.A.) Cayey Amalie (U.S.A.)
Mayagüez Coamo Vieques
Coamo Humacao VIEQUES
CABO ROJO • Ponce Salinas Guayama 18°
Christiansted
CARIBBEAN SEA
SAINT CROIX
(U.S.A.)

Scale 1:4 000 000
0 10 20 30 40 Miles
0 10 20 30 40 50 60 Kilometers
©RMcN.

c

LITTLE
LILLE 64°30'
HANS LOLLICK
OUTER BRASS HANS LOLLICK
INNER BRASS PICARA PT GRASS
STORMY PT ST. THOMAS THATCH CAY CAY
(U.S.A.)
Crown Mt. 18°
1558 Charlotte Amalie 20'
(St. Thomas)
WATER Nadir
FLAMINGO PT St. Thomas
Harbor

Scale 1:500 000
©RMcN.

W. VIRGINIA 80° 75° 70° 65°
Y Roanoke Richmond 67° 65°
VIRGINIA Chesapeake Bay
NC Norfolk
Raleigh 35°
ville NORTH CAROLINA CAPE HATTERAS
Mt. Mitchell Charlotte
6684 ATLANTIC
ANTA SOUTH Wilmington
Columbia CAPE FEAR
CAROLINA Charleston
ORGIA Augusta
Charleston
BERMUDA
Savannah (Br.)

llahassee Jacksonville
St. Augustine 30°
FLORIDA Ocala
Tampa CAPE CANAVERAL
pa Bay

NORTH AMERICAN
W. Palm
Beach BASIN
MIAMI GRAND
BAHAMA GREAT ABACO
CAPE SABLE ELEUTHERA
Key West Nassau CAT
FLORIDA KEYS San Salvador (Watling)
ANDROS

AVANA Guanabacoa LONG
ararianao Matanzas
rer del Río Cárdenas ACKLINS 20°
C Santa Clara
U Sancti Spíritus CAICOS TURKS
Cienfuegos B Ciego Nuevitas (Br.) (Br.)
Trinidad A de Ávila Camagüey GT. INAGUA
PUERTO RICO TRENCH
ISLA Holguín
DE LA PUNTA 28 374
JUVENTUD Manzanillo MAISI
Guantánamo Puerta Plata PUERTO RICO
SIERRA MAESTRA Cap-Haïtien Santiago de los SAMANA Mayagüez San Juan ST. VIRGIN IS. ANGUILLA
GRAND CAYMAN C. CRUZ Santiago Caballeros Sánchez ST. THOMAS I BARBUDA
(Br.) de Cuba Gonaïves HAITI Ponce Charlotte Amalie
W Montego Bay Mt. Denham Río HAITI DOMINICAN SAINT CROIX ST. KITTS ANTIGUA
3236 Port Antonio ÍLE DE LA Pico Duarte REPUBLIC PUERTO RICO (U.S.A.) NEVIS AND
Spanish Town GONAVE 10 417 Santo Domingo (U.S.A.) ST. CHRISTOPHER (ST. KITTS)—NEVIS V. Soufrière BARBUDA
JAMAICA Kingston Port-au-Prince HISPANIOLA MONTSERRAT 4869 GUADELOUPE
(Br.) Basse-Terre (Fr.)
ANTILLES DOMINICA

CARIBBEAN SEA MARTINIQUE (Fr.)
Fort-de-France

ST. LUCIA
ST. VINCENT BARBADOS
AND THE
GRENADINES Bridgetown
Kingstown
GRENADA

LESSER ANTILLES WINDWARD IS.
ARUBA SAN ROMAN
PUNTA DE GALLINAS (Neth.) CURAÇAO BONAIRE TOBAGO
PENÍNSULA (Neth.) (Neth.)
DE GUAJIRA Willemstad TRINIDAD AND TOBAGO
PEN. DE Port of Spain
Bluefields Golfo de PARAGUANÁ ISLA LA ISLA DE Carúpano Trinidad
Venezuela TORTUGA MARGARITA
Santa Marta Ciénaga Coro Puerto Cumaná
Barranquilla Maracaibo Cabello CARACAS
Soledad San Felipe La Guaira Puerto
AMERICA Cartagena Cabimas Maracay la Cruz Maturín
Lago de Valencia
osé Limón Barquisimeto El Tigre
Cartago Colón DE PANAMÁ Lorica Maracaibo
RICA Gulfo de PANAMÁ Sincelejo Mompós Trujillo Guanare Calabozo Morawhanna
Portobello Golfo del Darién Magangué Valera Ciudad Guayana
Panamá PANAMA Montería San Fernando Ciudad Bolívar
Antón Mérida de Apure Río
David PEN. DE Ocaña Puerto de Cerro Bolívar
COIBA Santiago AZUERO Cúcuta San Cristóbal Nutrias GUYANA
ISTMO Barrancabermeja VENEZUELA San Fernando
Bucaramanga Pamplona de Atabapo
Cerro Tolima
Medellín 7800 BRAZIL
Sonsón Tunja
Manizales COLOMBIA
Pereira
Armenia SERRA PACARAIMA
ISLA Ibagué Girardot Villavicencio
DE Buenaventura BOGOTÁ
MALPELO Cali San Fernando
(Colombia) Palmira de Atabapo

Relief
Meters Feet
3050 10 000
1525 5000
610 2000
305 1000
152.5 500
Sea Level 0
152.5 500
1525 5000
3050 10 000
6100 20 000

80° 75° 70° 65° 60°
Longitude West of Greenwich

0 50 100 200 300 400 500 Miles
0 100 200 400 600 800 Kilometers

Cities 0 to 50,000 500,000 to 1,000,000
and
Towns 50,000 to 500,000 1,000,000 and over

130

Continued on pages 124-125

106° 104° 102° 100°

24°

SIERRA

DURANGO

SIERRA MADRE DE NAYARIT

SINALOA

NAYARIT

22°

OCCIDENTAL

SIERRA DE VALLEJO

20°

JALISCO

SA. DEL CUALE

COLIMA

18°

SIERRA DE COALCOMÁN

ZACATECAS

ALTIPLANICIE

SIERRA MADRE OCCIDENTAL

MEXICANA

AGUASCALIENTES

SAN LUIS

POTOSI

GUANAJUATO

QUERÉTARO

HIDALGO

MICHOACÁN

MORELOS

SIERRA

MADRE

GUERRERO

NUEVO

LEÓN

TAMAULIPAS

SIERRA AZUL

SIERRA MADRE ORIENTAL

INTER-AMERICAN HY.

San Dimas
Durango
Miguel Auza
Juan Aldama
Ascensión
Aramberri
Hidalgo
Jiménez
Padilla
El Salto
Nombre de Dios
Nieves
Gruñidora
Vanegas
Cedral
Zaragoza
Ciudad Victoria
Soto la Marina
Pánuco
Mezquital
10 100
Sombrerete
Río Grande
Catorce
La Paz
Doctor Arroyo
C. Peña Nevada 13 300
Siqueros
Cancordia
Pueblo Nuevo
Chalchihuites
Sain Alto
Cañitas
Matehuala
Mier y Noriega
Miquihuana
Jaumave
Kicotencatl
Gonz
Villa Unión
△ 17 700
Santa María de Ocotán
Fresnillo
Calera
Víctor Rosales
Morelos
Troncoso
Charcas
Venado
Moctezuma
Villa de Guadalupe
Llera
Ocampo
Magiscatzin
Ciudad Mante
Escuinapa
Rosario
C. Pinal
Valparaíso
Huejuquilla el Alto
Ciudad García
Zacatecas
Calvillo
Ramos
Salinas
Ojocaliente
Bocas
Peotillos
Soledad Díez Gutiérrez
Cerritos
Guadalcázar
Ciudad del Maíz
Villa de Reyes
El Ebano
Laguna de Agua Brava
Ruiz
Mezquitic
Huejúcar
Villanueva
Rincón de Romoso
Asientos
Tepezalá
Villa García
San Luis Potosí
Pozos
Zaragoza
Ciudad Fernández
Ojo Caliente
Sta. María del Río
Ríoverde
Rayón
Tamuín
Cárdenas
Ciudad de Valles
Tuxpan
Monte Escobedo
Sta. María de los Angeles
Colotlán
Tabasco
Calvillo
Aguascalientes
Villa Hidalgo
Encarnación de Díaz
San Felipe
San Diego de la Unión
Villa de Reyes
Arroyo Seco
Lagunillas
General Pedro Antonio Santos
Xilitla
San Blas
Jalisco
Tepic
Pochotitán
Bolaños
Chimaltitán
J. (Tlaltenango)
Sánchez Román
Jalpa
Juchipila
Teocaltiche
Lagos de Moreno
León
La Luz
Guanajuato
San Miguel de Allende
San José Iturbide
Colón
Cadereyta
Zimapán
Zacualtipán
Jalpan
Jaltocan
Huejutla
Chico
Sta. María del Oro
San Pedro Lagunillas
Jala
Tomulco
García de la Cadena
Moyahua
Nochistlán
Mexticacán
San Juan de los Lagos
San Francisco del Rincón
Romita
Silao
Guanajuato
San Miguel de Allende
San José Iturbide
Comonfort
Querétaro
Cayetano Rubio
Tolimán
Tequisquiapan
Tecozautla
Ixmiquilpan
Huitzitzilingo
Jaltocan
Tamazunchale
Compostela
Ahuacatlán
Ixtlán del Río
Amatlán de Cañas
Ahualulco
Etzatlán
Zapopan
Guadalajara
Tlaquepaque
Tonalá
Zapotlanejo
Arandas
Atotonilco el Alto
Ayo el Chico
Ciudad Manuel Doblado
Irapuato
Juventino Rosas
Salamanca
Cortazar
Celaya
Jaral del Progreso
San Juan del Río
Amealco
Huichapan
Mixquiahuala
Tezontepec de Aldama
Atotonilco
Mineral del Chico
Mineral del Monte
Pachuca
Tulancingo
Cuautepec
Chignahu
Puerto Vallarta
Mascota
Talpa de Allende
S. Martín Hidalgo
Cocula
Tecolotlán
Jocotepec
Chapala
Degollado
Yurécuaro
La Piedad
Cabadas
Penjamo
Valle de Santiago
Salvatierra
Acámbaro
Maravatío
Temascalcingo
Tecuala
Tepeji del Río
Zumpango
Otumba
Apan
Calpulalpan
Tenamaxtlán
Ayutla
Autlán
Unión de Tula
Purificación
El Grullo
Venustiano Carranza
Zacoalco de Torres
Sayula
Teocuitatlán de Corona
Sahuayo de Díaz
Atoyac
Jiquilpan de Juárez
Tamazula de Gordiano
Zamora
Chavinda
Tangancícuaro
Purépero
Puruándiro
Moroleón
Cuitzeo
Zinapécuaro
El Oro
Tlalpujahua
Ixtlahuaca de Rayón
Almoloya
Toluca
Teoloyucan
Tepotzotlán
Teotihuacán
Texcoco
Coatepec
Chiconcuac
Tomatlán
Minatitlán
Comala
Villa de Alvarez
Colima
Nevado de Colima 13,993
Volcán de Colima 12,620
Ciudad Guzmán
Zapotiltic
Tuxpan
Tecalitlán
Cerro de Tancítaro 12,660
Paracho
Cherán
Chilchota
Zacapú
Villa Morelos
Coeneo de la Libertad
Quiroga
Pátzcuaro
Morelia
Ciudad Hidalgo
Angangueo
Zitácuaro
Valle de Bravo
Tenango
Nevado de Toluca 14,409
Tenancingo
Metepec
Tlalmanalco
Amecameca
Popocatépetl 17,887
Cholula
Atlixco
Manzanillo
Cihuatlán
Tepalcatepec
Apatzingán de la Constitución
Tancítaro
Tacámbaro de Cadallos
Tlacotepec
Texcaltitlán
Teipilco
Zacualpan
Ixtapan de la Sal
Tlatlaya
Sultepec
Taxco de Alarcón
Ixcateopan
Teloloapan
Arcelia
Cuernavaca
Yautepec
Jojutla
Cuautla
Axochiapan
Tepalcingo
Tepecoacuilco de Trujano
Huitzuco
Iguala
Huaquechula
Huatla
Tehuitzingo
Acatlá
Cuyutlán
Tecomán
Coalcomán de Matamoros
Aguililla
Churumuco
Huetamo de Núñez
Cutzamalá de Pinzón
Ciudad Altamirano
Coyuca de Catalán
Ajuchitlán del Progreso
Zirándaro
Coahuayutla
La Unión
Río Balsas
Cuetzala del Progreso
Apipilulco
Atliaca
Zitlala
Tlapa
Silacay
Juxt
Tumbiscatío
Presa del Infiernillo
Bahía de Petacalco
Bahía de Petacalco
Tlacotepec
Apango
Chilapa
Mochitlán
Hueycatenango
Zapotitlán
Tlacotepec
Olinalá
Huamuxtitlán
Atlixtac
Tixtla de Guerrero
Chilpancingo
Acatlá
Petatlán
Tecpan de Galeana
Atoyac de Alvarez
Coyuca de Benítez
San Jerónimo de Juárez
Acapulco
Ayutla
San Marcos
Cuautepec
Cozoyoapa
Ometepec
Azoyú
Malinaltepec
Acatla de C
Pinotepa Nacional
Tecoanapa
Puerto M

PUNTA DE MITA
BAHÍA DE BANDERAS
CABO CORRIENTES
PTA. FARALLÓN
PTA. TEJUPAN

P A C I F I C   O C E A N

Longitude West of Greenwich

DISTRITO FEDERAL
MÉXICO CITY
G.A. Madero
Azcapotzalco
Coyoacán
Tlalpan
Xochimilco
17 343

Relief

Meters		Feet
3050		10000
1525		5000
610		2000
305		1000
152.5		500
Sea Level		0
152.5		500
1525		5000
3050		10000

Cities and Towns

0 to 50,000	○	500,000 to 1,000,000 ◉
50,000 to 500,000 ⊙		1,000,000 and over

Scale 1:4 000 000; one inch to 64 miles. Conic Projecti
Elevations and depressions are given in feet

For larger scale coverage of Mexico City see page 60.

132

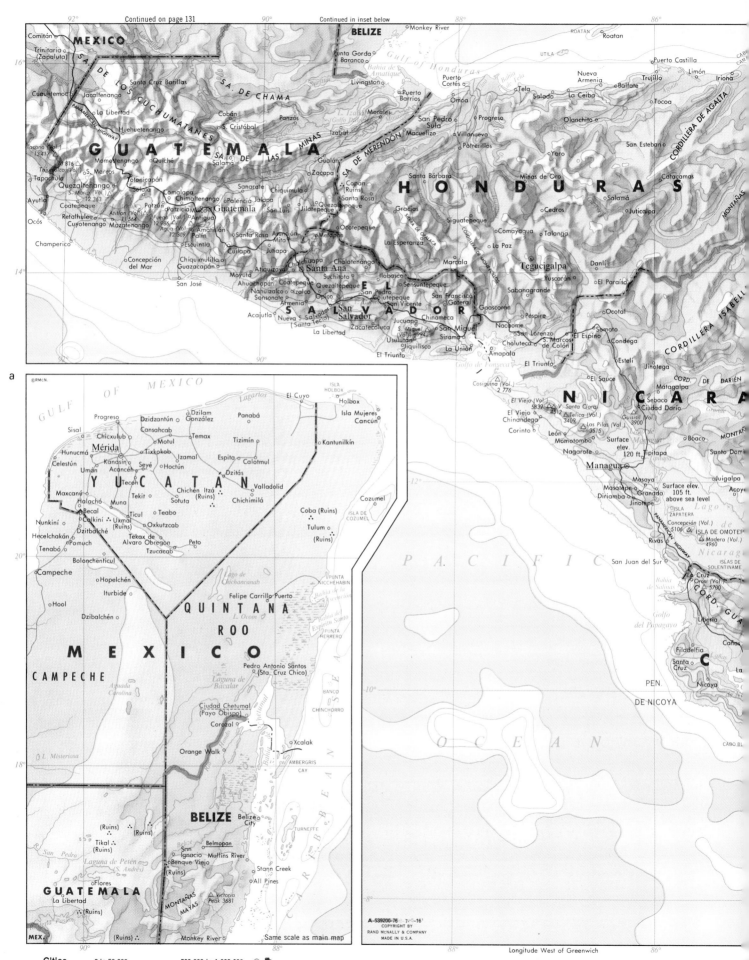

Continued on page 131

Continued in inset below

MEXICO

Comitán
Trinitaria
(Zapaluta)
Cuauhtémoc
Jacaltenango
La Libertad
Huehuetenango
Tacaná (Vol.)
13.417
18.876
Tajumulco (Vol.)
13.809
S. Marcos
Quezaltenango
S. María (Vol.)
12.363
Ayutla
Coatepeque
Retalhuleu
Atitlán (Vol.)
11.564
Fuego (Vol.)
12.986
Ocós
Cuyotenango
Mazatenango
Agua (Vol.)
12.309

GUATEMALA

SA. DE LOS CUCHUMATANES
PANAMERICAN HIGHWAY
Santa Cruz Barillas
Cobán
S. Cristóbal
SA. DE CHAMA
Momostenango
Totonicapán
Sololá
Patzún
Chimaltenango
Patzicía
Antigua
Amatitlán

SA. DE LAS MINAS
Panzós
Izabal
L. Izabal
Morales
SA. DE MERENDON
Salamá
Sanarate
Chiquimula
Zacapa
Gualán

BELIZE

Monkey River
Punta Gorda
Barranco
Gulf of Honduras
Livingston
Puerto Barrios
San Pedro Sula
Ompa
Copán (Ruins)
Santa Rosa
Quezaltepeque

ROATÁN
Roatán
UTILA
Puerto Castilla
Limón
Trujillo
Irriona
Balfate
Nueva Armenia
La Ceiba
Tela
Salado
Tocoa
Progreso
Villanueva
Olanchito
Yoro
San Esteban
CORDILLERA DE AGALTA
Catacamas

HONDURAS

Santa Bárbara
Minas de Oro
Salamá
Macuelizo
Potrerillos
Cedros
Juticalpa
Gracias
Siguatepeque
Comayagua
Talanga
La Esperanza
La Paz
Danlí
Tegucigalpa
Yuscarán
El Paraíso
MONTAÑAS

Guatemala
San Luis
Jalapa
Jilotepeque
Palencia
San José
Chiquimulilla
Guazacapán
Escuintla
Concepción del Mar
Champerico
Ayampuc
Mita
Metapán
Ocotepeque
SIERRA DE OPALACA
CORDILLERA DE MONTECILLOS
Mardala

Santa Rosa
Cuilapa
Jutiapa
Moyuta
Ahuachapán
Atiquizaya
Santa Ana
Chalchuapa
Coatepeque
Nahuizalco
Izalco
Sonsonate
Armenia
Nueva S. Salvador
(Santa Tecla)
Acajutla
La Libertad
Suchitoto
Quezaltepeque
San Pedro
Opico
San Salvador
Zacatecoluca

EL SALVADOR

Chalatenango
Ilobasco
Cojutepeque
Sensuntepeque
San Vicente
San Francisco Gotera
Jucuapa
Chinameca
Usulután
San Miguel
Sirama
Jiquilisco
La Unión
El Triunfo
Gaascorán
Golfo de Fonseca
Nacaome
Pespire
Choluteca
Amapala
El Triunfo

San Lorenzo
S. Marcos de Colón
El Espino
Somoto
Ocotal
Condega
Sabanagrande
Estelí
CORDILLERA ISABELL
Jinotega

Cosigüina (Vol.)
2.776
El Sauce
El Viejo (Vol.)
5839
Santa Clara
Telica (Vol.)
3409
Las Pilas (Vol.)
3515
Quisiil (Vol.)
3900
CORD. DE DARIÉN
Matagalpa
Sébaco
Ciudad Darío
NICARA

El Viejo
Chinandega
Corinto
León
Momotombo (Vol.)
Nagarote
Surface elev.
120 ft.
Tipitapa
Masaya
Masatepe
Diriamba
Jinotepe
ISLA ZAPATERA
Concepción (Vol.)
Boaco
Santo Domi
MONTA
Acoyi

Managua
Granada
Surface elev.
105 ft.
above sea level
Juigalpa
Lago de
Nicaragua
ISLA DE OMOTEP
Madera (Vol.)
4960
Rivas
San Juan del Sur
ISLAS DE SOLENTINAME
La Cruz
Orosi (Vol.)
5700
CORD. GUA
Liberia
Cañas
Filadelfia
Santa Cruz
Nicoya
PEN. DE NICOYA
La
CABO BL.

PACIFIC

OCEAN

---

a
(R) RMCN.

GULF OF MEXICO
Lagartos
El Cuyo
ISLA HOLBOX
Holbox
Progreso
Dzilam González
Panabá
Isla Mujeres
Cancún
Sisal
Chicxulub
Dzidzantún
Cansahcab
Temax
Tizimín
Espita
Kantunilkín
Hunucmá
Mérida
Motul
Tixkokob
Izamal
Calotmul
Celestún
Kanasín
Seyé
Hoctún
Dzitás
Umán
Acanceh
Chichén Itzá
(Ruins)
Maxcanú
Tecoh
Valladolid
Chichimilá
Tekit
YUCATÁN
Halachó
Muna
Sotuta
Cozumel
Becal
Teabo
Coba (Ruins)
ISLA DE COZUMEL
Nunkiní
Calkiní
Uxmal
(Ruins)
Oxkutzcab
Hecelchakán
Dzitbalché
Ticul
Teabo
Peto
Pomuch
Tekax de Alvaro Obregón
Tenabó
Tzucacab
Bolonchenticul
PUNTA NICCHEHABIN
Campeche
Hopelchén
Lago de Chichancanab
Bahía de la Ascensión
Iturbide
Felipe Carrillo Puerto
QUINTANA ROO
L. Ocom
PUNTA HERRERO
Dzibalchén
MEXICO
CAMPECHE
Aguada Carolina
Pedro Antonio Santos
(Sta. Cruz Chico)
BANCO CHINCHORRO
L. Misteriosa
Laguna de Bacalar
Ciudad Chetumal
(Payo Obispo)
Corozal
Xcalak
Orange Walk
AMBERGRIS CAY
BELIZE
Belize City
TURNEFFE
San Pedro
Benque Viejo
Muffins River
Belmopan
San Ignacio
Stann Creek
All Pines
GUATEMALA
Tikal
(Ruins)
Flores
La Libertad
Laguna de Petén
S. Andrés
(Ruins)
MONTAÑAS MAYAS
Victoria Peak 3681
CARIBBEAN SEA
MEX.
(Ruins)
Monkey River

Same scale as main map

Cities and Towns

0 to 50,000	•	500,000 to 1,000,000 ◎
50,000 to 500,000 ⊙		1,000,000 and over

Longitude West of Greenwich

Scale 1:4 000 000; one inch to 64 miles. Sinusoidal Projectio

Elevations and depressions are given in feet

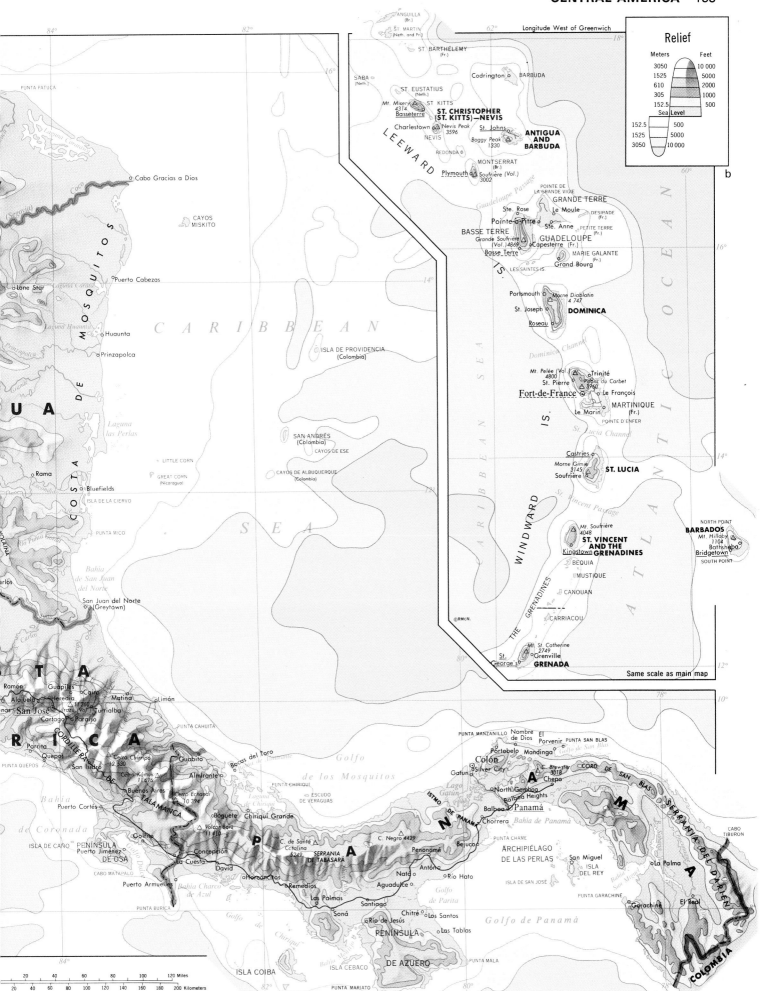

Longitude West of Greenwich

Relief

Meters	Feet
3050	10 000
1525	5000
610	2000
305	1000
152.5	500
Sea Level	
152.5	500
1525	5000
3050	10 000

b

ANGUILLA (Br.)
ST. MARTIN (Neth. and Fr.)
ST BARTHÉLEMY (Fr.)

Codrington ○ BARBUDA

SABA (Neth.)

ST. EUSTATIUS (Neth.)
ST KITTS
Mt. Misery 4314
Basseterre
ST. CHRISTOPHER (ST. KITTS)—NEVIS
Charlestown ○ Nevis Peak 3596
NEVIS
St. Johns
Boggy Peak 1330
REDONDA ○
ANTIGUA AND BARBUDA

L E E W A R D

MONTSERRAT (Br.)
Plymouth △ Soufrière (Vol.) 3002

POINTE DE LA GRANDE VIGIE
Ste. Rose ○ Le Moule
GRANDE TERRE
DÉSIRADE (Fr.)
Pointe-à-Pitre
Ste. Anne PETITE TERRE (Fr.)
BASSE TERRE
Grande Soufrière (Vol.) 4869 △ Capesterre (Fr.)
GUADELOUPE (Fr.)
Basse Terre
MARIE GALANTE
LES SAINTES IS.
Grand Bourg

I S.

Portsmouth ○ △ Morne Diablotin 4 747
St. Joseph ○
DOMINICA
Roseau ○

Dominica Channel

Mt. Pelée (Vol.) 4800 △
St. Pierre ○ Trinité
Pitons du Carbet 3960
Fort-de-France
Le François
MARTINIQUE (Fr.)
Le Marin
POINTE D'ENFER

St. Lucia Channel

Castries ○
Morne Gimie 3145 △
Soufrière ○
ST. LUCIA

I S.

St. Vincent Passage

W I N D W A R D

Mt. Soufrière 4048 △
Kingstown
ST. VINCENT AND THE GRENADINES
BEQUIA
○ MUSTIQUE

○ CANOUAN

T H E   G R E N A D I N E S

CARRIACOU

Mt. St. Catherine 2749 △
St. George's ○ Grenville
GRENADA

NORTH POINT
BARBADOS
Mt. Hillaby 1104
Bathsheba
Bridgetown
SOUTH POINT

C A R I B B E A N   S E A

A T L A N T I C   O C E A N

Same scale as main map

PUNTA PATUCA

○ Cabo Gracias a Dios

CAYOS MISKITO

○ Lone Star

○ Puerto Cabezas

○ Huaunta

○ Prinzapolca

M O S Q U I T O S

Laguna Carata

Laguna Huaunta

Coco (Segovia)

U A

D E

C O S T A

○ Rama

● Bluefields

ISLA DE LA CIERVO

PUNTA MICO

Laguna las Perlas

ISLA DE PROVIDENCIA (Colombia)

SAN ANDRÉS (Colombia)
CAYOS DE ESE

LITTLE CORN
GREAT CORN (Nicaragua)

CAYOS DE ALBUQUERQUE (Colombia)

C A R I B B E A N   S E A

Bahía de San Juan del Norte
San Juan del Norte (Greytown)

Carlos

TA

San José

Ramón ○ Guápiles ○ Cairo
Alajuela ○ Heredia ○
Matina ○ Limón
Cartago ○ Paraíso
Irazú Vol. 11 260 Turrialbo

R I C A

C O R D I L L E R A

Parrita ○
Quepos ○
PUNTA QUEPOS
Cerro Chirripó 12 530
Cerro Kámuk 11 696 △
San Isidro ○
Guabito ○
Buenos Aires ○
Cerro Echandi 10 394 △
Bahía de Coronada
Puerto Cortés ○
Volcán Barú 11 410 △
D E
Almirante ○
Bocas del Toro
Chiriquí Grande ○
Laguna de Chiriquí
ESCUDO DE VERAGUAS
Golfo de los Mosquitos
T A L A M A N C A
Golfito ○
ISLA DE CAÑO
PENÍNSULA DE OSA
Puerto Jiménez ○
CABO MATAPALO
Golfo Dulce
Boquete ○
Concepción ○
C. de Santa Catalina 5249
La Cuesta ○
David ○
Horconcitos ○
C. Negro 4429 △
SERRANÍA DE TABASARÁ
P A
Puerto Armuelles ○
Bahía Charco de Azul
PUNTA BURICA
Las Palmas ○
Remedios ○
Soná ○
Santiago ○
Río de Jesús ○
Chitré ○
Sona ○
Los Santos
Las Tablas ○
PENÍNSULA DE AZUERO
ISLA COIBA
ISLA CEBACO
PUNTA MALA
PUNTA MARIATO
ISLA JICARÓN
Golfo de Parita
Golfo de Panamá
Nató ○
Antón ○
Aguadulce ○
Río Hato ○
Penonomé ○
Bejuco ○
Chorrera ○
PUNTA CHAME
ARCHIPIÉLAGO DE LAS PERLAS
ISLA DE SAN JOSÉ
San Miguel ○ ISLA DEL REY
PUNTA GARACHINÉ
Garachiné ○
CABO TIBURÓN
La Palma ○
El Real ○
S E R R A N Í A   D E L   D A R I É N
C O L O M B I A

PUNTA MANZANILLO
Nombre de Dios
El Porvenir
PUNTA SAN BLAS
Portobelo ○ Mandinga ○
Golfo de San Blas
Colón ○
Silver City ○
Gatún ○
North Gamboa ○
Brewster 3018 △
Chepo ○
CORD. DE SAN BLAS
Lago Gatún
Balboa Heights ○
Balboa ○ Panamá
ISTMO DE PANAMÁ
Bahía de Panamá
N

20 40 60 80 100 120 Miles
20 40 60 80 100 120 140 160 180 200 Kilometers

©RMcN

GULF

OF

MEXICO

GULF OF MEXICO

Tropic of Cancer

FLORIDA

SANIBEL

Naples

SEMINOLE
IND. RES.

CAPE ROMANO

Everglades

TEN THOUSAND
ISLANDS

EVERGLADES

EVERGLADES

NATIONAL PARK

CAPE SABLE

PINE IS.

DRY TORTUGAS

MARQUESAS
KEYS

Key
West

THE EVERGLADES

Delray Beach

Fort Lauderdale

Dania

MIAMI ● Miami Beach

Biscayne
Bay

Homestead

KEY
LARGO

FLORIDA KEYS

Whitewater
Bay

Florida Bay

Straits of Florida

Santaren

LITTLE BAHAMA
BANK

GREAT SALE
CAY

SETTLEMENT PT.

West
End

Freeport GRAND BAHAMA

PINDER POINT

GREAT
ABACO

LITTLE
ABACO

Whale Cay

Carrion
Crow Harbor

GREAT

ABACO

MORES

Cross Harbor

Northwest Providence Channel

GREAT ISAAC

LITTLE ISAAC

BROTHERS

NORTH BIMINI

SOUTH BIMINI

N. CAT CAY

Barnett Harbor

Dollar Harbor

RIDING
ROCKS

ORANGE CAY

GREAT STIRRUP
CAY

GREAT
HARBOUR CAY

BERRY

ISLANDS

FRAZIERS HOG CAY

WHALE CAY

JOULTER'S CAYS

Nicolls Town

WILLIAMS

BONDS CAY

SOUTHWEST
PT.

CORNWALL

ROY

Nassau PARADISE

SIMMS PT.

NEW PROVIDENCE

Staniard Creek

SHIP CHANNEL CAY

HIGHBORNE CAY

SALVADOR PT.

North Bight

Middle Bight

South Bight

GREEN CAY

BOOBY

SNAP PT.

CURLY CUT CAYS

HURRICANE FLATS

NORTH ELBOW CAYS

DOG ROCKS

CAY SAL

CAY SAL
BANK

DAMAS
CAYS

ANGUILLA
CAYS

Nicholas Channel

Santaren Channel

Turner Sound

A
N
D
R
O
S

I
S
L
A
N
D

TONGUE OF THE OCEAN

SHROL

B
A
H
A
M
A

Old Bahama Channel

HAVANA
CIUDAD DE
LA HABANA
Marianao ⊙Guanabacoa
Regla

CAYO BLANCOS

CAYO

Bahía Matanzas

ARCHIPIÉLAGO DE SABANA

Guanajay

Pan de Guajaibón
2532 ▲
San Antonio de los Baños
Artemisa
Candelaria
H A B A N A
Güira de
Melena
Güines
Bejucal
Unión de Reyes
Batabanó

Matanzas ⊙Cárdenas

Corralillo

Bahía de
Cárdenas

Martí

Jovellanos

Quemado
de Güines

Sagua la
Grande

CAYO SANTA MARÍA

CAYO
FRAGOSO

ARCHIPIÉLAGO

Consolación del Sur

PINAR

Los Palacios

DE Pinar del Río **RIO**

VUELTABAJO

San Juan
Martínez

Guane

Mantua

SIERRA

PEN.
DE GUANAHACABIBES

CABO
FRANCES

CABO CORRIENTES

Bahía de
Guadiana

Santa Lucía

ARCHIPIÉLAGO
DE LOS COLORADOS

LOS ÓRGANOS

Ensenada
de Cortés

PUNTA GORDA

CAYOS DE SAN FELIPE

CAYOS DE LOS INDIOS

PTA. FRANCES

CABO PEPE

Nueva Gerona

CAYOS DE DIOS

ISLAS DE MANGLES

ARCHIPIÉLAGO
DE
LOS
CANARREOS

Santa Fé

ISLA DE LA
JUVENTUD

PINAR

CAYOS LAGUNA

CAYOS DE
JUAN LUIS

CAYO ROSARIO

CAYO
CANTILES

CAYO LARGO

Alacranes
Pedro
Betancourt
Navajas
Bolondrón
MATANZAS
Jagüey
Grande

PENÍNSULA DE ZAPATA

Ensenada
de la Broa

Golfo de
Batabanó

BANCO JARDINES

Colón

Aguada
de Pasajeros

Rodas

CIENFUEGOS
Cienfuegos

Palmira

Cruces

Santo
Domingo

Esperanza

VILLA CLARA

Santa
Clara

Remedios

Caibarién

Camajuaní
Zulueta

Yaguajay

CAYO
FRAGOSO

CAYO COCO

Bahía Buena Vista

TURIGUANO

CAYO SANTA MARÍA

CAYO LOBOS

CAYO
CRUZ

CAYO
ROMANO

Golfo de
Cazones

Bahía
Cienfuegos

Pico San Juan
1156

Florida

Placetas

SANCTI
SPIRITUS

SIERRA DE
TRINIDAD

Sancti
Spíritus

Casilda

Trinidad

Tunas de Zaza

Jatibonico

Morón

CIEGO DE
AVILA

Ciego de Ávila

Júcaro

Fomento

Minas

CAMAGÜEY

Camagüey

CAYO
GUAJABA

CAYO
SABINAL

Nuevitas

Puerto
LAS
TUNAS

Victoria de
las Tunas

CAYOS DE LA
ANA MARÍA

CAYOS CINCO BALAS

CAYOS
DE LAS DOCE LEGUAS

LABERINTO DE LAS
DOCE LEGUAS

Canal de Caballones

Santa Cruz
del Sur

Guayabal

Manzani

GRAN

SIERRA

GOLFO DE
GUACANAYABO

Campechuela

Niquero

Pico Ojo del Toro ▲
1748

CABO CRUZ

C A R I B B E A N

S

CAYMAN ISLANDS

LITTLE CAYMAN

CAYMAN BRAC
(Br.)

Georgetown

GRAND CAYMAN

Montego Bay

Lucea

Falmouth

St. Ann's Bay

JAMAICA

SOUTH NEGRIL PT.

Savanna la Mar

Mt. Denham ▲
3236

Annotto Ba

Buff Head
2728

Black River

May Pen

Kin

GT. PEDRO BLUFF

PORTLAND PT.

Portland
Bight

Longitude West of Greenwich

Relief

Meters	Feet
3050	10 000
1525	5000
610	2000
305	1000
152.5	500
0 Sea Level	
152.5	500
1525	5000
3050	10 000
6100	20 000

Cities
and
Towns

0 to 50,000 ○

50,000 to 500,000 ⊙

500,000 to 1,000,000 ⊚

1,000,000 and over

Scale 1:4 000 000; one inch to 64 miles. Conic Projec

Elevations and depressions are given in feet.

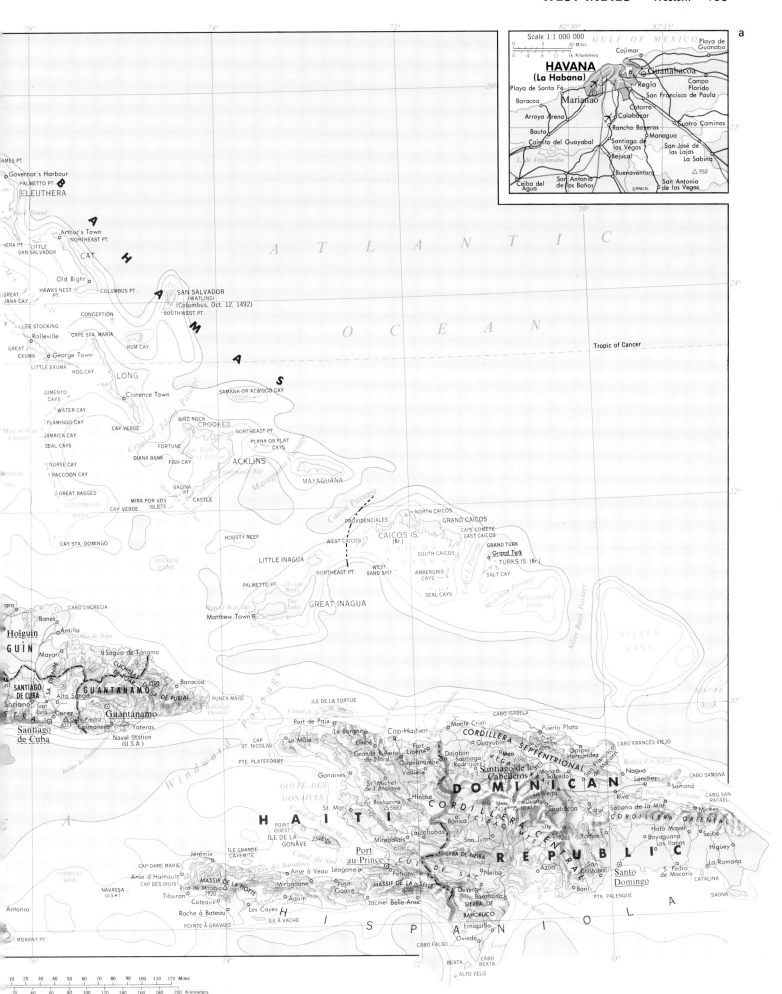

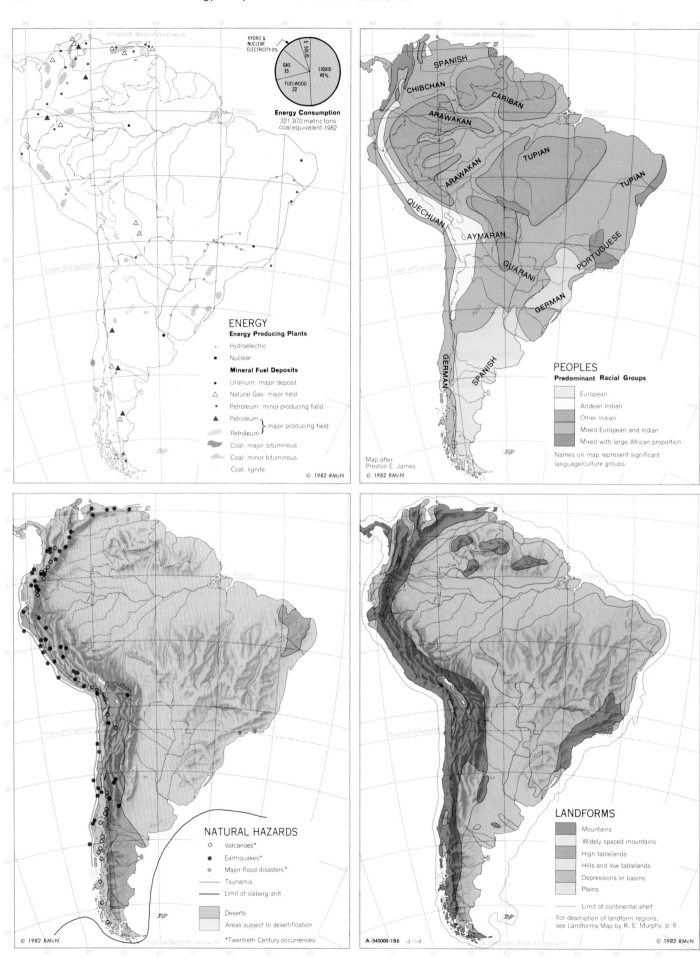

ENERGY

Energy Producing Plants

- Hydroelectric
- Nuclear

Mineral Fuel Deposits

- Uranium: major deposit
- △ Natural Gas: major field
- Petroleum: minor producing field
- ▲ Petroleum } major producing field
- Petroleum }
- Coal: major bituminous
- Coal: minor bituminous
- Coal: lignite

HYDRO. & NUCLEAR ELECTRICITY 9%
GAS 15
FUELWOOD 22
S SOLID
LIQUID 49%

Energy Consumption
321,970 metric tons
coal equivalent·1982

© 1982 RMcN

PEOPLES
Predominant Racial Groups

- European
- Andean Indian
- Other Indian
- Mixed European and Indian
- Mixed with large African proportion

Names on map represent significant
language/culture groups

Map after
Preston E. James
© 1982 RMcN

NATURAL HAZARDS

- ○ Volcanoes*
- ● Earthquakes*
- ● Major flood disasters*
- —— Tsunamis
- —— Limit of iceberg drift
- Deserts
- Areas subject to desertification

*Twentieth Century occurrences

© 1982 RMcN

LANDFORMS

- Mountains
- Widely spaced mountains
- High tablelands
- Hills and low tablelands
- Depressions or basins
- Plains
- —— Limit of continental shelf

For description of landform regions,
see Landforms Map by R. E. Murphy, p. 6

A-540000-1S6   -3-2-3

© 1982 RMcN

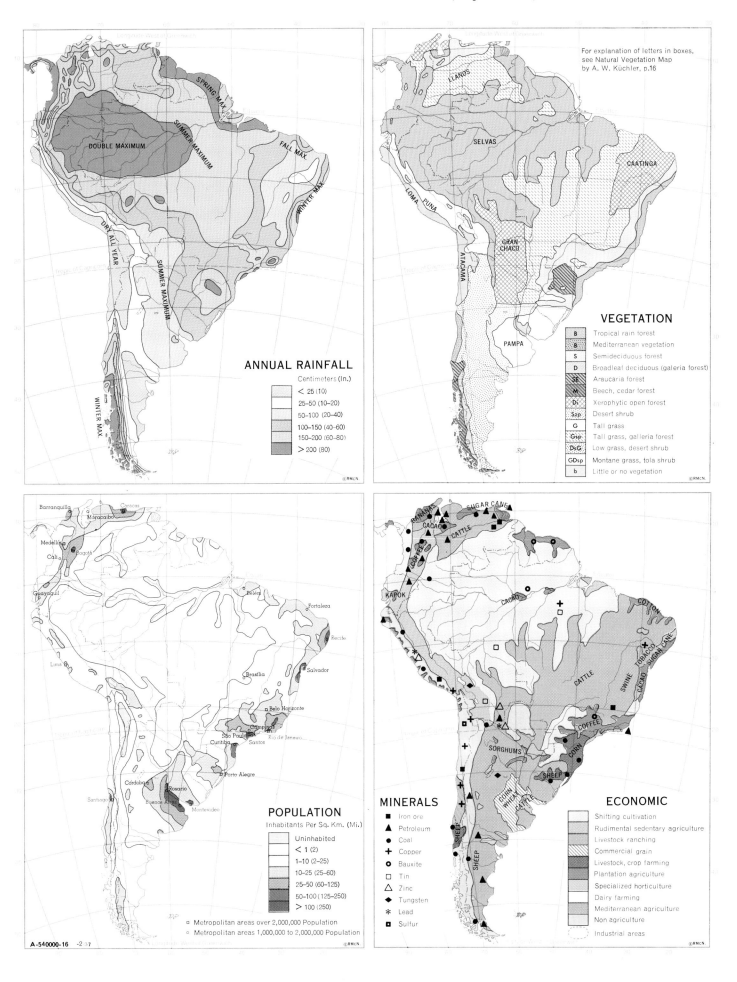

ANNUAL RAINFALL

Centimeters (In.)

- < 25 (10)
- 25–50 (10–20)
- 50–100 (20–40)
- 100–150 (40–60)
- 150–200 (60–80)
- > 200 (80)

For explanation of letters in boxes,
see Natural Vegetation Map
by A. W. Küchler, p.16

VEGETATION

B	Tropical rain forest
B	Mediterranean vegetation
S	Semideciduous forest
D	Broadleaf deciduous (galeria forest)
SE	Araucaria forest
M	Beech, cedar forest
Di	Xerophytic open forest
Szp	Desert shrub
G	Tall grass
Gsp	Tall grass, galleria forest
DsG	Low grass, desert shrub
GDsp	Montane grass, tola shrub
b	Little or no vegetation

POPULATION

Inhabitants Per Sq. Km. (Mi.)

- Uninhabited
- < 1 (2)
- 1–10 (2–25)
- 10–25 (25–60)
- 25–50 (60–125)
- 50–100 (125–250)
- > 100 (250)

□ Metropolitan areas over 2,000,000 Population
○ Metropolitan areas 1,000,000 to 2,000,000 Population

A-540000-16 -2-37

MINERALS

- ■ Iron ore
- ▲ Petroleum
- ● Coal
- + Copper
- ◉ Bauxite
- □ Tin
- △ Zinc
- ◆ Tungsten
- ✻ Lead
- ▪ Sulfur

ECONOMIC

- Shifting cultivation
- Rudimental sedentary agriculture
- Livestock ranching
- Commercial grain
- Livestock, crop farming
- Plantation agriculture
- Specialized horticulture
- Dairy farming
- Mediterranean agriculture
- Non agriculture
- Industrial areas

138

ATLANTIC

OCEAN

Tropic of Cancer

Equator

Recife

Fortaleza

Salvador

São Francisco

Belém

Brasília

Georgetown

Manaus

Amazon

Cuiabá

MATO GROSSO

Port of Spain
TRINIDAD

Negro

SELVAS

Orinoco

BAHAMAS

San Juan

PUERTO
RICO

CARACAS

Rio Branco

La Paz

HISPANIOLA

Maracaibo

LLANOS

Caribbean   Sea

Kingston

BOGOTÁ

JAMAICA

Iquitos

Barranquilla

ANDES

LIMA

Havana

Quito

CUBA

Panamá

Scale 1:24,000,000; one inch to 380 miles. Lambert Azimuthal Equal-Area Projection

RÍO DE JANEIRO

SÃO PAULO

Paraná

Porto Alegre

Asunción

Montevideo

San Miguel de Tucumán

Córdoba

BUENOS AIRES

Bahía Blanca

P A M P A S

G R A N

A N D E S

SANTIAGO

Puerto Montt

P A T A G O N I A

Punta Arenas

TIERRA DEL FUEGO

SOUTH GEORGIA

FALKLAND ISLANDS

Drake Passage

ANTARCTIC PENINSULA

A T L A N T I C

O C E A N

P A C I F I C

O C E A N

Tropic of Capricorn

A-540000-96

COPYRIGHT BY
RAND MCNALLY & COMPANY
MADE IN U.S.A.

- Urban
- Cropland
- Cropland & Woodland
- Cropland & Grazing Land
- Grassland, Grazing Land
- Forest, Woodland
- Swamp, Marshland
- Shrub, Sparse Grass, Wasteland (pattern)
- Barren Land

| 0 | 100 | 200 | 400 | 600 | 800 Miles |

| 0 | 150 | 300 | 600 | 900 | 1200 Kilometers |

CENTRAL AMERICA

HAVANA
CUBA
PEN. DE YUCATÁN
Bahía de Campeche
HISPANIOLA
San Juan
JAMAICA
PUERTO RICO (U.S.A.)
Gulf of Honduras
WEST INDIES
CARIBBEAN SEA
GUADELOUPE (Fr.)
MARTINIQUE (Fr.)
BARBADOS
TRINIDAD AND TOBAGO
Port of Spain

NORTH AMERICAN BASIN

ATLANTIC OCEAN

Tropic of Cancer

ISLA DEL COCO (Costa Rica)
ISLA DE MALPELO (Colombia)

Panamá
Golfo de Panamá

PUNTA DE GALLINAS
Barranquilla
Cartagena
Maracaibo
Valencia
La Guaira
CARACAS
VENEZUELA
Mérida
Ciudad Bolívar
Georgetown
Paramaribo
GUYANA
SURINAME
FR. GUIANA
Cayenne

Medellín
BOGOTÁ
COLOMBIA
Nevado del Tolima 17 110
Cerro (cutú) 7800
Boa Vista do Rio Branco
GUIANA HIGHLANDS

ARCHIPIÉLAGO DE COLÓN (GALÁPAGOS ISLANDS) (Ec.)

Quito
ECUADOR
Cotopaxi 19 347
Chimborazo 20 561
Guayaquil
Golfo de Guayaquil
Iquitos
Leticia
Rio Negro
Rio Amazonas
Rio Solimões (Amazonas)
Manaus (Manáos)
ILHA DE MARAJÓ
Belém (Pará)
São Luís (Maranhão)

Equator

ROCEDOS SÃO PEDRO E SÃO PAULO (Brazil)

Chiclayo
Trujillo
Nevs. Huascarán 22 205
PERU
LIMA
Callao
Cuzco
ANDES
Fortaleza (Ceará)
ARQUIPÉLAGO FERNANDO DE NORONHA (Brazil)
Teresina

BRAZIL
CHAPADA DE MATO GROSSO
Cuiabá
Brasília
Diamantina
BRAZILIAN HIGHLANDS
SERRA DO ESPINHAÇO

Cabo de São Roque
Natal
João Pessoa (Paraíba)
RECIFE (Pernambuco)
Maceió
Salvador (Bahia)

Volcán Misti 19 098
Arequipa
Mollendo
La Paz
Nev. Illimani 21 151
BOLIVIA
Sucre
Potosí
Belo Horizonte
Pico da Bandeira 9482
Vitória

Iquique
GRAN CHACO
PARAGUAY
Asunción
SÃO PAULO
Santos
RIO DE JANEIRO
CABO FRIO

Antofagasta
Salta
Tucumán
Corrientes
Cerro Azul (Copiapó) Vol.
Copiapó

Tropic of Capricorn

ISLA SAN FÉLIX (Chile)
ISLA DE SAN AMBROSIO (Chile)

Coquimbo
Córdoba
Santa Fe
Salto
URUGUAY
Rio Grande
Pôrto Alegre
Florianópolis

ISLAS DE JUAN FERNÁNDEZ (Chile)

Valparaíso
SANTIAGO
Mendoza
Rosario
BUENOS AIRES
La Plata
MONTEVIDEO
CHILE
ARGENTINA
PAMPAS
Concepción
Bahía Blanca
Valdivia
Viedma
Golfo San Matías

PACIFIC OCEAN

ATLANTIC OCEAN

Puerto Montt
ISLA DE CHILOÉ
ARCHIPIÉLAGO DE LOS CHONOS
Comodoro Rivadavia
Golfo San Jorge
Monte San Valentín 13 314

WELLINGTON
HANOVER
FALKLAND IS. (ISLAS MALVINAS) (Br.)
Río Gallegos
Stanley

Punta Arenas
DESOLACIÓN
Mt. Sarmiento 8100
TIERRA DEL FUEGO
ISLA DE LOS ESTADOS
Estrecho de Magallanes
CABO DE HORNOS (CAPE HORN)

SOUTH GEORGIA (Falkland Is.)

SOUTH SANDWICH ISLANDS

Drake Passage

SOUTH SHETLAND ISLANDS (B.A.T.)
SOUTH ORKNEY IS. (Falkland Is.)
SOUTH ORKNEY

Antarctic Circle
ANTARCTIC PENINSULA
Joinville
JAMES ROSS

Longitude West of Greenwich

A-540000-76 3-5-12
COPYRIGHT BY
RAND McNALLY & COMPANY
MADE IN U.S.A.

Relief		
Meters		Feet
3050		10 000
1525		5000
610		2000
305		1000
0	Sea Level	0
152.5		500
1525		5000
3050		10 000
6100		20 000

0 200 400 600 800 1000 Miles
0 400 800 1200 1600 Kilometers

Scale 1:40 000 000; one inch to 630 miles. Lambert's Azimuthal, Equal Area Projection
Elevations and depressions are given in feet

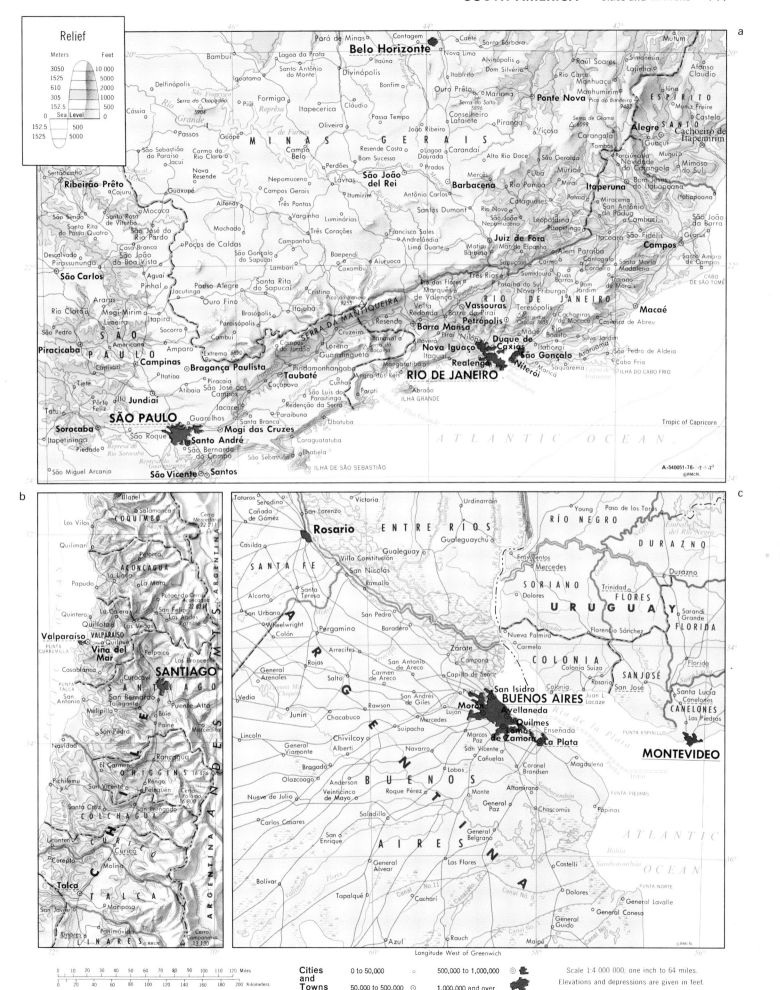

a

Relief

Meters	Feet
3050	10 000
1525	5000
610	2000
305	1000
152.5	500
0	Sea Level 0
152.5	500
1525	5000

Pará de Minas · Contagem · Caeté · Santa Bárbara · Mutum

Belo Horizonte

Bambuí · Lagoa da Prata · Itaúna · Nova Lima · Alvinópolis · Raúl Soares · Simonésia · Afonso Cláudio

Iguatama · Santo Antônio do Monte · Divinópolis · Itabirito · Dom Silvério · Rio Casca · Manhuaçu · Manhumirim · Iúna · ESPÍRITO

Delfinópolis · Serra do Chapadão 5904 · Piúí · Formiga · Itapecerica · Cláudio · Bonfim · Ouro Prêto · Mariana · Pico da Bandeira · 9482 · Muniz Freire · SANTO

Cássia · Rio Grande · Represa de Furnas · Passa Tempo · Conselheiro Lafaiete · Piranga · Serra de Grama · 6099 · Alegre · Castelo · Cachoeiro de Itapemirim

Passos · Oliveira · João Ribeiro · Itabira · Carangola · Tombos · Porciúncula · Guaçuí

São Sebastião do Paraíso · Carmo do Rio Claro · Jacuí · Campo Belo · Resende Costa · Lagoa Dourada · Carandaí · Alto Rio Doce · São Geraldo · Novidade do Carangola · Mimoso do Sul

Sertãozinho · Nova Resende · Perdões · Bom Sucesso · Prados · Mercês · Úba · Muriaé · Itaperuna · São João da Barra

Ribeirão Prêto · Guaxupé · MINAS GERAIS · **São João del Rei** · Antônio Carlos · Miracema · San Antônio de Pádua

São Simão · Cajuru · Mococa · Alfenas · Campos Gerais · Lavras · Itumirim · Barbacena · Rio Pomba · Mirai · Patma · Leopoldina · Pirapetinga · Cantagalo · Campos

Santa Rosa de Viterbo · Machado · Varginha · Luminárias · Santos Dumont · São João Nepomuceno · Itacoara · São Fidélis

Descalvado · São José do Rio Pardo · Poços de Caldas · Três Corações · Francisco Sales · Andrelândia · Juiz de Fora · Santo Amaro de Campos

Pirassununga · São João da Boa Vista · Campanha · Baependi · Caxambu · Lima Duarte · Mar de Espanha · Alem Paraíba · CABO DE SÃO TOMÉ

São Carlos · Aguaí · Santa Rita do Sapucaí · Aiuruoca · Matias Barbosa · Sapucaia · Carmo · Duas Barras · Trajano de Morais

Araras · Pinhal · Pouso Alegre · Lambari · RIO DE JANEIRO

Rio Claro · Mogi-Mirim · Ouro Fino · Cristina · Pico da Itatiaia 9255 · Rio das Flores · Três Rios · Paraíba do Sul · Bom Jardim · Macaé

São Pedro · Limeira · Itapira · Brasópolis · Itajubá · SERRA DA MANTIQUEIRA · Vassouras · Teresópolis · Cachoeiras de Macacu · Casimiro de Abreu

Piracicaba · Capivari · SÃO · Amparo · Extrema 6890 · Campos do Jordão · Cruzeiro · Resende · Barra do Piraí · **Petrópolis** · Rio Bonito · Silva Jardim

Tietê · Itatiba · Socorro · Piracaia · Lorena · Guaratinguetá · **Barra Mansa** · Pirai · Nilópolis · Magé · Itaboraí · São Pedro de Aldeia

Campinas · Bragança Paulista · PAULO · Atibaia · São José dos Campos · Pindamonhangaba · Piquete · **Nova Iguaçu** · **Duque de Caxias** · Cabo Frio

Pôrto Feliz · **Jundiaí** · **Taubaté** · Cunha · Angra dos Reis · Itaguaí · **Realengo** · **São Gonçalo** · ILHA DO CABO FRIO

Sorocaba · Guarulhos · Jacareí · Santa Branca · Paraty · **RIO DE JANEIRO** · **Viterói** · Maricá · Saquarema

Itapetininga · **SÃO PAULO** · São Roque · Mogi das Cruzes · São Luis do Paraitinga · ILHA GRANDE · Abraão · BAÍA DE ILHA GRANDE

Piedade · Represa de Guarapiranga · **Santo André** · Redenção da Serra · Ubatuba · Baía de Guanabara · Tropic of Capricorn

São Miguel Arcanjo · Represa do Rio Sorocaba · São Bernardo do Campo · Caraguatatuba · ATLANTIC OCEAN

São Vicente · **Santos** · São Sebastião · ILHA DE SÃO SEBASTIÃO · A-540051-76- -7 -1 -72 · ©RMCN.

b

Illapel · Salamanca · COQUIMBO · Cerro Mercedario 22 211

Los Vilos · Quilimarí · Pétorca · ACONCAGUA · ARGENTINA

Papudo · La Ligua · La Mora · Putaendo Cerro Aconcagua 22 831

Quintero · La Calera · San Felipe · Los Andes · Portillo

Quillota · Las Vegas · MTS.

Valparaíso · VALPARAÍSO · Quilpué · Polpaico · Las Bronces

PUNTA CURAUMILLA · **Viña del Mar** · ANDES

PUNTA TALCA · Casablanca · **SANTIAGO**

San Antonio · Curacaví · SAN · Puente Alto · CHILE

Melipilla · Talagante · Buin

San Pedro · Paine

Navidad · Mercedita

El Carmen · Rancagua

O'HIGGINS 16 876

Pichilemu · Rengo · Cerro el Palomo 16 600

Peralen · San Fernando

Santa Cruz · Cerro Campanario 13 130

COLCHAGUA

Licanten · CHILE

Curepto · Curicó

Molina · Mariposa

Talca

San Javier · Panimávida

LINARES · Linares · ©RMCN.

c

Totoras · Serodino · Victoria · Urdinarrain · Young · Paso de los Toros

Cañada de Gómez · San Lorenzo · RÍO NEGRO · Embalse del Río Negro

Rosario · ENTRE RÍOS · DURAZNO

Casilda · Gualeguay · Gualeguaychú · Fray Bentos · Mercedes · Durazno

SANTA FE · Villa Constitución · SORIANO · Trinidad · FLORES

Alcorta · San Nicolás · Ramallo · Dolores · URUGUAY · Florencio Sánchez · SARANDÍ Grande · FLORIDA

San Urbano · Santa Teresa · San Pedro · Nueva Palmira · Florida

Wheelwright · Colón · Baradero · Carmelo · Florida

Pergamino · Zárate · COLONIA · SAN JOSÉ

Arrecifes · San Antonio de Areco · Campona · Colonia Suiza · Santa Lucía · Canelones

Rojas · Capilla de Señor · Colonia · Rosario · San José · Las Piedras

General Arenales · Salto · Carmen de Areco · Juan L. Lacaze · CANELONES

Vedia · San Andrés de Giles · **San Isidro** · PUNTA ESPINILLO

Junín · Chacabuco · Luján · **Morón** · **BUENOS AIRES** · **MONTEVIDEO**

Lincoln · Suipacha · **Avellaneda**

Chivilcoy · Mercedes · **Quilmes** · Ensenada · PUNTA BRAVA

Alberti · Navarro · Marcos Paz · **Lomas de Zamora** · **La Plata**

General Viamonte · Bragado · San Vicente · Cañuelas

Olazcoaga · Lobos · Monte · Coronel Brandsen · Magdalena

Veinticinco de Mayo · Roque Pérez · ATLANTIC

Nueve de Julio · BUENOS · General Paz · Chascomús · Rápinas · PUNTA PIEDRAS

Carlos Casares · Saladillo · General Belgrano · OCEAN

San Enrique · AIRES · General Alvear · Las Flores · Castelli · Bahía

Bolívar · ARGENTINA · Tapalqué · Cachari · Dolores · Samborombón · General Lavalle

Azul · Rauch · Maipú · General Guido · General Conesa

Longitude West of Greenwich · ©RMCN.

0 10 20 30 40 50 60 70 80 90 100 110 120 Miles
0 20 40 60 80 100 120 140 160 180 200 Kilometers

Cities and Towns

| 0 to 50,000 | ○ | 500,000 to 1,000,000 | ◉ |
| 50,000 to 500,000 | ⊙ | 1,000,000 and over | ■ |

Scale 1:4 000 000; one inch to 64 miles.
Elevations and depressions are given in feet.

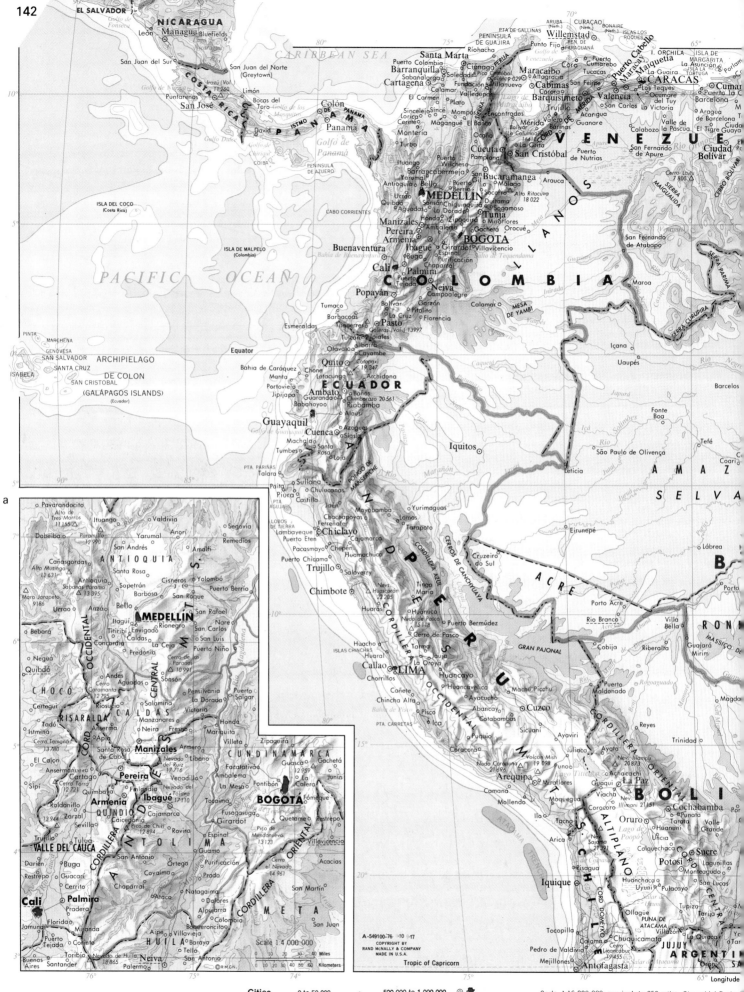

Cities and Towns

0 to 50,000 ○
50,000 to 500,000 ⊙
500,000 to 1,000,000 ◉
1,000,000 and over ▣

Scale 1:16 000 000, one inch to 250 miles. Sinusoidal Project
Elevations and depressions are given in feet

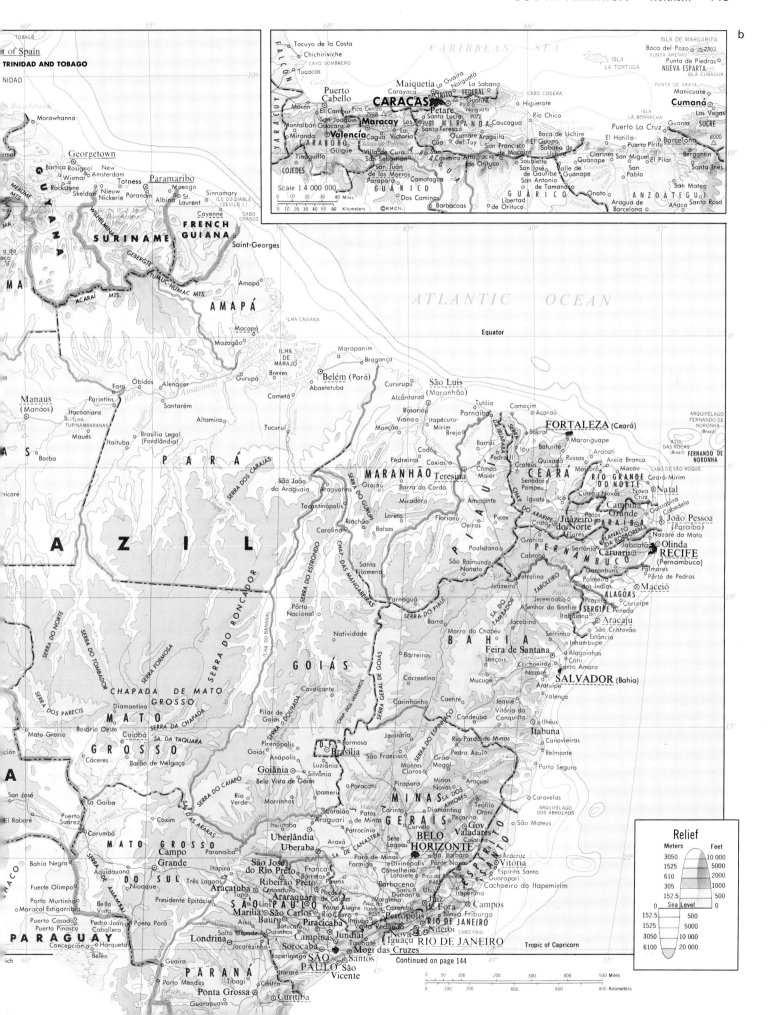

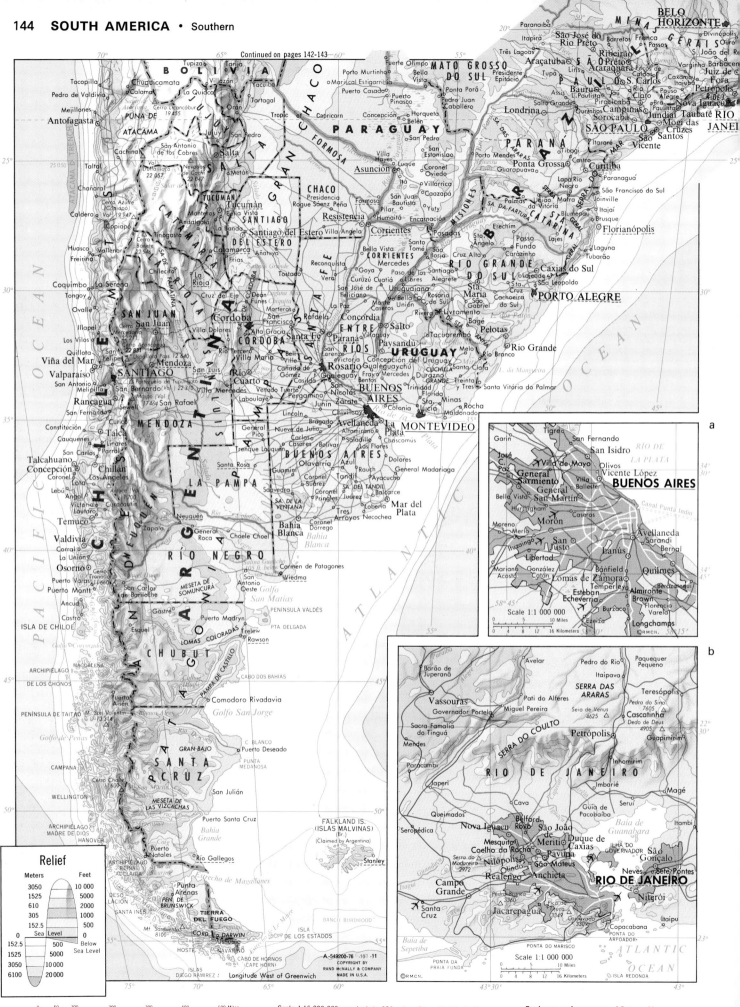

Continued on pages 142-143

a
BUENOS AIRES
Scale 1:1 000 000

b
Scale 1:1 000 000

Relief

Meters	Feet
3050	10 000
1525	5000
610	2000
305	1000
152.5	500
0 Sea Level	Sea Level
152.5	500 Below Sea Level
1525	5000
3050	10 000
6100	20 000

A-549200-76 -101 -11
COPYRIGHT BY
RAND MCNALLY & COMPANY
MADE IN U.S.A.

Scale 1:16 000 000; one inch to 250 miles. Sinusoidal Projection
Elevations and depressions are given in feet

For larger scale coverage of Buenos Aires, Rio de Janeiro, and São Paulo see pages 60 and 61

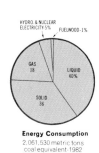

HYDRO. & NUCLEAR
ELECTRICITY·5% FUELWOOD·1%

GAS 18 LIQUID 40%

SOLID 36

Energy Consumption
2,061,530 metric tons
coal equivalent·1982

ENERGY

Energy Producing Plants

▽ Geothermal
· Hydroelectric
■ Nuclear

Mineral Fuel Deposits

· Uranium: major deposit
△ Natural Gas: major field
· Petroleum: minor producing field
▲ Petroleum } major producing field
Petroleum }
Coal: major bituminous and anthracite
Coal: minor bituminous and anthracite
Coal: lignite

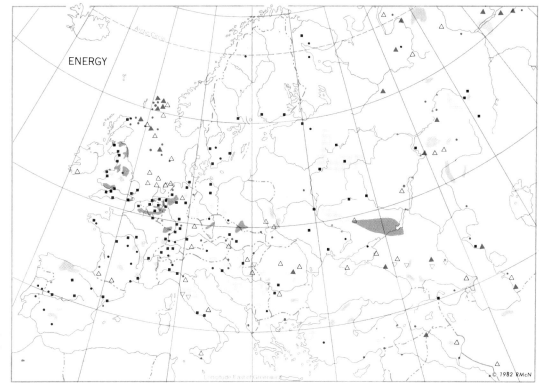

ENERGY

© 1982 RMcN

NATURAL HAZARDS

○ Volcanoes*
● Earthquakes*
● Major flood disasters*
— Tsunamis
— Limit of iceberg drift

Temporary pack ice
Areas subject to desertification

*Twentieth Century occurrences

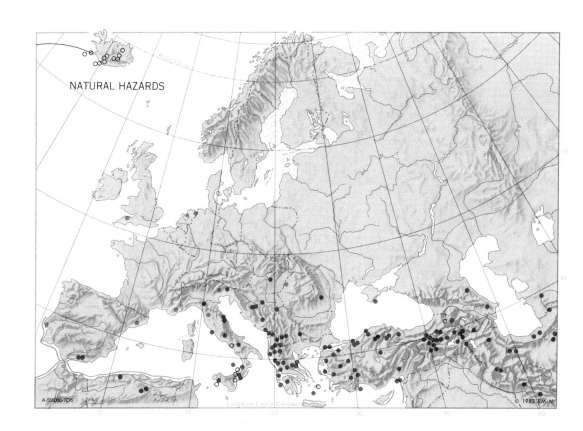

NATURAL HAZARDS

© 1982 RMcN

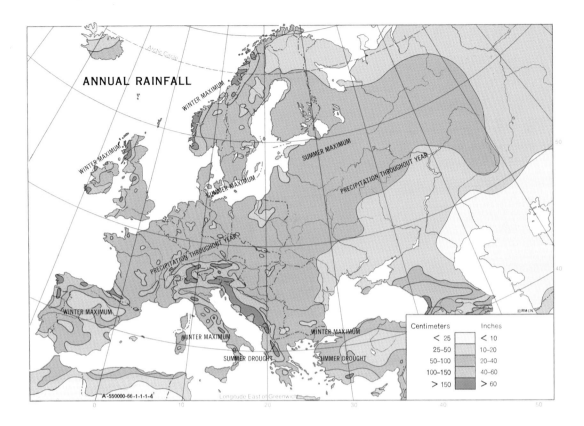

ANNUAL RAINFALL

WINTER MAXIMUM

WINTER MAXIMUM

WINTER MAXIMUM

SUMMER MAXIMUM

SUMMER MAXIMUM

SUMMER MAXIMUM

PRECIPITATION THROUGHOUT YEAR

PRECIPITATION THROUGHOUT YEAR

WINTER MAXIMUM

WINTER MAXIMUM

WINTER MAXIMUM

SUMMER DROUGHT

SUMMER DROUGHT

Centimeters	Inches
< 25	< 10
25–50	10–20
50–100	20–40
100–150	40–60
> 150	> 60

A-550000-66-1-1-1-4

Longitude East of Greenwich

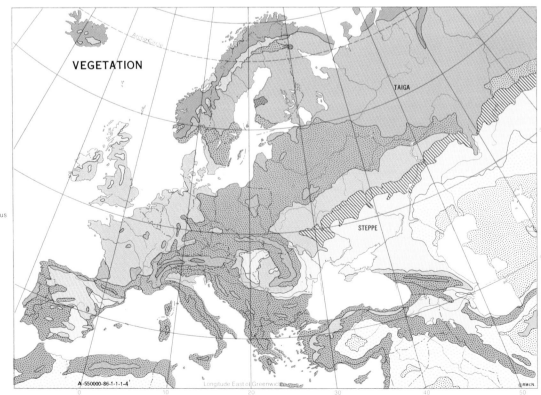

VEGETATION

TAIGA

STEPPE

VEGETATION

E	Coniferous forest
B, Bs	Mediterranean vegetation
M	Mixed forest: coniferous-deciduous
S	Semi-deciduous forest
D	Deciduous forest
DG	Wooded steppe
G	Grass (steppe)
Gp	Short grass
Dsp	Desert shrub
L	Heath and moor
L	Alpine vegetation, tundra
b	Little or no vegetation

For explanation of letters in boxes,
see Natural Vegetation Map
by A. W. Kuchler, **p. 16**

A-550000-86-1-1-1-4

Longitude East of Greenwich

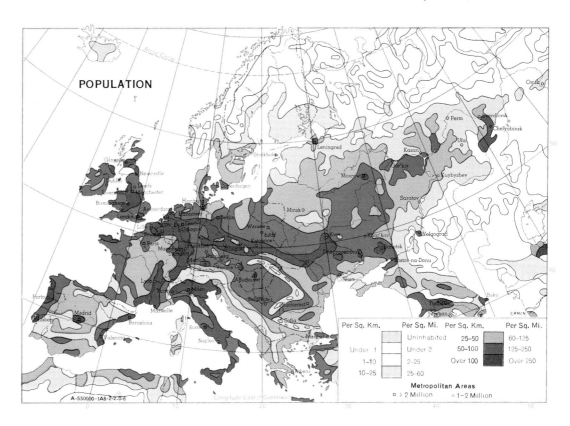

POPULATION

Per Sq. Km.	Per Sq. Mi.	Per Sq. Km.	Per Sq. Mi.
Uninhabited	25–50	60–125	
Under 1	Under 2	50–100	125–250
1–10	2–25	Over 100	Over 250
10–25	25–60		

Metropolitan Areas
□ > 2 Million   ○ 1–2 Million

A-550000-1A6-2-2-0-6

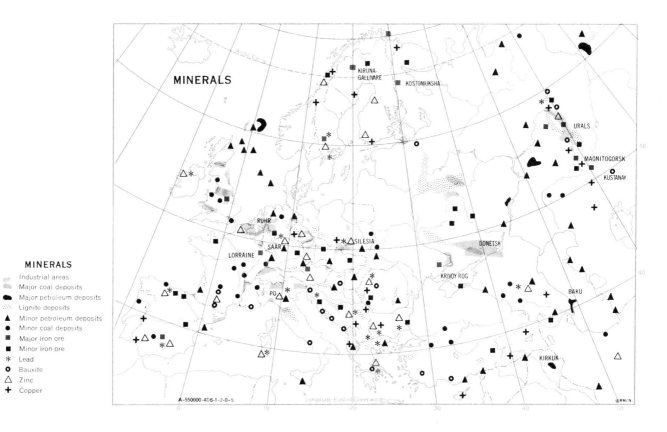

MINERALS

MINERALS

- Industrial areas
- Major coal deposits
- ⬤ Major petroleum deposits
- Lignite deposits
- ▲ Minor petroleum deposits
- ● Minor coal deposits
- ◼ Major iron ore
- ■ Minor iron ore
- ✳ Lead
- ○ Bauxite
- △ Zinc
- ✛ Copper

A-550000-4D6-1-2-0-5

Longitude East of Greenwich

148

Urban

Cropland

Cropland & Woodland

Cropland & Grazing Land

Grassland, Grazing Land

Forest, Woodland

Swamp, Marshland

Tundra

Shrub, Sparse Grass;
Wasteland (pattern)

Barren Land

Oasis

Reykjavik

ATLANTIC

OCEAN

North
Sea

Narvik
Murma

Trondheim
Ume
Gulf of Bothnia

Bergen
Oslo
Helsinki
LENINGRAD

Göteborg
Stockholm
Tallinn

Copenhagen
Rīga
Baltic Sea

Glasgow

Belfast

MANCHESTER
Dublin
LONDON

Amsterdam
Hamburg
Elbe
BERLIN
Kaliningrad
Minsk

Antwerp
Essen
Leipzig
Oder
Warsaw
Pripya

Brest
Frankfurt
Prague
Kraków
L'vov

PARIS
Seine
Strasbourg
Danube
VIENNA
CARPATHIANS

Loire
Rhine
Munich
Zürich
BUDAPEST
Tisza
Dv

Bay of Biscay
Lyon
ALPS
MILAN
Zagreb
Sava

La Coruña
Bordeaux
Garonne
Rhône
Venice
Belgrade
Bucharest

Bilbao
Genoa
Adriatic Sea
Danube

Douro
PYRENEES
Marseille
Sofia

Lisbon
MADRID
Ebro
BARCELONA
CORSICA
ROME
Tiranë

Sevilla
ISLAS BALEARES
SARDINIA
Naples

Tanger
Tyrrhenian Sea

Oran
Algiers
Mediterranean

Casablanca
ATLAS MOUNTAINS
Palermo
SICILY
Athens
Aegean Sea

Tunis

MALTA
Sea
CRETE

Longitude West of Greenwich   Longitude East of Greenwich

Scale 1: 16,000,000; one inch to 250 miles. Conic Projection

0 50 100   200   300   400   500 Miles
0   100   200   400   600   800 Kilometers

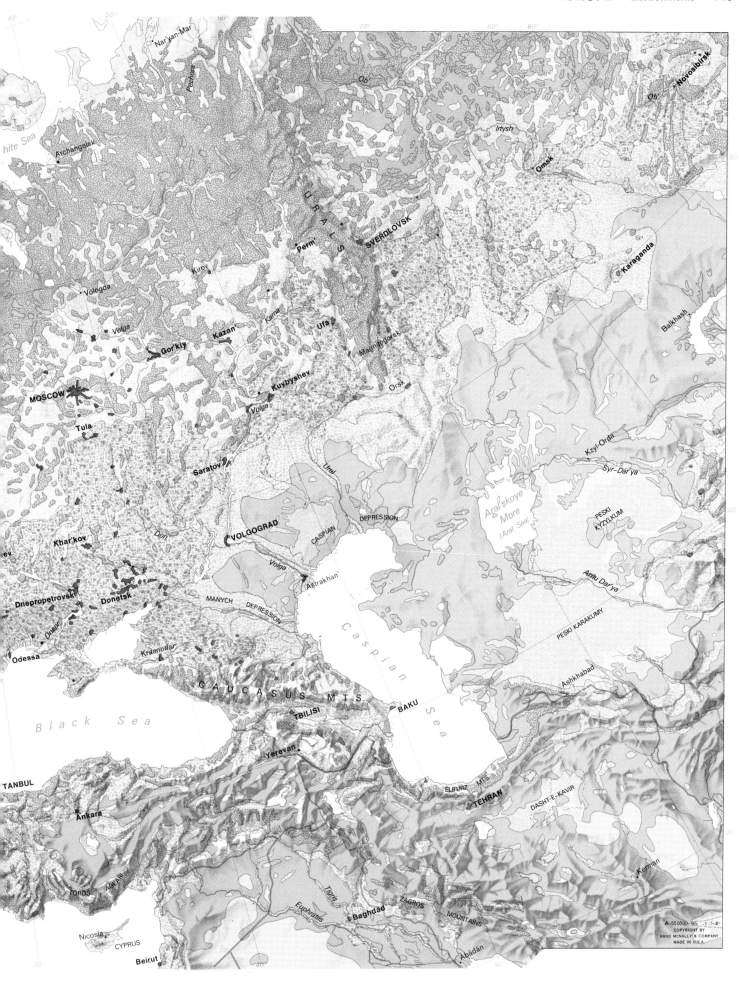

Scale 1:16 000 000, one inch to 250 miles. Conic Projection
Elevations and depressions are given in feet.

EUROPE LANGUAGES
BY
BOGDAN ZABORSKI

Scale 1:16,500,000; one inch to 260 miles Conic Projection

0   100   200   300   400   500   600 Miles

0   200   400   600   800   1000 Kilometers

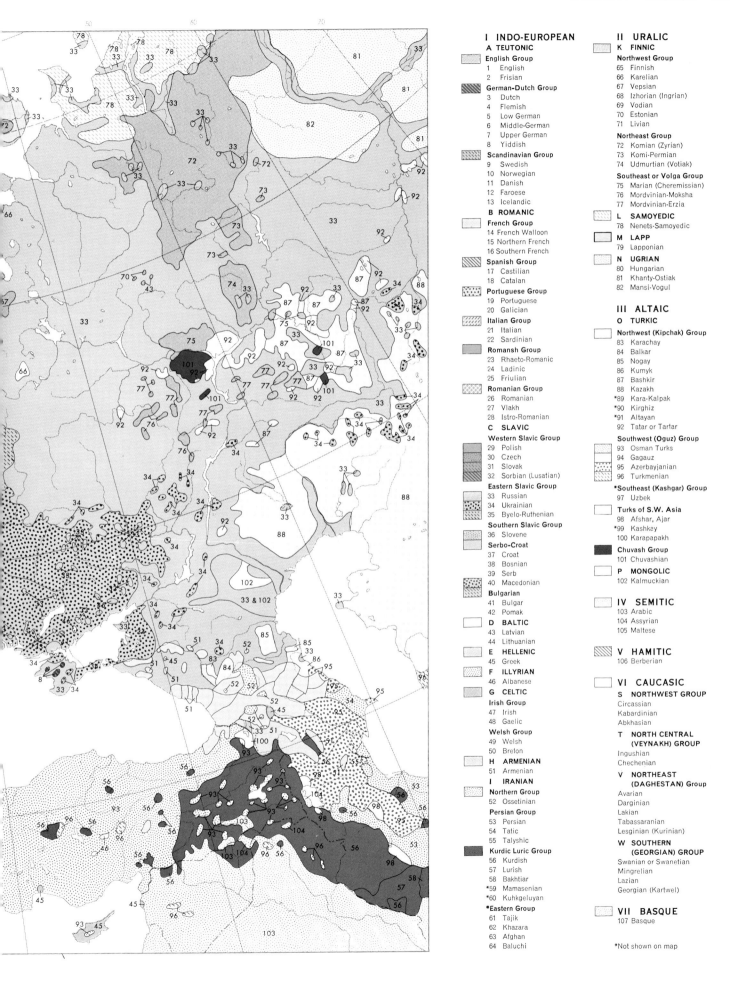

I INDO-EUROPEAN
A TEUTONIC
English Group
1 English
2 Frisian
German-Dutch Group
3 Dutch
4 Flemish
5 Low German
6 Middle-German
7 Upper German
8 Yiddish
Scandinavian Group
9 Swedish
10 Norwegian
11 Danish
12 Faroese
13 Icelandic
B ROMANIC
French Group
14 French Walloon
15 Northern French
16 Southern French
Spanish Group
17 Castilian
18 Catalan
Portuguese Group
19 Portuguese
20 Galician
Italian Group
21 Italian
22 Sardinian
Romansh Group
23 Rhaeto-Romanic
24 Ladinic
25 Friulian
Romanian Group
26 Romanian
27 Vlakh
28 Istro-Romanian
C SLAVIC
Western Slavic Group
29 Polish
30 Czech
31 Slovak
32 Sorbian (Lusatian)
Eastern Slavic Group
33 Russian
34 Ukrainian
35 Byelo-Ruthenian
Southern Slavic Group
36 Slovene
Serbo-Croat
37 Croat
38 Bosnian
39 Serb
40 Macedonian
Bulgarian
41 Bulgar
42 Pomak
D BALTIC
43 Latvian
44 Lithuanian
E HELLENIC
45 Greek
F ILLYRIAN
46 Albanese
G CELTIC
Irish Group
47 Irish
48 Gaelic
Welsh Group
49 Welsh
50 Breton
H ARMENIAN
51 Armenian
I IRANIAN
Northern Group
52 Ossetinian
Persian Group
53 Persian
54 Tatic
55 Talyshic
Kurdic Luric Group
56 Kurdish
57 Lurish
58 Bakhtiar
*59 Mamasenian
*60 Kuhkgeluyan
*Eastern Group
61 Tajik
62 Khazara
63 Afghan
64 Baluchi

II URALIC
K FINNIC
Northwest Group
65 Finnish
66 Karelian
67 Vepsian
68 Izhorian (Ingrian)
69 Vodian
70 Estonian
71 Livian
Northeast Group
72 Komian (Zyrian)
73 Komi-Permian
74 Udmurtian (Votiak)
Southeast or Volga Group
75 Marian (Cheremissian)
76 Mordvinian-Moksha
77 Mordvinian-Erzia
L SAMOYEDIC
78 Nenets-Samoyedic
M LAPP
79 Lapponian
N UGRIAN
80 Hungarian
81 Khanty-Ostiak
82 Mansi-Vogul

III ALTAIC
O TURKIC
Northwest (Kipchak) Group
83 Karachay
84 Balkar
85 Nogay
86 Kumyk
87 Bashkir
88 Kazakh
*89 Kara-Kalpak
*90 Kirghiz
*91 Altayan
92 Tatar or Tartar
Southwest (Oguz) Group
93 Osman Turks
94 Gagauz
95 Azerbayjanian
96 Turkmenian
*Southeast (Kashgar) Group
97 Uzbek
Turks of S.W. Asia
98 Afshar, Ajar
*99 Kashkey
100 Karapapakh
Chuvash Group
101 Chuvashian
P MONGOLIC
102 Kalmuckian

IV SEMITIC
103 Arabic
104 Assyrian
105 Maltese

V HAMITIC
106 Berberian

VI CAUCASIC
S NORTHWEST GROUP
Circassian
Kabardinian
Abkhasian
T NORTH CENTRAL
(VEYNAKH) GROUP
Ingushian
Chechenian
V NORTHEAST
(DAGHESTAN) Group
Avarian
Darginian
Lakian
Tabassaranian
Lesginian (Kurinian)
W SOUTHERN
(GEORGIAN) GROUP
Swanian or Swanetian
Mingrelian
Lazian
Georgian (Kartwel)

VII BASQUE
107 Basque

*Not shown on map

Relief

Meters		Feet
3050		10 000
1525		5000
610		2000
305		1000
152.5		500
0	Sea Level	0
152.5		500
1525		5000
3050		10 000

Below Sea Level

ICELAND

ATLANTIC OCEAN

ARCTIC

Arctic Circle

LAPLAND

IRELAND

UNITED KINGDOM
BRITISH ISLES

SWEDEN

NORWAY

FINLAND

NORTH SEA

DENMARK
COPENHAGEN
(København)

GERMAN DEM. REP.

POLAND
WARSAW

FRANCE

PARIS

SPAIN
MADRID

PORTUGAL
LISBON
(Lisboa)

MOROCCO

ALGERIA

TUNISIA

MEDITERRANEAN

MALTA

ITALY
ROME
(Roma)

NAPLES
(Napoli)

SICILY

YUGOSLAVIA

ROMANIA
BUCHAREST

BULGARIA

GREECE
ATHENS
(Athinai)

Scale 1: 16 000 000; one inch to 250 miles. Conic Projection

Elevations and depressions are given in feet

Continued on pages 224-225

Longitude West of Greenwich   Longitude East of Greenwich

0 50 100 200 300 400 500 Miles

0 100 200 400 600 800 Kilometers

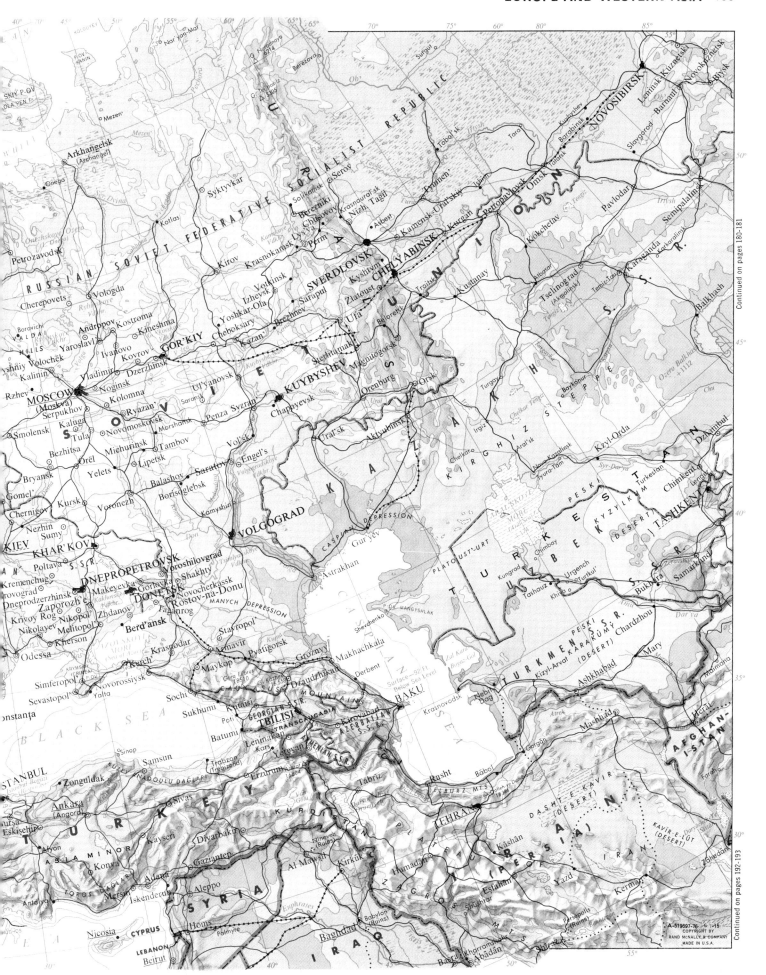

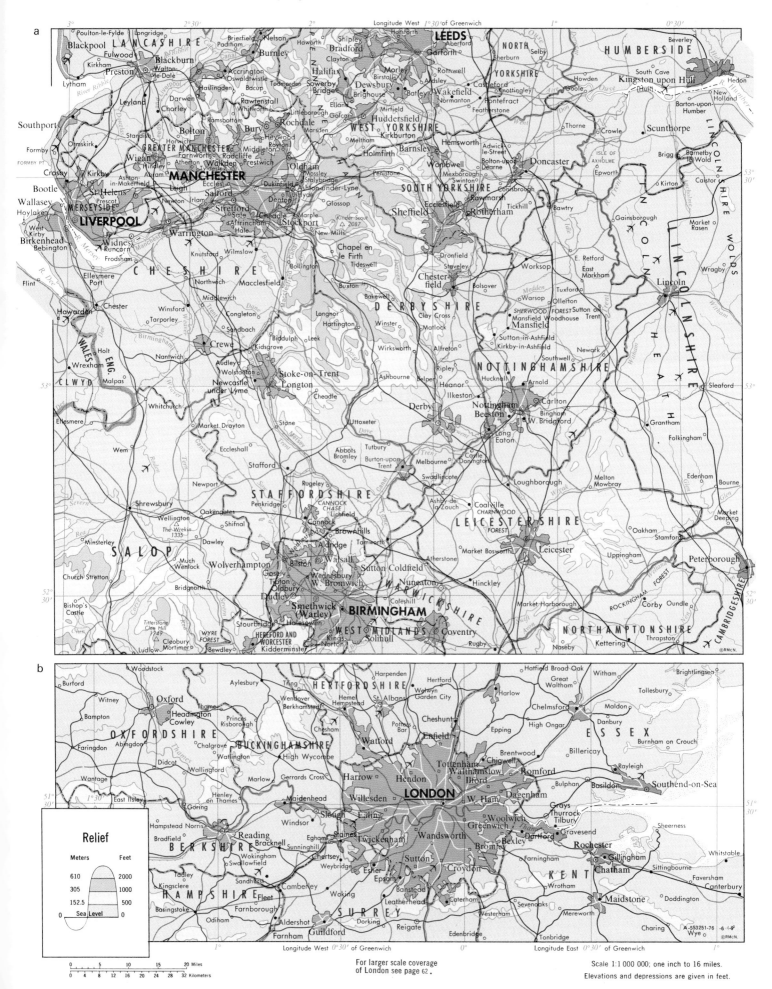

a

Blackpool LANCASHIRE
Poulton-le-Fylde Longridge
Fulwood Brierfield Nelson Shipley LEEDS
Kirkham Padiham Haworth Horsforth
Preston Burnley Bradford NORTH Selby
Blackburn Accrington Oswaldtwistle Clayton Morley YORKSHIRE Howden
Lytham Walton-le-Dale Haslingden Todmorden Sowerby Dewsbury Aidsley Castleford HUMBERSIDE
River Ribble Darwen Rawtenstall Bridge Brighouse Batley Wakefield Knottingley Pontefract Goole South Cave Kingston upon Hull
Southport Leyland Chorley Whitworth Littleborough Elland Mirfield WEST YORKSHIRE Normanton Featherstone Thorne Barton-upon-Humber (Hull) Hedon
Formby Ormskirk Standish Rochdale Marsden Huddersfield Kirkburton Barnsley Crowle Scunthorpe
FORMBY PT Crosby Kirkby Wigan GREATER MANCHESTER Middleton Royton Oldham Meltham Holmfirth Hemsworth Adwick le-Street Bolton-upon Epworth Brigg Barnetby le Wold
Bootle Hindley Abram Walkden Prestwich Penistone Wombwell Mexborough Dearne Conisbrough ISLE OF AXHOLME Kirton Caistor
Wallasey St Helens Leigh MANCHESTER Salford SOUTH YORKSHIRE Swinton Doncaster Market Rasen
LIVERPOOL Prescot Newton Irlam Eccles Dukinfield Ashton-under-Lyne Ecclesfield Rawmarsh Tickhill Bawtry Gainsborough
Hoylake Widnes Stretford Sale Denton Hyde Sheffield Rotherham
West Kirby Birkenhead Runcorn Altrincham Cheadle Marple Glossop Dronfield Staveley Worksop E. Retford East Markham Lincoln Wragby
Bebington Frodsham Hale Stockport New Mills Chesterfield Bolsover Tuxford Sutton on Trent Sleaford
Flint CHESHIRE Knutsford Wilmslow Chapel en le Frith Tideswell Kinder Scout Clay Cross SHERWOOD FOREST Ollerton Mansfield Woodhouse Newark
Ellesmere Port Northwich Macclesfield Bollington Buxton Bakewell Winster Matlock DERBYSHIRE Sutton-in-Ashfield Kirkby-in-Ashfield Southwell
Hawarden Chester Middlewich Congleton Langnor Hartington Wirksworth Alfreton Mansfield
WALES ENG. Tarporley Winsford Sandbach Leek Ashbourne Belper Ripley Hucknall Arnold NOTTINGHAMSHIRE
CLWYD Wrexham Holt Crewe Biddulph Kidsgrove Heanor Ilkeston Nottingham Carlton Bingham Grantham
Malpas Nantwich Audley Wolstanton Stoke-on-Trent Longton Cheadle Derby Beeston W. Bridgford Long Eaton Folkingham
Ellesmere Whitchurch Newcastle under Lyme Stone Uttoxeter Tutbury Burton-upon-Trent Melbourne Castle Donington Loughborough Melton Mowbray Edenham Bourne
Wem Market Drayton Eccleshall Abbots Bromley Swadlincote Ashby-de-la-Zouch Coalville Market Deeping
Newport Stafford Rugeley STAFFORDSHIRE CANNOCK CHASE Lichfield Cannock CHARNWOOD FOREST LEICESTERSHIRE Oakham Stamford Market
Shrewsbury Wellington Oakengates Shifnal Cannock Brownhills Tamworth Atherstone Market Bosworth Leicester Uppingham Peterborough
The Wrekin 1335 Dawley Aldridge Coleshill Nuneaton Hinckley ROCKINGHAM FOREST Oundle
SALOP Minsterley Much Wenlock Wolverhampton Bilston Walsall Sutton Coldfield WARWICKSHIRE Market Harborough Corby Thrapston NORTHAMPTONSHIRE CAMBRIDGESHIRE
Church Stretton Bridgnorth Gosely Tipton Wednesbury W. Bromwich BIRMINGHAM Coventry Rugby Kettering
Bishop's Castle Smethwick (Warley) Halesowen Solihull Naseby
Titterstone Clee Hill 1749 WYRE FOREST Stourbridge Kings Norton WEST MIDLANDS
Cleobury Mortimer HEREFORD AND WORCESTER
Ludlow Bewdley Kidderminster

b
Woodstock Harpenden Hatfield Broad Oak Brightlingsea
Burford Witney Aylesbury Tring HERTFORDSHIRE Hertford Great Waltham Witham Tollesbury
Oxford Thame Wendover Hemel Hempstead Welwyn Garden City Harlow Chelmsford Maldon
Bampton Headington Cowley Princes Risborough Berkhamsted St Albans Potters Bar Cheshunt Epping High Ongar Danbury ESSEX
Witney OXFORDSHIRE BUCKINGHAMSHIRE Chesham Watford Enfield Brentwood Burnham on Crouch
Faringdon Abingdon Chalgrove Watlington High Wycombe Tottenham Chigwell Romford Billericay Rayleigh
Didcot Marlow Gerrards Cross Harrow Walthamstow Ilford Bulphan Basildon Southend-on-Sea
Wantage Wallingford Henley on Thames Maidenhead Willesden LONDON W. Ham Dagenham Grays Thurrock Tilbury Sheerness
East Ilsley Goring Ealing Woolwich Greenwich Dartford Gravesend Whitstable
Windsor Slough Staines Twickenham Wandsworth Bexley Rochester
Reading BERKSHIRE Bracknell Egham Sutton Bromley Farningham Gillingham Chatham Sittingbourne Faversham Canterbury
Hampstead Norris Wokingham Sunninghill Chertsey Weybridge Esher Epsom Croydon KENT Maidstone Doddington
Bradfield Swallowfield Sandhurst Cobham Banstead Caterham Wrotham
HAMPSHIRE Fleet Camberley Woking Leatherhead Sevenoaks Mereworth
Basingstoke Farnborough SURREY Dorking Westerham Charing
Odiham Aldershot Guildford Reigate Edenbridge Tonbridge Wye
Bosingstoke Farnham

Relief

Meters	Feet
610	2000
305	1000
152.5	500
0	Sea Level 0

0 5 10 15 20 Miles
0 4 8 12 16 20 24 28 32 Kilometers

For larger scale coverage
of London see page 62.

Scale 1:1 000 000; one inch to 16 miles.
Elevations and depressions are given in feet.

A-553251-76 -6-1-8
©RMcN

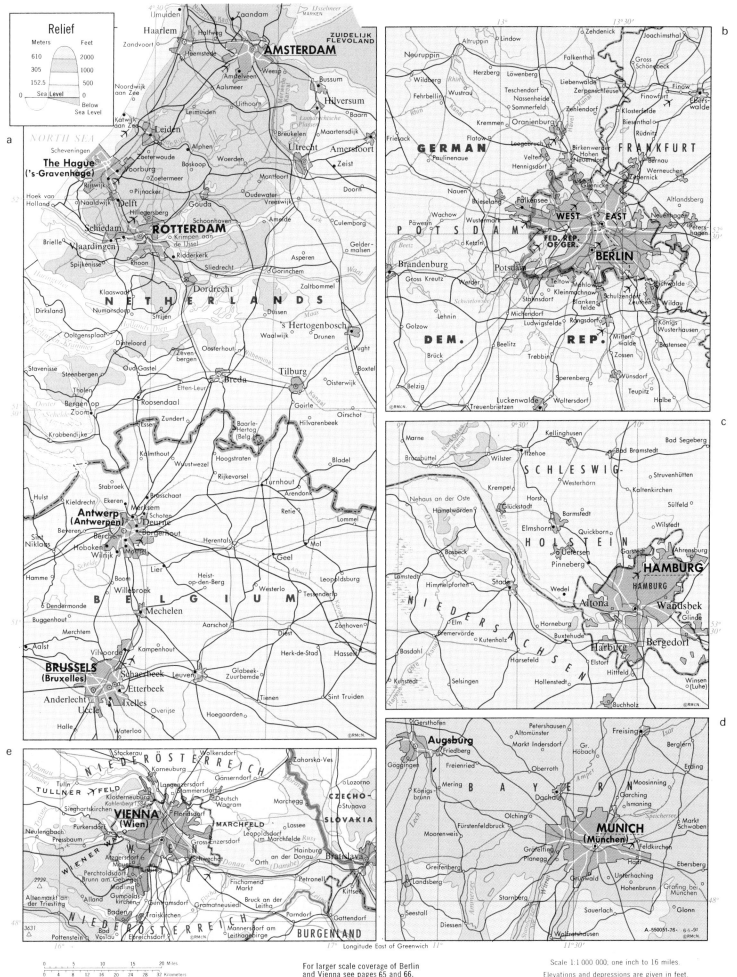

For larger scale coverage of Berlin and Vienna see pages 65 and 66.

Scale 1:1 000 000; one inch to 16 miles.
Elevations and depressions are given in feet.

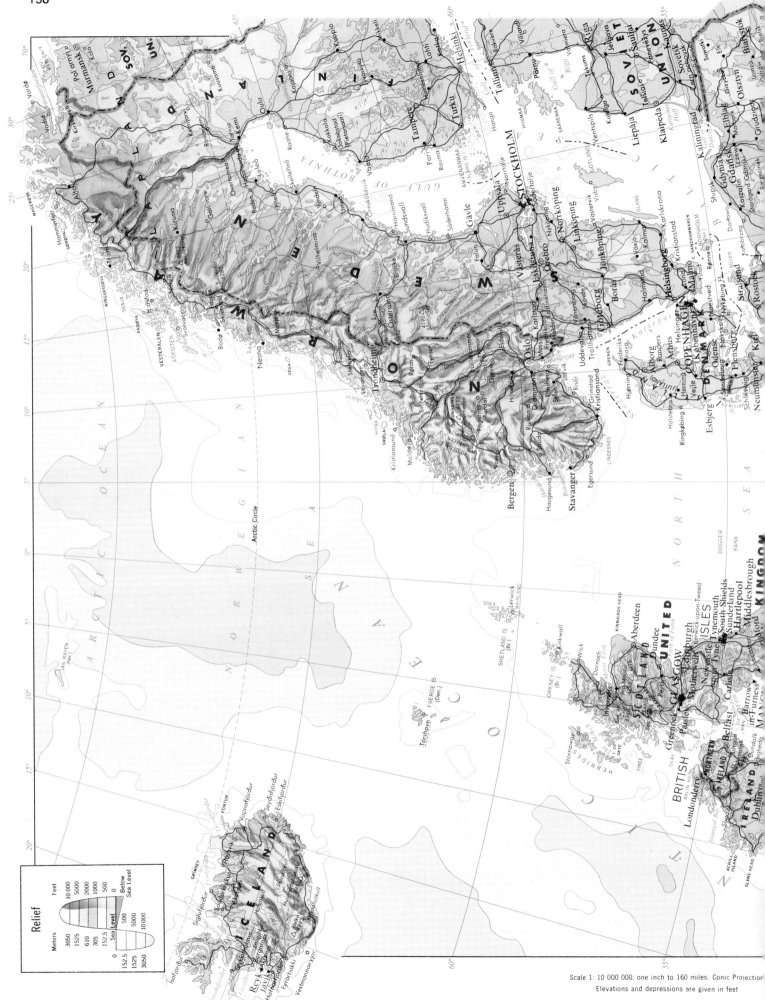

Scale 1: 10 000 000; one inch to 160 miles. Conic Projection
Elevations and depressions are given in feet

A-559400-76 -7-6-14
COPYRIGHT BY RAND McNALLY & COMPANY
MADE IN U.S.A.
Longitude West of Greenwich
Longitude East of Greenwich
0 50 100 150 200 250 300 Miles
0 100 200 300 400 500 Kilometers
FRANCE
SPAIN
PORTUGAL
ITALY
GERMANY
FEDERAL REPUBLIC OF GERMANY
SWITZERLAND
AUSTRIA
HUNGARY
YUGOSLAVIA
ALBANIA
CZECHOSLOVAKIA
POLAND
BELGIUM
NETHERLANDS
ENGLAND
WALES
ALGERIA
TUNISIA
MOROCCO
CORSICA (Fr.)
SARDINIA (It.)
ANDORRA
MONACO
SAN MARINO
MALTA
TYRRHENIAN SEA
IONIAN SEA
LIGURIAN SEA
MEDITERRANEAN SEA
BAY OF BISCAY
ENGLISH CHANNEL
ATLAS MOUNTAINS
SIERRA MORENA
CORDILLERA CANTABRICA
PARIS
MADRID
ROME
LISBON
BERLIN
PRAGUE (Praha)
VIENNA
BUDAPEST
BELGRADE
BRUSSELS
AMSTERDAM
LONDON
ALGIERS
TUNIS
TIRANE

160

Continued on pages 158-159

Relief

Meters		Feet
3050		10000
1525		5000
610		2000
305		1000
152.5		500
Sea Level		0
		Below
		Sea Level
152.5		500
1525		5000
3050		10000

A-558300-76 -12-6-21
COPYRIGHT BY
RAND McNALLY & COMPANY
MADE IN U.S.A.

Longitude West of Greenwich   0°   Longitude East of Greenwich

Scale 1: 10 000 000; one inch to 160 miles. Bonne's Projection
Elevations and depressions are given in feet

Continued on pages 178-179

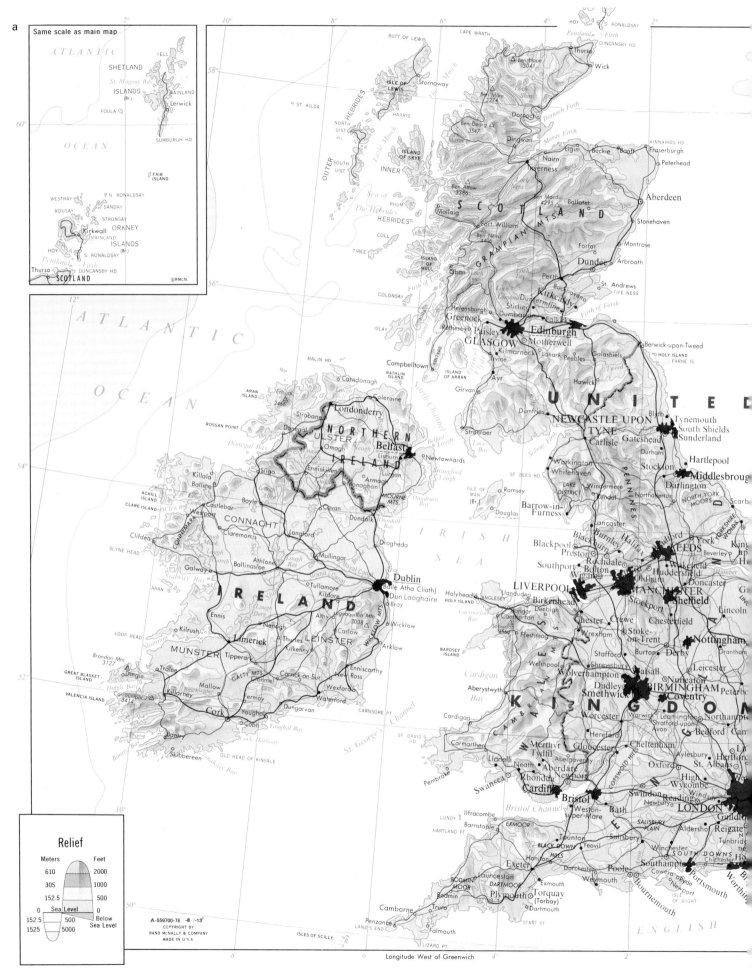

162

Same scale as main map

ATLANTIC

SHETLAND
ISLANDS
(Br.)

Lerwick

YELL

MAINLAND
(Br.)

St. Magnus Bay

FOULA

OCEAN

SUMBURGH HD.

FAIR
ISLAND

WESTRAY

N. RONALDSAY

ROUSAY
SANDAY

STRONSAY

Kirkwall

ORKNEY
ISLANDS
(Br.)

HOY

S. RONALDSAY

Pentland Firth

Thurso

SCOTLAND

DUNCANSBY HD.

©RMcN.

ATLANTIC

OCEAN

SCALE

Relief

Meters		Feet
610		2000
305		500
152.5		500
0	Sea Level	0
152.5	500	Below
1525	5000	Sea Level

A-559700-76 -8 /-13²
COPYRIGHT BY
RAND McNALLY & COMPANY
MADE IN U.S.A

Longitude West of Greenwich

Scale 1: 4 000 000; one inch to 64 miles. Conic Project
Elevations and depressions are given in feet

NORWAY
Egersund
Arendal
Flekkefjord
Grimstad
Lillesand
Farsund
Kristiansand
Mandal
LINDESNES

Kungälv Alingsås
Ulricehamn
Göteborg
Mölndal
Borås

SWEDEN

Varberg
Folkenberg
Oskarström

Skagerrak
Hirtshals
Hjørring
Skagen
GRENEN
Frederikshavn
LÆSØ
Brønderslev
Bolmen
Kattegat
Halmstad
Laholm

Thisted
Ålborg
Løgstør
Hobro
Mariager
Grenå
Ängelholm
Helsingborg
Helsingør
Landskrona

Skive
Viborg
Randers
ANHOLT

Nissum Fjord
JYLLAND
Struer
Holstebro
Silkeborg
Århus
Skanderborg
Nykøbing S
Hillerød
COPENHAGEN
København

N O R T H

Ringkøbing
Herning
Horsens
Roskilde
Lund
Malmö

Ringkøbing Fjord
Vejle
Fredericia
DENMARK
SJÆLLAND
Ringsted
Holbæk
Kalundborg
Køge
Trelleborg

Varde
Esbjerg
Kolding
Middelfart
Bogense
Slagelse
Næstved

FANØ
Ribe
Haderslev
Assens
Nyborg
Korsør
Vordingborg
MØN

RØMØ
Åbenrå
FYN
Fåborg
Svendborg
Rudkøbing
Nakskov
Nykøbing
FALSTER
Tønder
Sønderborg
Maribo

O G G E R
BANK
60—120 Ft.
ALS
LANGELAND
LOLLAND

S E A

SYLT
Flensburg
AERØ
BALTIC SEA
FØHR
Schleswig
SCHLESWIG
Husum
Kiel Bay
FEHMARN

Eckernförde
Rendsburg
Neustadt
in Holstein

HELGOLAND
Tønning
Heide
KIEL
HOLSTEIN
Lübecker Bucht
Rostock

Cuxhaven
Itzehoe
Bad Oldesloe
Neumünster
Lübeck
Wismar
Güstrow

ISLANDS
NORDERNEY LANGEOOG
Bremerhaven
Stade
Elmshorn
Schwerin
GERMAN
Parchim

FRISIAN
JUIST
Norden
HAMBURG
Schweriner See
MECKLENBURG
Pritzwalk
DEMOCRATIC

Wilhelmshaven
Emden
Lüneburg
LÜNEBURGER
Ludwigslust
Wittenberge
REPUBLIC

TERSCHELLING
AMELAND
BORKUM
Leer
Bremen
HEIDE
Uelzen
Salzwedel
Havel

VLIELAND
Harlingen
Leeuwarden
Delfzijl
Groningen
Oldenburg
Papenburg
Verden
NIEDERSACHSEN
Stendal
Tangermünde

TEXEL
Waddenzee
Assen
Emmen
Meppen
Lingen
Nienburg
Celle
Gardelegen

Den Helder
IJsselmeer
Meppel
Nordhorn
Hannover
Braunschweig

Alkmaar
NETHERLANDS
Zwolle
Almelo
Rheine
Minden
Hameln
Hildesheim
Wolfenbüttel
Magdeburg
Schönebeck

Zaandam
Haarlem
AMSTERDAM
Apeldoorn
Hengelo
Gronau
Osnabrück
Herford
Bielefeld
Detmold
Northeim
Quedlinburg
Aschersleben

Leiden
Utrecht
Deventer
Enschede
Münster
Gütersloh
Einbeck
Blankenburg
Bernburg

The Hague
('s-Gravenhage)
Delft
Arnhem
Ahlen
Paderborn
Göttingen
Nordhausen
Sangerhausen
Halle
Merseburg

Vlaardingen
Dordrecht
Nijmegen
Kleve
Hamm
Heiligenstadt
Sondershausen

ROTTERDAM
Bergen
op Zoom
Breda
's Hertogenbosch
Wesel
Gelsenkirchen
Dortmund
Arnsberg
Kassel
Eschwege
THÜRINGEN
Weimar

Vlissingen
Tilburg
Helmond
Oberhausen
Duisburg
ESSEN
Hagen
Iserlohn
Eisenach
Erfurt
Jena

Southend-
on-Sea
Roosendaal
Eindhoven
Weert
Mönchengladbach
Lüdenscheid
Wuppertal
Marburg
an der Lahn
Gotha
Arnstadt
Rudolstadt

Margate
Oostende
Brugge
Gent
Turnhout
ANTWERP
DÜSSELDORF
NORDRHEIN-WESTFALEN
COLOGNE
(Köln)
Siegen
Gummersbach
Bad Hersfeld
Schmalkalden
Zella-Mehlis
Suhl

Canterbury
Dover
Dunkerque
Mechelen
Düren
Bonn
Siegburg
Meiningen
Hildburghausen
Sonneberg
Neustadt b.C.
Coburg

Calais
FLANDERS
Torhout
Roeselare
Leuven
Maastricht
Aachen
Eupen
Ahrweiler
Netphen
Giessen
Fulda

Boulogne-
sur-Mer
Ieper
Kortrijk
BRUSSELS
Liège
Verviers
Spa
Andernach
Koblenz
Limburg
an der Lahn
FRANKFURT
AM MAIN
Schweinfurt
Bayreuth

Étaples
Béthune
Lille
Roubaix
Nivelles
Namur
Serang
Malmédy
RHEINLAND-
PFALZ
Bad
Kreuznach
Offenbach
Bamberg

Arras
Douai
Denain
Charleroi
Dinant
EIFEL
Wittlich
Bingen
Wiesbaden
Darmstadt
Würzburg
Erlangen

St. Valéry-
sur-Somme
Le Tréport
Abbeville
Cambrai
Maubeuge
Haumont
Givet
Fourmies
Bastogne
ARDENNES
LUX
Kirn
Bad
Main
Aschaffenburg

FRANCE
BELGIUM
Mons

10 20 30 40 50 60 70 80 90 100 110 120 Miles
20 40 60 80 100 120 140 160 180 200 Kilometers

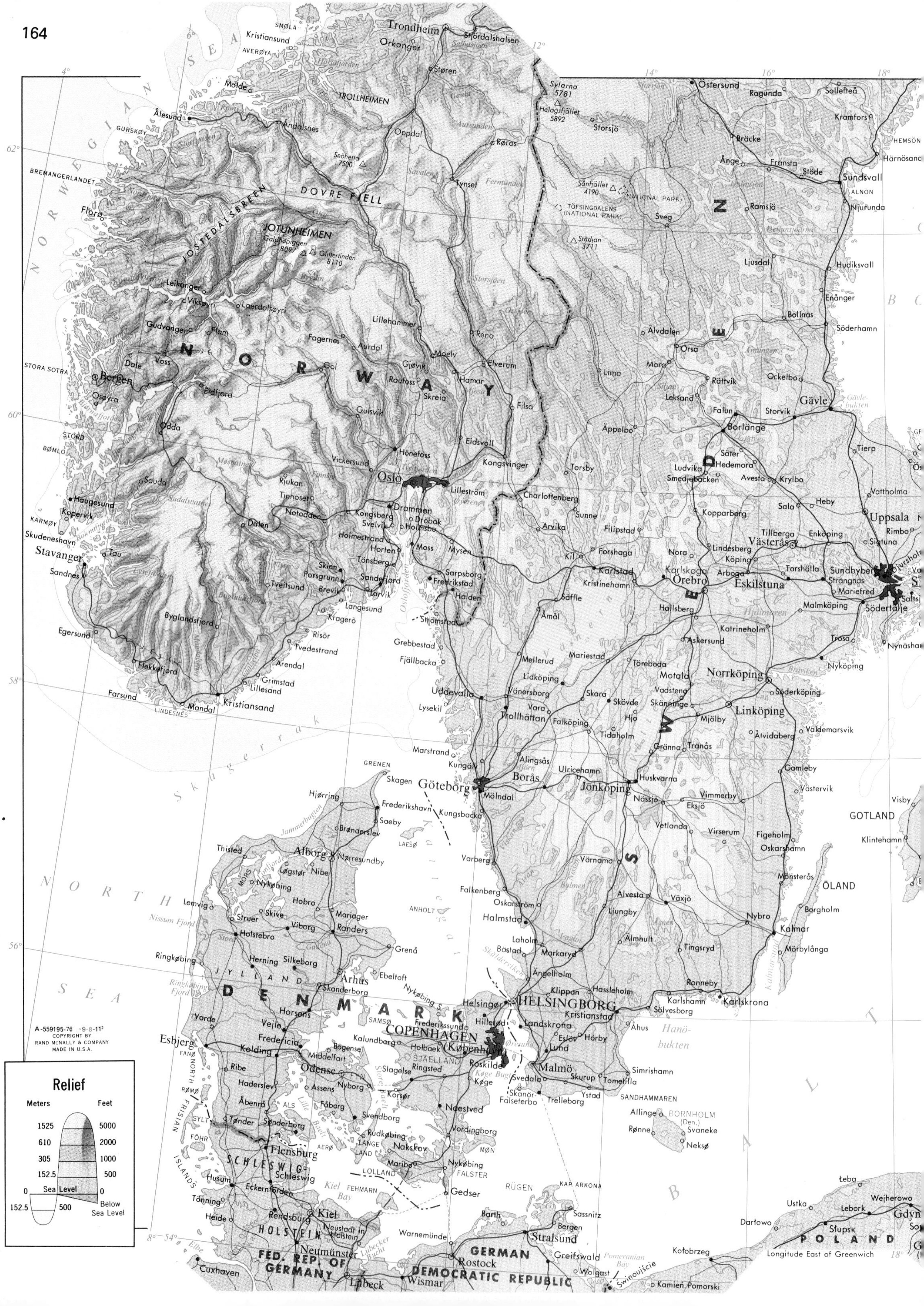

NORWEGIAN SEA

SMØLA
Kristiansund
Trondheim
Stjørdalshalsen
Orkanger
Averøya
Molde
TROLLHEIMEN
Åndalsnes
Oppdal
Støren
Røros
Østersund
Ragunda
Sollefteå
Sylarna 5781
Storsjön
HEMSÖN
Ålesund
GURSKØY
Snøhetta 7500
Tynset
Fermunden
Helagsfjället 5892
Storsjö
Kramfors
Härnösand
DOVRE FJELL
Sänfjället 4190 (NATIONAL PARK)
Ånge
Fransta
Stöde
Sundsvall
ALNÖN
Njurunda
BREMANGERLANDET
Floro
Aursunden
Töfsingdalens (NATIONAL PARK)
Sveg
Ramsjö

JOTUNHEIMEN
Galdhøpiggen 8097
Glittertinden 8110
JOSTEDALSBREEN
Stödjan 3711
Ljusdal
Hudiksvall

Leikanger
Viksøyri
Laerdalsøyri
Lillehammer
Rena
Älvdalen
Orsa
Enånger
Söderhamn
Gudvangen
Flåm
Fagernes
Aurdal
Moelv
Elverum
Mora
Ockelbo
Dale
Voss
NORWAY
Gol
Gjøvik
Hamar
Lima
Leksand
Rättvik
Gävle
Borgen
Raufoss
Skreia
Filsa
Äppelbo
Siljan
Gävlebukten
Osøyra
Etdfjord
Gulsvik
Falun
Storvik
STORA SOTRA
Odda
Eidsvoll
Ludvika
Hedemora
Borlänge
Säter
Tierp
STORD
Vickersund
Hönefoss
Kongsvinger
Torsby
Smedjebacken
Avesta
Krylbo
Vattholma
BØMLO
Rjukan
Tinnoset
Oslo
Lillestrøm
Charlottenberg
Sunne
Filipstad
Sala
Heby
Uppsala
Haugesund
Notodden
Kongsberg
Drammen
Arvika
Kil
Kopparberg
Nora
Lindesberg
Köping
Rimbo
Kopervik
Svelvik
Holmbu
Kristinehamn
Forshaga
Tillberga
Enköping
Sigtuna
KARMØY
Sauda
Holmestrand
Horten
Moss
Mysen
Karlstad
Karlskoga
Örebro
Arboga
Västerås
Torshälla
Sundbyberg
Skudeneshavn
Skien
Porsgrunn
Tønsberg
Sarpsborg
Säffle
Eskilstuna
Strängnäs
Mariefred
Stavanger
Tveitsund
Brevik
Sandefjord
Fredrikstad
Åmål
Hallsberg
Malmköping
Södertälje
Sandnes
Larvik
Halden
Mellerud
Askersund
Katrineholm
Trosa
Langesund
Strömstad
Mariestad
Motala
Söderköping
Nynäshamn
Egersund
Kragerø
Töreboda
Norrköping
Nyköping
Risør
Grebbestad
Skövde
Vadstena
Skänninge
Flekkefjord
Tvedestrand
Fjällbacka
Lidköping
Skara
Hjo
Mjölby
Linköping
Arendal
Uddevalla
Vänersborg
Vara
Tidaholm
Gränna
Tranås
Åtvidaberg
Farsund
Grimstad
Lillesand
Lysekil
Trollhättan
Falköping
Valdemarsvik
LINDESNES
Mandal
Kristiansand
Marstrand
Alingsås
Ulricehamn
Gamleby
Västervik
GRENEN
Kungälv
Borås
Jönköping
Nässjö
Vimmerby
Visby
Skagen
Göteborg
Mölndal
Eksjö
GOTLAND
Hjørring
Frederikshavn
Kungsbacka
Vetlanda
Virserum
Figeholm
Klintehamn
Saeby
LAESØ
Varberg
Värnamo
Oskarshamn
Thisted
Brønderslev
Falkenberg
Oskarström
Alvesta
Mönsterås
Ålborg
Nørresundby
Halmstad
Ljungby
Växjö
ÖLAND
Løgstør
Nibe
ANHOLT
Laholm
Markaryd
Almhult
Nybro
Borgholm
Nykøbing
Hobro
Båstad
Tingsryd
Kalmar
Lemvig
Struer
Skive
Mariager
Randers
Ängelholm
Ronneby
Mörbylånga
Holstebro
Viborg
Grenå
Klippan
Hässleholm
Karlshamn
Karlskrona
Ringkøbing
Herning
Silkeborg
Ebeltoft
Helsingør
Helsingborg
Kristianstad
Sölvesborg
JYLLAND
Århus
Skanderborg
Nykøbing
Landskrona
Eslöv
Hörby
Åhus
Hanöbukten
Yarde
Horsens
SAMSØ
Frederikssund
Hillerød
COPENHAGEN
København
Landskrona
Lund
Simrishamn
Esbjerg
FANØ
Vejle
Fredericia
Kalundborg
Holbaek
Roskilde
Malmö
DENMARK
Kolding
Middelfart
SJAELLAND
Køge
Skurup
Tomelilla
Ribe
Bogense
Odense
Slagelse
Ringsted
Svedala
Ystad
SANDHAMMAREN
Haderslev
Assens
FYN
Nyborg
Korsør
Naestved
Skanör-Falsterbo
Trelleborg
Allinge
BORNHOLM (Den.)
Åbenrå
Fåborg
Svendborg
Vordingborg
Rønne
Svaneke
ALS
Sønderborg
LANGE LAND
Rudkøbing
Nakskov
MØN
Nyköbing FALSTER
Neksø
NORTH FRISIAN ISLANDS
SYLT
Tønder
Aerø
LOLLAND
Maribo
FØHR
Husum
Flensburg
Schleswig
Gedser
RÜGEN
KAP ARKONA
Eckernførde
Sassnitz
Tønning
SCHLESWIG-HOLSTEIN
Rendsburg
Kiel
Neustadt in Holstein
Barth
Bergen
Dartowo
Łeba
Wejherowo
Heide
Kiel Bay
FEHMARN
Warnemünde
Stralsund
Greifswald
Wolgast
Kołobrzeg
Ustka
Lebork
GDY...
Neumünster
FED. REP. OF GERMANY
Cuxhaven
Lübecker Bucht
GERMAN DEMOCRATIC REPUBLIC
Rostock
Greifswald
Swinoujście
Słupsk
POLAND
Elbe
Lübeck
Wismar
Kamień Pomorski
Longitude East of Greenwich

SKAGERRAK
KATTEGAT
NORTH SEA
BALTIC SEA
Jammerbugten
Nissum Fjord
Ringkøbing Fjord

Relief

Meters	Feet
1525	5000
610	2000
305	1000
152.5	500
0 Sea Level	0
152.5	500 Below Sea Level

A-559195-76 · 9-8-11²
COPYRIGHT BY
RAND McNALLY & COMPANY
MADE IN U.S.A.

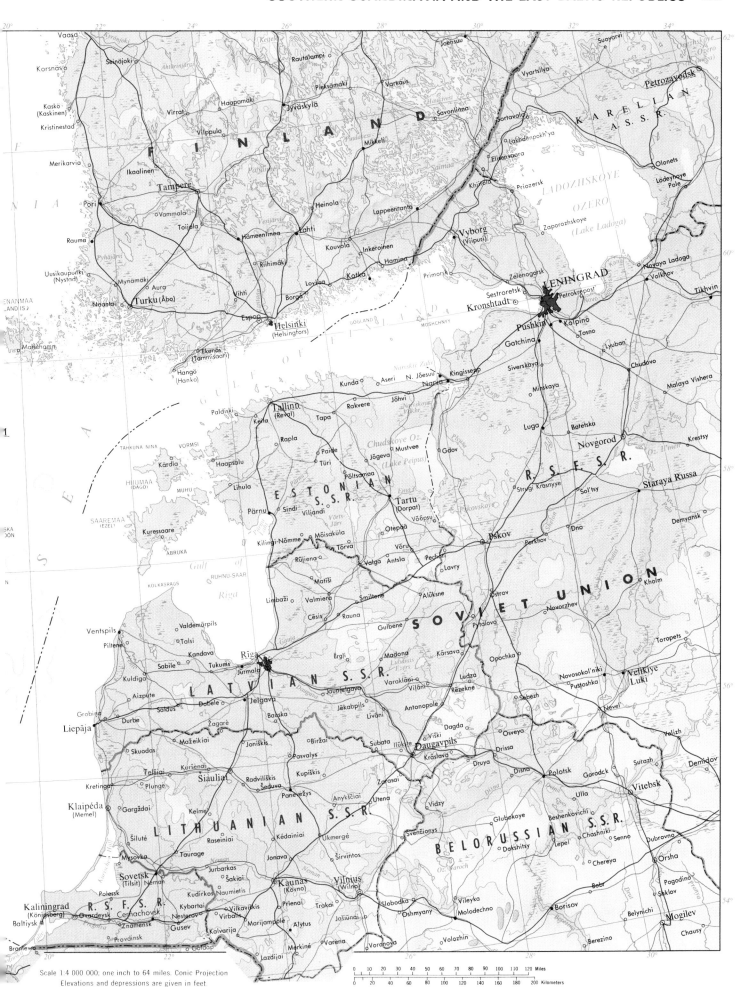

Scale 1:4 000 000; one inch to 64 miles. Conic Projection
Elevations and depressions are given in feet.

Continued on pages 168-169

Continued on pages 172-173

Scale 1:4 000 000, one inch to 64 miles. Conic Projection
Elevations and depressions are given in feet

Longitude East of Greenwich

Relief

Meters		Feet
3050		10 000
1525		5000
610		2000
305		1000
152.5		500
	Sea Level	0
152.5		500
1525		5000

A-550900-76-3-7-5-10²
COPYRIGHT BY
RAND McNALLY & COMPANY
MADE IN U.S.A.

a

Scale 1:1 000 000

Scale 1:4 000 000; one inch to 64 miles. Conic Project
Elevations and depressions are given in feet

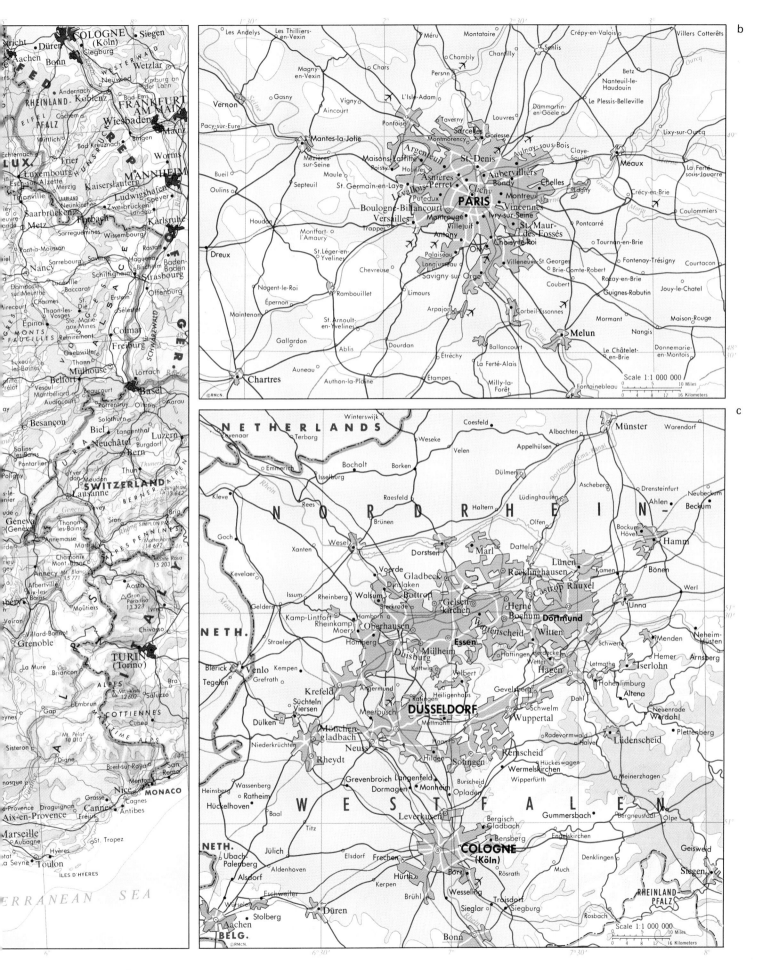

For larger scale coverage of Düsseldorf and Paris see pages 63 and 64.

Scale 1:4 000 000, one inch to 64 miles. Conic Projection
Elevations and depressions are given in feet

Longitude West of Greenwich

FRANCE

Toulouse · Montpellier · Béziers · Carcassonne · Narbonne · Perpignan

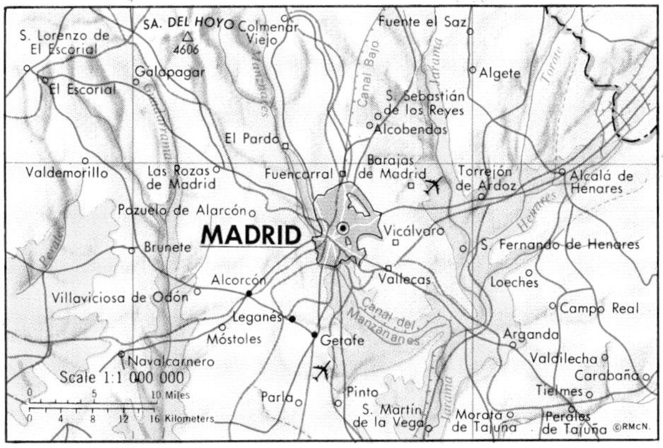

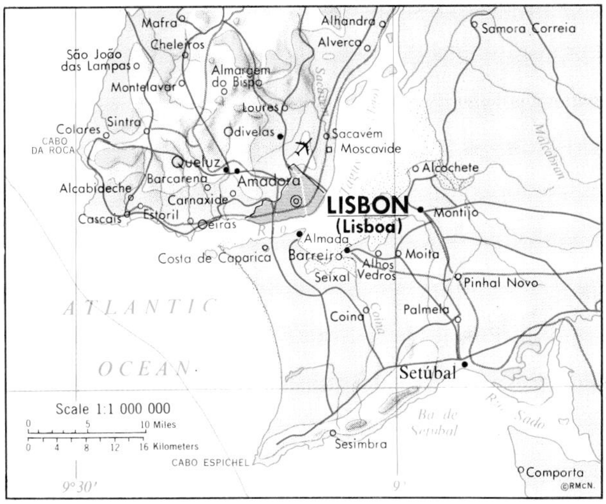

Golfe du Lion

PYRENEES · ANDORRA · Pico de Aneto · Mt. Perdido

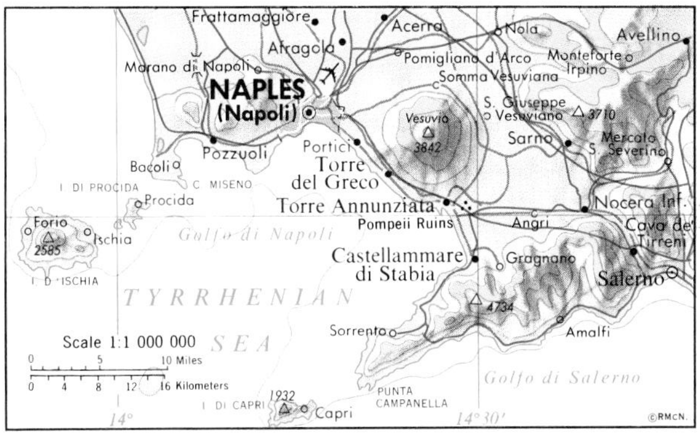

CATALUÑA (CATALONIA)

Lérida · Tarrasa · Sabadell · **BARCELONA** · Badalona · Mataró · Gerona · Manresa · Granollers · Reus · Tarragona · Villanueva y Geltrú

BALEARIC SEA · CABO DE TORTOSA

Castellón de la Plana · Valencia · Sagunto · Alicante · Elche · Torrevieja

ISLAS BALEARES (BALEARIC ISLANDS)

MENORCA (MINORCA) · Mahón · Ciudadela · MALLORCA (MAJORCA) · Palma · Manacor · Felanitx · CABRERA · IBIZA (IVIZA) · San Antonio Abad · Sta. Eulalia del Río · FORMENTERA

MEDITERRANEAN SEA

Algiers (Alger) · Blida · Médéa · Miliana · El Asnam (Orléansville) · Mostaganem · Mascara

ATLAS MOUNTAINS · **ALGERIA**

Longitude East of Greenwich

---

a — MADRID

S. DEL HOYO · El Escorial · Las Rozas de Madrid · Pozuelo de Alarcón · Alcorcón · Leganés · Móstoles · Getafe · Parla · Pinto · Vallecas · Vicálvaro · Alcalá de Henares · Torrejón de Ardoz · Barajas · Arganda

Scale 1:1 000 000 · 0 5 10 Miles · 0 4 8 12 16 Kilometers · ©RMcN

b — LISBON (Lisboa)

Mafra · Sintra · Queluz · Amadora · Estoril · Cascais · Barreiro · Seixal · Almada · Setúbal · Sesimbra · CABO DA ROCA · CABO ESPICHEL

ATLANTIC OCEAN · Baía de Setúbal

Scale 1:1 000 000 · 0 5 10 Miles · 0 4 8 12 16 Kilometers · ©RMcN

c — NAPLES (Napoli)

Afragola · Acerra · Nola · Avellino · Pozzuoli · Portici · Torre del Greco · Torre Annunziata · Pompeii Ruins · Castellammare di Stabia · Salerno · Amalfi · Sorrento · Vesuvius 3842 · Capri · I. DI CAPRI · I. DI ISCHIA · Ischia · Procida

Gulfo di Napoli · TYRRHENIAN SEA · Gulfo di Salerno

Scale 1:1 000 000 · 0 5 10 Miles · 0 4 8 12 16 Kilometers · ©RMcN

d — ROME (Roma) · VATICAN CITY

Tivoli · Guidonia · Mentana · Monterotondo · Frascati · Marino · Albano Laziale · Genzano di Roma · Velletri · Lanuvio · Aprilia · Anzio · Nettuno · Fiumicino · Ostia Antica · Lido di Roma · Pomezia · Cerveteri · Ladispoli

TYRRHENIAN SEA · COLLI ALBANI · AGRO PONTINO

Scale 1:1 000 000 · 0 5 10 Miles · 0 4 8 12 16 Kilometers · ©RMcN

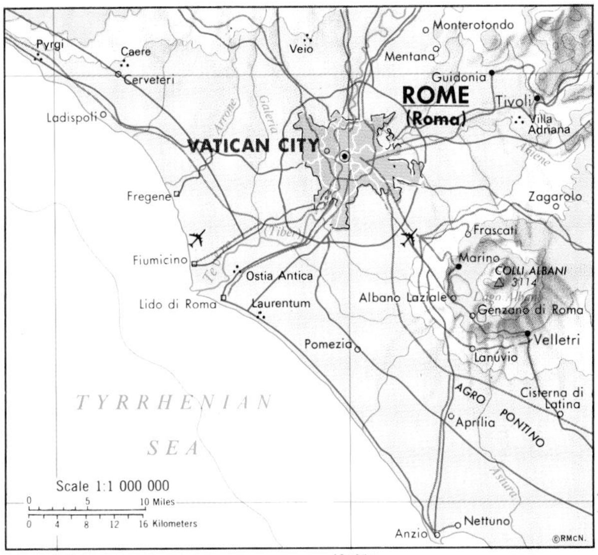

For larger scale coverage of Lisbon, Madrid, and Rome see pages 65 and 66.

Continued on pages 166-167

Continued on pages 168-169

a

Same scale
as main map

Scale 1:4 000 000; one inch to 64 miles. Conic Projection
Elevations and depressions are given in feet

Relief

Feet				
5000	2000	1000	500	0

Meters				Sea Level
1525	610	305	152.5	0
				152.5
				500

Cities
and
Towns

0 to 50,000   500,000 to 1,000,000

50,000 to 500,000   1,000,000 and over

Scale 1:4 000 000, one inch to 64 miles. Conic Projec
Elevations and depressions are given in feet

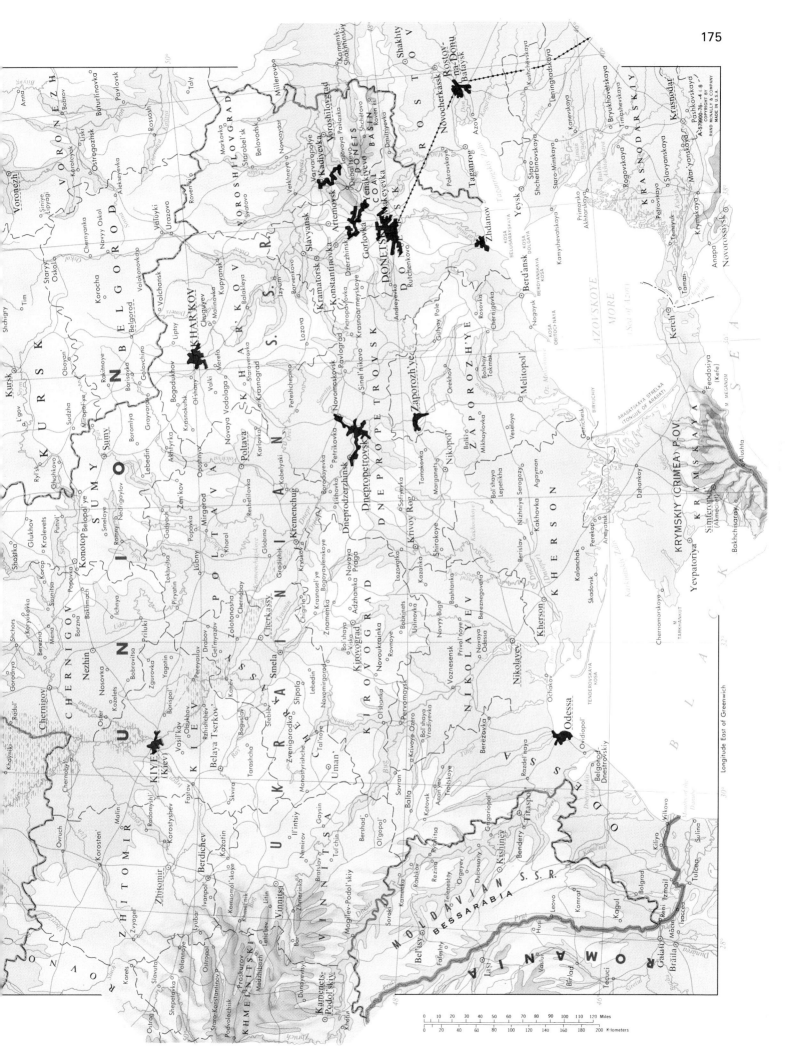

Scale 1:20 000 000; one inch to 315 Proj
Lambert's Azimuthal, Equal Area Proje
Elevations and depressions are given in

Scale 1:10 000 000; one inch to 160 miles. Conic Projection
Elevations and depressions are given in feet.

Continued on pages 160-161

SEVERNAYA ZEMLYA
(NORTHERN LAND)

MALYY TAMIR

M. CHELYUSKIN

NOVOSIBIRSKIYE O.VA
(NEW SIBERIAN ISLANDS)

NOVAYA SIBIR

FADDEYA

BEL'KOVSKIY

KOTEL-NYY

MALYY
LYAKHOVSKIYE

LYAKHOVSKIYE

BYRRANGA
TAYMYR

M. SVYATOY
NOS

STOLBOVOY

BOL'SHOY
BEGICHEV

Nordvik

M. BUOR
KHAYA

Tiksi

Ust'-Olenëk

Kazach'ye

Alloykha

Nizhne-Kolymsk

Ambarchik

Arctic Circle

Bulun

Srenne-
Kolymsk

Markova

Anadyr'

Zashiversk

Zyryanka

Penzhino

Ust'-Panzhino

Gizhiga

Thichki

Abyy

Zhigansk

Verkhoyansk

Gora Chen
10,171

KHREBET CHERSKOGO

Magadan

Yamsk

Ust'-Kamchatsk
Klyuchevskaya
(Vol)
15,584

M. OLYUTORSKIY

Palana

Verkhne-
Kamchatsk

KAMCHATKA

Vilyuysk

Yakutsk

Aldanskaya

Oymyakon

KARAGIN

Petropavlovsk-
Kamchatskiy

Suntar

Amga

Ust'-Maya

Okhotsk

Ust'-Bol'sheretsk

Mukhtuya

Olëkminsk

Tommot

Nel'kan

Ayan

Peleduy

Vitim

PATOM
5377

Aldan

Golets-Purpula
PLATEAU

ALDAN
PLATEAU

DZHUGDZHUR KHREBET

M. YELIZAVETY

Bodaybo

Golets-
Skalistyy
9186

STANOVOY KHREBET

Chumikan

SHANTAR

Okha

SAKHALIN
(Sov. Union)

KURIL ISLANDS
(Sov. Union)

Nikolayevsk-
na-Amure

Nizhne-Angarsk

BURYAT

Tyndinskiy

Aleksandrovsk

Komsomol'sk-
na-Amure

Poronaysk

M. TERPENIYA

Barguzin

Zeya

Skovorodino

Beketova

Uglegorsk

A.S.S.R.

KHREBET
BUREINSKIY

Malmyzh

Sovetskaya
Gavan'

Dolinsk

Ulan-Ude

Chita

Sretensk

Nerchinsk

Nerchinskiy
Zavod

Svobodnyy

Belogorsk

Ust'-Tyrma

Bureya

Birobidzhan

Khabarovsk

Yuzhno-Sakhalinsk

Kholmsk

Petrovsk-
Zabaykal'skiy

Baley

Zavitinsk

Raychikhinsk

YEVREY
AUT.
OBLAST

Korsakov

Kyakhta

Aginskoye

Blagoveshchensk

Aihun

Ulan Bator
(Ulaanbaatar)

Aksha

Borzya

Manzhouli

Hailar

Goukou

Longzhen

KHINGAN RANGE

Dalnerechensk

NEI
MONGGOL

GREATER KHINGAN RANGE

Qiqihar

Yilan

Swifenho

Spassk-Dal'niy
Arsen'yev

Ussuriysk

Artëm

Ol'ga

SIKHOTE ALIN'

Choybalsan

Ondörhaan

HEILUNGKIANG

Hulan

HARBIN

Ning an

Suchan

Nakhodka

Vladivostok

JAPAN

HOKKAIDO

Continued on pages 198-199

50 100 200 300 400 500 Miles
100 200 400 600 800 Kilometers

Relief

Meters	Feet
3050	10000
1525	5000
610	2000
305	1000
152.5	500
Sea Level	0
152.5	500
1525	5000
3050	10000

A-579300-76- -8-II°
COPYRIGHT BY
RAND McNALLY & COMPANY
MADE IN U.S.A.

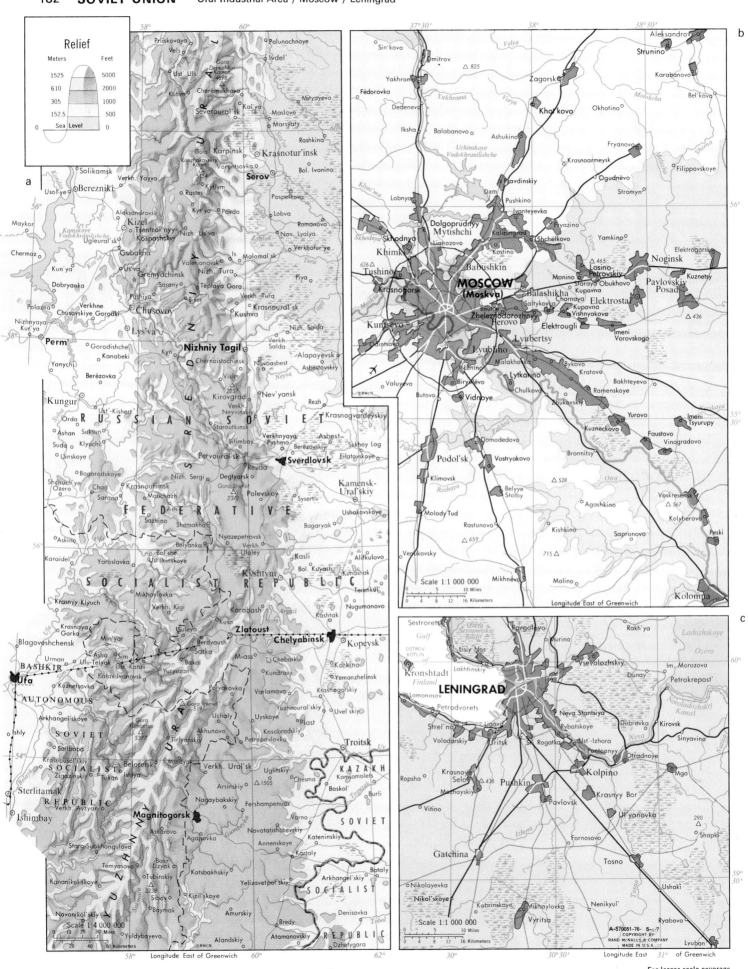

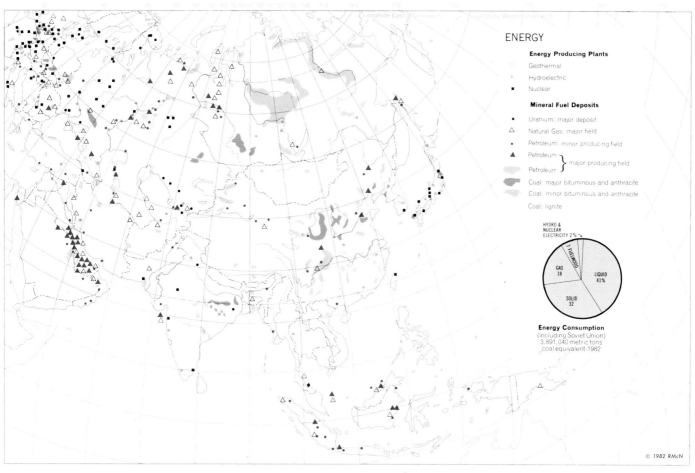

ENERGY

Energy Producing Plants

△ Geothermal

• Hydroelectric

■ Nuclear

Mineral Fuel Deposits

• Uranium: major deposit

△ Natural Gas: major field

• Petroleum: minor producing field

▲ Petroleum } major producing field

Petroleum }

Coal: major bituminous and anthracite

Coal: minor bituminous and anthracite

Coal: lignite

HYDRO & NUCLEAR ELECTRICITY 2%

FUELWOOD

GAS 18

LIQUID 41%

SOLID 32

Energy Consumption
(including Soviet Union)
3,891,040 metric tons
coal equivalent·1982

© 1982 RMcN

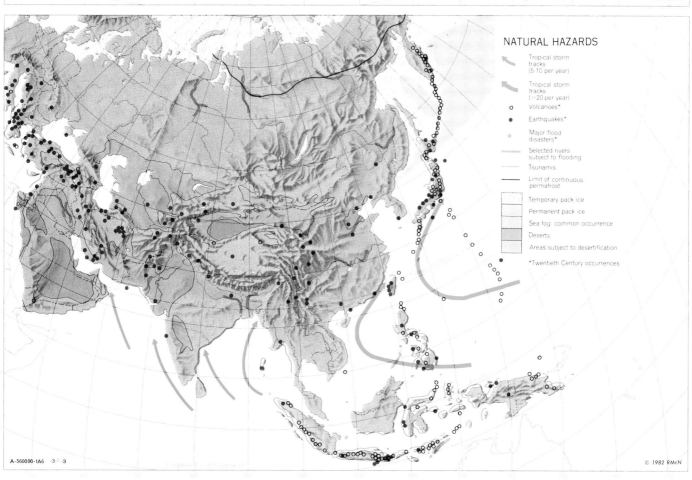

NATURAL HAZARDS

Tropical storm tracks (5-10 per year)

Tropical storm tracks (>20 per year)

○ Volcanoes*

● Earthquakes*

● Major flood disasters*

Selected rivers subject to flooding

Tsunamis

Limit of continuous permafrost

Temporary pack ice

Permanent pack ice

Sea fog: common occurrence

Deserts

Areas subject to desertification

*Twentieth Century occurrences

A-560000-1A6 -3 -3

© 1982 RMcN

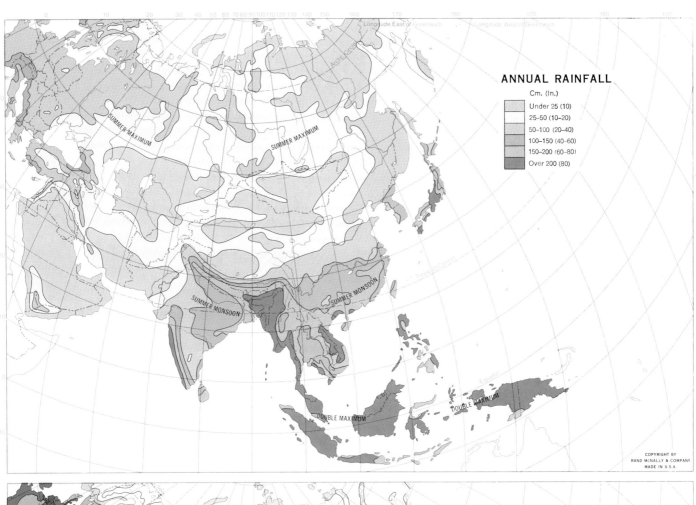

ANNUAL RAINFALL

Cm. (In.)

- Under 25 (10)
- 25–50 (10–20)
- 50–100 (20–40)
- 100–150 (40–60)
- 150–200 (60–80)
- Over 200 (80)

SUMMER MAXIMUM

SUMMER MAXIMUM

SUMMER MONSOON

SUMMER MONSOON

SUMMER MONSOON

DOUBLE MAXIMUM

DOUBLE MAXIMUM

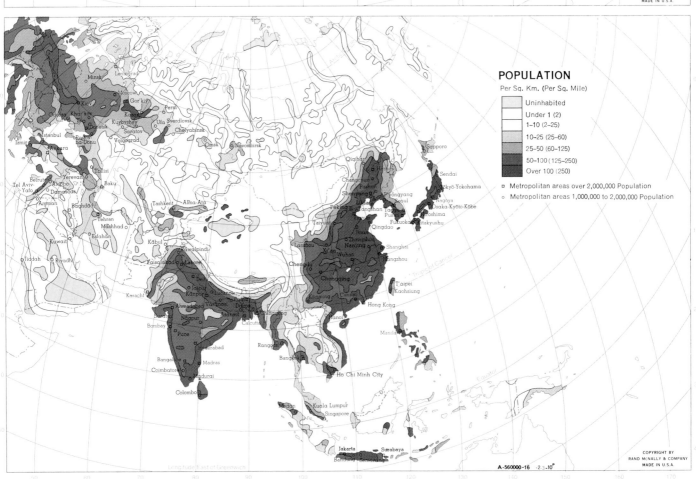

POPULATION

Per Sq. Km. (Per Sq. Mile)

- Uninhabited
- Under 1 (2)
- 1–10 (2–25)
- 10–25 (25–60)
- 25–50 (60–125)
- 50–100 (125–250)
- Over 100 (250)

□ Metropolitan areas over 2,000,000 Population

○ Metropolitan areas 1,000,000 to 2,000,000 Population

A-560000-16 -2-3-10"

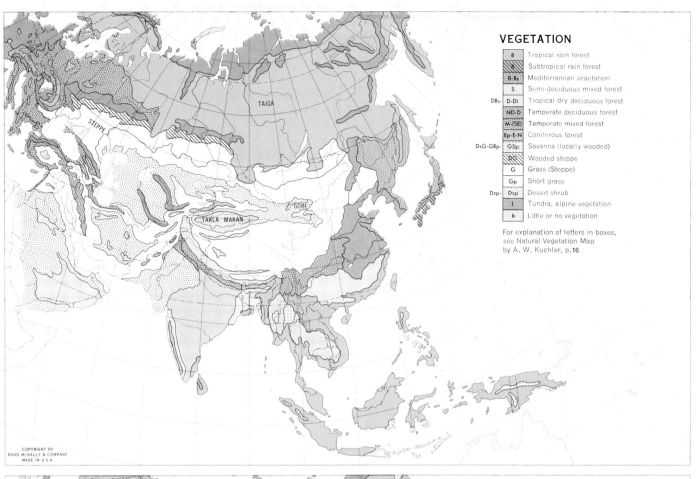

VEGETATION

B	Tropical rain forest
	Subtropical rain forest
B-Bs	Mediterranean vegetation
S	Semi-deciduous mixed forest
DBs- D-Di	Tropical dry deciduous forest
ND-D	Temperate deciduous forest
M-(SE)	Temperate mixed forest
Ep-E-N	Coniferous forest
DsG-GBp- GSp	Savanna (locally wooded)
DG	Wooded steppe
G	Grass (Steppe)
Gp	Short grass
Dzp- Dzp	Desert shrub
L	Tundra, alpine vegetation
b	Little or no vegetation

For explanation of letters in boxes,
see Natural Vegetation Map
by A. W. Kuchler, p.16

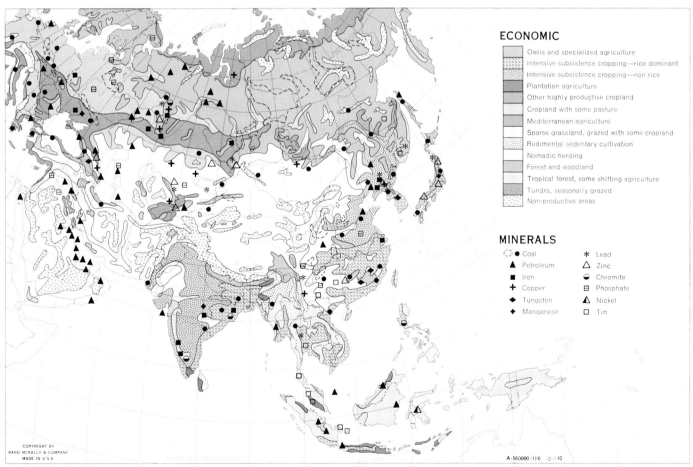

ECONOMIC

	Oasis and specialized agriculture
	Intensive subsistence cropping—rice dominant
	Intensive subsistence cropping—non rice
	Plantation agriculture
	Other highly productive cropland
	Cropland with some pasture
	Mediterranean agriculture
	Sparse grassland, grazed with some cropland
	Rudimental sedentary cultivation
	Nomadic herding
	Forest and woodland
	Tropical forest, some shifting agriculture
	Tundra, seasonally grazed
	Non-productive areas

MINERALS

●	Coal	✱	Lead
▲	Petroleum	△	Zinc
■	Iron	◖	Chromite
+	Copper	▣	Phosphate
◆	Tungsten	◭	Nickel
◆	Manganese	□	Tin

A-560000-1B6 -2-3-10

Urban
Cropland
Cropland & Woodland
Cropland & Grazing Land
Grassland, Grazing Land
Forest, Woodland
Swamp, Marshland
Tundra
Shrub, Sparse Grass,
Wasteland (pattern)
Barren Land
Oasis

ATLANTIC OCEAN

ARCTI

SPITSBERGEN

NOVAYA ZEMLYA

Kara Sea

Barents Sea

North Sea

Narvik

Murmansk

Kara

Gulf of Bothnia

Oslo

Stockholm

Baltic Sea

Arkangel'sk

Ob

BERLIN

MUNICH

LENINGRAD

Sukhona

U
R
A
L
S

Warsaw

BUDAPEST

MOSCOW

Kiev

Don

Kazan'

SVERDLOVSK

Danube

Volga

Novosib

ISTANBUL

Black Sea

Dnepr

VOLGOGRAD

Ural

Orsk

Irtysh

CAUCASUS MTS

Caspian Sea

Aral Sea

Karaganda

Mediterranean Sea

BAKU

Syr-Dar'ya

Ozero Balkhash

Beirut

CAIRO

Tigris

Baghdad

TEHRAN

Ashkhabad

Tashkent

TIEN SHAN

SYRIAN DESERT

Euphrates

ZAGROS MTS

DASHT-E KAVIR

Red Sea

AN NAFŪD

HINDU KUSH

TAKLA MAKAN

Kabul

Scale 1:24,000,000; one inch to 380 miles. Lambert Azimuthal Equal-Area Projection

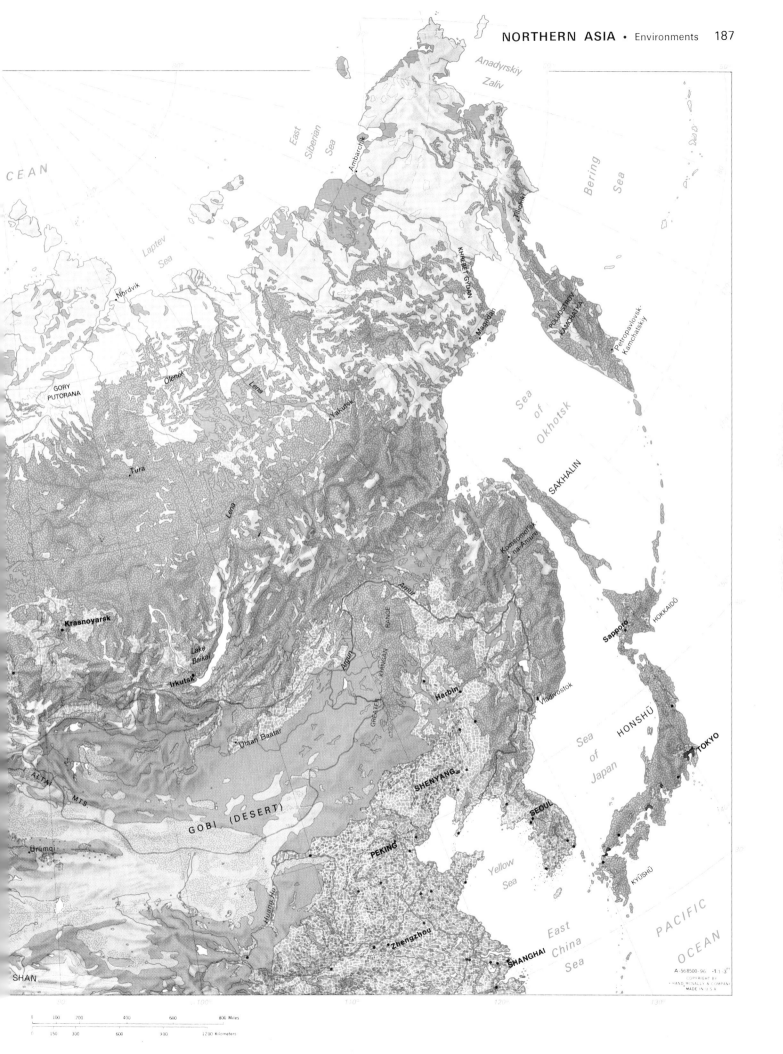

CEAN

Anadyrskiy
Zaliv

East
Siberian
Sea

Ambarchik

Laptev
Sea

Tiliohik

Bering
Sea

KHREBET GYDAN

POLUOSTROV KAMCHATKA

Nordvik

Magadan

Petropavlovsk-
Kamchatskiy

Olenek

Lena

GORY
PUTORANA

Yakutsk

Sea
of
Okhotsk

Tura

Lena

SAKHALIN

Komsomol'sk-
na-Amure

Amur

HOKKAIDŌ

Krasnoyarsk

Lake
Baikal

Sappporo

RANGE

Irkutsk

Argun

KHINGAN

Harbin

Vladivostok

HONSHŪ

Ulaan Baatar

GREATER

SHENYANG

Sea
of
Japan

TOKYO

ALTAI

MTS.

SEOUL

GOBI (DESERT)

PEKING

Ürümqi

Huang Ho

Yellow
Sea

KYŪSHŪ

East
China
Sea

Zhengzhou

PACIFIC
OCEAN

SHANGHAI

SHAN

A-568500-96 -1·1·3⁴¹

| 0 | 100 | 200 | 400 | 600 | 800 Miles |

| 0 | 150 | 300 | 600 | 900 | 1200 Kilometers |

Mediterranean Sea

CAUCASUS MTS.

BAKU

Caspian Sea

Aral Sea

Syr-Dar'ya

Karaganda

Ozero Balkhash

Beirut

CAIRO

30°

30°

SYRIAN DESERT

Tigris

Baghdad

Euphrates

TEHRAN

Ashkhabad

Tashkent

TIEN SHAN

TAKLA MAKAN

AN NAFŪD

ZAGROS MTS.

DASHT-E KAVIR

HINDU KUSH

Kabul.

Rawalpindi

Indus

PLA

Red Sea

20°

Mecca

Riyadh

Persian Gulf

Kermān

DELHI

DANAKIL

AR RUB' AL KHĀLĪ

Muscat

KARACHI

Nāgpur

10°

Aden

Gulf of Aden

Berbera

BOMBAY

Arabian Sea

WESTERN GHATS

EASTERN GHATS

MADRAS

Calicut

SRI LAN

Colombo

INDIAN OCEAN

■ • Urban

Cropland

Cropland & Woodland

Cropland & Grazing Land

Grassland, Grazing Land

Forest, Woodland

Swamp, Marshland

Tundra

Shrub, Sparse Grass, Wasteland (pattern)

Barren Land

• Oasis

A-568600-96   -1-17°
COPYRIGHT BY
RAND McNALLY & COMPANY
MADE IN U.S.A.

Scale 1:24,000,000, one inch to 380 miles. Lambert Azimuthal Equal-Area Projection

190

Continued on page 222

ATLANTIC OCEAN

ARCTIC OCEAN

North Pole

Meridian of Greenwich

Arctic Circle

GREENLAND (Den.)

ICELAND

BARENTS SEA

KARA SEA

LAPTEV SEA

SVALBARD (Nor.)

ZEMLYA FRANTSA IOSIFA (FRANZ JOSEF LAND)

NOVAYA ZEMLYA

SEVERNAYA ZEMLYA (NORTHERN LAND)

M. CHELYUSKIN

POV TAYMYR

BIRMINGHAM

LISBON

MADRID

LONDON

LIVERPOOL

Edinburgh

COPENHAGEN

HAMBURG

BERLIN

PARIS

Lyon

Bordeaux

Marseille

ROME

NAPLES

ATHENS

Tanger

Algiers Tunis

Tripoli

ATLAS MTS.

MEDITERRANEAN SEA

LIBYAN DESERT

ALEXANDRIA

CAIRO

Aswân

Khartoum

Mitsiwa

Addis Ababa

ETHIOPIAN PLATEAU

Lakes Victoria

AFRICA

OSLO

STOCKHOLM

Bergen

Helsinki

LENINGRAD

MOSCOW

GOR'KIY

Perm

Kazan

KUYBYSHEV

SVERDLOVSK

Tobol'sk

Orenburg

Omsk

Tomsk

Krasnoyarsk

Yeniseysk

NOVOSIBIRSK

Semipalatinsk

Kyzyl

SOVIET UNION

SIBERIA

Irkutsk

Ulan Bator

MONGO

GOBI

SAYAN

ALTAI MTS.

KHREBET

Hovd

Uliastay

Ûrûmqi

Hâmi

TIEN SHAN

TARIM BASIN (TAKLA-MAKAN DESERT)

ALTUN SHAN

KUNLUN SHAN

PLATEAU OF TIBET

CHINA

Lanzhou

CHENGDU

CHONGQI

KUNMING

Lhasa

NEPAL

BHUTAN

Mt. Everest

Kathmandu

Patna

BNGL.

Dacca

BURMA

Mandalay

DONETSK

Rostov-na-Donu

Odessa

BUCHAREST

Belgrade

BUDAPEST

VIENNA

PRAGUE

WARSAW

KIEV

CARPATHIANS

EUROPE

BLACK SEA

ISTANBUL

Ankara

Izmir

Trabzon

TURKEY

CYPRUS

CRETE

Beirut

Jerusalem

ISRAEL

LEB.

Aleppo

Damascus

SYRIA

IRAQ

Baghdad

Al Basrah

JORDAN

Amman

Suez

RED SEA

AL HIJAZ

Al Madinah

Jiddah

Mecca

Riyadh

NAJD

SAUDI ARABIA

AR RUB' AL KHALI

YEMEN

San'â

P.D.R. OF YEMEN

Aden (Adan)

Gulf of Aden

Berbera

SOCOTRA (P.D.R. of Yemen)

CAUCASUS MTS.

Batumi

Tbilisi

BAKU

Tabriz

TEHRAN

Esfahân

Shîrâz

Bûshehr

Kuwait

Al Hasâ

QATAR

UNITED ARAB EMIRATES

OMAN

Muscat

Gulf of Oman

CASPIAN SEA

CASPIAN DEPRESSION

Astrakhan

Gur'yev

KIRGHIZ STEPPE

KAZAKH

Ust'-Urt Plato

Ashkhabad

Mashhad

Mary

TURKESTAN

Bukhara

Samarkand

Dushanbe

Kokand

TASHKENT

Alma-Ata

Kapchagay

Ozero Balkhash

PAMIRS

HINDU KUSH

Herât

Kâbul

AFGHANISTAN

Quetta

Kermân

KARACHI

ARABIAN SEA

Peshawar

Islamâbâd

Rawalpindi

Srinagar

KARAKORAM RA.

Kashi

Shache

PAKISTAN

LAHORE

DELHI

New Delhi

Agra

KANPUR

Allahâbâd

Varanasi

INDIA

Ahmadâbâd

BOMBAY

Nâgpur

HYDERÂBÂD

DECCAN

WESTERN GHATS

EASTERN GHATS

BANGALORE

MADRAS

Calicut

Coimbatore

Madurai

CAPE COMORIN

LAKSHADWEEP (India)

SRI LANKA (CEYLON)

Colombo

DONDRA HEAD

MALDIVES

BAY OF BENGAL

Rangoon

PAGODA POINT

Moulmein

BANGKOK (Krung Thep)

THAILAND

ANDAMAN ISLANDS (India)

NICOBAR ISLANDS (India)

George Town

Banda Aceh

MALAY

SUMATRA

Gulf of Thailand

INDIAN OCEAN

Equator

Tropic of Cancer

Relief

Meters		Feet
3050		10 000
1525		5000
610		2000
305		1000
0	Sea Level	0
152.5		500 Below Sea Level
1525		5000
3050		10 000
6100		20 000

A-519695-76- -13-11 24
COPYRIGHT BY
RAND McNALLY & COMPANY
MADE IN U.S.A.

Scale 1:40 000 000; one inch to 630 miles. Lambert's Azimuthal, Equal Area Projection
Elevations and depressions are given in feet

Longitude East of Greenwich

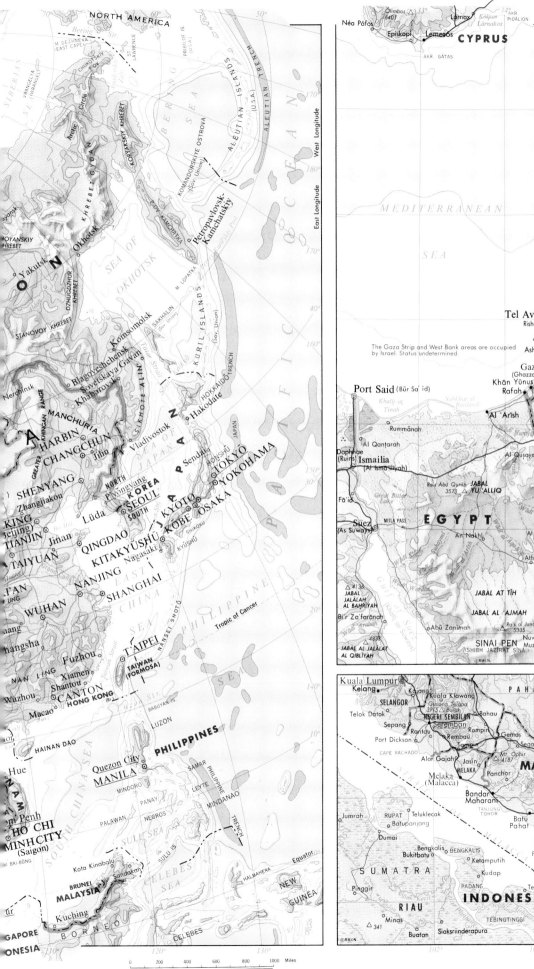

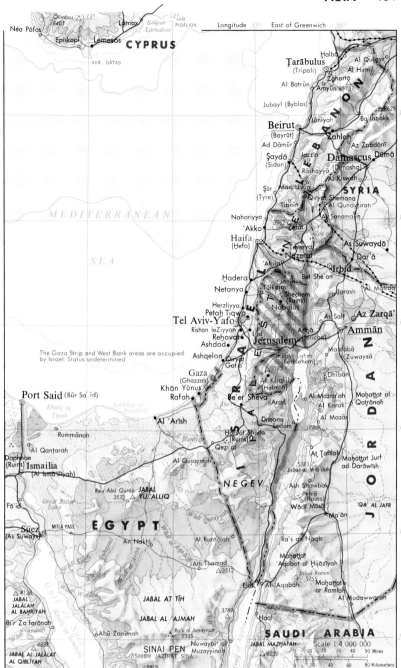

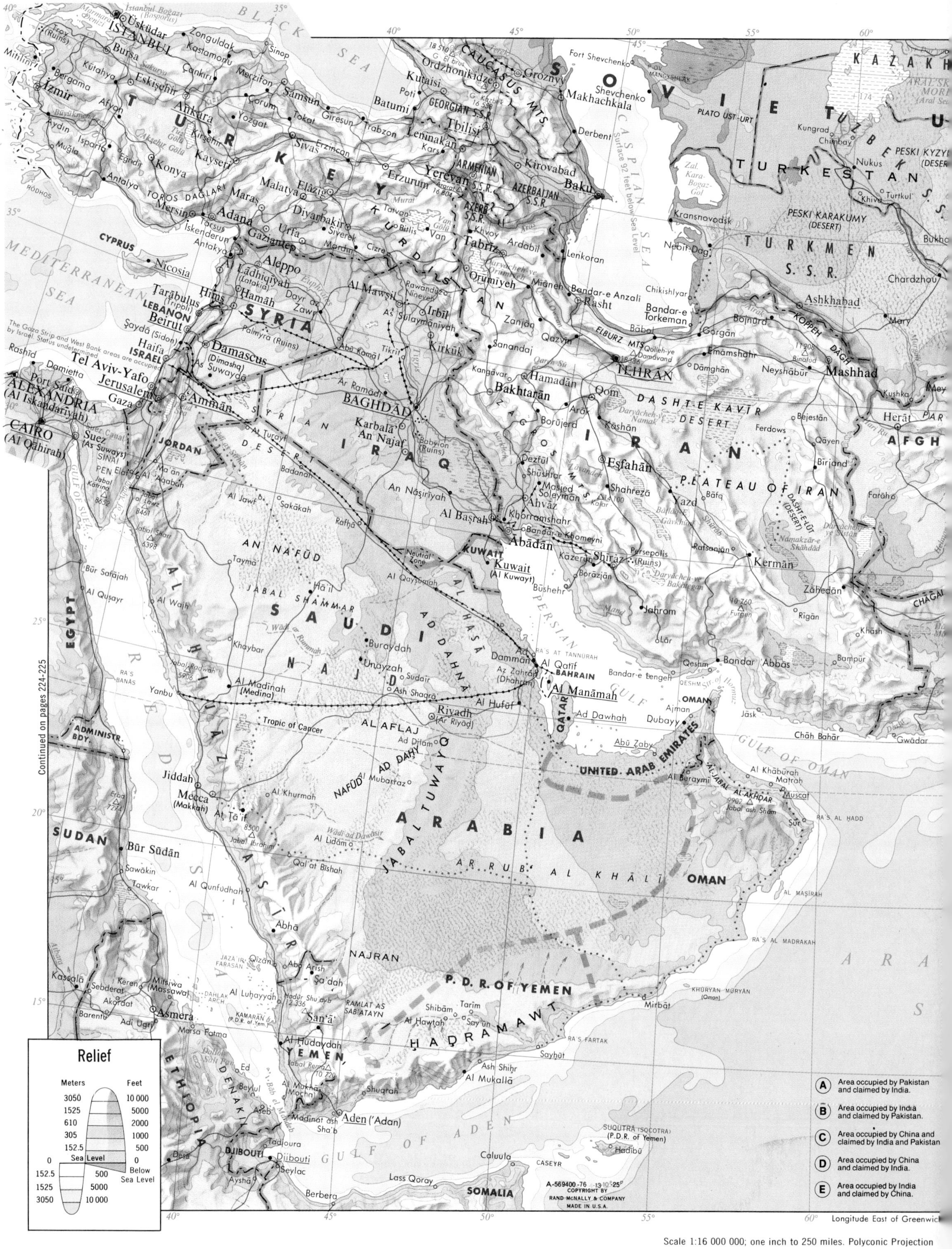

BLACK SEA

SOVIET UNION

CASPIAN SEA

TURKEY

KAZAKH

TURKESTAN

PESKI KARAKUMY (DESERT)

TURKMEN S.S.R.

CYPRUS

MEDITERRANEAN SEA

SYRIA

LEBANON

Beirut

ISRAEL

Tel Aviv-Yafo

Jerusalem

JORDAN

Damascus (Dimashq)

Amman

IRAQ

BAGHDAD

IRAN

TEHRAN

Esfahān

Mashhad

AFGH

PLATEAU OF IRAN

DASHT-E KAVIR DESERT

ZAGROS MTS

EGYPT

CAIRO (Al Qāhirah)

ALEXANDRIA

SUDAN

AN NAFŪD

SAUDI ARABIA

NAJD

AL HIJĀZ

Riyadh (Ar Riyāḍ)

KUWAIT

Kuwait (Al Kuwayt)

BAHRAIN

QATAR

Ad Dawhah

UNITED ARAB EMIRATES

Abū Ẓaby

OMAN

Dubayy

GULF OF OMAN

PERSIAN GULF

Muscat

Jiddah

Mecca (Makkah)

AR RUB' AL KHĀLĪ

Tropic of Cancer

ASĪR

NAJRAN

P.D.R. OF YEMEN

ḤAḌRAMAWT

YEMEN

San'ā

Al Ḥudaydah

Aden ('Adan)

GULF OF ADEN

ETHIOPIA

DJIBOUTI

SOMALIA

Berbera

SUQUTRA (SOCOTRA) (P.D.R. of Yemen)

Relief

Meters		Feet
3050		10 000
1525		5000
610		2000
305		1000
152.5		500
0	Sea Level	0
152.5		500
1525	Below Sea Level	5000
3050		10 000

Continued on pages 224-225

A — Area occupied by Pakistan and claimed by India.
B — Area occupied by India and claimed by Pakistan.
C — Area occupied by China and claimed by India and Pakistan
D — Area occupied by China and claimed by India.
E — Area occupied by India and claimed by China.

A-569400-76   13-10-25°
COPYRIGHT BY
RAND McNALLY & COMPANY
MADE IN U.S.A.

Scale 1:16 000 000; one inch to 250 miles. Polyconic Projection
Elevations and depressions are given in feet

Longitude East of Greenwich

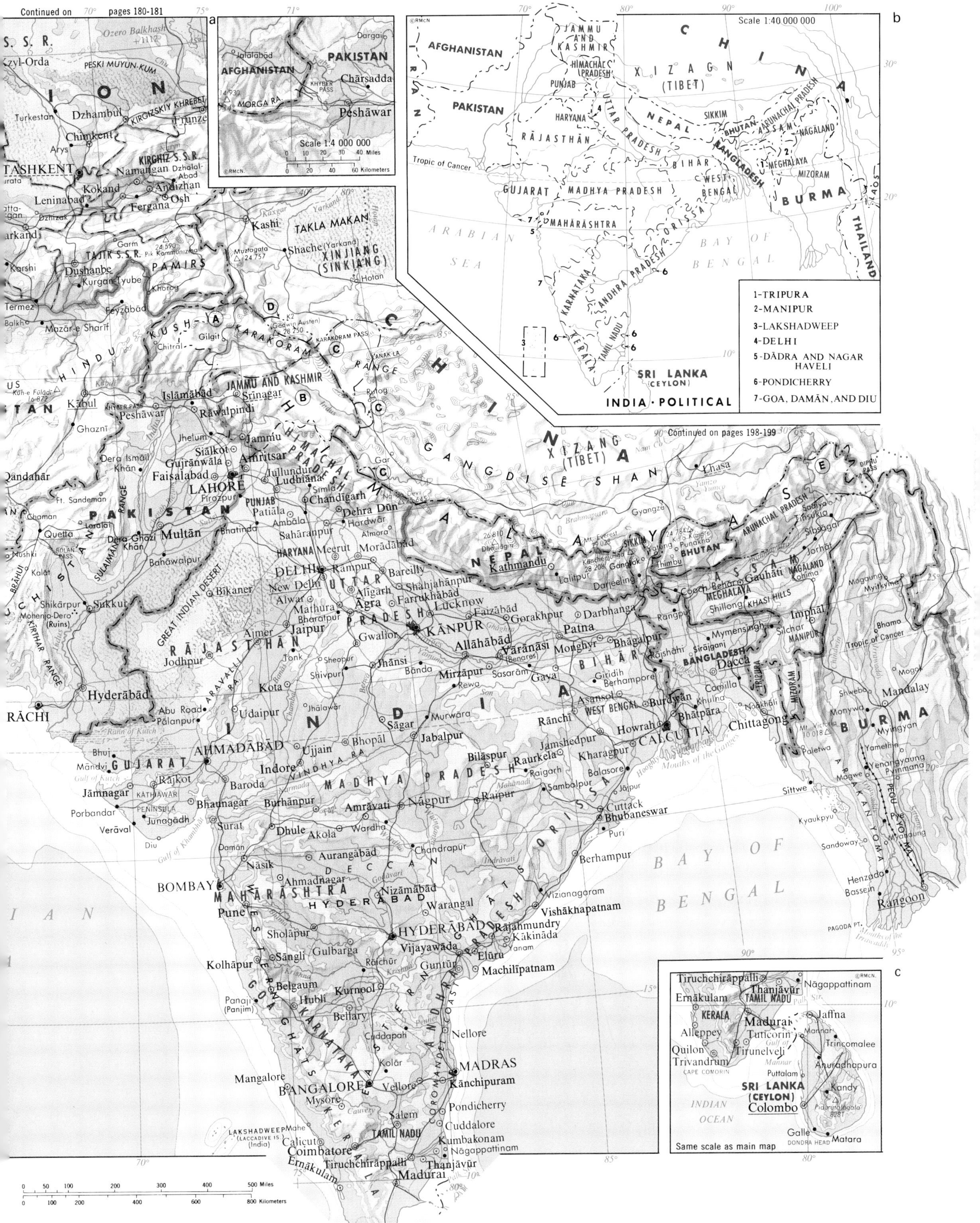

Continued on pages 180-181

PAKISTAN
AFGHANISTAN
Jalālābād
Dargai
KHYBER PASS
MORGA RA.
Chārsadda
Peshāwar
Scale 1:4 000 000
0 10 20 30 40 Miles
0 20 40 60 Kilometers

Scale 1:40 000 000

AFGHANISTAN
JAMMU AND KASHMIR
HIMACHAL PRADESH
PUNJAB
HARYANA
UTTAR PRADESH
NEPAL
SIKKIM
BHUTAN
ARUNACHAL PRADESH
ASSAM
NĀGĀLAND
MEGHALAYA
MIZORAM
PAKISTAN
RĀJASTHĀN
BIHAR
BANGLADESH
BURMA
Tropic of Cancer
GUJARAT
MADHYA PRADESH
WEST BENGAL
ORISSA
MAHĀRĀSHTRA
ARABIAN SEA
BAY OF BENGAL
KARNĀTAKA
ANDHRA PRADESH
THAILAND
KERALA
TAMIL NĀDU
SRI LANKA (CEYLON)
INDIA · POLITICAL
CHINA
XIZAGN (TIBET)

1-TRIPURA
2-MANIPUR
3-LAKSHADWEEP
4-DELHI
5-DĀDRA AND NAGAR HAVELI
6-PONDICHERRY
7-GOA, DAMĀN, AND DIU

S.S.R.
Kzyl-Orda
PESKI MUYUN-KUM
Ozero Balkhash
Turkestan
Dzhambul
KIRGIZSKIY KHREBET
Chimkent
Arys
Frunze
TASHKENT
Namangan
Dzhalal-Abad
KIRGHIZ S.S.R.
Leninabad
Kokand
Andizhan
Osh
Fergana
Dzhizak
TAKLA MAKAN
Kashi
Shache (Yarkand)
XINJIANG (SINKIANG)
Hotan
TAJIK S.S.R.
Garm
Pik Kommunizma
Muztagata
Dushanbe
Kurgan-Tyube
PAMIRS
Khorog
Karshi
Feyzābād
Termez
Balkh
Mazār-e Sharīf
HINDU KUSH
KARAKORAM RANGE
KARAKORAM PASS
Kābul
KHYBER PASS
Peshāwar
Ghaznī
Islāmābād
Srīnagar
JAMMU AND KASHMIR
Rāwalpindi
Jhelum
Jammū
HIMACHAL PRADESH
Lhasa
XIZANG (TIBET)
GANGDISÊ SHAN
HIMALAYA
Dera Ismāīl Khān
Siālkot
Gujrānwāla
Amritsar
LAHORE
Fīrozpur
PUNJAB
Ludhiāna
Chandīgarh
Simla
Dehra Dūn
Almora
PAKISTAN
Faisalābād
Jullundur
Patiāla
Ambāla
Sahāranpur
Mt. Everest
Kānchenjunga
Quetta
Multān
Bhatinda
Meerut
Morādābād
NEPAL
Kathmandu
SIKKIM
BHUTAN
Thimbu
ASSAM
Bahāwalpur
HARYANA
DELHI
Rampur
Bareilly
Shāhjahānpur
Lucknow
Gorakhpur
Darbhanga
Coch Behar
Gauhāti
NĀGĀLAND
Bīkaner
New Delhi
Aligarh
Mathura
UTTAR PRADESH
Faizābād
Darjeeling
Rangpur
MEGHALAYA
Shillong
KHĀSI HILLS
Imphāl
MANIPUR
GREAT INDIAN DESERT
Ajmer
Jaipur
Āgra
Farrukhābād
KĀNPUR
Allāhābād
Vārānasi (Benares)
Patna
Monghyr
Bhāgalpur
Mymensingh
Silchar
RĀJASTHĀN
Jodhpur
Tonk
Gwalior
Jhānsi
INDIA
Mirzāpur
Sāsarām
Gayā
Giridih
BIHAR
Rājshāhi
Sirājganj
Tropic of Cancer
Hyderābād
Udaipur
Ajmer
Kota
Shivpuri
Bānda
Rewa
Son
Rānchī
Āsansol
WEST BENGAL
Burdwān
Khulna
Comilla
RĀCHI
Ābu Road
Pālanpur
Sāgar
Murwāra
Jamshedpur
Howrah
CALCUTTA
Bhātpāra
Chittagong
BANGLADESH
Dacca
Bhuj
Mānḍvi
GUJARAT
AHMADĀBĀD
Ujjain
Bhopāl
Jabalpur
Bilāspur
Raurkela
Kharagpur
Balasore
Shwebo
Mandalay
BURMA
Myingyan
Jāmnagar
Rajkot
Baroda
Indore
NARMADA
NINDHYA RA.
MADHYA PRADESH
Raigarh
Sambalpur
ORISSA
Monywa
Porbandar
KATHIAWAR PENINSULA
Bhaunagar
Burhānpur
Amrāvati
Nāgpur
Raipur
Mahānadi
Cuttack
Bhubaneswar
Puri
Veraval
Junagādh
Surat
Dhule
Akola
Wardha
Chandrapur
Berhampur
Sittwe
Kyaukpyu
Henzada
Bassein
Rangoon
Diu
Damān
Nāsik
DECCAN
Aurangābād
EASTERN GHATS
BAY OF BENGAL
Sandoway
BOMBAY
Ahmadnagar
Nizāmābād
Vizianagaram
Vishākhapatnam
MAHĀRĀSHTRA
Pune
HYDERĀBĀD
Warangal
Rajahmundry
Kākināda
Yanam
Sholāpur
Sāngli
Gulbarga
Rāichūr
Vijayawāda
Elūru
Machilīpatnam
Guntūr
Kolhāpur
ANDHRA PRADESH
Belgaum
Kurnool
Bellary
Cuddapah
Nellore
Panaji (Panjim)
GOA
Hubli
KARNĀTAKA
WESTERN GHATS
Kolār
Mangalore
BANGALORE
Vellore
MADRAS
Mysore
Kānchipuram
LAKSHADWEEP (LACCADIVE IS.) (India)
Mahe
Salem
Pondicherry
Calicut
Coimbatore
Tiruchchirāppalli
Cuddalore
Kumbakonam
Nāgappattinam
Ernākulam
Thanjāvūr
Madurai
TAMIL NĀDU

INDIAN OCEAN

Continued on pages 198-199

Tiruchchirāppalli
Ernākulam
Thanjāvūr
TAMIL NĀDU
Nāgappattinam
KERALA
Alleppey
Madurai
Jaffna
Quilon
Tuticorin
Trincomalee
Trivandrum
Tirunelveli
CAPE COMORIN
Puttalam
SRI LANKA (CEYLON)
Colombo
Kandy
Galle
Matara
DONDRA HEAD
Anurādhapura
INDIAN OCEAN
Same scale as main map

0 50 100 200 300 400 500 Miles
0 100 200 400 600 800 Kilometers

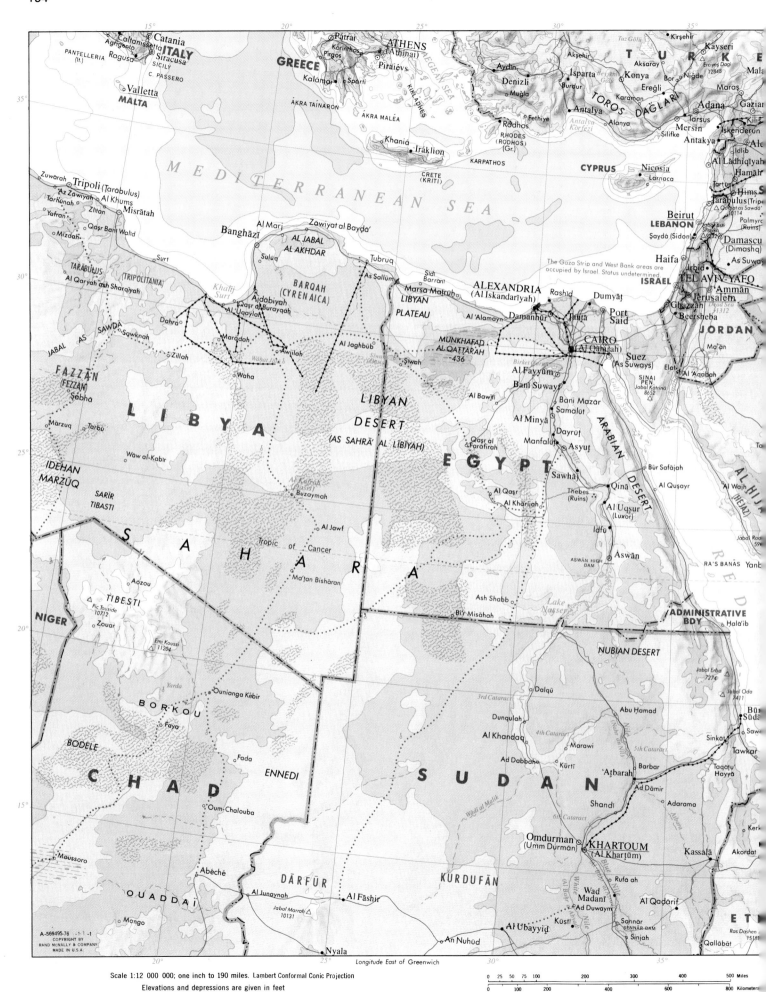

194

Scale 1:12 000 000; one inch to 190 miles. Lambert Conformal Conic Projection

Elevations and depressions are given in feet

Longitude East of Greenwich

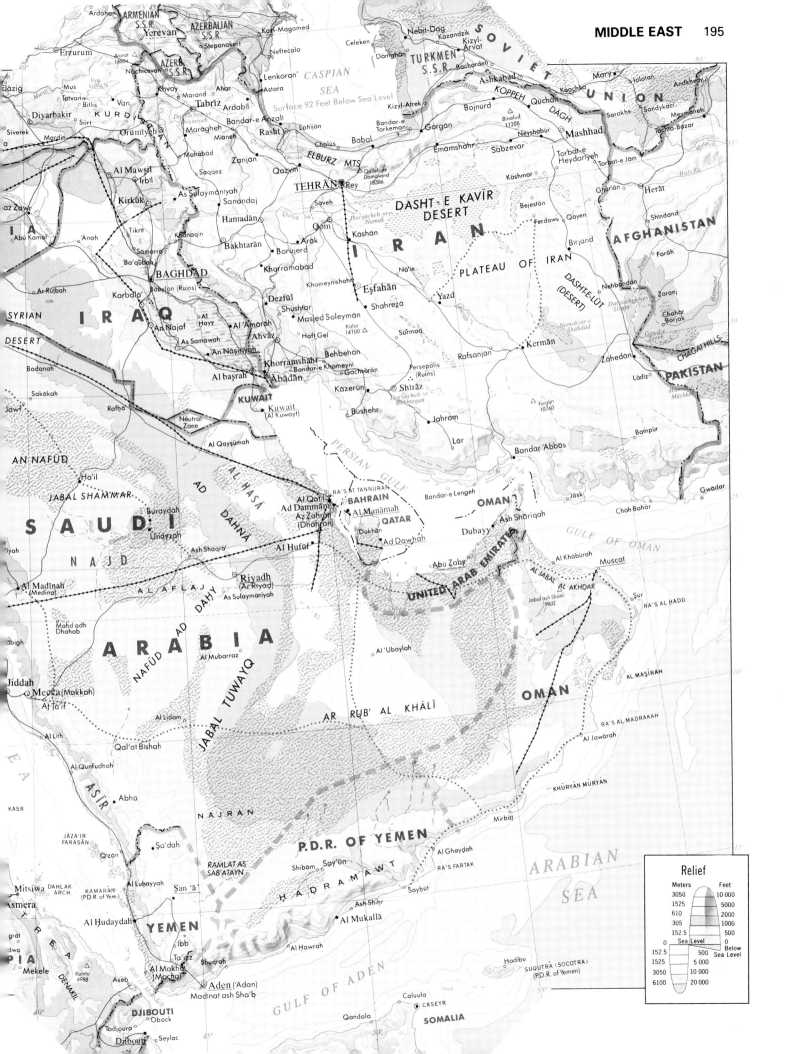

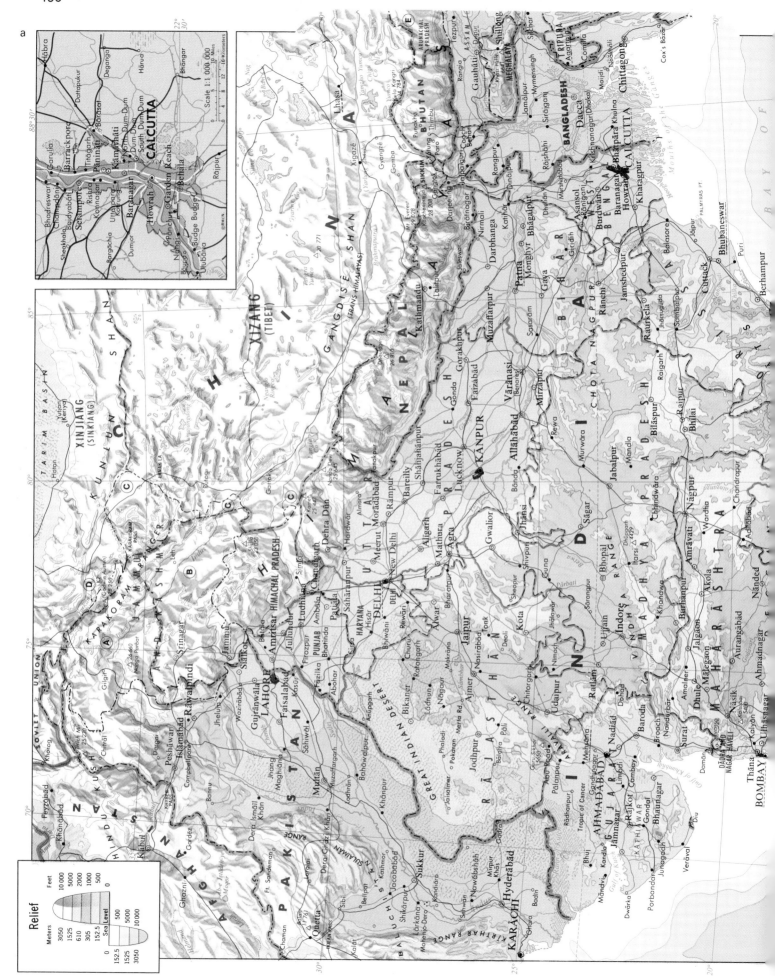

a

CALCUTTA

Scale 1:1 000 000

Relief

Meters	Feet
3050	10 000
1525	5000
610	2000
305	1000
152.5	500
0	0

Sea Level

152.5	500
1525	5000
3050	10 000

Scale 1:10 000 000; one inch to 160 miles. Lambert Conformal Conic Projection
Elevations and depressions are given in feet

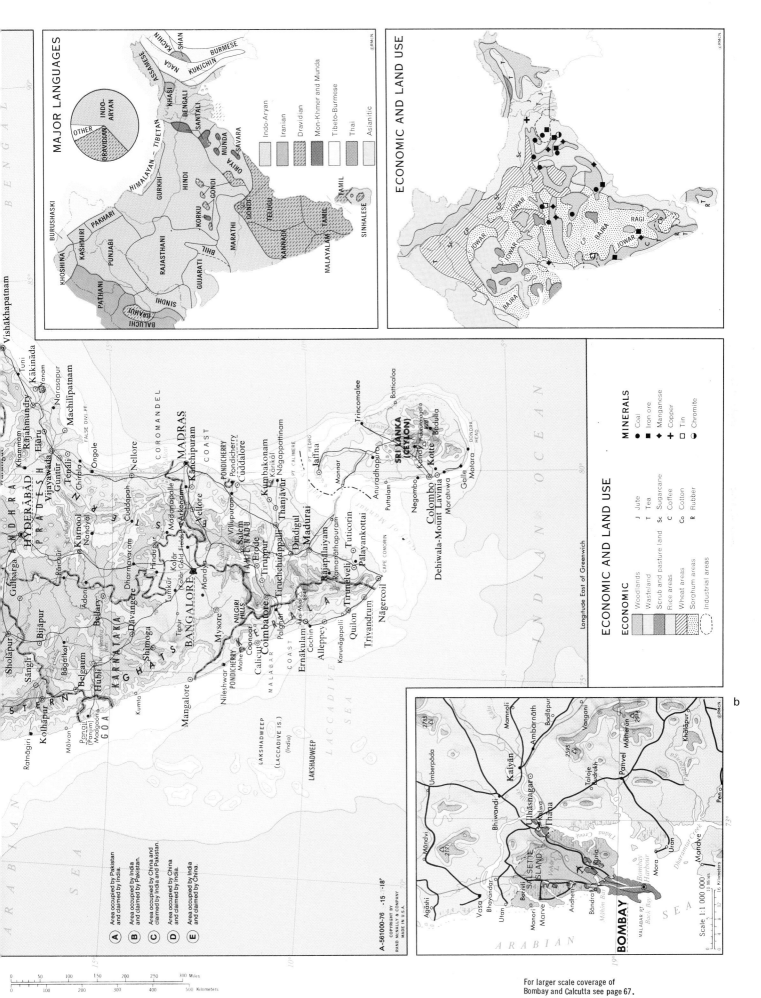

MAJOR LANGUAGES

Indo-Aryan
Iranian
Dravidian
Mon-Khmer and Munda
Tibeto-Burmese
Thai
Asianitic

OTHER · INDO-ARYAN · DRAVIDIAN

BURMESE
SHAN
KACHIN
NAGA
KUKICHIN
ASSAMESE
KHASI
BENGALI
SANTALI
MUNDA
SAVARA
ORIYA
GONDI
TELUGU
KANNADA
TAMIL
MALAYALAM
SINHALESE
HIMALAYAN — TIBETAN
GURKHI
HINDI
KORKU
GONDI
MARATHI
BHIL
GUJARATI
RAJASTHANI
PAKHARI
KASHMIRI
PUNJABI
SINDHI
PATHANI
BALUCHI
BRAHUI
KHOSHINA
BURUSHASKI

B E N G A L

ECONOMIC AND LAND USE

MINERALS

● Coal
■ Iron ore
■ Manganese
✦ Copper
□ Tin
◖ Chromite

ECONOMIC AND LAND USE

ECONOMIC

Woodlands
Wasteland
Scrub and pasture land
Rice areas
Wheat areas
Sorghum areas
Industrial areas

J Jute
T Tea
Sc Sugarcane
C Coffee
Co Cotton
R Rubber

Longitude East of Greenwich

I N D I A N   O C E A N

A R A B I A N   S E A

L A C C A D I V E   S E A

LAKSHADWEEP
(LACCADIVE IS.)
(India)

A-561000-76 -15--18°
COPYRIGHT BY
RAND MCNALLY & COMPANY
MADE IN U.S.A.

A · Area occupied by Pakistan and claimed by India.
B · Area occupied by India and claimed by Pakistan.
C · Area occupied by China and claimed by India and Pakistan.
D · Area occupied by China and claimed by India.
E · Area occupied by India and claimed by China.

BOMBAY

Scale 1:1 000 000

b

For larger scale coverage of
Bombay and Calcutta see page 67.

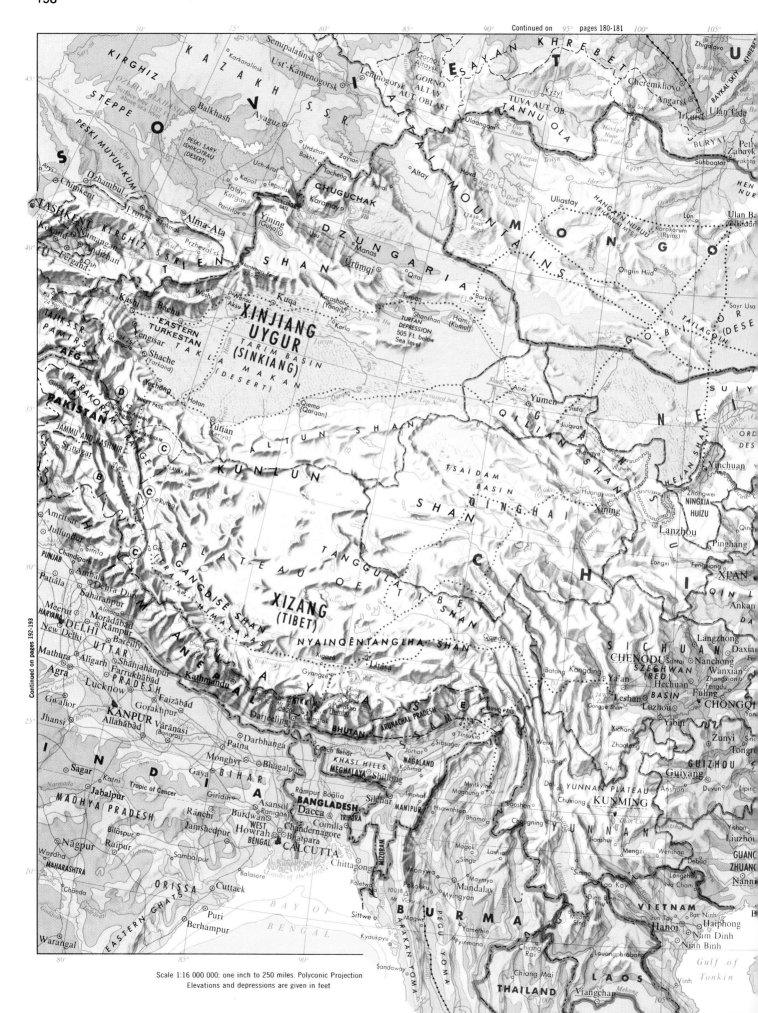

Continued on pages 180-181

Scale 1:16 000 000; one inch to 250 miles. Polyconic Projection
Elevations and depressions are given in feet

Chinese Provinces,
Autonomous Regions (AR)
and Municipalities (M)

Conventional Form — Pinyin Form

Anhwei	—	Anhui
Chekiang	—	Zhejiang
Fukien	—	Fujian
Heilungkiang	—	Heilongjiang
Honan	—	Henan
Hopeh	—	Hebei
Hunan	—	Hunan
Hupeh	—	Hubei
Inner Mongolia (AR)	—	Nei Monggol
Kansu	—	Gansu
Kiangsi	—	Jiangxi
Kiangsu	—	Jiangsu
Kirin	—	Jilin
Kwangsi (AR)	—	Guangxi Zhuangzu
Kwangtung	—	Guangdong
Kweichow	—	Guizhou
Liaoning	—	Liaoning
Ningsia Hui (AR)	—	Ningxia Huizu
Peking (M)	—	Beijing
Shanghai (M)	—	Shanghai
Shansi	—	Shanxi
Shantung	—	Shandong
Shensi	—	Shaanxi
Sinkiang (AR)	—	Xinjiang Uygur
Szechwan	—	Sichuan
Tibet (AR)	—	Xizang
Tientsin (M)	—	Tianjin
Tsinghai	—	Qinghai
Yunnan	—	Yunnan

(A) Area occupied by Pakistan and claimed by India.

(B) Area occupied by India and claimed by Pakistan.

(C) Area occupied by China and claimed by India and Pakistan.

(D) Area occupied by China and claimed by India.

(E) Area occupied by India and claimed by China.

A-569700-76 -12 -20P
COPYRIGHT BY
RAND MCNALLY & COMPANY
MADE IN U.S.A.

Relief

Meters		Feet
3050		10 000
1525		5000
610		2000
305		1000
152.5		500
0	Sea Level	0
152.5		Below Sea Level
1525		5000
3050		10 000
6100		20 000

Longitude East of Greenwich

Continued on pages 206-207

0 50 100   200   300   400   500 Miles
0   100   200   400   600   800 Kilometers

Cities and Towns

| 0 to 50,000 | ○ | 500,000 to 1,000,000 | ◉ |
| 50,000 to 500,000 | ⊙ | 1,000,000 and over | |

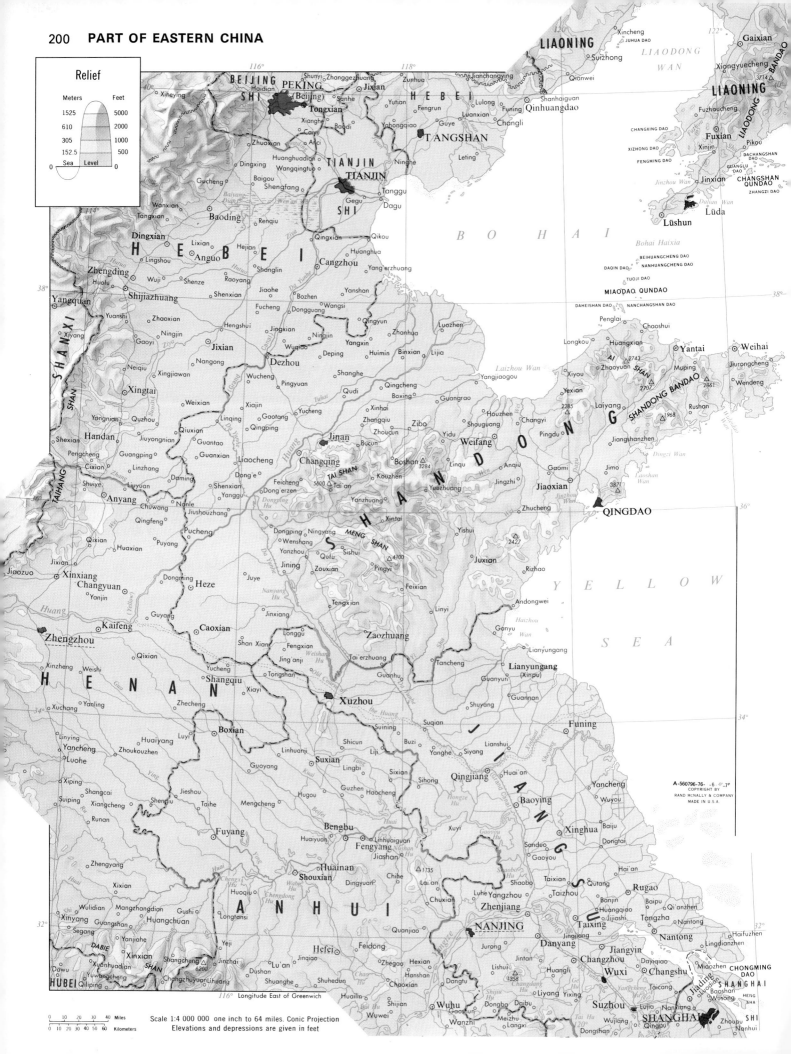

Relief

Meters	Feet
1525	5000
610	2000
305	1000
152.5	500
Sea Level	0

LIAONING

LIAODONG WAN

Gaixian

Xincheng
JUHUA DAO

Xiongyuecheng

3714△

LIAONING

Suizhong

Qianwei

Fuzhoucheng

LIAODONG BANDAO

CHANGXING DAO

Fuxian

XIZHONG DAO

Xinjin

DACHANGSHAN DAO

FENGMING DAO

GUANGLU DAO

CHANGSHAN QUNDAO

ZHANGZI DAO

Pikou

Jinxian

Lüshun   Lüda
Dalian Wan

Jianchangying

Shunyi Zhanggezhuang
BEIJING PEKING
Xiheying SHI (Beijing)
Haidian

Jixian   Zunhua

Sanhe

HEBEI

Shanhaiguan

Qinhuangdao

Tongxian   Yutian Fengrun
Xianghe Baodi   Luanxian Changli
Caiyu   Lulong
Anci Yahongqiao Guye
TANGSHAN
Zhuoxian Huanghuadian Ninghe   Leting
Dingxing Wangqingtuo
Baigou Shengfang TIANJIN
Gucheng   TIANJIN
Wanxian Baiyang- SHI
Tangxian Diang Wen'an Wa Tanggu
Baoding Renqiu Gegu Dagu
Dingxian Lixian Hejian Qingxian Qikou
Anguo   Ziya Qikou
Zhengding Shanglin Huanghua
HEBEI Wuji Raoyang Yang'erzhuang
Huolu Shenze
Yangquan Shijiazhuang Jiaohe Bozhen Yanshan
Yuanshi Shenxian Dongguang
Zhaoxian Fucheng Wangsi Qingyun Zhanhua
Xiyang Ningjin Hengshui Jingxian Ningjin Yangxin
SHAN Gaoyi Neiqiu Xingjiawan Wuqiao Deping Huimin Binxian Lijia
Xingtai Jixian Yucheng Qingcheng Boxing
Weixian Nangong Dezhou Shanghe Qudi Guangrao Houzhen Changyi
Yongnian Quzhou Wucheng Pingyuan Boshan Shouguang Pingdu
Handan Qiuxian Gaotang Xinhai Zhangqiu Zibo Yidu Weifang Anqiu Gaomi
Shexian Pengcheng Guantao Liaocheng Zhoucun Linqu Jingzhi Jiaoxian
Cixian Linzhang Guanxian Jinan Boshan△3284 Jimo
Daming Dong'e Changqing Bucun Kouzhen Yuezhuang
Anyang Chuwang Shenxian Feicheng TAI SHAN Zhucheng QINGDAO
Nanle Jiushouzhuang Yanggu 5000△Tai'an Yanzhuang
Qingfeng Dong'erzen Yishui 3871△
Qixian Pucheng Dongping Ningyang Xintai Juxian 2427△
Huaxian Puyang Wenshang MENG SHAN Yishui Rizhao
Jixian Dongming Yanzhou Qufu Sishui 4100△ Andongwei
Jiaozuo Changyuan Heze Juye Zouxian Pingyi Feixian Linyi
Xinxiang Yanjin Jining Tengxian Ganyu
Zhengzhou Guyang Caoxian Jinxiang Lianyungang
Kaifeng Shan Xian Zaozhuang Tancheng Lianyungang (Xinpu)
Qixian Longgu Weishan Tai'erzhuang Guannan
Xinzheng Weishi Fengxian Jing'anji Guanhu Shuyang Guannan
HENAN Yucheng Tongshan Xuzhou Suining Suqian Funing
Xuchang Yanling Shangqiu Xiayi Shicun Buzi JIANGSU
Linying Boxian Liji Sixian Yanghe Siyang
Yancheng Huaiyang Luyi Linhuaiji Lingbi Guzhen Haocheng Sihong Qingjiang Huai'an Yancheng
Luohe Zhoukouzhen Suxian Qingjiang Wuyou
Xiping Guoyang Hugou Huai'an Yancheng
Shangcai Shenqiu Jieshou Taihe Mengcheng Xinghua Baiju
Suiping Xiangcheng Bengbu Xuyi Baoying Dongtai
Runan Fuyang Huaiyuan Linhuaiguan Sanduo Hai'an
Zhengyang Fengyang Jiashan Gaoyou Hu Gaoyou Taixian Qutang Rugao
Xixian Huainan Chihe Shaobo Hu Taixing Banjin Baipu Qi'anzhen
Xinyang Huoqiu Shouxian Lai'an Luhe Yangzhou Taizhou Huangqiao Jijiashi Tangzha
Gushi Longtansi Dingyuan △1135 Chuxian Zhenjiang Taizhou Nantong
Wulidian Mangzhangdian Huangchuan ANHUI Zhenjiang Danyang Jiangyin Lingdianzhen Haifuzhen
DABIE Yeji Quanjiao NANJING Danyang Changzhou Dayiqiao CHONGMING DAO
Dawu Xinxian Shangcheng△6290 Jinzhai Feidong Jurong Jintan Changshu Miaozhen SHANGHAI
Yuwangcheng Changzhuyuanlin SHAN Lu'an Jinqiao Zhegao Hexian Lishui Wuxi Jiading
HUBEI Qiliping Changzhuyuanlin Hefei Feidong Hanshan Jintan Jiangyin Baoshan HENG SHA
Shangmao Dushan Shuanghe Shuhedun Dangtu △1358 Liyang Yixing SHANGHAI SHI
Huailin Shijian Chaoxian Taicang Wusong
Wuhu Daibu Suzhou Lujia SHANGHAI
Meizhou Wanzhi Dongba Nanxiang Nanhui
Langxi Wujiang Tai Hu Zhoupu
Dongshan Qingpu

BOHAI

Bohai Haixia

BEIHUANGCHENG DAO

DAQIN DAO NANHUANGCHENG DAO
TUOJI DAO
MIAODAO QUNDAO
DAHEISHAN DAO NANCHANGSHAN DAO
Penglai Chaoshui
Longkou Huangxian Yantai Weihai
AI △2743 Zhaoyuan Muping Jiurongcheng
Xiyou SHAN Laiyang △2861 Wendeng
2702△ △2285 △1968
Yangjiaogou Laiyang Rushan
Jiangshanzhen SHANDONG BANDAO
Dingzi Wan
Laoshan Wan

Jinzhou Wan
Laizhou Wan SHANDONG Jinzhou Whuf

YELLOW

Haizhou Wan

SEA

A-560796-76- -6 .4v_7P
COPYRIGHT BY
RAND McNALLY & COMPANY
MADE IN U.S.A.

Scale 1:4 000 000 one inch to 64 miles. Conic Projection
Elevations and depressions are given in feet

116° Longitude East of Greenwich

0 10 20 30 40 Miles
0 10 20 30 40 50 60 Kilometers

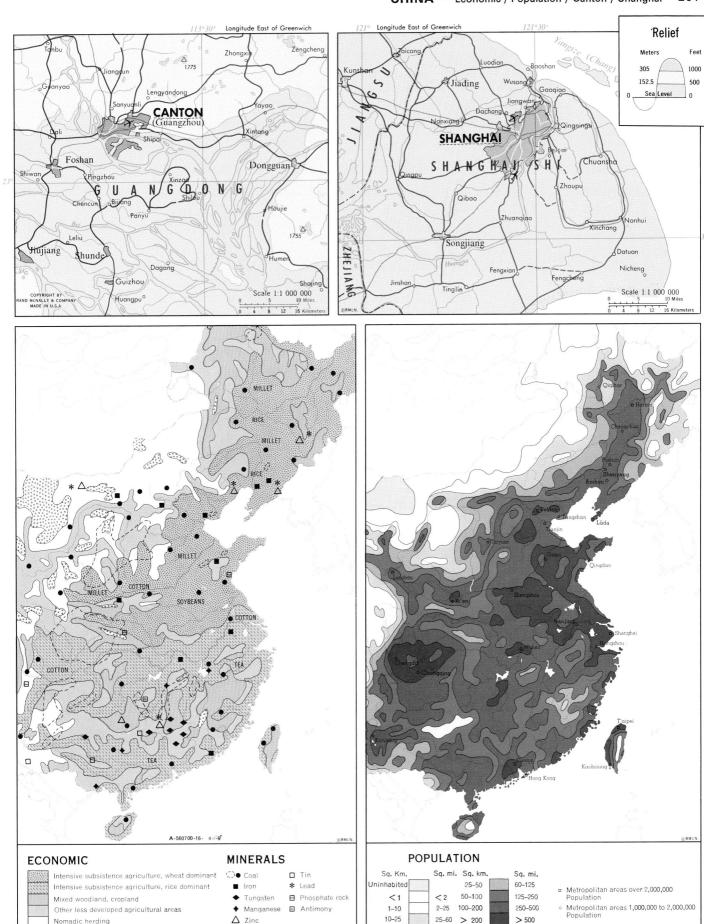

Relief

Meters	Feet
305	1000
152.5	500
0 Sea Level	0

Longitude East of Greenwich

Tanbu · Zhongxin · Zengcheng · Jiangcun · Jiangdun · Lengyandong · Yayao · Guanyao · Sanyuanli · **CANTON (Guangzhou)** · Shipai · Xintang · Dali · Foshan · Pingzhou · Xinzao · Dongguan · Shiwan · Chencun · Bijiang · Shilou · Houjie · Panyu · Leliu · Hujiang · Shunde · Dagang · Humen · Guizhou · Huangpu · Shajing

G U A N G D O N G

Bei

COPYRIGHT BY
RAND McNALLY & COMPANY
MADE IN U.S.A.

Scale 1:1 000 000
0   5   10 Miles
0 4 8 12 16 Kilometers

JIANGSU · ZHEJIANG

Taicang · Kunshan · Luodian · Baoshan · Jiading · Wusong · Gaoqiao · Nanxiang · Jiangwan · Qingningsi · **SHANGHAI** · Dachang · Beiçao · Chuansha · Qingpu · **SHANGHAI SHI** · Zhoupu · Qibao · Zhuanqiao · Nanhui · Zhuangqiao · Xinchang · Songjiang · Datuan · Jinshan · Fengxian · Nicheng · Tinglin · Fengcheng

Yangtze (Chang) · Huangpu

Scale 1:1 000 000
0   5   10 Miles
0 4 8 12 16 Kilometers

ECONOMIC

A-560700-16- 4-69

MINERALS

- ◌● Coal
- ■ Iron
- ◆ Tungsten
- ◆ Manganese
- △ Zinc
- □ Tin
- ✳ Lead
- ⊟ Phosphate rock
- ⊞ Antimony

Economic legend:
- Intensive subsistence agriculture, wheat dominant
- Intensive subsistence agriculture, rice dominant
- Mixed woodland, cropland
- Other less developed agricultural areas
- Nomadic herding
- Non-productive

Labels: MILLET, RICE, MILLET, RICE, COTTON, MILLET, SOYBEANS, COTTON, COTTON, TEA, TEA

POPULATION

Sq. Km.	Sq. mi.	Sq. km.	Sq. mi.
Uninhabited		25–50	60–125
<1	<2	50–100	125–250
1–10	2–25	100–200	250–500
10–25	25–60	> 200	> 500

□ Metropolitan areas over 2,000,000 Population
○ Metropolitan areas 1,000,000 to 2,000,000 Population

Cities: Qiqihar · Harbin · Changchun · Fushun · Shenyang · Anshan · Fengtian · Tangshan · Lüda · Tianjin · Taiyuan · Qingdao · Lanzhou · Jinan · Xi'an · Zhengzhou · Nanjing · Shanghai · Hangzhou · Chengdu · Wuhan · Chongqing · Fuzhou · T'aipei · Canton · Kaohsiung · Hong Kong

For larger scale coverage of Shanghai see page 68.

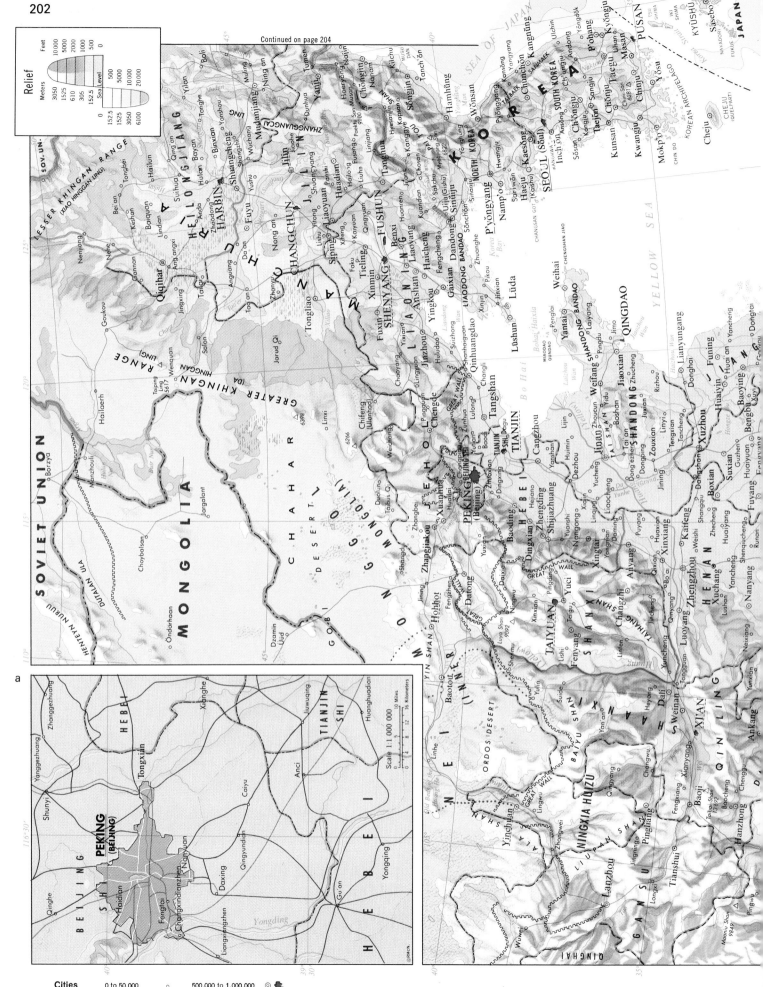

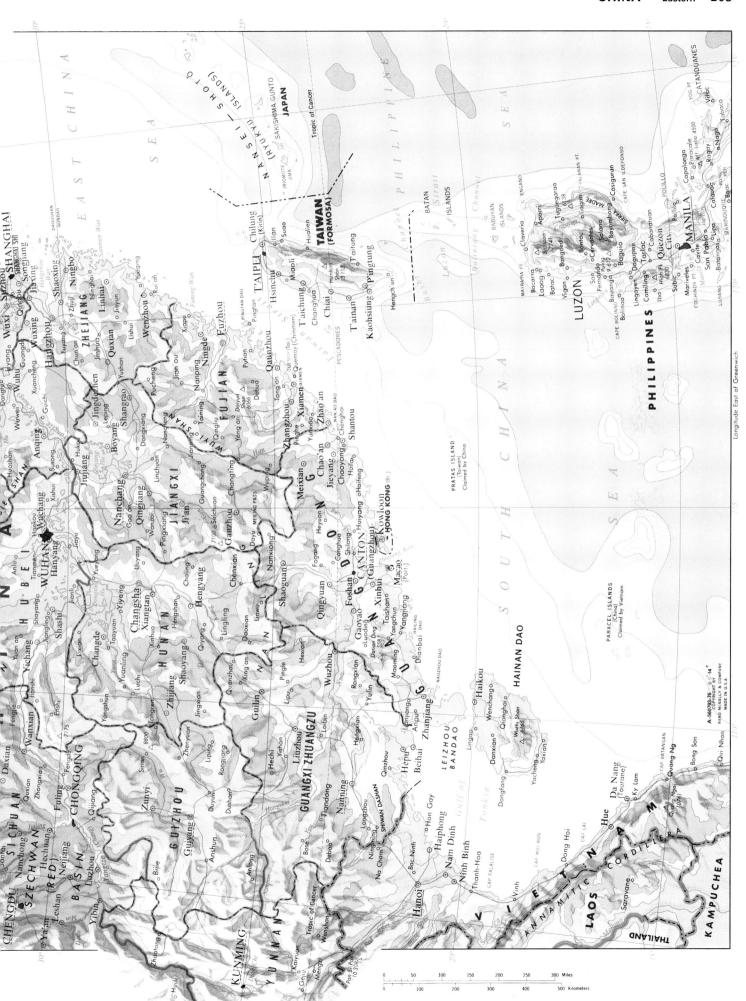

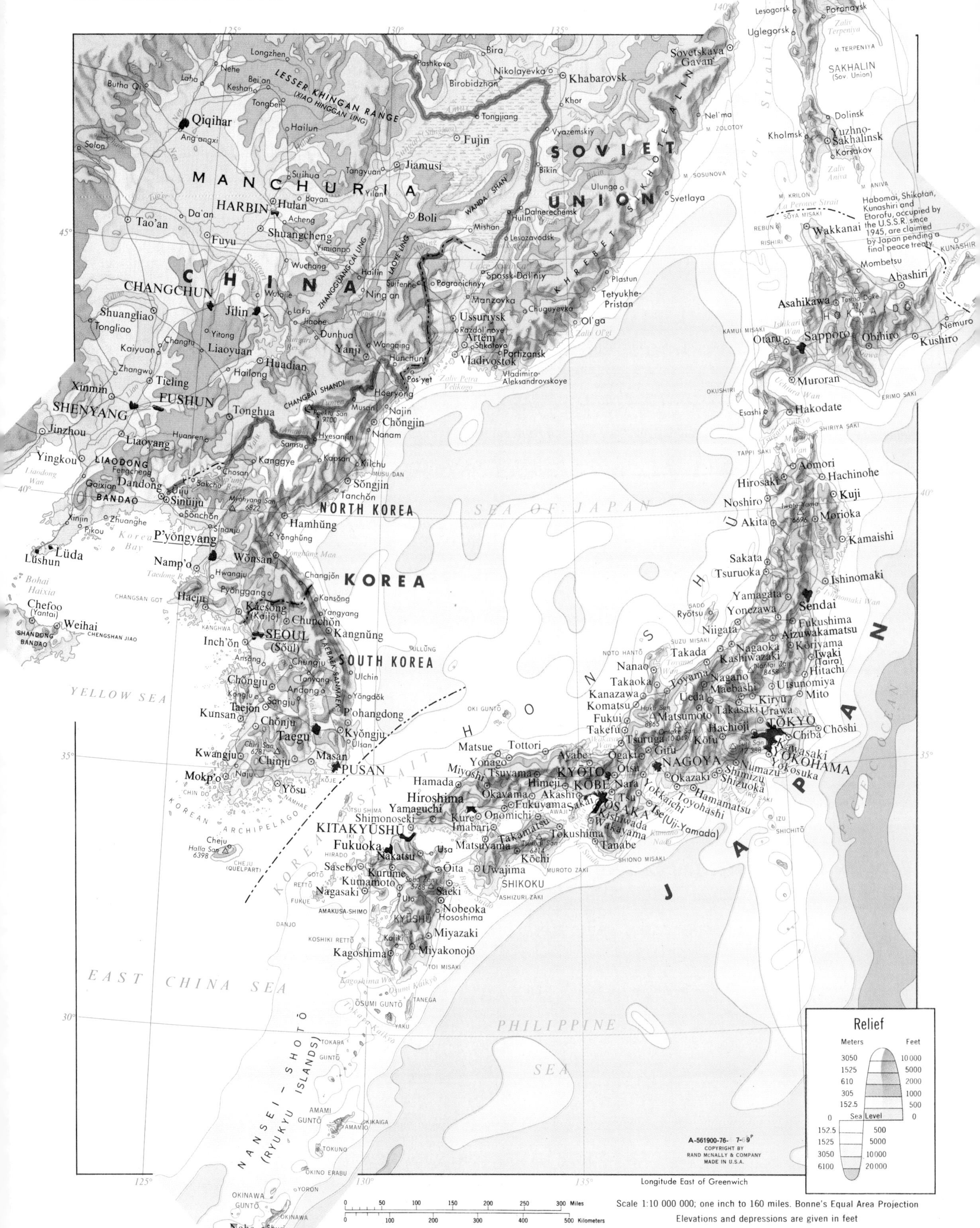

KOREA AND JAPAN

Relief

Meters	Feet
3050	10 000
1525	5000
610	2000
305	1000
152.5	500
0	Sea Level
152.5	500
1525	5000
3050	10 000
6100	20 000

A-561900-76- 7-9"
COPYRIGHT BY
RAND McNALLY & COMPANY
MADE IN U.S.A.

Longitude East of Greenwich

Scale 1:10 000 000; one inch to 160 miles. Bonne's Equal Area Projection

Elevations and depressions are given in feet

Habomai, Shikotan, Kunashiri and Etorofu, occupied by the U.S.S.R. since 1945, are claimed by Japan pending a final peace treaty.

a

For larger scale coverage of Tokyo, Ōsaka,
Kōbe, and Kyōto see page 68 and 69.

b

Scale 1:4 000 000, one inch to 64 miles. Conic Projection
Elevations and depressions are given in feet.

Scale 1:1 000 000

Scale 1:1 000 000

COPYRIGHT BY
RAND McNALLY & COMPANY
MADE IN U.S.A.

A-561992-76 -5- -82

Longitude East of Greenwich

SEA OF JAPAN

PACIFIC OCEAN

PHILIPPINE SEA

EAST CHINA SEA

KOREA

PUSAN

KITAKYŪSHŪ

KYŪSHŪ

SHIKOKU

TOKYO

YOKOHAMA

NAGOYA

ŌSAKA

KYŌTO

KŌBE

CHIBA

KANAGAWA

NARA

HYŌGO

Relief

Meters	Feet
3050	10 000
1525	5000
610	2000
305	1000
152.5	500
0	Sea Level 0
152.5	500
1525	5000
3050	10 000

Cities and Towns

0 to 50,000	○	500,000 to 1,000,000
50,000 to 500,000	⊙	1,000,000 and over

Relief

Meters		Feet
3050		10 000
1525		5000
610		2000
305		1000
152.5		500
Sea Level		
152.5		500
1525		5000
3050		10 000
6100		20 000

A-569800-76 8.10-23"
COPYRIGHT BY
RAND McNALLY & COMPANY
MADE IN U.S.A.

100°   105°   Longitude East of Greenwich   110°   115°   120°

Scale 1:16 000 000; one inch to 250 miles. Polyconic Projection
Elevations and depressions are given in feet

Continued on pages 198-199

PHILIPPINE

PHILIPPINES

SEA

PHILIPPINES

PHILIPPINE

SEA

SULU

SEA

LUZON

Cabugao
Banguod
Vigan
Narvacan
Candon
Cervantes
Luna
San Fernando
Bauang
Bolinao
Aringay
Bani
Alaminos
Agno
Burgos
Lingayen
San Carlos
Santa Cruz
Infanta
Mangatarem
Camiling
Candelaria
Iba
Palauig
Pinatubo
5771
S. Narciso
S. Antonio
Subic
Olongapo
Orani
Balanga
Mariveles
Orion
Cavite

Iguig
Tuguegarao
Bangued
Cabagan
Luboagan
Bontoc
Mt. Amuyao
8799
Cauayan
Santiago
Echague
Jones
Bagabag
Bayombong
Bambang
Dupax

Pulog
9626
S. Juan
Baguio
Salonge
San Fabian
Nicolas
Tayug
S. Quintin
Urdaneta
Rosales
Bayambang
San Jose
Muñoz
Gerona
Victoria
Tarlac
Cabanatuan
Concepcion
Gapan
S. Miguel
Angeles
Arayat
S. Fernando
Guagua
Malolos
Sta. Maria
Infanta
Malabon
Quezon City
MANILA
Pasig
Calamba

Divilacan Bay
PALANAN PT.
Palanan Bay

Cosiguran

DIJOHAN PT.
CAPE SAN ILDEFONSO

Baler Bay
Baler CAPE ENCANTO

Dingalan Bay

POLILLO IS.
POLILLO
PATNANONGAN
Polillo
JOMALIG

Lamon Bay
BALESIN
Capalonga
Paracale
Labo Talisay
Daet
Mt. Labo
5066
Lagonoy
Mt. Isarog
6450
Naga
Pili
Baao Buhi
Tabaco
Mayon
8077
Ligao
Legazpi

CALAGUAS ISLAND

San Miguel Bay

Iriga Bay

Ragay

CABALETE
ALABAT
Sta. Cruz
Mauban
Nagcarlan
S. Pablo
1777 Mt. Banahao
Atimonan
Gumaca
Macalelon
Catanauan
S. Narciso

LUBANG
IS.
Lubang
AMBIL
ISLAND
GOLD
ISLAND
Balayan
Nasugbu
Silang
Lemery
Lipa
Rosario
Batangas
Lobo
Naic
TALIM
Laguna Bay
Balayan Bay
MARICABAN
Verde I. Passage
VERDE
CAPE CALAVITE

CABRA ISLAND

Unisan
Boac
Gasan
Sta. Cruz
Torrijos
MARINDUQUE
ISLAND
DUMALI PT.
San Pascual
BURIAS
Jones
BANTON
Pinamalayan
ROMBLON ISLAND
Romblon
TABLAS
Odiongan
SIBUYAN
ISLAND
SIBUYAN
SEA
TICAO
ISLAND
S. Jacinto
Aroroy
Masbate
MASBATE

MINDORO
Paluan
Mt. Halcon
8471
Calapan
Naujan
Mamburao
Sablayan
Mt. Baco
8163
Calintaan

Knob Pk.
3031
S. Jose
Bulalacao
Looc
DONGON PT.
BUSUANGA
TARA
ILIN ISLAND

Scale 1:4 000 000

0 10 20 30 40 Miles
0 10 20 30 40 50 60 Kilometers

©RMCN

CATANDUANES
ISLAND
Sorsogon
Catbalogan
SAMAR
Tacloban
LEYTE
DINAGAT ISLAND
BOHOL
Butuan
Cagayan
MINDANAO
Apo
9692
Davao

Legazpi
Lucena

SOUTH CHINA SEA

CAIMAN PT.
Dasol Bay
SAMPALOC PT.
CORREGIDOR ISLAND

PALAU IS.
(T.T.P.I.)

PULAU MIANGAS

SONSOROL
ISLANDS

KEPULAUAN
TALAUD

PULAU SANGIHE

PULAU SIAU

Tondano
Ternate
HALMAHERA
MOROTAI
KEPULAUAN
MAPIA

Laut
Maluku
Molucca Sea

Labuha
KEPULAUAN OBI
PULAU
OBI
Sorong
Manokwari
BIAK
JAZIRAH
DOBERAI
PULAU
YAPEN

PULAU BACAN
PULAU
MANGOLE
PULAU
MISOOL
PULAU
NUMFOOR

KEPULAUAN
SULA
SERAM
Piru
Bula
Kaimana
Fakfak

Equator

NINIGO GROUP
HERMIT IS.
ADMIRALTY ISLANDS
MUSSAU
ISLAND
EMIRA
ISLAND
MANUS
ISLAND
NEW HANOVER
Kavieng
BISMARCK
NEW
IRELAND
ARCH.
Namatanai
Rabaul
Kokopo

TG. PERKAM
Jayapura
(Sukarnapura)
PEGUNUNGAN VAN REES
Aitape
Wewak

Teluk
Cenderawasih

SALAWATI
Teluk Berau

PULAU ADI

PEGUNUNGAN MAOKE
Puncak Jaya
16 503
Puncak Trikora
15 584

Sepik

KARKAR ISLAND
Madang
LONG ISLAND

WITU
ISLANDS
Talasea
The Father
7546

Ambon
PULAU AMBON

BURU
PULAU
WETAR

KEPULAUAN
BANDA

KEPULAUAN
KAI
KAI KECIL
Dobo
KEPULAUAN
ARU
KEPULAUAN
TRANGAN

NEW GUINEA
Mt. Giluwe 14 330
Mt. Bangeta
13 520
Mt. Wilhelm 14 793

BISMARCK RA.

PAPUA
NEW GUINEA
Lae
Morobe

Huon Gulf

NEW BRITAIN
NEW BRITAIN TRENCH

KEPULAUAN
LUCIPARA
LAUT BANDA
(BANDA SEA)

PULAU WETAR
PULAU
DAMAR
PULAU BABAR
YAMDENA
KEPULAUAN
TANIMBAR

Dili
PULAU
MOA
PULAU
SELARU
TANJUNG VALS
Merauke
Daru

PULAU
YOS
SUDARSA

Mt. Albert Edward
13 090
Buna
Port Moresby
Mt. Victoria
13 240
OWEN STANLEY RA.

Gulf
of Papua

TROBRIAND IS.
WOODLARK
ISLAND
D'ENTRECASTEAUX IS.
Samarai

TIMOR
SEA

ARAFURA SEA

MELVILLE
ISLAND
COBOURG
PEN.
CROKER ISLAND
BATHURST
ISLAND
Darwin

WESSEL IS.

C. ARNHEM

Gulf of Carpentaria

Torres Strait
C. YORK
CAPE
YORK
PEN.
GREAT BARRIER REEF

CORAL SEA

AUSTRALIA

0 50 100 200 300 400 500 Miles
0 100 200 400 600 800 Kilometers

Continued on pages 214-215

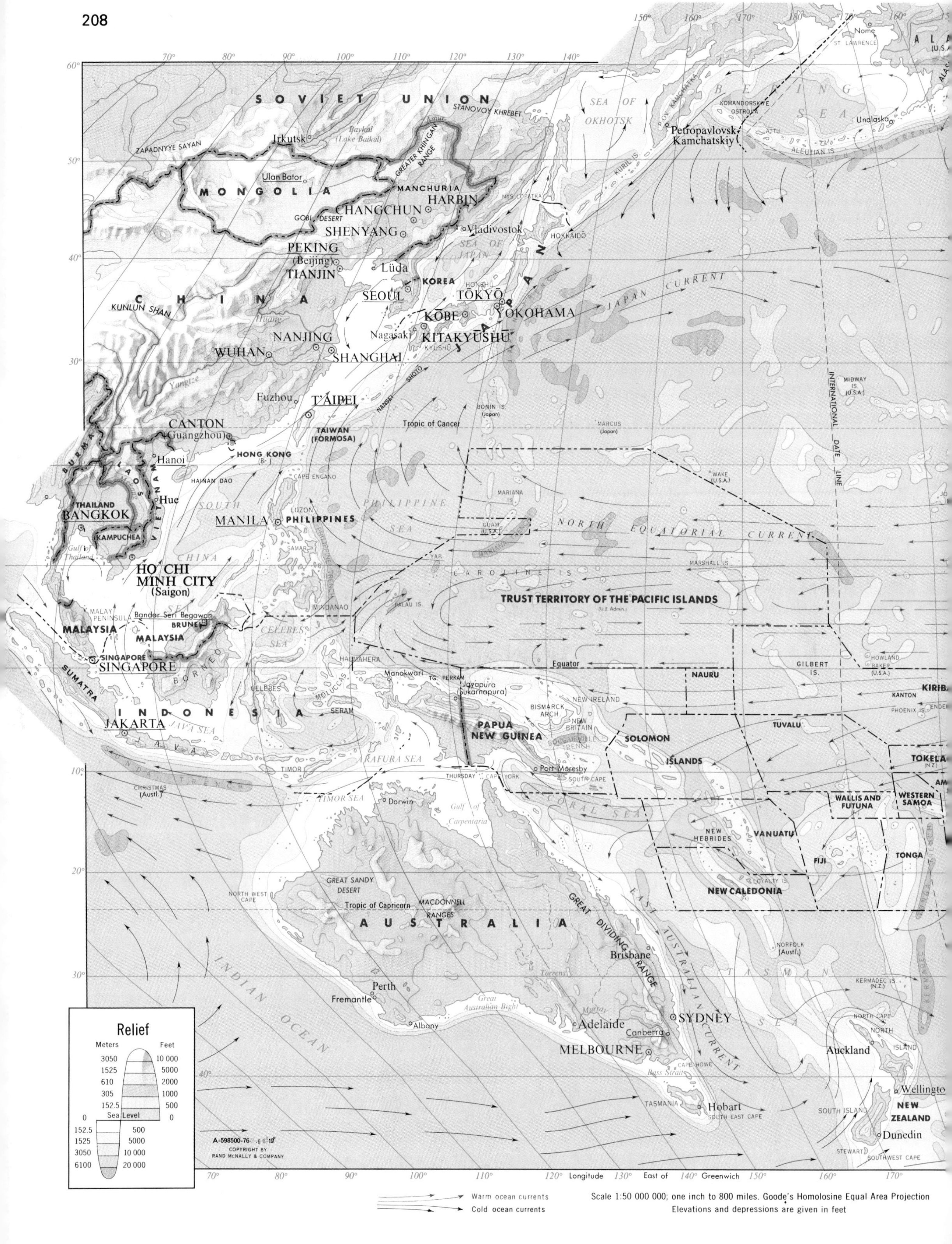

208

SOVIET UNION

Irkutsk
Baykal (Lake Baikal)
ZAPADNYYE SAYAN
STANOVOY KHREBET
SEA OF OKHOTSK
P-OV KAMCHATKA
KOMANDORSKIYE OSTROVA
Petropavlovsk-Kamchatskiy
Nome
ST. LAWRENCE
AL
(U.S.)
KURIL IS.
ATTU
ALEUTIAN IS.
Unalaska
BE RING SEA

Ulan Bator
MONGOLIA
GREATER KHINGAN RANGE
MANCHURIA
HARBIN
CHANGCHUN
SHENYANG
GOBI DESERT
MYS LOPATRA
HOKKAIDO

PEKING (Beijing)
TIANJIN
Lüda
Vladivostok
SEA OF JAPAN
KOREA
CHINA
KUNLUN SHAN
SEOUL
TOKYO
KOBE
YOKOHAMA
HONSHU
JAPAN CURRENT

NANJING
Hwang
Nagasaki
KITAKYUSHU
KYUSHU
NANSEI SHOTO
WUHAN
SHANGHAI
Yangtze

Fuzhou
T'AIPEI
TAIWAN (FORMOSA)
Tropic of Cancer
BONIN IS. (Japan)
MARCUS (Japan)
MIDWAY IS. (U.S.A.)
INTERNATIONAL DATE LINE

CANTON (Guangzhou)
HONG KONG (Br.)
HAINAN DAO
CAPE ENGAÑO
WAKE (U.S.A.)

Hanoi
BURMA
LAOS
VIETNAM
Hue
SOUTH CHINA SEA
PHILIPPINE SEA
LUZON
MANILA
PHILIPPINES
MARIANA IS.
NORTH EQUATORIAL CURRENT

THAILAND
BANGKOK
Gulf of Thailand
KAMPUCHEA
SAMAR
GUAM (U.S.A.)
MARSHALL IS.
CAROLINE IS.

HO CHI MINH CITY (Saigon)
MINDANAO
PALAU IS.
TRUST TERRITORY OF THE PACIFIC ISLANDS (U.S. Admin.)
KIRIB.
KANTON
PHOENIX IS.

MALAY PENINSULA
MALAYSIA
Bandar Seri Begawan
BRUNEI
CELEBES SEA
HALMAHERA
Equator
NAURU
GILBERT IS.
HOWLAND IS. (U.S.A.)

SINGAPORE
BORNEO
CELEBES
MOLUCCAS
SERAM
Manokwari
TG. PERKAM
Jayapura (Sukarnapura)
NEW IRELAND
BISMARCK ARCH.
NEW BRITAIN
TUVALU
TOKELAU (N.Z.)

SUMATRA
INDONESIA
JAKARTA
JAVA
JAVA SEA
ARAFURA SEA
PAPUA NEW GUINEA
BOUGAINVILLE TRENCH
SOLOMON ISLANDS
WESTERN SAMOA
WALLIS AND FUTUNA

JAVA TRENCH
CHRISTMAS (Austl.)
TIMOR
TIMOR SEA
THURSDAY
CAPE YORK
Port Moresby
SOUTH CAPE
CORAL SEA
NEW HEBRIDES
VANUATU
FIJI
TONGA

Darwin
Gulf of Carpentaria
NORTH WEST CAPE
GREAT SANDY DESERT
Tropic of Capricorn
MACDONNELL RANGES
AUSTRALIA
GREAT DIVIDING RANGE
EAST AUSTRALIAN CURRENT
LOYALTY IS.
NEW CALEDONIA

Brisbane
NORFOLK (Austl.)

Perth
Fremantle
Torrens
Murray
Great Australian Bight
Albany
SYDNEY
Adelaide
Canberra
TASMAN SEA
KERMADEC IS. (N.Z.)
NORTH CAPE
NORTH ISLAND
Auckland

MELBOURNE
Bass Strait
CAPE HOWE
Hobart
TASMANIA
SOUTH EAST CAPE
SOUTH ISLAND
NEW ZEALAND
Wellington
Dunedin
STEWART
SOUTHWEST CAPE

INDIAN OCEAN

Relief
Meters / Feet
3050 / 10 000
1525 / 5000
610 / 2000
305 / 1000
152.5 / 500
0 Sea Level 0
152.5 / 500
1525 / 5000
3050 / 10 000
6100 / 20 000

A-598500-76
COPYRIGHT BY
RAND McNALLY & COMPANY

Longitude East of Greenwich

Warm ocean currents
Cold ocean currents

Scale 1:50 000 000; one inch to 800 miles. Goode's Homolosine Equal Area Projection
Elevations and depressions are given in feet

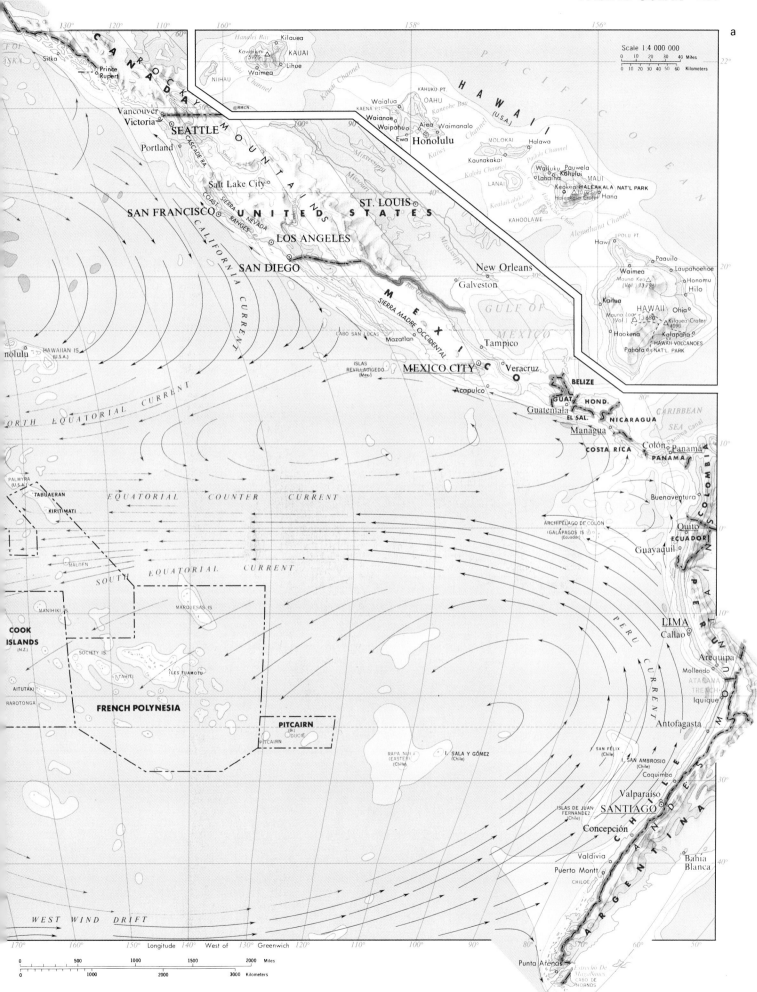

a

Scale 1:4 000 000
0 10 20 30 40 Miles
0 10 20 30 40 50 60 Kilometers

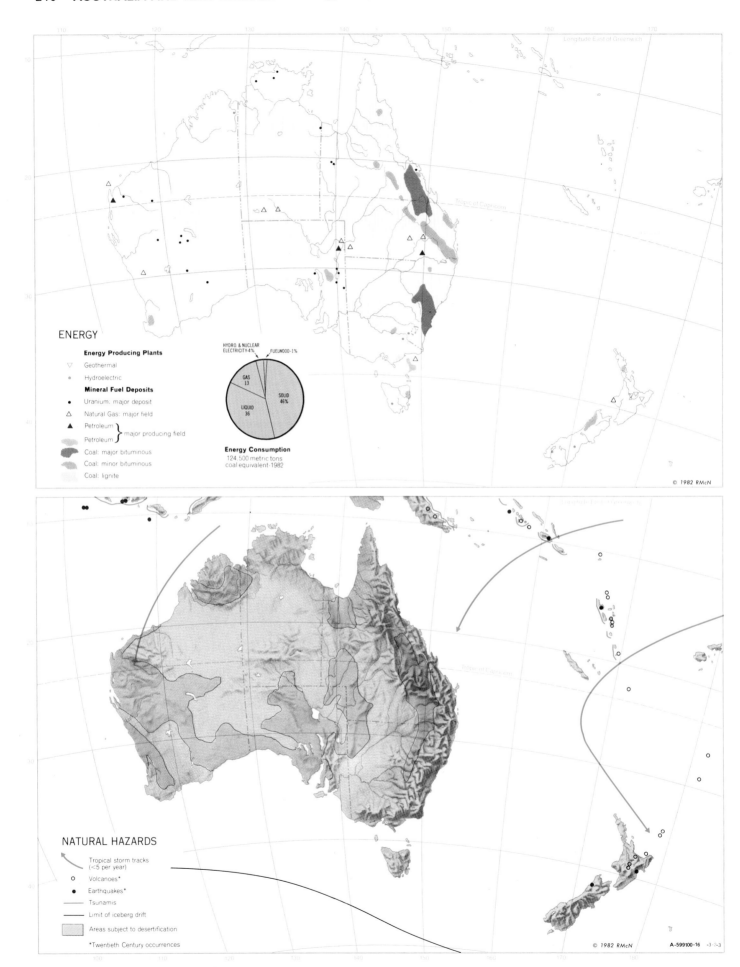

ENERGY

Energy Producing Plants

▽ Geothermal

• Hydroelectric

Mineral Fuel Deposits

• Uranium: major deposit

△ Natural Gas: major field

▲ Petroleum

Petroleum } major producing field

Coal: major bituminous

Coal: minor bituminous

Coal: lignite

HYDRO. & NUCLEAR ELECTRICITY-4%

FUELWOOD-1%

GAS 13

SOLID 46%

LIQUID 36

Energy Consumption
124,500 metric tons
coal equivalent-1982

© 1982 RMcN

NATURAL HAZARDS

↗ Tropical storm tracks (<5 per year)

○ Volcanoes*

● Earthquakes*

— Tsunamis

— Limit of iceberg drift

Areas subject to desertification

*Twentieth Century occurrences

© 1982 RMcN

A-599100-16 -3-3-3

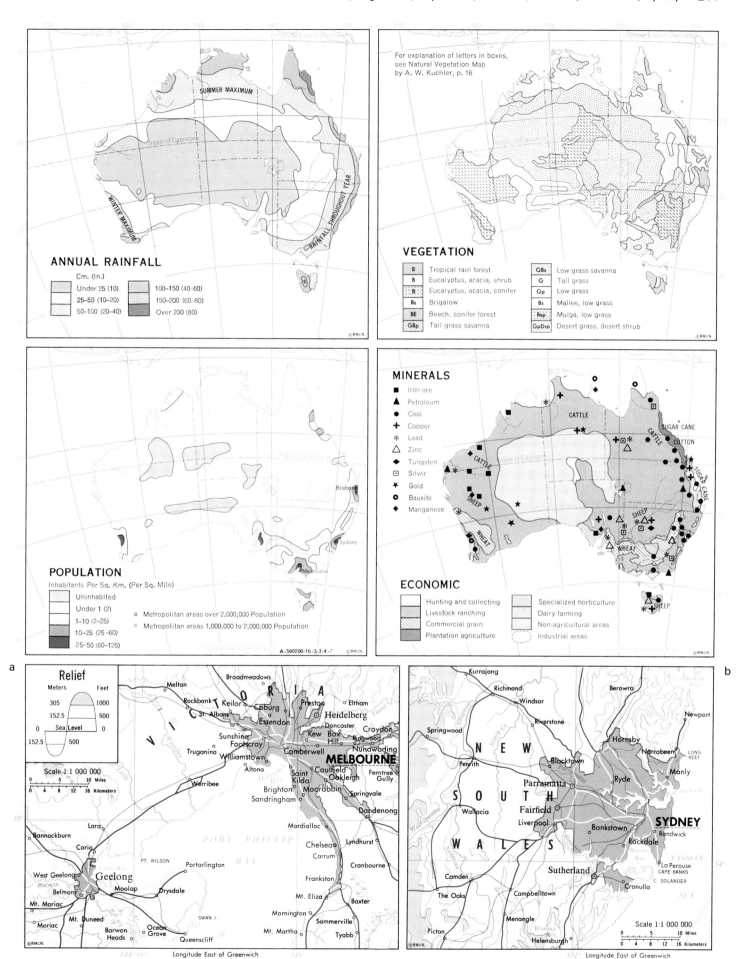

ANNUAL RAINFALL

Cm. (In.)

Under 25 (10)	100–150 (40–60)
25–50 (10–20)	150–200 (60–80)
50–100 (20–40)	Over 200 (80)

VEGETATION

For explanation of letters in boxes,
see Natural Vegetation Map
by A. W. Kuchler, p. 16

B	Tropical rain forest	GBs	Low grass savanna
B	Eucalyptus, acacia, shrub	G	Tall grass
B	Eucalyptus, acacia, conifer	Gp	Low grass
Bs	Brigalow	Bs	Mallee, low grass
BE	Beech, conifer forest	Bsp	Mulga, low grass
GBp	Tall grass savanna	GpDsp	Desert grass, desert shrub

POPULATION

Inhabitants Per Sq. Km. (Per Sq. Mile)

Uninhabited	
Under 1 (2)	
1–10 (2–25)	
10–25 (25–60)	
25–50 (60–125)	

□ Metropolitan areas over 2,000,000 Population
○ Metropolitan areas 1,000,000 to 2,000,000 Population

A-590200-16-3-3-4 -7   ©RMcN.

MINERALS

■	Iron ore
▲	Petroleum
●	Coal
+	Copper
✳	Lead
△	Zinc
◆	Tungsten
⊡	Silver
★	Gold
⦾	Bauxite
◆	Manganese

ECONOMIC

Hunting and collecting	Specialized horticulture
Livestock ranching	Dairy farming
Commercial grain	Non-agricultural areas
Plantation agriculture	Industrial areas

a

Relief

Meters	Feet
305	1000
152.5	500
0 Sea Level	0
152.5	500

Scale 1:1 000 000

0   5   10 Miles
0 4 8 12 16 Kilometers

Longitude East of Greenwich

b

Scale 1:1 000 000

0   5   10 Miles
0 4 8 12 16 Kilometers

Longitude East of Greenwich

For larger scale coverage of
Melbourne and Sydney see page 70

SINGAPORE

BORNEO

CELEBES

SERAM

Jaya

SUMATRA

Palembang

Banjarmasin

Ujung Pandang

Java Sea

JAKARTA

Surabaya

JAVA

SUMBA

TIMOR

Arafura Sea

CA
YO
PENIN

Timor
Sea

Darwin

Gulf
of
Carpentaria

INDIAN OCEAN

KIMBERLEY
PLATEAU

Daly

Victoria

Broome

Fitzroy

Mount Isa

GREAT SANDY DESERT

Alice Springs

GREAT
ARTESIA
BASIN

GIBSON DESERT

SIMPSON
DESERT

Tropic of Capricorn

Carnarvon

GREAT VICTORIA DESERT

Lake
Eyre

Kalgoorlie

NULLARBOR PLAIN

Lake
Gairdner

Broken
Hill

FLINDERS RANGES

Murray

DARLING RA.

Perth

Great Australian Bight

Adelaide

INDIAN OCEAN

Urban

Cropland

Cropland & Woodland

Cropland & Grazing Land

Grassland, Grazing Land

Forest, Woodland

Swamp, Marshland

Shrub, Sparse Grass,
Wasteland (pattern)

Barren Land

Scale 1:24,000,000; one inch to 380 miles. Lambert Azimuthal Equal-Area Projection

NEW
GUINEA

NEW BRITAIN

Moresby

SOLOMON ISLANDS

Equator

KIRIBATI

PACIFIC OCEAN

Coral Sea

Cairns

Townsville

VANUATU

SAMOA ISLANDS

Pago Pago

FIJI
ISLANDS

DIVIDING

RANGE

Rockhampton

NEW
CALEDONIA

ÎLES
LOYAUTÉ

Suva

Nouméa

TONGA ISLANDS

Brisbane

RANGE

SYDNEY

GREAT DIVIDING RANGE

Canberra

Tasman Sea

MELBOURNE

PACIFIC

TASMANIA

Auckland

NORTH ISLAND

Hobart

OCEAN

SOUTHERN ALPS

Wellington

Christchurch

SOUTH ISLAND

STEWART
ISLAND

Dunedin

0   100   200   400   600   800 Miles

0   150   300   600   900   1200 Kilometers

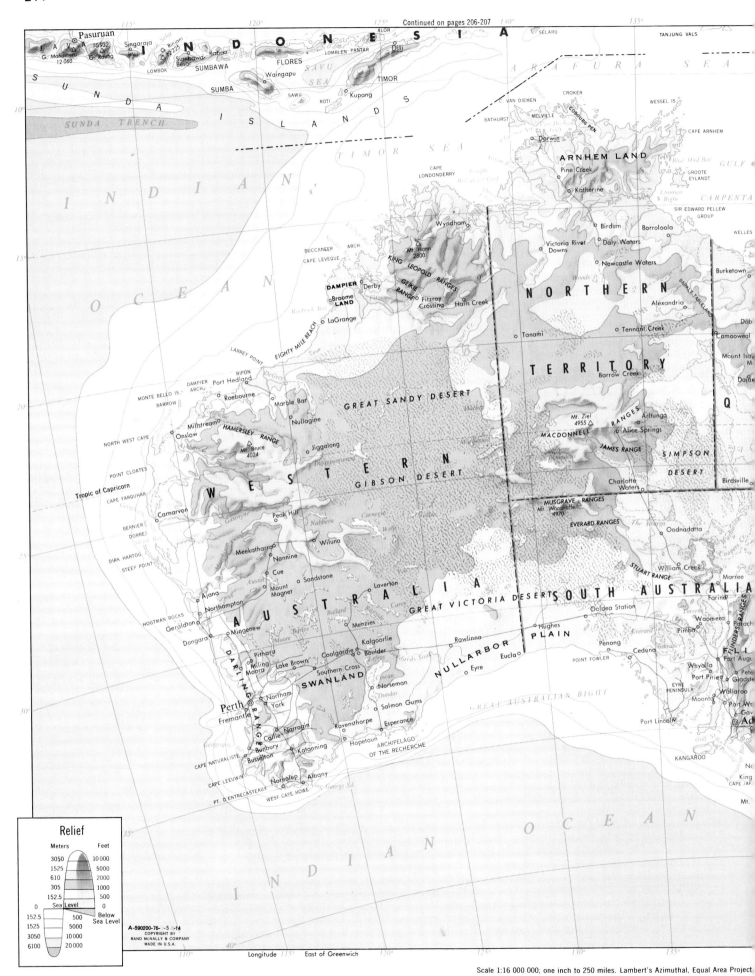

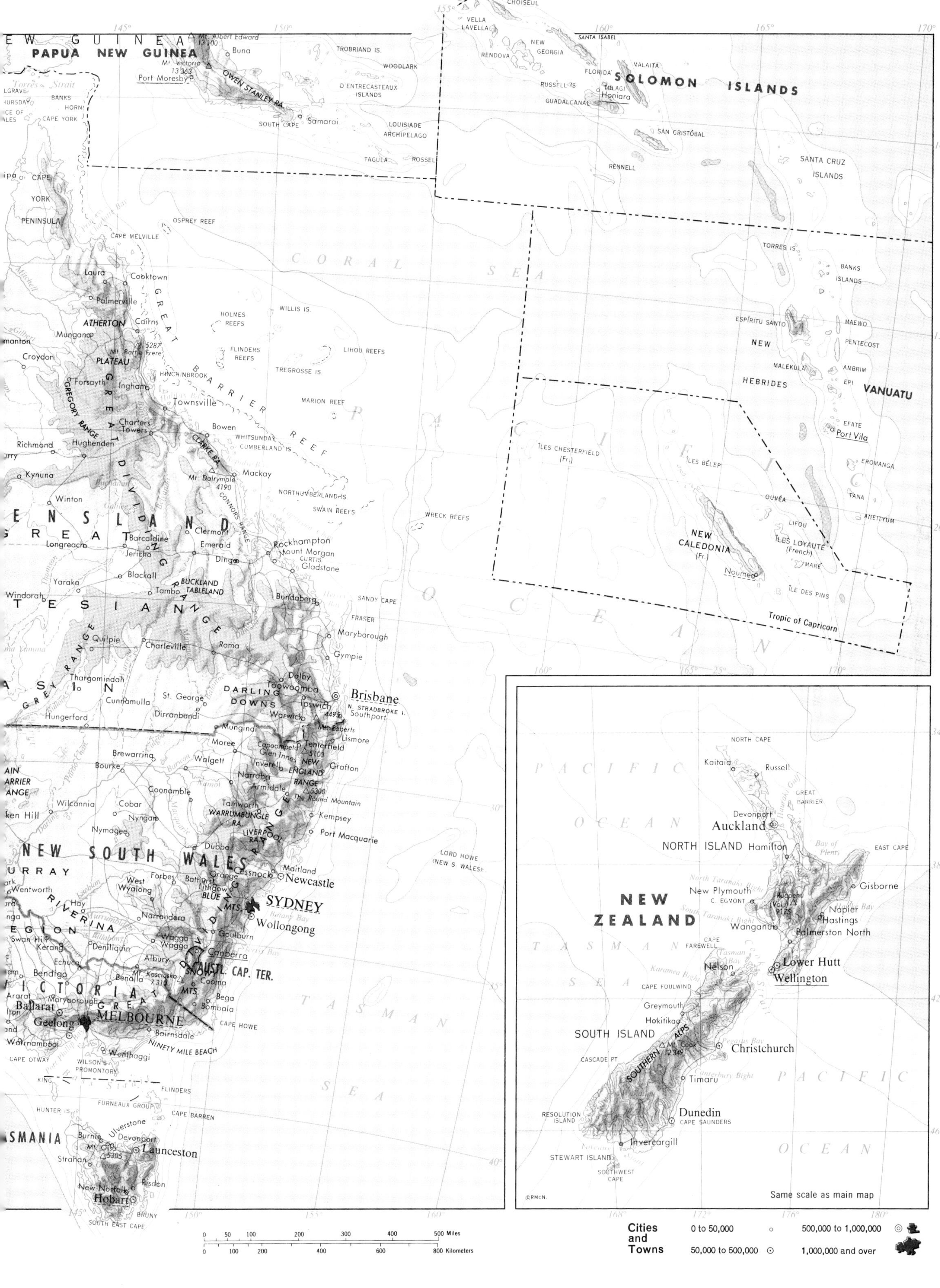

NEW GUINEA
PAPUA NEW GUINEA
Mt. Albert Edward 13,100
Buna
Mt. Victoria 13,363
Port Moresby
OWEN STANLEY RA.
TROBRIAND IS.
WOODLARK
D'ENTRECASTEAUX ISLANDS
SOUTH CAPE
Samarai
LOUISIADE ARCHIPELAGO
TAGULA
ROSSEL

CHOISEUL
VELLA LAVELLA
NEW GEORGIA
RENDOVA
SANTA ISABEL
FLORIDA
MALAITA
TULAGI
Honiara
SOLOMON ISLANDS
RUSSELL IS.
GUADALCANAL
SAN CRISTÓBAL
RENNELL
SANTA CRUZ ISLANDS

BANKS ISLANDS
TORRES IS.
ESPÍRITU SANTO
MAEWO
NEW
PENTECOST
MALEKULA
AMBRIM
EPI
HEBRIDES
VANUATU
EFATE
Port Vila
EROMANGA
ÎLES CHESTERFIELD (Fr.)
ÎLES BÉLEP
TANA
ANEITYUM
OUVÉA
LIFOU
NEW CALEDONIA (Fr.)
ÎLES LOYAUTÉ (French)
MARÉ
Nouméa
ÎLE DES PINS
Tropic of Capricorn

Torres Strait
LGRAVE
BANKS
HORN I.
HURSDAY
PRINCE OF WALES
CAPE YORK
CAPE YORK PENINSULA
ipa

CORAL SEA
OSPREY REEF
CAPE MELVILLE
Laura
Cooktown
Palmerville
ATHERTON
Cairns
PLATEAU
Mungana
Mt. Bartle Frere 5287
Forsayth
Inghams
HINCHINBROOK I.
Townsville
GREAT BARRIER REEF
HOLMES REEFS
WILLIS IS.
FLINDERS REEFS
TREGROSSE IS.
LIHOU REEFS
MARION REEF
GREGORY RANGE
Croydon
Richmond
Hughenden
Charters Towers
CLARKE RA.
Bowen
WHITSUNDAY I.
CUMBERLAND IS.
Mackay
NORTHUMBERLAND IS.
SWAIN REEFS
Kynuna
Winton
Mt. Dalrymple 4190
CONNORS RANGE
Longreach
Barcaldine
Jericho
Emerald
Clermont
Dingo
Rockhampton
Mount Morgan
CURTIS
Gladstone
QUEENSLAND
GREAT DIVIDING RANGE
Blackall
Tambo
BUCKLAND TABLELAND
Yaraka
Bundaberg
Windorah
Quilpie
Charleville
Roma
Sandy Cape
FRASER I.
Maryborough
GREY RANGE
Thargomindah
Cunnamulla
St. George
Dirranbandi
DARLING DOWNS
Toowoomba
Dalby
Gympie
Hungerford
WARRUMBUNGLE RA.
Brisbane
Ipswich
N. STRADBROKE I.
Southport
Warwick
Mt. Roberts 4495
LIVERPOOL RA.
Mungindi
Moree
Tenterfield
Glen Innes 5101
NEW ENGLAND RANGE
Lismore
Grafton
Inverell
Capoompeta 5100
Brewarrina
Bourke
Walgett
Narrabri
Armidale 5300
The Round Mountain
Kempsey
Port Macquarie
Wilcannia
Cobar
Goonamble
Tamworth
Nyngan
Nymagee
Dubbo
GREAT DIVIDING RANGE
ken Hill
NEW SOUTH WALES
LORD HOWE I. (NEW S. WALES)
MURRAY
DARLING
Forbes
West Wyalong
Orange
Bathurst
Lithgow
BLUE MTS.
Cessnock
Maitland
Newcastle
RIVERINA
Hay
Narrandera
Goulburn
SYDNEY
Wollongong
Wentworth
Swan Hill
Kerang
Echuca
Deniliquin
Wagga Wagga
Albury
Canberra
AUSTL. CAP. TER.
Cooma
BARRIER RANGE
Benalla
Kosciusko 7316
SNOWY MTS.
Bega
Bombala
Bendigo
VICTORIA
GREAT DIVIDING RANGE
Maryborough
CAPE HOWE
Ararat
Ballarat
MELBOURNE
Bairnsdale
NINETY MILE BEACH
Geelong
Warrnambool
Wonthaggi
CAPE OTWAY
WILSON'S PROMONTORY
KING I.
FLINDERS I.
FURNEAUX GROUP
CAPE BARREN
HUNTER IS.
TASMANIA
Burnie
Ulverstone
Devonport
MT. OSSA 5305
Launceston
Strahan
New Norfolk
Hobart
BRUNY I.
Risdon
SOUTH EAST CAPE

| | 50 | 100 | 200 | 300 | 400 | 500 Miles |
| 0 | 200 | 400 | 600 | 800 Kilometers |

a

NEW ZEALAND
NORTH CAPE
Kaitaia
Russell
PACIFIC OCEAN
GREAT BARRIER I.
Devonport
Auckland
NORTH ISLAND
Hamilton
Bay of Plenty
EAST CAPE
New Plymouth
C. EGMONT
Ruapehu (Vol.) 9175
Gisborne
Napier
Hastings
Wanganui
Palmerston North
CAPE FAREWELL
Nelson
Lower Hutt
Wellington
TASMAN SEA
CAPE FOULWIND
Greymouth
Hokitika
SOUTH ISLAND
SOUTHERN ALPS
Cook 12,349
Christchurch
CASCADE PT.
Timaru
RESOLUTION ISLAND
Dunedin
CAPE SAUNDERS
Invercargill
STEWART ISLAND
SOUTHWEST CAPE
PACIFIC OCEAN

Same scale as main map

| Cities and Towns | 0 to 50,000 ○ | 500,000 to 1,000,000 ◉ |
| | 50,000 to 500,000 ⊙ | 1,000,000 and over |

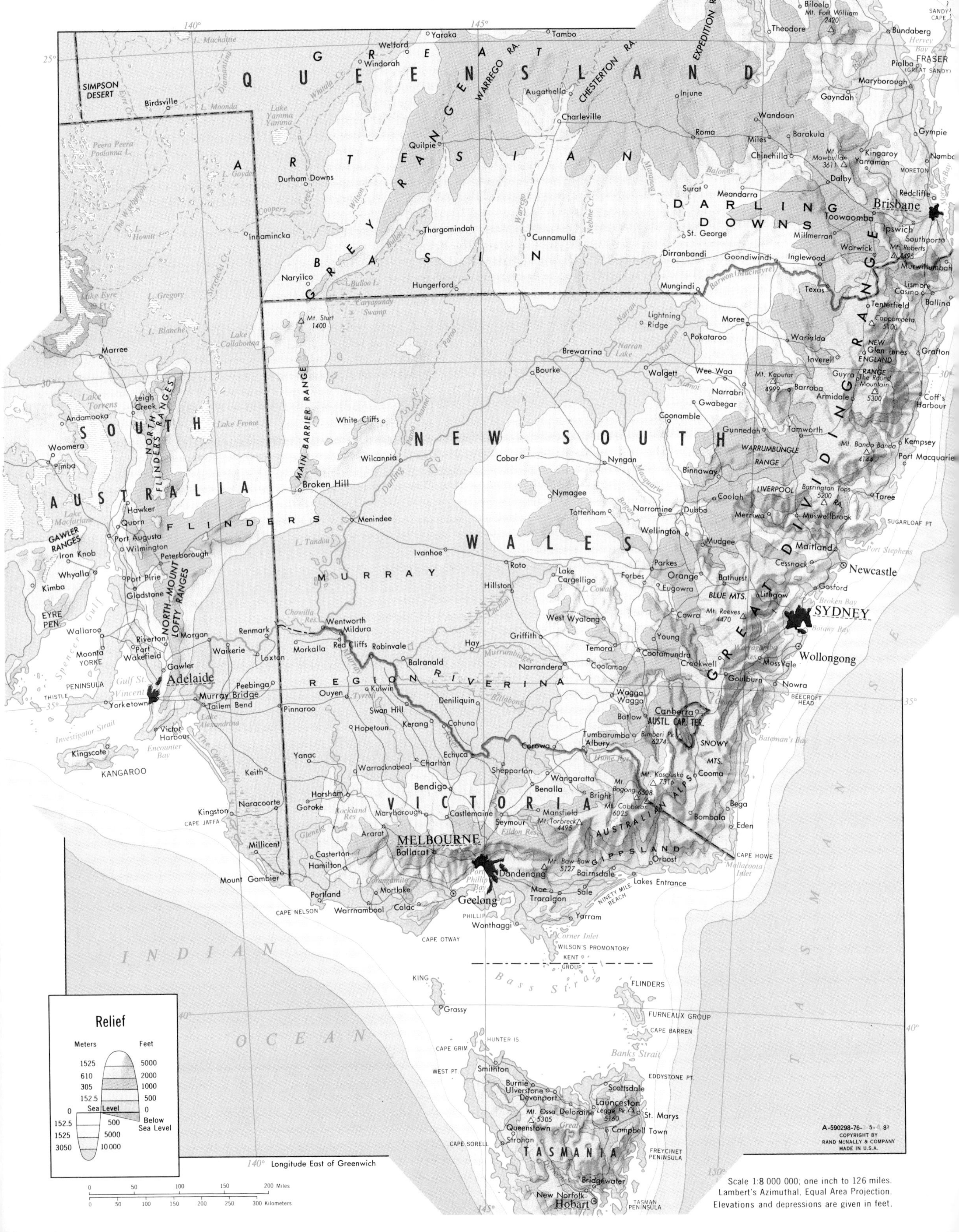

SIMPSON DESERT

Birdsville

Peera Peera Poolanna L.

Yaraka

Welford

Windorah

Tambo

L. Machattie

Diamantina

Whitula R.

WARREGO RA.

Warrego

Langlo R.

GREAT DIVIDING RA.

CHESTERTON RA.

EXPEDITION RA.

Gladstone

Biloela

Mt. Fort William 2420

Bundaberg

SANDY CAPE

Hervey Bay

FRASER I. (GREAT SANDY)

QUEENSLAND

Theodore

Piolba

Maryborough

Gympie

Nambo

MORETON

Durham Downs

Thargomindah

Augathella

Charleville

Injune

Wandoan

Barakula

Mt. Mowbullan 3611

Kingaroy

Yarraman

Dalby

Redcliffe

Brisbane

Ipswich

Southporto

Innamincka

Cunnamulla

Surat

Roma

Miles

Chinchilla

DARLING DOWNS

Meandarra

Millmerran

Toowoomba

Warwick

Mt. Roberts 4495

Murwillumbah

Lismore

Naryilco

Hungerford

Bullo L.

St. George

Dirranbandi

Goondiwindi

Inglewood

Texas

Tenterfield

Casino

Ballina

GREY RANGE

ARTESIAN BASIN

Mungindi

Barwon (Macintyre)

NEW ENGLAND

Glen Innes

Coff's Harbour

QUEENSLAND

Mt. Sturt 1400

Brewarrina

Lightning Ridge

Moree

Pokataroo

Wee Waa

Walgett

Cappeneeta 5100

RANGE The Round Mountain

Grafton

Andamooka

Marree

L. Gregory

L. Blanche

Lake Eyre

Lake Callabonna

Carapundy Swamp

Bulloo

Paroo

Narran

Narran Lake

Narrabri

Gwabegar

Mt. Kaputar 4999

Barraba

Armidale

5300

NEW

Guyra

Woomera

Pimba

Lake Torrens

Leigh Creek

FLINDERS RANGES

NORTH FLINDERS RANGES

White Cliffs

MAIN BARRIER RANGE

Coonamble

Tamworth

Gunnedah

WARRUMBUNGLE RANGE

Mt. Banda Banda 4144

Kempsey

Port Macquarie

SOUTH

Hawker

Quorn

Lake Frome

Wilcannia

Darling

Coonabarabran

Coolah

Merriwa

LIVERPOOL RANGE

Barrington Tops 5200

Taree

AUSTRALIA

FLINDERS

Broken Hill

Menindee

Nymagee

Narromine

Dubbo

Wellington

Mudgee

Muswellbrook

Sugarloaf Pt.

GAWLER RANGES

Iron Knob

Whyalla

Kimba

Port Augusta

Wilmington

Peterborough

FLINDERS

L. Tandou

Ivanhoe

Roto

Lake Cargelligo

L. Cowal

Forbes

Parkes

Orange

Eugowra

BLUE MTS.

Mt. Reeves 4470

Bathurst

Lithgow

Cessnock

Maitland

Port Stephens

Newcastle

EYRE PEN.

Wallaroo

Moonta

YORKE

Port Pirie

Gladstone

Riverton

Morgan

Renmark

Waikerie

Loxton

Wentworth

Mildura

Red Cliffs

Morkalla

Robinvale

Hay

Hillston

MURRAY

West Wyalong

Young

Cootamundra

Cowra

Crookwell

Goulburn

Mt. Kosciusko 7316

Gosford

Broken Bay

SYDNEY

Botany Bay

Moss Vale

Wollongong

BEECROFT HEAD

GREAT DIVIDING RANGE

Balranald

Griffith

Narrandera

Coleambally

Wagga Wagga

Batlow

Canberra

AUSTL. CAP. TER.

Bimberi Pk. 6274

SNOWY MTS.

Nowra

Adelaide

Gawler

NORTH MOUNT LOFTY RANGES

Murray Bridge

Tailem Bend

Pinnaroo

Ouyen

Tyrrell

Kulwin

Swan Hill

Kerang

Deniliquin

Cohuna

Corowa

Albury

Tumbarumba

Mt. Bogong 6508

AUSTRALIAN ALPS

Cooma

Bateman's Bay

Port Vincent

Yorketown

Victor Harbour

Encounter Bay

Lake Alexandrina

Lake Albert

The Coorong

Kingscote

KANGAROO

Keith

Yanac

Hopetoun

Warracknabeal

Charlton

Echuca

Shepparton

Wangaratta

Benalla

Bright

Mt. Cobberas 6025

Bombala

Eden

Gulf St. Vincent

Spencer Gulf

THISTLE I.

PENINSULA

Investigator Strait

Naracoorte

CAPE JAFFA

Kingston

Millicent

Horsham

Goroke

Rockland Res.

Maryborough

Castlemaine

Seymour

Eildon Res.

Mansfield

Mt. Torbreck 4495

Benalla

VICTORIA

Mt. Bogong

Mt. Baw Baw 5127

GIPPSLAND

Orbost

CAPE HOWE

Mallacoota Inlet

Mount Gambier

Casterton

Hamilton

Ararat

Glenelg

MELBOURNE

Ballarat

Dandenong

Moe

Bairnsdale

Sale

Lakes Entrance

NINETY MILE BEACH

Portland

Mortlake

Colac

Geelong

Traralgon

Yarram

Warrnambool

CAPE NELSON

Corangamite

Port Phillip Bay

PHILLIP I.

Wonthaggi

Corner Inlet

WILSON'S PROMONTORY

CAPE OTWAY

KENT GROUP

KING I.

Grassy

FLINDERS

FURNEAUX GROUP

CAPE BARREN

Bass Strait

CAPE GRIM

HUNTER IS.

Banks Strait

WEST PT.

Smithton

Burnie

Ulverstone

Devonport

Scottsdale

EDDYSTONE PT.

Mt. Ossa 5305

Deloraine

Launceston

Legges Pk. 5160

St. Marys

Queenstown

Strahan

Campbell Town

FREYCINET PENINSULA

CAPE SORELL

TASMANIA

New Norfolk

Bridgewater

Hobart

TASMAN PENINSULA

INDIAN

OCEAN

Longitude East of Greenwich

Relief

Meters		Feet
1525		5000
610		2000
305		1000
152.5		500
0	Sea Level	0
152.5		500
1525		5000
3050		10 000

Below Sea Level

0 50 100 150 200 Miles

0 50 100 150 200 250 300 Kilometers

A-590298-76- 5-6 8²
COPYRIGHT BY
RAND McNALLY & COMPANY
MADE IN U.S.A.

Scale 1:8 000 000; one inch to 126 miles.
Lambert's Azimuthal, Equal Area Projection.
Elevations and depressions are given in feet.

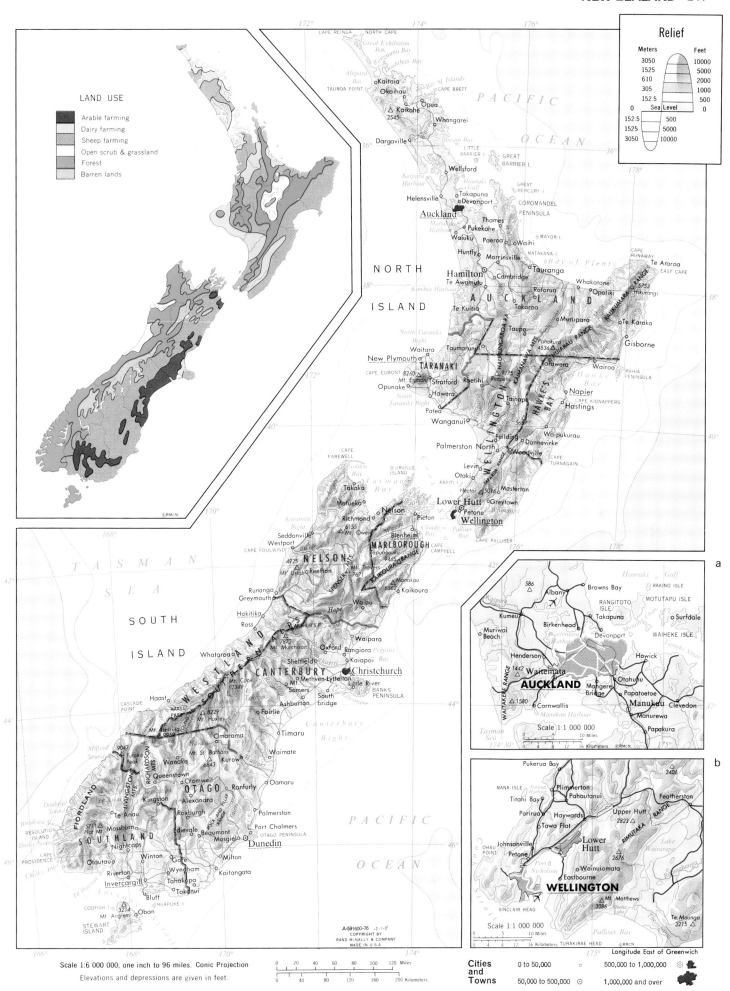

Relief

Meters		Feet
3050		10000
1525		5000
610		2000
305		1000
152.5		500
0	Sea Level	0
152.5		500
1525		5000
3050		10000

LAND USE

- Arable farming
- Dairy farming
- Sheep farming
- Open scrub & grassland
- Forest
- Barren lands

©RMcN

NORTH ISLAND

PACIFIC OCEAN

CAPE REINGA   NORTH CAPE
Great Exhibition Bay
Rangaunu Bay
Ahipara Bay   Doubtless Bay
Kaitaia   Bay of Islands
TAUROA POINT   Okaihau   CAPE BRETT
Kaikohe   Opua
2545   Whangarei
Dargaville   Bream Bay
LITTLE BARRIER I.   GREAT BARRIER I.
Wellsford   GREAT MERCURY I.
Kaipara Harbour   Hauraki Gulf
Helensville   Takapuna   COROMANDEL PENINSULA
Devonport
Auckland   Thames
Manukau Harbour   Pukekohe   MAYOR I.
Waiuku   Paeroa   MATAKANA I.
Huntly   Waihi   Bay of Plenty
Morrinsville   Tauranga   CAPE RUNAWAY
Hamilton   Te Araroa
Te Awamutu   Cambridge   Whakatane   EAST CAPE
AUCKLAND   Rotorua   Opotiki   Hikurangi   3753
Te Kuiti   Tokaroa   Murupara   RAUKUMARA RANGE
Kawhia Harbour   Te Karaka
Taupo
North Taranaki Bight   Taumarunu   Pohokura   Gisborne
Waitara   4536   Taupo   KAWEKA MTS   RUAHINE RANGE
New Plymouth   **TARANAKI**   Tarawera   Wairoa
CAPE EGMONT   8260   Raetihi   9175   Hawke Bay   MAHIA PENINSULA
Mt. Egmont   Stratford   Ruapehu   Taihape   **Napier**
Opunake   Hawera   5687   **Hastings**   CAPE KIDNAPPERS
South Taranaki Bight   Patea   Waipukurau
Wanganui   Feilding   Dannevirke
Palmerston North   Woodville
CAPE FAREWELL   Levin   CAPE TURNAGAIN
Levin   Otaki   Masterton
Golden Bay   D'URVILLE ISLAND   KAPITI I.   Hector   5016
Takaka   Tasman Bay   Greytown
Motueka   Richmond   **Lower Hutt**   Petone
Nelson   Picton   **Wellington**
6155   Blenheim   Cloudy Bay   Palliser Bay   CAPE PALLISER
Seddonville   Mt Owen   **MARLBOROUGH**
Westport   **NELSON**   Tapuaenuku   CAPE CAMPBELL
4925   9465   KAIKOURA RANGE
CAPE FOULWIND   Reefton   Mt Travers   7671
Mt Una   SPENSER MTS   Manakau   8562
Runanga   Kaikoura
Greymouth   Hope   Waiau
Hokitika   ARTHUR'S P.
Ross   Waipara
7873   Oxford   Rangiora   Pegasus Bay
Mt Murchison   Sheffield   Kaiapoi
Whataroa   **CANTERBURY**   **Christchurch**
Methven   Lyttelton
Somers   Little River   BANKS PENINSULA
Mt Cook   South bridge
12349   Ashburton
Haast   **WESTLAND**   Fairlie   Canterbury Bight
CASCADE POINT   HAAST PASS   8229
Mt Huxley   Timaru
Mt Aspiring   Omarama   Waimate
9959   Mt St Bathans
9042   6643   Kurow   PACIFIC OCEAN
Tutoko Peak   Wanaka   Ranfurly
RICHARDSON MTS   Queenstown   Cromwell   Oamaru
LIVINGSTONE MTS   Kingston   Alexandra   Palmerston
FIORDLAND   **OTAGO**   Roxburgh   Port Chalmers
Te Anau   OTAGO PENINSULA
Doubtful Sound   5371   Mossburn   Beaumont   Mosgiel   **Dunedin**
RESOLUTION ISLAND   Flat Mt   Nightcaps
Dusky Sound   **SOUTHLAND**   Otautau   Winton   Milton
CAPE PROVIDENCE   Gore   Milton
Chalky Inlet   Riverton   Wyndham   Kaitangata
Invercargill   Tahakopa
CODFISH I.   3214   Bluff   Tokanui
Mt Anglem   RUAPUKE I.
STEWART ISLAND   Oban

TASMAN SEA

SOUTH ISLAND

©RMcN

Scale 1:6 000 000; one inch to 96 miles. Conic Projection
Elevations and depressions are given in feet.

A-591600-76 -1-1-1'
COPYRIGHT BY
RAND McNALLY & COMPANY
MADE IN U.S.A.

0 20 40 60 80 100 120 Miles
0 40 80 120 160 200 Kilometers

a

PACIFIC OCEAN
Hauraki Gulf
586   Albany   Browns Bay   RAKINO ISLE
Kumeu   RANGITOTO ISLE   MOTUTAPU ISLE
Muriwai Beach   Birkenhead   Takapuna   Surfdale
Devonport   WAIHEKE ISLE
Henderson   Waitemata Harbour   Howick
WAITAKERE RANGE   1442   **AUCKLAND**   Otahuhu
△1580   Mangere Bridge   Papatoetoe   Clevedon
Cornwallis   **Manukau**   Manurewa
Manukau Harbour   Papakura
Tasman Sea

Scale 1:1 000 000
0 5 10 Miles
0 4 8 12 16 Kilometers
©RMcN

174° 30'   175°

b

Pukerua Bay   3406
MANA ISLE   Plimmerton   Featherston
Porirua Harbour   Pahautanui
Titahi Bay   Upper Hutt   RIMUTAKA RANGE
Porirua   Haywards   2823
Tawa Flat   Lake Wairarapa
OHAU POINT   Johnsonville   2676
Petone   **Lower Hutt**
Port Nicholson   Wainuiomata
WELLINGTON   Eastbourne
3086
SINCLAIR HEAD   Mt Matthews   Te Maunga
Palliser Bay   3215
TURAKIRAE HEAD

Scale 1:1 000 000
0 5 10 Miles
0 4 8 12 16 Kilometers   ©RMcN
Longitude East of Greenwich

Cities and Towns

| 0 to 50,000 | ○ | 500,000 to 1,000,000 | ◉ |
| 50,000 to 500,000 | ⊙ | 1,000,000 and over | ● |

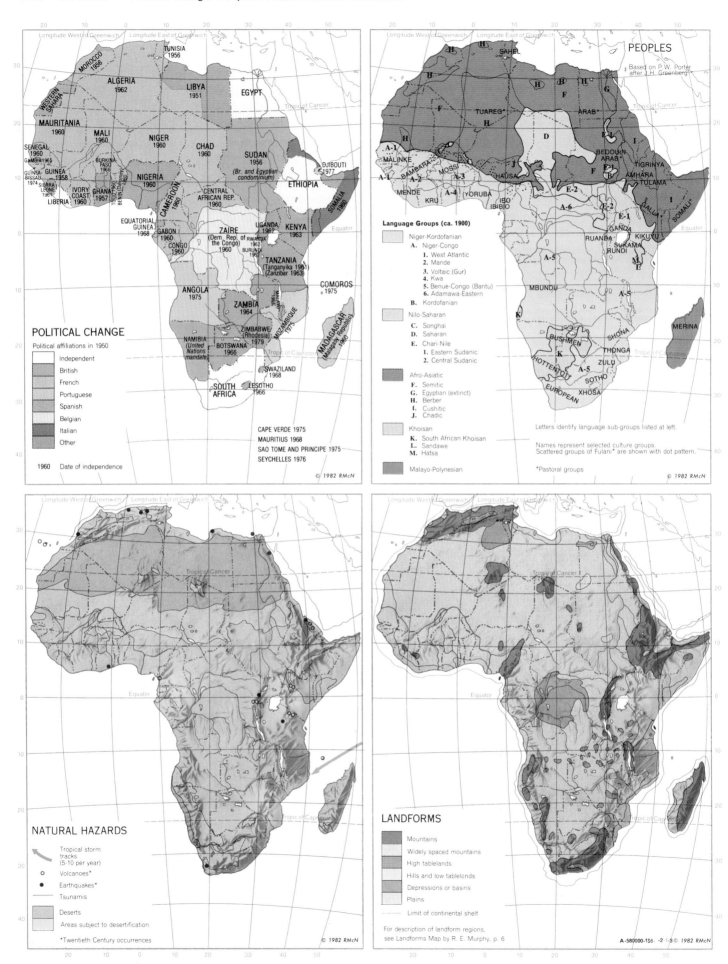

POLITICAL CHANGE

Political affiliations in 1950

- Independent
- British
- French
- Portuguese
- Spanish
- Belgian
- Italian
- Other

1960 Date of independence

MOROCCO 1956
TUNISIA 1956
ALGERIA 1962
LIBYA 1951
EGYPT
WESTERN SAHARA
MAURITANIA 1960
MALI 1960
NIGER 1960
CHAD 1960
SUDAN 1956 (Br. and Egyptian condominium)
SENEGAL 1960
GAMBIA 1965
GUINEA 1958
GUINEA-BISSAU 1974
SIERRA LEONE 1961
LIBERIA
IVORY COAST 1960
GHANA 1957
BURKINA FASO 1960
TOGO 1960
BENIN (Dahomey) 1960
NIGERIA 1960
CAMEROON 1960
CENTRAL AFRICAN REP. 1960
ETHIOPIA
DJIBOUTI 1977
SOMALIA 1960
EQUATORIAL GUINEA 1968
GABON 1960
CONGO 1960
ZAIRE (Dem. Rep. of the Congo) 1960
UGANDA 1962
KENYA 1963
RWANDA 1962
BURUNDI 1962
TANZANIA (Tanganyika 1961) (Zanzibar 1963)
COMOROS 1975
ANGOLA 1975
ZAMBIA 1964
MALAWI 1964
MOZAMBIQUE 1975
ZIMBABWE (Rhodesia) 1979
MADAGASCAR (Malagasy Republic) 1960
NAMIBIA (United Nations mandate)
BOTSWANA 1966
SWAZILAND 1968
SOUTH AFRICA
LESOTHO 1966

CAPE VERDE 1975
MAURITIUS 1968
SAO TOME AND PRINCIPE 1975
SEYCHELLES 1976

© 1982 RMcN

PEOPLES

Based on P.W. Porter after J.H. Greenberg

Language Groups (ca. 1900)

Niger-Kordofanian
  A. Niger-Congo
    1. West Atlantic
    2. Mande
    3. Voltaic (Gur)
    4. Kwa
    5. Benue-Congo (Bantu)
    6. Adamawa-Eastern
  B. Kordofanian

Nilo-Saharan
  C. Songhai
  D. Saharan
  E. Chari-Nile
    1. Eastern Sudanic
    2. Central Sudanic

Afro-Asiatic
  F. Semitic
  G. Egyptian (extinct)
  H. Berber
  I. Cushitic
  J. Chadic

Khoisan
  K. South African Khoisan
  L. Sandawe
  M. Hatsa

Malayo-Polynesian

Letters identify language sub-groups listed at left.

Names represent selected culture groups.
Scattered groups of Fulani* are shown with dot pattern.

*Pastoral groups

© 1982 RMcN

SAHEL
TUAREG
ARAB
BEDOUIN ARAB
TIGRINYA
AMHARA
TULAMA
MALINKE
BAMBARA
MOSSI
HAUSA
MENDE
KRU
YORUBA
IBO
IBIBIO
GALLA
SOMALI
GANDA
KIKUYU
RUANDA
SUKAMA
RUNDI
MBUNDU
BUSHMEN
SHONA
MERINA
HOTTENTOT
THONGA
ZULU
SOTHO
XHOSA
EUROPEAN

NATURAL HAZARDS

→ Tropical storm tracks (5-10 per year)
○ Volcanoes*
● Earthquakes*
— Tsunamis
  Deserts
  Areas subject to desertification

*Twentieth Century occurrences

© 1982 RMcN

LANDFORMS

- Mountains
- Widely spaced mountains
- High tablelands
- Hills and low tablelands
- Depressions or basins
- Plains
- Limit of continental shelf

For description of landform regions,
see Landforms Map by R. E. Murphy, p. 6

A-580000-1S6- -2-1-3 © 1982 RMcN

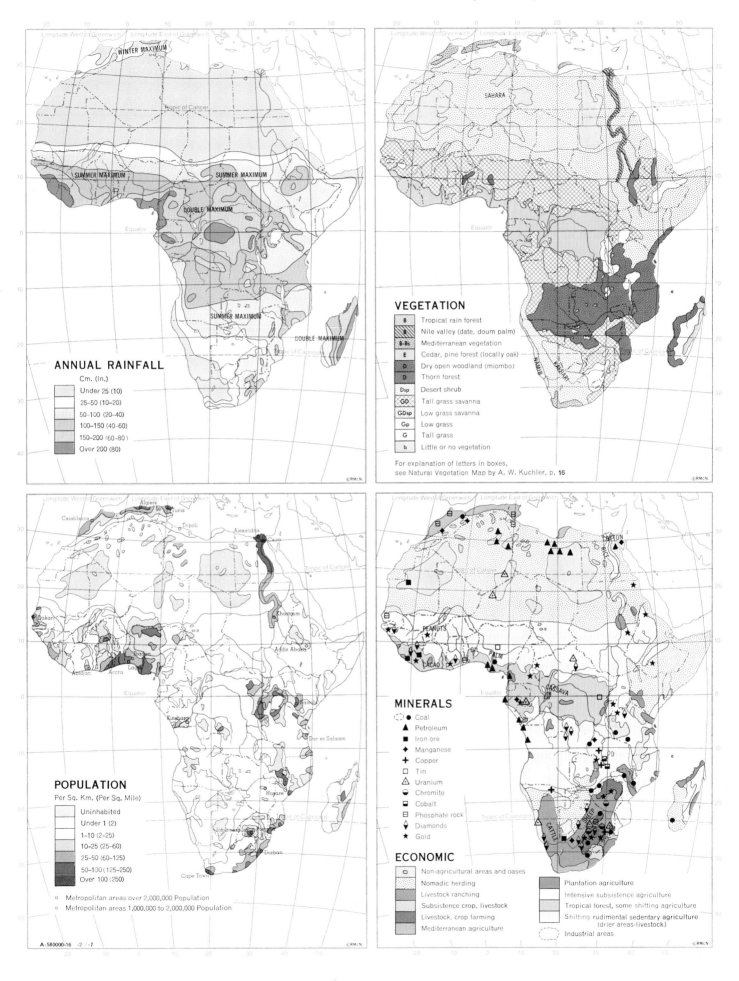

ANNUAL RAINFALL

Cm. (In.)

- Under 25 (10)
- 25–50 (10–20)
- 50–100 (20–40)
- 100–150 (40–60)
- 150–200 (60–80)
- Over 200 (80)

VEGETATION

B	Tropical rain forest
B	Nile valley (date, doum palm)
B–Bs	Mediterranean vegetation
E	Cedar, pine forest (locally oak)
D	Dry open woodland (miombo)
D	Thorn forest
Dsp	Desert shrub
GD	Tall grass savanna
GDsp	Low grass savanna
Gp	Low grass
G	Tall grass
b	Little or no vegetation

For explanation of letters in boxes,
see Natural Vegetation Map by A. W. Kuchler, p. 16

POPULATION

Per Sq. Km. (Per Sq. Mile)

- Uninhabited
- Under 1 (2)
- 1–10 (2–25)
- 10–25 (25–60)
- 25–50 (60–125)
- 50–100 (125–250)
- Over 100 (250)

□ Metropolitan areas over 2,000,000 Population
○ Metropolitan areas 1,000,000 to 2,000,000 Population

A-580000-16 -2 -7

MINERALS

- ◖● Coal
- ▲ Petroleum
- ■ Iron ore
- ◆ Manganese
- ✛ Copper
- ▢ Tin
- △ Uranium
- ◡ Chromite
- ▱ Cobalt
- ⊟ Phosphate rock
- ◊ Diamonds
- ★ Gold

ECONOMIC

- ○ Non-agricultural areas and oases
- Nomadic herding
- Livestock ranching
- Subsistence crop, livestock
- Livestock, crop farming
- Mediterranean agriculture
- Plantation agriculture
- Intensive subsistence agriculture
- Tropical forest, some shifting agriculture
- Shifting rudimental sedentary agriculture (drier areas-livestock)
- Industrial areas

Red Sea

ARABIAN DESERT

BERLIN

Athens

Alexandria

CAIRO

Nile

CRETE

Lake Nasser

NUBIAN DESERT

Nile

LONDON

A

PARIS

ROME

Banghāzī

LIBYAN DESERT

SICILY

MALTA

CORSICA

R

SARDINIA

PYRENEES

Tunis

Tripoli

ENNEDI

Al Faš

N

MADRID

Algiers

MOUNTAINS

GRAND ERG ORIENTAL

TIBESTI

A

ATLAS

GRAND ERG OCCIDENTAL

AHAGGAR

A

Casablanca

H

D

Lake Chad

Ndjamena

Tamanrasset

U

Kano

CANARY ISLANDS

ADRAR DES IFORAS

El Aaiun

S

S

Yaoundé

EL DJOUF

Niger

Tombouctou

Lagos

Niger

Gulf of Guinea

Bamako

Lake Volta

ATLANTIC OCEAN

Tropic of Cancer

Abidjan

ATLANTIC OCEAN

Dakar

CAPE VERDE ISLANDS

Freetown

Mediterranean Sea

ATLANTIC OCEAN

Scale 1:24,000,000; one inch to 380 miles. Lambert Azimuthal Equal-Area Projection

Urban

Cropland

Cropland & Woodland

Cropland & Grazing Land

Grassland, Grazing Land

Forest, Woodland

Swamp, Marshland

Shrub, Sparse Grass,
Wasteland (pattern)

Barren Land

Oasis

Gulf of Aden

Aden

Berbera

DANAKIL

Asmera

Blue Nile

Adis Abeba

White Nile

Mountain Nile

Muqdisho

SEYCHELLES

INDIAN OCEAN

Nairobi

Dar es Salaam

Lake Victoria

COMORO ISLANDS

MADAGASCAR

Antananarivo

Mozambique Channel

Uele

Kisangani

Lake Tanganyika

Lake Nyasa

Congo (Zaire)

Ubangi

Sangui

Lubumbashi

Blantyre

Kasai

Harare

Lusaka

Kinshasa

Congo (Zaire)

Zambezi

Limpopo

INDIAN OCEAN

Durban

Luanda

Johannesburg

KALAHARI DESERT

Orange

Windhoek

NAMIB DESERT

Orange

Cape Town

Tropic of Capricorn

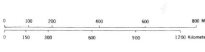

0	100	200	400	600	800 Miles
0	150	300	600	900	1200 Kilometers

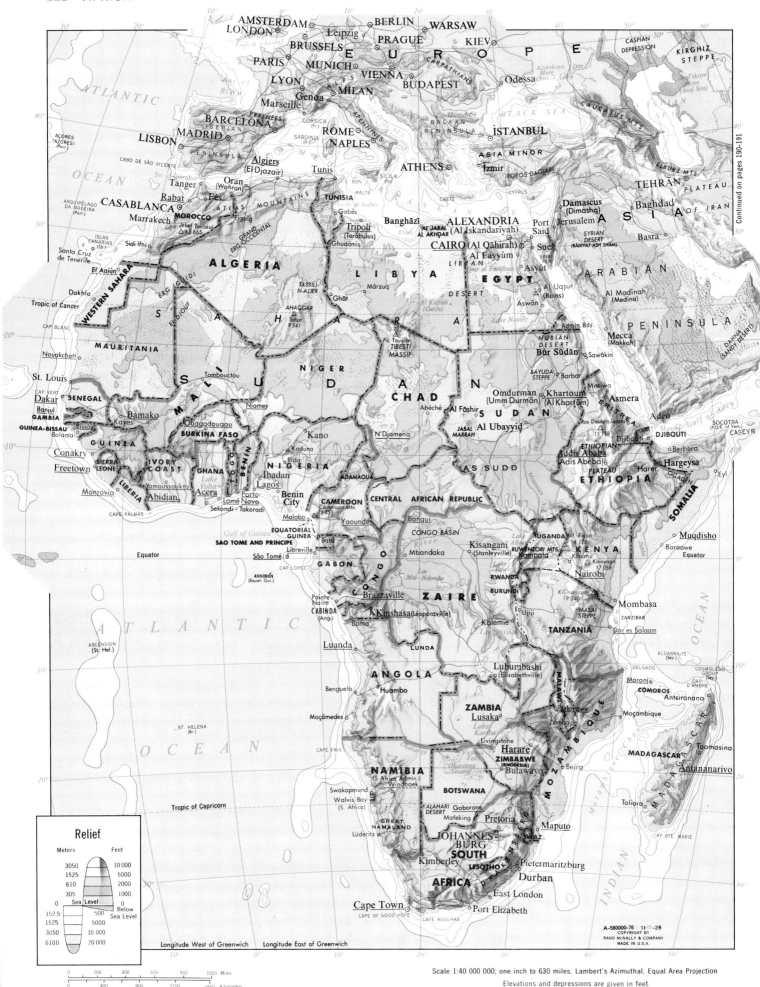

Continued on pages 190-191

Relief

Meters	Feet
3050	10 000
1525	5000
610	2000
305	1000
0 Sea Level	500
	0 Below Sea Level
152.5	500
1525	5000
3050	10 000
6100	20 000

Longitude West of Greenwich   Longitude East of Greenwich

0   200   400   600   800   1000 Miles

0   400   800   1200   1600 Kilometers

A-580000-76 11-28
COPYRIGHT BY
RAND McNALLY & COMPANY
MADE IN U.S.A.

Scale 1:40 000 000; one inch to 630 miles. Lambert's Azimuthal, Equal Area Projection
Elevations and depressions are given in feet.

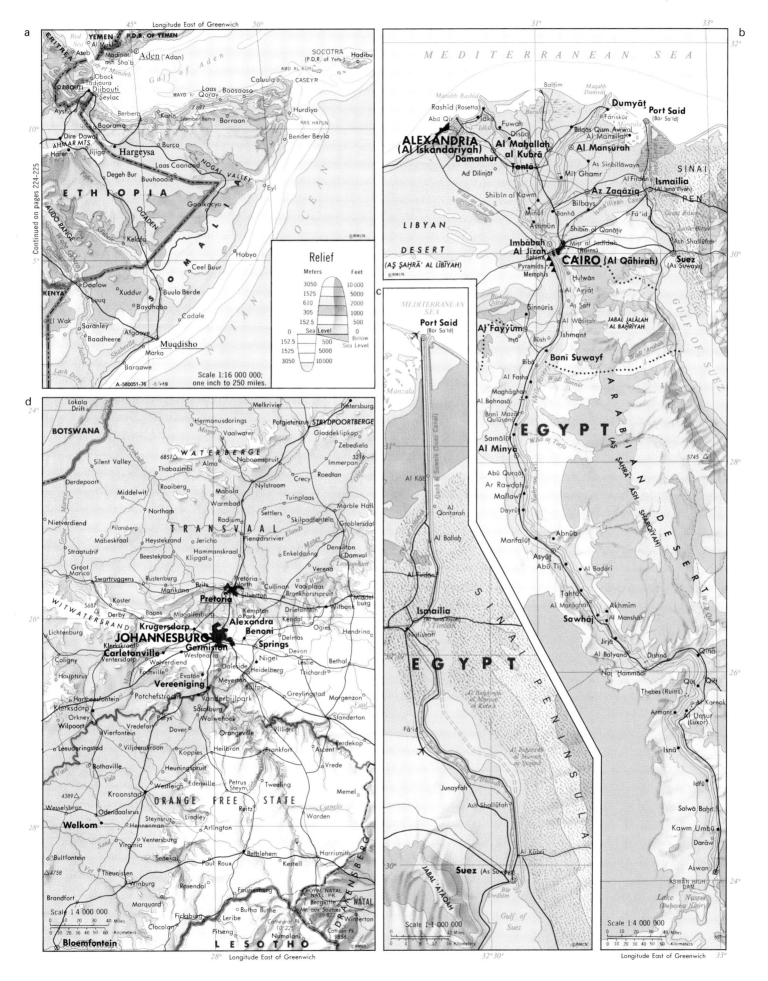

a

Continued on pages 224-225

45° Longitude East of Greenwich 50°

Red Sea
YEMEN
Al Mukha
Madīnat
ash Sha'b
Aden ('Adan)
P.D.R. OF YEMEN
ERITREA
Aseb
Bab el Mandeb
(P.D.R. of Yem.)
SOCOTRA
Hadibu
Obock
Tadjoura
DJIBOUTI
Djibouti
Seylac
ABD AL KŪRĪ
CASEYR
MAYD
Qoray
Caluula
Boosaaso
Aysha
Berbera
Karin
Shimber Berris
Borraan
RAS HAFUN
10°
Dire Dawa
Jijiga
Laas Caanood
Hurdiyo
AHMAR MTS.
Harer
Hargeysa
Burco
Bender Beyla
7 897
Degeh Bur
Buuhoodle
NOGAL VALLEY
Eyl
ETHIOPIA
OGADEN
Gaalkacyo
S
O
M
A
L
5°
Keldafo
Doolow
Xuddur
Buulo Berde
Ceel Buur
KENYA
Luuq
Baydhabo
Cadale
Hobyo
El Wak
Saranley
Afgooye
Baadheere
Muqdisho
Marka
INDIAN OCEAN
Baraawe
Jubba
Lach Dera
Shabeelle

Relief

Meters		Feet
3050		10 000
1525		5000
610		2000
305		1000
152.5		500
0	Sea Level	0
152.5		500 Below
1525		5000 Sea Level
3050		10 000

Scale 1:16 000 000;
one inch to 250 miles.

A-580051-76 -5 5-19

b

31° 33°
32°

M E D I T E R R A N E A N   S E A

Maşabb Rashīd
Baltīm
Maşabb
Dumyāṭ
Rashīd (Rosetta)
Dumyāṭ
Port Said
(Būr Sa'īd)
Abū Qīr
Idkū
Fuwah
Burullus
Fāriskūr
Disūq
Bilqās Qism Awwal
ALEXANDRIA
(Al Iskandarīyah)
Al Maḥallah
al Kubrā
Al Manzilah
Al Manşūrah
SINAI
Damanhūr
Ţanţā
As Sinbillāwayn
PEN.
Ad Dilinjāt
Mīt Ghamr
Al Firdān
Ismailia
(Al Ismā'īlīyah)
Shibīn al Kawm
Az Zaqāzīq
Ismā'īlīyah Canal
Great Bitter
Minūf
Banhā
Bilbays
Fā'id
LIBYAN
Ashmūn
Shibīn al Qanāṭir
Ash Shallūfah
DESERT
Imbābah
Al Jīzah
Mişr al Jadīdah
(Ruins)
Suez
(As Suways)
(AŞ ŞAḤRĀ' AL LĪBĪYAH)
Pyramids
Sphinx
CAIRO (Al Qāhirah)
Memphis
Hulwān
Al 'Ayyāt
Birkat
Qārūn
Al 'Ayyāt
GULF OF SUEZ
As Şaff
Al Fayyūm
Şinnūris
JABAL JALĀLAH
AL BAḤRĪYAH
Biba
Al Wāsiṭah
Ishmant
Itsā
Būsh
Banī Suwayf
Al Fashn
A
R
A
B
I
A
N
Maghāghah
Wādī Sinnūr
Banī Mazār
Qulūşanā
Wādī 'Araba
Al Bahnasā
Samālūṭ
Al Minyā
E
G
Y
P
T
5745
Abū Qurqāş
Ar Rawdah
Mallawī
Dayrūṭ
Abnūb
Manfalūṭ
Asyūţ
Abū Tīj
Al Badārī
Ţahṭā
Al Marāghah
Akhmīm
Al Manshāh
Sawhāj
ASH SHARQĪYAH
Al Maţā'nah
Jirjā
Al Balyanā
Dishnā
Naj' Ḥammādī
Qinā
Thebes (Ruins)
Qūş
Qifṭ
Armant
Al Uqşur
(Luxor)
Karnak
Isnā
Idfū
Salwā Baḥrī
Kawm Umbū
Darāw
ASWĀN HIGH
DAM
Aswan
Lake Nasser
(Buhayrat Naşir)

c

MEDITERRANEAN
SEA
Port Said
(Būr Sa'īd)
Manzala
Al Kāb
Al Qantarah
Al Ballāh
Al Firdān
Ismailia
(Al Ismā'īlīyah)
Nafīshah
S I N A I
Qanā al Suways (Suez Canal)
P E N I N S U L A
E G Y P T
Al Kubrā
Al Buḥayrah
al Murrah
al Kubrā
Fā'id
Junayfah
Ash Shallūfah
Suez (As Suways)
JABAL
ATAQAH
Gulf
of
Suez
Bi'r Ibrāhīm
30°

Scale 1:1 000 000
32°30' 33°
Longitude East of Greenwich

d

24°
BOTSWANA
Lokala
Drift
Melkrivier
Pietersburg
Hermanusdorings
Potgietersrus
STRYDPOORTBERGE
Vaalwater
Gladdeklipkop
WATERBERGE
Zebediela
6851
Naboomspruit
Immerpan
Silent Valley
Thabazimbi
Alma
Mogol
Derdepoort
3216
Middelwit
Rooiberg
Mabula
Nylstroom
Crecy
Roedtan
Northam
Warmbad
Settlers
Marble Hall
Pilansberg
Radium
Skilpadfontein
Groblersdal
T R A N S V A A L
Olifants
Straatsdrif
Groot
Marico
Mabeskraal
Heystekrand
Jericho
Piendarsrivier
Elands
Dennilton
Damval
Swartruggens
Rustenburg
Marikana
Brits
Moses
Verena
Loskopdam
Koster
Pretoria North
Silverton
Cullinan
Vaalplaas
Bronkhorstspruit
Middel-
burg
Derby
Boons
Magaliesburg
PRETORIA
Kempton
Park
Driefontein
Witbank
Lichtenburg
Klipgat
ALEXANDRA
Ogies
Hendrina
Coligny
KRUGERSDORP
BENONI
Kendal
WITWATERSRAND
5681
JOHANNESBURG
GERMISTON
SPRINGS
Delmas
Hauptrus
Westonaria
Nigel
Devon
Leslie
CARLETONVILLE
Evaton
Daleside
Heidelberg
Trichardt
Bethal
Fochville
Meyerton
VEREENIGING
Balfour
Hartbeesfontein
Vanderbijlpark
Greylingstad
Morgenzon
Klerksdorp
Potchefstroom
Sasolburg
Orkney
Vredefort
Wolwehoek
Standerton
Wilpoort
Parys
Dover
Orangeville
Villiers
Perdekop
Leeudoringstad
Vierfontein
Viljoenskroon
Koppies
Frankfort
Ascent
Bothaville
Heilbron
Vrede
ORANGE   FREE   STATE
Vaal
Heuningspruit
Edenville
Memel
Westleigh
Petrus
Steyn
Tweeling
4389
Kroonstad
Lindley
Reitz
Warden
Wesselsbron
Odendaalsrus
Steynsrus
Arlington
WELKOM
Hennenman
Ventersburg
Virginia
Senekal
Bethlehem
Harrismith
4758
Winburg
Paul Roux
ROYAL NATAL
NATL. PK.
Bultfontein
Bergville
NATAL
Brandfort
Rosendal
Fouriesburg
Mt. aux Sources
10 822
Marquard
Ficksburg
Butha Buthe
Winterton
Cathedral Pk.
9856
Leribe
DRAKENSBERG
Bloemfontein
Pitseng
Ntumolani
Clocolan
L E S O T H O

Scale 1:4 000 000
0   10 20 30 40 Miles
0 10 20 30 40 50 60 Kilometers

24°
28°
26°
28°
30°
28° Longitude East of Greenwich

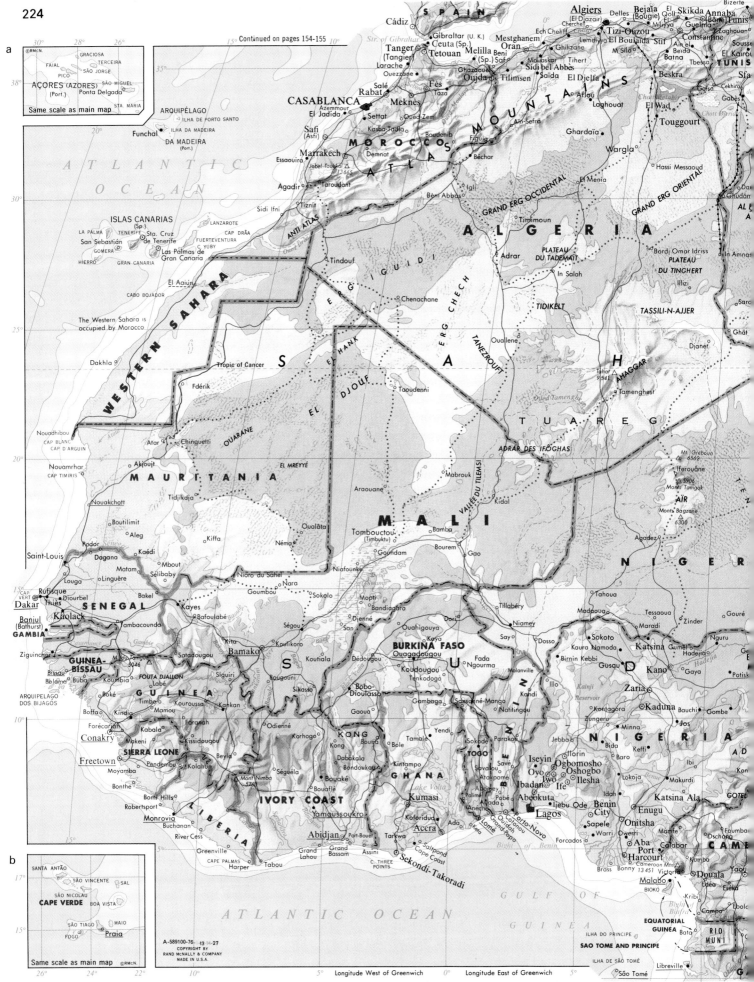

224

Continued on pages 154-155

a

AÇORES (AZORES)
(Port.)

Same scale as main map

FAIAL PICO GRACIOSA
TERCEIRA
SÃO JORGE
SÃO MIGUEL
Ponta Delgada
STA. MARIA

SPAIN

Cádiz
Gibraltar (U.K.)
Ceuta (Sp.)
Tanger (Tangier)
Tetouan
Larache
Salé
Rabat
Melilla (Sp.)
Beni

Algiers (El Djazair)
Delles
Béjaïa (Bougie)
El Skikda
Annaba (Bône)
Bizerte
Tizi-Ouzou
Chercheli
Lemdiya
El Bouicala
Sétif
Constantine
Guelma
TUNIS
Mestghanem
Oran
Sidi bel Abbès
Saïda
Tilmsen
El Djelfa
Aflou
Laghouat
Batna
El Kairol
Souss

CASABLANCA
Azemmour
El Jadida
Meknès
Fès
Taza
Oued-Zem
Kasba-Tadla
Ain-Sefra
Touggourt
El Wad

Safi (Asfi)
Settat
Boudenib
Figuig
Ghardaïa
Wargla

Essaouira
Marrakech
Demnat
Béchar
Hassi Messaoud

Jebel Toubkal
13665

Agadir
Taroudant
Igli
El Menia
Bordj Omar Idriss
In Amnas

Sidi Ifni
Tiznit
Béni Abbès
Adrar
In Salah
PLATEAU DU TINGHERT
Illizi

ISLAS CANARIAS (Sp.)
LANZAROTE
CAP YUBY
FUERTEVENTURA
La Palma
Tenerife
Sta. Cruz de Tenerife
San Sebastián
GOMERA
GRAN CANARIA
HIERRO
Las Palmas de Gran Canaria

ALGERIA

GRAND ERG OCCIDENTAL
Timimoun
PLATEAU DU TADEMAÏT
GRAND ERG ORIENTAL
TIDIKELT
TASSILI-N-AJJER

El Aaiún
CABO BOJADOR

WESTERN SAHARA

The Western Sahara is occupied by Morocco

Dakhla
Tropic of Cancer
Fdérik

ERG IGUIDI
ERG CHECH
Chenachane
Ouallene
Ghât
Djanet

S A H A R A

EL HANK
Taoudenni

TANEZROUFT
AHAGGAR
Tahar 9541
Tamenghest

Nouadhibou
CAP BLANC
CAP D'ARGUIN
Atar
Chinguetti
EL DJOUF
Mt. Gréboun 6562
Iferouâne
Monts Tamgak 5906

Nouamrhar
CAP TIMIRIS
OUARANE

T U A R E G
ADRAR DES IFÔGHAS
AÏR
Monts Bagzane 6300

MAURITANIA
EL MREYYÉ
Mabrouk
Agadez

Tidjikdja
Araouane

Nouakchott
Boutilimit
Aleg
Kiffa
Néma
Ouâlâta
Tombouctou (Timbuktu)
Bamba
Kidal

M A L I

Bourem
Gao

Podor
Saint-Louis
Dagana
Kaédi
Mbout
Sélibaby
Matam
Linguère
Nioro du Sahel
Nara
Goumbou
Sokolo
Goundam
Niafounké
Bourem

N I G E R

VALLÉE DU TILEMSI

Tahoua
Tessaoua
Gouré

CAP VERT
Dakar
Thiès
Diourbel
Louga
Rufisque
SENEGAL
Bakel
Kayes
Mopti
Bandiagara
Djenné
Tillabéry
Niamey
Say
Dosso
Madaoua
Zinder
Maradi
Katsina
Nguru

Banjul (Bathurst)
Kaolack
Tambacounda
Bafoulabé
Ségou
San
Ouahigouya
Kaya
Dori
Sokoto
Kaura Namoda
Hadejia
Gumel

GAMBIA
Ziguinchor
Kolda
GUINEA-BISSAU
Bissau
Bolama
FOUTA DJALLON
Labé
Mt. Tamgué 5046
Satadougou
Kita
Koulikoro
Bamako
BURKINA FASO
Ouagadougou
Fada Ngourma
Niamey
Gusau
Zaria
Kano
Gaya
Potiski

ARQUIPÉLAGO DOS BIJAGÓS
Buba
Boké
GUINEA
Timbe
Kouroussa
Siguiri
Koutiala
Dédougou
Koudougou
Tenkodogo
Malanville
Kandi
Kaduna
Kontagora
Bauchi
Gombe

Boffa
Kindia
Mamou
Dabola
Bobo-Dioulasso
Sikasso
Gaoua
Gambaga
Sansanné-Mango
Natitingou
Jebba
Minna
Jos

Forécariah
Conakry
Kabala
Kissidougou
Beyla
Odienné
Korhogo
KONG
Bouna
Bole
Tamale
Yendi
Sokodé
Parakou
Ilorin
NIGERIA
Kaffi

Freetown
SIERRA LEONE
Pendembu
Kolahun
Mt. Nimba 5741
Séguéla
Dabakala
Bondoukou
Kintampo
Savalou
TOGO
Iseyin
Oyo
Ogbomosho
Oshogbo
Ilesha
Ibi

Moyamba
Bonthe
Bomi Hills
Robertsport
Kabala
Bouaflé
Bouaké
GHANA
Kumasi
Palimé
Abomey
Pobé
Ibadan
Ife
Lokoja
Makurdi
Katsina Ala
GOTEL

Monrovia
Buchanan
River Cess
LIBERIA
IVORY COAST
Yamoussoukro
Koforidua
Accra
Anecho
Abeokuta
Ijebu Ode
Benin City
Enugu
Onitsha
Aba
Sapele
Warri
Owerri
CAME

Greenville
Harper
CAPE PALMAS
Tabou
Grand Lahou
Grand Bassam
Assini
C. THREE POINTS
Sekondi-Takoradi
Cape Coast
Salpond
Lomé
Cotonou
Porto-Novo
Lagos
Forcados
Port Harcourt
Brass
Bonny
Calabar
Kumba
Douala

ATLANTIC OCEAN
GULF OF GUINEA
Bight of Benin

EQUATORIAL GUINEA
SAO TOME AND PRINCIPE
ILHA DO PRINCIPE
Malabo
BIOKO
Bata
RIO MUNI
Kribi
Eséka
Yaou

ILHA DE SÃO TOMÉ
São Tomé
Libreville

b

CAPE VERDE

Same scale as main map

SANTA ANTÃO
SÃO VICENTE
SAL
SÃO NICOLAU
BOA VISTA
SÃO TIAGO
MAIO
FOGO
Praia

A-589100-76- 13 14-27
COPYRIGHT BY
RAND McNALLY & COMPANY
MADE IN U.S.A.

Longitude West of Greenwich   Longitude East of Greenwich

Scale 1:16 000 000; one inch to 250 miles. Sinusoidal Projection
Elevations and depressions are given in feet

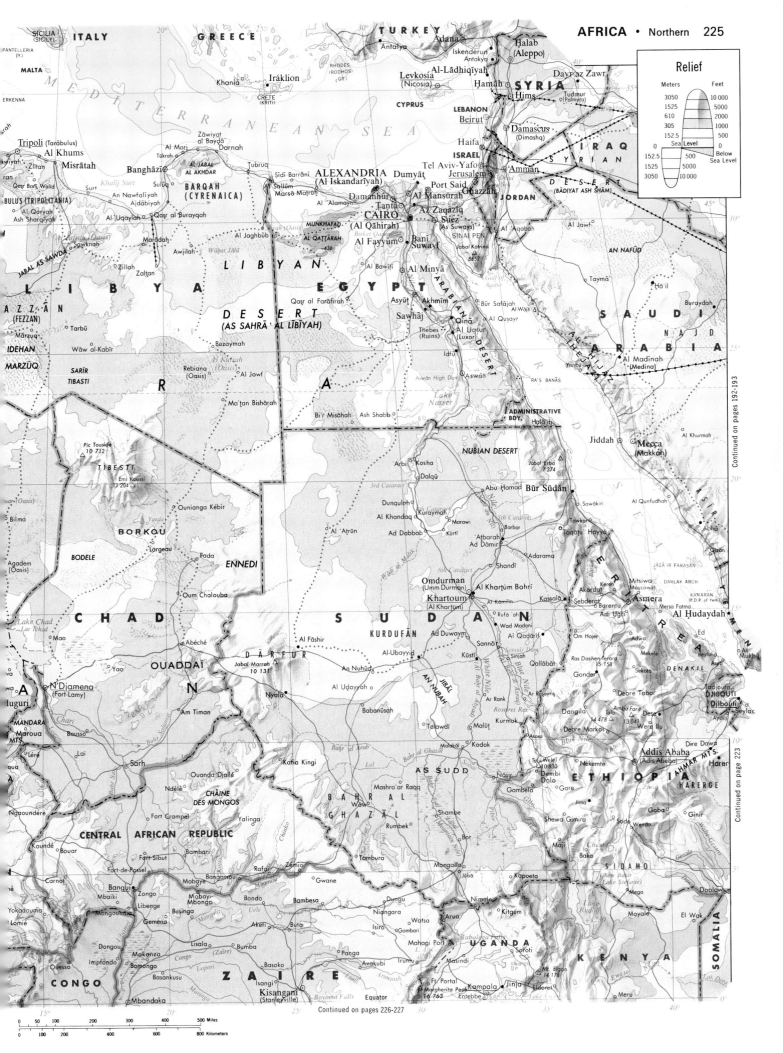

Continued on pages 224-225

The "Homelands" (Bophuthatswana, Ciskei, Transkei, Venda) were unilaterally created by South Africa and are not internationally recognized.

1 Bophuthatswana
2 Ciskei
3 Transkei
4 Venda

A-589200-76-13-11-25
COPYRIGHT BY
RAND McNALLY & COMPANY
MADE IN U.S.A.

CAPE TOWN
MOUILLE PT.

Scale 1:1 000 000

10 Miles
16 Kilometers

Scale 1:16 000 000; one inch to 250 miles. Sinusoidal Projection
Elevations and depressions are given in feet

15° Longitude East of Greenwich 20°

500 Miles
800 Kilometers

b

SOMALIA

Kismaayo
Buur Gaabo

Kinnyago
17058
Ft. Hall
Nairobi

Witu
Lamu

Malindi
Takaungu

Kilimanjaro
19 340

Mombasa
Vanga
Lushoto
Tanga
Pangani

ZANZIBAR
Zanzibar
Bagamoyo

Morogoro
Kisaki

Dar es Salaam

MAFIA

Utete

Kilwa Kivinje

Lindi

CABO DELGADO

Mikindani
Masasi

Moçímboa
da Praia
Ibo
Pemba
Lúrio

Memba
Nacala

Moçambique

António Enes
ILHA ANGOCHE

Pebane

ALDABRA IS.
(Sey.)

COSMOLEDO GROUP
(Sey.)

Moroni

GRANDE
COMORE   COMOROS
MOHELI   ANJOUAN

Dzaoudzi
MAYOTTE
(Fr.)

ÎLES GLORIEUSES
(Fr.)

CAP D'AMBRE

Antsiranana

NOSY BE

Iharana

Maromokotro

Maroantsetra

NOSY BORAHA

MADAGASCAR

Mahajanga
Mandritsara

Besalampy

CAP SAINT-
ANDRÉ

ÎLE JUAN DE NOVA
(Fr.)

NOSY BARREN

Maintirano

Ambatond
razaka

Fenoarivo
Atsinanana

Toamasina

Motamanga

Antananarivo

Vatomandry

Tsiroanomandidy
8621

Mahanoro

Antsirabe
Ambositra

Morondava

Fianarantsoa
Mananjary

Manakara

Ivohibé

BASSAS DA INDIA
(Fr.)

Farafangana

EUROPA
(Fr.)

Betroka

Morombe

Mahaly

Toliara

Trafonomby
4417
Faradofay

CAP STE. MARIE

Arlington

Paul Roux   Bethlehem

ORANGE FREE STATE

Fouriesburg

Ficksburg

Clocolan

Teyateyaneng

Senekal

Clarens

Kestell   Harrismith

ROYAL NATAL
NAT'L. PK.

Butha Buthe
Leribe

Pitseng

MALOTI MTS.   10 822
Mt. aux
Sources

Bergville   Winterton

Cathedral Pk.
9856

LESOTHO

Roma

Machache
9464

Mokhotlong

Thabana
Ntlenyana
11425

Cathkin Pk.
10438

Mt.
Giant
5803

10169

Mohale's
Hoek

The Twins
8820

DRAKENSBERG

Qacha's Nek

Matatiele

9326
Swartberg
7619

TRANSKEI

Zastron

Quthing

Cedarville   Mt. Currie
7426   7292

9684

TRANSKEI

Herschel

Wittles
2459

Lady Grey

Rhodes

Ben Macdhui
9846

Mount
Fletcher

Mount Frere

Maclear

Qumbu

Kokstad

Harding

Umzimkulu

Wolhuterskop
Jacksonstuin

MAGALIESBERG

Pretoria
North   Pretoria

Cullinan

Kosmos   Hartbeespoort

Swartspruit

Silverton
4426

Rayton

Skeerpoort
4549

Hennopsrivier

Voortrekkerhoogte

Valhalla

Irene

Tierpoort

WITWATERSBERG

Foothills

Olievenhoutpoort
4602

Halfway
House

Tarlton

Kaalfontein

Bapsfontein

Krugersdorp

Moddertontein

Kempton Park

Putfontein

JOHANNESBURG   Alexandra

Randfontein
5725

Roodepoort

Discovery

Florida
Maraisburg

Edenvale
Primrose

Boksburg   Benoni

Brakpan

Orlando
Pimville

Turffontein
Rosetten
-a ville

Germiston

Alberton
Springs

WITWATERSRAND

Scale 1:1 000 000

0   5   10 Miles
0   4   8   12   16 Kilometers

c

Dannhauser

Glencoe   Dundee

Nqutu

Mohlabetini

SOUTH

Wasbank

Babanango

Ladysmith   Pomeroy

Nkandla   Melmoth

Colenso   Weenen

Tugela Ferry

Estcourt   Greytown   Eshowe

Kranskop

Mooirivier

NATAL

AFRICA

Mapumulo

New
Hanover   Dalton

Wartburg

Stanger

Impendle

Nishoni
5851

Howick

Pietermaritzburg

Underberg

Bulwer

Verulam

Camper
down

Donnybrook

Richmond

Pinetown

Durban

Creighton

Mid Illovo

Isipingo

Ixopo

Umkomaas

Scottburgh

Park Rynie

Sezela

Umzinto

Umtentweni

Port Shepstone

Uvongo Beach

Margate

Port Edward

RAME HEAD

Mount
Ayliff

Bizana

Tabankulu

Flagstaff

Maclean

Libode

Tsolo

Umtata

Ngqeleni

Port St. Johns

Lusikisiki

Mqanduli

Elliotdale

Idutywa

Willowvale

Butterworth

Kentani

Komga

Kei Mouth
Morgan's Bay

Macleantown

SOUTH AFRICA

CAPE

Barkly East

Ugie

Rossouw
8430

Elliot

Jamestown

Molteno

STORMBERG

Dordrecht

Indwe

Cold

Sterkstroom

Engcobo

TRANSKEI

Ngamakwe

Tsomo

Tylden

Cofimvaba

Waverly

Queenstown

Lady Frere

Tarkastad

Cradock

BANKBERG
6606

WINTERBERG
7778

Whittlesea

Carthcart

Stutterheim
Frankfort

Seymour

Adelaide   CISKEI

Keiskammahoek

Bisho

Berlin

Pearston

Bedford

Fort
Beaufort

Fort
Alice

King William's
Town

Breidbach

Gonubie

East London

Somerset East

SUURBERGE

Riebeek-Oos

Alicedale

Grahamstown

Peddie

Kidd's Beach

Kirkwood

Adda

Salem

Bathurst

Hamburg

Uitenhage

Alexandria

Port Alfred (Kowie)

SAINT CROIX
ISLAND   BIRD ISLAND

Port Elizabeth

KAAP RECIFE

INDIAN   OCEAN

Scale 1:4 000 000

0   10   20   30   40 Miles
0   10   20   30   40   50   60 Kilometers

Longitude East of Greenwich

Relief

Meters		Feet
3050		10 000
1525		5000
610		2000
305		1000
152.5		500
0	Sea Level	0
152.5		500
1525		5000
3050		10 000

MOZAMBIQUE CHANNEL

INDIAN OCEAN

Equator

228

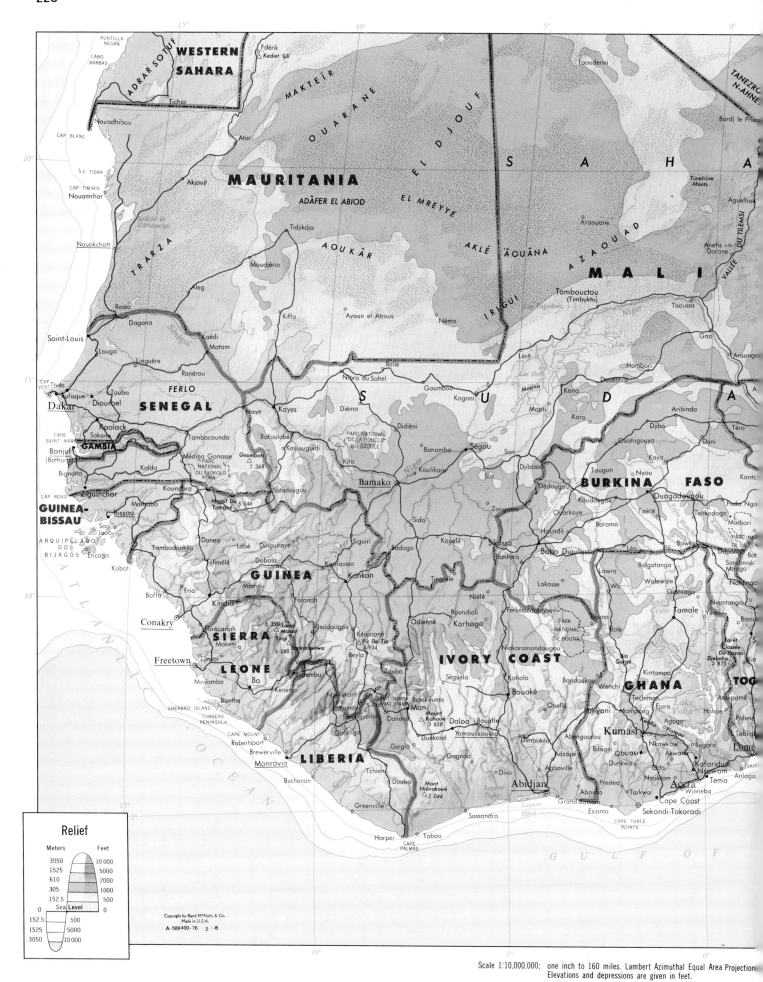

Relief

Meters	Feet
3050	10 000
1525	5000
610	2000
305	1000
152.5	500
0 Sea Level	0
152.5	500
1525	5000
3050	10 000

Copyright by Rand McNally & Co.
Made in U.S.A.
A-589400-76 2-8

Scale 1:10,000,000; one inch to 160 miles. Lambert Azimuthal Equal Area Projection
Elevations and depressions are given in feet.

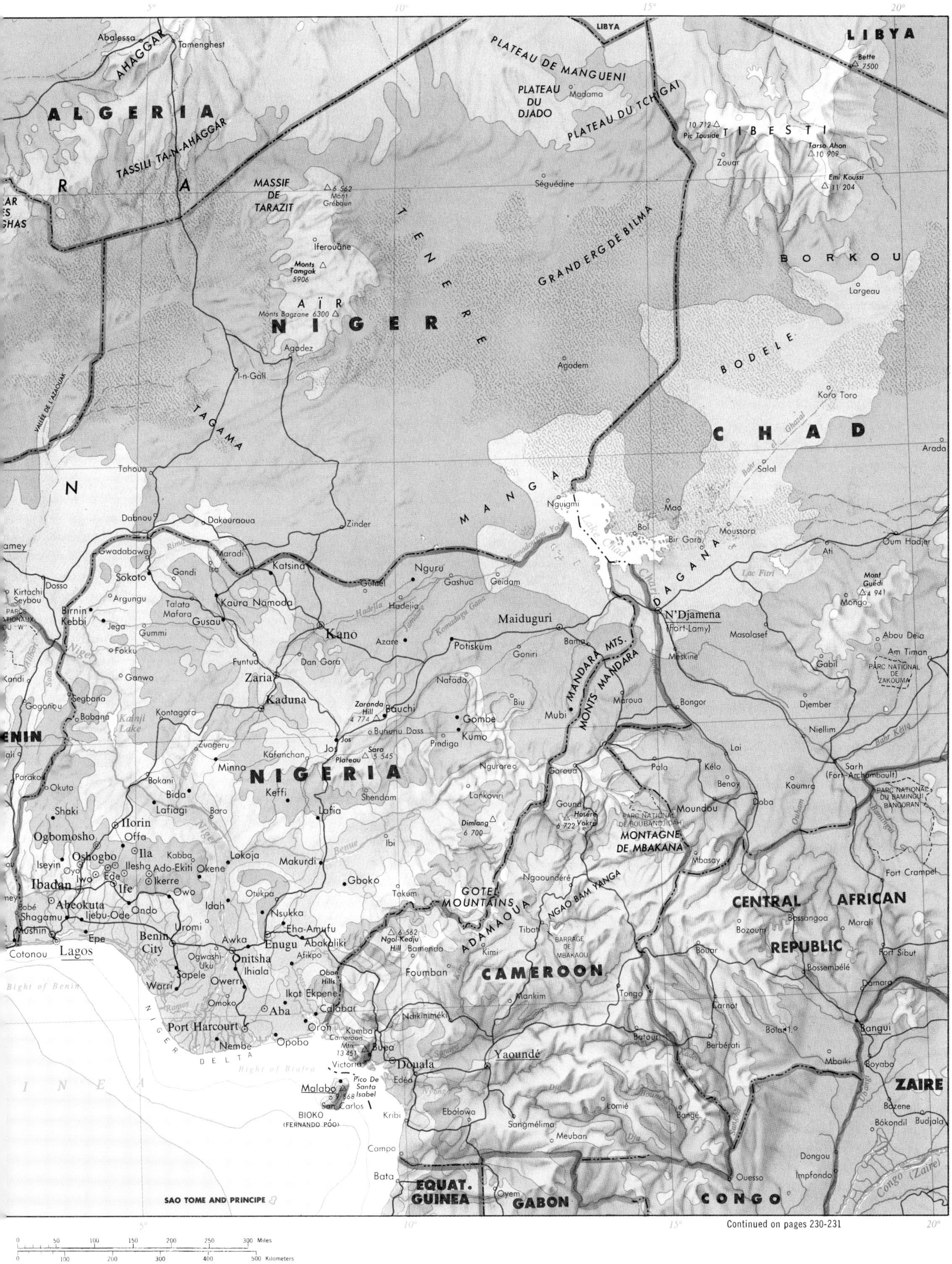

ALGERIA

AHAGGAR
Abalessa
Tamenghest

TASSILI TA-N-AHAGGAR

PLATEAU DE MANGUENI

LIBYA

PLATEAU
DU
DJADO
Madama

PLATEAU DU TCHIGAI

Bette △7500

LIBYA

MASSIF
DE
TARAZIT
△6 562
Mont
Grébaun

10 712 △ Pic Touside
TIBESTI
Zouar
Tarso Ahon △10 909

Séguédine

Emi Koussi △11 204

Iferouâne

Monts
Tamgak
5906

BORKOU

GRAND ERG DE BILMA

Largeau

Monts Bagzane 6300 △

AÏR

N I G E R

Agadez

BODELE

Koro Toro

I-n-Gall

TAGAMA

Agadem

C H A D

Tahoua

MANGA

DAGANA

Arada

Salal

N

Dabnou
Dakouraoua
Zinder

Nguigmi

Mao

Bir Gara
Moussoro

Bol

Lac Fitri

Ati

Oum Hadjer

amey
Gwadabawa
Maradi
Isa
Katsina
Guidel
Nguru
Gashua
Geidam

Lake Chad

N'Djamena
(Fort-Lamy)

Masalasef

Mont
Guédi △4 941
Mongo

Kirtachi
Seybou
Dosso
Sokoto
Gandi
Kaura Namoda
Hadejia
Hadejia

Maiduguri

Bama

Meskine

Abou Deïa

Am Timan

PARC
TIONAUX
DU W
Birnin
Kebbi
Argungu
Talata
Mafara
Gusau
Kano
Azare
Potiskum
Goniri
Mubi
MANDARA MTS.
MONTS MANDARA
Meroua
Bongor

Gabil
Djember
Niellim

PARC NATIONAL
DE
ZAKOUMA

Jega
Gummi
Fokku
Funtua
Dan Gora
Nafada
Biu

Goré

Lai

Segbana
Babana
Ganwo
Zaria
Bauchi
Gombe
Kumo

Pala
Kélo
Koumra

Sarh
(Fort-Archambault)

Goganou
Kontagora
Kaduna
Zoranda
Hill
4 774
Bunun Dass
Pindiga

Ngurare
Garoua

Benoy
Doba

PARC NATIONALE
DU BAMINGUI
BANGORAN

ENIN
Zungeru
Jos
Plateau
Sara △5 545
Jos
Minna
Kafanchan
Bokani
Bida
Keffi

NIGERIA

Lankoviri

Gound
Hosére △6 722 Yokra

Moundou

Fort Crampel

ali
Parakou
Okuta
Lafiagi
Baro
Lafia
Shendam
Ibi
Dimlang △6 700

MONTAGNE
DE MBAKANA

Mbasay

Shaki
Ilorin
Offa
Kabba
Lokoja
Makurdi
Gboko
Takum

Ngaoundéré

CENTRAL

AFRICAN

Bossangoa

Marali

Ogbomosho
Oshogbo Ila
Ilesha Ado-Ekiti Okene
Idah
Otukpa

GOTEL
MOUNTAINS

Ngaoundéré

Bozoum

REPUBLIC

Fort Sibut

Iseyin
Oyo
Iwo Ede Ife Ikerre Owo
Ondo
Uromi

ADAMAOUA

Tibati

BARRAGE
DE
MBAKAOU

Bouar

Bossembélé

be
Shagamu
Abeokuta Ijebu-Ode
Benin
City
Awka
Enugu Abakaliki
Afikpo
Eha-Amufu
Ngol-Kedju △6 562
Hill
Bamenda

Kimi

CAMEROON

Tongo

Carnot

Bola T.

Damaro

shin
Epe
Cotonou Lagos

Ogwashi-
Uku
Onitsha
Ihiala
Owerri
Ikot Ekpene
Oban
Hills

Foumban

Mankim

Batouri

Berbérati

Bangui

Warri
Sapele
Omoko
Aba

Calabar

Ndikinimeki

Yaoundé

Mbaiki

ZAIRE

Port Harcourt
Nembe
Opobo
Oron
Kumba
Cameroon
Mtn △13 451

Bafut
Buea

Douala

Bazene
Bokondil Budjala

NIGER
DELTA
Victoria
Malabo
Pico De
Santa
Isabel △9 868
San Carlos

Edéa
Kribi

Ebolowa

Lomié

Sangé

Dongou
Impfondo

BIOKO
(FERNANDO PÓO)

Sangmélima
Meuban

Ouesso

GUINEA
Bight of Biafra

Campo

Bata

SAO TOME AND PRINCIPE

EQUAT.
GUINEA
Oyem
GABON
CONGO
Congo (Zaire)

Continued on pages 230-231

Continued on pages 228-229

Opobo
NIGERIA
Cameroon Mtn. 13 451
Douala
Buea
Edéa
Malabo
San Carlos
BIOKO
(FERNANDO PÓO)
Kribi
Bight of Biafra

Yaoundé
Doumé
Batou
Berbérati
Bolai I.
Bangui
Boali
Fort de Possel

CENTRAL AFRICAN REPUBLIC
Kongbo
Bangassou
Rafai

CAMEROON
Sangmélima
Yokadouma
Lomié
Bangé
Mbaiki
Boyabo
Bosobolo
Mbaye
Yakoma
Bondo
Gitga

Ebolowa
Meuban
Souanké
Moloundou
Ouesso
Mongoumba
Gemena
Businga
Bodalang
Aketi
Zen

EQUATORIAL GUINEA
Campo
Bata
Oyem
Acalayong
Djoum
Dongou
Impfondo
Bomongo
Budjala
Lisala
Bumba
Basoko

CABO SAN JUAN
Mekambo
Djokoumatombi
Loka
Lakefa
Boende
Isangi
Bengam
Kisangan
(Stanleyville)

PRÍNCIPE
SAO TOME AND PRINCIPE
ISLA DE CORISCO
MONTS DE CRISTAL
Makokou
Lebango
Likouala
Mange
Lifanga
Boyabo
Bokungu
Ekoli
Litoko
São Tomé
SÃO TOMÉ
Libreville
Kango
Booué
Equator
Mbandaka
(Coquilhatville)
Lac Tumba
Bikoro
Boende
Yayama
Litoko

GABON
Bifoum
CONGO
Owando
ZAIRE
CAP LOPEZ
Mount Iboundji 5 184
Koula-Moutou
St. François
de Boandji
Gamboma
Lac Mai-Ndombe
Inongo
Monkoto
Lokolama
Ekanga
Katoi

Port-Gentil
Lambaréné
Franceville
Kiri
Omboué
Mouila
Monts De La Lékéti 3 412
Djambala
Fimi
Lokolama
Dekese
Esambo

Petit Loango
Mbinda
Mossendjo
Kindanba
Bandundu
Makaw
Lebo (Port-Francqui)
Yebo
Domiongo

Tchibanga
Sibiti
Lukenie
Dekese

Mayumba
Madingou
Brazzaville
Bandundu
Lusambo

Madingo
Loubomo
Kinshasa
(Léopoldville)
Masi-Manimba
Demba

Pointe-Noire
Tshela
Kisantu
Kikwit
Djokupunda
Mbuji-Ma
(Bakwanga)

CABINDA
(Ang.)
Cabinda
Boma
Matadi
Mbanza-Ngungu
Popokabaka
Kilembe
Bulunga
Kananga
(Luluabourg)

PONTA DO PADRÃO
Nqui
Kimvula
Kitenda
Tshikapa
Kanda-Kanda

Soyo
SERRA DO CONGO
Mbanza Congo
Quimbele
Kahemba
Luachimo
Kapanga
Kam

Nzeto
Mabaia
Damba
Kibenga
Luachimo
KATANGA

Ambriz
Uge
Marimba
Quimbonge
Caluango
Sambungo
Kangowa
Ki

Luanda
Caxito
Duque de Bragança
Quela
Saurima
Kapanga

PONTA DAS PALMEIRINHAS
Catete
Ndalatando
Dondo
Malange
Nova Gaia
Cacóla
Malanga
Nason

PARQUE NACIONAL DE QUICAMA
Luao
Lycano
PARQUE NACIONAL DA CAMEIA
Lumv

CABO DAS TRÊS PONTAS
Porto Amboim
Mussende
Saútar
Luena
Calunda

Ngunza
Gabela
Cela
Calucinga
ANGOLA
Curunga
KASHIJI PLAIN
Chitokoloki

Covelo
Alto-Uama
Coemba
Cangamba

SERRA CAMBONDA
SERRA MOCO 8 594
Kuito
Chitembo
Chá Pungana
LIUWA PLAIN
Ninda

Lobito
Benguela
Huambo
(Nova Lisboa)
Caconda
Mussuma
Mongu

SERRE DO CHILENGUE
Caculama
Caluquembe
Menongue
Lunga
Mavinga
BAROTSE PLAIN
Nangweshi

SERRA DA NEVE
Cacula
Kassinga
Caiundo
Cuando

CABO DE SANTA MARTA
São Nicolau
Lubango
PARQUE NACIONAL DO BIKUAR
SILOANA PLAINS
Luiana

Moçâmedes
Chiange
Catuala
Cuangar
Sambusu
NAMIBIA
BOTS.

PONTA ALBINA
Porto Alexandre
Cahama
Oncocua
Cuamato
Melunga
CAPRIVI STRIP
Kasina

PONTA DA MARCA
Baía dos Tigres
PARQUE NACIONAL DA IONA
Shakawe
CHOBE NATL P.

Foz do Cunene

Scale 1:10,000,000; one inch to 160 miles. Lambert Azimuthal Equal Area Projection
Elevations and depressions are given in feet.

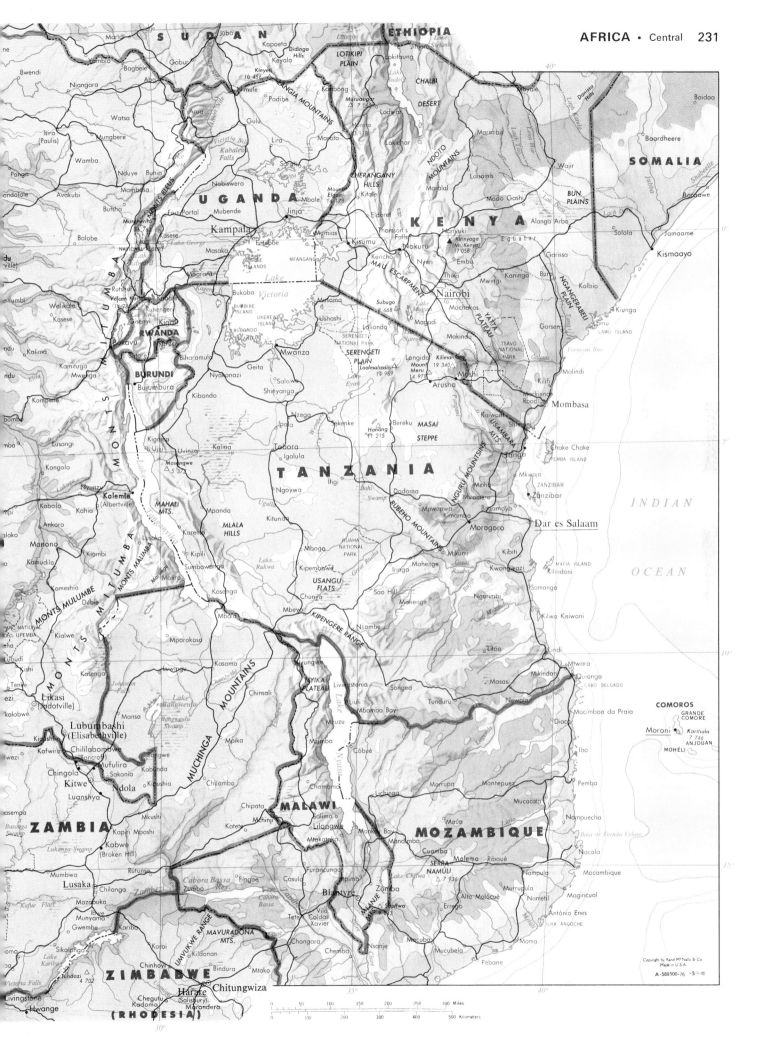

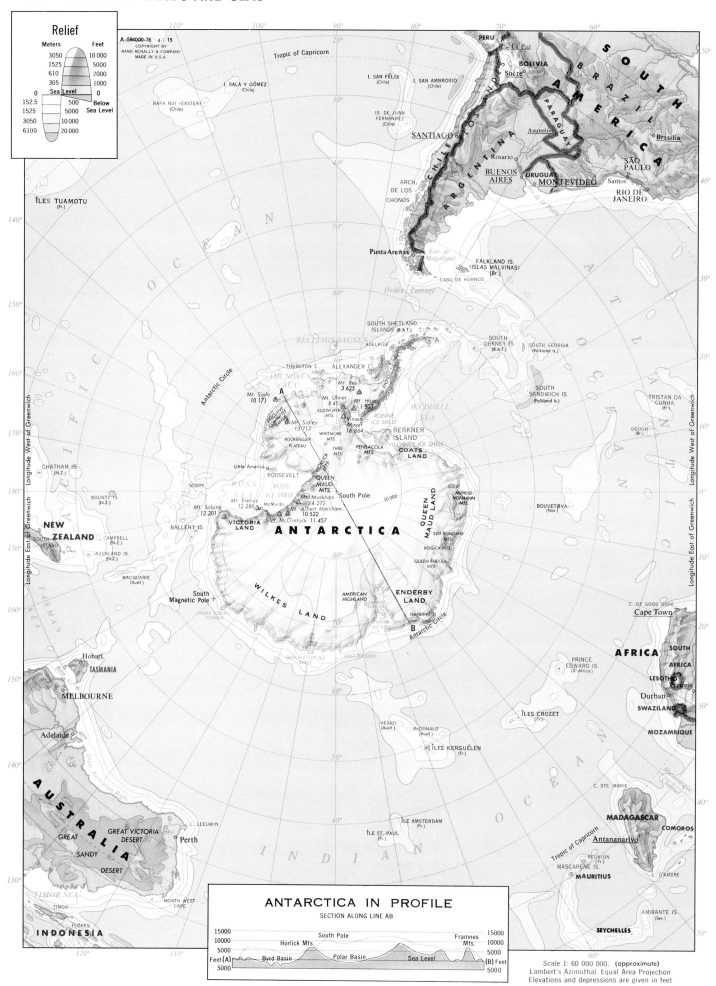

Relief

Meters		Feet
3050		10 000
1525		5000
610		2000
305		1000
0	Sea Level	0
152.5		500
1525	Below	5000
3050	Sea Level	10 000
6100		20 000

A-594000-76   4-7 15
COPYRIGHT BY
RAND McNALLY & COMPANY
MADE IN U.S.A.

ANTARCTICA IN PROFILE
SECTION ALONG LINE AB

Scale 1: 60 000 000; (approximate)
Lambert's Azimuthal. Equal Area Projection
Elevations and depressions are given in feet

plate tectonics and ocean floor maps

Plate Tectonics

Maps and atlases portray the position of the land and water masses and the surface features of the earth. In general they answer the question *where?* The plate tectonic theory of the earth's actions relates the physics of the earth's subsurface and its surface to explain *how* and *why* the surface features are where they are.

Stated concisely, the theory presumes the lithosphere—the outside crust and uppermost mantle of the earth—is divided into six major rigid plates and several smaller platelets that move relative to one another. The position and names of the plates are shown on the map below.

The motor that drives the plates is found deep in the mantle. The theory states that because of temperature differences in the mantle, slow convection currents circulate. Where two molten currents converge and move upward, they separate, causing the crustal plates to bulge and move apart in midoceanic regions. Lava wells up at these points to cause ridges and volcanic activity. The plates grow larger by accretion along these midocean regions, cause vast regions of the crust to move apart, and force different plates to move into one another. As the plates do so, they are destroyed at subduction zones, where the plates are consumed downward to form deep ocean trenches. Movement along these zones prompts earthquakes as well as changes in the coastline. Further movement results as plates slide past one another along transcurrent faults. The diagrams to the right illustrate the processes.

The overall result of tectonic movements is that the crustal plates move slowly and inexorably as relatively rigid entities, carrying the continents along with them. It is now accepted that the continents have moved and changed their positions during the past millions of years. The sequence of this continental drifting is illustrated on the following page. It begins with a single landmass, called the supercontinent of Pangaea, and the ancestral ocean, the Panthalassa Ocean. Pangaea first split into a northern landmass called Laurasia and a southern block called Gondwanaland and subsequently into the continents we map today.

Subduction Zone

Ocean Ridge Zone

World-Wide Distribution of Tectonic Plates

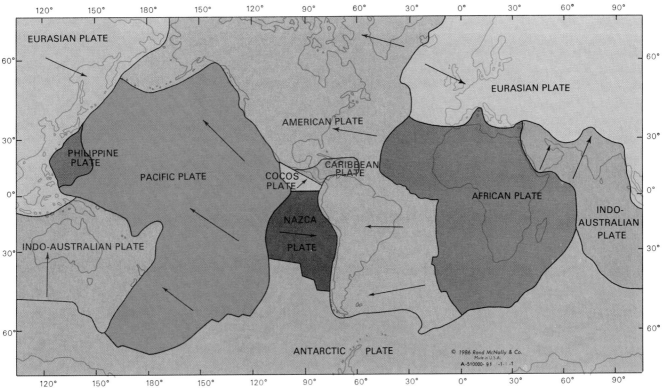

Credit: adapted from a drawing by Scripps Institution of Oceanography

Continental Drift

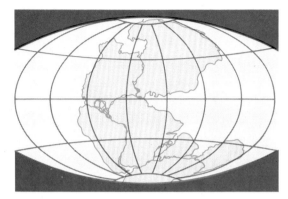

225 million years ago the supercontinent of Pangaea exists and Panthalassa forms the ancestral ocean. Tethys Sea separates Eurasia and Africa.

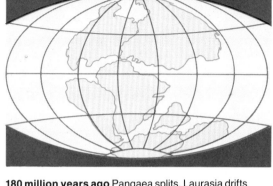

180 million years ago Pangaea splits, Laurasia drifts north. Gondwanaland breaks into South America/Africa, India, and Australia/Antarctica.

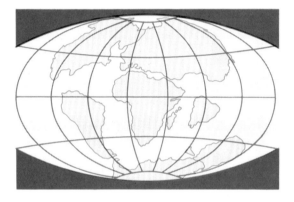

65 million years ago ocean basins take shape as South America and India move from Africa and the Tethys Sea closes to form the Mediterranean Sea.

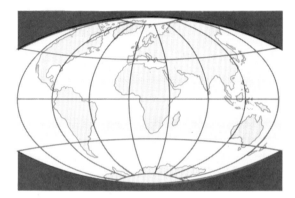

The present day: India has merged with Asia, Australia is free of Antarctica, and North America is free of Eurasia.

Ocean Floor Maps

The maps in this section convey an impression of the physical nature of the world's ocean floors. In general, the colors are those thought to exist on the ocean floors. For continental shelves or shallow inland seas, gray-green is used to correspond to terrigenous oozes, sediments washed from the continental areas. In deeper parts of the oceans, calcareous oozes derived from the skeletons of marine life appear in white, and the fine mud from land is red. In the Atlantic, materials accumulate relatively rapidly, have a high iron content, and thus are brighter red than elsewhere. Slower sedimentation in the Pacific and Indian oceans results in more manganese and hence darker colors. Undersea ridges are shown in black to suggest recent upswelling of molten rock. Small salt-and-pepper patches portray areas where manganese nodules are found. Around certain islands, white is used to show coral reefs. Differences in subsurface form are shown by relief-shading.

Many different features on the ocean floor are recognizable. Towering mountain ranges, vast canyons, broad plains, and a variety of other physiographic forms exceed in magnitude those found on the continents. One of the more pronounced is the Mid-Atlantic Ridge, a chain of mountains bisecting the Atlantic Ocean. One distinct characteristic of this ridge is a trough that runs along the entire center, in effect producing twin ridge lines. Away from the center there are parallel and lower crests, while at right angles to the crests are numerous fracture zones.

Measurements of temperature and magnetism indicate that the troughs in the Mid-Atlantic Ridge are younger than the paralleling crests, whose ages increase with distance from the center. It is believed that the central troughs mark a line where molten materials from the earth's interior rise to the ocean floor, where they form gigantic plates that move slowly apart. Where the plates meet certain continental areas or island chains, they plunge downward to replenish inner-earth materials and form trenches of profound depths. Along the northern and western edges of the Pacific Ocean, several lines of such gutters include some of the deepest known spots—Mariana Trench, Tonga Trench, Kuril Trench. Deep trenches also parallel the western coasts of Central and South America, the northern coasts of Puerto Rico and the Virgin Islands, and other coastal areas. Other identifiable features include the great sub-marine canyons that lead from the edges of the continents; seamounts that rise above the ocean floors; and the continental shelves, which appear to be underwater extensions of landmasses and which vary in shape from narrow fringes to broad plains.

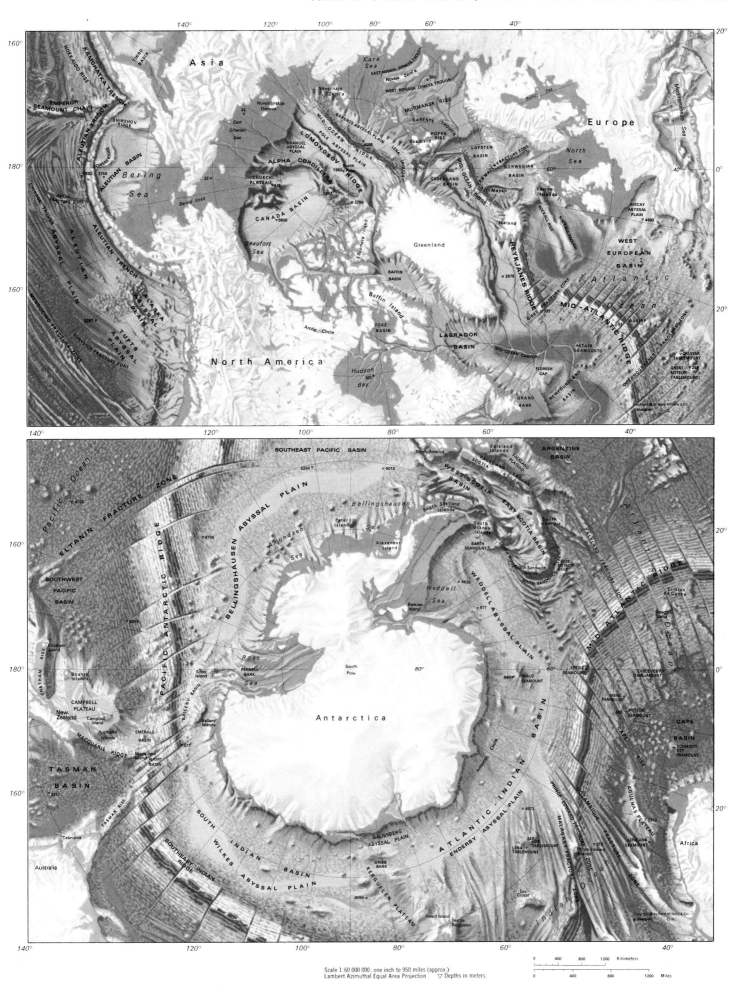

Scale 1:60 000 000; one inch to 950 miles (approx.)
Lambert Azimuthal Equal Area Projection   ▽ Depths in meters.

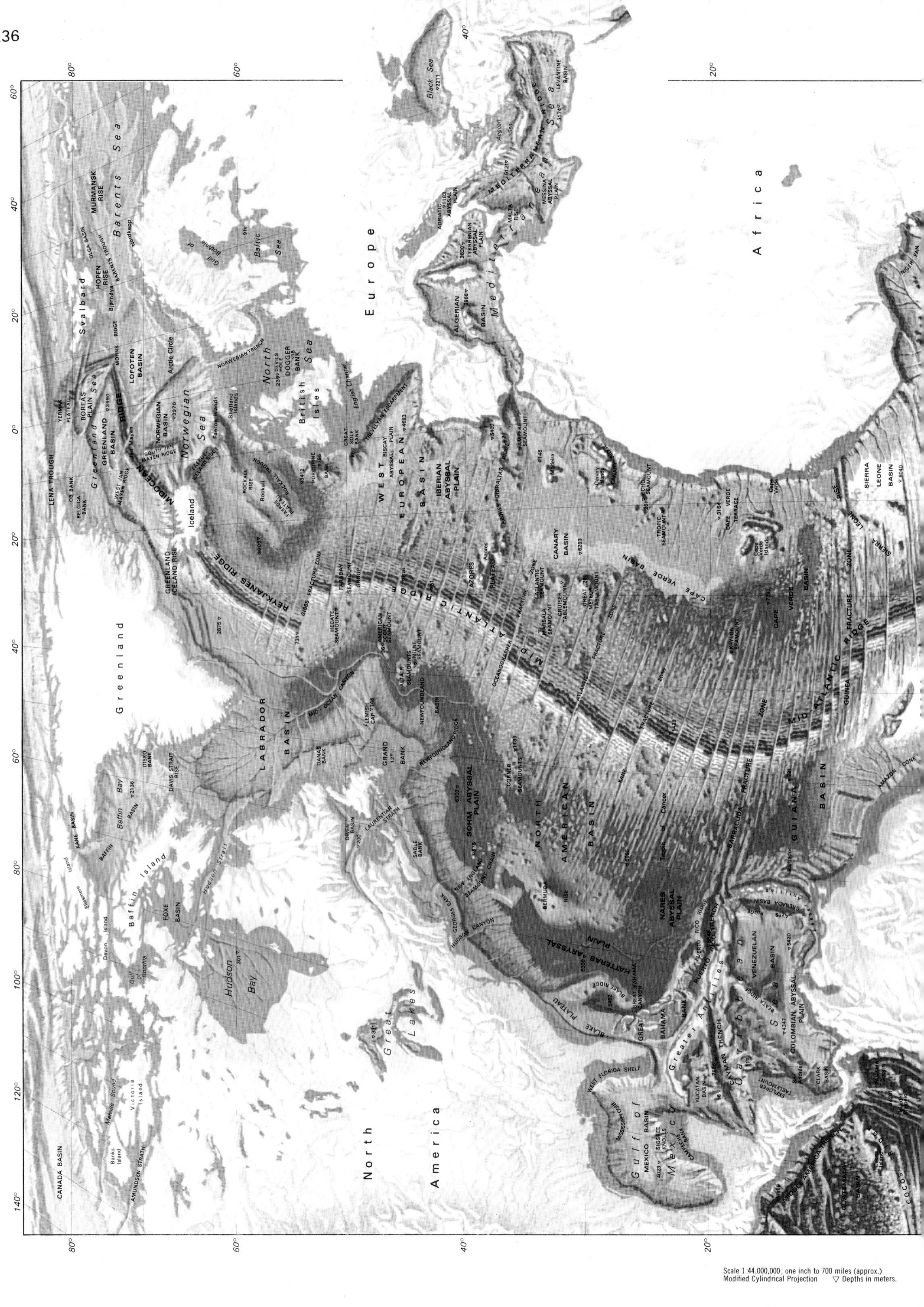
Greenland
Europe
Africa
North America
Iceland
Svalbard
Barents Sea
Norwegian Sea
North Sea
Baltic Sea
Gulf of Bothnia
British Isles
English Channel
Black Sea
Aegean Sea
Mediterranean Sea
MEDITERRANEAN RIDGE
LEVANTINE BASIN
MESSINA ABYSSAL PLAIN
MALTA RISE
ADRIATIC ABYSSAL PLAIN
TYRRHENIAN ABYSSAL PLAIN
ALGERIAN BASIN
MURMANSK RISE
HOPEN RISE
OLGA BASIN
BARENTS TROUGH
Bjørnøya
Nordkapp
LENA TROUGH
YERMAK PLATEAU
BOREAS PLAIN
Greenland Sea
GREENLAND BASIN
MOHNS RIDGE
LOFOTEN BASIN
Arctic Circle
NORWEGIAN BASIN
NORWEGIAN TRENCH
Jan Mayen
SOUTH JAN MAYEN RIDGE
WEST JAN MAYEN RIDGE
MIDOCEAN
OB BANK
BELGICA BANK
Faeroe Islands
Shetland Islands
FAEROE ICELAND RIDGE
DEVILS HOLE
DOGGER BANK
ROCKALL RISE
Rockall
ROCKALL TROUGH
FAEROE PLATEAU
PORCUPINE BANK
GREAT SOLE BANK
TREVELYAN ESCARPMENT
BISCAY ABYSSAL PLAIN
WEST EUROPEAN BASIN
IBERIAN ABYSSAL PLAIN
AZORES-GIBRALTAR RIDGE
AMPERE SEAMOUNT
Madeira
Canary Islands
CANARY BASIN
ECHO SEAMOUNT
TROPIC SEAMOUNT
CAPE VERDE TERRACE
Cape Verde
Cape Verde Islands
CAPE VERDE BASIN
SIERRA LEONE BASIN
SIERRA LEONE RISE
NIGER FAN
GREENLAND-ICELAND RISE
REYKJANES RIDGE
GIBBS FRACTURE ZONE
FARADAY SEAMOUNT GROUP
HECATE SEAMOUNTS
AZORES
AZORES PLATEAU
ATLANTIS SEAMOUNT
CRUISER TABLEMOUNT
GREAT METEOR TABLEMOUNT
MID ATLANTIC RIDGE
OCEANOGRAPHER FRACTURE ZONE
ATLANTIS FRACTURE ZONE
KANE FRACTURE ZONE
BARRACUDA FRACTURE ZONE
GUINEA FRACTURE ZONE
AMAZON CONE
KRYLOV SEAMOUNT
ALTAIR SEAMOUNTS
AMERICAN SCOUT SEAMOUNT
MILNE SEAMOUNT
LABRADOR BASIN
MID-OCEAN CANYON
FLEMISH CAP
NEWFOUNDLAND BASIN
NEWFOUNDLAND RIDGE
DANAS BANK
GRAND BANK
CORNER SEAMOUNTS
SOHM ABYSSAL PLAIN
NORTH AMERICAN BASIN
Tropic of Cancer
GUIANA BASIN
Barbados
DISKO BANK
DAVIS STRAIT RISE
Baffin Bay
BAFFIN BASIN
KANE BASIN
Baffin Island
Ellesmere Island
Devon Island
FOXE BASIN
Hudson Strait
Hudson Bay
Gulf of Boothia
LAURENTIAN STRAIT
OWEN BASIN
SABLE BANK
NEW ENGLAND SEAMOUNT CHAIN
GEORGES BANK
HUDSON CANYON
BERMUDA RISE
NARES ABYSSAL PLAIN
HATTERAS ABYSSAL PLAIN
PUERTO RICO RIDGE
PUERTO RICO TRENCH
BLAKE RIDGE
BLAKE PLATEAU
GREAT BAHAMA CANYON
GREAT BAHAMA BANK
Great Lakes
Greater Antilles
Lesser Antilles
GRENADA BASIN
AVES RIDGE
VENEZUELAN BASIN
BEATA RIDGE
COLOMBIAN ABYSSAL PLAIN
Caribbean Sea
CAYMAN TRENCH
YUCATAN BASIN
EXPLORER TABLEMOUNT
San Andrés
CLARK BASIN
PANAMA BASIN
WEST FLORIDA SHELF
MISSISSIPPI CONE
SIGSBEE KNOLLS
MEXICO BASIN
CAMPECHE BANK
Gulf of Mexico
MIDDLE AMERICA TRENCH
GUATEMALA BASIN
COCOS
Melville Sound
Victoria Island
Banks Island
AMUNDSEN STRAIT
CANADA BASIN
80°
60°
40°
20°
0°
100°
120°
140°

Scale 1:44,000,000; one inch to 700 miles (approx.)
Modified Cylindrical Projection ▽ Depths in meters.

South America

Antarctica

Antarctica

0 200 400 600 800 1000 Kilometers

0 200 400 600 800 1000 Miles

Scale 1:58 000 000; one inch to 900 miles (approx.)
Modified Cylindrical Projection ▽ Depths in meters.

160°　　　140°　　　120°　　　100°　　　80°　　　60°　　　40°

60°

Hudson Bay

LABRADOR BASIN

KODIAK GUYOT (SEAMOUNT)

ALASKA ABYSSAL PLAIN

ALEUTIAN TRENCH

LEUTIAN SAL PLAIN

▽ 3828

TUFTS ABYSSAL PLAIN

▽ 6257

North America

40°

NORTH

AMERICAN

BASIN

▽ 6383

Great Lakes

▽ 331

JUAN DE FUCA RIDGE

CASCADIA

MENDOCINO FRACTURE ZONE

BLANCO

FRACTURE ZONE

PIONEER FRACTURE ZONE

DELGADA FAN

MONTEREY FAN

MUSICIANS SEAMOUNTS

▽ 6253

MURRAY

FRACTURE

ZONE

8120 ▽

▽ 3008

Isla de Guadalupe

CEDROS TRENCH

Gulf of

MEXICO BASIN

SIGSBEE KNOLLS ▽ 4023

WEST FLORIDA SHELF

BLAKE PLATEAU

▽ 4786

MOLOKAI FRACTURE ZONE

BAJA CALIFORNIA SEAMOUNT PROVINCE

Mexico

CAMPECHE BANK

20°

MOLOKAI FRACTURE ZONE

PENSACOLA SEAMOUNT

1057

CLARION FRACTURE ZONE

SUITCASE SEAMOUNTS

RIVERA FRACTURE ZONE

OROZCO FRACTURE ZONE

Islas de Revillagigedo

MIDDLE

AMERICA

TRENCH

▽ 6669

CAYMAN TRENCH

Caribbean

BEATA RIDGE

PANAMA BASIN

▽ 11

Sea

▽ 7

EAST

PACIFIC

BASIN

CLARION FRACTURE ZONE

4808 ▽

▽ 6720

MATHEMATICIANS RIDGE

lle Clipperton

TEHUANTEPEC RIDGE

SIQUEIROS FRACTURE ZONE

GUATEMALA BASIN

▽ 4095

COCOS RIDGE

Isla del Melpelo

▽ 4201

0°

CHRISTMAS RIDGE

CLIPPERTON FRACTURE ZONE

Christmas Island

5349 ▽

Equator

GERMAINE BANK

20 ▽

GALAPAGOS FRACTURE ZONE

GALAPAGOS RISE

EAST PACIFIC RISE (ALBATROSS CORDILLERA)

Galapagos Islands

CARNEGIE RIDGE

PERU BASIN

▽ 5029

▽ 5485

5851 ▽

▽ 4388

Îles Marquises

MARQUESAS FRACTURE ZONE

Baltra

FRACTURE

ZONE

20°

▽ 731A

Îles de la Société

Bellis06

Îles Tuamotu

Tahiti

Pitcairn Island

▽ 4525

Rapa

NAZCA RIDGE

329 ▽

8069 ▽

Tropic of Capricorn

▽ 1068

SALA Y GOMEZ RIDGE

Sala y Gomez

EASTER ISLAND FRACTURE ZONE

Isla de Pascua (Easter Island)

Isla San Felix

Isla San Ambrosio

South America

SOUTHWEST PACIFIC BASIN

EAST PACIFIC RISE (ALBATROSS CORDILLERA)

CHALLENGER FRACTURE ZONE

FERNANDEZ

▽ 3841

CHILE

BASIN

Isla Juan Fernandez

GIFFORD SEAMOUNT

40°

▽ 4755

SOUTHEAST

PACIFIC

BASIN

▽ 3077

▽ 3447

FERNANDEZ FRACTURE ZONE

PERU-CHILE TRENCH

Atlantic Ocean

109 ▽

FALKLAND PLATEAU

501 ▽

ELTANIN FRACTURE ZONE

▽ 4876

Falkland Islands

SCOTIA RIDGE (SOUTH GEORGIA RIDGE)

WEST SCOTIA BASIN

160°　　　140°　　　120°　　　100°　　　80°　　　60°　　　40°

0　400　800　1200　Kilometers

0　400　800　1200　Miles

Scale 1:46 000 000; one inch to 730 miles (approx.)
Modified Cylindrical Projection   ▽ Depths in meters.

This table lists all countries and dependencies in the world, U.S. States, Canadian provinces, and other important regions and political subdivisions. Besides specifying the form of government for all political areas, the table classifies them into five groups according to their political status. Units labeled **A** are independent sovereign nations. (Several of these are designated as members of the British Commonwealth of Nations.) Units labeled **B** are independent as regards internal affairs, but for purposes of foreign affairs they are under the protection of another country. Units labeled **C** are colonies, overseas territories, dependencies, etc., of other countries. Together the **A, B,** and **C** areas comprise practically the entire inhabited area of the world. Units labeled **D** are states, provinces, soviet republics, or similar major administrative subdivisions of important countries. Units in the table with no letter designation are regions or other areas that do not constitute separate political units by themselves.

REGION OR POLITICAL DIVISION	Area* Sq. Mi.	Est. Pop. 1/1/85	Pop. Per. Sq. Mi.	Form of Government and Ruling Power		Capital; Largest City (if other)	Predominant Languages
Afars & Issas, see Djibouti							
Afghanistan†	250,000	14,650,000	59	Socialist Republic	A	Kābul	Dari, Pushtu
Africa	11,700,000	538,000,000	46			; Cairo	
Alabama	51,704	4,015,000	78	State (U.S.)	D	Montgomery; Birmingham	English
Alaska	591,004	515,000	0.9	State (U.S.)	D	Juneau; Anchorage	English, Amerindian languages, Eskimo
Albania†	11,100	2,935,000	264	Socialist Republic	A	Tiranë	Albanian
Alberta	255,285	2,370,000	9.3	Province (Canada)	D	Edmonton	English
Algeria†	919,595	21,695,000	24	Socialist Republic	A	Algiers (El Djazaïr)	Arabic, Berber, French
American Samoa	77	35,000	455	Unincorporated Territory (U.S.)	C	Pago Pago	Samoan, English
Andaman & Nicobar Is.	3,202	195,000	61	Territory (India)	D	Port Blair	Andaman, Nicobar Malay
Andorra	175	39,000	223	Coprincipality (French and Spanish protection)	B	Andorra	French, Spanish
Angola†	481,353	7,875,000	16	Socialist Republic	A	Luanda	Portuguese, indigenous languages
Anguilla	35	7,000	200	Associated State (U.K.)	B	The Valley; South Hill	English
Anhui	54,054	53,400,000	988	Province (China)	D	Hefei; Huainan	Chinese
Antarctica	5,400,000						
Antigua and Barbuda†	170	78,000	459	Parliamentary State (Comm. of Nations)	A	St. John's	English
Arabian Peninsula	1,160,000	24,270,000	21			; Riyadh	Arabic
Argentina†	1,068,301	30,340,000	28	Republic	A	Buenos Aires	Spanish
Arizona	114,002	3,040,000	27	State (U.S.)	D	Phoenix	English
Arkansas	53,191	2,375,000	45	State (U.S.)	D	Little Rock	English
Armenian S.S.R.	11,506	3,280,000	285	Soviet Socialist Republic (Sov. Un.)	D	Yerevan	Armenian, Russian
Aruba	75	65,000	867	Division of Netherlands Antilles (Neth.)	D	Oranjestad	Dutch, Spanish, English, Papiamento
Ascension	34	1,400	41	Dependency of St. Helena (U.K.)	C	Georgetown	English
Asia	17,250,000	2,946,200,000	171			; Tōkyō	
Australia†	2,967,909	15,565,000	5.2	Parliamentary State (Federal) (Commonwealth of Nations)	A	Canberra; Sydney	English
Australian Capital Territory	939	245,000	261	Territory (Australia)	D	Canberra	English
Austria†	32,377	7,580,000	234	Federal Republic	A	Vienna (Wien)	German
Azerbaijan S.S.R.	33,436	6,505,000	195	Soviet Socialist Republic (Sov. Un.)	D	Baku	Turkish, Russian, Armenian
Azores (Açores)	868	255,000	294	Autonomous Region (Portugal)	D	Ponta Delgada	Portuguese
Bahamas†	5,382	230,000	43	Parliamentary State (Commonwealth of Nations)	A	Nassau	English
Bahrain†	256	415,000	1,621	Constitutional Monarchy	A	Al Manāmah	Arabic, English
Balearic Is. (Islas Baleares)	1,936	695,000	359	Province (Spain)	D	Palma [de Mallorca]	Spanish
Baltic Republics	67,182	7,720,000	115	Part of Sov. Un. (3 Republics)		; Rīga	Lithuanian, Latvian, Estonian, Russian
Bangladesh†	55,598	101,130,000	1,819	Republic (Commonwealth of Nations)	A	Dacca (Dhaka)	Bangla, English
Barbados†	166	250,000	1,506	Parliamentary State (Commonwealth of Nations)	A	Bridgetown	English
Beijing Shi	6,487	10,055,000	1,550	Autonomous City (China)	D	Peking (Beijing)	Chinese
Belgium†	11,783	9,875,000	838	Constitutional Monarchy	A	Brussels (Bruxelles)	Dutch (Flemish), French
Belize (British Honduras)†	8,866	160,000	18	Parliamentary State (Commonwealth of Nations)	A	Belmopan; Belize City	English, Spanish, indigenous languages
Belorussian S.S.R.†	80,155	9,975,000	124	Soviet Socialist Republic (Sov. Un.)	D	Minsk	Byelorussian, Polish, Russian
Benelux	28,823	24,705,000	857	Economic Union		; Brussels	Dutch, French, Luxembourgish
Benin†	43,484	3,970,000	91	Socialist Republic	A	Porto-Novo; Cotonou	French, Fon, Adja, indigenous languages
Bermuda	21	70,000	3,333	Colony (U.K.)	C	Hamilton	English
Bhutan†	18,147	1,435,000	79	Monarchy (Indian protection)	B	Thimbu	Dzongkha, English, Nepalese dialects
Bolivia†	424,164	6,115,000	14	Republic	A	La Paz and Sucre;	Spanish, Quechua, Aymara
Bophuthatswana	15,610	1,440,000	92	Bantu Homeland (South Africa)††	B	Mmabatho	Sesotho, Afrikaans
Borneo, Indonesian (Kalimantan)	208,287	7,575,000	36	Part of Indonesia (4 Provinces)		; Banjarmasin	Indonesian
Botswana†	231,805	1,055,000	4.6	Republic (Commonwealth of Nations)	A	Gaborone	English, Setswana
Brazil†	3,286,487	134,340,000	41	Federal Republic	A	Brasilia; São Paulo	Portuguese
British Columbia	366,255	2,885,000	7.9	Province (Canada)	D	Victoria; Vancouver	English
British Honduras, see Belize							
British Indian Ocean Territory	23			Colony (U.K.)	C	Administered from London	
British Solomon Is., see Solomon Is.							
Brunei†	2,226	220,000	99	Constitutional Monarchy (Commonwealth of Nations)	A	Bandar Seri Begawan (Brunei)	Malay, English, Chinese
Bulgaria†	42,823	8,980,000	210	Socialist Republic	A	Sofia (Sofiya)	Bulgarian
Burkina Faso†	105,869	6,820,000	64	Provisional Military Government	A	Ouagadougou	French, indigenous languages
Burma†	261,228	36,795,000	141	Socialist Republic	A	Rangoon	Burmese, indigenous languages
Burundi†	10,747	4,760,000	443	Republic	A	Bujumbura	Kirundi, French, Swahili
California	158,704	25,620,000	161	State (U.S.)	D	Sacramento; Los Angeles	English
Cambodia, see Kampuchea							
Cameroon†	183,569	9,640,000	53	Republic	A	Yaoundé; Douala	English, French, indigenous languages
Canada†	3,831,033	25,270,000	6.6	Parliamentary State (Federal) (Commonwealth of Nations)	A	Ottawa; Toronto	English, French
Canary Is. (Islas Canarias)	2,808	1,475,000	525	Part of Spain (2 Provinces)		; Las Palmas de Gran Canaria	Spanish
Cape Verde†	1,557	300,000	193	Republic	A	Praia	Portuguese, Crioulo
Cayman Is.	100	22,000	220	Colony (U.K.)	C	Georgetown	English
Celebes (Sulawesi)	73,057	11,725,000	160	Part of Indonesia (4 Provinces)		; Ujung Pandang	Indonesian, Malay-Polynesian languages
Central African Republic†	240,535	2,620,000	11	Republic	A	Bangui	French, Sangho
Central America	202,000	25,495,000	126			; Guatemala	Spanish, Amerindian languages
Central Asia, Soviet	493,090	28,545,000	58	Part of Sov. Un (4 Republics)		; Tashkent	Uzbek, Russian, Kirghiz, Turkish, Tajik
Ceylon, see Sri Lanka							
Chad†	495,755	5,180,000	10	Republic	A	N'Djamena	French, Arabic, indigenous languages
Channel Is. (Guernsey, Jersey, etc.)	75	132,000	1,760	Dependency (U.K.)	C	; St. Helier	English, French
Chile†	292,135	11,740,000	40	Republic	A	Santiago	Spanish
China (excl. Taiwan)†	3,718,783	1,080,980,000	291	Socialist Republic	A	Peking (Beijing); Shanghai	Chinese dialects

† Member of the United Nations (1984).
* Areas include inland water.
†† Bophuthatswana, Ciskei, Transkei and Venda are not recognized by the United Nations.

REGION OR POLITICAL DIVISION	Area* Sq. Mi.	Est. Pop. 1/1/85	Pop. Per Sq. Mi.	Form of Government and Ruling Power		Capital; Largest City (if other)	Predominant Languages
China (Nationalist), see Taiwan							
Christmas I. (Indian Ocean)	52	3,300	63	External Territory (Australia)	C	; Flying Fish Cove	English, Tahitian
Ciskei	3,205	740,000	231	Bantu Homeland (South Africa)††	B	Bisho; Mdantsane	Xhosa, Afrikaans
Cocos (Keeling) Is.	5.4	600	111	Part of Australia	C		Malay, English
Colombia†	439,737	28,545,000	65	Republic	A	Bogotá	Spanish
Colorado	104,094	3,210,000	31	State (U.S.)	D	Denver	English
Commonwealth of Nations	10,650,000	1,196,620,000	112			; London	
Comoros†	838	460,000	549	Republic	A	Moroni	Arabic, French, Swahili
Congo†	132,047	1,770,000	13	Republic	A	Brazzaville	French, indigenous languages
Connecticut	5,019	3,160,000	630	State (U.S.)	D	Hartford	English
Cook Is.	91	16,000	176	Self-governing Territory (New Zealand)	B	Avarua	Malay-Polynesian languages, English
Corsica	3,352	220,000	66	Part of France (2 Departments)		; Ajaccio	French, Italian
Costa Rica†	19,730	2,725,000	138	Republic	A	San José	Spanish
Cuba†	44,218	9,770,000	221	Socialist Republic	A	Havana (La Habana)	Spanish
Curaçao	171	165,000	965	Division of Netherlands Antilles (Neth.)	D	Willemstad	Dutch, Spanish, English, Papiamento
Cyprus†	3,572	675,000	189	Republic (Commonwealth of Nations)	A	Nicosia	Greek, Turkish
Czechoslovakia†	49,381	15,490,000	314	Socialist Republic	A	Prague (Praha)	Czech, Slovak, Hungarian
Dahomey, see Benin							
Delaware	2,045	620,000	303	State (U.S.)	D	Dover; Wilmington	English
Denmark†	16,633	5,010,000	301	Constitutional Monarchy	A	Copenhagen (København)	Danish
Denmark and Possessions	857,177	5,110,000	6.0			Copenhagen	Danish, Faeroese, Eskimo
District of Columbia	69	610,000	8,841	District (U.S.)	D	Washington	English
Djibouti†	8,880	360,000	41	Republic	A	Djibouti	French, Somali, Afar, Arabic
Dominica†	290	74,000	255	Republic (Commonwealth of Nations)	A	Roseau	English, French
Dominican Republic†	18,704	6,205,000	332	Republic	A	Santo Domingo	Spanish
Ecuador†	109,483	9,235,000	84	Republic	A	Quito; Guayaquil	Spanish, Quechua
Egypt††	386,643	47,755,000	124	Socialist Republic	A	Cairo (Al Qāhirah)	Arabic
Ellice Is., see Tuvalu							
El Salvador†	8,124	4,905,000	604	Republic	A	San Salvador	Spanish
England	50,207	46,540,000	927	Administrative division of U.K.	D	London	English
Equatorial Guinea†	10,831	280,000	26	Republic	A	Malabo	Spanish, indigenous languages, English
Estonian S.S.R.	17,413	1,545,000	89	Soviet Socialist Republic (Sov. Un.)	D	Tallinn	Estonian, Russian
Ethiopia†	472,434	34,050,000	72	Provisional Military Government	A	Addis Ababa	Amharic, Arabic, indigenous languages
Eurasia	21,150,000	3,644,370,000	172			; Tōkyō	
Europe	3,800,000	673,900,000	177			; London	
Faeroe Is.	540	45,000	83	Part of Danish Realm	B	Tórshavn	Danish, Faeroese
Falkland Is. (excl. Deps.)	4,700	2,000	0.4	Colony (U.K.)△	C	Stanley	English
Fiji†	7,055	695,000	99	Parliamentary State (Commonwealth of Nations)	A	Suva	English, Fijian, Hindustani
Finland†	130,558	4,885,000	37	Republic	A	Helsinki	Finnish, Swedish
Florida	58,668	10,925,000	186	State (U.S.)	D	Tallahassee; Miami	English
France (excl. Overseas Depts)†	211,208	55,020,000	261	Republic	A	Paris	French
France and Possessions	260,661	56,680,000	217			Paris	French
French Guiana	35,135	81,000	2.3	Overseas Department (France)	D	Cayenne	French
French Polynesia	1,544	160,000	104	Overseas Territory (France)	C	Papeete	French, Tahitian,
French West Indies	1,112	640,000	576			; Fort-de-France	French
Fujian	47,491	27,890,000	587	Province (China)	D	Fuzhou	Chinese
Gabon†	103,347	975,000	9.4	Republic	A	Libreville	French, indigenous languages
Galapagos Is.	3,075	6,600	2.1	Province (Ecuador)	D	Puerto Baquerizo Moreno	Spanish
Gambia†	4,361	715,000	164	Republic (Commonwealth of Nations)	A	Banjul (Bathurst)	English, indigenous languages
Gansu	150,580	21,080,000	140	Province (China)	D	Lanzhou	Chinese, Mongolian, Tibetan dialects
Georgia	58,914	5,820,000	99	State (U.S.)	D	Atlanta	English
Georgian S.S.R.	26,911	5,210,000	194	Soviet Socialist Republic (Sov. Union)	D	Tbilisi	Georgic, Armenian, Russian
Germany (Entire)	137,794	77,990,000	566			; Essen	German
German Democratic Republic (East Germany)†	41,768	16,600,000	397	Socialist Republic	A	Berlin (East)	German
Germany, Federal Republic of (West Germany)†	96,019	61,390,000	639	Federal Republic	A	Bonn; Essen	German
Ghana†	92,100	14,030,000	152	Republic (Commonwealth of Nations)	A	Accra	English, Akan, indigenous languages
Gibraltar	2.3	30,000	13,043	Colony (U.K.)	C	Gibraltar	English, Spanish
Gilbert Is., see Kiribati							
Great Britain & Northern Ireland, see United Kingdom							
Greece†	50,944	10,030,000	197	Republic	A	Athens (Athínai)	Greek
Greenland	840,004	53,000	0.06	Part of Danish Realm	B	Godthåb	Danish, indigenous languages
Grenada†	133	114,000	857	Parliamentary State (Commonwealth of Nations)	A	St. George's	English
Guadeloupe (incl. Dependencies)	687	320,000	466	Overseas Department (France)	C	Basse-Terre; Pointe-à-Pitre	French, Creole
Guam	209	116,000	555	Unincorporated Territory (U.S.)	C	Agana	English, Chamorro
Guangdong	89,190	63,775,000	715	Province (China)	D	Canton (Guangzhou)	Chinese, Miao-Yao
Guangxi Zhuangzu	91,506	39,240,000	429	Autonomous Region (China)	D	Nanning	Chinese, Thai, Miao-Yao
Guatemala†	42,042	8,080,000	192	Republic	A	Guatemala	Spanish, indigenous languages
Guernsey (incl. Dependencies)	30	78,000	2,600	Bailiwick of Channel Islands (U.K.)	C	St. Peter Port	English, French
Guinea†	94,926	5,655,000	60	Republic	A	Conakry	French, indigenous languages
Guinea-Bissau†	13,948	850,000	61	Republic	A	Bissau	Portuguese, indigenous languages
Guizhou	67,182	30,810,000	459	Province (China)	D	Guiyang	Chinese, Thai, Miao-Yao
Guyana†	83,000	840,000	10	Republic (Commonwealth of Nations)	A	Georgetown	English
Haiti†	10,714	5,305,000	495	Republic	A	Port-au-Prince	French
Hawaii	6,473	1,045,000	161	State (U.S.)	D	Honolulu	English, Japanese, Hawaiian
Hebei	78,379	56,970,000	727	Province (China)	D	Shijiazhuang; Tangshan	Chinese
Heilongjiang	177,607	35,130,000	198	Province (China)	D	Harbin	Chinese, Mongolian, Tungus
Henan	64,479	79,990,000	1,241	Province (China)	D	Zhengzhou	Chinese
Hispaniola	29,418	11,510,000	391			; Santo Domingo	French, Spanish, Creole
Holland, see Netherlands							
Honduras†	43,277	4,500,000	104	Republic	A	Tegucigalpa	Spanish
Hong Kong	410	5,435,000	13,256	Colony (U.K.)	C	Hong Kong	Cantonese, English
Hubei	72,587	51,455,000	709	Province (China)	D	Wuhan	Chinese
Hunan	81,468	58,050,000	713	Province (China)	D	Changsha	Chinese, Miao-Yao
Hungary†	35,921	10,675,000	297	Socialist Republic	A	Budapest	Hungarian
Iceland†	39,769	240,000	6.0	Republic	A	Reykjavík	Icelandic
Idaho	83,566	1,020,000	12	State (U.S.)	D	Boise	English
Illinois	57,872	11,620,000	201	State (U.S.)	D	Springfield; Chicago	English
India (incl. part of Jammu and Kashmir)†	1,237,061	754,600,000	610	Federal Republic (Commonwealth of Nations)	A	New Delhi; Calcutta	Hindi, English, indigenous languages
Indiana	36,417	5,585,000	153	State (U.S.)	D	Indianapolis	English
Indonesia†	741,101	166,070,000	224	Republic	A	Jakarta	Indonesian, Malay-Polynesian languages
Inner Mongolia, see Nei Monggol							
Iowa	56,275	2,970,000	53	State (U.S.)	D	Des Moines	English

† Member of the United Nations (1984).
△ Claimed by Argentina.
* Areas include inland water.
†† Bophuthatswana, Ciskei, Transkei and Venda are not recognized by the United Nations.

REGION OR POLITICAL DIVISION	Area* Sq. Mi.	Est. Pop. 1/1/85	Pop. Per. Sq. Mi.	Form of Government and Ruling Power		Capital; Largest City (if other)	Predominant Languages
Iran†	636,296	44,500,000	70	Republic	A	Tehrān	Farsi, Turkish, Kurdish, Arabic
Iraq†	167,925	15,255,000	91	Republic	A	Baghdād	Arabic, Kurdish
Ireland†	27,136	3,595,000	132	Republic	A	Dublin	Irish Gaelic, English
Isle of Man	227	67,000	295	Self-governing Territory (U.K.)	B	Douglas	English
Israel†	8,302	4,189,000	505	Republic	A	Jerusalem; Tel Aviv-Yafo	Hebrew, Arabic, English
Israeli Occupied Territories	2,239	1,281,000	572			Gaza	Hebrew, Arabic
Italy†	116,319	56,940,000	490	Republic	A	Rome (Roma); Milan (Milano)	Italian
Ivory Coast†	123,847	9,325,000	75	Republic	A	Abidjan and Yamoussoukro; Abidjan	French, indigenous languages
Jamaica†	4,244	2,170,000	511	Parliamentary State (Commonwealth of Nations)	A	Kingston	English
Japan†	145,834	120,200,000	824	Constitutional Monarchy	A	Tōkyō	Japanese
Java (Jawa) (incl. Madura)	51,038	102,760,000	2,013	Part of Indonesia (5 Provinces)		Jakarta	Indonesian, Chinese, English
Jersey	45	54,000	1,200	Bailiwick of Channel Islands (U.K.)	C	St. Helier	English, French
Jiangsu	39,382	65,075,000	1,652	Province (China)	D	Nanjing	Chinese
Jiangxi	63,707	35,780,000	562	Province (China)	D	Nanchang	Chinese
Jilin	72,201	24,320,000	337	Province (China)	D	Changchun	Chinese, Mongolian, Korean
Jordan†	35,135	2,475,000	70	Constitutional Monarchy	A	'Ammān	Arabic, English
Kampuchea†	69,898	6,180,000	88	Socialist Republic	A	Phnom Penh	Khmer
Kansas	82,282	2,450,000	30	State (U.S.)	D	Topeka; Wichita	English
Kashmir, Jammu and	86,024	9,210,000	107	In dispute (India & Pakistan)		Srinagar and Jammu; Srinagar	Urdu, Kashmiri, Punjabi
Kazakh S.S.R.	1,049,155	15,710,000	15	Soviet Socialist Republic (Sov. Un.)	D	Alma-Ata	Turkish, Russian
Kentucky	40,414	3,780,000	94	State (U.S.)	D	Frankfort; Louisville	English
Kenya†	224,961	18,970,000	84	Republic (Commonwealth of Nations)	A	Nairobi	English, Swahili, indigenous languages
Kirghiz S.S.R.	76,641	3,855,000	50	Soviet Socialist Republic (Sov. Un.)	D	Frunze	Turkish, Farsi, Russian
Kiribati (Gilbert Is.)	275	62,000	225	Republic (Commonwealth of Nations)	A	Bairiki; Bikenibeu	English, Gilbertese
Korea (Entire)	85,052‡	62,170,000	731			; Seoul (Sŏul)	Korean
Korea, North	46,540	19,855,000	427	Socialist Republic	A	P'yŏngyang	Korean
Korea, South	38,025	42,315,000	1,113	Republic	A	Seoul (Sŏul)	Korean
Kuwait†	6,880	1,815,000	264	Constitutional Monarchy	A	Kuwait (Al Kuwayt)	Arabic, English
Labrador	112,826	32,000	0.3	Part of Newfoundland Province (Canada)		Labrador City	English, Eskimo dialects
Laos†	91,429	3,775,000	41	Socialist Republic	A	Viangchan	Lao, French
Latin America	8,000,000	397,610,000	50			; Mexico City	Spanish, Portuguese
Latvian S.S.R.	24,595	2,620,000	107	Soviet Socialist Republic (Sov. Un.)	D	Rīga	Latvian, Russian
Lebanon†	4,015	2,610,000	650	Republic	A	Beirut (Bayrūt)	Arabic, French, English
Lesotho†	11,720	1,495,000	128	Monarchy (Commonwealth of Nations)	A	Maseru	English, Sesotho
Liaoning	58,301	38,485,000	660	Province (China)	D	Shenyang (Mukden)	Chinese, Mongolian
Liberia†	43,000	2,195,000	51	Provisional Military Government	A	Monrovia	English, indigenous languages
Libya†	679,362	3,785,000	5.6	Socialist Republic	A	Tripoli	Arabic
Liechtenstein	62	27,000	435	Constitutional Monarchy	A	Vaduz	German
Lithuanian S.S.R.	25,174	3,555,000	141	Soviet Socialist Republic (Sov. Un.)	D	Vilnius	Lithuanian, Polish, Russian
Louisiana	47,750	4,515,000	95	State (U.S.)	D	Baton Rouge; New Orleans	English
Luxembourg†	998	365,000	366	Constitutional Monarchy	A	Luxembourg	Luxembourgish, French, German
Macao	6.0	310,000	51,667	Overseas Province (Portugal)	D	Macao	Portuguese, Chinese dialects
Madagascar (Malagasy Republic)†	226,658	9,775,000	43	Socialist Republic	A	Antananarivo	French, Malagasy
Madeira Is. (Arquipélago da Madeira)	307	260,000	847	Autonomous Region (Portugal)	D	Funchal	Portuguese
Maine	33,265	1,165,000	35	State (U.S.)	D	Augusta; Portland	English
Malagasy Republic see Madagascar							
Malawi†	45,747	6,940,000	152	Republic (Commonwealth of Nations)	A	Lilongwe; Blantyre	Chichewa, English
Malaya	50,700	12,850,000	253	Part of Malaysia (11 States)		; Kuala Lumpur	Malay, Chinese, English, Tamil
Malaysia†	128,430	15,500,000	121	Constitutional Monarchy (Comm. of Nations)	A	Kuala Lumpur	Malay, Chinese, English, Tamil
Maldives†	115	175,000	1,522	Republic (Commonwealth of Nations)	A	Male	Divehi
Mali†	478,766	7,650,000	16	Republic	A	Bamako	French, Bambara, indigenous languages
Malta†	122	360,000	2,951	Republic (Commonwealth of Nations)	A	Valletta	Maltese, English
Manitoba	251,000	1,060,000	4.2	Province (Canada)	D	Winnipeg	English
Maritime Provinces (excl. Newfoundland)	51,963	1,715,000	33	Part of Canada (3 Provinces)		; Halifax	English
Marshall Is.	70	34,000	486	Part of Trust Terr. of the Pacific Is.	B	Majuro (island); Jarej-Uliga-Delap	Malay-Polynesian languages, English
Martinique	425	320,000	753	Overseas Department (France)	D	Fort-de-France	French, Creole
Maryland	10,461	4,375,000	418	State (U.S.)	D	Annapolis; Baltimore	English
Massachusetts	8,286	5,820,000	702	State (U.S.)	D	Boston	English
Mauritania†	397,955	1,640,000	4.1	Provisional Military Government	A	Nouakchott	Arabic, French
Mauritius (incl. Dependencies)†	790	1,025,000	1,297	Parliamentary State (Commonwealth of Nations)	A	Port Louis	French, English
Mayotte	144	63,000	438	Overseas Department (France)	D	Dzaoudzi	Swahili, French
Mexico†	761,604	78,670,000	103	Federal Republic	A	Mexico City	Spanish
Michigan	97,107	9,090,000	94	State (U.S.)	D	Lansing; Detroit	English
Micronesia, Federated States of	271	80,000	295	Part of Trust Terr. of the Pacific Is.	B	Kolonia	Malay-Polynesian languages, English
Middle America	1,056,000	134,310,000	127			; Mexico City	Spanish, English
Midway Is.	2.0	500	250	Unincorporated Territory (U.S.)	C	Administered from Washington, D.C.	English
Minnesota	86,614	4,205,000	49	State (U.S.)	D	St. Paul; Minneapolis	English
Mississippi	47,691	2,640,000	55	State (U.S.)	D	Jackson	English
Missouri	69,697	5,040,000	72	State (U.S.)	D	Jefferson City; St. Louis	English
Moldavian S.S.R.	13,012	4,105,000	315	Soviet Socialist Republic (Sov. Un.)	D	Kishinëv	Moldavian, Russian, Ukrainian
Monaco	0.6	28,000	46,667	Constitutional Monarchy	A	Monaco	French, Italian, English, Monegasque
Mongolia†	604,250	1,885,000	3.1	Socialist Republic	A	Ulan Bator	Khalka Mongol
Montana	147,045	830,000	5.6	State (U.S.)	D	Helena; Billings	English
Montserrat	40	12,000	300	Colony (U.K.)	C	Plymouth	English
Morocco (excl. Western Sahara)†	172,414	21,750,000	126	Constitutional Monarchy	A	Rabat; Casablanca	Arabic, Berber dialects, French
Mozambique†	308,642	13,700,000	44	Socialist Republic	A	Maputo	Portuguese, indigenous languages
Namibia (excl. Walvis Bay)	318,261	1,095,000	3.4	Under South African Administration**	C	Windhoek	Afrikaans, indigenous languages
Nauru	8.2	7,800	951	Republic (Commonwealth of Nations)	A	Yaren District; ...	Nauruan, English
Nebraska	77,350	1,615,000	21	State (U.S.)	D	Lincoln; Omaha	English
Nei Monggol (Inner Mongolia)	463,323	20,865,000	45	Autonomous Region (China)	D	Hohhot; Baotou	Mongolian
Nepal†	56,135	16,785,000	299	Constitutional Monarchy	A	Kathmandu	Nepali
Netherlands†	16,042	14,465,000	902	Constitutional Monarchy	A	Amsterdam and The Hague ('s-Gravenhage); Amsterdam	Dutch
Netherlands Antilles	383	250,000	653	Self-governing Territory (Netherlands)	B	Willemstad	Dutch, Spanish, English, Papiamento
Netherlands Guiana, see Suriname							
Nevada	110,562	945,000	8.5	State (U.S.)	D	Carson City; Las Vegas	English
New Brunswick	28,354	715,000	25	Province (Canada)	D	Fredericton; Saint John	English, French
New Caledonia (incl. Deps.)	7,358	149,000	20	Overseas Territory (France)	C	Nouméa	French, Malay-Polynesian languages
New England	66,674	12,630,000	189	Part of U.S. (6 States)		; Boston	English
Newfoundland	156,185	585,000	3.7	Province (Canada)	D	St. John's	English

† Member of the United Nations (1984). ‡ Includes 487 sq. miles of demilitarized zone, not included in North or South Korea figures.
** The United Nations declared an end to the mandate of South Africa over Namibia in October 1966. Administration of the territory by South Africa is not recognized by the United Nations.
* Areas include inland water.

244

REGION OR POLITICAL DIVISION	Area* Sq. Mi.	Est. Pop. 1/1/85	Pop. Per. Sq. Mi.	Form of Government and Ruling Power		Capital; Largest City (if other)	Predominant Languages
Newfoundland (excl. Labrador) ..	43,359	553,000	13	Part of Newfoundland Province, Canada		.........; St. John's	English
New Hampshire	9,278	975,000	105	State (U.S.)	D	Concord; Manchester	English
New Hebrides, see Vanuatu							
New Jersey	7,787	7,555,000	970	State (U.S.)	D	Trenton; Newark	English
New Mexico	121,594	1,425,000	12	State (U.S.)	D	Santa Fe; Albuquerque	English, Spanish
New South Wales	309,433	5,415,000	17	State (Australia)	D	Sydney	English
New York	52,737	17,895,000	339	State (U.S.)	D	Albany; New York	English
New Zealand†	103,515	3,155,000	30	Parliamentary State (Commonwealth of Nations)	A	Wellington; Auckland	English, Maori
Nicaragua†	50,193	2,970,000	59	Republic	A	Managua	Spanish, English
Niger†	489,191	6,390,000	13	Provisional Military Government	A	Niamey	French, Hausa, indigenous languages
Nigeria†	356,669	89,650,000	251	Federal Republic (Commonwealth of Nations)	A	Lagos	English, Hausa, Yoruba, Ibo, indigenous languages
Ningxia Huizu	25,483	4,325,000	170	Autonomous Region (China)	D	Yinchuan	Chinese
Niue	102	2,900	28	Self-governing Territory (New Zealand)	B	Alofi	Malay-Polynesian languages, English
Norfolk Island	14	1,700	121	Part of Australia	C	Kingston	English
North America	9,400,000	397,400,000	42			.........; New York	....
North Borneo, see Sabah							
North Carolina	52,669	6,180,000	117	State (U.S.)	D	Raleigh; Charlotte	English
North Dakota	70,702	690,000	9.8	State (U.S.)	D	Bismarck; Fargo	English
Northern Ireland	5,452	1,555,000	285	Administrative division of United Kingdom	D	Belfast	English
Northern Mariana Is.	184	19,000	103	Part of Trust Terr. of the Pacific Is.	B	Saipan (island); Chalan Kanoa	Malay-Polynesian languages, English
Northern Territory	520,280	140,000	0.3	Territory (Australia)	D	Darwin	English, Aboriginal languages
Northwest Territories	1,304,903	51,000	0.04	Territory (Canada)	D	Yellowknife	English, Eskimo, indigenous languages
Norway (incl. Svalbard and Jan Mayen)†	149,158	4,150,000	28	Constitutional Monarchy	A	Oslo	Norwegian (Riksmål and Landsmål), Lappish
Nova Scotia	21,425	875,000	41	Province (Canada)	D	Halifax	English
Oceania (incl. Australia)	3,300,000	24,200,000	7.3			.........; Sydney	....
Ohio	44,786	10,760,000	240	State (U.S.)	D	Columbus; Cleveland	English
Oklahoma	69,957	3,375,000	48	State (U.S.)	D	Oklahoma City	English
Oman†	82,030	1,025,000	12	Monarchy	A	Muscat; Maṭraḥ	Arabic, Farsi
Ontario	412,582	8,985,500	22	Province (Canada)	D	Toronto	English
Oregon	97,076	2,710,000	28	State (U.S.)	D	Salem; Portland	English
Orkney Is.	376	19,000	51	Part of Scotland, U.K.		Kirkwall	English
Pacific Islands, Trust Territory of the	717	146,000	203	U.N. Trusteeship (U.S. Administration)	B	Saipan (island); Jarej-Uliga-Delap	Malay-Polynesian languages, English
Pakistan (incl. part of Jammu and Kashmir)†	339,732	101,300,000	298	Federal Republic	A	Islāmābād; Karāchi	Urdu, English, Punjabi, Sindhi
Palau (Belau)	192	13,000	68	Part of Trust Terr. of the Pacific Is.	B	Koror	Malay-Polynesian languages, English
Panama†	29,762	2,155,000	72	Republic	A	Panamá	Spanish, English
Papua New Guinea†	178,703	3,400,000	19	Parliamentary State (Commonwealth of Nations)	A	Port Moresby	English, Papuan and Negrito languages
Paraguay†	157,048	3,230,000	21	Republic	A	Asunción	Spanish, Guarani
Peking, see Beijing							
Pennsylvania	46,047	12,025,000	261	State (U.S.)	D	Harrisburg; Philadelphia	English
Peru†	496,224	19,520,000	39	Republic	A	Lima	Spanish, Quechua, Aymara
Philippines†	115,831	55,140,000	476	Republic	A	Manila	Pilipino, Spanish, English, Malay-Polynesian languages
Pitcairn (incl. Dependencies)	19	50	0.3	Colony (U.K.)	C	Adamstown	English, Tahitian
Poland†	120,728	37,055,000	307	Socialist Republic	A	Warsaw (Warszawa); Katowice	Polish
Portugal†	35,516	10,065,000	283	Republic	A	Lisbon (Lisboa)	Portuguese
Portuguese Guinea, see Guinea-Bissau							
Prairie Provinces	757,985	4,440,000	5.9	Part of Canada (3 Provinces)		.........; Winnipeg	English
Prince Edward Island	2,184	126,000	58	Province (Canada)	D	Charlottetown	English
Puerto Rico	3,515	3,350,000	953	Commonwealth (U.S.)	B	San Juan	Spanish, English
Qatar†	4,247	280,000	65	Monarchy	A	Ad Dawhah (Doha)	Arabic, English
Qinghai	278,380	4,325,000	16	Province (China)	D	Xining	Tibetan dialects, Mongolian, Turkish, Chinese
Quebec	594,860	6,585,000	11	Province (Canada)	D	Québec; Montréal	French, English
Queensland	667,000	2,500,000	3.7	State (Australia)	D	Brisbane	English
Reunion	969	545,000	562	Overseas Department (France)	D	St. Denis	French
Rhode Island	1,212	975,000	804	State (U.S.)	D	Providence	English
Rhodesia, see Zimbabwe							
Rodrigues	40	35,000	875	Part of Mauritius		.........; Port Mathurin	English, French
Romania†	91,699	22,860,000	249	Socialist Republic	A	Bucharest (Bucureşti)	Romanian
Russian S.F.S.R.	6,592,846	143,280,000	22	Soviet Federated Socialist Republic (Sov. Un.)	A	Moscow (Moskva)	Russian, Finno-Ugric languages, Farsi, Turkish, Mongolian
Rwanda†	10,169	5,935,000	584	Republic	A	Kigali	Kinyarwanda, French
Sabah (North Borneo)	29,388	1,155,000	39	State (Malaysia)	D	Kota Kinabalu; Sandakan	Malay, Chinese, English, indigenous languages
St. Christopher-Nevis†	104	45,000	433	Parliamentary State (Commonwealth of Nations)	A	Basseterre	English
St. Helena (incl. Dependencies) .	162	6,900	43	Colony (U.K.)	C	Jamestown	English
St. Lucia†	238	120,000	504	Parliamentary State (Commonwealth of Nations)	A	Castries	English, French
St. Pierre and Miquelon	93	6,200	67	Overseas Department (France)	D	St-Pierre	French
St. Vincent and the Grenadines† .	150	140,000	933	Parliamentary State (Commonwealth of Nations)	A	Kingstown	English
San Marino	24	23,000	958	Republic	A	San Marino	Italian
Sao Tome and Principe†	372	89,000	239	Republic	A	São Tomé	Portuguese, indigenous languages
Sarawak	48,342	1,495,000	31	State (Malaysia)	D	Kuching	Malay, Chinese, English, indigenous languages
Sardinia	9,301	1,600,000	172	Part of Italy (Sardegna Autonomous Region)	D	Cagliari	Italian
Saskatchewan	251,700	1,010,000	4.0	Province (Canada)	D	Regina	English
Saudi Arabia†	830,000	10,970,000	13	Monarchy	A	Riyadh; Jiddah	Arabic
Scandinavia (incl. Finland and Iceland)	510,000	22,665,000	44			.........; Copenhagen (København)	Swedish, Danish, Norwegian, Finnish, Icelandic
Scotland	30,416	5,130,000	169	Administrative division of United Kingdom	D	Edinburgh; Glasgow	English, Scots Gaelic
Senegal†	75,955	6,650,000	88	Republic	A	Dakar	French, Wolof, indigenous languages
Seychelles†	171	66,000	386	Republic (Commonwealth of Nations)	A	Victoria	French, English
Shaanxi (Shensi)	75,676	31,130,000	411	Province (China)	D	Xi'an	Chinese
Shandong	59,074	79,990,000	1,354	Province (China)	D	Jinan; Qingdao	Chinese
Shanghai Shi	2,239	12,865,000	5,745	Autonomous City (China)	D	Shanghai	Chinese
Shanxi (Shansi)	60,618	27,240,000	449	Province (China)	D	Taiyuan	Chinese
Shetland Is.	551	29,000	53	Part of Scotland, U.K.		Lerwick	English
Sichuan (Szechwan)	219,692	107,125,000	488	Province (China)	D	Chengdu; Chongging	Chinese, Tiberan dialects, Miao-Yao
Sicily	9,926	4,925,000	496	Part of Italy (Sicilia Autonomous Region)	D	Palermo	Italian
Sierra Leone†	27,925	3,855,000	138	Republic (Commonwealth of Nations)	A	Freetown	English, Krio, indigenous languages
Singapore†	224	2,545,000	11,361	Republic (Commonwealth of Nations)	A	Singapore	English, Chinese, Malay, Tamil
Soloman Is.†	11,506	270,000	23	Parliamentary State (Commonwealth of Nations)	A	Honiara	English, Malay-Polynesian languages
Somalia†	246,200	6,465,000	26	Socialist Republic	A	Muqdisho (Mogadisho)	Somali, Arabic, English, Italian
South Africa (incl. Walvis Bay)† .	433,680	26,855,000	62	Republic	A	Pretoria, Cape Town and Bloemfontein; Johannesburg	Afrikaans, English, indigenous languages
South America	6,900,000	263,300,000	38			.........; São Paulo	....
South Australia	380,070	1,355,000	3.6	State (Australia)	D	Adelaide	English

† Member of the United Nations (1984).
*Areas include inland water.

REGION OR POLITICAL DIVISION	Area* Sq. Mi.	Est. Pop. 1/1/85	Pop. Per. Sq. Mi.	Form of Government and Ruling Power	Capital; Largest City (if other)	Predōminant Languages
South Carolina	31,116	3,325,000	107	State (U.S.) .... D	Columbia; Charleston	English
South Dakota	77,120	715,000	9.3	State (U.S.) .... D	Pierre; Sioux Falls	English
Southern Yemen, see Yemen, People's Democratic Republic of	....	....		....		
South Georgia (incl. Dependencies)	1,580	22	0.01	Dependency of Falkland Is. (U.K.) C		English, Norwegian
South West Africa, see Namibia						
Soviet Union (Union of Soviet Socialist Republics)†	8,600,383	275,590,000	32	Federal Socialist Republic .... A	Moscow (Moskva)	Russian and other Slavic languages, various Altaic and Indo-European languages
Soviet Union in Europe	1,920,789	177,710,000	93	Part of Soviet Union ....; Moscow		Russian and other Slavic languages
Spain†	194,882	38,515,000	198	Constitutional Monarchy .... A	Madrid	Spanish
Spanish North Africa	12	137,000	11,417	Five Possessions (no central government) (Spain) C	.......; Ceuta	Spanish, Arabic, Berber
Spanish Sahara, see Western Sahara						
Sri Lanka (Ceylon)†	24,962	16,070,000	644	Socialist Republic (Commonwealth of Nations) .... A	Colombo	Sinhala, Tamil, English
Sudan†	967,500	21,390,000	22	Republic .... A	Al Kharṭum (Khartoum)	Arabic, indigenous languages, English
Sumatra (Sumatera)	182,860	31,555,000	173	Part of Indonesia (7 Provinces) ....; Medan		Indonesian, English, Chinese
Surinam†	63,037	375,000	5.9	Republic .... A	Paramaribo	Dutch, English, Hindi, Sranang Tongo, Javanese
Svalbard	23,958	4,200	0.2	Part of Norway ....; Longyearbyen		Norwegian, Russian
Swaziland†	6,704	660,000	98	Monarchy (Commonwealth of Nations) ...... A	Mbabane	English, siSwati
Sweden†	173,780	8,335,000	48	Constitutional Monarchy .... A	Stockholm	Swedish
Switzerland	15,943	6,485,000	408	Federal Republic .... A	Bern; Zürich	German, French, Italian
Syria†	71,498	10,485,000	147	Socialist Republic .... A	Damascus (Dimashq)	Arabic
Taiwan	13,900	19,090,000	1,373	Republic .... A	T'aipei	Chinese dialects
Tajik S.S.R.	55,251	4,300,000	78	Soviet Socialist Republic (Sov. Un.) .... D	Dushanbe	Tajik, Turkish, Russian
Tanzania†	364,900	21,525,000	59	Republic (Commonwealth of Nations) ...... A	Dar es Salaam	Swahili, English, indigenous languages
Tasmania	26,383	440,000	17	State (Australia) .... D	Hobart	English
Tennessee	42,143	4,755,000	113	State (U.S.) .... D	Nashville; Memphis	English
Texas	266,805	16,090,000	60	State (U.S.) .... D	Austin; Dallas	English, Spanish
Thailand†	198,115	52,220,000	264	Constitutional Monarchy .... A	Bangkok (Krung Thep)	Thai
Tianjin Shi	4,247	8,430,000	1,985	Autonomous City (China) .... D	Tianjin (Tientsin)	Chinese
Tibet, see Xizang						
Togo†	21,925	2,965,000	135	Republic .... A	Lomé	French, indigenous languages
Tokelau (Union Is.)	3.9	1,500	384	Island Territory (New Zealand) ....; Fakaofo		Malay-Polynesian languages, English
Tonga	270	107,000	396	Constitutional Monarchy (Comm. of Nations) .... A	Nuku'alofa	Tongan, English
Transcaucasia	71,853	14,995,000	209	Part of Soviet Union (3 Republics) ....; Baku		Russian, Armenian, Georgic, Turkish
Transkei	15,831	2,560,000	162	Bantu Homeland (South Africa)†† .... B	Umtata	Xhosa; Afrikaans
Trinidad and Tobago†	1,980	1,240,000	626	Republic (Commonwealth of Nations) ...... A	Port of Spain	English
Tristan da Cunha	40	300	7.5	Dependency of St. Helena (U.K.) C	Edinburgh	English
Tunisia†	63,170	7,295,000	115	Republic .... A	Tunis	Arabic, French
Turkey†	300,948	50,730,000	169	Republic .... A	Ankara; İstanbul	Turkish, Kurdish
Turkey in Europe	9,175	4,780,000	521	Part of Turkey ....; İstanbul		Turkish
Turkmen S.S.R.	188,456	3,085,000	16	Soviet Socialist Republic (Sov. Un.) .... D	Ashkhabad	Turkish, Russian
Turks and Caicos Is.	166	8,100	49	Colony (U.K.) C	Grand Turk	English
Tuvalu (Ellice Is.)	10	8,200	820	Parliamentary State (Commonwealth of Nations) ...... A	Funafuti	Tuvaluan, English
Uganda†	91,134	14,505,000	159	Republic (Commonwealth of Nations) ...... A	Kampala	English, Swahili, Luganda, indigenous languages
Ukrainian S.S.R.†	233,090	51,260,000	220	Federal Socialist Republic (Sov. Un.) .... D	Kiev	Ukrainian, Russian
Union of Soviet Socialist Republics, see Soviet Union						
United Arab Emirates†	32,278	1,600,000	50	Federation of Monarchs .... A	Abū Ẓaby (Abu Dhabi)	Arabic, Farsi, English
United Arab Republic, see Egypt						
United Kingdom†	94,092	56,040,000	596	Constitutional Monarchy (Commonwealth of Nations) ... A	London	English
United Kingdom & Possessions	102,111	61,820,000	605		London	English
United States†	3,679,245	237,640,000	65	Federal Republic .... A	Washington; New York	English
United States & Possessions	3,683,901	241,390,000	66		Washington; New York	English, Spanish
Upper Volta, see Burkina Faso						
Uruguay†	68,037	2,930,000	43	Republic .... A	Montevideo	Spanish
Utah	84,902	1,690,000	20	State (U.S.) .... D	Salt Lake City	English
Uzbek S.S.R.	172,742	17,305,000	100	Soviet Socialist Republic (Sov. Un.) .... D	Tashkent	Turkish, Sart, Russian
Vanuatu (New Hebrides)†	5,714	130,000	23	Republic (Commonwealth of Nations) ...... A	Port-Vila	Bislama, English, French
Vatican City (Holy See)	0.2	700	3,500	Ecclesiastical State .... A	Vatican City	Italian, Latin
Venda	2,774	400,000	144	Bantu Homeland (South Africa)†† .... B	Thohoyandou; Makearela	Venda, Afrikaans
Venezuela†	352,144	16,040,000	46	Federal Republic .... A	Caracas	Spanish
Vermont	9,614	535,000	56	State (U.S.) .... D	Montpelier; Burlington	English
Victoria	87,884	4,080,000	46	State (Australia) .... D	Melbourne	English
Vietnam†	127,242	58,930,000	463	Socialist Republic .... A	Ha-noi; Ho Chi Minh City (Saigon)	Vietnamese
Virginia	40,763	5,630,000	138	State (U.S.) .... D	Richmond; Norfolk	English
Virgin Is., British	59	13,000	220	Colony (U.K.) C	Road Town	English
Virgin Is. (U.S.)	133	105,000	789	Unincorporated Territory (U.S.) C	Charlotte Amalie	English, Spanish
Wake I.	3.0	300	100	Unincorporated Territory (U.S.) C	Administered from Washington, D.C.	English
Wales	8,017	2,815,000	351	Administrative division of U.K. .... D	Cardiff	English, Welsh
Wallis and Futuna	98	12,000	122	Overseas Territory (France) C	Mata-Utu	Uvean, Futunan, French
Washington	68,139	4,395,000	65	State (U.S.) .... D	Olympia; Seattle	English
Western Australia	975,920	1,390,000	1.4	State (Australia) .... D	Perth	English
Western Sahara	102,703	170,000	1.7	Occupied by Morocco .... A	El Aaiún	Arabic
Western Samoa†	1,097	160,000	146	Constitutional Monarchy (Comm. of Nations) .... A	Apia	Samoan, English
West Indies	92,000	30,150,000	328	....; Havana		Spanish, English, French, Creole
West Virginia	24,236	1,995,000	82	State (U.S.) .... D	Charleston; Huntington	English
White Russia, see Belorussian S.S.R.						
Wisconsin	66,213	4,800,000	72	State (U.S.) .... D	Madison; Milwaukee	English
World	57,850,000	4,843,000,000	84			
Wyoming	97,808	525,000	5.4	State (U.S.) .... D	Cheyenne	English
Xinjiang Uygur	635,910	14,160,000	22	Autonomous Region (China) .... D	Ürümqi	Turkish, Mongolian, Tungus
Xizang (Tibet)	471,817	2,160,000	4.6	Autonomous Region (China) .... D	Lhasa	Tibetan dialects
Yemen†	75,290	5,985,000	79	Republic .... A	Ṣan'ā'	Arabic
Yemen, People's Democratic Republic of,†	128,560	2,180,000	17	Socialist Republic .... A	Aden	Arabic
Yugoslavia†	98,766	23,075,000	234	Socialist Federal Republic .... A	Belgrade (Beograd)	Serbo-Croatian, Slovene, Macedonian
Yukon Territory	186,300	23,000	0.1	Territory (Canada) .... D	Whitehorse	English, Eskimo, Indian
Yunnan	168,341	35,025,000	208	Province (China) .... D	Kunming	Chinese, Tibetan dialects, Khmer, Miao-Yao
Zaire†	905,567	32,625,000	36	Republic .... A	Kinshasa	French, Lingala, Swahili, Kikongo, Tshiluba
Zambia†	290,586	6,660,000	23	Republic (Commonwealth of Nations) ...... A	Lusaka	English, indigenous languages
Zanzibar	641	555,000	866	Part of Tanzania ....; Zanzibar		Swahili, English, indigenous languages
Zhejiang	39,382	41,835,000	1,062	Province (China) .... D	Hangzhou	Chinese
Zimbabwe (Rhodesia)†	150,804	8,190,000	54	Republic (Commonwealth of Nations) ...... A	Harare	English, ChiShona, SiNdebele

† Member of the United Nations (1984).
* Areas include inland water.
†† Bophuthatswana, Ciskei, Transkei and Venda are not recognized by the United Nations.

world comparisons

General Information

Equatorial diameter of the earth, 7,926.68 miles
Polar diameter of the earth, 7,899.99 miles
Diameter of the mean sphere of the earth, 7,918.78 miles
Equatorial circumference of the earth, 24,901.46 miles
Polar circumference of the earth, 24,859.73 miles
Mean distance from the earth to the sun, 93,020,000 miles
Mean distance from the earth to the moon, 238,857 miles
Total area of the earth, 196,940,400 square miles

Highest elevation on the earth's surface, Mt. Everest, Asia, 29,028 feet
Lowest elevation on the earth's land surface, shores of the Dead Sea, Asia—1,312 feet below sea level
Greatest known depth of the ocean, south of the Mariana Islands, Pacific Ocean, 35,810 feet
Total land area of the earth, including inland water and Antarctica, 57,850,000 square miles.

Area of Africa, 11,700,000 square miles
Area of Antarctica, 5,400,000 square miles
Area of Asia, 17,250,000 square miles
Area of Europe, 3,800,000 square miles
Area of North America, 9,400,000 square miles
Area of Oceania, incl. Australia, 3,300,000 square miles
Area of South America, 6,900,000 square miles
Population of the earth (est. 1/1/85), 4,843,000,000

Principal Islands and Their Areas

ISLAND	Area (Sq. Mi.)
Baffin, Canada	183,810
Banks, Canada	27,038
Borneo, Asia	258,855
Bougainville, Papua New Guinea	3,880
Cape Breton, Canada	3,981
Celebes, Indonesia	73,057
Corsica, France	3,352
Crete, Greece	3,217
Cuba, North America	44,218
Cyprus, Asia	3,572
Devon, Canada	21,331
Ellesmere, Canada	83,896
Flores, Indonesia	5,513
Great Britain, U.K.	88,787
Greenland, North America	840,004
Guadalcanal, Solomon Is.	2,500
Hainan, China	13,127
Hawaii, U.S.	4,021
Hispaniola, North America	29,418
Hokkaidō, Japan	30,144
Honshū, Japan	87,805
Iceland, Europe	39,769
Ireland, Europe	32,588
Jamaica, North America	4,244
Jawa (Java), Indonesia	50,745
Kodiak, U.S.	3,670
Kyūshū, Japan	16,215
Leyte, Philippines	2,785
Luzon, Philippines	40,420
Madagascar, Africa	226,658
Melville, Canada	16,274
Mindanao, Philippines	36,537
Mindoro, Philippines	3,759
Negros, Philippines	4,907
New Britain, Papua New Guinea	14,592
New Caledonia, Oceania	5,671
Newfoundland, Canada	43,359
New Guinea, Oceania	303,090
New Ireland, Papua New Guinea	3,205
North East Land, Norway	6,350
North Island, New Zealand	44,279
Novaya Zemlya, Soviet Union	18,882
Palawan, Philippines	4,550
Panay, Philippines	4,446
Prince of Wales, Canada	12,872
Puerto Rico, North America	3,515
Sakhalin, Soviet Union	29,498
Samar, Philippines	5,050
Sardinia, Italy	9,301
Seram, Indonesia	6,046
Sicily, Italy	9,926
Shikoku, Japan	7,245
Somerset, Canada	9,570
Southampton, Canada	15,913
South Island, New Zealand	57,862
Spitsbergen, Norway	15,260
Sri Lanka, Asia	24,962
Sumatra, Indonesia	182,860
Taiwan, Asia	13,900
Tasmania, Australia	26,383
Tierra del Fuego, S. America	18,600
Timor, Indonesia	13,094
Vancouver, Canada	12,079
Victoria, Canada	81,930
Vrangelya, Soviet Union	2,819

Principal Lakes, Oceans, Seas, and Their Areas

LAKE Country	Area (Sq. Mi.)
Aral'skoye More (Aral Sea), Sov. Un	24,909
Arctic Ocean	5,400,000
Athabasca, L., Can	3,064
Atlantic Ocean	31,800,000
Balkhash, Ozero (L.), Sov. Un	7,115
Baltic Sea, Eur.	163,000
Baykal, Ozero (L. Baikal), Sov. Un	12,160
Bering Sea, Asia-N.A.	876,000
Black Sea, Eur.-Asia	178,000
Caribbean Sea, N.A.-S.A.	1,063,000
Caspian Sea, Asia	143,240
Chad, L., Chad-Cam.-Nig.	6,300
East China Sea, Asia	482,000
Erie, L., U.S.-Can.	9,910
Eyre, L., Austl.	2,970
Gairdner, L., Austl.	1,840
Great Bear L., Can.	12,028
Great Salt L., U.S.	1,680
Great Slave L., Can.	11,030
Hudson Bay, Can.	475,000
Huron, L., U.S.-Can.	23,000
Indian Ocean	28,900,000
Japan, Sea of, Asia	389,000
Koko Nor (Qinghai Hu) (L.), China	1,650
Ladozhskoye Ozero (Lake Ladoga), Sov. Un.	6,835
Mai-Ndombe, Lac, (L.), Zaire	3,100
Manitoba, L., Can.	1,800
Mediterranean Sea., Eur.-Afr.-Asia	967,000
Mexico, Gulf of, N.A.	596,000
Michigan, L., U.S.	22,300
Nicaragua, Lago de (L.), Nic.	3,150
North Sea, Eur.	222,000
Nyasa, L., Mwi,-Moz.-Tan	11,150
Okhotsk, Sea of, Asia	610,000
Onezhskoye Ozero (Lake Onega), Sov. Un.	3,720
Ontario, L., U.S.-Can.	7,540
Pacific Ocean	63,800,000
Red Sea, Afr.-Asia	169,000
Rudolf, L., Ken.-Eth.	2,473
Superior, L., U.S.-Can.	31,700
Tanganyika, L., Tan.-Zaire-Bdi.-Zam.	12,350
Titicaca, Lago (L.), Bol.-Peru	3,200
Torrens, L., Austl.	2,230
Vänern (L.), Swe.	2,156
Van Gölü (L.), Tur.	1,434
Victoria, L., Tan.-Ken.-Ug.	26,820
Winnipeg, L., Can.	9,417
Winnipegosis, L., Can.	2,075
Yellow Sea, China	480,000

Principal Mountains and Their Heights

MOUNTAIN Country	Elev. (Ft.)
Aconcagua, Argentina	22,831
Albert Edward, Papua New Guinea	13,091
Annapurna, Nepal	26,504
Antofalla, Argentina	20,013
Apo, Philippines	9,692
Ararat, Turkey	16,804
Bandeira, Brazil	9,482
Barú, Panama	11,410
Belukha, Soviet Union	14,783
Blanc, France-Italy	15,771
Blanca, Colorado, U.S.	14,317
Bolívar (La Columna), Venezuela	16,411
Borah, Idaho, U.S.	12,662
Cameroon, Cam	13,451
Chimborazo, Ecuador	20,561
Citlaltépetl, Mexico	18,701
Colima, Mexico	13,993
Cook, New Zealand	12,349
Cotopaxi, Ecuador	19,347
Cristóbal Colón, Colombia	19,029
Damāvand, Iran	18,386
Dhaulagiri, Nepal	26,810
Duarte, Dom. Rep.	10,417
Dykh-Tau, Soviet Union	17,070
Elbert, Colorado, U.S.	14,431
El'brus, Soviet Union	18,510
Elgon, Kenya	14,178
eNjesuthi, S. Africa	11,306
Erciyeş, Turkey	12,848
Erebus, Antarctia	12,280
Etna, Italy	10,902
Everest, Nepal-China	29,028
Finsteraarhorn, Switzerland	14,022
Foraker, Alaska, U.S.	17,395
Fuji, Japan	12,388
Gannett, Wyo., U.S.	13,785
Gasherbrum, Pak	26,470
Gerlachovský, Czech.	8,710
Glittertinden, Norway	8,110
Gongga Shan, China	24,902
Gosainthan, China	26,289
Grand Teton, Wyo., U.S.	13,766
Gran Paradiso, Italy	13,323
Grossglockner, Austria	12,461
Gunnbjørns, Greenland	12,139
Gurla Mandhata, China	25,354
Hekla, Iceland	4,892
Hood, Oregon, U.S.	11,239
Huascarán, Peru	22,205
Huila, Colombia	18,865
Hvannadalshnukur, Iceland	6,952
Illimani, Bolivia	21,151
Incahuasi, Argentina-Chile	21,719
Iztaccíhuatl, Mexico	17,343
Jaya, Indonesia	16,503
Jungfrau, Switzerland	13,668
K2 (Godwin Austen), Pak	28,250
Kailas, China (Tibet)	22,028
Kāmet, India	25,447
Kanchenjunga, Nepal-India	28,208
Kātrīnā, Egypt	8,652
Kazbek, Soviet Union	16,558
Kebnekaise, Sweden	6,926
Kerinci, Indonesia	12,467
Kilimanjaro, Tanzania	19,340
Kinabalu, Malaysia	13,455
Kirinyaga, Kenya	17,058
Klyuchevskaya, Soviet Union	15,584
Kommunizma, Soviet Union	24,590
Korab, Albania	9,026
Kosciusko, Australia	7,310
Koussi, Chad	11,204
Kula Kangri, Bhutan	24,784
Kwanmo, Korea	8,337
Lassen, California, U.S.	10,457
Lenina, Soviet Union	23,406
Llullaillaco, Argentina-Chile	22,057
Logan, Canada	19,524
McKinley, Alaska, U.S.	20,320
Makālu, China-Nepal	27,824
Margherita, Zaire-Uganda	16,763
Markham, Antarctica	14,272
Maromokotro, Madagascar	9,436
Matterhorn, Switz.-Italy	14,685
Mauna Kea, Hawaii, U.S.	13,796
Mauna Loa, Hawaii, U.S.	13,680
Mercedario, Argentina	22,211
Meru, Tanzania	14,978
Midi d'Ossau, France	10,322
Misti, Peru	19,098
Mitchell, North Carolina, U.S.	6,684
Moldaveneau, Romania	8,343
Munku-Sardyk, Mong. Soviet Union	11,457
Musala, Bulgaria	9,592
Muztag, China	25,338
Muztagata, China	24,388
Namcha Barwa, China	25,443
Nanda Devi, India	25,645
Nanga Parbat, Pak.	26,660
Narodnaya, Sov. Un.	6,217
Neblina, Brazil	9,888
Neiges, Reunion	10,069
Nevis, U.K.	4,406
Ntlenyana, Lesotho	11,424
Ojos del Salado, Argentina-Chile	22,615
Ólimbos, Greece	9,550
Orohena, Tahiti	7,352
Paektu, N. Korea-Sov. Un.	9,100
Paricutín, Mexico	9,213
Pelée, Martinique	4,800
Pico, Cape Verde	9,281
Pidurutalagala, Sri Lanka	8,281
Pikes Peak, Colorado, U.S.	14,110
Pissis, Argentina	22,241
Pobedy, China-Soviet Union	24,406
Popocatépetl, Mexico	17,887
Pulog, Philippines	9,626
Rainier, Washington, U.S.	14,410
Rakaposhi, Pak	25,550
Ras Dashen, Ethiopia	15,158
Rinjani, Indonesia	12,224
Rosa, Italy-Switzerland	15,200
Ruapehu, New Zealand	9,175
St. Elias, U.S.-Canada	18,008
Sajama, Bolivia	21,391
Sawdā, Lebanon	10,115
Semeru, Indonesia	12,060
Shām, Oman	9,902
Shasta, California, U.S.	14,162
Shkhara, Soviet Union	16,594
Sources, Lesotho-S. Afr.	10,822
Tahat, Algeria	9,541
Tajumulco, Guat.	13,816
Tirich Mīr, Pak.	25,230
Tocorpuri, Bolivia-Chile	19,137
Toubkal, Morocco	13,665
Trikora, Indonesia	15,584
Tsast Bogd, Mongolia	13,419
Tupungato, Argentina-Chile	22,310
Vesuvio (Vesuvius), Italy	3,842
Victoria, Papau New Guinea	13,242
Vinson Massif, Ant	16,864
Waddington, Canada	13,260
Washington, N.H., U.S.	6,288
Weisshorn, Switzerland	14,783
Whitney, California, U.S.	14,494
Wilhelm, Papua New Guinea	14,794
Wrangell, Alaska, U.S.	14,005
Yerupaja, Peru	21,765
Zugspitze, Austria	9,721

Principal Rivers and Their Lengths

RIVER Continent	Length (Mi.)
Albany, North America	610
Aldan, Asia	1,392
Amazonas-Ucayali, South America	3,902
Amu Dar'ya (Oxus), Asia	1,616
Amur, Asia	2,744
Araguaia, South America	1,367
Arkansas, North America	1,459
Athabasca, North America	765
Brahmaputra, Asia	1,802
Branco, South America	580
Brazos, North America	870
Canadian, North America	906
Churchill, North America	1,000
Colorado, North America	1,450
Columbia, North America	1,243
Congo (Zaïre), Africa	2,610
Cumberland, North America	720
Danube, Europe	1,777
Darling, Australia	1,690
Dnepr (Dnieper), Europe	1,368
Dnestr (Dniester), Europe	876
Don, Europe	1,162
Donets, Europe	735
Elbe, Europe	720
Euphrates, Asia	1,715
Fraser, North America	850
Gambia, Africa	680
Ganges, Asia	1,678
Gila, North America	630
Godāvari, Asia	930
Huang (Yellow), Asia	3,395
Indus, Asia	1,976
Irrawaddy, Asia	1,425
Japurá, South America	1,400
Juruá, South America	1,250
Kama, Europe	1,263
Kasai, Africa	1,338
Kolyma, Asia	1,600
Lena, Asia	2,734
Limpopo, Africa	1,100
Loire, Europe	625
Mackenzie, North America	2,635
Madeira-Mamore, South America	1,988
Magdalena, South America	950
Marañón, South America	1,000
Mekong, Asia	2,796
Meuse, Europe	575
Mississippi, North America	2,348
Mississippi-Missouri, North America	3,740
Missouri, North America	2,314
Murray, Australia	1,609
Negro, South America	1,305
Nelson-Saskatchewan, North America	1,600
Neman, Europe	582
Niger, Africa	2,585
Nile-Kagera, Africa	4,145
Ob'-Irtysh, Asia	3,362
Oder, Europe	565
Ohio, North America	981
Oka, Europe	920
Orange, Africa	1,300
Orinoco, South America	1,700
Ottawa, North America	696
Paraguay, South America	1,584
Paraná, South America	2,796
Paranaíba, South America	850
Peace, North America	1,195
Pechora, Europe	1,124
Pecos, North America	735
Pilcomayo, South America	1,550
Plata-Paraña, South America	2,920
Purús, South America	1,988
Red, North America	1,270
Rhine, Europe	820
Rhône, Europe	500
Rio Grande, North America	1,885
Roosevelt, South America	950
St. Lawrence, North America	800
Salado, South America	870
Salween, Asia	1,770
São Francisco, South America	1,802
Saskatchewan, North America	1,660
Sava, Europe	585
Snake, North America	1,038
Sungari (Songhua), Asia	1,140
Syr-Dar'ya, Asia	1,859
Tagus (Tajo, Tejo), Europe	625
Tarim, Asia	1,328
Tennessee, North America	652
Tigris, Asia	1,181
Tisza, Europe	607
Tobol, Asia	1,093
Tocantins, South America	1,640
Ucayali, South America	1,220
Ural, Asia	1,509
Uruguay, South America	1,025
Verkhnyaya Tunguska (Angara), Asia	1,549
Vilyuy, Asia	1,513
Volga, Europe	2,194
White, North America	720
Wisla (Vistula), Europe	630
Xingú, South America	1,230
Yangtze, Asia	3,915
Yellowstone, North America	671
Yenisey, Asia	2,543
Yukon, North America	1,979
Zambezi, Africa	1,653

principal cities of the world

Abidjan, Ivory Coast	1,500,000
Accra, Ghana (1,142,690)	1,045,381
Addis Ababa, Ethiopia	1,408,068
Adelaide, Australia (931,886)	12,656
Ahmadābād, India (2,400,000)	2,024,917
Aleppo (Halab), Syria	962,954
Alexandria (Al Iskandarīyah), Egypt (2,850,000)	2,409,000
Algiers (El Djazaïr), Algeria (1,724,705)	1,523,000
Al Kharṭūm (Khartoum), Sudan, (790,000)	333,921
Alma-Ata, Soviet Union (1,075,000)	1,046,000
Ammān, Jordan	648,587
Amsterdam, Netherlands (1,810,000)	687,397
Ankara (Angora), Turkey (1,975,000)	1,877,755
Anshan, China (1,210,000†)	1,030,000
Antwerp (Antwerpen), Belgium (1,100,000)	490,524
Asunción, Paraguay (700,000)	455,517
Athens (Athínai), Greece (3,027,331)	885,737
Atlanta, Georgia (2,112,400)	425,022
Auckland, New Zealand (778,200)	144,400
Baghdād, Iraq (2,183,800)	1,300,000
Baku, Soviet Union (1,880,000)	1,084,000
Baltimore, Maryland (1,901,100)	786,741
Bandung, Indonesia (1,525,000)	1,462,637
Bangalore, India (2,950,000)	2,482,507
Bangkok (Krung Thep), Thailand (5,700,000)	5,153,902
Barcelona, Spain (3,975,000)	1,754,900
Beirut, Lebanon (1,675,000)	474,870
Belfast, No. Ireland (710,000)	295,223
Belgrade (Beograd), Yugoslavia (1,400,000)	936,200
Belo Horizonte, Brazil (2,500,000)	1,781,924
Berlin, East, Ger. Dem. Rep. (*Berlin, West)	1,152,529
Berlin, West, Fed. Rep. of Ger. (3,790,000)	1,869,584
Bilbao, Spain (965,000)	433,030
Birmingham, England (2,675,000)	1,022,300
Bogotá, Colombia (4,150,000)	4,067,000
Bombay, India (9,950,000)	8,227,332
Bonn, Fed. Rep. of Ger. (570,000)	293,852
Boston, Massachusetts (3,732,300)	562,994
Brasília, Brazil	1,177,393
Bremen, Fed. Rep. of Ger. (800,000)	547,619
Brisbane, Australia (1,028,527)	689,378
Brussels (Bruxelles), Belgium (2,395,000)	137,738
Bucharest (București), Romania (2,175,000)	1,929,360
Budapest, Hungary (2,540,000)	2,064,000
Buenos Aires, Argentina (10,700,000)	2,908,001
Buffalo, New York (1,133,800)	357,870
Cairo (Al Qāhirah), Egypt (8,500,000)	5,278,000
Calcutta, India (11,100,000)	3,291,655
Cali, Colombia (1,340,000)	1,293,000
Canberra, Australia (239,798)	219,323
Canton (Guangzhou), China (3,120,000†)	2,380,000
Cape Town, South Africa (1,790,000)	859,940
Caracas, Venezuela (3,600,000)	3,041,000
Cardiff, Wales (625,000)	281,300
Casablanca, Morocco (1,575,000)	1,506,373
Changchun, China (1,740,000†)	1,340,000
Chelyabinsk, Soviet Union (1,245,000)	1,086,000
Chengdu, China (2,470,000)	1,410,000
Chicago, Illinois (7,823,000)	3,005,072
Chongqing (Chungking), China (2,650,800†)	1,940,000
Cincinnati, Ohio (1,472,200)	385,409
Cleveland, Ohio (2,160,800)	573,822
Cologne (Köln), Fed. Rep. of Ger. (1,810,000)	961,777
Colombo, Sri Lanka (1,600,000)	585,776
Columbus, Ohio (949,200)	565,032
Copenhagen (København), Denmark (1,470,000)	498,850
Dacca (Dhaka), Bangladesh (3,458,602)	1,850,000
Dakar, Senegal	979,000
Dallas, Texas (3,126,500)	904,570
Damascus (Dimashq), Syria (1,575,000)	1,201,000
Dar es Salaam, Tanzania	757,346
Delhi, India (7,200,000)	4,865,077
Denver, Colorado (1,559,200)	492,686
Detroit, Michigan (4,254,800)	1,203,368
Dnepropetrovsk, Soviet Union (1,525,000)	1,140,000
Donetsk (Stalino), Soviet Union (2,140,000)	1,064,000
Dresden, Ger. Dem. Rep. (640,000)	516,225
Dublin (Baile Atha Cliath), Ireland (1,110,000)	525,882
Durban, South Africa (1,550,000)	677,760
Düsseldorf, Fed. Rep. of Ger. (1,215,000)	583,445
Edinburgh, Scotland (630,000)	446,361
Essen, Fed. Rep. of Ger. (5,050,000)	638,812
Florence (Firenze), Italy (650,000)	453,293
Fortaleza, Brazil (1,550,000)	1,308,919
Frankfurt am Main, Fed. Rep. of Ger. (1,880,000)	620,186
Fukuoka, Japan (1,575,000)	1,088,588
Fushun, China (1,190,000†)	1,040,000
Gdańsk (Danzig), Poland (875,000)	464,600
Geneva (Génève), Switzerland (435,000)	158,900
Genoa (Genova), Italy (830,000)	760,300
Glasgow, Scotland (1,800,000)	767,456
Gor'kiy, Soviet Union (1,940,000)	1,392,000
Guadalajara, Mexico (2,300,000)	1,626,152
Guatemala, Guatemala (1,100,000)	749,784
Guayaquil, Ecuador	1,278,908
Hamburg, Fed. Rep. of Ger. (2,250,000)	1,623,848
Hannover, Fed. Rep. of Ger. (1,005,000)	526,253
Hanoi, Vietnam (1,500,000)	819,913
Harare, Zimbabwe (870,000)	656,011
Harbin, China (2,550,000†)	2,150,000
Hartford, Connecticut (1,058,800)	136,392
Havana (La Habana), Cuba (1,975,000)	1,924,886
Helsinki, Finland (900,000)	483,051
Hiroshima, Japan (1,525,000)	899,399
Ho Chi Minh City (Saigon), Vietnam (3,100,000)	2,441,185
Hong Kong, Hong Kong (4,515,000)	1,183,621
Honolulu, Hawaii (806,100)	365,048
Houston, Texas (3,085,700)	1,595,138
Hyderābād, India (2,750,000)	2,142,087
Ibadan, Nigeria	1,009,000
Indianapolis, Indiana (1,115,100)	700,807
Irkutsk, Soviet Union	589,000
İstanbul, Turkey (4,650,000)	2,772,708
İzmir, Turkey (1,200,000)	757,854
Jakarta (Batavia), Indonesia (7,000,000)	6,503,449
Jerusalem, Israel (440,000)	415,000
Jinan, China (1,320,000†)	1,040,000
Johannesburg, South Africa (3,650,000)	703,980
Kābul, Afghanistan	913,164
Kānpur, India (1,875,000)	1,531,345
Kansas City, Missouri (1,264,600)	448,028
Kaohsiung, Taiwan (1,640,000)	1,227,454
Karāchi, Pakistan (5,150,000)	4,776,000
Kathmandu, Nepal (320,000)	235,160
Katowice, Poland (2,720,000)	361,300
Kawasaki, Japan (*Tōkyō)	1,040,802
Kazan', Soviet Union (1,080,000)	1,039,000
Khar'kov, Soviet Union (1,825,000)	1,536,000
Kiev, Soviet Union (2,635,000)	2,409,000
Kingston, Jamaica	671,000
Kinshasa, Zaire	2,700,000
Kitakyūshū, Japan (1,515,000)	1,065,078
Kōbe, Japan (*Ōsaka)	1,367,390
Kowloon, Hong Kong (*Hong Kong)	799,123
Kuala Lumpur, Malaysia (1,250,000)	937,817
Kunming, China (1,430,000†)	1,020,000
Kuwait (Al Kuwayt), Kuwait (1,085,000)	60,365
Kuybyshev, Soviet Union (1,460,000)	1,250,000
Kyōto, Japan (*Ōsaka)	1,473,065
Lagos, Nigeria (2,000,000)	1,404,000
Lahore, Pakistan (2,975,000)	2,685,000
Lanzhou, China (1,430,000†)	1,080,000
La Paz, Bolivia	719,780
Leeds, England (1,540,000)	718,100
Leipzig, Ger. Dem. Rep. (710,000)	562,480
Leningrad, Soviet Union (5,550,000)	4,295,000
Liège, Belgium (755,000)	207,496
Lille, France (1,020,000)	168,424
Lima, Peru (4,608,010)	371,122
Lisbon (Lisboa), Portugal (2,250,000)	807,200
Liverpool, England (1,525,000)	518,900
Łódź, Poland (1,045,000)	848,500
London, England (11,100,000)	6,851,400
Los Angeles, California (10,339,800)	2,968,579
Louisville, Kentucky (882,700)	298,694
Luanda, Angola	475,328
Lucknow, India (1,060,000)	895,947
Lüda (Dairen), China (1,480,000†)	1,240,000
Lyon, France (1,180,000)	413,095
Madras, India (4,475,000)	3,266,034
Madrid, Spain (4,515,000)	3,188,297
Managua, Nicaragua	644,588
Manchester, England (2,775,000)	464,200
Manila, Philippines (6,800,000)	1,626,249
Mannheim, Fed. Rep. of Ger. (1,410,000)	302,621
Maracaibo, Venezuela	929,000
Marseille, France (1,090,000)	874,436
Mecca (Makkah), Saudi Arabia	550,000
Medan, Indonesia (1,450,000)	1,378,955
Medellín, Colombia (2,025,000)	1,477,000
Melbourne, Australia (2,722,817)	63,388
Memphis, Tennessee (847,300)	646,174
Mexico City, Mexico (14,600,000)	9,373,400
Miami, Florida (3,097,300)	346,865
Milan (Milano), Italy (3,775,000)	1,634,638
Milwaukee, Wisconsin (1,347,000)	636,297
Minneapolis, Minnesota (2,025,600)	370,951
Minsk, Soviet Union (1,450,000)	1,442,000
Monterrey, Mexico (2,015,000)	1,090,009
Montevideo, Uruguay (1,350,000)	1,229,748
Montréal, Canada (2,828,349)	980,354
Moscow (Moskva), Soviet Union (12,400,000)	8,202,000
Munich (München), Fed. Rep. of Ger. (1,955,000)	1,287,080
Nagoya, Japan (4,625,000)	2.087,902
Nāgpur, India (1,325,000)	1,215,425
Nairobi, Kenya	827,775
Nanjing, China (2,130,000)	1,740,000
Naples (Napoli), Italy (2,765,000)	1,210,503
Newcastle upon Tyne, England (1,300,000)	285,300
New Delhi, India (*Delhi)	271,990
New Orleans, Louisiana (1,236,500)	557,927
New York, New York (16,635,500)	7,071,639
Norfolk, Virginia (830,900)	266,979
Novosibirsk, Soviet Union (1,515,000)	1,384,000
Nürnberg, Fed. Rep. of Ger. (1,040,000)	479,035
Odessa, Soviet Union (1,165,000)	1,113,000
Oklahoma City, Oklahoma (813,300)	404,014
Omsk, Soviet Union (1,100,000)	1,094,000
Osaka, Japan (15,900,000)	2,648,180
Oslo, Norway (725,000)	448,747
Ottawa, Canada (717,978)	295,163
Palermo, Italy	699,691
Panamá, Panama (625,000)	388,638
Paris, France (9,450,000)	2,176,243
Peking (Beijing), China (6,100,000)	5,597,972
Perm', Soviet Union (1,105,000)	1,048,000
Perth, Australia (898,918)	79,398
Philadelphia, Pennsylvania (5,157,900)	1,688,210
Phnom Penh, Kampuchea	400,000
Phoenix, Arizona (1,652,700)	790,160
Pittsburgh, Pennsylvania (2,119,100)	423,959
Port-au-Prince, Haiti (800,000)	745,700
Portland, Oregon (1,249,600)	368,139
Porto (Oporto), Portugal (1,225,000)	327,400
Porto Alegre, Brazil (2,200,000)	1,125,901
Prague (Praha), Czechoslovakia (1,270,000)	1,185,693
Pretoria, South Africa (960,000)	435,100
Providence, Rhode Island (903,700)	156,804
Pune, India (1,775,000)	1,202,848
Pusan, Korea (South)	3,395,000
P'yŏngyang, Korea (North)	1,700,000
Qingdao, China (1,180,000†)	1,080,000
Qiqihar, China (1,222,000†)	920,000
Québec, Canada (576,075)	166,474
Quezon City, Philippines (*Manila)	1,165,865
Quito, Equador	918,884
Rabat, Morocco (540,000)	367,620
Rangoon, Burma (3,000,000)	2,276,000
Rawalpindi, Pakistan (1,040,000)	452,000
Recife (Pemambuco), Brazil (2,300,000)	1,204,738
Rīga, Soviet Union (950,000)	875,000
Rio de Janerio, Brazil (9,200,000)	5,093,232
Riyadh, Saudi Arabia	1,000,000
Rochester, New York (826,000)	241,741
Rome (Roma), Italy (3,115,000)	2,830,569
Rosario, Argentina (1,045,000)	935,471
Rostov-na-Donu, Soviet Union (1,110,000)	983,000
Rotterdam, Netherlands (1,090,000)	558,832
Sacramento, California (926,600)	275,741
St. Louis, Missouri (2,225,500)	452,801
St. Paul, Minnesota (*Minneapolis)	270,230
Salt Lake City, Utah (756,600)	163,034
Salvador, Brazil (1,700,000)	1,506,602
San Antonio, Texas, (1,104,500)	785,940
San Diego, California (1,746,500)	875,538
San Francisco, California (4,884,300)	678,974
San José, Costa Rica (560,000)	259,126
San Juan, Puerto Rico (1,535,000)	422,701
San Salvador, El Salvador (720,000)	397,100
Santiago, Chile (3,992,509)	425,924
Santo Domingo, Dominican Rep.	1,313,172
São Paulo, Brazil (12,700,000)	8,493,598
Sapporo, Japan (1,450,000)	1,401,757
Saratov, Soviet Union (1,125,000)	893,000
Seattle, Washington (2,173,800)	493,846
Seoul (Sŏul), Korea (South) (11,200,000)	8,366,756
Shanghai, China (9,000,000)	6,292,960
Sheffield, England (710,000)	547,600
Shenyang (Mukden), China (4,020,000†)	3,030,000
Singapore, Singapore (2,760,000)	2,502,000
Sofia (Sofiya), Bulgaria (1,142,582)	1.056,945
Stockholm, Sweden (1,402,426)	649,686
Stuttgart, Fed. Rep. of Ger. (1,935,000)	573,577
Surabaya, Indonesia (2,150,000)	2,027,913
Sverdlovsk, Soviet Union (1,505,000)	1,286,000
Sydney, Australia (3,204,696)	51,836
Taegu, Korea (South)	1,959,000
T'aipei, Taiwan (5,050,000)	2,270,983
Taiyuan, China (1,750,000†)	1,280,000
Tashkent, Soviet Union (2,165,000)	1,986,000
Tbilisi, Soviet Union (1,295,000)	1,140,000
Tegucigalpa, Honduras	444,749
Tehrān, Iran (4,700,000)	4,496,159
Tel Aviv-Yafo, Israel (1,380,000)	329,500
The Hague ('s-Gravenhage), Netherlands (775,000)	449,338
Tianjin (Tientsin), China (7,764,141†)	4,300,000
Tiranë, Albania	198,000
Tōkyō, Japan (26,200,000)	8,351,893
Toronto, Canada (2,998,947)	599,217
Tripoli (Tarābulus), Libya	858,500
Tunis, Tunisia (915,000)	550,404
Turin (Torino), Italy (1,600,000)	1,103,520
Ufa, Soviet Union (1,050,000)	1,048,000
Ulan Bator, Mongolia	435,400
Valencia, Spain (1,270,000)	751,734
Valparaíso, Chile (530,000)	266,502
Vancouver, Canada (1,268,183)	414,281
Venice (Venezia), Italy (1,465,000)	332,775
Vienna (Wien), Austria (1,875,000)	1,515,666
Vladivostok, Soviet Union	590,000
Volgograd (Stalingrad), Soviet Union (1,275,000)	969,000
Warsaw (Warszawa), Poland (2,145,000)	1,628,900
Washington, D.C. (3,329,800)	618,400
Wellington, New Zealand (343,200)	134,900
Winnipeg, Canada (584,842)	564,473
Wuhan, China (3,230,000†)	2,730,000
Wuppertal, Fed. Rep. of Ger. (855,000)	387,951
Xi'an, China (2,180,000†)	1,610,000
Xuzhou, China (773,000†)	668,000
Yerevan, Soviet Union (1,220,000)	1,114,000
Yokohama, Japan (*Tōkyō)	2,773,674
Zagreb, Yugoslavia	768,700
Zhengzhou, China (1,424,000†)	895,000
Zürich, Switzerland (780,000)	356,800

Metropolitan area populations are shown in parentheses.
* City is located within the metropolitan area of another city; for example, Kyōto, Japan (*Ōsaka).
† Population of entire municipality or district, including rural area.

glossary of foreign geographical terms

Annam ... Annamese
Arab ... Arabic
Bantu ... Bantu
Bur ... Burmese
Camb ... Cambodian
Celt ... Celtic
Chn ... Chinese
Czech ... Czech
Dan ... Danish
Du ... Dutch
Fin ... Finnish
Fr ... French
Ger ... German
Gr ... Greek
Hung ... Hungarian
Ice ... Icelandic
India ... India
Indian ... American Indian
Indon ... Indonesian
It ... Italian
Jap ... Japanese
Kor ... Korean
Mal ... Malayan
Mong ... Mongolian
Nor ... Norwegian
Per ... Persian
Pol ... Polish
Port ... Portuguese
Rom ... Romanian
Rus ... Russian
Siam ... Siamese
So. Slav ... Southern Slavonic
Sp ... Spanish
Swe ... Swedish
Tib ... Tibetan
Tur ... Turkish
Yugo ... Yugoslav

å, Nor., Swe ... brook, river
aa, Dan., Nor ... brook
aas, Dan., Nor ... ridge
āb, Per ... water, river
abad, India, Per ... town, city
ada, Tur ... island
adrar, Berber ... mountain
air, Indon ... stream
akrotírion, Gr ... cape
älf, Swe ... river
alp, Ger ... mountain
altipiano, It ... plateau
alto, Sp ... height
archipel, Fr ... archipelago
archipiélago, Sp ... archipelago
arquipélago, Port ... archipelago
arroyo, Sp ... brook, stream
ås, Nor., Swe ... ridge
austral, Sp ... southern
baai, Du ... bay
bab, Arab ... gate, port
bach, Ger ... brook, stream
backe, Swe ... hill
bad, Ger ... bath, spa
bahía, Sp ... bay, gulf
bahr, Arab ... river, sea, lake
baia, It ... bay, gulf
baía, Port ... bay
baie, Fr ... bay, gulf
bajo, Sp ... depression
bak, Indon ... stream
bakke, Dan., Nor ... hill
balkan, Tur ... mountain range
bana, Jap ... point, cape
banco, Sp ... bank
bandar, Mal., Per. ... town, port, harbor
bang, Siam ... village
bassin, Fr ... basin
batang, Indon., Mal ... river
ben, Celt ... mountain, summit
bender, Arab ... harbor, port
bereg, Rus ... coast, shore
berg, Du., Ger., Nor., Swe. ... mountain, hill
bir, Arab ... well
birkat, Arab ... lake, pond, pool
bit, Arab ... house
bjaerg, Dan., Nor ... mountain
bocche, It ... mouth
boğazı, Tur ... strait
bois, Fr ... forest, wood
boloto, Rus ... marsh
bolsón, Sp. ... flat-floored desert valley
boreal, Sp ... northern
borg, Dan., Nor., Swe ... castle, town
borgo, It ... town, suburb
bosch, Du ... forest, wood
bouche, Fr ... river mouth
bourg, Fr ... town, borough
bro, Dan., Nor., Swe ... bridge
brücke, Ger ... bridge
bucht, Ger ... bay, bight
bugt, Dan., Nor., Swe ... bay, gulf
bulu, Indon ... mountain
burg, Du., Ger ... castle, town
buri, Siam ... town
burun, burnu, Tur ... cape
by, Dan., Nor., Swe ... village
caatinga, Port. (Brazil) ... open brushland
cabezo, Sp ... summit
cabo, Port., Sp ... cape
campo, It., Port., Sp ... plain, field
campos, Port. (Brazil) ... plains
cañón, Sp ... canyon
cap, Fr ... cape
capo, It ... cape
casa, It., Port., Sp ... house
castello, It., Port ... castle, fort
castillo, Sp ... castle
càte, Fr ... hill
çay, Tur ... stream, river
cayo, Sp ... rock, shoal, islet
cerro, Sp ... mountain, hill
champ, Fr ... field
chang, Chn ... village, middle
château, Fr ... castle
chen, Chn ... market town
chiang, Chn ... river
chott, Arab ... salt lake
chou, Chn. capital of district; island
chu, Tib ... water, stream
cidade, Port ... town, city
cima, Sp ... summit, peak
città, It ... town, city
ciudad, Sp ... town, city
cochilha, Port ... ridge
col, Fr ... pass
colina, Sp ... hill
cordillera, Sp ... mountain chain
costa, It., Port., Sp ... coast
côte, Fr ... coast
cuchilla, Sp ... mountain ridge
dağ, Tur ... mountain(s)
dake, Jap ... peak, summit
dal, Dan., Du., Nor., Swe ... valley
dan, Kor ... point, cape
danau, Indon ... lake
dar, Arab ... house, abode, country
darya, Per ... river, sea
dasht, Per ... plain, desert
deniz, Tur ... sea
désert, Fr ... desert
deserto, It ... desert
desierto, Sp ... desert
détroit, Fr ... strait
dijk, Du ... dam, dike
djebel, Arab ... mountain
do, Kor ... island
dorf, Ger ... village
dorp, Du ... village
duin, Du ... dune
dzong, Tib. ... fort, administrative capital
eau, Fr ... water
ecuador, Sp ... equator
eiland, Du ... island
elv, Dan., Nor ... river, stream
embalse, Sp ... reservoir
erg, Arab ... dune, sandy desert
est, Fr., It ... east
estado, Sp ... state
este, Port., Sp ... east
estrecho, Sp ... strait
étang, Fr ... pond, lake
état, Fr ... state
eyjar, Ice ... islands
feld, Ger ... field, plain
festung, Ger ... fortress
fiume, It ... river
fjäll, Swe ... mountain
fjärd, Swe ... bay, inlet
fjeld, Nor ... mountain, hill
fjord, Dan., Nor ... fiord, inlet
fjördur, Ice ... fiord, inlet
fleuve, Fr ... river
flod, Dan., Swe ... river
flói, Ice ... bay, marshland
fluss, Ger ... river
foce, It ... river mouth
fontein, Du ... a spring
forêt, Fr ... forest
fors, Swe ... waterfall
forst, Ger ... forest
fos, Dan., Nor ... waterfall
fu, Chn ... town, residence
fuente, Sp ... spring, fountain
fuerte, Sp ... fort
furt, Ger ... ford
gang, Kor ... stream, river
gangri, Tib ... mountain
gat, Dan., Nor ... channel
gàve, Fr ... stream
gawa, Jap ... river
gebergte, Du ... mountain range
gebiet, Ger ... district, territory
gebirge, Ger ... mountains
ghat, India ... pass, mountain range
gobi, Mong ... desert
gol, Mong ... river
göl, gölü, Tur ... lake
golf, Du., Ger ... gulf, bay
golfe, Fr ... gulf, bay
golfo, It., Port., Sp ... gulf, bay
gomba, gompa, Tib ... monastery
gora, Rus., So. Slav ... mountain
góra, Pol ... mountain
gorod, Rus ... town
grad, Rus., So. Slav ... town
guba, Rus ... bay, gulf
gundung, Indon ... mountain
guntō, Jap ... archipelago
gunung, Mal ... mountain
haf, Swe ... sea, ocean
hafen, Ger ... port, harbor
haff, Ger ... gulf, inland sea
hai, Chn ... sea, lake
hama, Jap ... beach, shore
hamada, Arab ... rocky plateau
hamn, Swe ... harbor
hāmūn, Per ... swampy lake, plain
hantō, Jap ... peninsula
hassi, Arab ... well, spring
haus, Ger ... house
haut, Fr ... summit, top
hav, Dan., Nor ... sea, ocean
havn, Dan., Nor ... harbor, port
havre, Fr ... harbor, port
háza, Hung ... house, dwelling of
heim, Ger ... hamlet, home
hem, Swe ... hamlet, home
higashi, Jap ... east
hisar, Tur ... fortress
hissar, Arab ... fort
ho, Chn ... river
hoek, Du ... cape
hof, Ger ... court, farmhouse
höfn, Ice ... harbor
hoku, Jap ... north
holm, Dan., Nor., Swe ... island
hora, Czech ... mountain
horn, Ger ... peak
hoved, Dan., Nor ... cape
hsien, Chn ... district, district capital
hu, Chn ... lake
hügel, Ger ... hill
huk, Dan., Swe ... point
hus, Dan., Nor., Swe ... house
île, Fr ... island
ilha, Port ... island
indsö, Dan., Nor ... lake
insel, Ger ... island
insjö, Swe ... lake
irmak, irmagi, Tur ... river
isla, Sp ... island
isola, It ... island
istmo, It., Sp ... isthmus
järvi, jaur, Fin ... lake
jebel, Arab ... mountain
jima, Jap ... island
jökel, Nor ... glacier
joki, Fin ... river
jökull, Ice ... glacier
kaap, Du ... cape
kai, Jap ... bay, gulf, sea
kaikyō, Jap ... channel, strait
kalat, Per ... castle, fortress
kale, Tur ... fort
kali, Mal ... creek, river
kand, Per ... village
kang, Chn . mountain ridge; village
kap, Dan., Ger ... cape
kapp, Nor., Swe ... cape
kasr, Arab ... fort, castle
kawa, Jap ... river
kefr, Arab ... village
kei, Jap ... creek, river
ken, Jap ... prefecture
khor, Arab ... bay, inlet
khrebet, Rus ... mountain range
kiang, Chn ... large river
king, Chn ... capital city, town
kita, Jap ... north
ko, Jap ... lake
köbstad, Dan ... market-town
kol, Mong ... lake
kólpos, Gr ... gulf
kong, Chn ... river
kopf, Ger ... head, summit, peak
köpstad, Swe ... market-town
körfezi, Tur ... gulf
kosa, Rus ... spit
kou, Chn ... river mouth
köy, Tur ... village
kraal, Du. (Africa) ... native village
ksar, Arab ... fortified village
kuala, Mal ... bay, river mouth
kuh, Per ... mountain
kum, Tur ... sand
kuppe, Ger ... summit
küste, Ger ... coast
kyo, Jap ... town, capital
la, Tib ... mountain pass
labuan, Mal ... anchorage, port
lac, Fr ... lake
lago, It., Port., Sp ... lake
lagoa, Port ... lake, marsh
laguna, It., Port., Sp ... lagoon, lake
lahti, Fin ... bay, gulf
län, Swe ... county
landsby, Dan., Nor ... village
liehtao, Chn ... archipelago
liman, Tur ... bay, port
ling, Chn ... pass, ridge, mountain
llanos, Sp ... plains
loch, Celt. (Scotland) ... lake, bay
loma, Sp ... long, low hill
lough, Celt. (Ireland) ... lake, bay
machi, Jap ... town
man, Kor ... bay
mar, Port., Sp ... sea
mare, It., Rom ... sea
marisma, Sp ... marsh, swamp
mark, Ger ... boundary, limit
massif, Fr ... block of mountains
mato, Port ... forest, thicket
me, Siam ... river
meer, Du., Ger ... lake, sea
mer, Fr ... sea
mesa, Sp ... flat-topped mountain
meseta, Sp ... plateau
mina, Port., Sp ... mine
minami, Jap ... south
minato, Jap ... harbor, haven
misaki, Jap ... cape, headland
mont, Fr ... mount, mountain
montagna, It ... mountain
montagne, Fr ... mountain
montaña, Sp ... mountain
monte, It., Port., Sp. ... mount, mountain
more, Rus., So. Slav ... sea
morro, Port., Sp ... hill, bluff
mühle, Ger ... mill
mund, Ger ... mouth, opening
mündung, Ger ... river mouth
mura, Jap ... township
myit, Bur ... river
mys, Rus ... cape
nada, Jap ... sea
nadi, India ... river, creek
naes, Dan., Nor ... cape
nafud, Arab . . desert of sand dunes
nagar, India ... town, city
nahr, Arab ... river
nam, Siam ... river, water
nan, Chn., Jap ... south
näs, Nor., Swe ... cape
nez, Fr ... point, cape
nishi, nisi, Jap ... west
njarga, Fin ... peninsula
nong, Siam ... marsh
noord, Du ... north
nor, Mong ... lake
nord, Dan., Fr., Ger., It., Nor., Swe ... north
norte, Port., Sp ... north
nos, Rus ... cape
nyasa, Bantu ... lake
ö, Dan., Nor., Swe ... island
occidental, Sp ... western
ocna, Rom ... salt mine
odde, Dan., Nor ... point, cape
oeste, Port., Sp ... west
oka, Jap ... hill
oost, Du ... east
oriental, Sp ... eastern
óros, Gr ... mountain
ost, Ger., Swe ... east
öster, Dan., Nor., Swe ... eastern
ostrov, Rus ... island
oued, Arab ... river, stream
ouest, Fr ... west
ozero, Rus ... lake
pää, Fin ... mountain
padang, Mal ... plain, field
pampas, Sp. (Argentina) ... grassy plains
pará, Indian (Brazil) ... river
pas, Fr ... channel, passage
paso, Sp . mountain pass, passage
passo, It., Port. mountain pass, passage, strait
patam, India ... city, town
pei, Chn ... north
pélagos, Gr ... open sea
pegunungan, Indon ... mountains
peña, Sp ... rock
peresheyek, Rus ... isthmus
pertuis, Fr ... strait
peski, Rus ... desert
pic, Fr ... mountain peak
pico, Port., Sp ... mountain peak
piedra, Sp ... stone, rock
ping, Chn ... plain, flat
planalto, Port ... plateau
planina, Yugo ... mountains
playa, Sp ... shore, beach
pnom, Camb ... mountain
pointe, Fr ... point
polder, Du., Ger . . reclaimed marsh
polje, So. Slav ... plain, field
poluostrov, Rus ... peninsula
pont, Fr ... bridge
ponta, Port ... point, headland
ponte, It., Port ... bridge
pore, India ... city, town
porthmós, Gr ... strait
porto, It., Port ... port, harbor
potamós, Gr ... river
p'ov, Rus ... peninsula
prado, Sp ... field, meadow
presqu'île, Fr ... peninsula
proliv, Rus ... strait
pu, Chn ... commercial village
pueblo, Sp ... town, village
puerto, Sp ... port, harbor
pulau, Indon ... island
punkt, Ger ... point
punt, Du ... point
punta, It., Sp ... point
pur, India ... city, town
puy, Fr ... peak
qal'a, qal'at, Arab ... fort, village
qasr, Arab ... fort, castle
rann, India ... wasteland
ra's, Arab ... cape, head
reka, Rus., So. Slav ... river
represa, Port ... reservoir
rettō, Jap ... island chain
ría, Sp ... estuary
ribeira, Port ... stream
ribeirão, Port ... river
rio, It., Port ... stream, river
río, Sp ... river
rivière, Fr ... river
roca, Sp ... rock
rt, Yugo ... cape
rūd, Per ... river
saari, Fin ... island
sable, Fr ... sand
sahara, Arab ... desert, plain
saki, Jap ... cape
sal, Sp ... salt
salar, Sp ... salt flat, salt lake
salto, Sp ... waterfall
san, Jap., Kor ... mountain, hill
sat, satul, Rom ... village
schloss, Ger ... castle
sebkha, Arab ... salt marsh
see, Ger ... lake, sea
şehir, Tur ... town, city
selat, Indon ... stream
selvas, Port. (Brazil) ... tropical rain forests
seno, Sp ... bay
serra, Port ... mountain chain
serranía, Sp ... mountain ridge
seto, Jap ... strait
severnaya, Rus ... northern
shahr, Per ... town, city
shan, Chn ... mountain, hill, island
shatt, Arab ... river
shi, Jap ... city
shima, Jap ... island
shōtō, Jap ... archipelago
si, Chn ... west, western
sierra, Sp ... mountain range
sjö, Nor., Swe ... lake, sea
sö, Dan., Nor ... lake, sea
söder, södra, Swe ... south
song, Annam ... river
sopka, Rus ... peak, volcano
source, Fr ... a spring
spitze, Ger ... summit, point
staat, Ger ... state
stad, Dan., Du., Nor., Swe. ... city, town
stadt, Ger ... city, town
stato, It ... state
step', Rus ... treeless plain, steppe
straat, Du ... strait
strand, Dan., Du., Ger., Nor., Swe ... shore, beach
stretto, It ... strait
strom, Ger ... river, stream
ström, Dan., Nor., Swe. ... stream, river
stroom, Du ... stream, river
su, suyu, Tur ... water, river
sud, Fr., Sp ... south
süd, Ger ... south
suidō, Jap ... channel
sul, Port ... south
sund, Dan., Nor., Swe ... sound
sungai, sungei, Indon., Mal ... river
sur, Sp ... south
syd, Dan., Nor., Swe ... south
tafelland, Ger ... plateau
take, Jap ... peak, summit
tal, Ger ... valley
tanjung, tanjong, Mal ... cape
tao, Chn ... island
târg, târgul, Rom ... market, town
tell, Arab ... hill
teluk, Indon ... bay, gulf
terra, It ... land
terre, Fr ... earth, land
thal, Ger ... valley
tierra, Sp ... earth, land
tō, Jap ... east; island
tonle, Camb ... river, lake
top, Du ... peak
torp, Swe ... hamlet, cottage
tsangpo, Tib ... river
tsi, Chn ... village, borough
tso, Tib ... lake
tsu, Jap ... harbor, port
tundra, Rus . . treeless arctic plains
tung, Chn ... east
tuz, Tur ... salt
udde, Swe ... cape
ufer, Ger ... shore, riverbank
ujung, Indon ... point, cape
umi, Jap ... sea, gulf
ura, Jap ... bay, coast, creek
ust'ye, Rus ... river mouth
valle, It., Port., Sp ... valley
vallée, Fr ... valley
valli, It ... lake
vár, Hung ... fortress
város, Hung ... town
varoš, So. Slav ... town
veld, Du ... open plain, field
verkh, Rus ... top, summit
ves, Czech ... village
vest, Dan., Nor., Swe ... west
vik, Swe ... cove, bay
vila, Port ... town
villa, Sp ... town
villar, Sp ... village, hamlet
ville, Fr ... town, city
vostok, Rus ... east
wad, wādī, Arab. ... intermittent stream
wald, Ger ... forest, woodland
wan, Chn., Jap ... bay, gulf
weiler, Ger ... hamlet, village
westersch, Du ... western
wüste, Ger ... desert
yama, Jap ... mountain
yarimada, Tur ... peninsula
yug, Rus ... south
zaki, Jap ... cape
zaliv, Rus ... bay, gulf
zapad, Rus ... west
zee, Du ... sea
zemlya, Rus ... land
zuid, Du ... south

abbreviations of geographical names and terms

Afg.	Afghanistan
Afr.	Africa
Ak.	Alaska
Al.	Alabama
Alb.	Albania
Alg.	Algeria
And.	Andorra
Ang.	Angola
Ant.	Antarctica
Ar.	Arkansas
Arch.	Archipelago
Arc. O.	Arctic Ocean
Arg.	Argentina
A. S. S. R.	Autonomous Soviet Socialist Republic
Atl. O.	Atlantic Ocean
Aus.	Austria
Austl.	Australia
Aug.	Autonomous
Az.	Arizona
B.	Bay, Bahia
Ba.	Bahamas
B.A.T.	British Antarctic Territory
Bngl.	Bangladesh
Barb.	Barbados
Bdy.	Boundary
Bel.	Belgium
Bg.	Berg
Bhu.	Bhutan
Bk.	Bank
Bol.	Bolivia
Boph.	Bophuthatswana
Bots.	Botswana
Br.	British
Braz.	Brazil
Bru.	Brunei
Bul.	Bulgaria
Burkina	Burkina Faso
Bur.	Burma
C.	Cerro, Cape
Ca.	California
Cam.	Cameroon
Can.	Canal, Canada
Can. Is.	Canary Is.
Cen. Afr. Rep.	Central African Republic
Chan.	Channel
Co.	County, Colorado
Col.	Colombia
Con.	Congo
Comm.	Commonwealth
C. R.	Costa Rica
Cr.	Creek
Ct.	Connecticut
C. V.	Cape Verde
Czech.	Czechoslovakia
DC	District of Columbia
De.	Delaware
Den.	Denmark
Dept.	Department
Des.	Desert
D. F.	Distrito Federal
Dist.	District
Div.	Division
Dom. Rep.	Dominican Republic
E.	East
Ec.	Ecuador
Eng.	England
Equat. Gui.	Equatorial Guinea
Eth.	Ethiopia
Eur.	Europe
Faer.	Faeroe Is.
Falk. Is.	Falkland Is.
Fed. Rep. of Ger., F.R.G.	Federal Republic of Germany
Fin.	Finland
Fk.	Fork
Fl.	Florida
For.	Forest
Fr.	France
Fr. Gu.	French Guiana
Ft.	Fort
G.	Golfo, Gulf
Ga.	Georgia
Gam.	Gambia
Ger. Dem. Rep., G.D.R.	German Democratic Republic
Gib.	Gibraltar
Grc.	Greece
Grnld.	Greenland
Gt.	Great
Gt. Brit.	Great Britain
Guad.	Guadeloupe
Guat.	Guatemala
Gui.	Guinea
Guy.	Guyana
Hai.	Haiti
Har., Hbr.	Harbor, Harbour
Hd.	Head
Hi.	Hawaii
Hond.	Honduras
Hts.	Heights
Hung.	Hungary
I.	Island
Ia.	Iowa
Ice.	Iceland
Id.	Idaho
Il.	Illinois
In.	Inset, Indiana
Ind. O.	Indian Ocean
Indon.	Indonesia
Ind. Res.	Indian Reservation
Int., Intl.	International
Ire.	Ireland
Is.	Islands
Isr.	Israel
Isth.	Isthmus
It.	Italy
Jam.	Jamaica
Jap.	Japan
Jc.	Junction
Kamp.	Kampuchea
Ken.	Kenya
Km.	Kilometer, Kilometers
Kor.	Korea
Ks.	Kansas
Kuw.	Kuwait
Ky.	Kentucky
L.	Lago, Lake, Loch, Lough
La.	Louisiana
Lat.	Latitude
Leb.	Lebanon
Leso.	Lesotho
Lib.	Liberia
Liech.	Liechtenstein
Long.	Longitude
Lux.	Luxembourg
M.	Mile, Miles
Ma.	Massachusetts
Md.	Madagascar
Md. Is.	Madeira Islands
Mala.	Malaysia
Mand.	Mandate
Mart.	Martinique
Max.	Maximum
Max. surf. elev.	Maximum surface elevation
Md.	Maryland
Me.	Maine
Medit.	Mediterranean
Mex.	Mexico
Mi.	Mile, Miles, Michigan
Mn.	Minnesota
Mo.	Missouri
Mong.	Mongolia
Mor.	Morocco
Moz.	Mozambique
Ms.	Mississippi
Mt.	Mount, Montana
Mtn.	Mountain
Mts.	Mountains
N. A.	North America
Natl.	National
Ntal. Mon.	National Monument
Ne.	Nebraska
NC	North Carolina
N. Cal.	New Caledonia
ND	North Dakota
Neigh.	Neighborhood
Nep.	Nepal
Neth.	Netherlands
NH	New Hampshire
Nic.	Nicaragua
Nig.	Nigeria
N. Ire.	Northern Ireland
NJ	New Jersey
NM	New Mexico
Nor.	Norway
Nv.	Nevada
NY	New York
N. Z.	New Zealand
O.	Ocean
Obs.	Observatory
Oh.	Ohio
Ok.	Oklahoma
Om.	Oman
Or.	Oregon
O-va.	Ostrova
P.	Pass
Pa.	Pennsylvania
Pac. O.	Pacific Ocean
Pak.	Pakistan
Pan.	Panama
Pap. N. Gui.	Papua New Guinea
Par.	Paraguay
Pass.	Passage
P.D.R. of Yem.	Yemen, People's Democratic Republic of
Pen.	Peninsula
Phil.	Philippines
P. Int.	Point of Interest
Pk.	Peak, Park
Plat.	Plateau
Pln.	Plain
Pol.	Poland
Port.	Portugal
P-Ov.	Poluostrov
P. R.	Puerto Rico
Prov.	Province
Pt.	Point
Pta.	Punta
Pte.	Pointe
R.	River, Rio, Rivière
Ra.	Range, Ranges
Reg.	Region
Rep.	Republic
Res.	Reservation, Reservoir
Rf.	Reef
RI	Rhode Island
Rom.	Romania
R. R.	Railroad
R. S. F. S. R.	Russian Soviet Federated Socialist Republic
Rw.	Rwanda
Ry.	Railway
Rys.	Railways
S.	San, Santo, South
Sa.	Serra, Sierra
S. A.	South America
S. Afr.	South Africa
Sal.	El Salvador
Sau. Ar.	Saudi Arabia
SC	South Carolina
Scot.	Scotland
SD	South Dakota
Sd.	Sound
S. L.	Sierra Leone
Sol. Is.	Solomon Is.
Som.	Somalia
Sov. Un.	Soviet Union
Sp.	Spain
Spr., Sprs.	Spring, Springs
S. S. R.	Soviet Socialist Republic
St.	Saint
Sta.	Santa
Ste.	Sainte
Str.	Strait
Strm.	Stream
Sud.	Sudan
Sur.	Surinam
Swaz.	Swaziland
Swe.	Sweden
Switz.	Switzerland
Swp.	Swamp
Syr.	Syria
Tan.	Tanzania
Tas.	Tasmania
Ter.	Territory
Thai.	Thailand
Tn.	Tennessee
Trans.	Transkei
Trin.	Trinidad and Tobago
Tun.	Tunisia
Tur.	Turkey
Tx.	Texas
U.A.E.	United Arab Emirates
Ug.	Uganda
U. K.	United Kingdom of Gt. Brit. and N. Ire.
Ur.	Uruguay
U. S., U. S. A.	United States of America
Ut.	Utah
Va.	Virginia
Val.	Valley
Vdkhr.	Vodokhranilishche
Ven.	Venezuela
Viet.	Vietnam
Vir. Is.	Virgin Is.
Vol.	Volcano
Vt.	Vermont
Wa.	Washington
Wi.	Wisconsin
W. Sah.	Western Sahara
W. Sam.	Western Samoa
WV	West Virginia
Wy.	Wyoming
Yugo.	Yugoslavia
Zimb.	Zimbabwe

pronunciation of geographical names

key to the sound values of letters and symbols used in the index to indicate pronunciation

ă – ăt, căt, băttle
ă – *ă*ppeal, fin*ă*l
ā – rāte, elāte
a᷵ – inanima᷵te, sena᷵te
ä – cälm, ärm
ȧ – ȧsk, bȧth
ȧ – m*ȧ*rine, sof*ȧ* (short neutral or indeterminate sound)
â – fâre, prepâre
ch – church, choose
dh – as th in other, either
ē – bē, ēve
e᷵ – cre᷵ate, e᷵vent
ĕ – bĕt, ĕnd
ĕ – rec*ĕ*nt (short neutral or indeterminate sound)
ē – cratēr, cindēr
g – gō, gāme
gh – gutteral g
ĭ – wĭll, bĭt
ĭ – short neutral or indeterminate sound
ī – rīde, bīte
ᴋ – gutteral k as ch in German *ich*
ng – sing
ŋ – baŋk, liŋger
ɴ – indicates nasalized preceding vowel
ŏ – nŏd, ŏdd
ŏ – c*ŏ*mmit, c*ŏ*nnect
ō – ōld, bōld
o᷵ – o᷵bey, ho᷵tel
ô – ôrder, nôrth
oi – boil
o͞o – fo͞od, ro͞ot
o͝o – fo͝ot, wo͝od
ou – thou, out
s – as in soft, so, sane
sh – dish, finish
th – thin, thick
ū – pūre, cūre
u᷵ – u᷵nite, u᷵su᷵rp
û – ûrn, fûr
ŭ – stŭd, ŭp
ü – as in French *tu*
ŭ – circ*ŭ*s, s*ŭ*bmit
zh – as z in azure
' – indeterminate vowel sound

In many cases the spelling of foreign geographic names does not even remotely indicate the pronunciation to an American, i. e., Słupsk in Poland is pronounced swo͝opsk; Jujuy in Argentina is pronounced ho͞ohwē'; La Spezia in Italy is lä-spĕ'zyä.

This condition is hardly surprising, however, when we consider that in our own language Worcester, Massachusetts, is pronounced wo͝os'tĕr; Sioux City, Iowa, so͞o sĭ'tĭ; Schuylkill Haven, Pennsylvania, sko͞ol'kĭl hā-vĕn; Poughkeepsie, New York, p*ŏ*-kĭp'se.

The indication of pronunciation of geographic names presents several peculiar problems:

1. Many foreign tongues use sounds that are not present in the English language and which an American cannot normally articulate. Thus, though the nearest English equivalent sound has been indicated, only approximate results are possible.

2. There are several dialects in each foreign tongue which cause variation in the local pronunciation of names. This also occurs in identical names in the various divisions of a great language group, as the Slavic or the Latin.

3. Within the United States there are marked differences in pronunciation, not only of local geographic names, but also of common words, indicating that the sound and tone values for letters as well as the placing of the emphasis vary considerably from one part of the country to another.

4. A number of different letter and diacritical combinations could be used to indicate essentially the same or approximate pronunciations.

Some variation in pronunciation other than that indicated in this index may be encountered, but such a difference does not necessarily indicate that either is in error, and in many cases it is a matter of individual choice as to which is preferred. In fact, an exact indication of pronunciation of many foreign names using English letters and diacritical marks is extremely difficult and sometimes impossible.

a pronouncing index

of over 30,000 geographical names

This universal index includes in a single alphabetical list the important names that appear on the reference maps. Each place name is followed by the country or continent in which it is located, the pronunciation of the name, the page number of the map on which it appears, and the approximate geographic coordinates.

Local official names are used on the maps for nearly all cities and towns, with the exception of about 50 major world cities for which Anglicized conventional names have been preferred. For these exceptions, the index gives a cross-reference to the official local name.

The system of alphabetizing used in the index is standard. When more than one name (including political and physical names) with the same spelling is shown, the order of precedence is as follows: first, place names; second, political divisions; and third, physical features.

An explanation of the pronunciation system for names appears on page 249.

If a place is indexed to an inset map, the page number is followed by a lower-case letter which refers to the appropriate inset on that page.

Country names are followed by the continent in which they are located. Places in the U.S. are followed by their state. All other places are identified by the country in which they are located.

All minor political divisions are followed by a descriptive term (Dist., Reg., Prov., State, etc.) and the country in which they are located. The names of physical features and points of interest shown on the maps are listed in the index. Each of these entries is followed by a descriptive term (Bay, Hill, Island, etc.) to indicate its nature. A key to the abbreviations used for these descriptive terms appears on page 249.

PLACE (Pronounciation)	PAGE	Lat. °′	Long. °′
Aachen, F.R.G. (ä'kĕn)	169c	50.46 N	6.07 E
Aalen, F.R.G. (ä'lĕn)	166	48.49 N	10.08 E
Aalsmeer, Neth.	157a	52.16 N	4.44 E
Aalst, Bel.	157a	50.58 N	4.00 E
Aarau, Switz. (är'ou)	166	47.22 N	8.03 E
Aarschot, Bel.	157a	50.59 N	4.51 E
Aba, Nig.	229	5.06 N	7.21 E
Aba, Zaïre	231	3.52 N	30.14 E
Ābādān, Iran (ä-bŭ-dän')	192	30.15 N	48.30 E
Abaetetuba, Braz. (ä'bäĕ-tĕ-tōō'bȧ)	143	1.44 S	48.45 W
Abajo Pk., Ut. (ä-bȧ'hŏ)	121	37.51 N	109.28 W
Abakaliki, Nig.	229	6.21 N	8.06 E
Abakan (R.), Sov. Un.	180	53.00 N	91.06 E
Abakan, Sov. Un. (ŭ-bȧ-kän')	180	53.43 N	91.28 E
Abancay, Peru (ä-bän-kä'ē)	142	13.44 S	72.46 W
Abashiri, Jap. (ä-bä-shē'rē)	204	44.00 N	144.13 E
Abasolo, Mex. (ä-bä-sō'lō)	130	24.05 N	98.24 W
Abasolo, Mex.	124	27.13 N	101.25 W
Abay (R.), **see Blue Nile**			
Abaya L., Eth. (ȧ-bä'yȧ)	225	6.24 N	38.22 E
'Abbāsābād, Iran	68h	35.44 N	51.25 E
'Abbāsah, Tur'at al (Can.), Egypt	223c	30.45 N	32.15 E
Abbeville, Al. (ăb'ē-vĭl)	126	31.35 N	85.15 W
Abbeville, Fr. (ȧb-vēl')	168	50.08 N	1.49 E
Abbeville, Ga. (ăb'ē-vĭl)	126	31.53 N	83.23 W
Abbeville, La.	125	29.59 N	92.07 W
Abbeville, SC	127	34.09 N	82.25 W
Abbey Wood (Neigh.), Eng.	62	51.29 N	0.08 E
Abbiategrasso, It. (äb-byä'tä-gräs'sō)	172	45.23 N	8.52 E
Abbots Bromley, Eng. (ăb'ŭts brŭm'lē)	156	52.49 N	1.52 W
Abbotsford, Can. (ăb'ŭts-fērd)	118d	49.03 N	122.17 W
Abbots Langley, Eng.	62	51.43 N	0.25 W
Abd Al Kuri (I.), P.D.R. of Yem. (ăbd-ĕl-kōō'rē)	223a	12.12 N	51.00 E
'Abd al-Shāhīd, Egypt	71a	29.55 N	31.13 E
Abdulino, Sov. Un. (äb-dōō-lē'nō)	178	53.40 N	53.45 E
Abéché, Chad (ȧ-bĕ-shā')	225	13.48 N	20.39 E
Abengourou, Ivory Coast	228	6.44 N	3.29 W
Åbenrå, Den. (ō'bĕn-rō)	164	55.03 N	9.20 E
Abeokuta, Nig. (ä-bā-ō-kōō'tä)	229	7.10 N	3.26 E
Abercorn, see Mbala			
Aberdare, Wales (ăb-ēr-dâr')	162	51.45 N	3.35 W
Aberdeen (Xianggangzi), Hong Kong	68c	22.15 N	114.09 E
Aberdeen, Ms. (ăb-ēr-dēn')	126	33.49 N	88.33 W
Aberdeen, Scot.	162	57.10 N	2.05 W
Aberdeen, SD	114	45.28 N	98.29 W
Aberdeen, Wa.	116	47.00 N	123.48 W
Aberford, Eng. (ăb'ēr-fērd)	156	53.49 N	1.21 W
Abergavenny, Wales (ăb'ēr-gȧ-vĕn'ĭ)	162	51.45 N	3.05 W
Abert L., Or. (ā'bērt)	116	42.39 N	120.24 W
Aberystwyth, Wales (ă-bēr-ĭst'wĭth)	162	52.25 N	4.04 W
Abhā, Sau. Ar.	192	18.13 N	42.29 E
Abidjan, Ivory Coast (ä-bēd-zhäN')	228	5.19 N	4.02 W
Abiko, Jap. (ä-bē-kō)	205a	35.53 N	140.01 E
Abilene, Ks. (ăb'ĭ-lēn)	123	38.54 N	97.12 W
Abilene, Tx.	124	32.25 N	99.45 W
Abingdon, Eng.	156b	51.38 N	1.17 W
Abingdon, Il. (ăb'ĭng-dŭn)	115	40.48 N	90.21 W
Abingdon, Va.	127	36.42 N	81.57 W
Abington, Ma. (ăb'ĭng-tŭn)	105a	42.07 N	70.57 W
Abington, Pa.	56b	40.07 N	75.08 W
Abiquiu Res., NM	121	36.26 N	106.42 W
Abitibi (L.), Can. (ăb-ĭ-tĭb'ĭ)	97	48.27 N	80.20 W
Abitibi (R.), Can.	97	49.30 N	81.10 W

PLACE (Pronounciation)	PAGE	Lat. °′	Long. °′
Abkhaz A.S.S.R., Sov. Un.	179	43.10 N	40.45 E
Ablis, Fr. (ȧ-blē')	169b	48.31 N	1.50 E
Ablon-sur-Seine, Fr.	64c	48.43 N	2.25 E
Abnūb, Egypt (ȧb-nōōb')	223b	27.18 N	31.11 E
Abóbada, Port.	65d	38.43 N	9.20 W
Abohar, India	196	30.12 N	74.13 E
Aboisso, Ivory Coast	228	5.28 N	3.12 W
Abomey, Benin (ȧb-ō-mā')	229	7.11 N	1.59 E
Abony, Hung. (ŏ'bō-ny')	167	47.12 N	20.00 E
Åbo, see Turku			
Abou Deïa, Chad	229	11.27 N	19.17 E
Abra (R.), Phil (ä'brä)	207a	17.16 N	120.38 E
Abraão, Braz. (äbrä-ouN')	141a	23.10 S	44.10 W
Abraham's B., Ba.	135	22.20 N	73.50 W
Abram, Eng. (ā'brăm)	156	53.31 N	2.36 W
Abramcevo, Sov. Un.	66b	55.50 N	37.50 E
Abrantes, Port. (ȧ-brän'tĕs)	170	39.28 N	8.13 W
Abridge, Eng.	62	51.39 N	0.07 E
Abrolhos, Arquipélago dos (Arch.), Braz. (ä-rōōē-pĕ'lä-gō dōs ä-brō'l-yōs)	143	17.58 S	38.40 W
Abruka (I.), Sov. Un. (ȧ-brōō'kȧ)	165	58.09 N	22.30 E
Abrunheira, Port.	65d	38.46 N	9.21 W
Abruzzi E Molise (Reg.), It. (ä-brōōt'sē, mô'lē-zā)	172	42.10 N	13.55 E
Absaroka Ra. (Mts.), Wy. (ȧb-sȧ-rō-kă)	117	44.50 N	109.47 W
Abū an-Numrus, Egypt	71a	29.57 N	31.12 E
Abū Arīsh, Sau. Ar. (ä-bōō ȧ-rēsh')	192	16.48 N	43.00 E
Abu Ḩamad, Sud. (ä'bōō hä'-mĕd)	225	19.37 N	33.21 E
Abū Kamāl, Syr.	192	34.45 N	40.46 E
Abunã (R.), Bol-Braz. (ȧ-bōō-nä')	142	10.25 S	67.00 W
Abū Qīr, Egypt (ä'bōō kēr')	223b	31.18 N	30.06 E
Abū Qurqāṣ, Egypt (ā'bōō kōōr-käs')	223b	27.57 N	30.51 E
Abū Qurūn, Ra's (Mtn.), Egypt	191a	30.22 N	33.32 E
Aburatsu, Jap. (ä'bōō-rät'sōō)	205	31.33 N	131.20 E
Abu Road, India (ȧ'bōō)	196	24.38 N	72.45 E
Abū Şīr Pyramids (P. Int.), Egypt	71a	29.54 N	31.12 E
Abū Tīj, Egypt	223b	27.03 N	31.19 E
Abū Ẓaby, U.A.E.	192	24.15 N	54.28 E
Abū Zanīmah, Egypt	191a	29.03 N	33.08 E
Abyad, Al-Bahr al- (R.), **see White Nile**			
Abyy, Sov. Un.	181	68.24 N	134.00 E
Acacias, Col. (ȧ-kȧ'sēäs)	142a	3.59 N	73.44 W
Acadia Natl. Park, Me. (ă-kā'dĭ-ȧ)	104	44.19 N	68.01 W
Acajutla, Sal. (ä-kä-hōōt'lä)	132	13.37 N	89.50 W
Acala, Mex. (ä-kä'lä)	131	16.38 N	92.49 W
Acalayong, Equat. Gui.	230	1.05 N	9.40 E
Acàmbaro, Mex. (ä-käm'bä-rō)	130	20.03 N	100.42 W
Acancéh, Mex. (ä-kän-sĕ')	132a	20.50 N	89.27 W
Acapetlahuaya, Mex. (ä-kä-pĕt'lä-hwä'yä)	130	18.24 N	100.04 W
Acaponeta, Mex. (ä-kä-pō-nā'tă)	130	22.31 N	105.25 W
Acaponeta (R.), Mex.	130	22.47 N	105.23 W
Acapulco, Mex. (ä-kä-pōōl'kō)	130	16.49 N	99.57 W
Acaraí Mts., Braz.	143	1.30 N	57.40 W
Acaraú, Braz. (ä-kȧrhä-ōō')	143	2.55 S	40.04 W
Acarigua, Ven. (äkä-rē'gwä)	142	9.29 N	69.11 W
Acatlán de Osorio, Mex. (ä-kät-län'dā ō-sō'rē-ō)	130	18.11 N	98.04 W
Acatzingo de Hidalgo, Mex. (ä-kät-zĭŋ'gō dā ē-dhäl'gō)	131	18.58 N	97.47 W
Acayucan, Mex. (ä-kä-yōō'kän)	131	17.56 N	94.55 W
Accord, Ma.	54a	42.10 N	70.53 W
Accoville, WV (äk'kō-vĭl)	110	37.45 N	81.50 W
Accra, Ghana (ă'krȧ)	228	5.33 N	0.13 W
Accrington, Eng. (ăk'rĭng-tŭn)	156	53.45 N	2.22 W
Acerra, It. (ä-chĕ'r-rä)	171c	40.42 N	14.22 E

PLACE (Pronounciation)	PAGE	Lat. °′	Long. °′
Achacachi, Bol. (ä-chä-kä'chē)	142	16.11 S	68.32 W
Acheng, China (ä'chĕng')	204	45.32 N	126.59 E
Achill I., Ire. (ă-chĭl')	162	53.55 N	10.05 W
Achinsk, Sov. Un. (ȧ-chēnsk')	180	56.13 N	90.32 E
Acireale, It. (ä-chē-rā-ä'lā)	172	37.37 N	15.12 E
Ackia Battle Ground Natl. Mon., Ms. (ă-Kyū')	126	34.22 N	89.05 W
Acklins (I.), Ba. (ăk'lĭns)	135	22.30 N	73.55 W
Acklins, The Bight of (B.), Ba.	135	22.35 N	74.20 W
Acolman, Mex. (ä-kôl-mȧ'n)	131a	19.38 N	98.56 W
Aconcagua (Prov.), Chile (ä-kōn-kä'gwä)	141b	32.20 S	71.00 W
Aconcagua (R.), Chile	141b	32.43 S	70.53 W
Aconcagua, Cerro (Mtn.), Arg.	141b	32.38 S	70.00 W
Açores (Azores) (Is.), Atl. O. (ä-zō'rēs) (ȧ-zōrz')	224a	37.44 N	29.25 W
Acoyapa, Nic. (ä-kō-yä'pä)	132	11.54 N	85.11 W
Acqui, It. (äk'kwē)	172	44.41 N	8.22 W
Acre (R.), Braz.	142	10.33 S	68.34 W
Acre (State), Braz. (ä'krā)	142	8.40 S	70.45 W
Acton, Al. (ăk'tŭn)	112h	33.21 N	86.49 W
Acton, Can.	95d	43.38 N	80.02 W
Acton, Ma.	105a	42.29 N	71.26 W
Acton (Neigh.), Eng.	62	51.30 N	0.16 W
Actopan, Mex. (äk-tō-pän')	130	20.16 N	98.57 W
Actópan (R.), Mex. (äk-tŏ'pän)	131	19.25 N	96.31 W
Acuitzio del Canje, Mex. (ä-kwēt'zē-ō dĕl kän'hā)	130	19.28 N	101.21 W
Acul, Baie de l' (B.), Hai. (ä-kōōl')	135	19.55 N	72.20 W
Ada, Mn. (ā'dŭ)	114	47.17 N	96.32 W
Ada, Oh.	110	40.45 N	83.45 W
Ada, Ok.	123	34.45 N	96.43 W
Ada, Yugo. (ä'dä)	173	45.48 N	20.06 E
Adachi, Jap.	205a	35.50 N	39.36 E
Adachi (Neigh.), Jap.	69a	35.45 N	139.48 E
Adak, Ak. (ă-dăk')	107a	56.50 N	176.48 W
Adak (I.), Ak.	107a	51.40 N	176.28 W
Adak Str., Ak.	107a	51.42 N	177.16 W
Adalia, see Antalya			
Adamaoua (Mts.), Cam.-Nig.	229	6.30 N	11.50 E
Adams, Ma. (ăd'ămz)	111	42.35 N	73.10 W
Adams (R.), Can.	99	51.30 N	119.20 W
Adams, Wi.	115	43.55 N	89.48 W
Adams, Mt., Wa.	116	46.15 N	121.19 W
Adamsville, Al. (ăd'ămz-vĭl)	112h	33.36 N	86.57 W
Adana, Tur. (ä'dä-nä)	179	37.05 N	35.20 E
Adapazari, Tur. (ä-dä-pä-zä'rē)	179	40.45 N	30.20 E
Adarama, Sud. (ä-dä-rä'mä)	225	17.11 N	34.56 E
Adda (R.), It. (äd'dä)	172	45.43 N	9.31 E
Ad Dabbah, Sud.	225	18.04 N	30.58 E
Ad Dahnā (Des.), Sau. Ar.	192	26.05 N	47.15 E
Ad-Dāmir, Sud. (ad-dä'mĕr)	225	17.38 N	33.57 E
Ad Dammān, Sau. Ar.	192	26.27 N	49.59 E
Ad Dāmūr, Leb.	191a	33.44 N	35.27 E
Ad Dawhah, Qatar	192	25.02 N	51.28 E
Ad Dilam, Sau. Ar.	192	23.47 N	47.03 E
Ad Dilinjāt, Egypt	223b	30.48 N	30.32 E
Addington, Eng.	62	51.18 N	0.23 E
Addis Ababa (Ādis Abeda), Eth.	225	9.00 N	38.44 E
Addison, Tx. (ă'dĭ-sŭn)	119c	32.58 N	96.50 W
Addlestone, Eng.	62	51.22 N	0.30 W
Addo, S. Afr. (ădō)	227c	33.33 S	25.43 E
Ad-Duqqī, Egypt	71a	30.04 N	31.15 E
Ad Duwaym, Sud. (dōō-ām')	225	13.56 N	32.22 E
Addyston, Oh. (ăd'ē-stŭn)	113f	39.09 N	84.42 W
Adel, Ga. (ā-dĕl')	126	31.08 N	83.55 W
Adelaide, Austl. (ăd'ē-lād)	216	34.46 S	139.08 E
Adelaide, S. Afr. (ăd-ĕl'ād)	227c	32.41 S	26.07 E

ăt; finăl; rāte; senāte; ärm; ȧsk; sofȧ; fâre; ch-choose; dh-as th in other; bē; ēvent; bĕt; recĕnt; cratēr; g-gō; gh-guttural g; bĭt; ĭ-short neutral; rīde; K-guttural k as ch in German ich;

Havana

BARBADOS
Port of Spain
TRINIDAD and TOBAGO
Caracas
VENEZUELA
Georgetown
Paramaribo
GUIANA
SURINAME
Cayenne
FR. GUIANA
Bogota
COLOMBIA
Quito
ECUADOR
Manaus
Belém
São Luis
PERU
Recife
Lima
BOLIVIA
BRAZIL
La Paz
Brazil
PARAGUAY
São Paulo
Rio De Janeiro
Asunción
Porto Alegre
Cordoba
URUGUAY
Santiago
Buenos Aires
Montevideo
PAMPAS
CHILE
Bahia Blanca
ARGENTINA
Puerto montt

Capitols and other lg.
cities of S. America

Puerto Arenas
Terra Del Fuego
Falkland Is.

Statute Miles
0   200   400   600   800

Modified Orthographic Projection

Printed in U.S.A.   Published by DENOYER-GEPPERT CO., Chicago   Copyright

PLACE (Pronounciation)	PAGE	Lat. °′	Long. °′
Adelaide I., Ant.	232	67.15 S	68.40 W
Adelphi, Md.	56d	39.00 N	76.58 W
Aden ('Adan), P.D.R. of Yem. (ä'dĕn)	192	12.48 N	45.00 E
Aden, G. of, Asia	192	11.45 N	45.45 E
Aderklaa, Aus.	66e	48.17 N	16.32 E
Adige (R.), It. (ä'dē-jä)	172	46.38 N	10.43 E
Adige R., Aus.-Switz.	160	46.34 N	10.51 E
Adigrat, Eth.	195	14.17 N	39.28 E
Adilābād, India (ŭ-dĭl-ä-bäd')	196	19.47 N	78.30 E
Adi, Pulau (I.), Indon. (ä'dē)	207	4.25 S	133.52 E
Adirondack, Mts., NY (ăd-ĭ-rŏn'dăk)	111	43.45 N	74.40 W
Adis Abeba, see **Addis Ababa**			
Adi Ugri, Eth. (ä-dē o͞o'grē)	225	14.54 N	38.52 E
Adjud, Rom. (äd'zho͞od)	167	46.05 N	27.12 E
Adkins, Tx.	119d	29.22 N	98.18 W
Adlershof (Neigh.), G.D.R.	65a	52.26 N	13.33 E
Admiralty (I.), Ak.	107	57.50 N	133.50 W
Admiralty Inlet, Wa. (ăd'mĭrăl-tē)	118a	48.10 N	122.45 W
Admiralty Is., Pap. N. Gui.	207	1.40 S	146.45 E
Ado-Ekiti, Nig.	229	7.38 N	5.12 E
Adolph, Mn. (ā'dolf)	119h	46.47 N	92.17 W
Ādoni, India	197	15.42 N	77.18 E
Adour (R.), Fr. (á-do͞or')	168	43.43 N	0.38 W
Adra, Sp. (ä'drä)	170	36.45 N	3.02 W
Adrano, It. (ä-drä'nō)	172	37.42 N	14.52 E
Adria, It. (ä'drē-ä)	172	45.03 N	12.01 E
Adrian, Mi. (ā'drĭ-ăn)	110	41.55 N	84.00 W
Adrian, Mn.	114	43.39 N	95.56 W
Adrianople, see **Edirne**			
Adriatic Sea, Eur.	172	43.30 N	14.27 E
Adrir, Alg.	224	27.53 N	0.15 W
Adwa, Eth.	225	14.02 N	38.58 E
Adwick-le-Street, Eng. (ăd'wĭk-lē-strēt')	156	53.35 N	1.11 W
Adycha (R.), Sov. Un. (ä'dĭ-chá)	181	66.11 N	136.45 E
Adzhamka, Sov. Un. (ád-zhäm'ká)	175	48.33 N	32.28 E
Adzopé, Ivory Coast	228	6.06 N	3.52 W
Adz'va (R.), Sov. Un. (ädz'vá)	178	67.00 N	59.20 E
Aegean Sea, Asia-Eur. (ē-jē'ăn)	161	39.04 N	24.56 E
Aerø (I.), Den. (âr'ö)	163	54.52 N	10.22 E
Affton, Mo.	119e	38.33 N	90.20 W
Afghanistan, Asia (ăf-găn-ĭ-stăn')	190	33.00 N	63.00 E
Afgoi, Som. (äf-gô'ĭ)	223a	2.08 N	45.08 E
Afikpo, Nig.	229	5.53 N	7.56 E
Aflou, Alg. (ä-flo͞o')	224	33.59 N	2.04 E
Afognak (I.), Ak. (ä-fŏg-nák')	107	58.28 N	151.35 W
Afragola, It. (ä-frá'gō-lä)	171c	40.40 N	14.19 E
Africa (ăf'rĭ-ká)	218		
Afton, Mn. (ăf'tŭn)	119g	44.54 N	92.47 W
Afton, Ok.	123	36.42 N	94.56 W
Afton, Wy.	117	42.42 N	110.52 W
'Afula, Isr. (ä-fo͞o'là)	191a	32.36 N	35.17 E
Afyon, Tur. (ä-fē-ōn)	179	38.45 N	30.20 E
Agadem, Niger (ä'gá-dĕm)	229	16.50 N	13.17 E
Agadez, Niger (ä'gȧ-dĕs)	229	16.58 N	7.59 E
Agadir, Mor. (ä-gȧ-dēr)	224	30.30 N	9.37 W
Agalta, Cord. de (Mts.), Hond. (kôr-dĕl-yĕ'rä-dĕ-ä-gäl'-tä)	132	15.15 N	85.42 W
Agapovka, Sov. Un. (ä-gä-pôv'kä)	182a	53.18 N	59.10 E
Agartala, India	196	23.53 N	91.22 E
Agāshi, India	197b	19.28 N	72.46 E
Agashkino, Sov. Un. (á-gäsh'kĭ-nô)	182b	55.18 N	38.13 E
Agattu (I.), Ak. (á'gä-to͞o)	107a	52.14 N	173.40 E
Agayman, Sov. Un. (á-gä-ē-män')	175	46.39 N	34.20 E
Agboville, Ivory Coast	228	5.56 N	4.13 W
Agdam, Sov. Un. (äg'dăm)	179	40.00 N	47.00 E
Agde, Fr. (ägd)	168	43.19 N	3.30 E
Agege, Nig.	71d	6.37 N	3.20 E
Agen, Fr. (á-zhăN')	168	44.13 N	0.31 E
Agincourt (Neigh.), Can.	54c	43.48 N	79.17 W
Aginskoye, Sov. Un. (ä-hĭn'skô-yĕ)	181	51.15 N	113.15 E
Agno, Phil. (äg'nō)	207a	16.07 N	119.49 E
Agno (R.), Phil.	207a	15.42 N	120.28 E
Agnone, It. (än-yō'nä)	172	41.49 N	14.23 E
Agogo, Ghana	228	6.47 N	1.04 W
Agostinho Pôrto, Braz.	61c	22.47 S	43.23 W
Agra, India (ä'grä)	196	27.18 N	78.00 E
Ağri, Tur	179	39.50 N	43.10 E
Agri (R.), It. (ä'grē)	172	40.15 N	16.21 E
Agrícola Oriental, Mex.	60a	19.24 N	99.05 W
Agrínion, Grc. (á-grē'nyôn)	173	38.38 N	21.06 E
Agua (Vol.), Guat. (ä'gwä)	132	14.28 N	90.43 W
Agua Blanca, Río (R.), Mex. (rē'ō-ä-gwä-blä'n-kä)	130	21.46 N	102.54 W
Agua Brava, Laguna de (L.), Mex. (lä-go͞o'nä-dĕ-ä'gwä-brä'vä)	130	22.04 N	105.40 W
Agua Caliente Ind. Res., Ca. (ä'gwä kal-yĕn'tä)	120	33.50 N	116.24 W
Aguacate, Cuba	60b	22.59 N	81.49 W
Aguada, Cuba (ä-gwä'dȧ)	134	22.25 N	80.50 W
Aguada L., Mex.	132a	18.46 N	89.40 W
Aguadas, Col. (ä-gwä'dás)	142a	5.37 N	75.27 W
Aguadilla, P.R. (ä-gwä-dēl'yä)	129b	18.27 N	67.10 W
Aguadulce, Pan. (ä-gwä-do͞ol'sā)	133	8.15 N	80.33 W
Agua Escondida, Meseta de (Plat.), Mex. (mĕ-sĕ'tä-dĕ-ä'gwä-ĕs-kôn-dē'dä)	131	16.54 N	91.35 W
Agua Fria (R.), Az. (ä'gwä frē-ä)	121	33.43 N	112.22 W
Aguai, Braz. (ägwä-ē')	141a	22.04 S	46.57 W
Agualeguas, Mex. (ä-gwä-lā'gwäs)	124	26.19 N	99.33 W
Agualva-Cacém, Port.	65d	38.46 N	9.18 W
Aguanaval, R., Mex. (ä-guä-nä-väl')	124	25.12 N	103.28 W
Aguán R., Hond. (ä-gwä'n)	132	15.22 N	87.00 W
Aguanus (R.), Can. (ä-gwä'nŭs)	105	50.45 N	62.03 W
Aguascalientes, Mex. (ä'gwäs-käl-yĕn'tās)	130	21.52 N	102.17 W
Aguascalientes (State), Mex.	130	22.00 N	102.18 W
Águeda, Port. (ä-gwā'dȧ)	170	40.36 N	8.26 W
Agueda (R.), Sp. (ä-gē-dä)	170	40.50 N	6.44 W
Aguelhok, Mali	228	19.28 N	0.52 E
Aguilar, Co. (ä-gē-lär')	122	37.24 N	104.38 W
Aguilar, Sp.	170	37.32 N	4.39 W
Aguilas, Sp. (ä-gē-läs)	170	37.26 N	1.35 W
Aguililla, Mex. (ä-gē-lēl-yä)	130	18.44 N	102.44 W
Aguililla (R.), Mex.	130	18.30 N	102.48 W
Aguja, Pta. (Pt.), Peru (pŭn'tȧ á-go͞o' hä)	142	6.00 S	81.15 W
Agulhas, C., S. Afr. (ä-go͞ol'yäs)	226	34.47 S	20.00 E
Agusan (R.), Phil. (ä-go͞o'sän)	207	8.12 N	126.07 E
Ahaggar (Mts.), Alg. (á-há-gär')	224	23.14 N	6.00 E
Ahar, Iran	195	38.28 N	47.04 E
Ahlen, F.R.G. (ä'lĕn)	169c	51.45 N	7.52 E
Ahlenberg, F.R.G.	63	51.25 N	7.28 E
Ahmadābād, India (ŭ-mĕd-ä-bäd')	196	23.04 N	72.38 E
Ahmadnagar, India (ä'mûd-nû-gûr)	196	19.09 N	74.45 E
Ahmar Mts., Eth.	223a	9.22 N	42.00 E
Ahoskie, NC (ā-hŏs'kē)	127	36.15 N	77.00 W
Ahrensburg, F.R.G. (ä'rĕns-bo͞org)	157c	53.40 N	10.14 E
Ahrensfelde, G.D.R.	65a	52.35 N	13.35 E
Ahrweiler, F.R.G. (är'vī-lĕr)	166	50.34 N	7.05 E
Ähtärinjärvi (L.), Fin.	165	62.46 N	24.25 E
Ahuacatlán, Mex. (ä-wä-kät-län')	130	21.05 N	104.28 W
Ahuachapan, Sal. (ä-wä-chä-pän')	132	13.57 N	89.53 W
Ahualulco, Mex. (ä-wä-lo͞ol'kō)	130	20.43 N	103.57 W
Ahuatempan, Mex. (ä-wä-tĕm-pän)	130	18.11 N	98.02 W
Ahuntsic (Neigh.), Can.	54b	45.33 N	73.39 W
Åhus, Swe. (ô'ho͞os)	164	55.56 N	14.19 E
Ahvāz, Iran	192	31.15 N	48.54 E
Ahvenanmaa (Åland Is.), Fin. (ä'vĕ-nán-mô) (ô'länd)	165	60.36 N	19.55 E
Aiea, Hi.	106a	21.18 N	157.52 W
Aigburth (Neigh.), Eng.	64a	53.22 N	2.55 W
Aiken, SC (ā'kĕn)	127	33.32 N	81.43 W
Aimorès, Serra dos (Mts.), Braz. (sĕ'r-rä-dôs-ī-mō-rĕ's)	143	17.40 S	42.38 W
Aimoto, Jap. (ī-mô-tō)	205b	34.59 N	135.09 E
Aincourt, Fr. (âN-ko͞o'r)	169b	49.04 N	1.47 E
Ainsworth, Eng.	64b	53.35 N	2.22 W
Ainsworth, Ne. (ānz'wûrth)	114	42.32 N	99.51 W
Aintree, Eng.	64a	53.29 N	2.56 W
Aipe, Col. (ī'pĕ)	142a	3.13 N	75.15 W
Aire (R.), Eng.	156	53.42 N	1.00 W
Aire-sur-l'Adour, Fr. (âr)	168	43.42 N	0.17 W
Airhitam, Selat (Str.), Indon.	191b	0.58 N	102.38 E
Airport West, Austl.	70b	37.44 S	144.53 E
Aisne (R.), Fr. (ĕn)	168	49.28 N	3.32 E
Aitape, Pap. N. Gui. (ä-ē-tä'pā)	207	3.00 S	142.10 E
Aitkin, Mn. (āt'kĭn)	115	46.32 N	93.43 W
Aïn Beïtda, Alg. (ä'ĕn bā-dä')	224	35.57 N	7.25 E
Aïn Oussera, Alg. (ĕn o͞o-sā-rá)	171	35.25 N	2.50 E
Aïn Salah, Alg.	224	27.13 N	2.22 E
Aïn Témouchent, Alg. (ä'ĕntĕ-mo͞o-shaN')	159	35.20 N	1.23 W
Aitolikón, Grc. (â-tō'lĭ-kôn)	173	38.27 N	21.21 E
Aitos, Bul. (ä-ē'tôs)	173	42.42 N	27.17 E
Aïr (Mts.), Niger	229	18.00 N	8.30 E
Aitutaki (I.), Cook Is. (ī-to͞o-tä'kē)	209	19.00 S	162.00 W
Aiud, Rom. (ä'ē-o͞od)	167	46.19 N	23.40 E
Aiuruoca, Braz. (äē'o͞o-ro͞oô'-kà)	141a	21.57 S	44.36 W
Aiuruoca (R.), Braz.	141a	22.11 S	44.35 W
Aíyina, Grc.	173	37.37 N	22.12 E
Aíyina (I.), Grc.	173	37.43 N	23.35 E
Aíyion, Grc.	173	38.13 N	22.04 E
Aix-en-Provence, Fr. (ĕks-prô-väNs)	168a	43.32 N	5.27 E
Aix-les-Bains, Fr. (ĕks'-lā-băN')	169	45.42 N	5.56 E
Aiyáleo, Grc.	66d	37.59 N	23.41 E
Aizpute, Sov. Un. (ä'ēz-po͞o-tĕ)	165	56.44 N	21.37 E
Aizuwakamatsu, Jap.	205	37.27 N	139.51 E
Ajaccio, Fr. (ä-yät'chō)	172	41.55 N	8.42 E
Ajalpan, Mex. (ä-häl'pän)	131	18.21 N	97.14 W
Ajana, Austl. (ăj-ăn'ĕr)	214	28.00 S	114.45 E
Ajax Mt., Mt. (ā'jăks)	117	45.19 N	113.43 W
Ajdābiyah, Libya	225	30.56 N	20.16 E
Ajmah, Jabal al (Mts.), Egypt	191a	29.12 N	34.03 E
Ajman, U.A.E.	192	25.15 N	54.30 E
Ajmer, India (ŭj-mēr')	196	26.26 N	74.42 E
Ajo, Az. (ä'hō)	121	32.20 N	112.55 W
Ajuchitlán del Progreso, Mex. (ä-ho͞o-chet-lăn)	130	18.11 N	100.32 W
Ajuda (Neigh.), Port.	65d	38.43 N	9.12 W
Ajusco, Mex. (ä-ho͞o's-kō)	131a	19.13 N	99.12 W
Ajusco, Cerro (Mtn.), Mex. (sĕ'r-rô-ä-ho͞o's-kō)	131a	19.12 N	99.16 W
Akaishi-dake (Mtn.), Jap. (ä-kī-shē dä'kä)	205	35.30 N	138.00 E
Akashi, Jap. (ä'kä-shē)	205b	34.38 N	134.59 E
Akbarābād, Iran	68h	35.41 N	51.21 E
Aketi, Zaire (ä-kå-tē)	230	2.44 N	23.46 E
Akhaltsikhe, Sov. Un. (äkä'l-tsĭ-kĕ)	179	41.40 N	42.50 E
Akhdar, Al Jabal al (Mts.), Libya	225	32.00 N	22.00 E
Akhelóos (R.), Grc. (ä-hĕ'lô-ôs)	173	38.45 N	21.26 E
Akhisar, Tur. (äk-hĭs-sär')	179	38.58 N	27.58 E
Akhtarskaya, Bukhta (B.), Sov. Un. (bo͝ok'tä äK-tär'ská-yá)	175	45.53 N	38.22 E
Akhtopol, Bul. (äK'tô-pōl)	173	42.08 N	27.54 E
Akhtyrka, Sov. Un. (äK-tür'kä)	175	50.18 N	34.53 E
Akhunovo, Sov. Un. (ä-kŭ'nô-vô)	182a	54.13 N	59.36 E
Aki, Jap. (ä'kē)	205	33.31 N	133.51 E
Akiak, Ak. (äk'yák)	107	61.00 N	161.02 W
Akimiski (I.), Can. (ä-kĭ-mĭ'skĭ)	97	52.54 N	80.22 W
Akishima, Jap.	69a	35.41 N	139.22 E
Akita, Jap. (ä'kē-tä)	204	39.40 N	140.12 E
Akjoujt, Mauritania	228	19.45 N	14.23 W
'Akko, Isr.	191a	32.56 N	35.05 E
Aklavik, Can. (äk'lä-vĭk)	96	68.28 N	135.26 W
'Aklé'Āouâna (Dunes), Mali-Mauritania	228	18.07 N	6.00 W
Ako, Jap. (ä'kō)	205	34.44 N	134.22 E
Akola, India (á-kō'lä)	196	20.47 N	77.00 E
Akordat, Eth.	225	15.34 N	37.54 E
Akpatok (I.), Can. (ák'pá-tŏk)	97	60.30 N	67.10 W
Akranes, Ice.	158	64.18 N	21.40 W
Akron, Co. (ăk'rŭn)	122	40.09 N	103.14 W
Akron, Oh.	113d	41.05 N	81.30 W
Akrópolis (P. Int.), Grc.	66d	37.58 N	23.43 E
Aksaray, Tur. (äk-sá-rī')	179	38.30 N	34.05 E
Aksehir (L.), Tur.	179	38.40 N	31.30 E
Aksehir, Tur. (äk'shå-hēr)	179	38.20 N	31.20 E
Aksha, Sov.Un. (äk'shá)	181	50.28 N	113.00 E
Aksu, China (ä-kŭ-so͞o)	198	41.29 N	80.15 E
Aktyubinsk, Sov. Un. (äk'tyo͞o-bĕnsk)	179	50.20 N	57.00 E
Akune, Jap. (ä'ko͞o-nå)	205	32.03 N	130.16 E
Akureyri, Ice. (ä-ko͞o-rå'rē)	158	65.39 N	18.01 W
Akutan (I.), Ak. (ä-ko͞o-tän')	107a	53.58 N	169.54 W
Akwatia, Ghana	228	6.04 N	0.49 W
Alabama (State), U.S. (ăl-ȧ-băm'ȧ)	109	32.50 N	87.30 W
Alabama (R.), Al.	126	31.20 N	87.39 W
Alabat (I.), Phil. (ä-lä-bät')	207a	14.14 N	122.05 E
Alacam, Tur. (ä-lä-chăm')	179	41.30 N	35.40 E
Alacranes, Cuba (ä-lä-krä'nås)	134	22.45 N	81.35 W
Al Aflaj (Des.), Sau. Ar.	192	24.00 N	44.47 E
Alagôas (State), Braz. (ä-lä-gō'äzh)	143	9.50 S	36.33 W
Alagoinhas, Braz. (ä-lä-gō-ēn'yäzh)	143	12.13 S	38.12 W
Alagón (R.), Sp.	170	39.53 N	6.42 W
Alagón, Sp. (ä-lä-gōn')	170	41.46 N	1.07 W
Alaguntan, Nig.	71d	6.26 N	3.30 E
Alahuatán (R.), Mex. (ä-lä-wä-tà'n)	130	18.30 N	100.00 W
Alajuela, C.R. (ä-lä-hwa'lä)	133	10.01 N	84.14 W
Alajuela, L., Pan.	128a	9.15 N	79.34 W
Alakol (L.), Sov. Un.	180	45.45 N	81.13 E
Alalakeiki Chan., Hi. (ä-lä-lä-kā'kē)	106a	20.40 N	156.30 W
Al 'Alamayn, Egypt	225	30.53 N	28.52 E
Al 'Amārah, Iraq	195	31.50 N	47.09 E
Alameda, Ca. (ăl-ȧ-mā'dȧ)	118b	37.46 N	122.15 W
Alameda (R.), Ca.	118b	37.36 N	122.02 W
Alaminos, Phil. (ä-lä-mē'nôs)	207a	16.09 N	119.58 E
Al 'Amirīyah, Egypt	161	31.01 N	29.52 E
Alamo, Ca. (ă'lȧ-mō)	118b	37.51 N	122.02 W
Alamo, Mex. (ä'lä-mō)	131	20.55 N	97.41 W
Alamo, Nv. (ă'lá-mō)	120	37.22 N	115.10 W
Alamogordo, NM (ăl-ȧ-mō-gôr'dō)	121	32.55 N	106.00 W
Alamo Heights, Tx. (ă'lȧ-mō)	119d	29.28 N	98.27 W
Alamo Pk., NM (ă'lȧ-mō pēk)	124	32.50 N	105.55 W
Alamo, R., Mex. (ä'lä-mō)	124	26.33 N	99.35 W
Alamosa, Co. (ăl-ȧ-mō'sȧ)	121	37.25 N	105.50 W
Alandskiy, Sov. Un. (ä-länt'skĭ)	182a	52.14 N	59.48 E
Alanga Arba, Ken.	231	0.07 N	40.25 E
Alanya, Tur.	179	36.40 N	32.10 E
Alaotra (L.), Mad. (ä-lä-ō'trȧ)	227	17.15 S	48.17 E
Alapayevsk, Sov. Un. (ä-lä-pä'yĕfsk)	182a	57.50 N	61.35 E
Al 'Aqabah, Jordan	191a	29.32 N	35.00 E
Alaquines, Mex. (ä-lä-kē'nås)	130	22.07 N	99.35 W
Al 'Arīsh, Egypt (a-rēsh')	191a	31.08 N	33.48 E
Alaska (State), U.S. (ȧ-lăs'kȧ)	108a	64.00 N	150.00 W
Alaska, G. of, Ak.	107	57.42 N	147.40 W
Alaska Hy., Ak.	107	63.00 N	142.00 W
Alaska Pen., Ak.	107	55.50 N	162.10 W
Alaska Ra., Ak.	107	62.00 N	152.18 W
Al-'Atrūn, Sud.	225	18.13 N	26.44 E
Alatyr', Sov.Un. (ä'lä-tür)	178	54.55 N	46.30 E
Alausí, Ec. (á-lou-sē')	142	2.15 s	78.45 W
Al 'Ayyāt, Egypt (ä-ē-yät')	223b	29.38 N	31.18 E
Alba, It. (äl'bä)	172	44.41 N	8.02 E
Albacete, Sp. (äl-bä-thā'tā)	170	39.00 N	1.49 W
Albachten, F.R.G. (äl-bä'K-tĕn)	169c	51.55 N	7.31 E
Al Badārī, Egypt	223b	26.59 N	31.29 E
Alba de Tormes, Sp. (äl-bȧ dā tôr'mās)	170	40.48 N	5.28 W
Al Bahnasā, Egypt	223b	28.35 N	30.30 E
Alba Iulia, Rom. (äl-bä yo͞o'lyá)	167	46.05 N	23.32 E
Al Ballah, Egypt (bä'lä)	223c	30.46 N	32.20 E
Al Balyanā, Egypt	223b	26.12 N	32.00 E
Albania, Eur. (ăl-bā'nĭ-ȧ)	154	41.45 N	20.00 E
Albani, Colli (Mtn.), It.	171d	41.46 N	12.45 E
Albano, Lago (L.), It. (lä'-gō äl-bä'nō)	171d	41.45 N	12.44 E
Albano Laziale, It. (äl-bä'nō lät-zē-ä'lā)	171d	41.44 N	12.43 E
Albany, Austl. (ôl'bȧ-nĭ)	214	35.00 S	118.00 E
Albany, Ca.	118b	37.54 N	122.18 W
Albany, Ga.	126	31.35 N	84.10 W
Albany, Mo.	123	40.14 N	94.18 W
Albany, NY	111	42.40 N	73.50 W
Albany, Or.	116	44.38 N	123.06 W
Albany (R.), Can.	97	51.45 N	83.30 W
Albany Park (Neigh.), Il.	58a	41.58 N	87.43 W
Al-Barājīl, Egypt	71a	30.04 N	31.09 E
Al Başrah, Iraq	192	30.35 N	47.59 E
Al Batrūn, Leb. (bä-tro͞on')	191a	34.16 N	35.39 E
Al Bawītī, Egypt	225	28.19 N	29.00 E
Al Bayḑā, Libya	194	32.46 N	21.43 E
Albemarle, NC (ăl'bē-märl)	127	35.24 N	80.36 W
Albemarle Sd., NC	127	36.00 N	76.17 W
Albenga, It. (äl-bĕŋ'gä)	172	44.04 N	8.13 E
Alberche (R.), Sp. (äl-bĕr'chå)	170	40.08 N	4.19 W
Albergaria a-Velha, Port. (äl-bĕr-gȧ-rē'ä-ä-väl'yȧ)	170	40.47 N	8.31 W
Alberga, The (R.), Austl. (ăl-bŭr'gȧ)	214	27.15 S	135.00 E
Alberhill, Ca. (ăl'bēr-hĭl)	119a	33.43 N	117.23 W
Albert, Fr. (ál-bâr')	168	50.00 N	2.49 E
Albert (L.), Afr. (ăl'bērt) (ál-bâr')	231	1.50 N	30.40 E
Alberta (Prov.), Can. (ăl-bûr'tȧ)	96	54.33 N	117.10 W
Alberta, Mt., Can.	99	52.18 N	117.28 W
Albert Edward, Mt., Pap. N. Gui. (ăl'bērt ĕd'wērd)	207	8.25 S	147.25 E
Albertfalva (Neigh.), Hung.	66g	47.27 N	19.02 E
Alberti, Arg. (ál-bĕ'r-tē)	141c	35.01 S	60.16 W
Albert Kanaal (Can.), Bel.	157a	51.07 N	5.07 E
Albert Lea, Mn. (ăl'bērt lē')	115	43.38 N	93.24 W
Albert Nile (R.), Ug.	231	3.25 N	31.35 E
Alberton, Can. (ăl-bēr-tŭn)	104	46.49 N	64.04 W
Alberton, S. Afr.	227b	26.16 S	28.08 E
Albert, Parc Natl. (Natl. Pk.), Zaire	231	0.05 N	29.30 E
Albertson, NY	55	40.46 N	73.39 W
Albertville, Al. (ăl'bērt-vĭl)	126	34.15 N	86.10 W
Albertville, Fr. (ál-bêr-vēl')	169	45.42 N	6.25 E
Albertville (Neigh.), S. Afr.	71b	26.10 S	27.59 E

ng-sing; ŋ-baŋk; N-nasalized n; nŏd; cŏmmit; ōld; ôbey; ôrder; oi-boil; fo͞od; fo͝ot; ou-out; s-soft; sh-dish; th-thin; pūre; ŭnite; ûrn; stŭd; circŭs; ü-as in French tu; '-indeterminate vowel.

PLACE (Pronunciation)	PAGE	Lat. °'	Long. °'
Albertville, see Kalemie			
Albi, Fr. (ál-bē')	168	43.54 N	2.07 E
Albia, Ia. (ál-bī-à)	115	41.01 N	92.44 W
Albina, Sur. (ál-bē'à)	143	5.30 N	54.33 W
Albina, Ponta (Pt.), Ang.	230	15.51 S	11.44 E
Albino, Pt., Can. (ál-bē'nō)	113c	42.50 N	79.05 W
Albion, Austl.	70b	37.47 S	144.49 E
Albion, Mi. (ál'bī-ŭn)	110	42.15 N	84.50 W
Albion, Ne.	114	41.42 N	98.00 W
Albion, NY	111	43.15 N	78.10 W
Alboran, Isla del (I.), Sp.			
(ē's-lä-dĕl-äl-bô-rä'n)	170	35.58 N	3.02 W
Ålborg, Den. (ôl'bôr)	164	57.02 N	9.55 E
Al Buḥayrah al Murrah al Kubrā (Great Bitter) (Salt L.), Egypt	223c	30.24 N	32.27 E
Al Buḥayrah al Murrah aş Şughrā (Little Bitter) (Salt L.), Egypt	223c	30.10 N	32.36 E
Albuquerque, NM (ál-bŭ-kûr'kē)	121	35.05 N	106.40 W
Albuquerque, Cayus de (I.), Col.			
(ál-bŭ-kûr'kē)	133	12.12 N	81.24 W
Al Buraymī, Om.	192	23.45 N	55.39 E
Alburquerque, Sp. (ál-bōōr-kĕr'kä)	170	39.13 N	6.58 W
Albury, Austl. (ôl'bēr-ē)	216	36.00 S	147.00 E
Alcabideche, Port. (äl-kà-bē-dä'chä)	171b	38.43 N	9.24 W
Alcácer do Sal, Port.			
(äl-kä'sĕr dōō säl')	170	38.24 N	8.33 W
Alcalá de Henares, Sp.			
(äl-kä-lä' dä ā-na'räs)	171a	40.29 N	3.22 W
Alcalá la Real, Sp. (äl-kä-lä'lä rä-äl')	170	37.27 N	3.57 W
Alcamo, It. (äl'kä-mō)	172	37.58 N	13.03 E
Alcanadre (R.), Sp. (äl-kä-nä'drä)	171	41.41 N	0.18 W
Alcanar, Sp. (äl-kä-när')	171	40.35 N	0.27 E
Alcañiz, Sp. (äl-kän-yēth')	171	41.03 N	0.08 W
Alcântara, Braz. (äl-kän'tá-rá)	143	2.17 S	44.29 W
Alcântara (Neigh.), Port.	65d	38.42 N	9.10 W
Alcaraz, Sp. (äl-kä-räth')	170	38.39 N	2.28 W
Alcaudete, Sp. (äl-kou-dhä'tä)	170	37.38 N	4.05 W
Alcázar de San Juan, Sp.			
(äl-kä'thär dä sän hwän')	170	39.22 N	3.12 W
Alcira, Sp. (ä-thē'rä)	171	39.09 N	0.26 W
Alcoa, Tn. (äl-kō'à)	126	35.45 N	84.00 W
Alcobendas, Sp. (äl-kō-bĕn'däs)	171a	40.32 N	3.39 W
Alcochete, Port. (äl-kō-chä'ta)	171b	38.45 N	8.58 W
Alcorón, Sp. (äl-kô-rō'n)	171a	40.22 N	3.50 W
Alcorta, Arg. (äl-kôr'tä)	141c	33.32 S	61.08 W
Alcova Res., Wy. (äl-kō'vá)	117	42.31 N	106.33 W
Alcove, Can. (äl-kōv')	95c	45.41 N	75.55 W
Alcoy, Sp. (äl-koi')	171	38.42 N	0.30 W
Alcudia, Bahia de (B.), Sp.			
(bä-ē'ä-dĕ-äl-kōō-dhē'ä)	171	39.48 N	3.20 E
Aldabra Is., Afr. (äl-dä'brä)	227	9.16 S	46.17 E
Aldama, Mex. (äl-dä'mä)	130	22.54 N	98.04 W
Aldama, Mex.	124	28.50 N	105.54 W
Aldan (R.), Sov. Un.	181	63.30 N	132.14 E
Aldan, Sov.Un.	181	58.46 N	125.19 E
Aldan Plat., Sov. Un.	181	57.42 N	130.20 E
Aldanskaya, Sov. Un.	181	61.52 N	135.29 E
Aldeia, Braz.	61d	23.30 S	46.51 E
Aldeia de Carapicuiba, Braz.	61d	23.35 S	46.48 W
Aldenham, Eng.	62	51.40 N	0.21 W
Aldenhoven, F.R.G. (äl'dĕn-hō'vĕn)	169c	50.54 N	6.18 E
Aldenrade (Neigh.), F.R.G.	63	51.31 N	6.44 E
Aldergrove, Can. (ôl'dĕr-grōv)	118d	49.03 N	122.28 W
Alderney (I.), Guernsey (ôl'dĕr-nĭ)	168	49.43 N	2.11 W
Aldershot, Eng. (ôl'dĕr-shŏt)	156b	51.14 N	0.46 W
Alderson, WV (ôl-dēr-sŭn)	110	37.40 N	80.40 W
Alderwood Manor, Wa.			
(ôl'dĕr-wŏŏd män'ŏr)	118a	47.49 N	122.18 W
Aldridge-Brownhills, Eng.	156	52.38 N	1.55 W
Aledo, Il. (à-le'dō)	123	41.12 N	90.47 W
Aleg, Mauritania	228	17.03 N	13.55 W
Alegre, Braz. (àlē'grē)	141a	20.41 S	41.32 W
Alegre (R.), Braz.	144b	22.22 S	43.34 W
Alegrete, Braz. (ä-lå-grä'tä)	144	29.46 S	55.44 W
Aleksandrov, Sov. Un.			
(à-lyĕk-sän' drôf)	182b	56.24 N	38.45 E
Aleksandrovsk, Sov. Un.			
(à-lyĕk-sän'drôfsk)	182a	59.11 N	57.36 E
Aleksandrovsk, Sov. Un.	181	51.02 N	142.21 E
Aleksandrów Kujawski, Pol.			
(à-lĕk-säh'drōōv kōō-yav'skē)	167	52.54 N	18.45 E
Alekseyevka, Sov. Un.			
(à-lyĕk-sä-yēf'kà)	175	50.39 N	38.40 E
Aleksin, Sov. Un. (à-lyĕk-sēn)	174	54.31 N	37.07 E
Aleksinac, Yugo. (à-lyĕk-sē-nák')	173	43.33 N	21.42 E
Alem Paraíba, Braz.			
(ä-lĕ'm-pá-räē'ba)	141a	21.54 S	42.40 W
Alençon, Fr. (à-läN-sôN')	168	48.26 N	0.08 E
Alenquer, Braz. (ä-lĕŋ-kĕr')	143	1.58 S	54.44 W
Alenquer, Port.	170	39.04 N	9.01 W
Alentjo (Reg.), Port. (ä-lĕŋ-tä'zhōō)	170	38.05 N	7.45 W
Alenuihaha Chan., Hi.			
(ä'lå-nōō-ē-hä'hä)	106a	20.20 N	156.05 W
Aleppo, Syr. (à-lĕp-ō)	161	36.10 N	37.18 E
Alès, Fr. (à-lĕs')	168	44.07 N	4.06 E
Alessandria, It. (ä-lĕs-sän'drĕ-ä)	172	44.53 N	8.35 E
Alessio, see Lesh			
Ålesund, Nor. (ô'lĕ-sōōn')	164	62.28 N	6.14 E
Aleutian Is., Ak. (à-lu'shán)	107a	52.40 N	177.30 W
Aleutian Trench, Ak.	107a	50.40 N	177.10 E
Alevina, Mys (C.), Sov. Un.	181	58.49 N	151.44 E
Alexander Arch., Ak. (äl-ĕg-zän'dēr)	107	57.05 N	138.10 W
Alexander City, Al.	126	32.55 N	85.55 W
Alexander I., Ant.	232	71.00 N	71.00 W
Alexander Ind. Res., Can.	95g	53.47 N	114.00 W
Alexandra, S. Afr. (äl-ex-än'drà)	227b	26.07 S	28.07 E
Alexandra, Austl. (äl-ĕg-zän'drĭ-à)	216	37.11 S	145.42 E
Alexandria, Austl.	214	19.00 S	136.56 E
Alexandria, In.	110	40.20 N	85.20 W
Alexandria, La.	125	31.18 N	92.28 W
Alexandria, Mn.	114	45.53 N	95.23 W
Alexandria, Rom.	173	43.55 N	25.21 E
Alexandria, S. Afr. (äl-ĕx-än-drī-ä)	227c	33.40 S	26.26 E
Alexandria, SD	114	43.39 N	97.45 W
Alexandria, Va. (äl-ĕg-zän'drī-à)	112e	38.50 N	77.05 W
Alexandria Bay, NY	111	44.20 N	75.55 W
Alexandria, see Al Iskandarīyah			
Alexandroúpolis (Dedeagats), Grc.			
(ä-lĕk-sän-drōō'pō-lĭs)			
(de'dĕ-ä-gäts)	173	40.41 N	25.51 E
Alfaro, Sp. (äl-färō)	170	42.08 N	1.43 W
Al-Fāshir, Sud. (fä'shēr)	225	13.38 N	25.21 E
Al Fashn, Egypt	223b	28.47 N	30.53 E
Al Fayyūm, Egypt	225	29.14 N	30.48 E
Alfenas, Braz. (äl-fē'nás)	141a	21.26 S	45.55 W
Alfiós (R.), Grc.	173	37.33 N	21.50 E
Al Firdân, Egypt (fer-dän')	223b	30.43 N	32.20 E
Alfonso Claudio, Braz.			
(äl-fŏn'sō-klou'dēō)	141a	20.05 S	41.05 W
Alfortville, Fr.	64c	48.49 N	2.25 E
Alfred, Can. (äl'frĕd)	95c	45.34 N	74.52 W
Alfreton, Eng. (äl'fēr-tŭn)	156	53.06 N	1.23 W
Algarve (Reg.), Port. (äl-gär'vĕ)	170	37.15 N	8.12 W
Algeciras, Sp. (äl-hā-thē'räs)	170	36.08 N	5.25 W
Algeria, Afr. (äl-gē'rĭ-á)	222	28.45 N	1.00 E
Algés, Port.	65d	38.42 N	9.13 W
Algete, Sp. (äl-hā'tä)	171a	40.36 N	3.30 W
Al Ghaydah, P.D.R. of Yem.	195	16.12 N	52.15 E
Alghero, It. (äl-gā'rō)	172	40.32 N	8.22 E
Algiers, (El Djazaïr), Alg. (äl-jērs)	224	36.51 N	2.56 E
Algoa, Tx. (äl-gō'á)	125a	29.24 N	95.11 W
Algoabaai (B.), S. Afr. (äl'gôä)	227c	33.51 S	24.50 E
Algoma, Wa.	118a	47.17 N	122.15 W
Algoma, Wi.	115	44.38 N	87.30 W
Algona, Ia.	115	43.04 N	94.11 W
Algonac, Mi. (äl'gō-nák)	110	42.35 N	82.30 W
Algonquin, Il. (äl-gŏn'kwĭn)	113a	42.10 N	88.17 W
Algonquin Provincial Park, Can.	111	45.50 N	78.20 W
Alguierão-Mem Martins, Port.	65d	38.48 N	9.20 W
Alhama de Granada, Sp. (äl-hä'mä)	170	37.00 N	3.59 W
Alhama de Murcia, Sp.	170	37.50 N	1.24 W
Alhambra, Ca. (äl-häm'brá)	119a	34.05 N	118.08 W
Al Ḥammām, Egypt	161	30.46 N	29.42 E
Alhandra, Port. (äl-yän'drá)	171b	38.55 N	9.01 W
Al Hasā (Plain), Sau. Àr.	192	27.00 N	47.48 E
Alhaurín, Sp. (ä-lou-rēn')	170	36.40 N	4.40 W
Al-Hawāmidīyah, Egypt	71a	29.54 N	31.15 E
Al Hawrah, P.D.R. of Yem.	195	13.49 N	47.37 E
Al Hayy, Iraq	195	32.10 N	46.03 E
Al Ḥijāz (Reg.), Sau. Ar.	192	23.45 N	39.08 E
Al Ḥirmil, Leb.	191a	34.23 N	36.22 E
Al-Hoceima, Sp.	170	35.15 N	3.55 W
Alhos Vedros, Port. (äl'yōs'vä'drōs)	171b	38.39 N	9.02 W
Alhucemas, Baie d' (B.), Mor.	170	35.18 N	3.50 W
Al Ḥudaydah, Yemen	192	14.43 N	43.03 E
Al Hufūf, Sau. Ar.	192	25.15 N	49.43 E
Aliákmon (R.), Grc. (äl-ē-ák'mōn)	173	40.26 N	22.17 E
Alibori (R.), Benin	229	11.40 N	2.55 E
Alicante, Sp. (ä-lē-kän'tä)	171	38.20 N	0.30 W
Alice, S. Afr. (äl-ĭs)	227c	32.47 S	26.51 E
Alice, Tx. (äl'ĭs)	124	27.45 N	98.04 W
Alice Arm, Can.	98	55.29 N	129.29 W
Alicedale, S. Afr. (äl'ĭs-dāl)	227c	33.18 S	26.04 E
Alice, Punta (Pt.), It. (ä-lē'chē)	173	39.23 N	17.10 E
Alice Springs, Austl. (äl'ĭs)	214	23.38 S	133.56 E
Alicudi (I.), It. (ä-lē-kōō'dē)	172	38.34 N	14.21 E
Alifkulovo, Sov. Un. (ä-lĭf-kŭ'lô-vô)	182a	55.57 N	62.06 E
Al-Imām (Neigh.), Egypt	71a	30.01 N	31.10 E
Alingsås, Swe. (äl'ĭŋ-sôs)	164	57.57 N	12.30 E
Aligarh, India (ä-lē-gûr')	196	27.58 N	78.08 E
Alipore (Neigh.), India	67a	22.31 N	88.18 E
Aliquippa, Pa. (äl-ĭ-kwĭp'á)	113e	40.37 N	80.15 W
Al Iskandarīyah (Alexandria), Egypt	223b	31.12 N	29.58 E
Al Ismā'ī-līyah, see Ismailia			
Aliwal North, S. Afr. (ä-lē-wäl')	226	31.09 S	28.26 E
Al-Jabal Al-Akhḍar (Mts.), Om.	192	23.30 N	56.43 W
Al Jafr, Qa'al (L.), Jordan	191a	30.15 N	36.24 E
Al Jaghbūb, Libya	225	29.46 N	24.32 E
Al Jawārah, Om.	195	18.55 N	57.17 E
Al Jawf, Libya	225	24.14 N	23.15 E
Al Jawf, Sau. Ar.	192	29.45 N	39.30 E
Aljezur, Port. (äl-zhä-zōōr')	170	37.18 N	8.52 W
Al Jīzah, Egypt	223b	30.01 N	31.12 E
Al Jufrah (Oasis), Libya	224	29.30 N	15.16 E
Al Junaynah, Sud.	194	13.27 N	22.27 E
Aljustrel, Port. (äl-zhōō-strĕl')	170	37.44 N	8.23 W
Al Kāb, Egypt	223c	30.56 N	32.19 E
Al Kāmilīn, Sud. (käm-lēn')	225	15.09 N	33.06 E
Al Karak, Jordan (kĕ-räk')	191a	31.11 N	35.42 E
Al Karnak, Egypt (kär'nak)	223b	25.42 N	32.43 E
Al Khâbūrah, Om.	192	23.45 N	57.30 E
Al Khalil (Hebron), Jordan	191a	31.31 N	35.07 E
Al Khandaq, Sud. (kän-däk')	225	18.38 N	30.29 E
Al Khārijah, Egypt	194	25.26 N	30.33 E
Al Kharṭūm, see Khartoum			
Al Kharṭūm Bahrī, Sud.	225	15.43 N	32.41 E
Al Khums, Libya	225	32.35 N	14.10 E
Al Khurmah, Sau. Ar.	192	21.37 N	41.44 E
Al Kiswah, Syr.	191a	33.31 N	36.13 E
Alkmaar, Neth. (älk-mär')	163	52.39 N	4.42 E
Al Kūbrī, Egypt (kōō'brē)	223c	30.01 N	32.35 E
Al Kufrah (Oasis), Libya	225	24.45 N	22.45 E
Al-Kunayyisah, Egypt	71a	29.59 N	31.11 E
Al Kuntillah, Egypt	191a	29.59 N	34.42 E
Al Kuwayt (Kuwait), Kuw. (kōō-wit)	192	29.04 N	47.59 E
Al Lādhiqīyah (Latakia), Syr.	161	35.32 N	35.51 E
Allagash (R.), Me. (äl'à-gàsh)	104	46.50 N	69.24 W
Allāhābād, India (ŭl-ŭ-hä-bäd')	196	25.32 N	81.53 E
All American Can., Ca.			
(äl à-mĕr'ĭ-kàn)	120	32.43 N	115.12 W
Alland, Aus.	157e	48.04 N	16.05 E
Allariz, Sp. (äl-yä-rēth')	170	42.10 N	7.48 W
Allatoona (R.), Ga. (äl'à-tōōn'à)	126	34.05 N	84.57 W
Allauch, Fr. (ä-lē'ōō)	168a	43.21 N	5.30 E
Allaykha, Sov.Un. (ä-lī'κà)	181	70.32 N	148.53 E
Allegan, Mi. (ál'ē-gàn)	102	42.30 N	85.55 W
Allegany Ind. Res., NY (ál-ē-gä'nĭ)	111	42.05 N	78.55 W
Allegheny (R.), Pa.	111	41.10 N	79.20 W
Allegheny Front (Mts.), U.S.	111	38.12 N	80.03 W
Allegheny Mts., U.S.	109	37.35 N	81.55 W
Allegheny Plat., U.S.	110	39.00 N	81.15 W
Allegheny Res., Pa.	111	41.50 N	78.55 W
Allen, Ok. (ál'ĕn)	123	34.51 N	96.26 W
Allendale, NJ (ál'ĕn-dāl)	112a	41.02 N	74.08 W
Allendale, SC	127	33.00 N	81.19 W
Allende, Mex.	131	18.23 N	92.49 W
Allende, Mex.	124	28.20 N	100.50 W
Allen, Lough (B.), Ire. (lòk ál'ĕn)	162	54.07 N	8.09 W
Allen Park, Mi.	57c	42.15 N	83.13 W
Allentown, Pa. (ál'en-toun)	111	40.35 N	75.30 W
Alleppey, India (à-lĕp'ē)	197	9.33 N	76.22 E
Aller R., F.R.G. (äl'ēr)	166	52.43 N	9.50 E
Allerton, Ma.	54a	42.18 N	70.53 W
Allerton (Neigh.), Eng.	64a	53.22 N	2.53 W
Alliance, Ne. (à-lī'áns)	114	42.06 N	102.53 W
Alliance, Oh.	110	40.55 N	81.10 W
Al Lidām, Sau.Ar.	192	20.45 N	44.12 E
Allier (R.), Fr. (á-lyā')	168	46.43 N	3.03 E
Alligator Pt., La. (al'ĭ-gä-tēr)	112d	30.57 N	89.41 W
Allinge, Den. (äl'ĭŋ-ĕ)	164	55.16 N	14.48 E
Allison Park, Pa.	57b	40.34 N	79.57 W
Al Līth, Sau. Ar.	195	20.09 N	40.16 E
All Pines, Belize (ól pīnz)	132a	16.55 N	88.15 W
Allston (Neigh.), Ma.	54a	42.22 N	71.08 W
Al Luḥayyah, Yemen	192	15.58 N	42.48 E
Alluvial City, La.	112d	29.51 N	89.42 W
Allyn, Wa. (ál'ĭn)	118a	47.23 N	122.51 W
Alma, Can. (äl'má)	104	45.36 N	64.59 W
Alma, Can.	104	48.29 N	71.42 W
Alma, Ga.	127	31.33 N	82.31 W
Alma, Mi.	110	43.25 N	84.40 W
Alma, Ne.	122	40.08 N	99.21 W
Alma, S. Afr.	223d	24.30 S	28.05 E
Alma, Wi.	115	44.21 N	91.57 W
Alma-Ata, Sov. Un. (äl'má ä'tä)	180	43.19 N	77.08 E
Al Mabrak (R.), Sau. Ar.	191a	29.16 N	35.12 E
Almacuzac (R.), Mex.			
(ä-mä-kōō-zak)	130	18.00 N	99.03 W
Almada, Port. (äl-mä'dä)	171b	38.40 N	9.09 W
Almadén, Sp. (äl-mä-dhän)	170	38.47 N	4.50 W
Al Madīnah (Medina), Sau. Ar.	192	24.26 N	39.42 E
Al Mafraq, Jordan	191a	32.21 N	36.13 E
Almagre, Laguna (L.), Mex.			
(lä-gōō'nä-äl-mä'grē)	131	23.48 N	97.45 W
Almagro, Sp. (äl-mä'grō)	170	38.52 S	3.41 W
Al Maḥallah al Kubrā, Egypt	223b	31.00 N	31.10 E
Al Manāmah, Bahrain	192	26.01 N	50.33 E
Al-Manāwāt, Egypt	71a	29.55 N	31.14 E
Almanor (R.), Ca. (äl-ĕ-ák'mōn)	120	40.11 N	121.20 W
Almansa, Sp. (äl-män'sä)	170	38.52 N	1.09 W
Al Manshāh, Egypt	223b	26.31 N	31.46 E
Almansor (R.), Port. (äl-män-sôr)	170	38.41 N	8.27 W
Al Manṣūrah, Egypt	223b	31.02 N	31.25 E
Al Manzilah, Egypt (män'za-la)	223b	31.09 N	32.05 E
Almanzora (R.), Sp. (äl-män-thō'rä)	170	37.20 N	2.25 W
Al Marāghah, Egypt	223b	26.41 N	31.35 E
Almargem do Bispo, Port.			
(äl-mär-zhēN)	171b	38.51 N	9.16 W
Al-Marj, Libya	225	32.44 N	21.08 E
Al-Marj (Neigh.), Egypt	71a	30.09 N	31.20 E
Al Maşīrah (I.), Om.	192	20.43 N	58.58 E
Al Mawsil, Iraq	192	36.00 N	42.53 E
Almazán, Sp. (äl-mä-thän')	170	41.30 N	2.33 W
Al Mazār, Jordan	191a	31.04 N	35.41 E
Al Mazra'ah, Jordan	191a	31.17 N	35.33 E
Almeirim, Port. (äl-māĭ-rēN')	170	39.13 N	8.31 W
Almelo, Neth. (äl'mē-lō)	163	52.20 N	6.42 E
Almendra, Embalse de (Res.), Sp.	170	41.15 N	6.10 W
Almendralejo, Sp.			
(äl-mān-drä-lā'hō)	170	38.43 N	6.24 W
Almería, Sp. (äl-mā-rē'ä)	170	36.52 N	2.28 W
Almeria, Golfo de (G.), Sp.			
(gôl-fô-dĕ-äl-māĭ-rē'ä)	170	36.45 N	2.26 W
Älmhult, Swe. (älm'hōōlt)	164	56.35 N	14.08 E
Almina, Pta., Mor. (äl-mē'nä)	170	35.58 N	5.17 W
Al Minyā, Egypt	223b	28.04 N	30.45 E
Almirante, Pan. (äl-mäĭ-rĕn')	133	9.18 N	82.24 W
Almirante, Bahia de (B.), Pan.			
(bä-ē'ä-dĕ-äl-mē-rän'tä)	133	9.22 N	82.07 W
Almirós, Grc.	173	39.13 N	22.47 E
Almodóvar del Campo, Sp.			
(äl-mô-dhō'vär)	170	38.43 N	4.10 W
Almoi, India	196	29.41 N	79.42 E
Almoloya, Mex. (äl-mō-lō'yä)	130	19.32 N	99.44 W
Almoloya, Mex.	131a	19.11 N	99.28 W
Almonte, Can. (äl-mòn'tē)	111	45.15 N	76.15 W
Almonte (R.), Sp.	170	39.35 N	5.50 W
Almonte, Sp. (äl-mōn'tä)	170	37.16 N	6.32 W
Almora, India	196	29.20 N	79.40 E
Al Mubarraz, Sau.Ar.	192	22.31 N	46.27 E
Al Mudawwarah, Jordan	191a	29.20 N	36.01 E
Al Mukallā, P.D.R. of Yem.	192	14.27 N	49.05 E
Al Mukhā, Yemen	192	13.19 N	43.15 E
Almuñécar, Sp. (äl-mōōn-yä'kär)	170	36.44 N	3.43 W
Alnön (I.), Swe.	164	62.20 N	17.39 E
Aloha, Or. (ä'lô-hä)	118c	45.29 N	122.52 W
Alondra, Ca.	59	33.54 N	118.19 W
Álora, Sp. (ä'lô-rä)	170	36.49 N	4.42 W
Alor Gajah, Mala	191b	2.23 N	102.13 E
Alor, Pulau (I.), Indon.	207	8.07 S	125.00 E
Alor Setar, Mala. (ä'lôr stär)	206	6.10 N	100.16 E
Alouette (R.), Can. (ä-lōō-ĕt')	118d	49.16 N	122.32 W
Alpena, Mi. (äl-pē'ná)	110	45.05 N	83.30 W
Alphen, Neth.	157a	52.07 N	4.38 E
Alpiarça, Port. (äl-pyär'sá)	170	39.38 N	8.37 W
Alpine, NJ	55	40.56 N	73.56 W

PLACE (Pronounciation)	PAGE	Lat. °'	Long. °'
Alpine, Tx. (ăl'pīn)	124	30.21 N	103.41 W
Alps (Mts.), Eur. (ălps)	160	46.18 N	8.42 E
Alpujarra, Col. (àl-pōō-κä'rà)	142a	3.23 N	74.56 W
Alpujarras (Mts.), Sp. (äl-pōō-här'räs)	170	36.55 N	3.25 W
Al Qaḍārif, Sud.	225	14.03 N	35.11 E
Al Qāhirah (Cairo), Egypt	223b	30.00 N	31.17 E
Al Qanṭarah, Egypt	223c	30.51 N	32.20 E
Al Qaryah ash Sharqīyah, Libya	225	30.36 N	13.13 E
Al Qaṣr, Egypt	194	25.42 N	28.53 E
Al Qaṭīf, Sau. Ar.	192	26.30 N	50.00 E
Al Qayṣūmah, Sau. Ar.	192	28.15 N	46.20 E
Al Qunaytirah, Syr.	191a	33.09 N	35.49 E
Al Qunfudhah, Sau. Ar.	195	19.08 N	41.05 E
Al Quṣaymah, Egypt	191a	30.40 N	34.23 E
Al Qusayr, Egypt	191a	34.32 N	36.33 E
Al Quṣayr, Egypt	225	26.14 N	34.11 E
Als (I.), Den. (äls)	164	55.06 N	9.40 E
Alsace (Reg.), Fr. (äl-sà's)	169	48.25 N	7.24 E
Al Shan (Mts.), China (äī'shän)	200	37.27 N	120.35 E
Alsip, Il.	58a	41.40 N	87.44 W
Altadena, Ca. (ăl-tă-dē'nă)	119a	34.12 N	118.08 W
Alta Gracia, Arg. (äl'tä grä'sē-ä)	144	31.41 S	64.19 W
Altagracia, Ven.	142	10.42 N	71.34 W
Altagracia de Orituco, Ven. (ä'l-tà-grà'sēä-dě-ôrē-tōō'kô)	143b	9.53 N	66.22 W
Altai Mts., Asia (äl'tī')	198	49.11 N	87.15 E
Alta Loma, Ca. (ăl'tă lō'mä)	119a	34.07 N	117.35 W
Alta Loma, Tx. (ăl'tă lō-mă)	125a	29.22 N	95.05 W
Altamaha (R.), Ga. (ôl-tá-má-hô')	127	31.50 N	82.00 W
Altamira, Braz. (äl-tä-mē'rä)	143	3.13 S	52.14 W
Altamira, Mex.	131	22.25 N	97.55 W
Altamirano, Arg. (äl-tä-mē-rä'nō)	144	35.26 S	58.12 W
Altamura, It. (äl-tä-mōō'rä)	172	40.40 N	16.35 E
Altar of Heaven (P. Int.), China	67b	39.53 N	116.25 E
Altar of the Earth (P. Int.), China	67b	39.57 N	116.24 E
Altar of the Moon (P. Int.), China	67b	39.55 N	116.20 E
Altar of the Sun (P. Int.), China	67b	39.54 N	116.27 E
Altavista, Va. (ăl-tä-vĭs'tă)	127	37.08 N	79.14 W
Altay, China (äl-tä)	198	47.52 N	86.50 E
Altenburg, G.D.R. (äl-tĕn-bŏŏrgh)	166	50.59 N	12.27 E
Altenderne Oberbecker (Neigh.), F.R.G.	63	51.35 N	7.33 E
Altenessen (Neigh.), F.R.G.	63	51.29 N	7.00 E
Altenhagen (Neigh.), F.R.G.	63	51.22 N	7.28 E
Altenmarkt an der Triesting, Aus.	157e	48.02 N	16.00 E
Altenvoerde, F.R.G.	63	51.18 N	7.22 E
Alter do Chão, Port. (äl-tĕr'dōō shäɴ'ôɴ)	170	39.13 N	7.38 W
Altiplanicie Mexicana (Plat.), Mex. (äl-tē-plä-nē'syē-mě-κē-kà-nä)	130	22.38 N	102.33 W
Altiplano (Plat.), Bol. (äl-tē-plà'nō)	142	18.38 S	68.20 W
Altlandsberg, G.D.R. (ält länts'bĕrgh)	157b	52.34 N	13.44 E
Altlünun, F.R.G.	63	51.38 N	7.31 E
Altmannsdorf, (Neigh.), Aus.	66e	48.10 N	16.20 E
Alto, La. (ăl'tō)	125	32.21 N	91.52 W
Alto da Moóca, (Neigh.), Braz.	61d	23.34 S	46.35 W
Alto Marañón, Rio (R.), Peru (rē'ō-ál'tô-mä-rän-yō'n)	142	8.18 S	77.13 W
Alto Molócuè, Moz.	231	15.38 S	37.42 E
Altomünster, F.R.G. (äl'tō-mün'stĕr)	157d	48.24 N	11.16 E
Alton, Can. (ôl'tŭn)	95d	43.52 N	80.05 W
Alton, Il.	119e	38.53 N	90.11 W
Altona, Austl.	206a	37.52 S	144.50 E
Altona, Can.	101	49.06 N	97.33 W
Altona, F.R.G. (äl'tō-nà)	157c	53.33 N	9.54 E
Altona North, Austl.	70b	37.50 S	144.51 E
Altoona, Al. (ăl-tōō'nȧ)	126	34.01 N	86.15 W
Altoona, Pa.	111	40.25 N	78.25 W
Altoona, Wa.	118c	46.16 N	123.39 W
Alto Rio Doce, Braz. (äl'tô-rē'ô-dō'sě)	141a	21.02 S	43.23 W
Alto Songo, Cuba (äl-fō-sôŋ'gō)	135	20.10 N	75.45 W
Altotonga, Mex. (äl-tō-tôŋ'gä)	131	19.44 N	97.13 W
Alto-Uama, Ang.	230	12.14 S	15.33 E
Alto Velo (I.), Dom. Rep. (äl-tô-vě'lō)	135	17.30 N	71.35 W
Altrincham, Eng. (ôl'trĭng-ăm)	156	53.18 N	2.21 W
Altruppin, G.D.R. (ält rōō'ppēn)	157b	52.56 N	12.50 E
Altun Shan (Mts.), China (äl-tōōn shän)	198	36.58 N	85.09 E
Alturas, Ca. (ăl-tōō'rȧs)	116	41.29 N	120.33 W
Alturas, Serra das (Mts.), Port. (sě'r-rä-däs-äl-tōō'räs)	170	40.43 N	7.48 W
Altus, Ok. (ăl'tŭs)	122	34.38 N	99.20 W
Al 'Ubaylah, Sau. Ar.	195	21.59 N	50.57 E
Al-Ubayyiḍ, Sud.	225	13.15 N	30.15 E
Al-Uḍayyah, Sud.	225	12.06 N	28.16 E
Al-'Ugaylah, Libya	225	30.15 N	19.07 E
Alūksne, Sov. Un. (ä'lōōks-nĕ)	174	57.24 N	27.04 E
Alumette I., Can. (à-lü-mĕt')	111	45.50 N	77.00 W
Alum Rock, Ca.	118b	37.23 N	121.50 W
Al Uqṣur (Luxor), Egypt	223b	25.38 N	32.59 E
Alushta, Sov. Un. (ä'lshōō-tȧ)	175	44.39 N	34.23 E
Alva, Ok. (ăl'vȧ)	122	36.46 N	98.41 W
Alvanley, Eng.	64a	53.16 N	2.45 W
Alvarado, Mex. (äl-vä-rä'dhō)	131	18.48 N	95.45 W
Alvarado, Luguna de (L.), Mex. (lä-gōō'nä-dĕ-äl-vä-rä'dô)	131	18.44 N	96.45 W
Älvdalen, Swe. (ĕlv'dä-lĕn)	164	61.14 N	14.04 E
Alverca, Port. (al-vĕr'kȧ)	171b	38.53 N	9.02 W
Alvesta, Swe. (äl-vĕs'tä)	164	56.55 N	14.29 E
Alvin, Tx. (ăl'vĭn)	125a	29.25 N	95.14 W
Alvinópolis, Braz. (äl-vēnō'pō-lēs)	141a	20.07 S	43.03 W
Alviso, Ca. (ăl-vī'sō)	118b	37.26 N	121.59 W
Al Wajh, Sau. Ar.	192	26.15 N	36.32 E
Alwar, India (ŭl'wŭr)	196	27.39 N	76.39 E
Al Wāsiṭah, Egypt	223b	29.21 N	31.15 E
Alytus, Sov. Un. (ä'lē-tōōs)	165	54.24 N	24.05 E
Amadeus, (L.), Austl. (ăm-à-dē'ŭs)	214	24.30 S	131.25 E
Amadjuak (L.), Can. (ä-mädj'wäk)	97	64.50 N	69.20 W
Amadora, Port.	65d	38.45 N	9.14 W

PLACE (Pronounciation)	PAGE	Lat. °'	Long. °'
Amagasaki, Jap. (ä'mä-gä-sä'kē)	205b	34.43 N	135.25 E
Ama Keng, Singapore	67c	1.24 N	103.42 E
Amakusa-Shimo (I.), Jap. (ämä-kōō'sä shē-mō)	205	32.24 N	129.35 E
Åmål, Swe. (ô'môl)	164	59.05 N	12.40 E
Amalfi, Col. (ä'mà'l-fē)	142a	6.55 N	75.04 W
Amalfi, It. (ä-mä'l-fē)	171c	40.23 N	14.36 E
Amaliás, Grc. (à-mål'yàs)	173	37.48 N	21.23 E
Amalner, India	196	21.07 N	75.06 E
Amambai, Serra de (Mts.), Braz.	143	20.06 S	57.08 W
Amami Guntō (Is.), Jap. (ä'mä'mē gōōn'tō')	204	28.25 N	129.00 E
Amamio (I.), Jap. (ä-mä'mē-ō)	204	28.10 N	129.55 E
Amapá, Braz. (ä-mä-pà')	143	2.14 N	50.48 W
Amapá (State), Braz.	143	1.15 N	52.15 W
Amapala, Hond. (ä-mä-pä'lä)	132	13.16 N	87.39 W
Amarante, Braz. (ä-mä-rän'tä)	143	6.17 S	42.43 W
Amargosa (R.), Ca. (á'mär-gō'sȧ)	120	35.55 N	116.45 W
Amarillo, Tx. (ăm-à-rĭl'ō)	122	35.14 N	101.49 W
Amaro, Mt., It. (ä-mä'rō)	172	42.07 N	14.07 E
Amaroúsion, Grc.	66d	38.03 N	23.49 E
Amasya, Tur. (ä-mä'sē-à)	179	40.40 N	35.50 E
Amatenango, Mex. (ä-mä-tä-naŋ'gō)	131	16.30 N	92.29 W
Amatignak (I.), Ak. (ä-mà'tē-näk)	107a	51.12 N	178.30 W
Amatique, Bahía de (B.), Belize-Guat. (bä-ē'ä-dē-ä-mä-tē'kä)	132	15.58 N	88.50 W
Amatitlán, Guat. (ä-mä-tē-tlän')	132	14.27 N	90.39 W
Amatlán de Cañas, Mex. (ä-mät-län'dā kän-yäs)	130	20.50 N	104.22 W
Amazonas (State), Braz. (ä-mä-thō'näs)	142	4.15 S	64.30 W
Amazonas, Rio (R.), Braz. (rē'ō-ä-mä-thō'näs)	143	2.03 S	53.18 W
Ambāla, India (ŭm-bä'lŭ)	196	30.31 N	76.48 E
Ambalema, Col. (äm-bä-lā'mä)	142a	4.47 N	74.45 W
Ambarchik, Sov. Un. (ŭm-bär'chĭk)	181	69.39 N	162.18 E
Ambarnāth, India	197b	19.12 N	73.10 E
Ambato, Ec. (äm-bä'tō)	142	1.15 S	78.30 W
Ambatondrazaka, Mad.	227	17.58 S	48.43 E
Amberg, F.R.G. (äm'bĕrgh)	166	49.26 N	11.51 E
Ambergris Cay (I.), Belize (ăm'bēr-grēs kāz)	132	18.04 N	87.43 W
Ambergris Cays (Is.), Turks & Caicos Is.	135	21.20 N	71.40 W
Ambérieu-en-Bugey, Fr. (äɴ-bā-rē-u')	169	45.57 N	5.21 E
Ambert, Fr. (äɴ-bĕr')	168	45.32 N	3.41 E
Ambil I., Phil. (äm'bēl)	207a	13.51 N	120.25 E
Ambler, Pa. (ăm'blēr)	112f	40.09 N	75.13 W
Amboise, Fr. (äɴ-bwäz')	168	47.25 N	0.56 E
Ambon, Indon.	207	3.45 S	128.17 E
Ambon, Pulau (I.), Indon.	207	4.50 S	128.45 E
Ambositra, Mad. (äɴ-bô-sē'trä)	227	20.31 S	47.28 E
Amboy, Il. (ăm'boi)	110	41.41 N	89.15 W
Amboy, Wa.	118c	45.55 N	122.27 W
Ambre, Cap d' (C.), Mad.	227	12.06 S	49.15 E
Ambridge, Pa. (ăm'brĭdj)	113e	40.36 N	80.13 W
Ambrim (I.), Vanuatu	215	16.25 S	168.15 E
Ambriz, Ang.	230	7.50 S	13.06 E
Amchitka (I.), Ak. (ăm-chĭt'kä)	107a	51.25 N	178.10 E
Amchitka Pass., Ak.	107a	51.30 N	179.36 W
Amealco, Mex. (ä-mä-äl'kō)	130	20.12 N	100.08 W
Ameca, Mex. (ä-mĕ'kä)	130	20.34 N	104.02 W
Amecameca, Mex. (ä-mȧ-kä-mä'kä)	131a	19.06 N	98.46 W
Ameide, Neth.	157a	51.57 N	4.57 E
Ameixoera (Neigh.), Port.	65d	38.47 N	9.10 W
Ameland (I.), Neth.	163	53.29 N	5.54 E
Amelia, Oh. (ä-mēl'yä)	113f	39.01 N	84.12 W
American (R.), Ca. (ȧ-mĕr'ĭ-kăn)	120	38.43 N	120.45 W
Americana, Braz. (ä-mĕ-rē-kä'nȧ)	141a	22.46 S	47.19 W
American Falls, Id. (ȧ-mĕ-ĭ-kăn)	117	42.45 N	112.53 W
American Falls Res., Id.	117	42.56 N	113.18 W
American Fork, Ut.	121	40.20 N	111.50 W
American Highland, Ant.	232	72.00 S	79.00 E
American Samoa, (I.) Oceania	208	14.20 S	170.00 W
Americus, Ga. (ȧ-mĕr'ĭ-kŭs)	126	32.04 N	84.15 W
Amersfoort, Neth. (ä'mĕrz-fōrt)	157a	52.08 N	5.23 E
Amersham, Eng.	62	51.40 N	0.38 W
Amery, Can. (ā'mēr-ē)	101	56.34 N	94.03 W
Amery, Wi.	115	45.19 N	92.24 W
Ames, Ia. (āmz)	115	42.00 N	93.36 W
Amesbury, Ma. (āmz'bēr-ē)	105a	42.51 N	70.56 W
Amfissa, Grc. (ám-fī'sȧ)	173	38.32 N	22.26 E
Amga (R.), Sov. Un.	181	61.41 N	133.11 E
Amga, Sov. Un. (ŭm-gä')	181	61.08 N	132.09 E
Amgun (R.), Sov. Un.	181	53.33 N	137.57 E
Amherst, Can. (ăm'hērst)	104	45.49 N	64.14 W
Amherst (I.), Can.	103	44.08 N	76.45 W
Amherst, NY	57a	42.58 N	78.48 W
Amherst, Oh.	113d	41.24 N	82.13 W
Amiens, Fr. (ä-myäɴ')	168	49.54 N	2.18 E
Amirante Is., Sey.	232	6.02 S	52.30 E
Amisk L., Can.	101	54.35 N	102.13 W
Amistad Res., Tx.	124	29.20 N	101.00 W
Amite, La. (ă-mēt')	125	30.43 N	90.32 W
Amite R., La.	125	30.45 N	90.48 W
Amity, Pa. (ăm'ĭ-tĭ)	113e	40.02 N	80.11 W
Amityville, NY (ăm'ĭ-tĭ-vĭl)	112a	40.41 N	73.24 W
Amlia (I.), Ak. (ȧ'mlēȧ)	107a	52.00 N	173.28 W
'Ammān, Jordan (äm'mȧn)	191a	31.57 N	35.57 E
Ammersee (I.), F.R.G. (äm'mĕr)	157d	48.00 N	11.08 E
Amnicon R., Wi. (ăm'nē-kŏn)	119h	46.35 N	91.56 W
Amnok (R.), see Yalu			
Amorgós (I.), Grc. (ä-môr'gōs)	173	36.47 N	25.47 E
Amory, Ms. (ām'o-rē)	126	33.58 N	88.27 W
Amos, Can. (ā'mŭs)	103	48.31 N	78.04 W
Amoy, see Xiamen			
Amparo, Braz. (äm-pȧ'-rô)	141a	22.43 S	46.44 W
Amper R., F.R.G. (äm'pĕr)	157d	48.18 N	11.32 E
Amposta, Sp. (äm-pōs'tä)	171	40.42 N	0.34 E
Amqui, Can.	104	48.28 N	67.28 W
Amrāvati, India	196	20.58 N	77.47 E

PLACE (Pronounciation)	PAGE	Lat. °'	Long. °'
Amritsar, India (ŭm-rĭt'sŭr)	196	31.43 N	74.52 E
Amstelveen, Neth.	157a	52.18 N	4.51 E
Amsterdam, Neth. (äm-stĕr-däm')	157a	52.21 N	4.52 E
Amsterdam, NY (ăm'stĕr-dăm)	111	42.55 N	74.10 W
Amsterdam, Île (I.), Ind. O.	232	37.52 S	77.32 E
Amstetten, Aus. (äm'stĕt-ĕn)	166	48.09 N	14.53 E
Am Timan, Chad (äm'tē-män')	225	11.18 N	20.30 E
Amu Darya (R.), Asia (ä-mōō-dä'rēä)	192	40.40 N	62.00 E
Amukta Pass., Ak. (ä-mōōk'tá)	107a	52.30 N	172.00 W
Amundsen G., Can. (ä'mŭn-sĕn)	96	70.17 N	123.28 W
Amundsen Sea, Ant.	232	72.00 S	110.00 W
Amungen (L.), Swe.	164	61.07 N	16.00 E
Amurskiy, Sov. Un. (ä-mûr'skĭ)	182a	52.35 N	59.36 E
Amurskiy, Zaliv (B.), Sov. Un. (zä'lĭf ä-mōōr'skĭ)	204	43.20 N	131.40 E
Amusgos (San Pedro), Mex. (ä-mōō's-gôs) (sän-pĕ'drō)	130	16.39 N	98.09 W
Amuyao, Mt., Phil. (ä-mōō-yä'ō)	207a	17.04 N	121.09 E
Amvrakikos Kólpos (G.), Grc.	173	39.00 N	21.00 E
Amyun, Leb.	191a	34.18 N	35.48 E
Anabar (R.), Sov. Un. (ăn-à-bär')	181	71.15 N	113.00 E
Anaco, Ven. (ä-nä'kô)	143b	9.29 N	64.27 W
Anaconda, Mt. (ăn-ȧ-kŏn'dȧ)	117	46.07 N	112.55 W
Anacortes, Wa. (ăn-ȧ-kôr'tĕz)	118a	48.30 N	122.37 W
Anacostia (Neigh.), DC.	56d	38.52 N	76.59 W
Anadarko, Ok. (ăn-à-där'kō)	122	35.05 N	98.14 W
Anadoluhisarı (P. Int.), Tur.	66f	41.04 N	29.03 E
Anadyr', Sov.Un. (ŭ-nȧ-dĭr')	181	64.47 N	177.01 E
Anadyr (R.), Sov. Un.	181	65.30 N	172.45 E
Anadyrskiy Zaliv (B.), Sov. Un.	191	64.10 N	178.00 W
'Ānah, Iraq	195	34.28 N	41.56 E
Anaheim, Ca. (ăn'á-hīm)	119a	33.50 N	117.55 W
Anahuac, Tx. (ä-nä'wäk)	125a	29.46 N	94.41 W
Ānai Mudi (Mtn.), India	197	10.10 N	77.00 E
Anama Bay, Can.	101	51.56 N	98.05 W
Ana María, Cayos (Is.), Cuba (kä'yōs-ä'nȧ mȧ-rē'ȧ)	134	21.55 N	78.50 W
Anambas, Kepulauan (Is.), Indon. (ä-näm-bäs)	206	2.41 N	106.38 E
Anamosa, Ia. (ăn-ȧ-mō'sȧ)	115	42.06 N	91.18 W
Anan'yev, Sov. Un. (á-nä'nyĕf)	175	47.43 N	29.59 E
Anapa, Sov. Un. (á-nä'pä)	175	44.54 N	37.19 E
Anápolis, Braz. (ä-nà'pō-lēs)	143	16.17 S	48.47 W
Añatuya, Arg. (ä-nyä-tōō'yá)	144	28.22 S	62.45 W
Anchieta, Braz. (án-chyĕ'tä)	144b	22.49 S	43.24 W
Ancholme (R.), Eng. (ăn'chŭm)	156	53.28 N	0.27 W
Anchorage, Ak. (ăŋ'kēr-āj)	107	61.12 N	149.48 W
Anchorage, Ky.	113b	38.16 N	85.32 W
Anci, China (än-tsū)	202a	39.31 N	116.41 E
Ancienne-Lorette, Can. (äɴ-syĕn' lō-rĕt')	95b	46.48 N	71.21 W
Ancon, Pan. (äŋ-kōn')	128a	8.55 N	79.32 W
Ancona, It. (än-kō'nä)	172	43.37 N	13.32 E
Ancud, Chile (äŋ-kōōdh')	144	41.52 S	73.45 W
Ancud, G. de, Chile (gôl-fô-dĕ-äŋ-kōōdh')	144	41.15 S	73.00 W
Anda, China	202	46.20 N	125.20 E
Andalgalá, Arg. (á'n-däl-gá-lá')	144	27.35 S	66.14 W
Åndalsnes, Nor.	164	62.33 N	7.46 E
Andalucia (Reg.), Sp. (än-dä-lōō-sē'á)	170	37.35 N	5.40 W
Andalusia, Al. (ăn-dȧ-lōō'zhĭȧ)	126	31.19 N	86.19 W
Andaman Is., Andaman & Nicobar Is. (ăn-dȧ-măn')	206	11.38 N	92.17 E
Andaman Sea, Asia	206	12.44 N	95.45 E
Andarax (R.), Sp.	170	37.00 N	2.40 W
Anderlecht, Bel. (än'dĕr-lĕkt)	157a	50.49 N	4.16 E
Andernach, F.R.G. (än'dĕr-näk)	166	50.25 N	7.23 E
Anderson, Arg. (á'n-dĕr-sōn)	141c	35.15 S	60.15 W
Anderson, Ca. (ăn'dĕr-sŭn)	116	40.28 N	122.19 W
Anderson, In.	110	40.05 N	85.50 W
Anderson, SC	127	34.30 N	82.40 W
Anderson (R.), Can.	96	68.32 N	125.12 W
Andes Mts., S. A. (ăn'dēz) (än'dās)	140	13.00 S	75.00 W
Andheri (Neigh.), India	197b	19.08 N	72.50 E
Andhra Pradesh (State), India	197	16.00 N	79.00 E
Andikíthira (I.), Grc.	161	35.50 N	23.20 E
Andizhan, Sov. Un. (än-dē-zhän')	180	40.51 N	72.39 E
Andong, Kor. (än'dŭng')	204	36.31 N	128.42 E
Andongwei, China (än-dôŋ-wā)	200	35.08 N	119.19 E
Andorra, And. (än-dôr'rä)	171	42.38 N	1.30 E
Andorra, Eur.	159	42.30 N	2.00 E
Andover, Ma. (ăn'dô-vēr)	105a	42.39 N	71.08 W
Andover, NJ	112a	40.59 N	74.45 W
Andøya (I.), Nor. (änd-ûē)	158	69.12 N	14.58 E
Andreanof Is., Ak. (än-drå-ä'nôf)	107a	51.10 N	177.00 W
Andrelândia, Braz. (än-drĕ-lá'n-dyá)	141a	21.45 S	44.18 W
Andrésy, Fr.	64c	48.59 N	2.04 E
Andrew Johnson Natl. Mon., Tn. (ăn'drōō jŏn'sŭn)	126	36.15 N	82.55 W
Andrews, NC (ăn'drōōz)	126	35.12 N	83.48 W
Andrews, SC	127	33.25 N	79.32 W
Andrews Air Force Base (P. Int.), Md.	56d	38.48 N	76.52 W
Andreyevka, Sov. Un. (än-drå-yĕf'kä)	175	48.03 N	37.03 E
Andria, It. (än'drē-ä)	172	41.17 N	15.55 E
Andropov (Rybinsk), Sov. Un.	174	58.02 N	38.52 E
Andros, Grc. (ăn'dhrôs)	173	37.50 N	24.54 E
Ándros (I.), Grc. (ăn'drŏs)	173	37.59 N	24.55 E
Androscoggin (R.), Me. (ăn-drŭs-kŏg'ĭn)	104	44.25 N	70.45 W
Andros I., Ba. (ăn'drŏs)	134	24.30 N	78.00 W
Anefis i-n-Darane, Mali	228	18.03 N	0.36 E
Anegasaki, Jap. (ä'nå-gä-sä'kē)	205a	35.29 N	140.02 E
Aneityum (I.), Vanuatu (ä-nå-ē'tē-ŭm)	215	20.15 S	169.49 E
Aneta, ND (ă-nē'tȧ)	114	47.41 N	97.57 W
Angamacutiro, Mex. (äŋ'gä-mä-kōō-tē'rô)	130	20.08 N	101.44 W
Angangueo, Mex. (än-gäŋ'gwā-ō)	130	19.36 N	100.18 W
Ang'angxi, China (äŋ-äŋ-shyē)	202	47.05 N	123.58 E

ng-sing; ŋ-baŋk; ɴ-nasalized n; nŏd; cŏmmit; ōld; ōbey; ôrder; oi-boil; fōōd; fŏŏt; ou-out; s-soft; sh-dish; th-thin; pūre; ůnite; ûrn; stŭd; circŭs; ü-as in French tu; '-indeterminate vowel.

PLACE (Pronounciation)	PAGE	Lat. °'	Long. °'
Angara (R.), see **Verkhnyaya Tunguska**			
Angarsk, Sov. Un.	180	52.48 N	104.15 E
Ange, Swe. (ông'ĕ)	164	62.31 N	15.39 E
Angel De La Guarda (I.), Mex. (ä'n-hĕl-dĕ-lä-gwä'r-dä)	128	29.30 N	113.00 W
Angeles, Phil. (än'hā-lās)	207a	15.09 N	120.35 E
Ängelholm, Swe. (ĕng'ĕl-hôlm)	164	56.14 N	12.50 E
Angelina R., Tx. (ăn-jē lē'n*ȧ*)	125	31.30 N	94.53 W
Angel, Salto (Falls), Ven. (säl'tō-ä'n-hĕl)	142	5.44 N	62.27 W
Angels Camp, Ca. (ān'jĕls kămp')	120	38.03 N	120.33 W
Angerhausen, (Neigh.), F.R.G.	63	51.23 N	6.44 E
Ångermanälven (R.), Swe.	158	64.10 N	18.35 E
Angermund, F.R.G. (än'ngĕr-mŭnd)	169c	51.20 N	6.47 E
Angermünde, G.D.R. (äng'ĕr-mûn-dĕ)	166	53.02 N	14.00 E
Angers, Can. (äɴ-zhā')	95c	41.31 N	75.29 W
Angers, Fr.	168	47.29 N	0.36 W
Angkor (Ruins), Kamp. (ăng'kôr)	206	13.52 N	103.50 E
Anglesey, (I.), Wales (ăŋ'g'l-sē)	162	53.35 N	4.28 W
Angleton, Tx. (aŋ'g'l-t*ŭ*n)	125a	29.10 N	95.25 W
Angmagssalik, Grnld. (àŋ-mȧ'sȧ-lĭk)	94	65.40 N	37.40 W
Angoche, Ilha (I.), Moz. (ē'lä-ăn-gō'chā)	231	16.20 S	40.00 E
Angol, Chile (aŋ-gōl')	144	37.47 S	72.43 W
Angola, Afr.	222	14.15 S	16.00 E
Angola, In. (ăŋ-gō'lȧ)	110	41.35 S	85.00 W
Angono, Phil.	68g	14.31 N	121.08 E
Angora, see **Ankara**			
Angoulême, Fr. (äŋ'go͞o-lâm')	168	45.40 N	0.09 E
Angra dos Reis, Braz. (aŋ'grä dōs rā'ēs)	141a	23.01 S	44.17 W
Angri, It. (ä'n-grē)	171c	40.30 N	14.35 E
Anguang, China (än-gŭäŋ)	202	45.28 N	123.42 E
Anguilla, N.A.	129	18.15 N	62.54 W
Anguilla, Cays (Is.), Ba. (ăŋ-gwĭl'*ȧ*)	134	23.30 N	79.35 W
Anguille, C., Can. (äŋ-gē'y*ĕ*)	105	47.55 N	59.25 W
Anguo, China (än-gwō)	200	38.27 N	115.19 E
Angyalföld (Neigh.), Hung.	66g	47.33 N	19.05 E
Anholt (I.), Den. (än'hôlt)	164	56.43 N	11.34 E
Anhui (Prov.), China (än-hwā)	199	31.30 N	117.15 E
Aniak, Ak. (ä-nyȧ'k)	107	61.32 N	159.35 W
Anik (Neigh.), India	67e	19.02 N	72.53 E
Animas (R.), Co. (ä'nē-mȧs)	121	37.03 N	107.50 W
Anina, Rom. (ä-nē'nä)	173	45.03 N	21.50 E
Anita, Pa. (ȧ-nē'*ȧ*)	111	41.05 N	79.00 W
Aniva, Mys (Pt.), Sov.Un. (mĭs ȧ-nē'vȧ)	204	46.08 N	143.13 E
Aniva, Zaliv (B.), Sov. Un. (zä'lĭf ȧ-nē'vȧ)	204	46.28 N	143.30 E
Anjou, Can.	95a	45.37 N	73.33 W
Anjouan (I.), Comoros (äɴ-zhwäɴ)	227	12.14 S	44.47 E
Ankang, China (än-ĸäŋ)	202	32.38 N	109.10 E
Ankara (Angora), Tur. (än'k*ȧ*-r*ȧ*) (ăn-gō'r*ȧ*)	179	39.55 N	32.50 E
Anklam, G.D.R. (än'kläm)	166	53.52 N	13.43 E
Ankoro, Zaire (ăŋ-kō'rō)	231	6.45 S	26.57 E
Anloga, Ghana	228	5.47 N	0.50 E
Anlong, China (än-loŋ)	203	25.01 N	105.32 E
Anlu, China (än'lo͞o')	203	31.18 N	113.40 E
Anna, Il. (ăn'*ȧ*)	123	37.28 N	89.15 W
Anna, Sov. Un. (än'ä)	175	51.31 N	40.27 E
Annaba (Bône), Alg.	224	36.57 N	7.39 E
Annaberg-Bucholz, G.D.R. (än'ä-bĕrgh)	166	50.35 N	13.02 E
An Nafūd (Des.), Sau. Ar.	192	28.30 N	40.30 E
An Najaf, Iraq (än nä-jäf')	192	32.00 N	44.25 E
An Nakhl, Egypt	191a	29.55 N	33.45 E
Annamese Cordillera (Mts.), Laos-Viet.	206	17.34 N	105.38 E
Annandale, Va.	56d	38.50 N	77.12 W
Annapolis, Md. (ă-năp'ô-lĭs)	112e	39.00 N	76.25 W
Annapolis Royal, Can.	104	44.45 N	65.31 W
Ann Arbor, Mi. (ăn är'bẽr)	110	42.15 N	83.45 W
An-Narrānīyah, Egypt	71a	29.58 N	31.10 E
An Nāṣirīyah, Iraq	192	31.08 N	46.15 E
An Nawfalīyah, Libya	225	30.57 N	17.38 E
Ann, C., Ma. (ăn)	111	42.40 N	70.40 W
Annecy, Fr. (ȧn sē')	169	45.54 N	6.07 E
Annemasse, Fr. (ȧn'mäs')	169	46.09 N	6.13 E
Annen (Neigh.), F.R.G.	63	51.27 N	7.22 E
Annenskoye, Sov. Un. (ä-nĕn'skô-yĕ)	182a	53.09 N	60.25 E
Annet-sur-Marne, Fr.	64c	48.56 N	2.43 E
Annette I., Ak.	98	55.13 N	131.30 W
An-nhon, Viet.	206	13.55 N	109.00 E
Annieopsquotch Mts., Can.	105	48.37 N	57.17 W
Anniston, Al. (ăn'ĭs-t*ŭ*n)	126	33.39 N	85.47 W
Annobón (I.), Equat. Gui.	222	2.00 S	3.30 E
Annonay, Fr. (ȧ-nō-nĕ')	168	45.16 N	4.36 E
Annotto Bay, Jam. (än-nō'tō)	134	18.15 N	76.45 W
An Nuhūd, Sud.	225	12.39 N	28.18 E
Anoka, Mn. (*ȧ*-nō'k*ȧ*)	119g	45.12 N	93.24 W
Anori, Col. (ȧ-nō'rē)	142a	7.01 N	75.09 W
Áno Viánnos, Grc.	172a	35.02 N	25.26 E
Anpu, China (än-po͞o)	203	21.28 N	110.00 E
Anqing, China (än-chĭŋ)	203	30.32 N	117.00 E
Anqiu, China (än-chyō)	200	36.26 N	119.12 E
Ansbach, F.R.G. (äns'bäk)	166	49.18 N	10.35 E
Anschlag, F.R.G.	63	51.10 N	7.29 E
Anse à Veau, Hai. (äɴs' ä-vō')	135	18.30 N	73.25 W
Anse d' Hainault, Hai. (äɴs'dĕnō)	135	18.45 N	74.25 W
Anserma, Col. (ȧ'n-sĕ'r-mȧ)	142a	5.13 N	75.47 W
Ansermanuevo, Col. (ȧ'n-sĕ'r-mȧ-nwĕ'vō)	142a	4.47 N	75.59 W
Anshan, China	202	41.00 N	123.00 E
Anshun, China (än-sho͞on')	203	26.12 N	105.50 E
Anson, Tx. (ăn's*ŭ*n)	124	32.45 N	99.52 W
Anson B., Austl.	214	13.10 S	130.00 E
Ansŏng, Kor. (än'sŭng')	204	37.00 N	127.12 E
Ansongo, Mali	228	15.40 N	0.30 E
Ansonia, Ct. (ăn-sōnĭ-*ȧ*)	111	41.20 N	73.05 W
Antakya, Tur. (än-täk'yä)	179	36.20 N	36.10 E

PLACE (Pronounciation)	PAGE	Lat. °'	Long. °'
Antalya (Adalia), Tur. (än-tä'lē-ä) (ä-dä'lē-ä)	179	37.00 N	30.50 E
Antalya Körfezi (G.), Tur.	179	36.40 N	31.20 E
Antananarivo, Mad.	227	18.51 S	47.40 E
Antarctica,	232	80.15 S	127.00 E
Antartic Pen., Ant.	232	70.00 S	65.00 W
Antelope Cr., Wy. (ăn'tē-lōp)	117	43.29 N	105.42 W
Antequera, Sp. (än-tĕ-kĕ'rä)	170	37.01 N	4.34 W
Anthony, Ks. (ăn'thô-nē)	122	37.08 N	98.01 W
Anti Atlas (Mts.), Mor.	224	28.45 N	9.30 W
Antibes, Fr. (äɴ-tēb')	169	43.36 N	7.12 E
Anticosti, Île d' (I.), Can. (ăn-tĭ-kŏs'tē)	105	49.30 N	62.00 W
Antigo, Wi. (ăn'tĭ-gō)	115	45.09 N	89.11 W
Antigonish, Can. (ăn-tĭ-gô-nēsh')	105	45.35 N	61.55 W
Antigua, Guat. (än-tē'gwä)	132	14.32 N	90.43 W
Antigua, N.A.	129	17.15 N	61.15 W
Antigua (R.), Mex.	131	19.16 N	96.36 W
Antigua and Barbuda, N.A.	129	17.15 N	61.15 W
Antigua Veracruz, Mex. (än-tē'gwä vā-rä-kro͞oz')	131	19.18 N	96.17 W
Antiguo Lago de Texcoco, Vaso del (L.), Mex.	60a	19.30 N	99.00 W
Antilla, Cuba (än-tē'lyä)	135	20.50 N	75.50 W
Antilles, Greater (Is.), N.A.	129	20.30 N	79.15 W
Antilles, Lesser (Is.), N.A.	129	12.15 N	65.00 W
Antioch, Ca. (ăn'tĭ-ŏk)	118b	38.00 N	121.48 W
Antioch, Il.	113a	42.29 N	88.06 W
Antioch, Ne.	114	42.05 N	102.36 W
Antioquia, Col. (än-tē-ō'kēä)	142a	6.34 N	75.49 W
Antioquia (Dept.), Col.	142a	6.48 N	75.42 W
Antímano (Neigh.), Ven.	61a	10.28 N	66.59 W
Antlers, Ok. (ănt'lẽrz)	123	34.14 N	95.38 W
Antofagasta, Chile (än-tô-fä-gäs'tä)	144	23.32 N	70.21 W
Antofalla, Salar de (Des.), Arg. (sȧ-lȧr'de ȧn'tō-fä'lä)	144	26.00 S	67.52 W
Antón, Pan. (än-tōn')	133	8.24 N	80.15 W
Antongila, Helodrano (B.), Mad.	227	16.15 S	50.15 E
Antônio Carlos, Braz. (än-tō'nēo͞o-kȧ'r-lôs)	141a	21.19 S	43.45 W
António Enes, Moz. (ăn-to'nyō ĕn'ĕs)	231	16.14 S	39.58 E
Antonito, Co. (ăn-tô-nē'tō)	122	37.04 N	106.01 W
Antonopole, Sov. Un. (än'tô-nô-pō lyĕ)	174	56.19 N	27.11 E
Antony, Fr.	64c	48.45 N	2.18 E
Antsirabe, Mad. (änt-sē-rä'bā)	227	19.49 S	47.16 E
Antsiranana, Mad.	227	12.18 S	49.16 E
Antsla, Sov. Un. (änt'sl*ȧ*)	174	57.49 N	26.29 E
Antuco (Vol.), Chile (än-to͞o'kō)	144	37.30 S	72.30 W
Antwerp, S. Afr.	71b	26.06 S	28.10 E
Antwerpen (Antwerp), Bel. (änt'wĕrpĕn)	157a	51.13 N	4.24 E
Antwerp, see **Antwerpen**			
Anūpgarh, India (ŭ-no͞op'gŭr)	196	29.22 N	73.20 E
Anuradhapura, Sri Lanka (ŭ-no͞o'rä-dŭ-po͞o'r*ŭ*)	197	8.24 N	80.25 E
Anxi, China (än-shyē)	198	40.36 N	95.49 E
Anyang, China (än'yäng)	200	36.05 N	114.22 E
Anykščiai, Sov. Un. (aniksh-chä'ē)	165	55.34 N	25.04 E
Anzá, Col. (ȧn-zȧ')	142a	6.19 N	75.51 W
Anzhero-Sudzhensk, Sov. Un. (än'zhâ-rô-so͞od'zhĕnsk)	180	56.08 N	86.08 E
Anzio, It. (änt'zē-ō)	171d	41.28 N	12.39 E
Anzoátegui (State), Ven. (ȧn-zôȧ'tē-gē)	143b	9.38 N	64.45 W
Aomori, Jap. (äô-mō'rē)	204	40.45 N	140.52 E
Aosta, It. (ä-ôs'tä)	172	45.45 N	7.20 E
Aoukâr (Pln.), Mauritania	228	18.00 N	9.40 W
Aouk, Bahr (R.), Chad-Cen. Afr. Rep. (ä-o͞ok')	225	9.30 N	20.45 E
Aozou, Chad	194	21.49 N	17.25 E
Apalachicola, Fl. (ăp-*ȧ*-lăch-ĭ-kō'l*ȧ*)	126	29.43 N	84.59 W
Apan, Mex. (ä-pȧ'n)	131a	19.43 N	98.27 W
Apango, Mex. (ä-päŋ'gō)	130	17.41 N	99.22 W
Apaporis (R.), Col. (ä-pä-pô'rĭs)	142	0.48 N	72.32 W
Aparri, Phil. (ä-pär'rē)	206	18.15 N	121.40 E
Apasco, Mex. (ä-pȧ's-kō)	130	20.33 N	100.43 W
Apatin, Yugo. (ŏ'pŏ-tĭn)	173	45.40 N	19.00 E
Apatzingán de la Constitución, Mex. (ä-pät-zĭŋ-gän'dā lä cōn-stĭ-to͞o-sē-ōn')	130	19.07 N	102.21 W
Apeldoorn, Neth. (ä'pĕl-do͞orn)	163	52.14 N	5.55 E
Apese (Neigh.), Nig.	71d	6.25 N	3.25 E
Apía, Col. (ä-pē'ä)	142a	5.07 N	75.58 W
Apipilulco, Mex. (ä-pĭ-pĭ-lo͞ol'kō)	130	18.09 N	99.40 W
Apishapa (R.), Co. (ăp-ĭ-shä'p*ȧ*)	122	37.40 N	104.08 W
Apizaco, Mex. (ä-pē-zä'kō)	130	19.18 N	98.11 W
Aplerbeck (Neigh.), F.R.G.	63	51.29 N	7.33 E
Apo (Mtn.), Phil. (ä'pō)	207	6.56 N	125.05 E
Apopka, Fl. (ä-pŏp'k*ȧ*)	127a	28.37 N	81.30 W
Apopka (L.), Fl.	127a	28.38 N	81.50 W
Apoquindo, Chile	61b	33.24 S	70.32 W
Apostle Is., Wi. (ă-pŏs'l)	115	47.05 N	90.55 W
Appalachia, Va. (ăp*ȧ*-lăch'ĭ-*ȧ*)	126	36.54 N	82.49 W
Appalachian Mts., U.S. (ăp-*ȧ*-lăch'ĭ-*ȧ*n)	109	37.20 N	82.00 W
Appalachicola R., Fl. (ăp*ȧ*-lăch'ĭ-cōlă)	126	30.11 N	85.00 W
Äppelbo, Swe. (ĕp-*ĕ*l-bo͞o)	164	60.30 N	14.02 E
Appelhülsen, F.R.G. (ä'pĕl-hül'sĕn)	169c	51.55 N	7.26 E
Appennino (Mts.), It. (äp-pĕn-nē'nō)	172	43.48 N	11.06 E
Appleton, Mn. (ăp'l-t*ŭ*n)	114	45.10 N	96.01 W
Appleton, Wi.	115	44.14 N	88.27 W
Appleton City, Mo.	123	38.10 N	94.02 W
Appomattox (R.), Va. (ăp-ô-măt'*ŭ*ks)	127	37.22 N	78.09 W
Aprília, It. (*ȧ*-prē'ly*ȧ*)	171d	41.36 N	12.40 E
Apsheronskiy, P-Ov. (Pen.), Sov. Un.	179	40.20 N	50.30 E
Apt, Fr. (äpt)	169	43.54 N	5.19 E
Apulia (Reg.), see **Puglia**			
Apure (R.), Ven. (ä-po͞o'rä)	142	8.08 N	68.46 W
Apurimac (R.), Peru (ä-po͞o-rē-mäk')	142	11.39 S	73.48 W
Aqaba, G. of, Asia (ä'kȧ-bȧ)	161	28.30 N	34.40 E

PLACE (Pronounciation)	PAGE	Lat. °'	Long. °'
Aqabah, Wādī al (R.), Egypt	191a	29.48 N	34.05 E
Aquasco, Md. (ȧ'gwȧ'scō)	112e	38.35 N	76.44 W
Aquidauana, Braz. (ä-kē-däwä'nä)	143	20.24 S	55.46 W
Aquin, Hai. (ä-kăn')	135	18.20 N	73.25 W
Ara (R.), Jap. (ä-rä)	205a	35.40 N	139.52 E
'Arabah, Wādī, Egypt	223b	29.02 N	32.10 E
Arabatskaya Strelka (Tongue of Arabat) (Spit), Sov. Un. (ä-rä-băt' sk*ȧ*-y*ȧ* strĕl'k*ȧ*) (ä-r*ȧ*-băt')	175	45.50 N	35.05 E
Arab, Baḥr al- (R.), Sud.	225	9.46 N	26.52 E
Arabi, La.	112d	29.58 N	90.01 W
Arabian Des. (Aş Şaḥrā' ash Sharqīyah), Egypt (*ȧ*-rā'bĭ-*ă*n)	223b	27.06 N	32.49 E
Arabian Pen., Asia	222	28.00 N	40.00 E
Arabian Sea, Asia (*ȧ*-rā'bĭ-*ă*n)	190	16.00 N	65.15 E
Aracaju, Braz. (ä-rä'kä-zho͞o')	143	11.00 S	37.01 W
Aracati, Braz. (ä-rä'kä-tē')	143	4.31 S	37.41 W
Araçatuba, Braz. (ä-rä-sȧ-to͞o'bä)	143	21.14 S	50.19 W
Aracena, Sp.	170	37.53 N	6.34 W
Aracruz, Braz. (ä-rä-kro͞o's)	143	19.58 S	40.11 W
Araçuaí, Braz. (ä-rä-so͞o-ä-ē')	143	16.57 S	41.56 W
'Arad, Isr.	191a	31.20 N	35.15 E
Arad, Rom. (ŏ'rŏd)	167	46.10 N	21.18 E
Aradabīl, Iran	192	38.15 N	48.00 E
Arafura Sea, Oceania (ä-rä-fo͞o'rä)	208	8.40 S	130.00 E
Aragon (Reg.), Sp. (ä-rä-gōn')	171	40.55 N	0.45 W
Aragón (R.), Sp.	170	42.35 N	1.10 W
Aragua (State), Ven. (ä-rä'gwä)	143b	10.00 N	67.05 W
Aragua de Barcelona, Ven. (ä-rä'gwä dā bär-thā-lō'nä)	143b	9.29 N	64.48 W
Araguaía (R.), Braz. (ä-rä-gwä'yä)	143	8.37 S	49.43 W
Araguari, Braz. (ä-rä-gwä'rē)	143	18.43 S	48.03 W
Araguatins, Braz. (ä-rä-gwä-tēns)	143	5.41 S	48.04 W
Aragüita, Ven. (ärȧ-gwē'tȧ)	143b	10.13 N	66.28 W
Araj (Oasis), Egypt (ä-räj')	161	29.05 N	26.51 E
Arāk, Iran	192	34.08 N	49.57 E
Arakan Yoma (Mts.), Bur. (ŭ-rŭ-kŭn'yō'mȧ)	198	19.51 N	94.13 E
Arakawa (Neigh.), Jap.	69a	35.47 N	139.44 E
Arakhthos (R.), Grc. (är'äĸ-thôs)	173	39.10 N	21.05 E
Arakpur (Neigh.), India	67d	28.35 N	77.10 E
Aral Sea, see **Aral'skoye More**			
Aral'sk, Sov. Un. (*ȧ*-rälsk')	180	46.47 N	62.00 E
Aral'skoye More (Aral Sea), Sov. Un.	155	45.17 N	60.02 E
Aralsor (L.), Sov. Un. (ȧ-räl'sôr')	179	49.00 N	48.20 E
Aramberri, Mex. (ä-räm-bĕr-rē')	130	24.05 N	99.47 W
Arana, Sierra (Mts.), Sp.	170	37.17 N	3.28 W
Aranda de Duero, Sp. (ä-rän'dä dā dwā'rō)	170	41.43 N	3.45 W
Arandas, Mex. (ä-rän'däs)	130	20.43 N	102.18 W
Aran I., Ire. (ăr'ăn)	162	54.58 N	8.33 W
Aran Is., Ire.	162	53.04 N	9.59 W
Aranjuez, Sp. (ä-rän-hwāth')	170	40.02 N	3.24 W
Aransas Pass, Tx. (*ȧ*-răn'sȧs pȧs)	125	27.55 N	97.09 W
Araouane, Mali	228	18.54 N	3.33 W
Arapkir, Tur. (ä-räp-kēr')	179	39.00 N	38.10 E
Araraquara, Braz. (ä-rä-rä-kwȧ'rä)	143	21.47 S	48.08 W
Araras, Braz. (ä-rȧ'rȧs)	141a	22.21 S	47.22 W
Araras, Serra das (Mts.), Braz. (sĕ'r-rä-däs-ä-rä'räs)	143	18.03 S	53.23 W
Araras, Serra das (Mts.), Braz.	144b	22.24 S	43.15 W
Araras, Serra das (Mts.), Braz.	144	23.30 S	53.00 W
Ararat, Austl. (ăr'*ȧ*răt)	216	37.17 S	142.56 E
Ararat (Mtn.), Tur.	179	39.50 N	44.20 E
Arari (L.), Braz. (ä-rȧ'rē)	143	0.30 S	48.50 W
Araripe, Chapada do (Plain), Braz. (shä-pä'dä-dô-ä-rä-rē'pĕ)	143	5.55 S	40.42 W
Araruama, Braz. (ä-rä-ro͞o-ä'mä)	141a	22.53 S	42.19 W
Araruama, Lagoa de (L.), Braz. (lȧ-gôä-dĕ-ä-rä-ro͞o-ä'mä)	141a	23.00 S	42.15 W
Aras (R.), Iran-Sov. Un. (ä-räs)	179	39.15 N	47.10 E
Aratuípe, Braz. (ä-rä-to͞o-ē'pĕ)	143	13.12 S	38.58 W
Arauca, Col. (ä-rou'kä)	142	6.56 N	70.45 W
Arauca (R.), Ven.	142	7.13 N	68.43 W
Aravaca (Neigh.), Sp.	65b	40.28 N	3.46 W
Aravalli Ra., India (ä-rä'vŭ-lē)	196	24.15 N	72.40 E
Araxá, Braz. (ä-rä-shȧ')	143	19.41 S	46.46 W
Araya, Punta de (Pt.), Ven. (pŭn'tȧ-dĕ-ä-rä'yȧ)	143b	10.40 N	64.15 W
Arayat, Phil. (ä-rä'yät)	207a	15.10 N	120.44 E
'Arbi, Sud.	225	20.36 N	29.57 E
Arboga, Swe. (är-bō'gä)	164	59.26 N	15.50 E
Arborea, It. (är-bō-rē'ä)	172	39.50 N	8.36 E
Arbroath, Scot. (är-brōth')	162	56.36 N	2.25 W
Arcachon, Fr. (är-kä-shôɴ')	168	44.39 N	1.12 W
Arcachon, Bassin d' (Basin), Fr. (bä-sĕn' där-kä-shôn')	168	44.42 N	1.50 W
Arcadia, Ca. (är-kā'dĭ-*ȧ*)	119a	34.08 N	118.02 W
Arcadia, Fl.	127a	27.12 N	81.51 W
Arcadia, La.	125	32.33 N	92.56 W
Arcadia, Wi.	115	44.15 N	91.30 W
Arcata, Ca. (är-kȧ't*ȧ*)	116	40.54 N	124.05 W
Arc de Triomphe (P. Int.), Fr.	64c	48.53 N	2.17 E
Arc Dome Mtn., Nv. (ärk dōm)	120	38.51 N	117.21 W
Arcelia, Mex. (är-sä'lē-ä)	130	18.19 N	100.14 W
Archbald, Pa. (ärch'bôld)	111	41.30 N	75.35 W
Arches Natl. Park, Ut. (är'ches)	121	38.45 N	109.35 W
Archidona, Ec. (är-chē-do'nä)	142	1.01 S	77.49 W
Archidona, Sp. (är-chē-dō'nä)	170	37.08 N	4.24 W
Arcis-sur-Aube, Fr. (är-sēs'sûr-ōb')	168	48.31 N	4.04 E
Arco, Id. (är'kô)	117	43.39 N	113.15 W
Arcola, Tx.	125a	29.30 N	95.28 W
Arcola, Va. (ăr'cōlă)	112e	38.57 N	77.32 W
Arcos de la Frontera, Sp. (är'kōs-dĕ-lä-frōn-tē'rä)	170	36.44 N	5.48 W
Arctic Ocean (ärk'tĭk)	91		
Arcueil, Fr.	64c	48.48 N	2.20 E
Arda (R.), Bul. (är'dä)	173	41.36 N	25.18 E
Ardabīl, Iran	195	38.15 N	48.18 E
Ardahan, Tur. (är-dȧ-hän')	179	41.10 N	42.40 E
Ardatov, Sov. Un. (är-dȧ-tôf')	178	54.58 N	46.10 E

ăt; finăl; rāte; senāte; ärm; ȧsk; sofȧ; fâre; ch-choose; dh-as th in other; bē; ēvent; bĕt; recĕnt; cratẽr; g-gō; gh-guttural g; bĭt; ĭ-short neutral; rīde; ĸ-guttural k as ch in German ich;

PLACE (Pronunciation)	PAGE	Lat. °′	Long. °′
Ardennes (Mts.), Bel. (ȧr-dĕn')	163	50.01 N	5.12 E
Ardey (Neigh.), F.R.G.	63	51.26 N	7.23 E
Ardila (R.), Port. (är-dē'lȧ)	170	38.10 N	7.15 W
Ardmore, Md.	56d	38.56 N	76.52 W
Ardmore, Ok. (ärd'mōr)	123	34.10 N	97.08 W
Ardmore, Pa.	112f	40.01 N	75.18 W
Ardrossan, Can. (är-dros'ȧn)	95g	53.33 N	113.08 W
Ardsley, Eng. (ärdz'lē)	156	53.43 N	1.33 W
Åre, Swe.	158	63.12 N	13.12 E
Arecibo, P.R. (ä-rā-sē'bō)	129b	18.28 N	66.45 W
Areeiro, Port.	65d	38.39 N	9.12 W
Areia Branca, Braz. (ä-rĕ'yä-brä'n-kä)	143	4.58 S	37.02 W
Arena, Pt., Ca. (ä-rā'nȧ)	120	38.57 N	123.40 W
Arenas de San Pedro, Sp. (ä-rā'nås dā sän pā'drō)	170	40.12 N	5.04 W
Arenas, Punta (Pt.), Ven. (pōō'n-tä-rĕ'näs)	143b	10.57 N	64.24 W
Arendal, Nor. (ä'rĕn-däl)	164	58.29 N	8.44 E
Arendonk, Bel.	157a	51.19 N	5.07 E
Arequipa, Peru (ä-rå-kē'pä)	142	16.27 S	71.30 W
Arezzo, It. (ä-rĕt'sō)	172	43.28 N	11.54 E
Arga (R.), Sp. (är'gä)	170	42.35 N	1.55 W
Arganda, Sp. (är-gän'dä)	171a	40.18 N	3.27 W
Argazi (L.), Sov. Un. (är'gä-zĭ)	182a	55.24 N	60.37 E
Argazi R., Sov. Un.	182a	55.33 N	57.30 E
Argentan, Fr. (är-zhäN-täN')	168	48.45 N	0.01 W
Argentat, Fr. (ȧr-zhäN-ta')	168	45.07 N	1.57 E
Argenteuil, Fr. (är-zhäN-tû'y')	169b	48.56 N	2.15 E
Argentina, S.A. (är-jĕn-tē'nȧ)	140	35.30 S	67.00 W
Argentino (L.), Arg. (är-Kĕn-tē'nō)	144	50.15 S	72.45 W
Argenton-sur-Creuse, Fr. (är-zhäN'tôN-sür-krôs)	168	46.34 N	1.28 E
Argeş (R.), Rom. (ȧr'zhĕsh)	173	44.27 N	25.22 E
Argolikos Kólpos (G.), Grc.	173	37.20 N	23.00 E
Argonne (Mts.), Fr. (ä'r-gôn)	168	49.21 N	5.54 E
Argos, Grc. (är'gŏs)	173	37.38 N	22.45 E
Argostólion, Grc. (är-gŏs-tō'lē-ōn)	173	38.10 N	20.30 E
Arguello, Pt., Ca. (är-gwāl'yō)	120	34.35 N	120.40 W
Argungu, Nig.	229	12.45 N	4.31 E
Argun R., China-Sov. Un. (ȧr-gōōn')	181	50.15 N	118.45 E
Argyle, Can. (är'gīl)	95f	50.11 N	97.27 W
Argyle, Mn.	114	48.21 N	96.48 W
Århus, Den. (ôr'hōōs)	164	56.09 N	10.10 E
Ariakeno-Umi (Sea), Jap. (ä-rē'ä-Kā'nō ōō'nē)	205	33.03 N	130.18 E
Ariake-Wan (B.), Jap. (ä'rē-ä'kä wän)	205	31.19 N	131.15 E
Ariano, It. (ä-rē-ä'nō)	172	41.09 N	15.11 E
Ariari (R.), Col. (ä-ryä'rē)	142a	3.34 N	73.42 W
Aribinda, Upper Volta	228	14.14 N	0.52 W
Arica, Chile (ä-rē'kä)	142	18.34 S	70.14 W
Arichat, Can. (ä-rĭ-shät')	105	45.31 N	61.01 W
Ariège (R.), Fr. (ȧ-rē-ëzh')	168	43.26 N	1.29 E
Ariel, Wa. (ā'rĭ-ĕl)	118c	45.57 N	122.34 W
Arieşul (R.), Rom. (ä-rē-ā'shōōl)	167	46.25 N	23.15 E
Ariguanabo, L. de, Cuba (lä'gô-dĕ-ä-rē-gwä-nä'bô)	135a	22.17 N	82.33 W
Arikaree (R.), Co. (ä-rĭ-kȧ-rē')	122	39.51 N	102.18 W
Arima, Jap. (ä'rē-mä')	205b	34.48 N	135.16 E
Aringay, Phil. (ä-rĭŋ-gä'ē)	207a	16.25 N	120.20 E
Arino (Neigh.), Jap.	69b	34.50 N	135.14 E
Arinos (R.), Braz. (ä-rē'nōzh)	143	12.09 S	56.49 W
Arīḥā (Jericho), Jordan	191a	31.51 N	35.28 E
'Arīsh, Wādī al (R.), Egypt (ȧ-rēsh')	191a	30.36 N	34.07 E
Aripuanã (R.), Braz. (ȧ-rē-pwän'yȧ)	143	7.06 S	60.29 W
Aristazabal I., Can.	98	52.30 N	129.20 W
Arizona (State), U.S. (ăr-ĭ-zō'nȧ)	108	34.00 N	113.00 W
Arjona, Sp. (är-hō'nä)	170	37.58 N	4.03 W
Arka (R.), Sov. Un.	181	60.12 N	142.30 E
Arkabutla Res., Ms. (är-kȧ-bŭt'lȧ)	126	34.48 N	90.00 W
Arkadelphia, Ar. (är-kȧ-dĕl'fĭ-ȧ)	123	34.06 N	93.05 W
Arkansas (State), U.S. (är'kăn-sô) (är-kăn'sȧs)	109	34.50 N	93.40 W
Arkansas City, Ks.	123	37.04 N	97.02 W
Arkansas R., Ok.	123	35.20 N	94.56 W
Arkhangelsk (Archangel), Sov. Un. (ȧr-kän'gĕlsk)	178	64.30 N	40.25 E
Arkhangel'skiy, Sov. Un. (är-kän-gĕl'skĭ)	182a	52.52 N	61.53 E
Arkhangel'skoye, Sov. Un. (är-kän-gĕl'skô-yĕ)	182a	54.25 N	56.48 E
Arklow, Ire. (ärk'lō)	162	52.47 N	6.10 W
Arkona, Kap (C.), G.D.R. (är'kō-nä)	164	54.43 N	13.43 E
Arkonam, India (ăr-kō-năm')	197	13.05 N	79.43 E
Arlanza (R.), Sp. (är-län-thä')	170	42.08 N	3.45 W
Arlanzón (R.), Sp. (är-län-thōn')	170	42.12 N	3.58 W
Arlberg Tun., Aus. (ärl'bĕrgh)	166	47.05 N	10.15 E
Arles, Fr. (ärl)	168	43.42 N	4.38 E
Arlington, Ga. (är'lĭng-tun')	126	31.25 N	84.42 W
Arlington, Ma.	105a	42.26 N	71.13 W
Arlington, S. Afr.	223d	28.02 S	27.52 E
Arlington, SD (är'lēng-tŭn)	114	44.23 N	97.09 W
Arlington, Tx. (är'lĭng-tŭn)	119c	32.44 N	97.07 W
Arlington, Va.	112e	38.55 N	77.10 W
Arlington, Vt.	111	43.05 N	73.05 W
Arlington, Wa.	118a	48.11 N	122.08 W
Arlington Heights, Il. (är'lēng-tŭn-hī'ts)	113a	42.05 N	87.59 W
Arlington National Cemetery (P. Int.), Va.	56d	38.53 N	77.04 W
Arltunga, Austl. (ärl-tōōŋ'gȧ)	214	23.19 S	134.45 E
Arma, Ks. (är'mȧ)	123	37.34 N	94.43 W
Armagh, Can. (är-mä') (är-mäK')	95b	46.45 N	70.36 W
Armagh, N. Ire.	162	54.21 N	6.25 W
Armant, Egypt (är-mänt')	223b	25.37 N	32.32 E
Armaro, Col. (är-mȧ'rō)	142a	4.58 N	74.54 W
Armavir, Sov. Un. (är-mȧ-vĭr')	179	45.00 N	41.00 E
Armenia, Col. (ȧr-mē'nē̇ä)	142a	4.33 N	75.40 W
Armenia, Sal. (är-mā'nē-ä)	132	13.44 N	89.31 W
Armenian, S. S. R., Sov. Un.	176	41.00 N	44.39 E
Armentières, Fr. (ȧr-mäN-tyâr')	168	50.43 N	2.53 E
Armeria, Rio de (R.), Mex. (rē'ō-dĕ-är-mȧ-rē'ä)	130	19.36 N	104.10 W
Armherstburg, Can. (ärm'hĕrst-bōōrgh)	113b	42.06 N	83.06 W
Armidale, Austl. (är'mĭ-dāl)	216	30.27 S	151.50 E
Armour, SD (är'mēr)	114	43.18 N	98.21 W
Armstrong Station, Can. (ärm'strŏng)	102	50.21 N	89.00 W
Armyansk, Sov. Un. (ärm'yȧnsk)	175	46.06 N	33.42 E
Arnedo, Sp. (är-nā'dō)	170	42.12 N	2.03 W
Arnhem, Neth. (ärn'hĕm)	163	51.58 N	5.56 E
Arnhem, C., Austl.	214	12.15 S	137.00 E
Arnhem Land, (Reg.), Austl. (ärn'hĕm-lănd)	214	13.15 S	133.00 E
Arno (R.), It. (ä'r-nô)	172	43.45 N	10.42 E
Arnold, Eng. (är'nŭld)	156	53.00 N	1.08 W
Arnold, Mn. (ȧr'nŭld)	119h	46.53 N	92.06 W
Arnold, Pa.	113e	40.35 N	79.45 W
Arnouville-lès-Gonesse, Fr.	64c	49.00 N	2.25 E
Arnprior, Can. (ärn-prī'ēr)	111	45.25 N	76.20 W
Arnsberg, F.R.G. (ärns'bĕrgh)	163	51.25 N	8.02 E
Arnstadt, G.D.R. (ärn'shtät)	166	50.51 N	10.57 E
Aroab, Namibia (är'ō-ȧb)	226	25.40 S	19.45 E
Aroostook (R.), Me. (ȧ-rōōs'tōōk)	104	46.44 N	68.15 W
Aroroy, Phil. (ä-rô-rō'ē)	207a	12.30 N	123.24 E
Arpajon, Fr. (är-pä-jō'n)	169b	48.35 N	2.15 E
Arpoador, Ponta do (Pt.), Braz. (pô'n-tä-dō-är'pōä-dō'r)	144b	22.59 S	43.11 W
Arraiolos, Port. (är-rī-ō'lōzh)	170	38.47 N	7.59 W
Ar Ramādī, Iraq	192	33.30 N	43.12 E
Arran, Island of, Scot. (ă'răn)	162	55.25 N	5.25 W
Ar Rank, Sud.	225	11.45 N	32.53 E
Arras, Fr. (ȧ-räs')	168	50.21 N	2.40 E
Ar Rawḍah, Egypt	223b	27.47 N	30.52 E
Arrecifes, Arg. (är-rå-sē'fås)	141c	34.03 S	60.05 W
Arrecifes (R.), Arg.	141c	34.07 S	59.50 W
Arrée, Mts. d', Fr. (är-rā')	168	48.27 N	4.00 W
Arriaga, Mex. (är-rē̇ä'gä)	131	16.15 N	93.54 W
Ar Riyāḍ, see Riyadh			
Arrone (R.), It.	171d	41.57 N	12.17 E
Arrowhead, L., Ca. (lăk ăr'ōhĕd)	119a	34.17 N	117.13 W
Arrow R., Mt. (ăr'ō)	117	47.29 N	109.53 W
Arrowrock Res., Id. (ăr'ō-rŏk)	116	43.40 N	115.30 W
Arroya Arena, Cuba (är-rō'yä-rĕ'nä)	135a	23.01 N	82.30 W
Arroyo de la Luz, Sp. (är-rō'yō-dĕ-lä-lōō'z)	170	39.39 N	6.46 W
Arroyo Grande (R.), Mex. (är-rô'yō-grä'n-dĕ)	130	23.30 N	98.45 W
Arroyo Seco, Mex. (är-rō'yō sā'kō)	130	21.31 N	99.44 W
Ar Rub' Al Khālī (Des.), Sau. Ar.	192	20.30 N	49.15 E
Ar-Ruṣayriş, Sud.	225	11.38 N	34.42 E
Ar-Ruṭbah, Iraq	195	33.02 N	40.17 E
Arsen'yev, Sov. Un.	181	44.13 N	133.32 E
Arsinskiy, Sov. Un. (är-sĭn'skĭ)	182a	53.46 N	59.54 E
Árta, Grc. (är'tä)	173	39.08 N	21.02 E
Artarmon, Austl.	70a	33.49 S	151.11 E
Arteaga, Mex. (är-tā-ä'gä)	124	25.28 N	100.50 W
Artëm, Sov. Un. (ar-tyôm')	181	43.28 N	132.29 E
Artemisa, Cuba (är-tå-mē'sä)	134	22.50 N	82.45 W
Artëmovsk, Sov. Un. (ȧr-tyŏm'ōfsk)	175	48.37 N	38.00 E
Arteria, Ca.	59	33.52 N	118.05 W
Artesia, NM (är-tē'sĭ-ȧ)	122	32.44 N	104.23 W
Artesian Basin, The, Austl. (är-tē'zhăn)	216	26.45 S	141.40 E
Arthabaska, Can.	104	46.03 N	71.54 W
Arthur's Town, Ba.	135	24.40 N	75.40 W
Arti, Sov. Un. (är'tĭ)	182a	56.20 N	58.38 E
Artibonite (R.), Hai. (är-tē-bō-nē'tā)	135	19.00 N	72.25 W
Artigas (Neigh.), Ven.	61a	10.30 N	66.56 W
Arua, Ug. (ä'rōō-ä)	231	3.01 N	30.55 E
Aruba, (I.), Neth. Antilles (ä-rōō'bȧ)	142	12.29 N	70.00 W
Aru, Kepulauan (Is.), Indon.	207	6.20 S	133.00 E
Arunachal Pradesh (Union Ter.), India	198	27.35 N	92.56 E
Arundel Gardens, Md.	56c	39.13 N	76.37 W
Arundel Village, Md.	56c	39.13 N	76.36 W
Arusha, Tan. (ȧ-rōō'shä)	231	3.22 S	36.41 E
Arvida, Can.	103	48.26 N	71.11 W
Arvika, Swe. (är-vē'kȧ)	164	59.41 N	12.35 E
Arzamas, Sov. Un. (är-zä-mäs')	178	55.20 N	43.52 E
Arziw, Alg.	160	35.50 N	0.20 W
Arzua, Sp. (är-thōō'ä)	170	42.54 N	8.19 W
As, Czech. (äsh')	166	50.12 N	12.13 E
Asahi-Gawa (Strm.), Jap. (ä-sä'hē-gä'wä)	205	35.01 N	133.40 E
Asahikawa, Jap.	204	43.50 N	142.09 E
Asaka, Jap. (ä-sä'kä)	205a	35.47 N	139.36 E
Asālafpur (Neigh.), India	67d	28.38 N	77.05 E
Asansol, India	196	23.45 N	86.58 E
Asbest, Sov. Un. (äs-bĕst')	182a	57.02 N	61.28 E
Asbestos, Can. (ăs-bĕs'tōs)	104	45.49 N	71.52 W
Asbestovskiy, Sov. Un.	182a	57.46 N	61.23 E
Asbury Park, NJ (ăz'bĕr-ĭ)	112a	40.13 N	74.01 W
Ascención, Bahía de la (B.), Mex. (bä-ē'ä-dĕ-lä-äs-sĕn-sē-ōn')	132a	19.39 N	87.30 W
Ascensión, Mex. (äs-sĕn-sē-ōn')	130	24.21 N	99.54 W
Ascension (I.), Atl. O. (ȧ-sĕn'shŭn)	222	8.00 S	13.00 W
Ascent, S. Afr. (ăs-ĕnt')	223d	27.14 S	29.06 E
Aschaffenburg, F.R.G. (ä-shäf'ĕn-bōōrgh)	166	49.58 N	9.12 E
Ascheberg, F.R.G. (ä'shĕ-bĕrg)	169c	51.47 N	7.38 E
Aschersleben, G.D.R. (äsh'ērs-lā-bĕn)	166	51.46 N	11.28 E
Ascoli Piceno, It. (äs'kô-lēpē-chā'nō)	172	42.50 N	13.55 E
Aseb, Eth.	223a	12.52 N	43.39 E
Asenovgrad, Bul.	173	42.00 N	24.49 E
Aseri, Sov. Un. (ȧ'sĕ-rĭ)	174	59.26 N	26.58 E
Asfi, see Safi			
Asha, Sov. Un. (ä'shä)	182a	55.01 N	57.17 E
Ashabula (L.), ND (ăsh'ȧ-bū-lȧ)	114	47.07 N	97.51 W
Ashan, Sov. Un. (ä'shän)	182a	57.08 N	56.25 E
Ashbourne, Eng. (ăsh'bŭrn)	156	53.01 N	1.44 W
Ashburn, Ga. (ăsh'bŭrn)	126	31.42 N	83.42 W
Ashburn, Va.	112e	39.02 N	77.30 W
Ashburton (R.), Austl. (ăsh'bûr-tŭn)	214	22.30 S	115.30 E
Ashby-de-la-Zouch, Eng. (ăsh'bĭ-dē-lȧ zōōsh')	156	52.44 N	1.23 W
Ashdod, Isr.	191a	31.46 N	34.39 E
Ashdown, Ar. (ăsh'doun)	123	33.41 N	94.07 W
Asheboro, NC (ăsh'bŭr-ô)	127	35.41 N	79.50 W
Asherton, Tx. (ăsh'ēr-tŭn)	124	28.26 N	99.45 W
Asheville, NC (ăsh'vĭl)	127	35.35 N	82.35 W
Ashfield, Austl.	70a	33.53 S	151.08 E
Ashford, Eng.	62	51.26 N	0.27 W
Ash Fork, Az.	121	35.13 N	112.29 W
Ashikaga, Jap. (ä'shē-kä'gȧ)	205	36.22 N	139.26 E
Ashiya, Jap. (ä'shē-yä')	205	33.54 N	130.40 E
Ashiya, Jap.	205b	34.44 N	135.18 E
Ashizuri-Zaki (Pt.), Jap. (ä-shē-zōō-rē zä-kē)	205	32.43 N	133.04 E
Ashkhabad, Sov. Un. (ŭsh-kä-bät')	155	39.45 N	58.13 E
Ashland, Al. (ăsh'lȧnd)	126	33.15 N	85.50 W
Ashland, Ks.	122	37.11 N	99.46 W
Ashland, Ky.	110	38.25 N	82.40 W
Ashland, Ma.	105a	42.16 N	71.28 W
Ashland, Me.	104	46.37 N	68.26 W
Ashland, Ne.	114	41.02 N	96.23 W
Ashland, Oh.	110	40.50 N	82.15 W
Ashland, Or.	116	42.12 N	122.42 W
Ashland, Pa.	111	40.45 N	76.20 W
Ashland, Wi.	115	46.34 N	90.55 W
Ashley, Eng.	64b	53.21 N	2.20 W
Ashley, ND (ăsh'lē)	114	46.03 N	99.23 W
Ashley, Pa.	111	41.15 N	75.55 W
Ashley Green, Eng.	62	51.44 N	0.35 W
Ashmore Rf., Indon. (ăsh'mōr)	206	12.08 S	122.45 E
Ashmūn, Egypt (ȧsh-mōōn')	223b	30.19 N	30.57 E
Ashqelon, Isr. (äsh'kĕ-lōn)	191a	31.40 N	34.36 E
Ash Shabb, Egypt (shĕb)	225	22.34 N	29.52 E
Ash Shallūfah, Egypt (shäl'lōō-fȧ)	223c	30.09 N	32.33 E
Ash Shaqrā', Sau. Ar.	192	25.10 N	45.08 E
Ash Shāriqah, U.A.E.	195	25.22 N	55.23 E
Ash Shawbak, Jordan	191a	30.31 N	35.35 E
Ash Shiḥr, P.D.R. of Yem.	192	14.45 N	49.32 E
Ashtabula, Oh. (ăsh-tȧ-bū'lȧ)	110	41.55 N	80.50 W
Ashtead, Eng.	62	51.19 N	0.18 W
Ashton, Id. (ăsh'tŭn)	117	44.04 N	111.28 W
Ashton-in-Makerfield, Eng. (ăsh'tŭn-ĭn-măk'ēr-fēld)	156	53.29 N	2.39 W
Ashton-under-Lyne, Eng. (ăsh'tŭn-ŭn-dēr-līn')	156	53.29 N	2.04 W
Ashton upon Mersey, Eng.	64b	53.26 N	2.19 W
Ashuanipi (L.), Can. (ăsh-wȧ-nĭp'ĭ)	97	52.40 N	67.42 W
Ashukino, Sov. Un. (ȧ-shōō'kinô)	182b	56.10 N	37.57 E
Asia Minor, Asia (ā'zhȧ)	155	38.18 N	31.18 E
Asia (ā'zhȧ)	190		
Asientos, Mex. (ä-sē-ĕn'tōs)	130	22.13 N	102.05 W
Asilah, Mor.	170	35.30 N	6.05 W
Asinara (I.), It.	172	41.02 N	8.22 E
Asinara, Golfo dell' (G.), It. (gôl'fô-dĕl-ä-sē-nä'rä)	172	40.58 N	8.28 E
Asīr (Reg.), Sau. Ar. (ä-sēr')	192	19.30 N	42.00 E
Asir, Ras (C.), Som.	223a	11.55 N	51.30 E
Askarovo, Sov. Un. (äs-kä-rô'vô)	182a	53.21 N	58.32 E
Askersund, Swe. (äs'kĕr-sōōnd)	164	58.43 N	14.53 E
Askino, Sov. Un. (äs'kĭ-nô)	182a	56.06 N	56.29 E
Asmera, Eth. (äs-mä'rä)	225	15.17 N	38.56 E
Asnieres, Fr. (ä-nyâr')	169b	48.55 N	2.18 E
Asosa, Eth.	225	10.13 N	34.28 E
Asotin, Wa. (ȧ-sō'tĭn)	116	46.19 N	117.01 W
Aspen, Co. (ăs'pĕn)	121	39.15 N	106.55 W
Asperen, Neth.	157a	51.52 N	5.07 E
Aspern (Neigh.), Aus.	66e	48.13 N	16.29 E
Aspinwall, Pa.	57b	40.30 N	79.55 W
Aspy B., Can. (ăs'pē)	105	46.55 N	60.25 W
Aş Şaff, Egypt	223b	29.33 N	31.23 E
Aş Şaḥrā' al Lībīyah, see Libyan Des.			
Aş Şaḥrā' ash Sharqīyah, see Arabian Des.			
As Sallūm, Egypt	225	31.34 N	25.09 E
As Salt, Jordan	191a	32.02 N	35.44 E
Assam (State), India (ăs-săm')	196	26.00 N	91.00 E
As Samāwah, Iraq	195	31.18 N	45.17 E
Asseln (Neigh.), F.R.G.	63	51.32 N	7.35 E
Assens, Den. (äs'sĕns)	164	55.16 N	9.54 E
As Sinbillāwayn, Egypt	223b	30.53 N	31.37 E
Assini, Ivory Coast. (ä-sē-nē')	224	4.52 N	3.16 W
Assiniboia, Can.	100	49.38 N	105.59 W
Assiniboine (R.), Can. (ă-sĭn'ĭ-boin)	100	50.03 N	97.57 W
Assiniboine, Mt., Can.	99	50.52 N	115.39 W
Assis, Braz. (ä-sē's)	143	22.39 S	50.21 W
Assisi, It.	172	43.04 N	12.37 E
As-Sudd (Reg.), Sud.	225	8.45 N	30.45 E
As Sulaymānīyah, Iraq	192	35.47 N	45.23 E
As Sulaymānīyah, Sau. Ar.	195	24.09 N	46.19 E
As Suwaydā', Syr.	192	32.41 N	36.41 E
As Suways (Suez), Egypt	223c	29.58 N	32.34 E
Astakós, Grc. (äs'tä-kôs)	173	38.42 N	21.00 E
Astara, Sov. Un.	179	38.30 N	48.50 E
Asti, It. (äs'tē)	172	44.54 N	8.12 E
Astipálaia (I.), Grc.	161	36.31 N	26.19 E
Astley Bridge, Eng.	64b	53.36 N	2.26 W
Astorga, Sp. (äs-tôr'gä)	170	42.28 N	6.03 W
Astoria (Neigh.), NY	55	40.46 N	73.55 W
Astoria, Or. (äs-tō'rĭ-ȧ)	118c	46.11 N	123.51 W
Astrakhan' Sov. Un. (äs-trȧ-kän')	179	46.15 N	48.00 E
Astrida, Rw. (äs-trē'dȧ)	226	2.37 S	29.48 E
Asturias (Reg.), Sp. (äs-tōō'ryäs)	170	43.21 N	6.00 W
Asunción, Par. (ä-sōōn-syōn')	144	25.25 S	57.30 W
Asunción Mita, Guat. (ä-sōōn-syō'n-mē'tä)	132	14.19 N	89.43 W
Asunción, see Ixtaltepec			
Asunción, see Nochixtlán			
Åsunden (L.), Swe. (ô'sōōn-dĕn)	163	57.46 N	13.16 E
Aswān, Egypt (ä-swän')	223b	24.05 N	32.57 E

ng-sing; ŋ-baŋk; N-nasalized n; nŏd; cŏmmit; ōld; ôbey; ôrder; oi-boil; fōōd; fŏŏt; ou-out; s-soft; sh-dish; th-thin; pūre; ûnite; ûrn; stŭd; circŭs; ü-as in French tu; '-indeterminate vowel.

PLACE (Pronunciation)	PAGE	Lat. °′	Long. °′
Aswān High Dam, Egypt	223b	23.58 N	32.53 E
Asyūṭ, Egypt (ä-syōōt')	223b	27.10 N	31.10 E
Atacama, Desierto de (Des.), Chile-Peru (dĕ-syĕ'r-tô-dĕ-ä-tä-kà'mä)	140	23.50 s	69.00 w
Atacama, Puna de (Plat.), Bol. (pōō'nä-dĕ-ä-tä-kà'mä)	142	21.35 s	66.58 w
Atacama, Puna de (Reg.), Chile (pōō'nä-dĕ-ätä-kà'mä)	144	23.15 s	68.45 w
Atacama, Salar de (L.), Chile (sà-làr'dĕ-àtä-kà'mä)	144	23.38 s	68.15 w
Atacama Trench, S.A.	144	25.00 s	71.30 w
Ataco, Col. (ä-tà'kō)	142a	3.36 N	75.22 w
Atacora, Chaîne de l' (Mts.), Benin	228	10.15 N	1.15 E
Atā 'itah, Jabal al (Mts.), Jordan	191a	30.48 N	35.19 E
Atakpamé, Togo (ä'tàk-pà-mā')	228	7.32 N	1.08 E
Atamanovskiy, Sov. Un. (ä-tä-mä'nôv-skĭ)	182a	52.15 N	60.47 E
'Atāqah, Jabal (Mts.), Egypt	223c	29.59 N	32.20 E
Atar, Mauritania (ä-tär')	224	20.45 N	13.16 w
Atascadero, Ca. (ăt-ăs-kà-dâ'rō)	120	35.29 N	120.40 w
Atascosa R., Tx. (ăt-ăs-kō'sà)	124	28.50 N	98.17 w
Atauro, Ilha de (I.), Indon. (dĕ-ä-tä'ōō-rō)	207	8.20 s	126.15 E
'Aṭbarah, Sud. (ät'bà-rä)	225	17.45 N	33.15 E
Atbara R., Sud.	225	17.14 N	34.27 E
Atbasar, Sov. Un. (ät'bä-sär')	180	51.42 N	68.28 E
Atchafalaya B., La. (ăch-à-fà-lī'à)	125	29.25 N	91.30 w
Atchafalaya R., La.	125	30.53 N	91.51 w
Atchison, Ks. (ăch'ĭ-sŭn)	123	39.33 N	95.08 w
Atco, NJ (ăt'kō)	112f	39.46 N	74.53 w
Atempan, Mex. (ä-tĕm-pà'n)	131	19.49 N	97.25 w
Atenguillo (R.), Mex. (ä-tĕn-gē'l-yô)	130	20.18 N	104.35 w
Athabasca, Can. (ăth-à-băs'kà)	96	54.43 N	113.17 w
Athabasca (L.), Can.	96	59.04 N	109.10 w
Athabasca (R.), Can.	99	56.00 N	112.35 w
Athens, Al. (ăth'ĕnz)	126	34.47 N	86.58 w
Athens, Ga.	126	33.55 N	83.24 w
Athens, Oh.	110	39.20 N	82.10 w
Athens, Pa.	111	42.00 N	76.30 w
Athens, Tn.	126	35.26 N	84.36 w
Athens, Tx.	125	32.13 N	95.51 w
Athens, see Athínai			
Atherstone, Eng. (ăth'ēr-stŭn)	156	52.34 N	1.33 w
Atherton, Eng. (ăth'ēr-tŭn)	156	53.32 N	2.29 w
Atherton Plat., Austl. (ădh-ēr-tŏn)	215	17.00 s	144.30 E
Athi (R.), Ken. (ä'tē)	231	2.43 s	38.30 E
Athis-Mons, Fr.	64c	48.43 N	2.24 E
Athínai (Athens), Grc. (ä-thē'nĕ)	173	38.00 N	23.38 E
Athlone, Ire. (ăth-lōn')	162	53.24 N	7.30 w
Athos (Mtn.), Grc. (ăth'ŏs)	173	40.10 N	24.15 E
Ath Thamad, Egypt	191a	29.41 N	34.17 E
Athy, Ire. (à-thī)	162	52.59 N	7.08 w
Ati, Chad	229	13.13 N	18.20 E
Atibaia, Braz. (ä-tē-bà'yà)	141a	23.08 s	46.32 w
Atikonak (L.), Can.	97	52.34 N	63.49 w
Atimonan, Phil. (ä-tē-mō'nän)	207a	13.59 N	121.56 E
Atiquizaya, Sal. (ä'tē-kē-zä'yä)	132	14.00 N	89.42 w
Atitlan (Vol.), Guat. (ä-tē-tlän')	132	14.35 N	91.11 w
Atitlan L., Guat. (ä-tē-tlän')	132	14.38 N	91.23 w
Atizapán, Mex. (ä'tē-zà-pän')	131a	19.33 N	99.16 w
Atka, Ak. (ăt'kà)	107a	52.18 N	174.18 w
Atka (I.), Ak.	107a	51.58 N	174.30 w
Atkarsk, Sov. Un. (åt-kärsk')	179	51.50 N	45.00 E
Atkinson, Ne. (ăt'kĭn-sŭn)	114	42.32 N	98.58 w
Atlanta, Ga. (ăt-lăn'tà)	112c	33.45 N	84.23 w
Atlanta, Tx.	123	33.09 N	94.09 w
Atlantic, Ia. (ăt-lăn'tĭk)	115	41.23 N	94.58 w
Atlantic, NC	127	34.54 N	76.20 w
Atlantic Beach, NY	55	40.35 N	73.44 w
Atlantic City, NJ	111	39.20 N	74.30 w
Atlantic Highlands, NJ	112a	40.25 N	74.04 w
Atlantic O.	93	23.30 N	40.00 w
Atlas Mts., Alg.-Mor. (ăt'lăs)	224	31.22 N	4.57 w
Atliaca, Mex. (ät-lē-ä'kä)	130	17.38 N	99.24 w
Atlin (L.), Can. (ăt'lĭn)	96	59.34 N	133.20 w
Atlixco, Mex. (ät-lēz'kō)	130	18.52 N	98.27 w
Atmore, Al. (ăt'mōr)	126	31.01 N	87.31 w
Atoka, Ok. (à-tō'kà)	123	34.23 N	96.07 w
Atoka Res., Ok.	123	34.30 N	96.05 w
Atotonilco el Alto, Mex. (ä'tô-tô-nēl'kō ĕl äl'tō)	130	20.35 N	102.32 w
Atotonilco el Grande, Mex. (ä'tô-tô-nēl-kō ĕl grän'dā)	130	20.17 N	98.41 w
Atoui R., Mauritania-W. Sah. (à-tōō-ē')	224	21.00 N	15.32 w
Atoyac, Mex. (ä-tô-yäk')	130	20.01 N	103.28 w
Atoyac (R.), Mex.	130	18.35 N	98.16 w
Atoyac (R.), Mex.	131	16.27 N	97.28 w
Atoyac de Alvarez, Mex. (ä-tô-yäk'dā äl'vä-rāz)	130	17.13 N	100.29 w
Atoyatempan, Mex. (ä-tō'yà-tĕm-pän')	131	18.47 N	97.54 w
Atrak (R.), Iran	192	37.45 N	56.30 E
Atran (R.), Swe.	164	57.02 N	12.43 E
Atrato (R.), Col. (ä-trä'tō)	142a	5.48 N	76.19 w
Atrato, Rio (R.), Col. (rē'ō-ä-trä'tō)	142	7.15 N	77.18 w
Atsugi, Jap.	69a	35.27 N	139.22 E
Atta, India	67d	28.34 N	77.20 E
Aṭ Ṭafilah, Jordan (tä-fē'la)	191a	30.50 N	35.36 E
Aṭ Ṭā'if, Sau. Ar.	192	21.03 N	41.00 E
At-Talibīyah, Egypt	71a	30.00 N	31.11 E
Attalla, Al. (à-tăl'yà)	126	34.01 N	86.05 w
Attawapiskat (R.), Can. (ăt'à-wà-pĭs'kăt)	97	52.31 N	86.22 w
Attersee (L.) (Kammer), Aus.	166	47.57 N	13.25 E
Attica, NY (ăt'ĭ-kà)	111	42.55 N	78.15 w
Attleboro, Ma. (ăt''l-bŭr-ô)	112b	41.56 N	71.15 w
Attow, Ben (Mtn.), Scot. (bĕn ăt'tô)	162	57.15 N	5.25 w
Attoyac Bay, Tx. (ă-toi'yăk)	125	31.45 N	94.23 w
Attu (I.), Ak. (ät-tōō')	107a	53.08 N	173.18 E
Aṭ Ṭūr, Egypt	161	28.09 N	33.47 E
Aṭ Ṭurayf, Sau. Ar.	192	31.32 N	38.30 E
Åtvidaberg, Swe. (ôt-vē'dà-bĕrgh)	164	58.12 N	15.55 E
Atwood, Ks. (ăt'wŏŏd)	122	39.48 N	101.06 w
Atzalpur, India	67d	28.43 N	77.21 E
Atzcapotzalco, Mex. (ät'zkä-pô-tzäl'kō)	131a	19.29 N	99.11 w
Atzgersdorf, Aus.	157e	48.10 N	16.17 E
Auau Chan., Hi. (ä'ōō-ä'ōō)	106a	20.55 N	156.50 w
Aubagne, Fr. (ō-bän'y')	169	43.18 N	5.34 E
Aube (R.), Fr. (ōb)	168	48.42 N	3.49 E
Aubenas, Fr. (ōb-nä')	168	44.37 N	4.22 E
Aubervilliers, Fr. (ō-bĕr-vē-yā')	169b	48.54 N	2.23 E
Aubin, Fr. (ō-băN')	168	44.29 N	2.12 E
Aubrey, Can. (ô-brē')	95a	45.08 N	73.47 w
Auburn, Al. (ô'bŭrn)	126	32.35 N	85.26 w
Auburn, Austl.	70a	33.51 s	151.02 E
Auburn, Ca.	120	38.52 N	121.05 w
Auburn, Il.	123	39.36 N	89.46 w
Auburn, In.	110	41.20 N	85.05 w
Auburn, Ma.	105a	42.11 N	71.51 w
Auburn, Me.	104	44.04 N	70.24 w
Auburn, Ne.	123	40.23 N	95.50 w
Auburn, NY	111	42.55 N	76.35 w
Auburn, Wa.	118a	47.18 N	122.14 w
Auburndale, Ma.	54a	42.21 N	71.22 w
Auburn Hts., Mi.	113b	42.37 N	83.13 w
Aubusson, Fr. (ō-bü-sôN')	168	45.57 N	2.10 E
Auch, Fr. (ōsh)	168	43.38 N	0.35 E
Aucilla (R.), Fl.-Ga. (ô-sĭl'à)	126	30.15 N	83.55 w
Auckland, N.Z. (ôk'lănd)	215a	36.53 s	174.45 E
Auckland Is., N.Z.	232	50.30 s	166.30 E
Auckland Park (Neigh.), S. Afr.	71b	26.11 s	28.00 E
Aude (R.), Fr. (ōd)	168	42.55 N	2.08 E
Audenshaw, Eng.	64b	53.28 N	2.08 w
Audierne, Fr. (ō-dyĕrn')	168	48.02 N	4.31 w
Audincourt, Fr. (ō-dăn-kōōr')	169	47.30 N	6.49 E
Audley, Eng. (ôd'lĭ)	156	53.03 N	2.18 w
Audo Ra., Eth.	223a	6.58 N	41.18 E
Audubon, Ia. (ô'dŏŏ-bŏn)	115	41.43 N	94.57 w
Audubon, NJ	112f	39.54 N	75.04 w
Aue, G.D.R. (ou'ĕ)	166	50.35 N	12.44 E
Auf dem Kreinberge, F.R.G.	63	51.27 N	7.36 E
Auf dem Schnee (Neigh.), F.R.G.	63	51.26 N	7.25 E
Augathella, Austl. (ôr'gà'thē-là)	216	25.49 s	146.40 E
Aughton, Eng.	64a	53.32 N	2.56 w
Aughton Park, Eng.	64a	53.33 N	2.53 w
Augrabiesvalle (Falls), S. Afr.	226	28.30 s	20.00 E
Augsburg, F.R.G. (ouks'bŏŏrgh)	157d	48.23 N	10.55 E
Augusta, Ar. (ô-gŭs'tà)	123	35.16 N	91.21 w
Augusta, Ga.	127	33.26 N	82.00 w
Augusta, Ks.	123	37.41 N	96.58 w
Augusta, Ky.	110	38.45 N	84.00 w
Augusta, Me.	104	44.19 N	69.42 w
Augusta, NJ	112a	41.07 N	74.44 w
Augusta, Wi.	115	44.40 N	91.09 w
Augustow, Pol. (ou-gŏŏs'tŏŏf)	167	53.52 N	23.00 E
Aulnay-sous-Bois, Fr. (ō-nĕ'sōō-bwä')	169b	48.56 N	2.30 E
Aulne (R.), Fr. (ōn)	168	48.08 N	3.53 w
Auneau, Fr. (ō-nëū)	169b	48.28 N	1.45 E
Auob (R.), Namibia (ä'wŏb)	226	25.00 s	19.00 E
Aur (I.), Mala.	191b	2.27 N	104.51 E
Aura, Fin.	165	60.38 N	22.32 E
Aurangābād, India (ou-rŭŋ-gä-bäd')	196	19.56 N	75.19 E
Aurdal, Nor. (äûr-däl)	164	60.54 N	9.24 E
Aurès, Massif de l' (Mts.), Alg.	160	35.16 N	5.53 E
Aurillac, Fr. (ō-rē-yàk')	168	44.57 N	2.27 E
Aurora, Can.	103	43.59 N	79.25 w
Aurora, Il. (ô-rō'rà)	113a	41.45 N	88.18 w
Aurora, In.	113f	39.04 N	84.55 w
Aurora, Mn.	115	47.31 N	92.17 w
Aurora, Mo.	123	36.58 N	93.42 w
Aurora, Ne.	122	40.54 N	98.01 w
Aursunden (L.), Nor. (äûr-sûndĕn)	164	62.42 N	11.10 E
Au Sable (R.), Mi. (ô-sä'b'l)	110	44.40 N	84.25 w
Ausable (R.), NY	111	44.25 N	73.50 w
Austerlitz (P. Int.), Fr.	64c	48.50 N	2.22 E
Austin (L.), Austl.	214	27.45 s	117.30 E
Austin, Mn. (ôs'tĭn)	115	43.40 N	92.58 w
Austin (Neigh.), Il.	58a	41.54 N	87.45 w
Austin, Nv.	120	39.30 N	117.05 w
Austin, Tx.	125	30.15 N	97.42 w
Austin Bayou, Tx. (ôs'tĭn bī-ōō')	125a	29.17 N	95.21 w
Austral, Austl.	70a	33.56 s	150.48 E
Australian Alps (Mts.), Austl.	216	37.10 s	147.55 E
Australian Capital Ter., Austl. (ôs-trā'lĭ-ăn)	216	35.30 s	148.40 E
Australia, (ôs-trā'lĭ-à)	214	25.00 s	135.00 E
Austria, Eur. (ôs'trĭ-à)	154	47.15 N	11.53 E
Authon-la-Plaine, Fr. (ō-tô'N-lä-plĕ'n)	169b	48.27 N	1.58 E
Autlán, Mex. (ä-ōōt-län')	130	19.47 N	104.24 w
Autun, Fr. (ō-tŭN')	168	46.58 N	4.14 E
Auvergne (Mts.), Fr. (ō-vĕrn'y')	168	45.12 N	2.31 E
Auxerre, Fr. (ō-sâr')	168	47.48 N	3.32 E
Ava, Mo. (ā'và)	123	36.56 N	92.40 w
Avakubi, Zaire (ä-vá-kōō'bē)	231	1.20 N	27.34 E
Avallon, Fr. (à-và-lôN')	168	47.30 N	3.58 E
Avalon, Ca.	120	33.21 N	118.22 w
Avalon, Pa. (ăv'à-lŏn)	113e	40.31 N	80.05 w
Avanley, Eng.	64b	53.16 N	2.45 w
Aveiro, Port. (ä-vā'rōō)	170	40.38 N	8.38 w
Avelar, Braz. (ä'vĕ-là'r)	144b	22.20 s	43.25 w
Aveley, Eng.	62	51.30 N	0.16 E
Avellaneda, Arg. (ä-vĕl-yä-nä'dhä)	144a	34.25 s	58.23 w
Avellino, It. (ä-vĕl-lē'nō)	171c	40.40 N	14.46 E
Avenel, NJ	55	40.35 N	74.17 w
Averøya (I.), Nor. (ävĕr-ûê)	164	63.40 N	7.16 E
Aversa, It. (ä-vĕr'sä)	172	40.58 N	14.13 E
Avery, Tx. (ā'vĕr-ĭ)	123	33.34 N	94.46 w
Avesta, Swe. (ä-vĕs'tä)	164	60.16 N	16.09 E
Aveyron (R.), Fr. (ä-vâ-rôN)	168	44.07 N	1.45 E
Avezzano, It. (ä-vät-sä'nō)	172	42.03 N	13.27 E
Avigliano, It. (ä-vēl-yä'nō)	172	40.45 N	15.44 E
Avignon, Fr. (à-vē-nyôN')	168	43.55 N	4.50 E
Ávila, Sp. (ä-vē-lä)	170	40.39 N	4.42 w
Avilés, Sp. (ä-vē-lās')	170	43.33 N	5.55 w
Avoca, Ia. (à-vō'kà)	123	41.29 N	95.16 w
Avocado Heights, Ca.	59	34.03 N	118.00 w
Avon, Ct. (ā'vŏn)	111	41.40 N	72.50 w
Avon, Ma. (ā'vŏn)	105a	42.08 N	71.03 w
Avon, Oh.	113d	41.27 N	82.02 w
Avon (R.), Eng. (ā'vŭn)	162	52.05 N	1.55 w
Avondale, Ga.	112c	33.47 N	84.16 w
Avondale Heights, Austl.	70b	37.46 s	144.51 E
Avon Lake, Oh.	113d	41.31 N	82.01 w
Avonmore, Can. (ä'vŏN-mōr)	95c	45.11 N	74.58 w
Avon Park, Fl. (ā'vŏn pärk')	127a	27.35 N	81.29 w
Avranches, Fr. (à-vräNsh')	168	48.43 N	1.34 w
Awaji-Shima (I.), Jap. (ä'wä-jē shē-mä)	205b	34.32 N	135.02 E
Awe, Loch (L.), Scot. (lŏK ôr)	162	56.22 N	5.04 w
Awīn, Iran	68h	35.48 N	51.24 E
Awjilah, Libya	225	29.07 N	21.21 E
Awsīm, Egypt	71a	30.07 N	31.08 E
Ax-les-Thermes, Fr. (äks'lā tĕrm')	168	42.43 N	1.50 E
Axochiapan, Mex. (äks-ō-chyä'pän)	130	18.29 N	98.49 w
Ay (R.), Sov. Un.	178	55.55 N	57.55 E
Ayabe, Jap. (ä'yä-bĕ)	205	35.16 N	135.17 E
Ayachi, Arin' (Mtn.), Mor.	160	32.29 N	4.57 w
Ayacucho, Arg. (ä-yä-kōō'chō)	144	37.05 s	58.30 w
Ayacucho, Peru	142	12.12 s	74.03 w
Ayaguz, Sov. Un. (ä-yà-gōōz')	180	48.00 N	80.12 E
Ayamonte, Sp. (ä-yä-mô'n-tĕ)	170	37.14 N	7.28 w
Ayan, Sov. Un. (à-yän')	181	56.26 N	138.18 E
Ayase, Jap.	69a	35.26 N	139.26 E
Ayata, Bol. (ä-yä'tä)	142	15.17 s	68.43 w
Ayaviri, Peru (ä-yä-vē'rē)	142	14.46 s	70.38 w
Aydar (R.), Sov. Un. (ī-där')	175	49.15 N	38.48 E
Ayden, NC (ā'dĕn)	127	35.27 N	77.25 w
Aydın, Tur. (āīy-dĕn)	179	37.40 N	27.40 E
Ayer, Ma. (âr)	105a	42.33 N	71.36 w
Ayer Hitam, Mala.	191b	1.55 N	103.11 E
Ayiassos, Grc.	173	39.06 N	26.25 E
Áyion Óros (Mount Athos) (Reg.), Grc.	173	40.20 N	24.15 E
Ayíos Evstrátios (I.), Grc.	173	39.30 N	24.58 E
Ayía Varvára, Grc.	66d	37.59 N	23.39 E
Ayíou Orous, Kólpos (G.), Grc.	173	40.15 N	24.00 E
Aylesbury, Eng. (ālz'bĕr-ĭ)	156b	51.47 N	0.49 w
Aylmer (L.), Can. (āl'mēr)	96	64.27 N	108.22 w
Aylmer East, Can. (āl'mēr)	95c	45.24 N	75.50 w
Aylmer, Mt., Can.	99	51.19 N	115.26 w
Ayo el Chico, Mex. (ä'yô el chē'kō)	130	20.31 N	102.21 w
Ayon (I.), Sov. Un. (ī-ôn')	181	69.50 N	168.40 E
Ayorou, Niger	228	14.44 N	0.55 E
Ayotla, Mex. (ä-yōt'lä)	131a	19.18 N	98.55 w
Ayoun el Atrous, Mauritania	228	16.40 N	9.37 w
Ayr, Scot. (âr)	162	55.27 N	4.40 w
Aysha, Eth.	223a	10.48 N	42.32 E
Ayutla, Guat. (à-yōōt'lä)	132	14.44 N	92.11 w
Ayutla, Mex.	130	16.50 N	99.16 w
Ayutla, Mex.	130	20.09 N	104.20 w
Ayvalik, Tur. (āīy-wă-lĭk)	173	39.19 N	26.40 E
Azādpur (Neigh.), India	67d	28.43 N	77.11 E
Azaouad (Dunes), Mali	228	18.00 N	3.20 w
Azaouak, Vallée de l' (Val.), Mali	229	15.50 N	3.10 E
Azare, Nig.	229	11.40 N	10.11 E
Azcapotzalco, Mex.	60a	19.28 N	99.12 w
Azemmour, Mor. (à-zē-mōōr')	224	33.20 N	8.21 w
Azerbaijan (S.S.R.), Sov. Un. (ä'zēr-bä-ē-jän')	176	40.38 N	47.25 E
Azle, Tx. (ăz'lē)	119c	35.54 N	97.33 w
Azogues, Ec. (ä-sō'gās)	142	2.47 s	78.45 w
Azores (Is.), see Açores			
Azov, Sov. Un. (à-zôf') (ä-zôf)	175	47.07 N	39.19 E
Azov, Sea of, see Azovskoye More			
Azovskoye More (Sea of Azov), Sov. Un. (à-zôf'skô-yĕ mô'rĕ)	175	46.00 N	36.20 E
Azoyú, Mex. (ä-zô-yōō')	130	16.42 N	98.46 w
Azraq, Al-Bahr al- (R.), see Blue Nile			
Aztec, NM (ăz'tĕk)	121	36.40 N	108.00 w
Aztec Ruins Natl. Mon., NM	121	36.50 N	108.00 w
Azua, Dom. Rep. (ä'swä)	135	18.30 N	70.45 w
Azuaga, Sp. (ä-thwä'gä)	170	38.15 N	5.42 w
Azucar, Presa de (Res.), Mex. (prĕ'sä-dĕ-ä-zōō'kär)	124	26.06 N	98.44 w
Azuero, Peninsula de (Pen.), Pan. (ä-swā'rō)	133	7.30 N	80.34 w
Azufre, Cerro (Copiapó) (Vol.), Chile (sĕr'rō ä-sōō'frā) (kō-pē-äpō')	144	26.10 s	69.00 w
Azul, Arg. (ä-sōōl')	141c	36.46 s	59.51 w
Azul, Cordillera (Mts.), Peru (kô'r-dē-lyĕ'rä-zōō'l)	142	7.15 s	75.30 w
Azul, Sierra (Mts.), Mex. (sē-ĕ'r-rä-zōō'l)	130	23.20 N	98.28 w
Azusa, Ca. (à-zōō'sà)	119a	34.08 N	117.55 w
Az Zabdānī, Syr.	191a	33.45 N	36.06 E
Az Zahrān (Dhahran, Sau. Ar. (dä-rän')	192	26.13 N	50.00 E
Az-Zamālik (Neigh.), Egypt	71a	30.04 N	31.13 E
Az Zaqāzīq, Egypt	223b	30.36 N	31.36 E
Az Zarqā', Jordan	191a	32.03 N	36.07 E
Az Zawiyah, Libya	225	32.28 N	11.55 E

PLACE (Pronounciation)	PAGE	Lat. °′	Long. °′
B			
Baak, F.R.G.	63	51.25 N	7.10 E
Baal, F.R.G. (bäl)	169c	51.02 N	6.17 E
Baao, Phil. (bä'ō)	207a	13.27 N	123.22 E
Baardheere, Som.	223a	2.13 N	42.24 E
Baarle-Hertog, Bel.	157a	51.26 N	4.57 E
Baarn, Neth.	157a	52.12 N	5.18 E
Babaeski, Tur. (bä'bä-ĕs'kĭ)	173	41.25 N	27.05 E
Babahoyo, Ec. (bä-bä-ō'yō)	142	1.56 S	79.24 W
Babana, Nig.	229	10.36 N	3.50 E
Babanango, S. Afr.	227c	28.24 S	31.11 E
Babanūsah, Sud.	225	11.30 N	27.55 E
Babar, Pulau (I.), Indon. (bä'bär)	207	7.50 S	129.15 E
Bābarpur (Neigh.), India	67d	28.41 N	77.17 E
Bab-el-Mandeb, Str. of, Afr.-Asia (bäb'ĕl män-dĕb')	223a	13.17 N	42.49 E
Babelsberg (Neigh.), G.D.R.	65a	52.24 N	13.05 E
Babia, Arroyo de la, Mex. (är-rō'yō dā lä bä'bē-ȧ)	124	28.26 N	101.50 W
Babine (R.), Can.	98	55.10 N	127.00 W
Babine L., Can. (băb'ēn)	98	54.45 N	126.00 W
Bābol, Iran	192	36.30 N	52.48 E
Babson Park, Ma.	54a	42.18 N	71.23 W
Babushkin, Sov. Un. (bä'bo͞osh-kĭn)	181	51.47 N	106.08 W
Babushkin, Sov. Un.	182b	55.52 N	37.42 E
Babuyan Is., Phil. (bä-bo͞o-yän')	206	19.30 N	122.38 E
Babyak, Bul. (bäb'zhȧk)	173	41.59 N	23.42 E
Babylon, NY (băb'ĭ-lŏn)	112a	40.42 N	73.19 W
Babylon (Ruins), Iraq	192	32.15 N	45.23 E
Bacalar, Laguna de (L.), Mex. (lä-go͞o-nä-dĕ-bä-kä-lär')	132a	18.50 N	88.31 W
Bacan, Pulau (I.), Indon.	207	0.30 S	127.00 E
Bacarra, Phil. (bä-kär'rä)	203	18.22 N	120.40 E
Bacău, Rom.	167	46.34 N	27.00 E
Baccarat, Fr. (bȧ-kȧ-rȧ')	169	48.29 N	6.42 E
Bacchus, Ut. (băk'ŭs)	119b	40.40 N	112.06 W
Bachajón, Mex. (bä-chä-hōn')	131	17.08 N	92.18 W
Bachu, China (bä-cho͞o)	198	39.50 N	78.23 E
Back (R.), Can.	96	65.30 N	104.15 W
Bačka Palanka, Yugo. (bäch'kä pälän-kä)	173	45.14 N	19.24 E
Bačka Topola, Yugo. (bäch'kä tô'pō-lä')	173	45.48 N	19.38 E
Back B., India	67e	18.56 N	72.49 E
Back Bay, India (băk)	197b	18.55 N	72.45 E
Back Bay (Neigh.), Ma.	54a	42.21 N	71.05 W
Backstairs Pass., Austl. (băk-stârs')	214	35.50 S	138.15 E
Bac Ninh, Viet. (bäk'nēn'')	203	21.10 N	106.02 E
Bacoli, It. (bä-kō-lē')	171c	40.33 N	14.05 E
Bacolod, Phil. (bä-kō'lôd)	206	10.42 N	123.03 E
Baco, Mt., Phil. (bä'kō)	207a	12.50 N	121.11 E
Bacongo, Con.	71c	4.18 S	15.16 E
Bácsalmás, Hung. (bäch'ôl-mäs)	167	46.07 N	19.18 E
Bacup, Eng. (băk'ŭp)	156	53.42 N	2.12 W
Bad (R.), SD (băd)	114	44.04 N	100.58 W
Badajoz, Sp. (bȧ-dhä-hōth')	170	38.52 N	6.56 W
Badalona, Sp. (bä-dhä-lō'nä)	171	41.27 N	2.15 E
Badanah, Sau. Ar.	192	30.49 N	40.45 E
Bad Axe, Mi. (băd' ăks)	110	43.50 N	82.55 W
Bad Bramstedt, F.R.G. (bät bräm'shtĕt)	157c	53.55 N	9.53 E
Bad Ems, F.R.G. (bät ĕms)	169	50.20 N	7.45 E
Baden, Aus. (bä'dĕn)	157e	48.00 N	16.14 E
Baden, Switz.	166	47.28 N	8.17 E
Baden-Baden, F.R.G. (bä'dĕn-bä'dĕn)	166	48.46 N	8.11 E
Baden Württemberg (State), F.R.G. (bä'dĕn vür'tĕm-bĕrgh)	166	48.38 N	9.00 E
Bad Freienwalde, G.D.R. (bät frī'ĕn-väl'dĕ)	166	52.47 N	14.00 E
Badger's Mount, Eng.	62	51.20 N	0.09 E
Bad Hersfeld, F.R.G. (bät hĕrsh'fĕlt)	166	50.53 N	9.43 E
Bad Homberg, F.R.G. (bät hōm'bĕrgh)	163	50.14 N	8.35 E
Badin, NC (bă'dĭn)	127	35.23 N	80.08 W
Badīn, Pak.	196	24.47 N	69.51 E
Bad Ischl, Aus. (bät ĭsh''l)	166	47.46 N	13.37 E
Bad Kissingen, F.R.G. (bät kĭs'ĭng-ĕn)	166	50.12 N	10.05 E
Bad Kreuznach, F.R.G. (bät kroits'näk)	166	49.52 N	7.53 E
Badlands (Reg.), ND (băd' lănds)	114	46.43 N	103.22 W
Badlands (Reg.), SD	114	43.43 N	102.36 W
Badlands Natl. Park, SD	114	43.56 N	102.37 W
Badlāpur, India	197b	19.12 N	73.12 E
Bādli, India	67d	28.45 N	77.09 E
Badogo, Mali	228	11.02 N	8.13 W
Bad Oldeslow, F.R.G. (bät ōl'dĕs-lōē)	166	53.48 N	10.21 E
Bad Reichenhall, F.R.G. (bät rī'ĸĕn-häl)	166	47.43 N	12.53 E
Bad River Ind. Res., Wi. (băd)	115	46.41 N	90.36 W
Bad Segeberg, F.R.G. (bät sĕ'gĕ-bo͞orgh)	157c	53.56 N	10.18 E
Bad Tölz, F.R.G. (bät tûltz)	166	47.46 N	11.35 E
Badulla, Sri Lanka	197	6.55 N	81.07 E
Bad Vöslau, Aus.	157e	47.58 N	16.13 E
Badwater Cr., Wy. (băd'wô-tēr)	117	43.13 N	107.55 W
Baena, Sp. (bä-ā'nä)	170	37.38 N	4.20 W
Baependi, Braz. (bä-ā-pĕn'dĭ)	141a	21.57 S	44.51 W
Baerl, F.R.G.	63	51.29 N	6.41 E
Baffin B., Can. (băf'ĭn)	94	72.00 N	65.00 W
Baffin B., Tx.	125	27.11 N	97.35 W
Baffin I., Can.	94	67.20 N	71.00 W
Bafoulabé, Mali (bä-fo͞o-lä-bā')	228	13.48 N	10.50 W
Bāfq, Iran (bäfk)	192	31.48 N	55.23 E
Bafra, Tur. (bäf'rä)	179	41.30 N	35.50 E
Bagabag, Phil. (bä-gä-bäg')	207a	16.38 N	121.16 E
Bāgalkot, India	197	16.14 N	75.40 E
Bagamoyo, Tan. (bä-gä-mō'yō)	231	6.26 S	38.54 E
Bagaryak, Sov. Un. (bȧ-gȧr-yäk')	182a	56.13 N	61.32 E
Bagbele, Zaire	231	4.21 N	29.17 E
Bagé, Braz. (bä-zhā')	144	31.17 S	54.07 W
Baghdād, Iraq (bȧgh-dād') (băg'dăd)	192	33.14 N	44.22 E
Bagheria, It. (bä-gā-rē'ä)	172	38.03 N	13.32 E
Bagley, Mn. (băg'lē)	114	47.31 N	95.24 W
Bagnara, It. (bän-yä'rä)	172	38.17 N	15.52 E
Bagnell Dam, Mo. (băg'nĕl)	123	38.13 N	92.40 W
Bagnères-de-Bigorre, Fr. (bän-yâr'dē-bē-gor')	168	43.40 N	0.70 E
Bagnères-de-Luchon, Fr. (băn-yâr' dē-lu chôɴ')	168	42.46 N	0.36 E
Bagneux, Fr.	64c	48.48 N	2.18 E
Bagnolet, Fr.	64c	48.52 N	2.25 E
Bagnols-sur-Ceze, Fr. (bä-nyôl')	168	44.09 N	4.37 E
Bagoé R., Mali (bȧ-gō'ā)	224	12.22 N	6.34 W
Baguio, Phil. (bä-gē-ō')	207a	16.24 N	120.36 E
Bagzane, Monts (Mtn.), Niger	229	18.40 N	8.40 E
Bahamas, N.A. (bȧ-hā'mȧs)	129	26.15 N	76.00 W
Bahau, Mala.	191b	2.48 N	102.25 E
Bahāwalpur, Pak. (bŭ-hä'wŭl-po͞or)	196	29.29 N	71.41 E
Bahia (State), Braz.	143	11.05 S	43.00 W
Bahia Blanca, Arg. (bä-ē'ä bläŋ'kä)	144	38.45 S	62.07 W
Bahias, Cabo dos (C.), Arg. (kȧ'bō-dōs-bä-ē'äs)	144	44.55 S	65.35 W
Bahia, see Salvador			
Bahi Swp., Tan.	231	6.05 S	35.10 E
Bahía de Caráquez, Ec. (bä-e'ä dā kä-rä'kĕz)	142	0.45 S	80.29 W
Bahía, Islas de la (I.), Hond. (ē's-läs-dĕ-lä-bä-ē'ä)	128	16.15 N	86.30 W
Bahía Negra, Par. (bä-ē'ä nā'grä)	143	20.11 S	58.05 W
Bahoruco, Sierra de (Mts.), Dom. Rep. (sē-ĕ'r-rä-dĕ-bä-ō-ro͞o'kō)	135	18.10 N	71.25 W
Bahrain, Asia (bä-rān')	192	26.15 N	51.17 E
Baḥr al Ghazāl (Prov.), Sud. (bär ĕl ghä-zäl')	225	7.56 N	27.15 E
Baḥrīyah (Oasis), Egypt (bȧ-hȧ-rē'yä)	161	28.34 N	29.01 E
Baḥrīyah, Jabal Jalālah al (Plat.), Egypt	191a	29.15 N	32.20 E
Bahtīm, Egypt	71a	30.08 N	31.17 E
Baia de Criş, Rom. (bä'yä dā krēs')	167	46.11 N	22.40 E
Baia Mare, Rom. (bä'yä mä'rā)	167	47.40 N	23.35 E
Baidyabāti, India	196a	22.47 N	88.21 E
Baie-Comeau, Can.	104	49.13 N	68.10 W
Baie de Wasai, Mi. (bā dē wä-sä'ē)	119k	46.27 N	84.15 W
Baie-Saint Paul, Can. (bā'sănt-pôl')	103	47.27 N	70.30 W
Baigou, China (bī-gō)	200	39.08 N	116.02 E
Baihe, China (bī-hŭ)	202	32.30 N	110.15 E
Bai Hu (L.), China (bī-ho͞o)	200	31.22 N	117.38 E
Baiju, China (bī-jyo͞o)	200	33.04 N	120.17 E
Baikal. L., see Baykal, Ozero			
Baikal Mts., see Baykal'skiy Khrebet			
Baile Átha Cliath (Dublin), Ire. (bŏ'lĕŏ'hŏclē'ŏh)	162	53.20 N	6.15 W
Bailén, Sp. (bā-ē-lān')	170	38.05 N	3.48 W
Băileşti, Rom. (bă-ĭ-lĕsh'tē)	173	44.01 N	23.21 E
Baileys Crossroads, Va.	56d	38.51 N	77.08 W
Bainbridge, Ga. (bān'brĭj)	126	30.52 N	84.35 W
Bainbridge I., Wa.	118a	47.39 N	122.32 W
Bainchipota, India	67a	22.52 N	88.16 E
Baipu, China (bī-po͞o)	200	32.15 N	120.47 E
Baiquan, China (bī-chyuäŋ)	202	47.22 N	126.00 E
Baird, Tx. (bârd)	124	32.22 N	99.28 W
Bairdford, Pa. (bârd'fŏrd)	113e	40.37 N	79.53 W
Baird Mts., Ak.	107	67.35 N	160.10 W
Bairnsdale, Austl. (bârnz'dāl)	216	37.50 S	147.39 E
Baïse (R.), Fr. (bä-ēz')	168	43.52 N	0.23 E
Baía dos Tigres, Ang.	230	16.36 S	11.43 E
Baiyang Dian (L.), China (bī-yäŋ-dĭĕn)	200	39.00 N	115.45 E
Baiyunguan, China	67b	39.54 N	116.19 E
Baiyu Shan (Mts.), China (bī-yo͞o shän)	202	37.02 N	108.30 E
Baja, Hung. (bŏ'yŏ)	167	46.11 N	18.55 E
Baja California Norte (State), Mex. (bä-hä)	128	30.15 N	117.25 W
Baja California Sur (State), Mex.	128	26.00 N	113.30 W
Bakal, Sov. Un. (bä'kȧl)	182a	54.57 N	58.50 E
Baker (I.), Oceania	208	1.00 N	176.00 W
Baker (L.), Can.	96	63.51 N	96.10 W
Baker, Mt. (bā'kēr)	117	46.21 N	104.12 W
Baker, Or.	116	44.46 N	117.52 W
Baker Cr., Il.	113a	41.13 N	87.47 W
Baker, Mt., Wa.	116	48.46 N	121.52 W
Bakersfield, Ca. (bā'kērz-fēld)	120	35.23 N	119.00 W
Bakerstown, Pa. (bā'kerz-toun)	113e	40.39 N	79.56 W
Baker Street, Eng.	62	51.30 N	0.21 E
Bakewell, Eng. (bāk'wĕl)	156	53.12 N	1.40 W
Bakhchisaray, Sov. Un. (bȧĸ'chē-sȧ-rī')	175	44.46 N	33.54 E
Bakhmach, Sov. Un. (bȧĸ-mäch')	175	51.09 N	32.47 E
Bakhtarān, Iran	192	34.01 N	47.00 E
Bakhtegan, Daryācheh-ye (L.), Iran	192	29.29 N	54.31 E
Bakhteyevo, Sov. Un. (bȧk-tyĕ'yĕ-vô)	182b	55.35 N	38.32 E
Bakırköy (Neigh.), Tur.	66f	40.59 N	28.52 E
Bako, Eth. (bä'kö)	225	5.47 N	36.39 E
Bakony (Mts.), Hung. (bȧ-kōn'y')	167	46.57 N	17.30 E
Bakoye (R.), Mali (bȧ-kō'ē)	228	12.47 N	9.35 W
Bakr Uzyak, Sov. Un. (bȧkr o͞oz'yȧk)	182a	52.59 N	58.43 E
Baku, Sov. Un. (bȧ-ko͞o')	179	40.28 N	49.45 E
Bakwanga, see Mbuji-Mayi			
Balabac I., Phil. (bä'lä-bäk)	206	8.00 N	116.28 E
Balabac Str., Indon.-Phil.	206	7.23 N	116.30 E
Ba'labakk, Leb.	191a	34.00 N	36.13 E
Balabanovo, Sov. Un. (bȧ-lȧ-bä'nô-vô)	182b	56.10 N	37.44 E
Bala-Cynwyd, Pa.	56b	40.00 N	75.14 W
Balagansk, Sov. Un. (bä-lä-gänsk')	180	53.58 N	103.09 E
Balaguer, Sp. (bä-lä-gĕr')	171	41.48 N	0.50 E
Balakhta, Sov. Un. (bȧ'lȧk-tȧ')	180	55.22 N	91.43 E
Balakleya, Sov. Un. (bȧ'lȧ-klā'yȧ)	175	49.28 N	36.51 E
Balakovo, Sov. Un. (bȧ'lȧ-kô'vō)	179	52.00 N	47.40 E
Balancán, Mex. (bä-läŋ-kän')	131	17.47 N	91.32 W
Balanga, Phil. (bä-läŋ'gä)	207a	14.41 N	120.31 E
Balashikha, Sov. Un. (bȧ-lä'shĭ-kȧ)	182b	55.48 N	37.58 E
Balashov, Sov. Un. (bȧ'lȧ-shôf)	179	51.30 N	43.00 E
Balasore, India (bä-lȧ-sōr')	196	21.38 N	86.59 E
Balassagyarmat, Hung. (bô'lôsh-shô-dyôr'môt)	167	48.04 N	19.19 E
Balaton L., Hung. (bô'lô-tôn)	167	46.47 N	17.55 E
Balayan, Phil. (bä-lä-yān')	207a	13.56 N	120.44 E
Balayan B., Phil.	207a	13.46 N	120.46 E
Balboa Heights, Pan. (bäl-bô'ä)	133	8.59 N	79.33 W
Balboa Mt., Pan.	128a	9.05 N	79.44 W
Balcarce, Arg. (bäl-kär'sā)	144	37.49 S	58.17 W
Balchik, Bul.	173	43.24 N	28.13 E
Bald Eagle, Mn. (bôld ē'g'l)	119g	45.06 N	93.01 W
Bald Eagle L., Mn.	119g	45.08 N	93.03 W
Baldock L., Can.	101	56.33 N	97.57 W
Baldwin, NY	55	40.39 N	73.37 W
Baldwin, Pa.	57b	40.23 N	79.58 W
Baldwin Park, Ca. (bôld'wĭn)	119a	34.05 N	117.58 W
Baldwinsville, NY (bôld'wĭns-vĭl)	111	43.10 N	76.20 W
Baldy Mtn., Can.	101	51.28 N	100.44 W
Baldy Pk., Az. (bôl'dē)	121	33.55 N	109.35 W
Baldy Pk., Tx. (bôl'dē pēk)	124	30.38 N	104.11 W
Baleares, Islas (Balearic Is.), Sp. (e's-läs bä-lĕ-ă'rĕs)	171	39.25 N	1.28 E
Balearic Is., see Baleares, Islas			
Balearic Sea., Eur. (băl-ē-ăr'ĭk)	171	39.40 N	1.05 E
Baleine, Grande Rivière de la (R.), Can.	97	54.45 N	74.20 W
Baler, Phil. (bä-lar')	207a	15.46 N	121.33 E
Baler B., Phil.	207a	15.51 N	121.40 E
Balesin (I.), Phil.	207a	14.28 N	122.10 E
Baley, Sov. Un. (bȧl-yā')	181	51.29 N	116.12 E
Balfate, Hond. (bäl-fä'tē)	132	15.48 N	86.24 W
Balfour, S. Afr. (băl'fo͞or)	223d	26.41 S	28.37 E
Balgowlah, Austl.	70a	33.48 S	151.16 E
Bali (I.), Indon. (bä'lē)	206	8.00 S	115.22 E
Bālihāti, India	67a	22.44 N	88.19 E
Balikesir, Tur. (balĭk'ĭysĭr)	179	39.40 N	27.50 E
Balikpapan, Indon. (bä'lēk-pä'pän)	206	1.13 S	116.52 E
Balintang Chan., Phil. (bā-lĭn-täng')	206	19.50 N	121.08 E
Balizhuang, China	67b	39.52 N	116.28 E
Balkan Mts., see Stara Planina			
Balkh, Afg. (bälk)	193	36.48 N	66.50 E
Balkhash, Sov. Un. (bȧl-käsh')	180	46.58 N	75.00 E
Balkhash, Ozero (L.), Sov. Un.	180	45.58 N	72.15 E
Balki, Sov. Un. (bäl'kĭ)	175	47.22 N	34.56 E
Ballabhpur, India	67a	22.44 N	88.21 E
Ballancourt, Fr. (bä-äɴ-ko͞or')	169b	48.31 N	2.23 E
Ballarat, Austl. (băl'ȧ-răt)	216	37.37 S	144.00 E
Ballard (L.), Austl. (băl'ȧrd)	214	29.15 S	120.45 E
Ballater, Scot. (bäl'ȧ-tēr)	162	57.05 N	3.06 W
Ballé, Mali.	228	15.20 N	8.35 W
Ballenato, Punta (C.), Cuba	60b	23.06 N	82.30 W
Balleny Is., Ant. (băl'ĕ nē)	232	67.00 S	164.00 E
Ballina, Austl. (băl-ĭ-nä')	216	28.50 S	153.35 E
Ballina, Ire.	162	54.06 N	9.05 W
Ballinasloe, Ire. (băl'ĭ-nȧ-slō')	162	53.20 N	8.09 W
Ballinger, Tx. (băl'ĭn-jēr)	124	31.45 N	99.58 W
Ballston Spa, NY (bôls'tŭn spä')	111	43.05 N	73.50 W
Ballygunge (Neigh.), India	67a	22.31 N	88.21 E
Balmain, Austl.	70a	33.51 S	151.11 E
Balmazújváros, Hung. (bŏl'mŏz-o͞o'y'vä'rōsh)	167	47.35 N	21.23 E
Balobe, Zaire	231	0.05 N	28.00 E
Balonne (R.), Austl. (băl-ōn')	216	27.00 S	149.10 E
Bālotra, India	196	25.56 N	72.12 E
Balranald, Austl. (băl'-rȧn-ăld)	216	34.42 S	143.30 E
Balş, Rom. (bälsh)	173	44.21 N	24.05 E
Balsam (L.), Can. (bôl'sȧm)	111	44.30 N	78.50 W
Balsas, Braz. (bäl'säs)	143	7.09 S	46.04 W
Balsas (R.), Mex.	128	18.00 N	103.00 W
Balta, Sov. Un. (bȧl'tȧ)	175	47.57 N	29.38 E
Baltic Sea, Eur. (bôl'tĭk)	158	55.20 N	16.50 E
Baltimore, Md. (bôl'tĭ-mōr)	112e	39.20 N	76.38 W
Baltimore Highlands, Md.	56c	39.14 N	76.38 W
Baltīm, Egypt (bȧl-tēm')	223b	31.33 N	31.04 E
Baltiysk, Sov. Un. (bäl-tēysk')	165	54.40 N	19.55 E
Baluarte, Río del, Mex. (rē'ō-dĕl-bä-lo͞o'r-tĕ)	130	23.09 N	105.42 W
Baluchistān (Reg.), Pak. (bȧ-lo͞o-chĭ-stän')	193	27.30 N	65.30 E
Balwyn, Austl.	70b	37.49 S	145.05 E
Balzac, Can. (bôl'zăk)	95e	51.10 N	114.01 W
Bama, Nig.	229	11.30 N	13.41 E
Bamako, Mali (bä-mā-kō')	228	12.39 N	8.00 W
Bambang, Phil. (bäm-bäng')	207a	16.24 N	121.08 E
Bambari, Cen. Afr. Rep. (bäm-bȧ-rē)	225	5.44 N	20.40 E
Bamberg, F.R.G. (bäm'bĕrgh)	166	49.53 N	10.52 E
Bamberg, SC (băm'bûrg)	127	33.17 N	81.04 W
Bambuí, Braz. (bä'm-bo͞o-ē)	141a	20.01 S	45.59 W
Bamenda, Cam.	229	5.56 N	10.10 E
Bamingui (R.), Cen. Afr. Rep.	229	7.35 N	19.45 E
Bamingui Bangoran, Parc Nat'l. du (Natl. Park), Cen. Afr. Rep.	229	8.05 N	19.35 E
Bampton, Eng. (băm'tŭn)	156b	51.42 N	1.33 W
Bampūr, Iran (bŭm-po͞or')	192	27.15 N	60.22 E
Bam Yanga, Ngao (Mts.), Cam.	229	8.20 N	14.40 E
Banahao, Mt., Phil. (bä-nä-hä'ō)	207a	14.04 N	121.45 E
Banalia, Zaire	230	1.33 N	25.20 E
Banamba, Mali	228	13.33 N	7.27 W
Bananal, Braz. (bä-nä-näl')	141a	22.42 S	44.17 W
Bananal, Ilha do (I.), Braz. (ē'lä-dō-bä-nă-năl')	143	12.09 S	50.27 W
Banās (R.), India (băn-äs')	196	25.20 N	74.51 E
Banās, Ra's (C.), Egypt	225	23.48 N	36.39 E
Banat (Reg.), Rom.-Yugo. (bä-nät')	173	45.35 N	21.05 E
Banbidian, China	67b	39.54 N	116.32 E

ng-sing; nŋ-banŋk; ɴ-nasalized n; nŏd; cŏmmit; ōld; ôbey; ôrder; oi-boil; fo͞od; fo͝ot; ou-out; s-soft; sh-dish; th-thin; pūre; ûnite; ûrn; stŭd; circŭs; ü-as in French tu; '-indeterminate vowel.

PLACE (Pronounciation)	PAGE	Lat. °'	Long. °'
Bancroft, Can. (băn'krŏft)	111	45.05 N	77.55 W
Bancroft, see Chililabombwe			
Bānda, India (bän'dä)	196	25.36 N	80.21 E
Banda Aceh, Indon.	206	5.10 N	95.10 E
Banda Banda, Mt., Austl. (băn'dȧ băn'dȧ)	216	31.09 S	152.15 E
Banda, Kepulauan (Is.), Indon.	207	4.40 S	129.56 E
Banda Laut (Banda Sea), Indon.	207	6.05 S	127.28 E
Bandama Blanc (R.), Ivory Coast (bän-dä'mä)	228	6.15 N	5.00 W
Bandar Abbās, Iran (bän-där' ab-bäs')	192	27.04 N	56.22 E
Bandar-e Anzalī, Iran	195	37.28 N	49.27 E
Bandar-e Khomeynī, Iran	192	30.27 N	48.45 E
Bandar-e Lengeh, Iran	192	26.44 N	54.47 E
Bandar-e Torkeman, Iran	192	37.05 N	54.08 E
Bandar Maharani, Mala. (bän-där' mä-hä-rä'nē)	191b	2.02 N	102.34 E
Bandar Seri Begawan, Bru.	211	5.00 N	114.59 E
Bande, Sp.	170	42.02 N	7.58 W
Bandeira, Pico da (Pk.), Braz. (pē'koo dä bän dā'rä)	141a	20.27 S	41.47 W
Bāndel, India	67a	22.56 N	88.22 E
Bandelier Natl. Mon., NM (băn-dĕ-lēr')	121	35.50 N	106.45 W
Banderas, Bahía de (B.), Mex. (bä-ē'ä dĕ bän-dĕ'räs)	130	20.38 N	105.35 W
Bandir C., Indon.	68k	6.11 S	106.49 E
Bandirma, Tur. (bän-dĭr'mȧ)	179	40.25 N	27.50 E
Bandon, Or. (băn'dŭn)	116	43.06 N	124.25 W
Bāndra (Neigh), India	197b	19.04 N	72.49 E
Bandundu, Zaire	230	3.18 S	17.20 E
Bandung, Indon.	211	7.00 S	107.22 E
Banes, Cuba (bä'näs)	135	21.00 N	75.45 W
Banff, Can. (bănf)	99	51.10 N	115.34 W
Banff, Scot.	162	57.39 N	2.37 W
Banff Natl. Park, Can.	99	51.38 N	116.22 W
Bánfield, Arg. (bà'n-fyĕ'ld)	144a	34.44 S	58.24 W
Banfora, Upper Volta	228	10.38 N	4.46 W
Bangalore, India (băŋ'gȧ'lôr)	197	13.03 N	77.39 E
Bangassou, Cen. Afr. Rep. (bäN-gȧ-sōō')	225	4.47 N	22.49 E
Bangé, Cam.	229	3.01 N	15.07 E
Bangeta, Mt., Pap. N. Gui.	207	6.20 S	147.00 E
Banggai, Kepulauan (Is.), Indon. (bäng-gī')	207	1.05 N	123.45 E
Banggi, Pulau (I.), Mala.	206	7.12 N	117.10 E
Banghāzī, Libya (bĕn-gä'zē)	225	32.08 N	20.06 E
Bangka (I.), Indon. (băŋ'kȧ)	206	2.24 S	106.55 E
Bangkalan, Indon. (bäng-kȧ-län')	206	6.07 S	112.50 E
Bang Khun Thian, Thai.	68f	13.42 N	100.28 E
Bangkok, see Krung Thep			
Bangladesh, Asia	193	24.15 N	90.00 E
Bangong Co (L.), China (bäŋ-gôŋ tswo)	196	33.40 N	79.30 E
Bangor, Me. (băn'gēr)	104	44.47 N	68.47 W
Bangor, Mi.	110	42.20 N	86.05 W
Bangor, Pa.	111	40.55 N	75.10 W
Bangor, Wales (băŋ'ēr) (băŋ'ŏr)	162	53.13 N	4.05 W
Bangs, Mt., Az. (băngs)	121	36.45 N	113.50 W
Bangu (Neigh.), Braz.	61c	22.52 S	44.27 W
Bangued, Phil. (bän-gād')	207a	17.36 N	120.38 E
Bangui, Cen. Afr. Rep. (bäN-gē')	229	4.22 N	18.35 E
Bangweulu, L., Zambia (băng-wē-ōō'lōō)	231	10.55 S	30.10 E
Bangweulu Swp., Zambia	231	11.25 S	30.10 E
Banhā, Egypt	223b	30.24 N	31.11 E
Bani, Dom. Rep. (bä'-nĕ)	135	18.15 N	70.25 W
Bani, Phil. (bä'nē)	207a	16.11 N	119.51 E
Bani (R.), Mali	228	13.07 N	6.15 W
Bánica, Dom. Rep. (bä'-nē-kä)	135	19.00 N	71.35 W
Banī Majdūl, Egypt	71a	30.02 N	31.07 E
Banī Mazār, Egypt	223b	28.29 N	30.48 E
Banī Suwayf, Egypt	223b	29.05 N	31.06 E
Banī Walīd, Libya	194	31.45 N	14.01 E
Banjak, Kepulauan (I.), Indon.	206	2.08 N	97.15 E
Banja Luka, Yugo. (bän-yä-lōō'kȧ)	172	44.45 N	17.11 E
Banjarmasin, Indon. (bän-jēr-mä'sēn)	206	3.18 S	114.32 E
Banjin, China (bän-jyĭn)	200	32.23 N	120.14 E
Banjul (Bathurst), Gam.	228	13.28 N	16.39 W
Bankberg (Mts.), S. Afr. (baŋk'bûrg)	227c	32.18 S	25.15 E
Ban Khlong Samrong, Thai.	68f	13.39 N	100.36 E
Banks, Or. (bănks)	118c	45.37 N	123.07 W
Banks, C., Austl.	211b	34.01 S	151.17 E
Banks (Is.), Austl.	215	10.10 S	143.08 E
Banks I., Can.	94	73.00 N	123.00 W
Banks I., Can.	98	53.25 N	130.10 W
Banks Is., Vanuatu	215	13.38 S	168.23 E
Banksmeadow, Austl.	70a	33.58 S	151.13 E
Banks Pen., N.Z.	215a	43.45 S	172.20 E
Banks Str., Austl.	216	40.45 S	148.00 E
Bankstown, Austl.	70a	33.55 S	151.02 E
Ban Lat Phrao, Thai.	68f	13.47 N	100.36 E
Bann (R.), N. Ire. (băn)	162	54.50 N	6.29 W
Banning, Ca. (băn'ĭng)	119a	33.56 N	116.53 W
Bannister (R.), Va. (băn'ĭs-tēr)	127	36.45 N	79.17 W
Bannockburn, Austl.	211a	38.03 S	144.11 E
Bannu, Pak.	196	33.03 N	70.39 E
Baños, Ec. (bä'-nyôs)	142	1.30 S	78.22 W
Banská Bystrica, Czech. (bän'skä bē'strē-tzä)	167	48.46 N	19.10 E
Bansko, Bul. (bän'skō)	173	41.51 N	23.33 E
Banstala, India	67a	22.32 N	88.25 E
Banstead, Eng. (băn'stĕd)	156b	51.18 N	0.09 W
Banton, Phil. (bän-tōn')	207a	12.54 N	121.55 E
Bantry, Ire. (băn'trĭ)	162	51.39 N	9.30 W
Bantry B., Ire.	162	51.25 N	10.09 W
Banyuwangi, Indon. (bän-jōō-wäŋ'gē)	206	8.15 S	114.15 E
Baocheng, China (bou-chŭŋ)	202	33.15 N	106.58 E
Baodi, China (bou-dē)	200	39.44 N	117.19 E
Baoding, China (bou-dĭŋ)	200	38.52 N	115.31 E
Baoji, China (bou-jyē)	202	34.10 N	106.58 E
Baoshan, China (bou-shän)	198	25.14 N	99.03 E
Baoshan, China	201b	31.25 N	121.29 E
Baotou, China (bou-tō)	202	40.28 N	110.10 E
Baoying, China (bou-yĭŋ)	200	33.14 N	119.20 E
Bapsfontein, S. Afr. (băps-fŏn-tān')	227b	26.01 S	28.26 E
Ba 'qūbah, Iraq	195	33.45 N	44.38 E
Ba-queo, Viet.	68m	10.48 N	106.38 E
Baqueroncito, Col. (bä-kē-rô'n-sē-tô)	142a	3.18 N	74.40 W
Bar, Sov. Un. (bär)	175	49.02 N	27.44 E
Bara, India	67a	22.46 N	88.17 E
Baraawe, Som.	223a	1.20 N	44.00 E
Barabinsk, Sov. Un. (bȧ'rȧ-bĭnsk)	180	55.18 N	78.00 E
Baraboo, Wi. (bâr'ȧ-bōō)	115	43.29 N	89.44 W
Baracoa, Cuba (bä-rä-kō'ä)	135	20.20 N	74.25 W
Baracoa, Cuba	135a	23.03 N	82.34 W
Baradeo, Arg. (bä-rä-dĕ'ô)	141c	33.50 S	59.30 W
Baradères, Baie des (B.), Hai (bä-rä-dâr')	135	18.35 N	73.35 W
Baragwanath, S. Afr.	71b	26.16 S	27.59 E
Barahona, Dom. Rep. (bä-rä-ô'nä)	135	18.15 N	71.10 W
Barajas de Madrid, Sp. (bä-rä'häs dā mä-drēdh')	171a	40.28 N	3.35 W
Baranagar, India	196a	22.38 N	88.25 E
Baranco, Belize (bä-räŋ'kō)	132	16.01 N	88.55 W
Baranof (I.), Ak. (bä-rä'nôf)	107	56.48 N	136.08 W
Baranovichi, Sov. Un. (bä'rä-nô-vē'chē)	167	53.08 N	25.59 E
Baranpauh, Indon.	191b	0.40 N	103.28 E
Barão de Juperanã, Braz. (bä-rouN-dĕ-zhōō-pe-rä'nȧ)	144b	22.21 S	43.41 W
Barão de Melgaço, Braz. (bä-rouN-dĕ-mĕl-gä'sô)	143	16.12 S	55.48 W
Bārasat, India	67a	22.51 N	88.22 E
Bārāsat, India	196a	22.42 N	88.29 E
Barataria B., La.	125	29.13 N	89.90 W
Baraya, Col. (bä-rä'yä)	142a	3.10 N	75.04 W
Barbacena, Braz. (bär-bä-sā'nȧ)	141a	21.15 S	43.46 W
Barbacoas, Col. (bär-bä-kō'äs)	142	1.39 N	78.12 W
Barbacoas, Ven. (bä-bä-kô'äs)	143b	9.30 N	66.58 W
Barbados, N.A. (bär-bā'dōz)	129	13.30 N	59.00 W
Barbar, Sud.	225	18.11 N	34.00 E
Barbastro, Sp. (bär-bäs'trō)	171	42.05 N	0.05 E
Barbeau, Mi. (bȧr-bō')	119k	46.17 N	84.16 W
Barberton, Oh. (bär'bēr-tŭn)	113d	41.01 N	81.37 W
Barberton, S. Afr.	226	25.48 S	31.04 E
Barbezieux, Fr. (bärb-zyû')	168	45.30 N	0.11 W
Barbosa, Col. (bär-bô'-sȧ)	142a	6.26 N	75.19 W
Barboursville, WV (bär'bērs-vĭl)	110	38.20 N	82.20 W
Barbourville, Ky.	126	36.52 N	83.58 W
Barbuda (I.), Antigua (bär-bōō'dȧ)	129	17.45 N	61.15 W
Barcaldine, Austl. (bär'kôl-dīn)	215	23.33 S	145.17 E
Barcarena, Port. (bär-kä-rĕ'-nä)	171b	38.29 N	9.17 W
Barcarrota, Sp. (bär-kär-rō'tä)	170	38.31 N	6.50 W
Barcellona, It. (bä-chĕl-lō'nä)	172	38.07 N	15.15 E
Barcelona (Neigh.), Sp.	65b	40.22 N	3.34 E
Barcelona, Sp. (bär-thȧ-lō'nä)	171	41.25 N	2.08 E
Barcelona, Ven. (bär-sȧ-lō'nä)	143b	10.09 N	64.41 W
Barcelos, Braz. (bär-sĕ'lôs)	142	1.04 S	63.00 W
Barcelos, Port. (bär-thȧ'lōs)	170e	41.34 N	8.39 W
Barcroft, Lake (Res.), Md.	56d	38.51 N	77.09 W
Bardar-e Pahlavī, Iran	192	37.16 N	49.15 E
Bardawīl, Sabkhat al (B.), Egypt	191a	31.20 N	33.24 E
Bardejov, Czech. (bär'dyĕ-yôf)	167	49.18 N	21.18 E
Bardsey I., Wales (bärd'sē)	162	52.45 N	4.50 W
Bardstown, Ky. (bärds'toun)	110	37.50 N	85.30 W
Bardwell, Ky. (bärd'wĕl)	126	36.51 N	88.57 W
Bare Hills, Md.	56c	39.23 N	76.40 W
Barents Sea, Sov. Un. (bä'rĕnts)	176	72.14 N	37.28 E
Barentu, Eth. (bä-rĕn'tōō)	225	15.06 N	37.39 E
Barfleur, Pte. de (Pt.), Fr. (bȧr-flûr')	168	49.43 N	1.17 W
Barguzin, Sov. Un. (bär'gōō-zĭn)	181	53.44 N	109.28 E
Bar Harbor, Me. (bär här'bēr)	104	44.22 N	68.13 W
Bari, It. (bä'rē)	172	41.08 N	16.53 E
Barinas, Ven. (bä-rē'näs)	142	8.36 N	70.14 W
Baring, C., Can. (bâr'ĭng)	96	70.07 N	119.48 W
Barisan, Pegunungan (Mts.), Indon. (bä-rē-sän')	206	2.38 S	101.45 E
Bariti Bil (L.), India	67a	22.48 N	88.26 E
Barito (Strm.), Indon. (bä-rē'tō)	206	2.10 S	114.38 E
Barka (R.), Eth.	225	16.44 N	37.34 E
Barking (Neigh.), Eng.	62	51.33 N	0.06 E
Barkingside (Neigh.), Eng.	62	51.36 N	0.05 E
Barkley Sd., Can.	98	48.53 N	125.20 W
Barkly East, S. Afr. (bärk'lē ēst)	227c	30.58 S	27.37 E
Barkly Tableland (Plat.), Austl. (bär'klē)	214	18.15 S	137.05 E
Barkol, China (bär-kûl)	198	43.43 N	92.50 E
Barkshire (Co.), Eng.	156b	51.23 N	1.07 W
Bar-le-Duc, Fr. (bär-lē-dük')	168	48.47 N	5.05 E
Barlee (L.), Austl. (bär-lē')	214	29.45 S	119.00 E
Barletta, It. (bär-lĕt'tä)	172	41.19 N	16.20 E
Barmen (Neigh.), F.R.G.	63	51.17 N	7.13 E
Barmstedt, F.R.G. (bärm'shtĕt)	157c	53.47 N	9.46 E
Barnaul, Sov. Un. (bär-nä-ōōl')	180	53.18 N	83.23 E
Barnes (Neigh.), Eng.	62	51.28 N	0.15 W
Barnesboro, Pa. (bärnz'bēr-ô)	111	40.45 N	78.50 W
Barnesville, Ga. (bärnz'vĭl)	126	33.03 N	84.10 W
Barnesville, Mn.	114	46.38 N	96.25 W
Barnesville, Oh.	110	39.55 N	81.10 W
Barnet, Vt. (bär'nĕt)	111	44.20 N	72.00 W
Barnetby le Wold, Eng. (bär'nĕt-bĭ)	156	53.34 N	0.26 W
Barnett Hbr., Ba.	134	25.40 N	79.20 W
Barnsdall, Ok. (bärnz'dôl)	123	36.38 N	96.14 W
Barnsley, Eng. (bärnz'lĭ)	156	53.33 N	1.29 W
Barnstaple, Eng. (bärn'stā-p'l)	162	51.06 N	4.05 W
Barnston, Eng.	64a	53.21 N	3.05 W
Barnum Island, NY	55	40.36 N	73.39 W
Barnwell, SC (bärn'wĕl)	127	33.14 N	81.23 W
Baro, Nig. (bä'rô)	229	8.37 N	6.25 E
Baroda, India (bär-rō'dä)	196	22.21 N	73.12 E
Barotse Pln., Zambia	230	15.50 S	22.55 E
Barqah (Cyrenaica) (Prov.), Libya	225	31.09 N	21.45 E
Barquisimeto, Ven. (bär-kē-sē-mä'tō)	142	10.04 N	69.16 W
Barra, Braz. (bär'rä)	143	11.04 S	43.11 W
Barraba, Austl.	216	30.22 S	150.36 E
Barracas (Neigh.), Arg.	60d	34.38 S	58.22 W
Barrackpore, India	67a	22.46 N	88.21 E
Barrackpore Cantonment, India	67a	22.46 N	88.22 E
Barra do Corda, Braz. (bär'rä dōō cōr-dä)	143	5.33 S	45.13 W
Barra Funda (Neigh.), Braz.	61d	23.31 S	46.39 W
Barra Mansa, Braz. (bär'rä män'sä)	141a	22.35 S	44.09 W
Barrancabermeja, Col. (bär-räŋ'kä-bēr-mā'hä)	142	7.06 N	73.49 W
Barrancas, Chile	61b	33.27 S	70.46 W
Barranco, Peru	60c	12.09 S	77.02 W
Barranquilla, Col. (bär-rän-kēl'yä)	142	10.57 N	75.00 W
Barras, Braz. (bȧ'r-räs)	143	4.13 S	42.14 W
Barre, Vt. (băr'ē)	111	44.15 N	72.30 W
Barre do Piraí, Braz. (bȧr'rĕ-dô-pē'rä-ē')	141a	22.30 S	43.49 W
Barreiras, Braz. (bär-rā'räs)	143	12.13 S	44.59 W
Barreiro, Port. (bär-rĕ'ē-rōō)	171b	38.39 N	9.05 W
Barren (R.), Ky.	126	37.00 N	86.20 W
Barren, C., Austl. (băr'ĕn)	216	40.20 S	149.00 E
Barren, Nosy (Is.), Mad.	227	18.18 S	43.57 E
Barretos, Braz. (bär-rā'tōs)	143	20.40 S	48.36 W
Barrhead, Can. (băr-hĕd) (băr'ĭd)	99	54.08 N	114.24 W
Barriada Pomar Alto, Sp.	65e	41.29 N	2.14 E
Barrie, Can. (băr'ĭ)	111	44.25 N	79.45 W
Barrington, Can. (bă-rĕng-tŏn)	95a	45.07 N	73.35 W
Barrington, Il.	113a	42.09 N	88.08 W
Barrington, NJ	56b	39.52 N	75.04 W
Barrington, RI	112b	41.44 N	71.16 W
Barrington Tops (Mtn.), Austl.	216	32.00 S	151.25 E
Barrio Obrero Industrial, Peru	60c	12.04 S	77.04 W
Bar River, Can. (bär)	119k	46.27 N	84.02 W
Barron, Wi. (băr'ŭn)	115	45.24 N	91.51 W
Barrow, Ak. (băr'ō)	107	71.20 N	156.00 W
Barrow (I.), Austl.	214	20.50 S	115.00 E
Barrow Creek, Austl.	214	21.23 S	133.55 E
Barrow-in-Furness, Eng.	162	54.10 N	3.15 W
Barrow Pt., Ak.	107	71.20 N	156.00 W
Barrow R., Ire. (bȧ-rȧ)	162	52.35 N	7.05 W
Barstow, Ca. (bär'stō)	120	34.53 N	117.03 W
Barstow, Md.	112e	38.32 N	76.37 W
Barth, G.D.R. (bärt)	166	54.20 N	12.43 E
Bartholomew Bayou, Ar. (bär-thŏl'ô-mū bī-ōō')	123	33.53 N	91.45 W
Barthurst, Can. (bär-thŭrst')	104	47.38 N	65.40 W
Bartica, Guy (bär'tĭ-kȧ)	143	6.23 N	58.32 W
Bartin, Tur. (bär'tĭn)	179	41.35 N	32.12 E
Bartle Frere, Mt., Austl. (bärt''l frēr')	215	17.30 S	145.46 E
Bartlesville, Ok. (bär'tlz-vĭl)	123	36.44 N	95.58 W
Bartlett, Il. (bärt'lĕt)	113a	41.59 N	88.11 W
Bartlett, Tx.	125	30.48 N	97.25 W
Barton, Vt. (bär'tŭn)	111	44.45 N	72.05 W
Barton-upon-Humber, Eng. (bär'tŭn-ŭp'ŏn-hŭm'bēr)	156	53.41 N	0.26 W
Bartoszyce, Pol. (bär-tô-shĭ'tsȧ)	167	54.15 N	20.50 E
Bartow, Fl. (bär'tō)	127a	27.51 N	81.50 W
Baruta, Ven.	61a	10.26 N	66.53 W
Barú, Volcán (Vol.), Pan.	133	8.48 N	82.37 W
Barvenkovo, Sov. Un. (bär'vĕn-kô'vô)	175	48.55 N	36.59 E
Barwon (R.), Austl. (bär'wŭn)	216	29.45 S	148.25 E
Barwon Heads, Austl.	211a	38.17 S	144.29 E
Barycz R., Pol. (bä'rĭch)	166	51.30 N	16.38 E
Basai Dārāpur (Neigh.), India	67d	28.40 N	77.08 E
Basankusu, Zaire (bä-sän-kōō'sōō)	225	1.14 N	19.45 E
Basbeck, F.R.G. (bäs'bĕk)	157c	53.40 N	9.11 E
Basdahl, F.R.G. (bäs'däl)	157c	53.27 N	9.00 E
Basehor, Ks. (bās'hôr)	119f	39.08 N	94.55 W
Basel, Switz. (bä'z'l)	166	47.32 N	7.35 E
Bashee (R.), S. Afr. (bă-shē')	227c	31.47 S	28.25 E
Bashi Chan, Phil. (bäsh'ē)	203	21.20 N	120.22 E
Bashkir (A.S.S.R.), Sov. Un. (bȧsh-kēr')	178	54.12 N	57.15 E
Bashtanka, Sov. Un. (bȧsh-tän'kȧ)	175	47.24 N	32.31 E
Bashtīl, Egypt	71a	30.05 N	31.11 E
Basilan I., Phil.	206	6.37 N	122.07 E
Basildon, Eng.	62	51.35 N	0.25 E
Basilicata (Reg.), It. (bä-zē-lē-kä'tä)	172	40.30 N	15.55 E
Basin, Wy. (bā'sĭn)	117	44.22 N	108.02 W
Basingstoke, Eng. (bā'zĭng-stōk)	156b	51.14 N	1.06 W
Baška, Yugo. (bäsh'ka)	172	44.58 N	14.44 E
Baskale, Tur. (bäsh-kä'lĕ)	179	38.10 N	44.00 E
Baskatong Res., Can.	103	46.50 N	75.50 W
Baskunchak (L.), Sov. Un.	179	48.20 N	46.40 E
Basoko, Zaire (bȧ-sō'kō)	225	0.52 N	23.50 E
Bassano, Can. (bäs-sän'ō)	99	50.47 N	112.28 W
Bassano del Grappa, It.	172	45.46 N	11.44 E
Bassari, Togo	228	9.15 N	0.47 E
Bassas da India (I.), Afr. (bäs'säs dä ēn'dē-ȧ)	227	21.23 S	39.42 E
Bassein, Bur. (bŭ-sēn')	206	16.46 N	94.47 E
Basse Terre, Guad. (bȧs' târ')	133b	16.00 N	61.43 W
Basseterre, Saint Christopher-Nevis	133b	17.20 N	62.42 W
Basse Terre I., Guad.	133b	16.10 N	62.14 W
Bassett, Va. (băs'sĕt)	127	36.45 N	81.58 W
Bass Hill, Austl.	70a	33.54 S	151.00 E
Bass Is., Oh. (băs)	110	41.40 N	82.50 W
Bass Str., Austl.	216	39.40 S	145.40 E
Basswood (L.), Can.-Mn. (băs'wŏŏd)	115	48.10 N	91.36 W
Båstad, Swe. (bô'stät)	164	56.26 N	12.46 E
Bastia, Fr. (bäs'tē-ä)	172	42.43 N	9.27 E
Bastogne, Bel. (bäs-tôn'y')	163	50.02 N	5.45 E
Bastrop, La. (băs'trŭp)	125	32.47 N	91.55 W
Bastrop, Tx.	125	30.08 N	97.18 W
Bastrop Bayou, Tx.	125a	29.07 N	95.22 W

PLACE (Pronounciation)	PAGE	Lat. °′	Long. °′
Bāsudebpur, India	67a	22.49 N	88.25 E
Bata, Equat.Gui. (bä'tä)	230	1.51 N	9.45 E
Batabanó, Cuba (bä-tä-bä-nō')	134	22.45 N	82.20 W
Batabano, Golfo, de (G.), Cuba (gôl-fô-dĕ-bä-tä-bä'nō)	134	22.10 N	83.05 W
Batāla, India	196	31.54 N	75.18 E
Bataly, Sov. Un. (bá-tä'lĭ)	182a	52.51 N	62.03 E
Batam I., Indon. (bä-täm')	191b	1.03 N	104.00 E
Batang, China (bä-täŋ)	198	30.08 N	99.00 E
Batangan, C., Viet.	203	15.18 N	109.10 E
Batangas, Phil. (bä-tän'gäs)	207a	13.45 N	121.04 E
Batan Is., Phil. (bä-tän')	203	20.58 N	122.20 E
Bátaszék, Hung. (bä'tà-sĕk)	167	46.07 N	18.40 E
Batavia, Il. (bá-tā'vĭ-á)	113a	41.51 N	88.18 W
Batavia, NY	111	43.00 N	78.15 W
Batavia, Oh.	113f	39.05 N	84.10 W
Bataysk, Sov. Un. (bá-tīsk')	175	47.08 N	39.44 E
Bătdâmbâng, Kamp. (bàt-tàm-băng')	206	13.14 N	103.15 E
Batenbrock (Neigh.), F.R.G.	63	51.31 N	6.57 E
Batesburg, SC (bāts'bûrg)	127	33.53 N	81.34 W
Batesville, Ar. (bāts'vĭl)	123	35.46 N	91.39 W
Batesville, In.	110	39.15 N	85.15 W
Batesville, Ms.	126	34.17 N	89.55 W
Batetska, Sov. Un. (bá-tĕ'tská)	174	58.36 N	30.21 E
Bath, Can. (bàth)	104	46.31 N	67.36 W
Bath, Eng.	162	51.24 N	2.20 W
Bath, Me.	104	43.54 N	69.50 W
Bath, NY	111	42.25 N	77.20 W
Bath, Oh.	113d	41.11 N	81.38 W
Bathsheba, Barb.	133b	13.13 N	60.30 W
Bathurst, Austl. (bàth'ŭrst)	215	33.28 S	149.30 E
Bathurst (I.), Austl.	214	11.19 S	130.13 E
Bathurst, S. Afr. (băt-hûrst)	227c	33.26 S	26.53 E
Bathurst, C., Can. (báth'ŭrst)	107	70.33 N	127.55 W
Bathurst Inlet, Can.	96	68.10 N	108.00 W
Bathurst, see Banjul			
Batia, Benin	228	10.54 N	1.29 E
Batian (I.), Indon.	207	1.07 S	127.52 E
Bāṭlāq-E Gāvkhūnī (L.), Iran	192	31.40 N	52.48 E
Batley, Eng. (băt'lĭ)	156	53.43 N	1.37 W
Batna, Alg. (bät'nä)	224	35.41 N	6.12 E
Baton Rouge, La. (băt'ŭn rōōzh')	125	30.28 N	91.10 W
Batouri, Cam.	229	4.26 N	14.22 E
Battersea (Neigh.), Eng.	62	51.28 N	0.10 W
Batticaloa, Sri Lanka	197	8.40 N	81.10 E
Battle (R.), Can.	99	52.20 N	111.59 W
Battle (R.), Can.	100	53.05 N	109.40 W
Battle Creek, Mi. (băt''l krēk')	110	42.20 N	85.15 W
Battle Ground, Wa. (băt''l ground)	118c	45.47 N	122.32 W
Battle Harbour, Can. (băt''l här'bẽr)	97	52.17 N	55.33 W
Battle Mountain, Nv.	116	40.40 N	116.56 W
Battonya, Hung. (bät-tô'nyä)	167	46.17 N	21.00 E
Batu Kepulauan (I.), Indon. (bä'tōō)	206	0.10 S	99.55 E
Batumi, Sov. Un. (bŭ-tōō'mē)	179	41.40 N	41.30 E
Batu Pahat., Mala.	191b	1.51 N	102.56 E
Batupanjang, Indon.	191b	1.42 N	101.35 E
Baturité, Braz. (bä-tōō-rē-tā')	143	4.16 S	38.47 W
Bauang, Phil. (bä'wäng)	207a	16.31 N	120.19 E
Bauchi, Nig. (bà-ōō'chē)	229	10.19 N	9.50 E
Baudouinville, Zaire (bō-dwăN-vēl')	226	7.12 S	29.39 E
Bauernschaft, F.R.G.	63	51.34 N	6.33 E
Bauerstown, Pa.	57b	40.30 N	79.59 W
Baukau (Neigh.), F.R.G.	63	51.33 N	7.12 E
Bauld, C. Can.	105	51.38 N	55.25 W
Baulkham Hills, Austl.	70a	33.46 S	151.00 E
Baumschulenweg (Neigh.), G.D.R.	65a	52.28 N	13.29 E
Bāuria, India	196a	22.29 N	88.08 E
Bauru, Braz. (bou-rōō')	143	22.21 S	48.57 W
Bauska, Sov. Un. (bou'ská)	165	56.24 N	24.12 E
Bauta, Cuba (bà'ōō-tä)	135a	22.59 N	82.33 W
Bautzen, G.D.R. (bout'sĕn)	166	51.11 N	14.27 E
Bavaria (State), see Bayern			
Baw Baw, Mt., Austl. (bà-bà)	216	37.50 S	146.17 E
Bawean, Pulau (I.), Indon. (bà'vē-än)	206	5.50 S	112.40 E
Bawtry, Eng. (bôtrĭ)	156	53.26 N	1.01 W
Baxley, Ga. (băks'lĭ)	127	31.47 N	82.22 W
Baxter, Austl. (Băks'tẽr)	211a	38.12 S	145.10 E
Baxter Springs, Ks. (băks'tẽr springs')	123	37.01 N	94.44 W
Bayaguana, Dom. Rep. (bä-yä-gwä'nä)	135	18.45 N	69.40 W
Bay al Kabīr Wadi (R.), Libya	160	29.52 N	14.28 E
Bayambang, Phil. (bä-yäm-bäng')	207a	15.50 N	120.26 E
Bayamo, Cuba (bä-yä'mō)	134	20.25 N	76.35 W
Bayamón, P.R.	129b	18.27 N	66.13 W
Bayan, China (bä-yän)	202	46.00 N	127.20 E
Bayan-Aul, Sov. Un. (bä'yän-oul')	180	50.43 N	75.37 E
Bayard, Ne. (bā'ẽrd)	114	41.45 N	103.20 W
Bayard, WV	111	39.15 N	79.20 W
Bayburt, Tur. (bä'ĭ-bŏŏrt)	179	40.15 N	40.10 E
Baychabo, Som.	223a	3.19 N	44.20 E
Bay City, Mi. (bā)	110	43.35 N	83.55 W
Bay City, Tx.	125	28.59 N	95.58 W
Baydarag Gol (R.), Mong.	198	46.09 N	98.52 E
Baydaratskaya Guba (B.), Sov. Un.	178	69.20 N	66.10 E
Bay de Verde, Can.	105	48.05 N	52.54 W
Bayern (Bavaria) (State), F.R.G. (bī'ẽrn) (bà-vâ-rĭ-á)	166	49.00 N	11.16 E
Bayeux, Fr. (bá-yû')	168	49.19 N	0.41 W
Bayfield, Wi. (bā'fēld)	115	46.48 N	90.51 W
Bayford, Eng.	62	51.46 N	0.06 W
Baykal, Ozero (Baikal, L.), Sov. Un. (bī'käl') (bī'kôl)	181	53.00 N	109.28 E
Baykals'kiy Khrebet (Baikal Mts.), Sov. Un.	181	53.30 N	102.00 E
Baykit, Sov. Un. (bī-kēt')	180	61.43 N	96.39 E
Baykonur, Sov. Un. (bī-kô-nōōr')	180	47.46 N	66.11 E
Baymak, Sov. Un. (bày'mäk)	182a	52.35 N	58.21 E
Bay Mills, Mi. (bā mĭlls)	119k	46.27 N	84.36 W
Bay Mills Ind. Res., Mi.	115	46.19 N	85.03 W
Bay Minette, Al. (bā'mĭn-ĕt')	126	30.52 N	87.44 W
Bayombong, Phil. (bä-yôm-bŏng')	207a	16.28 N	121.09 E
Bayonne, Fr. (bá-yŏn')	168	43.28 N	1.30 W
Bayonne, NJ (bā-yōn')	112a	40.40 N	74.07 W
Bayou Bodcau Res., La. (bī'yōō bŏd'kō)	125	32.49 N	93.22 W
Bay Park, NY	55	40.38 N	73.40 W
Bayport, Mn. (bā'pōrt)	119g	45.02 N	92.46 W
Bayramic, Tur.	173	39.48 N	26.35 E
Bayreuth, F.R.G. (bī-roit')	166	49.56 N	11.35 E
Bay Ridge (Neigh.), NY	55	40.37 N	74.02 W
Bay Roberts, Can. (bā rŏb'ẽrts)	105	47.36 N	53.16 W
Bayrūt, see Beirut			
Bay Saint Louis, Ms. (bā' sănt lōō'ĭs)	126	30.19 N	89.20 W
Bay Shore, NY (bā' shôr)	112a	40.44 N	73.15 W
Bayside, Ma.	54a	42.18 N	70.53 W
Bayside (Neigh.), NY	55	40.46 N	73.46 W
Bays, L. of, Can. (bās)	111	45.15 N	79.00 W
Bayswater, Austl.	70b	37.51 S	145.16 E
Bayswater North, Austl.	70b	37.49 S	145.17 E
Bayt Lahm (Bethlehem), Jordan (bĕth'lē-hĕm)	191a	31.42 N	35.13 E
Baytown, Tx. (bā'town)	125a	29.44 N	95.01 W
Bayview, Al. (bā'vū)	112h	33.34 N	86.59 W
Bayview (Neigh.), Ca.	58b	37.44 N	122.23 W
Bayview, Wa.	118a	48.29 N	122.28 W
Bay Village, Oh. (bā)	113d	41.29 N	81.56 W
Bayville, NY	55	40.54 N	73.33 W
Baza, Sp. (bä'thä)	170	37.29 N	2.46 W
Bazar-Dyuzi (Mt.), Sov. Un. (bä'zàr-dyōōz'ĕ)	179	41.20 N	47.40 E
Bazaruto, Ilha do (I.), Moz. (bä-zá-rōō'tō)	226	21.42 S	36.10 E
Baza, Sierra de (Mts.), Sp.	170	37.19 N	2.48 W
Baziège, Fr.	168	43.25 N	1.41 E
Beach, ND (bēch)	114	46.55 N	104.00 W
Beachwood, Oh.	56a	41.34 N	81.28 W
Beachy Head, Eng. (bēchē hĕd)	163	50.40 N	0.25 E
Beacon, NY (bē'kŭn)	111	41.30 N	73.55 W
Beacon Hill, Austl.	70a	33.45 S	151.15 E
Beacon Hill (Mtn.), China	68c	22.21 N	114.09 E
Beaconsfield, Can. (bē'kŭnz-fēld)	95a	45.26 N	73.51 W
Beafort Mtn., NJ (bē'fōrt)	112a	41.08 N	74.23 W
Beals Cr., Tx. (bēls)	124	32.10 N	101.14 W
Bean, Eng.	62	51.25 N	0.17 E
Bear (L.), Id.-Ut.	117	41.56 N	111.10 W
Bear Brook (R.), Can.	95c	45.24 N	75.15 W
Bear Cr., Al. (bâr)	126	34.27 N	88.00 W
Bear Cr., Tx.	119c	32.56 N	97.09 W
Bear Creek, Mt. (bâr krēk)	117	45.11 N	109.07 W
Beardstown, Il. (bērds'toun)	123	40.01 N	90.26 W
Bearhead Mtn., Wa. (bâr'hĕd)	118a	47.01 N	121.49 W
Bear L., Can.	101	55.08 N	96.00 W
Bear R., Id.	117	42.17 N	111.42 W
Bear R., Ut.	119b	41.28 N	112.10 W
Beas de Segura, Sp. (bä'äs dā sä-gōō'rä)	170	38.16 N	2.53 W
Beata (I.), Dom. Rep. (bĕ-ä'tä)	135	17.40 N	71.40 W
Beata, Cabo (C.), Dom. Rep. (kä'bô-bĕ-ä'tä)	135	17.40 N	71.20 W
Beato (Neigh.), Port.	65d	38.44 N	9.06 W
Beatrice, Ne. (bē'á-trĭs)	123	40.16 N	96.45 W
Beatty, Nv. (bēt'ē)	120	36.58 N	116.48 W
Beattyville, Ky. (bēt'ē-vĭl)	110	37.35 N	83.40 W
Beaucaire, Fr. (bō-kâr')	168	43.49 N	4.37 E
Beaucourt, Fr. (bō-kōōr')	169	47.30 N	6.54 E
Beaufort, NC (bō'frt)	127	34.43 N	76.40 W
Beaufort, SC	127	32.25 N	80.40 W
Beaufort Sea, Ak.	107	70.30 N	138.40 W
Beaufort West, S. Afr.	226	32.20 S	22.45 E
Beauharnois, Can. (bō-är-nwä')	95a	45.23 N	73.52 W
Beaumont, Ca. (bō'mŏnt)	119a	33.57 N	116.57 W
Beaumont, Can.	95b	46.50 N	71.01 W
Beaumont, Can.	95g	53.22 N	113.18 W
Beaumont, Tx.	125	30.05 N	94.06 W
Beaune, Fr. (bōn)	168	47.02 N	4.49 E
Beauport, Can. (bō-pôr')	95b	46.52 N	71.11 W
Beaupré, Can. (bō-prā')	95b	47.03 N	70.53 W
Beauséjour, Can.	101	50.04 N	96.33 W
Beauvais, Fr. (bō-vĕ')	168	49.25 N	2.05 E
Beaver (I.), Mi.	110	45.40 N	85.30 W
Beaver, Ok. (bē'vẽr)	122	36.46 N	100.31 W
Beaver, Pa.	113e	40.42 N	80.18 W
Beaver (R.), Can.	100	54.20 N	111.10 W
Beaver, Ut.	121	38.15 N	112.40 W
Beaver City, Ne.	122	40.08 N	99.52 W
Beaver Cr., Co.	122	39.42 N	103.37 W
Beaver Cr., Ks.	122	39.44 N	101.05 W
Beaver Cr., Mt.	114	46.45 N	104.18 W
Beaver Cr., Wy.	114	43.46 N	104.25 W
Beaver Dam, Wi.	115	43.29 N	88.50 W
Beaverhead Mts., Mt. (bē'vẽr-hĕd)	117	44.33 N	112.59 W
Beaverhead R., Mt.	117	45.25 N	112.35 W
Beaver Ind. Res., Mi.	110	45.40 N	85.30 W
Beaverton, Or. (bē'vẽr-tŭn)	118c	45.29 N	122.49 W
Bebará', Col. (bĕ-bä-rá')	142a	6.07 N	76.39 W
Bebek (Neigh.), Tur.	66f	41.04 N	29.02 E
Bebington, Eng. (bē'bĭng-tŭn)	156	53.20 N	2.59 W
Beccar (Neigh.), Arg.	60d	34.28 S	58.31 W
Bečej, Yugo. (bĕ'chā)	173	45.36 N	20.03 E
Becerreá, Sp. (bā-thā'rē-ä)	170	42.49 N	7.12 W
Béchar, Alg.	224	31.39 N	2.14 W
Becharof (L.), Ak. (bĕk-á-rôf)	107	57.58 N	156.58 W
Becher B., Can. (bēch'ẽr)	118a	48.18 N	123.37 W
Beckenham (Neigh.), Eng.	62	51.24 N	0.02 W
Beckley, WV (bĕk'lĭ)	110	37.40 N	81.15 W
Bédarieux, Fr. (bā-dá-ryû')	168	43.36 N	3.11 E
Beddington (Neigh.), Eng.	62	51.22 N	0.08 W
Beddington Cr., Can. (bĕd'ĕng tŭn)	95e	51.14 N	114.13 W
Bedford, Can. (bĕd'fẽrd)	111	45.10 N	73.00 W
Bedford, Eng.	162	52.10 N	0.25 W
Bedford, Ia.	115	40.40 N	94.41 W
Bedford, In.	110	38.50 N	86.30 W
Bedford, Ma.	105a	42.30 N	71.17 W
Bedford, NY	112a	41.12 N	73.38 W
Bedford, Oh.	113d	41.23 N	81.32 W
Bedford, Pa.	111	40.05 N	78.20 W
Bedford, S. Afr.	227c	32.43 S	26.19 E
Bedford, Va.	127	37.19 N	79.27 W
Bedford Heights, Oh.	56a	41.22 N	81.30 W
Bedford Hills, NY	112a	41.14 N	73.41 W
Bedford Park, Il.	58a	41.46 N	87.49 W
Bedford Park (Neigh.), NY	55	40.52 N	73.53 W
Bedford-Stuyvesant (Neigh.), NY	55	40.41 N	73.55 W
Bedmond, Eng.	62	51.43 N	0.25 W
Bedok, Singapore	67c	1.19 N	103.57 E
Beebe, Ar. (bē'bē)	123	35.04 N	91.54 W
Beecher, Il. (bē'chŭr)	113a	41.20 N	87.38 W
Beechey Hd., Can. (bē'chĭ hĕd)	118a	48.19 N	123.40 W
Beech Grove, In. (bēch grōv)	113g	39.43 N	86.05 W
Beechview (Neigh.), Pa.	57b	40.25 N	80.02 W
Beeck (Neigh.), F.R.G.	63	51.29 N	6.44 E
Beeckerwerth (Neigh.), F.R.G.	63	51.29 N	6.41 E
Beecroft Hd., Austl. (bē'krûft)	216	35.03 S	151.15 E
Beelitz, G.D.R. (bē'lētz)	157b	52.14 N	12.59 E
Be'er Sheva', Isr. (bēr-shē'bá)	191a	31.15 N	34.48 E
Be'er Sheva' (R.), Isr.	191a	31.23 N	34.30 E
Beestekraal, S. Afr.	223d	25.22 S	27.34 E
Beeston, Eng. (bēs't'n)	156	52.55 N	1.11 W
Beetz R., G.D.R. (bĕtz)	157b	52.28 N	12.37 E
Beeville, Tx. (bē'vĭl)	125	28.24 N	97.44 W
Bega, Austl. (bā'gá)	216	36.50 S	149.49 E
Beggs, Ok. (bĕgz)	123	35.46 N	96.06 W
Bègles, Fr. (bĕ'gl')	168	44.47 N	0.34 W
Begoro, Ghana	228	6.23 N	0.23 W
Behala, India	196a	22.31 N	88.19 E
Behbehān, Iran	195	30.35 N	50.14 E
Behm Can., Ak.	98	55.41 N	131.35 W
Bei (R.), China (bā)	201a	22.54 N	113.08 E
Bei'an, China (bā-än)	202	48.05 N	126.26 E
Beicai, China (bā-tsī)	201b	31.12 N	121.33 E
Beifei (R.), China (bā-fā)	200	33.14 N	117.03 E
Beihai, China (bā-hī)	203	21.30 N	109.10 E
Beihuangcheng Dao (I.), China (bā-hûäŋ-chŭŋ dou)	200	38.23 N	120.55 E
Beijing (Peking), China (bā-jyĭŋ)	202a	39.55 N	116.23 E
Beijing Shi (Mun.), China (bā-jyĭŋ shr)	200	40.07 N	116.00 E
Beira, Moz. (bā'rá)	226	19.45 S	34.58 E
Beira (Reg.), Port. (bĕ'y-rä)	170	40.38 N	8.00 W
Beirut, (Bayrūt), Leb. (bā-rōōt')	191a	33.53 N	35.30 E
Beiyuan, China	67b	40.01 N	116.24 E
Beja, Port. (bä'zhä)	170	38.03 N	7.53 W
Béja, Tun.	159	36.52 N	9.20 E
Bejaïa (Bougie), Alg.	224	36.46 N	5.00 E
Béjar, Sp.	170	40.25 N	5.43 W
Bejestān, Iran	192	34.30 N	58.22 E
Bejucal, Cuba (bā-hōō-käl')	135a	22.56 N	82.23 W
Bejuco, Pan. (bĕ-kōō'kō)	133	8.37 N	79.54 W
Békés, Hung. (bā'kāsh)	167	46.45 N	21.08 E
Békéscsaba, Hung. (bā'kāsh-chô'bô)	167	46.39 N	21.06 E
Beketova, Sov. Un. (bĕk'e-to'vá)	199	53.23 N	125.21 E
Bela Crkva, Yugo. (bĕ'lä tsĕrk'vä)	173	44.53 N	21.25 E
Bel Air (Neigh.), Ca.	59	34.05 N	118.27 W
Bel Air, Va.	56d	38.52 N	77.10 W
Belalcázar, Sp. (bāl-á-kä'thär)	170	38.35 N	5.12 W
Belas, Port.	65d	38.47 N	9.16 W
Bela Vista (Neigh.), Braz.	61d	23.33 S	46.38 W
Bela Vista de Goia's, Braz.	143	16.57 S	48.47 W
Belawan, Indon. (bā-lä'wän)	206	3.43 N	98.43 E
Belaya (R.), Sov. Un. (byĕ'lĭ-yá)	178	52.30 N	56.15 E
Belaya Tserkov', Sov. Un. (byĕ'lĭ-yá tsĕr'kôf)	175	49.48 N	30.09 E
Belcher Is., Can. (bĕl'chẽr)	97	56.20 N	80.40 W
Belding, Mi. (bĕl'dĭng)	110	43.05 N	85.25 W
Belebey, Sov. Un. (byĕ'lĕ-bā'ĭ)	178	54.00 N	54.10 E
Belém (Neigh.), Port.	65d	38.42 N	9.12 W
Belém, (Pará), Braz. (bā-lĕN') (pä-rä)	143	1.18 S	48.27 W
Belen, NM (bĕ-lān')	121	34.40 N	106.45 W
Belén, Par. (bā-lān')	144	23.30 S	57.09 W
Belènzinho (Neigh.), Braz.	61d	23.32 S	46.35 W
Bélep, Isles (Is.), N. Cal.	215	19.30 S	160.32 E
Belëv, Sov. Un. (byĕl'yĕf)	174	53.49 N	36.06 E
Belfair, Wa. (bĕl'far)	118a	47.27 N	122.50 W
Belfast, Me. (bĕl'fást)	104	44.25 N	69.01 W
Belfast, N. Ire.	162	54.36 N	5.45 W
Belfast, Lough (B.), Ire. (lŏk bĕl'fást)	162	54.45 N	6.00 W
Belford Roxo, Braz.	61c	22.46 S	43.24 W
Belfort, Fr. (bā-fôr')	169	47.40 N	7.50 E
Belgaum, India	197	15.57 N	74.32 E
Belgium, Eur. (bĕl'jĭ-ŭm)	154	51.00 N	2.52 E
Belgorod (Oblast), Sov. Un.	175	50.40 N	36.42 E
Belgorod, Sov. Un. (byĕl'gŭ-rut)	175	50.36 N	36.32 E
Belgorod Dnestrovskiy, Sov. Un. (byĕl'gŭ-rŭd nyĕs-trôf'skē)	175	46.09 N	30.19 E
Belgrade, see Beograd			
Belgrano (Neigh.), Arg.	60d	34.34 S	58.28 W
Belgrave, Austl.	70b	37.55 S	145.21 E
Belhaven, NC (bĕl'hā-vĕn)	127	35.33 N	76.37 W
Belington, WV (bĕl'ĭng-tŭn)	111	39.00 N	79.55 W
Beli Timok (R.), Yugo. (bĕ'lĕ tē'mōk)	173	43.35 N	22.13 E
Belitung (I.), Indon.	206	3.30 S	107.30 E
Belize, N.A.	128	17.00 N	88.40 W
Belize City, Belize (bĕ-lēz')	132a	17.31 N	88.10 W
Belize R., Belize	132a	17.16 N	88.56 W
Bel'kovo, Sov. Un. (byĕl'kô-vô)	182b	56.15 N	38.49 E
Bel'kovskiy (I.), Sov. Un. (byĕl-kôf'skĭ)	181	75.52 N	133.00 E
Bell, Ca.	59	33.58 N	118.11 W
Bell (I.), Can. (bĕl)	105	50.45 N	55.35 W
Bell (R.), Can.	103	49.25 N	77.15 W
Bella Bella, Can.	98	52.10 N	128.07 W
Bella Coola, Can.	98	52.22 N	126.46 W

PLACE (Pronounciation)	PAGE	Lat. °′	Long. °′
Bellaire, Oh. (bĕl-âr')	110	40.00 N	80.45 W
Bellaire, Tx.	125a	29.43 N	95.28 W
Bellary, India (bĕl-lä'rē)	197	15.15 N	76.56 E
Bella Union, Ur. (bĕ'l-yà-ōō-nyō'n)	144	30.18 S	57.26 W
Bella Vista, Arg. (bā'lyà vēs'tà)	144	27.07 S	65.14 W
Bella Vista, Arg.	144a	34.18 S	58.41 W
Bella Vista, Arg.	144	28.35 S	58.53 W
Bella Vista, Braz.	143	22.16 S	56.14 W
Bellavista, Chile	61b	33.31 S	70.37 W
Bellavista, Peru	60c	12.04 S	77.08 W
Belle-Anse, Hai	135	18.15 N	72.00 W
Belle B., Can. (bĕl)	105	47.35 N	55.15 W
Belle Chasse, La. (bĕl shäs')	112d	29.52 N	90.00 W
Belle Farm Estates, Md.	56c	39.23 N	76.45 W
Bellefontaine, Oh. (bel-fŏn'tăn)	110	40.25 N	83.50 W
Bellefontaine Neighbors, Mo.	119e	38.46 N	90.13 W
Belle Fourche (R.), Wy.	114	44.29 N	104.40 W
Belle Fourche, SD (bĕl' fōōrsh')	114	44.28 N	103.50 W
Belle Fourche Res., SD	114	44.51 N	103.44 W
Bellegarde, Fr. (bĕl-gärd')	169	46.06 N	5.50 E
Belle Glade, Fl. (bĕl glăd)	127a	26.39 N	80.37 W
Bellehaven, Va.	56d	38.47 N	77.04 W
Belle-Île (I.), Fr. (bĕlēl')	168	47.15 N	3.30 W
Belle Isle, Str. of, Can.	105	51.35 N	56.30 W
Belle Mead, NJ (bĕl mēd)	112a	40.28 N	74.40 W
Belleoram, Can.	105	47.31 N	55.25 W
Belle Plaine, Ia. (bĕl plān')	115	41.52 N	92.19 W
Bellerose, NY	55	40.44 N	73.43 W
Belle Vernon, Pa. (bĕl vûr'năn)	113e	40.08 N	79.52 W
Belleville, Can. (bĕl'vĭl)	111	44.15 N	77.25 W
Belleville, Il.	119e	38.31 N	89.59 W
Belleville, Ks.	123	39.49 N	97.37 W
Belleville, Mi.	113b	42.12 N	83.29 W
Belleville, NJ	112a	40.47 N	74.09 W
Bellevue, Ia. (bĕl'vū)	115	42.14 N	90.26 W
Bellevue, Ky.	113f	39.06 N	84.29 W
Bellevue, Mi.	110	42.30 N	85.00 W
Bellevue, Oh.	110	41.15 N	82.45 W
Bellevue, Pa.	113e	40.30 N	80.04 W
Bellevue, Wa.	118a	47.37 N	122.12 W
Belley, Fr. (bĕ-lē')	169	45.46 N	5.41 E
Bellflower, Ca. (bĕl-flou'ēr)	119a	33.53 N	118.08 W
Bell Gardens, Ca.	119a	33.59 N	118.11 W
Bell I., Can.	105	50.44 N	55.35 W
Bellingham, Ma. (bĕl'ĭng-hăm)	105a	42.05 N	71.28 W
Bellingham, Wa.	118d	48.46 N	122.29 W
Bellingham B., Wa.	118d	48.44 N	122.34 W
Bellingshausen Sea, Ant. (bĕl'ĭngz houz'n)	232	72.00 S	80.30 W
Bellinzona, Switz. (bĕl-ĭn-tsō'nä)	172	46.10 N	9.09 E
Bellmawr, NJ	56b	39.51 N	75.06 W
Bellmore, NY (bĕl-mōr)	112a	40.40 N	73.31 W
Bello, Col. (bĕ'l-yô)	142a	6.20 N	75.33 W
Bello, Cuba	60b	23.07 N	82.24 W
Bellow Falls, Vt. (bĕl'ōz fôls)	111	43.10 N	72.30 W
Bellpat, Pak.	196	29.08 N	68.00 E
Bell Pen, Can.	97	63.50 N	81.16 W
Bells Corners, Can.	95c	45.20 N	75.49 W
Bells Mtn., Wa. (bĕls)	118c	45.50 N	122.21 W
Belluno, It. (bĕl-lōō'nō)	172	46.08 N	12.14 E
Bell Ville, Arg. (bĕl vēl')	144	32.33 S	62.36 W
Bellville, S.Afr.	226a	33.54 S	18.38 E
Bellville, Tx. (bĕl'vĭl)	125	29.57 N	96.15 W
Bellwood, Il.	58a	41.53 N	87.52 W
Bélmez, Sp. (bĕl'mĕth)	170	38.17 N	5.17 W
Belmond, Ia. (bĕl'mŏnd)	115	42.49 N	93.37 W
Belmont, Ca.	118b	37.34 N	122.18 W
Belmont, Ma.	54a	42.24 N	71.10 W
Belmonte, Braz. (bĕl-mōn'tå)	143	15.58 S	38.47 W
Belmopan, Belize	128	17.15 N	88.47 W
Belmore, Austl.	70a	33.55 S	151.05 E
Belogorsk, Sov.Un.	181	51.09 N	128.32 E
Belo Horizonte, Braz. (bĕ'lôre-sôn'-tĕ)	141a	19.54 S	43.56 W
Beloit, Ks. (bē-loit')	122	39.26 N	98.06 W
Beloit, Wi.	115	42.31 N	89.04 W
Belomorsk, Sov.Un. (byĕl-ō-môrsk')	178	64.30 N	34.42 E
Belopol'ye, Sov.Un. (byĕ'lô-pôl'yĕ)	175	51.10 N	34.19 E
Beloretsk, Sov.Un. (byĕ'lō-rĕtsk)	182a	53.58 N	58.25 E
Belorussian (S.S.R.), Sov.Un.	176	53.30 N	25.33 E
Belosarayskaya, Kosa (C.), Sov.Un. (kô-sä'byĕ'lô-sä-räy'skä'yä)	175	46.43 N	37.18 E
Belot, Cuba	60b	23.08 N	82.19 W
Belovo, Sov.Un. (byĕ'lŭ-vû)	180	54.17 N	86.23 E
Belovodsk, Sov.Un. (byĕ-lŭ-vôdsk')	175	49.12 N	39.36 E
Beloye (L.), Sov.Un.	178	60.10 N	38.05 E
Belozersk, Sov.Un. (byĕ-lŭ-zyôrsk')	178	60.00 N	38.00 E
Belper, Eng. (bĕl'pĕr)	156	53.01 N	1.28 W
Belt, Mt. (bĕlt)	117	47.11 N	110.58 W
Belt Cr., Mt.	117	47.19 N	110.58 W
Belton, Tx. (bĕl'tŭn)	125	31.04 N	97.27 W
Belton L., Tx.	125	31.15 N	97.35 W
Beltsville, Md. (belts-vĭl)	112e	39.03 N	76.56 W
Bel'tsy, Sov.Un. (bĕl'tsē)	175	47.47 N	27.57 E
Belukha, Gol'tsy (Mtn.), Sov.Un.	180	49.47 N	86.23 E
Belvedere, Ca.	58b	37.52 N	122.28 W
Belvedere (Neigh.), Eng.	62	51.29 N	0.09 E
Belvedere (P. Int.), Aus.	66e	48.11 N	16.23 E
Belvedere, Va.	56d	38.50 N	77.10 W
Belvidere, Il. (bĕl-vē-dēr')	115	42.14 N	88.52 W
Belvidere, NJ	111	40.50 N	75.05 W
Belyando (R.), Austl. (bĕl-yän'dō)	215	22.09 S	146.48 E
Belyanka, Sov. Un. (byĕl'yán-kà)	182a	56.04 N	59.16 E
Belynichi, Sov. Un. (byĕl-ĭ-nĭ'chĭ)	174	54.02 N	29.42 E
Belyy (I.), Sov. Un.	180	73.19 N	72.00 E
Belyy, Sov. Un. (byĕ'lē)	174	55.52 N	32.58 E
Belyye Stolby, Sov. Un. (byĕ'lĭ-ye stôl'bĭ)	182b	55.20 N	37.52 E
Belzig, G.D.R. (bĕl'tsēg)	157b	52.08 N	12.35 E
Belzoni, Ms. (bĕl-zō'nē)	126	33.09 N	90.30 W
Bembe, Ang. (bĕɴ'bĕ)	226	7.00 S	14.20 E
Bembézar (R.), Sp. (bĕm-bā-thär')	170	38.00 N	5.18 W
Bemidji, Mn. (bē-mĭj'ĭ)	115	47.28 N	94.54 W
Bena Dibele, Zaire (bĕn'à dē-bĕ'lĕ)	226	4.00 S	22.49 E
Benalla, Austl. (bĕn-ăl'à)	216	36.30 S	146.00 E
Benares, see Vārānasi			
Benavente, Sp. (bā-nä-vĕn'tā)	170	42.01 N	5.43 W
Ben Avon, Pa.	57b	40.31 N	80.05 W
Benbrook, Tx. (bĕn'brŏŏk)	119c	32.41 N	97.27 W
Benbrook Res., Tx.	119c	32.35 N	97.30 W
Bend, Or. (bĕnd)	116	44.04 N	121.17 W
Bendeleben, Mt., Ak. (bĕn-dĕl-bĕn)	107	65.18 N	163.45 W
Bender Beyla, Som.	223a	9.40 N	50.45 E
Bendery, Sov. Un. (bĕn-dyĕ're)	175	46.49 N	29.29 E
Bendigo, Austl. (bĕn'dĭ-gō)	216	36.39 S	144.20 E
Benedict, Md. (bĕnĕ'dĭct)	112e	38.31 N	76.41 W
Benešov, Czech. (bĕn'ĕ-shôf)	166	49.48 N	14.40 E
Benevento, It. (bā-nā-vĕn'tō)	172	41.08 N	14.46 E
Benfica (Neigh.), Braz., Braz.	61c	22.53 S	43.15 W
Benfica (Neigh.), Port., Port.	65d	38.45 N	9.12 W
Bengal, B. of, Asia (bĕn-gôl')	190	17.30 N	87.00 E
Bengamisa, Zaire	230	0.57 N	25.10 E
Bengbu, China (bŭŋ-bōō)	200	32.52 N	117.22 E
Bengkalis, Indon. (bĕng-kä'lĭs)	191b	1.29 N	102.06 E
Bengkulu, Indon.	206	3.46 S	102.18 E
Benguela, Ang. (bĕn-gĕl'à)	230	12.35 S	13.25 E
Beni (R.), Bol. (bā'nē)	142	13.41 S	67.30 W
Béni-Abbas, Alg. (bā'nē à-bĕs')	224	30.11 N	2.13 W
Benicarló, Sp. (bā-nē-kär-lō')	171	40.26 N	0.25 E
Benicia, Ca. (bē-nĭsh'ĭ-à)	118b	38.03 N	122.09 W
Benin, Afr.	222	8.00 N	2.00 E
Benin (R.), Nig. (bĕn-ēn')	229	5.55 N	5.15 E
Benin City, Nig.	229	6.19 N	5.41 E
Beni Saf, Alg. (bā'nē säf')	224	35.23 N	1.20 W
Benito (R.), Equat. Gui.	230	1.35 N	10.45 E
Benkelman, Ne. (bĕn-kĕl-măn)	122	40.05 N	101.35 W
Benkovac, Yugo. (bĕn'kō-vàts)	172	44.02 N	15.41 E
Ben Macdhui (Mtn.), Leso-S. Afr. (bĕn măk-dōō'ē)	227c	30.38 S	27.54 E
Bennettsville, SC (bĕn'ĕts vĭl)	127	34.35 N	79.41 W
Bennettswood, Austl.	70b	37.51 S	145.07 E
Benninghofen (Neigh.), F.R.G.	63	51.29 N	7.31 E
Bennington, Vt. (bĕn'ĭng-tŭn)	111	42.55 N	73.15 W
Benns Church, Va. (bĕnz' chûrch')	112g	36.47 N	76.35 W
Benoni, S. Afr. (bĕ-nō'nĭ)	227b	26.11 S	28.19 E
Benoni South, S. Afr.	71b	26.13 S	28.18 E
Be,Nosy (I.), Mad.	227	13.14 S	47.28 E
Benoy, Chad	229	8.59 N	16.19 E
Benque Viejo, Belize (bĕn-kĕ bĭē'hō)	132a	17.07 N	89.07 W
Benrath (Neigh.), F.R.G.	63	51.10 N	6.52 E
Bensberg, F.R.G.	169c	50.58 N	7.09 E
Bensenville, Il. (bĕn'sĕn-vĭl)	113a	41.57 N	87.56 W
Bensheim, F.R.G. (bĕns-hīm)	166	49.42 N	8.38 E
Benson, Az. (bĕn-sŭn)	121	32.00 N	110.20 W
Benson, Mn.	114	45.18 N	95.36 W
Bensonhurst (Neigh.), NY	55	40.35 N	73.59 E
Bentleigh, Austl.	70b	37.55 S	145.02 E
Bentleyville, Pa. (bent'lē vĭl)	113e	40.07 N	80.01 W
Benton, Ar. (bĕn'tŭn)	123	34.34 N	92.34 W
Benton, Can.	104	45.59 N	67.36 W
Benton, Ca.	120	37.44 N	118.22 W
Benton, Il.	110	38.00 N	88.55 W
Benton Harbor, Mi. (bĕn'tŭn här'bēr)	110	42.05 N	86.30 W
Bentonville, Ar. (bĕn'tŭn-vĭl)	123	36.22 N	94.11 W
Benue (R.), Nig. (bā'nōō-å)	229	7.55 N	8.55 E
Benut (R.), Mala.	191b	1.43 N	103.20 E
Benwood, WV (bĕn-wŏŏd)	110	39.55 N	80.45 W
Benxi, China (bŭn-shyē)	202	41.25 N	123.50 E
Beograd (Belgrade), Yugo. (bĕ-ō'gràd) (bĕl'grăd)	173	44.48 N	20.32 E
Beppu, Jap. (bĕ'pōō)	205	33.16 N	131.30 E
Bequia I., N.A. (bĕk-ē'ä)	133b	13.00 N	61.08 W
Berakit, Tanjung (C.), Indon.	191b	1.16 N	104.44 E
Berat, Alb. (bĕ-rät')	173	40.43 N	19.59 E
Berau, Teluk (B.), Indon.	207	2.22 S	131.40 E
Berazategui, Arg. (bĕ-rä-zá'tĕ-gē)	144a	34.46 S	58.14 W
Berbera, Som. (bûr'bûr-à)	223a	10.25 N	45.05 E
Berbérati, Cen. Afr. Rep.	229	4.16 N	15.47 E
Berchum, F.R.G.	63	51.23 N	7.32 E
Berck, Fr. (bĕrk)	168	50.26 N	1.36 E
Berd'ansk, Sov. Un.	161	46.45 N	36.47 E
Berdichev, Sov. Un. (bĕ-dē'chĕf)	175	49.53 N	28.32 E
Berdyanskaya, Kosa (C.), Sov. Un. (kô-sä' bĕ-dyän'skä-yä)	175	46.38 N	36.42 E
Berdyaush, Sov. Un. (bĕr'dyâûsh)	182a	55.10 N	59.12 E
Berea, Ky. (bĕ-rē'à)	126	37.30 N	84.19 W
Berea, Oh.	113d	41.22 N	81.51 W
Beregovo, Sov. Un. (bĕ'rĕ-gô-vô)	167	48.13 N	22.40 E
Bereku, Tan.	231	4.27 S	35.44 E
Berens (R.), Can. (bĕr'enz)	101	52.15 N	96.30 W
Berens I., Can.	101	52.18 N	97.40 W
Berens River, Can.	101	52.22 N	97.02 W
Beresford, SD (bĕr'ĕs-fērd)	114	43.05 N	96.46 W
Berettyóújfalu, Hung. (bĕ'rĕt-tyō-ōō'y'fô-lōō)	167	47.14 N	21.33 E
Berëza, Sov.Un. (bĕ-rā'zá)	167	52.29 N	24.59 E
Berezhany, Sov.Un. (bĕr-yĕ'zhá-nē)	167	49.25 N	24.58 E
Berezina (R.), Sov.Un. (bĕr-yĕ'zē-ná)	174	53.20 N	29.05 E
Berezino, Sov.Un. (bĕr-yä'zē-nô)	174	53.51 N	28.54 E
Berezna, Sov.Un. (bĕr-yôz'ná)	175	51.32 N	31.47 E
Bereznegovata, Sov.Un.	175	47.19 N	32.58 E
Berezniki, Sov.Un. (bĕr-yôz'nyē-kē)	182a	59.25 N	56.46 E
Berëzovka, Sov.Un. (bĕr-yôz'ôf-ká)	175	47.12 N	30.56 E
Berëzovka, Sov.Un.	182a	57.35 N	57.19 E
Berëzovo, Sov.Un. (bĭr-yô'zē-vû)	178	64.10 N	65.10 E
Berëzovskiy, Sov.Un. (bĕr-yô'zôf-skĭ)	182a	56.54 N	60.47 E
Berga, Sp. (bĕr'gä)	171	42.05 N	1.52 E
Bergama, Tur. (bĕr'gä-mä)	179	39.08 N	27.09 E
Bergamo, It. (bĕr'gä-mō)	172	45.43 N	9.41 E
Bergantin, Ven. (bĕr-gän-tē'n)	143b	10.04 N	64.23 W
Bergedorf, F.R.G. (bĕr'gē-dôrf)	157c	53.29 N	10.12 E
Bergen, G.D.R. (bĕr'gĕn)	166	54.26 N	13.26 E
Bergen, Nor.	164	60.24 N	5.20 E
Bergenfield, NJ	112a	40.55 N	73.59 W
Bergen op Zoom, Neth.	157a	51.29 N	4.16 E
Bergerac, Fr. (bĕr-zhĕ-rak')	168	44.49 N	0.28 E
Bergfelde, G.D.R.	65a	52.40 N	13.19 E
Berghausen, F.R.G.	63	51.18 N	7.17 E
Bergholtz, NY	57a	43.06 N	78.53 W
Bergisch-Born, F.R.G.	63	51.09 N	7.15 E
Bergisch Gladbach, F.R.G. (bĕrg'ĭsh-glät'bäk)	169c	50.59 N	7.08 E
Bergkamen, F.R.G.	63	51.38 N	7.38 E
Berglern, F.R.G. (bĕrgh'lĕrn)	157d	48.24 N	11.55 E
Bergneustadt, F.R.G.	169c	51.01 N	7.39 E
Bergville, S.Afr. (bĕrg'vĭl)	227c	28.46 S	29.22 E
Berhampur, India	196	19.19 N	84.48 E
Bering Sea, Asia-N.A. (bē'rĭng)	94	58.00 N	175.00 W
Bering Str., Ak.	107	64.50 N	169.50 W
Berislav, Sov.Un. (byĕr'ĭ-sláf)	175	46.49 N	33.24 E
Berja, Sp. (bĕr'hä)	170	36.50 N	2.56 W
Berkeley, Ca. (bûrk'lĭ)	118b	37.52 N	122.17 W
Berkeley, Il.	58a	41.53 N	87.55 W
Berkeley, Mo.	119e	38.45 N	90.20 W
Berkeley Hills, Pa.	57b	40.32 N	80.00 W
Berkeley Springs, WV (bûrk'lĭ springz)	111	39.40 N	78.10 W
Berkhamsted, Eng. (bĕk'hăm'stĕd)	156b	51.44 N	0.34 W
Berkley, Mi. (bûrk'lĭ)	113b	42.30 N	83.10 W
Berkovitsa, Bul. (bĕ-kō'vē-tsá)	173	43.14 N	23.08 E
Berland (R.), Can.	99	54.00 N	117.10 W
Berlenga (Is.), Port. (bĕr-lĕn'gäzh)	170	39.25 N	9.33 W
Berlin, NH (bûr-lĭn)	111	44.25 N	71.10 W
Berlin, NJ	112f	39.47 N	74.56 W
Berlin, S.Afr. (bĕr-lĭn)	227c	32.53 S	27.36 E
Berlin, Wi. (bûr-lĭn')	115	43.58 N	88.58 W
Berlin, East, G.D.R. (bĕr-lēn')	157b	52.31 N	13.28 E
Berlin, West, F.R.G.	157b	52.31 N	13.20 E
Bermejo (R.), Arg. (bĕr-mā'hō)	144	25.05 S	61.00 W
Bermeo, Sp. (bĕr-mā'yō)	170	43.23 N	2.43 W
Bermuda (I.), N.A.	129	32.20 N	65.45 W
Bern, Switz. (bĕrn)	166	46.55 N	7.25 E
Bernal, Arg. (bĕr-näl')	144a	34.27 S	58.17 W
Bernalillo, NM (bĕr-nä-lē'yō)	121	35.20 N	106.30 W
Bernard (L.), Can. (bĕr-närd')	111	45.45 N	79.25 W
Bernardsville, NJ (bûr nărds'vĭl)	112a	40.43 N	74.34 W
Bernau, G.D.R. (bĕr'nou)	157b	52.40 N	13.35 E
Bernau bei Berlin, G.D.R.	65a	52.40 N	13.35 E
Bernburg, G.D.R. (bĕrn'bŏŏrgh)	166	51.48 N	11.43 E
Berndorf, Aus. (bĕrn'dôrf)	166	47.57 N	16.05 E
Berne, In. (bûrn)	110	40.40 N	84.55 W
Berner Alpen (Mts.), Switz.	166	46.29 N	7.30 E
Bernier (I.), Austl. (bĕr-nēr')	214	24.58 S	113.15 E
Bernina Pizzo (Pk.), Switz.	166	46.23 N	9.58 E
Bero (R.), Ang.	230	15.10 S	12.20 E
Beroun, Czech. (bā'rōn)	166	49.57 N	14.03 E
Berounka R., Czech. (bĕ-rōn'ká)	166	49.53 N	13.40 E
Berowra, Austl.	211b	33.36 S	151.10 E
Berre, Étang de (L.), Fr. (ā-tôɴ' dĕ bâr')	168a	43.27 N	5.07 E
Berre-l'Étang, Fr. (bâr'lā-tôɴ')	168a	43.28 N	5.11 E
Berriozabal, Mex. (bā'rēō-zä-bäl')	131	16.47 N	93.16 W
Berriyyane, Alg.	160	32.50 N	3.49 E
Berry Creek (R.), Can.	99	51.15 N	111.40 W
Berryessa (R.), Ca. (bĕ'rĭ ĕs'à)	120	38.35 N	122.33 W
Berry Is., Ba.	134	25.40 N	77.50 W
Berryville, Ar. (bĕr'ē-vĭl)	123	36.21 N	93.34 W
Bershad', Sov.Un. (byĕr'shät)	175	48.22 N	29.31 E
Berthier, Can.	95b	46.56 N	70.44 W
Bertlich, F.R.G.	63	51.37 N	7.04 E
Bertrand (R.), Wa. (bûr'trand)	118d	48.58 N	122.31 W
Berwick, Pa. (bûr'wĭk)	111	41.05 N	76.10 W
Berwick-upon-Tweed, Eng. (bûr'ĭk)	162	55.45 N	2.01 W
Berwyn, Il. (bûr'wĭn)	113a	41.49 N	87.47 W
Berwyn Heights, Md.	56d	38.59 N	76.54 W
Besalampy, Mad. (bĕz-à-làm-pē')	227	16.48 S	40.40 E
Besançon, Fr. (bĕ-säɴ-sôn)	169	47.14 N	6.02 E
Besar, Gunong (Mt.), Mala.	191b	2.31 N	103.09 E
Besed' (R.), Sov.Un. (byĕ'syĕt)	174	52.58 N	31.36 E
Besedy, Sov. Un.	66b	55.37 N	37.47 E
Beshenkovichi, Sov.Un. (byĕ'shĕn-kōvĕ'chĭ)	174	55.04 N	29.29 E
Beşiktaş (Neigh.), Tur.	66f	41.03 N	29.01 E
Beskid (Mts.), Czech.-Pol.	167	49.23 N	19.00 E
Beskra, Alg.	224	34.52 N	5.39 E
Beskudnikovo (Neigh.), Sov. Un.	66b	55.52 N	37.34 E
Besós (R.), Sp.	65e	41.25 N	2.04 E
Bességes, Fr. (bĕ-sĕzh')	168	44.20 N	4.07 E
Bessemer, Al. (bĕs'ē-mĕr)	112h	33.24 N	86.58 W
Bessemer, Mi.	115	46.29 N	90.04 W
Bessemer City, NC	127	35.16 N	81.17 W
Bestensee, G.D.R. (bĕs'tĕn-zā)	157b	51.15 N	13.39 E
Betanzos, Sp. (bĕ-tän'thōs)	170	43.18 N	8.14 W
Betatakin Ruin, Az. (bĕt-à-tăk'ĭn)	121	36.40 N	110.29 W
Bethal, S.Afr. (bĕth'ăl)	223d	26.27 S	29.28 E
Bethalto, Il. (bá-thăl'tō)	119e	38.54 N	90.03 W
Bethanien, Namibia	226	26.20 S	16.10 E
Bethany, Mo.	123	40.15 N	94.04 W
Bethel, Ak. (bĕth'ĕl)	107	60.50 N	161.50 W
Bethel, Ct.	112a	41.22 N	73.24 W
Bethel, Vt.	111	43.50 N	72.40 W
Bethel Park, Pa.	113e	40.19 N	80.02 W
Bethesda, Md. (bĕ-thĕs'dá)	112e	39.00 N	77.10 W
Bethlehem, Pa. (bĕth'lē-hĕm)	111	40.40 N	75.25 W
Bethlehem, S.Afr.	223d	28.14 S	28.18 E
Bethlehem, see Bayt Lahm			
Bethnal Green (Neigh.), Eng.	62	51.32 N	0.03 W
Bethpage, NY	55	40.45 N	73.29 W
Béthune, Fr. (bā-tün')	168	50.32 N	2.37 E
Betroka, Mad. (bĕ-trōk'á)	227	23.13 S	46.17 E
Betsham, Eng.	62	51.25 N	0.19 E
Bet She'an, Isr.	191a	32.30 N	35.30 E
Betsiamites, Can.	104	48.57 N	68.36 W
Betsiamites, (R.), Can.	104	49.11 N	69.20 W
Betsiboka (R.), Mad. (bĕt-sĭ-bō'ká)	227	16.47 S	46.45 E

ăt; finăl; rāte; senāte; ärm; àsk; sofà; fâre; ch-choose; dh-as th in other; bē; ēvent; bĕt; recĕnt; cratĕr; g-gō; gh-guttural g; bĭt; ĭ-short neutral; rīde; ĸ-guttural k as ch in German ich;

PLACE (Pronounciation)	PAGE	Lat. °′	Long. °′
Bettles Field, Ak. (bĕt'tŭls)	107	66.58 N	151.48 W
Betwa (R.), India (bĕt'wȧ)	196	25.00 N	77.37 E
Betz, Fr. (bĕ)	169b	49.09 N	2.58 E
Beveren, Bel.	157a	51.13 N	4.14 E
Beverly, Eng. (bĕv'ẽr-lĭ)	156	53.50 N	0.25 W
Beverly, Ma.	105a	42.34 N	70.53 W
Beverly, NJ	112f	40.03 N	74.56 W
Beverly Hills, Austl.	70a	33.57 S	151.05 E
Beverly Hills, Ca.	119a	34.05 N	118.24 W
Beverly Hills, Mi.	57c	42.32 N	83.15 W
Bevier, Mo. (bē-vẽr')	123	39.44 N	92.36 W
Bewdley, Eng. (būd'lĭ)	156	52.22 N	2.19 W
Bexhill, Eng. (bĕks'hĭl)	163	50.49 N	0.25 E
Bexley, Austl.	70a	33.57 S	151.08 E
Bexley, Eng. (bĕks'ly)	156b	51.26 N	0.09 E
Beyenburg (Neigh.), F.R.G.	63	51.15 N	7.18 E
Beyla, Gui. (bā'lȧ)	228	8.41 N	8.37 W
Beylerbeyi (Neigh.), Tur.	66f	41.03 N	29.03 E
Beylul, Eth.	225	13.15 N	42.21 E
Beyoğlu (Neigh.), Tur.	66f	41.02 N	28.59 E
Beypazari, Tur. (bā-pȧ-zä'rĭ)	179	40.10 N	31.40 E
Beyşehir, Tur. (bā-shĕ'h'r)	179	38.00 N	31.45 E
Beyşehir Gölü (L.), Turk.	179	38.00 N	31.30 E
Beysugskiy, Liman (B.), Sov.Un. (lĭ-män' bĕy-sōōg'skĭ)	175	46.07 N	38.35 E
Bezhetsk, Sov.Un. (byĕ-zhĕtsk')	174	57.46 N	36.40 E
Bezhitsa, Sov.Un. (byĕ-zhĭ'tsȧ)	174	53.19 N	34.18 E
Béziers, Fr. (bā-zyā')	168	43.21 N	3.12 E
Bezons, Fr.	64c	48.56 N	2.13 E
Bhadreswar, India	196a	22.49 N	88.22 E
Bhāgalpur, India (bä'gŭl-po͞or)	196	25.15 N	86.59 E
Bhalswa (Neigh.), India	67d	28.44 N	77.10 E
Bhamo, Bur. (bŭ-mō')	198	24.00 N	96.15 E
Bhāngar, India	196a	22.30 N	88.36 E
Bharatpur, India (bẽrt'po͞or)	196	27.21 N	77.33 E
Bhatinda, India (bŭ-tĭn-dȧ)	196	30.19 N	74.56 E
Bhātpāra, India	67a	22.52 N	88.24 E
Bhaunagar, India (bäv-nŭg'ŭr)	196	21.45 N	72.58 E
Bhayandar, India	197a	19.20 N	72.50 E
Bhilai, India	196	21.14 N	81.23 E
Bhīma (R.), India (bē'mȧ)	196	17.15 N	75.55 E
Bhiwandi, India	197a	19.18 N	73.03 E
Bhiwāni, India	196	28.53 N	76.08 E
Bhopāl, India (bô-päl)	196	23.20 N	77.25 E
Bhopura, India	67d	28.42 N	77.20 E
Bhubaneswar, India (bo͞o-bŭ-nāsh'vûr)	196	20.21 N	85.53 E
Bhuj, India (bo͞oj)	196	23.22 N	69.39 E
Bhutan, Asia (bo͞o-tän')	193	27.15 N	90.30 E
Biafra, Bight of, Afr.	230	4.05 N	7.10 E
Biak (I.), Indon. (bē'äk)	207	1.00 S	136.00 E
Biala Podlaska, Pol. (byä'wä pōd-läs'kä)	167	52.01 N	23.08 E
Bialogard, Pol. (byä-wō'gärd)	166	54.00 N	16.01 E
Bialystok, Pol. (byä-wĭs'tôk)	167	53.08 N	23.12 E
Biankouma, Ivory Coast	228	7.44 N	7.37 W
Biarritz, Fr. (byä-rēts')	168	43.27 N	1.39 W
Bibā, Egypt (bē'bȧ)	223b	28.54 N	30.59 E
Bibb City, Ga. (bĭb' sĭ'tē)	126	32.31 N	84.56 W
Biberach, F.R.G. (bē'bēräk)	166	48.06 N	9.49 E
Bibiani, Ghana	228	6.28 N	2.20 W
Bic, Can. (bĭk)	104	48.22 N	68.42 W
Bickerstaffe, Eng.	64a	53.32 N	2.50 W
Bickley (Neigh.), Eng.	62	51.24 N	0.03 E
Bicknell, In. (bĭk'nĕl)	110	38.45 N	87.20 W
Bicske, Hung. (bĭsh'kē)	167	47.29 N	18.38 E
Bida, Nig. (bē'dä)	229	9.05 N	6.01 E
Biddeford, Me. (bĭd'ē-fẽrd)	104	43.29 N	70.29 W
Biddulph, Eng. (bĭd'ŭlf)	156	53.07 N	2.10 W
Bidston, Eng.	64a	53.24 N	3.05 W
Biebrza R., Pol. (byĕb'zhȧ)	167	53.18 N	22.25 E
Biel, Switz. (bēl)	166	47.09 N	7.12 E
Bielefeld, F.R.G. (bē'lē-fĕlt)	166	52.01 N	8.35 E
Biella, It. (byĕl'lä)	172	45.34 N	8.05 E
Bielsk Podlaski, Pol. (byĕlsk pŭd-lä'skĭ)	167	52.47 N	23.14 E
Bien Hoa, Viet.	206	10.59 N	106.49 E
Bienville, Lac (L.), Can.	97	55.32 N	72.45 W
Biesdorf (Neigh.), G.D.R.	65a	52.31 N	13.33 E
Biesenthal, G.D.R. (bē'sĕn-täl)	157b	52.46 N	13.38 E
Bièvres, Fr.	64c	48.45 N	2.13 E
Biferno (R.), It. (bē-fĕr'nō)	172	41.49 N	14.46 E
Bifoum, Gabon	230	0.22 S	10.23 E
Big (L.), Wa. (bĭg)	118a	48.23 N	122.14 W
Big (R.), Ar.	126	35.55 N	90.10 W
Biga, Tur. (bē'ghȧ)	173	40.13 N	27.14 E
Big Bay de Noc, Mi. (bĭg bā dē nok')	115	45.48 N	86.41 W
Big Bayou, Ar. (bĭg'bī'yo͞o)	123	33.04 N	91.28 W
Big Bear City, Ca. (bĭg bâr)	119a	34.16 N	116.51 W
Big Belt Mts., Mt. (bĭg bĕlt)	117	46.53 N	111.43 W
Big Bend Dam, SD (bĭg bĕnd)	114	44.11 N	99.33 W
Big Bend Natl. Park, Tx.	124	29.15 N	103.15 W
Big Black (R.), Ms. (bĭg blăk)	126	32.05 N	90.49 W
Big Blue (R.), Ne. (bĭg blo͞o)	123	40.53 N	97.00 W
Big Canyon, Tx. (bĭg kăn'yŭn)	124	30.27 N	102.19 W
Big Cr., Oh.	56a	41.27 N	81.41 W
Big Cypress Swp., Fl. (bĭg sī'prĕs)	127a	26.02 N	81.20 W
Big Delta, Ak. (bĭg dĕl'tȧ)	107	64.08 N	145.48 W
Big Fork (R.), Mn. (bĭg fôrk)	115	48.08 N	93.47 W
Biggar, Can.	100	52.04 N	108.00 W
Biggin Hill (Neigh.), Eng.	62	51.18 N	0.04 E
Big Hole (R.), Mt. (bĭg 'hōl)	117	45.53 N	113.15 W
Big Hole Natl. Battlefield, Mt. (bĭg hōl băt''l-fēld)	117	45.44 N	113.35 W
Big Horn Mts., Wy. (bĭg hôrn)	117	44.47 N	107.40 W
Bighorn R., Mt.	117	45.50 N	107.15 W
Big I., Can.	101	49.10 N	94.40 W
Big L., Can.	95g	53.35 N	113.47 W
Big Lake, Wa. (bĭg lāk)	118a	48.24 N	122.14 W
Big Mossy Pt., Can.	101	53.45 N	97.50 W
Big Muddy (R.), Il.	110	37.50 N	89.00 W
Big Muddy Cr., Mt. (bĭg mŭd'ĭ)	117	48.53 N	105.02 W
Bignona, Senegal	228	12.49 N	16.14 W
Big Quill L., Can.	100	51.55 N	104.22 W
Big Rapids, Mi. (bĭg răp'ĭdz)	110	43.40 N	85.30 W
Big River, Can.	100	53.50 N	107.01 W
Big Sandy (R.), Az. (bĭg sănd'ē)	121	34.59 N	113.36 W
Big Sandy (R.), Ky.-WV	110	38.15 N	82.35 W
Big Sandy Cr., Co.	122	39.08 N	103.36 W
Big Sandy Cr., Mt.	117	48.20 N	110.08 W
Bigsby I., Can.	101	49.04 N	94.35 W
Big Sioux (R.), SD (bĭg so͞o)	114	44.34 N	97.00 W
Big Spring, Tx. (bĭg sprĭng)	124	32.15 N	101.28 W
Big Stone (L.), Mn.-SD (bĭg stōn)	114	45.29 N	96.40 W
Big Stone Gap, Va.	126	36.50 N	82.50 W
Bigtimber, Mt. (bĭg'tĭm-bẽr)	117	45.50 N	109.57 W
Big Wood R., Id. (bĭg wo͝od)	117	43.02 N	114.30 W
Bihać, Yugo. (bē'häch)	172	44.48 N	15.52 E
Bihār (State), India (bē-här')	196	23.48 N	84.57 E
Biharamulo, Tan. (bē-hä-rä-mo͞o'lō)	231	2.38 S	31.20 E
Bihorului, Munţii (Mts.), Rom.	167	46.37 N	22.37 E
Bijagós, Arquipélago dos (Is.), Guinea-Bissau (är-kē-pā'lä-gō dôs bē-zhä-gôs)	228	11.20 N	17.10 W
Bijāpur, India	197	16.53 N	75.42 E
Bijeljina, Yugo.	173	44.44 N	19.15 E
Bijelo Polje, Yugo. (bē'yĕ-lō pô'lyĕ)	173	43.02 N	19.48 E
Bijiang, China (bē-jyän)	201a	22.57 N	113.15 E
Bijie, China (bē-jyĕ)	203	27.20 N	105.18 E
Bijou Cr., Co. (bē'zho͞o)	122	39.41 N	104.13 W
Bikin (R.), Sov.Un.	204	46.37 N	135.55 E
Bikin, Sov.Un. (bē-kēn')	204	46.41 N	134.29 E
Bikoro, Zaire (bē-kō'rō)	230	0.45 S	18.07 E
Bikuar, Parque Nacional do (Natl. Pk.), Ang.	230	15.07 S	14.40 E
Bilāspur, India (bē-läs'po͞or)	196	22.08 N	82.12 E
Bilauktaung (R.), Thai.	206	14.40 N	98.50 E
Bilbao, Sp. (bĭl-bä'ō)	170	43.12 N	2.48 W
Bilbays, Egypt	223b	30.26 N	31.37 E
Bileća, Yugo. (bē'lĕ-chä)	173	42.52 N	18.26 E
Bilecik, Tur. (bē-lĕd-zhēk')	179	40.10 N	29.58 E
Bilé Karpaty (Mts.), Czech.	167	48.53 N	17.35 E
Bilgoraj, Pol. (bēw-gō'rī)	167	50.31 N	22.43 E
Bilimbay, Sov.Un. (bē'lĭm-bāy)	182a	56.59 N	59.53 E
Billabong (R.), Austl. (bĭl'ă-bŏng)	216	35.15 S	145.20 E
Billerica, Ma. (bĭl'rĭk-ȧ)	105a	42.33 N	71.16 W
Billericay, Eng.	156b	51.38 N	0.25 E
Billings, Mt. (bĭl'ĭngz)	117	45.47 N	108.29 W
Billingsport, NJ	56b	39.51 N	75.14 W
Bill Williams (L.), Az. (bĭl-wĭl'yumz)	121	34.10 N	113.50 W
Bilma, Niger (bēl'mä)	225	18.41 N	13.20 E
Biloxi, Ms. (bĭ-lŏk'sĭ)	126	30.24 N	88.50 W
Bilqās Qism Awwal, Egypt	223b	31.14 N	31.25 E
Bimberi Pk., Austl. (bĭm'bẽrĭ)	216	35.45 S	148.50 E
Binalonan, Phil. (bē-nä-lō'nän)	207a	16.03 N	120.35 E
Binalud (Mtn.) Iran	192	36.32 N	58.34 E
Bingen, F.R.G. (bĭn'gĕn)	166	49.57 N	7.54 E
Bingham, Eng. (bĭng'ăm)	156	52.57 N	0.57 W
Bingham, Me.	104	45.03 N	69.51 W
Bingham Canyon, Ut.	119b	40.33 N	112.09 W
Bingham Farms, Mi.	57c	42.32 N	83.16 W
Binghamton, NY (bĭng'ăm-tŭn)	111	42.05 N	75.55 W
Bingo-Nada (Sea), Jap. (bĭn'gō nä-dä)	205	34.06 N	133.14 E
Binh-dong, Viet.	68m	10.43 N	106.39 E
Binjai, Indon.	206	3.59 N	108.00 E
Binnaway, Austl. (bĭn'ă-wā)	216	31.42 S	149.22 E
Binsheim, F.R.G.	63	51.31 N	6.42 E
Bintan (I.), Indon. (bĭn'tän)	191b	1.09 N	104.43 E
Bintulu, Mala. (bēn'to͞o-lo͞o)	206	3.07 N	113.06 E
Binxian, China (bĭn-shyän)	200	37.27 N	117.58 E
Binxian, China	202	45.40 N	127.20 E
Bio Gorge (Val.), Ghana	228	8.30 N	2.05 W
Bīkaner, India (bĭ-kă'nûr)	196	28.07 N	73.19 E
Bioko (Fernando Póo)(I.), Equat. Gui.	230	3.35 N	7.45 E
Bīrjand, Iran (bĕr'jänd)	192	33.07 N	59.16 E
Bira (R.), Sov.Un.	204	48.55 N	132.25 E
Bira, Sov.Un. (bē'rȧ)	204	49.00 N	133.18 E
Birātnagar, Nep. (bĭ-rät'nŭ-gŭr)	196	26.35 N	87.18 E
Birch, Eng.	64b	53.34 N	2.13 W
Birch B., Wa.	118d	48.55 N	122.52 W
Birch Bay, Wa. (bûrch)	118d	48.55 N	122.45 W
Birch I., Can.	101	52.25 N	99.55 W
Birch Mts., Can.	96	57.36 N	113.10 W
Birch Pt., Wa.	118d	48.57 N	122.50 W
Bird I., S.Afr. (bẽrd)	227c	33.51 S	26.21 E
Bird Rock (I.), Ba. (bûrd)	135	22.50 N	74.20 W
Birds Hill, Can. (bûrds)	95f	49.58 N	97.00 W
Birdsville, Austl. (bûrdz'vĭl)	216	25.50 S	139.31 E
Birdum, Austl. (bûrd'ŭm)	214	15.45 S	133.25 E
Birecik, Tur. (bē-rĕd-zhĕk')	179	37.10 N	37.50 E
Bir Gara, Chad.	229	13.11 N	15.58 E
Bīrjand, Iran	195	32.53 N	59.13 E
Birkenfeld, Or.	118c	45.59 N	123.20 W
Birkenhead, Eng. (bûr'kĕn-hĕd)	156	53.23 N	3.02 W
Birkenwerder, G.D.R. (bēr'kĕn-vĕr-dĕr)	157b	52.41 N	13.22 E
Birkholz, G.D.R.	65a	52.38 N	13.34 E
Birling, Eng.	62	51.19 N	0.25 E
Birmingham, Al. (bûr'mĭng-hăm)	112h	33.31 N	86.49 W
Birmingham, Eng.	156	52.29 N	1.53 W
Birmingham, Mi.	113b	42.32 N	83.13 W
Birmingham, Mo.	119f	39.10 N	94.22 W
Birmingham Can., Eng.	156	53.07 N	2.40 W
Bi'r Misāhah, Egypt	225	22.16 N	28.04 E
Birnin Kebbi, Nig.	229	12.32 N	4.12 E
Birobidzhan, Sov.Un. (bē'rō-bē-jän')	181	48.42 N	133.28 E
Bîrlad, Rom.	167	46.15 N	27.43 E
Birsk, Sov.Un. (bĭrsk)	178	55.25 N	55.30 E
Birstall, Eng. (bûr'stôl)	156	53.44 N	1.39 W
Biryuchiy (I.), Sov.Un. (bĭr-yo͞o'chĭ)	175	46.07 N	35.12 E
Biryulëvo, Sov.Un. (bēr-yo͞ol'yô-vô)	182b	55.35 N	37.39 E
Biryusa (R.), Sov.Un. (bēr-yo͞o'sä)	180	56.43 N	97.30 E
Bi'r Za'farānah, Egypt	191a	29.07 N	32.38 E
Biržai, Sov.Un. (bẽr-zhä'ē)	165	56.11 N	24.45 E
Bisbee, Az. (bĭz'bē)	121	31.30 N	109.55 W
Biscay, B. of, Eur. (bĭs'kā')	159	45.19 N	3.51 W
Biscayne B., Fl. (bĭs-kān')	127a	25.22 N	80.15 W
Bischeim, Fr. (bĭsh'hĭm)	169	48.40 N	7.48 E
Biscotasi L., Can.	102	47.20 N	81.55 W
Biser, Sov.Un. (bē'sẽr)	182a	58.24 N	58.54 E
Biševo (Is.), Yugo. (bē'shĕ-vō)	172	42.58 N	15.50 E
Bisho, Ciskei	227	32.50 S	27.20 E
Bishop, Ca. (bĭsh'ŭp)	120	37.22 N	118.25 W
Bishop, Tx.	125	27.35 N	97.46 W
Bishop's Castle, Eng. (bĭsh'ŏps käs'l)	156	52.29 N	2.57 W
Bishopville, SC (bĭsh'ŭp-vĭl)	127	34.11 N	80.13 W
Bismarck, ND (bĭz'märk)	114	46.48 N	100.46 W
Bismarck Arch, Pap. N. Gui.	207	3.15 S	150.45 E
Bismarck Ra., Pap. N. Gui.	207	5.15 S	144.15 E
Bissau, Guinea-Bissau (bē-sa'o͞o)	228	11.51 N	15.35 W
Bissett, Can.	101	51.01 N	95.45 W
Bissingheim (Neigh.), F.R.G.	63	51.24 N	6.49 E
Bistineau (L.), La. (bĭs-tĭ-nō')	125	32.19 N	93.45 W
Bistrita, Rom. (bĭs-trĭt-sȧ)	167	47.09 N	24.29 E
Bistrita R., Rom.	167	47.08 N	25.47 E
Bitlis, Tur. (bĭt-lēs')	179	38.30 N	42.00 E
Bitola (Monastir), Yugo. (bē'tô-lä) (mŏ'nä-stēr)	173	41.02 N	21.22 E
Bitonto, It. (bē-tôn'tō)	172	41.08 N	16.42 E
Bitter Cr., Wy. (bĭt'ẽr)	117	41.36 N	108.29 W
Bitterfeld, G.D.R. (bĭt'ẽr-fĕlt)	166	51.39 N	12.19 E
Bittermark (Neigh.), F.R.G.	63	51.27 N	7.28 E
Bitterroot R., Mt.	117	46.28 N	114.10 W
Bitterroot Ra., Mt. (bĭt'ẽr-o͞ot)	116	47.15 N	115.13 W
Bityrug (R.), Sov.Un. (bĭt'yo͞og)	175	51.23 N	40.33 E
Biu, Nig.	229	10.35 N	12.13 E
Biwabik, Mn. (bē-wä'bĭk)	115	47.32 N	92.24 W
Biwa-ko (L.), Jap. (bē-wä'kō)	205b	35.03 N	135.51 E
Biya (R.), Sov.Un. (bĭ'yȧ)	180	52.22 N	87.28 E
Biysk, Sov.Un. (bēsk)	180	52.32 N	85.28 E
Bizana, S.Afr. (bĭz-änä)	227c	30.51 S	29.54 E
Bizerte, Tun. (bē-zĕrt')	224	37.23 N	9.52 E
Bjelovar, Yugo. (byĕ-lō'vär)	172	45.54 N	16.53 E
Bjørnafjorden (Fd.), Nor.	164	60.11 N	5.26 E
Björneborg, see Pori			
Bla, Mali	228	12.57 N	5.46 W
Black (L.), Mi. (blăk)	110	45.25 N	84.15 W
Black (L.), NY	111	44.30 N	75.35 W
Black (R.), Ar.	123	35.47 N	91.22 W
Black (R.), Can.	102	49.20 N	81.15 W
Black (R.), NY	111	43.45 N	75.20 W
Black (R.), SC	127	33.55 N	80.10 W
Black (R.), Wi.	115	44.07 N	90.56 W
Blackall, Austl. (blăk'ŭl)	215	24.23 S	145.37 E
Black B., Can. (blăk)	115	48.36 N	88.32 W
Blackburn, Austl.	70b	37.49 S	145.09 E
Blackburn, Eng. (blăk'bûrn)	156	53.45 N	2.28 W
Blackburn Mt., Ak.	107	61.50 N	143.12 W
Black Canyon of the Gunnison Natl. Mon., Co. (blăk kăn'yŭn)	121	38.35 N	107.45 W
Black Creek Pioneer Village (P. Int.), Can.	54c	43.47 N	79.32 W
Black Diamond, Wa. (dī'mŭnd)	118a	47.19 N	122.00 W
Black Down Hills, Eng. (blăk'doun)	162	50.58 N	3.19 W
Blackduck, Mn. (blăk'dŭk)	115	47.41 N	94.33 W
Blackfoot, Id. (blăk'fo͝ot)	117	43.11 N	112.23 W
Blackfoot Ind. Res., Can.	99	50.45 N	113.00 W
Blackfoot Ind. Res., Mt.	117	48.49 N	112.53 W
Blackfoot R., Mt.	117	46.53 N	113.33 W
Blackfoot River Res., Id.	117	42.53 N	111.23 W
Black Hills, SD	114	44.08 N	103.47 W
Black I., Can.	101	51.10 N	96.30 W
Black Lake, Can.	104	46.02 N	71.24 W
Blackley (Neigh.), Eng.	64b	53.31 N	2.13 W
Black Mesa, Az. (blăk māsȧ)	121	36.33 N	110.40 W
Blackmore, Eng.	62	51.41 N	0.19 E
Blackmud Cr., Can. (blăk'mŭd)	95g	53.28 N	113.34 W
Blackpool, Eng. (blăk'po͞ol)	156	53.49 N	3.02 W
Black R., Viet.	203	20.56 N	104.30 E
Black Ra., NM	121	33.15 N	107.55 W
Black River, Jam. (blăk')	134	18.00 N	77.50 W
Black River Falls, Wi.	115	44.18 N	90.51 W
Black Rock, Austl.	70b	37.59 S	145.01 E
Black Rock Des., Nv. (rŏk)	116	40.55 N	119.00 W
Blacksburg, SC (blăks'bûrg)	127	35.09 N	81.30 W
Black Sea, Eur.-Asia	155	43.01 N	32.16 E
Blackshear, Ga. (blăk'shĭr)	127	31.20 N	82.15 W
Black Springs, Austl.	70b	37.46 S	145.19 E
Blackstone, Va. (blăk'stōn)	127	37.04 N	78.00 W
Black Sturgeon (R.), Can. (stû'jŭn)	115	49.12 N	88.41 W
Blacktown, Austl. (blăk'toun)	211b	33.47 S	150.55 E
Blackville, Can. (blăk'vĭl)	104	46.44 N	65.50 W
Blackville, SC	127	33.21 N	81.19 W
Black Volta (Volta Noire) (R.), Afr. (vōl'tȧ)	228	8.55 N	2.30 W
Black Warrior (R.), Al. (blăk wŏr'ĭ-ẽr)	126	32.37 N	87.42 W
Black Warrior (R.), Locust Fk., Al.	126	34.06 N	86.27 W
Black Warrior (R.), Mulberry Fk., Al.	126	34.06 N	86.32 W
Blackwater (R.), Ire. (blăk-wô'tẽr)	162	52.05 N	9.02 W
Blackwater (R.), Mo.	123	38.53 N	93.22 W
Blackwater (R.), Va.	127	37.07 N	77.10 W
Blackwell, Ok. (blăk'wĕl)	123	36.47 N	97.19 W
Bladel, Neth.	157a	51.22 N	5.15 E
Bladensburg, Md.	56d	38.56 N	76.55 W
Blagodarnoye, Sov.Un. (blä'gô-där-nō'yĕ)	179	45.00 N	43.30 E
Blagoevgrad (Gorna Dzhumaya), Bul.	173	42.01 N	23.06 E
Blagoveshchensk, Sov.Un. (blä'gō-vyĕsh'chĕnsk)	181	50.16 N	127.47 E
Blagoveshchensk, Sov.Un.	182a	55.03 N	56.00 E
Blaine, Mn. (blān)	119g	45.11 N	93.14 W
Blaine, Wa.	118d	48.59 N	122.49 W
Blaine, WV	111	39.25 N	79.10 W

ng-sing; ŋ-baŋk; ɴ-nasalized n; nŏd; cŏmmit; ōld; ôbey; ôrder; oi-boil; fo͞od; fo͝ot; ou-out; s-soft; sh-dish; th-thin; pūre; ůnite; ûrn; stŭd; circŭs; ü-as in French tu; '-indeterminate vowel.

PLACE (Pronounciation)	PAGE	Lat. °'	Long. °'
Blaine Hill, Pa.	57b	40.16 N	79.53 W
Blair, Ne. (blâr)	114	41.33 N	96.09 W
Blairmore, Can.	99	49.38 N	114.25 W
Blairsville, Pa. (blârs'vĭl)	111	40.30 N	79.40 W
Blakang Mati (I.), Singapore	67c	1.15 N	103.50 E
Blake (I.), Wa. (blāk)	118a	47.37 N	122.28 W
Blakehurst, Austl.	70a	33.59 S	151.07 E
Blakely, Ga. (blāk'lē)	126	31.22 N	84.55 W
Blanca, Bahia (B.), Arg. (bä-ē'ä-blän'kä)	144	39.30 S	61.00 W
Blanca Pk., Co. (blăŋ'kȧ)	122	37.36 N	105.22 W
Blanc, Cap (C.), Mauritania	224	20.39 N	18.08 W
Blanche, (R.), Can.	95c	45.34 N	75.38 W
Blanche, L., Austl. (blănch)	216	29.20 S	139.12 E
Blanchester, Oh. (blăn'chĕs-tẽr)	113f	39.18 N	83.58 W
Blanc, Mt., Fr.-It. (môɴ bläɴ)	169	45.50 N	6.53 E
Blanco (R.), Mex.	130	24.05 N	99.21 W
Blanco (R.), Mex.	131	18.42 N	96.03 W
Blanco, C., Arg. (bläŋ'kô)	144	47.08 S	65.47 W
Blanco, C., Or. (blăn'kō)	116	42.53 N	124.38 W
Blanco, Cabo (C.), C.R. (kä'bô-bläŋ'kō)	132	9.29 N	85.15 W
Blancos, Cayo (I.), Cuba (kä'yō-bläŋ'kōs)	134	23.15 N	80.55 W
Blanding, Ut.	121	37.40 N	109.31 W
Blankenburg, G.D.R. (bläŋ'kĕn-bo͞orgh)	163	51.45 N	11.15 E
Blankenburg (Neigh.), G.D.R.	65a	52.35 N	13.28 E
Blankenfelde, G.D.R. (blän'kĕn-fĕl-dĕ)	157b	52.20 N	13.24 E
Blankenfelde (Neigh.), G.D.R.	65a	52.37 N	13.23 E
Blankenstein, F.R.G.	63	51.24 N	7.14 E
Blanquefort, Fr.	168	44.53 N	0.38 W
Blanquilla, Arrecife (Reef), Mex. (är-rē-sē'fē-blän-kē'l-yä)	131	21.32 N	97.14 W
Blantyre, Malawi (blăn-tīyr)	231	15.47 S	35.00 E
Blasdell, NY (bläz'dĕl)	113c	42.48 N	78.51 W
Blato, Yugo. (blä'tō)	172	42.55 N	16.47 E
Blawnox, Pa.	57b	40.29 N	79.52 W
Blaye-et Sainte Luce, Fr. (blā'ā-sănt-lüs')	168	45.08 N	0.40 W
Blażowa, Pol. (bwä-zhō'vȧ)	167	49.51 N	22.05 E
Bleus, Monts (Mts.), Zaire	231	1.10 N	30.10 E
Bliedinghausen (Neigh.), F.R.G.	63	51.09 N	7.12 E
Bliersheim, F.R.G.	63	51.23 N	6.43 E
Blind River, Can. (blīnd)	102	46.10 N	83.09 W
Blissfield, Mi. (blĭs-fēld)	110	41.50 N	83.50 W
Blithe (R.), Eng. (blīth)	156	52.22 N	1.49 W
Blitta, Togo	228	8.19 N	0.59 E
Block (I.), RI (blŏk)	111	41.05 N	71.35 W
Bloedel, Can.	98	50.07 N	125.23 W
Bloemfontein, S.Afr. (blo͞om'fŏn-tān)	223d	29.09 S	26.16 E
Blois, Fr. (blwä)	168	47.36 N	1.21 E
Blombacher Bach (Neigh.), F.R.G.	63	51.15 N	7.14 E
Blood Ind. Res., Can.	99	49.30 N	113.10 W
Bloomer, Wi. (blo͞om'ẽr)	115	45.07 N	91.30 W
Bloomfield, Ia.	115	40.44 N	92.21 W
Bloomfield, In. (blo͞om'fēld)	110	39.00 N	86.55 W
Bloomfield, Mo.	123	36.54 N	89.55 W
Bloomfield, Ne.	114	42.36 N	97.40 W
Bloomfield, NJ	112a	40.48 N	74.12 W
Bloomfield Hills, Mi.	113b	42.35 N	83.15 W
Bloomfield Village, Mi.	57c	42.33 N	83.15 W
Blooming Prairie, Mn. (blo͞om'ĭng prā'rĭ)	115	43.52 N	93.04 W
Bloomington, Ca. (blo͞om'ĭng-tŭn)	119a	34.04 N	117.24 W
Bloomington, Il.	110	40.30 N	89.00 W
Bloomington, In.	110	39.10 N	86.35 W
Bloomington, Mn.	119g	44.50 N	93.18 W
Bloomsburg, Pa. (blo͞omz'bûrg)	111	41.00 N	76.25 W
Blossburg, Al. (blŏs'bûrg)	112h	33.38 N	86.57 W
Blossburg, Pa.	111	41.45 N	77.00 W
Bloubergstrand, S.Afr.	226a	33.48 S	18.28 E
Blountstown, Fl. (blŭnts'tun)	126	30.24 N	85.02 W
Bludenz, Aus. (blo͞o-dĕnts')	166	47.09 N	9.50 E
Blue Ash, Oh. (blo͞o ăsh)	113f	39.14 N	84.23 W
Blue Earth, Mn. (blo͞o ûrth)	115	43.38 N	94.05 W
Blue Earth (R.), Mn.	115	43.55 N	94.16 W
Bluefield, WV (blo͞o'fēld)	127	37.15 N	81.11 W
Bluefields, Nic. (blo͞o'fēldz)	133	12.03 N	83.45 W
Blue Island, Il.	113a	41.39 N	87.41 W
Blue Mesa Res., Co.	121	38.25 N	107.00 W
Blue Mosque (P. Int.), Egypt	71a	30.02 N	31.15 E
Blue, Mt., Can.	105	50.28 N	57.11 W
Blue Mts., Austl.	216	33.35 S	149.00 E
Blue Mts., Jam.	134	18.05 N	76.35 W
Blue Mts., Or.	116	45.15 N	118.50 W
Blue Mud B., Austl. (bo͞o mŭd)	214	13.20 S	136.45 E
Blue Nile (Abay) (R.), Eth. (ȧ-bä'ē)	225	9.45 N	37.23 E
Blue Nile (Al-Bahr al-Azraq) (R.), Sud. (bärĕlaz-räk')	225	12.50 N	34.10 E
Blue R., Mo.	119f	38.55 N	94.33 W
Blue Rapids, Ks. (blo͞o răp'ĭdz)	123	39.40 N	96.41 W
Blue Ridge (Mts.), U.S. (blo͞o rĭj)	109	35.30 N	82.50 W
Blue River, Can.	99	52.05 N	119.17 W
Bluff, Ut.	121	37.18 N	109.34 W
Bluff Park, Al.	112h	33.24 N	86.52 W
Bluffton, In. (blŭf-tŭn)	110	40.40 N	85.15 W
Bluffton, Oh.	110	40.50 N	83.55 W
Blumenau, Braz. (blo͞o'mĕn-ou)	144	26.53 S	48.58 W
Blumut, Gunong (Mt.), Mala.	191b	2.03 N	103.34 E
Blyth, Eng. (blĭth)	162	55.03 N	1.34 W
Blythe, Ca.	120	33.37 N	114.37 W
Blytheville, Ar. (blīth'vĭl)	123	35.55 N	89.51 W
Bo, S.L.	228	7.56 N	11.21 W
Boac, Phil.	207a	13.26 N	121.50 E
Boaco, Nic. (bô-ä'kō)	132	12.24 N	85.41 W
Bo'ai, China (bwo-ī)	202	35.10 N	113.08 E
Boa Vista do Rio Branco, Braz. (bō'ä vēsh'tä do͞o rē'o͞o brän'ko͞o)	143	2.46 N	60.45 W
Boa Vista I., C.V. (bō-ä-vēsh'tȧ)	224b	16.01 N	23.52 W

PLACE (Pronounciation)	PAGE	Lat. °'	Long. °'
Bobbingworth, Eng.	62	51.44 N	0.13 E
Bobërka, Sov.Un. (bō'bēr-kȧ)	167	49.36 N	24.18 E
Bobigny, Fr.	64c	48.54 N	2.27 E
Bobo Dioulasso, Burkina (bō'bô-dyo͞o-läs-sō')	228	11.12 N	4.18 W
Bóbr (R.), Pol. (bŭ'br)	166	51.44 N	15.13 E
Bobr, Sov.Un. (bô'b'r)	174	54.19 N	29.11 E
Bobrinets, Sov.Un. (bô'brē-nyĭts)	175	48.04 N	32.10 E
Bobrov, Sov.Un. (bŭb-rôf')	175	51.07 N	40.01 E
Bobrovitsa, Sov.Un. (bŭb-rô'vē-tsȧ)	175	50.43 N	31.27 E
Bobruysk, Sov.Un. (bŏ-bro͞o'ĭsk)	174	53.07 N	29.13 E
Boca (Neigh.), Arg.	60d	34.38 S	58.21 W
Boca del Pozo, Ven. (bô-kä-dĕl-pô'zō)	143b	11.00 N	64.21 W
Boca de Uchire, Ven. (bô-kä-dĕ-o͞o-chē'rĕ)	143b	10.09 N	65.27 W
Bocaina, Serra da (Mtn.), Braz. (sĕ'r-rä-dȧ-bô-kä'ē-nä)	141a	22.47 S	44.39 W
Bocanegra, Peru	60c	12.01 S	77.07 W
Bocas, Mex. (bō'käs)	130	22.29 N	101.03 W
Bocas del Toro, Pan. (bō'käs dĕl tō'rō)	133	9.24 N	82.15 W
Bochnia, Pol. (bōĸ'nyä)	167	49.58 N	20.28 E
Bocholt, F.R.G. (bō'ĸōlt)	169c	51.50 N	6.37 E
Bochum, F.R.G.-(bō'ĸo͞om)	169c	51.29 N	7.13 E
Böckel (Neigh.), F.R.G.	63	51.13 N	7.12 E
Bockum, F.R.G.	63	51.20 N	6.44 E
Bockum (Neigh.), F.R.G.	63	51.21 N	6.38 E
Bockum-Hövel, F.R.G. (bō'ĸo͞om-hû'fĕl)	169c	51.41 N	7.45 E
Bodalang, Zaire	230	3.14 N	22.14 E
Bodaybo, Sov.Un. (bō-dī'bō)	181	57.12 N	114.46 E
Bodele (Depression), Chad. (bō-dȧ-lā')	229	16.45 N	17.05 E
Bodelschwingh (Neigh.), F.R.G.	63	51.33 N	7.22 E
Boden, Swe.	158	65.51 N	21.29 E
Bodensee (L.), F.R.G.-Switz. (bō'dĕn zā)	166	47.48 N	9.22 E
Bodmin, Eng. (bŏd'mĭn)	162	50.29 N	4.45 W
Bodmin Moor, Eng. (bŏd'mĭn mo͞or)	162	50.36 N	4.43 W
Bodø, Nor. (bôd'û)	158	67.13 N	14.19 E
Bodrum, Tur.	179	37.10 N	27.07 E
Boende, Zaire (bô-ĕn'dȧ)	230	0.13 S	20.52 E
Boerne, Tx. (bō'ĕrn)	124	29.49 N	98.44 W
Boesmans (R.), S.Afr.	227c	33.29 S	26.09 E
Boeuf R., La. (bĕf)	125	32.23 N	91.57 W
Boffa, Gui. (bôf'ȧ)	228	10.10 N	14.02 W
Bōfu, Jap. (bō'fo͞o)	205	34.03 N	131.35 E
Bogalusa, La. (bō-gȧ-lo͞o'sȧ)	125	30.48 N	89.52 W
Bogan (R.), Austl. (bŏ'gĕn)	216	32.10 S	147.40 E
Bogense, Den. (bō'gĕn-sĕ)	164	55.34 N	10.09 E
Boggy Pk., Antigua (bŏg'ĭ-pēk)	133b	17.03 N	61.50 W
Bogodukhov, Sov.Un. (bŏ-gŏ-do͞o'ĸôf)	175	50.10 N	35.31 E
Bogong, Mt., Austl.	216	36.50 S	147.15 E
Bogor, Indon.	206	6.45 S	106.45 E
Bogoroditsk, Sov.Un. (bŏ-gŏ'rô-dĭtsk)	174	53.48 N	38.06 E
Bogorodsk, Sov.Un.	178	56.02 N	43.40 E
Bogorodskoje (Neigh.), Sov. Un.	66b	55.49 N	37.44 E
Bogorodskoye, Sov.Un. (bô-gô-rôd'skô-yĕ)	182a	56.43 N	56.53 E
Bogotá, Col. (bō-gō-tä')	142a	4.38 N	74.06 W
Bogota, NJ	55	40.53 N	74.02 W
Bogotá, Rio (R.), Col. (rē'ō-bō-gō-tä')	142a	4.27 N	74.38 W
Bogotol, Sov.Un. (bŏ'gô-tŏl)	180	56.15 N	89.45 E
Bogoyavlenskoye, Sov.Un. (bŏ'gô-yäf'lĕn-skō'yĕ)	175	48.46 N	33.19 E
Boguchar, Sov.Un. (bō'go͞o-chär)	179	49.40 N	41.00 E
Boguete, Pan. (bô-gĕ'tĕ)	133	8.54 N	82.29 W
Boguslav, Sov.Un. (bō'go͞o-släf)	175	49.34 N	30.51 W
Bohai Haixia (Str.), China (bwo-hī hī-shyä)	202	38.05 N	121.40 E
Bohain-en-Vermandois, Fr. (bô-ăɴ-ŏɴ-vâr-mäɴ-dwä')	168	49.58 N	3.22 E
Bohemia (Prov.), see Cechy			
Bohemian For., F.R.G. (bô-hē'mĭ-ăn)	166	49.35 N	12.27 E
Böhnsdorf (Neigh.), G.D.R.	65a	52.24 N	13.33 E
Bohol (I.), Phil. (bô-hôl')	207	9.28 N	124.35 E
Bohom, Mex. (bō-ô'm)	131	16.47 N	92.42 W
Boiestown, Can. (boiz'toun)	104	46.27 N	66.25 W
Bois Blanc (I.), Mi. (boi' blăŋk)	110	45.45 N	84.30 W
Boischâtel, Can. (bwä-shä-tĕl')	95b	46.54 N	71.08 W
Bois-Colombes, Fr.	64c	48.55 N	2.16 E
Bois-des-Filion, Can. (bo͞o-ä'dĕ-fē-yōɴ')	95a	45.40 N	73.46 W
Boise, Id. (boi'zē)	116	43.38 N	116.12 W
Boise (R.), Id.	116	43.43 N	116.30 W
Boise City, Ok.	122	36.42 N	102.30 W
Boissevain, Can. (bois'vān)	101	49.14 N	100.03 W
Boissy-Saint-Léger, Fr.	64c	48.45 N	2.31 E
Bojador, Cabo (C.), W.Sah. (kȧ'bô-bō-hä-dōr') (bŏj-ȧ-dōr')	224	26.21 N	16.08 W
Bojnūrd, Iran	192	37.29 N	57.13 E
Bokani, Nig.	229	9.26 N	5.13 E
Boké, Gui. (bō-kā')	224	10.58 N	14.15 W
Boknafjorden (Fd.), Nor.	164	59.12 N	5.37 E
Boksburg, S.Afr. (bŏks'bûrgh)	227b	26.13 S	28.15 E
Boksburg North, S. Afr.	71b	26.12 S	28.15 E
Boksburg South, S. Afr.	71b	26.14 S	28.15 E
Boksburg West, S. Afr.	71b	26.13 S	28.14 E
Bokungu, Zaire	230	0.41 S	22.19 E
Bol, Chad	229	13.28 N	14.43 E
Bolai I., Cen.Afr.Rep.	229	4.20 N	17.21 E
Bolama, Guinea-Bissau (bô-lä'mä)	224	11.34 S	15.41 W
Bolan (Mt.), Pak. (bô-län')	196	30.13 N	67.09 E
Bolaños, Mex. (bō-län'yôs)	130	21.40 N	103.48 W
Bolaños (R.), Mex.	130	21.26 N	103.54 W
Bolan P., Pak.	196	29.50 N	67.10 E
Bolbec, Fr. (bôl-bĕk')	168	49.37 N	0.26 E
Bole, Ghana (bō'lȧ)	228	9.02 N	2.29 W
Boleslawiec, Pol. (bō-lĕ-slä'vyĕts)	166	51.15 N	15.35 E

PLACE (Pronounciation)	PAGE	Lat. °'	Long. °'
Bolgatanga, Ghana	228	10.46 N	0.52 W
Bolgrad, Sov.Un. (bŏl-grȧt)	175	45.41 N	28.38 E
Boli, China (bwo-lē)	202	45.40 N	130.38 E
Bolinao, Phil. (bō-lē-nä'ô)	207a	16.24 N	119.53 E
Bolivar, Mo. (bŏl'ĭ-vȧr)	123	37.37 N	93.22 W
Bolivar, Tn.	126	35.14 N	88.56 W
Bolivar Pen., Tx. (bŏl'ĭ-vȧr)	125a	29.25 N	94.40 W
Bolivia, S.A. (bō-lĭv'ĭ-ȧ)	140	17.00 S	64.00 W
Bolívar, Arg. (bō-lē'vär)	141c	36.15 S	61.05 W
Bolívar, Col.	142	1.46 N	76.58 W
Bolívar (La Columna) (Mtn.), Ven. (bô-lē'vär) (lä-kô-lo͞o'm-nä)	142	8.44 N	70.54 W
Bölkenbusch, F.R.G.	63	51.21 N	7.06 E
Bolkhov, Sov. Un. (bŏl-ĸôf')	174	53.27 N	35.59 E
Bollate, It.	65c	45.33 N	9.07 E
Bollensdorf, G.D.R.	65a	52.31 N	13.43 E
Bollin (R.), Eng. (bŏl'ĭn)	156	53.18 N	2.11 W
Bollington, Eng. (bôl'ĭng-tŭn)	156	53.18 N	2.06 W
Bollington, Eng.	64b	53.22 N	2.25 W
Bollnäs, Swe. (bôl'nĕs)	164	61.22 N	16.20 E
Bollwerk, F.R.G.	63	51.10 N	7.35 E
Bolmen (L.), Swe. (bôl'mĕn)	164	56.58 N	13.25 E
Bolobo, Zaire (bō'lô-bô)	226	2.14 S	16.18 E
Bologna, It. (bô-lōn'yä)	172	44.30 N	11.18 E
Bologoye, Sov. Un. (bŏ-lŏ-gō'yĕ)	174	57.52 N	34.02 E
Bolonchenticul, Mex. (bô-lôn-chĕn-tē-ko͞o'l)	132a	20.03 N	89.47 W
Bolondrón, Cuba (bô-lôn-drōn')	134	22.45 N	81.25 W
Bol'šaja Ochta (Neigh.), Sov. Un.	66a	59.57 N	30.25 E
Bolseno, Lago di (L.), It. (lä'gō-dē-bôl-sā'nô)	172	42.35 N	11.40 E
Bol'shaya Anyuy (R.), Sov. Un.	181	67.58 N	161.15 E
Bol'shaya Chuva (R.), Sov. Un.	181	58.15 N	111.13 E
Bol'shaya Kinel' (R.), Sov. Un.	178	53.20 N	52.40 E
Bol'shaya Lepetikha, Sov. Un. (bôl-shȧ'yȧ'lyĕ'phyĕ-tē'ĸȧ)	175	47.11 N	33.58 E
Bol'shaya Viska, Sov. Un. (vĭs-kä')	175	48.34 N	31.54 E
Bol'shaya Vradiyevka, Sov. Un. (vrȧ-dyĕf'kȧ)	175	47.51 N	30.38 E
Bol'she Ust'ikinskoye, Sov. Un. (bôl'shĕ o͞os-tyĭ-kĕn'skô-yĕ)	182a	55.58 N	58.18 E
Bol'shoy Begichëv (I.), Sov. Un.	181	74.30 N	114.40 E
Bol'shoye Ivonino, Sov. Un. (ĭ-vô'nĭ-nô)	182a	59.41 N	61.12 E
Bol'shoy Kuyash, Sov. Un. (bôl'-shôy ko͞o'yȧsh)	182a	55.52 N	61.07 E
Bolshoy Tokmak, Sov. Un. (bŏl-shôy' tôk-mäk')	175	47.17 N	35.48 E
Bol'šoj Teatr (P. Int.), Sov. Un.	66b	55.46 N	37.37 E
Bolsover, Eng. (bōl'zō-vẽr)	156	53.14 N	1.17 W
Boltaña, Sp. (bôl-tä'nä)	171	42.28 N	0.03 E
Bolton, Can. (bōl'tŭn)	95d	43.53 N	79.44 W
Bolton, Eng.	156	53.35 N	2.26 W
Bolton-upon-Dearne, Eng. (bōl'tŭn-ŭp'ŏn-dûrn)	156	53.31 N	1.19 W
Bolu, Tur. (bō'lo͞o)	179	40.45 N	31.45 E
Bolva (R.), Sov. Un. (bôl'vä)	174	53.30 N	34.30 E
Bolvadin, Tur. (bŏl-vä-dēn')	179	38.50 N	30.50 E
Bolzano, It. (bôl-tsä'nō)	172	46.31 N	11.22 E
Boma, Zaire (bō'mä)	230	5.51 S	13.03 E
Bombala, Austl. (bŭm-bä'lȧ)	216	36.55 S	149.07 E
Bombay, India (bŏm-bā')	197b	18.58 N	72.50 E
Bombay Hbr., India	197b	18.55 N	72.52 E
Bomi Hills, Lib.	224	7.00 N	11.00 W
Bom Jardim, Braz. (bôn zhär-dēɴ')	141a	22.10 S	42.25 W
Bom Jesus do Itabapoana, Braz. (bôɴ-zhĕ-so͞o's-dô-ē-tȧ'bä-pô-ȧ'nä)	141a	21.08 S	41.51 W
Bømlo (I.), Nor. (bûmlô)	164	59.47 N	4.57 E
Bommerholz, F.R.G.	63	51.23 N	7.18 E
Bommern (Neigh.), F.R.G.	63	51.25 N	7.20 E
Bomongo, Zaire	230	1.22 N	18.21 E
Bom Retiro (Neigh.), Braz.	61d	23.32 S	46.38 W
Bom Sucesso, Braz. (bôn-so͞o-sĕ'sō)	141a	21.02 S	44.44 W
Bomu (R.), see Mbomou			
Bon Air, Pa.	56b	39.58 N	75.19 W
Bonaire (I.), Neth. Antilles (bô-nâr')	142	12.10 N	68.15 W
Bonavista, Can. (bŏ-nȧ-vĭs'tȧ)	105	48.39 N	53.07 W
Bonavista B., Can.	105	48.45 N	53.20 W
Bon, C., Tun. (bôɴ)	159	37.04 N	11.13 E
Bond, Co. (bŏnd)	122	39.53 N	106.40 W
Bondi, Austl.	70a	33.53 S	151.17 E
Bondo, Zaire (bôn'dô)	230	3.49 N	23.40 E
Bondoc Pen., Phil. (bôn-dŏk')	207a	13.24 N	122.30 E
Bondoukou, Ivory Coast (bŏn-do͞o'ko͞o)	228	8.02 N	2.48 W
Bonds Cay (I.), Ba. (bŏnds kē)	134	25.30 N	77.45 W
Bondy, Fr.	64c	48.54 N	2.28 E
Bône, see Annaba			
Bonete, Cerro (Mt.), Arg. (bô'nĕtĕh çĕrrô)	144	27.50 S	68.35 W
Bone, Teluk (G.), Indon.	206	4.09 S	121.00 E
Bonfim, Braz. (bôɴ-fē'ɴ)	141a	20.20 S	44.15 W
Bongor, Chad.	229	10.17 N	15.22 E
Bong Son, Viet.	203	14.20 N	109.10 E
Bonham, Tx. (bŏn'ăm)	123	33.35 N	96.09 W
Bonhomme, Pic (Pk.), Hai.	135	19.10 N	72.20 W
Bonifacio, Fr. (bō-nē-fä'chō)	172	41.23 N	9.10 E
Bonifacio, Str. of., Eur.	172	41.14 N	9.02 E
Bonifay, Fl. (bŏn-ĭ-fā')	126	30.46 N	85.40 W
Bonin Is., Asia (bō'nĭn)	208	26.30 N	141.00 E
Bonn, F.R.G. (bŏn)	169c	50.44 N	7.06 E
Bonne B., Can. (bŏn)	105	49.33 N	57.55 W
Bonners Ferry, Id. (bon'erz fĕr'ĭ)	116	48.41 N	116.19 W
Bonner Springs, Ks. (bŏn'ẽr sprĭngz)	119f	39.04 N	94.52 W
Bonne Terre, Mo. (bŏn târ')	123	37.55 N	90.32 W
Bonnet Pk., Can. (bŏn'ĭt)	99	51.26 N	115.53 W
Bonneuil-sur-Marne, Fr.	64c	48.46 N	2.29 E
Bonneville Dam, Or.-Wa. (bŏn'ē-vĭl)	116	45.37 N	121.57 W
Bonnie B., Can. (bŏn'ē)	105	49.38 N	58.15 W
Bonny, Nig. (bŏn'ē)	224	4.29 N	7.13 E
Bonny Lake, Wa. (bŏn'ē lăk)	118a	47.11 N	122.11 W

ăt; finăl; rāte; senāte; ärm; ȧsk; sofȧ; fâre; ch-choose; dh-as th in other; bē; ēvent; bĕt; recĕnt; cratẽr; g-gō; gh-guttural g; bĭt; ĭ-short neutral; rīde; ĸ-guttural k as ch in German ich;

PLACE (Pronounciation)	PAGE	Lat. °'	Long. °'
Bonnyrigg, Austl.	70a	33.54 S	150.54 E
Bonnyville, Can. (bŏn'e-vĭl)	99	54.16 N	110.44 W
Bonorva, It. (bô-nôr'vä)	172	40.26 N	8.46 E
Bonsúcesso (Neigh.), Braz.	61c	22.52 S	43.15 W
Bonthain, Indon. (bôn-tīn')	206	5.30 S	119.52 E
Bonthe, S.L.	228	7.32 N	12.30 W
Bontoc, Phil. (bôn-tŏk')	207a	17.10 N	121.01 E
Booby Rocks (I.), Ba. (bo͞o'bĭ rŏks)	134	23.55 N	77.00 W
Booker T. Washington Natl. Mon., Va. (bo͝ok'ẽr tē wŏsh'ĭng-tŭn)	127	37.07 N	79.45 W
Boom, Bel.	157a	51.05 N	4.22 E
Boone, Ia. (bo͞on)	115	42.04 N	93.51 W
Booneville, Ar. (bo͞on'vĭl)	123	35.09 N	93.54 W
Booneville, Ky.	110	37.25 N	83.40 W
Booneville, Ms.	126	34.37 N	88.35 W
Boons, S. Afr.	223d	25.59 S	27.15 E
Boonton, NJ (bo͞on'tŭn)	112a	40.54 N	74.24 W
Boonville, In.	110	38.00 N	87.15 W
Boonville, Mo.	123	38.57 N	92.44 W
Boorama, Som.	223a	10.05 N	43.08 E
Boosaaso, Som.	223a	11.19 N	49.10 E
Boothbay Harbor, Me. (bo͞oth'bā här'bẽr)	104	43.51 N	69.39 W
Boothia, G. of, Can. (bo͞o'thĭ-ȧ)	97	69.04 N	86.04 W
Boothia Pen., Can.	94	73.30 N	95.00 W
Boothstown, Eng.	64b	53.30 N	2.25 W
Bootle, Eng. (bo͞ot'l)	156	53.29 N	3.02 W
Booué, Gabon	230	0.06 S	11.56 E
Booysens (Neigh.), S. Afr.	71b	26.14 S	28.01 E
Bor, Sud. (bôr)	225	6.13 N	31.35 E
Bor, Tur. (bōr)	179	37.50 N	34.40 E
Boraha, Nosy (I.), Mad.	227	16.58 S	50.15 E
Borah Pk., Id. (bō'rä)	117	44.12 N	113.47 W
Borås, Swe. (bo͞o'rōs)	164	57.43 N	12.55 E
Borāzjān, Iran (bō-räz-jän')	192	29.13 N	51.13 E
Borba, Braz. (bôr'bä)	143	4.23 S	59.31 W
Borbeck (Neigh.), F.R.G.	63	51.29 N	6.57 E
Borborema, Planalto da (Plat.), Braz. (plä-näl'tô-dä-bôr-bō-rĕ'mä)	143	7.35 S	36.40 W
Bordeaux, Fr. (bôr-dō')	168	44.50 N	0.37 W
Bordeaux (Neigh.), Can.	54b	45.33 N	73.41 W
Bordeaux, S. Afr.	71b	26.06 S	28.01 E
Bordentown, NJ (bôr'dĕn-toun)	111	40.05 N	74.40 W
Bordj-bou-Arréridj, Alg. (bôrj-bo͞o-ȧ-rā-rēj')	159	36.03 N	4.48 E
Bordj Omar Idriss, Alg.	224	28.06 N	6.34 E
Borehamwood, Eng.	62	51.40 N	0.16 W
Borgå, Fin. (bôr'gō)	165	60.26 N	25.41 E
Borgarnes, Ice.	158	64.31 N	21.40 W
Borger, Tx. (bôr'gẽr)	122	35.40 N	101.23 W
Borgholm, Swe. (bôrg-hŏlm')	164	56.52 N	16.40 E
Borgne (L.), La. (bôrn'y')	125	30.03 N	89.36 W
Borgomanero, It. (bôr'gō-mä-nâ'rō)	172	45.40 N	8.28 E
Borgo Val di Taro, It. (bô'r-zhō-väl-dē-tä'rō)	172	44.29 N	9.44 E
Boring, Or. (bōring)	118c	45.26 N	122.22 W
Borislav, Sov. Un. (bô'rĭs-lôf)	167	49.17 N	23.24 E
Borisoglebsk, Sov. Un. (bŏ-rē sô-glyĕpsk')	179	51.20 N	42.00 E
Borisov, Sov. Un. (bŏ-rē'sôf)	174	54.16 N	28.33 E
Borisovka, Sov. Un. (bŏ-rē-sôf'kȧ)	175	50.38 N	36.00 E
Borispol', Sov. Un. (bo-rĭs'pol)	175	50.17 N	30.54 E
Borivli, India	197b	19.15 N	72.48 E
Borja, Sp. (bôr'hä)	170	41.50 N	1.33 W
Borjas Blancas, Sp. (bô'r-кäs-blä'n-käs)	171	41.29 N	0.53 E
Borken, F.R.G. (bōr'kĕn)	169c	51.50 N	6.51 E
Borkou (Reg.), Chad. (bôr-ko͞o')	225	18.11 N	18.28 E
Borkum I., F.R.G. (bōr'ko͞om)	166	53.31 N	6.50 E
Borlänge, Swe. (bôr-lĕng'gĕ)	164	60.30 N	15.24 E
Borle (Neigh.), India	67e	19.02 N	72.55 E
Borneo (I.), Asia (bôr'nē-ō)	206	0.25 N	112.39 E
Bornholm (I.), Den. (bôrn-hôlm)	164	55.16 N	15.15 E
Bornim (Neigh.), G.D.R.	65a	52.26 N	13.00 E
Bornstedt (Neigh.), G.D.R.	65a	52.25 N	13.02 E
Borodayevka, Sov. Un.	175	48.44 N	34.09 E
Boromlya, Sov. Un. (bŏ-rôm''l-yä)	175	50.36 N	34.58 E
Boromo, Upper Volta	228	11.45 N	2.56 W
Borough Green, Eng.	62	51.17 N	0.19 E
Borough Park (Neigh.), NY	55	40.38 N	74.00 W
Borovan, Bul. (bŏ-rō-vän')	173	43.24 N	23.47 E
Borovichi, Sov. Un. (bŏ-rō-vē'chē)	174	58.22 N	33.56 E
Borovsk, Sov. Un. (bô'rŏvsk)	174	55.13 N	36.26 E
Borraan, Som.	223a	10.38 N	48.30 E
Borracha, Isla la (I.), Ven. (ē's-lä-lä-bôr-rä'chä)	143b	10.18 N	64.44 W
Borroloola, Austl. (bŏr-rō-lo͞o'lȧ)	214	16.15 S	136.19 E
Borshchëv, Sov. Un. (bôrsh-chyôf')	167	48.47 N	26.04 E
Borth, F.R.G.	63	51.36 N	6.33 E
Bort-les-Orgues, Fr. (bôr-lā-zôrg)	168	45.26 N	2.26 E
Borūjerd, Iran	192	33.45 N	48.53 E
Borzna, Sov. Un. (bôrz'ná)	175	51.15 N	32.26 E
Borzya, Sov. Un. (bôrz'yȧ)	181	50.37 N	116.53 E
Bosa, It. (bō'sä)	172	40.18 N	8.34 E
Bosanska Dubica, Yugo. (bō'sän-skä do͞o'bĭt-sä)	172	45.10 N	16.49 E
Bosanska Gradiška, Yugo. (bō'sän-skä grä-dĭsh'kä)	172	45.08 N	17.15 E
Bosanski Novi, Yugo. (bō's sän-skĭ nō'vē)	172	45.00 N	16.22 E
Bosanski Petrovac, Yugo. (bō'sän-skĭ pĕt'rō-väts)	172	44.33 N	16.23 E
Bosanski Šamac, Yugo. (bō'sän-skĭ shä'mäts)	173	45.03 N	18.30 E
Boscobel, Wi. (bŏs'kō-bĕl)	115	43.08 N	90.44 W
Bose, China (bwo-sŭ)	203	24.00 N	106.38 E
Boshan, China (bwo-shan)	200	36.32 N	117.51 E
Boskol, Sov. Un. (bȧs-kôl')	182a	53.45 N	61.17 E
Boskoop, Neth.	157a	52.04 N	4.39 E
Boskovice, Czech. (bŏs'kō-vē-tsĕ)	166	49.26 N	16.37 E
Bosna (R.), Yugo.	173	44.19 N	17.54 E
Bosnia (Reg.), Yugo. (bŏs'nĭ-ȧ)	173	44.17 N	16.58 E
Bosobolo, Zaire	230	4.11 N	19.54 E
Bosporous (Str.), see İstanbul Boğazi			
Bossangoa, Cen. Afr. Rep.	229	6.29 N	17.27 E
Bossembélé, Cen. Afr. Rep.	229	5.16 N	17.39 E
Bossier City, La. (bŏsh'ẽr)	125	32.31 N	93.42 W
Bossley Park, Austl.	70a	33.52 S	150.54 E
Bostanci (Neigh.), Tur.	66f	40.57 N	29.05 E
Bosten Hu (L.), China (bwo-stŭn ho͞o)	198	42.06 N	88.01 E
Boston, Ga. (bôs'tŭn)	126	30.47 N	83.47 W
Boston, Ma.	105a	42.15 N	71.07 W
Boston, Pa.	57b	40.18 N	79.49 W
Boston B., Ma.	54a	42.22 N	70.54 W
Boston Garden (P. Int.), Ma.	54a	42.22 N	71.04 W
Boston Har., Ma.	54a	42.20 N	70.58 W
Boston Heights, Oh.	113d	41.15 N	81.30 W
Boston Mts., Ar.	123	35.46 N	93.32 W
Botafogo (Neigh.), Braz.	61c	22.57 S	43.11 W
Botafogo, Enseada de (B.), Braz.	61c	22.57 S	43.10 W
Botany, Austl.	70a	33.57 S	151.12 E
Botany B., Austl. (bŏt'ȧ-nĭ)	211b	33.58 S	151.11 E
Botany Bay (Neigh.), Eng.	62	51.41 N	0.07 W
Botevgrad, Bul.	173	42.54 N	23.41 E
Bothaville, S. Afr. (bō'tä-vĭl)	223d	27.24 S	26.38 E
Bothell, Wa. (bŏth'ĕl)	118a	47.46 N	122.12 W
Bothnia, G. of, Eur. (bŏth'nĭ-ȧ)	158	63.40 N	21.30 E
Botosani, Rom. (bô-tô-shȧn'ĭ)	167	47.46 N	26.40 E
Botswana, Afr. (bŏtswănă)	222	22.10 S	23.13 E
Bottineau, ND (bŏt-ĭ-nō')	114	48.48 N	100.28 W
Bottrop, F.R.G. (bŏt'trōp)	169c	51.31 N	6.56 E
Botucatú, Braz. (bô-to͞o-kä-to͞o')	143	22.50 S	48.23 W
Botwood, Can. (bŏt'wo͝od)	105	49.08 N	55.21 W
Bötzow, G.D.R.	65a	52.39 N	13.08 E
Bouafle, Ivory Coast (bo͞o-ȧ-flā')	228	6.59 N	5.45 W
Bouaké, Ivory Coast (bo͞o-ȧ-kā')	228	7.41 N	5.00 W
Bouar, Cen. Afr. Rep. (bo͞o-är)	229	5.57 N	15.36 E
Bou Areg, Sebkha (Marsh), Mor.	170	35.09 N	3.02 W
Boubandjidah, Parc Natl. de (Natl. Pk.), Cam.	229	8.20 N	14.40 E
Boucherville, Can. (bo͞o-shā-vēl')	95a	45.37 N	73.27 W
Boucherville, Îles de (Is.), Can.	54b	45.37 N	73.28 W
Boucle du Baoulé, Parc Natl. de la (Natl. Pk.), Mali	228	13.50 N	9.15 W
Boudenib, Mor. (bo͞o-dĕ-nēb')	224	32.14 N	3.04 W
Boudette, Mn. (bo͞o-dĕt)	115	48.42 N	94.34 W
Boudouaou, Alg.	171	36.44 N	3.25 E
Boufarik, Alg. (bo͞o-fȧ-rēk')	171	36.35 N	2.55 E
Bougainville Trench, Oceania (bo͞o-găɴ-vēl')	208	7.00 S	152.00 E
Bougie, see Bejaïa			
Bougouni, Mali (bo͞o-go͞o-nē')	224	11.27 N	7.30 W
Bouïra, Alg. (boo-ē'rȧ)	160	36.25 N	3.55 E
Bouïra-Sahary, Alg. (bwē-rȧ sȧ'ä-rē)	171	35.16 N	3.23 E
Bouka (R.), Gui.	228	11.05 N	10.40 W
Boukiéro, Con.	71c	4.12 S	15.18 E
Boulder, Austl. (bōl'dẽr)	214	31.00 S	121.40 E
Boulder, Co.	122	40.02 N	105.19 W
Boulder (R.), Mt.	117	46.10 N	112.07 W
Boulder City, Nv.	120	35.57 N	114.50 W
Boulder Cr., Id.	116	42.53 N	116.49 W
Boulder Pk., Id.	117	43.53 N	114.33 W
Boulogne (Neigh.), Arg.	60d	34.31 S	58.34 W
Boulogne-Billancourt, Fr. (bo͞o-lôn'y'-bē-yäɴ-ko͞or')	169b	48.50 N	2.14 E
Boulogne-sur-Mer, Fr. (bo͞o-lôn'y-sür-mâr')	168	50.44 N	1.37 E
Boumba (R.), Cam.	229	3.20 N	14.40 E
Bouna, Ivory Coast (bo͞o-nä')	228	9.16 N	3.00 W
Bouna, Park Natl. de (Natl. Pk.), Ivory Coast	228	9.20 N	3.35 W
Boundary B., Can. (boun'dȧ-rĭ)	118d	49.03 N	122.59 W
Boundary Pk., Nv.	120	37.52 N	118.20 W
Bound Brook, NJ (bound bro͝ok)	112a	40.34 N	74.32 W
Bountiful, Ut. (boun'tĭ-fo͝ol)	119b	40.55 N	111.53 W
Bountiful Pk., Ut. (boun'tĭ-fo͝ol)	119b	40.58 N	111.49 W
Bounty Is., N.Z.	232	47.42 S	179.05 E
Bourem, Mali (bo͞o-rĕm')	224	16.43 N	0.15 W
Bourg-en-Bresse, Fr. (bo͞or-gĕɴ-brĕs')	168	46.12 N	5.13 E
Bourges, Fr. (bo͞orzh)	168	47.06 N	2.22 E
Bourget, Can. (bo͞or-zhĕ')	95c	45.26 N	75.09 W
Bourg-la-Reine, Fr.	64c	48.47 N	2.19 E
Bourgoin, Fr. (bo͞or-gwăɴ')	169	45.46 N	5.17 E
Bourke, Austl. (bŭrk)	216	30.10 S	146.00 E
Bourne, Eng. (bōrn)	156	52.46 N	0.22 W
Bournebridge, Eng.	62	51.38 N	0.11 E
Bourne End, Eng.	62	51.45 N	0.32 W
Bournemouth, Eng. (bôrn'mŭth)	162	50.44 N	1.55 W
Bou Saâda, Alg. (bo͞o-sä'dä)	160	35.13 N	4.17 E
Bousso, Chad. (bo͞o-sō')	225	10.33 N	16.45 E
Boutilimit, Mauritania (bo͞o-tē-lē-mē')	224	17.30 N	14.54 W
Bouvert (I.), see Bouvetøya			
Bouvetøya (Bouvert) (I.), Alt. O.	232	54.26 S	3.24 E
Bövinghausen (Neigh.), F.R.G.	63	51.31 N	7.19 E
Bow (R.), Can. (bō)	99	50.35 N	112.15 W
Bowbells, ND (bō'bĕls)	114	48.50 N	102.16 W
Bowdle, SD (bōd''l)	114	45.28 N	99.42 W
Bowdon, Eng.	64b	53.23 N	2.22 W
Bowen, Austl. (bō'ĕn)	215	20.02 S	148.14 E
Bowie, Md. (bo͞o'ĭ) (bō'ē)	112e	38.59 N	76.47 W
Bowie, Tx.	122	33.34 N	97.50 W
Bowling Green, Ky. (bōlĭng grēn)	126	37.00 N	86.26 W
Bowling Green, Mo.	123	39.19 N	91.09 W
Bowling Green, Oh.	110	41.25 N	83.40 W
Bowman, ND (bō'mȧn)	114	46.11 N	103.23 W
Bowron (R.), Can. (bō'rŭn)	99	53.20 N	121.10 W
Boxelder Cr., Mt. (bŏks'ĕl-dẽr)	114	45.35 N	104.28 W
Boxelder Cr., Mt.	117	47.17 N	108.37 W
Box Hill, Austl.	70b	37.49 S	145.08 E
Boxian, China (bwo shyĕn)	200	33.52 N	115.47 E
Boxing, China (bwo-shyĭŋ)	200	37.09 N	118.08 E
Boxmoor, Eng.	62	51.45 N	0.29 W
Boxtel, Neth.	157a	51.40 N	5.21 E
Boyabo, Zaire	230	3.43 N	18.46 E
Boyacıköy (Neigh.), Tur.	66f	41.06 N	29.02 E
Boyang, China (bwo-yäŋ)	203	29.00 N	116.42 E
Boyer (R.), Can. (boi'ẽr)	95b	46.26 N	70.56 W
Boyer (R.), Ia.	114	41.45 N	95.36 W
Boyle, Ire. (boil)	162	53.59 N	8.15 W
Boyne (R.), Ire. (boin)	162	53.40 N	6.40 W
Boyne City, Mi.	110	45.15 N	85.05 W
Boyoma Falls, Zaire	230	0.30 N	25.12 E
Bozca Ada (I.), Tur.	173	39.50 N	26.00 E
Bozcaada, Tur. (bōz-cȧ'dä)	173	39.50 N	26.05 E
Bozeman, Mt. (bōz'mȧn)	117	45.41 N	111.00 W
Bozene, Zaire	230	2.56 N	19.12 E
Bozhen, China (bwo-jŭn)	200	38.05 N	116.35 E
Bozoum, Cen. Afr. Rep.	229	6.19 N	16.23 E
Bra, It. (brä)	172	44.41 N	7.52 E
Brač (I.), Yugo. (bräch)	172	43.18 N	16.36 E
Bracciano, Lago di (L.), It. (lä'gō-dē-brä-chä'nō)	172	42.05 N	12.00 E
Bracebridge, Can. (brās'brĭj)	111	45.05 N	79.20 W
Braceville, Il. (brās'vĭl)	113a	41.13 N	88.16 W
Bräcke, Swe. (brĕk'kĕ)	164	62.44 N	15.28 E
Brackenridge, Pa. (brăk'ĕn-rĭj)	113e	40.37 N	79.44 W
Brackettville, Tx. (brăk'ĕt-vĭl)	124	29.19 N	100.24 W
Braço Maior (R.), Braz.	143	11.00 S	51.00 W
Braço Menor (R.), Braz. (brä'zō-mē-nō'r)	143	11.38 S	50.00 W
Bradano (R.), It. (brä-dä'nō)	172	40.43 N	16.22 E
Braddock, Pa. (brăd'ŭk)	113e	40.24 N	79.52 W
Braddock Hills, Pa.	57b	40.25 N	79.51 W
Bradenburger Tor (P. Int.), G.D.R.	65a	52.31 N	13.23 E
Bradenton, Fl. (brā'dĕn-tŭn)	127a	27.28 N	82.35 W
Bradfield, Eng. (brăd'fēld)	156b	51.25 N	1.08 W
Bradford, Eng. (brăd'fẽrd)	156	53.47 N	1.44 W
Bradford, Oh.	110	40.10 N	84.30 W
Bradford, Pa.	111	42.00 N	78.40 W
Bradley, Il. (brăd'lĭ)	113a	41.09 N	87.52 W
Bradner, Can. (brăd'nẽr)	118d	49.05 N	122.26 W
Bradshaw, Eng.	64b	53.36 N	2.24 W
Brady, Tx. (brā'dĭ)	124	31.09 N	99.21 W
Braga, Port. (brä'gä)	170	41.20 N	8.25 W
Bragado, Arg. (brä-gä'dō)	141c	35.07 S	60.28 W
Bragança, Braz. (brä-gän'sä)	143	1.02 S	46.50 W
Bragança, Port.	170	41.48 N	6.46 W
Bragança Paulista, Braz. (brä-gän'sä-pä'o͞o-lē's-tȧ)	141a	22.58 S	46.31 W
Bragg Creek, Can. (brăg)	95a	50.57 N	114.35 W
Brahmaputra (R.), India (brä'mȧ-po͞o'trȧ)	193	26.45 N	92.45 E
Brāhui (Mts.), Pak.	193	28.32 N	66.15 E
Braidwood, Il. (brād'wo͝od)	113a	41.16 N	88.13 W
Brăila, Rom. (brē'ēlȧ)	175	45.15 N	27.58 E
Brainerd, Mn. (brān'ẽrd)	115	46.20 N	94.09 W
Braintree, Ma. (brān'trē)	105a	42.14 N	71.00 W
Braithwaite, La. (brāth'wīt)	112d	29.52 N	89.57 W
Brakpan, S. Afr. (brăk'păn)	227b	26.15 S	28.22 E
Bralorne, Can. (brā'lôrn)	98	50.47 N	122.49 W
Bramalea, Can.	95d	43.48 N	79.41 W
Bramhall, Eng.	64b	53.22 N	2.10 W
Brampton, Can. (brămp'tŭn)	95d	43.41 N	79.46 W
Branca, Pedra (Mtn.), Braz. (pĕ'drä-brä'ɴ-kä)	144b	22.55 S	43.28 W
Branchville, NJ (branch'vĭl)	112a	41.09 S	74.44 W
Branchville, SC	127	33.17 N	80.48 W
Branco (R.), Braz. (brän'kō)	143	2.21 N	60.38 W
Brandberg (Mtn.), Namibia	226	21.15 S	14.15 E
Brandenburg, G.D.R. (brän'dĕn-bo͞orgh)	157b	52.25 N	12.33 E
Brandenburg (Reg.), G.D.R.	166	52.12 N	13.31 E
Brandfort, S. Afr. (brăn'd-fôrt)	223d	28.42 S	26.29 E
Brandon, Can. (brăn'dŭn)	101	49.50 N	99.57 W
Brandon, Vt.	111	43.45 N	73.05 W
Brandon Mtn., Ire. (brăn-dŏn)	162	52.15 N	10.12 W
Brandywine, Md. (brăndĭ'wīn)	112e	38.42 N	76.51 W
Branford, Ct. (brăn'fẽrd)	111	41.15 N	72.50 W
Braniewo, Pol. (brä-nyĕ'vô)	167	54.23 N	19.50 E
Brańsk, Pol. (brän' sk)	167	52.44 N	22.51 E
Brantford, Can. (brănt'fẽrd)	95d	43.09 N	80.17 W
Bras d'Or L., Can. (brä-dôr')	105	45.52 N	60.50 W
Brasília Legal (Fordlândia), Braz. (brä-sē'lyä-lĕ-gál) (fô'rd-län-dyä)	143	3.45 S	55.46 W
Brasília, Braz. (brä-sē'lvä)	143	15.49 S	47.39 W
Brasópolis, Braz. (brä-sô'pô-lēs)	141a	22.30 S	45.36 W
Braşov (Oraşul-Stalin), Rom.	173	45.39 N	25.35 E
Brass, Nig. (brăs)	224	4.28 N	6.28 E
Bras Saint Michel (R.), Can.	95b	46.47 N	70.51 W
Brasschaat, Bel. (bräs'кät)	157a	51.19 N	4.30 E
Bratcevo (Neigh.), Sov. Un.	66b	55.51 N	37.24 E
Bratenahl, Oh. (bră'tĕn-ôl)	113d	41.34 N	81.36 W
Bratislava, Czech. (brä'tĭs-lä-vä)	157e	48.09 N	17.07 E
Bratsk, Sov. Un. (brätsk)	180	56.10 N	102.04 E
Bratskoye Vdkhr. (Res.), Sov. Un.	180	56.10 N	102.05 E
Bratslav, Sov. Un. (brät'släf)	175	48.48 N	28.59 E
Brattleboro, Vt. (brăt''l-bŭr-ô)	111	42.50 N	72.35 W
Braunau, Aus. (brou'nou)	166	48.15 N	13.05 E
Braunschweig, F.R.G. (broun'shvīgh)	166	52.16 N	10.32 E
Bråviken (R.), Swe.	164	58.40 N	16.40 E
Bravo del Norte, Rio (R.), see Grande, Rio			
Brawley, Ca. (brô'lĭ)	120	32.59 N	115.32 W
Bray, Ire. (brā)	162	53.10 N	6.05 W
Braybrook, Austl.	70b	37.47 S	144.51 E
Braymer, Mo. (brā'mẽr)	123	39.34 N	93.47 W
Brays Bay, Tx. (brās'bĭ'yo͞o)	125a	29.41 N	95.33 W
Brazeau (R.), Can.	99	52.55 N	116.10 W
Brazeau, Mt., Can. (brā-zō')	99	52.33 N	117.21 W
Brazil, In. (brȧ-zĭl')	110	39.30 N	87.00 W
Brazil, S.A.	140	9.00 S	53.00 W

ng-sing; ŋ-baŋk; ɴ-nasalized n; nŏd; cŏmmit; ōld; ôbey; ôrder; oi-boil; fo͞od; fo͝ot; ou-out; s-soft; sh-dish; th-thin; pūre; ûnite; ûrn; stŭd; circŭs; ü-as in French tu; '-indeterminate vowel.

PLACE (Pronounciation)	PAGE	Lat. °'	Long. °'
Brazilian Highlands (Mts.), Braz. (brȧ zīl yȧn hī-lȧndz)	140	14.00 S	48.00 W
Brazos (R.), Clear Fk., Tx.	124	32.56 N	99.14 W
Brazos (R.), Double Mountain Fk., Tx.	122	33.23 N	101.21 W
Brazos (R.), Salt Fk., Tx. (sôlt fôrk)	122	33.20 N	110.57 W
Brazos (R.), U.S. (brä'zōs)	108	33.10 N	98.50 W
Brazzaville, Con. (brȧ-zȧ-vēl')	230	4.16 S	15.17 E
Brčko, Yugo. (běrch'kô)	173	44.54 N	18.46 E
Brda R., Pol. (běr-dä)	167	53.18 N	17.55 E
Brea, Ca. (brē'ȧ)	119a	33.55 N	117.54 W
Breakeyville, Can.	95b	46.40 N	71.13 W
Brecheten (Neigh.), F.R.G.	63	51.35 N	7.28 E
Breckenridge, Mn. (brĕk'ĕn-rĭj)	114	46.17 N	96.35 W
Breckenridge, Tx.	124	32.46 N	98.53 W
Breckerfeld, F.R.G.	63	51.16 N	7.28 E
Brecksville, Oh. (brĕks'vĭl)	113d	41.19 N	81.38 W
Břeclav, Czech. (brzhĕl'läf)	166	48.46 N	16.54 E
Breda, Neth. (brā-dä')	157a	51.35 N	4.47 E
Bredasdorp, S. Afr. (brā'das-dôrp)	226	34.15 S	20.00 E
Bredbury, Eng.	64b	53.25 N	2.06 W
Bredell, S. Afr.	71b	26.05 S	28.17 E
Bredeney (Neigh.), F.R.G.	63	51.24 N	6.59 E
Bredenscheid-Stüter, F.R.G.	63	51.22 N	7.11 E
Bredy, Sov. Un. (brĕ'dĭ)	182a	52.25 N	60.23 E
Breezewood, Pa.	57b	40.34 N	80.03 W
Bregenz, Aus. (brā'gĕnts)	166	47.30 N	9.46 E
Bregovo, Bul. (brĕ'gô-vô)	173	44.07 N	22.45 E
Breidafjördur (Fd.), Ice.	158	65.15 N	22.50 W
Breidbach, S. Afr. (brĕd'bȧk)	227c	32.54 S	27.26 E
Breil-sur-Roya, Fr. (brĕ'y')	169	43.57 N	7.36 E
Breitscheid, F.R.G.	63	51.22 N	6.52 E
Brejo, Braz. (brâ'zhōō)	143	3.33 S	42.46 W
Bremangerlandet (I.), Nor.	164	61.51 N	4.25 E
Bremen, F.R.G. (brā-mĕn)	166	53.05 N	8.50 E
Bremen, In. (brē'mĕn)	110	41.25 N	86.05 W
Bremerhaven, F.R.G. (brām-ēr-hä'fĕn)	166	53.33 N	8.38 E
Bremerton, Wa. (brĕm'ēr-tŭn)	118a	47.34 N	122.38 W
Bremervörde, F.R.G. (brĕ'mĕr-fûr-dĕ)	157c	53.29 N	9.09 E
Bremner, Can. (brĕm'nēr)	95g	53.34 N	113.14 W
Bremond, Tx. (brĕm'ŭnd)	125	31.11 N	96.40 W
Breña, Peru	60c	12.04 S	77.04 W
Brenham, Tx. (brĕn'ăm)	125	30.10 N	96.24 W
Bren Mar Park, Md.	56d	38.48 N	77.09 W
Brenner P., Aus.-It. (brĕn'ēr)	166	47.00 N	11.30 E
Brentford (Neigh.), Eng.	62	51.29 N	0.18 W
Brenthurst, S. Afr.	71b	26.16 S	28.23 E
Brentwood, Eng. (brĕnt'wŏŏd)	156b	51.37 N	0.18 E
Brentwood, Md.	111	39.00 N	76.55 W
Brentwood, Mo.	119e	38.37 N	90.21 W
Brentwood, Pa.	113e	40.22 N	79.59 W
Brentwood Heights (Neigh.), Ca.	59	34.04 N	118.30 W
Brentwood Park, S. Afr.	71b	26.08 S	28.18 E
Brescia, It. (brā'shä)	172	45.33 N	10.15 E
Bressanone, It. (brĕs-sä-nō'nā)	172	46.42 N	11.40 E
Bresso, It.	65c	45.32 N	9.11 E
Bressuire, Fr. (grĕ-swēr')	168	46.49 N	0.14 W
Brest, Fr. (brĕst)	168	48.24 N	4.30 W
Brest, Sov. Un.	167	52.06 N	23.43 E
Brest (Oblast), Sov. Un.	174	52.30 N	26.50 E
Bretagne (Reg.), Fr. (brē-täN'yĕ)	168	48.00 N	3.00 W
Breton, Pertvis (Str.), Fr. (pâr-twē'brĕ-tôN')	168	46.18 N	1.43 W
Breton Sd., La. (brĕt'ŭn)	126	29.38 N	89.15 W
Breukelen, Neth.	157a	52.09 N	5.00 E
Brevard, NC (brē-värd')	126	35.14 N	82.45 W
Breves, Braz. (brā'vĕzh)	143	1.32 S	50.13 W
Brevik, Nor. (brĕ'vĕk)	164	59.04 N	9.39 E
Brewarrina, Austl. (brōō-ēr-rē'nȧ)	216	29.54 S	146.50 E
Brewer, Me. (brōō'ēr)	104	44.46 N	68.46 W
Brewerville, Lib.	228	6.26 N	10.47 W
Brewster, NY (brōō'stēr)	112a	41.23 N	73.38 W
Brewster, Cerro (Mtn.), Pan. (sĕ'r-rô-brōō'stēr)	133	9.19 N	79.15 W
Brewton, Al. (brōō'tŭn)	126	31.06 N	87.04 W
Brezhnev, Sov. Un.	178	55.42 N	52.19 E
Brežice, Yugo. (brē'zhē-tsĕ)	172	45.55 N	15.37 E
Breznik, Bul. (brĕs'nĕk)	173	42.44 N	22.55 E
Briancon, Fr. (brē-äN-sôN')	169	44.54 N	6.39 E
Briare, Fr. (brē-är')	168	47.40 N	2.46 E
Bridal Veil, Or. (brīd'ăl vāl)	118c	45.33 N	122.10 W
Bridesburg (Neigh.), Pa.	56b	40.00 N	75.04 W
Bridgeport, Al. (brĭj'pôrt)	126	34.55 N	85.42 W
Bridgeport, Ct.	112a	41.12 N	73.12 W
Bridgeport, IL.	110	38.40 N	87.45 W
Bridgeport (Neigh.), Il.	58a	41.51 N	87.39 W
Bridgeport, Ne.	114	41.40 N	103.06 W
Bridgeport, Oh.	110	40.00 N	80.45 W
Bridgeport, Pa.	112f	40.06 N	75.21 W
Bridgeport, Tx.	122	33.13 N	97.46 W
Bridge Pt., Ba. (brĭj)	134	25.35 N	76.40 W
Bridgeton, Al. (brĭj'tŭn)	112h	33.27 N	86.39 W
Bridgeton, Mo.	119e	38.45 N	90.23 W
Bridgeton, NJ	111	39.30 N	75.15 W
Bridgetown, Barb. (brĭj' toun)	133b	13.08 N	59.37 W
Bridgetown, Can.	104	44.51 N	65.18 W
Bridgeview, Il.	58a	41.45 N	87.48 W
Bridgeville, Pa. (brĭj'vĭl)	113e	40.22 N	80.07 W
Bridgewater, Austl. (brĭj'wô-tēr)	216	42.50 S	147.28 E
Bridgewater, Can.	104	44.23 N	64.31 W
Bridgnorth, Eng. (brĭj'nôrth)	156	52.32 N	2.25 W
Bridgton, Me. (brĭj'tŭn)	104	44.04 N	70.45 W
Bridlington, Eng. (brĭd'lĭng-tŭn)	162	54.06 N	0.10 W
Brie-Comte-Robert, Fr. (brē-KôNt-ĕ-rō-bâr')	169b	48.42 N	2.37 E
Brielle, Neth.	157a	51.54 N	4.08 E
Brierfield, Al. (brī'ēr-fēld)	126	33.01 N	86.55 W
Brierfield, Eng. (brī'ēr fēld)	156	53.49 N	2.14 W
Brier I., Can. (brī'ēr)	104	44.16 N	66.24 W
Brieselang, G.D.R. (brē'zĕ-läng)	157b	52.36 N	12.59 E
Briey, Fr. (brē-ĕ')	169	49.15 N	5.57 E
Brig, Switz. (brēg)	166	46.17 N	7.59 E
Brigg, Eng. (brĭg)	156	53.33 N	0.29 W
Brigham City, Ut. (brĭg'ăm)	119b	41.31 N	112.01 W
Brighouse, Eng. (brĭg'hous)	156	53.42 N	1.47 W
Bright, Austl. (brīt)	216	36.43 S	147.00 E
Bright, In. (brīt)	113f	39.13 N	84.51 W
Brightlingsea, Eng. (brī't-lĭng-sē)	156b	51.50 N	1.00 E
Brightmoor (Neigh.), Mi.	57c	42.24 N	83.14 W
Brighton, Al. (brīt'ŭn)	112h	33.27 N	86.56 W
Brighton, Austl.	70b	37.55 S	145.00 E
Brighton, Co.	122	39.58 N	104.49 W
Brighton, Eng.	162	50.47 N	0.07 W
Brighton, Ia.	115	41.11 N	91.47 W
Brighton, Il.	119e	39.03 N	90.08 W
Brighton (Neigh.), Ma.	54a	42.21 N	71.08 W
Brighton Le-Sands, Austl.	70a	33.58 S	151.09 E
Brightwood (Neigh.), DC	56d	38.58 N	77.02 W
Brigittenau (Neigh.), Aus.	66e	48.14 N	16.22 E
Brihuega, Sp. (brē-wā'gä)	170	40.32 N	2.52 W
Brilyn Park, Va.	56d	38.54 N	77.10 W
Brimley, Mi. (brĭm'lē)	119k	46.24 N	84.34 W
Brindisi, It. (brēn'dē-zē)	173	40.38 N	17.57 E
Brindley Heath, Eng.	62	51.12 N	0.03 W
Brinje, Yugo. (brēn'yĕ)	172	45.00 N	15.08 E
Brinkleigh, Md.	56c	39.18 N	76.50 W
Brinkley, Ar. (brĭŋk'lĭ)	123	34.52 N	91.12 W
Brinnon, Wa. (brĭn'ŭn)	118a	47.41 N	122.54 W
Brion (I.), Can. (brē-ôN')	105	47.47 N	61.29 W
Brioude, Fr. (brē-ōōd')	168	45.18 N	3.22 E
Brisbane, Austl. (brĭz'bān)	216	27.30 S	153.10 E
Brisbane, Ca.	58b	37.41 N	122.24 W
Bristol, Ct. (brĭs'tŭl)	111	41.40 N	72.55 W
Bristol, Eng.	162	51.29 N	2.39 W
Bristol, Pa.	112f	40.06 N	74.51 W
Bristol, RI	112b	41.41 N	71.14 W
Bristol, Tn.	127	36.35 N	82.10 W
Bristol, Va.	127	36.36 N	82.00 W
Bristol, Vt.	111	44.10 N	73.00 W
Bristol, Wi.	113a	42.32 N	88.04 W
Bristol B., Ak.	107	58.05 N	158.54 W
Bristol Chan., Eng.	162	51.20 N	3.47 W
Bristow, Ok. (brĭs'tō)	123	35.50 N	96.25 W
British Columbia (Prov.), Can. (brĭt'ĭsh kŏl'ŭm-bĭ-ȧ)	96	56.00 N	124.53 W
Brits, S. Afr.	223d	25.39 S	27.47 E
Britstown, S. Afr. (brĭts'toun)	226	30.30 S	23.40 E
Britt, Ia. (brĭt)	115	43.05 N	93.47 W
Britton, SD (brĭt'ŭn)	114	45.47 N	97.44 W
Brive-la-Gaillarde, Fr. (brēv-lä-gī-yärd'ĕ)	168	45.10 N	1.31 E
Briviesca, Sp. (brē-vyās'kȧ)	170	42.34 N	3.21 W
Brno, Czech. (b'r'nô)	166	49.18 N	16.37 E
Broach, India	196	21.47 N	72.58 E
Broad (R.), Ga. (brôd)	126	34.15 N	83.14 W
Broad (R.), NC	127	35.38 N	82.40 W
Broadheath, Eng.	64b	53.24 N	2.21 W
Broadley Common, Eng.	62	51.45 N	0.04 E
Broadmeadows, Austl. (brôd'mĕd-ōz)	211a	37.40 S	144.53 E
Broadmoor, Ca.	58b	37.41 N	122.29 W
Broadview Heights, Oh. (brôd'vū)	113d	41.18 N	81.41 W
Broa, Ensenada de la (B.), Cuba (ĕn-sĕ-nä'dä-dĕ-lä-brō'ä)	134	22.30 N	82.00 W
Brockenscheidt, F.R.G.	63	51.38 N	7.25 E
Brockport, NY (brŏk'pōrt)	111	43.15 N	77.55 W
Brockton, Ma. (brŏk'tŭn)	105a	42.04 N	71.01 W
Brockville, Can. (brŏk'vĭl)	103	44.35 N	75.40 W
Brockway, Mt. (brŏk'wā)	117	47.24 N	105.41 W
Brodnica, Pol. (brôd'nĭt-sȧ)	167	53.16 N	19.26 E
Brody, Sov. Un. (brô'dĭ)	167	50.05 N	25.10 E
Broich (Neigh.), F.R.G.	63	51.25 N	6.51 E
Broken Arrow, Ok. (brō'kĕn ăr'ō)	123	36.03 N	95.48 W
Broken B., Austl.	211b	33.34 S	151.20 E
Broken Bow, Ne. (brō'kĕn bō)	114	41.24 N	99.37 W
Broken Bow, Ok.	123	34.02 N	94.43 W
Broken Hill, Austl. (brōk'ĕn)	216	31.55 S	141.35 E
Broken Hill, see Kabwe			
Bromall, Pa.	56b	39.59 N	75.22 W
Bromborough, Eng.	64a	53.19 N	2.59 W
Bromley, Eng. (brŭm'lĭ)	156b	51.23 N	0.01 E
Bromley Common (Neigh.), Eng.	62	51.22 N	0.03 E
Bromptonville, Can. (brŭmp'tŭn-vĭl)	111	45.30 N	72.00 W
Brønderslev, Den. (brûn'dĕr-slĕv)	164	57.15 N	9.56 E
Bronkhorstspruit, S. Afr.	223d	25.50 S	28.48 E
Bronnitsy, Sov. Un. (brô-nyĭ'tsĭ)	182b	55.26 N	38.16 E
Bronson, Mi. (brŏn'sŭn)	110	41.55 N	85.15 W
Bronte Cr., Can.	95d	43.25 N	79.53 W
Bronx (Neigh.), NY	55	40.49 N	73.56 W
Bronxville, NY	55	40.56 N	73.50 W
Brood (R.), SC (brōōd)	127	34.46 N	81.25 W
Brookfield, Il. (brŏŏk'fēld)	113a	41.49 N	87.51 W
Brookfield, Mo.	123	39.45 N	93.04 W
Brookhaven, Ga. (brŏŏk'hāv'n)	112c	33.52 N	84.21 W
Brookhaven, Ms.	126	31.35 N	90.26 W
Brookhaven, Pa.	56b	39.52 N	75.23 W
Brookings, Or. (brŏŏk'ĭngs)	116	42.04 N	124.16 W
Brookings, SD	114	44.18 N	96.47 W
Brookland (Neigh.), DC.	56d	38.56 N	76.59 W
Brooklandville, Md.	56c	39.26 N	76.41 W
Brooklawn, NJ	56b	39.53 N	75.08 W
Brookline, Ma. (brŏŏk'līn)	105a	42.20 N	71.08 W
Brookline, NH	105a	42.44 N	71.37 W
Brooklyn (Neigh.), Md.	56c	39.14 N	76.36 W
Brooklyn, Oh. (brŏŏk'lĭn)	113d	41.26 N	81.44 W
Brooklyn Center, Mn.	119g	45.05 N	93.21 W
Brooklyn Heights, Oh.	56a	41.24 N	81.40 W
Brooklyn Park, Md.	56c	39.14 N	76.36 W
Brookmans Park, Eng.	62	51.43 N	0.12 W
Brookmont, Md.	56d	38.57 N	77.07 W
Brook Park, Oh. (brŏŏk)	113d	41.24 N	81.50 W
Brooks, Can.	99	50.35 N	111.53 W
Brooks Ra., Ak. (brŏŏks)	107	68.20 N	159.00 W
Brook Street, Eng.	62	51.37 N	0.17 E
Brooksville, Fl. (brōōks'vĭl)	127a	28.32 N	82.28 W
Brookvale, Austl.	70a	33.46 S	151.17 E
Brookville, In. (brŏŏk'vĭl)	110	39.20 N	85.00 W
Brookville, Ma.	54a	42.08 N	71.01 W
Brookville, NY	55	40.49 N	73.35 W
Brookville, Pa.	111	41.10 N	79.00 W
Brookwood, Al. (brŏŏk'wŏŏd)	126	33.15 N	87.17 W
Broome, Austl. (brōōm)	214	18.00 S	122.15 E
Broomfield, Eng.	62	51.14 N	0.38 E
Brossard, Can.	95a	45.26 N	73.28 W
Brothers (Is.), Ba. (brŭd'hērs)	134	26.05 N	79.00 W
Broughton, Pa.	57b	40.21 N	79.59 W
Broumov, Czech. (brōō'môf)	166	50.33 N	15.55 E
Brou-sur-Chantereine, Fr.	64c	48.53 N	2.38 E
Brown Bk., Ba.	135	21.30 N	74.35 W
Brownfield, Tx. (broun'fēld)	122	33.11 N	102.16 W
Browning, Mt. (broun'ĭng)	117	48.37 N	113.05 W
Brownsboro, Ky. (brounz'bô-rô)	113h	38.22 N	85.30 W
Brownsburg, Can. (brouns'bûrg)	95a	45.40 N	74.24 W
Brownsburg, In.	113g	39.51 N	86.23 W
Brownsmead, Or. (brounz'-mĕd)	118c	46.13 N	123.33 W
Brownstown, In. (brounz'toun)	110	38.50 N	86.00 W
Brownsville, Pa. (brounz'vĭl)	113e	40.01 N	79.53 W
Brownsville, Tn.	126	35.35 N	89.15 W
Brownsville, Tx.	125	25.55 N	97.30 W
Brownville Junction, Me. (broun'vĭl)	104	45.20 N	69.04 W
Brownwood (L.), Tx.	124	31.55 N	99.15 W
Brownwood, Tx. (broun'wŏŏd)	124	31.44 N	98.58 W
Broxbourne, Eng.	62	51.45 N	0.01 W
Brozas, Sp. (brō'thäs)	170	39.37 N	6.44 W
Bruce, Mt., Austl. (brōōs)	214	22.35 S	118.15 E
Bruce Pen, Can.	110	44.50 N	81.20 W
Bruceton, Tn. (brōōs'tŭn)	126	36.02 N	88.14 W
Bruchmühle, G.D.R.	65a	52.33 N	13.47 E
Bruchsal, F.R.G. (brŏŏk'zäl)	166	49.08 N	8.34 E
Bruck, Aus. (brŏŏk)	166	47.25 N	15.14 E
Brück, G.D.R. (brük)	157b	52.12 N	12.45 E
Bruck an der Leitha, Aus.	157e	48.01 N	16.47 E
Bruckhausen (Neigh.), F.R.G.	63	51.29 N	6.44 E
Bruderheim, Can. (brōō'dēr-hīm)	95g	53.47 N	112.56 W
Brugge, Bel.	163	51.13 N	3.05 E
Brügge, F.R.G.	63	51.13 N	7.34 E
Brugherio, It.	65c	45.33 N	9.18 E
Brühl, F.R.G. (brül)	169c	50.49 N	6.54 E
Bruneau (R.), Id. (brōō-nō')	116	42.47 N	115.43 W
Brunei, Asia (brōō-nī')	206	4.52 N	113.38 E
Brünen, F.R.G. (brü'nĕn)	169c	51.43 N	6.41 E
Brunete, Sp. (brōō-nā'tå)	171a	40.24 N	4.00 W
Brunette (I.), Can. (brōō-nĕt')	105	47.16 N	55.54 W
Brunn am Gebirge, Aus. (brōōn'äm gĕ-bĭr'gĕ)	157e	48.07 N	16.18 E
Brunoy, Fr.	64c	48.42 N	2.30 E
Brunsbüttel, F.R.G. (brōōns'büt-tĕl)	157c	53.58 N	9.10 E
Brunswick, Austl.	70b	37.46 S	144.58 E
Brunswick, Ga. (brŭnz'wĭk)	127	31.08 N	81.30 W
Brunswick, Md.	111	39.20 N	77.35 W
Brunswick, Me.	104	43.54 N	69.57 W
Brunswick, Mo.	123	39.25 N	93.07 W
Brunswick, Oh.	113d	41.14 N	81.50 W
Brunswick, Pen. de, Chile	144	53.25 S	71.15 W
Bruny (I.), Austl. (brōō'nē)	215	43.30 S	147.50 E
Brush, Co. (brŭsh)	122	40.14 N	103.40 W
Brusque, Braz. (brōō's-kōōĕ)	144	27.15 S	48.45 W
Brussels, Il. (brŭs'ĕls)	119e	38.57 N	90.36 W
Brussels, see Bruxelles			
Bruxelles (Brussels), Bel. (brü-sĕl') (brŭs'ĕls)	157a	50.51 N	4.21 E
Bryan, Oh. (brī'ăn)	110	41.25 N	84.30 W
Bryan, Tx.	125	30.40 N	96.22 W
Bryansk, Sov. Un. (b'r-yänsk')	174	53.12 N	34.23 E
Bryansk (Oblast), Sov. Un.	174	52.43 N	32.25 E
Bryant, SD (brī'ănt)	114	44.35 N	97.29 W
Bryant, Wa.	118a	48.14 N	122.10 W
Bryce Canyon Natl. Park, Ut. (brīs)	121	37.35 N	112.15 W
Bryn Mawr, Pa. (brĭn mär')	112f	40.02 N	75.20 W
Bryson City, NC (brīs'ŭn)	126	35.25 N	83.25 W
Bryukhovetskaya, Sov. Un. (b'ryŭk'ô-vyĕt-skä'yä)	175	45.56 N	38.58 E
Buatan, Indon.	191b	0.45 N	101.49 E
Buba, Guinea-Bissau (bōō'bȧ)	224	11.39 N	14.58 W
Buc, Fr.	64c	48.46 N	2.08 E
Bucaramanga, Col. (bōō-kä'rä-mäŋ'gä)	142	7.12 N	73.14 W
Buccaneer Arch, Austl. (bŭk-ȧ-nēr')	214	16.05 S	122.00 E
Buch (Neigh.), G.D.R.	65a	52.38 N	13.30 E
Buchach, Sov. Un. (bōō'chȧch)	167	49.04 N	25.25 E
Buchanan (L.), Austl. (bû-kăn'nŏn)	215	21.40 S	145.00 E
Buchanan, Lib. (bû-kăn'ăn)	228	5.57 N	10.02 W
Buchanan (L.), Tx. (bû-kăn'ăn)	124	30.55 N	98.40 W
Buchanan, Mi.	110	41.50 N	86.25 W
Buchans, Can.	105	48.49 N	56.52 W
Bucharest, see București			
Buchholtz, F.R.G. (bŏŏk'hōltz)	157c	53.19 N	9.53 E
Buchholz, G.D.R.	65a	52.35 N	13.47 E
Buchholz (Neigh.), F.R.G.	63	51.23 N	6.46 E
Buchholz (Neigh.), G.D.R.	65a	52.36 N	13.26 E
Buck Cr., In. (bŭk)	113g	39.43 N	85.58 W
Buckhannon, WV (bŭk-hăn'ŭn)	111	39.00 N	80.10 W
Buckhaven, Scot. (bŭk-hā'v'n)	162	56.10 N	3.10 W
Buckhorn Island State Park (P. Int.), NY	57a	43.03 N	78.59 W
Buckie, Scot. (bŭk'ĭ)	162	57.40 N	2.50 W
Buckingham, Can. (bŭk'ĭng-ăm)	95c	45.35 N	75.25 W
Buckingham (R.), India (bŭk'ĭng-ăm)	196	15.18 N	79.50 E
Buckingham Palace (P. Int.), Eng.	62	51.30 N	0.08 W
Buckinghamshire (Co.), Eng.	156b	51.45 N	0.48 W
Buckland, Can. (bŭk'lănd)	95b	46.37 N	70.33 W
Buckland Tableland (Reg.), Austl.	215	24.31 S	148.00 E
Buckley, Wa. (bŭk'lē)	118a	47.10 N	122.02 W
Buckow (Neigh.), F.R.G.	65a	52.25 N	13.26 E

PLACE (Pronunciation)	PAGE	Lat. °'	Long. °'
Bucksport, Me. (bŭks'pôrt)	104	44.35 N	68.47 W
Buctouche, Can. (bük-to͞osh')	104	46.28 N	64.43 W
Bucun, China (bo͞o-tso͞on)	200	36.38 N	117.26 E
Bucureşti (Bucharest), Rom. (bo͞o-ko͞o-rĕsh'tĭ) (bo͞o-ká-rĕst')	173	44.23 N	26.10 E
Bucyrus, Oh. (bů-sī'rŭs)	110	40.50 N	82.55 W
Buda (Neigh.), Hung.	66g	47.30 N	19.02 E
Budai-hegység (Mts.), Hung.	66g	47.31 N	19.57 E
Budakeszi, Hung.	66g	47.31 N	18.56 E
Budaörs, Hung.	66g	47.27 N	18.58 E
Budapest, Hung. (bo͞o'dá-pĕsht')	167	47.30 N	19.05 E
Budberg, F.R.G.	63	51.32 N	6.38 E
Büderich, F.R.G.	63	51.37 N	6.34 E
Buderus, F.R.G.	63	51.33 N	7.38 E
Budge Budge, India	196a	22.28 N	88.08 E
Budjala, Zaire	230	2.39 N	19.42 E
Buea, Cam.	229	4.09 N	9.14 E
Buechel, Ky. (bě-chûl')	113h	38.12 N	85.38 W
Bueil, Fr. (bwā')	169b	48.55 N	1.27 E
Buena Park, Ca. (bwā'nȧ pärk)	119a	33.52 N	118.00 W
Buenaventura, Col. (bwā'nä-vĕn-to͞o'rá)	142	3.46 N	77.09 W
Buenaventura, Bahia de (B.), Col. (bä-ē'ä-dě-bwä'nä-vĕn-to͞o'rá)	142	3.45 N	79.23 W
Buenaventura, Cuba	135a	22.53 N	82.22 W
Buena Vista, Co. (bū'nȧ vĭs'tȧ)	122	38.51 N	106.07 W
Buena Vista, Ga.	126	32.15 N	84.30 W
Buena Vista, Va.	111	37.45 N	79.20 W
Buena Vista, Bahía (B.), Cuba (bä-ē'ä-bwě-nä-vē's-tä)	134	22.30 N	79.10 W
Buena Vista Lake Res., Ca. (bū'nȧ vĭs'tȧ)	120	35.14 N	119.17 W
Buendia, Embalse de (Res.), Sp.	170	40.30 N	2.45 W
Buenos Aires, Arg. (bwā'nôs ī'rās)	144	34.20 S	58.30 W
Buenos Aires, Col.	142a	3.01 N	76.34 W
Buenos Aires, C. R.	133	9.10 N	83.21 W
Buenos Aires (L.), Arg.-Chile	144	46.30 S	72.15 W
Buenos Aires (Prov.), Arg.	144	36.15 S	61.45 W
Buer (Neigh.), F.R.G.	63	51.36 N	7.03 E
Buffalo, Mn. (buf'ȧ lō)	115	45.10 N	93.50 W
Buffalo, NY	113c	42.54 N	78.51 W
Buffalo (R.), Ar.	123	35.56 N	92.58 W
Buffalo (R.), S. Afr.	227c	28.35 S	30.27 E
Buffalo (R.), Tn.	126	35.24 N	87.10 W
Buffalo, Tx.	125	31.28 N	96.04 W
Buffalo, Wy.	117	44.19 N	106.42 W
Buffalo Bayou, Tx.	125a	29.46 N	95.32 W
Buffalo Cr., Mn.	115	44.46 N	94.28 W
Buffalo Har., NY	57a	42.51 N	78.52 W
Buffalo Head Hills, Can.	96	57.16 N	116.18 W
Buford, Can. (bū'fûrd)	95g	53.15 N	113.55 W
Buford, Ga. (bū'fērd)	126	34.05 N	84.00 W
Bug (R.), Pol. (bo͞og)	167	52.29 N	21.20 E
Bug (R.), Sov. Un. (bo͝ok)	175	48.12 N	30.13 E
Buga, Col. (bo͞o'gä)	142a	3.54 N	76.17 W
Buggenhout, Bel.	157a	51.01 N	4.10 E
Buggs Island L., NC-Va.	127	36.30 N	78.38 W
Buglandsfjorden (Fd.), Nor.	164	58.53 N	7.55 E
Bugojno, Yugo. (bo͞o-gō ĭ nō)	172	44.03 N	17.28 E
Bugul'ma, Sov. Un. (bo͞o-go͞ol'má)	178	54.40 N	52.40 E
Buguruslan, Sov. Un. (bo͞o-go͞o-ro͞os-lán')	178	53.30 N	52.32 E
Buhi, Phil. (bo͞o'ē)	207a	13.26 N	123.31 E
Buhl, Id. (būl)	116	42.36 N	114.45 W
Buhl, Mn.	115	47.28 N	92.49 W
Buin, Chile (bo͞o-ēn')	141b	33.44 S	70.44 W
Buinaksk, Sov. Un. (bo͞o'ē-näksk)	179	42.40 N	47.20 E
Buir Nur (L.), China-Mong. (bo͞o-ēr no͞or)	202	47.50 N	117.00 E
Bujalance, Sp. (bo͞o-hä-län'thā)	170	37.54 N	4.22 W
Bujumbura, Burundi	231	3.23 S	29.22 E
Bukama, Zaire (bo͞o-kä'mä)	226	9.08 S	26.00 E
Bukavu, Zaire	231	2.30 S	28.52 E
Bukhara, Sov. Un. (bo͞o-kä'rä)	155	39.31 N	64.22 E
Bukitbatu, Indon.	191b	1.25 N	101.58 E
Bukit Panjang, Singapore	67c	1.23 N	103.46 E
Bukit Timah, Singapore	67c	1.20 N	103.47 E
Bukittingg, Indon.	206	0.25 S	100.28 E
Bukoba, Tan.	231	1.20 S	31.49 E
Bukovina (Reg.), Sov. Un. (bo͞o-kô'vĭ-ná)	167	48.06 N	25.20 E
Bula, Indon. (bo͞o'lä)	207	3.00 S	130.30 E
Bulalacao, Phil. (bo͞o-lá-lä'kä-ō)	207a	12.30 N	121.20 E
Bulawayo, Zimb. (bo͞o-lá-wā'yō)	226	20.12 S	28.43 E
Buldir (I.), Ak. (bŭl dĭr)	107a	52.22 N	175.50 E
Bulgaria, Eur. (bo͝ol-gā'rĭ-ă)	154	42.12 N	24.13 E
Bulim, Singapore	67c	1.23 N	103.43 E
Bulkley Ra., Can. (bŭlk'lē)	98	54.30 N	127.30 W
Bullaque (R.), Sp. (bo͞o-lä'kå)	170	39.15 N	4.13 W
Bullas, Sp. (bo͞ol'yäs)	170	38.07 N	1.48 W
Bulldog Cr., Ut. (bŭl'dôg')	121	37.45 N	110.55 W
Bull Harbour, Can. (hăr'bēr)	98	50.45 N	127.55 W
Bull Head (Mtn.), Jam.	134	18.10 N	77.15 W
Bulloo (R.), Austl. (bŭ-lo͞o')	215	25.23 S	143.30 E
Bull Run (R.), Or. (bo͝ol)	118c	45.26 N	122.11 W
Bull Run Res., Or.	118c	45.29 N	122.11 W
Bull Shoals Res., Ar.-Mo. (bo͝ol shōlz)	123	36.35 N	92.57 W
Bulmke-Hüllen (Neigh.), F.R.G.	63	51.31 N	7.06 E
Bulphan, Eng. (bo͝ol'făn)	156b	51.33 N	0.21 E
Bultfontein, S. Afr. (bo͝olt'fōn-tān')	223d	28.18 S	26.10 E
Bulun, Sov. Un. (bo͞o-lo͞on')	181	70.48 N	127.27 E
Bulungu, Zaire (bo͞o-lo͞oŋ'go͞o)	230	6.04 S	21.54 E
Bulwer, S. Afr. (bo͝ol-wēr)	227c	29.49 S	29.48 E
Bumba, Zaire (bo͞om'bá)	230	2.11 N	22.28 E
Bumbles Green, Eng.	62	51.44 N	0.02 E
Bumire I., Tan.	231	1.40 S	32.05 E
Buna, Pap. N. Gui. (bo͞o'ná)	207	8.58 S	148.38 E
Bunbury, Austl. (bŭn'bŭrĭ)	214	33.25 S	115.45 E
Bundaberg, Austl. (bŭn'dá-bûrg)	216	24.45 S	152.18 E
Bundoora, Austl.	70b	37.42 S	145.04 E

PLACE (Pronunciation)	PAGE	Lat. °'	Long. °'
Bungo-Suidō (Chan.), Jap. (bo͞oŋ'gō so͞o-ē'dō)	205	33.26 N	131.54 E
Bunguran Utara, Kepulauan (Is.), Indon.	206	.322 N	108.00 E
Bunia, Zaire	231	1.34 N	30.15 E
Bunker Hill, Il. (bŭnk'ēr hĭl)	119e	39.03 N	89.57 W
Bunker Hill Monument (P. Int.), Ma.	54a	42.22 N	71.04 W
Bunkie, La. (bŭŋ'kĭ)	125	30.55 N	92.10 W
Bunkyō (Neigh.), Jap.	69a	35.43 N	139.45 E
Bun Plns, Ken.	231	0.55 N	40.35 E
Bununu Dass, Nig.	229	10.00 N	9.31 E
Buona Vista, Singapore	67c	1.16 N	103.47 E
Buor-Khaya, Guba (B.), Sov. Un.	181	71.45 N	131.00 E
Buor Khaya, Mys (C.), Sov. Un.	181	71.47 N	133.22 E
Bura, Ken.	231	1.06 S	39.57 E
Buraydah, Sau. Ar.	192	26.23 N	44.14 E
Burbank, Ca. (bûr'bănk)	119a	34.11 N	118.19 W
Burdekin (R.), Austl. (bûr'dē-kĭn)	215	19.22 S	145.07 E
Burdur, Tur. (bo͞or-do͞or')	179	37.50 N	30.15 E
Burdwān, India (bo͝od-wän')	196	23.29 N	87.53 E
Bureinskiy, Khrebet (Mts.), Sov. Un.	181	51.15 N	133.30 E
Bures-sur-Yvette, Fr.	64c	48.42 N	2.10 E
Bureya (R.), Sov. Un. (bo͞o-rā'yä)	181	51.00 N	130.14 E
Bureya, Sov. Un. (bo͞orā'ȧ)	181	49.55 N	130.00 E
Burford, Eng. (bûr-fērd)	156b	51.46 N	1.38 W
Burford (L.), NM	121	36.37 N	107.21 W
Burg, F.R.G.	63	51.08 N	7.09 E
Burgas, Bul. (bo͞or-gäs')	173	42.29 N	27.30 E
Burgas, Gulf of, Bul.	161	42.30 N	27.40 E
Burgaw, NC (bûr'gô)	127	34.31 N	77.56 W
Burgdorf, Switz. (bo͞org'dôrf)	166	47.04 N	7.37 E
Burgenland (State), Aus.	157e	47.58 N	16.57 E
Burgeo, Can.	105	47.36 N	57.34 W
Burger Township, S. Afr.	71b	26.05 S	27.46 E
Burgess, Va.	111	37.53 N	76.21 W
Burgh Heath, Eng.	62	51.18 N	0.13 W
Burgo, Som.	223a	9.20 N	45.45 E
Burgos, Mex. (bo͞or'gōs)	124	24.57 N	98.47 W
Burgos, Phil.	207a	16.03 N	119.52 E
Burgos, Sp. (bo͞o'r-gôs)	170	42.20 N	3.44 W
Burgsvik, Swe. (bo͞orgs'vĭk)	164	57.04 N	18.18 E
Burhānpur, India (bo͞or'hán-po͞or)	196	21.26 N	76.08 E
Burholme (Neigh.), Pa.	56b	40.03 N	75.05 W
Burias I., Phil. (bo͞o'rē-äs)	207a	12.56 N	122.56 E
Burias Pass, Phil. (bo͞o'rē-äs)	207a	13.04 N	123.11 E
Burica, Punta (Pt.), Pan. (po͞o'n-tä-bo͞o'rē-kä)	133	8.02 N	83.12 W
Burien, Wa. (bū'rĭ-ĕn)	118a	47.28 N	122.20 W
Burin, Can. (bûr'ĭn)	105	47.02 N	55.10 W
Burin Pen., Can.	105	47.00 N	55.40 W
Burkburnett, Tx. (bûrk-bûr'nĕt)	122	34.04 N	98.35 W
Burke, Vt. (bûrk)	111	44.40 N	72.00 W
Burke Chan., Can.	98	52.07 N	127.38 W
Burketown, Austl. (bûrk'toun)	214	17.50 S	139.30 E
Burkina Faso, Afr.	222	11.46 N	3.18 E
Burley, Id. (bûr'lĭ)	117	42.31 N	113.48 W
Burley, Wa.	118a	47.25 N	122.38 W
Burli, Sov. Un.	182a	53.36 N	61.55 E
Burlingame, Ca. (bûr'lĭn-gām)	118b	37.35 N	122.22 W
Burlingame, KS.	123	38.45 N	95.49 W
Burlington, Can. (bûr'lĭng-tŭn)	95d	43.19 N	79.48 W
Burlington, Co.	122	39.17 N	102.26 W
Burlington, Ia.	115	40.48 N	91.05 W
Burlington, Ks.	123	38.10 N	95.46 W
Burlington, Ky.	113f	39.01 N	84.44 W
Burlington, Ma.	105a	42.31 N	71.13 W
Burlington, NC	127	36.05 N	79.26 W
Burlington, NJ	112f	40.04 N	74.52 W
Burlington, Vt.	111	44.30 N	73.15 W
Burlington, Wa.	118a	48.28 N	122.20 W
Burlington, Wi.	113a	42.41 N	88.16 W
Burma, Asia (bûr'mȧ)	190	21.00 N	95.15 E
Burnaby, Can.	98	49.14 N	122.58 W
Burnage, Eng.	64b	53.26 N	2.12 W
Burnet, Tx. (bûrn'ĕt)	124	30.46 N	98.14 W
Burnham, Il.	58a	41.39 N	87.34 W
Burnham on Crouch, Eng. (bûrn'ăm-ŏn-krouch)	156b	51.38 N	0.48 E
Burnhamthorpe, Can.	54c	43.37 N	79.36 W
Burnie, Austl. (bûr'nē)	216	41.15 S	146.05 E
Burning Tree Estates, Md.	56d	39.01 N	77.12 W
Burnley, Eng. (bûrn'lē)	156	53.47 N	2.19 W
Burns, Or. (bûrnz)	116	43.35 N	119.05 W
Burnside, Ky. (bûrn'sīd)	126	36.57 N	84.33 W
Burns Lake, Can. (bûrnz lăk)	98	54.14 N	125.46 W
Burnsville, Can. (bûrnz'vĭl)	104	47.44 N	65.07 W
Burnt R., Or. (bûrnt)	116	44.26 N	117.53 W
Burntwood (R.), Can.	101	55.53 N	97.30 W
Burrard Inlet, Can. (bûr'ȧrd)	118d	49.19 N	123.15 W
Burriana, Sp. (bo͞or-rē-á'nä)	171	39.53 N	0.05 W
Burrowhill, Eng.	62	51.21 N	0.36 W
Burr Ridge, Il.	58a	41.46 N	87.55 W
Bursa, Tur. (bo͞or'sȧ)	179	40.10 N	28.10 E
Būr Safājah, Egypt	225	26.57 N	33.56 E
Būr Sa'īd (Port Said), Egypt	223c	31.15 N	32.19 E
Burscheid, F.R.G. (bo͞or'shīd)	169c	51.05 N	7.07 E
Būr Sūdān, Sud. (so͞o-dän')	225	19.30 N	37.10 E
Burt (L.), Mi. (bûrt)	110	45.25 N	84.45 W
Burt, NY (bûrt)	113c	43.19 N	78.45 W
Burton, Eng.	64a	53.16 N	3.01 W
Burton, Wa. (bûr'tŭn)	118a	47.24 N	122.28 W
Burton Res., Ga.	126	34.46 N	83.40 W
Burtonsville, Md. (bûrtŏns-vil)	112e	39.07 N	76.57 W
Burton-upon-Trent, Eng. (bûr'tŭn-ŭp'-ŏn-trĕnt)	156	52.48 N	1.37 W
Buru (I.), Indon.	207	3.30 S	126.30 E
Burullus (L.), Egypt	223b	31.20 N	30.58 E
Burundi, Afr.	222	3.00 S	29.30 E
Burwell, Ne. (bûr'wĕl)	114	41.46 N	99.08 W
Burwood, Austl.	70b	37.51 S	145.06 E
Bury, Eng. (bĕr'ĭ)	156	53.36 N	2.17 W
Buryat A.S.S.R., Sov. Un.	181	55.15 N	112.00 E

PLACE (Pronunciation)	PAGE	Lat. °'	Long. °'
Bury Saint Edmunds, Eng. (bĕr'ĭ-sānt ĕd'mŭndz)	163	52.14 N	0.44 E
Burzaco, Arg. (bo͞or-zá'kô)	144a	34.35 S	58.23 W
Busanga Swp., Zambia	231	14.10 S	25.50 E
Busby, Austl.	70a	33.54 S	150.53 E
Buschhausen (Neigh.), F.R.G.	63	51.30 N	6.51 E
Būsh, Egypt (bo͞osh)	223b	29.13 N	31.08 E
Būshehr, Iran	192	28.48 N	50.53 E
Bushey, Eng.	62	51.39 N	0.22 W
Bushey Heath, Eng.	62	51.38 N	0.20 W
Bush Hill, Va.	56d	38.48 N	77.07 W
Bushmanland (Reg.), S. Afr. (bo͝osh-măn lănd)	226	29.15 S	18.45 E
Bushnell, Il. (bo͝osh'nĕl)	123	40.33 N	90.28 W
Bushwick (Neigh.), NY	55	40.42 N	73.55 W
Businga, Zaire (bo͞o-sĭŋ'gȧ)	230	3.20 N	20.53 E
Busira (R.), Zaire	230	0.05 S	19.20 E
Busk, Sov. Un. (bo͞o'sk)	167	49.58 N	24.39 E
Busselton, Austl. (bûs'l-tŭn)	214	33.40 S	115.30 E
Bussum, Neth.	157a	52.16 N	5.10 E
Bustamante, Mex. (bo͞os-tá-män'tå)	124	26.34 N	100.30 W
Bustleton (Neigh.), Pa.	56b	40.05 N	75.02 W
Busto Arsizio, It. (bo͞os'tō är-sēd'zē-ō)	172	45.47 N	8.51 E
Busuanga (I.), Phil. (bo͞o-swäŋ'gä)	207a	12.20 N	119.43 E
Buta, Zaire (bo͞o'tá)	230	2.48 N	24.44 E
Butantã (Neigh.), Braz.	61d	23.34 S	46.43 W
Butendorf (Neigh.), F.R.G.	63	51.33 N	6.59 E
Butha Buthe, Leso. (bo͞o-thá-bo͞o'thå)	227c	28.49 S	28.16 E
Butha Qi, China (bo͞o-thä chē)	204	47.59 N	122.56 E
Butler, Al. (bŭt'lēr)	126	32.05 N	88.10 W
Butler, In.	110	41.25 N	84.50 W
Butler, Md.	112e	39.32 N	76.46 W
Butler, NJ	112a	41.00 N	74.20 W
Butler, Pa.	111	40.50 N	79.55 W
Butovo, Sov. Un. (bo͞o-tô'vô)	182b	55.33 N	37.36 E
Butsha, Zaire	231	0.57 N	29.13 E
Buttahatchie (R.), Al.-Ms. (bŭt-á-hăch'ē)	126	34.02 N	88.05 W
Butte, Mt. (būt)	117	46.00 N	112.31 W
Butterworth, S. Afr. (bŭ tēr'wûrth)	227c	32.20 S	28.09 E
Büttgen, F.R.G.	63	51.12 N	6.36 E
Butt of Lewis (C.), Scot. (bŭt ŏv lū'ĭs)	162	58.34 N	6.15 W
Butuan, Phil. (bo͞o-to͞o'än)	207	8.40 N	125.33 E
Butung (I.), Indon.	206	5.00 S	122.55 E
Buturlinovka, Sov. Un. (bo͞o-to͞o'lē-nôf'ka)	175	50.47 N	40.35 E
Buuhoodle, Som.	223a	8.15 N	46.20 E
Buulo Berde, Som.	223a	3.53 N	45.30 E
Burr Gaabo, Som.	227	1.14 N	51.47 E
Buxtehude, F.R.G. (bo͞oks-tē-ho͞o'dē)	157c	53.29 N	9.42 E
Buxton, Eng. (bŭks't'n)	156	53.15 N	1.55 W
Buxton, Or.	118c	45.41 N	123.11 W
Buy, Sov. Un. (bwē)	178	58.30 N	41.48 E
Buzău, Rom. (bo͞o-zĕ'o͞o)	173	45.09 N	26.51 E
Buzău (R.), Rom.	175	45.17 N	27.22 E
Buzaymah, Libya	225	25.14 N	22.13 E
Buzi, China (bo͞o-dz)	200	33.48 N	118.13 E
Buzuluk, Sov. Un. (bo͞o-zo͞o-lo͝ok')	179	52.50 N	52.10 E
Bvkhovo, Sov. Un. (bĭ-ĸô'vô)	174	53.32 N	30.15 E
Bwendi, Zaire	231	4.01 N	26.41 E
Byala, Bul.	173	43.26 N	25.44 E
Byala Slatina, Bul. (byä'la slä'tēnä)	173	43.26 N	23.56 E
Byblos, see Jubayl			
Byculla (Neigh.), India	67e	18.58 N	72.49 E
Bydgoszcz, Pol. (bĭd'gôshch)	167	53.07 N	18.00 E
Byesville, Oh. (bīz-vĭl)	110	39.55 N	81.35 W
Byfang (Neigh.), F.R.G.	63	51.24 N	7.06 E
Byfleet, Eng.	62	51.20 N	0.29 W
Bygdin (L.), Nor. (bügh-dĕn')	164	61.24 N	8.31 E
Byglandsfjord, Nor. (bügh'lănds-fyôr)	164	58.40 N	7.49 E
Bykovo, Sov. Un. (bĭ-kô'vô)	182b	55.38 N	38.05 E
Bymea Bay, Austl.	70a	34.03 S	151.06 E
Byrranga, Gory (Mts.), Sov. Un.	180	74.15 N	94.28 E
Bytantay (R.), Sov. Un. (byän'tāy)	181	68.15 N	132.15 E
Bytom, Pol. (bĭ'tŭm)	167	50.21 N	18.55 E
Bytosh', Sov. Un. (bĭ-tôsh')	174	53.48 N	34.06 E
Bytow, Pol. (bĭ'tŭf)	167	54.10 N	17.30 E

C

PLACE (Pronunciation)	PAGE	Lat. °'	Long. °'
Caazapá, Par. (kä-zä-pä')	144	26.14 S	56.18 W
Cabagan, Phil. (kä-bä-gän')	207a	17.27 N	121.50 E
Cabalete (I.), Phil. (kä-bä-lā'tå)	207a	14.19 N	122.00 E
Caballito (Neigh.), Arg.	60d	34.37 S	58.27 W
Caballones, Canal de (Chan.), Cuba (kä-nä'l-dĕ-kä-bäl-yô'nĕs)	134	20.45 N	79.20 W
Caballo Res., NM (kä-bä-lyō')	121	33.00 N	107.20 W
Cabanatuan, Phil. (kä-bä-nä-twän')	207a	15.30 N	120.56 E
Cabano, Can. (kä-bä-nō')	104	47.41 N	68.54 W
Cabarruyan (I.), Phil. (kä-bä-ro͞o'yän)	207a	16.21 N	120.10 E
Cabedelo, Braz. (kä-bĕ-dā'lo͞o)	143	6.58 S	34.49 W
Cabeza, Arrecife (Reef), Mex. (är-rĕ-sē'fĕ-kä-bĕ-zä)	131	19.07 N	95.52 W

PLACE (Pronounciation)	PAGE	Lat. °'	Long. °'
Cabeza del Buey, Sp. (kȧ-bā'thä dĕl bwā')	170	38.43 N	5.18 W
Cabimas, Ven. (kä-bē'mäs)	142	10.21 N	71.27 W
Cabinda, Ang. (kä-bĭn'dȧ)	222	5.10 S	10.00 E
Cabinda, Ang.	230	5.33 S	12.12 E
Cabinet Mts., Mt. (kăb'ĭ-nĕt)	116	48.13 N	115.52 W
Cabin John, Md.	56d	38.58 N	77.09 W
Cabo Frio, Braz. (kä'bô-frē'ô)	141a	22.53 S	42.02 W
Cabo Frio, Ilha do, Braz. (ē'lä-dô-kä'bô frē'ô)	141a	23.01 S	42.00 W
Cabonga Res., Can.	103	47.25 N	76.35 W
Cabot Hd., Can. (kăb'ŭt)	110	45.15 N	81.20 W
Cabot Str., Can. (kăb'ŭt)	105	47.35 N	60.00 W
Cabra I., Phil.	207a	13.55 N	119.55 E
Cabra, Sp. (käb'rä)	170	37.28 N	4.29 W
Cabramatta, Austl.	70a	33.54 S	150.56 E
Cabrera (I.), Sp. (kä-brā'rä)	171	39.08 N	2.57 E
Cabrera, Sierra de la (Mts.), Sp.	170	42.15 N	6.45 W
Cabriel (R.), Sp. (kä-brē-ĕl')	170	39.25 N	1.20 W
Cabrillo Natl. Mon., Ca. (kä-brēl'yō)	120a	32.41 N	117.03 W
Cabrobó, Braz. (kä-brō-bô')	143	8.34 S	39.13 W
Cabuçu (R.), Braz. (kä-bōō'-sōō)	144b	22.57 S	43.36 W
Cabugao, Phil. (kä-bōō'gä-ô)	207a	17.48 N	120.28 E
Čačak, Yugo. (chä'chȧk)	173	43.51 N	20.22 E
Caçapava, Braz. (kä'sä-pä'vä)	141a	23.05 S	45.52 W
Cáceres, Braz. (kȧ'sĕ-rĕs)	143	16.11 S	57.32 W
Cáceres, Sp. (kȧ'thå-rās)	170	39.28 N	6.20 W
Cachan, Fr.	64c	48.48 N	2.20 E
Cachapoal (R.), Chile (kä-chä-pô-ȧ'l)	141b	34.23 S	70.19 W
Cacharí, Arg. (kä-chä-rē')	141c	36.23 S	59.29 W
Cache (R.), Ar. (kȧsh)	123	35.24 N	91.12 W
Cache Cr., Can. (kȧsh)	120	38.53 N	122.24 W
Cache Creek, Can.	99	50.48 N	121.19 W
Cache la Poudre (R.), Co. (kȧsh lȧ pōōd'r')	122	40.43 N	105.39 W
Cachinal, Chile (kä-chē-näl')	144	24.57 S	69.33 W
Cachi, Nevados de (Pk.), Arg. (nĕ-vȧ'dôs-dĕ-kȧ'chē)	144	25.05 S	66.40 W
Cachoeira, Braz. (kä-shô-ā'rä)	143	12.32 S	38.47 W
Cachoeirá do Sul, Braz. (kä-shô-ā'rä-dô-sōō'l)	144	30.02 S	52.49 W
Cachoeiras de Macacu, Braz. (kä-shô-ā'räs-dĕ-mä-kȧ'kōō)	141a	22.28 S	42.39 W
Cachoeiro de Itapemirim, Braz. (kä-shô-ā'rô-dĕ-ē'tä-pĕmē-rē'ɴ)	141a	20.51 S	41.06 W
Cacilhas, Port.	65d	38.41 N	9.09 W
Cacólo, Ang.	230	10.07 S	19.17 E
Caconda, Ang. (kä-kōn'dä)	230	13.43 S	15.06 E
Cacouna, Can.	104	47.54 N	69.31 W
Cacula, Ang.	230	14.29 S	14.10 E
Cadale, Som.	223a	2.45 N	46.15 E
Caddo (L.), La.-Tx. (kăd'ō)	125	32.37 N	94.15 W
Cadereyta, Mex. (kä-dȧ-rā'tä)	130	20.42 N	99.47 W
Cadereyta Jimenez, Mex. (kä-dä-rā'tä hē-mā'nāz)	124	25.36 N	99.59 W
Cadillac, Mi. (kăd'ĭ-lăk)	110	44.15 N	85.25 W
Cadishead, Eng.	64b	53.25 N	2.26 W
Cadi, Sierra de (Mts.), Sp. (sē-ĕ'r-rä-dĕ-kä'dē)	171	42.17 N	1.34 E
Cadiz, Ca. (kā'dĭz)	120	34.33 N	115.30 W
Cadiz, Oh.	110	40.15 N	81.00 W
Cádiz, Sp. (kȧ'dēz)	170	36.34 N	6.20 W
Cádiz, Golfo de (G.), Sp. (gôl-fô-dĕ-kȧ'dēz)	170	36.50 N	7.00 W
Caen, Fr. (käɴ)	168	49.13 N	0.22 W
Caernarfon, Wales	162	53.08 N	4.17 W
Caernarfon B., Wales	162	53.09 N	4.56 W
Caeté, Braz. (kä'ĕ-tē')	141a	19.53 S	43.41 W
Caetité, Braz. (kä-å-tē-tā')	143	14.02 S	42.14 W
Cagayan, Phil. (kä-gä-yän')	207	8.13 N	124.30 E
Cagayan (R.), Phil.	206	16.45 N	121.55 E
Cagayan Is., Phil.	206	9.40 N	120.30 E
Cagayan Sulu (I.), Phil. (kä-gä-yän sōō'lōō)	206	7.00 N	118.30 E
Cagli, It. (käl'yē)	172	43.35 N	12.40 E
Cagliari, It. (käl'yä-rē)	172	39.16 N	9.08 E
Cagliari, Golfo di (G.), It. (gôl-fô-dē-käl'yä-rē)	172	39.08 N	9.12 E
Cagnes, Fr. (kän'y')	169	43.40 N	7.14 E
Cagua, Ven. (kä'gwä)	143b	10.12 N	67.27 W
Caguas, P.R. (kä'gwäs)	129b	18.12 N	66.01 W
Cahaba (R.), Al. (kȧ hä-bä)	126	32.50 N	87.15 W
Cahama, Ang. (kä-ȧ'mä)	230	16.17 S	14.19 E
Cahokia, Il. (kȧ-hō'kĭ-ȧ)	119e	38.34 N	90.11 W
Cahora-Bassa (Gorge), Moz.	231	15.40 S	32.50 E
Cahors, Fr. (kȧ-ôr')	168	44.27 N	1.27 E
Cahuacán, Mex. (kä-wä-kä'n)	131a	19.38 N	99.25 W
Cahuita, Punta (Pt.), C.R. (pōō'n-tä-kä-wē'tȧ)	133	9.47 N	82.41 W
Caiapó, Serra do (Mts.), Braz. (sĕ'r-rä-dô-kä-yä-pô')	143	17.52 S	52.37 W
Caibarién, Cuba (kī-bä-rē-ĕn')	134	22.35 N	79.30 W
Caicedonia, Col. (kī-sĕ-dô-nêä)	142a	4.21 N	75.48 W
Caicos Bk., Ba. (kī'kōs)	135	21.35 N	72.00 W
Caicos Is., Turks & Caicos Is.,	135	21.45 N	71.50 W
Caicos Passage (Str.), Ba.	135	21.55 N	72.45 W
Caillou B., La. (kȧ-yōō')	125	29.07 N	91.00 W
Caimanera, Cuba (kī-mä-nä'rä)	135	20.00 N	75.10 W
Caiman Pt., Phil. (kī'män)	207a	15.56 N	119.33 E
Caimito, (R.), Pan. (kä-ē-mē'tô)	128a	8.50 N	79.45 W
Caimito del Guayabal, Cuba (kä-ē-mē'tō-dĕl-gwä-yä-bä'l)	135a	22.57 N	82.36 W
Cairns, Austl. (kârnz)	215	17.02 S	145.49 E
Cairo, C.R. (kī'rô)	133	10.06 N	83.47 W
Cairo, Ga. (kā'rō)	126	30.48 N	84.12 W
Cairo, Il.	123	36.59 N	89.11 W
Cairo, see Al Qāhirah			
Caistor, Eng. (kâs'tĕr)	156	53.30 N	0.20 W
Caiundo, Ang.	230	15.46 S	17.28 E
Caiyu, China (tsī-yōō)	202a	39.39 N	116.36 E
Cajamarca, Col. (kä-ĸä-mȧ'r-kä)	142	4.25 N	75.25 W
Cajamarca, Peru (kä-hä-mär'kä)	142	7.16 S	78.30 W
Čajniče, Yugo. (chī'nĭ-chĕ)	173	43.32 N	19.04 E
Cajon, Ca. (kȧ-hōn')	119a	34.18 N	117.28 W
Caju (Neigh.), Braz.	61c	22.53 S	43.13 W
Çajuru, Braz. (kȧ-zhōō'rōō)	141a	21.17 S	47.17 W
Čakovec, Yugo. (chȧ'kō-vĕts)	172	46.23 N	16.27 E
Cala, S. Afr. (cä-lȧ)	227c	31.33 S	27.41 E
Calabar, Nig. (kăl-ȧ-bär')	229	4.57 N	8.19 E
Calabazar, Cuba (kä-lä-bä-zä'r)	135a	23.02 N	82.25 W
Calabozo, Ven. (kä-lä-bō'zō)	142	8.48 N	67.27 W
Calabria (Reg.), It. (kä-lä'brē-ä)	172	39.26 N	16.23 E
Calafat, Rom. (kȧ-lȧ-fȧt')	173	43.59 N	22.56 E
Calaguas Is., Phil. (kä-läg'wäs)	207a	14.30 N	123.06 E
Calahoo, Can. (kă-lȧ-hōō')	95g	53.42 N	113.58 W
Calahorra, Sp. (kä-lä-ôr'rä)	170	42.18 N	1.58 W
Calais, Fr. (kȧ-lĕ')	168	50.56 N	1.51 E
Calais, Me.	104	45.11 N	67.15 W
Calama, Chile (kä-lä'mä)	144	22.17 S	68.58 W
Calamar, Col. (kä-lä-mär')	142	10.24 N	75.00 W
Calamar, Col.	142	1.55 N	72.33 W
Calamba, Phil. (kä-läm'bä)	207a	14.12 N	121.10 E
Calamian Group (Is.), Phil. (kä-lä-myän')	206	12.14 N	118.38 E
Calañas, Sp. (kä-län'yäs)	170	37.41 N	6.52 W
Calanda, Sp.	171	40.53 N	0.20 W
Calapan, Phil. (kä-lä-pän')	207a	13.25 N	121.11 E
Călăraşi, Rom. (kŭ-lŭ-rȧsh'ĭ)	161	44.09 N	27.20 E
Calatayud, Sp. (kä-lä-tä-yōōdh')	170	41.23 N	1.37 W
Calauag B., Phil.	207a	14.07 N	122.10 E
Calaveras Res., Ca. (kăl-ȧ-vĕr'ăs)	118b	37.29 N	121.47 W
Calavite, C., Phil. (kä-lä-vē'tä)	207a	13.29 N	120.00 E
Calcasieu (R.), La. (kăl'kȧ-shū)	125	30.22 N	93.08 W
Calcasieu L., La.	125	29.58 N	93.08 W
Calcutta, India (kăl-kŭt'ȧ)	196a	22.32 N	88.22 E
Caldas, Col. (kȧ'l-däs)	142a	6.06 N	75.38 W
Caldas (Dept.), Col.	142a	5.20 N	75.38 W
Caldas da Rainha, Port. (käl'däs dä rīn'yȧ)	170	39.25 N	9.08 W
Calder (R.), Eng. (kôl'dĕr)	156	53.39 N	1.30 W
Caldera, Chile (käl-dā'rä)	144	27.02 S	70.53 W
Calder Can., Eng.	156	53.48 N	2.25 W
Caldwell, Id. (kôld'wĕl)	116	43.40 N	116.43 W
Caldwell, Ks.	123	37.04 N	97.36 W
Caldwell, NJ	55	40.51 N	74.17 W
Caldwell, Oh.	110	39.40 N	81.30 W
Caldwell, Tx.	125	30.30 N	96.40 W
Caledon, Can. (kăl'ē-dŏn)	95d	43.52 N	79.59 W
Caledonia, Mn. (kăl-ē-dō'nĭ-ȧ)	115	43.38 N	91.31 W
Calella, Sp. (kä-lĕl'yä)	171	41.37 N	2.39 E
Calera Victor Rosales, Mex. (kä-lā'rä-vē'k-tôr-rô-sȧ'lĕs)	130	22.57 N	102.42 W
Calexico, Ca. (kȧ-lĕk'sĭ-kō)	120	32.41 N	115.30 W
Calgary, Can. (kăl'gȧ-rĭ)	95e	51.03 N	114.05 W
Calhariz (Neigh.), Port.	65d	38.44 N	9.12 W
Calhoun, Ga. (kăl-hōōn')	126	34.30 N	84.56 W
Cali, Col. (kä'lē)	142a	3.26 N	76.30 W
Calicut, India (kăl'ĭ-kŭt)	197	11.19 N	75.49 E
Caliente, Nv. (käl-yĕn'tä)	121	37.38 N	114.30 W
California, Mo. (kăl-ĭ-fôr'nĭ-ȧ)	123	38.38 N	92.38 W
California, Pa.	113e	40.03 N	79.53 W
California (State), U.S.	108	38.10 N	121.20 W
California, Golfo de (G.), Mex. (gôl-fô-dĕ-kä-lē-fôr-nyä)	128	30.30 N	113.45 W
California, University of (U.C.L.A.) (P. Int.), Ca.	59	34.04 N	118.26 W
Călimani, Munţii (Mts.), Rom.	167	47.05 N	24.47 E
Calimere, Pt., India	197	10.20 N	80.20 E
Calimesa, Ca. (kă-lĭ-mā'sȧ)	119a	34.00 N	117.04 W
Calipatria, Ca. (kăl-ĭ-pȧt'rĭ-ȧ)	120	33.03 N	115.30 W
Calkini, Mex. (käl-kē-nē')	131	20.21 N	90.06 W
Callabonna, L., Austl. (călă'bŏnȧ)	216	29.35 S	140.28 E
Callao, Peru (käl-yä'ō)	142	12.02 S	77.07 W
Calling (L.), Can. (kôl'ĭng)	99	55.15 N	113.12 W
Calmar, Can. (kăl'mär)	95g	53.16 N	113.49 W
Calmar, Ia.	115	43.12 N	91.54 W
Calnali, Mex. (käl-nä-lē')	130	20.53 N	98.34 W
Caloocan, Phil.	68g	14.39 N	120.59 E
Calooshatchee (R.), Fl. (kȧ-loo-sȧ-hăch'ē)	127a	26.45 N	81.41 W
Calotmul, Mex. (kä-lôt-mōōl)	132a	20.58 N	88.11 W
Calpulalpan, Mex. (käl-pōō-läl'pän)	130	19.35 N	98.33 W
Caltagirone, It. (käl-tä-jē-rō'nå)	172	37.14 N	14.32 E
Caltanissetta, It. (käl-tä-nē-sĕt'tä)	172	37.30 N	14.02 E
Caluango, Ang.	230	8.21 S	19.40 E
Calucinga, Ang.	230	11.18 S	16.12 E
Calumet, Mi. (kă-lū-mĕt')	115	47.15 N	88.29 W
Calumet City, Il.	113a	41.37 N	87.33 W
Calumet, L., Il.	113a	41.43 N	87.36 W
Calumet Park, Il.	58a	41.44 N	87.33 W
Calumet Sag Chan., Il.	58a	41.42 N	87.57 W
Calunda, Ang.	230	12.06 S	23.23 E
Caluquembe, Ang.	230	13.47 S	14.44 E
Caluula, Som.	223a	11.53 N	50.40 E
Calvert, Tx. (kăl'vērt)	125	30.59 N	96.41 W
Calvert I., Can.	98	51.35 N	128.00 W
Calvi, Fr. (käl'vē)	172	42.33 N	8.35 E
Calvillo, Mex. (käl-vēl'yō)	130	21.51 N	102.44 E
Calvinia, S. Afr. (kăl-vĭn'ĭ-ȧ)	226	31.20 S	19.50 E
Cam (R.), Eng. (kăm)	162	52.15 N	0.05 E
Camagüey, Cuba (kä-mä-gwā')	134	21.25 N	78.00 W
Camagüey (Prov.), Cuba	134	21.30 N	78.10 W
Camajuani, Cuba (kä-mä-hwä'nē)	134	22.25 N	79.50 W
Camaná, Peru (kä-mä'nä)	142	16.37 S	72.33 W
Camano, Wa. (kä-mä'no)	118a	48.10 N	122.32 W
Camano I., Wa.	118a	48.11 N	122.29 W
Camargo, Mex. (kä-mär gō)	124	26.19 N	98.49 W
Camarón, Cabo (C.), Hond. (kȧ'bô-kä-mä-rōn')	132	16.06 N	85.05 W
Camas, Wa. (kăm'ȧs)	118c	45.36 N	122.24 W
Camas Cr., Id.	117	44.10 N	112.09 W
Camatagua, Ven. (kä-mä-tȧ'gwä)	143b	9.49 N	66.55 W
Ca-Mau, Mui (Pt.), Viet.	206	8.36 N	104.43 E
Cambay, India (kăm-bā')	196	22.22 N	72.39 E
Camberwell, Austl.	70b	37.50 S	145.04 E
Cambonda, Serra (Mts.), Ang.	230	12.10 S	14.15 E
Camborne, Eng. (kăm'bôrn)	162	50.15 N	5.28 W
Cambrai, Fr. (käɴ-brĕ')	168	50.10 N	3.15 E
Cambrian Mts., Wales (kăm'brĭ-ăn)	162	52.05 N	4.05 W
Cambridge, Eng. (kām'brĭj)	162	52.12 N	0.11 E
Cambridge, Ma.	105a	42.23 N	71.07 W
Cambridge, Md.	111	38.35 N	76.10 W
Cambridge, Mn.	115	45.35 N	93.14 W
Cambridge, Ne.	122	40.17 N	100.10 W
Cambridge, Oh.	110	40.00 N	81.35 W
Cambridge Bay, Can.	96	69.15 N	105.00 W
Cambridge City, In.	110	39.45 N	85.15 W
Cambridgeshire (Co.), Eng.	156	52.26 N	0.19 W
Cambuci, Braz. (käm-bōō'sē)	141a	21.35 S	41.54 W
Cambuci (Neigh.), Braz.	61d	23.34 S	46.37 W
Cambuí, Braz. (käm-bōō-ē')	141a	22.38 S	46.02 W
Camby, In. (kăm'bē)	113g	39.40 N	86.19 W
Camden, Al. (kăm'dĕn)	126	31.58 N	87.15 W
Camden, Ar.	123	33.36 N	92.49 W
Camden, Austl.	211b	34.03 S	150.42 E
Camden, Me.	104	44.11 N	69.05 W
Camden (Neigh.), Eng.	62	51.33 N	0.10 W
Camden, NJ	112f	39.56 N	75.06 W
Camden, SC	127	34.14 N	80.37 W
Cameia, Parque Nacional da (Natl. Pk.), Ang.	230	11.40 S	21.20 E
Cameron, Mo. (kăm'ēr-ŭn)	123	39.44 N	94.14 W
Cameron, Tx.	125	30.52 N	96.57 W
Cameron, WV	110	39.40 N	80.35 W
Cameron Hills, Can.	96	60.13 N	120.20 W
Cameroon, Afr.	222	5.48 N	11.00 E
Cameroon, (Mtn.), Cam.	229	4.12 N	9.11 E
Cametá, Braz. (kä-må-tä')	143	1.14 S	49.30 W
Camiling, Phil. (kä-mē-lĭng')	207a	15.42 N	120.24 E
Camilla, Ga. (kȧ-mĭl'ȧ)	126	31.13 N	84.12 W
Caminha, Port. (kä-mĭn'yȧ)	170	41.52 N	8.44 W
Camoçim, Braz. (kä-mô-sēɴ')	143	2.56 S	40.55 W
Camooweal, Austl.	214	20.00 S	138.13 E
Campana, Arg. (käm-pä'nä)	141c	34.10 S	58.58 W
Campana (I.), Chile (käm-pän'yä)	144	48.20 S	75.15 W
Campanario, Sp. (kä-pä-nä'rē-ō)	170	38.51 N	5.36 W
Campanella, Punta (C.), It. (pōō'n-tä-käm-pä-nĕ'lä)	171c	40.20 N	14.21 E
Campanha, Braz. (käm-pän-yäɴ')	141a	21.51 S	45.24 W
Campania (Reg.), It. (käm-pän'yä)	172	41.00 N	14.40 E
Campbell, Ca. (kăm'bĕl)	118b	37.17 N	121.57 W
Campbell (Is.), N.Z.	232	52.30 S	169.00 E
Campbell, Mo.	123	36.29 N	90.04 W
Campbellfield, Austl.	70b	37.41 S	144.57 E
Campbellpore, Pak.	196	33.49 N	72.24 E
Campbell River, Can.	98	50.01 N	125.15 W
Campbellsville, Ky. (kăm'bĕlz-vĭl)	126	37.19 N	85.20 W
Campbellton, Can. (kăm'bĕl-tŭn)	104	48.00 N	66.40 W
Campbelltown, Austl. (kăm'bĕl-toun)	211b	34.04 S	150.49 E
Campbelltown, Scot. (kăm'b'l-toun)	162	55.25 N	5.50 W
Camp Dennison, Oh. (dĕ'nĭ-sŏn)	113f	39.12 N	84.17 W
Campeche, Mex. (käm-pā'chå)	131	19.51 N	90.32 W
Campeche (State), Mex.	128	18.55 N	90.20 W
Campeche, Bahía de (B.), Mex. (bä-ē'ä-dĕ-käm-pā'chā)	128	19.30 N	93.40 W
Campechuela, Cuba (käm-på-chwā'lä)	134	20.15 N	77.15 W
Camperdown, S. Afr. (kăm'pĕr-doun)	227c	29.14 S	30.33 E
Campina Grande, Braz. (käm-pē'nä grän'dĕ)	143	7.15 S	35.49 W
Campinas, Braz. (käm-pē'näzh)	141a	22.53 S	47.03 W
Camp Ind. Res., Ca. (kămp)	120	32.39 N	116.26 W
Campo, Cam. (käm'pō)	229	2.22 N	9.49 E
Campoalegre, Col. (kä'm-pô-ȧlĕ'grĕ)	142	2.34 N	75.20 W
Campobasso, It. (käm'pô-bäs'sō)	172	41.35 N	14.39 E
Campo Belo, Braz.	141a	20.52 S	45.15 W
Campo de Criptana, Sp. (käm'pô dā krēp-tä'nä)	170	39.24 N	3.09 W
Campo Florido, Cuba (kä'm-pō flō-rē'dō)	135a	23.07 N	82.07 W
Campo Grande, Braz. (käm-pōō grän'dĕ)	143	20.28 S	54.32 W
Campo Grande, Braz.	144b	22.54 S	43.33 W
Campo Grande (Neigh.), Port.	65d	38.45 N	9.09 W
Campo Maior, Braz. (käm-pōō mä-yôr')	143	4.48 S	42.12 W
Campo Maior, Port.	170	39.03 N	7.06 W
Campo Real, Sp. (käm'pō rå-äl')	171a	40.21 N	3.23 W
Campos, Braz. (kä'm-pôs)	141a	21.46 S	41.19 W
Campos do Jordão, Braz. (kä'm-pôs-dô-zhôr-dou'ɴ)	141a	22.45 S	45.35 W
Campos Gerais, Braz. (kä'm-pôs-zhĕ-rä'es)	141a	21.17 S	45.43 W
Camps Bay, S. Afr. (kămps)	226a	33.57 S	18.22 E
Campsie, Austl.	70a	33.55 S	151.06 E
Camp Springs, Md. (cămp sprĭngz)	112e	38.48 N	76.55 W
Camp Springs, Md.	56d	38.48 N	76.55 W
Camp Wood, Tx. (kămp wŏŏd)	124	29.39 N	100.02 W
Camrose, Can. (kăm-rōz)	100	53.01 N	112.50 W
Camu (R.), Dom. Rep. (kä'mōō)	135	19.05 N	70.15 W
Canada, N.A. (kăn'ȧ-dȧ)	94	50.00 N	100.00 W
Canada B., Can.	105	50.43 N	56.10 W
Cañada de Gómez, Arg. (kä-nyä'dä-dĕ-gô'mĕz)	141c	32.49 S	61.24 W
Canadian, Tx. (kȧ-nā'dĭ-ăn)	122	35.54 N	100.24 W
Canadian R., Ok.	123	34.53 N	97.06 W
Canajoharie, NY (kăn-ȧ-jô-hăr'ē)	111	42.55 N	74.35 W
Çanakkale, Tur. (chä-näk-kä'lĕ)	173	40.10 N	26.26 E
Çanakkale Boğazi (Dardanelles) (Str.), Tur. (chä-näk-kä'lē) (där-dȧ-nĕlz')	173	40.05 N	25.50 E
Canandaigua (L.), NY	111	42.45 N	77.20 W
Canandaigua, NY (kăn-ăn-dā'gwȧ)	111	42.55 N	77.20 W
Cananea, Mex. (kä-nä-nĕ'ä)	128	31.00 N	110.20 W

PLACE (Pronounciation)	PAGE	Lat. °′	Long. °′
Canarias, Islas (Is.), Sp. (ĕ's-läs-kä-nä'ryäs)	224	29.15 N	16.30 W
Canarreos, Arch. de los (Is.), Cuba (är-chē-pyĕ'lä-gô-dĕ-lôs-kä-när-rĕ'ōs)	134	21.35 N	82.20 W
Canarsie (Neigh.), NY	55	40.38 N	73.53 W
Cañas, C.R. (kä'-nyäs)	132	10.26 N	85.06 W
Cañasgordas, Col. (kä'nyäs-gô'r-däs)	142a	6.44 N	76.01 W
Cañas R., C.R.	132	10.20 N	85.21 W
Canastota, NY (kăn-ȧs-tō'tȧ)	111	43.05 N	75.45 W
Canastra, Serra de (Mts.), Braz. (sĕ'r-rä-dĕ-kä-nä's-trä)	143	19.53 S	46.57 W
Canatlán, Mex. (kä-nät-län')	124	24.30 N	104.45 W
Canaveral, C., Fl.	127a	28.30 N	80.23 W
Canavieiras, Braz. (kä-nȧ-vē-ā'räs)	143	15.40 S	38.49 W
Canberra, Austl. (kăn'bĕr-ȧ)	216	35.21 S	149.10 E
Canby, Mn. (kăn'bĭ)	114	44.43 N	96.15 W
Canchyauya, Cerros de (Mts.), Peru (sĕ'r-rôs-dĕ-kän-choo-ȧ'ïä)	142	7.30 S	74.30 W
Cancuc, Mex. (kän-kook)	131	16.58 N	92.17 W
Cancún, Mex.	132a	21.25 N	86.50 W
Candelaria, Cuba (kän-dĕ-lä'ryä)	134	22.45 N	82.55 W
Candelaria, Phil. (kän-dȧ-lä'rē-ä)	207a	15.39 N	119.55 E
Candelaria (R.), Mex. (kän-dĕ-lä-ryä)	131	18.25 N	91.21 W
Candeleda, Sp. (kän-dhā-lā'dhä)	170	40.09 N	5.18 W
Candia, see **Iráklion**			
Candle, Ak. (kăn'd'l)	107	65.00 N	162.04 W
Cando, ND (kăn'dō)	114	48.27 N	99.13 W
Candon, Phil. (kän-dōn')	207a	17.13 N	120.26 E
Canelones (Dept.), Ur.	141c	34.34 S	56.15 W
Canelones, Ur. (kä-nĕ-lô-nĕs)	141c	34.32 S	56.19 W
Cañete, Peru (kän-yā'tȧ)	142	13.06 S	76.17 W
Caney, Cuba (kä-nā') (kā'nĭ)	135	20.05 N	75.45 W
Caney, Ks. (kā'nĭ)	123	37.00 N	95.57 W
Caney (R.), Tn.	126	36.10 N	85.50 W
Cangamba, Ang.	230	13.40 S	19.54 E
Cangas, Sp. (kän'gäs)	170	42.15 N	8.43 W
Cangas de Narcea, Sp. (kä'n-gäs-dĕ-när-sĕ-ä)	170	43.08 N	6.36 W
Cangzhou, China (tsäŋ-jō)	200	38.21 N	116.53 E
Caniapiscau (L.), Can.	97	54.10 N	71.13 E
Caniapiscau (R.), Can.	97	57.00 N	68.45 W
Canicatti, It. (kä-nē-kät'tē)	172	37.18 N	13.58 E
Canillas (Neigh.), Sp.	65b	40.28 N	3.38 W
Canillejas (Neigh.), Sp.	65b	40.27 N	3.37 W
Cañitas, Mex. (kän-yē'täs)	130	23.38 N	102.44 W
Çankırı, Tur. (chän-kē'rē)	179	40.40 N	33.40 E
Cannell, Can.	95g	53.35 N	113.38 W
Cannelton, In. (kăn'ĕl-tŭn)	110	37.55 N	86.45 W
Cannes, Fr. (kȧn)	169	43.34 N	7.05 E
Canning, Can. (kăn'ĭng)	104	45.09 N	64.25 W
Cannock, Eng. (kăn'ŭk)	156	52.41 N	2.02 W
Cannock Chase (Reg.), Eng. (kăn'ŭk chās)	156	52.43 N	1.54 W
Cannon (R.), Mn. (kăn'ŭn)	115	44.18 N	93.24 W
Cannonball (R.), ND (kăn'ŭn-bäl)	114	46.17 N	101.35 W
Canoe (R.), Can. (kȧ-noo)	99	52.20 N	119.00 W
Canoga Park, Ca. (kä-nō'gȧ)	119a	34.07 N	118.36 W
Caño, Isla de (I.), C.R. (ĕ's-lä-dĕ-kä'nō)	133	8.38 N	84.00 W
Canon City, Co. (kăn'yŭn)	122	38.27 N	105.16 W
Canonsburg, Pa. (kăn'ŭnz-bûrg)	113e	40.16 N	80.11 W
Canoochee (R.), Ga. (kȧ-noo'chē)	127	32.25 N	82.11 W
Canora, Can. (kȧ-nōrȧ)	101	51.37 N	102.26 W
Canosa, It. (kä-nō'sä)	172	41.14 N	16.03 E
Canouan (I.), Saint Vincent	133b	12.44 N	61.10 W
Cansaheab, Mex. (kän-sä-ĕ-äb)	132a	21.11 N	89.05 W
Canso, Can. (kăn'sō)	105	45.20 N	61.00 W
Canso, C., Can.	105	45.21 N	60.46 W
Canso, Str. of, Can.	105	45.37 N	61.25 W
Cantabrica, Cordillera (Mts.),Sp. (kôr-dēl-yĕ'rä-kan-tä'brē-kä)	170	43.05 N	6.05 W
Cantagalo, Braz. (kän-tä-gȧ'lo)	141a	21.59 S	42.22 W
Cantanhede, Port. (kän-täN-yā'dȧ)	170	40.22 N	8.35 W
Canterbury, Eng. (kăn'tĕr-bĕr-ē)	156b	51.17 N	1.06 E
Canterbury, Austl., Austl.	70b	37.49 S	145.05 E
Canterbury Bight, N.Z.	215a	44.15 S	172.08 E
Canterbury Woods, Va.	56d	38.49 N	77.15 W
Cantiles, Cayo (I.), Cuba (ky-ō-kän-tē'lås)	134	21.40 N	82.00 W
Canto do Pontes, Braz.	61c	22.58 S	43.04 W
Canton, Ga.	126	34.13 N	84.29 W
Canton, Il.	123	40.34 N	90.02 W
Canton, Ma.	105a	42.09 N	71.09 W
Canton, Mo.	123	40.08 N	91.33 W
Canton, Ms.	126	32.36 N	90.01 W
Canton, NC	126	35.32 N	82.50 W
Canton, Oh.	110	40.50 N	81.25 W
Canton, Pa.	111	41.50 N	76.45 W
Canton, SD	114	43.17 N	96.37 W
Canton, see **Guangzhou**			
Canton, (I.), see **Kanton** (I.)			
Cantu, It. (kän-too')	172	45.43 N	9.09 E
Cañuelas, Arg. (kä-nyooĕ'-läs)	141c	35.03 S	58.45 W
Canumã (R.), Braz. (kä-noo-mȧ')	143	6.20 S	58.57 W
Canyon, Ca.	118b	37.49 N	122.09 W
Canyon (R.), Wa.	118a	48.09 N	121.48 W
Canyon, Tx. (kăn'yŭn)	122	34.59 N	101.57 W
Canyon De Chelly Natl. Mon., Az.	121	36.14 N	110.00 W
Canyonlands Natl. Park, Ut.	121	38.10 N	110.00 W
Caoxian, China (tsou shyĕn)	200	34.48 N	115.33 E
Capalonga, Phil. (kä-pä-lôŋ'gä)	207a	14.20 N	122.30 E
Capannori, It. (kä-pän'nô-rē)	172	43.50 N	10.30 E
Capão Redondo (Neigh.), Braz.	61d	23.40 S	46.46 W
Caparica, Port.	65d	38.40 N	9.12 W
Capaya (R.), Ven. (kä-pä-ïä)	143b	10.28 N	66.15 W
Cap-Chat, Can. (kȧp-shä')	97	48.02 N	65.20 W
Cap-de-la-Madeleine, Can. (kȧp dē lá mȧ-d'lĕn')	104	46.23 N	72.30 W
Cape (Prov.), S. Afr. (kāp)	226	31.50 S	21.15 E
Cape Breton (I.), Can. (kāp brĕt'ŭn)	105	45.48 N	59.50 W
Cape Breton Highlands Natl. Park, Can.	105	46.45 N	60.45 W
Cape Charles, Va. (kāp chärlz)	127	37.13 N	76.02 W
Cape Coast, Ghana	228	5.05 N	1.15 W
Cape Fear (R.), NC (kāp fēr)	127	34.43 N	78.41 W
Cape Flats, S. Afr. (kāp flăts)	226a	34.01 S	18.37 E
Cape Girardeau, Mo. (jē-rär-dō')	123	37.17 N	89.32 W
Cape May, NJ (kāp mā)	111	38.55 N	74.50 W
Cape May C.H., NJ	111	39.05 N	75.00 W
Capenhurst, Eng.	64a	53.15 N	2.57 W
Cape Romanzof, Ak. (rō' män zôf)	107	61.50 N	165.45 W
Capesterre, Guad.	133b	16.02 N	61.37 W
Cape Tormentine, Can.	104	46.08 N	63.47 W
Cape Town, S. Afr. (kāp toun)	226a	33.48 S	18.28 E
Cape Verde, Afr.	224b	15.48 N	26.02 W
Cape York Pen., Austl. (kāp yôrk)	215	12.30 S	142.35 E
Cap-Haïtien, Hai. (kȧp ȧ-ē-syăn')	135	19.45 N	72.15 W
Capilla de Señor, Arg. (kä-pēl'yä dā sän-yôr')	141c	34.18 S	59.07 W
Capitachouane, (R.), Can.	103	47.50 N	76.45 W
Capitol Heights, Md.	56d	38.53 N	76.55 W
Capitol Reef Natl. Park, Ut. (kăp'ĭ-tŏl)	121	38.15 N	111.10 W
Capitol View, Md.	56d	39.01 N	77.04 W
Capivari, Braz. (kä-pē-vȧ'rē)	141a	22.59 S	47.29 W
Capivari (R.), Braz.	144b	22.39 S	43.19 W
Capoompeta (Mtn.), Austl. (kă-poom-pē'tȧ)	216	29.15 S	152.12 E
Capraia (I.), It. (kä-prä'yä)	172	43.02 N	9.51 E
Caprara Pt., It. (kä-prä'rä)	172	41.08 N	8.20 E
Capreol, Can.	102	46.43 N	80.56 W
Caprera (I.), It. (kä-prā'rä)	172	41.12 N	9.28 E
Capri, It.	171c	40.18 N	14.16 E
Capricorn Chan., Austl. (kăp'rĭ-kôrn)	215	22.27 S	151.24 E
Capri, I. di, It. (ē'-sō-lä-dē-kä'prē)	171c	40.19 N	14.10 E
Caprivi Strip (Reg.), Namibia	226	18.00 S	22.00 E
Cap-Rouge, Can. (kȧp roozh')	95b	46.45 N	71.21 W
Cap-Saint Ignace, Can. (kĭp săN-tē-nyȧs')	95b	47.02 N	70.27 W
Captain Cook Bridge (P. Int.), Austl.	70a	34.00 S	151.08 E
Capua, It. (kä'pwä)	172	41.07 N	14.14 E
Capuáva, Braz.	61d	23.39 S	46.29 W
Capulhuac, Mex. (kä-pool-hwäk')	130	19.33 N	99.43 W
Capulin Mountain Natl. Mon., NM (kȧ-pū'lĭn)	122	36.15 N	103.58 W
Capultitlán, Mex. (kä-poo'l-tē-tlä'n)	131a	19.15 N	99.40 W
Caputh, G.D.R.	65a	52.21 N	13.00 E
Caquetá (R.), Col. (kä-kā-tä')	142	0.23 S	73.22 W
Caraballeda, Ven.	61a	10.37 N	66.50 W
Carabaña, Sp. (kä-rä-bän'yä)	171a	40.16 N	3.15 W
Carabanchel Alto (Neigh.), Sp.	65b	40.22 N	3.45 W
Carabanchel Bajo (Neigh.), Sp.	65b	40.23 N	3.47 W
Carabelle, Fl. (kăr'ȧ-bĕl)	126	29.50 N	84.40 W
Carabobo (State), Ven. (kä-rä-bô'-bô)	143b	10.07 N	68.06 W
Caracal, Rom. (kȧ-rȧ-kȧl')	173	44.06 N	24.22 E
Caracas, Ven. (kä-rä'käs)	143b	10.30 N	66.58 W
Carácuaro de Morelos, Mex. (kä-rä'kwä-rō-dĕ-mô-rĕ-lôs)	130	18.44 N	101.04 W
Caraguatatuba, Braz. (kä-rä-gwä-tȧ-too'bä)	141a	23.37 S	45.26 W
Carajás, Serra dos (Mts.), Braz. (sĕ'r-rä-dôs-kä-rä-zhȧ's)	143	5.58 S	51.45 W
Caramanta, Cerro (Mtn.), Col. (sĕ'r-rô-kä-rä-mȧ'n-tä)	142a	5.29 N	76.01 W
Caramarca, Arg. (kä-rä-mȧ'r-kä)	144	28.29 S	65.45 W
Carandaí, Braz. (kä-rän-dȧē')	141a	20.57 S	43.47 W
Carangola, Braz. (kä-rän'gō'lä)	141a	20.46 S	42.02 W
Caransebeş, Rom. (kȧ-rȧn-sȧ'bĕsh)	173	45.24 N	22.13 E
Carapicuíba, Braz.	61d	23.31 S	46.50 W
Caraquet, Can. (kă-rȧ-kĕt')	104	47.48 N	64.57 W
Carata, Laguna (L.), Nic. (lä-goo'nä-kä-rä'tä)	133	13.59 N	83.41 W
Caratasca, Laguna (L.), Hond. (lä-goo'nä-kä-rä-täs'kä)	133	15.20 N	83.45 W
Caravaca, Sp. (kä-rä-vä'kä)	170	38.05 N	1.51 W
Caravelas, Braz. (kȧ-rä-vĕl'äzh)	143	17.46 S	39.06 W
Carayaca, Ven. (kȧ-rä-ïä'kä)	143b	10.32 N	67.07 W
Carazinho, Braz. (kä-rȧ'zē-nyō)	144	28.22 S	52.33 W
Carballino, Sp. (kär-bäl-yē'nō)	170	42.26 N	8.04 W
Carballo, Sp. (kär-bäl'yō)	170	43.13 N	8.40 W
Carbon (R.), Wa. (kär'bŏn)	118a	47.06 N	122.08 W
Carbonado, Wa. (kär-bō-nä'dō)	118a	47.05 N	122.03 W
Carbonara, C., It. (kär-bō-nä'rä)	172	39.08 N	9.33 E
Carbondale, Can. (kär'bŏn-dāl)	95g	53.45 N	113.32 W
Carbondale, Il.	123	37.42 N	89.12 W
Carbondale, Pa.	111	41.35 N	75.30 W
Carbonear, Can. (kär-bō-nēr')	105	47.45 N	53.14 W
Carbon Hill, Al. (kär'bŏn hĭl)	126	33.53 N	87.34 W
Carcagente, Sp. (kär-kä-hĕn'tä)	171	39.09 N	0.29 W
Carcans, Étang de (L.), Fr. (ā-taN-dĕ-kär-kăn)	168	45.12 N	1.00 W
Carcassonne, Fr. (kär-kȧ-sôn')	168	43.12 N	2.23 E
Carcross, Can. (kär'krôs)	96	60.18 N	134.54 W
Cárdenas, Cuba (kär'dȧ-näs)	134	23.00 N	81.10 W
Cárdenas, Mex. (kȧ'r-dĕ-näs)	131	17.59 N	93.23 W
Cárdenas, Mex.	130	22.01 N	99.38 W
Cardenas, Bahía de (B.), Cuba (bä-ē'ä-dĕ-kär'dȧ-näs)	134	23.10 N	81.10 W
Cardiff, Can. (kär'dĭf)	95g	53.46 N	113.36 W
Cardiff, Wales	162	51.30 N	3.18 W
Cardigan, Wales (kär'dĭ-găn)	162	52.05 N	4.40 W
Cardigan B., Wales	162	52.35 N	4.40 W
Cardston, Can. (kärds'tŭn)	99	49.12 N	113.18 W
Carei, Rom. (kä-rē')	167	47.42 N	22.28 E
Carentan, Fr. (kä-rôN-täN')	168	49.19 N	1.14 W
Carey (L.), Aust. (kâr'ē)	214	29.20 S	123.35 E
Carey, Oh. (kā'rē)	110	40.55 N	83.25 W
Carhaix-Plouguer, Fr. (kär-ĕ')	168	48.17 N	3.37 W
Caribbean Sea, N.A.-S.A. (kăr-ĭ-bē'ăn)	129	14.30 N	75.30 W
Caribe, Arroyo (R.), Mex. (är-ro'ï-kä-rē'bĕ)	131	18.18 N	90.38 W
Cariboo Mts., Can. (kă'rĭ-boo)	99	53.00 N	121.00 W
Caribou (I.), Can.	102	47.22 N	85.42 W
Caribou, Me.	104	46.51 N	68.01 W
Caribou L., Mn.	119h	46.54 N	92.16 W
Caribou Mts., Can.	96	59.20 N	115.30 W
Caringbah, Austl.	70a	34.03 S	151.08 E
Carinhanha, Braz. (kä-rĭ-nyän'yä)	143	14.14 S	43.44 W
Carini, It. (kä-rē'nē)	172	38.09 N	13.10 E
Carinthia (State), see **Kärnten**			
Carleton Place, Can. (kärl'tŭn)	103	45.15 N	76.10 W
Carletonville, S. Afr.	223d	26.20 S	27.23 E
Carlingford, Austl.	70a	33.47 S	151.03 E
Carlinville, Il. (kär'lĭn-vĭl)	123	39.16 N	89.52 W
Carlisle, Eng. (kär-līl')	162	54.54 N	3.03 W
Carlisle, Ky.	110	38.20 N	84.00 W
Carlisle, Pa.	111	40.10 N	77.15 W
Carloforte, It. (kär'lō-fôr-tȧ)	172	39.11 N	8.28 E
Carlos Casares, Arg. (kär-lôs-kä-sȧ'rĕs)	141c	35.38 S	61.17 W
Carlow, Ire. (kär'lō)	162	52.50 N	7.00 W
Carlsbad, NM (kärlz'băd)	124	32.24 N	104.12 W
Carlsbad Caverns Nat'l Park, NM	124	32.08 N	104.30 W
Carlstadt, NJ	55	40.50 N	74.06 W
Carlton, Eng. (kärl'tŭn)	156	52.58 N	1.05 W
Carlton, Mn.	119h	46.40 N	92.26 W
Carlton Center, Mi. (kärl'tŭn sĕn'tĕr)	110	42.45 N	85.20 W
Carlyle, Il. (kärlīl')	123	38.37 N	89.23 W
Carmagnolo, It. (kär-mä-nyô'lä)	172	44.52 N	7.48 E
Carman, Can. (kär'mȧn)	101	49.32 N	98.00 W
Carmarthen, Wales (kär-mär'thĕn)	162	51.50 N	4.20 W
Carmarthen B., Wales (kär-mär'thĕn)	162	51.33 N	4.50 W
Carmaux, Fr. (kȧr-mō')	168	44.05 N	2.09 E
Carmel, NY (kär'mĕl)	112a	41.25 N	73.42 W
Carmelo, Ur. (kär-mĕ'lo)	141c	33.59 S	58.15 W
Carmen de Areco, Arg. (kär'mĕn' dā ä-rā'kō)	141c	34.21 S	59.50 W
Carmen de Patagones, Arg. (kȧ'r-mĕn-dĕ-pä-tä-gō'nĕs)	144	41.00 S	63.00 W
Carmen, Isla del (I.), Mex. (ē's-lä-dĕl-kȧ'r-mĕn)	131	18.43 N	91.40 W
Carmen, Laguna del (L.), Mex. (lä-goo'nä-dĕl-kȧ'r-mĕn)	131	18.15 N	93.26 W
Carmi, Il. (kär'mī)	110	38.05 N	88.10 W
Carmo, Braz. (kȧ'r-mô)	141a	21.57 S	42.06 W
Carmo do Rio Clara, Braz. (kȧ'r-mô-dô-rē'ô-klä'rä)	141a	20.57 S	46.04 W
Carmona, Sp.	170	37.28 N	5.38 W
Carnarvon, Austl. (kär-när'vŭn)	214	24.45 S	113.45 E
Carnarvon, S. Afr.	226	31.00 S	22.15 E
Carnation, Wa. (kär-nä'shŭn)	118a	47.39 N	121.55 W
Carnaxide, Port. (kär-nä-shē'dĕ)	171b	38.44 N	9.15 W
Carndonagh, Ire. (kärn-dō-nä')	162	55.15 N	7.15 W
Carnegie, Ok. (kär-nĕg'ĭ)	122	35.06 N	98.38 W
Carnegie, Pa.	113e	40.24 N	80.06 W
Carnegie Institute (P. Int.), Pa.	57b	40.27 N	79.57 W
Carnetin, Fr.	64c	48.54 N	2.42 E
Carneys Point, NJ (kär'nēs)	111	39.45 N	75.25 W
Carnic Alps (Mts.), Aus.-It.	166	46.43 N	12.38 E
Carnide (Neigh.), Port.	65d	38.46 N	9.11 W
Carnot, Alg. (kär nō')	171	36.15 N	1.40 E
Carnot, Cen. Afr. Rep.	229	5.00 N	15.52 E
Carnsore Pt., Ire. (kärn'sôr)	162	52.10 N	6.16 W
Caro, Mi. (kȧ'rō)	110	43.30 N	83.25 W
Carolina, Braz. (kä-rô-lē'nä)	143	7.26 S	47.16 W
Carolina (L.), Mex. (kä-rō-lē'nä)	132a	18.41 N	89.40 W
Carolina, S. Afr. (kăr-ô-lī'nȧ)	226	26.07 S	30.09 E
Caroline Is., Pac. Is. Trust Ter. (kăr'ô-līn)	208	9.30 N	143.00 E
Caroni (R.), Ven. (kä-rō'nē)	142	5.49 N	62.57 W
Carora, Ven. (kä-rō'rä)	142	10.09 N	70.12 W
Carpathians (Mts.), Eur. (kär-pā'thĭ-ăn)	161	49.23 N	20.14 E
Carpaţii Meridionali (Transylvanian Alps) (Mts.), Rom.	173	45.30 N	23.30 E
Carpentaria, G. of, Austl. (kär-pĕn-târ'ĭȧ)	214	14.45 S	138.50 E
Carpentras, Fr. (kär-päN-träs')	168	44.04 N	5.01 E
Carpi, It.	172	44.48 N	10.54 E
Carrara, It. (kä-rä'rä)	172	44.05 N	10.05 E
Carrauntoohil, Ire. (kă-rȧn-too'ĭl)	162	52.01 N	9.48 W
Carretas, Punta (Pt.), Peru (poo'n-tä-kär-rĕ'tĕ'räs)	142	14.15 S	76.25 W
Carriacou (I.), Grenada (kär-ē-ȧ-koo')	133b	12.28 N	61.20 W
Carrick-on-Sur, Ire. (kăr'-ĭk)	162	52.20 N	7.35 W
Carrier, Can. (kăr'ĭ-ĕr)	95b	46.43 N	71.05 W
Carriere, Ms. (kȧ-rēr')	126	30.37 N	89.37 W
Carrières-sous-Bois, Fr.	64c	48.57 N	2.07 E
Carrières-sous-Poissy, Fr.	64c	48.57 N	2.03 E
Carrières-sur-Seine, Fr.	64c	48.55 N	2.11 E
Carriers Mills, Il. (kăr'ĭ-ĕrs)	110	37.40 N	88.40 W
Carrington, Eng.	64b	53.26 N	2.24 W
Carrington, ND (kăr'ĭng-tŭn)	114	47.26 N	99.06 W
Carr Inlet, Wa. (kăr ĭn'lĕt)	118a	47.20 N	122.42 W
Carrion Crow Hbr., Ba. (kăr'ĭŭn krō)	134	26.35 N	77.55 W
Carrión de los Condes, Sp. (kär-rē-ōn' dā los kōn'dȧs)	170	42.20 N	4.35 W
Carrizo Cr., NM (kär-rē'zō)	122	36.22 N	103.39 W
Carrizo Springs, Tx.	124	28.32 N	99.51 W
Carrizozo, NM (kär-rē-zō'zō)	121	33.40 N	105.55 W
Carroll, Ia. (kăr'ŭl)	115	42.03 N	94.51 W
Carrollton, Ga. (kăr-ŭl-tŭn)	126	33.35 N	84.05 W
Carrollton, Il.	123	39.18 N	90.22 W
Carrollton, Ky.	110	38.45 N	85.15 W
Carrollton, Mi.	110	43.30 N	83.55 W
Carrollton, Mo.	123	39.21 N	93.29 W
Carrollton, Oh.	110	40.35 N	81.10 W
Carrollton, Tx.	119c	32.58 N	96.53 W
Carrols, Wa. (kăr'ŭlz)	118c	46.05 N	122.51 W
Carron (L.), Scot. (kȧ'rŭn)	162	57.25 N	5.25 W

PLACE (Pronounciation)	PAGE	Lat. °′	Long. °′
Carrot (R.), Can.	100	53.12 N	103.50 W
Carry-le-Rouet, Fr. (kä-rē'lẽ-rōō-ā')	168a	43.20 N	5.10 E
Carsamba, Tur. (chär-shäm'bä)	179	41.05 N	36.40 E
Carshalton (Neigh.), Eng.	62	51.22 N	0.10 W
Carson, Ca.	59	33.50 N	118.16 W
Carson (R.), Nv. (kär'sŭn)	120	39.15 N	119.25 W
Carson City, Nv.	120	39.10 N	119.45 W
Carsondale, Md.	56d	38.57 N	76.50 W
Carson Sink, Nv.	120	39.51 N	118.25 W
Cartagena, Col. (kär-tä-hā'nä)	142	10.30 N	75.40 W
Cartagena, Sp. (kär-tä-κē'nä)	171	37.46 N	1.00 W
Cartago, Col. (kär-tä'gō)	142a	4.44 N	75.54 W
Cartago, C. R.	133	9.52 N	83.56 W
Cartaxo, Port. (kär-tä'shō)	170	39.10 N	8.48 W
Carteret, NJ (kär'tē-ret)	112a	40.35 N	74.13 W
Cartersville, Ga. (kär'tẽrs-vĭl)	126	34.09 N	84.47 W
Carthage, Il. (kär'thåj)	123	40.27 N	91.09 W
Carthage, Mo.	123	37.10 N	94.18 W
Carthage, NC	127	35.22 N	79.25 W
Carthage, NY	111	44.00 N	75.45 W
Carthage, Tun.	224	37.04 N	10.18 E
Carthage, Tx.	125	32.09 N	94.20 W
Carthcart, S. Afr. (cärth-cȧ't)	227c	32.18 S	27.11 E
Cartwright, Can. (kärt'rít)	97	53.36 N	57.00 W
Caruaru, Braz. (kä-rōō-ȧ-rōō')	143	8.19 S	35.52 W
Carúpano, Ven. (kä-rōō'pä-nō)	142	10.45 N	63.21 W
Caruthersville, Mo. (kȧ-rŭdh'ẽrz-vĭl)	123	36.09 N	89.41 W
Carver, Or. (kärv'ẽr)	118c	45.24 N	122.30 W
Carvoeiro, Cabo (C.), Port. (kȧ'bō-kär-vō-ĕ'y-rō)	170	39.22 N	9.24 W
Cary, Il. (kā'rē)	113a	42.13 N	88.14 W
Casablanca, Chile (kä-sä-bläŋ'kä)	141b	33.19 S	71.24 W
Casablanca, Mor.	224	33.32 N	7.41 W
Casa Branca, Braz. (kȧ'sä-brȧ'ɴ-kä)	141a	21.47 S	47.04 W
Casa Grande, Az. (kä'sä grän'dā)	121	32.50 N	111.45 W
Casa Grande Natl. Mon., Az.	121	33.00 N	111.33 W
Casale Monferrato, It. (kä-sä'lā)	172	45.08 N	8.26 E
Casalmaggiore, It. (kä-säl-mäd-jō'rā)	172	45.00 N	10.24 E
Casa Loma (P. Int.), Can.	54c	43.41 N	79.25 W
Casamance (R.), Senegal (kä-sä-mäɴs')	228	12.43 N	16.00 W
Cascade Pt., N.Z. (kăs-kād')	217	43.59 S	168.23 E
Cascade Ra., U.S.	108	42.50 N	122.20 W
Cascade Tun., Wa.	116	47.41 N	120.53 W
Cascais, Port. (käs-kȧ-ēzh)	171b	38.42 N	9.25 W
Case Inlet, Wa. (kās)	118a	47.22 N	122.47 W
Caseros, Arg. (kä-sā'rōs)	144a	34.35 S	58.34 W
Caserta, It. (kä-zĕr'tä)	172	41.04 N	14.21 E
Casey, Il. (kā'sĭ)	110	39.20 N	88.00 W
Cashmere, Wa. (kăsh'mĭr)	116	47.30 N	120.28 W
Casiguran, Phil. (käs-sē-gōō'rän)	207a	16.15 N	122.10 E
Casiguran Sd., Phil.	207a	16.02 N	121.51 E
Casilda, Arg. (kä-sē'l-dä)	141c	33.02 S	61.11 W
Casilda, Cuba	134	21.50 N	80.00 W
Casimiro de Abreu, Braz. (kä'sē-mē'ro-dĕ-ȧ-brĕ'ōō)	141a	22.30 S	42.11 W
Casino, Austl. (kȧ-sē'nō)	216	28.35 S	153.10 E
Casiquiare (R.), Ven. (kä-sē-kyä'rä)	142	2.11 N	66.15 W
Caspe, Sp. (käs'pā)	171	41.18 N	0.02 W
Casper, Wy. (kăs'pẽr)	117	42.51 N	106.18 W
Caspian Dep., Sov. Un. (kăs'pĭ-ȧn)	178	47.40 N	52.35 E
Caspian Sea, Asia	176	40.00 N	52.00 E
Cass, WV (kăs)	111	38.25 N	79.55 W
Cass (L.), Mn.	115	47.23 N	94.28 W
Cassai (R.), Ang. (kä-sä'ē)	230	7.30 S	21.45 E
Cass City, Mi. (kăs)	110	43.35 N	83.10 W
Casselman, Can. (kăs''l-mȧn)	95c	45.18 N	75.05 W
Casselton, ND (kăs''l-tŭn)	114	46.53 N	97.14 W
Cássia, Braz. (kȧ'syä)	141a	20.36 S	46.53 W
Cassin, Tx. (kăs'ĭn)	119d	29.16 N	98.29 W
Cassino, It. (käs-sē'nō)	172	41.30 N	13.50 E
Cass Lake, Mn. (kăs)	115	47.23 N	94.37 W
Cassopolis, Mi. (kăs-ŏ'pô-lĭs)	110	41.55 N	86.00 W
Cassville, Mo. (kăs'vĭl)	123	36.41 N	93.52 W
Castanheira de Pêra, Port. (käs-tän-yā'rä-dĕ-pĕ'rä)	170	40.00 N	8.07 W
Castellammare di Stabia, It. (käs-tĕl-läm-mä'rā-dē-stä'byä)	171c	40.26 N	14.29 E
Castellbisbal, Sp.	65e	41.29 N	1.59 E
Castelli, Arg. (kȧs-tĕ'zhē)	141c	36.07 S	57.48 W
Castellón de la Plana, Sp. (käs-tĕl-yô'n-dĕ-lä-plä'nä)	171	39.59 N	0.05 W
Castelnaudary, Fr. (kȧs'tĕl-nō-dȧ-rē')	168	43.20 N	1.57 E
Castelo, Braz. (käs-tĕ'lô)	141a	21.37 S	41.13 W
Castelo Branco, Port. (käs-tā'lōō bräŋ'kōō)	170	39.48 N	7.37 W
Castelo de Vide, Port. (käs-tā'lōō dĭ vē'dĭ)	170	39.25 N	7.25 W
Castelsarrasin, Fr. (kȧs'tĕl-sȧ-rȧ-zăɴ')	168	44.03 N	1.05 E
Castelvetrano, It. (käs'tĕl-vĕ-trä'nō)	172	37.43 N	12.50 E
Castilla, Peru (kȧs-tē'l-yä)	142	5.18 S	80.40 W
Castilla La Nueva (Reg.), Sp. (käs-tē'lyä lä nwā'vȧ)	170	39.15 N	3.55 W
Castilla La Vieja (Reg.), Sp. (käs-tēl'yä lä vyā'hä)	170	40.48 N	4.24 W
Castillo De San Marcos Natl. Mon., Fl. (käs-tē'lyä de-sän mär-kōs)	127	29.55 N	81.25 W
Castle (I.), Ba. (kȧs''l)	135	22.05 N	74.20 W
Castlebar, Ire. (kȧs''l-bär)	162	53.55 N	9.15 W
Castlecrag, Austl.	70a	33.48 S	151.13 E
Castle Dale, Ut. (kȧs'l dāl)	121	39.15 N	111.00 W
Castle Donington, Eng. (dŏn'ĭng-tŭn)	156	52.50 N	1.21 W
Castleford, Eng. (kȧs'l-fẽrd)	156	53.43 N	1.21 W
Castlegar, Can. (kȧs''l-gär)	99	49.19 N	117.40 W
Castle Hill, Austl.	70a	33.44 S	151.00 E
Castlemaine, Austl. (kăs''l-mān)	216	37.05 S	114.10 E
Castle Pk., Co.	121	39.00 N	106.50 W
Castlerock, Wa. (kȧs''l-rŏk)	116	46.17 N	122.53 W
Castle Rock Flowage (Res.), Wi.	115	44.03 N	89.48 W
Castle Shannon, Pa. (shăn'ŭn)	113e	40.22 N	80.02 W
Castleton, Eng.	64b	53.35 N	2.11 W
Castleton, In. (kȧs''l-tŏn)	113g	39.54 N	86.03 W
Castor (R.), Can (kăs'tôr)	95c	45.16 N	75.14 W
Castor (R.), Mo.	123	36.59 N	89.53 W
Castres, Fr. (kȧs'tr')	168	43.36 N	2.13 E
Castries, Saint Lucia (kȧs-trē')	133b	14.01 N	61.00 W
Castro, Braz. (käs'trōō)	144	24.56 S	50.00 W
Castro, Chile (käs'tro)	144	42.27 S	73.48 W
Castro Daire, Port. (käs'trōō dīr'ĭ)	170	40.56 N	7.57 W
Castro del Río, Sp. (käs-trô-dĕl rē'ō)	170	37.42 N	4.28 W
Castrop Rauxel, F.R.G. (käs'trōp rou'ksĕl)	169c	51.33 N	7.19 E
Castro Urdiales, Sp. (käs'trō ōōr-dyä'lās)	170	43.23 N	3.11 W
Castro Valley, Ca.	118b	37.42 N	122.05 W
Castro Verde, Port. (käs-trō vĕr'dĕ)	170	37.43 N	8.05 W
Castrovillari, It. (käs'trō-vēl-lyä'rē)	172	39.48 N	16.11 E
Castuera, Sp. (käs-tōō-ā'rä)	170	38.43 N	5.33 W
Casula, Moz.	231	15.25 S	33.40 E
Cat (I.), Ba.	135	25.30 N	75.30 W
Catacamas, Hond. (kä-tä-kä'mäs)	132	14.52 N	85.55 W
Cataguases, Braz. (kä-tä-gwȧ'sĕs)	141a	21.23 S	42.42 W
Catahoula (L.), La. (kăt-ȧ-hōō'lȧ)	125	31.35 N	92.20 W
Catalão, Braz. (kä-tä-louɴ')	143	18.09 S	47.42 W
Catalina (I.), Dom. Rep. (kä-tä-lē'nä)	135	18.20 N	69.00 W
Cataluma (Reg.), Sp. (kä-tä-lōō'mä)	171	41.23 N	0.50 E
Cataluña, Museo de Arte de (P. Int.), Sp.	65e	41.23 N	2.09 E
Catamarca (Prov.), Arg. (kä-tä-mär'kä)	144	27.15 S	67.15 W
Catanaun, Phil. (kä-tä-nä'wän)	207a	13.36 N	122.20 E
Catanduanes I., Phil. (kä-tän-dwä'nĕs)	207	13.55 N	125.00 E
Catanduva, Braz. (kä-tȧn-dōō'vä)	143	21.12 S	48.47 W
Catania, It. (kä-tä'nyä)	172	37.30 N	15.09 E
Catania, Golfo di (G.), It. (gôl-fô-dē-kä-tä'nyä)	172	37.24 N	15.28 E
Catanzaro, It. (kä-tän-dzä'rō)	172	38.53 N	16.34 E
Catarroja, Sp. (kä-tär-rō'hä)	171	39.24 N	0.25 W
Catawba (L.), SC	127	35.02 N	81.21 W
Catawba (R.), NC (kȧ-tô'bȧ)	127	35.25 N	80.55 W
Catazajá, Laguna de (L.), Mex. (lä-gōō'nä-dĕ-kä-tä-zä-hȧ')	131	17.45 N	92.03 W
Catbalogan, Phil. (kät-bä-lō'gän)	207	11.45 N	124.52 E
Catemaco, Mex. (kä-tā-mä'kō)	131	18.26 N	95.06 W
Catemaco, Lago (L.), Mex. (lä'gô-kä-tā-mä'kō)	131	18.23 N	95.04 W
Caterham, Eng. (kā'tẽr-ŭm)	156b	51.16 N	0.04 W
Catete, Ang. (kä-tĕ'tĕ)	230	9.06 S	13.43 E
Catete (Neigh.), Braz.	61c	22.55 S	43.10 W
Catford (Neigh.), Eng.	62	51.27 N	0.01 W
Cathedral Mt., Tx. (kȧ-thē'drăl)	124	30.09 N	103.46 W
Cathedral Pk., S. Afr. (kă-thē'drȧl)	227c	28.53 S	29.04 E
Catherine, L., Ar. (kă-thẽr-ĭn)	123	34.26 N	92.47 W
Cathkin Pk., S. Afr. (kăth'kĭn)	227c	29.08 S	29.22 E
Cathlamet, Wa. (kăth-lăm'ĕt)	118c	46.12 N	123.22 W
Catia (Neigh.), Ven.	61a	10.31 N	66.57 W
Catlettsburg, Ky. (kăt'lĕts-bûrg)	110	38.20 N	82.35 W
Catoche, C., Mex. (kä-tô'chĕ)	128	21.30 N	87.15 W
Catonsville, Md. (kā'tŭnz-vĭl)	112e	39.16 N	76.45 W
Catorce, Mex. (kä-tôr'sȧ)	130	23.41 N	100.51 W
Catskill, NY (kăts'kĭl)	111	42.15 N	73.50 W
Catskill Mts., NY	111	42.20 N	74.35 W
Cattaraugus Ind. Res., NY (kăt'tȧ-rȧ-gŭs)	111	42.30 N	79.05 W
Catu, Braz. (kȧ-tōō)	143	12.26 S	38.12 W
Catuala, Ang.	230	16.29 S	19.03 E
Catumbela (R.), Ang. (kä'tŏm-bĕl'ȧ)	230	12.40 S	14.10 E
Cauayan, Phil. (kou-ä'yän)	207a	16.56 N	121.46 E
Cauca (R.), Col. (kou'kä)	142	7.30 N	75.26 W
Caucagua, Ven. (käōō-kȧ'gwä)	143b	10.17 N	66.22 W
Caucasus Mts., Sov. Un. (kô'kȧ-sŭs)	179	43.20 N	42.00 E
Cauchon L., Can. (kô-shŏn')	101	55.25 N	96.30 W
Caughnawaga, Can.	95a	45.24 N	73.41 W
Caulfield, Austl.	70b	37.53 S	145.03 E
Caulonia, It. (kou-lō'nyä)	172	38.24 N	16.22 E
Cauquenes, Chile (kou-kā'nās)	144	35.54 S	72.14 W
Caura (R.), Ven. (kou'rä)	142	6.48 N	64.40 W
Causapscal, Can.	104	48.22 N	67.14 W
Caution, C., Can. (kô'shŭn)	98	51.10 N	127.47 W
Cauto (R.), Cuba (kou'tō)	135	20.33 N	76.20 W
Cauvery (R.), India	196	11.15 N	78.06 E
Cava, Braz. (kä'vä)	144b	22.41 S	43.26 W
Cava de' Tirreni, It. (kä'vä-dĕ-tēr-rĕ'nē)	171c	40.27 N	14.43 E
Cávado (R.), Port. (kä-vä'dō)	170	41.43 N	8.08 W
Cavalcante, Braz. (kä-väl-kän'tā)	143	13.45 S	47.33 W
Cavalier, ND (kăv-ȧ-lēr')	114	48.45 N	97.39 W
Cavally (R.), Ivory Coast-Lib.	228	4.40 N	7.30 W
Cavan, Ire. (kăv'ȧn)	162	54.01 N	7.00 W
Cavarzere, It. (kä-vär'dzā-rā)	172	45.08 N	12.06 E
Cavendish, Vt. (kăv'ĕn-dĭsh)	111	43.25 N	72.35 W
Caviana, Ilha (I.), Braz. (kä-vyä'nä)	143	0.45 N	49.33 W
Cavite, Phil. (kä-vē'tā)	207a	14.30 N	120.54 E
Caxambu, Braz. (kä-shȧ'm-bōō)	141a	22.00 S	44.45 W
Caxias, Braz. (kä'shē-äzh)	143	4.48 S	43.16 W
Caxias, Port.	65d	38.42 N	9.16 W
Caxias do Sul, Braz. (kä'shē-äzh-dô-sōō'l)	144	29.13 S	51.03 W
Caxito, Ang. (kä-shē'tōō)	230	8.33 S	13.36 E
Cayambe, Ec. (kȧ-ĭä'm-bĕ)	142	0.03 N	79.09 W
Cayenne, Fr. Gu. (kā-ĕn')	143	4.56 N	52.18 W
Cayetano Rubio, Mex. (kä-yĕ-tȧ-nô-rōō'byô)	130	20.37 N	100.21 W
Cayey, P. R.	129b	18.05 N	66.12 W
Cayman Brac (I.), Cayman Is. (kī-män' brȧk)	134	19.45 N	79.50 W
Cayman Is., N. A.	134	19.30 N	80.30 W
Cay Sal Bk., Ba. (kē-săl)	134	23.55 N	80.20 W
Cayuga (L.), NY (kā-yōō'gȧ)	111	42.35 N	76.35 W
Cazalla de la Sierra, Sp. (kä-thäl'yä-dĕ-lä-sē-ĕ'r-rä)	170	37.55 N	5.48 W
Cazaux, Étang de (L.), Fr. (ā-täɴ' dĕ kä-zō')	168	44.32 N	0.59 W
Cazenovia, NY (kăz-ē-nō'vĭ-ȧ)	111	42.55 N	75.50 W
Cazenovia Cr., NY	113c	42.49 N	78.45 W
Čazma, Yugo. (chäz'mä)	172	45.44 N	16.39 E
Cazombo, Ang. (kä-zô'm-bō)	226	11.54 S	22.52 E
Cazones (R.), Mex. (kä-zô'nĕs)	131	20.37 N	97.28 W
Cazones, Ensenada de (B.), Cuba (ĕn-sĕ-nä-dä-dĕ-kä-zō'nås)	134	22.05 N	81.30 W
Cazones, Golfo de (G.), Cuba (gôl-fô-dĕ-kä-zō'nås)	134	23.55 N	81.15 W
Cazorla, Sp. (kä-thôr'lå)	170	37.55 N	2.58 W
Cea (R.), Sp. (thā'ä)	170	42.18 N	5.10 W
Ceará-Mirim, Braz. (sā-ä-rä'mē-rē'ɴ)	143	6.00 S	35.13 W
Ceará, see Fortaleza			
Ceará (State), Braz. (sā-å-rä')	143	5.13 S	39.43 W
Cebaco, Isla (I.), Pan. (ē's-lä-sā-bä'kō)	133	7.27 N	81.08 W
Cebolla Cr., Co. (sē-bōl'yä)	121	38.15 N	107.10 W
Cebreros, Sp. (sē-brĕ'rôs)	170	40.28 N	4.28 W
Cebu, Phil. (sā-bōō')	207	10.22 N	123.49 E
Cecchignola (Neigh.), It.	66c	41.49 N	12.29 E
Čechy (Bohemia) (Prov.), Czech. (bô-hē'mĭ-ȧ)	166	49.51 N	13.55 E
Cecil, Pa. (sē'sĭl)	113e	40.20 N	80.10 W
Cecil Park, Austl.	70a	33.52 S	150.51 E
Cedar (R.), Ia.	115	42.23 N	92.07 W
Cedar (R.), Wa.	118c	45.56 N	122.32 W
Cedar, West Fk. (R.), Ia.	115	42.49 N	93.10 W
Cedar Bayou, Tx.	125a	29.54 N	94.58 W
Cedar Breaks Natl. Mon., Ut.	121	37.35 N	112.55 W
Cedarbrook, Pa.	56b	40.05 N	75.10 W
Cedarburg, Wi. (sē'dẽr bûrg)	115	43.23 N	88.00 W
Cedar City, Ut.	121	37.40 N	113.10 W
Cedar Cr., ND	114	46.05 N	102.10 W
Cedar Falls, Ia.	115	42.31 N	92.29 W
Cedar Grove, NJ	55	40.51 N	74.14 W
Cedar Heights, Pa.	56b	40.05 N	75.17 W
Cedarhurst, NY	55	40.38 N	73.44 W
Cedar Keys, Fl.	126	29.06 N	83.03 W
Cedar L., In.	113a	41.23 N	87.25 W
Cedar Lake, In.	113a	41.22 N	87.27 W
Cedar Rapids, Ia.	115	42.00 N	91.43 W
Cedar Springs, Mi.	110	43.15 N	85.40 W
Cedartown, Ga. (sē'dẽr-toun)	126	34.00 N	85.15 W
Cedarville, S. Afr. (cĕdȧr'vĭl)	227c	30.23 S	29.04 E
Cedral, Mex. (sā-dräl')	130	23.47 N	100.42 W
Cedros, Hond. (sā'drōs)	132	14.36 N	87.07 W
Cedros (I.), Mex.	128	28.10 N	115.10 W
Ceduna, Austl. (sē-dōō'nȧ)	214	32.15 S	133.55 E
Ceel Buur, Som.	223a	4.35 N	46.40 E
Cefalù, It. (chā-fä-lōō')	172	38.01 N	14.01 E
Cega (R.), Sp. (thā'gä)	170	41.25 N	4.27 W
Cegléd, Hung. (tsā'glād)	167	47.10 N	19.49 E
Ceglie, It. (chĕ'lyĕ)	173	40.39 N	17.32 E
Cehegín, Sp. (thā-å-hēn')	170	38.05 N	1.48 W
Ceiba del Agua, Cuba (sā'bä-dĕl-ȧ'gwä)	135a	22.53 N	82.38 W
Cekhira, Tun.	224	34.17 N	10.00 E
Cela, Ang. (sĕ-lȧ)	230	11.25 S	15.07 E
Celaya, Mex. (sā-lä'yä)	130	20.33 N	100.49 W
Celebes (Sulawesi) (I.), Indon.	206	2.15 S	120.30 E
Celebes Sea, Indon.	206	3.45 N	121.52 E
Celestún, Mex. (sĕ-lĕs-tōō'n)	132a	20.57 N	90.18 W
Celina, Oh. (sĕlī'na)	110	40.30 N	84.35 W
Celje, Yugo. (tsĕl'yĕ)	172	46.13 N	15.17 E
Celle, F.R.G. (tsĕl'ĕ)	166	52.37 N	10.05 E
Cement, Ok. (sē-mĕnt')	122	34.56 N	98.07 W
Cenderawasih Teluk (B.), Indon.	207	2.20 S	135.30 E
Ceniza, Pico (Mtn.), Ven. (pē'kô-sē-nē'zä)	143b	10.24 N	67.26 W
Center, Tx. (sĕn'tẽr)	125	31.50 N	94.10 W
Centerhill Res., Tn. (sĕn'tẽr-hĭl)	126	36.02 N	86.00 W
Center Line, Mi. (sĕn'tẽr līn)	113b	42.29 N	83.01 W
Centerville, Ia. (sĕn'tẽr-vĭl)	115	40.44 N	92.48 W
Centerville, Mn.	119g	45.10 N	93.03 W
Centerville, Pa.	113e	40.02 N	79.58 W
Centerville, SD	114	43.07 N	96.56 W
Centerville, Ut.	119b	40.55 N	111.53 W
Centocelle (Neigh.), It.	66c	41.53 N	12.34 E
Central African Republic, Afr.	222	7.50 N	21.00 E
Central America, N. A. (ä-mĕr'ĭ-kȧ)	128	10.45 N	87.15 W
Central City, Ky. (sĕn'trȧl)	126	37.15 N	87.09 W
Central City, Ne. (sĕn'trȧl sĭ'tĭ)	114	41.07 N	98.00 W
Central, Cordillera (Cibao Mts.), Dom. Rep. (kôr-dēl-yā'rȧ sĕn'träl) (sē-bä'ō)	135	19.05 N	71.30 W
Central, Cordillera (Mts.), Bol. (kôr-dēl-yĕ'rä-sĕn-trä'l)	142	19.18 S	65.29 W
Central, Cordillera (Mts.), Col.	142a	3.58 N	75.55 W
Central Cordillera (Mts.), Phil. (kôr-dēl-yĕ'rä-sĕn-träl)	207a	17.05 N	120.55 E
Central Falls, RI (sĕn'trȧl fôlz)	112b	41.54 N	71.23 W
Central Highlands, Pa.	57b	40.16 N	79.50 W
Centralia, Il. (sĕn-trā'lĭ-ȧ)	110	38.35 N	89.05 W
Centralia, Mo.	123	39.11 N	92.07 W
Centralia, Wa.	116	46.42 N	122.58 W
Central Intelligence Agency (P. Int.), Va.	56d	38.57 N	77.09 W
Central Park (P. Int.), NY	55	40.47 N	73.58 W
Central Plat, Sov. Un.	178	55.00 N	33.30 E
Central Valley, NY	112a	41.19 N	74.07 W
Centre Island, NY	55	40.54 N	73.32 W
Centreville, Il. (sĕn'tẽr-vĭl)	119e	38.33 N	90.06 W
Centreville, Md.	111	39.05 N	76.05 W
Centro Simón Bolívar (P. Int.), Ven.	61a	10.30 N	66.55 W
Century, Fl. (sĕn'tū-rĭ)	126	30.57 N	87.15 W
Century City (Neigh.), Ca.	59	34.03 N	118.26 W
Cephalonia (I.), see Kefallinéa			
Céret, Fr. (sā-rĕ')	168	42.29 N	2.47 E

PLACE (Pronounciation)	PAGE	Lat. °′	Long. °′
Cereté, Col. (sĕ-rĕ-tĕ')	142	8.56 N	75.58 W
Cerignola, It. (chā-rē-nyô'lä)	172	41.16 N	15.55 E
Cerknica, Yugo. (tsĕr'knē-tsȧ)	172	45.48 N	14.21 E
Cern'achovsk, Sov. Un. (chĕr-nyä'ĸôfsk)	165	55.38 N	21.17 E
Čer'omuski (Neigh.), Sov. Un.	66b	55.41 N	37.35 E
Cerralvo, Mex. (sĕr-räl'vō)	124	26.05 N	99.37 W
Cerralvo (I.), Mex.	128	24.00 N	109.59 W
Cerrito, Col. (sĕr-rē'-tô)	142	3.41 N	76.17 W
Cerritos, Mex. (sĕr-rē'tôs)	130	22.26 N	100.16 W
Cerro de Pasco, Peru (sĕr'rō dā päs'kō)	142	10.45 S	76.14 W
Cerro Gordo, Arroyo de, Mex. (är-rô-yō-dĕ-sĕ'r-rô-gôr-dō)	124	26.12 N	104.06 W
Čertanovo (Neigh.), Sov. Un.	66b	55.38 N	37.37 E
Certegui, Col. (sĕr-tĕ'gē)	142a	5.21 N	76.35 W
Cervantes, Phil. (sĕr-vän'tās)	207a	16.59 N	120.42 E
Cervera del Río Alhama, Sp. (thĕr-vā'rȧ dĕl rē'ō-äl-ä'mä)	170	42.02 N	1.55 W
Cerveteri, It. (chĕr-vĕ'tĕ-rē)	171d	42.00 N	12.06 E
Cesano Boscone, It.	65c	45.27 N	9.06 E
Cesena, It. (chĕ'sĕ-nä)	172	44.08 N	12.16 E
Cēsis, Sov. Un. (sā'sĭs)	165	57.19 N	25.17 E
Česká Lípa, Czech. (chĕs'kä lē'pa)	166	50.41 N	14.31 E
České Budějovice, Czech. (chĕs'kā bōō'dyĕ-yô-vĕt-sĕ)	166	49.00 N	14.30 E
Českomoravaska Vysočina (Mts.), Czech.	166	49.21 N	15.40 E
Český Těšín, Czech.	167	49.43 N	18.22 E
Cesme, Tur. (chĕsh'mĕ)	173	38.20 N	26.20 E
Cessnock, Austl.	216	32.58 S	151.15 E
Cestos (R.), Lib.	228	5.40 N	9.25 W
Cetinje, Yugo. (tsĕt'in-yĕ)	173	42.23 N	18.55 E
Ceuta (Sp.), Aft. (thā-ōō'tä)	224	36.04 N	5.36 W
Cévennes (Reg.), Fr. (sā-vĕn')	168	44.20 N	3.48 E
Ceyhan (R.), Tur.	161	37.19 N	36.06 E
Ceylon, see Sri Lanka			
Chabot (L.), Ca. (sha'bŏt)	118b	37.44 N	122.06 W
Chacabuco, Arg. (chä-kä-bōō'kō)	141c	34.37 S	60.27 W
Chacaltianguis, Mex. (chä-käl-tē-äŋ'gwēs)	131	18.18 N	95.50 W
Chacao, Ven.	61a	10.30 N	66.51 W
Chachapoyas, Peru (chä-chä-poi'yäs)	142	6.16 S	77.48 W
Chaco (Prov.), Arg. (chä'kō)	144	26.00 S	60.45 W
Chaco Canyon Natl. Mon., NM (chä'kô)	121	35.38 N	108.06 W
Chad, Afr.	222	17.48 N	19.00 E
Chad, Sov. Un. (chäd)	182a	56.33 N	57.11 E
Chadbourn, NC (chăd'bŭrn)	127	34.19 N	78.55 W
Chadderton, Eng.	64b	53.33 N	2.08 W
Chad, L., Afr.	229	13.55 N	13.40 E
Chadron, Ne. (chăd'rŭn)	114	42.50 N	103.10 W
Chadstone, Austl.	70b	37.53 S	145.05 E
Chadwell Saint Mary, Eng.	62	51.29 N	0.22 E
Chafarinas (C.), Mor.	170	35.08 N	2.20 W
Chaffee, Mo. (chăf'ē)	123	37.10 N	89.39 W
Chāgal Hills, Afg.-Pak.	192	29.15 N	63.28 E
Chagodoshcha (R.), Sov. Un. (chä-gō-dôsh-chä)	174	59.08 N	35.13 E
Chagres R., Pan. (chä'grĕs)	133	9.18 N	79.22 W
Chagrin Falls, Oh. (shȧ'grĭn fôls)	113d	41.26 N	81.23 W
Chagrin R., Oh. (shȧ'grĭn)	113d	41.34 N	81.24 W
Chahar (Reg.), China (chä-här)	202	44.25 N	115.00 E
Chahār Borjak, Afg.	195	30.17 N	62.03 E
Chāh Bahār, Iran (chä'h' bä'hăr)	192	25.18 N	60.45 E
Chakdaha, India	67a	22.20 N	88.20 E
Chake Chake, Tan.	231	5.15 S	39.46 E
Chalatenango, Sal. (chäl-ä-tĕ-näŋ'gō)	132	14.04 N	88.54 W
Chalbi Des., Ken.	231	3.40 N	36.50 E
Chalcatongo, Mex. (chäl-kä-tôŋ'gō)	131	17.04 N	97.41 W
Chalchihuites, Mex. (chäl-chē-wē'tås)	130	23.28 N	103.57 W
Chalchuapa, Sal. (chäl-chwä'pä)	132	14.01 N	89.39 W
Chalchyn (R.), China-Mong. (chäl-chyn)	181	48.00 N	118.45 E
Chalco, Mex. (chäl-kō)	131a	19.15 N	98.54 W
Chaldon, Eng.	62	51.17 N	0.07 W
Chaleur B., Can. (shȧ-lûr')	104	47.58 N	65.33 W
Chalfant, Pa.	57b	40.25 N	79.52 W
Chalfont Common, Eng.	62	51.38 N	0.33 W
Chalfont Saint Giles, Eng.	62	51.38 N	0.34 W
Chalfont Saint Peter, Eng.	62	51.37 N	0.33 W
Chalgrove, Eng. (chăl'grôv)	156b	51.38 N	1.05 W
Chaling, China (chä'lĭng)	203	27.00 N	113.31 E
Chalk, Eng.	62	51.26 N	0.25 E
Chalmette, La. (shăl-mĕt')	112d	29.57 N	89.57 W
Châlons-sur-Marne, Fr. (shȧ-lôN'sür-märn)	168	48.57 N	4.23 E
Chalon-sur-Saône, Fr.	168	46.47 N	4.54 E
Chaltel, Cerro (Mtn.), Arg.-Chile (sĕ'r-rô-chäl'tĕl)	144	48.10 S	73.18 W
Chālūs, Iran	195	36.38 N	51.26 E
Chama (R.), NM (chä'mä)	121	36.19 N	106.31 W
Chamama, Malawi	231	12.55 S	33.43 E
Chaman, Pak. (chŭm-än')	196	30.58 N	66.21 E
Chama, Sierra de (Mts.), Guat. (sē-ĕ'r-rä-dĕ-chä-mä)	132	15.48 N	90.20 W
Chambal (R.), India (chŭm-bäl')	196	26.05 N	76.37 E
Chamberlain, SD (chām'bĕr-lĭn)	114	43.48 N	99.21 W
Chamberlain (L.), Me.	104	46.15 N	69.10 W
Chambersburg, Pa. (chām'bĕrz-bûrg)	111	40.00 N	77.40 W
Chambéry, Fr. (shäm-bā-rē')	169	45.35 N	5.54 E
Chambeshi (R.), Zambia	231	10.35 S	31.20 E
Chamblee, Ga. (chăm-blē')	112c	33.55 N	84.18 W
Chambly, Can. (shäN-blē')	95a	45.27 N	73.17 W
Chambly, Fr.	169b	49.11 N	2.14 E
Chambord, Can.	97	48.22 N	72.01 W
Chambourcy, Fr.	64c	48.54 N	2.03 E
Chamelecón (R.), Hond. (chä-mĕ-lĕ-kô'n)	132	15.09 N	88.42 W
Chame, Punta (Pt.), Pan. (pōō'n-tä-chä'mā)	133	8.41 N	79.27 W
Chamo (L.), Eth.	225	5.58 N	37.00 E
Chamonix-Mont-Blanc, Fr. (shȧ-mô-nē')	169	45.55 N	6.50 E
Champagne (Reg.), Fr. (shäm-pän'yĕ)	168	48.53 N	4.48 E
Champaign, Il. (shăm-pān')	110	40.10 N	88.15 W
Champdāni, India	196b	22.48 N	88.21 E
Champerico, Guat. (chăm-pȧ-rē'kō)	132	14.18 N	91.55 W
Champigny-sur-Marne, Fr.	64c	48.49 N	2.31 E
Champion, Mi. (chăm'pĭ-ŭn)	115	46.30 N	87.59 W
Champlain, L., NY-Vt. (shăm-plān')	111	44.45 N	73.20 W
Champlan, Fr.	64c	48.43 N	2.16 E
Champlitte-et-le-Prálot, Fr. (shäN-plēt')	169	47.38 N	5.28 E
Champotón, Mex. (chäm-pō-tōn')	131	19.21 N	90.43 W
Champotón (R.), Mex.	131	19.19 N	90.15 W
Champs-sur-Marne, Fr.	64c	48.51 N	2.36 E
Chāmrāil, India	67a	22.38 N	88.18 E
Chañaral, Chile (chän-yä-räl')	144	26.20 S	70.46 W
Chandannagar, India	67a	22.51 N	88.21 E
Chandeleur Is., La. (shăn-dĕ-lōōr')	126	29.53 N	88.35 W
Chandeleur Sd., La.	126	29.47 N	89.08 W
Chandīgarh, India	196	30.51 N	77.13 E
Chandler, Can. (chăn'dlẽr)	97	48.21 N	64.41 W
Chandler, Ok.	123	35.42 N	96.52 W
Chandler's Cross, Eng.	62	51.40 N	0.27 W
Chandrapur, India	196	19.58 N	79.21 E
Chang (R.), see Yangtze			
Changane (R.), Moz.	226	22.42 S	32.46 E
Changara, Moz.	231	16.54 S	33.14 E
Changchun, China (chäŋ-chōōn)	202	43.55 N	125.25 E
Changdang Hu (L.), China (chäŋ-däŋ hōō)	200	31.37 N	119.29 E
Changde, China (chäŋ-dŭ)	203	29.00 N	111.38 E
Changdian, China	67b	40.01 N	116.32 E
Changhua, Taiwan (chäng'hwä')	203	24.02 N	120.32 E
Changi, Singapore	67c	1.23 N	103.59 E
Changjŏn, Kor. (chäng'jŭn')	204	38.40 N	128.05 E
Changli, China (chäŋ-lē)	200	39.46 N	119.10 E
Changning, China (chäŋ-nĭŋ)	198	24.34 N	99.49 E
Changping, China (chäŋ-pĭŋ)	202	40.12 N	116.10 E
Changqing, China (chäŋ-chyĭŋ)	200	36.33 N	116.42 E
Changsan Cot (I.), Kor.	204	38.06 N	124.50 E
Changsha, China (chäŋ-shä)	203	28.20 N	113.00 E
Changshan Quandao (Is.), China (chäŋ-shän chyōōn-dou)	200	39.08 N	122.26 E
Changshu, China (chäŋ-shōō)	200	31.40 N	120.45 E
Changting, China	203	25.50 N	116.18 E
Changtu, China	204	43.00 N	124.02 E
Changwu, China (chäng'wōō')	202	35.12 N	107.45 E
Changxindianzhen, China (chäŋ-shyĭn-dĭĕn-jŭn)	202a	39.49 N	116.12 E
Changxing Dao (I.), China (chäŋ-shyĭŋ dou)	200	39.38 N	121.10 E
Changyi, China (chäŋ-yē)	200	36.51 N	119.23 E
Changyuan, China (chyäŋ-yuän)	200	35.10 N	114.41 E
Changzhi, China (chäŋ-jr)	202	35.58 N	112.58 E
Changzhou, China (chäŋ-jō)	200	31.47 N	119.56 E
Changzhuyuan, China (chäŋ-jōō-yuän)	200	31.33 N	115.17 E
Chanhassen, Mn. (shăn'hăs-sĕn)	119g	44.52 N	93.32 W
Chanh-hung, Viet.	68m	10.43 N	106.41 E
Channel Is., Eur. (chăn'ĕl)	154	49.15 N	3.30 W
Channel-Port-auz-Basques, Can.	105	47.35 N	59.11 W
Channelview, Tx. (chăn'elvū)	125a	29.46 N	95.07 W
Chantada, Sp. (chän-tä'dä)	170	42.38 N	7.36 W
Chanteloup-les-Vignes, Fr.	64c	48.59 N	2.02 E
Chanthaburi, Thai.	206	12.37 N	102.04 E
Chantilly, Fr. (shäN-tē-yē')	169b	49.12 N	2.30 E
Chantilly, Va. (shăn'tĭlē)	112e	38.53 N	77.26 W
Chantrey Inlet, Can. (chăn-trē)	96	67.49 N	95.00 W
Chanute, Ks. (shȧ-nōōt')	123	37.41 N	95.27 W
Chany (L.), Sov. Un. (chä'nē)	180	54.15 N	77.31 E
Chao'an, China (chou-än)	203	23.48 N	116.35 E
Chao Hu (L.), China (chou hōō)	200	31.31 N	117.28 E
Chao Hu (L.), China	203	31.45 N	116.59 E
Chao Phraya, (R.), Thai.	206	16.13 N	99.33 E
Chaor (R.), China (chou-r)	202	47.20 N	121.40 E
Chaoshui, China (chou-shwā)	200	37.43 N	120.56 E
Chaoxian, China (chou shyĕn)	200	31.37 N	117.50 E
Chaoyang, China	202	41.32 N	120.20 E
Chaoyang, China (chou-yäŋ)	203	23.18 N	116.32 E
Chapadão, Serra do (Mtn.), Braz. (sĕ'r-rä-dô-shä-pȧ-dou'N)	141a	20.31 S	46.20 W
Chapada, Serra da (Mts.), Braz. (sĕ'r-rä-dä-shä-pä'dä)	143	14.57 S	54.34 W
Chapala, Mex. (chä-pä'lä)	130	20.18 N	103.10 W
Chapalagana (R.), Mex. (chä-pä-lä-gȧ'nä)	130	22.11 N	104.09 W
Chapala, Lago de (L.), Mex. (lä'gô-dĕ-chä-pä'lä)	130	20.14 N	103.02 W
Chaparral, Col. (chä-pär-rȧ'l)	142a	3.44 N	75.28 W
Chapayevsk, Sov. Un. (châ-pī'ĕfsk)	179	53.00 N	49.30 E
Chapel Hill, NC (chăp''l hĭl)	127	35.55 N	79.05 W
Chapel Oaks, Md.	56d	38.54 N	76.55 W
Chapeltown, Eng.	64b	53.38 N	2.24 W
Chaplain (L.), Wa. (chăp'lĭn)	118a	47.58 N	121.50 W
Chapleau, Can. (chă-plō')	97	47.43 N	83.28 W
Chapman, Mt., Can. (chăp'mȧn)	99	51.50 N	118.20 W
Chapman's B., S. Afr. (chăp'mȧns bā)	226a	34.06 S	18.17 E
Chapman Woods, Ca.	59	34.08 N	118.05 W
Chappell, Ne. (chă-pĕl')	114	41.06 N	102.29 W
Chapultenango, Mex. (chä-pōōl-tĕ-näŋ'gō)	131	17.19 N	93.08 W
Chapultepec, Castillo de (P. Int.), Mex.	60a	19.25 N	99.11 W
Chá Pungana, Ang.	230	13.44 S	18.39 E
Charcas, Mex. (chär'käs)	130	23.09 N	101.09 W
Charco de Azul, Bahía (B.), Pan. (bä-ē'ä-chä'r-kô-dĕ-ä-zōō'l)	133	8.14 N	82.45 W
Chardzhou, Sov. Un. (chĕr-jô'ōō)	155	38.52 N	63.37 E
Charente (R.), Fr. (shȧ-räNt')	168	45.48 N	0.28 W
Charenton-le-Pont, Fr.	64c	48.49 N	2.25 E
Chari (R.), Chad (shä-rē')	229	12.45 N	14.55 E
Charing, Eng. (chă'rĭng)	156b	51.13 N	0.49 E
Chariton, Ia. (châr'ĭ-tŭn)	115	41.02 N	93.16 W
Chariton (R.), Mo.	123	40.24 N	92.38 W
Charlemagne, Can. (shärl-mäny')	95a	45.43 N	73.29 W
Charleroi, Bel. (shȧr-lĕ-rwä')	163	50.25 N	4.35 E
Charleroi, Pa. (shär'lĕ-roi)	113e	40.08 N	79.54 W
Charles (R.), Ma.	54a	42.22 N	71.03 W
Charlesbourg, Can. (shȧrl-bōōr')	95b	46.51 N	71.16 W
Charles, C., Va. (chärlz)	127	37.05 N	75.48 W
Charles City, Ia. (chärlz)	115	43.03 N	92.40 W
Charles de Gaulle, Aéroport (Arpt.), Fr.	64c	49.00 N	2.34 E
Charleston, Il. (chärlz'tŭn)	110	39.30 N	88.10 W
Charleston, Mo.	123	36.53 N	89.20 W
Charleston, Ms.	126	34.00 N	90.02 W
Charleston, SC	127	32.47 N	79.56 W
Charleston, WV	110	38.20 N	81.35 W
Charlestown, In. (chärlz'toun)	113h	38.46 N	85.39 W
Charlestown, Saint Christopher-Nevis	133b	17.10 N	62.32 W
Charleville, Austl. (chär'lē-vĭl)	216	26.16 S	146.28 E
Charleville Mézières, Fr. (shärl-vēl')	168	49.48 N	4.41 E
Charlevoix, Mi. (shär'lē-voi)	110	45.20 N	85.15 W
Charlevoix, L., Mi.	115	45.17 N	85.43 W
Charlotte, Mi. (shär'lŏt)	110	42.35 N	84.50 W
Charlotte, NC	127	35.15 N	80.50 W
Charlotte Amalie (Saint Thomas), Virgin Is. (U.S.A.) (shär-lŏt'ĕ ä-mä'lĭ-ȧ)	129c	18.21 N	64.54 W
Charlotte Hbr., Fl.	127a	26.49 N	82.00 W
Charlotte L., Can.	98	52.07 N	125.30 W
Charlottenberg, Swe. (shär-lŭt'ĕn-bĕrg)	164	59.53 N	12.17 E
Charlottenburg (Neigh.), F.R.G.	65a	52.31 N	13.16 E
Charlottenburg, Schloss (P. Int.), G.D.R.	65a	52.31 N	13.14 E
Charlottesville, Va. (shär'lŏtz-vĭl)	111	38.00 N	78.25 W
Charlottetown, Can. (shär'lŏt-toun)	105	46.14 N	63.08 W
Charlotte Waters, Austl. (shär'lŏt)	214	26.00 S	134.50 E
Charlton (Neigh.), Eng.	62	51.29 N	0.02 E
Charmes, Fr. (shärm)	169	48.23 N	6.19 E
Charneca (Neigh.), Port.	65d	38.47 N	9.08 W
Charnwood For., Eng. (chärn'wŏŏd)	156	52.42 N	1.15 W
Charny, Can. (shär-nē')	95b	46.43 N	71.16 W
Chars, Fr. (shär)	169b	49.09 N	1.57 E
Chārsadda, Pak. (chŭr-sä'dä)	193a	34.17 N	71.43 E
Charters Towers, Austl. (chär'tẽrz)	215	20.03 S	146.20 E
Charterwood, Pa.	57b	40.33 N	80.00 W
Chartres, Fr. (shärt'r')	169b	48.26 N	1.29 E
Chascomús, Arg. (chäs-kō-mōōs')	141c	35.32 S	58.01 W
Chase City, Va. (chās)	127	36.45 N	78.27 W
Chashniki, Sov. Un. (chäsh'nyē-kē)	174	54.51 N	29.08 E
Chaska, Mn. (chăs'kȧ)	119g	44.48 N	93.36 W
Châteaubriant, Fr. (shȧ-tō-brē-äN')	168	47.43 N	1.23 W
Châteaudun, Fr. (shä-tō-dăN')	168	48.04 N	1.23 E
Châteaufort, Fr.	64c	48.44 N	2.06 E
Château-Gontier, Fr. (chȧ-tō-gôN'tyā')	168	47.48 N	0.43 W
Châteauguay, Can. (chȧ-tō-gā)	95a	45.22 N	73.45 W
Châteauguay (R.), Can.	95a	45.13 N	73.51 W
Châteauneaut, Fr.	168a	43.23 N	5.11 E
Château-Renault, Fr. (shȧ-tō-rĕ-nō')	168	47.36 N	0.57 E
Château-Richer, Can. (shȧ-tō'rē-shā')	95b	47.00 N	71.01 W
Châteauroux, Fr. (shȧ-tō-rōō')	168	46.47 N	1.39 E
Château-Thierry, Fr. (shȧ-tō'ty-ĕr-rē')	168	49.03 N	3.22 E
Châtellerault, Fr. (shä-tĕl-rō')	168	46.48 N	0.31 E
Châtenay-Malabry, Fr.	64c	48.46 N	2.17 E
Chatfield, Mn. (chăt'fēld)	115	43.50 N	92.10 W
Chatham, Can. (chăt'ȧm)	102	42.25 N	82.10 W
Chatham, Can.	104	47.02 N	65.28 W
Chatham, Eng. (chăt'ŭm)	156b	51.23 N	0.32 E
Chatham, NJ (chăt'ȧm)	112a	40.44 N	74.23 W
Chatham, Oh.	113d	41.06 N	82.01 W
Chatham Is., N. Z.	208	44.00 S	178.00 W
Chatham Sd., Can.	98	54.32 N	130.35 W
Chatham Str., Ak.	107	57.00 N	134.40 W
Châtillon, Fr.	64c	48.48 N	2.17 E
Chatou, Fr.	64c	48.54 N	2.09 E
Chatpur (Neigh.), India	67a	22.36 N	88.23 E
Chatswood, Austl.	70a	33.48 S	151.12 E
Chatsworth, Ca. (chătz'wûrth)	119a	34.16 N	118.36 W
Chatsworth Res., Ca.	119a	34.15 N	118.41 W
Chattahoochee, Fl. (chăt-tȧ-hōō' chee)	126	30.42 N	84.47 W
Chattahoochee (R.), Al.-Ga.	126	31.17 N	85.10 W
Chattanooga, Tn. (chăt-ȧ-nōō'gȧ)	126	35.01 N	85.15 W
Chattooga (R.), Ga.-SC (chȧ-tōō'gȧ)	126	34.47 N	83.13 W
Chaudière (R.), Can. (shō-dyĕr')	103	46.26 N	71.10 W
Chaumont, Fr. (shō-môN')	168	48.08 N	5.07 E
Chaunskaya Guba (B.), Sov. Un.	181	69.15 N	170.00 E
Chauny, Fr. (shō-nē')	168	49.40 N	3.09 E
Chau-phu, Kamp.	206	10.49 N	104.57 E
Chausy, Sov. Un. (chou'sĭ)	174	53.57 N	30.58 E
Chautauqua (L.), NY (shȧ-tô'kwȧ)	111	42.10 N	79.25 W
Chavaniga, Sov. Un.	178	66.02 N	37.50 E
Chavenay, Fr.	64c	48.51 N	1.59 E
Chaves, Port. (chä'vĕzh)	170	41.44 N	7.30 W
Chaville, Fr.	64c	48.48 N	2.10 E
Chavinda, Mex. (chä-vē'n-dä)	130	20.01 N	102.27 W
Chazumba, Mex. (chä-zōō'm'bä)	131	18.11 N	97.41 W
Cheadle, Eng. (chē'd'l)	156	52.59 N	1.59 W
Cheadle Hulme, Eng.	64b	53.22 N	2.12 W
Cheam (Neigh.), Eng.	62	51.21 N	0.13 W
Cheat R., WV (chēt)	111	39.35 N	79.40 W
Cheb, Czech. (ĸĕb)	166	50.05 N	12.23 E

PLACE (Pronounciation)	PAGE	Lat. °'	Long. °'
Chebarkul, Sov. Un. (chĕ-bár-kûl')	182a	54.59 N	60.22 E
Cheboksary, Svo. Un. (chyĕ-bôk-sä'rē)	178	56.00 N	47:20 E
Cheboygan, Mi. (shē-boi'găn)	110	45.40 N	84.30 W
Chechen' (I.), Sov. Un. (chyĕch'ĕn)	179	44.00 N	48.10 E
Chech, Erg (Dune), Alg.	224	24.45 N	2.07 W
Checotah, Ok. (chē-kō'tá)	123	35.27 N	95.32 W
Chedabucto B., Can. (chĕd-á-bŭk-tō)	105	45.23 N	61.10 W
Cheduba I., Bur.	206	18.45 N	93.01 E
Cheecham Hills, Can. (chēē'hăm)	100	56.20 N	111.10 W
Cheektowaga, NY (chēk-tō-wä'gá)	113c	42.54 N	78.46 W
Cheetham Hill (Neigh.), Eng.	64b	53.31 N	2.15 W
Chefoo, see Yantai			
Chegutu, Zimb	231	18.18 S	30.10 E
Chehalis, Wa. (chē-hā'lĭs)	116	46.39 N	122.58 W
Chehalis R., Wa.	116	46.47 N	123.17 W
Cheju, Kor. (chĕ'jōō')	204	33.29 N	126.40 E
Cheju (Quelpart) (I.), Kor.	204	33.20 N	126.25 E
Chekalin, Sov. Un. (chĕ-kä'lĭn)	174	54.05 N	36.13 E
Chelan (L.), Wa.	116	48.09 N	120.20 W
Chelan, Wa. (chē-lăn')	116	47.51 N	119.59 W
Chelas (Neigh.), Port.	65d	38.45 N	9.07 W
Chela, Serra da (Mts.), Ang. (sĕr'rá dä shä'lá)	226	15.30 S	13.30 E
Cheleiros, Port. (shĕ-la'rŏzh)	171b	38.54 N	9.19 W
Chéliff (R.), Alg. (shā-lĕf)	171	36.17 N	1.22 E
Chelkar (L.), Sov. Un.	179	50.30 N	51.30 E
Chelkar, Sov. Un. (chyĕl'kär)	180	47.52 N	59.41 E
Chelkar Tengiz (L.), Sov. Un. (chyĕl'kär tĕn'yēz)	180	47.42 N	61.45 E
Chelles, Fr.	64c	48.53 N	2.36 E
Chelm, Pol. (kĕlm)	167	51.08 N	23.30 E
Chelmno, Pol. (kĕlm'nō)	167	53.20 N	18.25 E
Chelmsford, Can.	102	46.35 N	81.12 W
Chelmsford, Eng. (chĕlm's-fērd)	156b	51.44 N	0.28 E
Chelmsford, Ma.	105a	42.36 N	71.21 W
Chelsea, Al. (chĕl'sē)	112h	33.20 N	86.38 W
Chelsea, Austl.	211a	38.05 S	145.08 E
Chelsea, Can.	95c	45.30 N	75.46 W
Chelsea, Ma.	105a	42.23 N	71.02 W
Chelsea, Mi.	110	42.20 N	84.00 W
Chelsea, Ok.	123	36.32 N	95.23 W
Cheltenham, Eng. (chĕlt'nŭm)	162	51.57 N	2.06 W
Cheltenham, Md. (chĕltĕn-hăm)	112e	38.45 N	76.50 W
Chelva, Sp. (chĕl'vä)	171	39.43 N	1.00 W
Chelyabinsk, Sov. Un. (chĕl-yä-bĕnsk')	182a	55.10 N	61.25 E
Chelyuskin, Mys (C.), Sov. Un. (chĕl-yōōs'-kĭn)	181	77.45 N	104.45 E
Chemba, Moz.	231	17.08 S	34.52 E
Chembür (Neigh.), India	67e	19.04 N	72.54 E
Chemillé, Fr. (shē-mē-yā')	168	47.13 N	0.46 W
Chemnitz, see Karl-Marx-Stadt			
Chemung (R.), NY (shē-mŭng)	111	42.20 N	77.25 W
Chenāb (R.), Pak. (chē-näb)	196	31.33 N	72.28 E
Chenachane, Alg. (shē-ná-shän')	224	26.14 N	4.14 W
Chencun, China (chŭn-tsōōn)	201a	22.58 N	113.14 E
Cheney, Wa. (chē'nå)	116	47.29 N	117.34 W
Chengde, China (chŭŋ-dŭ)	202	40.50 N	117.50 E
Chengdong Hu (L.), China (chŭŋ-dôŋ hōō)	200	32.22 N	116.32 E
Chengdu, China (chŭŋ-dōō)	203	30.30 N	104.10 E
Chenggu, China (chŭŋ-gōō)	202	33.05 N	107.25 E
Chenghai, China (chŭŋ-hī)	203	23.22 N	116.40 E
Chën, Gora (Mtn.), Sov. Un.	181	65.13 N	142.12 E
Chengshan, Jiao (C.), China (jyou chŭŋ-shän)	202	37.28 N	122.40 E
Chengxi Hu (L.), China (chŭŋ-shyē hōō)	200	32.31 N	116.04 E
Chenies, Eng.	62	51.41 N	0.32 W
Chennevières, Fr.	64c	49.00 N	2.07 E
Chenxian, China (chŭn-shyĕn)	203	25.40 N	113.00 E
Chepén, Peru (chĕ-pĕ'n)	142	7.17 S	79.24 W
Chepo, Pan. (chā'pō)	133	9.12 N	79.06 W
Chepo R., Pan.	133	9.10 N	78.36 W
Cher (R.), Fr. (shâr)	168	47.14 N	1.34 E
Cherán, Mex. (chā-rän')	130	19.41 N	101.54 W
Cherangany Hills, Ken.	231	1.25 N	35.20 E
Cheraw, SC (chē'rô)	127	34.40 N	79.52 W
Cherbourg, Fr. (shär-bōōr')	168	49.39 N	1.43 W
Cherchell, Alg. (shĕr-shĕl')	224	36.38 N	2.09 E
Cherdyn', Sov. Un. (chĕr-dyĕn')	178	60.25 N	56.32 E
Cheremkhovo, Sov. Un. (chĕr'yĕm-kô-vô)	180	52.58 N	103.18 E
Cherëmukhovo, Sov. Un. (chĕr-yĕ-mû-kô-vô)	182a	60.20 N	60.00 E
Cherepanovo, Sov. Un. (chĕr'yĕ pä-nô'vô)	180	54.13 N	83.18 E
Cherepovets, Sov. Un. (chĕr-yĕ-pô'vyĕtz)	174	59.08 N	37.59 E
Chereya, Sov. Un. (chĕr-ā'yä)	174	54.38 N	29.16 E
Chergui (I.), Tun.	160	34.50 N	11.40 E
Chergui, Chott ech (L.), Alg. (chĕr gē)	160	34.12 N	0.10 W
Cherikov, Sov. Un. (chĕ'rē-kôf)	174	53.34 N	31.22 E
Cherkassy (Oblast), Sov. Un.	175	48.58 N	30.55 E
Cherkassy, Sov. Un. (chĕr-ká'sĭ)	175	49.26 N	32.03 E
Cherlak, Sov. Un. (chĭr-läk')	180	54.04 N	74.28 E
Chermoz, Sov. Un. (chĕr-môz')	182a	58.47 N	56.08 E
Chern', Sov. Un. (chĕrn)	174	53.28 N	36.49 E
Chërnaya Kalitva (R.), Sov. Un. (chôr'ná yá ká-lēt'vá)	175	50.15 N	39.16 E
Chernigov (Oblast), Sov. Un. (chĕr-nē'gôf)	175	51.23 N	31.15 E
Chernigov, Sov. Un. (chĕr-nē'gôf)	175	51.28 N	31.18 E
Chernigovka, Sov. Un.	175	47.08 N	36.20 E
Chernobay, Sov. Un. (chĕr-nō-bī')	175	49.41 N	32.24 E
Chernobyl', Sov. Un. (chĕr-nō-bĭl')	175	51.17 N	30.14 E
Chernogorsk, Sov. Un. (chĕr-nŏ-gôrsk')	180	54.01 N	91.07 E
Chernoistochinsk, Sov. Un. (chĕr-nôy-stô'chĭnsk)	182a	57.44 N	59.55 E

PLACE (Pronounciation)	PAGE	Lat. °'	Long. °'
Chërnomorskoye, Sov. Un. (chĕr-nô-môr'skô-yĕ)	175	45.29 N	32.43 E
Chernovtsy (Cernăuţi), Sov. Un. (chĭr-nôf'tsē) (chĕr-nou'tsē)	167	48.18 N	25.56 E
Chernyanka, Sov. Un. (chĕrn-yäŋ'kä)	175	50.56 N	37.48 E
Cherokee, Ia. (chĕr-ô-kē')	114	42.43 N	95.33 W
Cherokee, Ks.	123	37.21 N	94.50 W
Cherokee, Ok.	122	36.44 N	98.22 W
Cherokee (L.), Tn.	126	36.22 N	83.22 W
Cherokee Indian Res., NC	126	35.33 N	83.12 W
Cherokees, L. of the, Ok. (chĕr-ô-kēz')	123	36.32 N	95.14 W
Cherokee Sound Ba.	134	26.15 N	76.55 W
Cherry City, Pa.	57b	40.29 N	79.58 W
Cherryfield, Me. (chĕr'ĭ-fēld)	104	44.37 N	67.56 W
Cherry Grove, Or.	118c	45.27 N	123.15 W
Cherry Hill (Neigh.), Md.	56c	39.15 N	76.38 W
Cherry Hill, NJ	56b	39.55 N	75.01 W
Cherryvale, Ks.	123	37.16 N	95.33 W
Cherryville, NC (chĕr'ĭ-vĭl)	127	35.32 N	81.22 W
Cherskogo, Khrebet (Mts.), Sov. Un.	181	66.15 N	138.30 E
Chertsey, Eng.	62	51.24 N	0.30 W
Cherven', Sov. Un. (chĕr'vyĕn)	174	53.43 N	28.26 E
Chervonoye (L.), Sov. Un. (chĕr-vô'nô-yĕ)	174	52.24 N	28.12 E
Chesaning, Mi. (chĕs'á-nĭng)	110	43.10 N	84.10 W
Chesapeake, Va. (chĕs'á-pēk)	112g	36.48 N	76.16 W
Chesapeake B., Md.	111	38.20 N	76.15 W
Chesapeake Beach, Md.	112e	38.42 N	76.33 W
Chesham, Eng. (chĕsh'ŭm)	156b	51.41 N	0.37 W
Chesham Bois, Eng.	62	51.41 N	0.37 W
Cheshire (Co.), Eng.	156	53.16 N	2.30 W
Cheshire, Mi. (chĕsh'ĭr)	110	42.25 N	86.00 W
Chëshskaya Guba (B.), Sov. Un.	178	67.25 N	46.00 E
Cheshunt, Eng.	62	51.43 N	0.02 W
Chesma, Sov. Un. (chĕs'má)	182a	53.50 N	60.42 E
Chesnokovka, Sov. Un. (chĕs-nŏ-kôf'ká)	180	53.28 N	83.41 E
Chessington (Neigh.), Eng.	62	51.21 N	0.18 W
Chester, Eng. (chĕs'tēr)	156	53.12 N	2.53 W
Chester, Il.	123	37.54 N	89.48 W
Chester, Pa.	56b	39.51 N	75.21 W
Chester, Pa.	112f	39.51 N	75.22 W
Chester, SC	127	34.42 N	81.11 W
Chester, Va.	127	37.20 N	77.24 W
Chester, WV	110	40.35 N	80.30 W
Chesterbrook, Va.	56d	38.55 N	77.09 W
Chesterfield, Eng. (chĕs'tēr-fēld)	156	53.14 N	1.26 W
Chesterfield (Inlet), Can.	96	63.59 N	92.09 W
Chesterfield, Iles, N. Cal.	215	19.38 S	160.08 E
Chesterfield Inlet, Can.	96	63.19 N	91.11 W
Chestermere L., Can. (chĕs'tē-mēr)	95e	51.03 N	113.45 W
Chesterton, In. (chĕs'tēr-tŭn)	110	41.35 N	87.05 W
Chestertown, Md. (chĕs'tēr-toun)	111	39.15 N	76.05 W
Chestnut Hill, Ma.	54a	42.20 N	71.10 W
Chestnut Hill, Md.	56c	39.17 N	76.47 W
Chesuncook (L.), Me. (chĕs'ŭn-kŏŏk)	104	46.03 N	69.40 W
Cheswick, Pa.	57b	40.32 N	79.47 W
Chetek, Wi. (chĕ'tĕk)	115	45.18 N	91.41 W
Chetumal, Bahia de (B.), Belize (bä-ē-ä dĕ chĕt-ōō-mäl')	132a	18.07 N	88.05 W
Chevelon Cr., Az. (shĕv'á-lŏn)	121	34.35 N	111.00 W
Chevening, Eng.	62	51.18 N	0.08 E
Cheverly, Md.	56d	38.55 N	76.55 W
Chevilly-Larue, Fr.	64c	48.46 N	2.21 E
Cheviot, Oh. (shĕv'ĭ-ŭt)	113f	39.10 N	84.37 W
Chevreuse, Fr. (shĕ-vrûz')	169b	48.42 N	2.02 E
Chevy Chase, Md. (shĕvĭ chās)	112e	38.58 N	77.06 W
Chevy Chase View, Md.	56d	39.01 N	77.05 W
Chew Bahir (Lake Stefanie), Eth. (stĕf-a-nē)	225	4.46 N	37.31 E
Chewelah, Wa. (chē-wē'lä)	116	48.17 N	117.42 W
Cheyenne (R.), SD	114	44.20 N	102.15 W
Cheyenne, Wy. (shī-ĕn')	114	41.10 N	104.49 W
Cheyenne River Ind. Res., SD	114	45.07 N	100.46 W
Cheyenne Wells, Co.	122	38.46 N	102.21 W
Chhalera Bāngar, India	67d	28.33 N	77.20 E
Chhināmor, India	67a	22.48 N	88.18 E
Chhindwāra, India	196	22.08 N	78.57 E
Chiai, Taiwan (chī'ī')	203	23.28 N	120.28 E
Chiang Mai, Thai.	198	18.38 N	98.44 E
Chiang Rai, Thai.	206	19.53 N	99.48 E
Chiange, Ang.	230	15.45 S	13.48 E
Chiapa de Corzo, Mex. (chē-ä'pä dā kōr'zō)	131	16.44 N	93.01 W
Chiapa, Rio de (R.), Mex. (rē'-ō-dĕ-chē-ä'pä)	132	16.00 N	92.20 W
Chiapas (State), Mex. (chē-ä'päs)	128	17.10 N	93.00 W
Chiapas, Cordilla de (Mts.), Mex. (kôr-dĕl-yĕ'rä-dĕ-chyá'räs)	131	15.55 N	93.15 W
Chiari, It. (kyä'rē)	172	45.31 N	9.57 E
Chiasso, Switz.	166	45.50 N	8.57 E
Chiautla, Mex. (chyä-ōōt'lá)	130	18.16 N	98.37 W
Chiavari, It. (kyä-vä'rē)	172	44.18 N	9.21 E
Chiba, Jap. (chē'bá)	205a	35.37 N	140.08 E
Chiba (Pref.), Jap.	205a	35.47 N	140.02 E
Chibougamau, Can. (chē-bōō'gä-mou)	103	49.57 N	74.23 W
Chibougamau (L.), Can.	103	49.53 N	74.21 W
Chicago, Il. (shĭ-kô-gō) (chĭ-kä'gō)	113a	41.49 N	87.37 W
Chicago Heights, Il.	113a	41.30 N	87.38 W
Chicago Lawn (Neigh.), Il.	58a	41.47 N	87.41 W
Chicago, North Branch (R.), Il.	58a	41.53 N	87.38 W
Chicago-O'Hare International Arpt., Il.	58a	41.59 N	87.54 W
Chicago Ridge, Il.	58a	41.42 N	87.47 W
Chicago Sanitary and Ship Canal (Can.), Il.	58a	41.42 N	87.58 W
Chicapa (R.), Ang. (chē-kä'pä)	230	7.45 S	20.25 E
Chicbul, Mex. (chēk-bōō'l)	131	18.45 N	90.56 W
Chic-Chocs. Mts., Can.	104	48.38 N	66.37 W
Chichagof (I.), Ak. (chē-chä'gôf)	107	57.50 N	137.00 W

PLACE (Pronounciation)	PAGE	Lat. °'	Long. °'
Chichâncanab, Lago de (L.), Mex. (lä'gô-dĕ-chē-chän-kä-nä'b)	132a	19.50 N	88.28 W
Chichen Itzá (Ruins), Mex. (chē-chĕ'n-ē-tsá')	132a	20.38 N	88.35 W
Chichester, Eng. (chĭch'ĕs-tēr)	162	50.50 N	0.55 W
Chichimila, Mex. (chē-chē-mē'lä)	132a	20.36 N	88.14 W
Chichiriviche, Ven. (chē-chē-rē-vē-chĕ)	143b	10.56 N	68.17 W
Chickamauga, Ga. (chĭk-á-mô'gá)	126	34.50 N	85.15 W
Chickamauga, (L.), Tn.	126	35.18 N	85.22 W
Chickasawhay (R.), Ms. (chĭk-á-sô'wā)	126	31.45 N	88.45 W
Chickasha, Ok. (chĭk'á-shā)	122	35.04 N	97.56 W
Chiclana de la Frontera, Sp. (chē-klä'nä)	170	36.25 N	6.09 W
Chiclayo, Peru (chē-klä'yō)	142	6.46 S	79.50 W
Chico, Ca. (chē'kō)	120	39.43 N	121.51 W
Chico (R.), Arg.	144	44.30 S	66.00 W
Chico (R.), Arg.	144	49.15 S	69.30 W
Chico (R.), Phil.	207a	17.33 N	121.24 E
Chico, Wa.	118a	47.37 N	122.43 W
Chicoa, Moz.	231	15.37 S	32.24 E
Chicoloapan, Mex. (chē-kō-lwä'pän)	131a	19.24 N	98.54 W
Chiconautla, Mex. (chē-kō-nä-ōō'tlá)	131a	19.39 N	99.01 W
Chicontepec, Mex. (chē-kōn'tē-pĕk')	130	20.58 N	98.08 W
Chicopee, Ma. (chĭk'ō-pē)	111	42.10 N	72.35 W
Chicoutimi, Can. (shē-kōō'tē-mē')	103	48.26 N	71.04 W
Chicxulub, Mex. (chēk-sōō-lōō'b)	132a	21.10 N	89.30 W
Chidley, C., Can. (chĭd'lĭ)	97	60.32 N	63.56 W
Chief Joseph Dam, Wa.	116	48.00 N	119.39 W
Chiefland, Fl. (chēf'lănd)	126	29.30 N	82.50 W
Chiemsee (L.), F.R.G. (kēm zā)	166	47.58 N	12.20 E
Chieri, It. (kyâ'rē)	172	45.03 N	7.48 E
Chieti, It. (kyĕ'tē)	172	42.22 N	14.22 E
Chifeng (Ulanhad), China (chr-fŭŋ)	202	42.18 N	118.52 E
Chigirin, Sov. Un. (chē-gē'rĕn)	175	49.02 N	32.39 E
Chignall Saint James, Eng.	62	51.46 N	0.25 E
Chignanuapan, Mex. (chē'g-ŋä-nwä-pá'n)	130	19.49 N	98.02 W
Chignecto B., Can. (shĭg-nĕk'tō)	104	45.33 N	64.50 W
Chignik, Ak. (chĭg'nĭk)	107	56.14 N	158.12 W
Chignik B., Ak.	107	56.18 N	157.22 W
Chigu Co (L.), China (chr-gōō tswo)	196	28.55 N	91.47 E
Chigwell, Eng.	62	51.38 N	0.05 E
Chigwell Row, Eng.	62	51.37 N	0.07 E
Chihe, China (chr-hŭ)	200	32.32 N	117.57 E
Chihuahua, Mex. (chē-wä'wä)	124	28.37 N	106.06 W
Chihuahua (State), Mex.	128	29.00 N	107.30 W
Chikishlyar, Sov. Un. (chē-kēsh-lyär')	179	37.40 N	53.50 E
Chilanga, Zambia	231	15.34 S	28.17 E
Chilapa, Mex. (chē-lä'pä)	130	17.34 N	99.14 W
Chilchota, Mex. (chēl-chō'tä)	130	19.40 N	102.04 W
Chilcotin (R.), Can. (chĭl-kō'tĭn)	98	52.20 N	124.15 W
Childer Thornton, Eng.	64a	53.17 N	2.57 W
Childress, Tx. (chĭld'rĕs)	122	34.26 N	100.11 W
Chile, S.A. (chē'lā)	140	35.00 S	72.00 W
Chilecito, Arg. (chē-lå-sē'tō)	144	29.06 S	67.25 W
Chilengue, Serra do (Mts.), Ang.	230	13.20 S	15.00 E
Chilibre, Pan. (chē-lē'brĕ)	128a	9.09 N	79.37 W
Chililabombwe (Bancroft), Zambia	231	12.18 S	27.43 E
Chilí, Pico de (Pk.), Col. (pē'kō-dĕ chē-lē')	142a	4.14 N	75.38 W
Chilka (L.), India	196	19.26 N	85.42 E
Chilko (R.), Can. (chĭl'kō)	98	51.53 N	123.53 W
Chilko L., Can.	98	51.20 N	124.05 W
Chillán, Chile (chēl-yän')	144	36.44 S	72.06 W
Chillicothe, Il. (chĭl-ĭ-kŏth'ē)	110	41.55 N	89.30 W
Chillicothe, Mo.	123	39.46 N	93.32 W
Chillicothe, Oh.	110	39.20 N	83.00 W
Chilliwack, Can. (chĭl'ĭ-wăk)	99	49.10 N	121.57 W
Chillum, Md.	56d	38.58 N	76.59 W
Chilly-Mazarin, Fr.	64c	48.42 N	2.19 E
Chiloé, Isla de (I.), Chile (ē's-lä-dĕ-chē-lō-ā')	144	43.00 S	75.00 W
Chilpancingo, Mex. (chēl-pän-sēŋ'gō)	130	17.32 N	99.30 W
Chilton, Wi. (chĭl'tŭn)	115	44.00 N	88.12 W
Chilung (Kirin), Taiwan (chī'lung)	203	25.02 N	121.48 E
Chilwa, L. Malawi-Moz.	231	15.12 S	36.30 E
Chimacum, Wa. (chĭm'ä-kŭm)	118a	48.01 N	122.47 W
Chimalpa, Mex. (chē-mäl'pä)	131a	19.26 N	99.22 W
Chimaltenango, Guat. (chē-mäl-tā-näŋ'gō)	132	14.39 N	90.48 W
Chimaltitan, Mex. (chēmäl-tē-tän')	130	21.36 N	103.50 W
Chimbay, Sov. Un. (chĭm-bī')	155	43.00 N	59.44 E
Chimborazo (Mtn.), Ec. (chēm-bō-rä'zō)	142	1.35 S	78.45 W
Chimbote, Peru (chēm-bō'tå)	142	9.02 S	78.33 W
Chimkent, Sov. Un. (chĭm-kĕnt)	180	42.17 N	69.42 E
Chimki, Sov. Un.	66b	55.54 N	37.26 E
Chimki-Chovrino (Neigh.), Sov. Un.	66b	55.51 N	37.30 E
China, Asia (chī'ná)	190	36.45 N	93.00 E
China, Mex. (chē'nä)	124	25.43 N	99.13 W
Chinameca, Sal. (Chē-nä-mä'kä)	132	13.31 N	88.18 W
Chinandega, Nic. (chē-nän-dä'gä)	132	12.38 N	87.08 W
Chinati Pk., Tx. (chĭ-nä'tē)	124	29.56 N	104.29 W
Chinatown (Neigh.), Ca.	58b	37.48 N	122.26 W
Chincha Alta, Peru (chĭn'chä äl'tä)	142	13.24 S	76.04 W
Chinchas, Islas (Is.), Peru (ē's-läs-chē'n-chäs)	142	11.27 S	79.05 W
Chinchilla, Austl. (chĭn-chĭl'á)	216	26.44 S	150.36 E
Chinchorro, Banco (Bk.), Mex. (bä'n-kô-chēn-chô'r-rô)	132a	18.43 N	87.25 W
Chincilla de Monte Aragon, Sp.	170	38.54 N	1.43 W
Chinde, Moz. (shēn'dē)	226	17.39 S	36.34 E
Chin Do (I.), Kor.	204	34.30 N	125.43 E
Chindwin R., Bur. (chĭn-dwĭn)	198	23.30 N	94.34 E
Chingford (Neigh.), Eng.	62	51.38 N	0.01 E
Chingmei, Taiwan	68d	24.59 N	121.32 E
Chingola, Zambia (chĭng-gōlä)	231	12.32 S	27.52 E

ăt; finăl; rāte; senåte; ärm; åsk; sofá; fâre; ch-choose; dh-as th in other; bē; ēvent; bĕt; recĕnt; cratēr; g-gō; gh-guttural g; bĭt; ĭ-short neutral; rīde; ĸ-guttural k as ch in German ich;

PLACE (Pronounciation)	PAGE	Lat. °'	Long. °'
Chinguar, Ang. (chĭng-gär)	226	12.35 S	16.15 E
Chinguetti, Mauritania (chēn-gĕt'ē)	224	20.34 N	12.34 W
Chinhoyi, Zimb	231	17.22 S	30.12 E
Chinju, Kor. (chĭn'jo͞o)	204	35.13 N	128.10 E
Chinko (R.), Cen. Afr. Rep. (shĭn'kō)	225	6.37 N	24.31 E
Chinmen, see Quemoy			
Chino, Ca. (chē'nō)	119a	34.01 N	117.42 W
Chinon, Fr. (shē-nôN')	168	47.09 N	0.13 E
Chinook, Mt. (shĭn-o͝ok')	117	48.35 N	109.15 W
Chinook, Wa. (shĭn-o͝ok')	118c	46.17 N	123.57 W
Chinsali, Zambia	231	10.34 S	32.03 E
Chinteche, Malawi (chĭn-tĕ'chĕ)	226	11.48 S	34.14 E
Chioggia, It. (kyôd'jä)	172	45.12 N	12.17 E
Chipata, Zambia	231	13.39 S	32.40 E
Chipera, Moz. (zhē-pĕ'rä)	226	15.16 S	32.30 E
Chipley, Fl. (chĭp'lĭ)	126	30.45 N	85.33 W
Chipman, Can. (chĭp'măn)	104	46.11 N	65.53 W
Chipola (R.), Fl. (chĭ-pō'lȧ)	126	30.40 N	85.14 W
Chippawa, Can. (chĭp'ē-wä)	113c	43.03 N	79.03 W
Chipperfield, Eng.	62	51.42 N	0.29 W
Chippewa (R.), Mn. (chĭp'ē-wä)	114	45.07 N	95.41 W
Chippewa (R.), Wi.	115	45.07 N	91.19 W
Chippewa Falls, Wi.	115	44.55 N	91.26 W
Chippewa Lake, Oh.	113d	41.04 N	81.54 W
Chipping Ongar, Eng.	62	51.43 N	0.15 E
Chipstead, Eng.	62	51.17 N	0.09 E
Chipstead, Eng.	62	51.18 N	0.10 W
Chiputneticook L., Can. (chĭ-po͞ot-nĕt'ĭ-ko͝ok)	104	45.47 N	67.45 W
Chiquimula, Guat. (chē-kē-mo͞o'lä)	132	14.47 N	89.31 W
Chiquimulilla, Guat. (chē-kē-mo͞o-lē'l-yä)	132	14.08 N	90.23 W
Chiquinquira, Col. (chē-kēn'kē-rä')	142	5.33 N	73.49 W
Chiquita, Laguna Mar (L.), Arg. (lä-go͞o'nä-mär-chē-kē'tä)	141c	34.25 S	61.10 W
Chirāgh Delhi (Neigh.), India	67d	28.32 N	77.14 E
Chirald, India	197	15.52 N	80.22 E
Chirchik, Sov. Un. (chĭr-chĕk')	180	41.28 N	69.18 E
Chire (R.), Moz.	231	17.15 S	35.25 E
Chiricahua Natl. Mon., Az. (chĭ-rä-cä'hwä)	121	32.02 N	109.18 W
Chirikof (I.), Ak. (chĭ'rĭ-kôf)	107	55.50 N	155.35 W
Chiriqui, Punta (Pt.), Pan. (po͞o'n-tä-chē-rē-kē')	133	9.13 N	81.39 W
Chiriquí, Golfo de (G.), Pan. (gôl-fô-dĕ-chē-rē-kē')	133	7.56 N	82.18 W
Chiriquí Grande, Pan. (chē-rē-kē' grän'dä)	133	8.57 N	82.08 W
Chiriqui, Laguna de (L.), Pan. (lä-go͞o'nä-dĕ-chē-rē-kē')	133	9.06 N	82.02 W
Chiri San (Mt.), Kor. (chĭ'rĭ-sän')	204	35.20 N	127.39 E
Chiromo, Malawi	226	16.34 S	35.13 E
Chirpan, Bul.	173	42.12 N	25.19 E
Chirripó, Cerro (Mtn.), C. R. (chē-rē'pō)	133	9.30 N	83.31 W
Chirripo, Rio (R.), C. R.	133	9.50 N	83.20 W
Chisholm, Mn. (chĭz'ŭm)	115	47.28 N	92.53 W
Chislehurst (Neigh.), Eng.	62	51.25 N	0.04 E
Chistopol', Sov. Un. (chĭs-tô'pôl-y')	178	55.18 N	50.30 E
Chiswellgreen, Eng.	62	51.44 N	0.22 W
Chiswick (Neigh.), Eng.	62	51.29 N	0.16 W
Chita, Sov. Un. (chē-tá')	181	52.09 N	113.39 E
Chitambo, Zambia	231	12.55 S	30.39 E
Chitembo, Ang.	230	13.34 S	16.40 E
Chitina, Ak. (chĭ-tē'nȧ)	107	61.28 N	144.35 W
Chitokoloki, Zambia	230	13.50 S	23.13 E
Chitorgarh, India	196	24.59 N	74.42 E
Chitrāl, Pak. (chē-träl')	196	35.58 N	71.48 E
Chitré, Pan. (chē'trā)	133	7.59 N	80.26 W
Chittagong, Bngl. (chĭt-ȧ-gông')	196	22.26 N	90.51 E
Chitungwiza, Zimb	226	17.51 S	31.05 E
Chiumbe (R.), Ang. (chē-o͞om'bȧ)	230	9.05 S	21.00 E
Chivasso, It. (kē-väs'sō)	172	45.13 N	7.52 E
Chivhu, Zimb	226	19.59 S	30.58 E
Chivilcoy, Arg. (chē-vēl-koi')	141c	34.51 S	60.03 W
Chixoy (R.), Guat. (chē-Koi')	132	15.40 N	90.35 W
Chizu, Jap. (chē-zo͞o')	205	35.16 N	134.15 E
Chloride, Az. (klō'rīd)	121	35.25 N	114.15 W
Chmielnik, Pol. (Kmyĕl'nēK)	167	50.36 N	20.46 E
Choa Chu Kang, Singapore	67c	1.22 N	103.41 E
Choapa (R.), Chile (chô-á'pä)	141b	31.56 S	70.48 W
Chobham, Eng.	62	51.21 N	0.36 W
Chocó (Dept.), Col. (chô-kô')	142a	5.33 N	76.28 W
Choctawhatchee (R.), Fl.-Ga.	126	30.37 N	85.56 W
Choctawhatchee, B., Fl. (chôk-tô-hăch'ē)	126	30.15 N	86.32 W
Chodziez, Pol. (Kôj'yĕsh)	166	52.59 N	16.55 E
Choele Choel, Arg. (chô-ĕ'lĕ-chôĕ'l)	144	39.14 S	66.46 W
Chōfu, Jap. (chō'fo͞o')	205a	35.39 N	139.33 E
Chōgo, Jap. (chō-gō)	205a	35.25 N	139.28 E
Choisel, Fr.	64c	48.41 N	2.01 E
Choiseul, (I.), Sol. Is. (shwä-zûl')	215	7.30 S	157.30 E
Choisy-le-Roi, Fr.	64c	48.46 N	2.25 E
Chojnice, Pol. (Kôĭ-nē-tsĕ)	167	53.41 N	17.34 E
Cholet, Fr. (shô-lĕ')	168	47.06 N	0.54 W
Cho-lon (Neigh.), Viet.	68m	10.46 N	106.40 E
Cholula, Mex. (chō-lo͞o'lä)	130	19.04 N	98.19 W
Choluteca, Hond. (chō-lo͞o-tā'kä)	132	13.18 N	87.12 W
Choluteco (R.), Hond.-Nic.	132	13.34 N	86.59 W
Cho Moi, Viet.	68m	10.51 N	106.38 E
Chomutov, Czech. (kō'mo͞o-tôf)	166	50.27 N	13.23 E
Chona (R.), Sov. Un. (chō'nä)	181	60.45 N	109.15 E
Chone, Ec. (chô'nĕ)	142	0.48 S	80.06 W
Chŏngjin, Kor. (chŭng-jĭn')	204	41.48 N	129.46 E
Chŏngju, Kor. (chŭng-jo͞o')	204	36.35 N	127.30 E
Chongming Dao (I.), China (chôŋ-mĭŋ dou)	203	31.40 N	122.30 E
Chong Pang, Singapore	67c	1.26 N	103.50 E
Chongqing, China (chôŋ-chyĭŋ)	203	29.38 N	107.30 E
Chŏnju, Kor. (chŭn-jo͞o')	204	35.48 N	127.08 E
Chorley, Eng. (chôr'lĭ)	156	53.40 N	2.38 W
Chorleywood, Eng.	62	51.39 N	0.31 W

PLACE (Pronounciation)	PAGE	Lat. °'	Long. °'
Chorlton-cum-Hardy (Neigh.), Eng.	64b	53.27 N	2.17 W
Chornaya, Sov. Un.	182b	55.45 N	38.04 E
Chorošovo (Neigh.), Sov. Un.	66b	55.47 N	37.28 E
Chorrera de Managua, Cuba	60b	23.02 N	82.19 E
Chorrillos, Peru (chôr-rē'l-yōs)	142	12.17 S	76.55 W
Chortkov, Sov. Un. (chôrt'kôf)	167	49.01 N	25.48 E
Chosan, Kor. (chō-sän')	204	40.44 N	125.48 E
Chosen, Fl. (chō'z'n)	127a	26.41 N	80.41 W
Chōshi, Jap. (chō'shē)	204	35.40 N	140.55 E
Choszczno, Pol. (chôsh'chnō)	166	53.10 N	15.25 E
Chota Nagpur (Reg.), India	196	23.40 N	82.50 E
Choteau, Mt. (shō'tō)	117	47.51 N	112.10 W
Chowan (R.), NC (chô-wän')	127	36.13 N	76.46 W
Chowilla Res., Austl.	216	34.05 S	141.20 E
Chown, Mt., Can. (choun)	99	53.24 N	119.22 W
Choybalsan, Mong.	202	47.50 N	114.15 E
Christchurch, N.Z. (krīst'chûrch)	215a	43.30 S	172.38 E
Christian (I.), Can. (krĭs'chăn)	110	44.50 N	80.00 W
Christiansburg, Va. (krĭs'chănz-bûrg)	127	37.08 N	80.25 W
Christiansted, Vir. Is. (U.S.A.)	129b	17.45 N	64.44 W
Christmas (I.), see Kiritimati (I.)			
Christmas I., Austl.	206	10.35 S	105.40 E
Christopher, Il. (krĭs'tô-fēr)	123	37.58 N	89.04 W
Chrudim, Czech. (Kro͞o'dyĕm)	166	49.57 N	15.46 E
Chrzanów, Pol. (Kzhä'no͞of)	167	50.08 N	19.24 E
Chuansha, China (chŭän-shä)	201b	31.12 N	121.41 E
Chubut (Prov.), Arg. (cho͞o-bo͞ot')	144	44.00 S	69.15 W
Chubut (R.), Arg. (cho͞o-bo͞ot')	144	43.05 S	69.00 W
Chuckatuck, Va. (chŭck ȧ-tŭck)	112g	36.51 N	76.35 W
Chucunaque (R.), Pan. (cho͞o-ko͞o-nä'kȧ)	133	8.36 N	77.48 W
Chudovo, Sov. Un. (cho͞o'dô-vô)	174	59.03 N	31.56 E
Chudskoye Oz. (Peipus, L.), Sov. Un. (cho͞ot'skô-yĕ)	174	58.43 N	26.45 E
Chuguchak (Reg.), China (cho͞o'go͞o-chäk')	198	46.09 N	83.58 E
Chuguyev, Sov. Un. (cho͞o'go͞o-yĕf)	175	49.52 N	36.40 E
Chuguyevka, Sov. Un. (cho͞o-go͞o'yĕf-kȧ)	204	43.58 N	133.49 E
Chugwater Cr., Wy. (chŭg'wô-tēr)	114	41.43 N	104.54 W
Chukot Natl. Okrug (Reg.), Sov. Un.	181	68.15 N	170.00 E
Chukotskiy (Chukot) P-Ov (Pen.), Sov. Un.	181	66.12 N	175.00 W
Chukotskoye Nagor'ye (Mts.), Sov. Un.	181	66.00 N	166.00 E
Chula Vista, Ca. (cho͞o'lȧ vĭs'tȧ)	120a	32.38 N	117.05 W
Chulkovo, Sov. Un. (cho͞ol-kô vô)	182b	55.33 N	38.04 E
Chulucanas, Peru (cho͞o-lo͞o-kä'näs)	142	5.13 S	80.13 W
Chulum (R.), Sov. Un.	180	57.52 N	84.45 E
Chumikan, Sov. Un. (cho͞o-mē-kän')	181	54.47 N	135.09 E
Chun'an, China (cho͞on-än)	203	29.38 N	119.00 E
Chunchŏn, Kor. (cho͞on-chŭn')	204	37.51 N	127.46 E
Chungju, Kor. (chŭng'jo͞o')	204	37.00 N	128.19 E
Chŭngsanha-ri (Neigh.), Kor.	68b	37.35 N	126.54 E
Chunya (R.), Sov. Un. (cho͞on'yä')	180	61.45 N	101.28 E
Chunya, Tan.	231	8.32 S	33.25 E
Chūō (Neigh.), Jap.	69a	35.40 N	139.47 E
Chuquicamata, Chile (cho͞o-kē-kä-mä'tä)	144	22.08 S	68.57 W
Chur, Switz. (ko͞or)	166	46.51 N	9.32 E
Churchill, Can. (chûrch'ĭl)	96	58.50 N	94.10 W
Churchill, Pa.	57b	40.27 N	79.51 W
Churchill, Va.	56d	38.54 N	77.10 W
Churchill (R.), Can.	101	57.20 N	96.30 W
Churchill, C., Can.	96	59.07 N	93.50 W
Churchill Falls, Can.	97	53.35 N	64.27 W
Churchill L., Can.	100	56.12 N	108.40 W
Churchill Pk., Can.	96	58.10 N	125.14 W
Church Street, Eng.	62	51.26 N	0.28 E
Church Stretton, Eng. (chûrch strĕt'ŭn)	156	52.32 N	2.49 W
Churchton, Md.	112e	38.49 N	76.33 W
Churu, India	196	28.22 N	75.00 E
Churumuco, Mex. (cho͞o-ro͞o-mo͞o'kō)	130	18.39 N	101.40 W
Chuska Mts., Az.-NM (chŭs-kȧ)	121	36.21 N	109.11 W
Chusovaya R., Sov. Un. (cho͞o-sô-vä'yȧ)	182a	58.08 N	58.35 E
Chusovoy, Sov. Un. (cho͞o-sô-vôy')	182a	58.18 N	57.50 E
Chust, Sov. Un. (cho͞ost)	180	41.05 N	71.28 E
Chuvash A. S. S. R., Sov. Un. (cho͞o'vàsh)	178	55.45 N	46.00 E
Chuviscar (R.), Mex. (cho͞o-vēs-kär')	124	28.34 N	105.36 W
Chuwang, China (cho͞o-wäŋ)	200	36.08 N	114.53 E
Chuxian, China (cho͞o shyĕn)	200	32.19 N	118.19 E
Chuxiong, China (cho͞o-shyôŋ)	198	25.19 N	101.34 E
Cicero, Il. (sĭs'ēr-ō)	113a	41.50 N	87.46 W
Cide, Pur. (jē'dĕ)	179	41.50 N	33.00 E
Ciechanów, Pol. (tsyĕ-kä'no͞of)	167	52.52 N	20.39 E
Ciego dę Avila, Cuba (syā'gō dā ä'vē-lä)	134	21.50 N	78.45 W
Ciego de Avila (Prov.), Cuba	134	22.00 N	78.40 W
Ciempozuelos, Sp. (thyĕm-pô-thwā'lōs)	170	40.09 N	3.36 W
Ciénaga, Col. (syā'nä-gä)	142	11.01 N	74.15 W
Cienfuegos, Cuba (syĕn-fwā'gōs)	134	22.10 N	80.30 W
Cienfuegos (Prov.), Cuba	134	22.15 N	80.40 W
Cienfuegos, Bahía (B.), Cuba (bä-ē'ä-syĕn-fwā'gōs)	134	22.00 N	80.35 W
Ciervo, Isla de la (I.), Nic. (ē's-lä-dĕ-lä-syĕ'r-vô)	133	11.56 N	83.20 W
Cieszyn, Pol. (tsyĕ'shĕn)	167	49.47 N	18.45 E
Cieza, Sp. (thyā'thä)	170	38.13 N	1.25 W
Cigüela (R.), Sp.	170	39.53 N	2.54 W
Cihuatlán, Mex. (sē-wä-tlä'n)	130	19.13 N	104.36 W
Cihuatlán (R.), Mex.	130	19.11 N	104.30 W
Cijara, Embalse de (Res.), Sp.	170	39.25 N	5.00 W
Cilician Gates P.), Tur.	179	37.30 N	35.30 E
Cimarron (R.), North Fk., Co.	122	37.13 N	102.30 W
Cimarron R., U.S. (sĭm-ȧ-rōn')	108	36.26 N	98.27 W

PLACE (Pronounciation)	PAGE	Lat. °'	Long. °'
Cinca (R.), Sp. (thēŋ'kä)	171	42.09 N	0.08 E
Cincinnati, Oh. (sĭn-sĭ-năt'ĭ)	113f	39.08 N	84.30 W
Cinco Balas, Cayos (Is.), Cuba (kä'yōs-thēŋ'kō bä'läs)	134	21.05 N	79.25 W
Cinderella, S. Afr.	71b	26.15 S	28.16 E
Cinisello Balsamo, It.	65c	45.33 N	9.13 E
Cinkota (Neigh.), Hung.	66g	47.31 N	19.14 E
Cintalapa, Mex. (sēn-tä-lä'pä)	131	16.41 N	93.44 W
Cinto, Mt., Fr. (chēn'tō)	172	42.24 N	8.54 E
Circle, Ak. (sûr'k'l)	107	65.49 N	144.22 W
Circleville, Oh. (sûr'k'lvĭl)	110	39.35 N	83.00 W
Cirebon, Indon.	206	6.50 S	108.33 E
Cîmpina, Rom.	173	45.08 N	25.47 E
Cîmpulung, Rom.	173	45.15 N	25.03 E
Cîmpulung Moldovenesc, Rom.	167	47.31 N	25.36 E
Cisco, Tx. (sĭs'kō)	124	32.23 N	98.57 W
Cisliano, It.	65c	45.27 N	8.59 E
Cisneros, Col. (sēs-nĕ'rôs)	142a	6.33 N	75.05 W
Cisterna di Latina, It. (chēs-tĕ'r-nä-dē-lä-tē'nä)	171d	41.36 N	12.53 E
Cistierna, Sp. (thēs-tyĕr'nä)	170	42.48 N	5.08 W
Citlaltépetl (Vol.), Mex. (sē-tlăl-tĕ'pĕtl)	131	19.04 N	97.14 W
Citronelle, Al. (cĭt-rô'nĕl)	126	31.05 N	88.15 W
Cittadella, It. (chēt-tä-dĕl'lä)	172	45.39 N	11.51 E
Città di Castello, It. (chēt-tä'dē käs-tĕl'lō)	172	43.27 N	12.17 E
City College of New York (P. Int.), NY	55	40.49 N	73.57 W
City Island (Neigh.), NY	55	40.51 N	73.47 W
City of Baltimore, Md.	56d	39.18 N	76.37 W
City of Commerce, Ca.	59	33.59 N	118.08 W
City of Industry, Ca.	59	34.01 N	117.57 W
City of London (Neigh.), Eng.	62	51.31 N	0.05 W
City of Westminster (Neigh.), Eng.	62	51.30 N	0.09 W
Ciudad Altamirano, Mex. (syo͞o-dä'd-äl-tä-mē-rä'nô)	130	18.24 N	100.38 W
Ciudad Bolívar, Ven. (syo͞o-dhädh' bô-lē'vär)	142	8.07 N	63.41 W
Ciudad Camargo (Santa Rosalia), Mex. (syo͞o-dhädh' kä-mär'gō) (sän'tȧ rō-sä'lēȧ)	124	27.42 N	105.10 W
Ciudad Chetumal (Payo Obispo), Mex. (syo͞o-dhädh' chĕt-o͞o-mäl) (pä'yō ō-bēs'pō)	132a	18.30 N	88.17 W
Ciudad Darío, Nic. (syo͞o-dhädh'dä'rē-ō)	132	12.44 N	86.08 W
Ciudad de la Habana (Prov.), Cuba	134	23.20 N	82.10 W
Ciudad de las Casas, Mex. (syo͞o-dä'd-dĕ-lä-kä'säs)	131	16.44 N	92.39 W
Ciudad del Carmen, Mex. (syo͞o-dä'd-dĕl-kà'r-mĕn)	131	18.39 N	91.49 W
Ciudad del Maíz, Mex. (syo͞o-dhädh'del mä-ēz')	130	22.24 N	99.37 W
Ciudad de Naucalpan de Juárez, Mex.	60a	19.28 N	99.14 W
Ciudad Deportive (P. Int.), Mex.	60a	19.24 N	99.06 W
Ciudad de Valles, Mex. (syo͞o-dhädh'dā vä'lyās)	130	21.59 N	99.02 W
Ciudadela, Sp. (thyo͞o-dhä-dhā'lä)	171	40.00 N	3.52 E
Ciudad Fernández, Mex. (syo͞o-dhädh'fĕr-nän'dĕz)	130	21.56 N	100.03 W
Ciudad García Mex. (syo͞o-dhädh'gär-sē'ä)	130	22.39 N	103.02 W
Ciudad General Belgrano, Arg.	60d	34.44 S	58.32 W
Ciudad Guayana Ven.	142	8.30 N	62.45 W
Ciudad Guzmán, Mex. (syo͞o-dhädh'go͞oz-män)	130	19.40 N	103.29 W
Ciudad Hidalgo, Mex. (syo͞o-dä'd-ē-dä'l-gô)	130	19.41 N	100.35 W
Ciudad Juárez, Mex. (syo͞o-dhädh hwä'räz)	125	31.44 N	106.28 W
Ciudad Lineal (Neigh.), Sp.	65b	40.27 N	3.40 W
Ciudad Madero, Mex. (syo͞o-dä'd-mä-dĕ'rô)	131	22.16 N	97.52 W
Ciudad Mante, Mex. (syo͞o-dä'd-män'tĕ)	130	22.34 N	98.58 W
Ciudad Manual Doblado, Mex. (syo͞o-dä'd-män-wäl'dō-blä'dō)	130	20.43 N	101.57 W
Ciudad Obregón, Mex. (syo͞o-dhädh-ô-brē-gō'n)	128	27.40 N	109.58 W
Ciudad Real, Sp. (thyo͞o-dhädh'rā-äl')	170	38.59 N	3.55 W
Ciudad Rodrigo, Sp. (thyo͞o-dhädh'rô-drē'gō)	170	40.38 N	6.34 W
Ciudad Serdán, Mex. (syo͞o-dä'd-sĕr-dà'n)	131	18.58 N	97.26 W
Ciudad Universitaria (Neigh.), Sp.	65b	40.27 N	3.44 W
Ciudad Victoria, Mex. (syo͞o-dhädh'vēk-tō'rē-ä)	130	23.43 N	99.09 W
Civitavecchia, It. (chē'vē-tä-vĕk'kyä)	172	42.06 N	11.49 E
Cixian, China (tsē shyĕn)	200	36.22 N	114.23 E
Clackamas, Or. (klăc-kȧ'măs)	118c	45.25 N	122.34 W
Claire (L.), Can. (klâr)	96	58.33 N	113.16 W
Clair Engle L., Ca.	116	40.51 N	122.41 W
Clairton, Pa. (klârtŭn)	113e	40.17 N	79.53 W
Clamart, Fr.	64c	48.48 N	2.16 E
Clanton, Al. (klăn'tŭn)	126	32.50 N	86.38 W
Clare, Mi. (klâr)	110	43.50 N	84.45 W
Clare I., Ire.	162	53.46 N	10.00 W
Claremont, Ca. (klâr'mŏnt)	119a	34.06 N	117.43 W
Claremont, Eng.	62	51.21 N	0.22 W
Claremont, NH (klâr'mŏnt)	111	43.20 N.	72.20 W
Claremont, WV	110	37.55 N	81.00 W
Claremore, Ok. (klâr'mōr)	123	36.16 N	95.37 W
Claremorris, Ire. (klâr-mŏr'ĭs)	162	53.46 N	9.05 W
Clarence Str., Ak.	98	55.25 N	132.00 W
Clarence Str., Austl. (klăr'ĕns)	214	12.15 S	130.05 E
Clarence Town, Ba.	135	23.05 N	75.00 W
Clarendon, Ar. (klăr'ĕn-dŭn)	123	34.42 N	91.17 W
Clarendon, Tx.	122	34.55 N	100.52 W
Clarens, S. Afr. (clâ-rĕns)	227c	28.34 S	28.26 E
Claresholm, Can. (klâr'ĕs-hōlm)	100	50.02 N	113.35 W

PLACE (Pronounciation)	PAGE	Lat. °'	Long. °'
Clarinda, Ia. (klȧ-rĭn'dȧ)	115	40.42 N	95.00 W
Clarines, Ven. (klä-rē'nës)	143b	9.57 N	65.10 W
Clarion, Ia. (klăr'ĭ-ŭn)	115	42.43 N	93.45 W
Clarion, Pa.	111	41.10 N	79.25 W
Clark, NJ	55	40.38 N	74.19 W
Clark, SD (klärk)	114	44.52 N	97.45 W
Clarkdale, Az (klärk-dāl)	121	34.45 N	112.05 W
Clarke City, Can.	104	50.12 N	66.38 W
Clarke Ra, Austl.	215	20.30 S	148.00 E
Clark Fork (R.), Mt.	117	47.50 N	115.35 W
Clark Hill Res., Ga.-SC (klärk-hĭl)	127	33.50 N	82.35 W
Clark, Pt, Can.	110	44.05 N	81.50 W
Clarksburg, WV (klärkz'bûrg)	111	39.15 N	80.20 W
Clarksdale, Ms. (klärks-dāl)	126	34.10 N	90.31 W
Clark's Harbour, Can. (klärks)	104	43.26 N	65.38 W
Clarkson, Can.	54c	43.31 N	79.37 W
Clarkston, Ga. (klärks'tŭn)	112c	33.49 N	84.15 W
Clarkston, Wa.	116	46.24 N	117.01 W
Clarksville, Ar. (klärks-vĭl)	123	35.28 N	93.26 W
Clarksville, Tn.	126	36.30 N	87.23 W
Clarksville, Tx.	123	33.37 N	95.02 W
Clatskanie, Or.	118c	46.04 N	123.11 W
Clatskanie (R.), Or. (klăt-skā'nē)	118c	46.06 N	123.11 W
Clatsop Spit, Or. (klăt-sŏp)	118c	46.13 N	124.04 W
Cláudio, Braz. (klou'-dēō)	141a	20.26 S	44.44 W
Claveria, Phil. (klä-vå-rē'ä)	203	18.38 N	121.08 E
Clawson, Mi. (klô's'n)	113b	42.32 N	83.09 W
Claxton, Ga. (klăks'tŭn)	127	32.07 N	81.54 W
Clay, Ky. (klā)	126	37.28 N	87.50 W
Clay Center, Ks. (klā sĕn'tẽr)	123	39.23 N	97.08 W
Clay City, Ky. (klā sĭ'tĭ)	110	37.50 N	83.55 W
Claycomo, Mo. (kla-kō'mo)	115f	39.12 N	94.30 W
Clay Cross, Eng. (klā krŏs)	156	53.10 N	1.25 W
Claye-Souilly, Fr. (klĕ-sōō-yē')	169b	48.56 N	2.43 E
Claygate, Eng.	62	51.22 N	0.20 W
Claygate Cross, Eng.	62	51.16 N	0.19 E
Claymont, De. (klā-mŏnt)	112f	39.48 N	75.28 W
Clayton, Al. (klā'tŭn)	126	31.52 N	85.25 W
Clayton, Ca.	118b	37.56 N	121.56 W
Clayton, Eng.	156	53.47 N	1.49 W
Clayton, Mo.	119e	38.39 N	90.20 W
Clayton, NC	127	35.40 N	78.27 W
Clayton, NM	122	36.26 N	103.12 W
Clear (L.), Ca.	120	39.05 N	122.50 W
Clear Boggy Cr., Ok. (klēr bŏg'ĭ krēk)	123	34.21 N	96.22 W
Clear Cr., Az.	121	34.40 N	111.05 W
Clear Cr., Tx.	125a	29.34 N	95.13 W
Clear Cr., Wy.	117	44.35 N	106.20 W
Clearfield, Pa. (klēr-fēld)	111	41.00 N	78.25 W
Clearfield, Ut.	119b	41.07 N	112.01 W
Clear Hills, Can.	96	57.11 N	119.20 W
Clearing (Neigh.), Il.	58a	41.47 N	87.47 W
Clear Lake, Ia.	115	43.09 N	93.23 W
Clear Lake, Wa.	118a	48.27 N	122.14 W
Clear Lake Res., Ca.	116	41.53 N	121.00 W
Clearwater, Fl. (klēr-wô'tẽr)	127a	27.43 N	82.45 W
Clearwater (R.), Can.	99	52.00 N	114.50 W
Clearwater (R.), Can.	99	52.00 N	120.10 W
Clearwater (R.), Can.	100	56.10 N	110.40 W
Clearwater (R.), Id.	116	46.27 N	116.33 W
Clearwater (R.) Middle Fork, Id.	116	46.10 N	115.48 W
Clearwater (R.) North Fork, Id.	116	46.34 N	116.08 W
Clearwater (R.) South Fork, Id.	116	45.46 N	115.53 W
Clearwater Mts., Id.	116	45.56 N	115.15 W
Clearwater Res., Mo.	123	37.20 N	91.04 W
Cleburne, Tx. (klē'bŭrn)	125	32.21 N	97.23 W
Cle Elum, Wa. (klē ĕl'ŭm)	116	47.12 N	120.55 W
Clementon, NJ (klē'mĕn-tŭn)	112f	39.49 N	75.00 W
Cleobury Mortimer, Eng. (klēō-bĕr'ĭ môr'tĭ-mĕr)	156	52.22 N	2.29 W
Clermont, Austl. (klēr'mŏnt)	215	23.02 S	147.46 E
Clermont, Can.	104	47.45 N	70.20 W
Clermont-Ferrand, Fr. (klĕr-môn'fĕr-răn')	168	45.47 N	3.03 E
Cleveland, Ms. (klēv'lănd)	126	33.45 N	90.42 W
Cleveland, Oh.	113d	41.30 N	81.42 W
Cleveland, Ok.	123	36.18 N	96.28 W
Cleveland, Tn.	126	35.09 N	84.52 W
Cleveland, Tx.	125	30.18 N	95.05 W
Cleveland Heights, Oh.	113d	41.30 N	81.35 W
Cleveland Museum of Art (P. Int.), Oh.	56a	41.31 N	81.37 W
Cleveland Park (Neigh.), DC	56d	38.56 N	77.04 W
Cleveland Pen., Ak.	98	55.45 N	132.00 W
Cleves, Oh. (klē'vĕs)	113f	39.10 N	84.45 W
Clew B., Ire. (kloo)	162	53.47 N	9.45 W
Clewiston, Fl. (klē'wis-tŭn)	127a	26.44 N	80.55 W
Clichy, Fr. (klē-shē')	169b	48.54 N	2.18 E
Clichy-sous-Bois, Fr.	64c	48.55 N	2.33 E
Clifden, Ire. (klĭf'dĕn)	162	53.31 N	10.04 W
Cliffside Park, NJ	55	40.49 N	73.59 W
Clifton, Az. (klĭf'tŭn)	121	33.05 N	109.20 W
Clifton, Ma.	54a	42.29 N	70.53 W
Clifton, NJ	112a	40.52 N	74.09 W
Clifton, SC	127	35.00 N	81.47 W
Clifton, Tx.	125	31.45 N	97.31 W
Clifton Forge, Va.	111	37.50 N	79.50 W
Clifton Heights, Pa.	56b	39.56 N	75.18 W
Clinch (R.), Tn.-Va. (klĭnch)	126	36.30 N	83.19 W
Clingmans Dome (Mtn.), NC (klĭng'măns dōm)	126	35.37 N	83.26 W
Clinton, Can. (klĭn-'tŭn)	99	51.05 N	121.35 W
Clinton, Ia.	115	41.50 N	90.13 W
Clinton, Il.	110	40.10 N	88.55 W
Clinton, In.	110	39.40 N	87.25 W
Clinton, Ky.	126	36.39 N	88.56 W
Clinton, Ma.	105a	42.25 N	71.41 W
Clinton, Md.	112e	38.46 N	76.54 W
Clinton, Mo.	123	38.23 N	93.46 W
Clinton, NC	127	35.58 N	78.20 W
Clinton, Ok.	122	35.31 N	98.56 W

PLACE (Pronounciation)	PAGE	Lat. °'	Long. °'
Clinton, SC	127	34.27 N	81.53 W
Clinton, Tn.	126	36.05 N	84.08 W
Clinton, Wa.	118a	47.59 N	122.22 W
Clinton-Colden (L.), Can.	96	63.58 N	106.34 W
Clinton R., Mi.	113b	42.36 N	83.00 W
Clintonville, Wi. (klĭn'tŭn-vĭl)	115	44.37 N	88.46 W
Clio, Mi. (klē'ō)	110	43.10 N	83.45 W
Cloates, Pt., Austl. (klōts)	214	22.47 S	113.45 E
Clocolan, S. Afr.	223d	28.56 S	27.35 E
Clonakilty B., Ire. (klŏn-ȧ-kĭltē)	162	51.30 N	8.50 W
Cloncurry, Austl. (klŏn-kŭr'ē)	214	20.58 S	140.42 E
Clonmel, Ire. (klŏn-mĕl)	162	52.21 N	7.45 W
Clontarf, Austl.	70a	33.48 S	151.16 E
Cloquet, Mn. (klô-kā')	119h	46.42 N	92.28 W
Closter, NJ (klōs'tẽr)	112a	40.58 N	73.57 W
Cloud Pk., Wy. (kloud)	117	44.23 N	107.11 W
Clover, SC (klō'vẽr)	127	35.08 N	81.08 W
Clover Bar, Can. (klō'vẽr bär)	95g	53.34 N	113.20 W
Cloverdale, Can.	118d	49.06 N	122.44 W
Cloverdale, Ca. (klō'vẽr-dāl)	120	38.47 N	123.03 W
Cloverdene, S. Afr.	71b	26.09 S	28.22 E
Cloverport, Ky. (klō'vẽr pōrt)	110	37.50 N	86.35 W
Clovis, NM (klō'vĭs)	122	34.24 N	103.11 W
Cluj-Napoca, Rom.	167	46.46 N	23.34 E
Clun (R.), Eng. (klŭn)	156	52.25 N	2.56 W
Cluny, Fr. (klü-nē')	168	46.27 N	4.40 E
Clutha (R.), N.Z. (kloo'thȧ)	215a	45.52 S	169.30 E
Clwyd (Co.), Wales	156	53.01 N	2.59 W
Clyde, Ks.	123	39.34 N	97.23 W
Clyde, Oh.	110	41.15 N	83.00 W
Clyde (R.), Scot.	162	55.35 N	3.50 W
Clyde, Firth of, Scot. (fûrth ŏv klīd)	162	55.28 N	5.01 W
Côa (R.), Port. (kô'ä)	170	40.28 N	6.55 W
Coacalco, Mex. (kō-ä-käl'kō)	131a	19.37 N	99.06 W
Coachella, Can., Ca. (kō'chĕl-lȧ)	120	33.15 N	115.25 W
Coahuayana, Rio de (R.), Mex. (rē'ō-dĕ-kō-ä-wä-yä'nä)	130	19.00 N	103.33 W
Coahuayutla, Mex. (kō'ä-wī-yōōt'lä)	130	18.19 N	101.44 W
Coahuila (State), Mex. (kō-ä-wē'lä)	128	27.30 N	103.00 W
Coal City, Il. (kōl sĭ'tĭ)	113a	41.17 N	88.17 W
Coalcomán de Matamoros, Mex. (kō-äl-kō-män'dä mä-tä-mō'rôs)	130	18.46 N	103.10 W
Coalcomán, Rio de (R.), Mex. (rē'ō-dĕ-kō-äl-kō-män')	130	18.45 N	103.15 W
Coalcomán, Sierra de (Mts.), Mex. (svĕr'rä dā kō-äl-kō-män')	130	18.30 N	102.45 W
Coaldale, Can. (kōl'dāl)	100	49.43 N	112.37 W
Coaldale, Nv.	120	38.02 N	117.57 W
Coalgate, Ok. (kōl'gāt)	123	34.44 N	96.13 W
Coal Grove, Oh. (kōl grōv)	110	38.20 N	82.40 W
Coal Hill Park (P. Int.), China	67b	39.56 N	116.23 E
Coalinga, Ca. (kō-ȧ-lĭŋ'gȧ)	120	36.09 N	120.23 W
Coalville, Eng. (kōl'vĭl)	156	52.43 N	1.21 W
Coamo, P.R. (kō-ä'mō)	129b	18.05 N	66.21 W
Coari, Braz. (kō-är'ē)	142	4.06 S	63.10 W
Coast Mts., Can. (kōst)	98	54.10 N	128.00 W
Coast Ranges (Mts.), U.S.	108	41.28 N	123.30 W
Coatepec, Mex. (kō-ä-tā-pĕk)	130	19.23 N	98.44 W
Coatepec, Mex.	131d	19.08 N	99.25 W
Coatepec, Mex.	131	19.26 N	96.56 W
Coatepeque, Guat. (kō-ä-tå-pā'kå)	132	14.40 N	91.52 W
Coatepeque, Sal.	132	13.56 N	89.30 W
Coatesville, Pa. (kōts'vĭl)	111	40.00 N	75.50 W
Coatetelco, Mex. (kō-ä-tå-tĕl'kō)	130	18.43 N	99.47 W
Coaticook, Can. (kō'tĭ-ko͝ok)	111	45.10 N	71.55 W
Coatlinchán, Mex. (kô-ä-tlē'n-chä'n)	131a	19.26 N	98.52 W
Coats (I.), Can. (kōts)	97	62.23 N	82.11 W
Coats Land (Reg.), Ant.	232	74.00 S	30.00 W
Coatzacoalcos (Puerto México), Mex. (kō-ät'zä-kô-äl'kōs) (pwĕ'r-tô-mĕ'-kē-kō)	131	18.09 N	94.26 W
Coatzacoalcos (R.), Mex.	131	17.40 N	94.41 W
Coba (Ruins), Mex. (kô'bä)	132a	20.23 N	87.23 W
Cobalt, Can. (kō'bôlt)	97	47.21 N	79.40 W
Cobán, Guat. (kō-bän')	132	15.28 N	90.19 W
Cobar, Austl.	216	31.28 S	145.50 E
Cobberas, Mt., Austl. (cŏ-bĕr-ăs)	216	36.45 S	148.15 E
Cobequid Mts., Can.	104	45.35 N	64.10 W
Cobh, Ire. (kôv)	162	51.52 N	8.09 W
Cobham, Eng.	62	51.23 N	0.24 E
Cobija, Bol. (kō-bē'hä)	142	11.12 S	68.49 W
Cobourg, Can. (kō'bo͝orgh)	111	43.55 N	78.05 W
Cobre (R.), Jam. (kō'brā)	134	18.05 N	77.00 W
Cóbuè, Moz.	231	12.04 S	34.50 E
Coburg, Austl.	70b	37.45 S	144.58 E
Coburg, F.R.G. (kō'bo͝org)	166	50.16 N	10.57 E
Cocentaina, Sp. (kō-thĕn-tä-ē'nȧ)	171	38.44 N	0.27 W
Cochabamba, Bol. (kō-chä-bäm'bä)	142	17.30 S	66.08 W
Cochem, F.R.G. (kō'kĕm)	169	50.10 N	7.06 E
Cochin, India (kō-chĭn')	197	9.58 N	76.19 E
Cochinos, Bahia (B.), Cuba (bä-ē'ä-kô-chē'nōs)	134	22.05 N	81.10 W
Cochinos Bks., Ba.	135	22.20 N	76.15 W
Cochita Res., NM	121	35.45 N	106.10 W
Cochran, Ga. (kŏk'răn)	126	32.23 N	83.23 W
Cochrane, Can. (kŏk'răn)	97	49.01 N	81.06 W
Cochrane, Can.	95e	51.11 N	114.28 W
Cockburn (I.), Can. (kŏk-bûrn)	110	45.55 N	83.25 W
Cockeysville, Md. (kŏk'ĭz-vĭl)	112e	39.30 N	76.40 W
Cockfosters (Neigh.), Eng.	62	51.39 N	0.09 W
Cockrell Hill, Tx. (kŏk'rĕl)	119c	32.44 N	96.53 W
Coco (Segovia) (R.), Hond-Nic. (kō-kō) (sĕ-gô'vyä)	133	14.55 N	83.45 W
Cocoa, Fl. (kō'kō)	127a	28.21 N	80.44 W
Cocoa Beach, Fl.	127a	28.20 N	80.35 W
Coco, Cayo (I.), Cuba (kä'-yō-kō'kô)	134	22.30 S	78.30 W
Coco, Isla del (I.), C.R. (ē's-lä-dĕl-kô-kô)	128	5.33 N	87.02 W
Cocoli, Pan. (kō-kō'lē)	128a	8.58 N	79.36 W
Coconino, Plat., Az. (kō kō nē'nō)	121	35.45 N	112.28 W
Cocos (Keeling) Is., Oceania (kō'kôs) (kē'lĭng)	7	11.50 S	90.50 E

PLACE (Pronounciation)	PAGE	Lat. °'	Long. °'
Coco Solito, Pan. (kô-kô-sō-lē'tō)	128a	9.21 N	79.53 W
Cocotá (Neigh.), Braz.	61c	22.49 S	43.11 W
Cocula, Mex. (kō-ko͞o'lä)	130	20.23 N	103.47 W
Cocula (R.), Mex.	130	18.17 N	99.11 W
Codajás, Braz. (kō-dä-häzh')	142	3.44 N	62.09 W
Codera, Cabo (C.), Ven. (kä'bô-kō-dĕ'rä)	143b	10.35 N	66.06 W
Codó, Braz. (kō'dō)	143	4.21 S	43.52 W
Codogno, It. (kô-dō'nyō)	172	45.08 N	9.43 E
Codrington, Antigua (kŏd'rĭng-tŭn)	133	17.39 N	61.49 W
Cody, Wy. (kō'dĭ)	11	44.31 N	109.02 W
Côe d'Or (hill), Fr. (kōr-dōr')	168	47.02 N	4.35 E
Coelho da Rocha, Braz.	61c	22.47 S	43.23 W
Coemba, Ang.	230	12.08 S	18.05 E
Coesfeld, F.R.G. (kûs'fĕld)	169c	51.56 N	7.10 E
Coeur d' Alene, Id. (kûr dȧ-lān')	116	47.43 N	116.35 W
Coeur d' Alene (L.), Id.	116	47.32 N	116.39 W
Coeur d' Alene (R.), Id.	116	47.26 N	116.35 W
Coffeyville, Ks. (kŏf'ĭ-vĭl)	123	37.01 N	95.38 W
Coff's Harbour, Austl.	216	30.20 S	153.10 E
Cofimvaba, S. Afr. (căfĭm'vä-bȧ)	227c	32.01 S	27.37 E
Coghinas (R.), It. (kō'gē-nàs)	172	40.31 N	9.00 E
Cognac, Fr. (kôn-yak')	168	45.41 N	0.22 W
Cohasset, Ma. (kō-hăs'ĕt)	105a	42.14 N	70.48 W
Cohoes, NY (kō-hōz')	111	42.50 N	73.40 W
Coig (R.), Arg. (kô'ĕk)	144	51.15 S	71.00 W
Coimbatore, India (kō-ēm-bȧ-tôr')	197	11.03 N	76.56 E
Coimbra, Port. (kō-ēm'brä)	170	40.14 N	8.23 W
Coina, Port. (kō-ē'nȧ)	171b	38.35 N	9.03 W
Coina (R.), Port. (kô'y-nä)	171b	38.35 N	9.02 W
Coipasa, Salar de (Salt Flat), Chile (sä-lä'r-dĕ-koi-pä'-sä)	142	19.12 S	69.13 W
Coín, Sp. (kō-ēn')	170	36.40 N	4.45 W
Coixtlahuaca, Mex. (kō-ēks'tlä-wä'kä)	131	17.42 N	97.17 W
Cojedes (State), Ven. (kô-kĕ'dĕs)	143b	9.50 N	68.21 W
Cojimar, Cuba (kō-hē-mär')	135a	23.10 N	82.19 W
Cojutepeque, Sal. (kô-hōō-tĕ-pā'kå)	132	13.45 N	88.50 W
Cokato, Mn. (kō-kā'tō)	115	45.03 N	94.11 W
Cokeburg, Pa. (kōk bŭgh)	113e	40.06 N	80.03 W
Coker, Nig.	71d	6.29 N	3.20 E
Colāba (Neigh.), India	67e	18.54 N	72.48 E
Colac, Austl. (kŏ'lȧc)	216	38.25 S	143.40 E
Colares, Port. (kô-lä'rĕs)	171b	38.47 N	9.27 W
Colatina, Braz. (kō-lä-tē'nä)	143	19.33 S	40.42 W
Colby, Ks. (kōl'bĭ)	122	39.23 N	101.04 W
Colchagua (Prov.), Chile (kôl-chá'gwä)	141b	34.42 S	71.24 W
Colchester, Eng. (kōl'chĕs-tẽr)	163	51.52 N	0.50 E
Coldblow (Neigh.), Eng.	62	51.26 N	0.10 E
Cold L., Can. (kōld)	100	54.33 N	110.05 W
Coldwater, Ks. (kōld'wô-tẽr)	122	37.14 N	99.21 W
Coldwater, Mi.	110	41.55 N	85.00 W
Coldwater (R.), Ms.	126	34.25 N	90.12 W
Coldwater Cr., Tx.	122	36.10 N	101.45 W
Coleman, Tx. (kōl'mȧn)	124	31.50 N	99.25 W
Colenso, S.Afr. (kō-lĕnz'ō)	227c	28.48 S	29.49 E
Coleraine, Mn. (kōl-rān')	115	47.16 N	93.29 W
Coleraine, N. Ire.	162	55.08 N	6.40 W
Coleshill, Eng. (kōlz'hĭl)	156	52.30 N	1.42 W
Colfax, Ia. (kōl'făks)	115	41.40 N	93.13 W
Colfax, La.	125	31.31 N	92.42 W
Colfax, Wa.	116	46.53 N	117.21 W
Colhué Huapi (L.), Arg. (kôl-wā'o͞oá'pē)	144	45.30 S	68.45 W
Coligny, S.Afr.	223d	26.20 S	26.18 E
Colima, Mex. (kōlē'mä)	130	19.13 N	103.45 W
Colima (State), Mex.	130	19.10 N	104.00 W
Colima, Nevado de (Mtn.), Mex. (nĕ-vä'dô-dĕ-kō-lē'mä)	130	19.30 N	103.38 W
Coll (I.), Scot. (kŏl)	162	56.42 N	6.23 W
College, Ak.	107	64.43 N	147.50 W
College Park, Ga. (kŏl'ĕj)	112c	33.39 N	84.27 W
College Park, Md.	112e	38.59 N	76.58 W
College Point (Neigh.), NY	55	40.47 N	73.51 W
Collegeville, Pa. (kŏl'ĕj-vĭl)	112f	40.11 N	75.27 W
Collie, Austl. (kŏl'ē)	214	33.20 S	116.20 E
Collier B., Austl. (kōl-yẽr)	214	15.30 S	123.30 E
Collier Row (Neigh.), Eng.	62	51.36 N	0.10 E
Collingdale, Pa.	56b	39.55 N	75.17 W
Collingswood, NJ (kŏl'ĭngz-wo͝od)	112f	39.54 N	75.04 W
Collingwood, Austl.	70b	37.48 S	145.00 E
Collingwood, Can.	110	44.30 N	80.20 W
Collins, Ms. (kŏl'ĭns)	126	31.40 N	89.34 W
Collinsville, Il. (kŏl'ĭnz-vĭl)	119e	38.41 N	89.59 W
Collinsville, Ok.	123	36.21 N	95.50 W
Colmar, Fr. (kôl'mär)	169	48.03 N	7.25 E
Colmenar de Oreja, Sp. (kôl-mā-när'dāōrā'hä)	170	40.06 N	3.25 W
Colmenar Viejo, Sp. (kôl-mā-när'vyā'hō)	171a	40.40 N	3.46 W
Colnbrook, Eng.	62	51.29 N	0.31 W
Colney Heath, Eng.	62	51.44 N	0.15 W
Colney Street, Eng.	62	51.42 N	0.20 W
Cologne, see Köln			
Cologno Monzese, It.	65c	45.32 N	9.17 E
Colombes, Fr.	64c	48.55 N	2.15 E
Colombia, Col. (kô-lôm'bē-ä)	142a	3.23 N	74.48 W
Colombia, S.A.	140	3.30 N	72.30 W
Colombo, Sri Lanka (kô-lôm'bō)	197	6.58 N	79.52 W
Colón, Arg. (kō-lōn')	141c	33.55 S	61.08 W
Colón, Cuba (kô-lô'n)	134	22.45 N	80.55 W
Colón, Mex. (kō-lōn')	130	20.46 N	100.02 W
Colón, Pan. (kō-lō'n)	128a	9.22 N	79.54 W
Colonail Park, Md.	56c	39.19 N	76.45 W
Colon, Arch. de (Galápagos Is.), Ec. (är-chē-pyĕ'l-ägō-dĕ-kō-lōn') (gä-lá'pägōs)	142	0.10 S	87.45 W
Colonia (Dept.), Ur.	141c	34.08 S	57.50 W
Colonia, NJ	55	40.35 N	74.18 W
Colonia, Ur. (kō-lō'nē-ä)	141c	34.27 S	57.50 W

ăt; finăl; rāte; senåte; ärm; ȧsk; sofȧ; fâre; ch-choose; dh-as th in other; bē; ēvent; bĕt; recĕnt; cratẽr; g-gō; gh-guttural g; bĭt; ĭ-short neutral; rīde; K-guttural k as ch in German ich;

PLACE (Pronounciation)	PAGE	Lat. °′	Long. °′
Colonial Manor, NJ	56b	39.51 N	75.09 W
Colonia Suiza, Ur. (kô-lô'nēä-sōōē'zä)	141c	34.17 S	57.15 W
Colōn, Montañas de (Mts.), Hond. (môn-tä'n-yäs-dĕ-kŏ-lô'n)	133	14.58 N	84.39 W
Colonna, Capo (C.), It.	173	39.02 N	17.15 E
Colonsay (I.), Scot. (kŏl-ŏn-sā')	162	56.08 N	6.08 E
Coloradas, Lomas (Hills), Arg. (lô'mäs-kō-lō-rä'däs)	144	43.30 S	68.00 W
Colorado (R.), Tx.	125	30.08 N	97.33 W
Colorado (State), U.S.	108	39.30 N	106.55 W
Colorado City, Tx. (kŏl-ô-rä'dō sĭ'tĭ)	124	32.24 N	100.50 W
Colorado Natl. Mon., Co.	121	39.00 N	108.40 W
Colorado Plat, U.S.	108	36.20 N	109.25 W
Colorado R., U.S.	108	36.25 N	112.00 W
Colorado, Rio (R.), Arg.	144	38.30 S	66.00 W
Colorado River Aqueducts, Ca.	120	33.38 N	115.43 W
Colorado River Ind. Res., Az.	121	34.03 N	114.02 W
Colorados, Arch. de los (Is.), Cuba (är-chē-pyĕ-lä-gô-dĕ-lôs-kô-lô-rä'dôs)	134	22.25 N	84.25 W
Colorado Springs, Co. (kŏl-ô-rä'dō)	122	38.49 N	104.48 W
Colosseo (P. Int.), It.	66c	41.54 N	12.29 E
Colotepec (R.), Mex. (kô-lô'tĕ-pĕk)	131	15.56 N	96.57 W
Colotlán, Mex. (kô-lô-tlän')	130	22.06 N	103.14 W
Colotlán (R.), Mex.	130	22.09 N	103.17 W
Colquechaca, Bol. (kôl-kā-chä'kä)	142	18.47 S	66.02 W
Colstrip, Mt. (kōl'strĭp)	117	45.54 N	106.38 W
Colton, Ca. (kōl'tŭn)	119a	34.04 N	117.20 W
Columbia, Il. (kô-lŭm'bĭ-ā)	119e	38.26 N	90.12 W
Columbia, Ky.	126	37.06 N	85.15 W
Columbia, Md.	112e	39.15 N	76.51 W
Columbia, Mo.	123	38.55 N	92.19 W
Columbia, Ms.	126	31.15 N	89.49 W
Columbia, Pa.	111	40.00 N	76.25 W
Columbia, SC	127	34.00 N	81.00 W
Columbia, TN	126	35.36 N	87.02 W
Columbia (R.), Can.-U.S.	96	46.20 N	123.00 W
Columbia (R.), Can.	99	51.30 N	119.00 W
Columbia City, In.	110	41.10 N	85.30 W
Columbia City, Or.	118c	45.53 N	112.49 W
Columbia Heights, Mn.	119g	45.03 N	93.15 W
Columbia Icefield, Can.	99	52.08 N	117.26 W
Columbia, Mt., Can.	99	52.09 N	117.25 W
Columbia Mts., Can.	99	51.30 N	118.30 W
Columbiana, Al. (kô-ŭm-bĭ-ă'nā)	126	33.10 N	86.35 W
Columbia University (P. Int.), NY	55	40.48 N	73.58 W
Columbretes (I.), Sp. (kô-lōōm-brĕ'tĕs)	171	39.54 N	0.54 E
Columbus, Ga. (kô-lŭm'bŭs)	126	32.29 N	84.56 W
Columbus, In.	110	39.15 N	85.55 W
Columbus, Ks.	123	37.10 N	94.50 W
Columbus, Ms.	126	33.30 N	88.25 W
Columbus, Mt.	117	45.39 N	109.15 W
Columbus, Ne.	114	41.25 N	97.25 W
Columbus, NM	121	31.50 N	107.40 W
Columbus, Oh.	110	40.00 N	83.00 W
Columbus, Tx.	125	29.44 N	96.34 W
Columbus, Wi.	115	43.20 N	89.01 W
Columbus Bk., Ba. (kô-lŭm'bŭs)	135	22.05 N	75.30 W
Columbus Grove, Oh.	110	40.55 N	84.05 W
Columbus Pt., Ba.	135	24.10 N	75.15 W
Colusa, Ca. (kô-lū'să)	120	39.12 N	122.01 W
Colville (R.), Ak.	107	69.00 N	156.25 W
Colville, Wa. (kŏl'vĭl)	116	48.33 N	117.53 W
Colville R, Wa.	116	48.25 N	117.58 W
Colvos Pass., Wa. (kŏl'vōs)	118a	47.24 N	122.32 W
Colwood, Can. (kŏl'wŏŏd)	118a	48.26 N	123.30 W
Colwyn, Pa.	56b	39.55 N	75.15 W
Comacchio, It. (kô-mäk'kyō)	172	44.42 N	12.12 E
Comala, Mex. (kō-mä-lä')	130	19.22 N	103.47 W
Comalapa, Guat. (kō-mä-lä'-pä)	132	14.43 N	90.56 W
Comalcalco, Mex. (kō-mäl-käl'kō)	131	18.16 N	93.13 W
Comanche, Ok. (kô-măn'chē)	122	34.20 N	97.58 W
Comanche, Tx.	124	31.54 N	98.37 W
Comanche Cr., Tx.	124	31.02 N	102.47 W
Comas, Peru	60c	11.57 S	77.04 W
Comayagua, Hond. (kō-mä-yä'gwä)	132	14.24 N	87.36 W
Combahee (R.), SC (kŏm-bă-hē')	127	32.42 N	80.40 W
Comer, Ga. (kŭm'ēr)	126	34.02 N	83.07 W
Comete, C., Turks & Caicos (kō-mā'tā)	135	21.45 N	71.25 W
Comilla, Bngl. (kô-mĭl'ä)	196	23.33 N	91.17 E
Comino, C., It. (kô-mē'nō)	172	40.30 N	9.48 E
Comitán, Mex. (kô-mē-tän')	132	16.16 N	92.09 W
Commencement B., Wa. (kŏ-mĕns'mĕnt bā)	118a	47.17 N	122.21 W
Commentry, Fr. (kŏ-mäN-trē')	168	46.16 N	2.44 E
Commerce, Ga. (kŏm'ẽrs)	126	34.10 N	83.27 W
Commerce, Ok.	123	36.57 N	94.54 W
Commerce, Tx.	123	33.15 N	95.52 W
Como, Austl.	70a	34.00 S	151.04 E
Como, It. (kō'mō)	172	45.48 N	9.03 E
Comodoro Rivadavia, Arg. (kō'mō-dō'rō rē-vä-dä'vē-ä)	144	45.47 S	67.31 W
Como-Est, Can.	95a	45.27 N	74.08 W
Como, Lago di (L.), It. (lä'gō-dē-kō'mō)	172	46.00 N	9.30 E
Comonfort, Mex. (kô-mōn-fô'rt)	130	20.43 N	100.47 W
Comorin C., India (kŏ'mô-rĭn)	197	8.05 N	78.05 E
Comoros, Afr.	222	12.30 S	42.45 E
Comox, Can. (kō'mŏks)	98	49.40 N	124.55 W
Compainalá, Mex. (kôm-pä-ē-nä-lä')	131	17.05 N	93.11 W
Companario, Cerro (Mtn.), Arg.-Chile (sĕ'r-rô-kôm-pä-nä'ryô)	141b	35.54 S	70.23 W
Compans, Fr.	64c	49.00 N	2.40 E
Compiègne, Fr. (kôN-pyĕn'y')	168	49.25 N	2.49 E
Comporta, Port. (kôm-pôr'tă)	171b	38.24 N	8.48 W
Compostela, Mex. (kŏm-pō-stā'lä)	130	21.41 N	104.54 W
Compton, Ca. (kŏmpt'tŭn)	119a	33.54 N	118.14 W
Cona (R.), Ga. (kô-nà)	126	34.40 N	84.51 W
Conakry, Gui. (kô-nà-krē')	228	9.31 N	13.43 W

PLACE (Pronounciation)	PAGE	Lat. °′	Long. °′
Conanicut (I.), RI (kŏn'ă-nĭ-kŭt)	112b	41.34 N	71.20 W
Concarneau, Fr. (kôN-kär-nō')	168	47.54 N	3.52 W
Concepción, Bol. (kôn-sĕp'syōn')	143	15.47 S	61.08 W
Concepción, Chile	144	36.51 S	72.59 W
Concepción, Pan.	133	8.31 N	82.38 W
Concepción, Par.	144	23.29 S	57.18 W
Concepcion, Phil.	207a	15.19 N	120.40 E
Concepción (R.), Mex.	128	30.25 N	112.20 W
Concepción (Vol.), Nic.	132	11.36 N	85.43 W
Concepción del Mar, Guat. (kôn-sĕp-syōn'dĕl mär')	132	14.07 N	91.23 W
Concepción del Oro, Mex. (kôn-sĕp-syōn' dĕl ō'rō)	124	24.39 N	101.24 W
Concepción del Uruguary, Arg. (kôn-sĕp-syô'n-dĕl-ōō-rōō-gwī')	144	32.31 S	58.10 W
Conception (I.), Ba.	135	23.50 N	75.05 W
Conception B., Can. (kŏn-sĕp'shŭn)	105	47.50 N	52.50 W
Conception, Pt., Ca.	120	34.27 N	120.28 W
Conchali, Chile	61b	33.24 S	70.39 W
Concho (R.), Tx. (kŏn'chō)	124	31.34 N	100.00 W
Conchos (R.), Mex. (kōn'chōs)	124	25.03 N	99.00 W
Conchos (R.), Mex.	124	29.08 N	105.02 W
Concord, Austl.	70a	33.52 S	151.06 E
Concord, Ca. (kŏŋ'kẽrd)	118b	37.58 N	122.02 W
Concord, Can., Can.	54c	43.48 N	79.29 W
Concord, Ma.	105a	42.28 N	71.21 W
Concord, NC	127	35.23 N	80.11 W
Concord, NH	111	43.10 N	71.30 W
Concordia, Arg. (kôn-kôr'dĭ-ä)	144	31.18 S	57.59 W
Concordia, Col.	142a	6.04 N	75.54 W
Concordia, Ks.	123	39.32 N	97.39 W
Concordia, Mex. (kôn-kô'r-dyä)	130	23.17 N	106.06 W
Concord West, Austl.	70a	33.51 S	151.05 E
Concrete, Wa. (kŏn-'krēt)	116	48.33 N	121.44 W
Conde, Fr.	168	48.50 N	0.36 W
Conde, SD (kŏn-dē')	114	45.10 N	98.06 W
Condega, Nic. (kŏn-dĕ'gä)	132	13.20 N	86.27 W
Condeúba, Braz. (kōn-dā-ōō'bä)	143	14.47 S	41.44 W
Condom, Fr.	168	43.58 N	0.22 E
Condon, Or. (kŏn'dŭn)	116	45.14 N	120.10 W
Conecun (R.), Al. (kô-nē'kū)	126	31.05 N	86.52 W
Conegliano, It. (kō-nāl-yä'nō)	172	45.59 N	12.17 E
Conejos (R.), Co. (kô-nā'hōs)	121	37.07 N	106.19 W
Conemaugh, Pa. (kŏn'ē-mô)	111	40.25 N	78.50 W
Coney I., NY (kō'nĭ)	112a	40.34 N	73.27 W
Coney Island (Neigh.), NY	55	40.34 N	74.00 W
Conflans-Sainte-Honorine, Fr.	64c	48.59 N	2.06 E
Confolens, Fr. (kôN-fä-läN')	168	46.01 N	0.41 E
Congaree (R.), SC (kŏŋ-gă-rē')	127	33.53 N	80.55 W
Conghua, China (tsōŋ-hwä)	203	23.30 N	113.40 E
Congleton, Eng. (kŏŋ'g'l-tŭn)	156	53.10 N	2.13 W
Congo, Afr. (kŏn'gō)	222	3.00 S	13.48 E
Congo (Zaire) (R.), Afr.	230	1.10 N	18.25 E
Congo Basin, Zaire	222	2.47 N	20.58 E
Congo, Serra do (Mts.), Ang.	230	6.25 S	18.30 E
Congo, The, see Zaire			
Congress Heights (Neigh.), DC.	56d	38.51 N	77.00 W
Conisbrough, Eng. (kŏn'ĭs-bŭr-ō)	156	53.29 N	1.13 W
Coniston, Can.	103	46.29 N	80.51 W
Conklin, Can. (kōŋk'lĭn)	99	55.38 N	111.05 W
Conley, Ga. (kŏn'lĭ)	112c	33.38 N	84.19 W
Connacht (Reg.), Ire. (cŏn'ăt)	162	53.50 N	8.45 W
Connaughton, Pa.	56b	40.05 N	75.19 W
Conneaut, Oh. (kŏn-ē-ôt')	110	41.55 N	80.35 W
Connecticut (State), U.S. (kŏ-nĕt'ĭ-kŭt)	109	41.40 N	73.10 W
Connecticut R., U.S.	111	43.55 N	72.15 W
Connellsville, Pa. (kŏn'nĕlz-vĭl)	111	40.00 N	79.40 W
Connemara (Mts.), Ire. (kŏn-nē-mà'rà)	162	53.30 N	9.54 W
Connersville, In. (kŏn'ĕrz-vĭl)	110	39.35 N	85.10 W
Conn, Lough (L.), Ire. (lŏk kŏn)	162	53.56 N	9.25 W
Connors Ra., Austl. (kŏn'nŏrs)	215	22.15 S	149.00 E
Conrad, Mt. (kŏn'răd)	117	48.11 N	111.56 W
Conrich, Can. (kŏn'rĭch)	95e	51.06 N	113.51 W
Conroe, Tx. (kŏn'rō)	125	30.18 N	95.23 W
Conselheiro Lafaiete, Braz. (kôn-sē-lā'rô-lä-fä'ē-tē)	141a	20.40 S	43.46 W
Conshohocken, Pa. (kŏn-shô-hŏk'ĕn)	112f	40.04 N	75.18 W
Consolação (Neigh.), Braz.	61d	23.33 S	46.39 W
Consolación del Sur, Cuba (kôn-sô-lä-syōn')	134	22.30 N	83.55 W
Consolidated Main Reef Mines (P. Int.), S. Afr.	71b	26.11 S	27.56 E
Con Son (Is.), Viet.	206	8.30 N	106.28 E
Constance, Mt., Wa. (kŏn'stăns)	118a	47.46 N	123.08 W
Constanța, Rom. (kōn-stan'tsä)	161	44.12 N	28.36 E
Constantina, Sp. (kōn-stän-tē'nä)	170	37.52 N	5.39 W
Constantine, Alg. (kôN-stäN-tēn')	224	36.28 N	6.38 E
Constantine, Mi. (kŏn'stăn-tēn)	110	41.50 N	85.40 W
Constitución, Chile (kŏn'stĭ-tōō-syōn')	144	35.24 S	72.25 W
Constitución (Neigh.), Arg.	60d	34.37 S	58.23 W
Constitution, Ga. (kŏn-stĭ-tū'shŭn)	112c	33.41 N	84.20 W
Contagem, Braz. (kôn-tà'zhĕm)	141a	19.54 S	44.05 W
Contepec, Mex. (kôn-tĕ-pĕk')	130	20.04 N	100.07 W
Contreras, Mex. (kôn-trĕ'räs)	131a	19.18 N	99.14 W
Contwoyto (L.), Can.	96	65.42 N	110.50 W
Converse, Tx. (kŏn'vērs)	119d	29.31 N	98.17 W
Conway, Ar. (kŏn'wā)	123	35.06 N	92.27 W
Conway, NH	111	44.00 N	71.10 W
Conway, SC	127	33.49 N	79.01 W
Conway, Wa.	118a	48.20 N	122.20 W
Conyers, Ga. (kŏn'yōrz)	126	33.41 N	84.01 W
Cooch Behār, India (kōōch bē-här')	196	26.25 N	89.34 E
Coogee, Austl.	70a	33.55 S	151.16 E
Cook, Pt., Austl.	70b	37.55 S	144.48 E
Cook, C., Can. (kŏŏk)	98	50.08 N	127.55 W
Cookeville, Tn. (kŏŏk'vĭl)	126	36.07 N	85.30 W
Cooking L., Can.	95g	53.25 N	113.02 W
Cooking Lake, Can. (kŏŏk'ĭng)	95g	53.10 N	113.08 W
Cook Inlet, Ak.	107	60.50 N	151.38 W

PLACE (Pronounciation)	PAGE	Lat. °′	Long. °′
Cook Is., Oceania	209	20.00 S	158.00 W
Cook, Mt., N.Z.	215a	43.27 S	170.13 E
Cooksmill Green, Eng.	62	51.44 N	0.22 E
Cook Str., N.Z.	215a	40.37 S	174.15 E
Cooktown, Austl. (kŏŏk'toun)	215	15.40 S	145.20 E
Cooleemee, NC (kōō-lē'mē)	127	35.50 N	80.32 W
Coolgardie, Austl. (kōōl-gär'dē)	214	31.00 S	121.25 E
Cooma, Austl. (kōō'mà)	216	36.22 S	149.10 E
Coonamble, Austl. (kōō-năm'b'l)	216	31.00 S	148.30 E
Coonoort, India	197	10.22 N	76.15 E
Coon Rapids, Mn. (kōōn)	119g	45.09 N	93.17 W
Cooper, Tx. (kōōp'ēr)	123	33.23 N	95.40 W
Cooper Center, Ak. (kōōp'ēr sĕn'tēr)	107	61.54 N	15.30 W
Coopersale Common, Eng.	62	51.42 N	0.08 E
Coopers Cr., Austl. (kōō'pērz)	216	27.32 N	141.19 E
Cooperstown, ND	114	47.26 N	98.07 W
Cooperstown, NY (kōōp'ērs-toun)	111	42.45 N	74.55 W
Coorong, The (L.), Austl. (kōō'rŏng)	216	36.07 N	319.45 E
Coosa, Al. (kōō'să)	126	32.43 N	86.25 W
Coosa (R.), Al.	126	34.00 N	86.00 W
Coosawattee (R.), Ga. (kōō-să-wôt'ē)	126	34.37 N	84.45 W
Coos B., Or.	116	43.19 N	124.40 W
Coos Bay, Or. (kōōs)	116	43.21 N	124.12 W
Cootamundra, Austl. (kōōtă-mŭnd'ră)	216	34.25 S	148.00 E
Copacabana, Braz. (kô'pä-kà-bà'nä)	144b	22.57 S	43.11 W
Copalita (R.), Mex. (kô-pä-lē'tä)	131	15.55 N	96.06 W
Copán (Ruins), Hond. (kō-pän')	132	14.50 N	89.10 W
Copano B., Tx. (kō-pän'ō)	125	28.08 N	97.25 W
Copenhagen, see København			
Copiapó, Chile (kō-pyä-pō')	144	27.16 S	70.28 W
Copley, Oh. (kŏp'lē)	113d	41.06 N	81.38 W
Copparo, It. (kôp-pä'rō)	172	44.53 N	11.50 E
Coppell, Tx. (kŏp'pĕl)	119c	32.57 N	97.00 W
Copper (R.), Ak. (kŏp'ēr)	107	62.38 N	145.00 W
Copper Cliff, Can.	102	46.28 N	81.04 W
Copper Harbor, Mi.	115	47.27 N	87.53 W
Copperhill, Tn. (kŏp'ēr hĭl)	126	35.00 N	84.22 W
Copperinine (R.), Can.	96	66.48 N	114.59 W
Coppermine, Can. (kŏp'ēr-mīn)	96	67.46 N	115.19 W
Copper Mtn., Ak.	98	55.14 N	132.36 W
Copperton, Ut. (kŏp'ēr-tŭn)	119b	40.34 N	112.06 W
Coquilee, Or. (kō-kēl')	116	43.11 N	124.11 W
Coquilhatville, see Mbandaka			
Coquimbo, Chile (kô-kēm'bō)	144	29.58 S	71.31 W
Coquimbo (Prov.), Chile	141b	31.50 S	71.05 W
Coquitlam (L.) (kō-kwĭt-lăm)	118d	49.23 N	122.44 W
Corabia, Rom. (kô-rä'bĭ-ā)	173	43.45 N	24.29 E
Coracora, Peru (kō'rä-kō'rä)	142	15.12 S	73.42 W
Coral Gables, Fl.	127a	25.43 N	80.14 W
Coral Rapids, Can. (kŏr'ăl)	102	50.18 N	81.49 W
Coral Sea, Oceania (kŏr'ăl)	208	13.30 S	150.00 E
Coralville Res., Ia.	115	41.45 N	91.50 W
Corangamite, L., Austl. (cŏr-ăŋg'á-mīt)	216	38.05 S	142.55 E
Coraopolis, Pa. (kō-rä-ŏp'ō-lĭs)	113e	40.30 N	80.09 W
Corato, It. (kô'rä-tô)	172	41.08 N	16.28 E
Corbeil-Essonnes, Fr. (kôr-bā'yĕ-sŏn')	169b	48.31 N	2.29 E
Corbett, Or. (kôr'bĕt)	118c	45.31 N	122.17 W
Corbie, Fr. (kôr-bē')	168	49.55 N	2.27 E
Corbin, Ky. (kôr'bĭn)	126	36.55 N	84.06 W
Corby, Eng. (kôr'bĭ)	156	52.29 N	0.38 W
Corcovado (Mtn.(, Braz. (kôr-kō-vä'dōō)	144b	22.57 S	43.13 W
Corcovado, Golfo (G.), Chile (kôr-kō-vä'dhō)	144	43.40 S	75.00 W
Cordeiro, Braz. (kôr-dā'rō)	141a	22.03 S	42.22 W
Cordele, Ga. (kôr-dēl')	126	31.55 N	83.50 W
Cordell, Ok. (kôr-dĕl')	122	35.19 N	98.58 W
Cordilleran Highlands (Reg.), N.A. (kōr dĭl'lūr ăn)	94	55.00 N	125.00 W
Córdoba, Arg. (kôr'dô-vä)	144	30.20 S	64.03 W
Córdoba, Mex. (kô'r-dô-bä)	131	18.53 N	96.54 W
Córdoba (Prov.), Arg. (kôr'dô-vä)	144	32.00 S	64.00 W
Córdoba, Sp. (kô'r-dô-bä)	170	37.55 N	4.45 W
Córdoba, Sa. de (Mts.), Arg.	144	31.15 S	64.30 W
Cordova, Ak. (kôr-dō-vä)	107	60.34 N	145.38 W
Cordova, Al. (kôr'dô-ā)	126	33.45 N	86.22 W
Cordova B., Ak.	98	54.55 N	132.35 W
Corfu (I.), see Kérkira			
Corigliano, It. (kō-rē-lyä'nō)	172	39.35 N	16.30 E
Corinth, Ms. (kŏr'ĭnth)	126	34.55 N	88.30 W
Corinth, see Kórinthos			
Corinto, Braz. (kô-rē'n-tō)	143	18.20 S	44.16 W
Corinto, Col.	142a	3.09 N	76.12 W
Corinto, Nic. (kōr-ĭn'to)	132	12.30 N	87.12 W
Corio, Austl.	211a	38.05 S	144.22 E
Corio B., Austl.	211a	38.07 S	144.25 E
Corisco, It.	65c	45.26 N	9.07 E
Corisco, Isal de (I.), Equat. Gui.	230	0.50 N	8.40 E
Cork, Ire. (kôrk)	162	51.54 N	8.25 W
Cork Hbr., Ire.	162	51.44 N	8.15 W
Corleone, It. (kôr-lā-ō'nā)	172	37.48 N	13.18 E
Cormano, It.	65c	45.33 N	9.10 E
Cormeilles-en-Parisis, Fr.	64c	48.59 N	2.12 E
Cormorant L., Can.	101	54.13 N	100.47 W
Cornelia, Ga. (kôr-nē'lyā)	126	34.31 N	83.30 W
Cornelis (R.), S. Afr. (kôr-nē'lĭs)	223d	27.48 S	29.15 E
Cornell, Ca. (kôr-nĕl')	119a	34.06 N	118.46 W
Cornell, Wi.	115	45.10 N	91.10 W
Cornellá, Sp.	65e	41.21 N	2.04 E
Corner Brook, Can. (kôr'nēr)	105	48.57 N	57.57 W
Corner Inlet, Austl.	216	38.55 S	146.45 E
Corning, Ar. (kôr'nĭng)	123	36.26 N	90.35 W
Corning, Ia.	115	40.58 N	94.40 W
Corning, NY	111	42.10 N	77.05 W
Corno, Monte (Mtn.), It. (kôr'nō)	172	42.28 N	13.37 E
Cornwall, Ba.	134	25.55 N	77.15 W
Cornwall, Can. (kôrn'wôl)	111	45.05 N	74.35 W

PLACE (Pronounciation)	PAGE	Lat. °′	Long. °′
Coro, Ven. (kō'rō)	142	11.22 N	69.43 W
Corocoro, Bol. (kō-rō-kō'rō)	142	17.15 S	68.21 W
Coromandel Coast, India (kŏr-ô-man'dĕl)	197	13.30 N	80.30 E
Coromandel Pen., N.Z.	215a	36.50 S	176.00 E
Corona, Al. (kô-rō'nȧ)	126	33.42 N	87.28 W
Corona, Ca.	119a	33.52 N	117.34 W
Coronada, Bahía de (B.), C.R. (bä-ē'ä-dĕ-kō-rō-nä'dō)	133	8.47 N	84.04 W
Corona del Mar, Ca. (kô-rō'nȧ dĕl mär)	119a	33.36 N	117.53 W
Coronado, Ca. (kŏr-ô-nä'dō)	120a	32.42 N	117.12 W
Coronation G., Can. (kŏr-ô-nā'shŭn)	96	68.07 N	112.50 W
Coronel, Chile (kō-rô-nĕl')	144	37.00 S	73.10 W
Coronel Brandsen, Arg. (kō-rô-nĕl-brä'nd-sĕn)	141c	35.09 S	58.15 W
Coronel Dorrego, Arg. (kō-rô-nĕl-dôr-rē'gō)	144	38.43 S	61.16 W
Coronel Oviedo, Par. (kō-rō-nĕl-ō-vē'dō)	144	25.28 S	56.22 W
Coronel Pringles, Arg. (kō-rô-nĕl-prēn'glĕs)	144	37.54 S	61.22 W
Coronel Suárez, Arg. (kō-rô-nĕl-swä'rās)	144	37.27 S	61.49 W
Corowa, Austl. (cŏr-ôwȧ)	216	36.02 S	146.23 E
Corozal, Belize (cŏr-ŏth-äl')	132a	18.25 N	88.23 W
Corpus Christi, Tx. (kôr'pŭs krĭs'tē)	125	27.48 N	97.24 W
Corpus Christi B., Tx.	125	27.47 N	97.14 W
Corpus Christi L., Tx.	124	28.08 N	98.20 W
Corral, Chile (kō-räl')	144	39.57 S	73.15 W
Corral de Almaguer, Sp. (kō-räl'dā äl-mä-gâr')	170	39.45 N	3.10 W
Corralillo, Cuba (kō-rä-lē-yō)	134	28.00 N	80.40 W
Corregidor I, Phil. (kō-rā-hē-dōr')	207a	14.21 N	120.25 E
Correntina, Braz. (kō-rĕn-tē-nȧ)	143	13.18 S	44.33 W
Corrib, Lough (L.), Ire. (lŏk kŏr'ĭb)	162	53.56 N	9.19 W
Corrientes, Arg. (kō-ryĕn'tās)	144	27.25 S	58.39 W
Corrientes (Prov.)	144	28.45 S	58.00 W
Corrientes, Cabo (C.), Cuba (kȧ'bô-kôr-rē-ĕn'tĕs)	134	21.50 N	84.25 W
Corrientes, Cabo (C.), Col. (kȧ'bô-kō-ryĕn'tās)	142	5.34 N	77.35 W
Corrientes, Cabo (C.), Mex.	130	20.25 N	105.41 W
Corringham, Eng.	62	51.31 N	0.28 E
Corroios, Port.	65d	38.38 N	9.09 W
Corry, Pa. (kŏr'ĭ)	111	41.55 N	79.40 W
Corse, C., Fr. (kôrs)	172	42.59 N	9.19 E
Corsica (I.), Fr. (kô'r-sē-kä)	172	42.10 N	8.55 E
Corsicana, Tx. (kôr-sĭ-kăn'ȧ)	125	32.06 N	96.28 W
Cortazar, Mex. (kôr-tä-zär)	130	20.30 N	100.57 W
Corte, Fr. (kôr'tā)	172	42.18 N	9.10 E
Cortegana, Sp. (kôr-tā-gä'nä)	170	37.54 N	6.48 W
Corte Madera, Ca.	58b	37.55 N	122.31 W
Cortes (P. Int.), Sp.	65b	40.25 N	3.41 W
Cortés, Ensenada de (B.), Cuba (ĕn-sĕ-nä-dä-dĕ-kôr-tās')	134	22.05 N	83.45 W
Cortez, Co.	121	37.21 N	108.35 W
Cortland, NY (kôrt'lănd)	111	42.35 N	76.10 W
Cortona, It. (kôr-tō'nä)	172	43.16 N	12.00 E
Corubal (R.), Guinea-Bissau	228	11.43 N	14.40 W
Coruche, Port. (kô-rōō'she)	170	38.58 N	8.34 W
Coruh (R.), Tur. (chō-rōōk')	179	40.30 N	41.10 E
Corum, Tur. (chô-rōōm')	179	40.34 N	34.45 E
Corumbá, Braz. (kō-rōōm-bä')	143	19.01 S	57.28 W
Corunna, Mi. (kô-rŭn'ȧ)	110	43.00 N	84.05 W
Coruripe, Braz. (kō-rōō-rē'pĭ)	143	10.09 S	36.13 W
Corvallis, Or. (kŏr-văl'ĭs)	116	44.34 N	123.17 W
Corve (R.), Eng. (kôr'vē)	156	52.28 N	2.43 W
Corviale (Neigh.), It.	66c	41.52 N	12.25 E
Corydon, Ia.	115	40.45 N	93.20 W
Corydon, In. (kŏr'ĭ-dŭn)	110	38.10 N	86.05 W
Corydon, Ky.	110	37.45 N	87.40 W
Cosamaloápan, Mex. (kô-sä-mä-lwä'pän)	131	18.21 N	95.48 W
Coscomatepec, Mex. (kôs'kōmä-tē-pĕk')	131	19.04 N	97.03 W
Cosenza, It. (kō-zĕnt'sä)	172	39.18 N	16.15 E
Cosfanero, Canal de (Can.), Arg.	60d	34.34 S	58.22 W
Coshocton, Oh. (kô-shŏk'tŭn)	110	40.15 N	81.55 W
Cosigüina (Vol.), Nic.	110	12.59 N	83.35 W
Cosmoledo Group (Is.), Afr. (kŏs-mô-lā'dō)	227	9.42 S	47.45 E
Cosmopolis, Wa. (kŏz-mŏp'ô-lĭs)	116	46.58 N	123.47 W
Cosne-sur-Loire, Fr. (kōn-sür-lwär')	168	47.25 N	2.57 E
Cosoleacaque, Mex. (kō sō lā-ä-kä'kē)	131	18.01 N	94.38 W
Costa de Caparica, Port.	171b	38.40 N	9.12 W
Costa Mesa, Ca. (kŏs'tȧ mā'sȧ)	119a	33.39 N	118.54 W
Costa Rica, N.A. (kŏs'tȧ rē'kȧ)	129	10.30 N	84.30 W
Cosumnes (R.), Ca. (kŏ-sŭm'nĕz)	120	38.21 N	121.17 W
Cotabambas, Peru (kô-tä-bȧm'bäs)	142	13.49 S	72.17 W
Cotabato, Phil. (kō-tä-bä'tō)	207	7.06 N	124.13 E
Cotaxtla, Mex. (kō-täs'tlä)	131	18.49 N	96.22 W
Cotaxtla (R.), Mex.	131	18.54 N	96.21 W
Coteau-du-Lac, Can. (cō-tō'dü-läk)	95a	45.17 N	74.11 W
Coteau-Landing, Can.	95a	45.15 N	74.13 W
Coteaux, Hai.	135	18.15 N	74.05 W
Côte-Saint-Luc, Can.	54b	45.28 N	73.40 W
Côte Visitation (Neigh.), Can.	54b	45.33 N	73.36 W
Cotija de la Paz, Mex. (kô-tē'-ĸä-dĕ-lä-pȧ'z)	130	19.46 N	102.43 W
Cotonou, Benin (kō-tô-nōō')	229	6.21 N	2.26 E
Cotopaxi (Mtn.), Ec. (kō-tô-păk'sē)	142	0.40 S	78.26 W
Cotorro, Cuba (kô-tôr-rō)	135a	23.03 N	82.17 W
Cotswold Hills, Eng. (kŭtz'wōld)	162	51.35 N	2.16 W
Cottage City, Md.	56d	38.56 N	76.57 W
Cottage Grove, Mn. (kŏt'āj grōv)	119g	44.50 N	92.52 W
Cottage Grove, Or.	116	43.48 N	123.04 W
Cottbus, G.D.R. (kōtt'bōōs)	166	51.47 N	14.20 E
Cottienes Alps (Mts.), Fr.-It.	169	44.46 N	7.02 E
Cottonwood (R.), Mn. (kŏt'ŭn-wōōd)	114	44.25 N	95.35 W
Cottonwood Cr., Ca.	116	40.24 N	122.50 W
Cotuí, Dom. Rep. (kô-tōō'-ē)	135	19.05 N	70.10 W
Cotulla, Tx. (kō-tŭl'lȧ)	124	28.26 N	99.14 W
Coubert, Fr. (kōō-bâr')	169b	48.40 N	2.43 E
Coudersport, Pa. (kou'dērz-port)	111	41.45 N	78.00 W
Coudres, Île aux (I.), Can.	104	47.17 N	70.12 W
Coulommiers, Fr. (kōō-lô-myā')	169b	48.49 N	3.05 E
Coulsdon (Neigh.), Eng.	62	51.19 N	0.08 W
Coulto, Serra do (Mts.), Braz. (sĕ'r-rä-dô-kô-ōō'tô)	144b	22.33 S	43.27 W
Council Bluffs, Ia. (koun'sĭl blŭf)	114	41.16 N	95.53 W
Council Grove, Ks. (koun'sĭl grōv)	123	38.39 N	96.30 W
Coupeville, Wa. (kōōp'vĭl)	118a	48.13 N	122.41 W
Courantyne (R.), Guy.-Sur. (kôr'ăntīn)	143	4.28 N	57.42 W
Courbevoie, Fr.	64c	48.54 N	2.15 E
Courcelle, Fr.	64c	48.42 N	2.06 E
Courtenay, Can. (cōōrt-nā')	98	49.41 N	125.00 W
Courtleigh, Md.	56c	39.22 N	76.46 W
Courtry, Fr.	64c	48.55 N	2.36 E
Coushatta, La. (kou-shăt'ȧ)	125	32.02 N	93.21 W
Coutras, Fr. (kōō-trȧ')	168	45.02 N	0.07 W
Cova da Piedade, Port.	65d	38.40 N	9.10 W
Covelo, Ang.	230	12.06 S	13.55 E
Cove Neck, NY	55	40.53 N	73.31 W
Coventry, Eng. (kŭv'ĕn-trĭ)	156	52.25 N	1.29 W
Covilhã, Port. (kô-vēl'yăN)	170	40.18 N	7.29 W
Covina, Ca. (kō-vē'nȧ)	119a	34.06 N	117.54 W
Covington, Ga. (kŭv'ĭng-tŭn)	126	33.36 N	83.50 W
Covington, In.	110	40.10 N	87.15 W
Covington, Ky.	113f	39.05 N	84.31 W
Covington, La.	125	30.30 N	90.06 W
Covington, Oh.	110	40.10 N	84.20 W
Covington, Ok.	123	36.18 N	97.32 W
Covington, Tn.	126	35.33 N	89.40 W
Covington, Va.	111	37.50 N	80.00 W
Cowal, L., Austl. (kou'ăl)	216	33.30 S	147.10 E
Cowan, (L.), Austl. (kou'ăn)	214	32.00 S	122.30 E
Cowan Heights, Ca.	59	33.47 N	117.47 W
Cowansville, Can.	104	45.13 N	72.47 W
Cow Cr., Or. (kou)	116	42.45 N	123.35 W
Cowes, Eng. (kouz)	162	50.43 N	1.25 W
Cowichan L., Can.	98	48.54 N	124.20 W
Cowley (Neigh.), Eng.	62	51.32 N	0.29 W
Cowlitz (R.), Wa. (kou'lĭts)	116	46.30 N	122.45 W
Cowra, Austl. (kou'rȧ)	216	33.50 S	148.33 E
Coxim, Braz. (kō-shēN')	143	18.32 S	54.43 W
Coxquihui, Mex. (kōz-kē-wē')	131	20.10 N	97.34 W
Cox's Bāzār, Bngl.	190	21.32 N	92.00 E
Coyaima, Col. (kô-yăē'mä)	142a	3.48 N	75.11 W
Coyame, Mex. (kō-yä'mā)	124	29.26 N	105.05 W
Coyanosa Draw, Tx. (kō yá-nō'sä)	124	30.55 N	103.07 W
Coyoacán, Mex. (kô-yô-á-kän')	131a	19.21 N	99.10 W
Coyote (R.), Ca. (kī'ōt)	118b	37.37 N	121.57 W
Coyuca de Benítez, Mex. (kō-yōō'kä dā bā-nē'tāz)	130	17.04 N	100.06 W
Coyuca de Catalán, Mex. (kō-yōō'kä dā kä-tä-län')	130	18.19 N	100.41 W
Coyutla, Mex. (kō-yōō'tlä)	131	20.13 N	97.40 W
Cozad, Ne. (kō'zăd)	122	40.53 N	99.59 W
Cozaddale, Oh. (kō-zăd-dāl)	113f	39.16 N	84.09 W
Cozoyoapan Mex. (kō-zō-yō-ä-pȧ'n)	130	16.45 N	98.17 W
Cozumel, Mex. (kŏ-zōō-mĕ'l)	132a	20.31 N	86.55 W
Cozumel, Isla de (I.), Mex. (ē's-lä-dĕ-kŏ-zōō-mĕ'l)	132a	20.26 N	87.10 W
Crab Cr., Wa. (krăb)	116	46.47 N	119.43 W
Crab Cr., Wa.	116	47.21 N	119.09 W
Cradock, S. Afr. (kră'dŭk)	227c	32.12 S	25.38 E
Crafton, Pa. (krăf'tŭn)	113e	40.26 N	80.04 W
Craig, Co. (krāg)	117	40.32 N	107.31 W
Craighall (Neigh.), S. Afr.	71b	26.07 S	28.02 E
Craighall Park (Neigh.), S. Afr.	71b	26.08 S	28.01 E
Craiova, Rom. (krȧ-yō'vȧ)	173	44.18 N	23.50 E
Cranberry (L.), NY (krăn'bĕr-ĭ)	111	44.10 N	74.50 W
Cranbourne, Austl.	211a	38.07 S	145.16 E
Cranbrook, Can. (krăn'brŏŏk)	99	49.31 N	115.46 W
Cranbury, NJ (krăn'bē-rĭ)	112a	40.19 N	74.31 W
Crandon, Wi. (krăn'dŭn)	115	45.35 N	88.55 W
Cranford, NJ	55	40.39 N	74.19 W
Crank, Eng.	64a	53.29 N	2.45 W
Cranston, RI (krăns'tŭn)	112b	41.46 N	71.25 W
Crater L., Or. (krā'tēr)	116	43.00 N	122.08 W
Crater Lake Natl. Park, Or.	116	42.58 N	122.40 W
Craters of the Moon Natl. Mon., Id. (krā'tēr)	117	43.28 N	113.15 W
Crateús, Braz. (krä-tā-ōōzh')	143	5.09 S	40.35 W
Crato, Braz. (krä'tōō)	143	7.19 S	39.13 W
Crawford, Ne. (krô'fērd)	114	42.41 N	103.25 W
Crawford, Wa.	118c	45.49 N	122.24 W
Crawfordsville, In. (krô'fērdz-vĭl)	110	40.00 N	86.55 W
Crazy Mts., Mt. (krā'zĭ)	117	46.11 N	110.25 W
Crazy Woman Cr., Wy.	117	44.08 N	106.40 W
Crecy, S. Afr. (krĕ-sē)	223d	24.38 S	28.52 E
Crécy-en-Brie, Fr. (krā-sē'-ĕN-brē')	169b	48.52 N	2.55 E
Crécy-en-Ponthieu, Fr.	168	50.13 N	1.48 E
Credit (R.), Can.	95d	43.41 N	79.55 W
Cree (L.), Can. (krē)	96	57.35 N	107.52 W
Creekmouth (Neigh.), Eng.	62	51.31 N	0.06 E
Creighton, Ne. (krā'tŭn)	114	42.27 N	97.54 W
Creighton, S. Afr. (cre-tŏn)	227c	30.02 S	28.52 E
Creil, Fr. (krĕ'y')	168	49.18 N	2.28 E
Crema, It. (krā'mä)	172	45.21 N	9.53 E
Cremona, It. (krā-mō'nä)	172	45.09 N	10.02 E
Crépy-en-Valois, Fr. (krā-pē'ĕN-vä-lwä')	169b	49.14 N	2.53 E
Cres (I.), Yugo.	172	44.50 N	14.31 E
Cres, Yugo. (Tsrĕs)	172	44.58 N	14.21 E
Crescent (L.), Fl. (krĕs'ĕnt)	127	29.33 N	81.30 W
Crescent (L.), Or.	116	43.25 N	121.58 W
Crescent Beach, Can.	118d	49.03 N	122.58 W
Crescent City, Ca. (krĕs'ĕnt)	116	41.46 N	124.13 W
Crescent City, Fl.	127	29.26 N	81.35 W
Crescentville (Neigh.), Pa.	56b	40.02 N	75.05 W
Cresco, Ia. (krĕs'kō)	115	43.23 N	92.07 W
Cresskill, NJ	55	40.57 N	73.57 W
Crested Butte, Co. (krĕst'ĕd būt)	121	38.50 N	107.00 W
Crest Haven, Md.	56d	39.02 N	76.59 W
Crestline, Ca. (krĕst-līn)	119a	34.15 N	117.17 W
Crestline, Oh.	110	40.50 N	82.40 W
Crestmore, Ca. (krĕst'môr)	119a	34.02 N	117.23 W
Creston, Can. (krĕs'tŭn)	99	49.06 N	116.31 W
Creston, Ia.	115	41.04 N	94.22 W
Creston, Oh.	113d	40.59 N	81.54 W
Crestview, Fl. (krĕst'vū)	126	30.44 N	86.35 W
Crestwood, Il.	58a	41.39 N	87.44 W
Crestwood, Ky. (krĕst'wŏŏd)	113h	38.20 N	85.28 W
Crestwood, Mo.	119e	38.33 N	90.23 W
Crete, Il. (krēt)	113a	41.26 N	87.38 W
Crete (I.), Grc.	172a	35.15 N	24.30 E
Crete, Ne.	123	40.38 N	96.56 W
Créteil, Fr.	64c	48.48 N	2.28 E
Creus, Cabo de (C.), Sp. (kȧ'-bô-dĕ-krē-ōōs)	171	42.16 N	3.18 E
Creuse (R.), Fr. (krûz)	168	46.51 N	0.49 E
Creve Coeur, Mo. (krēv kōōr)	119e	38.40 N	90.27 W
Crevillente, Sp. (krā-vē-lyĕn'tā)	171	38.12 N	0.48 W
Crewe, Eng. (krōō)	156	53.06 N	2.27 W
Crewe, Va.	127	37.09 N	78.08 W
Crimea P-Ov (Pen.), see Krymskiy			
Crimmitschau, G.D.R. (krĭm'ĭt-shou)	166	50.49 N	12.22 E
Cripple Creek, Co. (krĭp''l)	122	38.44 N	105.12 W
Crisfield, Md. (krĭs-fēld)	111	38.00 N	75.50 W
Cristal, Monts de (Mts.), Gabon	230	0.50 N	10.30 E
Cristina, Braz. (krēs-tē'-nä)	141a	22.13 S	45.15 W
Cristobal Colón, Pico (Pk.), Col. (pē'kô-krēs-tô'bäl-kō-lôn')	142	11.00 N	74.00 W
Cristo Redentor, Estatua do (P. Int.), Braz.	61c	22.57 S	43.13 W
Crişul Alb (R.), Rom. (krē'shōōl älb)	167	46.20 N	22.15 E
Crna (R.), Yugo. (ts'r'nȧ)	173	41.03 N	21.46 E
Crna Gora (Montenegro)(Reg.), Yugo. (ts'r-nȧ-gō'rȧ) (mōn-tā-nā'grō) (mōn-tē-nē'grō)	173	42.55 N	18.52 E
Črnomelj, Yugo. (ch'r'nō-māl')	172	45.35 N	15.11 E
Croatia (Reg.), see Hrvatska			
Crockenhill, Eng.	62	51.23 N	0.10 E
Crockett, Ca. (krŏk'ĕt)	118b	38.03 N	122.14 W
Crockett, Tx.	125	31.19 N	95.28 W
Crofton, Md.	112e	39.01 N	76.43 W
Crofton, Ne.	114	42.44 N	97.32 W
Croissy-Beaubourgh, Fr.	64c	48.50 N	2.40 E
Croissy-sur-Seine, Fr.	64c	48.53 N	2.09 E
Croix, Lac la (L.), Can.-Mn. (läk lä krōō-ä')	115	48.19 N	91.53 W
Croker (I.), Austl. (krŏ'kȧ)	214	10.45 S	132.25 E
Cromer, Austl.	70a	33.44 S	151.17 E
Cronenberg (Neigh.), F.R.G.	63	51.12 N	7.08 E
Cronton, Eng.	64a	53.23 N	2.46 W
Cronulla, Austl. (krō-nŭl'ȧ)	211b	34.03 S	151.09 E
Crooked (I.), Ba.	135	22.45 N	74.10 W
Crooked (L.), Can.	105	48.25 N	56.05 W
Crooked (R.), Can.	98	54.30 N	122.55 W
Crooked (R.), Or.	116	44.07 N	120.30 W
Crooked Cr., Il. (krŏŏk'ĕd)	123	40.21 N	90.49 W
Crooked Cr., Or.	116	42.23 N	118.14 W
Crooked Island Passage (Str.), Ba.	135	22.40 N	74.50 W
Crookston, Mn. (krŏŏks'tŭn)	114	47.44 N	96.35 W
Crooksville, Oh. (krŏŏks'vĭl)	110	39.45 N	82.05 W
Crosby, Eng.	64a	53.30 N	3.02 W
Crosby, Mn. (krôz'bĭ)	115	46.29 N	93.58 W
Crosby, ND	114	48.55 N	103.18 W
Crosby (Neigh.), S. Afr.	71b	26.12 S	27.59 E
Crosby, Tx.	125a	29.55 N	95.04 W
Crosne, Fr.	64c	48.43 N	2.28 E
Cross (L.), Can. (krôs)	111	44.55 N	76.55 W
Cross (L.), La.	125	32.33 N	93.58 W
Cross (R.), Nig.	229	5.35 N	8.05 E
Cross City, Fl.	126	29.55 N	83.25 W
Crossett, Ar. (krôs'ĕt)	123	33.08 N	92.00 W
Cross Hbr., Ba.	134	25.55 N	77.105 W
Cross L., Can.	101	54.45 N	97.30 W
Cross Lake, Can.	101	54.37 N	97.47 W
Cross River Res., NY (krôs)	112a	41.14 N	73.34 W
Cross Sd., Ak. (krŏs)	107	58.12 N	137.20 W
Crosswell, Mi. (krôz'wĕl)	110	43.15 N	82.35 W
Crotch (R.), Can.	103	45.02 N	76.55 W
Crotone, It. (krō-tô'nĕ)	173	39.05 N	17.08 E
Croton Falls Res., NY (krōtŭn)	112a	41.22 N	73.44 W
Croton-on-Hudson, NY (krō'tŭn-ŏn hŭd'sŭn)	112a	41.12 N	73.53 W
Crouse Run (R.), Pa.	57b	40.35 N	79.58 W
Crow (L.), Can.	115	49.13 N	93.29 W
Crow Agency, Mt.	117	45.36 N	107.27 W
Crow Cr., Co.	122	41.08 N	104.25 W
Crow Creek Ind. Res., SD	114	44.17 N	99.17 W
Crow Ind. Res., Mt. (krō)	117	45.26 N	108.12 W
Crowle, Eng. (kroul)	156	53.36 N	0.49 W
Crowley, La. (krou'lē)	125	30.13 N	92.22 W
Crown Mtn., Can. (kroun)	118d	49.24 N	123.05 W
Crown Mtn., Vir.Is.(U.S.A.)	129c	18.22 N	64.58 W
Crown Point, In. (kroun point')	113a	41.25 N	87.22 W
Crown Point, NY	111	44.00 N	73.25 W
Crows Nest, Austl.	70a	33.50 S	151.12 E
Crowsnest P., Can.	99	49.39 N	114.45 W
Crow Wing (R.), Mn. (krō)	115	44.50 N	94.01 W
Crow Wing (R.), Mn.	115	46.42 N	94.48 W
Crow Wing (R.),North Fork, Mn.	115	45.16 N	94.28 W
Crow Wing (R.),South Fork, Mn.	115	44.59 N	94.42 W
Croxley Green, Eng.	62	51.39 N	0.27 W
Croydon, Austl. (kroi'dŭn)	215	18.15 S	142.15 E
Croydon, Austl.	211a	37.48 S	145.17 E
Croydon, Eng.	156b	51.22 N	0.06 W
Croydon, Pa.	112f	40.05 N	74.55 W
Crozet, Îles, Ind. O. (krō-zē')	232	46.20 S	51.30 E
Cruces, Cuba (krōō'sås)	134	22.20 N	80.20 W

ăt; finȧl; rāte; senåte; ärm; åsk; sofȧ; fâre; ch-choose; dh-as th in other; bē; ēvent; bĕt; recĕnt; cratēr; g-gō; gh-guttural g; bĭt; ĭ-short neutral; rīde; ĸ-guttural k as ch in German ich;

PLACE (Pronounciation)	PAGE	Lat. °'	Long. °'
Cruces, Arroyo de, Mex. (är-rō'yô-dĕ-krōō'sĕs)	124	26.17 N	104.32 W
Cruillas, Mex. (krōō-ēl'yäs)	124	24.45 N	98.31 W
Crum Lynne, Pa.	56b	39.52 N	75.20 W
Cruz Alta, Braz. (krōōz äl'tä)	144	28.41 S	54.02 W
Cruz, Cabo (C.), Cuba (kä'-bô-krōōz)	134	19.50 N	77.45 W
Cruz, Cayo (I.), Cuba (kä'yō-krōōz)	134	22.15 N	77.50 W
Cruz del Eje, Arg. (krōō's-dĕl-ĕ-kĕ)	144	30.46 S	64.45 W
Cruzeiro, Braz. (krōō-zā'rōō)	141a	22.36 S	44.57 W
Cruzeiro do Sul, Braz. (krōō-zā'rōō dōō sōōl)	142	7.34 S	72.40 W
Crysler, Can.	95c	45.13 N	75.09 W
Crystal Beach, Can.	57a	42.52 N	79.04 W
Crystal City, Tx. (krĭs'tăl sĭ'tĭ)	124	28.40 N	99.90 W
Crystal Falls, Mi. (krĭs'tăl fôls)	115	46.06 N	88.21 W
Crystal Lake, Il. (krĭs'tăl lāk)	113a	42.15 N	88.18 W
Crystal Springs, Ms. (krĭs'tăl sprĭngz)	126	31.58 N	90.20 W
Crystal Sprs., Ca.	118b	37.31 N	122.26 W
Csömör, Hung.	66g	47.33 N	19.14 E
Csongrád, Hung. (chôn'gräd)	167	46.42 N	20.09 E
Csorna, Hung. (chôr'nä)	167	47.39 N	17.11 E
Cúa, Ven. (kōō'ä)	143b	10.10 N	66.54 W
Cuajimalpa, Mex. (kwä-hē-mäl'pä)	131a	19.21 N	99.18 W
Cuale, Sierra del (Mts.), Mex. (sē-ĕ'r-rä-dĕl-kwä'lĕ)	130	20.20 N	104.58 W
Cuamato, Ang. (kwä-mä'tō)	230	17.05 S	15.09 E
Cuamba, Moz.	231	14.49 S	36.33 E
Cuando, Ang. (kwän'dō)	230	16.32 S	22.07 E
Cuando (R.), Ang.	230	16.50 S	22.40 E
Cuangar, Ang.	230	17.36 S	18.39 E
Cuango (Kwango) (R.), Afr. (kwäŋ'gō)	230	6.35 S	16.50 E
Cuanza (R.), Ang. (kwän'zä)	230	9.05 S	13.15 E
Cuarto Saladillo (R.), Arg. (kwär'tō-sä-lä-dē'l-yō)	144	33.00 S	63.25 W
Cuatro Caminos, Cuba (kwä'trô-kä-mē'nôs)	135a	23.01 N	82.13 W
Cuatro Caminos, Cuba	60b	22.54 N	82.23 W
Cuatro Ciénegas, Mex. (kwä'trō syā'nā-gäs)	124	26.59 N	102.03 W
Cuauhtemoc, Mex. (kwä-ōō-tē-mōk')	132	15.43 N	91.57 W
Cuautepec, Mex. (kwä-ōō-tē-pĕk)	130	16.41 N	99.04 W
Cuautepec, Mex.	130	20.01 N	98.19 W
Cuautepec el Alto, Mex.	60a	19.34 N	99.08 W
Cuautitlán, Mex. (kwä-ōō-tēt-län')	131a	19.40 N	99.12 W
Cuautla, Mex. (kwä-ōō'tlä)	130	18.47 N	98.57 W
Cuba, N.A. (kū'bȧ)	129	22.00 N	79.00 W
Cuba, Port. (kōō'bä)	170	38.10 N	7.55 W
Cubagua, Isla (I.), Ven. (ē's-lä-kōō-bä'gwä)	143b	10.48 N	64.10 W
Cubango (Okavango)(R.), Ang.-Namibia (kōō-bäŋ'gō)	230	17.10 S	18.20 E
Cub Hills, Can. (kŭb)	100	54.20 N	104.30 W
Cucamonga, Ca. (kōō-kȧ-mōŋ'gȧ)	119a	34.05 N	117.35 W
Cuchi, Ang.	226	14.40 S	16.50 E
Cuchillo Parado, Mex. (kōō-chē'lyō pä-rä'dō)	124	29.26 N	104.52 W
Cuchumatanes, Sierra de los (Mts.), Guat.	132	15.35 N	91.10 W
Cúcuta, Col. (kōō'kōō-tä)	142	7.56 N	72.30 W
Cudahy, Wi. (kŭd'ȧ-hĭ)	113a	42.57 N	87.52 W
Cuddalore, India (kŭd ȧ-lōr')	197	11.49 N	79.46 E
Cuddapah, India (kŭd'ȧ-pä)	191	14.31 N	78.52 E
Cudham (Neigh.), Eng.	62	51.19 N	0.05 E
Cue, Austl. (kū)	214	27.30 S	118.10 E
Cuéllar, Sp. (kwā'lyär')	170e	41.24 N	4.15 W
Cuenca, Ec. (kwĕn'kä)	142	2.52 S	78.54 W
Cuenca, Sp.	170	40.05 N	2.07 W
Cuencame, Mex. (kwĕn-kä-mā')	124	24.52 N	103.42 W
Cuenca, Sierra de (Mts.), Sp. (sē-ĕ'r-rä-dĕ-kwĕ'n-kä)	170	40.02 N	1.50 W
Cuerámaro, Mex. (kwā-rä'mä-rō)	130	20.39 N	101.44 W
Cuernavaca, Mex. (kwĕr-nä-vä'kä)	131a	18.55 N	99.15 W
Cuero, Tx. (kwā'rō)	125	29.05 N	97.16 W
Cuetzalá del Progreso, Mex. (kwĕt-zä-lä dĕl prō-grā'sō)	130	18.07 N	99.51 W
Cuetzalan del Progreso, Mex. (kwĕt-zä-län dĕl prō-grā'sō)	131	20.02 N	97.33 W
Cuevas del Almanzora, Sp. (kwĕ'väs-dĕl-äl-män-zō-rä)	170	37.19 N	1.54 W
Cuffley, Eng.	62	51.47 N	0.07 W
Cuglieri, It. (kōō-lyā'rē)	172	40.11 N	8.37 E
Cuiabá, Braz. (kōō-yä-bä')	143	15.33 S	56.03 W
Cuicatlán, Mex. (kwē-kä-tlän')	131	17.46 N	96.57 W
Cuigezhuang, China	67b	40.01 N	116.28 E
Cuilapa, Guat. (kōō-ē-lä'pä)	132	14.16 N	90.20 W
Cuilo (R.), Ang.	230	9.15 S	19.30 E
Cuito (R.), Ang. (kōō-ē-'tō)	230	14.15 S	19.00 E
Cuitzeo, Mex. (kwēt'zā-ō)	130	19.57 N	101.11 W
Cuitzeo, Laguna de (L.), Mex. (lä-ōō'nä-dĕ-kwēt'zā-ō)	130	19.58 N	101.05 W
Culcross, Can. (kŭl'rôs)	95f	49.43 N	97.54 W
Cul de Sac (R.), Dom. Rep.-Hai. (kōō'l-dĕ-sä'k)	135	18.35 N	72.05 W
Culebra, (I.), P.R. (kōō-lā'brä)	129b	18.19 N	65.32 W
Culemborg, Neth.	157a	51.57 N	5.14 E
Culgoa (R.), Austl. (kŭl-gō'ȧ)	215	29.21 S	147.00 E
Culiacán, Mex. (kōō-lyä-kä'n)	128	24.45 N	107.30 W
Culion, Phil. (kōō-lē-ōn')	206	11.43 N	119.58 E
Cúllar de Baza, Sp. (kōō'l-yär-dĕ-bä'zä)	170	37.36 N	2.35 W
Cullera, Sp. (kōō-lyā'rä)	171	39.12 N	0.15 W
Cullinan, S. Afr. (kōō'lĭ-nán)	227b	25.41 S	28.32 E
Cullman, Ala. (kŭl'măn)	126	34.10 N	86.50 W
Culmore, Va.	56d	38.51 N	77.08 W
Culpeper, Va. (kŭl'pĕp-ẽr)	111	38.30 N	77.55 W
Culver, In. (kŭl'vẽr)	110	41.15 N	86.25 W
Culver City, Ca.	119a	34.00 N	118.23 W
Culverstone Green, Eng.	62	51.20 N	0.21 E
Cumaná, Ven. (kōō-mä-nä')	143b	10.28 N	64.10 W
Cumberland, Can. (kŭm'bẽr-lănd)	95c	45.31 N	75.25 W
Cumberland, Md.	111	39.40 N	78.40 W
Cumberland, Wa.	118a	47.17 N	121.55 W
Cumberland, Wi.	115	45.31 N	92.01 W
Cumberland (R.), U.S.	126	36.45 N	85.33 W
Cumberland Is., Austl.	215	20.20 S	149.46 E
Cumberland, L., Ky.	126	36.55 N	85.20 W
Cumberland Pen., Can.	97	65.59 N	64.05 W
Cumberland Plat., Tn.	126	35.25 N	85.30 W
Cumberland Sd., Can.	97	65.27 N	65.44 W
Cundinamarca (Dept.), Col. (kōōn-dē-nä-mä'r-kȧ)	142a	4.57 N	74.27 W
Cunduacán, Mex. (kōōn-dōō-ȧ-kän')	131	18.04 N	93.23 W
Cunene (Kunene)(R.), Ang.-Namibia	230	17.05 S	12.35 E
Cuneo, It. (kōō'nā-ō)	172	44.24 N	7.31 E
Cunha, Braz. (kōō'nyȧ)	141a	23.05 S	44.56 W
Cunnamulla, Austl. (kŭn-ȧ-mŭl-ȧ)	216	28.00 S	145.55 E
Cupula, Pico (Mtn.) (pē'kō-kōō'pōō-lä)	128	24.45 N	111.10 W
Cuquío, Mex. (kōō-kē'ō)	130	20.55 N	103.03 W
Curaçao (I.), Neth. Antilles (kōō-rä-sä'ō)	142	12.12 N	68.58 W
Curacautín, Chile (kä-rä-kaōō-tē'n)	144	38.25 S	71.53 W
Curacaví, Chile (kōō-rä-kä-vē')	141b	33.23 S	71.09 W
Curaumilla, Punta (Pt.), Chile (kōō-rou-mē'lyä)	141b	33.05 S	71.44 W
Curepto, Chile (kōō-rĕp-tô)	141b	35.06 S	72.02 W
Curicó, Chile (kōō-rē-kō')	141b	34.57 S	71.14 W
Curicó (Prov.), Chile	141b	34.55 S	71.15 W
Curitiba, Braz. (kōō-rē-tē'bȧ)	144	25.20 S	49.15 W
Curly Cut Cays (I.), Ba.	134	23.40 N	77.40 W
Currais Novos, Braz. (kōōr-rä'ēs nō-vōs)	143	6.02 S	36.39 W
Curran, Can. (kŭ-räN')	95c	45.30 N	74.59 W
Current (I.), Ba. (kŭ-rĕnt)	134	25.20 N	76.50 W
Current (R.), Mo. (kûr'ĕnt)	123	37.18 N	91.21 W
Currie, Mt., S. Afr. (kŭ-rē)	227c	30.28 S	29.23 E
Currituck Sd., NC (kûr'ĭ-tŭk)	127	36.27 N	75.42 W
Curtea-de-Argeş, Rom. (kōōr'tĕ-ȧ dĕ ȧr'zhĕsh)	173	45.09 N	24.40 E
Curtis (I.), Austl.	215	23.38 S	151.43 E
Curtis, Ne. (kûr'tĭs)	122	40.36 N	100.29 W
Curtis B, Md.	56c	39.13 N	76.35 W
Curtisville, Pa. (kûr'tĭs-vĭl)	113e	40.38 N	79.50 W
Curuá (R.), Braz. (kōō-rōō-ä')	143	6.26 S	54.39 W
Curug, Yugo. (chōō'rōōg)	173	45.27 N	20.26 E
Curunga, Ang.	230	12.51 S	21.12 E
Curupira, Serra (Mts.), Braz.-Ven. (sĕr'rȧ kōō-rōō-pē'rȧ)	142	1.00 N	65.30 W
Cururupu, Braz. (kōō-rōō-rōō-pōō')	143	1.40 S	44.56 W
Curuzú Cuatiá, Arg. (kōō-rōō-zōō'kwä-tē-ä')	144	29.45 S	57.58 W
Curvelo, Braz. (kōōr-vĕl'ōō)	143	18.47 S	44.14 W
Cusano Milanino, It.	65c	45.33 N	9.11 E
Cushing, Ok. (kŭsh'ĭng)	123	35.58 N	96.46 W
Custer, SD (kŭs'tẽr)	114	43.46 N	103.36 W
Custer, Wa.	118d	48.55 N	122.39 W
Custer Battlefield Nat'l Mon., Mt. (kŭs'tẽr băt''l-fēld)	117	45.44 N	107.15 W
Cut Bank, Mt. (kŭt bănk)	117	48.38 N	112.19 W
Cuthbert, Ga. (kŭth'bẽrt)	126	31.47 N	84.48 W
Cuttack, India (kŭ-tăk')	196	20.38 N	85.53 E
Cutzamala (R.), Mex. (kōō-tzä-mä-lä')	130	18.57 N	100.41 W
Cutzamalá de Pinzón, Mex. (kōō-tzä-mä-lä'dĕ-pēn-zō'n)	130	18.28 N	100.36 W
Cuvo (R.), Ang. (kōō'vō)	230	10.55 S	14.00 E
Cuxhaven, F.R.G. (kōōks'hä-fĕn)	166	53.51 N	8.43 E
Cuxton, Eng.	62	51.22 N	0.27 E
Cuyahoga Falls, Oh.	113d	41.08 N	81.29 W
Cuyahoga Heights, Oh.	56a	41.26 N	81.39 W
Cuyahoga R., Oh. (kī-ȧ-hō'gȧ)	113d	41.22 N	81.38 W
Cuyapaire Ind. Res., Ca. (kū-yȧ-pâr)	120	32.46 N	116.20 W
Cuyo Is., Phil. (kōō'yō)	206	10.54 N	120.08 E
Cuyotenango, Guat. (kōō-yô-tĕ-näŋ'gô)	132	14.30 N	91.35 W
Cuyuni (R.), Guy.-Ven. (kōō-yōō'nē)	143	6.40 N	60.44 W
Cuyutlán, Mex. (kōō-yōō-tlän')	130	18.54 N	104.04 W
Cuzco, Peru	142	13.36 S	71.52 W
Cynthiana, Ky. (sĭn-thĭ-ăn'ȧ)	110	38.20 N	84.20 W
Cypress, Ca. (sī'prĕs)	119a	33.50 N	118.03 W
Cypress Hills, Can.	100	49.40 N	110.20 W
Cypress L., Can.	100	49.28 N	109.43 W
Cyprus, Asia (sī'prŭs)	190	35.00 N	31.00 E
Cyrenaica (Prov.), see Barqah			
Cyrildene (Neigh.), S. Afr.	71b	26.11 S	28.06 E
Czechoslovakia, Eur. (chĕk'ô-slô-vä'kĭ-ȧ)	154	49.28 N	16.00 E
Czersk, Pol. (chĕrsk)	167	53.47 N	17.58 E
Częstochowa, Pol. (chăN-stô kô'vȧ)	167	50.49 N	19.10 E

D

PLACE (Pronounciation)	PAGE	Lat. °'	Long. °'
Da'an, China (dä-än)	202	45.25 N	124.22 E
Dabakala, Ivory Coast (dä-bä-kä'lä)	224	8.16 N	4.36 W
Daba Shan (Mts.), China (dä-bä shän)	202	32.25 N	108.20 E
Dabeiba, Col. (dȧ-bā'bä)	142a	7.01 N	76.16 W
Dabie Shan (Mts.), China (dä-bĭĕ shän)	203	31.40 N	114.50 E
Dabnou, Niger	229	14.09 N	5.22 E
Dabob B., Wa. (dā'bŏb)	118a	47.50 N	122.50 W
Dabola, Gui.	228	10.45 N	11.07 W
Dąbrowa Bialostocka, Pol. (dōN-brō'vȧ)	167	53.37 N	23.18 E
Dacca (Dhaka), Bngl. (dä'kä) (dăk'ȧ)	196	23.45 N	90.29 E
Dachang, China (dä-chäŋ)	201b	31.18 N	121.25 E
Dachangshan Dao (I.), China (dä-chäŋ-shän dou)	200	39.21 N	122.31 E
Dachau, F.R.G. (dä'kou)	157d	48.16 N	11.26 E
Dacotah, Can. (dȧ-kō'tȧ)	95f	49.52 N	97.38 W
Dadar (Neigh.), India	67e	19.01 N	72.50 E
Dade City, Fl. (dād)	127a	28.22 N	82.09 W
Dadeville, Al. (dād'vĭl)	126	32.48 N	85.44 W
Dādra & Nagar Haveli (Union Ter.), India	196	20.00 N	73.00 E
Dadu (R.), China (dä-dōō)	203	29.20 N	103.03 E
Daet (Mtn.), Phil. (dä'ĕt)	207a	14.07 N	122.59 E
Dafoe (R.), Can.	101	55.50 N	95.50 W
Dafter, Mi. (dăf'tẽr)	119k	46.21 N	84.26 W
Dagana, Senegal (dä-gä'nä)	228	16.31 N	15.30 W
Dagana (Reg.) Chad	229	12.20 N	15.15 E
Dagang, China (dä-gäŋ)	201a	22.48 N	113.24 E
Dagda, Sov. Un. (dȧg'dȧ)	174	56.04 N	27.30 E
Dagenham, Eng. (dăg'ĕn-ăm)	156b	51.32 N	0.09 E
Dagestan (Reg.), Sov. Un. (dä-gĕs-tän')	179	43.40 N	46.10 E
Daggafontein, S. Afr.	71b	26.18 S	28.28 E
Daggett, Ca. (dăg'ĕt)	120	34.50 N	116.52 W
Dagu, China (dä-gōō)	200	39.00 N	117.42 E
Dagu (R.), China	200	36.29 N	120.06 W
Dagupan, Phil. (dä-gōō'pän)	207a	16.02 N	120.20 E
Daheishan Dao (I.), China (dȧ-hā-shän dou)	200	37.57 N	120.37 E
Da Hinggan Ling, see Greater Khingan Range			
Dahīrpur (Neigh.), India	67d	28.43 N	77.12 E
Dahl, F.R.G. (däl)	169c	51.18 N	7.33 E
Dahlak Arch. (Is.), Eth.	225	15.45 N	40.30 E
Dahlem (Neigh.), F.R.G.	65a	52.28 N	13.17 E
Dahlerau, F.R.G.	63	51.13 N	7.19 E
Dahlwitz, G.D.R.	65a	52.30 N	13.38 E
Dahomey, see Benin			
Dahra, Libya	194	29.34 N	17.50 E
Daibu, China (dī-bōō)	200	31.22 N	119.29 E
Daigo, Jap. (dī-gō)	205b	34.57 N	135.49 E
Daimiel Manzanares, Sp. (dī-myĕl'män-zä-nä'rĕs)	170	39.05 N	3.36 W
Dairy (R.), East Fk. Or.	118c	45.40 N	123.03 W
Dairy (R.), Or. (dâr'ĭ)	118c	45.33 N	123.04 W
Dai-Sen (Mtn.), Jap. (dī'sĕn')	205	35.22 N	133.35 E
Dai-Tenjo-dake (Mtn.), Jap. (dī-tĕn'jō dä-kä)	205	36.21 N	137.38 E
Daitō, Jap.	205b	34.42 N	135.38 E
Daiyun Shan (Mtn.), China (dī-yōōn shän)	203	25.40 N	118.08 E
Dajabón, Dom. Rep. (dä-kä-bô'n)	135	19.35 N	71.40 W
Dajarra, Austl. (dȧ-jăr'ȧ)	214	21.45 S	139.30 E
Dakar, Senegal (dȧ-kär')	228	14.40 N	17.26 W
Dakhla, W. Sah.	224	23.45 N	16.04 W
Dakouraoua, Niger	229	13.58 N	6.15 E
Dakovica, Yugo.	173	42.33 N	20.28 E
Dalälven (R.), Swe.	164	60.26 N	15.50 E
Dalby, Austl. (dôl'bē)	216	27.10 S	151.15 E
Dalcour, La. (dăl-kour)	112d	29.49 N	89.59 W
Dale, Nor. (dä'lĕ)	164	60.35 N	5.55 E
Dale Hollow (L.), Tn. (dāl hŏl'ō)	126	36.33 N	85.03 W
Dalemead, Can. (dä'lĕ-mēd)	95e	50.53 N	113.38 W
Dalen, Nor. (dä'lĕn)	164	59.28 N	8.01 E
Daleside, S. Afr. (dāl'sīd)	223d	26.30 S	28.03 E
Dalesville, Can. (dālz'vĭl)	95a	45.42 N	74.23 W
Daley Waters, Austl. (dā lē)	214	16.15 S	133.30 E
Dalhart, Tx. (dăl härt)	122	36.04 N	102.32 W
Dalhousie, Can. (dăl-hōō'zē)	104	48.04 N	66.23 W
Dali, China (dä-lē)	201a	23.27 N	113.06 E
Dali, China	198	26.00 N	100.08 E
Dali, China	198	35.00 N	109.38 E
Dalian Wan (B.), China (dä-lĭĕn wän)	200	38.55 N	121.50 E
Dalías, Sp. (dä-lē'ȧs)	170	36.49 N	2.50 W
Dall (I.), Ak. (dăl)	107	54.50 N	133.10 W
Dallas, Or. (dăl'lȧs)	116	44.55 N	123.20 W
Dallas, SD	114	43.13 N	99.34 W
Dallas, Tx.	119c	32.45 N	96.48 W
Dalles Dam, Or.	116	45.36 N	121.08 W
Dallgow, G.D.R.	65a	52.32 N	13.05 E
Dall I., Ak.	98	54.50 N	132.55 W
Dalmacija (Reg.), Yugo. (däl-mä'tsē-yä)	172	43.25 N	16.37 E
Dalnerechensk, Sov. Un.	181	46.07 N	133.21 E
Daloa, Ivory Coast	228	6.53 N	6.27 W
Dalqū, Sud. (dĕl'gô)	225	20.07 N	30.41 E
Dalroy, Can. (dăl'roi)	95e	51.07 N	113.39 W
Dalrymple, Mt., Austl. (dăl'rĭm-p'l)	215	21.14 S	148.46 E
Dalton, Eng.	64a	53.34 N	2.46 W
Dalton, Ga. (dôl'tŭn)	126	34.46 N	84.58 W
Dalton, S. Afr. (dôl'tŏn)	227c	29.21 S	30.41 E
Daly (R.), Austl. (dā'lĭ)	214	14.15 S	131.15 E
Daly City, Ca. (dā'lē)	118b	37.42 N	122.27 W
Damān, India	196	20.32 N	72.53 E
Damanhūr, Egypt (dä-män-hōōr')	223b	30.59 N	30.31 E
Damaraland (Reg.), Namibia (dă'nȧ-rȧ-lănd)	226	22.15 S	16.15 E
Damara Rep., Cen. Afr. Rep.	229	4.58 N	18.42 E
Damar, Pulau (I.), Indon.	207	7.15 S	129.15 E
Damas Cays (Is.), Ba. (dä'mäs)	134	23.50 N	79.50 W
Damascus, see Dimashq			
Damba, Ang. (däm'bä)	230	6.41 S	15.08 E
Dame Marie, Cap (C.), Hai. (dām mȧrē')	135	18.35 N	74.50 W
Dāmghān, Iran (dām-gān')	192	35.50 N	54.15 E

ng-sing; ŋ-baŋk; N-nasalized n; nŏd; cŏmmit; ōld; ôbey; ôrder; oi-boil; fōōd; fŏŏt; ou-out; s-soft; sh-dish; th-thin; pūre; ûnite; ûrn; stŭd; circŭs; ü-as in French tu; '-indeterminate vowel.

PLACE (Pronounciation)	PAGE	Lat. °'	Long. °'
Dāmghān, Iran	195	39.09 N	54.22 E
Daming, China (dä-mĭŋ)	200	36.15 N	115.09 E
Dammartin-en-Goële, Fr. (däɴ-mär-tăɴ-äɴ-gô-ĕl')	169b	49.03 N	2.40 E
Dampier Arch, Austl. (dăn-pyår')	214	20.15 S	116.25 E
Dampier Land (Penin), Austl.	214	17.30 S	122.25 E
Dampier, Selat (Str.), Indon. (däm'pēr)	207	0.40 S	131.15 E
Dan (R.), NC (dăn)	127	36.26 N	79.40 W
Danané, Ivory Coast	228	7.16 N	8.09 W
Da Nang (Tourane), Viet.	203	16.08 N	108.22 E
Danbury, Ct. (dăn'bēr-ĭ)	112a	41.23 N	73.27 W
Danbury, Eng.	156b	51.42 N	0.34 E
Danbury, Tx.	125a	29.14 N	95.22 W
Dandenong, Austl. (dăn'dĕ-nông)	211a	37.59 S	145.13 E
Dandong, China (dän-dôŋ)	202	40.10 N	124.30 E
Dane (R.), Eng. (dān)	156	53.11 N	2.14 W
Danea, Gui.	228	11.27 N	13.12 W
Danforth, Me.	104	45.38 N	67.53 W
Dongila, Eth.	225	11.17 N	37.00 E
Dan Gora, Nig.	229	11.30 N	8.09 E
Dangtu, China (däŋ-tōō)	200	31.35 N	118.28 E
Dani, Burkina	228	13.43 N	0.10 W
Dania, Fl. (dā'nĭ-à)	127a	26.01 N	80.10 W
Daniels, Md.	56c	39.26 N	77.03 W
Danilov, Sov. Un. (dä'nē-lôf)	174	58.12 N	40.08 E
Danissa Hills, Ken.	231	3.20 N	40.55 E
Dankov, Sov. Un. (däŋ'kôf)	174	53.17 N	39.09 E
Danlí, Hond. (dän'lē)	132	14.02 N	86.35 W
Dannemora, NY (dăn-ē-mō'rȧ)	111	44.45 N	73.45 W
Dannhauser, S. Afr. (dän'hou-zēr)	227c	28.07 S	30.04 E
Dansville, NY (dănz'vĭl)	111	42.30 N	77.40 W
Danube (Donau,Duna)(R.), Eur.	166	48.35 N	10.38 E
Danube, Mouths of the, Rom. (dăn'ūb)	175	45.13 N	29.37 E
Danvers, Ma. (dăn'vērz)	105a	42.34 N	70.57 W
Danville, Ca. (dăn'vĭl)	118b	37.49 N	122.00 W
Danville, Il.	110	40.10 N	87.35 W
Danville, In.	110	39.45 N	86.30 W
Danville, Ky.	110	37.35 N	84.50 W
Danville, Pa.	111	41.00 N	76.35 W
Danville, Va.	127	36.35 N	79.24 W
Danxian, China (dän shyĕn)	203	19.30 N	109.38 E
Danyang, China (dän-yäŋ)	200	32.01 N	119.32 E
Danzig, G. of, Pol. (dàn'tsĭk)	158	54.41 N	19.01 E
Daoxian, China (dou shyĕn)	203	25.35 N	111.27 E
Dapango, Upper Volta	228	10.52 N	0.12 E
Daphnae (Ruins), Egypt	191a	30.43 N	32.12 E
Daqin Dao (I.), China (dä-chyĭn dou)	200	38.18 N	120.50 E
Dar'ā, Syria	191a	32.37 N	36.07 E
Darabani, Rom. (dă-ră-băn'ĭ)	167	48.13 N	26.38 E
Daraj, Libya	224	30.12 N	10.14 E
Darakeh, Iran	68h	35.48 N	51.23 E
Dār as-Salām, Egypt	71a	29.59 N	31.13 E
Darāw, Egypt (dȧ-rä'ōō)	223b	24.24 N	32.56 E
Darband, Iran	68h	35.49 N	51.26 E
Darbhanga, India (dŭr-bŭŋ'gä)	196	26.03 N	85.09 E
Darby (I.), Ba.	135	23.50 N	76.20 W
Darby, Pa. (där'bĭ)	112f	39.55 N	75.16 W
Dardanelles (Str.), see **Çanakkale Boğazi**			
Dar es Salaam, Tan. (där ĕs sȧ-läm')	231	6.48 S	39.17 E
Dārfūr (Prov.), Sud. (där-fōōr')	225	13.21 N	23.46 E
Dargai, Pak. (dŭr-gä'ē)	193a	34.35 N	72.00 E
D'Arguin, Cap (C.), Mauritania	224	20.28 N	17.46 W
Darien, Col. (dā-rĭ-ĕn')	142a	3.56 N	76.30 W
Darien, Ct. (dâ-rē-ĕn')	112a	41.04 N	73.28 W
Darién, Cordillera de (Mts.), Nic.	132	13.00 N	85.42 W
Darien, Serrania del (Ra.), Pan. (sĕr-ä-nē'ä dĕl dä-rē-ĕn')	133	8.13 N	77.28 W
Darjeeling, India (dŭr-jē'lĭng)	196	27.05 N	88.16 E
Darling(L.), ND (där'lĭng)	114	48.35 N	101.25 W
Darling (R.), Austl.	216	31.50 S	143.20 E
Darling Downs (Reg.), Austl.	216	27.22 S	105.00 E
Darling Ra, Austl.	214	30.30 S	115.45 E
Darlington, Eng. (där'lĭng-tŭn)	162	54.32 N	1.35 W
Darlington, SC	127	34.15 N	79.52 W
Darlington, Wi.	115	42.41 N	90.06 W
Darlowo, Pol. (där-lô'vô)	166	54.26 N	16.23 E
Darmstadt, F.R.G. (därm'shtät)	166	49.53 N	8.40 E
Darnah, Libya	225	32.44 N	22.41 E
Darnley B., Ak. (därn'lē)	107	70.00 N	124.00 W
Daroca, Sp. (dä-rō-kä)	170	41.08 N	1.24 W
Dartford, Eng.	62	51.27 N	0.14 E
Dartmoor, Eng. (därt'mōōr)	162	50.35 N	4.05 W
Dartmouth, Can. (därt'mŭth)	104	44.40 N	63.34 W
Dartmouth, Eng.	162	50.33 N	3.28 W
Daru I., Pap. N. Gui. (dä'rōō)	207	9.04 S	143.21 E
Daruvar, Yugo. (där'rōō-vär)	172	45.37 N	17.16 E
Darwen, Eng. (där'wĕn)	156	53.42 N	2.28 W
Darwin, Austl. (där'wĭn)	214	12.25 S	131.00 E
Darwin, Cordillera (Mts.), Chile-Arg. (kôr-dēl-yĕ'rä-där'wĕn)	144	54.40 S	69.30 W
Dash Point, Wa. (dăsh)	118a	47.19 N	122.25 W
Dasht (R.), Pak. (dŭsht)	192	25.30 N	62.30 E
Dasht-e Kavīr Des., Iran (dŭsht-ē-ka-vēr')	192	34.41 N	53.30 E
Dasht-e-Lūt (Des.), Iran (dă'sht-ē-lōōt)	192	31.47 N	58.38 E
Dasol B., Phil. (dä-sōl')	207a	15.53 N	119.40 E
Datchet, Eng.	62	51.29 N	0.34 W
Datian Ding (Mtn.), China (dä-tĭĕn dĭŋ)	203	22.25 N	111.20 E
Datong, China (dä-tôŋ)	202	40.00 N	113.30 E
Dattapukur, India	196a	22.45 N	88.32 E
Datteln, F.R.G. (dät'tĕln)	169c	51.39 N	7.20 E
Datuan, China (dä-tůän)	201b	30.57 N	121.43 E
Datu, Tandjung (C.), Indon.	206	2.08 N	110.15 E
Daugava (R.), Sov. Un.	165	56.40 N	24.40 E
Daugavpils, Sov. Un. (dä'ōō-gäv-pēls)	174	55.52 N	26.32 E
Dauphin, Can. (dô'fĭn)	101	51.09 N	100.00 W
Dauphin L., Can.	101	51.17 N	99.48 W
Dāvangere, India	197	14.30 N	75.55 E
Davao, Phil. (dä'vä-ô)	207	7.05 N	125.30 E
Davao G., Phil.	207	6.30 N	125.45 E
Davenport, Ia. (dăv'ĕn-pōrt)	115	41.34 N	90.38 W
Davenport, Wa.	116	47.39 N	118.07 W
Daveyton Location, S. Afr.	71b	26.09 S	28.25 E
David, Pan. (dȧ-vēdh')	133	8.27 N	82.27 W
David City, Ne. (dā'vĭd)	114	41.15 N	97.10 W
David-Gorodok, Sov. Un. (dȧ-vēt' gô-rō'dôk)	167	52.02 N	27.14 E
Davis, Ok. (dā'vĭs)	123	34.34 N	97.08 W
Davis, WV	111	39.15 N	79.25 W
Davis L., Or.	116	43.38 N	121.43 W
Davis Mts., Tx.	124	30.45 N	104.17 W
Davisson Lake (Res.), Wa.	116	46.20 N	122.10 W
Davis Str., Can.	94	66.00 N	60.00 W
Davlekanovo, Sov. Un.	178	54.15 N	55.05 E
Davos, Switz. (dä'vōs)	166	46.47 N	9.50 E
Davyhulme, Eng.	64b	53.27 N	2.22 W
Dawa (R.), Eth.	225	4.34 N	41.34 E
Dawāsir, Wādī ad (R.), Sau. Ar.	192	20.48 N	44.07 E
Dawen (R.), China (dä-wŭn)	200	35.58 N	116.53 E
Dawley, Eng. (dô'lĭ)	156	52.38 N	2.28 W
Dawna Ra., Bur. (dô'nȧ)	206	17.02 N	98.01 E
Dawson, Can. (dô'sŭn)	107	64.04 N	139.22 W
Dawson, Ga.	126	31.45 N	84.29 W
Dawson, Mn.	114	44.54 N	96.03 W
Dawson (R.), Austl.	216	24.20 S	149.45 E
Dawson B., Can.	101	52.55 N	100.50 W
Dawson Creek, Can.	99	55.46 N	120.14 W
Dawson Ra., Can.	107	62.15 N	138.10 W
Dawson Springs, Ky.	126	37.10 N	87.40 W
Dawu, China (dä-wōō)	200	31.33 N	114.07 E
Dawuji, China	67b	39.51 N	116.30 E
Dax, Fr. (dȧks)	168	43.42 N	1.06 W
Daxian, China (dä-shyĕn)	203	31.12 N	107.30 E
Daxing, China (dä-shyĭŋ)	202a	39.44 N	116.19 E
Dayiqiao, China (dä-yē-chyou)	200	31.43 N	120.40 E
Dayr az Zawr, Syr. (dā-ĕr'ez-zôr')	192	35.15 N	40.01 E
Dayrūţ, Egypt	223b	27.33 N	30.48 E
Dayton, Ky. (dā'tŭn)	113f	39.07 N	84.28 W
Dayton, NM	122	32.44 N	104.23 W
Dayton, Oh.	110	39.54 N	84.15 W
Dayton, Tn.	126	35.30 N	85.00 W
Dayton, Tx.	125	30.03 N	94.53 W
Dayton, Wa.	116	46.18 N	117.59 W
Daytona Beach, Fl. (dā-tō'nȧ)	127	29.11 N	81.02 W
Dayu, China (dä-yōō)	203	25.20 N	114.20 E
Da Yunhe (Grand Canal), China (dä yōōn-hŭ)	200	34.23 N	117.57 E
Dayville, Ct. (dā'vĭl)	111	41.50 N	71.55 W
De Aar, S. Afr. (dē-är')	226	30.45 S	24.05 E
Dead (L.), Mn. (dĕd)	114	46.28 N	96.00 W
Dead Sea, Isr.-Jordan	191a	31.30 N	35.30 E
Deadwood, SD (dĕd'wŏŏd)	114	44.23 N	103.43 W
Deal Island, Md. (dēl-ī'lănd)	111	38.10 N	75.55 W
Dean (R.), Can. (dēn)	98	52.45 N	125.30 W
Dean Chan, Can.	98	52.33 N	127.13 W
Deán Funes, Arg. (dĕ-ȧ'n-fōō-nĕs)	144	30.26 S	64.12 W
Dean Row, Eng.	64b	53.20 N	2.11 W
Dearborn, Mi. (dēr'bŭrn)	113b	42.18 N	83.15 W
Dearborn Heights, Mi.	57c	42.19 N	83.14 W
Dearg, Ben (Mtn.), Scot. (bĕn dŭrg)	162	57.48 N	4.59 W
Dease Str., Can. (dēz)	96	68.50 N	108.20 W
Death Valley, Ca.-Nv.	120	36.55 N	117.12 W
Death Valley Junction, Ca.	120	36.18 N	116.26 W
Death Valley Natl. Mon., Ca.	120	36.34 N	117.00 W
Debal'tsevo, Sov. Un. (dyĕb'ál-tsyĕ'vô)	175	48.23 N	38.29 E
Debao, China (dŭ-bou)	203	23.18 N	106.40 E
Debar (Dibra), Yugo. (dĕ'bär) (dĭ'brä)	173	41.31 N	20.32 E
Deblin, Pol. (dăɴ'blĭn)	167	51.34 N	21.49 E
Debno, Pol. (dĕb-nô')	166	52.47 N	13.43 E
Debo, Lac (L.), Mali	228	15.15 N	4.40 W
Debrecen, Hung. (dĕ'brĕ-tsĕn)	167	47.32 N	21.40 E
Debre Markos, Eth.	225	10.15 N	37.45 E
Debre Tabor, Eth.	225	11.57 N	38.09 E
Decatur, Al. (dē-kā'tŭr)	126	34.35 N	87.00 W
Decatur, Ga.	112c	33.47 N	84.18 W
Decatur, Il.	123	39.50 N	88.59 W
Decatur, In.	110	40.50 N	84.55 W
Decatur, Mi.	110	42.10 N	86.00 W
Decatur, Tx.	122	33.14 N	97.33 W
Decazeville, Fr. (dē-käz'vēl')	168	44.33 N	2.16 E
Deccan (Plat.), India (dĕk'ăn)	196	19.05 N	76.40 E
Deception L., Can.	100	56.33 N	104.15 W
Deception P., Wa. (dē-sĕp'shŭn)	118a	48.24 N	122.44 W
Děčín, Czech. (dyĕ'chēn)	166	50.47 N	14.14 E
Decorah, Ia. (dē-kō'rȧ)	115	43.18 N	91.48 W
Dedeagats, see **Alexandroúpolis**			
Dedenevo, Sov. Un. (dyĕ-dyĕ'nyĕ-vô)	182b	56.14 N	37.31 E
Dedham, Ma. (dĕd'ăm)	105a	42.15 N	71.11 W
Dedo do Deus (Mt.), Braz. (dĕ-dô-dĕ'ōōs)	144b	22.30 S	43.02 W
Dédougou, Burkina (dā-dōō-gōō')	228	12.38 N	3.28 W
Dee (R.), Scot.	162	57.05 N	2.25 W
Deep (R.), NC (dēp)	127	35.36 N	79.32 W
Deep Fk. (R.), OK.	123	35.35 N	96.42 W
Deep River, Can.	103	46.06 N	77.20 W
Deepwater, Mo. (dep-wô-tēr)	123	38.15 N	93.46 W
Deer (I.), Me.	104	44.07 N	68.38 W
Deerfield, IL. (dēr'fēld)	113a	42.10 N	87.51 W
Deer Island, Or.	118c	45.56 N	122.51 W
Deer L., Can.	101	52.40 N	94.30 W
Deer Lake, Can.	105	49.10 N	57.25 W
Deer Lodge, Mt. (dēr lŏj)	117	46.23 N	112.42 W
Deer Park, Oh.	113f	39.12 N	84.24 W
Deer Park, Wa.	116	47.58 N	117.28 W
Deer River, Mn.	115	47.20 N	93.49 W
Dee Why, Austl.	70a	33.45 S	151.17 E
Dee Why Head, Austl.	70a	33.46 S	151.19 E
Dee Why Lagoon, Austl.	70a	33.45 S	151.18 E
Defiance, Oh. (dē-fī'ăns)	110	41.15 N	84.20 W
DeFuniak Springs, Fl. (dē fū'nĭ-ăk)	126	30.42 N	86.06 W
Deganga, India	196a	22.41 N	88.41 E
Degeh Bur, Eth.	223a	8.10 N	43.25 E
Deggendorf, F.R.G. (dĕ'ghĕn-dôrf)	166	48.50 N	12.59 E
Degollado, Mex. (dā-gô-lyä'dō)	130	20.27 N	102.11 W
DeGrey (R.), Austl. (dē grā')	214	20.20 S	119.25 E
Degtyarsk, Sov. Un. (dĕg-ty'arsk)	182a	56.42 N	60.05 E
Dehiwala-Mount Lavinia, Sri Lanka	197	6.47 N	79.55 E
Dehra Dūn, India (dā'rŭ)	196	30.09 N	78.07 E
Dehua, China (dŭ-hwä)	203	25.30 N	118.15 E
Dej, Rom. (dāzh)	167	47.09 N	23.53 E
De Kalb, Il. (dē kălb')	115	41.54 N	88.46 W
Dekese, Zaire	230	3.27 S	21.24 E
Delacour, Can. (dĕ-lä-kōōr')	95e	51.09 N	113.45 W
Delagua, Co. (dĕl-ä'gwä)	122	37.19 N	104.42 W
Delair, NJ	56b	39.59 N	75.03 W
De Land, Fl. (dē lănd')	127	29.00 N	81.19 W
Delano, Ca. (dĕl'ȧ-nō)	120	35.47 N	119.15 W
Delano Pk., Ut.	121	38.25 N	112.25 W
Delavan, Wi. (dĕl'ȧ-văn)	115	42.39 N	88.38 W
Delaware, Oh. (dĕl'ȧ-wâr)	110	40.15 N	83.05 W
Delaware (State), U.S.	109	38.40 N	75.30 W
Delaware (R.), Ks.	123	39.45 N	95.47 W
Delaware (R.), U.S.	111	41.50 N	75.20 W
Delaware B., De.-NJ	111	39.05 N	75.10 W
Delaware Res., Oh.	110	40.30 N	83.05 W
Delémont, Switz. (dē-lā-mōɴ')	166	47.21 N	7.18 E
De Leon, Tx. (dē lē-ŏn')	124	32.06 N	98.33 W
Delfinópolis, Braz. (dĕl-fē'nô'pō'-lĕs)	141a	20.20 S	46.50 W
Delft, Neth. (dĕlft)	157a	52.01 N	4.20 E
Delfzijl, Neth.	163	53.20 N	6.50 E
Delgada Pta. (Pt.), Arg. (pōō'n-tä-dĕl-gä'dȧ)	144	43.46 S	63.46 W
Delgado, Cabo (C.), Moz. (kȧ'bô-dĕl-gä'dō)	231	10.40 S	40.35 E
Delhi, Il. (dĕl'hī)	119e	39.03 N	90.16 W
Delhi, India	196	28.54 N	77.13 E
Delhi, La.	125	32.26 N	91.29 W
Delhi (State), India	196	28.30 N	76.50 E
Delhi Cantonment, India	67d	28.36 N	77.08 E
Delitzsch, G.D.R. (dā'lĭch)	166	51.32 N	12.18 E
Delles, Alg. (dĕ'lĕs')	224	36.59 N	3.40 E
Dell Rapids, SD (dĕl)	114	43.50 N	96.43 W
Dellwig (Neigh.), F.R.G.	63	51.29 N	6.56 E
Dellwood, Mn. (dĕl'wŏŏd)	119g	45.05 N	92.58 W
Del Mar, Ca. (dĕl mär')	120a	32.57 N	117.16 W
Delmas, S. Afr. (dĕl'mȧs)	223d	26.08 S	28.43 E
Delmenhorst, F.R.G. (dĕl'mĕn-hôrst)	166	53.03 N	8.38 E
Del Norte, Co. (dĕl nôrt')	121	37.40 N	106.25 W
De-Longa (I.), Sov. Un.	181	76.30 N	153.00 E
De Long Mts., Ak. (dē'lông)	107	68.38 N	162.30 W
Deloraine, Austl. (dĕ-lŭ-rān)	216	41.30 S	146.40 E
Delphi, In. (dĕl'fī)	110	40.35 N	86.40 W
Delphos, Oh. (dĕl'fŏs)	110	40.50 N	84.20 W
Delran, NJ	56b	40.02 N	74.58 W
Delray Beach, Fl. (dĕl-rā')	127a	26.27 N	80.05 W
Del Rio, Tx. (dĕl rē'ō)	124	29.21 N	100.52 W
Delson, Can. (dĕl'sŭn)	95a	45.24 N	73.32 W
Delta, Co.	121	38.45 N	108.05 W
Delta, Ut.	121	39.20 N	112.35 W
Delta Beach, Can.	95f	50.10 N	98.20 W
Delta Mendota Can, Ca.	120	37.10 N	121.02 W
Delvine, Alb. (dĕl'vē-nȧ)	173	39.58 N	20.10 E
Del Viso, Arg.	60d	34.26 S	58.46 W
Dĕma (R.), Sov. Un. (dyĕm'ä)	178	53.40 N	54.30 E
Demarest, NJ	55	40.57 N	73.58 W
Demba, Zaire	230	5.30 S	22.16 E
Dembi Dolo, Eth.	225	8.46 N	34.46 E
Demidov, Sov. Un. (dzyĕ'mē-dô'f)	174	55.16 N	31.32 E
Deming, NM (dĕm'ĭng)	121	32.15 N	107.45 W
Demmeltrath (Neigh.), F.R.G.	63	51.11 N	7.03 E
Demmin, G.D.R. (dĕm'mēn)	166	53.54 N	13.04 E
Demnat, Mor. (dĕm-nät)	224	31.58 N	7.03 W
Demopolis, Al. (dē-mŏp'ō-lĭs)	126	32.30 N	87.50 W
Demotte, In. (dē'mŏt)	113a	41.12 N	87.13 W
Dempo, Gunung (Vol.), Indon. (dĕm'pō)	206	4.04 S	103.11 E
Dem'yanka (R.), Sov. Un. (dyĕm-yän'kä)	180	59.07 N	72.58 E
Demyansk, Sov. Un. (dyĕm-yänsk')	174	57.39 N	32.26 E
Denain, Fr. (dē-năɴ')	168	50.23 N	3.21 E
Denakil Pln., Eth.	225	12.45 N	41.01 E
Denali Natl. Park, Ak.	107	63.48 N	153.02 W
Denbigh, Wales (dĕn'bĭ)	162	53.15 N	3.25 W
Dendermonde, Bel.	157a	51.02 N	4.04 E
Dendron, Va. (dĕn'drŭn)	127	37.02 N	76.53 W
Denenchōfu (Neigh.), Jap.	69a	35.35 N	139.41 E
Denezhkin Kamen, Gora (Mtn.), Sov. Un. (dzyĕ-ŋĕ'zhkĕn kămĭēŋ)	182a	60.26 N	59.35 E
D'Enfer, Pointe (Pt.), Mart.	133b	14.21 N	60.48 W
Denham, Mt., Jam.	134	18.20 N	77.30 W
Den Helder, Neth. (dĕn hĕl'dĕr)	163	52.55 N	5.45 E
Denia, Sp. (dā'nyä)	171	38.48 N	0.06 E
Deniliquin, Austl. (dĕ-nĭl'ĭ-kwĭn)	216	35.20 S	144.52 E
Denison, Ia. (dĕn'ĭ-sŭn)	114	42.01 N	95.22 W
Denison, Tx.	123	33.45 N	97.02 W
Denisovka, Sov. Un. (dĕ-nē'sof-kȧ)	182a	52.26 N	61.45 E
Denizli, Tur. (dĕn-ĭz-lē')	179	37.40 N	29.10 E
Denklingen, F.R.G. (dĕn'klĕn-gĕn)	169c	50.54 N	7.40 E
Denmark, Eur.	154	56.14 N	8.30 E
Denmark, SC (dĕn'märk)	127	33.18 N	81.09 W
Denmark Str., Grnld.	94	66.30 N	27.00 W
Dennilton, S. Afr. (dĕn-ĭl-tŭn)	223d	25.18 S	29.13 E
Dennison, Oh. (dĕn'ĭ-sŭn)	110	40.25 N	81.20 W
Denpasar, Indon.	206	8.35 S	115.10 E
Denshaw, Eng.	64b	53.35 N	2.02 W
Denton, Eng. (dĕn'tŭn)	156	53.27 N	2.07 W
Denton, Md.	111	38.55 N	75.50 W
Denton, Tx.	123	33.12 N	97.06 W

ăt; finăl; rāte; senåte; ärm; åsk; sofȧ; fâre; ch-choose; dh-as th in other; bē; ēvent; bĕt; recĕnt; cratēr; g-gō; gh-guttural g; bĭt; ĭ-short neutral; rīde; ĸ-guttural k as ch in German ich;

PLACE (Pronounciation)	PAGE	Lat. °′	Long. °′
D'Entrecasteaux Is., Pap. N. Gui. (däN-tr'-lás-tō')	207	9.45 S	152.00 E
D'Entrecasteaux, Pt., Austl. (däN-tr'kás-tō')	214	34.50 S	114.45 E
Denver, Co. (děn'vẽr)	122	39.44 N	104.59 W
Deoli, India	196	25.52 N	75.23 E
De Pere, Wi. (dē pēr')	115	44.25 N	88.04 W
Depew, NY (dē-pū')	113c	42.55 N	78.43 W
Deping, China (dŭ-pĭŋ)	200	37.28 N	116.57 E
Deptford (Neigh.), Eng.	62	51.28 N	0.02 W
Depue, Il. (dē pū)	110	41.15 N	89.55 W
De Queen, Ar. (dē kwēn')	123	34.02 N	94.21 W
De Quincy, La. (dē kwĭn'sĭ)	125	30.27 N	93.27 W
Dera Ghāzi Khān, Pak. (dā'rŭ gä-zē' ĸän')	196	30.09 N	70.39 E
Dera Ismāīl Khān, Pak. (dā'rŭ ĭs-mä-ēl' ĸän')	196	31.55 N	70.51 E
Derbent, Sov. Un. (děr-běnt')	179	42.00 N	48.10 E
Derby, Austl. (där'bē) (dûr'bē)	214	17.20 S	123.40 E
Derby, Ct. (dûr'bē)	111	41.20 N	73.05 W
Derby, Eng. (där'bē)	156	52.55 N	1.29 W
Derby, S. Afr. (där'bĭ)	223d	25.55 S	27.02 E
Derbyshire (Co.), Eng.	156	53.11 N	1.30 W
Derdepoort, S. Afr.	223d	24.39 S	26.21 E
Dere, Lak (R.), Ken.	231	0.45 N	40.15 E
Derendorf (Neigh.), F.R.G.	63	51.15 N	6.48 E
Derg, Lough (L.), Ire. (lŏk dĕrg)	162	53.00 N	8.09 W
De Ridder, La. (dē rĭd'ēr)	125	30.50 N	93.18 W
Dermott, Ar. (dûr'mŏt)	123	33.32 N	91.24 W
Derne (Neigh.), F.R.G.	63	51.34 N	7.31 E
Derry, NH (dâr'ĭ)	105a	42.53 N	71.22 W
Derventa, Yugo. (děr'ven-tá)	173	45.58 N	17.58 E
Derwent (R.), Austl. (dēr'wěnt)	216	42.21 S	146.30 E
Derwent (R.), Eng.	156	52.54 N	1.24 W
Des Arc, Ar. (dāz ärk')	123	34.59 N	91.31 W
Descalvado, Braz. (děs-käl-vá-dô)	141a	21.55 S	47.37 W
Descartes, Fr.	168	46.58 N	0.42 E
Deschambault L., Can.	100	54.40 N	103.35 W
Deschênes, Can.	95c	45.23 N	75.47 W
Deschenes, L., Can.	95c	45.25 N	75.53 W
Deschutes R., Or. (dā-shōōt')	116	44.25 N	121.21 W
Desdemona, Tx. (děz-dē-mō'ná)	124	32.16 N	98.33 W
Dese, Eth.	225	11.00 N	39.51 E
Deseado, Rio (R.), Arg. (rē-ō-dā-sä-ä'dhō)	144	46.50 S	67.45 W
Desirade I., Guad. (dā-zē-rás')	133b	16.21 N	60.51 W
De Smet, SD (dē smět')	114	44.23 N	97.33 W
Des Moines, Ia. (dē moin')	115	41.35 N	93.37 W
Des Moines, NM	122	36.42 N	103.48 W
Des Moines (R.), U.S.	109	43.45 N	94.20 W
Des Moines, Wa.	118a	46.24 N	122.20 W
Desna (R.), Sov. Un. (dyĕs-ná')	175	51.05 N	31.03 E
Desolación (I.), Chile (dě-sô-lä-syô'n)	144	53.05 S	74.00 W
De Soto, Mo. (dē sō'tō)	123	38.07 N	90.32 W
Des Peres, Mo. (děs pěr'ěs)	119e	38.36 N	90.26 W
Des Plaines, Il. (děs plānz')	113a	42.02 N	87.54 W
Des Plaines R., Il.	113a	41.39 N	87.56 W
Dessau, G.D.R. (děs'ou)	166	51.50 N	12.15 E
Detmold, G.D.R. (dět'mōld)	166	51.57 N	8.55 E
Detroit, Mi. (dē-troit')	113b	42.22 N	83.10 W
Detroit, Tx.	123	33.41 N	95.16 W
Detroit (R.), Mi.	57c	42.06 N	83.08 W
Detroit Lakes, Mn. (dē-troit'lākz)	114	46.48 N	95.51 W
Detroit Metropolitan-Wayne County Arpt., Mi.	57c	42.13 N	83.22 W
Detva, Czech. (dyĕt'vá)	167	48.32 N	19.21 E
Deuil-la-Barre, Fr.	64c	48.59 N	2.20 E
Deurne, Bel.	157a	51.13 N	4.27 E
Deusen (Neigh.), F.R.G.	63	51.33 N	7.26 E
Deutsch Wagram, Aus.	157e	48.19 N	16.34 E
Deux-Montagnes, Can.	54b	45.33 N	73.53 W
Deux Montagnes, Lac des (L.), Can.	95a	45.28 N	74.00 W
Deva, Rom. (dā'vä)	173	45.52 N	22.52 E
Dévaványa, Hung. (dā'vô-vän-yô)	167	47.01 N	20.58 E
Develi, Tur. (dě'vá-lē)	179	38.20 N	35.10 E
Deventer, Neth. (děv'ěn-tēr)	163	52.14 N	6.07 E
Devils I., see Diable, Ile du			
Devils (L.), ND (děv''lz)	114	47.57 N	99.04 W
Devils Lake, ND	108	48.10 N	98.55 W
Devils Lake Ind. Res, ND	114	48.08 N	99.40 W
Devils Postpile Natl. Mon., Ca.	120	37.42 N	119.12 W
Devils (R.), Tx.	124	29.55 N	101.10 W
Devils Tower Natl. Mon., Wy.	117	44.38 N	105.07 W
Devoll (R.), Alb.	173	40.55 N	20.10 E
Devon, Can.	95g	53.23 N	113.43 W
Devon, S. Afr. (děv'ŭn)	223d	26.23 S	28.47 E
Devonport, Austl. (děv'ŭn-pôrt)	216	41.20 S	146.30 E
Devonport, N.Z.	215a	36.50 S	174.45 E
Devore, Ca. (dē-vôr')	119a	34.13 N	117.24 W
Dewatto, Wa. (dē-wát'ō)	118a	47.27 N	123.04 W
Dewey, Ok. (dū'ĭ)	123	36.48 N	95.55 W
De Witt, Ar. (dē wĭt')	123	34.17 N	91.22 W
De Witt, Ia.	115	41.46 N	90.34 W
Dewsbury, Eng. (dūz'bēr-ĭ)	156	53.42 N	1.39 W
Dexter (L.), Fl.	127	29.07 N	81.24 W
Dexter, Me. (děks'tēr)	104	45.01 N	69.19 W
Dexter, Mo.	123	36.46 N	89.56 W
Dezfūl, Iran	192	32.14 N	48.37 E
Dezhnëva, Mys (East Cape), Sov. Un. (dyězh'nyĭf)	191	68.00 N	172.00 W
Dezhou, China (dŭ-jō)	200	37.28 N	116.17 E
Dháfni, Grc.	66d	37.48 N	22.01 E
Dhahran, see Aẓ Ẓahrān			
Dharamtar Cr., India	197b	18.49 N	72.54 E
Dharmavaram, India	197	14.32 N	77.43 E
Dhaulāgiri (Mtn.), Nep. (dou-lá-gē'rē)	196	28.42 N	83.31 E
Dhenoúsa (I.), Grc.	173	37.09 N	25.53 E
Dhidhimótikhon, Grc.	173	41.20 N	26.27 E
Dhībān, Jordan	191a	31.30 N	35.46 E
Dhodhekánisos (Dodecanese) (Is.), Grc.	173	38.00 N	26.10 E
Dhule, India	196	20.58 N	74.43 E

PLACE (Pronounciation)	PAGE	Lat. °′	Long. °′
Día (I.), Grc. (dē'ä)	172a	35.27 N	25.17 E
Diable, Ile du (Devils I.), Fr. Gu.	143	5.15 N	57.10 W
Diablo Heights, Pan. (dyä'blō)	128a	8.58 N	79.34 W
Diablo, Mt., Ca. (dyä'blō)	118b	37.52 N	121.55 W
Diablo Range (Mts.), Ca.	118b	37.47 N	121.50 W
Diaca, Moz.	231	11.30 S	39.59 E
Diaka (R.), Mali	228	14.40 N	5.00 E
Diamantina, Braz.	143	18.14 S	43.32 W
Diamantina (R.), Austl. (dī'man-tē'ná)	214	25.38 S	139.53 E
Diamantino, Braz. (dê-á-män-tē'no)	143	14.22 S	56.23 W
Diamond Creek, Austl.	70b	37.41 S	145.09 E
Diamond Pk., Or.	116	43.32 N	122.08 W
Diana Bk., Ba. (dī'ǎn'á)	135	22.30 N	74.45 W
Dianbai, China (dĭĕn-bī)	203	21.30 N	111.20 E
Dian Chi (L.), China (dĭĕn chē)	203	24.58 N	103.18 E
Diancun, China	67b	39.55 N	116.14 E
Dibra, see Debar			
Dickinson, ND (dĭk'ĭn-sŭn)	114	46.52 N	102.49 W
Dickinson, Tx. (dĭk'ĭn-sŭn)	125a	29.28 N	95.02 W
Dickinson Bayou, Tx.	125a	29.26 N	95.08 W
Dickson, Tn. (dĭk'sŭn)	126	36.03 N	87.24 W
Dickson City, Pa.	111	41.25 N	75.40 W
Dicle (R.), Tur. (dĭj'lå)	179	37.50 N	40.40 E
Didcot, Eng. (dĭd'cŏt)	156b	51.35 N	1.15 W
Didiéni, Mali	228	13.53 N	8.06 W
Didsbury (Neigh.), Eng.	64b	53.25 N	2.14 W
Die, Fr. (dē)	169	44.45 N	5.22 E
Diefenbaker (Res.), Can.	96	51.20 N	108.10 W
Diefenbaker L., Can.	100	51.00 N	106.55 W
Diego de Ocampo, Pico (Pk.), Dom. Rep. (pē'-kô-dyě'gô-dě-ō-kä'm-pô)	135	19.40 N	70.45 W
Diego Ramirez, Islas (Is.), Chile (dē á'gō rä-mē'rāz)	144	56.15 S	70.15 W
Diéma, Mali	228	14.32 N	9.12 W
Dien Bien Phu, Viet.	198	21.38 N	102.49 E
Diepensee, G.D.R.	65a	52.22 N	13.31 E
Dieppe, Can. (dē-ěp')	104	46.06 N	64.45 W
Dieppe, Fr.	168	49.54 N	1.05 E
Dierks, Ar. (dērks)	123	34.06 N	94.02 W
Diersfordt, F.R.G.	63	51.42 N	6.33 E
Diessem (Neigh.), F.R.G.	63	51.20 N	6.35 E
Diessen, F.R.G. (dēs'sěn)	157d	47.57 N	11.06 E
Diest, Bel.	157a	50.59 N	5.05 E
Digby, Can. (dĭg'bĭ)	104	44.37 N	65.46 W
Dighton, Ma. (dī-tŭn)	112b	41.49 N	71.05 W
Digmoor, Eng.	64a	53.32 N	2.45 W
Digne, Fr. (dēn'y')	169	44.07 N	6.16 E
Digoin, Fr. (dē-gwäN')	168	46.28 N	4.06 E
Digra, India	67a	22.50 N	88.20 E
Digul (R.), Indon.	207	7.00 S	140.27 E
Dijohan Pt., Phil. (dē-kô-än)	207a	16.24 N	122.25 E
Dijon, Fr. (dē-zhôN')	168	47.21 N	5.02 E
Dikson, Sov. Un. (dĭk'sŏn)	180	73.30 N	80.35 E
Dikwa, Nig. (dē'kwá)	225	12.06 N	13.53 E
Dili, Indon. (dĭl'ē)	207	8.35 S	125.35 E
Di Linosa I., It. (dē-lē-nō'sä)	160	36.01 N	12.43 E
Dilizhan, Sov. Un.	179	40.45 N	45.00 E
Dillingham, Ak. (dĭl'ěng-hăm)	107	59.10 N	158.38 W
Dillon, Mt. (dĭl'ŭn)	117	45.12 N	112.40 W
Dillon, SC	127	34.24 N	79.28 W
Dillon Park, Md.	56d	38.52 N	76.56 W
Dillon Res., Oh.	110	40.05 N	82.05 W
Dilolo, Zaire, (dē-lō'lō)	226	10.19 S	22.23 E
Dimashq (Damascus), Syria (dá-más'kŭs)	192	33.31 N	36.18 E
Dimbokro, Ivory Coast	228	6.39 N	4.42 W
Dimbovita (R.), Rom.	173	44.43 N	25.41 E
Dimitrovo, See Pernik			
Dimlang (Mtn.), Nig.	229	8.24 N	11.47 E
Dimona, Isr.	191a	31.03 N	35.01 E
Dinagate (I.), Phil.	207	10.15 N	126.15 E
Dinājpur, Bngl.	196	25.38 N	87.39 E
Dinan, Fr. (dē-näN')	168	48.27 N	2.03 W
Dinant, Bel. (dē-näN')	163	50.17 N	4.50 E
Dinara (Mts.), Yugo. (dē'nä-rä)	172	43.50 N	16.15 E
Dinard, Fr.	168	48.38 N	2.04 W
Dindigul, India	197	10.25 N	78.03 E
Dingalan B., Phil. (dĭŋ-gä'län)	207a	15.19 N	121.33 E
Dingle, Ire. (dĭng''l)	162	52.10 N	10.13 W
Dingle (Neigh.), Eng.	64a	53.23 N	2.57 W
Dingle B., Ire.	162	52.02 N	10.15 W
Dingo, Austl. (dĭŋ'gō)	215	23.45 S	149.26 E
Dinguiraye, Gui.	228	11.18 N	10.43 W
Dingwall, Scot. (dĭng'wôl)	162	57.37 N	4.23 W
Dingxian, China (dĭŋ shyěn)	200	38.30 N	115.00 E
Dingxing, China (dĭŋ-shyĭŋ)	200	39.18 N	115.50 E
Dingyuan, China (dĭŋ-yüän)	200	32.32 N	117.40 E
Dingzi Wan (B.), China	200	36.33 N	121.06 E
Dinosaur Natl. Mon., Co.-Ut. (dī'nō-sôr)	117	40.45 N	109.17 W
Dinslaken, F.R.G. (děns'lä-kěn)	169c	51.33 N	6.44 E
Dinslakener Bruch, F.R.G.	63	51.35 N	6.43 E
Dinteloord, Neth.	157a	51.38 N	4.21 E
Dinuba, Ca. (dĭ-nū'bá)	120	36.33 N	119.29 W
Dinwiddie, S. Afr.	71b	26.16 S	28.10 E
Dios, Cayo de (I.), Cuba (kä'yō-dě-dē-ōs')	134	22.05 N	83.05 W
Diourbel, Senegal (dē-ōōr-běl')	228	14.40 N	16.15 W
Diphu Pass, China (dĭ-pōō)	193	28.15 N	96.45 E
Diquis (R.), C.R. (dē-kēs')	133	8.59 N	83.24 W
Dire Dawa, Eth.	223a	9.40 N	41.47 E
Diriamba, Nic. (dēr-yäm'bä)	132	11.52 N	86.15 W
Dirk Hartog (I.), Austl.	214	26.25 S	113.15 E
Dirksland, Neth.	157a	51.45 N	4.04 E
Dirranbandi, Austl. (dĭ-rá-băn'dē)	216	28.24 S	148.29 E
Dirty Devil (R.), Ut. (dûr'tĭ děv''l)	121	38.20 N	110.30 W
Disappointment (L.), Austl.	214	23.20 S	120.20 E
Disappointment, C., Wa. (dĭs'á-point'ment)	118c	46.16 N	124.11 W
D'Ischia, I., It. (dē'sh-kyä)	171c	40.26 N	13.55 E
Discovery (Is.), Can. (dĭs-kŭv'ēr-ē)	118a	48.25 N	123.13 W

PLACE (Pronounciation)	PAGE	Lat. °′	Long. °′
Discovery, S. Afr. (dĭs-kŭv'ēr-ĭ)	227b	26.10 S	27.53 E
Dishnā, Egypt (dēsh'ná)	223b	26.08 N	32.27 E
Disko (I.), Grnld. (dĭs'kō)	94	70.00 N	54.00 W
Dismal Swp., NC-Va. (dĭz'mál)	127	36.35 N	76.34 W
Disna, Sov. Un. (dēs'ná)	174	55.34 N	28.15 E
Disneyland (P. Int.), Ca.	59	33.48 N	117.55 W
Dispur, India	196	26.00 N	91.50 E
Disraëli, Can. (dĭs-rā'lĭ)	104	45.53 N	71.23 W
Disteln, F.R.G.	63	51.36 N	7.09 E
District Heights, Md.	56d	38.51 N	76.53 W
District of Columbia, U.S.	109	38.50 N	77.00 W
Distrito Federal (Dist.), Braz. (dēs-trē'tô-fě-dě-rä'l)	143	15.49 S	47.39 W
Distrito Federal (Dist.), Mex.	131	19.14 N	99.08 W
Disūq, Egypt (dē-sōōk')	223b	31.07 N	30.41 E
Ditton, Eng.	62	51.18 N	0.27 E
Diu, India (dē'ōō)	196	20.48 N	70.58 E
Divilacan B., Phil. (dē-vē-lä'kän)	207a	17.26 N	122.25 E
Divinópolis, Braz. (dē-vē-nô'pō-lēs)	141a	20.10 S	44.53 W
Divo, Ivory Coast	228	5.50 N	5.22 W
Dixie, Can.	54c	43.36 N	79.36 W
Dixon, Il. (dĭks'ŭn)	115	41.50 N	89.30 W
Dixon Entrance, Ak.-Can.	98	54.25 N	132.00 W
Diyarbakir, Tur. (dē-yär-běk'ĭr)	179	38.00 N	40.10 E
Dja (R.), Cam.	229	3.25 N	13.17 E
Djakovo (Neigh.), Sov. Un.	66b	55.39 N	37.40 E
Djambala, Con.	230	2.33 S	14.45 E
Djanet, Alg.	224	24.29 N	9.26 E
Djebob (Mtn.), Ghana	228	8.20 N	0.37 E
Djedi, Oued (R.), Alg.	160	34.18 N	4.39 E
Djelo-Binza, Zaire	71c	4.23 S	15.16 E
Djember, Chad.	229	10.25 N	17.50 E
Djerba, Ile de (I.), Tun.	160	33.53 N	11.26 E
Djerid, Chott (L.), Tun. (jěr'ĭd)	224	33.15 N	8.29 E
Djibasso, Burkina	228	13.07 N	4.10 W
Djibo, Burkina	228	14.06 N	1.38 W
Djibouti, Afr.	222	11.35 N	48.08 E
Djibouti, Djibouti (jē-bōō-tē')	223a	11.34 N	43.00 E
Djokoumatombi, Con.	230	0.47 N	15.22 E
Djokupunda, Zaire	230	5.27 S	20.58 E
Djoua (R.), Con.-Gabon	230	1.25 N	13.40 E
Djoué (R.), Con.	71c	4.19 S	15.14 E
Djursholm, Swe. (djōōrs'hōlm)	164	59.26 N	18.01 E
Dmitriyevka, Sov. Un. (d'mē-trē-yěf'ká)	175	47.57 N	38.56 E
Dmitriyev-L'govskiy, Sov. Un. (d'mē'trĭ-yěf l'gôf'skĭ)	175	52.07 N	35.05 E
Dmitrov, Sov. Un. (d'mē'trôf)	182b	56.21 N	37.32 E
Dmitrovsk, Sov. Un. (d'mē'trôfsk)	174	52.30 N	35.10 E
Dnepr (Dnieper) (R.), Sov. Un. (nē'pēr)	175	46.47 N	32.57 E
Dneprodzerzhinsk, Sov. Un. (d'nyěp'rô-zēr-shĭnsk)	175	48.32 N	34.38 E
Dneprodzerzhinskoye Vdkhr. (Res.), Sov. Un.	176	49.00 N	34.10 E
Dnepropetrovsk (Oblast), Sov. Un.	175	48.15 N	34.08 E
Dnepropetrovsk, Sov. Un. (d'nyěp'rô-pā-trôfsk)	175	48.23 N	34.10 E
Dnepr Zaliv (B.), Sov. Un. (dnyěp'r zá'lĭf)	175	46.33 N	31.45 E
Dnestr (Dniester) (R.), Sov. Un. (nēst'rōōl) (nēs'tēr)	175	48.21 N	28.10 E
Dnestrovskiy Lĭman (B), Sov. Un.	175	46.13 N	29.50 E
Dnieper (R.), see Dnepr			
Dniester (R.), see Dnestr			
Dno, Sov.Un. (d'nô')	174	57.49 N	29.59 E
Doba, Chad	229	8.39 N	16.51 E
Dobbs Ferry, NY (dŏbz'fĕ'rē)	112a	41.01 N	73.53 W
Dobbyn, Austl. (dôb'ĭn)	214	19.45 S	140.02 E
Dobele, Sov.Un. (dô'bĕ-lĕ)	165	56.37 N	23.18 E
Döbeln, G.D.R. (dû'běln)	166	51.08 N	13.07 E
Doberai Jazirah (Pen.), Indon.	207	1.25 S	133.15 E
Döbling (Neigh.), Aus.	66e	48.15 N	16.22 E
Dobo, Indon.	207	6.00 S	134.18 E
Doboj, Yugo. (dō'boi)	173	44.42 N	18.04 E
Dobryanka, Sov. Un. (dôb-ryän'ká)	182a	58.27 N	56.26 E
Dobšina, Czech. (dôp'shē-nä)	167	48.48 N	20.25 E
Doce (R.), Braz. (dō'sā)	143	19.01 S	42.14 W
Doce Leguas, Cayos de las (Is.), Cuba (kä'yōs-dě-lás-dō-sě-lě'gwäs)	134	20.55 N	79.05 W
Doctor Arroyo, Mex. (dōk-tōr' är-rō'yō)	130	23.41 N	100.10 W
Doddinghurst, Eng.	62	51.40 N	0.18 E
Doddington, Eng. (dŏd'dĭng-tŏn)	156b	51.17 N	0.47 E
Dodecanese (S.), see Dhodhekánisos			
Dodge City, Ks. (dŏj)	122	37.44 N	100.01 W
Dodgeville, Wi. (dŏj'vĭl)	115	42.58 N	90.07 W
Dodoma, Tan. (dō'dô-má)	231	6.11 S	35.45 E
Dog (L.), Can. (dŏg)	115	48.42 N	89.24 W
Dogger Bk., Eur. (dŏg'gēr)	163	55.07 N	2.25 E
Dogubayazit, Tur.	179	39.35 N	44.00 E
Dohad, India	196	22.52 N	74.18 E
Doiran (L), Grc.	173	41.10 N	23.00 E
Dōjō, Jap. (dō-jō)	205b	34.51 N	135.14 E
Dokshitsy, Sov. Un. (dôk-shētsĕ)	174	54.53 N	27.49 E
Do, Lac (L.), Mali.	228	15.50 N	2.20 W
Dolbeau, Can.	103	48.52 N	72.16 W
Dole, Fr. (dōl)	169	47.07 N	5.28 E
Dolgaya, Kosa (C.), Sov. Un. (kô'sá dôl-gä'yä)	175	46.42 N	37.42 E
Dolgeville, NY	111	43.10 N	74.45 W
Dolgiy (I.), Sov. Un.	178	69.20 N	59.20 E
Dolgoprudnyy, Sov. Un.	182b	55.57 N	37.33 E
Dolina, Sov. Un. (dô-lyē'ná)	167	48.57 N	24.01 E
Dolinsk, Sov. Un. (dá-lēnsk')	204	47.29 N	142.31 E
Dollard-des-Ormeaux, Can.	54b	45.29 N	73.49 W
Dollar Hbr, Ba.	134	25.30 N	79.15 W
Dolo, Som.	225	4.01 N	42.14 E
Dolomite, Al. (dŏl'ō-mīt)	112h	33.28 N	86.57 W
Dolomiti, Alpi (Mts.), It. (äl-pē-dô-lô'mē-tē)	172	46.16 N	11.43 E
Dolores, Arg. (dô-lō'rěs)	141c	36.20 S	57.42 W
Dolores, Col.	142a	3.33 N	74.54 W

PLACE (Pronunciation)	PAGE	Lat. °′	Long. °′
Dolores, Phil. (dô-lô-rĕs)	207a	17.40 N	120.43 E
Dolores, Tx. (dô-lō'rĕs)	124	27.42 N	99.47 W
Dolores, Ur.	141c	33.32 S	58.15 W
Dolores (R.), Co.-Ut.	121	38.35 N	108.50 W
Dolores Hidalgo, Mex. (dô-lô'rĕs-ē-däl'gō)	130	21.09 N	100.56 W
Dolphin and Union Str., Can. (dŏl'fĭn ūn'yŭn)	96	69.22 N	117.10 W
Dolton, Il.	58a	41.39 N	87.37 W
Domažlice, Czech. (dō'mäzh-lē-tsĕ)	166	49.27 N	12.55 E
Dombasle-sur-Meurthe, Fr. (dôN-bäl')	169	48.38 N	6.18 E
Dombóvár, Hung. (dŏm'bō-vär)	167	46.22 N	18.08 E
Domeyko, Cordillera (Mts.), Chile (kôr-dēl-yĕ'rä-dô-mā'kô)	142	20.50 S	69.02 W
Dominguez, Ca.	59	33.50 N	118.31 W
Dominica, N.A. (dŏ-mĭ-nē'kȧ)	129	15.30 N	60.45 W
Dominica Chan., N.A.	133b	15.00 N	61.30 W
Dominican Republic, N.A. (dô-mĭn'ĭ-kăn)	129	19.00 N	70.45 W
Dominion, Can. (dô-mĭn'yŭn)	105	46.13 N	60.01 W
Domiongo, Zaire	230	4.37 S	21.15 E
Domitilla, Catacombe di (P. Int.), It.	66c	41.52 N	12.31 E
Domodedovo, Sov. Un. (dô-mô-dyĕ'do-vô)	182b	55.27 N	37.45 E
Dom Silvério, Braz. (doN-sĕl-vĕ'ryō)	141a	20.09 S	42.57 W
Don (R.), Can.	54c	43.39 N	79.21 W
Don (R.), Eng.	156	53.39 N	0.58 W
Don (R.), Scot.	162	57.19 N	2.39 W
Don (R.), Sov.Un.	176	49.50 N	41.30 E
Don (R.), Eng. (dŏn)	156	53.27 N	1.34 W
Donaldson, Mi. (dŏn'ăl-sŭn)	119k	46.19 N	84.22 W
Donaldsonville, La. (dŏn'ăld-sŭn-vĭl)	123	30.05 N	90.58 W
Donalsonville, Ga.	126	31.02 N	84.50 W
Donau (R.), See Danube			
Donaufeld (Neigh.), It.	66c	48.15 N	16.25 E
Donaustadt (Neigh.), Aus.	66e	48.13 N	16.30 E
Donauturm (P. Int.), Aus.	66e	48.14 N	16.25 E
Donawitz, Aus. (dō'ná-vĭts)	166	47.23 N	15.05 E
Don Benito, Sp. (dōn'bå-nē'tō)	170	38.55 N	6.08 W
Dönberg, F.R.G.	63	51.18 N	7.10 E
Don Bosco (Neigh.), Arg.	60d	34.42 S	58.19 W
Doncaster, Austl. (doŋ'kăs-tēr)	211a	37.47 S	145.08 E
Doncaster, Can.	54c	43.48 N	79.25 W
Doncaster, Eng. (doŋ'kăs-tēr)	156	53.32 N	1.07 W
Doncaster East, Austl.	70b	37.47 S	145.10 E
Dondo, Ang. (dōn'dō)	230	9.38 S	14.25 E
Dondo, Moz.	226	19.33 S	34.47 E
Dondra Hd., Sri Lanka	197	5.52 N	80.52 E
Donegal, Ire. (dŏn-ē-gôl')	162	54.44 N	8.05 W
Donegal Bay, Ire. (dŏn-ē-gôl')	162	54.35 N	8.36 W
Donets (R.), Sov. Un. (dō-nyĕts')	175	48.48 N	38.42 E
Donets Coal Basin (Reg.), Sov. Un. (dō-nyĕts')	175	48.15 N	38.50 E
Donetsk (Stalino), Sov. Un. (dō-nyĕts'k) (stä'lĭ-nō)	175	48.00 N	37.35 E
Donetsk (Oblast), Sov. Un.	175	47.55 N	37.40 E
Dong (R.), China (dôŋ)	199	34.13 N	115.08 E
Dongara, Austl. (dôn-gă'rȧ)	214	29.15 S	115.00 E
Dongba, China	67b	39.58 N	116.32 E
Dongba, China (dôŋ-bä)	200	31.40 N	119.02 E
Dongbahe, China	67b	39.58 N	116.27 E
Dong'e, China (dôŋ-ŭ)	200	36.21 N	116.14 E
Dong'erzen, China (dôŋ-är-dzŭn)	200	36.11 N	116.16 E
Dongfang, China (dôŋ-fäŋ)	203	19.08 N	108.42 E
Donggala, Indon. (dôn-gä'lä)	206	0.45 S	119.32 E
Dongguan, China (dôŋ-gūän)	201a	23.03 N	113.46 E
Dongguang, China (dôŋ-gūäŋ)	200	37.54 N	116.33 E
Donghai, China (dôŋ-hī)	200	34.35 N	119.05 E
Dong Hoi, Viet. (dông-hô-ē')	203	17.25 N	106.42 E
Dongming, China (dôŋ-mĭŋ)	200	35.16 N	115.06 E
Dongo, Ang. (dôŋ'gō)	226	14.45 S	15.30 E
Dongon Pt., Phil (dông-ôn')	207a	12.43 N	120.35 E
Dongou, Con. (dôŋ-gōō')	230	2.02 N	18.04 E
Dongping, China (dôŋ-pĭŋ)	200	35.50 N	116.24 E
Dongping Hu (L.), China (dôŋ-pĭŋ hōō)	200	36.06 N	116.24 E
Dongsha Dao (I.), see Pratas			
Dongshan, China (doŋ-shän)	200	31.05 N	120.24 E
Dongshi, China	67b	39.49 N	116.34 E
Dongtai, China	200	32.51 N	120.20 E
Dongting Hu (L.), China (dôŋ-tĭŋ hōō)	203	29.10 N	112.30 E
Dongxiang, China (dôŋ-shyän)	203	28.18 N	116.38 E
Doniphan, Mo. (dŏn'ĭ-făn)	123	36.37 N	90.50 W
Donji Vakuf, Yugo. (dōn'yĭ väk'ōōf)	172	44.08 N	17.25 E
Don Martin, Presa de (Res.), Mex. (prĕ'sä-dĕ-dôn-mär-tē'n)	124	27.35 N	100.38 W
Donnacona, Can.	104	46.40 N	71.46 W
Donnemarie-en-Montois, Fr. (dôn-mä-rē'ĕN-môN-twä')	169b	48.29 N	3.09 E
Donner und Blitzen (R.), Or. (dŏn'ēr ōōnt'blĭ'tsĕn)	116	42.45 N	118.57 W
Donnybrook, S. Afr. (dŏ-nĭ-brŏŏk)	227c	29.56 S	29.54 E
Donora, Pa. (dŏ-nō'rȧ)	113e	40.10 N	79.51 W
Don Torcuato, Arg.	60d	34.30 S	58.40 W
Doolow, Som.	223a	4.10 N	42.05 E
Doonerak, Mt., Ak. (dōō'nē-răk)	107	68.00 N	150.34 W
Doorn, Neth.	157a	52.02 N	5.21 E
Door Pen., Wi. (dōr)	115	44.40 N	87.36 W
Dora Baltea (R.), It. (dō'rä bäl'tā-ä)	172	45.40 N	7.34 E
Doraville, Ga. (dō'rá-vĭl)	112c	33.54 N	84.17 W
Dorchester, Eng. (dôr'chĕs-tēr)	162	50.45 N	2.34 W
Dorchester Heights National Historic Site (P. Int.), Ma.	54a	42.20 N	71.03 W
Dordogne (R.), Fr. (dôr-dôn'yĕ)	168	44.53 N	0.16 E
Dordrecht, Neth. (dôr'drĕKt)	157a	51.48 N	4.39 E
Dordrecht, S. Afr. (dôr'drĕKt)	227c	31.24 S	27.06 E
Doré L., Can.	100	54.31 N	107.06 W
Dorgali, It. (dôr'gä-lē)	172	40.18 N	9.37 E
Dörgön Nuur (L.), Mong	200	47.47 N	94.01 E
Dorion-Vaudreuil, Can. (dôr-yō)	95a	45.23 N	74.01 W
Dorking, Eng. (dôr'kĭng)	156b	51.12 N	0.20 W
D'Orleans, Ile (I.), Can. (yl dôr-lē-äN')	95b	46.56 N	71.00 W
Dormont, Pa. (dôr'mŏnt)	113e	40.24 N	80.02 W
Dornap, F.R.G.	63	51.15 N	7.04 E
Dornbirn, Aus. (dōrn'bĭrn)	166	47.24 N	9.45 E
Dornoch, Scot. (dôr'nŏK)	162	57.55 N	4.01 W
Dornoch Firth, Scot. (dôr'nŏK fûrth)	162	57.55 N	3.55 W
Dorogobuzh, Sov. Un. (dôrôgô'-bōō'zh)	174	54.57 N	33.18 E
Dorohoi, Rom. (dō-rô-hoi')	167	47.57 N	26.28 E
Dorpat, see Tartu			
Dorre (I.), Austl. (dôr)	214	25.19 S	113.10 E
Dorseyville, Pa.	57b	40.35 N	79.53 W
Dorstfield (Neigh.), F.R.G.	63	51.31 N	7.25 E
Dorstsen, F.R.G.	169c	51.40 N	6.58 E
Dortmund, F.R.G. (dôrt'mōōnt)	169c	51.31 N	7.28 E
Dortmund-Ems-Kanal (Can.), F.R.G. (dōrt'mōōnd-ĕms'kä-näl')	169c	51.50 N	7.25 E
Dörtyol, Tur. (dûrt'yôl)	179	36.50 N	36.20 E
Dorval, Can. (dôr-väl')	95a	45.26 N	73.44 W
Dos Caminos, Ven. (dôs-kä-mē'nŏs)	143b	9.38 N	67.17 W
Dosewallips (R.), Wa. (dō'sē-wäl'lĭps)	118a	47.45 N	123.04 W
Dos Hermanas, Sp. (dōsĕr-mä'näs)	170	37.17 N	5.56 W
Dosso, Niger (dôs-ō')	229	13.03 N	3.12 E
Dothan, Al. (dō'thăn)	126	31.13 N	85.23 W
Douai, Fr. (dōō-ā')	168	50.23 N	3.04 E
Douala, Cam. (dōō-ä'lä)	229	4.03 N	9.42 E
Douarnenez, Fr. (dōō-är nē-nĕs')	168	48.06 N	4.18 W
Double Bayou, Tx. (dŭb''l bī'yōō)	125a	29.40 N	94.38 W
Douentza, Mali	228	15.00 N	2.57 W
Douglas, Ak. (dŭg'lăs)	107	58.18 N	134.35 W
Douglas, Ar.	121	31.20 N	109.30 W
Douglas, Ga.	126	31.30 N	82.53 W
Douglas, Isle of Man (dŭg'lăs)	162	54.10 N	4.24 W
Douglas, Wy. (dŭg'lăs)	117	42.45 N	105.21 W
Douglas (R.), Eng. (dŭg'lăs)	156	53.38 N	2.48 W
Douglas (R.), Tn. (dŭg'lăs)	126	36.00 N	83.35 W
Douglas Chan, Can.	98	53.30 N	129.12 W
Douglas Lake Ind. Res., Can.	99	50.10 N	120.49 W
Douglasville, Ga. (dŭg'lăs-vĭl)	126	33.45 N	84.47 W
Doumé, Cam. (dōō-mā')	225	4.41 N	13.26 E
Dourada, Serra (Mts.), Braz. (sĕ'r-rä-dōōō-rá'dă)	143	15.11 S	49.57 W
Dourdan, Fr. (dōōr-däN')	169b	48.32 N	2.01 E
Douro (R.), Port. (dô'ōō-rô)	170	41.03 N	8.12 W
Dove (R.), Eng. (dŭv)	156	52.53 N	1.47 W
Dover, De. (dō vēr)	111	39.10 N	75.30 W
Dover, Eng.	163	51.08 N	1.19 E
Dover, NH	111	43.15 N	71.00 W
Dover, NJ	112a	40.53 N	74.33 W
Dover, Oh.	110	40.35 N	81.30 W
Dover, S. Afr.	223d	27.05 S	27.44 E
Dover-Foxcroft, Me. (dō'vēr fôks'krôft)	104	45.10 N	69.15 W
Dover Heights, Austl.	70a	33.53 S	151.17 E
Dover, Str. of, Eur.	163	50.50 N	1.15 W
Doveton, Austl.	70b	38.00 S	145.14 E
Dovlekanovo, Sov. Un. (dôv'lyĕk-á-nô-vô)	178	54.15 N	55.05 E
Dovre Fjell (Plat.), Nor. (dôv'rĕ fyĕl')	164	62.03 N	8.36 E
Dow, Il. (dou)	119e	39.01 N	90.20 W
Dowagiac, Mi. (dô-wô'jăk)	110	42.00 N	86.05 W
Dowlatābād, Iran	68h	35.37 N	51.27 E
Downers Grove, Il. (dou'nērz grōv)	113a	41.48 N	88.00 W
Downey, Ca. (dou'nĭ)	119a	33.56 N	118.08 W
Downieville, Ca. (dou'nĭ-nĭl)	120	39.35 N	120.48 W
Downs, Ks. (dounz)	122	39.29 N	98.32 W
Doylestown, Oh. (doilz'toun)	113d	40.58 N	81.43 W
Drâa, C., Mor. (drá)	224	28.39 N	12.15 W
Drâa, Oued (R.), Mor.	224	28.00 N	9.31 W
Drabov, Sov. Un. (drä'bôf)	175	49.57 N	32.14 E
Drac (R.), Fr. (dräk)	169	44.50 N	5.47 E
Dracut, Ma. (dră'kŭt)	105a	42.40 N	71.19 W
Draganovo, Bul. (drä-gä-nō'vô)	173	43.13 N	25.45 E
Drăgăşani, Rom. (drä-gá-shän'ĭ)	173	44.39 N	24.18 E
Draguignan, Fr. (drä-gēn-yäN')	169	43.35 N	6.28 E
Drakensberg Mts.), Leso-S.Afr. (drä'kĕnz-bĕrgh)	226	29.15 S	29.07 E
Drake Passage, S.A.-Ant. (drāk păs'ĭj)	140	57.00 S	65.00 W
Dráma, Grc. (drä'mä)	173	41.09 N	24.10 E
Drammen, Nor. (dräm'ĕn)	164	59.45 N	10.15 E
Drancy, Fr.	64c	48.56 N	2.27 E
Drau (R.), Aus. (drou)	166	46.44 N	13.45 E
Drava (R.), Yugo. (Drä'vä)	172	46.37 N	15.17 E
Draveil, Fr.	64c	48.41 N	2.25 E
Dravograd, Yugo. (Drä'vô-gräd')	172	46.37 N	15.01 E
Dravosburg, Pa.	57b	40.21 N	79.51 W
Drawsko Pomorskie, Pol. (dräv'skō pō-mōr'skyĕ)	166	53.31 N	15.50 E
Drayton Hbr., Wa. (drā'tŭn)	118d	48.58 N	122.40 W
Drayton Plains, Mi.	113b	42.41 N	83.23 W
Drayton Valley, Can.	99	53.13 N	114.59 W
Drensteinfurt, F.R.G. (drĕn'shtīn-fōōrt)	169c	51.47 N	7.44 E
Dresden, G.D.R. (drās'dĕn)	166	51.05 N	13.45 E
Dreux, Fr. (drû)	169b	48.44 N	1.24 E
Drewitz (Neigh.), G.D.R.	65a	52.22 N	13.08 E
Drexel Hill, Pa.	56b	39.57 N	75.19 W
Driefontein, S. Afr.	223d	25.53 S	29.10 E
Drin (R.), Alb. (drēn)	173	42.13 N	20.13 E
Drina (R.), Yugo. (drē'nä)	173	44.09 N	19.30 E
Drinit, Pelgi (B.), Alb.	173	41.42 N	19.17 E
Dr. Ir. W. J. van Blommestein Meer (Res.), Sur.	143	4.45 N	55.05 W
Drissa (R.), Sov. Un.	174	55.44 N	28.58 E
Drissa, Sov. Un. (drĭs'sä)	174	55.48 N	27.59 E
Driver, Va.	112g	36.50 N	76.30 W
Dröbak, Nor. (drû'bäk)	164	59.40 N	10.35 E
Drobeta-Turnu-Severin, Rom. (sĕ-vĕ-rēn')	173	43.54 N	24.49 E
Drogheda, Ire. (drŏ'hē-dȧ)	162	53.43 N	6.15 W
Drogichin, Sov. Un. (drō-gē'chĭn)	167	52.10 N	25.11 E
Drogobych, Sov. Un. (drō-hô'bĭch)	167	49.21 N	23.31 E
Drôme (R.), Fr. (drōm)	168	44.42 N	4.53 E
Dronfield, Eng. (drŏn'fēld)	156	53.18 N	1.28 W
Droylsden, Eng.	64b	53.29 N	2.10 W
Drumheller, Can. (drŭm-hĕl-ēr)	99	51.28 N	112.42 W
Drummond (I.), Mi. (drŭm'ŭnd)	110	46.00 N	83.50 W
Drummondville, Can. (drŭm'ŭnd-vĭl)	104	45.53 N	72.33 W
Drummoyne, Austl.	70a	33.51 S	151.09 E
Drumright, Ok. (drŭm'rīt)	123	35.59 N	96.37 W
Drunen, Neth.	157a	51.41 N	5.10 E
Drut' (R.), Sov.Un. (drōōt)	174	53.40 N	29.45 E
Druya, Sov.Un. (drōō'yá)	174	55.45 N	27.26 E
Družba, Sov. Un.	66b	55.53 N	37.45 E
Drweca R., Pol. (d'r-văn'tsá)	167	53.06 N	19.13 E
Dryden, Can. (drī-dĕn)	97	49.47 N	92.50 W
Drysdale, Austl.	211a	38.11 S	144.34 E
Dry Tortugas (I.), Fl. (tôr-tōō'gäz)	127a	24.37 N	82.45 W
Dschang, Cam. (dshäng)	224	5.34 N	10.09 E
Duabo, Lib.	228	5.40 N	8.05 W
Duagh, Can.	95g	53.43 N	113.24 W
Duarte, Ca.	59	34.08 N	117.58 W
Duarte, Pico (Mtn.), Dom. Rep. (dĭŭ'ărtĕh pēcô)	129	19.00 N	71.00 W
Duas Barras, Braz. (dōō'äs-bà'r-räs)	141a	22.03 S	42.30 W
Dubawnt (L.), Can. (dōō-bônt')	96	63.27 N	103.30 W
Dubawnt (R.), Can.	96	61.30 N	103.49 W
Dubayy, U.A.E.	192	25.18 N	55.26 E
Dubbo, Austl. (dŭb'ō)	216	32.20 S	148.42 E
Dubie, Zaire	231	8.33 S	28.32 E
Dublin, Ca. (dŭb'lĭn)	118b	37.42 N	121.56 W
Dublin, Ga.	126	32.33 N	82.55 W
Dublin, Tx.	124	32.05 N	98.20 W
Dublin, see Baile Átha Cliath			
Dubno, Sov.Un. (dōō'b-nô)	167	50.24 N	25.44 E
Du Bois, Pa. (dōō-bois')	111	41.10 N	78.45 W
Dubossary, Sov. Un. (dōō-bŏ-sä'rĭ)	175	47.16 N	29.11 E
Dubovka, Sov. Un. (dōō-bôf'ká)	179	49.00 N	44.50 E
Dubrovka, Sov. Un. (dōō-brôf'kȧ)	182c	59.51 N	30.56 E
Dubrovnik (Ragusa), Yugo. (dōō'brôv-nĕk) (rä-gōō'sä)	173	42.40 N	18.10 E
Dubrovno, Sov. Un. (dōō-brôf'nō)	174	54.39 N	30.54 E
Dubuque, Ia. (dōō-būk')	115	42.30 N	90.43 W
Duchesne (R.), Ut.	121	40.20 N	110.50 W
Duchesne, Ut. (dōō-shān')	121	40.12 N	110.23 W
Duchess, Austl. (dŭch'ĕs)	214	21.30 S	139.55 E
Ducie I., Oceania (dü-sē')	209	25.30 S	126.20 W
Duck (R.), Tn.	126	35.55 N	87.40 W
Duckabush (R.), Wa. (dŭk'á-bōōsh)	118a	47.41 N	123.09 W
Duck Lake, Can.	100	52.47 N	106.13 W
Duck Mtn., Can.	101	51.35 N	101.00 W
Ducktown, Tn. (dŭk'toun)	126	35.03 N	84.20 W
Duck Valley Ind. Res., Id.-Nv.	116	42.02 N	115.49 W
Duckwater Pk., Nv. (dŭk-wô-tēr)	120	39.00 N	115.31 W
Duda (R.), Col. (dōō'dä)	142a	3.25 N	74.23 W
Dudinka, Sov. Un. (dōō-dĭn'kȧ)	180	69.15 N	85.42 E
Dudley, Eng. (dŭd'lĭ)	156	52.28 N	2.07 E
Duékoué, Ivory Coast	228	6.45 N	7.21 W
Duero (R.), Sp. (dwĕ'rō)	170	41.30 N	5.10 W
Dugger, In. (dŭg'ēr)	110	39.00 N	87.10 W
Dugi Otok (I.), Yugo. (dōō'gē o'tôk)	172	44.03 N	14.40 E
Dugny, Fr.	64c	48.57 N	2.25 E
Duisburg, F.R.G. (dōō'ĭs-bŏŏrgh)	169c	51.26 N	6.46 E
Duissern (Neigh.), F.R.G.	63	51.26 N	6.47 E
Dukhān, Qatar	195	25.25 N	50.48 E
Dukhovshchina, Sov. Un. (dōō-Kôfsh-'chēnȧ)	174	55.13 N	32.26 E
Dukinfield, Eng. (dŭk'ĭn-fēld)	156	53.28 N	2.05 W
Dukla P., Pol. (dōō'klä)	167	49.25 N	21.44 E
Dulce, Golfo (G.), C.R. (gōl'fô dōōl'sä)	133	8.25 N	83.13 W
Dulcigno, see Ulcinj			
Dülken, F.G.R. (dül'kĕn)	169c	51.15 N	6.21 E
Dülmen, F.R.G. (dül'mĕn)	169c	51.50 N	7.17 E
Duluth, Mn. (dŏŏ-lōōth')	119h	46.50 N	92.07 W
Dulwich (Neigh.), Eng.	62	51.26 N	0.05 W
Dūmā, Syria	191a	33.34 N	36.17 E
Dumaguete City, Phil. (dōō-mä-gā'tā)	207	9.14 N	123.15 E
Dumai, Indon.	191b	1.39 N	101.30 E
Dumali Pt., Phil. (dōō-mä'lē)	207a	13.07 N	121.42 E
Dumas, Tx.	122	35.52 N	101.58 W
Dumbarton, Scot. (dŭm'băr-tŭn)	162	56.00 N	4.35 W
Dum-Dum, India	196a	22.37 N	88.25 E
Dumfries, Scot. (dŭm-frēs')	162	54.05 N	3.40 W
Dumjor, India	196a	22.37 N	88.14 E
Dumont, NJ (dōō'mŏnt)	112a	40.56 N	74.00 W
Dümpten (Neigh.), F.R.G.	63	51.27 N	6.54 E
Dumyāt, Egypt	223b	31.22 N	31.50 E
Dumyāţ, Maşabb (Chan.), Egypt	223b	31.36 N	31.45 E
Duna (R.), Hung. (dōō'nä)	167	46.07 N	18.45 E
Duna (R.), see Danube			
Dunaföldvár, Hung. (dōō'nô-fûld'vär)	167a	46.48 N	18.55 E
Dunajec (R.), Pol. (dōō-nä'yĕts)	167	49.52 N	20.53 E
Dunaújváros, Hung.	167	46.57 N	18.55 E
Dunay, Sov. Un. (dōō'nĭ)	182c	59.59 N	30.57 E
Dunayevtsy, Sov. Un. (dōō-nä'yĕf-tsĭ)	175	48.52 N	26.51 E
Dunbar, WV	110	38.20 N	81.45 W
Duncan, Can. (dŭŋ'kăn)	96.	48.47 N	123.42 W
Duncan, Ok.	122	34.29 N	97.56 W
Duncan (R.), Can.	99	50.30 N	116.45 W
Duncan Dam, Can.	99	50.15 N	116.55 W
Duncan L, Can.	99	50.20 N	117.00 W
Duncansby Hd., Scot. (dŭn'kănz-bĭ)	162a	58.40 N	3.01 W
Duncanville, Tx. (dŭn'kăn-vĭl)	119c	32.39 N	96.55 W
Dundalk, Ire. (dŭn'kôk)	162	54.00 N	6.18 W
Dundalk, Md.	112e	39.16 N	76.31 W

ăt; finăl; rāte; senåte; ärm; ȧsk; sofȧ; fåre; ch-choose; dh-as th in other; bē; ēvent; bĕt; recĕnt; cratēr; g-gō; gh-guttural g; bĭt; ĭ-short neutral; rīde; K-guttural k as ch in German ich;

PLACE (Pronounciation)	PAGE	Lat. °′	Long. °′
Dundalk B., Ire. (dŭn'dôk)	162	53.55 N	6.15 W
Dundas, Austl.	70a	33.48 S	151.02 E
Dundas, Can. (dŭn-dăs')	95d	43.16 N	79.58 W
Dundas (L.), Austl. (dŭn-dȧs)	214	32.15 S	122.00 E
Dundas I, Can.	98	54.33 N	130.55 W
Dundas Str., Austl.	214	10.35 S	131.15 E
Dundedin, Fl. (dŭn-ē'dĭn)	127a	28.00 N	82.43 W
Dundee, Il. (dŭn-dē)	113a	42.06 N	88.17 W
Dundee, S. Afr	227c	28.14 S	30.16 E
Dundee, Scot	162	56.30 N	2.55 W
Dundrum B., Ire. (dŭn-drŭm')	162	54.13 N	5.47 W
Dunedin, N.Z.	215a	45.48 S	170.32 E
Dunellen, NJ (dŭn-ĕl'l'n)	112a	40.36 N	74.28 W
Dunfermline, Scot. (dŭn-fĕrm'lĭn)	162	56.05 N	3.30 W
Dungarvan, Ire. (dŭn-gȧr'vă̇n)	162	52.06 N	7.50 W
Dungeness (R.), Wa.	118a	48.03 N	123.10 W
Dungeness, Wa. (dŭnj-nĕs')	118a	48.09 N	123.07 W
Dungeness Spit, Wa.	118a	48.11 N	123.03 W
Dunham Town, Eng.	64b	53.23 N	2.24 W
Dunheved, Austl.	70a	33.45 S	150.47 E
Dunhua, China (do͞on-hwä)	202	48.18 N	128.10 E
Dunkerque, Fr. (dŭn-kĕrk')	168	51.02 N	2.37 E
Dunkirk, In. (dŭn'kûrk)	110	40.20 N	85.25 W
Dunkirk, NY	111	42.30 N	79.20 W
Dunkwa, Ghana	228	5.22 N	1.12 W
Dun Laoghaire, Ire. (dŭn-lā'rĕ)	162	53.16 N	6.09 W
Dunlap, Ia. (dŭn'lăp)	114	41.53 N	95.33 W
Dunlap, Tn.	126	35.23 N	85.23 W
Dunmore, Pa. (dŭn'mōr)	111	41.25 N	75.30 W
Dunn, NC (dŭn)	127	35.18 N	78.37 W
Dunnellon, Fl. (dŭn-ĕl'ŏn)	127	29.02 N	82.28 W
Dunn Loring, Va.	56d	38.53 N	77.14 W
Dunnville, Can. (dŭn'vĭl)	111	42.55 N	79.40 W
Dunqulah, Sud.	225	19.21 N	30.19 E
Dunsmuir, Ca. (dŭnz'mûr)	116	41.08 N	122.17 W
Dunton Green, Eng.	62	51.18 N	0.11 E
Dunton Wayletts, Eng.	62	51.35 N	0.24 E
Dunvegan, S. Afr.	71b	26.09 S	28.09 E
Dunwoody, Ga. (dŭn-wo͝od'ĭ)	112c	33.57 N	84.20 W
Duolun, China (dwô-lo͞on)	202	42.12 N	116.15 E
Duomo (P. Int.), It.	65c	45.27 N	9.11 E
Du Page R., Il. (do͞o pāj)	113a	41.41 N	88.11 W
Du Page R., E. Br., Il.	113a	41.49 N	88.05 W
Du Page R., W. Br., Il.	113a	41.48 N	88.10 W
Dupax, Phil. (do͞o'päks)	207a	16.16 N	121.06 E
Dupo, Il. (dū'pō)	119e	38.31 N	90.12 W
Duque de Bragança, Ang. (do͞o'kå dȧ brä-gȧN'sä)	230	9.06 S	15.57 E
Duque de Caxias, Braz. (do͞o'kĕ-dĕ-kȧ'shyȧs)	144b	22.46 S	43.18 W
Duquesne, Pa. (do͞o-kān')	113e	40.22 N	79.51 W
Du Quoin, Il. (do͞o-kwoin')	123	38.01 N	89.14 W
Durance (R.), Fr. (dü-räNs')	169	43.46 N	5.52 E
Durand, Mi. (dů-rănd')	110	42.50 N	84.00 W
Durand, Wi.	115	44.37 N	91.58 W
Durango, Co. (do͞o-răŋ'gō)	121	37.15 N	107.55 W
Durango, Mex. (do͞o-rä'n-gô)	130	24.02 N	104.42 W
Durango (State), Mex.	128	25.00 N	106.00 W
Durant, Ms. (dů-rănt')	126	33.05 N	89.50 W
Durant, Ok.	123	33.59 N	96.23 W
Duratón (R.), Sp. (do͞o-rä-tōn')	170	41.55 N	3.55 W
Durazno (Dept.), Ur.	141c	33.00 S	56.35 W
Durazno, Ur. (do͞o-räz'nō)	141c	33.21 S	56.31 W
Durban, S. Afr. (dûr'bă̇n)	227c	29.48 S	31.00 E
Durban Roodepoort Deep Gold Mines (P. Int.), S. Afr.	71b	26.10 S	27.51 E
Durbanville, S. Afr. (dûr-bȧn'vĭl)	226a	33.50 S	18.39 E
Durbe, Sov. Un. (do͞or'bĕ)	165	56.36 N	21.24 E
Durchholz, F.R.G.	63	51.23 N	7.17 E
Durdevac, Yugo.(dūr'dyĕ-vȧts')	172	46.03 N	17.03 E
Düren, F.R.G. (dü'rĕn)	169c	50.48 N	6.30 E
Durham, Eng. (dûr'ăm)	162	54.47 N	1.46 W
Durham, NC	127	36.00 N	78.55 W
Durham Downs, Austl.	216	27.30 S	141.55 E
Durrës, Alb. (do͞or'ĕs)	173	41.19 N	19.27 E
Duryea, Pa. (do͞or-yā')	111	41.20 N	75.50 W
Dushan, China (do͞o-shän)	203	25.50 N	107.42 E
Dushan, China	200	31.38 N	116.16 E
Dushanbe, Sov. Un.	193	38.30 N	68.45 E
Düssel, F.R.G.	63	51.16 N	7.03 E
Düsseldorf, F.R.G. (düs'ĕl-dôrf)	169c	51.14 N	6.47 E
Dussen, Neth.	157a	51.43 N	4.58 E
Dutalan Ula (Mtn.), Mong.	202	49.25 N	112.40 E
Dutch Harbor, Ak. (dŭch här'bĕr)	107a	53.58 N	166.30 W
Duvall, Wa. (do͞o'vâl)	118a	47.44 N	121.59 W
Duvergé, Dom. Rep. (do͞o-vĕr-hĕ')	135	18.20 N	71.20 W
Duwamish (R.), Wa. (do͞o-wăm'ĭsh)	118a	47.24 N	122.18 W
Duyun, China (do͞o-yo͞on)	203	26.18 N	107.40 E
Dvina, Western, (R.), see Zapadnaya Dvina			
Dvinskaya Guba (G.), Sov. Un.	178	65.10 N	38.40 E
Dvůr Králové, Czech. (dvo͞or' krä'lô-vā)	166	50.28 N	15.43 E
Dwārka, India	196	22.18 N	68.59 E
Dwight, Il. (dwīt)	110	41.00 N	88.20 W
Dworshak Res, Id.	116	46.45 N	115.50 W
Dyat'kovo, Sov. Un. (dyät'kō-vō)	174	53.36 N	34.19 E
Dyer, In. (dī'ēr)	113a	41.30 N	87.31 W
Dyersburg, Tn. (dī'ērz-bûrg)	126	36.02 N	89.23 W
Dyersville, Ia. (dī'ērz-vĭl)	115	42.28 N	91.09 W
Dyes Inlet, Wa. (dīz)	118a	47.37 N	122.45 W
Dyment, Can. (dī'mĕnt)	101	49.37 N	92.19 W
Dzabhan (R.), Mong.	198	48.19 N	94.08 E
Dzamiin Üüd, Mong.	202	44.38 N	111.32 E
Dzaoudzi, Mayotte (dzou'dzĭ)	227	12.44 S	45.15 E
Dzaudzhikau, Sov. Un. (dzou-jĭ-kou')	155	48.00 N	44.52 E
Dzerzhinsk, Sov. Un. (dzhĕr-zhĭnsk')	175	48.24 N	37.58 E
Dzerzhinsk, Sov. Un.	174	53.41 N	27.14 E
Dzerzhinsk, Sov. Un.	178	56.20 N	43.50 E
Dzeržinskij, Sov. Un.	66b	55.38 N	37.50 E
Dzhalal-Abad, Sov. Un. (jȧ-läl'ȧ-bät')	180	41.13 N	73.35 E
Dzhambul, Sov. Un. (dzhäm-bo͞ol')	180	42.51 N	71.29 E
Dzhankoy, Sov. Un. (dzhän'koi)	175	45.43 N	34.22 E
Dzhetygara, Sov. Un. (dzhĕt'-gä'rȧ)	182a	52.12 N	61.18 E
Dzhizak, Sov. Un. (dzhĕ'zäk)	180	40.13 N	67.58 E
Dzhugdzhur Khrebet (Mts.), Sov. Un. (jo͞og-jo͞or')	181	56.15 N	137.00 E
Działoszyce, Pol. (jyä-wō-shē'tsĕ)	167	50.21 N	20.22 E
Dzibalchén, Mex. (zē-bäl-chĕ'n)	132a	19.25 N	89.39 W
Dzidzantún, Mex. (zĕd-zän-to͞o'n)	132a	21.18 N	89.00 W
Dzierzoniów, Pol. (dzyĕr-zhôn'yŭf)	166	50.44 N	16.38 E
Dzilam González, Mex. (zē-lä'm-gôn-zä'lĕz)	132a	21.21 N	88.53 W
Dzitás, Mex. (zē-tä's)	132a	20.47 N	88.32 W
Dzitbalché, Mex. (dzēt-bäl-chā')	132a	20.18 N	90.03 W
Dzungaria (Reg.), China (dzo͞oŋ-gä'rĭ-ȧ)	198	44.39 N	86.13 E
Dzungarian Gate (P.), China	198	45.00 N	88.00 E

E

PLACE (Pronounciation)	PAGE	Lat. °′	Long. °′
Eagle, Ak (ē'g'l)	107	64.42 N	141.20 W
Eagle (R.), Co.	121	39.32 N	106.28 W
Eagle, WV	110	38.10 N	81.20 W
Eaglecliff, Wa (ē'gl-klĭf)	118c	46.10 N	123.13 W
Eagle Cr., In.	113g	39.54 N	86.17 W
Eagle Grove, Ia.	115	42.39 N	93.55 W
Eagle L, Ca.	116	40.45 N	120.52 W
Eagle Lake, Me.	104	47.03 N	68.38 W
Eagle Lake, Tx.	125	29.37 N	96.20 W
Eagle Mountain L, Tx.	119c	32.56 N	97.27 W
Eagle Pass, Tx.	124	28.49 N	100.30 W
Eagle Pk, Ca.	116	41.18 N	120.11 W
Eagle Rock (Neigh.), Ca.	59	34.09 N	118.12 W
Ealing, Eng. (ē'lĭng)	156b	51.29 N	0.19 W
Earle, Ar. (ûrl)	123	35.14 N	90.28 W
Earlington, Ky. (ûr'lĭng-tŭn)	126	37.15 N	87.31 W
Easley, SC (ēz'lĭ)	127	34.48 N	82.37 W
East (R.), NY	55	40.48 N	73.48 W
East Alton, Il. (ôl'tŭn)	119e	38.53 N	90.08 W
East Angus, Can. (ăŋ'gŭs)	103	45.35 N	71.40 W
East Arlington, Ma.	54a	42.25 N	71.08 W
East Aurora, NY (ô-rō'rȧ)	113c	42.46 N	78.38 W
East B, Tx	125a	29.30 N	94.41 W
East Barnet (Neigh.), Eng.	62	51.38 N	0.09 W
East Bedfont (Neigh.), Eng.	62	51.27 N	0.26 W
East Berlin, G.D.R. (bĕr-lēn')	157b	52.31 N	13.28 E
East Bernstadt, Ky (bûrn'stát)	126	37.09 N	84.08 W
Eastbourne, Eng. (ēst'bôrn)	163	50.48 N	0.16 E
East Braintree, Ma.	54a	42.13 N	70.58 W
East Burwood, Austl.	70b	37.51 S	145.09 E
Eastbury, Eng.	62	51.37 N	0.25 W
East Caicos (I.), Turk & Caicos Is. (kī'kōs)	135	21.40 N	71.35 W
East Cape (C.), N.Z.	217	37.37 S	178.33 E
East Cape, see Dezhnëva, Mys			
East Carondelet, Il. (kȧ-rŏn'dĕ-lĕt)	119e	38.33 N	90.14 W
Eastchester, NY	55	40.57 N	73.49 W
East Chicago, In. (shĭ-kô'gō)	113a	41.39 N	87.29 W
East China Sea, Asia	199	30.28 N	125.52 E
East Cleveland, Oh (klēv'lănd)	113d	41.33 N	81.35 W
Eastcote (Neigh.), Eng.	62	51.35 N	0.24 W
East Cote Blanche B., La. (kōt blänsh')	125	29.30 N	92.07 W
East Des Moines (R.), Ia. (dē moin')	115	42.57 N	94.17 W
East Detroit, Mi (dē-troit')	113b	42.28 N	82.57 W
Easter (I.), see Rapa Nui			
Eastern Ghāts (Mts.), India	197	13.50 N	78.45 E
Eastern Native (Neigh.), S. Afr.	71b	26.13 S	28.05 E
Eastern Turkestan (Reg), China (to͞or-kĕ-stän')(tûr-kĕ-stăn')	198	39.40 N	78.20 E
East Falls (Neigh.), Pa.	56b	40.01 N	75.11 W
East Grand Forks, Mn. (grănd fôrks)	114	47.56 N	97.02 W
East Greenwich, RI (grĭn'ĭj)	112b	41.40 N	71.27 W
Eastham, Eng.	64a	53.19 N	2.58 W
East Ham (Neigh.), Eng.	62	51.32 N	0.03 E
Easthampton, Ma. (ēst-hămp'tŭn)	111	42.15 N	72.45 W
East Hartford, Ct (härt'fērd)	111	41.45 N	72.35 W
East Helena, Mt. (hĕ-hē'nȧ)	117	46.31 N	111.50 W
East Hills, Austl.	70a	33.58 S	150.59 E
East Hills, NY	55	40.47 N	73.38 W
East Ilsley, Eng. (ĭl'slē)	156b	51.30 N	1.18 W
East Jordan, Mi. (jôr'dă̇n)	110	45.05 N	85.05 W
East Kansas City, Mo. (kăn'zȧs)	119f	39.09 N	94.30 W
East Lamma Chan., Asia	68c	22.15 N	114.07 E
Eastland, Tx (ēst'lănd)	124	32.24 N	98.47 W
East Lansdowne, Pa.	56b	39.56 N	75.16 W
East Lansing, Mi (lăn'sĭng)	110	42.45 N	84.30 W
Eastlawn, Mi	113b	42.15 N	83.35 W
East Leavenworth, Mo (lĕv'ĕn-wûrth)	119f	39.18 N	94.50 W
East Liberty (Neigh.), Pa.	57b	40.27 N	79.55 W
East Lindfield, Austl.	70a	33.46 S	151.11 E
East Liverpool, Oh. (lĭv'ēr-po͞ol)	110	40.40 N	80.35 W
East London, S. Afr. (lŭn'dŭn)	227c	33.02 S	27.54 E
East Los Angeles, Ca (lōs ăŋ'hȧ-lās)	119a	34.01 N	118.09 W
Eastmain (R.), Can. (ēst'mān)	97	52.12 N	73.19 W
East Malling, Eng.	62	51.17 N	0.26 E
Eastman, Ga. (ēst'mă̇n)	126	32.10 N	83.11 W
East Meadow, NY	55	40.43 N	73.34 W
East Millstone, NJ (mĭl'stōn)	112a	40.30 N	74.35 W
East Molesey, Eng.	62	51.24 N	0.21 W
East Moline, Il. (mô-lēn')	115	41.31 N	90.28 W
East, Mt., Pan.	128a	9.09 N	79.46 W
East Newark, NJ	55	40.45 N	74.10 W
East New York (Neigh.), NY	55	40.40 N	73.53 W
East Nishnabotna R.), Ia. (nĭsh-nȧ-bŏt'nȧ)	121	40.53 N	95.23 W
East Norwich, NY	55	40.50 N	73.32 W
Easton, Md. (ēs'tŭn)	111	72.45 N	76.05 W
Easton, Pa.	111	40.45 N	75.15 W
Easton L, Ct.	112a	41.18 N	73.17 W
East Orange, NJ (ŏr'ĕnj)	112a	40.46 N	74.12 W
East Palo Alto, Ca	118b	37.27 N	122.07 W
East Peoria, Il. (pē-ō'rĭ-ȧ)	110	40.40 N	89.30 W
East Pittsburgh, Pa (pĭts'bûrg)	113e	40.24 N	79.50 W
East Point, GA	112c	33.41 N	84.27 W
Eastport, Me. (ēst'pōrt)	104	44.53 N	67.01 W
East Providence, RI (prŏv'ĭ-dĕns)	112b	41.49 N	71.22 W
East Retford, Eng. (rĕt'fērd)	156	53.19 N	0.56 W
East Richmond, Ca.	58b	37.57 N	122.19 W
East Rochester, NY (rŏch'ĕs-tēr)	111	43.10 N	77.30 W
East Rockaway, NY	55	40.39 N	73.40 W
East Saint Louis, Il. (sānt lo͞o'ĭs)(lo͞o-ĭ)	119e	38.38 N	90.10 W
East Siberian Sea, Sov. Un. (sī-bĭr'y'n)	176	73.00 N	153.28 E
Eastsound, Wa. (ēst-sound)	118d	48.42 N	122.42 W
East Stroudsburg, Pa (stroudz'bûrg)	111	41.00 N	75.10 W
East Syracuse, NY (sĭr'ȧ-kūs)	111	43.05 N	76.00 W
East Tavaputs Plat., Ut. (tă-vă'-pŭts)	121	39.25 N	109.45 W
East Tawas, Mi (tô'wȧs)	110	44.15 N	83.30 W
East Tilbury, Eng.	62	51.28 N	0.26 E
East Tustin, Ca.	59	33.46 N	117.49 W
East Walker (R.), Nv (wôk'ēr)	120	38.36 N	119.02 W
East Walpole, Ma.	54a	42.10 N	71.13 W
East Watertown, Ma.	54a	42.22 N	71.10 W
East Weymouth, Ma.	54a	42.13 N	70.55 W
Eastwick (Neigh.), Pa.	56b	39.55 N	75.14 W
East Wickham (Neigh.), Eng.	62	51.28 N	0.07 E
Eastwood, Austl.	70a	33.48 S	151.05 E
East York, Can.	95d	43.41 S	79.20 W
Eaton, Co. (ē'tŭn)	113	40.31 N	104.42 W
Eaton, Oh.	110	39.45 N	84.40 W
Eaton Estates, Oh.	113d	41.19 N	82.01 W
Eaton Rapids, Mi. (răp'ĭdz)	110	42.30 N	84.40 W
Eatonton, GA (ētŭn-tŭn)	126	33.20 N	83.24 W
Eatontown, NJ (ē'tŭn-toun)	112a	40.18 N	74.04 W
Eaubonne, Fr.	64c	49.00 N	2.17 E
Eau Claire, Wi. (ō klâr')	115	44.47 N	91.32 W
Ebeltoft, Den. (ĕ'bĕl-tŭft)	164	56.11 N	10.39 E
Ebensburg, Pa.	111	40.29 N	78.44 W
Ebersberg, F.R.G. (ĕ'bĕrs-bĕrgh)	157d	48.05 N	11.58 E
Ebina, Jap.	69a	35.26 N	139.25 E
Ebingen, F.R.G. (ā'bĭng-ĕn)	166	48.13 N	9.04 E
Ebinur Hu (L.), China (ä-bē-no͞or ho͞o)	198	45.09 N	83.15 E
Eboli, It. (ĕb'ô-lē)	172	40.38 N	15.04 E
Ebolowa, Cam.	229	2.54 N	11.09 E
Ebreichsdorf, Aus.	157e	47.58 N	16.24 E
Ebrie, Lagune (Lagoon), Ivory Coast	228	5.20 N	4.50 W
Ebro (R.), Sp. (ā'brō)	171	41.30 N	0.35 W
Ebute-ikorodu, Nig.	71d	6.37 N	3.30 E
Eccles, Eng. (ĕk''lz)	156	53.29 N	2.20 W
Eccles, WV	110	37.45 N	81.10 W
Eccleshall, Eng. (ĕk''lz-hôl)	156	52.51 N	2.15 W
Eccleston, Eng.	64a	53.27 N	2.47 W
Eccleston, Md.	56c	39.24 N	76.44 W
Eceabat (Maidos), Tur.	173	40.10 N	26.21 E
Echague, Phil. (ä-chä'gwä)	207a	16.43 N	121.40 E
Echandi, Cerro (Mt.), Pan. (sĕ'r-rô-ĕ-chä'nd)	133	9.05 N	82.51 W
Ech Cheliff (Orléansville), Alg.	160	36.14 N	1.32 E
Echimamish (R.), Can.	101	54.15 N	97.30 W
Echo Bay, Can. (ĕk'ō)	119k	46.29 N	84.04 W
Echoing (R.), Can. (ĕk'ō-ĭng)	101	55.15 N	91.30 W
Echternach, Lux. (ĕk'tĕr-näk)	169	49.48 N	6.25 E
Echuca, Austl. (ḗ-cho͞o'kȧ)	216	36.10 S	144.47 E
Écija, Sp. (ā'thē-hä)	170	37.20 N	5.07 W
Eckernförde, F.R.G.	166	54.27 N	9.51 E
Eclipse, Va (ḗ-klĭps')	112g	36.55 N	76.29 W
Ecorse, Mi (ḗ-kôrs')	113b	42.15 N	83.09 W
Ecuador, S.A. (ĕk'wȧ-dôr)	140	0.00 N	78.30 W
Ed, Eth.	225	13.57 N	41.37 E
Eda (Neigh.), Jap.	69a	35.34 N	139.34 E
Eddyville, Ky. (ĕd'ĭ-vĭl)	126	37.03 N	88.03 W
Ede, Nig.	229	7.44 N	4.27 E
Edéa, Cam. (ĕ-dā'ä)	229	3.48 N	10.08 E
Eden (R.), Eng. (ē'dĕn)	162	54.40 N	2.35 W
Eden, Tx.	124	31.13 N	99.51 W
Eden, Ut.	119b	41.18 N	111.49 W
Edenbridge, Eng. (ē'dĕn-brĭj)	156b	51.11 N	0.05 E
Edendale, S. Afr.	71b	26.09 S	28.09 E
Edenham, Eng. (ē'd'n-ăm)	156	52.46 N	0.25 W
Eden Prairie, Mn. (prâr'ĭ)	119g	44.51 N	93.29 W
Edenton, NC (ē'dĕn-tŭn)	127	36.02 N	76.37 W
Edenton, Oh	113f	39.14 N	84.02 W
Edenvale, S. Afr. (ĕd'ĕn-vāl)	227b	29.06 N	28.10 E
Edenvale Location, S. Afr.	71b	26.08 S	28.11 E
Edenville, S. Afr. (ē'd'n-vĭl)	223d	27.33 S	27.42 E
Eder R., F.R.G. (ā'dēr)	166	51.05 N	8.52 E
Edgefield, SC (ĕj'fēld)	127	33.52 N	81.55 W
Edge Hill (Neigh.), Eng.	64a	53.24 N	2.57 W
Edgeley, ND (ĕj'lĭ)	114	46.24 N	98.43 W
Edgemere, Md.	56c	39.14 N	76.27 W
Edgemont, SD (ĕj'mŏnt)	114	43.19 N	103.50 W
Edgerton, Wi. (ĕj'ēr-tŭn)	115	42.49 N	89.06 W
Edgewater, Al. (ĕj-wô-tēr)	112h	33.31 N	86.52 W
Edgewater, Md.	112e	38.58 N	76.35 W
Edgewater, NJ	55	40.50 N	73.58 W
Edgewood, Can. (ĕj'wo͝od)	99	49.47 N	118.08 W

PLACE (Pronounciation)	PAGE	Lat. °'	Long. °'
Edgware (Neigh.), Eng.	62	51.37 N	0.17 W
Edgwater, NY	57a	43.03 N	78.55 W
Edgworth, Eng.	64b	53.39 N	2.24 W
Édhessa, Grc.	173	40.48 N	22.04 E
Edina, Minn. (ě-dī'nā)	119g	44.55 N	93.20 W
Edina, Mo.	123	40.10 N	92.11 W
Edinburg, In. (ěd'n-bûrg)	110	39.20 N	85.55 W
Edinburg, Tx.	124	26.18 N	98.08 W
Edinburgh, Scot. (ěd'n-bûr-ô)	162	55.57 N	3.10 W
Edirne (Adrianople), Tur. (ě-dīr'ně)(ä-drī-ăn-ō'p'l)	173	41.41 N	26.35 E
Edison Park (Neigh.), Il.	58a	42.01 N	87.49 W
Edisto (R.), North Fk, SC	127	33.42 N	81.24 W
Edisto, (R.), SC (ěd'Ĭs-tō)	127	33.10 N	80.50 W
Edisto (R.), South Fk, SC	127	33.43 N	81.35 W
Edisto Island, SC	127	32.32 N	80.20 W
Edmond, Ok. (ěd'mŭnd)	123	35.39 N	97.29 W
Edmonds, Wa. (ěd'mŭndz)	118a	47.49 N	122.23 W
Edmonston, Md.	56d	38.57 N	76.56 W
Edmonton, Can.	95c	53.33 N	113.28 W
Edmonton (Neigh.), Eng.	62	51.37 N	0.04 W
Edmundston, Can. (ěd'mŭn-stŭn)	104	47.22 N	68.20 W
Edna, Tx. (ěd'nà)	125	28.59 N	96.39 W
Edo (R.), Jap.	69a	35.41 N	139.53 E
Edogawa (Neigh.), Jap.	69a	35.42 N	139.52 E
Edremit, Tur. (ěd-rě-mět')	173	39.35 N	27.00 E
Edremit Körfezi (G.), Tur.	173	39.28 N	26.35 E
Edson, Can. (ěd'sŭn)	99	53.35 N	116.26 W
Edward (I.), Can. (ěd'wěrd)	102	48.21 N	88.29 W
Edward (L.), Zaire	231	0.25 s	29.40 E
Edwardsville, Il. (ěd'wěrdz-vĭl)	119e	38.49 N	89.58 W
Edwardsville, In	113h	38.17 N	85.53 W
Edwardsville, Ks.	119f	39.04 N	94.49 W
Eel (R.), Ca. (ěl)	116	40.39 N	124.15 W
Eel (R.), In.	110	40.05 N	85.55 W
Efate (I.), Vanuatu (å-fä'tä)	215	18.02 s	168.29 E
Effigy Mounds Natl. Mon., Ia. (ěf'ĭ-jū mounds)	115	43.04 N	91.15 W
Effingham, Il. (ěf'ĭng-hăm)	110	39.05 N	88.30 W
Ega (R.), Sp. (ā'gä)	170	42.40 N	2.20 W
Egadi, Isole (Is.), It. (ě'sō-lě-ě'gä-dě)	172	38.01 N	12.00 E
Egea de los Caballeros, Sp. (å-kä'ä dä lōs kä-bäl-yä'rōs)	170	42.07 N	1.05 W
Egegik, Ak. (ěg'ě-jǐt)	107	58.10 N	157.22 W
Eger, Hung. (ě gěr)	167	47.53 N	20.24 E
Egersund, Nor. (ě'ghěr-sōōn')	164	58.29 N	6.01 E
Egg Harbor, NJ (ěg här'běr)	111	39.30 N	74.35 W
Egham, Eng. (ěg'ŭm)	156b	51.24 N	0.33 W
Egiyn (R.), Mong.	198	49.41 N	100.40 E
Egmont, C., N.Z. (ěg'mŏnt)	217	39.18 s	173.49 E
Egota (Neigh.), Jap.	69a	35.43 N	139.40 E
Egridir Gölü (L.), Tur. (ä-rī-dīr')	179	38.10 N	30.00 E
Eguilles, Fr (ě-gwě')	168a	43.34 N	5.21 E
Egypt, Afr. (ē'jǐpt)	222	26.58 N	27.01 E
Eha-Amufu, Nig.	229	6.40 N	7.46 E
Ehingen (Neigh.), F.R.G.	63	51.22 N	6.42 E
Ehringhausen, F.R.G.	63	51.11 N	7.33 E
Ehringhausen, F.R.G.	63	51.09 N	7.11 E
Eibar, Sp. (ā'ě-bär)	170	43.12 N	2.20 W
Eiche, G.D.R.	65a	52.34 N	13.36 E
Eichlinghofen (Neigh.), F.R.G.	63	51.29 N	7.24 E
Eichstätt, F.R.G. (īk'shtät)	166	48.54 N	11.14 E
Eichwalde, G.D.R. (īk'väl-dě)	157b	52.22 N	13.37 E
Eickerend, F.R.G.	63	51.13 N	6.34 E
Eidfjord, Nor. (ěid'fyŏr)	164	60.28 N	7.04 E
Eidsvoll, Nor. (īdhs'vôl)	164	60.19 N	11.15 E
Eifel (Plat), F.R.G. (ī'fěl)	166	50.08 N	6.30 E
Eiffel, Tour (P. Int.), Fr.	64c	48.51 N	2.18 E
Eigen (Neigh.), F.R.G.	63	51.33 N	6.57 E
Eighty Mile Beach, Austl.	214	20.45 s	121.00 E
Eilenburg, G.D.R. (ī'lěn-bōōrgh)	166	51.27 N	12.38 E
Eilliot, S. Afr.	227c	31.19 s	27.52 E
Eilpe (Neigh.), F.R.G.	63	51.21 N	7.29 E
Einbeck, F.R.G. (īn'běk)	166	51.49 N	9.52 E
Eindhoven, Neth. (īnd'hō-věn)	163	51.29 N	5.20 E
Eirunepé, Braz. (ā-rōō-ně-pě')	142	6.37 s	69.58 W
Eisenach, G.D.R. (ī'zěn-äк)	166	50.58 N	10.18 E
Eisenhüttenstadt, G.D.R.	166	52.08 N	14.40 E
Eisleben, G.D.R. (īs'lä'běn)	166	51.31 N	11.33 E
Ejura, Ghana	228	7.23 N	1.22 W
Ejutla de Crespo, Mex. (å-hōōt'lä dä krās'pō)	131	16.34 N	96.44 W
Ekanga, Zaire	230	2.23 s	23.14 E
Ekenäs (Tammisaari), Fin. (ě'kě-nás)(täm'ǐ-sä'rǐ)	165	59.59 N	23.25 E
Ekeren, Bel.	157a	51.17 N	4.27 E
Ekoli, Zaire	230	0.23 s	24.16 E
Eksára, India	67a	22.38 N	88.17 E
Eksjö, Swe. (ěk'shŭ)	164	57.41 N	14.55 E
El Aaiún, W. Sah.	224	26.45 N	13.15 W
El Affroun, Alg. (ěl äf-froun')	171	36.28 N	2.38 E
El Aguacate, Ven.	61a	10.28 N	66.59 W
Elands (R.), S. Afr. (ělånds)	227c	31.48 s	26.09 E
Elands (R.), S. Afr.	223d	25.11 s	28.52 E
Elandsfontein, S. Afr.	71b	26.10 s	28.12 E
El Arahal, Sp. (ěl ä-rä-äl')	170	37.17 N	5.32 W
El Arba, Alg.	171	36.35 N	3.10 E
Elat, Isr.	191a	29.34 N	34.57 E
Eláziğ, Tur. (ěl-ä'zěz)	179	38.40 N	39.00 E
Elba, Al. (ěl'bá)	126	31.25 N	86.01 W
Elba, Isola d' (I.), It. (ě-sō lä-d-ěl'bá)	172d	42.42 N	10.25 E
El Banco, Col. (ěl bän'cō)	142	9.58 N	74.01 W
Elbansan, Alb. (ěl-bä-sän')	173	41.08 N	20.05 E
El Barco de Valdeorras, Sp (ěl bär'kō)	170	42.26 N	6.58 W
Elbe (Labe)(R.), Czech.-G.D.R. (ěl'bě)(lä'bě)	166	53.47 N	9.20 E
Elberfeld (Neigh.), F.R.G.	63	51.16 N	7.08 E
Elbert, Mt., Co. (ěl'běrt)	121	39.05 N	106.25 W
Elberton, Ga. (ěl'běr-tŭn)	126	34.05 N	82.53 W
Elbeuf, Fr. (ěl-bŭf')	168	49.16 N	0.59 E
El Beyadh, Alg.	160	33.42 N	1.06 E
Elbistan, Tur. (ěl-bē-stän')	179	38.20 N	37.10 E
Elblag, Pol. (ěl'bläg)	167	54.11 N	19.25 E
El Bonillo, Sp. (ěl bō-nēl'yō)	170	38.56 N	2.31 W
El Boulaïda, Alg.	224	36.33 N	2.45 E
Elbow (R.), Can. (ěl'bō)	95e	51.03 N	114.24 W
Elbow Cay (I.), Ba	134	26.25 N	77.55 W
Elbow Lake, Mn.	114	46.00 N	95.59 W
El'brus, Gora (Mt.), Sov. Un. (ěl'brōōs')	179	43.20 N	42.25 E
El Burgo de Osma, Sp.	170	41.35 N	3.02 W
Elburz Mts., Iran, (ěl'bōōrz')	179	36.30 N	51.00 E
El Cajon, Ca.	120a	32.48 N	116.58 W
El Cajon, Col (ěl-kä-kô'n)	142a	4.50 N	76.35 W
El Calvario (Neigh.), Cuba	60b	23.05 N	82.24 W
El Cambur, Ven. (käm-bōōr')	143b	10.24 N	68.06 W
El Campamento (Neigh.), Sp.	65b	40.24 N	3.46 W
El Campo, Tx. (käm'pō)	125	29.13 N	96.17 W
El Caribe, Ven.	61a	10.37 N	66.49 W
El Carmen, Chile (ká'r-měn)	141b	34.14 s	71.23 W
El Carmen, Col. (ká'r-měn)	142	9.54 N	75.12 W
El Casco, Ca. (kás'kô)	119a	33.59 N	117.08 W
El Centro, Ca. (sěn'trō)	120	32.47 N	115.33 W
El Cerrito, Ca. (sěr-rě'tō)	118b	37.55 N	122.19 W
Elche, Sp. (ěl'chä)	171	38.15 N	0.42 W
El Cojo, Ven.	61a	10.37 N	66.53 W
El Corozo, Ven.	61a	10.35 N	66.58 W
El Cotorro, Cuba	60b	23.03 N	82.16 W
El Cuyo, Mex.	132a	21.30 N	87.42 W
Elda, Sp. (ěl'dä)	171	38.28 N	0.44 W
Elder Mills, Can.	54c	43.49 N	79.38 W
El Djazaïr, see Algiers			
El Djelfa, Alg. (jěl'fa)	224	34.40 N	3.17 E
El Djouf (Des.), Mauritania (ěl djōōf)	224	21.45 N	7.05 W
Eldon, Ia. (ěl-dŭn)	115	40.55 N	92.15 W
Eldon, Mo.	121	38.21 N	92.36 W
Eldora, Ia. (ěl-dō'rá)	115	42.21 N	93.08 W
El Dorado, Ar. (ěl dō-rä'dō)	123	33.13 N	92.39 W
El Dorado, Il.	110	37.50 N	88.30 W
El Dorado, Ks.	123	37.49 N	96.51 W
Eldorado Springs, Mo. (springz)	123	37.51 N	94.02 W
Eldoret, Ken. (ěl-dō-rět')	231	0.31 N	35.17 E
El Ebano, Mex. (ā-bā'nō)	130	22.13 N	98.26 W
Electra, Tx. (ē-lěk'trá)	122	34.02 N	98.54 W
Electric Pk., Mt. (ē-lěk'trǐk)	117	45.03 N	110.52 W
Elektrogorsk, Sov. Un. (ěl-yěk'trō-gôrsk)	182b	55.53 N	38.48 E
Elektrostal, Sov. Un. (ěl-yěk'trō-stàl)	182b	55.47 N	38.27 E
Elektrougli, Sov. Un.	182b	55.43 N	38.13 E
El Encantado, Ven.	61a	10.27 N	66.47 W
Elephanta I. (Ghārp uri), India	67e	18.57 N	72.55 E
Elephant Butte Res., NM	121	33.25 N	107.10 W
El Escorial, Sp (ěl-ěs-kô-ryä'l)	171a	40.38 N	4.08 W
El Espino, Nic. (ěl-ěs-pě'nō)	132	13.26 N	86.48 W
Eleuthera (I.), Ba. (ē-lŭ'thěr-à)	135	25.05 N	76.10 W
Eleuthera Pt., Ba.	135	24.35 N	76.05 W
Eleven Point (R.), Mo. (ē-lěv'ěn)	123	36.53 N	91.39 W
El Ferrol, Sp. (fā-rōl')	170	43.30 N	8.12 W
Elgin, Il (ěl'jǐn)	113a	42.03 N	88.16 W
Elgin, Ne.	114	41.58 N	98.04 W
Elgin, Or.	116	45.34 N	117.58 W
Elgin, Scot.	162	57.40 N	3.30 W
Elgin, Tx.	125	30.21 N	97.22 W
Elgin, Wa.	118a	47.23 N	122.42 W
Elgon, Mt., Ken. (ěl'gŏn)	231	1.00 N	34.25 E
El Granada, Ca.	58b	37.30 N	122.28 W
El Grara, Alg.	160	32.50 N	4.26 E
El Grullo, Mex. (grōōl-yō)	130	19.46 N	104.10 W
El Guapo, Ven. (gwá'pō)	143b	10.07 N	66.00 W
El Guarapo, Ven.	61a	10.36 N	66.58 W
El Hank (Bluffs), Mauritania-Mali	116	23.44 N	6.45 W
El Hatillo, Ven. (ä-tě'l-yō)	143b	10.26 N	65.13 W
Elie, Can. (ē'lē)	95f	49.55 N	97.45 W
Elila (R.), Zaire (ē-lē'lä)	231	3.00 s	26.50 E
Elisa (I.), Wa. (ē-lī'sá)	118d	48.43 N	122.37 W
Élisabethville, see Lubumbashi			
Elisenvaara, Sov. Un. (ā-lē'sěn-vä'rá)	165	61.25 N	29.46 E
Elizabeth, La. (ē-lĭz'á-běth)	125	30.50 N	92.47 W
Elizabeth, NJ	112a	40.40 N	74.13 W
Elizabeth, Pa.	113e	40.16 N	79.53 W
Elizabeth City, NC	127	36.15 N	76.15 W
Elizabethton, Tn (ē-lĭz-á-běth'tŭn)	127	36.19 N	82.12 W
Elizabethtown, Ky. (ē-lĭz'á-běth-toun)	110	37.40 N	85.55 W
El Jadida, Mor.	224	33.14 N	8.34 W
Elk, Pol.	167	53.53 N	22.23 E
Elk (R.), Can.	99	50.00 N	115.00 W
Elk (R.), Tn.	126	35.05 N	86.36 W
Elk (R.), WV	110	38.30 N	81.05 W
El Kairouan, Tun. (kěr-ōō-än)	224	35.46 N	10.04 E
Elk City, Ok. (ělk)	122	35.23 N	99.23 W
El Kef, Tun. (xěf')	159	36.14 N	8.42 E
Elkhart, In. (ělk'härt)	110	41.40 N	86.00 W
Elkhart, Ks.	122	37.00 N	101.54 W
Elkhart, Tx	125	31.38 N	95.35 W
Elkhorn, (R.), Ne.	114	42.08 N	97.46 W
Elkhorn, Wi (ělk'hôrn)	115	42.39 N	88.32 W
Elk I, Can.	101	50.45 N	96.32 W
Elk Island Natl. Park, Can. (ělk ī'lånd)	99	53.37 N	112.45 W
Elko, Nv. (ěl'kō)	116	40.51 N	115.46 W
Elk Point, SD	114	42.41 N	96.41 W
Elk Rapids, Mi. (răp'ĭdz)	110	44.55 N	85.25 W
Elk River, Id. (rǐv'ěr)	116	46.47 N	116.11 W
Elk River, Mn.	115	45.17 N	93.33 W
Elkton, Ky. (ělk'tŭn)	126	36.47 N	87.08 W
Elkton, Md.	111	39.35 N	75.50 W
Elkton, SD	114	44.15 N	96.28 W
Elland, Eng. (el'ånd)	156	53.41 N	1.50 W
Ellendale, ND	114	46.01 N	98.33 W
Ellen, Mt., Ut. (ěl'ěn)	121	38.05 N	110.50 W
Ellensburg, Wa. (ěl'ěnz-bûrg)	116	47.00 N	120.31 W
Ellenville, NY	111	41.40 N	74.25 W
Ellerslie, Can. (ěl'ěrz-lě)	95g	53.25 N	113.30 W
Ellesmere, Eng. (ělz'měr)	156	52.55 N	2.54 W
Ellesmere I, Can.	94	81.00 N	80.00 W
Ellesmere Park, Eng.	64b	53.29 N	2.20 W
Ellesmere Port, Eng.	156	53.17 N	2.54 W
Ellice Is., see Tuvalu			
Ellicott City, Md. (ěl'Ĭ-kŏt sǐ'tě)	112e	39.16 N	76.48 W
Ellicott Cr., NY	113c	43.00 N	78.46 W
El Limoncito, Ven.	61a	10.29 N	66.47 W
Ellinghorst , (Neigh.), F.R.G.	63	51.34 N	6.57 E
Elliot, Wa. (ěl'ī-ŭt)	118a	47.28 N	122.08 W
Elliotdale, S. Afr.	227c	31.58 s	28.42 E
Elliot Lake, Can.	102	46.23 N	82.39 W
Ellis, Ks. (ěl'ǐs)	122	38.56 N	99.34 W
Ellisville, Ms. (ěl'ǐs-vǐl)	126	31.37 N	89.10 W
Ellisville, Mo.	119e	38.35 N	90.35 W
Ellsworth, Ks. (ělz'wûrth)	122	38.43 N	98.14 W
Ellsworth, Me.	104	44.33 N	68.26 W
Ellsworth Highland, Ant.	232	77.00 s	90.00 W
Ellwangen, F.R.G. (ěl'väŋ-gěn)	166	48.47 N	10.08 E
Elm, F.R.G. (ělm)	157c	53.31 N	9.13 E
Elm (R.), SD	114	45.47 N	98.28 W
Elm (R.), WV	110	38.30 N	81.05 W
Elma, Wa. (ěl'má)	116	47.02 N	123.20 W
El Mahdia, Tun. (mä-dě'a)(mä'dě-à)	159	35.30 N	11.09 E
Elm Cr, Tx.	123	29.15 N	97.25 W
Elmendorf, Tx (ěl'měn-dôrf)	119d	29.16 N	98.20 W
El Menia, Alg.	224	30.39 N	2.52 E
Elm Fork, Tx. (ěl'm fôrk)	119c	32.55 N	96.56 W
Elmhurst, Il (ělm'hûrst)	113a	41.54 N	87.56 W
Elmhurst (Neigh.), NY	55	40.44 N	73.53 W
El Miliyya, Alg. (mě'à)	224	36.30 N	6.16 E
Elmira, NY (ěl-mī'rá)	111	42.05 N	76.50 W
Elmira Heights, NY	111	42.10 N	76.50 W
El Misti (Vol.), Peru (mě's-tē)	142	16.04 s	71.20 W
El Modena, Ca. (mō-dē'nô)	119a	33.47 N	117.48 W
El Molinito, Mex.	60a	19.27 N	99.15 W
Elmont, NY	55	40.42 N	73.42 W
El Monte, Ca. (mōn'tå)	119a	34.04 N	118.02 W
El Morro Natl. Mon., NM	121	35.05 N	108.20 W
El Mreyyé (Des.), Mauritania	228	19.15 N	7.50 W
Elmshorn, F.R.G. (ělms'hôrn)	157c	53.45 N	9.39 E
Elmwood (Neigh.), Pa.	56b	39.56 N	75.14 W
Elmwood Park, Il.	58a	41.55 N	87.49 W
Elmwood Place, Oh. (ělm'wŏod plås)	113f	39.11 N	84.30 W
Elokomin (R.), Wa. (ē-lō'kô-mǐn)	118c	46.16 N	123.16 W
El Oro, Mex.	130	19.49 N	100.04 W
El Palmar, Ven.	61a	10.38 N	66.52 W
El Pao, Ven. (ěl pá'ō)	142	8.08 N	62.37 W
El Paraíso, Hond. (pä-rä-ē'sō)	132	13.55 N	86.35 W
El Pardo, Sp. (pä'r-dô)	171a	40.31 N	3.47 W
El Paso, Tx. (pas'ō)	124	31.47 N	106.27 W
El Pedregal (Neigh.), Ven.	61a	10.30 N	66.51 W
El Pilar, Ven. (pě-lá'r)	143b	9.56 N	64.48 W
El Plantío (Neigh.), Sp.	65b	40.28 N	3.49 W
El Porvenir, Pan. (pôr-vä-něr')	133	9.34 N	78.55 W
El Puerto de Sta. María, Sp. (pwěr tō dä sän tä mä-rē'ä)	170	36.36 N	6.18 W
El Qala, Alg.	159	36.52 N	8.23 E
El Qoll, Alg.	224	37.02 N	6.29 E
El Real, Pan. (rä-äl)	133	8.07 N	77.43 W
El Recreo (Neigh.), Ven.	61a	10.30 N	66.53 W
El Reloj, Mex.	60a	19.18 N	99.08 W
El Reno, Ok. (rě'nō)	122	35.31 N	97.57 W
El Rincón de La Florida, Chile	61b	33.33 s	70.34 W
El Roboré, Bol. (rô-bō-rě')	143	18.23 s	59.43 W
Elroy, Wi. (ěl'roi)	115	43.44 N	90.17 W
Elsa, Can.	107	63.55 N	135.25 W
Elsah, Il. (ěl'zà)	119e	38.57 N	90.22 W
El Salto, Mex. (säl'tō)	130	22.00 N	105.22 W
El Salvador, N.A.	128	14.00 N	89.30 W
El Sauce, Nic. (ěl-sá'ōō-sě)	132	13.00 N	86.40 W
Elsberry, Mo. (ělz'běr-ǐ)	123	39.09 N	90.44 W
Elsburg, S. Afr.	71b	26.15 s	28.12 E
Elsdorf, F.R.G. (ěls'dôrf)	169c	50.56 N	6.35 E
El Segundo, Ca (sěgŭn'dō)	119a	33.55 N	118.24 W
Elsey, F.R.G.	63	51.22 N	7.34 E
Elsinore, Ca. (ěl'sǐ-nôr)	119a	33.40 N	117.19 W
Elsinore L., Ca	119a	33.38 N	117.21 W
Elstorf, F.R.G. (ěls'tôrf)	157c	53.25 N	9.48 E
Elstree, Eng.	62	51.39 N	0.16 W
Eltham, Austl. (ěl'thăm)	211	37.43 s	145.08 E
Eltham (Neigh.), Eng.	62	51.27 N	0.04 E
El Tigre, Ven. (tě'grě)	142	8.49 N	64.15 W
Elton, Eng.	64a	53.16 N	2.49 W
El'ton (L.), Sov. Un.	179	49.10 N	47.00 E
El Toreo (P. Int.), Mex.	60a	19.27 N	99.13 W
El Toro, Ca. (tō'rō)	119a	33.37 N	117.42 W
El Triunfo, Hond. (ěl-trē-ōō'n-fô)	132	13.06 N	87.00 W
El Triunfo, Sal.	132	13.17 N	88.32 W
Elūru, India	193	16.44 N	80.09 E
El Vado Res, NM	121	36.37 N	106.30 W
El Valle (Neigh.), Ven.	61a	10.27 N	66.55 W
Elvas, Port. (ěl'väzh)	170	38.53 N	7.11 W
Elverum, Nor. (ěl'vě-rōōm)	164	60.53 N	11.33 E
El Viego, Nic. (ěl-vyě'ко)	132	12.10 N	87.10 W
El Viejo (Vol.), Nic.	132	12.44 N	87.03 W
Elvins, Mo. (ěl'vǐnz)	123	37.49 N	90.31 W
El Wad, Alg.	224	33.23 N	6.49 E
El Wak, Ken. (wäk')	225	3.00 N	41.00 E
Elwood, Il. (ě'wŏod)	113a	41.24 N	88.07 W
Elwood, In.	110	40.15 N	85.50 W
Ely, Eng. (ē'lǐ)	163	52.25 N	0.17 E
Ely, Mn.	115	47.54 N	91.53 W
Ely, Nv.	120	39.16 N	114.53 W

PLACE (Pronounciation)	PAGE	Lat. °'	Long. °'
Elyria, Oh. (ē-lĭr'ĭ-ȧ)	113d	41.22 N	82.07 W
El Zamural, Ven.	61a	10.27 N	67.00 W
El Zig-Zag, Ven.	61a	10.33 N	66.58 W
Ema (R.), Sov. Un. (å'mȧ)	165	58.25 N	27.00 E
Emāmshahr, Iran	195	36.25 N	55.01 E
Emån (R.), Swe.	164	57.15 N	15.46 E
Emba (R.), Sov. Un. (yĕm'bȧ)	179	46.50 N	54.10 E
Embalse Guri (L.), Ven.	142	7.30 N	63.00 W
Embarrass (R.), Il. (ĕm-băr'ăs)	110	39.15 N	88.05 W
Embrun, Can. (ĕm'brŭn)	95c	45.16 N	75.17 W
Embrun, Fr. (äN-brûN')	169	44.35 N	6.32 E
Embu, Braz.	61d	23.39 S	46.51 W
Embu, Ken.	231	0.32 S	37.27 E
Emden, F.R.G. (ĕm'dĕn)	166	53.21 N	7.15 E
Emerald, Austl. (ĕm'ēr-ăld)	215	28.34 S	148.00 E
Emerson, Can. (ĕm'ēr-sŭn)	101	49.00 N	97.12 W
Emerson, NJ	55	40.58 N	74.02 W
Emeryville, Ca (ĕm'ēr-ĭ-vĭl)	118b	37.50 N	122.17 W
Emi Koussi, (Mtn.), Chad (ā'mē kōō-sē')	229	19.50 N	18.30 E
Emiliano Zapata, Mex. (ĕ-mē-lyá'nō-zä-pá'tä)	131	17.45 N	91.46 W
Emilia-Romagna (Reg.), It. (ĕ-mēl'yä rō-má'n-yä)	172	44.35 N	10.48 E
Eminence, Ky. (ĕm'ĭ-nĕns)	110	38.25 N	85.15 W
Emira I., Pap. N. Gui. (ā-mē-rä')	207	1.40 S	150.28 E
Emmarentia (Neigh.), S. Afr.	71b	26.10 S	28.01 E
Emmen, Neth. (ĕm'ĕn)	163	52.48 N	6.55 E
Emmerich, F.R.G. (ĕm'ēr-ĭk)	169c	51.51 N	6.16 E
Emmetsburg, Ia. (ĕm'ĕts-bûrg)	115	43.07 N	94.41 W
Emmett, Id. (ĕm'ĕt)	116	43.53 N	116.30 W
Emmons Mt., Ut. (ĕm'ŭnz)	117	40.43 N	110.20 W
Emory Pk., Tx. (ĕ'mō-rē pēk)	124	29.13 N	103.20 W
Empoli, It. (ām'pō-lē)	172	43.43 N	10.55 E
Emporia, Ks. (ĕm-pō'rĭ-ȧ)	123	38.24 N	96.11 W
Emporia, Va.	127	37.40 N	77.34 W
Emporium, Pa. (ĕm-pō'rĭ-ŭm)	111	41.30 N	78.15 W
Ems R., F.R.G. (ĕms)	166	52.52 N	7.16 E
Emst (Neigh.), F.R.G.	63	51.21 N	7.30 E
Ems-Weser (Can.), F.R.G. (vā'zēr)	166	52.23 N	8.11 E
Emsworth, Pa.	57b	40.30 N	80.04 W
Enånger, Swe. (ĕn-ôŋ'gēr)	166	61.36 N	16.55 E
Encantada, Cerro de la (Mtn.), Mex. (sĕ'r-rô-dĕ-lä-ĕn-kän-tä'dä)	128	31.58 N	115.15 W
Encanto, C., Phil. (ĕn-kän'tō)	207a	15.44 N	121.46 E
Encarnação (Neigh.), Port.	65d	38.47 N	9.06 W
Encarnación, Par. (ĕn-kär-nä-syōn')	144	27.26 S	55.52 W
Encarnación de Diaz, Mex. (ĕn-kär-nä-syōn dā dē'áz)	130	21.34 N	102.15 W
Encinal, Tx. (ĕn'sĭ-nôl)	124	28.02 N	99.22 W
Encino (Neigh.), Ca.	59	34.09 N	118.30 W
Encontrados, Ven. (ĕn-kōn-trä'dōs)	142	9.01 N	72.10 W
Encounter B., Austl. (ĕn-koun'tēr)	216	35.50 S	138.45 E
Endako (R.), Can.	98	54.05 N	125.30 W
Endau (R.), Mala.	191b	2.29 N	103.40 E
Enderbury (I.), Oceania (ĕn'dēr-bûrĭ)	208	2.00 S	107.50 W
Enderby Land (Reg.), Ant. (ĕn'dēr bĭĭ)	232	72.00 S	52.00 E
Enderlin, ND (ĕn'dēr-lĭn)	114	46.38 N	97.37 W
Endicott, NY (ĕn'dĭ-kŏt)	111	42.05 N	76.00 W
Endicott Mts., Ak.	107	67.30 N	153.45 W
Enez, Tur.	173	40.42 N	26.05 E
Enfield, Austl.	70a	33.53 S	151.06 E
Enfield, Ct. (ĕn'fēld)	111	41.55 N	72.35 W
Enfield, Eng.	156b	51.38 N	0.06 W
Enfield, NC	127	36.10 N	77.41 W
Engang, Cabo (C.), Dom.Rep. (kà'-bô- ĕn-gä-nô)	135	18.40 N	68.30 W
Engcobo, S. Afr. (ĕŋg-cô-bô)	227c	31.41 S	27.59 E
Engel's, Sov. Un. (ĕn'gĕls)	179	51.20 N	45.40 E
Engelskirchen, F.R.G. (ĕn'gĕls-kēr'kĕn)	169c	50.59 N	7.25 E
Engenho de Dentro (Neigh.), Braz.	61c	22.54 S	43.18 W
Engenho do Mato, Braz.	61c	22.52 S	43.01 W
Engenho Nôvo (Neigh.), Braz.	61c	22.55 S	43.17 W
Enggano, Pulau (I.), Indon. (ĕng-gä'nō)	206	5.22 S	102.18 E
Enghien-les-Bains, Fr.	64c	48.58 N	2.19 E
England, Ar. (ĭŋ'glănd)	123	34.33 N	91.58 W
England (Reg.), U.K. (ĭŋ'glănd)	162	51.35 N	1.40 W
Engleé, Can. (ĕn-glee)	105	50.44 N	56.06 W
Englefield Green, Eng.	62	51.26 N	0.35 W
Englewood, Co. (ĕn'g'l-wŏŏd)	122	39.39 N	105.00 W
Englewood (Neigh.), Il.	58a	41.47 N	87.39 W
Englewood, NJ	112a	40.54 N	73.59 W
Englewood Cliffs, NJ	55	40.53 N	73.57 W
English, In. (ĭn'glĭsh)	110	38.15 N	86.25 W
English (R.), Can.	97	50.31 N	94.12 W
English Chan, Eng.	159	49.45 N	3.06 W
Énguera, Sp. (ān'gärä)	171	38.58 N	0.42 W
Enid, Ok. (ē'nĭd)	122	36.25 N	97.52 W
Enid Res., Ms.	126	34.13 N	89.47 W
Enkeldoring, S. Afr (ĕŋ'k'l-dôr-ĭng)	223d	25.24 S	28.43 E
Enköping, Swe. (ĕn'kû-pĭng)	164	59.39 N	17.05 E
Ennedi (Plat.), Chad (ĕn-nĕd'ē)	225	16.45 N	22.45 E
Ennepetal, F.R.G.	63	51.18 N	7.22 E
Ennis, Ire. (ĕn'ĭs)	162	52.54 N	9.05 W
Ennis, Tx.	125	32.20 N	96.38 W
Enniscorthy, Ire. (ĕn-ĭs-kôr'thĭ)	162	52.33 N	6.27 W
Enniskillen, N. Ire (ĕn-ĭs-kĭl'ĕn)	162	54.20 N	7.25 W
Enns (R.), Aus. (ĕns)	166	47.37 N	14.35 E
Enoree, SC (ē-nō'rē)	127	34.43 N	81.58 W
Enoree (R.), SC	127	34.35 N	81.55 W
Enriquillo, Dom. Rep. (ĕn-rē-kē'l-yō)	135	17.55 N	71.15 W
Enriquillo, Lago (L.), Dom. Rep. (lä'gô-ĕn-rē-kē'l-yô)	135	18.35 N	71.35 W
Enschede, Neth. (ĕns'kā-dĕ)	163	52.10 N	6.50 E
Enseñada, Arg.	141c	34.50 S	57.55 W
Ensenada, Mex. (ĕn-sĕ-nä'dä)	128	32.00 N	116.30 W
Enshi, China (ŭn-shr)	203x	30.18 N	109.25 E
Enshū-Nada (Sea), Jap. (ĕn'shōō nä-dä)	205	34.25 N	137.14 E
Enterprise, Al. (ĕn'tēr-prīz)	126	31.20 N	85.50 W
Enterprise, Or.	116	45.25 N	117.16 W
Entiat, L, Wa.	116	45.43 N	120.11 W
Entraygues, Fr. (ĕN-trĕg')	168	44.39 N	2.33 E
Entre Rios (Prov.), Arg.	144	31.30 S	59.00 W
Enugu, Nig. (ĕ-nōō'gōō)	229	6.27 N	7.27 E
Enumclaw, Wa. (ĕn'ŭm-klô)	118a	47.12 N	121.59 W
Envigado, Col. (ĕn-vē-gá'dŏ)	142a	6.10 N	75.34 W
Eolie, Isole (Is.), It. (ĕ'sō-lĕ-ĕ-ô'lyĕ)	172	38.43 N	14.43 E
Epe, Nig.	229	6.37 N	3.59 E
Épernay, Fr. (ā-pĕr-nĕ')	168	49.02 N	3.54 E
Épernon, Fr. (ā-pĕr-nôN')	169b	48.36 N	1.41 E
Ephraim, Ut. (ē'frâ-ĭm)	121	39.20 N	111.40 W
Ephrata, Wa. (ĕfrā'tȧ)	116	47.18 N	119.35 W
Epi, Vanuatu (ā'pē)	215	16.59 S	168.29 E
Épila, Sp. (ā'pē-lä)	170	41.38 N	1.15 W
Épinal, Fr. (ā-pē-nàl')	169	48.11 N	6.27 E
Episkopi, Cyprus	191a	34.38 N	32.55 E
Eppendorf (Neigh.), F.R.G.	63	51.27 N	7.11 E
Eppenhausen (Neigh.), F.R.G.	63	51.21 N	7.31 E
Epping, Austl.	70a	33.46 S	151.05 E
Epping, Eng. (ĕp'ĭng)	156b	51.41 N	0.06 E
Epping Green, Eng.	62	51.44 N	0.05 E
Epping Upland, Eng.	62	51.43 N	0.06 E
Epsom, Eng.	62	51.20 N	0.16 W
Epupa Falls, Ang.	230	17.00 S	13.05 E
Epworth, Eng. (ĕp'wûrth)	156	53.31 N	0.50 W
Equatorial Guinea, Afr.	224	2.00 N	7.15 E
Eramosa (R.), Can. (ĕr-ȧ-mō'sȧ)	95d	43.39 N	80.08 W
Erba, Jabal (Mtn.), Sud. (ĕr-bȧ)	225	20.53 N	36.45 E
Erciyeş Daği (Mtn.), Tur.	161	38.30 N	35.36 E
Erda, Ut. (ēr'dä)	119b	40.41 N	112.17 W
Erding, F.R.G. (ĕr'dĕng)	157d	48.19 N	11.54 E
Erechim, Braz. (ĕ-rĕ-shē'N)	144	27.43 S	52.11 W
Ereğli, Tur. (ĕ-râ'ĭ-le)	179	37.40 N	34.00 E
Ereğli, Tur.	179	41.15 N	31.25 E
Erenköy (Neigh.), Tur.	66f	40.58 N	29.04 E
Erfurt, G.D.R. (ĕr'fōōrt)	166	50.59 N	11.04 E
Ergene (R.), Tur. (ĕr'gĕ-nĕ)	173	41.17 N	26.50 E
Erges (R.), Port.-Sp. (ĕr'-zhĕs)	170	39.45 N	7.01 W
Ergli, Sov. Un.	165	56.54 N	25.38 E
Ergste, F.R.G.	63	51.25 N	7.34 E
Eria (R.), Sp. (ā-rē'ä)	170	42.10 N	6.08 W
Erick, Ok. (âr'ĭk)	122	35.14 N	99.51 W
Erie, Ks. (ē'rĭ)	123	37.35 N	95.17 W
Erie, Pa.	111	42.05 N	80.05 W
Erie, L., U.S.-Can.	109	42.15 N	81.25 W
Erimo Saki (C.), Jap. (ā'rē-mō sä-kē)	204	41.53 N	143.20 E
Erin, Can. (ĕ'rĭn)	95d	43.46 N	80.04 W
Erith (Neigh.), Eng.	62	51.29 N	0.10 E
Eritrea (Reg.), Eth. (ā-rē-trā'ȧ)	225	16.15 N	38.30 E
Erkrath, F.R.G.	63	51.13 N	6.55 E
Erlangen, F.R.G. (ĕr'läng-ĕn)	166	49.36 N	11.03 E
Erlanger, Ky. (ĕr'lăng-ēr)	113f	39.01 N	84.36 W
Erle (Neigh.), F.R.G.	63	51.33 N	7.05 E
Ermont, Fr.	64c	48.59 N	2.16 E
Ermoúpolis, Grc.	173	37.30 N	24.56 E
Ernākulam, India	197	9.58 N	76.23 E
Erne, Lower Lough (L.), N. Ire.	162	54.30 N	7.40 W
Erne, Upper Lough (L.), N. Ire. (lŏk ûrn)	162	54.20 N	7.24 W
Erode, India	197	11.20 N	77.45 E
Eromanga (I.), Vanuatu	215	18.58 S	169.18 E
Eros, La. (ē'rōs)	125	32.23 N	92.22 W
Errego, Moz.	231	16.02 S	37.14 E
Errigal (Mtn.), Ire. (ĕr-ĭ-gôl')	162	55.02 N	8.07 W
Errol Heights, Or.	118c	45.29 N	122.38 W
Erskine Park, Austl.	70a	33.49 S	150.47 E
Erstein, Fr. (ĕr'shtīn)	169	48.27 N	7.40 E
Erwin, NC (ûr'wĭn)	127	35.16 N	78.40 W
Erwin, Tn.	127	36.07 N	82.25 W
Erzgebirge (Ore.Mts.), G.D.R. (ĕrts'gĕ-bē'gĕ)	166	50.29 N	12.40 E
Erzincan, Tur. (ĕr-zĭn-jän')	179	39.50 N	39.30 E
Erzurum, Tur. (ĕrz'rōōm')	179	39.55 N	41.10 E
Esambo, Zaire	230	3.40 S	23.24 E
Esashi, Jap. (ĕs'ä-shē)	204	41.50 N	140.10 E
Esbjerg, Den. (ĕs'byĕrgh)	164	55.29 N	8.25 E
Esborn, F.R.G.	63	51.23 N	7.20 E
Escalante (R.), Ut.	121	37.40 N	111.20 W
Escalante, Ut. (ĕs-kȧ-lăn'tē)	121	37.50 N	111.40 W
Escalón, Mex.	124	26.45 N	104.20 W
Escambia (R.), Fl. (ĕs-kăm'bĭ-ȧ)	126	30.38 N	87.20 W
Escanaba, Mi. (ĕs-kȧ-nô'bȧ)	115	45.44 N	87.05 W
Escanaba (R.), Mi.	115	46.10 N	87.22 W
Escarpada Point, Phil.	206	18.40 N	122.45 E
Esch-sur-Alzette, Lux.	169	49.32 N	6.21 E
Eschwege, F.R.G. (ĕsh'vā-gē)	166	51.11 N	10.02 E
Eschweiler, F.R.G. (ĕsh'vī-lēr)	169c	50.49 N	6.15 E
Escocesá, Bahia (B.), Dom. Rep. (bä-ē'ä-ĕs-kō-sĕ'sä)	135	19.25 N	69.40 W
Escondido, Ca. (ĕs-kŏn-dē'dō)	120	33.07 N	117.00 W
Escondido R., Nic.	133	12.04 N	84.09 W
Escondido, Rio (R.), Mex. (rē'ō-ĕs-kŏn-dē'dô)	124	28.30 N	100.45 W
Escuadrón 201, Mex.	60a	19.22 N	99.06 W
Escudo de Veraguas I., Pan. (ĕs-kōō'dä dā vä-rä'gwäs)	133	9.07 N	81.25 W
Escuinapa, Mex. (ĕs-kwē-nä'pä)	130	22.49 N	105.44 W
Escuintla, Guat. (ĕs-kwēn'tlä)	132	14.16 N	90.47 W
Escuintla, Mex.	131	15.20 N	92.45 W
Ese, Cayos de (I.), Col.	133	12.24 N	81.07 W
Esfahān, Iran	192	32.38 N	51.30 E
Esgueva (R.), Sp. (ĕs-gĕ'vä)	170	41.48 N	4.10 W
Esher, Eng.	62	51.23 N	0.22 W
Eshowe, S. Afr. (ĕsh'ô-wĕ)	227c	28.54 S	31.28 E
Esiama, Ghana	228	4.56 N	2.21 W
Eskdale, WV (ĕsk'dāl)	110	38.05 N	81.25 W
Eskifjördur, Ice. (ĕs'kē-fyûr'dōōr)	158	65.04 N	14.01 W
Eskilstuna, Swe. (å'shĕl-stü-na)	164	59.23 N	16.28 E
Eskimo Lakes (L.), Can. (es'kĭ-mō)	96	69.40 N	130.10 W
Eskişehir, Tur. (ĕs-kē-shĕ'h'r)	179	39.40 N	30.20 E
Esko, Mn. (ĕs'kô)	119h	46.27 N	92.22 W
Esla (R.), Sp. (ĕs-lä)	170	41.50 N	5.48 W
Eslöv, Swe. (ĕs'lûv)	164	55.50 N	13.17 E
Esmeraldas, Ec. (ĕs-mȧ-räl'däs)	142	0.58 N	79.45 W
Espada, Punta (Pt.), Dom. Rep. (pōō'n-tä-ĕs-pä'dä)	135	18.30 N	68.30 W
Espanola, Can. (ĕs-pȧ-nō'lȧ)	102	46.11 N	81.59 W
Esparta, C.R. (ĕs-pär'tä)	133	9.59 N	84.40 W
Esperance, Austl. (ĕs'pē-rǎns)	214	33.45 S	122.07 E
Esperanza, Cuba (ĕs-pĕ-rä'n-zä)	134	22.30 N	80.10 W
Espichel, Cabo (C.), Port. (kà'bō-ĕs-pē-shĕl')	171b	38.25 N	9.13 W
Espinal, Col. (ĕs-pē-näl')	142a	4.10 N	74.53 W
Espinhaço, Serra do (Mts.), Braz. (sĕ'r-rä-dô-ĕs-pē-nà-sô)	143	16.06 S	44.56 W
Espinillo, Punta (Pt.), Ur. (pōō'n-tä-ĕs-pē-nē'l-yô)	141c	34.49 S	56.27 W
Espírito Santo, Braz. (ĕs-pē'rē-tô-sán'tô)	143	20.27 S	40.18 W
Espírito Santo (State), Braz.	143	19.57 S	40.58 W
Espiritu Santo (I.), Vanuatu (ĕs-pē'rē-tōō sän'tō)	215	15.45 S	166.50 E
Espíritu Santo, Bahia del (B.), Mex. (bä-ē'ä-dĕl-ĕs-pē'rē-tōō-sän'tô)	132a	19.25 N	87.28 W
Espita, Mex. (ĕs-pē'tä)	132a	20.57 N	88.22 W
Esplugas, Sp.	65e	41.23 N	2.06 E
Espoo, Fin.	165	60.13 N	24.41 E
Esposende, Port. (ĕs-pō-zĕn'dā)	170	41.33 N	8.45 W
Esquel, Arg. (ĕs-kĕ'l)	144	42.47 S	71.22 W
Esquimalt, Can. (ĕs-kwī'mŏlt)	118a	48.26 N	123.24 W
Essaouira, Mor.	224	31.34 N	9.44 W
Essel (Neigh.), F.R.G.	63	51.37 N	7.15 E
Essen, Bel.	157a	51.28 N	4.27 E
Essen, F.R.G. (ĕs'sĕn)	169c	51.26 N	6.59 E
Essenberg, F.R.G.	63	51.26 N	6.42 E
Essendon, Austl.	70b	37.46 S	144.55 E
Essequibo (R.), Guy. (ĕs-ā-kē'bō)	143	4.26 N	58.17 W
Essex, Il.	113a	41.11 N	88.11 W
Essex, Ma.	105a	42.38 N	70.47 W
Essex, Md.	112e	39.19 N	76.29 W
Essex, Vt.	111	44.30 N	73.05 W
Essex Fells, NJ (ĕs'ĕks fĕlz)	112a	40.50 N	74.16 W
Essexville, Mi. (ĕs'ĕks-vĭl)	110	43.35 N	83.50 W
Essington, Pa.	56b	39.52 N	75.18 W
Essling (Neigh.), Aus.	66e	48.13 N	16.32 E
Esslingen, F.R.G. (ĕs'slĕn-gĕn)	166	48.45 N	9.19 E
Estacado, Llano (Plain), U.S. (yá-nō ĕs-tȧcȧ-dō')	108	33.50 N	103.20 W
Estados, Isla de los, S.A.	144	55.05 S	63.00 W
Estância, Braz. (ĕs-tän'sĭ-ä)	143	11.17 S	37.18 W
Estarreja, Port. (ĕ-tär-rä'zhä)	170	40.44 N	8.39 W
Estats, Pique d' (Pk.), Fr.	171	42.43 N	1.30 E
Estcourt, S. Afr. (ĕst-coort)	227c	29.04 S	29.53 E
Este, It. (ĕs'tā)	172	45.13 N	11.40 E
Estelí, Nic. (ĕs-tā-lē')	132	13.10 N	86.23 W
Estella, Sp. (ĕs-tāl'yä)	170	42.40 N	2.01 W
Estepa, Sp. (ĕs-tā'pä)	170	37.18 N	4.54 W
Estepona, Sp. (ĕs-tȧ-pō'nä)	170	36.26 N	5.08 W
Esterhazy, Can. (ĕs'tēr-hä-zē)	101	50.40 N	102.08 W
Esteros, B., Ca. (ĕs-tä'rōs)	120	35.22 N	121.04 W
Estevan, Can. (ĕ-stē'văn)	100	49.07 N	103.05 W
Estevan Group (Is.), Can.	98	53.05 N	129.40 W
Estherville, Ia. (ĕs'tēr-vĭl)	115	43.24 N	94.49 W
Estill, SC (ĕs'tĭl)	127	32.46 N	81.15 W
Eston, Can.	100	51.10 N	108.45 W
Estonian S.S.R., Sov. Un. (ĕs-tō'nĭ-ăn)	176	59.10 N	25.00 E
Estoril, Port. (ĕs-tô-rĕl')	171b	38.45 N	9.24 W
Estrêla (R.), Braz. (ĕs-trĕ'là)	144b	22.39 S	43.16 W
Estrêla, Serra da (Mts.), Port. (sĕr'rȧ dä ĕs-trĕ'lȧ)	170	40.25 N	7.45 W
Estrella, Cerro de la (Mtn.), Mex.	60a	19.21 N	99.05 W
Estremadura (Reg.), Port. (ĕs-trā-mä-dōō'rȧ)	170	41.35 N	8.36 W
Estremoz, Port. (ĕs-trā-mōzh')	170	38.50 N	7.35 W
Estrondo, Serra do (Mts.), Braz. (sĕr'ī dōō ĕs-trôn'dōō)	143	9.52 S	48.56 W
Esumba, Ile (I.), Zaire	230	2.00 N	21.12 E
Esztergom, Hung. (ĕs'tēr-gōm)	167	47.46 N	18.45 E
Etah, Grnld. (ē'tȧ)	94	78.20 N	72.42 W
Étampes, Fr. (ā-täNp')	169b	48.26 N	2.09 E
Étaples, Fr. (ā-täp'l')	168	50.32 N	1.38 E
Etchemin (R.), Can. (ĕch'ĕ-mĭn)	95b	46.39 N	71.03 W
Ethiopa, Afr. (ē-thē-ō'pē-ȧ)	222	7.53 N	37.55 E
Eticoga, Guinea-Bissau	228	11.09 N	16.08 W
Etiwanda, Ca. (ē-tĭ-wän'dȧ)	119a	34.07 N	117.31 W
Etlatongo, see San Mateo			
Etna, Pa. (ĕt'nȧ)	113e	40.30 N	79.55 W
Etna, Mt. (Vol.), It.	172	37.48 N	15.00 E
Etobicoke, Can.	95d	43.39 N	79.34 W
Etobicoke Cr., Can.	95d	43.44 N	79.48 W
Etolin Str., Ak. (ĕt ō lĭn)	107	60.35 S	165.40 W
Eton, Eng.	62	51.31 N	0.37 W
Etorofu (I.), see Iturop			
Etoshapan (L.), Namibia (ĕtō'shä)	226	19.07 S	15.30 E
Etowah (R.), Ga.	126	34.23 N	84.19 W
Etowah, Tn. (ĕt'ô-wä)	126	35.18 N	84.31 W
Étréchy, Fr. (ā-trā-shē')	169b	48.29 N	2.12 E
Etten-Leur, Neth.	157a	51.34 N	4.38 E
Etterbeek, Bel. (ĕt'ēr-bāk)	157a	50.51 N	4.24 E
Etzatlán, Mex. (ĕt-zä-tlän')	130	20.44 N	104.04 W
Eucla, Austl. (ū'klȧ)	214	31.45 S	128.50 E
Euclid, Oh. (ū'klĭd)	113d	41.34 N	81.32 W
Eudora, Ar. (u-dō'rȧ)	123	33.07 N	91.16 W
Eufaula, Al. (û-fô'lȧ)	126	31.53 N	85.09 W
Eufaula, Ok.	123	35.16 N	95.35 W
Eufaula Res., Ok.	123	35.00 N	94.45 W
Eugene, Or. (û-jēn')	116	44.02 N	123.06 W
Euless, Tx. (ū'lĕs)	119c	32.50 N	97.05 W
Eunice, La. (ū'nĭs)	125	30.30 N	92.25 W
Eupen, Bel. (oi'pĕn)	163	50.39 N	6.05 E
Euphrates (R.), Asia (û-frā'tēz)	192	36.00 N	39.30 E
Eure (R.), Fr. (ûr)	168	49.03 N	1.22 E

ng-sing; ŋ-baŋk; N-nasalized n; nŏd; cŏmmit; ōld; ôbey; ôrder; oi-boil; fōōd; fŏŏt; ou-out; s-soft; sh-dish; th-thin; pūre; ûnite; ûrn; stŭd; circŭs; ü-as in French tu; '-indeterminate vowel.

PLACE (Pronounciation)	PAGE	Lat. °′	Long. °′
Eureka, Ca. (û-rē'kà)	116	40.45 N	124.10 W
Eureka, Ks.	123	37.48 N	96.17 W
Eureka, Mt.	116	48.53 N	115.07 W
Eureka, Nv.	120	39.33 N	115.58 W
Eureka, SD	114	45.46 N	99.38 W
Eureka, Ut.	121	39.55 N	112.10 W
Eureka Springs, Ar.	123	36.24 N	93.43 W
Eurgun (Mtn.), Iran	192	28.47 N	57.00 E
Europe, (ū'rŭp)	154	50.00 N	15.00 E
Eustis, Fl. (ūs'tĭs)	127	28.50 N	81.41 W
Eutaw, Al. (ū-tå)	126	32.48 N	87.50 W
Eutsuk L., Can. (o͞ot'sŭk)	98	53.20 N	126.44 W
Evanston, Il. (ĕv'ăn-stŭn)	113a	42.03 N	87.41 W
Evanston, Wy.	117	41.17 N	111.02 W
Evansville, In. (ĕv'ănz-vĭl)	110	38.00 N	87.30 W
Evansville, Wi.	115	42.46 N	89.19 W
Evart, Mi. (ĕv'ērt)	110	43.55 N	85.10 W
Evaton, S. Afr. (ĕv'á-tŏn)	223d	26.32 S	27.53 E
Eveleth, Mn. (ĕv'ē-lĕth)	115	47.27 N	92.35 W
Everard (L.), Austl. (ĕv'ēr-árd)	214	36.20 S	134.10 E
Everard Ra., Austl.	214	27.15 S	132.00 E
Everest, Mt., Nep.-China (ĕv'ēr-ĕst)	196	28.00 N	86.57 E
Everett, Ma. (ĕv'ēr-ĕt)	105a	42.24 N	71.03 W
Everett, Wa. (ĕv'ēr-ĕt)	118a	47.59 N	122.11 W
Everett Mts., Can.	97	62.34 N	68.00 W
Everglades, Fl. (ĕv'ēr-glādz)	127a	25.50 N	81.25 W
Everglades Natl. Park, Fl.	127a	25.39 N	80.57 W
Everglades, The (Swp.), Fl.	134	25.35 N	80.55 W
Evergreen, Al. (ĕv'ēr-grēn)	126	31.25 N	87.56 W
Evergreen Park, Il.	113a	41.44 N	87.42 W
Everman, Tx. (ĕv'ēr-măn)	119c	32.38 N	97.17 W
Everson, Wa. (ĕv'ēr-sŭn)	118d	48.55 N	122.21 W
Everton (Neigh.), Eng.	64a	53.25 N	2.58 W
Eving (Neigh.), F.R.G.	63	51.33 N	7.29 E
Évora, Port. (ĕv'ô-rä)	170	38.35 N	7.54 W
Évreux, Fr. (ā-vrû')	168	49.02 N	1.11 E
Evrótas (R.), Grc. (ĕv-rō'täs)	173	37.15 N	22.17 E
Évvoia (I.), Grc.	173	38.38 N	23.45 E
Ewa Beach, Hi. (ē'wä)	106	21.17 N	158.03 E
Ewaso Ng'iro (R.), Ken.	225	0.59 N	37.47 E
Éden, Braz.	61c	22.48 S	43.24 W
Ewell, Eng.	62	51.21 N	0.15 W
Émerainville, Fr.	64c	48.49 N	2.37 E
Épinay-sous-Sénart, Fr.	64c	48.42 N	2.31 E
Épinay-sur-Seine, Fr.	64c	48.57 N	2.19 E
Ewu, Nig.	71d	6.33 N	3.19 E
Excelsior, Mn. (ĕk-sel'sĭ-ŏr)	119g	44.54 N	93.35 W
Excelsior Springs, Mo.	123	39.20 N	94.13 W
Exe (R.), Eng. (ĕks)	162	50.57 N	3.37 W
Exeter, Ca. (ĕk'sē-tēr)	120	36.18 N	119.09 W
Exeter, Eng.	162	50.45 N	3.33 W
Exeter, NH	111	43.00 N	71.00 W
Exmoor, Eng. (ĕks'mo͝or)	162	51.10 N	3.55 W
Exmouth, Eng. (ĕks'mŭth)	162	50.40 N	3.20 W
Exmouth, G., Austl.	214	21.45 S	114.30 E
Exploits (R.), Can. (ĕks-ploits')	105	48.50 N	56.15 W
Extórrax (R.), Mex. (ĕx-tó'ráx)	130	21.04 N	99.39 W
Extrema, Braz. (ĕsh-trē'mä)	141a	22.52 S	46.19 W
Extremadura (Reg.), Sp. (ĕks-trä-mä-doo'rä)	170	38.43 N	6.30 W
Exuma Sd, Ba. (ĕk-so͞o'mä)	135	24.20 N	76.20 W
Eyasi, L., Tan. (å-yä'sē)	231	3.25 S	34.55 E
Eyjafjördur (Fd.), Ice.	158	66.21 N	18.20 W
Eyl, Som.	223a	7.53 N	49.45 E
Eynsford, Eng.	62	51.22 N	0.13 E
Eyrarbakki, Ice.	158	63.51 N	20.52 W
Eyre, Austl. (âr)	214	32.15 S	126.20 E
Eyre (L.), Austl.	216	28.43 S	137.50 E
Eyre Pen, Austl.	214	33.30 S	136.00 E
Eyüp (Neigh.), Tur.	66f	41.03 N	28.55 E
Ezbekīyah (Neigh.), Egypt	71a	30.03 N	31.15 E
Ezeiza, Arg. (ĕ-zā'zä)	144a	34.36 S	58.31 W
Ezine, Tur. (å'zĭ-nå)	173	39.47 N	26.18 E

F

PLACE (Pronounciation)	PAGE	Lat. °′	Long. °′
Fabens, Tx. (fā'bĕnz)	124	31.30 N	106.07 W
Fåborg, Den. (fô'bôrg)	164	55.06 N	10.19 E
Fabreville (Neigh.), Can.	54b	45.34 N	73.50 W
Fabriano, It. (fä-brē-ä'nô)	172	43.20 N	12.55 E
Facatativá, Col. (fä-kä-tä-tē-vá')	142a	4.49 N	74.09 W
Fada, Chad (fä'dä)	225	17.06 N	21.18 E
Fada Ngourma, Burkina (fä'dä' 'n go͞or'mä)	228	12.04 N	0.21 E
Faddeya (I.), Sov. Un. (fád-yä')	181	76.12 N	145.00 E
Faenza, It. (fä-ĕnd'zä)	172	44.16 N	11.53 E
Faeroe Is., Eur. (fā'rō)	154	62.00 N	5.45 W
Fafe, Port. (fä'fā)	170	41.30 N	8.10 W
Fafen (R.), Eth.	223a	8.15 N	42.40 E
Făgăras, Rom. (fá-gä'rásh)	173	45.50 N	24.55 E
Fagerness, Nor. (fä'ghēr-nĕs)	164	61.00 N	9.10 E
Fagnano (L.), Arg.-Chile (fäk-nä'nô)	144	54.35 S	68.20 W
Faguibine, Lac (L.), Mali	228	16.50 N	4.20 W
Fahrland, G.D.R.	65a	52.28 N	13.01 E
Faial I., Acores (fä-yä'l)	224a	38.40 N	29.19 W
Fā'id, Egypt (fä-yēd')	223c	30.19 N	32.18 E
Failsworth, Eng.	64b	53.31 N	2.09 W
Fairbanks, Ak. (fâr'bănks)	107	64.50 N	147.48 W
Fairbury, Il. (fâr'bĕr-ĭ)	110	40.45 N	88.25 W
Fairbury, Ne.	123	40.09 N	97.11 W
Fairchild Cr., Can. (fâr'chīld)	95d	43.18 N	80.10 W
Fairfax, Mn. (fâr'făks)	115	44.29 N	94.44 W
Fairfax, SC	127	32.29 N	81.13 W
Fairfax, Va.	112e	38.51 N	77.20 W
Fairfield, Al. (fâr'fēld)	112h	33.30 N	86.50 W
Fairfield, Austl.	211b	33.52 S	150.57 E
Fairfield, Ct.	112a	41.08 N	73.22 W
Fairfield, Ia.	115	41.00 N	91.59 W
Fairfield, Il.	110	38.25 N	88.20 W
Fairfield, Me.	104	44.35 N	69.38 W
Fairfield, NJ.	55	40.53 N	74.17 W
Fairhaven, Ma. (fâr-hā'vĕn)	111	41.35 N	70.55 W
Fairhaven, Md.	56d	38.47 N	77.05 W
Fair Haven, Vt.	111	43.35 N	73.15 W
Fair I., Scot. (fâr)	162a	59.34 N	1.41 W
Fair Lawn, NJ	55	40.56 N	74.07 W
Fairlee, Md.	56d	38.52 N	77.16 W
Fairmont, Mn. (fâr'mŏnt)	115	43.39 N	94.26 W
Fairmont, WV	111	39.30 N	80.10 W
Fairmont City, Il.	119e	38.39 N	90.05 W
Fairmount, In.	110	40.25 N	85.45 W
Fairmount, Ks.	119f	39.12 N	95.55 W
Fairmount Heights, Md.	56d	38.54 N	76.55 W
Fair Oaks, Ga. (fâr ōks)	112c	33.56 N	84.33 W
Fairport, NY (fâr'pōrt)	111	43.05 N	77.30 W
Fairport Harbor, Oh.	110	41.45 N	81.15 W
Fairseat, Eng.	62	51.30 N	0.20 E
Fairview, NJ	55	40.49 N	74.00 W
Fairview, Ok. (fâr'vū)	122	36.16 N	98.28 W
Fairview, Or.	118c	45.32 N	112.26 W
Fairview, Ut.	121	39.35 N	111.30 W
Fairview Park, Oh.	113d	41.27 N	81.52 W
Fairweather, Mt., Can. (fâr-wĕdh'ēr)	107	59.12 N	137.22 W
Faisalabad, Pak.	196	31.29 N	73.06 E
Faith, SD (fāth)	114	45.02 N	120.02 W
Faizābād, India	196	26.50 N	82.17 E
Fajardo, P.R.	129b	18.20 N	65.40 W
Fakfak, Indon.	207	2.56 S	132.25 E
Faku, China, (fä-ko͞o)	202	42.28 N	123.20 E
Falaise, C, Viet.	203	19.20 N	106.18 E
Falcón (State), Ven. (fäl-kô'n)	143b	11.00 N	68.28 W
Falconer, NY (fô'k'n-ēr)	111	42.10 N	79.10 W
Falcon Heights, Mn. (fô'k'n)	119g	44.59 N	93.10 W
Falcon Res., Tx. (fôk'n)	124	26.47 N	99.03 W
Falemé (R.), Afr. (fá-lā-mā')	228	13.40 N	12.00 W
Faleshty, Sov. Un. (fä-lĕsh'tĭ)	175	47.33 N	27.46 E
Falfurrias, Tx. (făl'fo͞o-rē'ás)	124	27.15 N	98.08 W
Falher, Can. (făl'ēr)	99	55.44 N	117.12 W
Falkenberg, Swe. (fäl'kĕn-bĕrgh)	164	56.54 N	12.25 E
Falkensee, G.D.R. (fäl'kĕn-zā)	157b	52.34 N	13.05 E
Falkenthal, G.D.R. (fäl'kĕn-täl)	157b	52.54 N	13.18 E
Falkirk, Scot. (fôl'kûrk)	162	55.59 N	3.55 W
Falkland Is., S.A. (fôk'lănd)	144	50.45 S	61.00 W
Falköping, Swe. (fäl'chûp-ĭng)	164	58.09 N	13.30 E
Fall City, Wa.	118a	47.34 N	121.53 W
Fall Cr., In. (fôl)	113g	39.52 N	86.04 W
Fallon, Nv. (făl'ŭn)	120	39.30 N	118.48 W
Fall River, Ma.	112b	41.42 N	71.07 W
Falls Church, Va. (fôlz chûrch)	112e	38.53 N	77.10 W
Falls City, Ne.	123	40.04 N	95.37 W
Fallston, Md. (fâls'ton)	112e	39.32 N	76.26 W
Falmouth, Eng. (făl'mŭth)	162	50.08 N	5.04 W
Falmouth, Jam.	134	18.30 N	77.40 W
Falmouth, Ky.	110	38.40 N	84.20 W
False (B.), see Valsbaai			
False Divi Pt., India	191	15.45 N	80.50 E
Falso, Cabo (C.), Dom.Rep. (ká'bô-fäl-sô)	135	17.45 N	71.55 W
Falster (I.), Den. (fäls'tēr)	164	54.48 N	11.58 E
Fălticeni, Rom. (fŭl-tē-chān'y')	167	47.27 N	26.17 E
Falun, Swe. (fä-lo͞on')	164	60.38 N	15.35 E
Famadas, Sp.	65e	41.21 N	2.05 E
Famagusta, Cyprus (fä-mä-go͞os'tä)	161	35.08 N	33.59 E
Famatina, Sierra de (Mts.), Arg. (sē-ĕ'r-rä-dĕ-fä-mä-tē'nä)	144	29.00 S	67.50 W
Fangxian, China (fäŋ-shyĕn)	203	32.05 N	110.45 E
Fanning (I.), see Tabuaeran (I.)			
Fannystelle, Can. (făn'ĭ-stĕl)	95f	49.45 N	97.46 W
Fanø (I.), Den. (fän'û)	164	55.24 N	8.10 E
Fano, It. (fä'nō)	172	43.49 N	13.01 E
Farafangana, Mad. (fä-rä-fäŋ-gä'nä)	227	21.18 S	47.59 E
Farāh, Afg. (fä-rä')	192	32.15 N	62.13 E
Farallón, Punta (Pt.), Mex. (po͞o'n-tä-fä-rä-lōn)	130	19.21 N	105.03 W
Faranah, Gui (fä-rä'nä)	228	10.02 N	10.44 W
Farasān, Jaza'ir (Is.), Eth.	225	16.45 N	41.08 E
Farazād, Iran	68h	35.47 N	51.21 E
Faregh, Wadi al (R.), Libya (wädē ĕl fä-rĕg')	161	30.10 N	19.34 E
Farewell, C., N.Z. (fâr-wĕl')	217	40.37 S	172.40 E
Fargo, ND (fär'gō)	114	46.53 N	96.48 W
Far Hills, NJ (fär hĭlz)	112a	40.41 N	74.38 W
Faribault, Mn. (fâ'rĭ-bō)	115	44.19 N	93.16 W
Farilhões (Is.), Port. (fä-rē-lyônzh')	170	39.28 N	9.32 W
Faringdon, Eng. (fă'rĭng-dŏn)	156b	51.38 N	1.35 W
Fāriskūr, Egypt (fä-rĕs-ko͞or')	223b	31.19 N	31.46 E
Farit, Amba (Mt.), Eth.	225	10.51 N	37.52 E
Farley, Mo (fär'lē)	119f	39.16 N	94.49 W
Farmers Branch, Tx. (fär'mērz branch)	119c	32.56 N	96.53 W
Farmersburg, In. (fär'mērz-bûrg)	110	39.15 N	87.25 W
Farmersville, Tx. (fär'mērz-vĭl)	123	33.11 N	96.22 W
Farmingdale, NJ (färm'ĕng-dāl)	112a	40.11 N	74.10 W
Farmingdale, NY	112a	40.44 N	73.26 W
Farmingham, Ma. (färm-ĭng-hăm)	105a	42.17 N	71.25 W
Farmington, Il. (färm-ĭng-tŭn)	123	40.42 N	90.01 W
Farmington, Me.	104	44.40 N	70.10 W
Farmington, Mi.	113b	42.28 N	83.23 W
Farmington, Mo.	123	37.46 N	90.26 W
Farmington, NM	121	36.40 N	108.10 W
Farmington, Ut.	119b	40.59 N	111.53 W
Farmington Hills, Mi.	57c	42.28 N	83.23 W
Farmville, NC (färm-vĭl)	127	35.35 N	77.35 W
Farmville, Va.	127	37.15 N	78.23 W
Farnborough, Eng. (färn'bŭr-ō)	156b	51.15 N	0.45 W
Farnborough (Neigh.), Eng.	62	51.21 N	0.04 E
Farne (I.), Eng. (färn)	162	55.40 N	1.32 W
Farnham, Can. (fär'năm)	111	45.15 N	72.55 W
Farningham, Eng. (fär'nĭng-ŭm)	156	51.22 N	0.14 E
Farnworth, Eng. (färn'wŭrth)	156	53.34 N	2.24 W
Faro, Braz. (fä'ro͞o)	143	2.05 S	56.32 W
Faro, Port.	170	37.01 N	7.57 W
Farodofay, Mad.	227	24.59 S	46.58 E
Fåron (I.), Swe.	165	57.57 N	19.10 E
Farquhar, C., Austl. (fär'kwár)	214	23.50 S	112.55 E
Farrell, Pa. (făr'ĕl)	110	41.10 N	80.30 W
Far Rockaway (Neigh.), NY	55	40.36 N	73.45 W
Farrukhābād, India (fŭ-ro͞ok-hä-bäd')	196	27.29 N	79.35 E
Fársala (Pharsalus), Grc.	173	39.18 N	22.25 E
Farsund, Nor. (fär'so͞on)	164	58.05 N	6.47 E
Fartura, Serra da (Mts.), Braz. (sĕ'r-rä-dá-fär-to͞o'rä)	144	26.40 S	53.15 W
Farvel, Kap (C.), Grnld.	94	60.00 N	44.00 W
Farwell, Tx. (fär'wĕl)	122	34.24 N	103.03 W
Fasano, It. (fä-zä'nō)	173	40.50 N	17.22 E
Fastov, Sov. Un. (fäs'tôf)	175	50.04 N	29.57 E
Fatëzh, Sov. Un.	175	52.06 N	35.51 E
Fatima, Port.	170	39.36 N	9.36 E
Fatsa, Tur. (fät'sä)	179	40.50 N	37.30 E
Faucilles, Monts. (Mts.), Fr. (môn' fō-sēl')	169	48.07 N	6.13 E
Fauske, Nor.	158	67.15 N	15.24 E
Faust, Can. (foust)	99	55.19 N	115.38 W
Faustovo, Sov. Un.	182b	55.27 N	38.29 E
Faversham, Eng. (fă'vēr-sh'm)	156b	51.19 N	0.54 E
Favoriten (Neigh.), Aus.	66e	48.11 N	16.23 E
Fawkham Green, Eng.	62	51.22 N	0.17 E
Fawkner, Austl.	70b	37.43 S	144.58 E
Fawsett Farms, Md.	56d	38.59 N	77.14 W
Faxaflói (B.), Ice.	158	64.33 N	22.40 W
Faya, Chad	194	17.55 N	19.07 E
Fayette, Al. (fā-yĕt')	126	33.40 N	87.54 W
Fayette, Ia.	115	42.49 N	91.49 W
Fayette, Mo.	123	39.09 N	92.41 W
Fayette, Ms.	126	31.43 N	91.00 W
Fayetteville, Ar. (fā-yĕt'vĭl)	123	36.03 N	94.08 W
Fayetteville, NC	127	35.02 N	78.54 W
Fayetteville, Tn.	126	35.10 N	86.33 W
Fazao, Forêt Classée du (For.), Togo	228	8.50 N	0.40 E
Fazilka, India	196	30.30 N	74.02 E
Fazzān (Fezzan) (Prov.), Libya	225	26.45 N	13.01 E
Fdérik, Mauritania	224	22.45 N	12.38 W
Fear, C., NC (fēr)	127	33.52 N	77.48 W
Feather (R.), Ca. (fĕth'ēr)	120	38.56 N	121.41 W
Feather, Middle Fk. of (R.), Ca.	120	39.49 N	121.10 W
Feather, North Fk. of (R.), Ca.	120	40.00 N	121.20 W
Featherstone, Eng. (fĕdh'ēr stŭn)	156	53.39 N	1.21 W
Fécamp, Fr. (fā-kän')	168	49.45 N	0.20 E
Federal, Distrito (Dist.), Ven. (dēs-trē'tô-fĕ-dĕ-rä'l)	143b	10.34 N	66.55 W
Federal Way, Wa.	118a	47.20 N	122.20 W
Fëdorovka, Sov. Un. (fyô'dô-rôf-kà)	182b	56.15 N	37.14 E
Fehmarn I., F.R.G. (fā'märn)	166	54.28 N	11.15 E
Fehrbellin, G.D.R. (fĕr'bĕl-lēn)	157b	52.49 N	12.46 E
Feia, Logoa (L.), Braz. (lô-gôä-fĕ'yä)	141a	21.54 S	41.45 W
Feicheng, China (fā-chŭŋ)	200	36.18 N	116.45 E
Feidong, China (fā-dôŋ)	200	31.53 N	117.28 E
Feira de Santana, Braz. (fĕ'ê-rä dä sänt-än'ä)	143	12.16 S	38.46 W
Feixian, China (fā-shyĕn)	200	35.17 N	117.59 E
Felanitx, Sp. (fā-lä-nēch')	171	39.29 N	3.09 E
Feldkirch, Aus. (fĕlt'kĭrk)	166	47.15 N	9.36 E
Feldkirchen, F.R.G. (fĕld'kēr-kĕn)	157d	48.09 N	11.44 E
Felipe Carrillo Puerto, Mex. (fĕ-lē'pĕ-kär-rē'l-yô-pwĕ'r-tô)	132a	19.36 N	88.04 W
Feltre, It. (fĕl'trā)	172	46.02 N	11.56 E
Femunden (L.), Nor.	164	62.17 N	11.40 E
Fengcheng, China (fŭŋ-chŭŋ)	202	40.28 N	124.03 E
Fengcheng, China	201b	30.55 N	121.38 E
Fengdu, China (fŭŋ-do͞o)	203	29.58 N	107.50 E
Fengjie, China (fŭŋ-jyĕ)	203	31.02 N	109.30 E
Fengming Dao (I.), China (fŭŋ-mĭŋ dou)	200	39.19 N	121.15 E
Fengrun, China (fŭŋ-ro͞on)	200	39.51 N	118.06 E
Fengtai, China (fŭŋ-tī)	202a	39.51 N	116.19 E
Fengxian, China (fŭŋ-shyĕn)	201b	30.55 N	121.26 E
Fengxian, China	200	34.41 N	116.36 E
Fengxiang, China (fŭŋ-shyäŋ)	202	34.25 N	107.20 E
Fengyang, China (fŭng'yäng')	200	32.55 N	117.32 E
Fengzhen, China (fŭŋ-jŭn)	202	40.28 N	113.20 E
Fenimore, Pass. Ak. (fĕn-ĭ-mōr)	107a	51.40 N	175.38 W
Fenoarivo Atsinanana, Mad.	227	17.30 S	49.31 E
Fenton, Mi. (fĕn-tŭn)	110	42.50 N	83.40 W
Fenton, Mo.	119e	38.31 N	90.27 W
Fenyang, China	202	37.20 N	111.48 E
Feodosiya (Kefe), Sov. Un. (fĕ-ô-dô'sē'yá) (kyĕ'fĕ)	175	45.02 N	35.21 E
Ferbitz, G.D.R.	65a	52.30 N	13.01 E
Ferdows, Iran	192	34.00 N	58.13 E
Ferencváros (Neigh.), Hung.	66g	47.28 N	19.06 E
Ferentino, It. (fā-rĕn-tē'nō)	172	41.42 N	13.18 E
Fergana, Sov. Un.	180	40.16 N	72.07 E
Fergus Falls, Mn. (fûr'gŭs)	114	46.17 N	96.03 W
Ferguson, Mo. (fûr-gŭ-sŭn)	119e	38.45 N	90.18 W
Ferkéssédougou, Ivory Coast	228	9.36 N	5.12 W
Fermo, It. (fĕr'mō)	172	43.10 N	13.43 E
Fermoselle, Sp. (fĕr-mō-säl'yå)	170	41.20 N	6.23 W
Fermoy, Ire. (fûr-moi')	162	52.05 N	8.06 W
Fernandina Beach, Fl. (fûr-năn-dē'ná)	127	30.38 N	81.29 W

ăt; finăl; rāte; senâte; ärm; àsk; sofá; fâre; ch-choose; dh-as th in other; bē; ēvent; bĕt; recĕnt; cratēr; g-gō; gh-guttural g; bĭt; ĭ-short neutral; rīde; ĸ-guttural k as ch in German ich;

PLACE (Pronounciation)	PAGE	Lat. °′	Long. °′
Fernando de Noronha (Prov.), Braz. (är-kĕ-pĕ′lä-gô-fĕr-nän-dō-dĕ-nô-rō′n-yä)	143	3.51 s	32.25 w
Fernando Póo (I.), see Bioko			
Fernãn-Núñez, Sp. (fĕr-nän′nōōn′yåth)	170	37.42 n	4.43 w
Fernão Veloso, Baia de (B.), Moz.	231	14.20 s	40.55 e
Ferndale, Ca. (fûrn′dāl)	116	40.34 n	124.18 w
Ferndale, Md.	56c	39.11 n	76.38 w
Ferndale, Mi.	57c	42.28 n	83.08 w
Ferndale, Mi.	113b	42.27 n	83.08 w
Ferndale, Wa.	118d	48.51 n	122.36 w
Fernie, Can. (fûr′nĭ)	99	49.30 n	115.03 w
Fern Prairie, Wa. (fûrn prâr′ĭ)	118c	45.38 n	122.25 w
Ferntree Gully, Austl.	211	37.53 s	145.18 e
Ferny Creek, Austl.	70b	37.53 s	145.21 e
Ferrara, It. (fĕr-rä′rä)	172	44.50 n	11.37 e
Ferrat, Cap (C.), Alg. (kăp fĕr-răt)	171	35.49 n	0.29 w
Ferraz de Vasconcelos, Braz.	61d	23.32 s	46.22 w
Ferreira do Alentejo, Port. (fĕr-rē′ê-rä dōō ä-lĕn-tā′zhōō)	170	38.03 n	8.06 w
Ferreira do Zezere, Port (fĕr-rĕ′ê-rä dōō zā-zā′rĕ)	170	39.49 n	8.17 w
Ferrelview, Mo. (fĕr′rĕl-vū)	119f	39.18 n	94.40 w
Ferreñafe, Peru (fĕr-rĕn-yä′fĕ)	142	6.38 s	79.48 w
Ferriday, La. (fĕr′ĭ-dā)	125	31.38 n	91.33 w
Ferrières, Fr.	64c	48.49 n	2.42 e
Ferry Village, NY	57a	43.58 n	78.57 w
Fershampenuaz, Sov. Un. (fĕr-shȧm′pĕn-wäz)	182a	53.32 n	59.50 e
Fertile, Mn. (fur′tĭl)	114	47.33 n	96.18 w
Fès, Mor. (fĕs)	224	34.08 n	5.00 w
Fessenden, ND (fĕs′ĕn-dĕn)	114	47.39 n	99.40 w
Festus, Mo. (fĕst′ŭs)	123	38.12 n	90.22 w
Fetcham, Eng.	62	51.17 n	0.22 w
Fethiye, Turk. (fĕt-hē′yĕ)	179	36.40 n	29.05 e
Feuilles, Rivière aux (R.), Can.	97	58.30 n	70.50 w
Fezzan (Prov.), see Fazzān			
Ffestiniog, Wales	162	52.59 n	3.58 w
Fianarantsoa, Mad. (fyȧ-nä′rȧn-tsō′ȧ)	227	21.21 s	47.15 e
Fichtenau, G.D.R.	65a	52.27 n	13.42 e
Ficksburg, S. Afr (fĭks′bûrg)	223d	28.53 s	27.53 e
Fidalgo I., Wa. (fĭ-dăl′gō)	118a	48.28 n	122.39 w
Fiddlers Hamlet, Eng.	62	51.41 n	0.08 e
Fieldbrook, Ca. (fēld′brŏŏk)	118	40.59 n	124.02 w
Fier, Alb. (fyĕr)	173	40.43 n	19.34 e
Fife Ness (C.), Scot. (fĭf′nes′)	162	56.15 n	2.19 w
Fifth Cataract, Sud.	225	18.27 n	33.38 e
Figeac, Fr. (fē-zhȧk′)	168	44.37 n	2.02 e
Figeholm, Swe. (fē-ghĕ-hōlm)	164	57.24 n	16.33 e
Figueira da Foz, Port. (fē-gwĕy-rä-dȧ-fô′z)	170	40.10 n	8.50 w
Figuig, Mor.	224	32.20 n	1.30 w
Fiji, Oceania (fē′jē)	208	18.40 s	175.00 e
Filadelfia, C.R. (fĭl-ȧ-dĕl′fĭ-ȧ)	132	10.26 n	85.37 w
Filatovskoye, Sov. Un. (fĭ-lä′tôf-skô-yĕ)	182a	56.49 n	62.20 e
Filbert, WV (fĭl′bĕrt)	127	37.18 n	81.29 w
Filchner Ice Shelf, Ant. (fĭlk′nĕr)	232	80.00 s	35.00 w
Fili (Neigh.), Sov. Un.	66b	55.45 n	37.31 e
Filiatrá, Grc.	173	37.10 n	21.35 e
Filicudi (I.), It. (fē′le-kōō′dē)	172	38.34 n	14.39 e
Filigas (R.), Tur.	161	41.10 n	32.53 e
Filippovskoye, Sov. Un. (fĭ-lĭ-pôf′skô-yĕ)	182b	56.06 n	38.38 e
Filipstad, Swe. (fĭl′ĭps-städh)	164	59.44 n	14.09 e
Fillmore, Ut. (fĭl′môr)	121	39.00 n	112.20 w
Filsa, Nor.	164	60.35 n	12.03 e
Fimi (R.), Zaire	230	2.43 s	17.50 e
Finaalspan, S. Afr.	71b	26.17 s	28.15 e
Finch, Can. (fĭnch)	95c	45.09 n	75.06 w
Finchley (Neigh.), Eng.	62	51.36 n	0.10 w
Findlay, Oh. (fĭnd′lā)	110	41.05 n	83.40 w
Fingoe, Moz.	231	15.12 s	31.50 e
Finisterre, Cabo de (C.), Sp. (kȧ′bô-dĕ-fĭn-ĭs-târ′)	170	42.52 n	9.48 w
Finke (R.), Austl. (fĭŋ′kē)	214	25.25 s	134.30 e
Finkenkrug, G.D.R.	65a	52.34 n	13.03 e
Finland, Eur. (fĭn′lănd)	154	62.45 n	26.13 e
Finland, G. of, Eur. (fĭn′lănd)	165	59.35 n	23.35 e
Finlandia, Col. (fēn-lä′n-dēä)	142a	4.38 n	75.39 w
Finlay (R.), Can. (fĭn′lā)	96	57.45 n	125.30 w
Finow, G.D.R. (fē′nōv)	157b	52.50 n	13.44 e
Finowfurt, G.D.R. (fē′nō-fōōrt)	157b	52.50 n	13.41 e
Finsterwalde, G.D.R. (fĭn′stĕr-väl-dĕ)	166	51.38 n	13.42 e
Firat (R.), Tur. (fē-rät′)	179	39.40 n	38.30 e
Fircrest, Wa. (fûr′krĕst)	118a	47.14 n	122.31 w
Firenze (Florence), It. (fē-rĕnt′sä)	172	43.47 n	11.15 e
Firenzuola, It. (fē-rĕnt-swô′lä)	172	44.08 n	11.21 e
Firgrove, Eng.	64b	53.37 n	2.08 w
Firozpur, India	196	30.58 n	74.39 e
Fischa (R.), Aus.	157e	48.04 n	16.33 e
Fischamend Markt, Aus.	157e	48.07 n	16.37 e
Fischeln (Neigh.), F.R.G.	63	51.18 n	6.35 e
Fish (R.), Namibia (fĭsh)	226	27.30 s	17.45 e
Fish Cay (I.), Ba.	135	22.30 n	74.20 w
Fish Cr., Can. (fĭsh)	95e	50.52 n	114.21 w
Fisher, La. (fĭsh′ĕr)	125	31.28 n	93.30 w
Fisher B., Can.	101	51.30 n	97.16 w
Fisher Chan, Can.	98	52.10 n	127.42 w
Fisherman's Wharf (P. Int.), Ca.	58b	37.48 n	122.25 w
Fisher Str., Can.	97	62.43 n	84.28 w
Fisherville, Can.	54c	43.47 n	79.28 w
Fishing L., Can. (fĭsh′ĭng)	101	52.07 n	95.25 w
Fishpool, Eng.	64b	53.35 n	2.17 w
Fitchburg, Ma. (fĭch′bûrg)	105a	42.35 n	71.48 w
Fitri, Lac (L.), Chad	229	12.50 n	17.28 e
Fitzgerald, Ga. (fĭts-jĕr′ăld)	126	31.42 n	83.17 w
Fitz Hugh Sd., Can. (fĭts hū)	98	51.40 n	127.57 w
Fitzroy, Austl.	70b	37.48 s	144.59 e
Fitzroy (R.), Austl. (fĭts-roi′)	214	18.00 s	124.05 e
Fitzroy (R.), Austl.	215	23.45 s	150.02 e
Fitzroy Crossing, Austl.	214	18.08 s	126.00 e
Fitzwilliam (I.), Can. (fĭts-wĭl′yŭm)	110	45.30 n	81.45 w
Fiume, see Rijeka			
Fiumicino, It. (fyōō-mē-chē′nô)	171d	41.47 n	12.19 e
Five Dock, Austl.	70a	33.52 s	151.08 e
Fjällbacka, Swe. (fyĕl′bäk-ȧ)	164	58.37 n	11.17 e
Flagstaff, Az. (flăg-stȧf)	121	35.15 n	111.40 w
Flagstaff, S. Afr. (flăg′stäf)	227c	31.06 s	29.31 e
Flagstaff (L.), Me. (flăg-stȧf)	111	45.05 n	70.30 w
Flalow, G.D.R. (flä′lōv)	157b	52.44 n	12.58 e
Flåm, Nor. (flôm)	164	60.15 n	7.01 e
Flambeau (R.), Wi. (flăm-bō′)	115	45.32 n	91.05 w
Flaming Gorge Res., Wy.	117	41.13 n	109.30 w
Flamingo, Fl. (flȧ-mĭŋ′gô)	127	25.10 n	80.55 w
Flamingo Cay (I.), Ba. (flȧ-mĭŋ′gô)	135	22.50 n	75.50 w
Flamingo Pt, Vir. Is. (U.S.A.)	129c	18.19 n	65.00 w
Flanders (Reg.), Fr. (flăn′dĕrz)	163	50.53 n	2.29 e
Flandreau, SD (flăn′drō)	114	44.02 n	96.35 w
Flatbush (Neigh.), NY	55	40.39 n	73.56 w
Flathead (R.), Can.	99	49.30 n	114.30 w
Flathead L., Mt. (flăt′hĕd)	117	47.57 n	114.20 w
Flathead R., Mt.	117	48.45 n	114.20 w
Flathead R., Middle Fork, Mt.	117	48.30 n	113.47 w
Flathead R., South Fork, Mt.	117	48.05 n	113.45 w
Flat Rock, Mi. (flăt rŏk)	113b	42.06 n	83.17 w
Flattery C., Wa. (flăt′ĕr-ĭ)	116	48.22 n	125.45 w
Flat Willow Cr., Mt. (flat wĭl′ô)	117	46.45 n	108.47 w
Flaunden, Eng.	62	51.42 n	0.32 w
Flehe (Neigh.), F.R.G.	63	51.12 n	6.47 e
Flekkefjord, Nor. (flăk′kē-fyôr)	164	58.19 n	6.38 e
Flemingsburg, Ky. (flĕm′ĭngz-bûrg)	110	38.25 n	83.45 w
Flensburg, F.R.G. (flĕns′bŏŏrgh)	166	54.48 n	9.27 e
Flers, Fr. (flĕr)	168	48.43 n	0.37 w
Fletcher, NC	127	35.26 n	82.30 w
Fley (Neigh.), F.R.G.	63	51.23 n	7.30 e
Flinders (I.), Austl.	216	39.35 s	148.10 e
Flinders (R.), Austl.	215	18.48 s	141.07 e
Flinders (Reg.), Austl. (flĭn′dĕrz)	214	32.15 s	138.45 e
Flinders Rfs., Austl.	215	17.30 s	149.02 e
Flin Flon, Can. (flĭn flŏn)	110	54.46 n	101.53 w
Flingern (Neigh.), F.R.G.	63	51.14 n	6.49 e
Flint, Mi.	110	43.00 n	83.45 w
Flint (R.), Ga. (flĭnt)	126	31.25 n	84.15 w
Flint, Wales	156	53.15 n	3.07 w
Flora, Il. (flō′rȧ)	110	38.40 n	88.25 w
Flora, In.	110	40.25 n	86.30 w
Florala, Al. (flŏr-ăl′ȧ)	126	31.01 n	86.19 w
Floral Park, NY (flôr′ăl pärk)	112a	40.42 n	73.42 w
Florence, Al. (flŏr′ĕns)	126	34.46 n	87.40 w
Florence, Az.	121	33.00 n	111.25 w
Florence, Ca.	59	33.58 n	118.15 w
Florence, Co.	122	38.23 n	105.08 w
Florence, Ks.	123	38.14 n	96.56 w
Florence, SC	127	34.10 n	79.45 w
Florence, Wa.	118a	48.13 n	122.21 w
Florence, see Firenze			
Florencia, Col. (flō-rĕn′sē-ȧ)	142	1.31 n	75.13 w
Florencio Sanchez, Ur. (flō-rĕn-sēō-sä′n-chĕz)	141c	33.52 s	57.24 w
Florencio Varela, Arg. (flō-rĕn′sē-o vä-rā′lä)	144a	34.34 s	58.16 w
Florentia, S. Afr.	71b	26.16 s	28.08 e
Flores, Braz. (flō′rĕzh)	143	7.57 s	37.48 w
Flores (Dept.), Ur.	141c	33.33 s	57.00 w
Flores, Guat.	132a	16.53 n	89.54 w
Flores (I.), Indon.	206	8.14 s	121.08 e
Flores (Neigh.), Arg.	60d	34.38 s	58.28 w
Flores (R.), Arg.	141c	36.13 s	60.28 w
Flores Laut (Flores Sea), Indon.	206	7.09 n	120.30 e
Floresta (Neigh.), Arg.	60d	34.38 s	58.29 w
Floresville, Tx. (flō′rĕs-vĭl)	124	29.10 n	98.08 w
Floriano, Braz. (flō-rȧ-ä′nōō)	143	6.17 s	42.58 w
Florianópolis, Braz. (flō-rē-ä-nō′pō-lēs)	144	27.30 s	48.30 w
Florida, Col. (flō-rē′dä)	142a	3.20 n	76.12 w
Florida, Cuba	134	22.10 n	79.50 w
Florida, NY (flŏr′ĭ-dȧ)	112a	41.20 n	74.21 w
Florida, S. Afr.	227b	26.11 s	27.56 e
Florida, Ur. (flō-rē-dhä)	141c	34.06 s	56.14 w
Florida, (State), U.S. (flŏr′ĭ-dȧ)	109	30.30 n	84.40 w
Florida (Dept.), Ur. (flō-rē′dhä)	141c	33.48 s	56.15 w
Florida (I.), Sol. Is.	215	8.56 s	159.45 e
Florida B., Fl. (flŏr′ĭ-dȧ)	127a	24.55 n	80.55 w
Florida Keys (Is.), Fl.	127a	24.33 n	81.20 w
Florida Mts., NM	121	32.10 n	107.35 w
Florida, Strs. of, N.A.	134	24.10 n	81.00 w
Florido, R., Mex. (flō-rē′dō)	124	27.21 n	104.48 w
Floridsdorf, Aus. (flō′rĭds-dôrf)	157e	48.16 n	16.25 e
Florina, Grc. (flō-rē′nä)	173	40.48 n	21.24 e
Florissant, Mo. (flŏr′ĭ-sȧnt)	119e	38.47 n	90.20 w
Florø, Nor. (flō′ü)	164	61.36 n	5.01 e
Flotantes, Jardines (P. Int.), Mex.	60a	19.16 n	99.06 w
Flourtown, Pa.	56b	40.07 n	75.13 w
Flower Hill, NY	55	40.49 n	73.41 w
Floyd (R.), Ia. (floid)	114	42.38 n	96.15 w
Floydada, Tx. (floi-dā′dȧ)	122	33.59 n	101.19 w
Floyds Fk. (R.), Ky. (floi-dz)	113h	38.08 n	85.30 w
Flumendosa, R., It. (flōō-mĕn-dō′sä)	172	39.45 n	9.18 e
Flushing, Mi. (flûsh′ĭng)	110	43.05 n	83.50 w
Flushing (Neigh.), NY	55	40.45 n	73.49 w
Fly (R.), Pap. N. Gui. (flī)	207	8.00 s	141.45 e
Foča, Yugo. (fō′chä)	173	43.29 n	18.48 e
Fochville, S. Afr. (fŏk′vĭl)	223d	26.29 s	27.29 e
Focsani, Rom. (fŏk-shä′nē)	167	45.41 n	27.17 e
Fogang, China (fwo-găŋ)	203	23.50 n	113.35 e
Foggia, It. (fôd′jä)	172	41.30 n	15.34 e
Fogo, Can. (fō′gō)	103	49.43 n	54.17 w
Fogo I, Can.	103	49.40 n	54.13 w
Fogo I, C.V.	224b	14.46 n	24.51 w
Fohnsdorf, Aus. (fōns′dôrf)	166	47.13 n	14.40 e
Föhr I., F.R.G. (fûr)	166	54.47 n	8.30 e
Foix, Fr. (fwä)	168	42.58 n	1.34 e
Fokku, Nig.	229	11.40 n	4.31 e
Folcroft, Pa.	56b	39.54 n	75.17 w
Folgares, Ang.	230	14.54 s	15.08 e
Foligno, It. (fō-lēn′yō)	172	42.58 n	12.41 e
Folkeston, Eng.	163	51.05 n	1.18 e
Folkingham, Eng. (fō′kĭng-ăm)	156	52.53 n	0.24 w
Folkston, Ga.	127	30.50 n	82.01 w
Folsom, NM (fōl′sŭm)	122	36.47 n	103.56 w
Folsom, Pa.	56b	39.54 n	75.19 w
Folsom City, Ca.	120	38.40 n	121.10 w
Fomento, Cuba (fō-mĕ′n-tō)	134	21.35 n	78.20 w
Fómeque, Col. (fō′mĕ-kĕ)	142a	4.29 n	73.52 w
Fonda, Ia. (fŏn′dȧ)	115	42.33 n	94.51 w
Fond du Lac, Wi. (fŏn dū lăk′)	115	43.47 n	88.29 w
Fond du Lac Ind. Res., Mn.	115	46.44 n	93.04 w
Fondi, It. (fōn′dē)	172	41.23 n	13.25 e
Fonsagrada, Sp. (fōn-sä-grä′dhä)	170	43.08 n	7.07 w
Fonseca, Golfo de (G.), Hond. (gōl-fō-dĕ-fōn-sä′kä)	132	13.09 n	87.55 w
Fontainebleau, Fr. (fōn-tĕn-blō′)	169b	48.24 n	2.42 e
Fontainebleau, S. Afr.	71b	26.07 s	27.59 e
Fontana, Ca. (fŏn-tă′nȧ)	119a	34.06 n	117.27 w
Fonte Boa, Braz. (fōn′tå bō′ȧ)	142	2.32 s	66.05 w
Fontenay-aux-Roses, Fr.	64c	48.47 n	2.17 e
Fontenay-le-Comte, Fr. (fôɴt-nĕ′lĕ-kôɴt′)	168	46.28 n	0.53 w
Fontenay-le-Fleury, Fr.	64c	48.49 n	2.30 e
Fontenay-sous-Bois, Fr.	64c	48.51 n	2.29 e
Fontenay-Trésigny, Fr. (fôɴ-te-hā′ tra-sēn-yē′)	169b	48.43 n	2.53 e
Fontenelle Res., Wy.	117	42.05 n	110.05 w
Fontera, Punta (Pt.), Mex. (pōō′n-tä-fōn-tĕ′rä)	131	18.36 n	92.43 w
Fontibón, Col. (fōn-tē-bōn′)	142a	4.42 n	74.09 w
Fontur (Pt.), Ice.	158	66.21 n	14.02 w
Foothills, S. Afr. (fōōt-hĭls)	227b	25.55 s	27.36 e
Footscray, Austl.	70b	37.48 s	144.54 e
Foraker, Mt., Ak. (fôr′ȧ-kĕr)	107	62.40 n	152.40 w
Fora, Ponta de (C.), Braz.	61c	22.57 s	43.07 w
Forbach, Fr. (fôr′bäĸ)	169	49.12 n	6.54 e
Forbes, Austl. (fôrbz)	216	33.24 s	148.05 e
Forbes, Mt., Can.	99	51.52 n	116.56 w
Forbidden City (P. Int.), China	67b	39.55 n	116.23 e
Forchheim, F.R.G. (fôrĸ′hīm)	166	49.43 n	11.05 e
Fordham University (P. Int.), NY	55	40.51 n	73.53 w
Fordlândia, see Brasília Legal			
Fords, NJ	55	40.32 n	74.19 w
Fordsburg (Neigh.), S. Afr.	71b	26.13 s	28.02 e
Fordyce, Ar. (fôr′dīs)	123	33.48 n	92.24 w
Forecariah, Gui. (fōr-kȧ-rē′ä′)	228	9.26 n	13.06 w
Forel, Mt., Grnld.	94	65.50 n	37.41 w
Forest, Ms. (fŏr′ĕst)	126	32.22 n	89.29 w
Forest (R.), ND	114	48.08 n	97.45 w
Forest City, Ia.	115	43.14 n	93.40 w
Forest City, NC	127	35.20 n	81.52 w
Forest City, Pa.	111	41.35 n	75.30 w
Forest Gate (Neigh.), Eng.	62	51.33 n	0.02 e
Forest Grove, Or. (grōv)	118c	45.31 n	123.07 w
Forest Heights, Md.	56d	38.49 n	77.00 w
Forest Hill, Austl.	70b	37.50 s	145.11 e
Forest Hill, Md.	112e	39.35 n	76.26 w
Forest Hill, Tx.	119c	32.40 n	97.16 w
Forest Hill (Neigh.), Can.	54c	43.42 n	79.24 w
Forest Hills, Pa.	57b	40.26 n	79.52 w
Forest Hills (Neigh.), NY	55	40.42 n	73.51 w
Forest Park, Il.	58a	41.53 n	87.50 w
Forest Park (Neigh.), Md.	56c	39.19 n	76.41 w
Forestville, Austl.	70a	33.46 s	151.13 e
Forestville, Can. (fŏr′ĕst-vĭl)	104	48.45 n	69.06 w
Forestville, Md.	112e	38.51 n	76.55 w
Forez, Mts. du, Fr. (môɴ dü fô-rā′)	168	44.55 n	3.43 e
Forfar, Scot. (fôr′fȧr)	162	57.10 n	2.55 w
Forillon, Parc Natl. (Natl. Pk.), Can.	104	48.50 n	64.05 w
Forio (Mtn.), It. (fô′ryō)	171c	40.29 n	13.55 e
Forked Cr., Il. (fôrk′d)	113a	41.16 n	88.01 w
Forked Deer (R.), Tn.	122	35.53 n	89.29 w
Forli, It. (fōr-lē′)	172	44.13 n	12.03 e
Formby, Eng. (fôrm′bē)	156	53.34 n	3.04 w
Formby Pt., Eng.	156	53.33 n	3.06 w
Formentera, Isla de (I.), Sp. (ē′s-lä-dĕ-fōr-mĕn-tā′rä)	171	38.43 n	1.25 e
Formiga, Braz. (fōr-mē′gȧ)	141a	20.27 s	45.25 w
Formigas Bk., N.A. (fōr-mē′gäs)	135	18.30 n	75.40 w
Formosa, Arg. (fōr-mō′sä)	144	27.25 s	58.12 w
Formosa, Braz.	143	15.32 s	47.10 w
Formosa (I.), see Taiwan			
Formosa (Prov.), Arg.	144	24.30 s	60.45 w
Formosa B, Ken.	231	2.45 s	40.30 e
Formosa, Serra (Mts.), Braz. (sĕ′r-rä)	143	12.59 s	55.11 w
Formosa Str., see Taiwan Str.			
Fornosovo, Sov. Un. (fôr-nô′sô vô)	182c	59.35 n	30.34 e
Forrest City, Ar. (for′ĕst sĭ′tĭ)	123	35.00 n	90.46 w
Forsayth, Austl. (fôr-sīth′)	215	18.33 s	143.42 e
Forshaga, Swe. (fôrs′hä′gä)	164	59.34 n	13.25 e
Forst, G.D.R. (fôrst)	166	51.45 n	14.38 e
Forsyth, Ga. (fôr-sīth′)	126	33.02 n	83.56 w
Forsyth, Mt.	117	46.15 n	106.41 w
Fort (Neigh.), India	67e	18.56 n	72.50 e
Fort Albany, Can. (fôrt ôl′bȧ nĭ)	97	52.20 n	81.30 w
Fort Alexander Ind. Res., Can.	101	50.27 n	96.15 w
Fortaleza (Ceará), Braz. (fôr′tä-lā′zȧ) (sä-ä-rä′)	143	3.35 s	38.31 w
Fort Apache Ind. Res., Az. (ȧ-păch′ē)	121	34.02 n	110.27 w
Fort Atkinson, Wi. (ăt′kĭn-sŭn)	115	42.55 n	88.46 w
Fort Beaufort, S. Afr. (bō′fôrt)	227c	32.47 s	26.39 e
Fort Bellefontaine, Mo. (bĕl-fōn-tān′)	119e	38.50 n	90.15 w
Fort Benton, Mt. (bĕn′tŭn)	117	47.51 n	110.40 w

PLACE (Pronounciation)	PAGE	Lat. °′	Long. °′
Fort Berthold Ind. Res., ND (bĕrth'ôld)	114	47.47 N	103.28 W
Fort Branch, In. (brănch)	110	38.15 N	87.35 W
Fort Chipewyan, Can.	96	58.46 N	111.15 W
Fort Cobb Res., Ok.	122	35.12 N	98.28 W
Fort Collins, Co. (kŏl'ĭns)	122	40.36 N	105.04 W
Fort Crampel, Cen. Afr. Rep. (krȧm-pĕl')	229	6.59 N	19.11 E
Fort-de-France, Mart. (dē fräNs)	133b	14.37 N	61.06 W
Fort Deposit, Al. (dē-pŏz'ĭt)	126	31.58 N	86.35 W
Fort-de-Possel, Cen. Afr. Rep. (dē pô-sĕl')	225	5.03 N	19.11 E
Fort Dodge, Ia. (dŏj)	115	42.31 N	94.10 W
Fort Edward, NY (wẽrd)	111	43.15 N	73.30 W
Fort Erie, Can. (ē'rĭ)	113c	42.55 N	78.56 W
Fortescue (R.), Austl. (fôr'tĕs-kū)	214	21.25 S	116.50 E
Fort Fairfield, Me. (fâr'fēld)	104	46.46 N	67.53 W
Fort Fitzgerald, Can. (fĭts-jĕr'ăld)	96	59.48 N	111.50 W
Fort Frances, Can. (frăn'sĕs)	101	48.36 N	93.24 W
Fort Frederica Natl. Mon., Ga. (frĕd'ĕ-rĭ-kȧ)	127	31.13 N	85.25 W
Fort Gaines, Ga. (gānz)	126	31.35 N	85.03 W
Fort George, Can. (jôrj)	97	53.40 N	78.58 W
Fort Gibson, Ok. (gĭb'sŭn)	123	35.50 N	95.13 W
Fort Good Hope, Can. (go͝od hōp)	96	66.19 N	128.52 W
Fort Hall, Ken. (hôl)	225	0.47 S	37.13 E
Fort Hall Ind. Res., Id.	117	43.02 N	112.21 W
Forth, Firth of, Scot. (fûrth ôv fôrth)	162	56.04 N	3.03 W
Fort Howard, Md.	56c	39.12 N	76.27 W
Fort Huachuca, Az. (wä-cho͞o'kä)	121	31.30 N	110.25 W
Fortier, Can. (fôr'tyā')	95f	49.56 N	97.55 W
Fort Jameson, Zambia (jām'sŭn)	226	13.35 S	32.43 E
Fort Jefferson Natl. Mon., Fl. (jĕf'ẽr-sŭn)	127a	24.42 N	83.02 W
Fort Johnston, Malawi	226	14.16 S	35.14 E
Fort Kent, Me. (kĕnt)	104	47.14 N	68.37 W
Fort Langley, Can. (lăng'lĭ)	118d	49.10 N	122.35 W
Fort Lauderdale, Fl. (lô'dẽr-dāl)	127a	26.07 N	80.09 W
Fort Lee, NJ	112a	40.50 N	73.58 W
Fort Liard, Can.	96	60.16 N	123.34 W
Fort Liberté, Hai. (lē-bĕr-tā')	135	19.40 N	71.50 W
Fort Louden (R.), Tn. (fôrt lou'dĕn)	126	35.52 N	84.10 W
Fort Lupton, Co. (lŭp'tŭn)	122	40.04 N	104.54 W
Fort Matanzas, Fl. (mä-tän'zäs)	127	29.39 N	81.17 W
Fort McDermitt Ind. Res., Or. (măk dẽr'mĭt)	116	42.04 N	118.07 W
Fort McHenry National Monument (P. Int.), Md.	56c	39.16 N	76.35 W
Fort Macleod, Can. (mȧ-Kloud')	99	49.43 N	113.25 W
Fort McMurray, Can. (măk-mŭr'ĭ)	100	56.44 N	111.23 W
Fort McNair (P. Int.), DC	56d	38.52 N	77.04 W
Fort McPherson, Can. (măk-fŭr's'n)	96	67.37 N	134.59 W
Fort Madison, Ia. (măd'ĭ-sŭn)	115	40.40 N	91.17 W
Fort Meade, Fl. (mēd)	127a	27.45 N	81.48 W
Fort Mill, SC (mĭl)	127	35.03 N	80.57 W
Fort Mohave Ind. Res., Ca. (mō-hä'vā)	120	34.59 N	115.02 W
Fort Morgan, Co. (môr'găn)	122	40.14 N	103.49 W
Fort Myers, Fl. (mī'ẽrz)	127a	26.36 N	81.45 W
Fort Nelson, Can. (nĕl'sŭn)	96	58.57 N	122.30 W
Fort Nelson (R.), Can. (nĕl'sŭn)	96	58.44 N	122.20 W
Fort Payne, Al. (pān)	126	34.26 N	85.41 W
Fort Peck, Mt. (pĕk)	117	47.58 N	106.30 W
Fort Peck Ind. Res., Mt.	114	48.22 N	105.40 W
Fort Peck Res., Mt.	117	47.52 N	106.59 W
Fort Pierce, Fl. (pērs)	127a	27.25 N	80.20 W
Fort Portal, Ug. (pôr'tȧl)	231	0.40 N	30.16 E
Fort Providence, Can. (prŏv'ĭ-dĕns)	96	61.27 N	117.59 W
Fort Pulaski Natl. Mon., Ga. (pu-lăs'kĭ)	127	31.59 N	80.56 W
Fort Qu'Appelle, Can.	100	50.46 N	103.55 W
Fort Randall Dam, U.S.	114	42.48 N	98.35 W
Fort Resolution, Can. (rĕz'ô-lū'shŭn)	96	61.08 N	113.42 W
Fort Riley, Ks. (rī'lĭ)	123	39.05 N	96.46 W
Fort Saint James, Can. (fôrt sānt jāmz)	98	54.26 N	124.15 W
Fort Saint John, Can. (sānt jŏn)	99	56.15 N	120.51 W
Fort Sandeman, Pak. (săn'da-măn)	196	31.28 N	69.29 E
Fort Saskatchewan, Can. (săs-kăt'cho͞o-ăn)	95g	53.43 N	113.13 W
Fort Scott, Ks. (skŏt)	123	37.50 N	94.43 W
Fort Severn, Can. (sĕv'ẽrn)	97	56.58 N	87.50 W
Fort Shevchenko, Sov. Un. (shĕv-chĕn'kô)	179	44.30 N	50.18 E
Fort Sibut, Cen. Afr. Rep. (fôr sē-bü')	229	5.44 N	19.05 E
Fort Sill, Ok. (fôrt sĭl)	122	34.41 N	98.25 W
Fort Simpson, Can. (sĭmp'sŭn)	96	61.52 N	121.48 W
Fort Smith, Ar. (smĭth)	123	35.23 N	94.24 W
Fort Smith, Can.	96	60.09 N	112.08 W
Fort Stockton, Tx. (stŏk'tŭn)	124	30.54 N	102.51 W
Fort Sumner, NM (sŭm'nẽr)	122	34.30 N	104.17 W
Fort Sumter Natl. Mon., SC (sŭm'tẽr)	127	32.43 N	79.54 W
Fort Thomas, Ky. (tŏm'ăs)	113f	39.05 N	84.27 W
Fortuna, Ca. (fôr-tū'nȧ)	116	40.36 N	124.10 W
Fortune, Can. (fôr'tŭn)	105	47.04 N	55.51 W
Fortune (I.), Ba.	135	22.35 N	74.20 W
Fortune B, Can.	105	47.25 N	55.25 W
Fort Union Natl. Mon., NM (ūn'yŭn)	122	35.51 N	104.57 W
Fort Valley, Ga. (văl'ĭ)	126	32.33 N	83.53 W
Fort Vermilion, Can. (vẽr-mĭl'yŭn)	96	58.23 N	115.50 W
Fort Victoria, see Mzsvingo.			
Fortville, In. (fôrt-vĭl)	110	40.00 N	85.50 W
Fort Wayne, In. (wān)	110	41.00 N	85.10 W
Fort Wayne Military Museum (P. Int.), Mi.	57c	42.18 N	83.06 W
Fort William (P. Int.), India	67a	22.33 N	88.20 E
Fort William, Scot. (wĭl'yŭm)	162	56.50 N	3.00 W
Fort William, Mt., Austl. (wĭ'ĭ-ăm)	216	24.45 S	151.15 E
Fort Worth, Tx. (wûrth)	119c	32.45 N	97.20 W
Fort Yukon, Ak. (yo͞o'kŏn)	107	66.30 N	145.00 W
Fort Yuma Ind. Res., Ca. (yo͞o'mä)	120	32.54 N	114.47 W

PLACE (Pronounciation)	PAGE	Lat. °′	Long. °′
Foshan, China	201a	23.02 N	113.07 E
Fossano, It. (fôs-sä'nō)	172	44.34 N	7.42 E
Fossil Cr., Tx. (fŏs-ĭl)	119c	32.53 N	97.19 W
Fossombrone, It. (fôs-sôm-brō'nā)	172	43.41 N	12.48 E
Foss Res, Ok.	122	35.38 N	99.11 W
Fosston, Mn. (fôs'tŭn)	114	47.34 N	95.44 W
Fosterburg, Il. (fôs'tẽr-bûrg)	119e	38.58 N	90.04 W
Foster City, Ca.	58b	37.34 N	122.16 W
Fostoria, Oh. (fŏs-tō'rĭ-ȧ)	110	41.10 N	83.20 W
Fougéres, Fr. (fo͞o-zhâr')	168	48.23 N	1.14 W
Foula (I.), Scot. (fou'lȧ)	162a	60.08 N	2.04 W
Foulwind, C., N.Z. (foul'wĭnd)	217	41.45 S	171.00 E
Foumban, Cam. (fo͞om-bän')	229	5.43 N	10.55 E
Fountain Cr., Co. (foun'tĭn)	122	38.36 N	104.37 W
Fountain Valley, Ca.	119a	33.42 N	117.57 W
Fourche le Fave (R.), Ar. (fo͞orsh lä fäv')	123	34.46 N	93.45 W
Fouriesburg, S. Afr. (fo͞o'rēz-bûrg)	223d	28.38 S	28.13 E
Fourmies, Fr. (fo͞or-mē')	168	50.01 N	4.01 E
Four Mts., Is. of the, Ak. (fōr)	107a	52.58 N	170.40 W
Fourqueux, Fr.	64c	48.53 N	2.04 E
Fourth Cataract, Sud.	225	18.52 N	32.07 E
Fouta Djallon (Mts.), Gui. (fo͞o'tä jä-lôN)	224	11.37 N	12.29 W
Foveaux Str., N.Z. (fô-vō')	217	46.30 S	167.43 E
Fowler, Co. (foul'ẽr)	122	38.04 N	104.02 W
Fowler, In.	110	40.35 N	87.20 W
Fowler, Pt., Austl.	214	32.05 S	132.30 E
Fowlerton, Tx. (foul'ẽr-tŭn)	124	28.26 N	98.48 W
Fox (I.), Wa. (fŏks)	118a	47.15 N	122.08 W
Fox (R.), Il.	115	41.35 N	88.43 W
Fox, (R.), Wi.	115	44.18 N	88.23 W
Foxboro, Ma. (fŏks'bŭrô)	105a	42.04 N	71.15 W
Fox Chapel, Pa.	57b	40.30 N	79.55 W
Foxe Basin, Can. (fŏks)	96	67.35 N	79.21 W
Foxe Chan, Can.	97	64.30 N	79.23 W
Foxe Pen, Can.	97	64.57 N	77.26 W
Fox Is., Ak. (fŏks)	107a	53.04 N	167.30 W
Fox L., Il.	113a	42.24 N	88.07 W
Fox Lake, Il. (lăk)	113a	42.24 N	88.11 W
Fox Point, Wi.	113a	43.10 N	87.54 W
Fox Valley, Austl.	70a	33.45 S	151.06 E
Foyle, Lough (B.), Ire. (lŏk foil')	162	55.07 N	7.08 W
Foz do Cunene, Ang.	230	17.16 S	11.50 E
Fraga, Sp. (frä'gä)	171	41.31 N	0.20 E
Fragoso, Cayo (I.), Cuba (kä'yō-frä-gō'sō)	134	22.45 N	79.30 W
Franca, Braz. (frä'n-kä)	143	20.28 S	47.20 W
Francavilla, It. (fräŋ-kä-vēl'lä)	173	40.32 N	17.37 E
France, Eur. (frȧns)	154	46.39 N	0.47 E
Frances (L.), Can. (frăn'sĭs)	96	61.27 N	128.28 W
Frances, Cabo (C.), Cuba (kä'bô-frän-sĕ's)	134	21.55 N	84.05 W
Frances, Punta (Pt.), Cuba (po͞o'n-tä-frän-sĕ's)	134	21.45 N	83.10 W
Frances Viejo, Cabo (C.), Dom. Rep. (kä'bô-frän'sås vyā'hô)	135	19.40 N	69.35 W
Franceville, Gabon (fräNs-vēl')	230	1.38 S	13.35 E
Francis Case, L., SD (frăn'sĭs)	114	43.15 N	99.00 W
Francisco Sales, Braz. (frän-sē's-kô-sá'lĕs)	141a	21.42 S	44.26 W
Francistown, Bots. (frăn'sis-toun)	226	21.17 S	27.28 E
Franconville, Fr.	64c	48.59 N	2.14 E
Frank, Pa.	57b	40.16 N	79.48 W
Frankby, Eng.	64a	53.22 N	3.08 W
Frankford (Neigh.), Pa.	56b	40.01 N	75.05 W
Frankfort, Il. (frăŋk'fẽrt)	113a	41.30 N	87.51 W
Frankfort, In.	110	40.15 N	86.30 W
Frankfort, Ks.	123	39.42 N	96.27 W
Frankfort, Ky.	110	38.10 N	84.55 W
Frankfort, Mi.	110	44.40 N	86.15 W
Frankfort, NY	111	43.05 N	75.05 W
Frankfort, S. Afr. (frănk'fŏrt)	227c	32.43 S	27.28 E
Frankfort, S. Afr	223d	27.17 S	28.30 E
Frankfurt (Dist.), G.D.R. (fraŋk'fo͞ort)	157b	52.42 N	13.37 E
Frankfurt am Main, F.R.G.	166	50.07 N	8.40 E
Frankfurt an der Oder, G.D.R.	166	52.20 N	14.31 E
Franklin, In. (frănk'lĭn)	110	39.25 N	86.00 W
Franklin, Ky.	126	36.42 N	86.34 W
Franklin, La.	125	29.47 N	91.31 W
Franklin, Ma.	105a	42.05 N	71.24 W
Franklin, Mi.	57c	42.31 N	83.18 W
Franklin, Ne.	122	40.06 N	99.01 W
Franklin, NH	111	43.25 N	71.40 W
Franklin, NJ	112a	41.08 N	74.35 W
Franklin, Oh.	110	39.30 N	84.20 W
Franklin, Pa.	111	41.25 N	79.50 W
Franklin, S. Afr.	227c	30.19 S	29.28 E
Franklin, Tn.	126	35.54 N	86.54 W
Franklin, Va.	127	36.41 N	76.57 W
Franklin (L.), Nv.	120	40.23 N	115.10 W
Franklin, Dist. of, Can.	96	70.46 N	105.22 W
Franklin D. Roosevelt L., Wa.	116	48.12 N	118.43 W
Franklin Mts., Can.	96	65.36 N	125.55 W
Franklin Park, Il.	113a	41.56 N	87.53 W
Franklin Park, Pa.	57b	40.35 N	80.06 W
Franklin Park, Va.	56d	38.55 N	77.09 W
Franklin Roosevelt Park (Neigh.), S. Afr.	71b	26.09 S	27.59 E
Franklin Square, NY	112a	40.43 N	73.40 W
Franklinton, La. (frăŋk'lĭn-tŭn)	125	30.49 N	90.09 W
Frankston, Austl.	211a	38.09 S	145.08 E
Franksville, Wi. (frănkz'vĭl)	113a	42.46 N	87.55 W
Fransta, Swe.	164	62.30 N	16.04 E
Franz Josef Land (Is.), see Zemlya Frantsa Iosifa			
Frascati, It. (fräs-kä'tē)	171d	41.49 N	12.45 E
Fraser (Great Sandy) (I.), Austl. (frā'zẽr)	216	25.12 S	153.00 E
Fraser, Mi. (frā'zẽr)	113b	42.32 N	82.57 W
Fraser (R.), Can.	98	52.20 N	122.35 W
Fraserburgh, Scot. (frā'zẽr-bûrg)	162	57.40 N	2.01 W

PLACE (Pronounciation)	PAGE	Lat. °′	Long. °′
Fraser Plateau, Can.	98	51.30 N	122.00 W
Frattamaggiore, It. (frät-tä-mäg-zhyō'rē)	171c	40.41 N	14.16 E
Fray Bentos, Ur. (frī bĕn'tōs)	141c	33.10 S	58.19 W
Frazee, Mn. (frā-zē')	114	46.42 N	95.43 W
Fraziers Hog Cay (I.), Ba.	134	25.25 N	77.55 W
Frechen, F.R.G. (frĕ'Kĕn)	169c	50.54 N	6.49 E
Fredericia, Den. (frĕdh-ĕ-rē'tsē-ȧ)	164	55.35 N	9.45 E
Frederick, Md. (frĕd'ẽr-ĭk)	111	39.25 N	77.25 W
Frederick, Ok.	122	34.23 N	99.01 W
Frederick House (R.), Can.	102	49.05 N	81.20 W
Fredericksburg, Tx. (frĕd'ẽr-ĭkz-bûrg)	124	30.16 N	98.52 W
Fredericksburg, Va.	111	38.20 N	77.30 W
Fredericktown, Mo. (frĕd'ẽr-ĭk-toun)	123	37.32 N	90.16 W
Fredericton, Can. (frĕd'ẽr-ĭk-tŭn)	104	45.48 N	66.39 W
Frederikshavn, Den. (frĕdh'ĕ-rĕks-houn)	164	57.27 N	10.31 E
Frederikssund, Den. (frĕdh'ĕ-rĕks-so͞on)	164	55.51 N	12.04 E
Fredersdorf bei Berlin, G.D.R.	65a	52.31 N	13.44 E
Fredonia, Col. (frē-dō'nyȧ)	142a	5.55 N	75.40 W
Fredonia, Ks. (frē-dō'nĭ-ȧ)	123	36.31 N	95.50 W
Fredonia, NY	111	42.25 N	79.20 W
Fredrikstad, Nor. (frădh'rĕks-stȧd)	164	59.14 N	10.58 E
Freeburg, Il. (frē'bûrg)	119e	38.26 N	89.59 W
Freehold, NJ (frē'hōld)	112a	40.15 N	74.16 W
Freeland, Pa. (frē'lănd)	112	41.00 N	75.50 W
Freeland, Wa.	118a	48.01 N	122.32 W
Freels, C., Can. (frēlz)	105	46.37 N	53.45 W
Freelton, Can. (frēl'tŭn)	95d	43.24 N	80.02 W
Freeport, Ba.	134	26.30 N	78.45 W
Freeport, Il. (frē'pōrt)	115	42.19 N	89.30 W
Freeport, NY	112a	40.39 N	73.35 W
Freeport, Tx.	119	28.56 N	95.21 W
Freetown, S.L. (frē'toun)	228	8.30 N	13.15 W
Fregenal de la Sierra, Sp. (frā-hå-näl' dä lä syĕr'rä)	170	38.09 N	6.40 W
Fregene, It. (frĕ-zhĕ'-nĕ)	171d	41.52 N	12.12 E
Freiberg, G.D.R. (frī'bĕrgh)	166	50.54 N	13.18 E
Freiburg, G.D.R.	166	48.00 N	7.50 E
Freienried, F.R.G. (frī'ĕn-rēd)	157d	48.20 N	11.08 E
Freirina, Chile (frå-ĭ-rē'nä)	144	28.35 S	71.26 W
Freisenbruch (Neigh.), F.R.G.	63	51.27 N	7.06 E
Freising, F.R.G. (frī'zĭng)	157d	48.25 N	11.45 E
Fréjus, Fr. (frā-zhüs')	169	43.28 N	6.46 E
Fremantle, Austl. (frē'măn-t'l)	214	32.03 S	116.05 E
Fremont, Ca. (frē-mŏnt')	118b	37.33 N	122.00 W
Fremont, Mi.	110	43.25 N	85.55 W
Fremont, Ne.	114	41.26 N	96.30 W
Fremont, Oh.	110	41.20 N	83.05 W
Fremont (R.), Ut.	121	38.20 N	111.30 W
Fremont Pk., Wy.	117	43.05 N	109.35 W
French Broad (R.), Tn.-NC (frĕnch brôd)	126	35.59 N	83.01 W
French Frigate Shoals (Rocks), Hi.	106b	23.30 N	167.10 W
French Guiana, S.A. (gē-ä'nä)	140	4.20 N	53.00 W
French Lick, In. (frĕnch lĭk)	110	38.35 N	86.35 W
Frenchman (R.), Can.	100	49.25 N	108.30 W
Frenchman Cr., Mt. (frĕnch-măn)	117	48.51 N	107.20 W
Frenchman Cr., Ne.	122	40.24 N	101.50 W
Frenchman Flat, Nv.	120	36.55 N	116.11 W
French Polynesia, Pac. O.	209	15.00 S	140.00 W
French River, Mn.	119h	46.54 N	91.54 W
French's Forest, Austl.	70a	33.45 S	151.14 E
Freshfield, Eng.	64a	53.34 N	3.04 W
Freshfield, Mt., Can. (frĕsh'fēld)	99	51.44 N	116.57 W
Fresh Meadows (Neigh.), NY	55	40.44 N	73.48 W
Fresnillo, Mex. (frås-nēl'yō)	130	23.10 N	102.52 W
Fresno, Ca. (frĕz'nō)	120	36.43 N	119.47 W
Fresno, Col. (frĕs'nō)	142a	5.10 N	75.01 W
Fresno (R.), Ca. (frĕz'nō)	120	37.00 N	120.24 W
Fresno Slough, Ca.	120	36.39 N	120.12 W
Freudenstadt, F.R.G. (froi'den-shtät)	166	48.28 N	8.26 E
Freycinet Pen., Austl. (frā-sē-nĕ')	216	42.13 S	148.56 E
Fria, Gui.	228	10.05 N	13.32 W
Fria (R.), Az. (frē-ä)	121	34.03 N	112.12 W
Fria, C., Namibia (frĭȧ)	226	18.15 S	12.10 E
Frias, Arg. (frē-äs)	144	28.43 S	65.03 W
Fribourg, Switz. (frē-bo͞or')	166	46.48 N	7.07 E
Fridley, Mn. (frĭd'lĭ)	119g	45.05 N	93.16 W
Frieburg, F.R.G. (frī'bo͞orgh)	166	47.59 N	7.50 E
Friedberg, F.R.G. (frēd'bĕrgh)	157d	48.22 N	11.00 E
Friedenau (Neigh.), F.R.G.	65a	52.28 N	13.20 E
Friedland, G.D.R. (frēt'länt)	166	53.39 N	13.34 E
Friedrichsfeld, F.R.G.	63	51.38 N	6.39 E
Friedrichsfelde (Neigh.), G.D.R.	65a	52.31 N	13.31 E
Friedrichshafen, F.R.G. (frē-drĕks-häf'ĕn)	166	47.39 N	9.28 E
Friedrichshagen (Neigh.), G.D.R.	65a	52.27 N	13.38 E
Friedrichshain (Neigh.), G.D.R.	65a	52.31 N	13.27 E
Friemersheim, F.R.G.	63	51.23 N	6.42 E
Friend, Ne. (frĕnd)	123	40.40 N	97.16 W
Friends Colony (Neigh.), India	67d	28.34 N	77.16 E
Friendship International Arpt., Md.	56c	39.11 N	76.40 W
Friendswood, Tx. (frĕnds'wo͝od)	125a	29.31 N	95.11 W
Friern Barnet (Neigh.), Eng.	62	51.37 N	0.10 W
Fries, Va. (frēz)	127	36.42 N	80.59 W
Friesack, G.D.R. (frē'säk)	157b	52.44 N	12.35 E
Frillendorf (Neigh.), F.R.G.	63	51.28 N	7.05 E
Frio, Cabo (C.), Braz. (kä'bō-frē'ō)	143	22.58 S	42.08 W
Frio R, Tx.	124	29.00 N	99.15 W
Frisian (Is.), Neth. (frē'zhăn)	163	53.30 N	5.20 E
Friuli-Venezia Giulia (Reg.), It.	172	46.20 N	13.20 E
Frobisher B., Can.	97	62.49 N	66.41 W
Frobisher Bay, Can.	97	63.48 N	68.31 W
Frobisher L., Can. (frŏb'ĭsh'ẽr)	100	56.25 N	108.20 W
Frodsham, Eng. (frŏdz'ăm)	156	53.18 N	2.48 W
Frohavet (Sea), Nor.	158	63.49 N	9.12 E
Frohnau (Neigh.), F.R.G.	65a	52.38 N	13.18 E
Frohnhausen (Neigh.), F.R.G.	63	51.27 N	6.58 E
Frome, L., Austl. (fro͞om)	216	30.40 S	140.13 E

PLACE (Pronunciation)	PAGE	Lat. °'	Long. °'
Frontenac, Ks. (frŏn'tĕ-năk)	123	37.27 N	94.41 W
Frontera, Mex. (frŏn-tā'rä)	131	18.34 N	92.38 W
Front Ra., Wy. (frŭnt)	117	42.17 N	105.53 W
Front Royal, Va. (frŭnt)	111	38.55 N	78.10 W
Frosinone, It. (frō-zē-nō'nå)	172	41.38 N	13.22 E
Frostburg, Md. (frŏst'bûrg)	111	39.40 N	78.55 W
Fruita, Co. (frōōt-å)	121	39.10 N	108.45 W
Frunze, Sov.Un. (frōōn'zĕ)	180	42.49 N	74.42 E
Fryanovo, Sov.Un. (f'ryä'nô-vô)	182b	56.08 N	38.28 E
Fryazino, Sov.Un. (f'ryä'zĭ-nô)	182b	55.58 N	38.05 E
Frydlant, Czech. (frēd'länt)	166	50.56 N	15.05 E
Fryerning, Eng.	62	51.41 N	0.22 E
Fucheng, China (fōō-chŭŋ)	200	37.53 N	116.08 E
Fuchu, Jap. (fōō'chōō)	205a	35.41 N	139.29 E
Fuchun (R.), China (fōō-chōōn)	203	29.50 N	120.00 E
Fuego (Vol.), Guat. (fwā'gŏ)	132	14.29 N	90.52 W
Fuencarral, Sp. (fuän-kär-räl')	171a	40.29 N	3.42 W
Fuensalida, Sp. (fwän-sä-lē'dä)	170	40.04 N	4.15 W
Fuente, Mex. (fwĕ'n-tĕ')	124	28.39 N	100.34 W
Fuente de Cantos, Sp. (fwĕn'tå dä kän'tōs)	170	38.15 N	6.18 W
Fuente el Saz, Sp. (fwĕn'tå ĕl säth')	171a	40.39 N	3.30 W
Fuenteobejuna, Sp.	170	38.15 N	5.30 W
Fuentesauco, Sp. (fwĕn-tå-sä-ōō'kō)	170	41.18 N	5.25 W
Fuerte Olimpo, Par. (fwĕr'tå ō-lĕm-pō)	143	21.10 S	57.49 W
Fuerte, Rio del (R.), Mex. (rē'ō-dĕl-fōō-ĕ'r-tĕ')	128	26.15 N	108.50 W
Fuerteventura I., Can.Is. (fwĕr'tå-vĕn-tōō'rä)	224	28.24 N	13.21 W
Fuhai, China	198	47.01 N	87.07 E
Fuhlenbrock (Neigh.), F.R.G.	63	51.32 N	6.54 E
Fuji, Jap. (jōō'jĕ)	205	35.11 N	138.44 E
Fuji (R.), Jap.	205	35.20 N	138.23 E
Fujian (Prov.), China (fōō-jyĕn)	199	25.40 N	117.30 E
Fujidera, Jap.	205	34.34 N	135.37 E
Fujiidera, Jap.	69b	34.34 N	135.36 E
Fujin, China (fōō-jyĭn)	199	47.13 N	132.11 E
Fuji-san (Mtn.), Jap. (fōō'jĕ sän)	205	35.23 N	138.44 E
Fujisawa, Jap. (fōō'jĕ-sä'wa)	205a	35.20 N	139.29 E
Fukagawa (Neigh.), Jap.	69a	35.03 N	139.48 E
Fukiai (Neigh.), Jap.	69b	34.42 N	135.12 E
Fukuchiyama, Jap. (fōō'kōō-chē-yä'ma)	205	35.18 N	135.07 E
Fukue (I.), Jap. (fōō-kōō'ā)	205	32.40 N	129.02 E
Fukui, Jap. (fōō'kōō-ē)	205	36.05 N	136.14 E
Fukuoka, Jap.	205	33.35 N	130.23 E
Fukuoka, Jap.	205a	31.52 N	139.31 E
Fukushima, Jap. (fōō'kōō-shē'må)	204	37.45 N	140.29 E
Fukushima (Neigh.), Jap.	69b	34.42 N	135.29 E
Fukuyama, Jap. (fōō-kōō-yä'má)	205	34.31 N	133.21 E
Fülädï, Kūh-e (Mtn.), Afg.	193	34.38 N	67.55 E
Fulda R., F.R.G. (fŏōl'dä)	166	51.05 N	9.40 E
Fulerum (Neigh.), F.R.G.	63	51.26 N	6.57 E
Fuling, China (fōō-lĭŋ)	203	29.40 N	107.30 E
Fullerton, Ca.	119a	33.53 N	117.56 W
Fullerton, La.	125	31.00 N	93.00 W
Fullerton, Ne.	114	41.21 N	97.59 W
Fulmer, Eng.	62	51.33 N	0.34 W
Fulton, Ky. (fŭl'tŭn)	126	36.30 N	88.53 W
Fulton, Mo.	123	38.51 N	91.56 W
Fulton, NY	111	43.20 N	76.25 W
Fultondale, Al. (fŭl'tŭn-dāl)	112h	33.37 N	86.48 W
Funabashi, Jap. (fōō'nä-bä'shē)	205a	35.43 N	139.59 E
Funasaka, Jap.	69b	34.49 N	135.17 E
Funaya, Jap. (fōō-nä'yä)	205b	34.45 N	135.52 E
Funchal, Mad.Is. (fōōn-shäl')	224	32.41 N	16.15 W
Fundación, Col. (fōōn-dä-syō'n)	142	10.43 N	74.13 W
Fundão, Port. (fōōn-douN')	170	40.08 N	7.32 W
Fundão, Ilha do (I.), Braz.	61c	22.51 S	43.14 W
Funde, India	67e	18.54 N	72.58 E
Fundy, B. of, Can. (fŭn'dĭ)	102	45.00 N	66.00 W
Fundy Natl.Park, Can.	102	45.38 N	65.00 W
Funing, China, (fōō-nīŋ)	200	33.55 N	119.54 E
Funing, China	200	39.55 N	119.16 E
Funing Wan. (B.), China	203	26.48 N	120.35 E
Funtua, Nig.	229	11.31 N	7.17 E
Furancungo, Moz.	231	14.55 S	33.35 E
Furbero, Mex. (fōōr-bĕ'rŏ)	131	20.21 N	97.32 W
Furmanov, Sov.Un. (fūr-mä'nŏf)	174	57.14 N	41.11 E
Furnas, Reprêsa de (Res.), Braz.	144b	21.00 S	46.00 W
Furneaux Group (Is.), Austl. (fûr'nō)	215	40.15 S	146.27 E
Fürstenfeld, Aus. (fŏōr'stĕn-fĕlt)	166	47.02 N	16.03 E
Fürstenfeldbruck, F.R.G. (fur'stĕn-fĕld'brŏōk)	157d	48.11 N	11.16 E
Fürstenwalde, G.D.R. (für'stĕn-väl-dĕ)	166	52.21 N	14.04 E
Fürth, F.R.G. (fürt)	166	49.28 N	11.03 E
Furuichi, Jap. (fōō'rōō-ē'chē)	205b	34.33 N	135.37 E
Fusa, Jap. (fōō'sä)	205a	35.52 N	140.08 E
Fusagasugá, Col. (fōō-sä-gä-sōō-gá')	142a	4.22 N	74.22 W
Fuse, Jap.	205b	34.40 N	135.43 E
Fushimi, Jap. (fōō'shē-mē)	205b	34.57 N	135.47 E
Fushun, China (fōō'shōōn')	202	41.50 N	124.00 E
Fusong, China	202	42.12 N	127.12 E
Futatsubashi, Jap.	69a	35.29 N	139.30 E
Futtsu, Jap. (fōō'tsōō')	205a	35.19 N	139.49 E
Futtsu Misaki (C.), Jap. (fŏōt'tsōō' mē-sä'kĕ)	205a	35.19 N	139.46 E
Fuwah, Egypt (fōō'wä)	223b	31.13 N	30.35 E
Fuxian, China (fōō shyĕn)	200	39.36 N	121.59 E
Fuxin, China (fōō-shyĭn)	202	42.05 N	121.40 E
Fuyang, China	200	32.53 N	115.48 E
Fuyang, China	203	30.10 N	119.58 E
Fuyang (R.), China (fōō-yäŋ)	200	36.59 N	114.48 E
Fuyu, China (fōō-yōō)	202	45.20 N	125.09 E
Fuyuan, China (fōō-yŭän)	203	28.39 N	104.13 E
Fuzhou, China (fōō-jō)	203	26.02 N	119.18 E
Fuzhou, China	200	39.38 N	121.43 E
Fuzhoucheng, China (fōō-jō-chŭŋ)	200	39.46 N	121.44 E
Fyfield, Eng.	62	51.45 N	0.16 E
Fyn (I.), Den. (fü'n)	164	55.24 N	10.33 E
Fyne, Loch (L.), Scot. (fīn)	162	56.14 N	5.10 W
Fyresvatn (L.), Nor.	164	59.04 N	7.55 E

G

PLACE (Pronunciation)	PAGE	Lat. °'	Long. °'
Gaalkacyo, Som.	223a	7.00 N	47.30 E
Gabela, Ang.	230	10.48 S	14.20 E
Gabés, Tun. (gä'bĕs)	224	33.51 N	10.04 E
Gabés, Golfe de (G.), Tun.	224	33.22 N	10.59 E
Gabil, Chad	229	11.09 N	18.12 E
Gabin, Pol (gä'bēn)	167	52.23 N	19.47 E
Gabon, Afr. (gà-bôN')	222	0.30 S	10.45 E
Gaborone, Bots.	226	24.28 S	25.59 E
Gabriel R., Tx. (gä'brĭ-ĕl)	125	30.38 N	97.15 W
Gabrovo, Bul. (gäb'rŏ-vô)	173	42.52 N	25.19 E
Gachetá, Col. (gä-chá'tä)	142a	4.50 N	73.36 W
Gachsārān Iran	195	30.12 N	50.47 E
Gacko, Yugo. (gäts'kô)	173	43.10 N	18.34 E
Gadsden, Al. (gädz'dĕn)	126	34.00 N	86.00 W
Gadyach, Sov.Un. (gäd-yäch')	175	50.22 N	33.59 E
Găeşti, Rom. (gä-yĕsh'tĕ)	173	44.43 N	25.21 E
Gaeta, It. (gä-ā'tä)	172	41.18 N	13.34 E
Gaffney, SC (găf'nĭ)	127	35.04 N	81.47 W
Gafsa, Tun. (gäf'sä)	224	34.16 N	8.37 E
Gagarin, Sov.Un.	174	55.32 N	34.58 E
Gagnoa, Ivory Coast	228	6.08 N	5.56 W
Gagny, Fr.	64c	48.53 N	2.32 E
Gagrary (I.), Phil. (gä-grä-rĕ)	207a	13.23 N	123.58 E
Gahmen (Neigh.), F.R.G.	63	51.36 N	7.32 E
Gaillac-sur-Tarn, Fr. (gá-yäk'sür-tärn')	154	43.54 N	1.52 E
Gaillard Cut, Pan. (gä-ēl-yä'rd)	128a	9.03 N	79.42 W
Gainesville, Fl. (gānz'vĭl)	127	29.40 N	82.20 W
Gainesville, Ga.	126	34.16 N	83.48 W
Gainesville, Tx.	123	33.38 N	97.08 W
Gainsborough, Eng. (gānz'bŭr-ô)	156	53.23 N	0.46 W
Gairdner, L., Austl. (gârd'nĕr)	216	32.20 S	136.30 E
Gaithersburg, Md. (gā'thĕrs'bûrg)	112e	39.08 N	77.13 W
Gaixian, China (gī-shyĕn)	200	40.25 N	122.20 E
Galana (R.), Ken.	231	3.00 S	39.30 E
Galapagar, Sp. (gä-lä-pä-gär')	171a	40.36 N	4.00 W
Galápagos Is., see Colon, Arch. de			
Galaria (R.), It.	171d	41.58 N	12.21 E
Galashiels, Scot. (gǎl-á-shēlz)	162	55.41 N	2.57 W
Galata (Neigh.), Tur.	66f	41.01 N	28.58 E
Galata Köprüsü (P. Int.)	66f	41.00 N	28.57 E
Galati, Rom. (gä-lätz'ĭ)	175	45.25 N	28.05 E
Galatina, It. (gä-lä-tē'nä)	173	40.10 N	18.12 E
Galátsion, Grc.	66d	38.01 N	23.45 E
Galaxídhion, Grc.	173	38.26 N	22.22 E
Galdhopiggen (Mtn.), Nor.	164	61.37 N	8.17 E
Galeana, Mex. (gä-lä-ä'nä)	124	24.50 N	100.04 W
Galena, Il. (gá-lē'ná)	115	42.26 N	90.27 W
Galena, In.	113h	38.21 N	85.55 W
Galena, Ks.	123	37.06 N	94.39 W
Galena Pk., Tx.	125a	29.44 N	95.14 W
Galera, Cerro (Mtn.), Pan. (sĕ'r-rô-gä-lĕ'rä)	128a	8.55 N	79.38 W
Galeras (Vol.), Col.	142	0.57 N	77.27 W
Gales (R.), Or. (gālz)	118c	45.33 N	123.11 W
Galesburg, Il. (gālz'bûrg)	123	40.56 N	90.21 W
Galesville, Wi. (gālz'vĭl)	115	44.04 N	91.22 W
Galeton, Pa. (gāl'tŭn)	111	41.45 N	77.40 W
Galich, Sov.Un. (gäl'ĭch)	178	58.20 N	42.38 E
Galicia (Reg.), Pol.-Sov.Un. (gà-lĭsh'ĭ-à)	167	49.48 N	21.05 E
Galicia (Reg.), Sp. (gä-lē'thyä)	170	43.35 N	8.03 W
Galilee (L.), Austl. (gäl'ĭ-lē)	215	22.23 S	145.09 E
Galilee, Sea of, Isr.	191a	32.53 N	35.45 E
Galina Pt., Jam. (gä-lē'nä)	134	18.25 N	76.50 W
Galion, Oh. (gäl'ĭ-ŭn)	129	40.45 N	82.50 W
Galisteo, NM (gä-lĭs-tā'ō)	123	35.20 N	106.00 W
Galite, La. I., Alg. (gä-lēt)	159	37.36 N	8.03 E
Gallarate, It. (gäl-lä-rä'tĕ)	172	45.57 N	8.48 E
Gallardon, Fr. (gä-lär-dôN')	169b	48.31 N	1.40 E
Gallatin, Mo. (gäl'á-tĭn)	123	39.55 N	93.58 W
Gallatin, Tn.	126	36.23 N	86.28 W
Gallatin R., Mt.	117	45.12 N	111.10 W
Galle, Sri Lanka (gäl)	197	6.13 N	80.10 E
Gállego (R.), Sp. (gäl-yā'gŏ)	171	42.27 N	0.37 W
Gallinas, Pta. de (Pt.), Col. (gä-lyē'näs)	142	12.10 N	72.10 W
Gallipoli, It. (gäl-lē'pŏ-lē)	173	40.03 N	17.58 E
Gallipoli Pen., Tur.	173	40.23 N	25.10 E
Gallipolis, Oh. (gäl-ĭ-pô-lēs)	110	38.50 N	82.10 W
Gallipoli, see Gelibolu			
Gällivare, Swe. (yĕl-ĭ-vär'ĕ)	158	68.06 N	20.29 E
Gallo (R.), Sp. (gäl'yō)	170	40.43 N	1.42 W
Gallup, NM (gäl'ŭp)	123	35.30 N	108.45 W
Galnale Doria R., Eth.	225	5.35 N	40.26 E
Galt, Can.	110	43.22 N	80.19 W
Galty Mts., Ire.	162	52.19 N	8.20 W
Galva, Il. (gäl'vä)	123	41.11 N	90.02 W
Galveston, Tx. (gäl'vĕs-tŭn)	125a	29.18 N	94.48 W
Galveston B., Tx.	125	29.39 N	94.45 W
Galveston I, Tx.	125a	29.12 N	94.53 W
Galvin, Austl.	70b	37.51 S	144.49 E
Galway, Ire.	162	53.16 N	9.05 W
Galway B., Ire. (gôl'wä)	162	53.10 N	9.47 W
Gamba, China (gäm-bä)	196	28.23 N	89.42 E
Gambaga, Ghana (gäm-bä'gä)	228	10.32 N	0.26 W
Gambela, Eth. (gäm-bä'lá)	225	8.15 N	34.33 E
Gambia, Afr. (gäm'bĕ-á)	224	13.38 N	19.38 W
Gambia (R.), (Gambie), Afr.	228	13.20 N	15.55 W
Gambie (R.), (Gambia), Afr.	228	13.20 N	15.55 W
Gamboma, Con. (gäm-bō'mä)	230	1.53 S	15.51 E
Gamleby, Swe. (gäm'lĕ-bü)	164	57.54 N	16.20 E
Gan (R.), China (gän)	203	26.50 N	115.00 E
Gandak (R.), India	196	26.37 N	84.22 E
Gander, Can. (gän'dĕr)	105	48.57 N	54.34 W
Gander (R.), Can.	105	49.10 N	54.35 W
Gander L., Can.	105	48.55 N	55.40 W
Gandhinagar, India	196	23.30 N	72.47 E
Gandi, Nig.	229	12.55 N	5.49 E
Gandía, Sp. (gän-dē'ä)	171	38.56 N	0.10 W
Gangdisê Shan (Trans Himalayas)(Mts.), China (gän-dē-sŭ shän) (träns-hī-mä-lá-yás)	198	30.25 N	83.43 E
Ganges (R.), India (găn'jēz)	196	24.32 N	87.58 E
Ganges, Mouths of, India (găn'jēz)	196	21.18 N	88.40 E
Gangi, It. (gän'jē)	172	37.48 N	14.15 E
Gangtok, India	198	27.15 N	88.30 E
Gannan, China (gän-nän)	202	47.50 N	123.30 E
Gannett Pk., Wy. (gän'ĕt)	117	43.10 N	109.38 W
Gano, Oh. (g'nô)	113f	39.18 N	84.24 W
Gänserndorf, Aus.	157e	48.21 N	16.43 E
Gansu (Prov.), China (gän-sōō)	198	38.50 N	101.10 E
Ganwo, Nig.	229	11.13 N	4.42 E
Ganyu, China (gän-yōō)	200	34.52 N	119.07 E
Ganzhou, China (gän-jō)	203	25.50 N	114.30 E
Gao, Mali (gä'ō)	228	16.16 N	0.03 W
Gao'an, China (gou-än)	203	28.30 N	115.02 E
Gaobaita, China	67b	39.53 N	116.30 E
Gaobeidian, China	67b	39.54 N	116.33 E
Gaomi, China, (gou-mē)	200	36.23 N	119.46 E
Gaoqiao, China	201b	31.21 N	121.35 E
Gaoshun, China (gou-shōōn)	200	31.22 N	118.50 E
Gaotang, China	200	36.52 N	116.12 E
Gaoyao, China (gou-you)	203	23.08 N	112.25 E
Gaoyi, China (gou-yĕ)	200	37.37 N	114.39 E
Gaoyou, China (gou-yō)	200	32.46 N	119.26 E
Gaoyou Hu (L.), China (gou-yō hōō)	200	32.59 N	119.04 E
Gap, Fr. (gàp)	169	44.34 N	6.08 E
Gapan, Phil. (gä-pän)	207a	15.18 N	120.56 E
Garachiné, Pan. (gä-rä-chĕ'nå)	133	8.02 N	78.22 W
Garachiné, Punta (Pt.), Pan. (pōō'n-tä-gä-rä-chĕ'nå)	133	8.08 N	78.35 W
Garanhuns, Braz. (gä-rän-yōōNsh')	143	8.49 S	36.28 W
Garbagnate Milanese, It.	65c	45.35 N	9.05 E
Garbatella (Neigh.), It.	66c	41.52 N	12.29 E
Garber, Ok. (gär'bĕr)	123	36.28 N	97.35 W
Garches, Fr.	64c	48.51 N	2.11 E
Garching, F.R.G. (gär'ĸĕng)	157d	48.15 N	11.39 E
Garcia, Mex. (gär-sē'ä)	124	25.90 N	100.37 W
Garcia de la Cadena, Mex. (dĕ-lä-kä-dĕ-nä)	130	21.14 N	103.26 W
Garda, Lago di (L.), It. (lä-gō-dē-gär'dä)	172	45.43 N	10.26 E
Gardanne, Fr. (gär-dàn')	168a	43.28 N	5.29 E
Gardelegen, G.D.R. (gär-dĕ-lä'ghĕn)	166	52.32 N	11.22 E
Garden (I.), Mi. (gär'd'n)	110	45.50 N	85.50 W
Gardena, Ca. (gär-dĕ'nå)	119a	33.53 N	118.19 W
Garden City, Ks.	122	37.58 N	100.52 W
Garden City, Mi.	113b	42.20 N	83.21 W
Garden City, NY	55	40.44 N	73.37 W
Garden City Park, NY	55	40.44 N	73.40 W
Garden Grove, Ca. (gär'd'n grŏv)	119a	33.47 N	117.56 W
Garden' Reach), India	196a	22.33 N	88.17 E
Garden River, Can.	119k	46.33 N	84.10 W
Gardēz, Afg.	196	33.43 N	69.09 E
Gardiner, Me. (gärd'nĕr)	104	44.12 N	69.46 W
Gardiner, Mt.	117	45.03 N	110.43 W
Gardiner, Wa.	118a	48.03 N	122.55 W
Gardiner Dam, Can.	100	51.17 N	106.51 W
Gardner, Ma.	111	42.35 N	72.00 W
Gardner Canal, Can.	98	53.28 N	128.15 W
Gardner Pinnacles (Rocks), Hi.	106b	25.10 N	167.00 W
Gareloi (I.), Ak. (gär-lōō-ä')	107a	51.40 N	178.48 W
Garenfeld, F.R.G.	63	51.24 N	7.31 E
Garfield, NJ (gär'fĕld)	112a	40.53 N	74.06 W
Garfield, NJ	55	40.53 N	74.07 W
Garfield, Ut.	119b	40.45 N	112.10 W
Garfield Heights, Oh	113d	41.25 N	81.36 W
Gargaliánoi, Grc. (gär-gä-lyä'nĕ)	173	37.07 N	21.50 E
Garges-lès-Gonesse, Fr.	64c	48.58 N	2.25 E
Gargždai, Sov.Un. (gärgzh'dī)	165	55.43 N	20.09 E
Garibaldi, Mt., Can. (gär-ĭ-bäl'dĕ)	98	49.51 N	123.01 W
Garin, Arg. (gä-rē'n)	144a	34.10 S	58.44 W
Garissa, Ken.	231	0.28 S	39.38 E
Garland, Md.	56c	39.11 N	76.39 W
Garland, Tx. (gär'lănd)	119c	32.55 N	96.39 W
Garland, Ut.	117	41.45 N	112.10 W
Garm, Sov.Un.	180	39.12 N	70.28 E
Garmisch-Partenkirchen, F.R.G. (gär'mĕsh pär'tĕn-kĕr'ĸĕn)	166	47.30 N	11.10 E
Garnett, Ks. (gär'nĕt)	123	38.16 N	95.15 W
Garonne Rivière (R.), Fr. (gä-rŏn)	168	44.43 N	0.25 E
Garoua, Cam.	229	9.18 N	13.24 E
Garrett, In. (gär'ĕt)	110	41.20 N	85.10 W
Garrison, Md.	56c	39.24 N	76.45 W
Garrison, ND	114	47.38 N	101.24 W
Garrison, NY (gär'ĭ-sŭn)	112a	41.23 N	73.57 W
Garrovillas, Sp. (gä-rŏ-vēl'yäs)	170	39.42 N	6.30 W
Garry (L.), Can. (gär'ĭ)	96	66.16 N	99.23 W
Garsen, Ken.	231	2.16 S	40.07 E
Garson, Can.	104	46.34 N	80.52 W
Garsted, F.R.G. (gär'shtĕt)	157c	53.40 N	9.58 E
Garston, Eng.	62	51.41 N	0.23 W
Garston (Neigh.), Eng.	64a	53.21 N	2.53 W
Gartenstadt (Neigh.), F.R.G.	63	51.30 N	7.26 E

ng-sing; nꞧ-banꞧk; N-nasalized n;   nŏd; cŏmmit; ōld; ŏbey; ôrder; oi-boil; fōōd; fŏŏt; ou-out;   s-soft; sh-dish;   th-thin;   pūre; ûnite; ûrn; stŭd; circŭs; ü-as in French tu;   '-indeterminate vowel.

PLACE (Pronounciation)	PAGE	Lat. °′	Long. °′
Gartok, China (gär-tŏk')	196	31.11 N	80.35 E
Garulia, India	196a	22.48 N	88.23 E
Garwolin, Pol. (gär-vō'lēn)	167	51.54 N	21.40 E
Garwood, NJ	55	40.39 N	74.19 W
Gary, In. (gā'rĭ)	113a	41.35 N	87.21 W
Garza-Little Elm Res., Tx.	125	33.16 N	96.54 W
Garzón, Col. (gär-thōn')	142	2.13 N	75.44 W
Gasan, Phil. (gä-sän')	207a	13.19 N	121.52 E
Gasan-Kuli, Sov.Un.	179	37.25 N	53.55 E
Gas City, In. (găs)	110	40.30 N	85.40 W
Gascogne, (Reg.), Fr. (gäs-kôn'yĕ)	168	43.45 N	1.49 W
Gasconade (R.), Mo. (găs-kō-nād')	123	37.46 N	92.15 W
Gascoyne, (R.), Austl. (găs-koin')	214	25.15 S	117.00 E
Gashland, Mo. (găsh'-lănd)	119f	39.15 N	94.35 W
Gashua, Nig.	229	12.54 N	11.00 E
Gasny, Fr. (gäs-nē')	169b	49.05 N	1.36 E
Gaspé, Can.	104	48.50 N	64.29 W
Gaspé, Baie de (B.), Can. (gas'pā)(gas-pā')	104	48.35 N	63.45 W
Gaspé, Cape de (C.), Can.	104	48.45 N	63.34 W
Gaspé, Péninsule de (Pen.), Can.	104	48.23 N	65.42 W
Gasper Hernandez, Dom.Rep. (gäs-pär' ĕr-nän'dāth)	135	19.40 N	70.15 W
Gassaway, WV (găs'á-wā)	110	38.40 N	80.45 W
Gaston, Or. (găs'tŭn)	118c	45.26 N	123.08 W
Gastonia, NC (găs-tô'nĭ-á)	127	35.15 N	81.14 W
Gastre, Arg. (gäs-trĕ)	144	42.12 S	68.50 W
Gata, Cabo de (C.), Sp. (kä'bô-dĕ-gä'tä)	170	36.42 N	2.00 W
Gata, Sierra de (Mts.), Sp. (syĕr'rä dä gä'tä)	170	40.12 N	6.39 W
Gatchina, Sov.Un. (gä-chē'ná)	182c	59.33 N	30.08 E
Gateacre (Neigh.), Eng.	64a	53.23 N	2.51 W
Gátes, Akrotírion (C.), Cyprus	191a	34.30 N	33.15 E
Gateshead, Eng. (gāts'hĕd)	162	54.56 N	1.38 W
Gatesville, Mex. (gāts'vĭl)	125	31.26 N	97.34 W
Gateway of India (P. Int.), India	67e	18.55 N	72.50 E
Gatineau, Can. (gá'tē-nō)	95c	45.29 N	75.38 W
Gatineau (R.), Can.	95c	45.45 N	75.50 W
Gatineau, Parc de la (Natl. Pk.), Can.	95c	45.32 N	75.53 W
Gâtine, Hauteurs de (Hills), Fr.	168	46.40 N	0.50 W
Gatley, Eng.	64b	53.23 N	2.14 W
Gato Negro, Ven.	61a	10.33 N	66.57 W
Gattendorf, Aus.	157e	48.01 N	17.00 E
Gatun, Pan. (gä-tōōn')	128a	9.16 N	79.25 W
Gatun (R.), Pan.	128a	9.21 N	79.10 W
Gatún, L., Pan.	128a	9.13 N	79.24 W
Gatun Locks, Pan.	128a	9.16 N	79.27 W
Gauhāti, India	196	26.09 N	91.51 E
Gauja (R.), Sov.Un. (gá'ōō-yá)	165	57.10 N	24.30 E
Gaula (R.), Nor.	164	62.55 N	10.45 E
Gauttier-Gebergte (Mts.), Indon. (gō-tyā')	207	2.30 S	138.45 E
Gāvanpāda, India	67e	18.57 N	73.01 E
Gávdhos (I.), Grc. (gäv'dôs)	172a	34.48 N	24.08 E
Gávea (Neigh.), Braz.	61c	22.58 S	43.14 W
Gavins Point Dam, Ne. (gă'-vĭns)	114	42.47 N	97.47 W
Gävle, Swe. (yĕv'lĕ)	164	60.40 N	17.07 E
Gavle-bukten (B.), Swe.	164	60.45 N	17.30 E
Gavrilov Posad, Sov.Un. (gá'vrē-lôf'ka po-sát)	174	56.34 N	40.09 E
Gavrilov-Yam, Sov.Un. (gá'vrē-lôf yäm')	174	57.17 N	39.49 E
Gawler, Austl. (gô'lēr)	216	34.35 S	138.47 E
Gawler Ra., Austl.	216	32.35 S	136.30 E
Gaya, India (gŭ'yä)(gī'á)	196	24.53 N	85.00 E
Gaya, Nig. (gä'yä)	224	11.58 N	9.05 E
Gaylord, Mi. (gā'lôrd)	110	45.00 N	84.35 W
Gayndah, Austl. (gān'däh)	216	25.43 S	151.33 E
Gaysin, Sov.Un.	175	48.46 N	29.22 E
Gayton, Eng.	64a	53.19 N	3.06 W
Gaza, see Ghazzah			
Gaziantep, Tur. (gä-zē-än'tĕp)	179	37.10 N	37.30 E
Gbarnga, Lib.	228	7.00 N	9.29 W
Gdańsk (Danzig), Pol. (g'dänsk)(dän'tsĕg)	167	54.20 N	18.40 E
Gdov, Sov.Un. (g'dôf')	174	58.44 N	27.51 E
Gdynia, Pol. (g'dēn'yá)	167	54.29 N	18.30 E
Geary, Ok. (gē'rĭ)	122	35.36 N	98.19 W
Géba (R.), Guinea-Bissau	228	12.25 N	14.35 W
Gebo, Wy. (gĕb'ō)	117	43.49 N	108.13 W
Ged, La. (gĕd)	125	30.07 N	93.36 W
Gediz (R.), Tur.	161	38.44 N	28.45 E
Gedney, (I.), Wa. (gĕd-nē)	118a	48.01 N	122.18 W
Gedser, Den.	166	54.35 N	12.08 E
Gee Cross, Eng.	64b	53.26 N	2.04 W
Geel, Bel.	157a	51.09 N	5.01 E
Geelong, Austl. (jē-lông')	211a	38.06 S	144.13 E
Geelvink-baai (B.), Indon. (gäl'vĭŋk)	207	2.20 S	135.30 E
Gegu, China (gŭ-gōō)	200	39.00 N	117.30 E
Ge Hu (L.), China (gŭ hōō)	200	31.37 N	119.57 E
Geidam, Nig.	229	12.57 N	11.57 E
Geikie Ra., Austl. (gē'kē)	214	17.35 S	125.32 E
Geislingen, F.R.G. (gis'lĭng-ĕn)	166	48.37 N	9.52 E
Geist Res., In. (gēst)	113g	39.57 N	85.59 W
Geita, Tan.	231	2.52 S	32.10 E
Gejiu, China (gŭ-jĭo)	203	23.32 N	102.50 E
Geldermalsen, Neth.	157a	51.53 N	5.18 E
Geldern, F.R.G. (gĕl'dĕrn)	169c	51.31 N	6.20 E
Gelibolu (Gallipoli), Tur. (gĕl-lē'pô-lē)(gĕ-lĭb'ō-lōō)	173	40.25 N	26.40 E
Gellep-Stratum (Neigh.), F.R.G.	63	51.20 N	6.41 E
Gellibrand, Pt., Austl.	70b	37.52 S	144.54 E
Gel'myazov, Sov.Un.	175	49.49 N	31.54 E
Gelsenkirchen, F.R.G. (gĕl-zĕn-kĭrk-ĕn)	169c	51.31 N	7.05 E
Gemas, Mala. (jĕm'ás)	191b	2.35 N	102.37 E
Gemena, Zaire	230	3.15 N	19.46 E
Gemlik, Tur. (gĕm'lĭk)	179	40.30 N	29.10 E
Genale (R.), Eth.	223	5.00 N	41.15 E
General Alvear, Arg. (gĕ-nĕ-räl'ál-vĕ-á'r)	141c	36.04 S	60.02 W
General Arenales, Arg. (ä-rĕ-nä'lĕs)	141c	34.19 S	61.16 W
General Belgrano, Arg. (bĕl-grá'nô)	141c	35.45 S	58.32 W
General Cepeda, Mex. (sĕ-pĕ'dä)	124	25.24 N	101.29 W
General Conesa, Arg. (kō-nĕ'sä)	141c	36.30 S	57.19 W
General Guido, Arg. (gē'dō)	141c	36.41 S	57.48 W
General Lavalle, Arg. (lá-vá'l-yĕ)	141c	36.25 S	56.55 W
General Madariaga, Arg. (män-dá-rēä'gä)	144	36.59 S	57.14 W
General Pacheco, Arg.	60d	34.28 S	58.40 W
General Paz, Arg. (pá'z)	141c	35.30 S	58.20 W
General Pedro Antonio Santios, Mex. (pĕ'drô-än-tô'nyô-sän-tyōs)	130	21.37 N	98.58 W
General Pico, Arg. (pē'kô)	144	36.46 S	63.44 W
General Roca, Arg. (rô-kä)	144	39.01 S	67.31 W
General San Martín, Arg. (sän-mår-tē'n)	144a	34.19 S	58.32 W
General San Martín, Arg.	60d	34.35 S	58.30 W
General Sarmiento (San Miguel), Arg.	60d	34.33 S	58.43 W
General Urquiza (Neigh.)	60d	34.34 S	58.29 W
General Viamonte, Arg. (vēá'môn-tē)	141c	35.01 S	60.59 W
General Zuazua, Mex. (zwä'zwä)	124	25.54 N	100.07 W
Genesee (R.), NY (jĕn-ē-sē')	111	42.25 N	78.10 W
Geneseo, Il. (jē-nĕs'eō)	110	41.28 N	90.11 W
Geneva, Al. (jē-nē'vá)	126	31.03 N	85.50 W
Geneva, Il.	113a	41.53 N	88.18 W
Geneva, Ne.	123	40.32 N	97.37 W
Geneva, NY	111	42.50 N	77.00 W
Geneva, Oh.	110	41.45 N	80.55 W
Geneva, L., Switz.	166	46.28 N	6.30 E
Geneva, see Génève			
Génève (Geneva), Switz. (zhē-nĕv')	166	46.14 N	6.04 E
Genichesk, Sov.Un. (gĕnē-chyĕsk')	175	46.11 N	34.47 E
Genil (R.), Sp. (hå-nēl')	170	37.15 N	4.05 W
Gennebreck, F.R.G.	63	51.19 N	7.12 E
Gennevilliers, Fr.	64c	48.56 N	2.18 E
Genoa, Ne. (jen'ô-á)	123	41.26 N	97.43 W
Genoa City, Wi.	113a	42.31 N	88.19 W
Genoa, see Genova			
Genova (Genoa), It. (jĕn'ō-vä)	172	44.23 N	9.52 E
Genova, Golfodi (G.), It. (gôl-fô-dē-jĕn'ō-vä)	172	44.10 N	8.45 E
Genovesa (I.), Ec. (ĕ's-lä-gĕ-nō-vĕ-sä)	128	0.08 N	90.15 W
Gent, Bel.	163	51.05 N	3.40 E
Genthin, G.D.R. (gĕn-tēn')	166	52.24 N	12.10 E
Gentilly, Fr.	64c	48.49 N	2.21 E
Genzano di Roma, It., (gzhĕnt-zá'-nô-dē-rô'mä)	171d	41.43 N	12.49 E
Geographe B., Austl. (jē-ô-graf')	214	33.00 S	114.00 E
Geographic Chan., Austl. (jēô'gră-fĭk)	214	24.15 S	112.50 E
Geokchay, Sov. Un. (gĕ-ôk'chī)	179	40.40 N	47.40 E
George (L.), Fl. (jôr-ĭj)	127	29.10 N	81.50 W
George (L.), NY (jôrj)	111	43.40 N	73.30 W
George L., Can.-U.S. (jôrg)	119k	46.26 N	84.09 W
George, L., In.	113a	41.31 N	87.17 W
George, L., Ug.	231	0.02 N	30.25 E
Georges (R.), Austl.	211b	33.57 S	151.00 E
Georges Hall, Austl.	70a	33.55 S	150.59 E
George Town, Ba.	135	23.30 N	75.50 W
Georgetown, Can. (jôrg-toun)	95d	43.39 N	79.56 W
Georgetown, Can. (jôr-ĭj-toun)	105	46.11 N	62.32 W
Georgetown, Cayman Is.	134	19.20 N	81.20 W
Georgetown, Ct.	112	41.15 N	73.25 W
Georgetown, De.	111	38.40 N	75.20 W
Georgetown, Guy. (jôrj'toun)	143	7.45 N	58.04 W
Georgetown, Il.	110	40.00 N	87.40 W
Georgetown, Ky.	110	38.10 N	84.35 W
Georgetown, Ma. (jôrg-toun)	105a	42.43 N	71.00 W
Georgetown, Md.	111	39.25 N	75.55 W
Georgetown (Neigh.), DC	56d	38.54 N	77.03 W
George Town, (Pinang), Mala.	206	5.21 N	100.09 E
Georgetown, S.C. (jôr-ĭj-toun)	127	33.22 N	79.17 W
Georgetown, Tx. (jôrg-toun)	125	30.37 N	97.40 W
Georgetown University (P. Int.), DC	56d	38.54 N	77.04 W
George Washington Birthplace Natl. Mon., Va. (jôrj wŏsh'ĭng-tŭn)	111	38.10 N	77.00 W
George Washington Carver Natl. Mon., Mo. (jôrg wăsh-ĭng-tŭn kär'vēr)	123	36.58 N	94.21 W
George West, Tx.	124	28.20 N	98.07 W
Georgia (State), U.S. (jôr'ji-ă)	109	32.40 N	83.50 W
Georgian (S.S.R.), Sov. Un.	176	42.17 N	43.00 E
Georgiana, Al. (jôr-jē-ăn'á)	126	31.39 N	86.44 W
Georgian B., Can.	102	45.15 N	80.50 W
Georgian Bay Is. Natl. Pk, Can.	102	45.20 N	81.40 W
Georgia, Str. of, Can.	98	49.20 N	124.00 W
Georgia, Str. of, Wa.	118d	48.56 N	123.06 W
Georgina (R.), Austl. (jôr-jē'ná)	214	22.00 S	138.15 E
Georgiyevsk, Sov. Un. (gyôr-gyĕfsk')	179	44.05 N	43.30 E
Gera, G.D.R. (gā'rä)	166	50.52 N	12.06 E
Geral de Goiás, Serra (Mts.), Braz. (zhå-räl'-dĕ-gô-yá's)	161	14.22 S	45.40 W
Geraldton, Austl. (jĕr'ăld-tŭn)	214	28.40 S	114.35 E
Geraldton, Can.	97	49.43 N	87.00 W
Geral, Serra (Mts.), Braz. (sĕr'rá zhå-räl')	144	28.30 S	51.00 W
Gerdview, S. Afr.	71b	26.10 S	28.11 E
Gérgal, Sp. (gĕr'gäl)	170	37.08 N	2.29 E
Gering, Ne. (gē'rĭng)	114	41.49 N	103.41 W
Gerlachovský Štít (Mtn.), Czech.	167	49.12 N	20.08 E
Gerli (Neigh.), Arg.	60d	34.41 S	58.23 W
German Democratic Republic, Eur.	154	53.30 N	12.30 E
Germantown (Neigh.), Pa.	56b	40.03 N	75.11 W
Germantown, Oh. (jûr'măn-toun)	110	39.35 N	84.25 W
Germany, Federal Republic of, Eur. (jûr'má-nĭ)	154	51.45 N	8.30 E
Germiston, S. Afr. (jûr'mĭs-tŭn)	227b	26.19 S	28.11 E
Gerona, Phil. (hā-rō'nä)	207a	15.36 N	120.36 E
Gerona, Sp. (hĕ-rô'nä)	170	41.55 N	2.48 E
Gerrards Cross, Eng. (jĕr'ards krŏs)	156b	51.34 N	0.33 W
Gers (R.), Fr. (zhĕr)	171	43.25 N	0.30 E
Gersthofen, F.R.G. (gĕrst-hō'fĕn)	157d	48.26 N	10.54 E
Getafe, Sp. (hā-tä'fā)	171a	40.19 N	3.44 W
Gettysburg, Pa. (gĕt'ĭs-bûrg)	111	39.50 N	77.15 W
Gettysburg, SD	114	45.01 N	99.59 W
Getzville, NY	57a	43.01 N	78.46 W
Gevelsberg, F.R.G. (gĕ-fĕls'bĕrgh)	169c	51.18 N	7.20 E
Geweke (Neigh.), F.R.G.	63	51.22 N	7.25 E
Ghāghra (R.), India	196	27.19 N	81.22 E
Ghana, Afr. (gän'ä)	222	8.00 N	2.00 W
Ghanzi, Bots. (gän'zē)	226	21.30 S	22.00 E
Ghārāpuri, India	67e	18.54 N	72.56 E
Ghardaïa, Alg. (gär-dä'ē-ä)	224	32.29 N	3.38 E
Gharo, Pak.	196	24.50 N	68.35 E
Ghāt, Libya	224	24.52 N	10.16 E
Ghātkopar (Neigh.), India	67e	19.05 N	72.54 E
Ghazāl, Bahr al- (R.), Sud.	225	9.11 N	29.37 E
Ghazal, Bahr el (R.), Chad. (bär ĕl ghä-zäl')	229	14.30 N	17.00 E
Ghāzipur (Neigh.), India	67d	28.38 N	77.19 E
Ghaznī, Afg. (gŭz'nē)	196	33.43 N	68.18 E
Ghazzah, Gaza Strip (Gaza)	191a	31.30 N	34.29 E
Gheorgheni, Rom.	167	46.48 N	25.30 E
Gherla, Rom. (gĕr'lä)	167	47.01 N	23.55 E
Ghilizane, Alg.	160	35.43 N	0.43 E
Ghonda (Neigh.), India	67d	28.41 N	77.16 E
Ghondi (Neigh.), India	67d	28.42 N	77.16 E
Ghost Lake, Can.	95e	51.15 N	114.46 W
Ghudāmis, Libya	224	30.07 N	9.26 E
Ghūrīān, Afg.	195	34.21 N	61.30 E
Ghushuri, India	67a	22.37 N	88.22 E
Gia-dinh, Viet.	68m	10.48 N	106.42 E
Giannutri, I. di, It. (jän-nōō'trē)	172	42.15 N	11.06 E
Gibara, Cuba (hē-bä'rä)	135	21.05 N	76.10 W
Gibbsboro, NJ	56b	39.50 N	74.58 W
Gibeon, Namibia (gĭb'ē-ŭn)	226	24.45 S	16.40 E
Gibraleón, Sp. (hē-brä-lå-ōn')	170	37.24 N	7.00 W
Gibraltar, Eur. (hē-bräl-tä'r)	159	36.08 N	5.22 W
Gibraltar, Bay of, Sp.	170	35.04 N	5.10 W
Gibraltar Pt., Can.	54c	43.36 N	79.23 W
Gibraltar, Str. of, Afr.-Eur.	170	35.55 N	5.45 W
Gibson City, Il. (gĭb'sŭn)	110	40.25 N	88.20 W
Gibson Des, Austl.	214	24.45 S	123.15 E
Gibson Island, Md.	112e	39.05 N	76.26 W
Gibson Res., Ok.	123	36.07 N	95.08 W
Giddings, Tx. (gĭd'ĭngz)	125	30.11 N	96.55 W
Gidea Park (Neigh.), Eng.	62	51.35 N	0.12 E
Gideon, Mo. (gĭd'ē-ŭn)	123	36.27 N	89.56 W
Gien, Fr. (zhē-ăN')	168	47.43 N	2.37 E
Giessen, F.R.G. (gēs'sĕn)	166	50.35 N	8.40 E
Gif-sur-Yvette, Fr.	64c	48.42 N	2.08 E
Gifu, Jap. (gē'fōō)	205	35.25 N	136.45 E
Gig Harbor, Wa. (gĭg)	118a	47.20 N	122.36 W
Giglio, I. di, It. (jēl'yō)	172	42.23 N	10.55 E
Gijón, Sp. (hē-hōn')	170	43.33 N	5.37 W
Gila (R.), Az. (hē'lá)	121	32.41 N	113.50 W
Gila Bend, Az.	121	32.59 N	112.41 W
Gila Bend Ind. Res., Az.	121	33.02 N	112.48 W
Gila Cliffs Dwellings Natl. Mon., NM	121	33.15 N	108.20 W
Gila River Ind. Res., Az.	121	33.11 N	112.38 W
Gilbert, Mn. (gĭl'bērt)	115	47.27 N	92.29 W
Gilbert (R.), Austl. (gĭl-bērt)	215	17.15 S	142.09 E
Gilbert, Mt., Can.	98	50.51 N	124.20 W
Gilbert Islands (I.), Kiribati	208	0.30 S	174.00 E
Gilboa, Mt., S. Afr. (gĭl-bôá)	227c	29.13 N	30.17 W
Gilford I., Can. (gĭl'fērd)	98	50.45 N	126.25 W
Gilgit, Pak. (gĭl'gĭt)	196	35.58 N	73.48 E
Gil I., Can. (gĭl)	98	53.13 N	129.15 W
Gillen (I.), Austl. (jĭl'ĕn)	214	26.15 S	125.15 E
Gillett, Ar. (jĭ-lĕt')	123	34.07 N	91.22 W
Gillette, Wyo.	117	44.17 N	105.30 W
Gillingham, Eng. (gĭl'ĭng ăm)	156b	51.23 N	0.33 E
Gilman, Il. (gĭl'măn)	110	40.45 N	87.55 W
Gilman Hot Springs, Ca.	119a	33.49 N	116.57 W
Gilmer, Tx. (gĭl'mēr)	125	32.43 N	94.57 W
Gilmore, Ga. (gĭl'môr)	112c	33.51 N	84.29 W
Gilo (R.), Eth.	225	7.40 N	34.17 E
Gilroy, Ca. (gĭl-roi')	120	37.00 N	121.34 W
Giluwe, Mt., Pap. N. Gui.	207	6.04 S	144.00 E
Gimli, Can. (gĭm'lē)	101	50.39 N	97.00 W
Gimone (R.), Fr. (zhē-mōn')	168	43.26 N	0.36 E
Ginir, Eth.	225	7.13 N	40.44 E
Ginosa, It. (jē-nō'zä)	172	40.35 N	16.48 E
Ginza (Neigh.), Jap.	69a	35.40 N	139.47 E
Ginzo, Sp. (hēn-thō')	170	42.03 N	7.43 W
Gioia del Colle, It. (jō'yä dĕl kôl'lā)	172	40.48 N	16.55 E
Gi-Paraná (R.), Braz. (zhē-pä-rä-ná')	143	9.33 S	61.35 W
Girard, Ks. (jĭ-rärd')	123	37.30 N	94.50 W
Girardot, Col. (hē-rär-dōt')	142a	4.19 N	75.47 W
Giresun, Tur. (ghĕr'ĕ-sōōn')	179	40.55 N	38.20 E
Girgaum (Neigh.), India	67e	18.57 N	72.48 E
Giridih, India (jē-rē-dē)	196	24.12 N	81.18 E
Gironde (Est.), Fr. (zhē-rônd')	168	45.31 N	1.00 W
Girvan, Scot. (gûr'văn)	162	55.15 N	5.01 W
Gisborne, N.Z. (gĭz'bŭrn)	217	38.40 S	178.08 E
Gisenyi, Rw.	231	1.43 S	29.15 E
Gisors, Fr. (zhē-zôr')	168	49.19 N	1.47 E
Gitambo, Zaire	230	4.21 N	24.45 E
Gitega, Burundi	226	3.39 S	30.05 E
Giurgiu, Rom. (jōōr'jōō)	173	43.53 N	25.58 E
Givet, Fr. (zhē-vĕ')	168	50.80 N	4.47 E
Givors, Fr. (zhē-vôr')	168	45.35 N	4.46 E
Giza Pyramids (P. Int.), Egypt	71a	29.59 N	31.08 E
Gizhiga, Sov. Un. (gē'zhi-gá)	181	61.59 N	160.46 E
Gizycko, Pol. (gĭ'zhĭ-ko)	167	54.03 N	21.48 E
Gjirokastër, Alb.	173	40.04 N	20.10 E
Gjøvik, Nor. (gyû'vĕk)	164	60.47 N	10.36 E
Glabeek-Zuurbemde, Bel.	157a	50.52 N	4.59 E
Glace Bay, Can. (gläs bā)	105	46.12 N	59.57 W
Glacier Bay Natl. Park, Ak. (glā'shēr)	107	58.40 N	136.50 W
Glacier Natl. Park, Can.	99	51.45 N	117.35 W
Glacier Pk., Wa.	116	48.07 N	121.10 W

ăt; finăl; rāte; senāte; ärm; ȧsk; sofȧ; fâre; ch-choose; dh-as th in other; bē; ēvent; bĕt; recĕnt; cratēr; g-gō; gh-guttural g; bĭt; ĭ-short neutral; rīde; ĸ-guttural k as ch in German ich;

PLACE (Pronounciation)	PAGE	Lat. °′	Long. °′
Glacier Pt., Can.	118a	48.24 N	123.59 W
Gladbeck, F.R.G. (gläd'bĕk)	169c	51.35 N	6.59 E
Gladdeklipkop, S. Afr.	223d	24.17 S	29.36 E
Gladesville, Austl.	70a	33.50 S	151.08 E
Gladstone, Austl. (glăd'stōn)	216	23.45 S	150.00 E
Gladstone, Austl.	216	33.15 S	138.20 E
Gladstone, Mi.	115	45.50 N	87.04 W
Gladstone, NJ	112a	40.43 N	74.39 W
Gladstone, Or.	118c	45.23 N	122.36 W
Gladwin, Mi. (glăd'wĭn)	110	44.00 N	84.25 W
Gladwyne, Pa.	56b	40.02 N	75.17 W
Glåma (R), Nor.	164	61.22 N	11.02 E
Glamoč, Yugo. (gläm'ôch)	172	44.03 N	16.51 E
Glarus, Switz. (glä'ro͞os)	166	47.02 N	9.03 E
Glasgow, Ky.	126	37.00 N	85.55 W
Glasgow, Mo.	123	39.14 N	92.48 W
Glasgow, Mt.	117	48.14 N	106.39 W
Glasgow, Scot. (glås'gō)	162	55.54 N	4.25 W
Glashütte (Neigh.), F.R.G.	63	51.13 N	6.52 E
Glassmanor, Md.	56d	38.49 N	76.59 W
Glassport, Pa. (glås'pōrt)	113e	40.19 N	79.53 W
Glassport, Pa.	57b	40.19 N	79.54 W
Glauchau, G.D.R. (glou'ĸou)	166	50.51 N	12.28 E
Glazov, Sov. Un. (glä'zôf)	178	58.05 N	52.52 E
Glehn, F.R.G.	63	51.10 N	6.35 E
Glen (R.), Eng. (glĕn)	156	52.44 N	0.18 W
Glénan, Iles de (Is.), Fr. (ēl-dē-glā-näɴ')	168	47.43 N	4.42 W
Glenarden, Md.	56d	38.56 N	76.52 W
Glen Burnie, Md. (bûr'nē)	112e	39.10 N	76.38 W
Glen Canyon Dam, Az. (glĕn kăn'yŭn)	121	36.57 N	111.25 W
Glen Carbon, Il. (kär'bŏn)	119e	38.45 N	89.59 W
Glencoe, Il.	113a	42.08 N	87.45 W
Glencoe, Mn. (glĕn'kō)	115	44.44 N	94.07 W
Glencoe, S. Afr. (glĕn-cō)	227c	28.14 S	30.09 E
Glen Cove, NY (kōv)	112a	40.51 N	73.38 W
Glendale, Az. (glĕn'dāl)	121	33.30 N	112.15 W
Glendale, Ca.	119a	34.09 N	118.15 W
Glendale, Oh.	113f	31.16 N	84.22 W
Glendive, Mt. (glĕn'dīv)	117	47.08 N	104.41 W
Glendo, Wy.	117	42.32 N	104.54 W
Glendora, Ca. (glĕn-dō'rȧ)	119a	34.08 N	117.52 W
Glendora, NJ	56b	39.50 N	75.04 W
Glen Echo, Md	56d	38.58 N	77.08 W
Glenelg (R.), Austl.	216	37.20 S	141.30 E
Glen Ellyn, Il. (glĕn ĕl'-lĕn)	113a	41.53 N	88.04 W
Glenfield, Austl.	70a	33.58 S	150.54 E
Glen Head, NY	55	40.50 N	73.37 W
Glenhuntly, Austl.	70b	37.54 S	145.03 E
Glen Innes, Austl. (ĭn'ĕs)	216	29.45 S	152.02 E
Glenmore, Md.	56c	39.11 N	76.36 W
Glenns Ferry, Id. (fĕr'ĭ)	116	42.58 N	115.21 W
Glen Olden, Pa. (ōl'd'n)	112f	39.54 N	75.17 W
Glenomra, La. (glĕn-mō'rȧ)	125	30.58 N	92.36 W
Glen Ridge, NJ	55	40.49 N	74.13 W
Glen Rock, NJ	55	40.58 N	74.08 W
Glenrock, Wy. (glĕn'rŏk)	117	42.50 N	105.53 W
Glenroy, Austl.	70b	37.42 S	144.55 E
Glens Falls, NY (glĕnz fôlz)	111	43.20 N	73.40 W
Glenshaw, Pa. (glĕn'shô)	113e	40.33 N	79.57 W
Glenside, Pa.	56b	40.06 N	75.09 W
Glen Ullin, ND (glĕn'ŭl'ĭn)	114	46.47 N	101.49 W
Glen Valley, Can.	118d	49.09 N	122.30 W
Glenview, IL (glĕn'vū)	113a	42.04 N	87.48 W
Glenville, Ga. (glĕn'vĭl)	127	31.55 N	81.56 W
Glen Waverley, Austl.	70b	37.53 S	145.10 E
Glenwood, Ia.	114	41.03 N	95.44 W
Glenwood, Mn.	114	45.39 N	95.23 W
Glenwood Landing, NY	55	40.50 N	73.39 W
Glenwood Springs, Co.	121	39.35 N	107.20 W
Glienicke, G.D.R. (glē'nē-kĕ)	157b	52.38 N	13.19 E
Glinde, F.R.G. (glēn'dĕ)	157c	53.32 N	10.13 E
Glittertinden (Mtn.), Nor.	164	61.39 N	8.12 E
Gliwice, Pol. (gwĭ-wĭt'sĕ)	167	50.18 N	18.40 E
Globe, Az. (glōb)	121	33.20 N	110.50 W
Globino, Sov. Un. (glôb'ĕ-nô)	175	49.22 N	33.17 E
Głogów, Pol. (gwō'go͞ov)	166	51.40 N	16.04 E
Glommen (R.), Nor. (glôm'ĕn)	164	60.03 N	11.15 E
Glonn, F.R.G. (glônn)	157d	47.59 N	11.52 E
Glorieuses, Iles (Is.), Afr.	227	11.28 S	47.50 E
Glossop, Eng. (glŏs'ŭp)	156	53.26 N	1.57 W
Gloster, Ms. (glŏs'tēr)	126	31.10 N	91.00 W
Gloucester, Eng. (glŏs'tēr)	162	51.54 N	2.11 W
Gloucester, Ma.	105a	42.37 N	70.40 W
Gloucester City, NJ	112f	39.53 N	75.08 W
Glouster, Oh. (glŏs'tēr)	110	39.35 N	82.05 W
Glover I., Can. (glŭv'ēr)	105	48.44 N	57.45 W
Gloversville, NY (glŭv'ērz-vĭl)	111	43.05 N	74.20 W
Glovertown, Can. (glŭv'ēr-toun)	105	48.41 N	54.02 W
Glubokoye, Sov. Un. (glo͞o-bô-kō'yĕ)	174	55.08 N	27.44 E
Glückstadt, F.R.G. (glük-shtät)	157c	53.47 N	9.25 E
Glukhov, Sov. Un. (glo͞o'ĸôf')	175	51.42 N	33.52 E
Glushkovo, Sov. Un. (glo͞osh'kô-vô)	175	51.21 N	34.43 E
Gmünden, Aus. (g'mo͞on'dĕn)	166	47.57 N	13.47 E
Gniezno, Pol. (g'nyăz'nô)	167	52.32 N	17.34 E
Gnjilane, Yugo. (gnyē'lȧ-nĕ)	173	42.28 N	21.27 E
Goa (Ter.), India (gō'ȧ)	197	15.45 N	74.00 E
Goascorán, Hond. (gō-äs'kō-rän')	132	13.37 N	87.43 W
Goba, Eth. (gō'bä)	225	7.17 N	39.58 E
Gobabis, Namibia (gō-bä'bĭs)	226	22.25 S	18.50 E
Gobi or Shamo (Des.), Mong. (gō'be)	198	43.29 N	103.15 E
Goble, Or. (gō'b'l)	118c	46.01 N	122.53 W
Goch, F.R.G. (gōĸ)	169c	51.35 N	6.10 E
Godāvari (R.), India (gô-dä'vŭ-rē)	196	17.42 N	81.15 E
Goddards Soak (Swp.), Austl. (gŏd'ărdz)	214	31.20 S	123.30 E
Goderich, Can. (gŏd'rĭch)	110	43.45 N	81.45 W
Godfrey, Il. (gŏd'frē)	119e	38.57 N	90.12 W
Godhavn, Grnld. (gōdh'hävn)	94	69.15 N	53.30 W
Gods (R.), Can. (gŏdz)	101	55.17 N	93.35 W
Gods Lake, Can.	101	54.40 N	94.09 W
Godthåb, Grnld. (gŏt'hōb)	94	64.10 N	51.32 W
Godwin Austen (Mtn.), See K2			
Goéland, Lac au (L.), Can.	103	49.47 N	76.41 W
Goffs, Ca. (gôfs)	120	34.57 N	115.06 W
Goff's Oak, Eng.	62	51.43 N	0.05 W
Gogebic (L.), Mi. (gô-gē'bĭk)	115	46.24 N	89.25 W
Gogebic Ra, Mi.	115	46.37 N	89.48 W
Goggingen, F.R.G. (gûg'gĕn-gĕn)	157d	48.21 N	10.53 E
Gogland (I.), Sov. Un.	165	60.04 N	26.55 E
Gogonou, Benin	229	10.50 N	2.50 E
Gogorrón, Mex. (gō-gô-rōn')	130	21.51 N	100.54 W
Goiânia, Braz. (gô-yȧ'nyä)	143	16.41 S	48.57 W
Goiás, Braz. (gô-yá's)	143	15.57 S	50.10 W
Goiás (State), Braz.	143	12.35 S	48.38 W
Goirle, Neth.	157a	51.31 N	5.06 E
Gökçeada (I.), Tur.	173	40.10 N	25.27 E
Göksu (R.), Tur. (gûk'so͞o')	179	36.40 N	33.30 E
Gol, Nor. (gûl)	164	60.58 N	8.54 E
Golabāri, India	67a	22.36 N	88.20 E
Golax, Va. (gō'lăks)	127	36.41 N	80.56 W
Golcar, Eng. (gŏl'kȧr)	156	53.38 N	1.52 W
Golconda, Il. (gŏl-kŏn'dȧ)	123	37.21 N	88.32 W
Goldap, Pol. (gôl'dăp)	167	54.17 N	22.17 E
Golden, Can.	99	51.18 N	116.58 W
Golden, Co.	122	39.44 N	105.15 W
Goldendale, Wa. (gōl'dĕn-dāl)	116	45.49 N	120.48 W
Golden Gate (Str.), Ca. (gōl'dĕn gāt)	118b	37.48 N	122.32 W
Golden Hinde, Can. (hīnd)	98	49.40 N	125.45 W
Golden's Bridge, NY	112a	41.17 N	73.41 W
Golden Valley, Mn.	119g	44.58 N	93.23 W
Golders Green (Neigh.), Eng.	62	51.35 N	0.12 W
Goldfield, Nv. (gōld'fēld)	120	37.42 N	117.15 W
Gold Hill (Mtn.), Pan.	128a	9.03 N	79.08 W
Gold Mtn., Wa. (gōld)	118a	47.33 N	122.48 W
Goldsboro, NC (gōldz-bûr'ô)	127	35.23 N	77.59 W
Goldthwaite, Tx. (gōld'thwāt)	124	31.27 N	98.34 W
Goleniów, Pol. (gō-lĕ-nyūf')	166	53.33 N	14.51 E
Golets-Purpula, Gol'tsy (Mtn.), Sov. Un.	181	59.08 N	115.22 E
Golf, Il.	58a	42.03 N	87.48 W
Golfito, C.R. (gôl-fē'tō)	133	8.40 N	83.12 W
Golfo Dulce, see Izabal, L.			
Golf Park Terrace, Il.	58a	42.03 N	87.51 W
Goliad, Tx. (gō-lĭ-ăd')	125	28.40 N	97.12 W
Golo I., Phil. (gō'lō)	207a	13.38 N	120.17 E
Golo (R.), Fr.	172	42.28 N	9.18 E
Golovchino, Sov. Un. (gō-lôf'chĕ-nō)	175	50.34 N	35.52 E
Golyamo Konare, Bul. (gō'lȧ-mō-kō'nä-rĕ)	173	42.16 N	24.33 E
Golzow, G.D.R. (gōl'tsōv)	157b	52.17 N	12.36 E
Gombari, Zaire (go͞om-bä-rē)	231	2.45 N	29.00 E
Gombe, Nig.	229	10.19 N	11.02 E
Gomel', Sov. Un. (Oblast)	174	52.18 N	29.00 E
Gomel', Sov. Un. (go'mĕl')	174	52.20 N	31.03 E
Gomera I., Can. Is. (gô-mä'rä)	224	28.00 N	18.01 W
Gomez Farias, Mex. (gō'mäz fä-rē'äs)	124	24.59 N	101.02 W
Gómez Palacio, Mex. (pä-lä'syō)	124	25.35 N	103.30 W
Gonaïves, Hai. (gō-nȧ-ēv')	135	19.25 N	72.45 W
Gonaïves, Golfe des (G.), Hai. (gō-nȧ-ēv')	135	19.20 N	73.20 W
Gonâve, Ile De La (I.); Hai. (gô-nȧv')	135	18.50 N	73.30 W
Gonda, India	196	27.13 N	82.00 E
Gondal, India	196	22.02 N	70.47 E
Gonder, Eth.	225	12.39 N	37.30 E
Gonesse, Fr. (gô-nĕs')	169b	48.59 N	2.28 E
Gongga Shan (Mt.), China (gôŋ-gä shän)	198	29.16 N	101.46 E
Goniri, Nig.	229	11.30 N	12.20 E
Gonor, Can. (gō'nŏr)	95f	50.04 N	96.57 W
Gonō (R.), Jap. (gō'nō)	205	35.00 N	132.25 E
Gonubie, S. Afr. (gŏn'o͞o-bē)	227c	32.56 S	28.02 E
Gonzales, Mex. (gōn-zá'lĕs)	130	22.47 N	98.26 W
Gonzales, Tx. (gŏn-zä'lĕz)	125	29.31 N	97.25 W
González Catán, Arg. (gōn-zá'lĕz-kä-tȧ'n)	144a	34.31 S	58.39 W
Good Hope, C. of, S. Afr. (kăp ov go͝od hōp)	226a	34.21 S	18.29 E
Good Hope Mtn., Can.	98	51.09 N	124.10 W
Gooding, Id. (go͝od'ĭng)	116	42.55 N	114.43 W
Goodland, In. (go͝od'lănd)	110	40.50 N	87.15 W
Goodland, Ks.	122	39.19 N	101.43 W
Goodwood, S. Afr. (go͝od'wo͝od)	226a	33.54 S	18.33 E
Goole, Eng. (go͞ol)	156	53.42 N	0.52 W
Goose (R.), ND	114	47.40 N	97.41 W
Goose Bay, Can.	97	53.19 N	60.33 W
Gooseberry Cr., Wy. (go͞os-bĕr'ĭ)	117	44.04 N	108.35 W
Goose Cr., Id. (go͞os)	117	42.07 N	113.53 W
Goose L., Ca.	116	41.56 N	120.35 W
Gorakhpur, India (gō'rŭk-po͞or)	196	26.45 N	82.39 E
Gorda Cay, Ba. (gôr'dä)	134	26.05 N	77.30 W
Gorda, Punta (Pt.), Cuba (po͞o'n-tä-gôr-dä)	134	22.25 N	82.10 W
Gordon, Can. (gôr'dŭn)	95f	50.00 N	97.20 W
Gordon, Ne.	114	42.47 N	102.14 W
Gordons Corner, Md.	56d	39.50 N	76.57 W
Gore, Eth. (gō'rē)	225	8.12 N	35.34 E
Gore Hill, Austl.	70a	33.49 S	151.11 E
Gorgān, Iran	192	36.44 N	54.30 E
Gorgona, Isola di, It. (gôr-gō'nä)	172	43.27 N	9.55 E
Gori, Sov. Un. (gō'rē)	179	42.00 N	44.08 E
Gorinchem, Neth. (gō'rĭn-ĸĕm)	157a	51.50 N	4.59 E
Goring, Eng. (gôr'ĭng)	156b	51.30 N	1.08 W
Gorizia, It. (gō-rē'tsē-yä)	172	44.56 N	13.40 E
Gor'kiy, Sov. Un. (gôr'kē)	178	56.15 N	44.05 E
Gor'kovskoye, Sov. Un.	178	56.38 N	43.40 E
Gor'kovskoye Vdkhr. (Res.), Sov. Un. (gôr-kôf-skô-yĕ)	174	57.38 N	41.18 E
Gorlice, Pol. (gôr-lē'tsĕ)	167	49.38 N	21.11 E
Görlitz, G.D.R. (gŭr'lĭts)	166	51.10 N	15.01 E
Gorlovka, Sov. Un. (gôr'lôf-kȧ)	175	48.17 N	38.03 E
Gorman, Tx. (gôr'măn)	124	32.13 N	98.40 W
Gorna Oryakhovitsa, Bul. (gôr'nä-ôr-yĕk'ô-vē-tsȧ)	173	43.08 N	25.40 E
Gornji Milanovac, Yugo (gôrn'yē-mē'la-nô-väts)	173	44.02 N	20.29 E
Gorno-Altay Aut. Oblast, Sov. Un.	180	51.00 N	86.00 E
Gorno-Altaysk, Sov. Un. (gôr'nŭ'ŭl-tīsk')	180	52.28 N	82.45 E
Gorodënka, Sov. Un. (gō-rô-deŋ'kä)	167	48.40 N	25.30 E
Gorodets (Res.), Sov. Un.	178	57.00 N	43.55 E
Gorodishche, Sov. Un. (gô-rô'dĭsh-chĕ)	182a	57.57 N	57.03 E
Gorodnya, Sov. Un. (gô-rôd''nyä)	175	51.54 N	31.31 E
Gorodok, Sov. Un. (gō-rô-dôk')	167	49.37 N	23.40 E
Gorodok, Sov. Un.	174	55.27 N	29.58 E
Gorodok, Sov. Un.	180	50.30 N	103.58 E
Gorontalo, Indon. (gō-rōn-tä'lo)	206	0.40 N	123.04 E
Gorton (Neigh.), Eng.	64b	53.27 N	2.10 W
Goryn' R., Sov. Un. (gō'rĕn')	167	50.55 N	26.07 E
Gorzow Wielkopolski, Pol. (gō-zho͞ov'vyĕl-ko-pōl'skē)	166	53.44 N	15.15 E
Gosely, Eng.	156	52.33 N	2.10 W
Gosen, G.D.R.	65a	52.24 N	13.43 E
Goshen, In. (gō'shĕn)	110	41.35 N	85.50 W
Goshen, Ky.	113h	38.24 N	85.34 W
Goshen, NY	112a	41.24 N	74.19 W
Goshen, Oh.	113f	39.14 N	84.09 W
Goshute Ind. Res., Ut. (gō-sho͞ot')	121	39.50 N	114.00 W
Goslar, F.R.G. (gôs'lär)	166	51.55 N	10.25 E
Gospa (R.), Ven. (gôs-pä)	143b	9.43 N	64.23 W
Gospić, Yugo. (gôs'pĭch)	172	44.31 N	15.03 E
Gostivar, Yugo. (gos'tē-vär)	173	41.46 N	20.58 E
Gostynin, Pol. (gôs-tē'nĭn)	167	52.24 N	19.30 E
Göta (R.), Swe. (gōĕtä)	164	58.11 N	12.03 E
Göta Kanal (Can.), Swe. (yû'tȧ)	164	58.35 N	15.24 E
Gotanno (Neigh.), Jap.	69a	35.46 N	139.49 E
Göteborg, Swe. (yû'tĕ-bôrgh)	164	57.39 N	11.56 E
Gotel Mts., Cam.-Nig.	229	7.05 N	11.20 E
Gotera, Sal. (gō-tā'rä)	132	13.41 N	88.06 W
Gotha, G.D.R. (gō'tȧ)	166	50.47 N	10.43 E
Gothenburg, Ne. (gŏth'ĕn-bûrg)	122	40.57 N	100.08 W
Gotland (I.), Swe.	164	57.35 N	17.35 E
Gotō-Rettō (Is.), Jap. (gō'tō rĕt'tō)	205	33.06 N	128.54 E
Gotska Sandön (I.), Swe.	165	58.24 N	19.15 E
Götterswickerhamm, F.R.G.	63	51.35 N	6.40 E
Göttin, G.D.R.	65a	52.27 N	12.54 E
Göttingen, F.R.G. (gŭt'ĭng-ĕn)	166	51.32 N	9.57 E
Gouda, Neth. (gou'dä)	157a	52.00 N	4.42 E
Gough (I.), Atl. O. (gŏf)	232	40.00 S	10.00 W
Gouin, Rés, Can.	97	48.15 N	74.15 W
Goukou, China (gō-kō)	202	48.45 N	121.42 E
Goulais (R.), Can.	102	46.45 N	84.10 W
Goulburn, Austl. (gōl'bŭrn)	216	34.47 S	149.40 E
Goumbati (Mtn.), Senegal	228	13.08 N	12.06 W
Goumbou, Mali (go͞om-bo͞o')	228	14.59 N	7.27 W
Gouna, Cam.	229	8.32 N	13.34 E
Goundam, Mali (go͞on-däɴ')	224	16.29 N	3.37 W
Gouré, Niger (go͞o-ra')	224	13.53 N	10.44 E
Gournay-sur-Marne, Fr.	64c	48.52 N	2.34 E
Goussainville, Fr.	64c	49.01 N	2.28 E
Gouverneur, NY (gŭv-ēr-no͞or')	111	44.20 N	75.25 W
Go-vap, Viet.	68m	10.49 N	106.42 E
Govenlock, Can. (gŭvĕn-lŏk)	100	49.15 N	109.48 W
Governador Ilhado (I.), Braz. (gô-vĕr-nä-dō'r-ē-lä'dō)	144b	22.48 S	43.13 W
Governador Portela, Braz. (pōr-tĕ'lá)	144b	22.28 S	43.30 W
Governador Valadares, Braz. (vä-lä-dä'rĕs)	143	18.47 S	41.45 W
Governor's Harbour, Ba.	135	25.15 N	76.15 W
Gowanda, NY (gô-wŏn'dȧ)	111	42.30 N	78.55 W
Goya, Arg. (gō'yä)	144	29.06 S	59.12 W
Goyt (R.), Eng. (goit)	156	53.19 N	2.03 W
Graaff-Reinet, S. Afr. (gräf'rī'nĕt)	226	32.10 S	24.40 E
Gracac, Yugo. (grä'chäts)	172	44.16 N	15.50 E
Gračanico, Yugo.	173	44.42 N	18.19 E
Graceville, Fl. (grās'vĭl)	126	30.57 N	85.30 W
Graceville, Mn.	114	45.33 N	96.25 W
Gracias, Hond. (grä'sē-äs)	132	14.35 N	88.37 W
Gracias a Dios, Cabo (C.) (kȧ'bô-grä-syäs-ä-dyô's)	133	15.00 N	83.13 W
Graciosa I., Açores (grä-syō'sä)	224a	39.07 N	27.30 W
Gradačac, Yugo. (gra-dä'chats)	173	44.50 N	18.28 E
Gradizhsk, Sov. Un. (grä-dēzhsk')	175	49.12 N	33.06 E
Grado, Sp. (grä'dō)	170	43.24 N	6.04 W
Gräfelging, F.R.G. (grä'fĕl-fĕng)	157d	48.07 N	11.27 E
Grafenberg (Neigh.), F.R.G.	63	51.14 N	6.50 E
Grafing bei München, F.R.G. (grä'fĕng)	157d	48.03 N	11.58 E
Grafton, Austl. (graf'tŭn)	216	29.38 S	153.05 E
Grafton, Il.	119e	38.58 N	90.26 W
Grafton, Ma.	105a	42.13 N	71.41 W
Grafton, ND	114	48.24 N	97.25 W
Grafton, Oh.	113d	41.16 N	82.04 W
Grafton, WV	111	39.20 N	80.00 W
Gragnano, It. (grän-yä'nō)	171c	40.27 N	14.32 E
Graham, NC (grā'ăm)	127	36.03 N	79.23 W
Graham, Tx.	122	33.07 N	98.34 W
Graham, Wa.	118a	47.03 N	122.18 W
Graham (I.), Can.	96	53.50 N	132.40 W
Grahamstown, S. Afr. (grā'ămș'toun)	227c	33.19 S	26.33 E
Grajaú, Braz. (grá-zhȧ-o͞o')	143	5.59 S	46.03 W
Grajaú (R.), Braz.	143	4.24 S	46.04 W
Grajewo, Pol. (grä-yä'vo)	167	53.38 N	22.28 E
Gramada, Bul. (grä'mä-dä)	173	43.46 N	22.41 E
Grama, Serra de (Mtn.), Braz. (sĕ'r-rä-dē-grá'má)	141a	23.42 S	42.28 W
Gramatneusiedl, Aus.	157e	48.02 N	16.29 E
Grammichele, It. (gräm-mē-kĕ'lā)	172	37.15 N	14.40 E
Grampian Mts., Scot. (grăm'pĭ-ăn)	162	56.30 N	4.55 W
Granada, Nic. (grä-nä'dhä)	132	11.55 N	85.58 W

ng-sing; nŋ-banŋk; ɴ-nasalized n; nŏd; cŏmmit; ōld; ôbey; ôrder; oi-boil; fo͞od; fo͝ot; ou-out; s-soft; sh-dish; th-thin; pūre; ûnite; ûrn; stŭd; circŭs; ü-as in French tu; '-indeterminate vowel.

PLACE (Pronounciation)	PAGE	Lat. °′	Long. °′
Granada, Sp. (grä-nä'dä)	170	37.13 N	3.37 W
Gran Bajo (Pln.), Arg. (grán'bä'kō)	144	47.35 S	68.45 W
Granbury, Tx. (grăn'bĕr-ĭ)	125	32.26 N	97.45 W
Granby, Can. (grăn'bĭ)	111	45.30 N	72.40 W
Granby (L.), Co.	122	40.07 N	105.40 W
Granby, Mo.	123	36.54 N	94.15 W
Gran Canal del Desagüe (Can.), Mex.	60a	19.29 N	99.05 W
Gran Canaria I., Can. Is. (grän'kä-nä'rē-ä)	224	27.39 N	15.39 W
Gran Chaco (Reg.), Arg.-Par. (grán'chá'kō)	144	25.30 S	62.15 W
Grand (I.), Mi.	115	46.37 N	86.38 W
Grand (L.), Can.	104	45.17 N	67.42 W
Grand (L.), Can.	104	66.15 N	45.59 W
Grand (R.), Can.	103	43.45 N	80.20 W
Grand (R.), Mi.	110	42.58 N	85.13 W
Grand (R.), Mo.	123	39.50 N	93.52 W
Grand (R.), North Fork, SD	114	45.52 N	102.49 W
Grand (R.), SD	114	45.40 N	101.55 W
Grand (R.), South Fork, SD	114	45.38 N	102.56 W
Grand Bahama (I.), Ba.	134	26.35 N	78.30 W
Grand Bank, Can. (grănd băngk)	105	47.06 N	55.47 W
Grand Bassam, Ivory Coast (grän bá-sän')	228	5.12 N	3.44 W
Grand Bourg, Guad. (grän bōōr')	133b	15.54 N	61.20 W
Grand Caicos (I.), Turks & Caicos Is. (grănd kä-ē'kōs)	135	21.45 N	71.50 W
Grand Canal, Ire.	162	53.21 N	7.15 W
Grand Canal, see Da Yunhe			
Grand Canyon, Az. (grănd kăn yŭn)	121	36.05 N	112.10 W
Grand Canyon (canyon), Az.	121	35.50 N	113.16 W
Grand Canyon Natl. Park, Az.	121	36.15 N	112.20 W
Grand Cayman (I.), Cayman Is. (kā'măn)	134	19.15 N	81.15 W
Grand Coulee Dam, Wa. (kōō'lē)	116	47.58 N	119.28 W
Grande (R.), Chili	141b	35.25 S	70.14 W
Grande, (R.), Mex.	131	17.37 N	96.41 W
Grande (R.), Ur.	141c	33.19 S	57.15 W
Grande, Bahía (B.), Arg. (bä-ē'ä-grän'dě)	144	50.45 S	68.00 W
Grande, Boca (Est.), Ven. (bō'kä-grä'n-dě)	143	8.46 N	60.17 W
Grande Cayemite, Ile (I.), Hai.	135	18.45 N	73.45 W
Grande, Ciri (R.), Pan. (sē'rē-grä'n'dě)	128a	8.55 N	80.04 W
Grande Comore, Comoros (grä'n-dě-kō-mō-rē)	227	11.44 S	42.38 E
Grande, Cuchilla (Mts.), Ur. (kōō-chē'l-yä)	144	33.00 S	55.15 W
Grande de Otoro, Hond. (grä'dā dā ō-tō'rō)	132	14.42 N	88.21 W
Grande, Ilha (I.), Braz. (grän'dě)	141a	23.11 S	44.14 W
Grande Pointe, Can. (grănd point')	95f	49.47 N	97.03 W
Grande Prairie, Can. (prâr'ĭ)	99	55.10 N	118.48 W
Grande R., Nic. (grän'dě)	133	13.01 N	84.21 W
Grand Erg Occidental (Dunes), Alg.	224	29.37 N	6.04 E
Grande, Rio (R.), Bol.	142	16.49 S	63.19 W
Grande, Rio (R.), (Bravo del Norte, Rio), Mex.-U.S. (grän'dā)	108	26.50 N	99.10 W
Grande, Rio (R.), Braz.	143	19.48 S	49.54 W
Grande Rivière du Nord, Hai. (rē-vyâr' dü nôr')	135	19.35 N	72.10 W
Grande Ronde R., Or. (rŏnd')	116	45.32 N	117.52 W
Grande, Salinas (F.), Arg. (sä-lē'näs)	144	29.45 S	65.00 W
Grande, Salto (Falls), Braz. (säl-tô)	143	16.18 S	39.38 W
Gran Desierto (Des.), Mex. (grän-dě-syě'r-tô)	120	32.14 N	114.28 W
Grande Soufriere Vol., Guad. (sōō-frē-âr')	133b	16.06 N	61.42 W
Grande Terre I., Guad. (târ')	133b	16.28 N	61.13 W
Grande Vigie, Pointe de la (Pt.), Guad. (gränd vē-gē')	133b	16.32 N	61.25 W
Grand Falls, Can. (fôlz)	105	48.56 N	55.40 W
Grandfather, Mt., NC (grănd-fä-thēr)	101	36.07 N	81.48 W
Grandfield, Ok. (grănd'fēld)	122	34.13 N	98.39 W
Grand Forks, Can. (fôrks)	99	49.02 N	118.27 W
Grand Forks, ND	114	47.55 N	97.05 W
Grand Haven, Mi (hā'v'n)	110	43.05 N	86.15 W
Grand I, NY	113c	43.03 N	78.58 W
Grand Island, Ne. (ī'lănd)	122	40.56 N	98.20 W
Grand Island, NY	57a	42.49 N	78.58 W
Grand Junction, Co. (jŭngk'shŭn)	121	39.05 N	108.35 W
Grand L., Can. (lăk)	105	49.00 N	57.10 W
Grand L., La.	125	29.57 N	91.25 W
Grand L., Mn.	119h	46.54 N	92.26 W
Grand Ledge, Mi. (lěj)	110	42.45 N	84.50 W
Grand Lieu, L. de, Fr. (grän'-lyû)	168	46.00 N	1.45 W
Grand Manan (I.), Can. (mă-năn)	104	44.40 N	66.50 W
Grand Mère, Can. (grän mâr')	103	46.36 N	72.43 W
Grand Morin (R.), Fr. (mô-răn')	169b	48.23 N	2.19 E
Grândola, Port. (grăn'dô-là)	170	38.10 N	8.36 W
Grand Portage Ind. Res., Mn. (pōr'tĭj)	115	47.54 N	89.34 W
Grand Portage Natl. Mon., Mi.	115	47.59 N	89.47 W
Grand Prairie, Tx. (prē'rē)	119c	32.45 N	97.00 W
Grand Quivira Natl. Mon., NM (kē-vē'rá)	121	34.10 N	106.05 W
Grand Rapids, Can.	101	53.08 N	99.20 W
Grand Rapids, Mi. (răp'ĭdz)	110	43.00 N	85.45 W
Grand Rapids, Mn.	115	47.16 N	93.33 W
Grand Rapids Forebay (Res.), Can.	101	53.10 N	100.00 W
Grand-Riviere, Can.	104	48.26 N	64.30 W
Grand Teton Mt., Wy.	117	43.46 N	110.50 W
Grand Teton Natl. Park, Wy. (tē'tŏn)	117	43.54 N	110.15 W
Grand Traverse B., Mi. (trăv'ērs)	110	45.00 N	85.30 W
Grand Turk (I.), Turks & Caicos Is.	125	21.30 N	71.10 W
Grand Turk, Turks & Caicos Is. (tûrk)	135	21.30 N	71.10 W
Grandview, Mo. (grănd'vyōō)	119f	38.53 N	94.32 W
Grand Wash (R.), Az. (wŏsh)	121	36.20 N	113.52 W
Grandyle, NY	57a	43.00 N	78.57 W
Grange Hill, Eng.	62	51.37 N	0.05 E

PLACE (Pronounciation)	PAGE	Lat. °′	Long. °′
Granger, Wy. (grān'jēr)	117	41.37 N	109.58 W
Grangeville, Id. (grānj'vĭl)	116	45.56 N	116.08 W
Granite, Md.	56c	39.21 N	76.51 W
Granite City, Il. (grăn'ĭt sĭt'ĭ)	119e	38.42 N	90.09 W
Granite Falls, Mn. (fôlz)	114	44.46 N	95.34 W
Granite Falls, NC	127	35.49 N	81.25 W
Granite Falls, Wa.	118a	48.05 N	121.59 W
Granite L., Can.	105	48.01 N	57.00 W
Granite Pk., Mt.	117	45.13 N	109.48 W
Graniteville, SC (grăn'ĭt-vĭl)	127	33.35 N	81.50 W
Granito, Braz. (grä-nē'tō)	143	7.39 S	39.34 W
Granma (Prov.), Cuba	134	20.10 N	76.50 W
Gränna, Swe. (grĕn'á)	164	58.02 N	14.38 E
Granollers, Sp. (grä-nôl-yěrs')	171e	41.36 N	2.19 E
Gran Pajonal (Marsh), Peru (grä'n-pä-ĸō-näl')	142	11.14 S	71.45 W
Gran Piedra (Mtn.), Cuba (grän-pyě'drä)	125	20.00 N	75.40 W
Grantham, Eng. (grăn'tăm)	156	52.54 N	0.38 W
Grant Park, Il. (grănt pärk)	113a	41.14 N	87.39 W
Grant Park (P. Int.), Il.	58a	41.52 N	87.37 W
Grants Pass, Or. (grănts pȧs)	116	42.26 N	123.20 W
Granville, Austl.	70a	33.50 S	151.01 E
Granville, Fr. (grän-vēl')	168	48.52 N	1.35 W
Granville (L.), Can.	101	56.18 N	100.30 W
Granville, NY (grăn'vĭl)	111	43.25 N	73.15 W
Grão Mogol, Braz. (groun' mōō-gôl')	143	16.34 S	42.35 W
Grapevine, Tx. (grāp'vīn)	119c	32.56 N	97.05 W
Gräso (I.), Swe.	164	60.30 N	18.35 E
Grass (R.), NY	111	44.45 N	75.10 W
Grass Cay (I.), Vir. Is.(U.S.A.)	129c	18.22 N	64.50 W
Grasse, Fr. (gräs)	169	43.39 N	6.57 E
Grassendale (Neigh.), Eng.	64a	53.21 N	2.54 W
Grass Mtn., Wa. (grȧs)	118a	47.13 N	121.48 W
Grates Pt., Can. (grāts)	105	48.09 N	52.57 W
Gravelbourg, Can. (grăv'ĕl-bôrg)	100	49.53 N	106.34 W
Gravesend, Eng. (grāvz'ĕnd')	156b	51.26 N	0.22 E
Gravina, It. (grä-vē'nä)	172	40.48 N	16.27 E
Gravois, Pte., Hai. (grá-vwä')	135	18.00 N	74.20 W
Gray, Fr. (grā)	169	47.26 N	5.35 E
Grayling, Mi. (grā'lĭng)	110	44.40 N	84.40 W
Grays, Eng.	62	51.29 N	0.20 E
Grayslake, Il. (grāz'lāk)	113a	42.20 N	88.20 W
Grays Pk., Co. (grāz)	122	39.29 N	105.52 W
Grayvoron, Sov. Un. (grá-ē'vô-rôn)	175	50.28 N	35.41 E
Graz, Aus. (gräts)	166	47.05 N	15.26 E
Greasby, Eng.	64a	53.23 N	3.07 W
Great Abaco (I.), Ba. (ä'bä-kō)	134	26.30 N	77.05 W
Great Altcar, Eng.	64a	53.33 N	3.01 W
Great Artesian Basin (Reg.), Austl. (är-tēzh-ăn bā-sĭn)	215	23.16 S	143.37 E
Great Australian Bight, Austl. (ôs-trā'lĭ-ăn bīt)	214	33.30 S	127.00 E
Great Bahama Bk., Ba (bȧ-hā'mȧ)	134	25.00 N	78.50 W
Great Barrier (I.), N.Z. (băr'ĭ-ēr)	217	37.00 S	175.31 E
Great Barrier Rf., Austl. (bă-rĭ-ēr rēf)	215	16.43 S	146.34 E
Great Basin, U.S. (grāt bā's'n)	108	40.08 N	117.10 W
Great Bear L., Can. (bâr)	96	66.10 N	119.53 W
Great Bend, Ks. (bĕnd)	122	38.41 N	98.46 W
Great Bitter, see Al Buḩayrah al Murrah al Kubrā			
Great Blasket I., Ire. (blăs'kĕt)	162	52.05 N	10.55 W
Great Bookham, Eng.	62	51.16 N	0.22 W
Great Britain, U.K. (brĭt'n)	154	56.53 N	0.02 W
Great Burstead, Eng.	62	51.36 N	0.25 E
Great Corn I., Nic.	133	12.10 N	82.54 W
Great Crosby, Eng.	64a	53.29 N	3.01 W
Great Divide Basin, Wyo. (dĭ-vīd' bā's'n)	117	42.10 N	108.10 W
Great Dividing Ra., Austl. (dĭ-vī-dĭng rānj)	215	35.16 S	146.38 E
Great Duck (I.), Can. (dŭk)	102	45.40 N	83.22 W
Greater Khingan Range (Da Hinggan Ling), China (dä hĭŋ-gän lĭŋ)	202	46.30 N	120.00 E
Greater Leech Ind. Res., Mn. (grāt'ēr lēch)	115	47.39 N	94.27 W
Greater Manchester (Co.), Eng.	156	53.34 N	2.41 W
Greater Sunda Is., Indon.	206	4.00 S	108.00 E
Great Exuma (I.), Ba. (ĕk-sōō'mä)	135	23.35 N	76.00 W
Great Falls, Mt. (fôlz)	117	47.30 N	111.15 W
Great Falls, SC	127	34.32 N	80.53 W
Great Falls, Va.	56d	39.00 N	77.17 W
Great Guana Cay (I.), Ba. (gwä'nä)	135	24.00 N	76.20 W
Great Harbor Cay (I.), Ba. (kē)	134	25.45 N	77.50 W
Great Inagua (I.), Ba. (ē-nä'gwä)	135	21.00 N	73.15 W
Great Indian Des., India	196	27.35 N	71.37 E
Great Isaac (I.), Ba. (ī'zăk)	134	26.05 N	79.05 W
Great Karroo (Mts.), S. Afr. (grāt kȧ'rōō)	226	32.45 S	22.00 E
Great Kills (Neigh.), NY	55	40.33 N	74.10 W
Great Namaland (Reg.), Namibia	226	25.45 S	16.15 E
Great Neck, NY (nĕk)	112a	40.48 N	73.44 W
Great Nicobar I., Andaman & Nicobar Is. (nĭk-ô-bär')	206	7.00 N	94.18 E
Great Oxney Green, Eng.	62	51.44 N	0.25 E
Great Parndon, Eng.	62	51.45 N	0.05 E
Great Pedro Bluff (Hd.), Jam.	134	17.50 N	78.05 W
Great Plains, The (Reg.), N.A. (plāns)	94	45.00 N	104.00 W
Great Ragged (I.), Ba.	135	22.10 N	75.45 W
Great Ruaha (R.), Tan.	231	7.45 S	34.50 E
Great Saint Bernard Pass, Switz-It. (sānt bēr-närd')	172	45.53 N	7.15 E
Great Salt L., Ut. (sôlt lāk)	117	41.19 N	112.48 W
Great Salt Lake Des., U.S.	108	41.00 N	113.30 W
Great Salt Plains Res., Ok.	122	36.56 N	98.14 W
Great Sand Dunes Natl. Mon., Co.	122	37.56 N	105.25 W
Great Sand Hills, Can. (sănd)	100	50.35 N	109.05 W
Great Sandy (I.), see Fraser			
Great Sandy Des., Austl. (săn'dē)	214	21.50 S	123.10 E
Great Sandy Des., Or. (săn'dĭ)	116	43.43 N	120.44 W

PLACE (Pronounciation)	PAGE	Lat. °′	Long. °′
Great Sitkin (I.), Ak. (sĭt-kĭn)	107a	52.18 N	176.22 W
Great Slave (L.), Can. (slāv)	96	61.37 N	114.58 W
Great Smoky Mts. Natl. Park, NC-Tn. (smōk-ē)	126	35.43 N	83.20 W
Great Stirrup Cay (I.), Ba. (stĭr-ŭp)	134	25.50 N	77.55 W
Great Sutton, Eng.	64a	53.17 N	2.56 W
Great Victoria Des., Austl. (vĭk-tō'rĭ-ȧ)	214	29.45 S	124.30 E
Great Waltham, Eng. (wôl'thŭm)	156	51.47 N	0.27 E
Great Warley, Eng.	62	51.35 N	0.17 E
Great Yarmouth, Eng. (yär-mŭth)	163	52.35 N	1.45 E
Grebbestad, Swe. (grĕb-bĕ-städh)	164	58.42 N	11.15 E
Gréboun, Mont (Mtn.), Niger	229	20.00 N	8.35 E
Greco (Neigh.), It.	65c	45.30 N	9.13 E
Gredos, Sierra de (Mts.) (syĕr'rä dā grā'dōs)	170	40.13 N	5.30 W
Greece, Eur. (grēs)	154	39.00 N	21.30 E
Greeley, Co. (grē'lĭ)	122	40.25 N	104.41 W
Green (R.), Ky (grēn)	126	37.13 N	86.30 W
Green (R.), ND	114	47.05 N	103.05 W
Green (R.), U.S.	108	38.30 N	110.10 W
Green (R.), Ut.	121	38.30 N	110.05 W
Green (R.), Wa.	118a	47.17 N	121.57 W
Green B., U.S.	109	44.55 N	87.40 W
Greenbank, Wa. (grēn'bănk)	118a	48.06 N	122.35 W
Green Bay, Wi.	115	44.30 N	88.04 W
Green Bayou, Tx.	125a	29.53 N	95.13 W
Greenbelt, Md. (grĕn'bĕlt)	112e	38.59 N	76.53 W
Greenbrae, Ca.	58b	37.57 N	122.31 W
Greencastle, In. (grēn-kȧs''l)	110	39.40 N	86.50 W
Green Cay (I.)	134	24.05 N	77.10 W
Green Cove Springs, Fl. (kōv)	127	29.56 N	81.42 W
Greendale, Wi. (grēn'dāl)	113a	42.56 N	87.59 W
Greenfield, Ia.	115	41.16 N	94.30 W
Greenfield, In. (grēn'fēld)	110	39.45 N	85.40 W
Greenfield, Ma.	111	42.35 N	72.35 W
Greenfield, Mo.	123	37.23 N	93.48 W
Greenfield, Oh.	110	39.15 N	83.25 W
Greenfield, Tn.	126	36.08 N	88.45 W
Greenfield Park, Can.	95a	45.29 N	73.29 W
Greenhills, Oh. (grēn-hĭls)	113f	39.16 N	84.31 W
Greenhithe, Eng.	62	51.27 N	0.17 E
Greenland, N.A. (grēn'lănd)	94	74.00 N	40.00 W
Green Meadows, Md.	56d	38.58 N	76.57 W
Greenmount, Eng.	64b	53.37 N	2.20 W
Green Mountain Res., Co.	121	39.50 N	106.20 W
Green Mtn., Or.	118c	45.52 N	123.24 W
Green Mts., Vt.	111	43.10 N	73.05 W
Greenock, Scot. (grēn'ŭk)	162	55.55 N	4.45 W
Green Pond Mtn., NJ (pŏnd)	112a	41.00 N	74.32 W
Greenport, NY	111	41.06 N	72.22 W
Green R., Blacks Fk., Wy.	117	41.08 N	110.27 W
Green R., Hams Fk., Wy.	117	41.55 N	110.40 W
Green River, Ut. (grēn rĭv'ēr)	121	39.00 N	110.05 W
Green River, Wy.	117	41.32 N	109.26 W
Greensboro, Al. (grēnz'bŭro)	126	32.42 N	87.36 W
Greensboro, Ga. (grēns-bûr'ô)	126	33.34 N	83.11 W
Greensboro, NC	127	36.04 N	79.45 W
Greensborough, Austl.	70b	37.42 S	145.06 E
Greensburg, In. (grēnz'bûrg)	110	39.20 N	85.30 W
Greensburg, Ks. (grēns-bûrg)	122	37.36 N	99.17 W
Greensburg, Pa.	111	40.20 N	79.30 W
Greenside (Neigh.), S. Afr.	71b	26.09 S	28.01 E
Greenstead, Eng.	62	51.42 N	0.14 E
Green Street, Eng.	62	51.40 N	0.16 W
Green Street Green (Neigh.), Eng.	62	51.21 N	0.04 E
Greenvale, NY	55	40.49 N	73.38 W
Greenville, Al. (grēn'vĭl)	126	31.49 N	86.39 W
Greenville, Il.	123	38.52 N	89.22 W
Greenville, Ky.	126	37.11 N	87.11 W
Greenville, Lib.	228	5.01 N	9.03 W
Greenville, Me.	104	45.26 N	69.35 W
Greenville, Mi.	110	43.10 N	85.25 W
Greenville, Ms.	126	33.25 N	91.00 W
Greenville, NC	127	35.35 N	77.22 W
Greenville, Oh.	110	40.05 N	84.35 W
Greenville, Pa.	110	41.20 N	80.25 W
Greenville, SC	127	34.50 N	82.25 W
Greenville, Tn.	126	36.08 N	82.50 W
Greenville, Tx.	123	33.09 N	96.07 W
Greenwich, Ct.	112a	41.01 N	73.37 W
Greenwich, Eng. (grĭn'ĭj)	156b	51.28 N	0.00
Greenwich (Neigh.), Eng.	62	51.28 N	0.02 E
Greenwich Observatory (P. Int.), Eng.	62	51.28 N	0.00
Greenwich Village (Neigh.), NY	55	40.44 N	74.00 W
Greenwood, Ar. (grēn-wŏŏd)	123	35.13 N	94.15 W
Greenwood, In.	113g	39.37 N	86.07 W
Greenwood, Ma.	54a	42.29 N	71.04 W
Greenwood, Ms.	126	33.30 N	90.09 W
Greenwood (R.), SC	127	34.17 N	81.55 W
Greenwood, SC	127	34.10 N	82.10 W
Greenwood L., NY	112a	41.13 N	74.20 W
Greer, SC (grēr)	127	34.55 N	81.56 W
Grefrath, F.R.G. (grĕf'rät)	169c	51.20 N	6.21 E
Gregory, SD (grĕg'ô-rĭ)	114	43.12 N	99.27 W
Gregory, L., Austl. (grĕg'ô-rē)	216	29.47 S	139.15 E
Gregory Ra, Austl.	215	19.23 S	143.45 E
Greifenberg, F.R.G. (grī'fĕn-bĕrgh)	157d	48.04 N	11.06 E
Greiffenburg (P. Int.), F.R.G.	63	51.20 N	6.38 E
Greifswald, G.D.R. (grīfs'vält)	166	54.05 N	13.24 E
Greiz, G.D.R. (grīts)	166	50.39 N	12.14 E
Gremyachinsk, Sov. Un. (grâ'myà-chĭnsk)	182a	58.35 N	57.53 E
Grenå, Den. (grĕn'ô)	164	56.25 N	10.51 E
Grenada, Ms. (grē-nā'da)	126	33.45 N	89.47 W
Grenada, N.A.	129	12.02 N	61.15 W
Grenada Res., Ms.	126	33.52 N	89.30 W
Grenadines, The (Is.), Grenada-Saint Vincent (grĕn'ȧ-dēnz)	133b	12.37 N	61.35 W
Grenen (Pt.), Den.	164	57.43 N	10.31 E
Grenoble, Fr. (grē-nô'bl')	169	45.14 N	5.45 E
Grenora, ND (grĕ-nō'ra)	114	48.38 N	103.55 W

PLACE (Pronounciation)	PAGE	Lat. °′	Long. °′
Grenville, Can. (grĕn'vĭl)	111	45.40 N	74.35 W
Grenville, Grenada	133b	12.07 N	61.38 W
Gresham, Or. (grĕsh'ăm)	118c	45.30 N	122.25 W
Gretna, La. (grĕt'nȧ)	112d	29.56 N	90.03 W
Grevel (Neigh.), F.R.G.	63	51.34 N	7.33 E
Grevelingen Krammer, R., Neth.	157a	51.42 N	4.03 E
Grevená, Grc. (grĕ'vå-nȧ)	173	40.02 N	21.30 E
Grevenbroich, F.R.G. (grĕ'fĕn-broik)	169c	51.05 N	6.36 E
Grey (R.), Can. (grā)	105	47.53 N	57.00 W
Greybull, Wy. (grā'bo͝ol)	117	44.28 N	108.05 W
Greybull R., Wy.	117	44.13 N	108.43 W
Greylingstad, S. Afr. (grā-lĭng'shtȧt)	223d	26.40 S	29.13 E
Greymouth, N.Z. (grā'mouth)	217	42.27 S	171.17 E
Grey, Pt., Can.	118d	49.22 N	123.16 W
Grey Ra., Austl.	216	28.40 S	142.05 E
Greys Hbr., Wa. (grās)	116	46.55 N	124.23 W
Greystanes, Austl.	70a	33.49 S	150.58 E
Greytown, S. Afr. (grā'toun)	227c	29.07 S	30.38 E
Greytown, see San Juan del Norte			
Grey Wolf Pk., Wa. (grā wo͝olf)	118a	48.53 N	123.12 W
Gridley, Ca. (grĭd'lĭ)	120	39.22 N	121.43 W
Griffin, Ga. (grĭf'ĭn)	126	33.15 N	84.16 W
Griffith, Austl. (grĭf-ĭth)	216	34.16 S	146.10 E
Griffith, In.	113a	41.31 N	87.26 W
Grigoriopol', Sov. Un. (grĭ'gor-ĭ-ô'pôl)	175	47.09 N	29.18 E
Grijalva (R.), Mex. (grē-häl'vä)	131	17.25 N	93.23 W
Grim, C., Austl. (grĭm)	216	40.43 S	144.30 E
Grimlinghausen (Neigh.), F.R.G.	63	51.10 N	6.44 E
Grimma, G.D.R. (grĭm'ȧ)	166	51.14 N	12.43 E
Grimsby, Can. (grĭmz'bĭ)	95d	43.11 N	79.33 W
Grimstad, Nor. (grĭm-städh)	164	58.21 N	8.30 E
Grindstone Island, Can.	105	47.25 N	61.51 W
Grinnel, Ia. (grĭ-nĕl')	115	41.44 N	92.44 W
Grinzing (Neigh.), Aus.	66e	48.15 N	16.21 E
Griswold, Ia. (grĭz'wŭld)	115	41.11 N	95.05 W
Griva, Sov. Un. (grē'vȧ)	174	55.51 N	26.31 E
Grímsey (I.), Ice. (grĭms'ā)	158	66.30 N	17.50 W
Groais I., Can.	105	50.57 N	55.35 W
Grobina, Sov. Un. (grō'bĭnĭa)	165	56.35 N	21.10 E
Groblersdal, S. Afr.	223d	25.11 S	29.25 E
Grodno, Sov. Un. (grôd'nō)	167	53.40 N	23.49 E
Grodzisk, Pol. (grō'jēsk)	166	52.14 N	16.22 E
Grodzisk Masowiecki, Pol. (grō'jēsk mä-zō-vyĕts'ke)	167	52.06 N	20.40 E
Groesbeck, Tx. (grōs'bĕk)	125	31.32 N	96.31 W
Groix, Île de (I.), Fr. (ēl dē grwä')	168	47.39 N	3.28 W
Grójec, Pol. (gro͞o'yĕts)	167	51.53 N	20.52 E
Gronau, F.R.G. (grō'nou)	166	52.12 N	7.05 E
Groningen, Neth. (grō'nĭng-ĕn)	163	53.13 N	6.30 E
Groote Eylandt (I.), Austl. (grō'tē ī'länt)	214	13.50 S	137.30 E
Grootfontein, Namibia (grōt'fōn-tān')	226	18.15 S	19.30 E
Groot-Kei, S. Afr. (kē)	227c	32.17 S	27.30 E
Grootkop, (Mtn.), S. Afr.	226a	34.11 S	18.23 E
Groot Marico, S. Afr.	223d	25.36 S	26.23 E
Groot R., S. Afr.	223d	25.13 S	26.20 E
Groot-Vis (R.), S. Afr.	227c	33.04 S	36.08 E
Groot Vloer (L.), S. Afr. (grōt' vlōōr')	227c	33.00 S	20.16 E
Gros Morne (Mtn.), Can. (grō môrn')	105	49.36 N	57.48 W
Gros Morne Natl. Pk., Can.	97	49.45 N	59.15 W
Gros Pate (Mtn.), Can.	105	50.16 N	57.25 W
Grossbeeren, G.D.R.	65a	52.21 N	13.18 E
Grosse I., Mi. (grōs)	113b	42.08 N	83.09 W
Grosse Isle, Can. (īl')	95f	50.04 N	97.27 W
Grossenbaum (Neigh.), F.R.G.	63	51.22 N	6.47 E
Grossenhain, G.D.R. (grōs'ĕn-hīn)	166	51.17 N	13.33 E
Gross-Enzersdorf, Aus.	157e	48.13 N	16.33 E
Grosse Pointe, Mi. (point')	113b	42.23 N	82.54 W
Grosse Pointe Farms, Mi. (färm)	113b	42.25 N	82.53 W
Grosse Pointe Park, Mi. (pärk)	113b	42.23 N	82.55 W
Grosse Pointe Woods, Mi.	57c	42.27 N	82.55 W
Grosseto, It. (grôs-sā'tō)	172	42.46 N	11.09 E
Grossglockner Pk, Aus. (glôk'nĕr)	166	47.06 N	12.45 E
Gross Höbach, F.R.G. (hû'bäk)	157d	48.21 N	11.36 E
Grossjedlersdorf (Neigh.), Aus.	66e	48.17 N	16.25 E
Gross Kreutz, G.D.R. (kroitz)	157b	52.24 N	12.47 E
Gross Schönebeck, G.D.R. (shō'nĕ-bĕk)	157b	52.54 N	13.32 E
Gross Ziethen, G.D.R.	65a	52.24 N	13.27 E
Gros Ventre R., Wy. (grōvĕn't'r)	117	43.38 N	110.34 W
Groton, Ct. (grŏt'ŭn)	111	41.20 N	72.00 W
Groton, Ma.	105a	42.37 N	71.34 W
Groton, SD	114	45.25 N	98.04 W
Grottaglie, It. (grôt-täl'yā)	173	40.32 N	17.26 E
Grouard Mission, Can.	99	55.31 N	116.09 W
Groveland, Ma. (grōv'land)	105a	42.25 N	71.02 W
Groveton, NH (grōv'tŭn)	111	44.35 N	71.30 W
Groveton, Tx.	125	31.04 N	95.07 W
Groznyy, Sov. Un. (grōz'nĭ)	179	43.20 N	45.40 E
Grudziądz, Pol. (gro͞o'jyôNts)	167a	53.30 N	18.48 E
Grues, Ile aux (I.), Can. (ō grü)	95b	47.05 N	70.32 W
Gruiten, F.R.G.	63	51.14 N	7.01 E
Grumme (Neigh.), F.R.G.	63	51.30 N	7.14 E
Grumpholds-Kirchen, Aus.	157e	48.03 N	16.17 E
Grünau (Neigh.), G.D.R.	65a	52.25 N	13.34 E
Grundy Center, Ia. (grŭn'dĭ sĕn'tĕr)	115	42.22 N	92.45 W
Grünewald, F.R.G.	63	51.13 N	7.37 E
Grunewald (Neigh.), F.R.G.	65a	52.30 N	13.17 E
Gruñidora, Mex. (gro͞o-nyē-dō'rō)	130	24.10 N	101.49 W
Grünwald, F.R.G. (gro͞on'väld)	157d	48.04 N	11.34 E
Gryazi, Sov. Un. (gryä'zĭ)	174	52.31 N	39.59 E
Gryazovets, Sov. Un. (gryä'zō-vĕts)	154	58.52 N	40.14 E
Gryfice, Pol. (grĭ'fĭ-tsĕ)	166	53.55 N	15.11 E
Gryfino, Pol. (grĭ'fē-nō)	166	53.16 N	14.30 E
Guabito, Pan. (gwä-bē'tō)	133	9.30 N	82.33 W
Guacanayabo, Golfo de (G.), Cuba (gôl-fō-dĕ-gwä-kä-nä-yä'bō)	134	20.30 N	77.40 W
Guacara, Ven. (gwȧ'kä-rä)	143b	10.16 N	67.48 W
Guacarí, Col. (gwä-kä-rē')	142a	3.45 N	76.20 W
Guaçuí, Braz. (gwä'so͞o-ē')	141a	20.47 S	41.40 W
Guadalajara, Mex. (gwä-dhä-lä-hä'rä)	130	20.41 N	103.21 W
Guadalajara, Sp. (gwä-dä-lä-kä'rä)	170	40.37 N	3.10 W
Guadalcanal, Sp. (gwä-dhäl-kä-näl')	170	38.05 N	5.48 W
Guadalcanal (I.), Sol. Is.	215	9.48 S	158.43 E
Guadalcázar, Mex. (gwä-dhäl-kä'zär)	130	22.38 N	100.24 W
Guadalete (R.), Sp. (gwä-dhä-lā'tȧ)	170	38.53 N	5.38 W
Guadalhorce (R.), Sp. (gwä-dhäl-ôr'thā)	170	37.05 N	4.50 W
Guadalimar (R.), Sp. (gwä-dhä-lē-mär')	170	38.29 N	2.53 W
Guadalope (R.), Sp. (gwä-dä-lô-pē)	171	40.48 N	0.10 W
Guadalquivir, Río (R.), Sp. (rē'ō-gwä-dhäl-kē-vēr')	170	36.35 N	6.00 W
Guadalupe, Mex.	124	31.23 N	106.06 W
Guadalupe, Basílica de (P. Int.), Mex.	60a	19.29 N	99.07 W
Guadalupe I., Mex.	128	29.00 N	118.45 W
Guadalupe Mts., NM-Tx	124	32.00 N	104.55 W
Guadalupe Pk., Tx.	124	31.55 N	104.55 W
Guadalupe R., Tx. (gwä-dhä-lo͞o'pȧ)	124	29.54 N	99.03 W
Guadalupe, Sierra de (Mts.), Sp. (syĕr'rä dā gwä-dhä-lo͞o'pā)	170	39.30 N	5.25 W
Guadarrama (R.), Sp. (gwä-dhär-rä'mä)	171a	40.34 N	3.58 W
Guadarrama, Sierra de (Mts.), Sp. (gwä-dhär-rä'mä)	170	41.00 N	3.40 W
Guadatentin (R.), Sp.	170	37.43 N	1.58 W
Guadeloupe, N.A. (gwä-dē-lo͞op)	129	16.40 N	61.10 W
Guadeloupe Pass, N.A.	133b	16.26 N	62.00 W
Guadiana (R.), Port. (gwä-dvä'nä)	170	37.43 N	7.43 W
Guadiana Alto (R.), Sp. (äl'tō)	170	39.02 N	2.52 W
Guadiana, Bahia de (B.), Cuba (bä-ē'ä-dĕ-gwä-dhē-ä'nä)	134	22.10 N	84.35 W
Guadiana Menor (R.), Sp. (mā'nôr)	170	37.43 N	2.45 W
Guadiaro (R.), Sp. (gwä-dhē-ä rō)	170	37.38 N	5.25 W
Guadiela (R.), Sp. (gwä-dhē-ā'lä)	170	40.27 N	2.05 W
Guadix, Sp. (gwä-dēsh')	170	37.18 N	3.09 W
Guaianazes (Neigh.), Braz.	61d	23.33 S	46.25 W
Guaira, Braz. (gwä-ē-rä)	143	24.03 S	44.02 W
Guaire (R.), Ven. (gwī'rē)	143b	10.25 N	66.43 W
Guajaba, Cayo (I.), Cuba (kä'yō-gwä-hä'bä)	134	21.50 N	77.35 W
Guajará Mirim, Braz. (gwä-zhä-rä'mē-rēN')	142	10.58 S	65.12 W
Guajira, Pen. de (Pen.), Col.-Ven. (pĕ-nē'ng-so͞o-lä-dĕ-gwä-Kē'rä)	142	12.35 N	73.00 W
Gualán, Guat. (gwä-län')	132c	15.08 N	89.21 W
Gualeguay, Arg. (gwä-lĕ-gwä'y)	141c	33.10 S	59.20 W
Gualeguay (R.), Arg.	141c	32.49 S	59.05 W
Gualeguaychú, Arg. (gwä-lȧ-gwī-cho͞o')	141c	33.01 S	58.32 W
Gualeguaychú (R.), Arg.	141c	32.58 S	58.27 W
Gualicho, Salina (F.), Arg. (sä-lē'nä-gwä-lē'chō)	144	40.20 S	65.15 W
Guam, Oceania (gwäm)	208	14.00 N	143.20 E
Guaminí, Arg. (gwä-mē-nē')	144	37.02 S	62.21 W
Guamo, Col. (gwá'mō)	142a	4.02 N	74.58 W
Gu'an, China (go͞o-än)	202a	39.25 N	116.18 E
Guan (R.), China (gůän)	200	31.56 N	115.19 E
Guanabacoa, Cuba (gwä-nä-bä-kō'ä)	135a	23.08 N	82.19 W
Guanabara, Baia de (B.), Braz.	144b	22.44 S	43.09 W
Guanacaste Cord. (Mts.), C.R. (kôr-dĕl-yĕ'rä-gwä-nä-käs'tä)	132	10.54 N	85.27 W
Guanacevi, Mex. (gwä-nä-sĕ-vē')	128	25.30 N	105.45 W
Guanahacabibes, Pen. de, Cuba (pĕ-nĕn-so͞o-lä-dĕ-gwä-nä hä-kä-bē'bȧs)	134	21.55 N	84.35 W
Guanajay, Cuba (gwäŋä-hī')	134	22.55 N	82.40 W
Guanajuato, Mex. (gwä-nä-hwä'tō)	130	21.01 N	101.16 W
Guanajuato (State), Mex.	128	21.00 N	101.00 W
Guanape (R.), Ven.	143b	9.52 N	65.20 W
Guanape, Ven. (gwä-nä'pē)	143b	9.55 N	65.32 W
Guanare, Ven. (gwä-nä'rȧ)	142	8.57 N	69.47 W
Guanduçu (R.), Braz. (gwä'n-do͞o'so͞o)	144b	22.50 S	43.40 W
Guane, Cuba (gwä'nȧ)	134	22.10 N	84.05 W
Guangchang, China (gůäŋ-chäŋ)	203	25.50 N	116.18 E
Guangde, China (gůäŋ-dŭ)	203	30.40 N	119.20 E
Guangdong (Prov.), China (gůäŋ-dôŋ)	199	23.45 N	113.15 E
Guanglu Dao (I.), China (gůäŋ-lo͞o dou)	200	39.13 N	122.21 E
Guangping, China (gůäŋ-pĭŋ)	200	36.30 N	114.57 E
Guangrao, China (gůäŋ-rou)	200	37.04 N	118.24 E
Guangshan, China (gůäŋ-shän)	200	32.02 N	114.53 E
Guangxi Zhuangzu (Aut. Reg.), China (gůäŋ-shyē)	198	24.00 N	108.30 E
Guangzhou (Canton), China (gůäŋ-jō)	201a	23.07 N	113.15 E
Guanhu, China (gůän-ho͞o)	200	34.26 N	117.59 E
Guannan, China (gůän-nän)	200	34.17 N	119.17 E
Guanta, Ven. (gwän'tä)	143b	10.15 N	64.35 W
Guantanamo, Cuba (gwän-tä'nä-mō)	135	20.10 N	75.10 W
Guantánamo (Prov.), Cuba	135	20.10 N	75.05 W
Guantanamo, Bahía de (B.), Cuba (bä-ē'ä-dē)	135	19.35 N	75.35 W
Guantao, China (gůän-tou)	200	36.39 N	115.25 E
Guanxian, China (gůän-shyĕn)	200	36.30 N	115.28 E
Guanyao, China (gůän-you)	201a	23.13 N	113.04 E
Guanyintang, China	67b	39.52 N	116.31 E
Guanyun, China (gůän-yo͞on)	200	34.28 N	119.16 E
Guapé, Braz. (gwȧ-pĕ)	141a	20.45 S	45.55 W
Guapiles, C.R. (gwä-pē-lĕs)	133	10.05 N	83.54 W
Guapimirim, Braz. (gwä-pē-mē-rē'N)	144b	22.31 S	42.59 W
Guaporé (R.), Bol.-Braz. (gwä-pô-rä')	142	12.11 S	63.47 W
Guaqui, Bol. (guä'kē)	142	16.42 S	68.47 W
Guarabira, Braz. (gwä-rä-bē'rȧ)	143	6.49 S	35.27 W
Guaracarumbo, Ven.	61a	10.34 N	66.59 W
Guaranda, Ec. (gwä-rän'dä)	142	1.39 S	78.57 W
Guarapari, Braz. (gwä-rä-pä'rē)	143	20.34 S	40.31 W
Guarapiranga, Represa do (Res.), Braz. (r'ĕ-prĕ-sȧ-dô-gwä'rä-pē-rȧ'n-gä)	141a	23.45 S	46.44 W
Guarapuava, Braz. (gwä-rä-pwä'vȧ)	144	25.29 S	51.26 W
Guara, Sierra de (Mts.), Sp. (sē-ĕ'r-rä-dē-gwä'rä)	171	42.24 N	0.15 W
Guaratinguetá, Braz. (guä-rä-tĭN-gȧ-tä')	141a	22.49 S	45.10 W
Guarda, Port. (gwär'dä)	170	40.32 N	7.17 W
Guardiato (R.), Sp.	170	38.10 N	5.05 W
Guarena, Sp. (gwä-rā'nyä)	170	38.52 N	6.08 W
Guaribe (R.), Ven. (gwä-rē'bē)	143b	9.48 N	65.17 W
Guárico (State), Ven.	143b	9.42 N	67.25 W
Guárico (R.), Ven.	143b	9.50 N	67.07 W
Guarulhos, Braz. (gwä-ro͞o'l-yôs)	141a	32.28 S	46.30 W
Guarus, Braz. (gwá'ro͞os)	141a	21.44 S	41.19 W
Guasca, Col. (gwäs'kä)	142a	4.52 N	73.52 W
Guasipati, Ven. (gwä-sē-pä'tē)	143	7.26 N	61.57 W
Guastalla, It. (gwäs-täl'lä)	172	44.53 N	10.39 E
Guasti, Ca. (gwäs'tĭ)	119a	34.04 N	117.35 W
Guatemala, Guat. (guä-tȧ-mä'lä)	132	14.37 N	90.32 W
Guatemala, N.A.	128	15.45 N	91.45 W
Guatire, Ven. (gwä-tē'rē)	143b	10.28 N	66.34 W
Guaxupé, Braz. (gwä-sho͞o-pĕ')	141a	21.18 S	46.42 W
Guayabal, Cuba (gwä-yä-bä'l)	134	20.40 N	77.40 W
Guayalejo (R.), Mex. (gwä-yä-lĕ'hō)	130	23.24 N	99.09 W
Guayama, P.R. (gwä-yä'mä)	129b	18.00 N	66.08 W
Guayamouc (R.), Hai.	135	19.05 N	72.00 W
Guayaquil, Ec. (gwī-ä-kēl')	142	2.16 S	79.53 W
Guayaquil, Golfo de (G.), Ec. (gôl-fô-dĕ)	142	3.03 S	82.12 W
Guayiare (R.), Col. (gwä-yá'rē)	142	3.35 N	69.28 W
Guaymas, Mex. (gwá'y-mäs)	128	27.49 N	110.58 W
Guayubin, Dom. Rep. (gwȧ-yo͞o-bē'n)	135	19.40 N	71.25 W
Guazacapán, Guat. (gwä-zä-kä-pän')	132	14.04 N	90.26 W
Gubakha, Sov. Un. (go͞o-bä'kȧ)	182a	58.53 N	57.35 E
Gubbio, It. (go͞ob'byō)	172	43.23 N	12.36 E
Gucheng, China (go͞o-chŭŋ)	200	39.09 N	115.43 E
Gudar, Sierra de (Mts.), Sp. (syĕr'rä dā go͞o'dhär)	171	40.28 N	0.47 W
Gudena (R.), Den.	164	56.20 N	9.47 E
Gudvangen, Nor. (go͞odh'väŋ-gĕn)	164	60.52 N	6.45 E
Guebwiller, Fr. (gĕb-vē-lâr')	169	47.53 N	7.10 E
Guédi, Mont (Mtn.), Chad	229	12.14 N	18.58 E
Guelma, Alg. (gwĕl'mä)	224	36.32 N	7.17 E
Guelph, Can. (gwĕlf)	95d	43.33 N	80.15 W
Güere (R.), Ven. (gwĕ'rē)	143b	9.39 N	65.00 W
Guéret, Fr. (gā-rĕ')	168	46.09 N	1.52 E
Guermantes, Fr.	64c	48.51 N	2.42 E
Guernsey (I.), Eur. (gûrn'zĭ)	168	49.27 N	2.36 W
Guerrero, Mex. (gĕr-rā'rō)	124	26.47 N	99.20 W
Guerrero, Mex.	124	28.20 N	100.24 W
Guerrero (State), Mex.	130	17.45 N	100.15 W
Gueydan, La. (gā'dăn)	125	30.01 N	92.31 W
Guia de Pacobaíba, Braz. (gwē'ä-dĕ-pä'kō-bī'bä)	144b	22.42 S	43.10 W
Guiana Highlands (Mts.), Braz.	140	3.20 N	60.00 W
Guichi, China (gwā-chr)	203	30.35 N	117.28 E
Guichicovi (San Juan), Mex. (gwē-chē-kō'vē)	131	16.58 N	95.10 W
Guidonia, It. (gwē-dō'nyä)	171d	42.00 N	12.45 E
Guiglo, Ivory Coast	228	6.33 N	7.29 W
Guignes, Fr. (gēN'yĕ)	169b	48.38 N	2.48 E
Güigüe, Ven. (gwē'gwĕ)	143b	10.05 N	67.48 W
Guija, L., Sal. (gē'hä)	132	14.16 N	89.21 W
Guildford, Austl.	70a	33.51 S	150.59 E
Guildford, Eng. (gĭl'fērd)	156b	51.13 N	0.34 W
Guilford, In. (gĭl'fērd)	113f	39.10 N	84.55 W
Guilin, China (gwā-lĭn)	203	25.18 N	110.22 E
Guimarães, Port. (gē-mä-räNsh')	170	41.27 N	8.22 W
Guinea, Afr. (gĭn'ē)	222	10.48 N	12.28 W
Guinea, G. of, Afr.	222	2.00 N	1.00 E
Guinea-Bissau, Afr. (gĭn'ē)	222	12.00 N	20.00 W
Güines, Cuba (gwē'nās)	134	22.50 N	82.05 W
Guingamp, Fr. (gäN-gäN')	168	48.35 N	3.10 W
Guir (R.), Mor.-Alg.	160	31.55 N	2.48 W
Güira de Melena, Cuba (gwē'rä dā mȧ-lā'nä)	134	22.45 N	82.30 W
Güiria, Ven. (gwē-rē'ä)	142	10.43 N	62.16 W
Guise, Fr. (güēz)	169	49.54 N	3.37 E
Guisisil (Vol.), Nic. (gē-sē-sēl')	132	12.40 N	86.11 W
Guiyang, China (gwā-yäŋ)	203	26.45 N	107.00 E
Guizhou, China (gwā-jō)	201a	22.46 N	113.15 E
Guizhou (Prov.), China	198	27.00 N	106.10 E
Gujānwāla, Pak. (go͞oj-rän'va-lȧ)	196	32.08 N	74.14 E
Gujarat (State), India	196	22.54 N	79.00 E
Gulbarga, India (go͞ol-bûr'gȧ)	197	17.25 N	76.52 E
Gulbene, Sov. Un. (go͞ol-bā'nē)	174	57.09 N	26.49 E
Gulfport, Ms. (gŭlf'pōrt)	126	30.24 N	89.05 W
Gulja, see Yining			
Gull L., Can.	98	52.35 N	114.00 W
Gull Lake, Can.	100	50.10 N	108.25 W
Gulph Mills, Pa.	56b	40.04 N	75.21 W
Gulu, Ug.	231	2.47 N	32.18 E
Gulyay Pole, Sov. Un.	175	47.39 N	36.12 E
Gumaca, Phil. (go͞o-mä-kä')	207a	13.55 N	122.06 E
Gumbeyka R., Sov. Un. (go͞om-bĕy'kȧ)	182a	53.20 N	59.42 E
Gumel, Nig.	229	12.39 N	9.22 E
Gummersbach, F.R.G. (go͞om'ĕrs-bäk)	166	51.02 N	7.34 E
Gummi, Nig.	229	12.09 N	5.09 E
Gumpoldskirchen, Aus.	157	48.04 N	16.15 E
Guna, India	196	24.44 N	77.17 E
Gunisao (R.), Can. (gŭn-ĭ-sä'ō)	101	53.40 N	97.35 W
Gunisao L., Can.	101	53.54 N	97.58 W
Gunnedah, Austl. (gŭ'nē-dä)	216	31.00 S	150.10 E
Gunnison, Co. (gŭn'ĭ-sŭn)	121	38.33 N	106.56 W
Gunnison, (R.), Col.	121	38.30 N	106.40 W
Gunnison, Ut.	121	39.10 N	111.50 W
Guntersville, Al. (gŭn'tērz-vĭl)	126	34.20 N	86.19 W
Guntersville L., Al.	126	34.30 N	86.20 W

PLACE (Pronounciation)	PAGE	Lat. °′	Long. °′
Guntramsdorf, Aus.	157e	48.04 N	16.19 E
Guntūr, India (go͞on'to͞or)	197	16.22 N	80.29 E
Guo (R.), China (gwô)	200	33.04 N	117.16 E
Guoyang, China (gwô-yäŋ)	200	33.32 N	116.10 E
Gurdon, Ar. (gûr'dŭn)	123	33.56 N	93.10 W
Gurgucia (R.), Braz. (go͞or-go͞o'syä)	143	8.12 S	43.49 W
Gurnee, Il. (gûr'nē)	113a	42.22 N	87.55 W
Gurskøy (I.), Nor. (go͞orskûė)	164	62.18 N	5.20 E
Gurupá, Braz. (go͞o-ro͞o-pä')	143	1.28 S	51.32 W
Gurupi, Serra do (Mts.) (sĕ'r-rä-dô-go͞o-ro͞o-pē')	143	5.32 S	47.02 W
Gurupí (R.), Braz. (go͞o-ro͞o-pē')	143	2.37 S	46.45 W
Guru Sikhar Mt., India	196	29.42 N	72.50 E
Gur'yev, Sov. Un. (go͞or'yĕf)	179	47.10 N	51.50 E
Gur'yevsk, Sov. Un. (go͞or-yĭfsk')	180	54.14 N	86.07 E
Gusau, Nig. (go͞o-zä'o͞o)	229	12.12 N	6.40 E
Gusev, Sov. Un. (go͞o'sĕf)	165	54.35 N	22.15 E
Gushi, China (go͞o-shr)	200	32.11 N	115.39 E
Gushiago, Ghana	228	9.55 N	0.12 W
Gusinje, Yugo. (go͞o-sēn'yĕ)	173	42.34 N	19.54 E
Gus'-Khrustal'nyy, Sov. Un. (go͞os-kro͞o-stäl'ny')	174	55.39 N	40.41 E
Gustavo A. Madero, Mex. (go͞os-tä'vô-ȧ-mä-dĕ'rô)	131a	19.29 N	99.07 W
Güstrow, G.D.R. (güs'trō)	166	53.48 N	12.12 E
Gütersloh, F.R.G. (gü'tērs-lo)	166	51.54 N	8.22 E
Guthrie, Ok. (gŭth'rĭ)	123	35.52 N	97.26 W
Guthrie Center, Ia.	115	41.41 N	94.33 W
Gutiérrez Zamora, Mex. (go͞o-tĭ-âr'rāz zä-mō'rä)	131	20.27 N	97.17 W
Guttenberg, Ia. (gŭt'ĕn-bûrg)	115	42.48 N	91.09 W
Guttenberg, NJ	55	40.48 N	74.01 W
Guyana, S.A. (gŭy'ănă)	140	7.45 N	59.00 W
Guyancourt, Fr.	64c	48.46 N	2.04 E
Guyang, China (go͞o-yäŋ)	200	34.56 N	114.57 E
Guye, China (go͞o-yŭ)	200	39.46 N	118.23 E
Guymon, Ok. (gī'mŏn)	122	36.41 N	101.29 W
Guysborough, Can. (gīz'bŭr-ô)	105	45.23 N	61.30 W
Guzhen, China (go͞o-jŭn)	200	33.20 N	117.18 E
Gvardeysk, Sov. Un. (gvȧr-dĕysk')	165	54.39 N	21.11 E
Gwadabawa, Nig.	229	13.20 N	5.15 E
Gwādar, Pak. (gwä'dŭr)	192	25.15 N	62.29 E
Gwane, Zaire (gwän)	231	4.43 N	25.50 E
Gwda (R.), Pol.	166	53.27 N	16.52 E
Gwembe, Zambia	231	16.30 S	27.35 E
Gweru, Zimb.	226	19.15 S	29.48 E
Gwinn, Mi. (gwĭn)	115	46.15 N	87.30 W
Gyangzê, China (gyäŋdzŭ)	198	29.00 N	89.28 E
Gyaring Co. (L.), China (gyä-rĭŋ)	196	30.37 N	88.33 E
Gydan, Khrebet (Kolymskiy), (Mts.), Sov. Un.	181	61.45 N	155.00 E
Gydanskiy, P-Ov (Pen.), Sov. Un.	180	70.42 N	76.03 E
Gympie, Austl. (gĭm'pē)	216	26.20 S	152.50 E
Gyöngyös, Hung. (dyûn'dyûsh)	167	47.47 N	19.55 E
Györ, Hung. (dyûr)	167	47.40 N	17.37 E
Gyōtoku, Jap. (gyō'tô-ko͞o')	205a	35.42 N	139.56 E
Gypsumville, Can. (jĭp'sŭm'vĭl)	101	51.45 N	98.35 W
Gyula, Hung. (dyo͞o'lä)	167	46.38 N	21.18 E

H

PLACE (Pronounciation)	PAGE	Lat. °′	Long. °′
Haan, F.R.G. (hän)	169c	51.12 N	7.00 E
Haapamäki, Fin. (häp'ä-mĕ-kē)	165	62.16 N	24.20 E
Haapsalu, Sov. Un. (häp'sä-lo͞o)	165	58.56 N	23.33 E
Haar, F.R.G. (här)	157d	48.06 N	11.44 E
Haar (Neigh.), F.R.G.	63	51.26 N	7.13 E
Ha 'Arava (Wādī al Jayb), Isr.	191a	30.33 N	35.10 E
Haarlem, Neth. (här'lĕm)	157a	52.22 N	4.37 E
Habana (Prov.), Cuba (hä-vä'nä)	134	22.45 N	82.25 W
Haberfield, Austl.	70a	33.53 S	151.08 E
Habikino, Jap.	205b	34.32 N	135.37 E
Hābra, India	196a	22.49 N	88.38 E
Hachinohe, Jap. (hä'chē-nō'hā)	204	40.29 N	141.40 E
Hachiōji, Jap. (hä'chē-ō'jē)	205	35.39 N	139.18 E
Hacienda Heights, Ca.	59	33.58 N	117.58 W
Hackensack, NJ (hăk'ĕn-săk)	112a	40.54 N	74.03 W
Hacketts, Eng.	62	51.45 N	0.05 W
Hackney (Neigh.), Eng.	62	51.33 N	0.03 W
Haddonfield, NJ (hăd'ŭn-fēld)	112f	39.53 N	75.02 W
Haddon Heights, NJ (hăd'ŭn hīts)	112f	39.53 N	75.03 W
Hadd, Ra's al (C.), Om.	192	22.29 N	59.46 E
Hadejia, Nig. (hä-dā'jä)	229	12.30 N	9.59 E
Hadejia (R.), Nig.	229	12.15 N	9.40 E
Hadera, Isr. (ĸȧ-dĕ'rȧ)	191a	32.26 N	34.55 E
Hadersdorf (Neigh.), Aus.	66e	48.13 N	16.14 E
Haderslev, Den. (hä'dhĕrs-lĕv)	164	55.17 N	9.28 E
Hadfield, Austl.	70b	37.42 S	144.56 E
Hadibu, P.D.R. of Yem.	223a	12.40 N	53.50 E
Hadlock, Wa. (hăd'lŏk)	118a	48.02 N	122.46 W
Ḩaḑramawt (Reg.), P.D.R. of Yem.	192	15.22 N	48.40 E
Hadur Shuayb, Jabal (Mtn.), Yemen	192	15.45 N	43.45 E
Haeju, Kor. (hä'ĕ-jŭ)	204	38.03 N	125.42 E
Haemgon-ni (Neigh.), Kor.	68b	37.35 N	126.49 E
Hafnarfjördur, Ice.	158	64.02 N	21.32 W
Haft Gel, Iran	195	31.27 N	49.27 E
Hafun, Ras. (C.), Som. (hä-fo͞on')	223a	10.15 N	51.35 E
Hageland, Mt. (hăge'lănd)	117	48.53 N	108.43 W
Hagen, F.R.G. (hä'gĕn)	169c	51.21 N	7.29 E
Hagerstown, In. (hā'gērz-toun)	110	39.55 N	85.10 W
Hagerstown, Md.	111	39.40 N	77.45 W
Hagi, Jap. (hä'gĭ)	205	34.25 N	131.25 E
Hague, C. de la, Fr. (dē lȧ ȧg')	168	49.44 N	1.55 W
Haguenau, Fr. (ȧg'nō')	169	48.47 N	7.48 E
Hague, The, see 's Gravenhagen			
Hahnenberg, F.R.G.	63	51.12 N	7.24 E
Hai'an, China (hī-än)	200	32.35 N	120.25 E
Haibara, Jap. (hä'ē-bä'rä)	205	34.29 N	135.57 E
Haicheng, China (hī-chŭŋ)	202	40.58 N	122.45 E
Haidārpur (Neigh.), India	67d	28.43 N	77.09 E
Haidian, China (hī-dĭĕn)	202a	39.59 N	116.17 E
Haifa (Hefa), Isr. (hä'ē-fȧ)	191a	32.48 N	35.00 E
Haifeng, China (hä'ē-fĕng')	203	23.00 N	115.20 E
Haifuzhen, China (hī-fo͞o-jŭn)	200	31.57 N	121.48 E
Haijima, Jap.	69a	35.42 N	139.21 E
Haikou, China (hī-kō)	203	20.00 N	110.20 E
Ḩā'il, Sau. Ar. (hāl)	190	27.30 N	41.47 E
Hailaerh, China	202	49.10 N	118.40 E
Hailey, Id. (hā'lĭ)	117	43.31 N	114.19 W
Haileybury, Can.	103	47.27 N	79.38 W
Haileyville, Ok. (hā'lĭ-vĭl)	123	34.51 N	95.34 W
Hailin, China (hä'ē-lēn')	204	44.31 N	129.11 E
Hailing Dao (I.), China (hī-lĭŋ dou)	203	21.30 N	112.15 E
Hailong, China (hī-loŋ)	202	42.32 N	125.52 E
Hailun, China (hä'ē-lo͞on')	202	47.18 N	126.50 E
Hainan Dao (I.), China (hī-nän dou)	203	19.00 N	111.10 E
Hainault (Neigh.), Eng.	62	51.36 N	0.06 E
Hainburg an der Donau, Aus.	157e	48.09 N	16.57 E
Haines, Ak. (hānz)	107	59.10 N	135.38 W
Haines City, Fl.	127a	28.05 N	81.38 W
Haiphong, Viet. (hī'fông')(hä'ēp-hŏng)	203	20.52 N	106.40 E
Haiti, N.A. (hā'tĭ)	129	19.00 N	72.15 W
Haizhou Wan (B.), China	202	35.49 N	120.35 E
Hajduböszormény, Hung. (hôl'do͞o-bû'sûr-mān')	167	47.41 N	21.30 E
Hajdúhadház, Hung. (hô'ĭ-do͞o-hôd'häz)	167	47.32 N	21.32 E
Hajdúnánás, Hung. (hô'ĭ-do͞o-nä'näsh)	167	47.52 N	21.27 E
Hajduszoboszló, Hung. (hô'ĭ-do͞o-sô'bôs-lō)	167	47.24 N	21.25 E
Hakodate, Jap. (hä-kō-dä't ā)	204	41.46 N	140.42 E
Haku-San (Mtn.), Jap. (hä'ko͞o-sän')	205	36.11 N	136.45 E
Halachó, Mex. (ä-lä-chō')	131	20.28 N	90.06 W
Halā'ib, Egypt (hä-lä'ēb)	225	22.10 N	36.40 E
Ḩalbā, Leb.	191a	34.33 N	36.03 E
Halbe, G.D.R. (häl'bĕ)	157b	52.07 N	13.43 E
Halberstadt, G.D.R. (häl'bĕr-shtät)	166	51.54 N	11.07 E
Halcon, Mt., Phil. (häl-kōn')	207a	13.19 N	120.55 E
Halden (Neigh.), F.R.G.	63	51.23 N	7.31 E
Halden, Nor. (häl'dĕn)	164	59.10 N	11.21 E
Haldensleben, G.D.R.	166	52.18 N	11.23 E
Hale, Eng. (hāl)	156	53.22 N	2.20 W
Haleakala Crater, Hi. (hä'lā-ä'kä-lä)	106a	20.44 N	156.15 W
Haleakala Natl. Park, Hi.	106a	20.46 N	156.00 W
Halebarns, Eng.	64b	53.22 N	2.19 W
Haledon, NJ	55	40.56 N	74.11 W
Hales Corners, Wi. (hālz kŏr'nērz)	113a	42.56 N	88.03 W
Halesowen, Eng. (hālz'ô-wĕn)	156	52.26 N	2.03 W
Halethorpe, Md. (hāl-thôrp)	112e	39.15 N	76.40 W
Halewood, Eng.	64a	53.22 N	2.49 W
Haleyville, Al. (hā'lĭ-vĭl)	126	34.11 N	87.36 W
Half Moon Bay, Ca. (hăf'mo͞on)	118b	37.28 N	122.26 W
Halfway House, S. Afr. (häf-wā hous)	227b	26.00 S	28.08 E
Halfweg, Neth.	157a	52.23 N	4.45 E
Haliç (B.), Tur.	66f	41.02 N	28.58 E
Halifax, Can. (hăl'ĭ-făks)	104	44.39 N	63.36 W
Halifax, Eng.	156	53.44 N	1.52 W
Halifax B., Austl. (hăl'ĭ-făx)	215	18.56 S	147.07 E
Halifax Hbr., Can.	104	44.35 N	63.31 W
Halkett, C., Ak.	107	70.50 N	151.15 W
Hallam, Austl.	70b	38.01 S	145.06 E
Hallam Park, Can.	99	52.11 N	118.46 E
Halla San (Mt.), Kor. (häl'lȧ-sän)	204	33.20 N	126.37 E
Halle, Bel. (häl'lĕ)	157a	50.45 N	4.13 E
Halle, G.D.R.	166	51.30 N	11.59 E
Hallettsville, Tx. (hăl'ĕts-vĭl)	125	29.26 N	96.55 W
Hallock, Mn. (hăl'ŭk)	114	48.46 N	96.57 W
Hall Pen, Can. (hôl)	97	63.14 N	65.40 W
Halls Bayou, Tx.	125a	29.55 N	95.23 W
Hallsberg, Swe. (häls'bĕrgh)	164	59.04 N	15.04 E
Halls Creek, Austl. (hôlz)	214	18.15 S	127.45 E
Halmahera (I.), Indon. (häl-mä-hā'rä)	207	0.45 N	128.45 E
Halmahera, Laut (Halmahera Sea), Indon.	207	1.00 S	129.00 E
Halmstad, Swe. (hälm'städ)	164	56.40 N	12.46 E
Halsafjorden, Nor. (häl'sĕ fyôrd)	164	63.03 N	8.23 E
Halstead, Eng.	62	51.20 N	0.08 E
Halstead, Ks. (hôl'stĕd)	123	38.02 N	97.36 W
Haltern, F.R.G. (häl'tĕrn)	169c	51.45 N	7.10 E
Haltom City, Tx. (hôl'tŏm)	119c	32.48 N	97.13 W
Halvarenbeek, Neth.	157a	51.29 N	5.10 E
Halver, F.R.G.	63	51.11 N	7.30 E
Ham (Neigh.), Eng.	62	51.26 N	0.19 W
Hamadān, Iran (hŭ-mŭ-dān')	192	34.45 N	48.07 E
Ḩamāh, Syr. (hä'mä)	161	35.08 N	36.53 E
Hamamatsu, Jap. (hä'mä-mät'so͞o)	205	34.41 N	137.43 E
Hamar, Nor. (hä'mär)	164	60.49 N	11.05 E
Hamasaka, Jap. (hă'mȧ-sä'kȧ)	201	35.57 N	134.27 E
Hamberg, S. Afr.	71b	26.11 S	27.53 E
Hamborn, F.R.G. (häm'bōrn)	169c	51.30 N	6.43 E
Hamburg, Ar. (hăm'bûrg)	123	33.15 N	91.49 W
Hamburg, F.R.G. (häm'bo͞orgh)	157c	53.34 N	10.02 E
Hamburg, Ia.	114	40.39 N	95.40 W
Hamburg, NJ	112a	41.09 N	74.35 W
Hamburg, NY	113c	42.44 N	78.51 W
Hamburg, S. Afr. (hăm'bŭrg)	227c	33.18 S	27.28 E
Hamburg (State), F.R.G.	157c	53.35 N	10.00 E
Hamden, Ct. (hăm'dĕn)	111	41.20 N	72.55 W
Hämeenlinna, Fin. (hĕ'mān-lĭn-nȧ)	165	61.00 N	24.29 E
Hameln, F.R.G. (hä'mĕln)	166	52.06 N	9.23 E
Hamelwörden, F.R.G. (hä'mĕl-vûr-dĕn)	157c	53.47 N	9.19 E
Hamersley ., Austl. (hăm'ērz-lē)	214	22.15 S	117.50 E
Hamhŭng, Kor. (häm'ho͞ong')	204	39.57 N	127.35 E
Hami (Kumul), China (hä-mē)(kô-mo͞ol')	198	42.58 N	93.14 E
Hamilton, Al.	126	34.09 N	88.01 W
Hamilton, Austl. (hăm'ĭl-tŭn)	216	37.50 S	142.10 E
Hamilton, Can.	95d	43.15 N	79.52 W
Hamilton, Ma.	105a	42.37 N	70.52 W
Hamilton, Mo.	123	39.43 N	93.59 W
Hamilton, Mt.	117	46.15 N	114.09 W
Hamilton, N.Z.	217	37.45 S	175.28 E
Hamilton, Oh.	113f	39.22 N	84.33 W
Hamilton, Tx.	124	31.42 N	98.07 W
Hamilton Hbr., Can.	95d	43.17 N	79.50 W
Hamilton Inlet, Can.	97	54.20 N	56.57 W
Hamilton, L., Ar.	123	34.25 N	93.32 W
Hamina, Fin. (hȧ'mē-nȧ)	165	60.34 N	27.15 E
Hamlet, NC (hăm'lĕt)	127	35.52 N	79.46 W
Hamlin, Tx. (hăm'lĭn)	122	32.54 N	100.08 W
Hamm, F.R.G. (häm)	169c	51.40 N	7.48 E
Hamm (Neigh.), F.R.G.	63	51.12 N	6.44 E
Hammanskraal, S. Afr. (hä-mȧns-kräl')	223d	25.24 S	28.17 E
Hamme, Bel.	157a	51.06 N	4.07 E
Hamme-Oste Kanal (Can.), F.R.G. (hä'mĕ-ōs'tĕ kä-näl)	157c	53.20 N	8.59 E
Hammerfest, Nor. (hä'mĕr-fĕst)	158	70.38 N	23.59 E
Hammersmith (Neigh.), Eng.	62	51.30 N	0.14 W
Hammond, In. (hăm'ŭnd)	113a	41.37 N	87.31 W
Hammond, La.	125	30.30 N	90.28 W
Hammond, Or.	118c	46.12 N	123.57 W
Hammondville, Austl.	70a	33.57 S	150.57 E
Hammonton, NJ (hăm'ŭn-tŭn)	111	39.40 N	74.45 W
Hampden, Me. (hăm'dĕn)	104	44.44 N	68.51 W
Hampshire Downs, Eng. (hămp'shĭr dounz)	162	51.01 N	1.05 W
Hampstead, Md.	112e	39.36 N	76.54 W
Hampstead (Neigh.), Eng.	62	51.33 N	0.11 W
Hampstead Heath (P. Int.), Eng.	62	51.34 N	0.10 W
Hampstead Norris, Eng. (hămp-stĕd nŏ'rĭs)	156b	51.27 N	1.14 W
Hampton, Austl.	70b	37.56 S	145.00 E
Hampton, Can. (hămp'tŭn)	104	45.32 N	65.51 W
Hampton, Ia.	115	42.43 N	93.15 W
Hampton (Neigh.), Eng.	62	51.25 N	0.22 W
Hampton, Va.	112g	37.02 N	76.21 W
Hampton National Historic Site (P. Int.), Md.	56c	39.25 N	76.35 W
Hampton Roads (Inlet), Va.	112g	36.56 N	76.23 W
Ḩamrā, Al- Ḩammadah al- (Plat.), Libya	224	29.39 N	10.53 E
Hamtramck, Mi. (hăm-trăm'ĭk)	113b	42.24 N	83.03 W
Hāmūn-i Māshkel (L.), Pak. (hā-mo͞on'ē māsh-kĕl')	192	28.28 N	64.13 E
Han (R.), China (hän)	203	25.00 N	116.35 E
Han (R.), China	203	31.40 N	112.04 E
Han (R.), Kor.	204	37.10 N	127.40 E
Hana, Hi. (hä'nä)	106a	20.43 N	155.59 W
Hanábana (R.), Cuba (hä-nä-bä'nä)	134	22.30 N	80.55 W
Hanalei B., Hi. (hä-nä-lā'ē)	106a	22.15 N	159.40 W
Hanang (Mtn.), Tan.	231	4.26 S	35.24 E
Hanau, F.R.G. (hä'nou)	166	50.08 N	8.56 E
Hancock, Mi. (hăn'kŏk)	115	47.08 N	88.37 W
Handan, China (hän-dän)	200	36.37 N	114.30 E
Handforth, Eng.	64b	53.21 N	2.13 W
Haney, Can. (hā-nē)	99	49.13 N	122.36 W
Hanford, Ca. (hăn'fērd)	120	36.20 N	119.38 W
Han-gang (R.), Kor.	68b	37.36 N	126.47 E
Hangayn Nuruu (Khangai Mts.), Mong.	198	48.03 N	99.45 E
Hangchou, China (hăng'chō')	203	30.17 N	120.12 E
Hang Hau Town, China	68c	22.19 N	114.16 E
Hango, Fin. (häŋ'gû)	165	59.49 N	22.56 E
Hangzhou Wan (B.), China (häŋ-jō wän)	203	30.20 N	121.25 E
Hankamer, Tx. (hăn'kȧ-mēr)	125a	29.52 N	94.42 W
Hankinson, ND (häŋ'kĭn-sŭn)	114	46.04 N	96.54 W
Hankou, China (hän-kō)	203	30.42 N	114.22 E
Hanna, Can. (hăn'ȧ)	99	51.38 N	111.54 W
Hanna, Wy.	117	41.51 N	106.34 W
Hannah, ND	114	48.58 N	98.42 W
Hannibal, Mo. (hăn'ĭ băl)	123	39.42 N	91.22 W
Hann, Mt., Austl. (hän)	214	16.05 S	126.07 E
Hannover, F.R.G. (hän-ō'vĕr)	166	52.22 N	9.45 E
Hanö-bukten (B.), Swe.	164	55.54 N	14.55 E
Hanoi, Viet. (hä-noi')	203	21.04 N	105.50 E
Hanover, Can. (hăn'ô-vēr)	110	44.10 N	81.05 W
Hanover (I.), Chile	144	51.00 S	74.45 W
Hanover, Ma.	105a	42.07 N	70.49 W
Hanover, Md.	56c	39.11 N	76.42 W
Hanover, NH	111	43.45 N	72.15 W
Hanover, Pa.	111	39.50 N	77.00 W
Hanshan, China (hän'shän')	200	31.43 N	118.06 E
Hans Lollick (I.), Vir. Is. (U.S.A.) (häns'lôl'ĭk)	129c	18.24 N	64.55 W
Hanson, Ma. (hăn'sŭn)	105a	42.04 N	70.53 W
Hansville, Wa. (hăns'-vĭl)	118a	47.55 N	122.33 W
Hantengri Feng (Mtn.), China (hän-tŭŋ-rē fŭŋ)	198	42.10 N	80.20 E
Hantsport, Can. (hănts'pōrt)	104	45.04 N	64.11 W
Hanworth (Neigh.), Eng.	62	51.26 N	0.23 W
Hanyang, China (han'yäng')	203	30.30 N	114.10 E
Hanzhong, China (hän-jôŋ)	202	33.02 N	107.00 E
Haocheng, China (hou-chŭŋ)	200	33.19 N	117.33 E
Haparanda, Swe. (hä-pa-rän'dä)	158	65.54 N	23.57 E
Hapeville, Ga. (hāp'vĭl)	112c	33.39 N	84.25 W
Hapsford, Eng.	64a	53.16 N	2.48 W
Haql, Sau. Ar.	191a	29.15 N	34.57 E
Haramachida, Jap.	69a	35.33 N	139.27 E

PLACE (Pronounciation)	PAGE	Lat. °′	Long. °′
Harar (Prov.), Eth.	225	8.15 N	41.00 E
Harare (Salisbury), Zimb.	231	17.50 S	31.03 E
Harbin, China	202	45.40 N	126.30 E
Harbor Beach, Mi. (här'bẽr bēch)	110	43.50 N	82.40 W
Harbor City (Neigh.), Ca.	59	33.48 N	118.17 W
Harbord, Austl.	70a	33.45 S	151.26 E
Harbor Isle, NY	55	40.36 N	73.40 W
Harbor Springs, Mi.	110	45.25 N	85.05 W
Harbour Breton, Can. (brĕt'ŭn) (brē-tôN')	105	47.29 N	55.48 W
Harbour Grace, Can. (grās)	105	47.32 N	53.13 W
Harburg, F.R.G. (här-bo͝orgh)	157c	53.28 N	9.58 E
Hardangerfjorden (Fd.), Nor. (här-däng'ẽr fyôrd)	164	59.58 N	6.30 E
Hardin, Mt. (här'dĭn)	117	45.44 N	107.36 W
Harding (L.), Al.-Ga.	126	32.43 N	85.00 W
Harding, S. Afr. (här'dĭng)	227c	30.34 S	29.54 E
Hardwār, India (hŭr'dvär)	196	29.56 N	78.06 E
Hardy (R.), Mex. (här'dĭ)	120	32.04 N	115.10 W
Hare B., Can. (hâr)	103	51.18 N	55.50 W
Harefield (Neigh.), Eng.	62	51.36 N	0.29 W
Harerge, Eth.	225	9.43 N	42.10 E
Hargeysa, Som. (här-gā'ē-sȧ)	223a	9.20 N	43.57 E
Harghita, Munţii (Mts.), Rom.	167	46.25 N	25.40 E
Harima-Nada (Sea), Jap. (hä'rē-mä nä-dä)	205	34.34 N	134.37 E
Haringey (Neigh.), Eng.	62	51.35 N	0.07 W
Haringvliet (R.), Neth.	157a	51.49 N	4.03 E
Harker Village, NJ	56b	39.51 N	75.09 W
Har, Laga (R.), Ken.	231	2.15 N	39.30 E
Harlan, Ia. (här'lăn)	124	41.40 N	95.10 W
Harlan, Ky.	126	36.50 N	83.19 W
Harlan Co. Res., Ne.	122	40.03 N	99.51 W
Harlem, Mt. (hár'lĕm)	117	48.33 N	108.50 W
Harlem (Neigh.), NY	55	40.49 N	73.56 W
Harlesden (Neigh.), Eng.	62	51.32 N	0.15 W
Harlingen, Neth. (här'lĭng-ĕn)	163	53.10 N	5.24 E
Harlingen, Tx.	125	26.12 N	97.42 W
Harlington (Neigh.), Eng.	62	51.29 N	0.26 W
Harlow, Eng. (här'lō)	156b	51.46 N	0.08 E
Harlowton, Mt. (här'lō-tun)	117	46.26 N	109.50 W
Harmar Heights, Pa.	57b	40.33 N	79.49 W
Harmarville, Pa.	57b	40.32 N	79.51 W
Harmony, In. (här'mō-nĭ)	110	39.35 N	87.00 W
Harney Basin, Or. (här'nĭ)	116	43.26 N	120.19 W
Harney L., Or.	116	43.11 N	119.23 W
Harney Pk., SD	114	43.52 N	103.32 W
Härnosand, Swe. (hẽr-nû-sänd)	164	62.37 N	17.54 E
Haro, Sp. (ä'rō)	170	42.35 N	2.49 W
Harola, India	67d	28.36 N	77.19 E
Harold Hill (Neigh.), Eng.	62	51.36 N	0.13 E
Harold Wood (Neigh.), Eng.	62	51.36 N	0.14 E
Haro Str., Can.-U.S. (hă'rō)	118a	48.27 N	123.11 W
Harpen (Neigh.), F.R.G.	63	51.29 N	7.16 E
Harpenden, Eng. (här'pĕn-d'n)	156b	51.48 N	0.22 W
Harper, Ks. (här'pẽr)	122	37.17 N	98.02 W
Harper, Lib.	228	4.25 N	7.43 W
Harper, Wa.	118a	47.31 N	122.32 W
Harpers Ferry, WV (här'pẽrz)	111	39.20 N	77.45 W
Harper Woods, Mi.	57c	42.24 N	82.55 W
Harpurhey (Neigh.), Eng.	64b	53.31 N	2.13 W
Harricana (R.), Can.	103	50.10 N	78.50 W
Harriman, Tn. (hăr'ĭ-măn)	126	35.55 N	84.34 W
Harrington, De. (hăr'ĭng-tŭn)	111	38.55 N	75.35 W
Harri Rud (R.), Afg.	192	34.29 N	61.16 E
Harris (I.), Scot. (hăr'ĭs)	162	57.55 N	6.40 W
Harris (L.), Fl.	127a	28.43 N	81.40 W
Harrisburg, Il. (hăr'ĭs-bûrg)	110	37.45 N	88.35 W
Harrisburg, Pa.	111	40.15 N	76.50 W
Harrismith, S. Afr. (hă-rĭs'mĭth)	223d	28.17 S	29.08 E
Harrison, Ar. (hăr'ĭ-sŭn)	123	36.13 N	93.06 W
Harrison, NJ	55	40.45 N	74.10 W
Harrison, NY	55	40.58 N	73.43 W
Harrison, Oh.	113f	39.16 N	84.45 W
Harrisonburg, Va. (hăr'ĭ-sŭn-bûrg)	111	38.30 N	78.50 W
Harrison L., Can.	99	49.31 N	121.59 W
Harrisonville, Md.	56c	39.23 N	77.50 W
Harrisonville, Mo. (hăr-ĭ-sŭn-vĭl)	123	38.39 N	94.21 W
Harris Park, Austl.	70a	33.49 S	151.01 E
Harrisville, Ut. (hăr'ĭs-vĭl)	119b	41.17 N	112.00 W
Harrisville, WV	110	39.10 N	81.05 W
Harrodsburg, Ky. (hăr'ŭdz-bûrg)	110	37.45 N	84.50 W
Harrods Cr., Ky. (hăr'ŭdz)	113h	38.24 N	35.33 W
Harrow, Eng. (hăr'ō)	156b	51.34 N	0.21 W
Harrow on the Hill (Neigh.), Eng.	62	51.34 N	0.20 W
Harsefeld, F.R.G. (här'zĕ-fĕld')	157c	53.27 N	9.30 E
Harstad, Nor. (här'städh)	158	68.49 N	16.10 E
Hart, Mi. (härt)	110	43.40 N	86.25 W
Hartbeesfontein, S. Afr.	223d	26.46 S	26.25 E
Hartbeespoortdam (L.), S. Afr.	227b	25.47 S	27.43 E
Hartford, Al. (härt'fẽrd)	126	31.05 N	85.42 W
Hartford, Ar.	123	35.01 N	94.21 W
Hartford, Ct.	111	41.45 N	72.40 W
Hartford, Il.	119e	38.50 N	90.06 W
Hartford, Ky.	126	37.25 N	86.50 W
Hartford, Mi.	110	42.15 N	86.15 W
Hartford, Wi.	115	43.19 N	88.25 W
Hartford City, In.	110	40.35 N	85.25 W
Hartington, Eng. (härt'ĭng-tŭn)	156	53.08 N	1.48 W
Hartington, Ne.	114	42.37 N	97.18 W
Hartland Pt., Eng.	162	51.03 N	4.40 W
Hartlepool, Eng. (här't'l-po͞ol)	162	54.40 N	1.12 W
Hartley, Eng.	62	51.23 N	0.19 E
Hartley, Ia. (härt'lĭ)	114	43.12 N	95.29 W
Hartley Bay, Can.	98	53.25 N	129.15 W
Hart Mtn., Can. (härt)	101	52.25 N	101.30 W
Hartsbeespoort, S. Afr.	227b	25.44 S	27.51 E
Hartselle, Al. (härt'sĕl)	126	34.24 N	86.55 W
Hartshorne, Ok. (härts'hôrn)	123	34.49 N	95.34 W
Hartsville, SC (härts'vĭl)	127	34.20 N	80.04 W
Hartwell, Ga. (härt'wĕl)	126	34.21 N	82.56 W
Hartwell Res., Ga.	126	34.30 N	83.00 W
Hārua, India	196a	22.36 N	88.40 E
Har Us Nuur (L.), Mong	198	48.00 N	92.32 E
Harvard, Il. (här'vȧrd)	115	42.25 N	88.39 W
Harvard, Ma.	105a	42.30 N	71.35 W
Harvard, Ne.	122	40.36 N	98.08 W
Harvard, Mt., Co.	121	38.55 N	106.20 W
Harvel, Eng.	62	51.21 N	0.22 E
Harvey, Can.	104	45.44 N	64.46 W
Harvey, Il.	113a	41.37 N	87.39 W
Harvey, La.	112d	29.54 N	90.05 W
Harvey, ND	114	47.46 N	99.55 W
Harwich, Eng. (här'wĭch)	163	51.53 N	1.13 E
Harwick, Pa.	57b	40.34 N	79.48 W
Harwood, Eng.	64b	53.35 N	2.23 W
Harwood, Md.	56c	38.52 N	76.37 W
Harwood Heights, Il.	58a	41.59 N	87.48 W
Harwood Park, Md.	56c	39.12 N	76.44 W
Haryana (State), India	196	29.00 N	75.45 E
Harz Mts., G.D.R. (härts)	166	51.42 N	10.50 E
Hasanābād, Iran	68h	35.44 N	51.19 E
Hasā, Wādī al (R.), Jordan	191a	30.55 N	35.50 E
Hasbrouck Heights, NJ	55	40.52 N	74.04 W
Hashimoto, Jap. (hä'shē-mō'tō)	205	34.19 N	135.37 E
Haskayne, Eng.	64a	53.34 N	2.58 W
Haskell, Ok. (hăs'kĕl)	123	35.49 N	95.41 W
Haskell, Tx.	122	33.09 N	99.43 W
Hasköy (Neigh.), Tur.	66f	41.02 N	28.58 E
Haslingden, Eng. (hăz'lĭng dĕn)	156	53.43 N	2.19 W
Hasselbeck-Schwarzbach, F.R.G.	63	51.16 N	6.53 E
Hasseleholm, Swe. (häs'lĕ-hôlm)	164	56.10 N	13.44 E
Hassels (Neigh.), F.R.G.	63	51.10 N	6.53 E
Hasselt, Bel. (häs'ĕlt)	157a	50.56 N	5.23 E
Hassi Messaoud, Alg.	224	31.17 N	6.13 E
Hasslinghausen, F.R.G.	63	51.20 N	7.17 E
Hästen (Neigh.), F.R.G.	63	51.09 N	7.06 E
Hasten (Neigh.), F.R.G.	63	51.12 N	7.09 E
Hastings, Eng. (hās'tĭngz)	163	50.52 N	0.28 E
Hastings, Mi.	110	42.40 N	85.20 W
Hastings, Mn.	119g	44.44 N	92.51 W
Hastings, Ne.	122	40.34 N	98.42 W
Hastings, N.Z.	217	39.33 S	176.53 E
Hastings-on-Hudson, NY (ŏn-hŭd'sŭn)	112a	40.59 N	75.53 W
Hastingwood, Eng.	62	51.45 N	0.09 E
Hatchie (R.), Tn. (hăch'ē)	126	35.28 N	89.14 W
Haţeg, Rom. (kät-säg')	173	45.35 N	22.57 E
Hatfield Broad Oak, Eng. (hăt-fēld brôd ōk)	156	51.50 N	0.14 E
Hatogaya, Jap. (hä'tō-gä-yä)	205a	35.50 N	139.45 E
Hatsukaichi, Jap. (hät'so͞o-kȧ'ē-chē)	205	34.22 N	132.19 E
Hatteras, C., NC (hăt'ẽr-ȧs)	127	35.15 N	75.24 W
Hattiesburg, Ms. (hăt'ĭz-bûrg)	126	31.20 N	89.18 W
Hattingen, F.R.G. (hä'tĕn-gĕn)	169c	51.24 N	7.11 E
Hatton (Neigh.), Eng.	62	51.28 N	0.25 W
Hattori, Jap.	69b	34.46 N	135.27 E
Hatvan, Hung. (hôt'vôn)	167	47.39 N	19.44 E
Hatzfeld (Neigh.), F.R.G.	63	51.17 N	7.11 E
Haugesund, Nor. (hou'gē-soon')	164	59.26 N	5.20 E
Haughton Green, Eng.	64b	53.27 N	2.06 W
Haukivesi (L.), Fin. (hou'kē-vē'sē)	165	62.02 N	29.02 E
Haultain (R.), Can.	100	56.15 N	106.35 W
Hauptsrus, S. Afr.	223d	26.35 S	26.16 E
Hauraki, G., N.Z. (hä-o͞o-rä'kē)	217	36.30 S	175.00 E
Haut Atlas (Mts.), Mor.	160	32.10 N	5.49 W
Hauterive, Can.	104	49.11 N	68.16 W
Haut, Isle au, Me. (hō)	104	44.03 N	68.13 W
Hauula, Hi.	106a	21.37 N	157.45 W
Hauz Rāni (Neigh.), India	67d	28.32 N	77.13 E
Havana, Cuba	60b	23.08 N	82.22 W
Havana, Il. (hȧ-vă'nȧ)	123	40.17 N	90.02 W
Havana, see La Habana			
Havasu L., Az. (hăv'ȧ-so͞o)	121	34.26 N	114.09 W
Havel-Kanal (Can.), G.D.R.	65a	52.36 N	13.12 E
Havel R., G.D.R. (hä'fĕl)	166	53.09 N	13.10 E
Haverford, Pa.	56b	40.01 N	75.18 W
Haverhill, Ma. (hā'vẽr-hĭl)	105a	42.46 N	71.05 W
Haverhill, NH	111	44.00 N	72.05 W
Havering (Neigh.), Eng.	62	51.34 N	0.14 E
Havering-atte-Bower (Neigh.), Eng.	62	51.37 N	0.11 E
Havering's Grove, Eng.	62	51.38 N	0.23 E
Haverstraw, NY (hā'vẽr-strô)	112a	41.11 N	73.58 W
Havertown, Pa.	56b	39.59 N	75.18 W
Havlíčkův Brod, Czech.	166	49.38 N	15.34 E
Havre, Mt. (hăv'ẽr)	117	48.34 N	109.42 W
Havre-Bouche Boucher, Can. (hăv'rȧ-bo͞o-shā')	105	45.42 N	61.30 W
Havre de Grace, Md. (hăv'ẽr dē grȧs')	111	39.35 N	76.05 W
Havre-Saint Pierre, Can.	105	50.15 N	63.36 W
Haw (R.), NC (hô)	127	36.17 N	79.46 W
Hawaii (State), U.S.	108c	20.00 N	157.40 W
Hawaii (I.), Hi (häw wī'ē)	106b	19.50 N	157.15 W
Hawaiian Gardens, Ca.	59	33.50 N	118.04 W
Hawaiian Is., U.S. (hä-wī'ȧn)	108c	22.00 N	158.00 W
Hawaii Volcanoes Natl. Pk., Hi.	106a	19.30 N	155.25 W
Hawarden, Ia. (hā'wȧr-dĕn)	114	43.00 N	96.28 W
Hawf, Jabal (Hills), Egypt	71a	29.55 N	31.21 E
Hawi, Hi. (hä'wē)	106a	20.16 N	155.48 W
Hawick, Scot. (hô'ĭk)	162	55.25 N	2.55 W
Hawke B., N.Z. (hôk)	217	39.17 S	177.20 E
Hawker, Austl. (hô'kẽr)	216	31.58 S	138.12 E
Hawkesbury, Can. (hôks'bẽr-ĭ)	111	45.35 N	74.35 W
Hawkinsville, Ga. (hô'kĭnz-vĭl)	126	32.15 N	83.30 W
Hawks Nest Pt., Ba.	135	24.05 N	75.30 W
Hawley, Eng.	62	51.25 N	0.14 E
Hawley, Mn. (hô'lĭ)	114	46.52 N	96.18 W
Haworth, Eng. (hä'wûrth)	156	53.50 N	1.57 W
Haworth, NJ	55	40.58 N	73.59 W
Hawtah, Sau. Ar.	192	15.58 N	48.26 E
Hawthorn, Austl.	70b	37.49 S	145.02 E
Hawthorne, Ca. (hô'thôrn)	119a	33.55 N	118.22 W
Hawthorne, NJ	55	40.57 N	74.09 W
Hawthorne, Nv.	120	38.33 N	118.39 W
Haxtun, Co. (hăks'tŭn)	122	40.39 N	102.38 W
Hay (R.), Austl. (hā)	214	23.00 S	136.45 E
Hay (R.), Can.	96	60.21 N	117.14 W
Hayama, Jap. (hä-yä'mä)	205a	35.16 N	139.35 E
Hayashi, Jap. (hä-yä'shē)	205a	35.13 N	139.38 E
Hayden, Az. (hā'dĕn)	121	33.00 N	110.50 W
Hayes (Neigh.), Eng.	62	51.23 N	0.01 E
Hayes (R.), Can.	111	55.25 N	93.55 W
Hayes, Mt., Ak. (hāz)	107	63.32 N	146.40 W
Haynesville, La. (hānz'vĭl)	125	32.55 N	93.08 W
Hayrabolu, Tur.	173	41.14 N	27.05 E
Hay River, Can.	106	60.50 N	115.53 W
Hays, Ks. (hāz)	122	38.51 N	99.20 W
Haysī, Wādī al (R.), Egypt	191	29.24 N	34.32 E
Haystack Mtn., Wa. (hā-stăk')	118a	48.26 N	122.07 W
Hayward, Ca. (hā'wẽrd)	118b	37.40 N	122.06 W
Hayward, Wi.	115	46.01 N	91.31 W
Hazard, Ky. (hăz'ȧrd)	126	37.13 N	83.10 W
Hazel Grove, Eng.	64b	53.23 N	2.08 W
Hazelhurst, Ga. (hā'z'l-hûrst)	127	31.50 N	82.36 W
Hazelhurst, Ms.	126	31.52 N	90.23 W
Hazel Park, Mi.	113b	42.28 N	83.06 W
Hazelton, Can. (hā'z'l-tŭn)	98	55.15 N	127.40 W
Hazelton Mts., Can.	98	55.00 N	128.00 W
Hazleton, Pa.	111	41.00 N	76.00 W
Headland, Al. (hĕd'lănd)	126	31.22 N	85.20 W
Headley, Eng.	62	51.17 N	0.16 W
Heald Green, Eng.	64b	53.22 N	2.14 W
Healdsburg, Ca. (hēldz'bûrg)	120	38.37 N	122.52 W
Healdton, Ok. (hēld'tŭn)	123	34.13 N	97.28 W
Heanor, Eng. (hēn'ŏr)	156	53.01 N	1.22 W
Heard I., Ind. O. (hûrd)	232	53.10 S	74.35 E
Hearne, Tx. (hûrn)	125	30.53 N	96.35 W
Hearst, Can. (hûrst)	97	49.36 N	83.40 W
Heart (R.), ND (härt)	114	46.46 N	102.34 W
Heart Lake Ind. Res., Can.	99	55.02 N	111.30 W
Heart's Content, Can. (härts kŏn'tĕnt)	105	47.52 N	53.22 W
Heathmont, Austl.	70b	37.49 S	145.15 E
Heath Pte., Can. (hēth)	105	49.06 N	61.45 W
Heaton Moor, Eng.	64b	53.25 N	2.11 W
Heavener, Ok. (hēv'nẽr)	123	34.52 N	94.36 W
Heaverham, Eng.	62	51.18 N	0.15 E
Heaviley, Eng.	64b	53.24 N	2.09 W
Hebbronville, Tx. (hē'brŭn-vĭl)	124	27.18 N	98.40 W
Hebbville, Md.	56c	39.20 N	77.46 W
Hebei (Prov.), China (hŭ-bā)	199	39.15 N	115.40 E
Heber, Ut. (hē'bẽr)	121	40.30 N	111.25 W
Heber Springs, Ar.	123	35.28 N	91.59 W
Hebgen Res., Mt. (hĕb'gĕn)	117	44.47 N	111.38 W
Hebrides, Sea of, Scot.	162	57.00 N	7.00 W
Hebron, Can. (hĕb'rŭn)	97	58.11 N	62.56 W
Hebron, In.	113a	41.19 N	87.13 W
Hebron, Ky.	113f	39.04 N	84.43 W
Hebron, ND	114	46.54 N	102.04 W
Hebron, Ne.	123	40.11 N	97.36 W
Hebron, see Al Khalīl			
Heby, Swe. (hĭ'bü)	164	59.56 N	16.48 E
Hecate Str., Can. (hĕk'ȧ-tē)	98	53.00 N	131.00 W
Hecelchakán, Mex. (ā-sĕl-chä-kän')	131	20.10 N	90.09 W
Hechi, China (hŭ-chr)	203	24.50 N	108.18 E
Hechuan, China (hŭ-chyuän)	203	30.00 N	106.20 E
Hecla I., Can.	101	51.08 N	96.45 W
Hedemora, Swe. (hĭ-dĕ-mō'rä)	164	60.16 N	15.55 E
Hedon, Eng. (hĕ-dŭn)	156	53.44 N	0.12 W
Heemstede, Neth.	157a	52.20 N	4.36 E
Heerdt (Neigh.), F.R.G.	63	51.13 N	6.43 E
Heerlen, Neth.	163	50.55 N	5.58 E
Hefa, see Haifa			
Hefei, China (hŭ-fā)	200	31.51 N	117.15 E
Heflin, Al. (hĕf'lĭn)	126	33.40 N	85.33 W
Heide, F.R.G. (hī'dĕ)	166	54.13 N	9.06 E
Heide (Neigh.), F.R.G.	63	51.31 N	6.52 E
Heidelberg, Austl. (hī'dĕl-bûrg)	211	37.45 S	145.04 E
Heidelberg, F.R.G. (hīdĕl-bĕrgh)	166	49.24 N	8.43 E
Heidelberg, Pa.	57b	40.23 N	80.05 W
Heidenheim, F.R.G. (hī'dĕn-hīm)	166	48.41 N	10.09 E
Heil, F.R.G.	63	51.38 N	7.35 E
Heilbron, S. Afr. (hĭl'brōn)	223d	27.17 S	27.58 E
Heilbronn, F.R.G. (hīl'brōn)	166	49.09 N	9.16 E
Heiligenhaus, F.R.G. (hī'lē-gĕn-houz)	169c	51.19 N	6.58 E
Heiligensee (Neigh.), F.R.G.	65a	52.36 N	13.13 E
Heiligenstadt, G.D.R. (hī'lē-gĕn-shtät)	166	51.21 N	10.10 E
Heilong (R.), China-Sov. Un. (hā-loŋ)	202	49.38 N	127.25 E
Heilongjiang, China (hā-lôŋ-jyäŋ)	199	46.36 N	128.07 E
Heinersdorf, G.D.R.	65a	52.23 N	13.20 E
Heinersdorf (Neigh.), G.D.R.	65a	52.34 N	13.27 E
Heinola, Fin. (hā-nō'lȧ)	165	61.13 N	26.03 E
Heinsberg, F.R.G. (hīnz'bĕrgh)	169c	51.04 N	6.07 E
Heisingen (Neigh.), F.R.G.	63	51.25 N	7.04 E
Heist-op-den-Berg, Bel.	157a	51.05 N	4.14 E
Hejaz, see Al Hijāz			
Hejian, China (hŭ-jyĕn)	200	38.28 N	116.05 E
Hel, Pol. (hāl)	167	54.37 N	18.53 E
Helagsfjället (Mtn.), Swe.	164	62.54 N	12.24 E
Helan Shan (Mts.), China (hŭ-län shän)	198	38.02 N	105.20 E
Helena, Ar. (hē-lē'nȧ)	123	34.33 N	90.35 W
Helena, Mt. (hĕ-lĕ'nȧ)	117	46.35 N	112.01 W
Helensburgh, Austl. (hĕl'ĕnz-bŭr-ō)	211b	34.11 S	150.59 E
Helensburgh, Scot.	162	56.01 N	4.53 W
Helgoland I., F.R.G. (hĕl'gō-länd)	166	54.13 N	7.30 E
Heliopolis (P. Int.), Egypt	71a	30.08 N	31.17 E
Heliopolis, see Misr al-Jadīdah (Neigh.), Egypt	71a	30.06 N	31.20 E
Helka (Vol.), Ice. (hĕl'kȧ)	158	63.53 N	19.37 W
Hellier, Ky. (hĕl'yẽr)	127	37.16 N	82.27 W
Hellín, Sp. (ĕl-yĕn')	170	38.30 N	1.40 W
Helmand (R.), Afg. (hĕl'mŭnd)	192	31.00 N	63.48 E

PLACE (Pronunciation)	PAGE	Lat. °′	Long. °′
Helmond, Neth. (hĕl'mŏnt) (ĕl'môN')	163	51.35 N	5.04 E
Helmstedt, F.R.G. (hĕlm'shtĕt)	166	52.14 N	11.03 E
Helotes, Tx. (hē'lōts)	119d	29.35 N	98.41 W
Helper, Ut. (hĕlp'ēr)	121	39.40 N	110.55 W
Helsby, Eng.	64a	53.16 N	2.46 W
Helsingborg, Swe. (hĕl'sĭng-bôrgh)	164	56.04 N	12.40 E
Helsingfors, see Helsinki			
Helsingør, Den. (hĕl-sĭng-ûr')	164	56.03 N	12.33 E
Helsinki (Helsingfors), Fin. (hĕl'sēn-kē) (hĕl'sĭng-fôrs')	165	60.10 N	24.53 E
Hemel Hempstead, Eng. (hĕm'ĕl hĕmp'stĕd)	156b	51.43 N	0.29 W
Hemer, F.R.G.	169c	51.32 N	7.46 E
Hemet, Ca. (hĕm'ĕt)	119a	33.45 N	116.57 W
Hemingford, Ne. (hĕm'ĭng-fērd)	114	42.21 N	103.30 W
Hemphill, Tx. (hĕmp'hĭl)	125	31.20 N	93.48 W
Hempstead, NY (hĕmp'stĕd)	112a	40.42 N	73.37 W
Hempstead, Tx.	125	30.07 N	96.05 W
Hemse, Swe. (hĕm'sĕ)	164	57.15 N	18.25 E
Hemsön (I.), Swe.	164	62.43 N	18.22 E
Henan (Prov.), China (hŭ-nän)	199	33.58 N	112.33 E
Henares (R.), Sp. (å-nä'rås)	170	40.50 N	2.55 W
Henderson, Ky. (hĕn'dēr-sŭn)	110	37.50 N	87.30 W
Henderson, NC	127	36.18 N	78.24 W
Henderson, Nv.	120	36.09 N	115.04 W
Henderson, Tn.	126	35.25 N	88.40 W
Henderson, Tx.	125	32.09 N	94.48 W
Hendersonville, NC (hĕn'dēr-sŭn-vĭl)	127	35.17 N	82.28 W
Hendon, Eng. (hĕn'dŭn)	156b	51.34 N	0.13 W
Hendrina, S. Afr. (hĕn-drē'nå)	223d	26.10 S	29.44 E
Hengch'un, Taiwan (hĕng'chŭn')	203	22.00 N	120.42 E
Hengelo, Neth. (hĕngĕ-lō)	163	52.20 N	6.45 E
Hengshan, China (hĕng'shän')	203	27.20 N	112.40 E
Hengshui, China (hĕng'shōō-ē')	200	37.43 N	115.42 E
Hengxian, China (hŭŋ shyĕn)	203	22.40 N	104.20 E
Hengyang, China	203	26.58 N	112.30 E
Henley on Thames, Eng. (hĕn'lē ŏn tĕmz)	156b	51.31 N	0.54 W
Henlopen, C., De. (hĕn-lō'pĕn)	111	38.45 N	75.05 W
Hennebont, Fr. (ĕn-bôN')	168	47.47 N	3.16 W
Hennenman, S. Afr.	223d	27.59 S	27.03 E
Hennessey, Ok. (hĕn'ĕ-sĭ)	122	36.04 N	97.53 W
Hennigsdorf, G.D.R. (hĕ'nēngz-dōrf))	157b	52.39 N	13.12 E
Hennops (R.), S. Afr. (hĕn'ŏps)	227b	25.51 S	27.57 E
Hennopsrivier, S. Afr.	227b	25.50 S	27.59 E
Henrietta, Ok. (hĕn-rĭ-ĕt'å)	123	35.25 N	95.58 W
Henrietta, Tx. (hen-rĭ-ĕ'tå)	122	33.47 N	98.11 W
Henrietta Maria, C., Can. (hĕn-rĭ-ĕt'å)	97	55.10 N	82.20 W
Henry Mts., Ut. (hĕn'rĭ)	121	38.55 N	110.45 W
Henteyn Nuruu (Mts.), Sov. Un.	202	49.40 N	111.00 E
Hentiyn Nuruu (Mts.), Mong.	198	49.25 N	107.51 E
Henzada, Bur.	206	17.38 N	95.28 E
Heppner, Or. (hĕp'nēr)	116	45.21 N	119.33 W
Hepu, China (hŭ-pōō)	203	21.28 N	109.10 E
Herāt, Afg. (hĕ-rät')	192	34.28 N	62.13 E
Herbede, F.R.G.	63	51.25 N	7.16 E
Hercegovina (Reg.), Yugo. (hĕr-tsĕ-gô'vē-nå)	173	43.23 N	17.52 E
Hercules, Can.	95g	53.27 N	113.20 W
Herdecke, F.R.G. (hĕr'dĕ-kĕ)	169c	51.24 N	7.26 E
Heredia, C.R. (ā-rā'dhē-ä)	133	10.04 N	84.06 W
Hereford, Eng. (hĕrĕ'fērd)	162	52.05 N	2.44 W
Hereford, Md.	112e	39.35 N	76.42 W
Hereford, Tx. (hĕr'ĕ-fērd)	122	34.47 N	102.25 W
Hereford and Worcester (Co.), Eng.	156	52.24 N	2.15 W
Herencia, Sp. (å-rān'thē-ä)	170	39.23 N	3.22 W
Herentals, Bel.	157a	51.10 N	4.51 E
Herford, F.R.G. (hĕr'fôrt)	166	52.06 N	8.42 E
Herington, Ks. (hĕr'ĭng-tŭn)	123	38.41 N	96.57 W
Herisau, Switz. (hā'rē-zou)	166	47.23 N	9.18 E
Herk-de-Stad, Bel.	157a	50.56 N	5.13 E
Herkimer, NY (hûr'kĭ-mēr)	111	43.05 N	75.00 W
Hermann, Mo. (hûr'măn)	123	38.41 N	91.27 W
Hermannskogel (Mtn.), Aus.	66e	48.16 N	16.18 E
Hermansville, Mi. (hûr'măns-vĭl)	110	45.40 N	87.35 W
Hermantown, Mn. (hĕr'măn-toun)	119h	46.46 N	92.12 W
Hermanusdorings, S. Afr.	223d	24.08 S	27.46 E
Herminie, Pa. (hûr-mĭ'nē)	113e	40.16 N	79.45 W
Hermitage B., Can. (hûr'mĭ-tĕj)	105	47.35 N	56.05 W
Hermit Is., Pap. N. Gui. (hûr'mĭt)	207	1.48 S	144.55 E
Hermosa Beach, Ca. (hĕr-mō'så)	119a	33.51 N	118.24 W
Hermosillo, Mex. (ĕr-mô-sē'l-yō)	128	29.00 N	110.57 W
Hermsdorf (Neigh.), F.R.G.	65a	52.37 N	13.18 E
Hernals (Neigh.), Aus.	66e	48.13 N	16.20 E
Herndon, Va. (hĕrn'don)	112e	38.58 N	77.22 W
Herne, F.R.G. (hĕr'nĕ)	169c	51.32 N	7.13 E
Herning, Den. (hĕr'nĭng)	164	56.08 N	8.55 E
Hernwood Heights, Md.	56c	39.22 N	77.50 W
Héroes Chapultepec, Cuba	60a	19.28 N	99.04 W
Héroes de Churubusco, Cuba	60a	19.22 N	99.06 W
Heron (L.), Mn. (hĕr'ŭn)	114	43.42 N	95.23 W
Herongate, Eng.	62	51.36 N	0.21 E
Heron Lake, Mn.	114	43.48 N	95.20 W
Heronsgate, Eng.	62	51.38 N	0.31 W
Herrero, Punta (pt.), Mex. (pōō'n-tä-ĕr-rĕ'rō)	132	19.18 N	87.24 W
Herrin, Il. (hĕr'ĭn)	110	37.50 N	89.00 W
Herschel, S. Afr. (hēr'-shĕl)	227c	30.37 S	27.12 E
Herscher, Il. (hēr'shēr)	113a	41.03 N	88.06 W
Hersham, Eng.	62	51.22 N	0.23 W
Herstal, Bel. (hĕr'stäl)	163	50.42 N	5.32 E
Herten, F.R.G.	63	51.35 N	7.07 E
Hertford, NC (hûrt'fērd)	127	36.10 N	76.30 W
Hertfordshire (Co.), Eng.	156	51.46 N	0.05 W
Hertzberg, G.D.R. (hĕrtz'bĕrgh)	157b	52.54 N	12.58 E
Hervás, Sp.	170	40.16 N	5.51 W
Herzliyya, Isr.	191a	32.10 N	34.49 E
Hessen, (State), F.R.G. (hĕs'ĕn)	166	50.42 N	9.00 E

PLACE (Pronunciation)	PAGE	Lat. °′	Long. °′
Heswall, Eng.	64a	53.20 N	3.06 W
Hetch Hetchy Aqueduct, Ca. (hĕtch hĕt'chĭ ăk'wē-dŭkt)	120	37.27 N	120.54 W
Hettinger, ND (hĕt'ĭn-jēr)	114	45.58 N	102.36 W
Hetzendorf (Neigh.), Aus.	66e	48.10 N	16.18 E
Heuningspruit, S. Afr.	223d	27.28 S	27.26 E
Heven (Neigh.), F.R.G.	63	51.26 N	7.17 E
Hewlett, NY	55	40.38 N	73.42 W
Hewlett Harbor, NY	55	40.38 N	73.41 W
Hexian, China (hŭ shyĕn)	203	24.20 N	111.28 E
Hexian, China	200	31.44 N	118.20 E
Hextable, Eng.	62	51.25 N	0.11 E
Heyang, China (hŭ-yäŋ)	202	35.18 N	110.18 E
Heystekrand, S. Afr.	223d	25.16 S	27.14 E
Heyuan, China (hŭ-yůän)	203	23.48 N	114.45 E
Heywood, Eng. (hā'wŏŏd)	156	53.36 N	2.12 W
Heze, China (hŭ-dzŭ)	200	35.13 N	115.28 E
Hialeah, Fl. (hī-ă-lē'ăh)	127a	25.49 N	80.18 W
Hiawatha, Ks. (hī-ȧ-wô'thȧ)	123	39.50 N	95.33 W
Hiawatha, Ut.	121	39.25 N	111.05 W
Hibbing, Mn. (hĭb'ĭng)	115	47.26 N	92.58 W
Hickman, Ky. (hĭk'măn)	126	34.33 N	89.10 W
Hickory, NC (hĭk'ô-rĭ)	127	35.43 N	81.21 W
Hickory Hills, Il.	58a	41.43 N	87.49 W
Hicksville, NY (hĭks'vĭl)	112a	40.47 N	73.25 W
Hicksville, OH	110	41.15 N	84.45 W
Hico, Tx. (hī'kō)	124	32.00 N	98.02 W
Hidalgo, Mex. (ē-dhäl'gō)	120	24.14 N	99.25 W
Hidalgo, Mex.	124	27.49 N	99.53 W
Hidalgo (State), Mex.	128	20.45 N	99.30 W
Hidalgo del Parral, Mex. (ē-dä'l-gō-dĕl-pär-rä'l)	124	26.55 N	105.40 W
Hidalgo Yalalag, Mex. (ē-dhäl'gō-yä-lä-läg)	131	17.12 N	96.11 W
Hiddinghausen, F.R.G.	63	51.22 N	7.17 E
Hiedelberg, S. Afr.	223d	26.32 S	28.22 E
Hierro I., Can.Is. (yĕ'r-rô)	224	27.37 N	18.29 W
Hiesfeld, F.R.G.	63	51.33 N	6.46 E
Hietzing (Neigh.), Aus.	66e	48.11 N	16.18 E
Higashi (Neigh.), Jap.	69b	34.41 N	135.31 E
Higashimurayama, Jap.	205a	35.46 N	139.28 E
Higashinada (Neigh.), Jap.	69b	34.43 N	135.16 E
Higashinakano, Jap.	69a	35.38 N	139.25 E
Higashinari (Neigh.), Jap.	69b	34.40 N	135.33 E
Higashiōizumi (Neigh.), Jap.	69a	35.45 N	139.36 E
Higashiōsaka, Jap.	205b	34.40 N	135.44 E
Higashisumiyoshi (Neigh.), Jap.	69b	34.37 N	135.32 E
Higashiyama (Neigh.), Jap.	68e	34.52 N	135.48 E
Higashiyodogawa (Neigh.) Jap.	69b	34.44 N	135.29 E
Higgins (L.), Mi. (hĭg'ĭnz)	110	44.20 N	84.45 W
Higginsville, Mo. (hĭg'ĭnz-vĭl)	123	39.05 N	93.44 W
High (I.), Mi.	110	45.45 N	85.45 W
Higham Upshire, Eng.	62	51.26 N	0.28 E
High Beach, Eng.	62	51.39 N	0.02 E
High Bluff, Can.	95f	50.01 N	98.08 W
Highborne Cay, Ba. (hībôrn kē)	134	24.45 N	76.50 W
Highcliff, Pa.	57b	40.32 N	80.03 W
Higher Broughton (Neigh.), Eng.	64b	53.30 N	2.15 W
Highgrove, Ca. (hī'grōv)	119a	34.01 N	117.20 W
High Island, Tx.	125a	29.34 N	94.24 W
Highland, Ca. (hī'lănd)	119a	34.08 N	117.13 W
Highland, Il.	123	38.44 N	89.41 W
Highland, In.	113a	41.33 N	87.28 W
Highland, Mi.	113b	42.38 N	83.37 W
Highland, Pa.	57b	40.33 N	80.04 W
Highland Park, Il.	113a	42.11 N	87.47 W
Highland Park, Md.	56d	38.54 N	76.54 W
Highland Park, Mi.	113b	42.24 N	83.06 W
Highland Park, NJ	112a	40.30 N	74.25 W
Highland Park, Tx.	119c	32.49 N	96.48 W
Highlands, NJ (hī-lăndz)	112a	40.24 N	73.59 W
Highlands, Tx.	125a	29.49 N	95.01 W
Highlands North (Neigh.), S. Afr.	71b	26.09 S	28.05 E
High Laver, Eng.	62	51.45 N	0.13 E
Highmore, SD (hī'mōr)	114	44.30 N	99.26 W
High Ongar, Eng. (on'gēr)	156b	51.43 N	0.15 E
High Pk., Phil.	207a	51.38 N	120.05 E
High Point, NC	127	35.55 N	80.00 W
High Prairie, Can.	99	55.26 N	116.29 W
High Ridge, Mo.	115e	38.27 N	90.32 W
High River, Can.	99	50.35 N	113.52 W
Highrock (R.), NC (hī'-rŏk)	127	35.40 N	80.15 W
High Springs, Fl.	127	29.48 N	82.38 W
High Tatra Mts., Czech.-Pol.	167	49.15 N	19.40 E
Hightown, Eng.	64a	53.32 N	3.04 W
Hightstown, NJ (hīts-toun)	112a	40.16 N	74.32 W
High Wycombe, Eng. (wĭ-kŭm)	156b	51.36 N	0.45 W
Higuero, Pta (Pt.), P.R.	129b	18.21 N	67.11 W
Higuerote, Ven. (ē-gĕ-rô'tĕ)	143b	10.29 N	66.06 W
Higüey, Dom. Rep. (ē-gwĕ'y)	135	18.40 N	68.45 W
Hiiumaa (D'Ago), Sov. Un. (hē'ōōm-ô)	165	58.47 N	22.05 E
Hikone, Jap. (hē'kô-nĕ)	205	35.15 N	136.15 E
Hildburghausen, G.D.R. (hĭld'bŏŏrg hou-zĕn)	166	50.26 N	10.45 E
Hilden, F.R.G. (hĕl'dĕn)	169c	51.10 N	6.56 E
Hildesheim, F.R.G. (hĭl'dĕs-hĭm)	166	52.08 N	9.56 E
Hillaby, Mt., Barb. (hĭl'ȧ-bĭ)	133b	13.15 N	59.35 W
Hillbrow (Neigh.), S. Afr.	71b	26.11 S	28.03 E
Hill City, Ks. (hĭl)	122	39.22 N	99.54 W
Hill City, Mn.	115	46.58 N	93.38 W
Hill Crest, Pa.	56b	40.05 N	75.11 W
Hillcrest Heights, Md.	56d	38.52 N	76.57 W
Hillegersberg, Neth.	157a	51.57 N	4.29 E
Hillen (Neigh.), F.R.G.	63	51.37 N	7.13 E
Hillerød, Den. (hē'lĕ-rûdh)	164	55.56 N	12.17 E
Hillingdon (Neigh.), Eng.	62	51.32 N	0.27 W
Hillsboro, IL. (hĭlz'bŭr-ō)	123	39.09 N	89.28 W
Hillsboro, Ks.	123	38.22 N	97.11 W
Hillsboro, ND	114	47.23 N	97.05 W
Hillsboro, NH	111	43.05 N	71.55 W
Hillsboro, Oh.	110	39.10 N	83.40 W

PLACE (Pronunciation)	PAGE	Lat. °′	Long. °′
Hillsboro, Or.	118c	45.31 N	122.59 W
Hillsboro, Tx.	125	32.01 N	97.06 W
Hillsboro, Wi.	115	43.39 N	90.20 W
Hillsburgh, Can. (hĭlz'bûrg)	95d	43.48 N	80.09 W
Hills Creek Res., Or.	116	43.41 N	122.26 W
Hillsdale, Mi. (hĭls-dāl)	120	41.55 N	84.35 W
Hillside, Md.	56d	38.52 N	76.55 W
Hillside (Neigh.), NY	55	40.42 N	73.47 W
Hillwood, Va.	56d	38.52 N	77.10 W
Hilo, Hi. (hē'lō)	106a	19.44 N	155.01 W
Hiltrop (Neigh.), F.R.G.	63	51.30 N	7.15 E
Hilversum, Neth. (hĭl'vēr-sŭm)	157a	52.13 N	5.10 E
Himachal Pradesh (State), India	196	36.03 N	77.41 E
Himalaya Mts., Asia (hĭ-mä'lȧ-yȧ)	193	29.30 N	85.02 E
Himeji, Jap. (hē'mā-jē)	205	34.50 N	134.42 E
Himmelgeist (Neigh.), F.R.G.	63	51.10 N	6.49 E
Himmelpforten, F.R.G. (hē'mĕl-pfōr-tĕn)	157c	53.37 N	9.19 E
Hims, Syr.	195	34.44 N	36.43 E
Hinche, Hai. (hēn'chå) (ăNsh)	135	19.10 N	72.05 W
Hinchinbrook (I.), Austl. (hĭn-chĭn-brŏŏk)	215	18.23 S	146.57 W
Hinckley, Eng. (hĭnk'lĭ)	156	52.32 N	1.21 W
Hindley, Eng. (hĭnd'lĭ)	156	53.32 N	2.35 W
Hindu Kush (Mts.), Asia (hĭn'dōō kōōsh')	193	35.15 N	68.44 E
Hindupur, India (hĭn'dōō-pōōr)	197	13.52 N	77.34 E
Hingham, Ma. (hĭng'ăm)	105a	42.14 N	70.53 W
Hinkley, Oh. (hĭnk'-lĭ)	113d	41.14 N	81.45 W
Hino, Jap.	69a	35.41 N	139.24 E
Hinojosa del Duque, Sp. (ē-nô-kō'sä)	170	38.30 N	5.09 W
Hinsdale, Il. (hĭnz'dāl)	113a	41.48 N	87.56 W
Hinsel (Neigh.), F.R.G.	63	51.26 N	7.05 E
Hinton, Can. (hĭn'tŭn)	99	53.25 N	117.34 W
Hinton, WV (hĭn'tŭn)	110	37.40 N	80.55 W
Hirado (I.), Jap. (hē'rä-dō)	205	33.19 N	129.18 E
Hirakata, Jap. (hē'rä-kä'tä)	205b	34.49 N	135.40 E
Hiratsuka, Jap. (hē-rät-sōō'kå)	205	35.20 N	139.19 E
Hirosaki, Jap. (hē'rô-sä'kē)	204	40.31 N	140.38 E
Hirose, Jap. (hē'rô-sä)	205	35.20 N	133.11 E
Hiroshima, Jap. (hē-rô-shē'mȧ)	205	34.22 N	132.25 E
Hirota, Jap.	69b	34.45 N	135.21 E
Hirschstetten (Neigh.), Aus.	66e	48.14 N	16.29 E
Hirson, Fr. (ēr-sôN')	168	49.54 N	4.00 E
Hisar, India	199	29.15 N	75.47 E
Hispaniola (I.), N.A. (hĭ'spăn-ĭ-ō-lȧ)	129	17.30 N	73.15 W
Hitachi, Jap. (hē-tä'chē)	204	36.42 N	140.47 E
Hitchcock, Tx. (hĭch'kŏk)	125a	29.21 N	95.01 W
Hitdorf, F.R.G. (hē'dōrf)	169c	51.04 N	6.56 E
Hither Green (Neigh.), Eng.	62	51.27 N	0.01 W
Hitoyoshi, Jap. (hē'tō-yō'shē)	205	32.13 N	130.45 E
Hitra (I.), Nor. (hĭträ)	158	63.34 N	7.37 E
Hittefeld, F.R.G. (hē'tĕ-fĕld)	157c	53.23 N	9.59 E
Hiwasa, Jap. (hē'wȧ-sä)	205	33.44 N	134.31 E
Hiwassee (R.), Tn. (hī-wôs'sē)	126	35.10 N	84.35 W
Hjälmaren (L.), Swe.	164	59.07 N	16.05 E
Hjo, Swe. (yō)	164	58.19 N	14.11 E
Hjørring, Den. (jûr'ĭng)	164	57.27 N	9.59 E
Hlohovec, Czech. (hlō'ho-vĕts)	167	48.24 N	17.49 E
Hobart, Austl. (hō'bȧrt)	216	43.00 S	147.30 E
Hobart, In.	113a	41.31 N	87.15 W
Hobart, Ok.	122	35.02 N	99.06 W
Hobart, Wa.	118a	47.25 N	121.58 W
Hobbs, NM (hŏbs)	122	32.41 N	104.04 W
Hoboken, Bel. (hō'bō-kĕn)	157a	51.11 N	4.20 E
Hoboken, NJ	112a	40.43 N	74.03 W
Hobro, Den. (hô-brô')	164	56.38 N	9.47 E
Hobson, Va. (hŏb'sŭn)	112g	36.54 N	76.31 W
Hobson's B., Austl. (hŏb'sŭnz)	211a	37.54 S	144.45 E
Hobsons B., Austl.	70b	37.51 S	144.56 E
Hobyo, Som.	223a	5.24 N	48.28 E
Hochdahl, F.R.G.	63	51.13 N	6.56 E
Hochheide, F.R.G.	63	51.27 N	6.41 E
Ho Chi Minh City (Saigon), Viet.	206	10.46 N	106.34 E
Hochlar (Neigh.), F.R.G.	63	51.36 N	7.10 E
Höchsten, F.R.G.	63	51.27 N	7.29 E
Hockinson, Wa. (hŏk'ĭn-sŭn)	118c	45.44 N	122.29 W
Hoctún, Mex. (ôk-tōō'n)	132a	20.52 N	89.10 W
Hodgenville, Ky. (hŏj'ĕn-vĭl)	110	37.35 N	85.45 W
Hodges Hill (Mtn.), Can. (hŏj'ĕz)	103	49.04 N	55.53 W
Hodgkins, Il.	58a	41.46 N	87.51 W
Hódmezövásárhely, Hung. (hōd'mĕ-zû-vô'shôr-hĕl-y')	167	46.24 N	20.21 E
Hodna, Chott el (L.), Alg.	159	35.20 N	3.27 E
Hodonin, Czech. (hē'dô-nén)	167	48.50 N	17.06 E
Hoegaarden, Bel.	157a	50.46 N	4.55 E
Hoek van Holland, Neth.	157a	51.59 N	4.05 E
Hoeryŏng, Kor. (hwĕr'yŭng)	204	42.28 N	129.39 E
Hof, F.R.G. (hōf)	166	50.19 N	11.55 E
Hofburg (P. Int.), Aus.	66e	48.12 N	16.22 E
Hofsjökull (Gl.), Ice. (hōfs'yŭ'kōōl)	158	64.55 N	18.40 W
Hog (I.), Mi.	110	45.50 N	85.20 W
Hogansville, Ga. (hō'gănz-vĭl)	126	33.10 N	84.54 W
Hogar y Redención, Mex.	60a	19.22 N	99.13 W
Hog Cay (I.), Ba.	135	23.35 N	75.30 W
Hogsty Rf., Ba.	135	21.45 N	73.50 W
Hohenbrunn, F.R.G. (hō'hĕn-brōōn)	157d	48.03 N	11.42 E
Hohenlimburg, F.R.G. (hō'hĕn lĕm'bŏŏrg)	169c	51.20 N	7.35 E
Hohen Neuendorf, G.D.R. (hō'hĕn noi'ĕn-dōrf)	157b	52.40 N	13.22 E
Hohenschönhausen (Neigh.), G.D.R.	65a	52.33 N	13.30 E
Hohensyburg (P. Int.), F.R.G.	63	51.25 N	7.29 E
Hohe Tauern (Mts.), Aus. (hō'ĕ tou'ērn)	166	47.11 N	12.12 E
Hohhot, China (hŭ-hōō-tŭ)	202	41.05 N	111.50 E
Hohoe, Ghana	228	7.09 N	0.28 E
Hohokus, NJ (hō-hō-kŭs)	112a	41.01 N	74.08 W
Höhscheid (Neigh.), F.R.G.	63	51.09 N	7.04 E
Hoisington, Ks. (hoi'zĭng-tŭn)	122	38.30 N	98.46 W
Hoisten, F.R.G.	63	51.08 N	6.42 E

ăt; finăl; rāte; senåte; ärm; åsk; sofȧ; fâre; ch-choose; dh-as th in other; bē; ēvent; bĕt; recĕnt; cratēr; g-gō; gh-guttural g; bĭt; ĭ-short neutral; rīde; K-guttural k as ch in German ich;

PLACE (Pronounciation)	PAGE	Lat. °′	Long. °′
Hojo, Jap. (hō'jô)	205	33.58 N	132.50 E
Hokitika, N.Z. (hō-kĭ-tē'kä)	217	42.43 S	170.59 E
Hokkaido (I.), Jap. (hôk'kī-dō)	204	43.30 N	142.45 E
Holbaek, Den. (hôl'běk)	164	55.42 N	11.40 E
Holborn (Neigh.), Eng.	62	51.31 N	0.07 W
Holbox, Mex. (ôl-bô'x)	132a	21.33 N	87.19 W
Holbox, Isla (I.), Mex. (ē's-lä-ôl-bô'x)	132a	21.40 N	87.21 W
Holbrook, Az. (hōl'brŏŏk)	121	34.55 N	110.15 W
Holbrook, Ma.	105a	42.10 N	71.01 W
Holden, Ma. (hōl'dĕn)	105a	42.21 N	71.51 W
Holden, Mo.	123	38.42 N	94.00 W
Holden, WV	110	37.45 N	82.05 W
Holdenville, Ok. (hōl'dĕn-vĭl)	123	35.05 N	96.25 W
Holdrege, Ne. (hōl'drĕj)	122	40.25 N	99.28 W
Holguín, Cuba (ôl-gēn')	135	20.55 N	76.15 W
Holguín (Prov.), Cuba	135	20.40 N	76.15 W
Holidaysburg, Pa. (hŏl'ĭ-dāz-bûrg)	111	40.30 N	78.30 W
Hollabrunn, Aus.	166	48.33 N	16.04 E
Holland, Mi. (hŏl'ănd)	110	42.45 N	86.10 W
Holland Diep (Chan.), Neth.	157a	51.43 N	4.25 E
Hollenstedt, F.R.G. (hō'lĕn-shtĕt)	157c	53.22 N	9.43 E
Hollins, Eng.	64b	53.34 N	2.17 W
Hollis (Neigh.), NY	55	40.43 N	73.46 W
Hollis, NH (hŏl'ĭs)	105a	42.30 N	71.29 W
Hollis, Ok.	122	34.39 N	99.56 W
Hollister, Ca. (hŏl'ĭs-tēr)	120	36.50 N	121.25 W
Holliston, Ma. (hŏl'ĭs-tŭn)	105a	42.12 N	71.25 W
Holly, Mi. (hŏl'ĭ)	110	42.45 N	83.30 W
Holly, Wa.	118a	47.34 N	122.58 W
Holly Springs, Ms. (hŏl'ĭ sprĭngz)	126	34.45 N	89.28 W
Hollywood, Ca. (hŏl'ē-wŏŏd)	119a	34.06 N	118.20 W
Hollywood, Fl.	127a	26.00 N	80.11 W
Hollywood Bowl (P. Int.), Ca.	59	34.07 N	118.20 W
Holmes, Pa.	56b	39.54 N	75.19 W
Holmes Rfs., Austl. (hōmz)	215	16.33 S	148.43 E
Holmes Run Acres, Va.	56d	38.51 N	77.13 W
Holmestrand, Nor. (hôl'mĕ-strän)	164	59.29 N	10.17 E
Holmsbu, Nor. (hôlms'bōō)	164	59.36 N	10.26 E
Holmsjön (L.), Swe.	164	62.23 N	15.43 E
Holroyd, Austl.	70a	33.50 S	150.58 E
Holstebro, Den. (hôl'stĕ-brô)	164	56.22 N	8.39 E
Holston (R.), Tn. (hōl'stŭn)	126	36.02 N	83.42 W
Holt, Eng. (hōlt)	156	53.05 N	2.53 W
Holten (Neigh.), F.R.G.	63	51.31 N	6.48 E
Holthausen (Neigh.), F.R.G.	63	51.34 N	7.26 E
Holton, Ks. (hōl'tŭn)	123	39.27 N	95.43 W
Holy Cross, Ak. (hō'lĭ krôs)	107	62.10 N	159.40 W
Holyhead, Wales (hŏl'ē-hĕd)	162	53.48 N	4.45 W
Holy I., Eng.	162	55.43 N	1.48 W
Holy I., Wales (hō'lĭ)	162	53.45 N	4.45 W
Holyoke, Co. (hōl'yōk)	122	40.36 N	102.18 W
Holyoke, Ma.	111	42.10 N	72.40 W
Holzen, F.R.G.	63	51.26 N	7.31 E
Holzheim, F.R.G.	63	51.09 N	6.39 E
Holzwickede, F.R.G.	63	51.30 N	7.36 E
Homano, Jap. (hō-mä'nō)	205a	35.33 N	140.08 E
Homberg, F.R.G. (hōm'bĕrgh)	169c	51.27 N	6.42 E
Hombori, Mali	228	15.17 N	1.42 W
Home Gardens, Ca. (hōm gär'd'nz)	119a	33.53 N	117.32 W
Homeland, Ca. (hōm'lănd)	119a	33.44 N	117.07 W
Homer, Ak. (hō'mēr)	107	59.42 N	151.30 W
Homer, La.	125	32.46 N	93.05 W
Homestead, Fl. (hōm'stĕd)	127a	25.27 N	80.28 W
Homestead, Mi.	119k	46.20 N	84.07 W
Homestead, Pa.	113e	40.29 N	79.55 W
Homestead Natl. Mon. of America, Ne.	124	40.16 N	96.51 W
Hometown, Il.	58a	41.44 N	87.44 W
Homewood, Al. (hōm'wŏŏd)	112h	33.28 N	86.48 W
Homewood, Il.	113a	41.34 N	87.40 W
Homewood (Neigh.), Pa.	57b	40.27 N	79.54 W
Hominy, Ok. (hŏm'ĭ-nĭ)	124	36.25 N	96.24 W
Homochiho (R.), Ms. (hō-mō-chĭt'ō)	126	31.23 N	91.15 W
Homs, Syr. (hōms)	161	34.42 N	36.52 E
Honda, Col. (hōn'dȧ)	142a	5.13 N	74.45 W
Honda, Bahía (B.), Cuba (bä-ē'ä-ô'n-dä)	134	23.10 N	83.20 W
Hondo (R.), NM	122	33.22 N	105.06 W
Hondo, Tx.	124	29.20 N	99.08 W
Hondo, Rio (R.), Belize (hon-dō')	132a	18.16 N	88.32 W
Honduras, N.A. (hŏn-dōō'rȧs)	128	14.30 N	88.00 W
Honduras, Gulf of, N.A.	128	16.30 N	87.30 W
Honea Path, SC (hŭn'ĭ păth)	127	34.25 N	82.16 W
Hönefoss, Nor. (hē'nē-fôs)	164	60.10 N	10.15 E
Honesdale, Pa. (hōnz'dāl)	111	41.30 N	75.15 W
Honey (R.), Ca. (hŭn'ĭ)	120	40.11 N	120.34 W
Honey Grove, Tx. (hŭn'ĭ grōv)	123	33.35 N	95.54 W
Honfleur, Can. (ôN-flûr')	95b	46.39 N	70.53 W
Honfleur, Fr. (ôN-flûr')	168	49.26 N	0.13 E
Hon Gay, Viet.	203	20.58 N	107.10 E
Hong Kong, Asia (hŏng' kŏng')	199	21.45 N	115.00 E
Hongshui (R.), China (hôŋ-shwā)	203	25.00 N	107.22 E
Honguedo, Détroit d' (Str.), Can.	104	49.08 N	63.45 W
Hongze Hu (L.), China (hôŋ-dzŭ hōō)	200	33.17 N	118.37 E
Honiara, Sol. Is.	215	9.15 S	159.45 E
Honiton, Eng. (hŏn'ĭ-tŏn)	162	50.49 N	3.10 W
Honolulu, Hi. (hŏn-ō-lōō'lōō)	106a	21.18 N	157.50 W
Honomu, Hi. (hŏn'ō-mōō)	106a	19.50 N	155.04 W
Honshū (I.), Jap. (hŏn'shōō)	204	36.50 N	135.20 E
Höntrop (Neigh.), F.R.G.	63	51.27 N	7.08 E
Hood Can., Wa. (hŏŏd)	118a	47.45 N	122.45 W
Hood, Mt., Or.	116	45.20 N	121.43 W
Hood River, Or.	116	45.42 N	121.30 W
Hoodsport, Wa. (hŏŏdz'pōrt)	118a	47.25 N	123.09 W
Hooghly-Chinsura, India	67a	22.54 N	88.24 E
Hoogly (R.), India (hōōg'lĭ)	196	21.35 N	87.50 E
Hoogstraten, Bel.	157a	51.24 N	4.46 E
Hooker, Ok. (hŏŏk'ēr)	122	36.49 N	101.13 W
Hool, Mex. (ōō'l)	132a	19.32 N	90.22 W
Hoonah, Ak. (hōō'nä)	107	58.05 N	135.25 W

PLACE (Pronounciation)	PAGE	Lat. °′	Long. °′
Hoopa Valley Ind. Res., Ca. (hōō'pȧ)	116	41.18 N	123.35 W
Hooper, Ne. (hŏŏp'ēr)	123	41.37 N	96.31 W
Hooper, Ut.	119b	41.10 N	112.08 W
Hooper Bay, Ak.	107	61.32 N	166.02 W
Hoopeston, Il. (hōōps'tŭn)	110	40.35 N	87.40 W
Hoosick Falls, NY (hōō'sĭk)	111	42.55 N	73.15 W
Hooton, Eng.	64a	53.18 N	2.57 W
Hoover Dam, Nv. (hōō'vēr)	120	36.00 N	115.06 W
Hopatcong, L., NJ (hō-păt'kong)	112a	40.57 N	74.38 W
Hope, Ak. (hōp)	107	60.54 N	149.48 W
Hope, Ar.	123	33.41 N	93.35 W
Hope, Can.	99	49.23 N	121.26 W
Hope, ND	114	47.17 N	97.45 W
Hope, Ben (Mtn.), Scot. (bĕn hōp)	162	58.25 N	4.25 W
Hopedale, Can. (hōp'dāl)	97	55.26 N	60.11 W
Hopedale, Ma. (hōp'dāl)	105a	42.08 N	71.33 W
Hopelchén, Mex. (o-pĕl-chĕ'n)	132a	19.47 N	89.51 W
Hopes Advance, C., Can. (hōps ăd-vans')	97	61.05 N	69.35 W
Hopetoun, Austl. (hōp'toun)	214	33.50 S	120.15 E
Hopetown, S. Afr. (hōp'toun)	226	29.35 S	24.10 E
Hopewell, Va. (hōp'wĕl)	127	37.14 N	77.15 W
Hopi Ind. Res., Az. (hō'pē)	121	36.20 N	110.30 W
Hopkins, Mn. (hŏp'kĭns)	119g	44.55 N	93.24 W
Hopkinsville, Ky. (hŏp'kĭns-vĭl)	126	36.50 N	87.28 W
Hopkinton, Ma. (hŏp'kĭn-tŭn)	105a	42.14 N	71.31 W
Hoppegarten, G.D.R.	65a	52.31 N	13.40 E
Hoquiam, Wa. (hō'kwĭ-ăm)	116	47.00 N	123.53 W
Horby, Swe. (hûr'bü)	164	55.50 N	13.41 E
Horconcitos, Pan. (ŏr-kôn-sē'-tôs)	133	8.18 N	82.11 W
Hörde (Neigh.), F.R.G.	63	51.29 N	7.30 E
Horgen, Switz. (hôr'gĕn)	166	47.16 N	8.35 E
Horicon, Wi. (hŏr'ĭ-kŏn)	115	43.26 N	88.40 W
Horinouchi (Neigh.), Jap.	69a	35.41 N	139.40 E
Hormuz, Str. of, Asia (hôr'mŭz')	192	26.30 N	56.30 E
Horn (Is.), Austl. (hôrn)	215	10.30 S	143.30 E
Hornavan (L.), Swe.	158	65.54 N	16.17 E
Hornchurch (Neigh.), Eng.	62	51.34 N	0.12 E
Horn, C., see Hornos, Cabo de			
Horndon on the Hill, Eng.	62	51.31 N	0.25 E
Horneburg, F.R.G. (hôr'nĕ-bŏŏrgh)	157c	53.30 N	9.35 E
Horneburg, F.R.G.	63	51.38 N	7.18 E
Hornell, NY (hôr-nĕl')	111	42.10 N	77.40 W
Horn Hill, Eng.	62	51.37 N	0.32 W
Horn Mts., Can.	96	62.12 N	120.29 W
Hornos, C. de (Horn, C.), Chile (kä'-bô-dĕ-ô'r-nôs) (kā'p-hôr'n)	144	56.00 S	67.00 W
Hornsby, Austl. (hôrnz'bĭ)	211b	33.43 S	151.06 E
Hornsey (Neigh.), Eng.	62	51.35 N	0.07 W
Horqueta, Par. (ŏr-kĕ'tä)	144	23.20 S	57.00 W
Horse Cr., Co. (hôrs)	122	38.49 N	103.48 W
Horse Cr., Wy.	114	41.33 N	104.39 W
Horse Is., Can.	105	50.11 N	55.45 W
Horsell, Eng.	62	51.19 N	0.34 W
Horsens, Den. (hôrs'ĕns)	164	55.50 N	9.49 E
Horseshoe B., Can. (hôrs-shōō)	118d	49.23 N	123.16 W
Horsforth, Eng. (hôrs'fŭrth)	156	53.50 N	1.38 W
Horsham, Austl. (hôr'shăm) (hôrs'ăm)	216	36.42 S	142.17 E
Horsley, Austl.	70a	33.51 S	150.51 E
Horst, F.R.G. (hôrst)	157c	53.49 N	9.37 E
Horst (Neigh.), F.R.G.	63	51.32 N	7.02 E
Horsthausen (Neigh.), F.R.G.	63	51.33 N	7.13 E
Horstmar (Neigh.), F.R.G.	63	51.36 N	7.33 E
Hortaleza (Neigh.), Sp.	65b	40.28 N	3.39 W
Horten, Nor. (hôr'tĕn)	164	59.26 N	10.27 E
Horton, Ks. (hôr'tŭn)	124	39.38 N	95.32 W
Horton (R.), Ak. (hôr'tŭn)	107	68.38 N	122.00 W
Horton Kirby, Eng.	62	51.23 N	0.15 E
Horwich, Eng. (hŏr'ĭch)	156	53.36 N	2.33 W
Hösel, F.R.G.	63	51.19 N	6.54 E
Hoséré Vokré (Mtn.), Cam.	229	8.20 N	13.15 E
Hososhima, Jap. (hō'sō-shē'mä)	205	32.25 N	131.40 E
Hospitalet, Sp.	65e	41.22 N	2.08 E
Hoste (I.), Chile (ŏs'tā)	144	55.20 S	70.45 W
Hostotipaquillo, Mex. (ôs-tō'tĭ-pä-kēl'yō)	130	21.09 N	104.05 W
Hota, Jap. (hō'tä)	205a	35.08 N	139.50 E
Hotan, China (hwô-tän)	198	37.11 N	79.50 E
Hotan (R.), China	198	39.09 N	81.08 E
Hoto Mayor, Dom. Rep. (ô-tō-mä-yō'r)	135	18.45 N	69.10 W
Hot Springs, Ak. (hŏt sprĭngs)	107	65.00 N	150.20 W
Hot Springs, Ar.	123	34.29 N	93.02 W
Hot Springs, SD	114	43.28 N	103.32 W
Hot Springs, Va.	111	38.00 N	79.55 W
Hot Springs Natl. Park, Ar.	123	34.30 N	93.00 W
Hotte, Massif de la (Mts.), Hai.	135	18.25 N	74.00 W
Hotville, Ca. (hŏt'vĭl)	120	32.50 N	115.24 W
Houdan, Fr. (ōō-däN')	169b	48.47 N	1.36 E
Hough Green, Eng.	64a	53.23 N	2.47 W
Houghton, (L.), Mi.	110	44.20 N	84.45 W
Houghton, Mi. (hō'tŭn)	115	47.06 N	88.36 W
Houilles, Fr. (ōō-yēs')	169b	48.55 N	2.11 E
Houjie, China (hwô-jyĕ)	201a	22.58 N	113.39 E
Houlton, Me. (hōl'tŭn)	104	46.07 N	67.50 W
Houma, La. (hōō'mȧ)	125	29.36 N	90.43 W
Houndé, Burkina	228	11.30 N	3.31 W
Hounslow (Neigh.), Eng.	62	51.29 N	0.22 W
Housatonic (R.), Ct.-Ma. (hōō-sȧ-tŏn'ĭk)	111	41.50 N	73.25 W
House Springs, Mo. (hous sprĭngs)	119e	38.24 N	90.34 W
Houston, Ms. (hūs'tŭn)	126	33.53 N	89.00 W
Houston, Tx.	125a	29.46 N	95.21 W
Houston Ship Chan., Tx.	125a	29.38 N	94.57 W
Houtbaai, S. Afr.	226a	34.03 S	18.22 E
Houtman Rocks (Is.), Austl. (hout'män)	214	28.15 S	112.45 E
Houzhen, China (hwō-jŭn)	200	36.59 N	118.59 E
Houd, Mong.	198	48.08 N	91.40 E
Houd, (R.) Mong.	198	49.06 N	91.16 E

PLACE (Pronounciation)	PAGE	Lat. °′	Long. °′
Hove, Eng. (hōv)	162	50.50 N	0.09 W
Hovenweep Natl. Mon., Co.-Ut. (hō'v'n-wēp)	121	37.27 N	108.50 W
Hövsgöl Nuur (Koso Lake), Mong.	198	51.11 N	99.11 E
Howard, Ks. (hou'ȧrd)	123	37.27 N	96.10 W
Howard, SD	114	44.01 N	97.31 W
Howard Beach (Neigh.), NY	55	40.40 N	73.51 W
Howden, Eng. (hou'dĕn)	156	53.44 N	0.52 W
Howe C., Austl. (hou)	216	37.30 S	150.40 E
Howell, Mi. (hou'ĕl)	110	42.40 N	84.00 W
Howe Sd., Can.	98	49.22 N	123.18 W
Howick, Can. (hou'ĭk)	95a	45.11 N	73.51 W
Howick, S. Afr.	227c	29.29 S	30.16 E
Howland (I.), Oceania (hou'lănd)	208	1.00 N	176.00 W
Howrah, India (hou'rä)	196b	22.33 N	88.20 E
Howrah Bridge (P. Int.), India	67a	22.35 N	88.21 E
Howse Pk., Can.	99	51.30 N	116.40 W
Howson Pk., Can.	98	54.25 N	127.45 W
Hoxie, Ar. (kŏh'sĭ)	123	36.03 N	91.00 W
Hoxton Park, Austl.	70a	33.55 S	150.51 E
Hoy (I.), Scot. (hoi)	162a	58.53 N	3.10 W
Hōya, Jap.	205a	35.45 N	139.35 E
Hoylake, Eng. (hoi-lāk')	156	53.23 N	3.11 W
Hoyo, Sierra del (Mts.), Sp. (sē-ĕ'r-rä-dĕl-ô'yō)	171a	40.39 N	3.56 W
Hradec Králové, Czech. (hrä'dĕts krä'lô-vā)	166	50.14 N	15.50 E
Hranice, Czech. (hrän'yē-tsĕ)	167	49.33 N	17.45 E
Hrinová, Czech. (hrēn'yô-vä)	167	48.36 N	19.32 E
Hron R., Czech.	167	48.22 N	18.42 E
Hrubieszów, Pol. (hrōō-byä'shōōf)	167	50.48 N	23.54 E
Hrvatska (Croatia) (Reg.), Yugo. (hr-väts'kä)	172	45.24 N	15.18 E
Hsawnhsup, Bur.	198	24.29 N	94.45 E
Hsiaoku Ho (R.), China (sĭou'gōō hŭ)	200	36.29 N	120.06 E
Hsich'ang, China	203	26.50 N	102.25 E
Hsiliao (R.), China	202	43.23 N	121.40 E
Hsinchiang (Mts.), China	196	41.52 N	81.20 E
Hsinchu, Taiwan (hsĭn'chōō')	203	24.48 N	121.00 E
Hsinchuang, Taiwan	68d	25.02 N	121.26 E
Hsinkao Shan (Mtn.), Taiwan	203	23.38 N	121.05 E
Huadian, China (hwä-dĭĕn)	202	42.38 N	126.45 E
Huai (R.), China (hwī)	199	32.07 N	114.38 E
Huai'an, China (hwī-än)	200	33.31 N	119.11 E
Huailai, China	202	40.20 N	115.45 E
Huailin, China (hwī-lĭn)	200	31.27 N	117.36 E
Huainan, China	200	32.38 N	117.02 E
Huaiyang, China (hōōäī'yang)	200	33.45 N	114.54 E
Huaiyuan, China (hwī-yūän)	200	32.53 N	117.13 E
Huajicori, Mex. (wä-jē-kō'rē)	130	22.41 N	105.24 W
Huajuapan de León, Mex. (wäj-wä'päm dā lä-ón')	131	17.46 N	97.45 W
Hualapai Ind. Res., Az. (wäl'apĭ)	121	35.41 N	113.38 W
Hualapai Mts., Az.	121	34.53 N	113.54 W
Hualien, Taiwan (hwä'lyĕn')	203	23.58 N	121.58 E
Huallaga (R.), Peru (wäl-yä'gä)	142	8.12 S	76.34 W
Huamachuco, Peru (wä-mä-chōō'kō)	142	7.52 S	78.11 W
Huamantla, Mex. (wä-män'tlä)	131	19.18 N	97.54 W
Huambo (Nova Lisboa), Ang.	230	12.44 S	15.47 E
Huamuxtitlán, Mex. (wä-mōōs-tē-tlän')	130	17.49 N	98.38 W
Huan (R.), China (hŭän)	198	36.45 N	106.30 E
Huancavelica, Peru (wän'kä-vä-lē'kä)	142	12.47 S	75.02 W
Huancayo, Peru (wän-kä'yō)	142	12.09 S	75.04 W
Huanchaca, Bol. (wän-chä'kä)	142	20.09 S	66.40 W
Huang (Yellow River), China (hŭäŋ)	199	35.06 N	113.39 E
Huangchuan, China (hŭäŋ-chŭän)	200	32.07 N	115.01 E
Huangcun, China	67b	39.56 N	116.11 E
Huang He, Old Course of the (R.), China (hŭäŋ-hŭ)	200	34.28 N	116.59 E
Huanghua, China (hŭäŋ-hwä)	200	38.28 N	117.18 E
Huanghuadian, China (hŭäŋ-hwä-dĭĕn)	202a	39.22 N	116.53 E
Huangli, China (hōōäNg'lē)	200	31.39 N	119.42 E
Huang, Old Beds of the (Yellow) (R.), China	199	40.28 N	106.34 E
Huangpu, China (hŭäŋ-pōō)	201a	22.44 N	113.20 E
Huangpu (R.), China	201b	30.56 N	121.16 E
Huangqiao, China (hŭän-chyou)	200	32.15 N	120.13 E
Huangxian, China (hŭäŋ shyĕn)	200	37.39 N	120.32 E
Huangyuan, China (hŭäŋ-yūän)	198	37.00 N	101.01 E
Huanren, China (hŭän-rŭn)	202	41.10 N	125.30 E
Huánuco, Peru (wä-nōō'kō)	142	9.50 S	76.17 W
Huánuni, Bol. (wä-nōō'nē)	142	18.11 S	66.43 W
Huapí, Montañas de (Mts.), Nic. (môn-tä'n-yäs-dĕ-wä'pē')	133	12.35 N	84.43 W
Huaquechula, Mex. (wä-kĕ-chōō'lä)	130	18.44 N	98.37 W
Huaral, Peru (wä-rä'l)	142	11.28 S	77.11 W
Huarás, Peru (ōōä'rȧ's)	142	9.32 S	77.29 W
Huascarán, Nevs. (Pk.), Peru (wäs-kä-rän')	142	9.05 S	77.50 W
Huasco, Chile (wäs'kō)	144	28.32 S	71.16 W
Huatla de Jiménez, Mex. (wä'tlä-dĕ-Ke-mĕ'nĕz)	131	18.08 N	96.49 W
Huatlatlauch, Mex. (wä'tlä-tlä-ōō'ch)	131	18.40 N	98.04 W
Huatusco, Mex. (wä-tōōs'kō)	131	19.09 N	96.57 W
Huauchinango, Mex. (wä-ōō-chē-näŋ'gō)	130	20.09 N	98.03 W
Huaunta, Nic. (wä-ōō'n-tä)	133	13.30 N	83.32 W
Huaunta, Laguna (L.), Nic. (lä-gōō'nä-wä-ōō'n-tä)	133	13.35 N	83.46 W
Huautla, Mex. (wä-ōō'tlä)	130	21.04 N	98.13 W
Huaxian, China (hwä shyĕn)	200	35.34 N	114.32 E
Huaynamota, Rió de (R.), Mex. (rē'ō-dĕ-wäy-nä-mō'tä)	130	22.10 N	104.36 W
Huazolotitlán (Santa María), Mex. (wäzō-lō-tlē-tlän')	131	16.18 N	97.55 W
Hubbard, NH (hŭb'ērd)	105a	42.53 N	71.12 W
Hubbard, Tx.	125	31.53 N	96.46 W

PLACE (Pronounciation)	PAGE	Lat. °'	Long. °'
Hubbard (L.), Mi.	110	44.45 N	83.30 W
Hubbard Creek Res., Tx.	124	32.50 N	98.55 W
Hubbelrath, F.R.G.	63	51.16 N	6.55 E
Hubei (Prov.), China (hōō-bā)	199	31.20 N	111.58 E
Hubli, India (hŏŏ'blē)	197	15.25 N	75.09 E
Hückeswagen, F.R.G. (hü'kĕs-vä'gĕn)	169c	51.09 N	7.20 E
Hucknall, Eng. (hŭk'nǎl)	156	53.02 N	1.12 W
Huddersfield, Eng. (hŭd'ẽrz-fēld)	156	53.39 N	1.47 W
Hudiksvall, Swe. (hōō'dĭks-väl)	164	61.44 N	17.05 E
Hudson, Can. (hŭd'sŭn)	95a	45.26 N	74.08 W
Hudson, Ma.	105a	42.24 N	71.34 W
Hudson, Mi.	110	41.50 N	84.15 W
Hudson, NY	111	42.15 N	73.45 W
Hudson, Oh.	113d	41.15 N	81.27 W
Hudson, Wi.	119g	44.59 N	92.45 W
Hudson B., Can.	97	60.15 N	85.30 W
Hudson Bay, Can.	101	52.52 N	102.25 W
Hudson Falls, NY	111	43.20 N	73.30 W
Hudson Heights, Can.	95a	45.28 N	74.09 W
Hudson R., NY	110	41.55 N	73.55 W
Hudson Str., Can.	97	63.25 N	74.05 W
Hue, Viet. (ü-ā')	203	16.28 N	107.42 E
Huebra (R.), Sp. (wĕ'brä)	170	40.44 N	6.17 W
Huehuetenango, Guat. (wā-wā-tā-näŋ'gō)	132	15.19 N	91.26 W
Huejotzingo, Mex. (wā-hō-tzĭŋ'gō)	130	19.09 N	98.24 W
Huejúcar, Mex. (wā-hōō'kär)	130	22.26 N	103.12 W
Huejuquilla el Alto, Mex. (wā-hōō-kēl'yä ĕl äl'tō)	130	22.42 N	102.54 W
Huejutla, Mex. (wā-hōō'tlä)	130	21.08 N	98.26 W
Huelma, Sp. (wĕl'mä)	170	37.39 N	3.36 W
Huelva, Sp. (wĕl'vä)	170	37.16 N	6.58 W
Huércal-Overa, Sp. (wĕr-käl' ō-vä'rä)	170	37.12 N	1.58 W
Huerfano (R.), Co. (wâr'fȧ-nō)	122	37.41 N	105.13 W
Huésca, Sp. (wĕs-kä)	171	42.07 N	0.25 W
Huéscar, Sp. (wās'kär)	170	37.50 N	2.34 W
Huetamo de Múñez, Mex. (wā-tä'mō dā-mōōn'yĕz)	130	18.34 N	100.53 W
Huete, Sp. (wā'tā)	170	40.09 N	2.42 W
Hueycatenango, Mex. (wĕy-kä-tĕ-nä'n-gō)	130	17.31 N	99.10 W
Hueytlalpan, Mex. (wā'ī-tlăl'păn)	131	20.03 N	97.41 W
Hueytown, Al.	112h	33.28 N	86.59 W
Huffman, Al. (hŭf'mȧn)	112h	33.36 N	86.42 W
Hügel, Villa (P. Int.), F.R.G.	63	51.25 N	7.01 E
Hugh Butler (L.), Ne.	122	40.21 N	100.40 W
Hughenden, Austl. (hū'ĕn-dĕn)	215	20.58 S	144.13 E
Hughes, Austl. (hūz)	214	30.45 S	129.30 E
Hughesville, Md.	112e	38.32 N	76.48 W
Hugo, Mn. (hū'gō)	119g	45.10 N	93.00 W
Hugo, Ok.	123	34.01 N	95.32 W
Hugoton, Ks. (hū'gō-tŭn)	122	37.10 N	101.28 W
Hugou, China (hōō-gō)	200	33.22 N	117.07 E
Huichapan, Mex. (wē-chä-pän')	130	20.22 N	99.39 W
Huila (Dept.), Col. (wē'lä)	142a	3.10 N	75.20 W
Huilai, China	203	23.02 N	116.18 E
Huila, Nevado de (Pk.), Col. (nĕ-vä-dô-de-wē'lä)	142a	2.59 N	76.01 W
Huili, China	203	26.48 N	102.20 E
Huimanguillo, Mex. (wē-män-gēl'yō)	131	17.50 N	93.16 W
Huimin, China (hōōī mĭn)	200	37.29 N	117.32 E
Huipulco, Mex.	60a	19.17 N	99.09 W
Huitzilac, Mex. (ōōē't-zē-lä'k)	131a	19.01 N	99.16 W
Huitzitzilingo, Mex. (wē-tzē-tzē-lē'n-gō)	130	21.11 N	98.42 W
Huitzuco, Mex. (wē-tzōō'kō)	130	18.16 N	99.20 W
Huixquilucan, Mex. (ōōē'x-kē-lōō-kä'n)	131a	19.21 N	99.22 W
Huixtla, Mex. (wēs'tlä)	131	15.12 N	92.28 W
Huiyang, China	203	23.05 N	114.25 E
Hukou, China (hōō-kō)	203	29.58 N	116.20 E
Hulan, China (hōō'län')	202	45.58 N	126.32 E
Hulan (R.), China	202	42.20 N	126.30 E
Hulin, China (hōō'lĭn')	204	45.45 N	133.25 E
Hull, Can. (hŭl)	95c	45.26 N	75.43 W
Hull, Ma.	105a	42.18 N	70.54 W
Hull (R.), Eng.	156	53.47 N	0.20 W
Hülscheid, F.R.G.	63	51.16 N	7.34 E
Hulst, Neth. (hōōlst)	157a	51.17 N	4.01 E
Huludao, China (hōō-lōō-dou)	202	40.40 N	122.55 E
Hulun Nur (L.), China (hōō-lōōn nōōr)	202	48.50 N	116.45 E
Hulwān, Egypt (hĕl'wän)	223b	29.51 N	31.20 E
Humacao, P.R. (ōō-mä-kä'ō)	129b	18.09 N	65.49 W
Humaitá, Braz. (ōō-mä-ē-tä')	130	7.37 S	62.58 W
Humaitá, Par.	142	27.08 S	58.18 W
Humansdorp, S. Afr. (hōō'mäns-dôrp)	226	33.57 S	24.45 E
Humbe, Ang. (hōōm'bā)	226	16.50 S	14.55 E
Humber (L.), Eng. (hŭm'bẽr)	162	53.38 N	0.40 W
Humber (R.), Can.	95d	43.53 N	79.40 W
Humbermouth, Can. (hŭm'bẽr-mŭth)	105	48.58 N	57.55 W
Humberside (Co.), Eng.	156	53.47 N	0.36 W
Humble, Tx. (hŭm'b'l)	125	29.58 N	95.15 W
Humboldt, Can. (hŭm'bōlt)	100	52.12 N	105.07 W
Humboldt, Ia.	115	42.43 N	94.11 W
Humboldt, Ks.	123	37.48 N	95.26 W
Humboldt, Ne.	123	40.10 N	95.57 W
Humboldt (R.), U.S.	108	40.30 N	116.50 W
Humboldt B., Ca.	116	40.48 N	124.25 W
Humboldt, Planetario (P. Int.), Ven.	61a	10.30 N	66.50 W
Humboldt R., East Fork, Nv.	116	40.59 N	115.21 W
Humboldt R., North Fork, Nv.	116	41.25 N	115.45 W
Humbolt, Tn.	126	35.47 N	88.55 W
Humbolt Ra., Nv.	120	40.12 N	118.16 W
Humbolt Salt Marsh, Nv.	120	39.49 N	117.41 W
Humbolt Sink, Nv.	120	39.58 N	118.54 W
Humen, China (hōō-mŭn)	201a	22.49 N	113.39 E
Humphreys Pk., Az. (hŭm'frĭs)	121	35.20 N	111.40 W
Humpolec, Czech. (hōōm'pō-lĕts)	166	49.33 N	15.21 E
Humuya R., Hond. (ōō-mōō'yä)	132	14.38 N	87.36 W
Hunaflói (B.), Ice. (hōō'nä-flō'ĭ)	158	65.41 N	20.44 W
Hunan (Prov.), China (hōō'nän')	199	28.08 N	111.25 E
Hunchun, China (hōōn-chŭn)	199	42.53 N	130.34 E
Hunedoara, Rom. (ĸōō'nĕd-wä'rȧ)	173	45.45 N	22.54 E
Hungary, Eur. (hŭŋ'gȧ-rĭ)	154	46.44 N	17.55 E
Hungerford, Austl. (hŭn'gẽr-fẽrd)	216	28.50 S	144.32 E
Hungry Horse Res., Mt. (hŭŋ'gȧ-rĭ hôrs)	117	48.11 N	113.30 W
Hunsrück (Mts.), F.G.R. (hōōns'rûk)	166	49.43 N	7.12 E
Hunte R., F.R.G. (hōōn'tĕ)	166	52.45 N	8.26 E
Hunter Is., Austl. (hŭn-tẽr)	215	40.33 S	143.36 E
Hunters Hill, Austl.	70a	33.50 S	151.09 E
Huntingburg, In. (hŭnt'ĭng-bûrg)	110	38.15 N	86.55 W
Huntingdon, Can. (hŭnt'ĭng-dŭn)	111	45.10 N	74.05 W
Huntingdon, Can.	118d	49.00 N	122.16 W
Huntingdon, Tn.	126	36.00 N	88.23 W
Huntington, In.	110	40.55 N	85.30 W
Huntington, Pa.	111	40.30 N	78.00 W
Huntington, Va.	56d	38.48 N	77.15 W
Huntington, WV	110	38.25 N	82.25 W
Huntington Beach, Ca.	119a	33.39 N	118.00 W
Huntington Park, Ca.	119a	33.59 N	118.14 W
Huntington Station, NY	112a	40.51 N	73.25 W
Huntington Woods, Mi.	57c	42.29 N	83.10 W
Huntley, Mt.	117	45.54 N	108.01 W
Hunt's Cross (Neigh.), Eng.	64a	53.21 N	2.51 W
Huntsville, Al. (hŭnts'vĭl)	126	34.44 N	86.36 W
Huntsville, Can.	111	45.20 N	79.15 W
Huntsville, Md.	56d	38.55 N	76.54 W
Huntsville, Mo.	123	39.24 N	92.32 W
Huntsville, Tx.	125	30.44 N	95.34 W
Huntsville, Ut.	119b	41.16 N	111.46 W
Hunucmá, Mex. (hōō-nōōk-mä')	131	21.01 N	89.54 W
Huolu, China (hōōŭ lōō)	200	38.05 N	114.20 E
Huon G., Pap. N. Gui.	207	7.15 S	147.45 E
Huoqiu, China (hwô-chyô)	200	32.19 N	116.17 E
Huoshan, China (hwô-shän)	203	31.30 N	116.25 E
Ḩuraydin, Wādī (R.), Egypt	191a	30.55 N	34.12 E
Hurd, C., Can. (hûrd)	110	45.15 N	81.45 W
Hurdiyo, Som.	223a	10.43 N	51.05 E
Hurley, Wi. (hûr'lĭ)	115	46.26 N	90.11 W
Hurlingham, Arg. (ōō'r-lēn-gäm)	144a	34.20 S	58.38 W
Huron, Oh. (hū'rŏn)	110	41.20 N	82.35 W
Huron, SD	114	44.22 N	98.15 W
Huron, L., U. S.-Can. (hū'rŏn)	109	45.15 N	82.40 W
Huron Mts., Mi. (hū'rŏn)	115	46.47 N	87.52 W
Huron R., Mi.	113b	42.12 N	83.26 W
Hurricane, Ak. (hŭr'ĭ-kān)	107	63.00 N	149.30 W
Hurricane, Ut.	121	37.10 N	113.20 W
Hurricane Flats (Shoal), Ba. (hŭ-rĭ-kȧn flăts)	134	23.35 N	78,30 W
Hurst, Tx.	119c	32.48 N	97.12 W
Hurstville, Austl.	70a	33.58 S	151.06 E
Húsavik, Ice.	158	66.00 N	17.10 W
Husen (Neigh.), F.R.G.	63	51.33 N	7.36 E
Huşi, Rom. (kōōsh')	175	46.52 N	28.04 E
Huskvarna, Swe. (hōōsk-vär'nȧ)	164	57.48 N	14.16 E
Husum, F.R.G. (hōō'zōōm)	166	54.29 N	9.04 E
Hutchins, Tx. (hŭch'ĭnz)	119c	32.38 N	96.43 W
Hutchinson, Ks. (hŭch'ĭn-sŭn)	122	38.02 N	97.56 W
Hutchinson, Mn.	115	44.53 N	94.23 W
Hut'o Ho (R.), China (hōō'tō'hō')	202	38.10 N	114.00 E
Hütteldorf (Neigh.), Aus.	66e	48.12 N	16.16 E
Hüttenheim (Neigh.), F.R.G.	63	51.22 N	6.43 E
Hutton, Eng.	62	51.38 N	0.22 E
Huttrop (Neigh.), F.R.G.	63	51.27 N	7.03 E
Huy, Bel. (û-ē') (hû'ē)	163	50.33 N	5.14 E
Hvannadalshnúkur (Mtn.), Ice.	158	64.09 N	16.46 W
Hvar (I.), Yugo. (ĸhvär)	172	43.08 N	16.28 E
Hwange, Zimb	231	18.22 S	26.29 E
Hwangju, Kor. (hwäng'jōō')	204	38.39 N	125.49 E
Hyargas Nuur (L.), Mong	198	49.18 N	94.21 E
Hyattsville, Md. (hī'ăt's-vĭl)	112e	38.57 N	76.58 W
Hydaburg, Ak. (hī-dă'bûrg)	107	55.12 N	132.49 W
Hyde, Eng. (hīd)	156	53.27 N	2.05 W
Hyde Park (Neigh.), Il.	58a	41.48 N	87.36 W
Hyderābād, India (hī-dẽr-ȧ-băd')	197	17.29 N	79.28 E
Hyderābād, Pak.	196	25.29 N	68.28 E
Hyderabad (State), India	197	23.29 N	76.50 E
Hyéres, Fr. (ē-âr')	169	43.09 N	6.08 E
Hyéres, Îles d' (Is.), Fr. (ēl'dyâr')	169	42.57 N	6.17 E
Hyesanjin, Kor. (hyĕ'sän-jĭn')	204	41.11 N	128.12 E
Hymera, In. (hī-mē'rȧ)	110	39.10 N	87.20 W
Hyndman Pk., Id. (hīnd'mǎn)	117	43.38 N	114.04 W
Hyōgo (Neigh.), Jap.	69b	34.47 N	135.10 E
Hyōgo (Pref.), Jap. (hĭyō'gō)	205b	34.54 N	135.15 E
Hythe, Can.	106	55.20 N	119.33 W
Hythe End, Eng.	62	51.27 N	0.32 W

I

PLACE (Pronunciation)	PAGE	Lat. °'	Long. °'
Ia (R.), Jap. (ē'ä)	205b	34.54 N	135.34 E
Ialomiţa (R.), Rom.	173	44.37 N	26.42 E
Iasi, Rom. (yä'shē)	167	47.10 N	27.40 E
Iba, Phil. (ē'bä)	207a	15.20 N	119.59 E
Ibadan, Nig. (ē-bä'dän)	229	7.17 N	3.30 E
Ibagué, Col. (ē-bȧ-gā')	142a	4.27 N	75.13 W
Ibar (R.), Yugo. (ē'bär)	173	43.22 N	20.35 E
Ibaraki, Jap. (ē-bä'rä-gē)	205b	34.49 N	135.35 E
Ibarra, Ec. (ē-bär'rä)	142	0.19 N	78.08 W
Ibb, Yemen	195	14.01 N	44.10 E
Idlib, Syr.	195	35.55 N	36.38 E
Iberian Pen., Port.-Sp.	222	41.00 N	0.07 W
Iberoamericana, Universidad (P. Int.), Mex.	60a	19.21 N	99.08 W
Iberville, Can. (ē-bär-vēl') (ī'bẽr-vĭl)	104	45.14 N	73.01 W
Ibese, Nig.	71d	6.33 N	3.29 E
Ibi, Nig. (ē'bē)	229	8.12 N	9.45 E
Ibiapaba, Serra da (Mts.), Braz. (sĕ'r-rä-dä-ē-byä-pȧ'bä)	143	3.30 S	40.55 W
Ibirapuera (Neigh.), Braz.	61d	23.37 S	46.40 W
Ibiza, (Iviza) (I.), Sp. (ē-bē'zä)	171	39.07 N	1.05 E
Ibiza, Sp. (ē-bē'thä)	171	38.55 N	1.24 E
Ibo, Moz. (ē'bō)	231	12.20 S	40.35 E
Iboundji, Mont. (Mtn.), Gabon	230	1.08 S	11.48 E
Ibrahim, Jabal (Mtn.), Sau. Ar.	192	20.31 N	41.17 E
Ibrāhīm, Būr (B.), Egypt	223	29.57 N	32.33 E
Ibwe Munyama, Zambia	231	16.09 S	28.34 E
Ica, Peru (ē'kȧ)	142	14.09 S	75.42 W
Icá (R.), Braz. (ē-kȧ')	142	2.56 S	69.12 W
Içana, Braz. (ē-sä'nä)	142	0.15 N	67.19 W
Ice Harbor Dam, Wa.	116	46.15 N	118.54 W
Iceland, Eur. (īs'lǎnd)	154	65.12 N	19.45 W
Ichāpur, India	67a	22.50 N	88.24 E
Ichibusayama (Mt.), Jap. (ē'chē-bōō'sȧ-yä'mä)	205	32.19 N	131.08 E
Ichihara, Jap.	205a	35.31 N	140.05 E
Ichikawa, Jap. (ē'chē-kä'wä)	205a	35.44 N	139.54 E
Ichinomiya, Jap. (ē'chē-nō-mē'yȧ)	205	35.19 N	136.49 E
Ichinomoto, Jap. (ē-chē'nō-mō-tō)	205b	34.37 N	135.50 E
Ichnya, Sov.Un. (ĭch'nyä)	175	50.47 N	32.23 E
Ickenham (Neigh.), Eng.	62	51.34 N	0.27 W
Ickern (Neigh.), F.R.G.	63	51.36 N	7.21 E
Icó, Braz. (ē-kō')	143	6.25 S	38.43 W
Icutú, Cerro (Mtn.), Ven. (sĕ'r-rō-ē-kōō-tōō')	142	7.07 N	65.30 W
Icy C., Ak. (ī'sĭ)	107	70.20 N	161.40 W
Idabel, Ok. (ī'dȧ-bĕl)	123	33.52 N	94.47 W
Idagrove, Ia. (ī'dȧ-grōv)	114	42.22 N	95.29 W
Idah, Nig. (ē'dä)	229	7.07 N	6.43 E
Idaho (State), U. S. (ī'dȧ-hō)	108	44.00 N	115.10 W
Idaho Falls, Id.	117	43.30 N	112.01 W
Idaho Springs, Co.	122	39.43 N	105.32 W
Idanha-a-Nova, Port. (ē-dän'yȧ-ä-nō'vȧ)	170	39.58 N	7.13 W
Iddo (Neigh.), Nig.	71d	6.28 N	3.23 E
Ider (R.), Mong.	198	48.58 N	98.38 E
Idfū, Egypt (ĕd'fōō)	223b	24.57 N	32.53 E
Idhra (I.), Grc.	173	37.20 N	23.30 E
Idi, Indon. (ē'dē)	206	4.58 N	97.47 E
Idkū, Egypt (ĕd'kōō)	223b	31.18 N	30.20 E
Idkū L., Egypt	223b	31.13 N	30.22 E
Idle (R.), Eng. (īd''l)	156	53.22 N	0.56 W
Idlib, Syr.	195	35.55 N	36.38 E
Idriaj, Yugo. (ē'drē-ȧ)	172	46.01 N	14.01 E
Idutywa, S. Afr. (ē-dōō-tī'wȧ)	227c	32.06 S	28.18 E
Idylwood, Va.	56d	38.54 N	77.12 W
Ieper, Bel.	163	50.50 N	2.53 E
Ierápetra, Grc.	172a	35.01 N	25.48 E
Iesi, It. (yā'sē)	172	43.37 N	13.20 E
Ife, Nig.	229	7.30 N	4.30 E
Iferouâne, Niger (ēf'rōō-än')	229	19.04 N	8.24 E
Iforas, Adrar des (Mts.), Alg.-Mali (ä-drär')	229	19.55 N	2.00 E
Igalula, Tan.	231	5.14 S	33.00 E
Iganmu (Neigh.), Nig.	71d	6.29 N	3.22 E
Igarka, Sov. Un. (ē-gär'kȧ)	180	67.22 N	86.16 E
Igbobi, Nig.	71d	6.32 N	3.22 E
Ightham, Eng.	62	51.17 N	0.17 E
Iglesias, It. (ē-lĕ'syôs)	172	39.20 N	8.34 E
Igli, Alg. (ē-glē')	224	30.32 N	2.15 W
Igloolik, Can.	97	69.33 N	81.18 W
Ignacio, Ca. (ĭg-nā'cĭ-ō)	118b	38.05 N	122.32 W
Iguaçu (R.), Braz. (ē-gwä-sōō')	144b	22.42 S	43.19 W
Iguala, Mex. (ē-gwä'lä)	130	18.18 N	99.34 W
Igualada, Sp. (ē-gwä-lä'dä)	171	41.35 N	1.38 E
Iguassu (R.), Braz. (ē-gwä-sōō')	144	25.45 S	52.30 W
Iguassu Falls, Braz.	144	25.40 S	54.16 W
Iguatama, Braz. (ē-gwä-tä'mä)	141a	20.13 S	45.40 W
Iguatu, Braz. (ē-gwä-tōō')	143	6.22 S	39.17 W
Iguidi, Erg (Dune), Alg.	224	26.22 N	6.53 W
Iguig, Phil. (ē-gēg')	207a	17.46 N	121.44 E
Iharana, Mad.	227	13.35 S	50.05 E
Ihiala, Nig.	229	5.51 N	6.51 E
Iida, Jap. (ē'ē-dȧ)	205	35.39 N	137.53 E
Iijoki (R.), Fin. (ē'yō'kĭ)	178	65.28 N	27.00 E
Iizuka, Jap. (ē'ē-zōō-kȧ)	205	33.39 N	130.39 E
Ijebu-Ode, Nig. (ē-jĕ'bōō ōdȧ)	229	6.50 N	3.56 E
IJmuiden, Neth.	157a	52.27 N	4.36 E
IJsselmeer (L.), Neth. (ī'sĕl-mār)	163	52.46 N	5.14 E
Ikaalinen, Fin. (ē'kä-lĭ-nĕn)	165	61.47 N	22.55 E
Ikaría (I.), Grc. (ē-kä'ryȧ)	173	37.43 N	26.07 E
Ikeda, Jap. (ē'kȧ-dä)	205b	34.49 N	135.26 E
Ikeja, Nig.	71d	6.36 N	3.21 E
Ikerre, Nig.	229	7.31 N	5.14 E
Ikhtiman, Bul. (ēk'tē-män)	173	42.26 N	23.49 E
Iki (I.), Jap. (ē'kē)	205	33.46 N	129.44 E
Ikoma, Jap.	205b	34.41 N	135.43 E
Ikoma, Tan. (ē-kō'mä)	226	2.08 S	34.47 E
Ikorodu, Nig.	71d	6.37 N	3.31 E
Ikoyi (Neigh.), Nig.	71d	6.27 N	3.26 E
Ikoyi I., Nig.	71d	6.27 N	3.26 E
Iksha, Sov. Un. (ĭk'shȧ)	182b	56.10 N	37.30 E
Ikuno (Neigh.), Jap.	69b	34.39 N	135.33 E
Ikuta (Neigh.), Jap.	69b	34.42 N	135.11 E
Ila, Nig.	229	8.01 N	4.55 E
Ilagen, Phil. (ē-lä'gän)	207a	17.09 N	121.52 E

PLACE (Pronounciation)	PAGE	Lat. °′	Long. °′
Ilan, Taiwan (ē'län')	203	24.50 N	121.42 E
Ilawa, Pol. (ê-lä'vȧ)	167	53.35 N	19.36 E
Ilchester, Md.	56c	39.15 N	76.46 W
Île-à-la-Crosse, Can.	100	55.34 N	108.00 W
Ilebo (Port-Franqui), Zaire	230	4.19 S	20.35 E
Île-Cadieux, Can.	54b	45.25 N	74.01 W
Ilek (R.), Sov. Un.	179	51.20 N	53.10 E
Ilek, Sov. Un. (ē'lyĕk)	179	51.30 N	53.10 E
Île-Perrot, Can. (yl-pĕ-rōt')	95a	45.21 N	73.54 W
Ilesha, Nig.	229	7.38 N	4.45 E
Ilford, Eng. (ĭl'fērd)	156b	51.33 N	0.06 E
Ilfracombe, Eng. (ĭl-frȧ-kōōm')	162	51.13 N	4.08 W
Ilhabela, Braz. (ē'lä-bĕ'lä)	141a	23.47 S	45.21 W
Ilha Grande, Baia de (B.), Braz. (ēl'yȧ grän'dĕ)	141a	23.17 S	44.25 W
Ílhavo, Port. (ēl'yȧ-vô)	170	40.36 N	8.41 W
Ilhéus, Braz. (ē-lĕ'ōōs)	143	14.52 S	39.00 W
Iliamna, Ak. (ē-lē-ăm'nȧ)	107	59.45 N	155.05 W
Iliamna (L.), Ak.	107	59.25 N	155.30 W
Iliamna (Vol.), Ak.	107	60.18 N	153.25 W
Ilim (R.), Sov. Un. (ē-lyēm')	180	57.28 N	103.00 E
Ilimsk, Sov. Un. (ē-lyēmsk')	180	56.47 N	103.43 E
Ilin I., Phil. (ē-lyēn')	207a	12.16 N	120.57 E
Il'intsiy, Sov.Un.	175	49.07 N	29.13 E
Ilion, NY (ĭl'ĭ-ŭn)	111	43.00 N	75.05 W
Ilioúpolis, Grc.	66d	37.56 N	23.45 E
Ili R., Sov. Un. (ē'lē)	198	43.46 N	77.41 E
Ilkeston, Eng. (ĭl'kĕs-tŭn)	156	52.58 N	1.19 W
Illampu, Nevado (Pk.), Bol. (nĕ-vá'dô-ēl-yäm-pōō')	142	15.50 S	68.15 W
Illapel, Chile (ē-zhä-pĕ'l)	141b	31.37 S	71.10 W
Iller R., F.R.G. (ĭl'er)	166	47.52 N	10.06 E
Illimani, Nevado (Pk.), Bol. (nĕ-vá'dô-ēl-yē-mä'nē)	142	16.50 S	67.38 W
Illinois (R.), Il.	123	40.52 N	89.31 W
Illinois (State), U. S. (ĭl-ĭ-noi') (ĭl-ĭ-noiz')	109	40.25 N	90.40 W
Illizi, Alg.	224	26.35 N	8.24 E
Illovo, S. Afr.	71b	26.08 S	28.03 E
Il'men', Ozero (L.), Sov. Un. (ô'zĕ-rô el''men'') (ĭl'mĕn)	174	58.18 N	32.00 E
Ilo, Peru	142	17.46 S	71.13 W
Ilobasco, Sal. (ē-lô-bäs'kô)	132	13.57 N	88.46 W
Iloilo, Phil. (ē-lô-ē'lō)	206	10.49 N	112.33 E
Ilopango, L., Sal. (ē-lô-päŋ'gō)	132	13.48 N	88.50 W
Ilorin, Nig. (ē-lô-rēn')	229	8.30 N	4.32 E
Ilūkste, Sov. Un.	174	55.59 N	26.20 E
Ilverich, F.R.G.	63	51.17 N	6.42 E
Ilwaco, Wa. (ĭl-wä'kô)	118c	46.19 N	124.02 W
Ilych (R.), Sov. Un. (ē'lĭch)	178	62.30 N	57.30 E
Imabari, Jap. (ē'mä-bä'rē)	205	34.05 N	132.58 E
Imai, Jap. (ē-mī')	205b	34.30 N	135.47 E
Iman (R.), Sov. Un. (ē-män')	204	45.40 N	134.31 E
Imandra (L.), Sov. Un. (ē-män'drȧ)	178	67.40 N	32.30 E
Imbābah, Egypt (ēm-bä'bȧ)	223b	30.06 N	31.09 E
Imbarié, Braz. (ēm-bä-ryĕ')	144b	22.38 S	43.13 W
Imeni Morozova, Sov. Un. (ĭm-yĕ'nyĭ mô rô'zô vá)	182c	59.58 N	31.02 E
Imeni Moskvy, Kanal (Moscow Can.), Sov. Un. (kȧ-näl'ĭm-yä'nĭ mŏs-kvĭ)	174	56.33 N	37.15 E
Imeni Tsyurupy, Sov. Un.	182b	55.30 N	38.39 E
Imeni Vorovskogo, Sov. Un.	182b	55.43 N	38.21 E
Imlay City, Mi. (ĭm'lā)	110	43.00 N	83.15 W
Immenstadt, F.R.G. (ĭm'ĕn-shtät)	166	47.34 N	10.12 E
Immerpan, S. Afr. (ĭmēr-păn)	223d	24.29 S	29.14 E
Imola, It. (ē'mô-lä)	172	44.19 N	11.43 E
Imotski, Yugo. (ē-môts'kē)	172	43.25 N	17.15 E
Impameri, Braz.	143	17.44 S	48.03 W
Impendle, S. Afr. (ĭm-pĕnd'lā)	227c	29.38 S	29.54 E
Imperia, It. (ēm-pā'rē-ä)	172	43.52 N	8.00 E
Imperial, Pa. (ĭm-pē'rĭ-ăl)	113e	40.27 N	80.15 W
Imperial Beach, Ca.	120a	32.34 N	117.08 W
Imperial Res., Az.	121	32.57 N	114.19 W
Imperial Valley, Ca.	120	33.00 N	115.22 W
Impfondo, Con. (ĭmp-fōn'dō)	230	1.37 N	18.04 E
Imphāl, India (ĭmp'hŭl)	193	24.42 N	94.00 E
Ina (R.), Jap. (ē-nä')	205b	34.56 N	135.21 E
Inagi, Jap.	69a	35.38 N	139.30 E
Inaja Ind. Res., Ca. (ē-nä'hä)	120	32.56 N	116.37 W
Inari (L.), Fin.	158	69.02 N	26.22 E
Inatsuke (Neigh.), Jap.	69a	35.46 N	139.43 E
Inca, Sp. (ēŋ'kä)	171	39.43 N	2.53 E
Ince, Eng.	64a	53.17 N	2.49 W
Ince Blundell, Eng.	64a	53.31 N	3.02 W
Ince Burun (C.), Tur. (ĭn'jȧ)	179	42.00 N	35.00 E
Inch'ŏn, Kor. (ĭn'chŭn)	204	37.26 N	126.46 E
Incudine, Mt. (Mtn.), Fr. (ēn-kōō-dē'nā) (äN-kü-dēn')	172	41.53 N	9.17 E
Indalsälven (R.), Swe.	164	62.50 N	16.50 E
Indé, Mex. (ēn'dā)	124	25.53 N	105.15 W
Independence, Ks. (ĭn-dē-pĕn'dĕns)	123	37.14 N	95.42 W
Independence, Mo.	119f	39.06 N	94.26 W
Independence, Oh.	113d	41.23 N	81.39 W
Independence, Or.	116	44.49 N	123.13 W
Independence Mts., Ny.	116	41.15 N	116.02 W
Independence National Historical Park NJ (P. Int.), Md.	56b	39.57 N	75.09 W
Inder (L.), Sov. Un.	179	48.20 N	52.10 E
In der Bredde, F.R.G.	63	51.20 N	7.23 E
India, Asia (ĭn'dĭ-ȧ)	190	23.00 N	77.30 E
India Gate (P. Int.), India	67d	28.37 N	77.18 E
Indian (L.), Mi. (ĭn'dĭ-ăn)	115	46.04 N	86.34 W
Indian (R.), NY	111	44.05 N	75.45 W
Indiana, Pa. (ĭn-dĭ-ăn'ȧ)	111	40.40 N	79.10 W
Indiana (State), U. S.	109	39.50 N	86.45 W
Indianapolis, In. (ĭn-dĭ-ăn-ăp'ô-lĭs)	113g	39.45 N	86.08 W
Indian Arm (R.), Can. (ĭn'dĭ-ăn ärm)	118d	49.21 N	122.55 W
Indian Head, Can.	100	50.29 N	103.44 W
Indian Head Park, Il.	58a	41.47 N	87.54 W
Indian L., Can.	102	47.00 N	82.00 W
Indianola, Ia. (ĭn-dĭ-ăn-ō'lȧ)	115	41.22 N	93.33 W
Indianola, Ms.	126	33.29 N	90.35 W

PLACE (Pronounciation)	PAGE	Lat. °′	Long. °′
Indianola, Pa.	57b	40.34 N	79.51 W
Indianópolis (Neigh.), Braz.	61d	23.36 S	46.38 W
Indian O.	190	0	70.00 E
Indian Springs, Va.	56d	38.49 N	77.10 W
Indigirka (R.), Sov. Un. (ēn-dē-gēr'kȧ)	181	67.45 N	145.45 E
Indio (R.), Pan. (ē'n-dyô)	128a	9.13 N	78.28 W
Indochina (Reg.), Asia (ĭn-dô-chī'nȧ)	206	17.22 N	105.18 E
Indonesia, Asia (ĭn'dô-nē-zhȧ)	206	4.38 S	118.45 E
Indonesian Culture, Museum of (P. Int.), Indon.	68k	6.09 S	106.49 E
Indore, India (ĭn-dōr')	196	22.48 N	76.51 E
Indragiri (R.), Indon. (ĭn-drȧ-jē'rē)	206	0.27 S	102.05 E
Indrāvati (R.), India (ĭn-drŭ-vä'tē)	132	19.15 N	80.54 E
Indre (R.), Fr. (ăN'dr')	168	47.13 N	0.29 E
Indus, Can. (ĭn'dŭs)	95e	50.55 N	113.45 W
Indus (R.), Pak.	196	26.43 N	67.41 E
Industria (Neigh.), S. Afr.	71b	26.12 S	27.59 E
Indwe, S. Afr. (ĭnd'wā)	227c	31.30 S	27.21 E
Inebolu, Tur. (ē-nā-bō'lōō)	179	41.50 N	33.40 E
Inego, Tur. (ē'nā-gŭ)	179	40.05 N	29.20 E
Infanta, Phil. (ēn-fän'tä)	207a	14.44 N	121.39 E
Infanta, Phil.	207a	15.50 N	119.53 E
Inferror, Laguna (L.), Mex. (lä-gōō'nä-ēn-fĕr-rôr)	131	16.18 N	94.40 W
Infiernillo, Presa de (Res.), Mex.	130	18.50 N	101.50 W
Infiesto, Sp. (ēn-fyĕ's-tô)	170	43.21 N	5.24 W
I-n-Gall, Niger	229	16.47 N	6.56 E
Ingatestone, Eng.	62	51.41 N	0.22 E
Ingeniero Budge (Neigh.), Arg.	60d	34.43 S	58.28 W
Ingersoll, Can. (ĭn'gēr-sŏl)	110	43.05 N	81.00 W
Ingham, Austl. (ĭng'ăm)	215	18.45 S	146.14 E
Ingleburn, Austl.	70a	34.00 S	150.52 E
Ingles, Cayos (Is.), Cuba (kä-yōs-ē'n-glē's)	134	21.55 N	82.35 W
Ingleside (Neigh.), Ca.	58b	37.43 N	122.28 W
Inglewood, Ca. (ĭn'g'l-wōōd)	119a	33.57 N	118.22 W
Inglewood, Can.	95d	43.48 N	79.56 W
Ingoda (R.), Sov. Un. (ēn-gō'dȧ)	181	51.29 N	112.32 E
Ingolstadt, F.R.G. (iŋ'gôl-shtät)	166	48.46 N	11.27 E
Ingomar, Pa.	57b	40.35 N	80.05 W
Ingram, Pa.	57b	40.26 N	80.04 W
Ingrave, Eng.	62	51.36 N	0.21 E
Ingul (R.), Sov. Un. (ēn-gōōl')	175	47.22 N	32.52 E
Ingulets (R.), Sov. Un. (ēn-gōōl'yĕts')	175	47.12 N	33.12 E
Ingur (R.), Sov. Un. (ēn-gōōr')	179	42.30 N	42.00 E
Inhambane, Moz. (ēn-äm-bä'-nĕ)	226	23.47 S	35.28 E
Inhambupe, Braz. (ēn-yäm-bōō'pä)	143	11.47 S	38.13 W
Inharrime, Moz. (ēn-yär-rē'mä)	226	24.17 S	35.07 E
Inhomirim, Braz. (ē-nô-mē-rē'N)	144b	22.34 S	43.11 W
Inirida (R.), Col. (ē-nē-rē'dä)	142	2.25 N	70.38 W
Injune, Austl. (ĭn'jōōn)	216	25.52 S	148.30 E
Inkeroinem, Fin. (ĭn'kĕr-oi-nĕn)	165	60.42 N	26.50 E
Inkster, Mi. (ĭngk'stēr)	113b	42.18 N	83.19 W
Innamincka, Austl. (ĭnn-ȧ'mĭn-kȧ)	216	27.50 S	140.48 E
Inner Brass (I.), Vir. Is. (U.S.A.) (bräs)	129c	18.23 N	64.58 W
Inner Hebrides (Is.), Scot.	162	57.20 N	6.20 W
Inner Mongolia, (Aut. Reg.), see Nei Monggol			
Innisfail, Can.	99	52.02 N	113.57 W
Inn R., F.R.G.-Aus. (ĭn)	166	48.19 N	13.16 E
Innsbruck, Aus. (ĭns'brōōk)	166	47.15 N	11.25 E
Ino, Jap. (ē'nô)	205	33.34 N	133.23 E
Inongo, Zaire (ē-nôŋ'gō)	230	1.57 S	18.16 E
Inowroclaw, Pol. (ē-nô-vrôts'läf)	167	52.48 N	18.16 E
In Salah, Alg.	224	27.13 N	2.22 E
Inscription House Ruin, Az. (ĭn'skrĭp-shŭn hous rōō'ĭn)	121	36.45 N	110.47 W
Inter-American Hy., Mex. (ĭn'tēr ȧ-mĕr'ĭ-kăn)	130	22.30 N	99.08 W
International Falls, Mn. (ĭn'tēr-năsh'ŭn-ăl fôlz)	115	48.34 N	93.26 W
Inuvik, Can.	96	68.40 N	134.10 W
Inuyama, Jap. (ē'nōō-yä'mä)	205	35.24 N	137.01 E
Invercargil, N. Z. (ĭn-vēr-kär'gĭl)	217	46.25 S	68.27 E
Inverel, Austl. (ĭn-vēr-el')	216	29.50 S	151.32 E
Invergrove Hts., Mn. (ĭn'vēr-grōv)	119g	44.51 N	93.01 W
Inverness, Can. (ĭn-vēr-nĕs')	105	46.14 N	61.18 W
Inverness, Fl.	127	28.48 N	82.22 W
Inverness, Scot.	162	57.30 N	4.07 W
Investigator Str., Austl. (ĭn-vĕst'ĭ'gā-tôr)	216	35.33 S	137.00 E
Inwood, NY	55	40.37 N	73.45 W
Inyangani, Mt., Zimb. (ēn-yän-gä'nē)	226	18.06 S	32.37 E
Inyokern, Ca.	120	35.39 N	117.51 W
Inyo Mts., Ca. (ĭn'yō)	120	36.55 N	118.04 W
Inzer R., Sov. Un. (ĭn'zĕr)	182a	54.24 N	57.17 E
Inzersdorf (Neigh.), Aus.	66e	48.09 N	16.21 E
Inzia (R.), Zaire	230	5.55 S	17.50 E
Iō (I.), Jap. (ē'wō)	205	30.46 N	130.15 E
Ioánnina (Yannina), Grc. (yô-ä'nē-nȧ) (yä'nē-nȧ)	173	39.39 N	20.52 E
Ioco, Can.	118d	49.18 N	122.53 W
Iola, Ks. (ī-ō'lȧ)	123	37.55 N	95.23 W
Iôna, Parque Nacional do (Natl. Pk.), Ang.	230	16.35 S	12.00 E
Ionia, Mi. (ī-ō'nĭ-ȧ)	110	43.00 N	85.10 W
Ionian Is., Grc. (ī-ō'nĭ-ăn)	173	39.10 N	20.05 E
Ionian Sea, Eur.	161	38.59 N	18.48 E
Ios (I.), Grc. (ĭ'ŏs)	173	36.48 N	25.25 E
Iowa (State), U.S. (ī'ô-wȧ)	109	42.05 N	94.20 W
Iowa (R.), Ia.	115	41.55 N	92.20 W
Iowa City, Ia.	115	41.39 N	91.31 W
Iowa Falls, Ia.	115	42.32 N	93.16 W
Iowa Park, Tx.	122	33.57 N	98.39 W
Ipala, Tan.	231	4.30 S	32.53 E
Ipanema (Neigh.), Braz.	61c	22.59 S	43.12 W
Ipeirus (Reg.), Grc.	173	39.35 N	20.45 E
Ipel' (R.), Czech.-Hung. (ē'pĕl)	167	48.08 N	19.00 E
Ipiales, Col. (ē-pē-ä'lās)	142	0.48 N	77.45 W
Ipoh, Mala.	206	4.45 N	101.05 E
Ipswich, Austl. (ĭps'wĭch)	216	27.40 S	152.50 E
Ipswich, Eng.	163	52.05 N	1.05 E

PLACE (Pronounciation)	PAGE	Lat. °′	Long. °′
Ipswich, Ma.	105a	42.41 N	70.50 W
Ipswich, SD	114	45.26 N	99.01 W
Ipu, Braz. (ē-pōō)	143	4.11 S	40.45 W
Iput' (R.), Sov. Un. (ē-pōōt')	174	52.53 N	31.57 E
Iquique, Chile (ē-kē'kĕ)	142	20.16 S	70.07 W
Iquitos, Peru (ē-kē'tōs)	142	3.39 S	73.18 W
Iráklion (Candia), Grc.	172a	35.20 N	25.10 E
Iran, Asia (ē-rän')	190	31.15 N	53.30 E
Iran Mts., Mala.	206	2.30 N	114.30 E
Iran, Plat. of, Iran	192	32.28 N	58.00 E
Irapuato, Mex. (ē-rä-pwä'tō)	130	20.41 N	101.24 W
Iraq, Asia (ē-räk')	190	32.00 N	42.30 E
Irazu Vol, C.R. (ē-rä-zōō')	133	9.58 N	83.54 W
Irbid, Jordan (ēr-bēd')	191a	32.33 N	35.51 E
Irbil, Iraq	179	36.10 N	44.00 E
Irbit, Sov. Un. (ēr-bēt')	178	57.40 N	63.10 E
Irby, Eng.	64b	53.21 N	3.07 W
Irébou, Zaire (ē-rā'bōō)	226	0.40 S	17.48 E
Ireland, Eur. (īr-lănd)	154	53.33 N	8.00 W
Iremel', Gora (Mt.), Sov. Un. (gȧ-rä'ĭ-rē'mĕl)	182a	54.32 N	58.52 E
Irene, S. Afr. (ĭ-rē-nē)	227b	25.53 S	28.13 E
Irgiz, Sov. Un. (ĭr-gēz')	180	48.30 N	61.17 E
Irgiz (R.), Sov. Un.	180	49.30 N	60.32 E
Iriklinskoye Vdkhr (Res.), Sov. Un.	178	52.20 N	58.50 E
Iringa, Tan. (ē-rĭŋ'gä)	231	7.46 S	35.42 E
Iriomote Jima (I.), Jap. (ērē'-ō-mō-tā)	203	24.20 N	123.30 E
Iriona, Hond. (ē-rē-ō'nä)	132	15.53 N	85.12 W
Irīgui (Reg.), Mali-Mauritania	228	16.45 N	5.35 W
Irish Sea, Eur. (ī'rĭsh)	162	53.55 N	5.25 W
Irkutsk, Sov. Un. (ĭr-kōōtsk')	180	52.16 N	104.00 E
Irlam, Eng. (ûr'lăm)	156	53.26 N	2.26 W
Irois, Cap des (C.), Hai.	135	18.25 N	74.50 W
Iron Cove (B.), Austl.	70a	33.52 S	151.10 E
Irondale, Al. (ī'ērn-dăl)	112h	33.32 N	86.43 W
Iron Gate (Gorge), Yugo.-Rom.	173	44.43 N	22.32 E
Iron Knob, Austl. (ĭ-ăn nŏb)	216	32.47 S	137.10 E
Iron Mountain, Mi. (ī'ērn)	115	45.49 N	88.04 W
Iron River, Mi.	115	46.09 N	88.39 W
Ironton, Oh. (ī'ērn-tŭn)	110	38.30 N	82.45 W
Ironwood, Mi. (ī'ērn-wōōd)	115	46.28 N	90.10 W
Iroquois (R.), Il.-In. (ĭr'ō-kwoi)	110	40.55 N	87.20 W
Iroquois Falls, Can.	97	48.41 N	80.39 W
Irō-Saki (C.), Jap. (ē'rō sä'kē)	205	34.35 N	138.54 E
Irpen' (R.), Sov. Un. (ĭr-pĕn')	175	50.13 N	29.55 E
Irrawaddy (R.), Bur. (ĭr-ȧ-wäd'ē)	193	23.27 N	96.25 E
Irtysh (R.), Sov. Un. (ĭr-tĭsh')	180	58.32 N	68.31 E
Irumu, Zaire (ē-rōō'mōō)	225	1.30 N	29.52 E
Irun, Sp. (ē-rōōn')	170	43.20 N	1.47 W
Irvine, Ca. (ûr'vĭn)	119a	33.40 N	117.45 W
Irvine, Ky.	110	37.40 N	84.00 W
Irvine, Scot.	162	55.39 N	4.40 W
Irving, Tx. (ûr'vēng)	119c	32.49 N	96.57 W
Irving Park (Neigh.), Il.	58a	41.57 N	87.43 W
Irvington (Neigh.), Md.	56c	39.17 N	76.41 W
Irvington, NJ (ûr'vēng-tŭn)	112a	40.43 N	74.15 W
Irwin, Pa. (ûr'wĭn)	113e	40.19 N	79.42 W
Is, Sov. Un. (ēs)	182a	58.48 N	59.44 E
Isa, Nig.	229	13.14 N	6.24 E
Isaacs, Mt., Pan. (ē-sä-ȧ'ks)	128a	9.22 N	79.01 W
Isabela (I.), Ec. (ē-sä-bā'lä)	142	0.47 S	91.35 W
Isabela (I.), Mex. (ē-sä-bĕ'-lä)	130	21.56 N	105.53 W
Isabela, Cabo (C.), Dom. Rep. (kȧ'bô-ē-sä-bĕ'lä)	135	20.00 N	71.00 W
Isabella, Cord. (Mts.), Nic. (kôr-dĕl-yĕ'rä-ē-sä-bĕlä)	132	13.20 N	85.37 W
Isabella Ind. Res., Mi. (ĭs-ȧ-bĕl'-lȧ)	110	43.35 N	84.55 W
Isaccea, Rom. (ē-säk'chä)	175	45.16 N	28.26 E
Ísafjördur, Ice. (ēs'ȧ-fŷr-dōōr)	158	66.09 N	22.39 W
Isando, S. Afr.	71b	26.09 S	28.12 E
Isangi, Zaire (ē-säŋ'gē)	230	0.46 N	24.15 E
Isarco (R.), It. (ē-sär'kō)	172	46.37 N	11.25 E
Isarog, Mt., Phil. (ē-sä-rô-g)	207a	13.40 N	123.23 E
Isar R., F.R.G. (ē'zär)	166	48.27 N	12.02 E
Ischia, It. (ēs'kyä)	171c	40.29 N	13.58 E
Ise (Uji-Yamada), Jap. (ĭs'hē) (ŭ'gē-yä'mä'dȧ)	205	34.30 N	136.43 E
Iselin, NJ	55	40.34 N	74.19 W
Iseo, Lago d' (L.), It. (lä-'gō-dē-ē-zĕ'ō)	172	45.50 N	9.55 E
Isére (R.), Fr. (ē-zâr')	169	45.24 N	6.04 E
Iserlohn, F.R.G. (ē'zĕr-lōn)	169c	51.22 N	7.42 E
Isernia, It. (ē-zĕr'nyä)	172	41.35 N	14.14 E
Ise-Wan (B), Jap. (ē'sē wän)	205	34.49 N	136.44 E
Iseyin, Nig.	229	7.58 N	3.36 E
Ishikari Wan (B.), Jap. (ē'shē-kä-rē wän)	204	43.30 N	141.05 E
Ishim, Sov. Un. (ĭsh-ĕm')	180	56.07 N	69.13 E
Ishim (R.), Sov. Un.	180	53.17 N	67.45 E
Ishimbay, Sov. Un. (ē-shĕm-bī')	182a	53.28 N	56.02 E
Ishinomaki, Jap. (ĭsh-nō-mä'kē)	204	38.22 N	141.22 E
Ishinomaki Wan (B.), Jap. (ē-shē-nō-mä'kē wän)	204	38.10 N	141.40 E
Ishly, Sov. Un. (ĭsh'lĭ)	182a	54.13 N	55.55 E
Ishlya, Sov. Un. (ĭsh'lyȧ)	182a	53.54 N	57.48 E
Ishmant, Egypt	223b	29.17 N	31.15 E
Ishpeming, Mi. (ĭsh'pē-mĭng)	115	46.28 N	87.42 W
Isidro Casanova, Arg.	60d	34.42 S	58.35 W
Isipingo, S. Afr. (ĭs-ĭ-pĭŋ-gō)	227c	29.59 S	30.58 E
Isiro (Paulis), Zaire	231	2.47 N	27.37 E
Iskenderun, Tur. (ĭs-kĕn'dĕr-ōōn)	179	36.45 N	36.15 E
Iskenderun Körfezi (G.), Turk.	161	36.22 N	35.25 E
Iskilip, Tur. (ēs'kĭ-lēp')	179	40.40 N	34.30 E
Iskūr (R.), Bul. (ĭs'k'r)	173	43.05 N	23.37 E
Isla-Cristina, Sp. (ī'lä-krē-stē'nä)	170	37.13 N	7.20 W
Islāmābād, Pak.	193	33.55 N	73.05 E
Isla Mujeres, Mex. (ē's-lä-mōō-kĕ'rĕs)	132a	21.25 N	86.53 W
Island L., Can.	101	53.47 N	94.25 W
Island Park, NY	55	40.36 N	73.40 W
Islands, B. of, Can. (ī'lăndz)	105	49.10 N	58.15 W

PLACE (Pronounciation)	PAGE	Lat. ° '	Long. ° '
Islay (I.), Scot. (ī'lä)	162	55.55 N	6.35 W
Isle (R.), Fr. (ēl)	168	45.02 N	0.29 E
Isle of Axholme (Reg.), Eng. (āks'-hōm)	156	53.33 N	0.48 W
Isle of Man, Eur. (măn)	162	54.26 N	4.21 W
Isle Royale Nat'l Park, U. S. (īl'roi-ăl')	115	47.57 N	88.37 W
Isleta, NM (ēs-lā'tá) (ī-lē'tá)	121	34.55 N	106.45 W
Isle Verte, Can. (ēl vĕrt')	104	48.01 N	69.20 W
Isleworth (Neigh.), Eng.	62	51.28 N	0.20 W
Islington (Neigh.), Can.	54c	43.39 N	79.32 W
Islington (Neigh.), Eng.	62	51.34 N	0.06 W
Ismailia (Al Isma 'ilīyah), Egypt (ēs-mä-ēl'ēá)	223c	30.35 N	32.17 E
Ismā'īlīyah (Neigh.), Egypt	71a	30.03 N	31.14 E
Ismā'īlīyah Can., Egypt	223c	30.25 N	31.45 E
Ismaning, F.R.G. (ēz'mä-nēng)	157d	48.14 N	11.41 E
Isnā, Egypt (ēs'ná)	223b	25.17 N	32.33 E
Isparta, Tur. (ē-spär'tá)	179	37.50 N	30.40 E
Israel, Asia	192	32.40 N	34.00 E
Issaquah, Wa. (Iz'sä-kwäh)	118a	47.32 N	122.02 W
Isselburg, F.R.G. (ē'sĕl-bōōrg)	169c	51.50 N	6.28 E
Issoire, Fr. (ē-swär')	168	45.32 N	3.13 E
Issoudun, Fr. (ē-sōō-dāN')	168	46.56 N	2.00 E
Issum, F.R.G. (ē'sōōm)	169c	51.32 N	6.24 E
Issyk-Kul, Ozero (L.), Sov. Un.	180	42.13 N	76.12 E
Issy-les-Moulineaux, Fr.	64c	48.49 N	2.17 E
Istādeh-ye Moqor, Ab-e (L.), Afg.	196	32.35 N	68.00 E
Istanbul, Tur. (ē-stän-bōōl')	179	41.02 N	29.00 E
Istanbul Boğazi (Bosporous) (Str.), Tur.	179	41.10 N	29.10 E
Istead Rise, Eng.	62	51.24 N	0.22 E
Istiaía, Grc. (ēs-tyī'yä)	173	38.58 N	23.11 E
Istmina, Col. (ēst-mē'nä)	142a	5.10 N	76.40 W
Istokpoga (L.), Fl. (Is-tŏk-pō'gá)	127a	27.20 N	81.33 W
Istra (Pen.), Yugo. (ē-strä)	172	45.18 N	13.48 E
Istranca Dağlari (Mts.), Bul.-Turk. (ī-strän'jä)	173	41.50 N	27.25 E
Istres, Fr. (ēs'tr')	168a	43.30 N	5.00 E
Itá, Par. (ē-tä')	144	25.39 S	57.14 W
Itabaiana, Braz. (ē-tä-bä-yá-nä)	143	10.42 S	37.17 W
Itabapoana, Braz. (ē-tä'-bä-pōä'nä)	141a	21.19 S	40.58 W
Itabapoana (R.), Braz.	141a	21.11 S	41.18 W
Itabirito, Braz. (ē-tä-bē-rē'tò)	141a	20.15 S	43.46 W
Itaboraí, Braz. (ē-tä-bō-räē')	141a	22.46 S	42.50 W
Itabuna, Braz. (ē-tä-bōō'nä)	143	14.47 S	39.17 W
Itacoara, Braz. (ē-tä-kwä'rä)	141a	21.41 S	42.04 W
Itacoatiara, Braz. (ē-tá-kwá-tyä'rá)	143	3.03 S	58.18 W
Itaguaí, Braz. (ē-tä-gwä-ē')	141a	22.52 S	43.46 W
Itagüi, Col. (ē-tä'gwĕ)	142a	6.11 N	75.36 W
Itagui (R.), Braz.	144b	22.53 S	43.43 W
Itaipava, Braz. (ē-tī-pá'-vä)	144b	22.23 S	43.09 W
Itaipu, Braz. (ē-tī'pōō)	144b	22.58 S	43.02 W
Itaipu, Ponta de (C.), Braz.	61c	22.59 S	43.03 W
Itaituba, Braz. (ē-tä'I-tōō'bá)	143	4.12 S	56.00 W
Itajaí, Braz. (ē-tä-zhī')	144	26.52 S	48.39 W
Itajubá, Braz. (ē-tä-zhōō-bá')	141a	22.26 S	45.27 W
Italy, Eur. (It'á-lē)	154	43.58 N	11.14 E
Italy, Tx.	125	32.11 N	96.51 W
Itambi, Braz. (ē-tä'm-bē)	144b	22.44 S	42.57 W
Itami, Jap. (ē'tä'mē')	205b	34.47 N	135.25 E
Itapecerica, Braz. (ē-tä-pě-sě-rē'ká)	141a	21.29 S	45.08 W
Itapecurú (R.), Braz. (ē-tä-pě-kōō-rōō')	143	4.05 S	43.49 W
Itapēcuru-Mirim, Braz. (ē-tä-pě'kōō-rōō-mē-rèN')	143	3.17 S	44.15 W
Itaperuna, Braz. (ē-tá-pä-rōō'nä)	141a	21.12 S	41.53 W
Itapetininga, Braz. (ē-tä-pě-tě-nē'N-gä)	141a	23.37 S	48.03 W
Itapira, Braz. (ē-tä-pē'rä)	143	20.42 S	51.19 W
Itapira, Braz.	141a	21.27 S	46.47 W
Itaquaquecetuba, Braz.	61d	23.29 S	46.21 W
Itarsi, India	196	22.43 N	77.45 E
Itasca (L.), Mn.	115	47.13 N	95.14 W
Itasca, Tx. (ī-tās'ká)	125	32.09 N	97.08 W
Itatiaia, Pico da (Pk.), Braz. (pē'-kō-dä-ē-tä-tyä'bä)	141a	22.18 S	44.41 W
Itatiba, Braz. (ē-tä-tē'bä)	141a	23.01 S	46.48 W
Itaúna, Braz. (ē-tä-ōō'nä)	141a	20.05 S	44.35 W
Itaverá, Braz. (ē-tä-vē-rá')	141a	22.44 S	44.07 W
Ithaca, Mi. (Ith'á-ká)	110	43.20 N	84.35 W
Ithaca, NY	111	42.25 N	76.30 W
Itháka (I.), Grc. (ē'thä-kē)	173	38.27 N	20.48 E
Itigi, Tan.	231	5.42 S	34.29 E
Itimbiri (R.), Zaire	230	2.40 N	23.30 E
Itire, Nig.	71d	6.31 N	3.21 E
Itoko, Zaire	226	1.13 S	22.07 E
Itsā, Egypt (ēt'sá)	223b	29.13 N	30.47 E
Itu, Braz. (ē-tōō')	141a	23.16 S	47.16 W
Ituango, Col. (ē-twäN'gō)	142a	7.07 N	75.44 W
Ituiutaba, Braz. (ē-tōō-ēōō-tä'bä)	143	18.56 S	49.17 W
Itumirim, Braz. (ē-tōō-mē-rē'N)	141a	21.20 S	44.51 W
Itundujia Santa Cruz, Mex. (ē-tōōn-dōō-hē'á sä'n-tä krōō'z)	131	16.50 N	97.43 W
Iturbide, Mex. (ē'tōōr-bē'dhá)	132a	19.38 N	89.31 W
Iturup (Etorofu) (I.), Sov. Un. (ē-tōō-rōōp')	181	45.35 N	147.15 E
Ituzaingo, Arg. (ē-tōō-zä-ē'n-gō)	144a	34.24 S	58.40 W
Itzehoe, F.R.G. (ē'tzē-hō)	157c	53.55 N	9.31 E
Iuka, Ms. (ī-ū'ká)	126	34.47 N	88.10 W
Iúna, Braz. (ē-ōō'-nä)	141a	20.22 S	41.32 W
Iupeba, Braz.	61d	23.41 S	46.22 W
Iva (R.),	180	53.45 N	99.30 E
Ivanhoe, Austl. (īv'ăn-hō)	216	32.53 S	144.10 E
Ivanhoe, Austl.	70b	37.46 S	145.03 E
Ivano-Frankovsk, Sov. Un.	167	48.53 N	24.46 E
Ivanovo (Oblast), Sov. Un.	174	56.55 N	40.30 E
Ivanovo, Sov. Un. (ē-vä'nô-vô)	174	57.02 N	41.54 E
Ivanpol, Sov. Un. (ē-vän'pôl)	175	49.51 N	28.11 E
Ivanteyevka, Sov. Un. (ē-vän-tyĕ'yĕf-ká)	182b	55.58 N	37.56 E
Ivdel', Sov. Un. (īv'dyĕl)	182a	60.42 N	60.27 E
Iver, Eng.	62	51.31 N	0.30 W
Iver Heath, Eng.	62	51.32 N	0.31 W
Iviza (I.), see Ibiza			
Ivohibé, Mad. (ē-vô-hē-bä')	227	22.28 S	46.59 E
Ivory Coast, Afr.	222	7.43 N	6.30 W
Ivrea, It. (ē-vrē'ä)	172	45.25 N	7.54 E
Ivry-sur-Seine, Fr.	64c	48.49 N	2.23 E
Ivujivik, Can.	97	62.17 N	77.52 W
Iwaki (Taira), Jap.	204	37.03 N	140.57 E
Iwate Yama (Mt.), Jap. (ē-wä-tĕ-yä'mä)	204	39.50 N	140.56 E
Iwatsuki, Jap.	205a	35.48 N	139.43 E
Iwaya, Jap. (ē'wä-yä)	205b	34.35 N	135.01 E
Iwo, Nig.	229	7.38 N	4.11 E
Ixcateopán, Mex. (ēs-kä-tä-ō-pän')	130	18.29 N	99.49 W
Ixelles, Bel.	157a	50.49 N	4.23 E
Ixhuatlan, Mex. (ēs-wät-län')	130	20.41 N	98.01 W
Ixhuatán (San Francisco), Mex. (ēs-hwä-tän')	131	16.19 N	94.30 W
Ixmiquilpan, Mex. (ēs-mē-kēl'pän)	130	20.30 N	99.12 W
Ixopo, S. Afr.	227c	30.10 S	30.04 E
Ixtacalco, Mex. (ēs-tá-käl'kò)	131a	19.23 N	99.07 W
Ixtaltepec (Asunción), Mex. (ēs-täl-tē-pěk')	131	16.33 N	95.04 W
Ixtapalapa, Mex. (ēs'tä-pä-lä'pä)	131a	19.21 N	99.06 W
Ixtapaluca, Mex. (ēs'tä-pä-lōō'kä)	131a	19.18 N	98.53 W
Ixtepec, Mex. (ēks-tē'pěk)	131	16.37 N	95.09 W
Ixtlahuaca, Mex. (ēs-tlä-wä'kä)	131a	19.34 N	99.46 W
Ixtlán de Juárez, Mex. (ēs-tlän' dä hwä'räz)	131	17.20 N	96.29 W
Ixtlán del Río, Mex. (ēs-tlän'děl rē'ō)	130	21.05 N	104.22 W
Iyo-Nada (Sea), Jap. (ē'yō nä-dä)	205	33.33 N	132.07 E
Izabal, Guat. (ē'zä-bäl')	132	15.23 N	89.10 W
Izabal, L. (Golfo Dulce), Guat. (gôl'fō dōōl'sä)	132	15.30 N	89.04 W
Izalco, Sal. (ē-zäl'kō)	132	13.50 N	89.40 W
Izamal, Mex. (ē-zä-mä'l)	132a	20.55 N	89.00 W
Izhevsk, Sov. Un. (ē-zhyĕfsk')	178	56.50 N	53.15 E
Izhma (R.), Sov. Un. (Izh'má)	178	64.00 N	53.00 E
Izhma, Sov. Un. (Izh'má)	178	65.00 N	54.05 E
Izhora R., Sov. Un. (ēz'hô-rá)	182c	59.36 N	30.20 E
Izmail, Sov. Un. (ēz-má-ēl)	175	45.00 N	28.49 E
Izmir, Tur. (īz-mēr')	179	38.25 N	27.05 E
Izmir Körfezi (G.), Tur.	173	38.43 N	26.37 E
Izmit, Tur. (īz-mēt')	179	40.45 N	29.45 E
Iznajar, Embalse de (Res.), Sp.	170	37.15 N	4.30 W
Iztaccíhuatl (Mtn.), Mex.	131a	19.10 N	98.38 W
Izuhara, Jap. (ē'zōō-hä'rä)	205	34.11 N	129.18 E
Izu (I.), Jap. (ē'zōō)	205	34.32 N	139.25 E
Izumi-Ōtsu, Jap. (ē'zōō-mōō ō'tsōō)	205b	34.30 N	135.24 E
Izumo, Jap. (ē'zōō-mō)	205	35.22 N	132.45 E

J

PLACE (Pronounciation)	PAGE	Lat. ° '	Long. ° '
Jaachimsthal, G.D.R. (yä'kĕm-stäl)	157b	52.58 N	13.45 E
Jabal, Bahr al (R.), Sud.	225	7.02 N	30.45 E
Jabalpur, India	196	23.18 N	79.59 E
Jabavu, S. Afr.	71b	26.15 S	27.53 E
Jablonec nad Nisou, Czech. (yäb'lô-nyĕts)	166	50.43 N	15.12 E
Jablunkov P., Czech. (yäb'lōōn-kôf)	167	49.31 N	18.35 E
Jaboatão, Braz. (zhä-bô-ä-touN)	143	8.14 S	35.08 W
Jaca, Sp. (hä'kä)	171	42.35 N	0.30 W
Jacala, Mex. (hä-kä'lä)	130	21.01 N	99.11 W
Jacaltenango, Guat. (hä-käl-tē-nán'gò)	132	15.39 N	91.41 W
Jacareí, Braz. (zhä-kä-rē-ē')	141a	23.19 S	45.57 W
Jacarepaguá, Braz. (zhä-kä-rā'pä-gwä')	144b	22.55 S	43.22 W
Jacarezinho, Braz. (zhä-kä-rē'zĕ-nyó)	143	23.13 S	49.58 W
Jachymov, Czech. (yä'chī-môf)	166	50.22 N	12.51 E
Jacinto City, Tx. (hä-sěn'tò)	125a	29.45 N	95.14 W
Jacksboro, Tx. (jäks'bŭr-ô)	122	33.13 N	98.11 W
Jackson, Al. (jăk'sŭn)	126	31.31 N	87.52 W
Jackson, Ca.	120	38.22 N	120.47 W
Jackson, Ga.	126	33.19 N	83.55 W
Jackson, Ky.	126	37.32 N	83.17 W
Jackson, La.	126	30.50 N	91.13 W
Jackson, Mi.	110	42.15 N	84.25 W
Jackson, Mn.	115	43.37 N	95.00 W
Jackson, Mo.	123	37.23 N	89.40 W
Jackson, Ms.	126	32.17 N	90.10 W
Jackson, Oh.	110	39.00 N	82.40 W
Jackson, Tn.	126	35.37 N	88.49 W
Jackson Heights (Neigh.), NY	55	40.45 N	73.53 W
Jackson L., Wy.	117	43.57 N	110.28 W
Jacksonville, Al. (jăk'sŭn-vĭl)	126	33.52 N	85.45 W
Jacksonville, Fl.	127	30.20 N	81.40 W
Jacksonville, Il.	123	39.43 N	90.12 W
Jacksonville, Tx.	125	31.58 N	95.18 W
Jacksonville Beach, Fl.	127	31.18 N	81.25 W
Jacmel, Hai. (zhäk-mĕl')	135	18.15 N	72.30 W
Jacobābad, Pak.	196	28.22 N	68.30 E
Jacobina, Braz. (zhä-kô-bē'ná)	143	11.13 S	40.30 W
Jaco, L., Mex. (hä'kō)	124	27.51 N	103.50 W
Jacomino, Cuba	60b	23.06 N	82.20 W
Jacques-Cartier, (R.), Can.	95b	47.04 N	71.28 W
Jacques Cartier, Détroit de (Str.), Can.	105	50.07 S	63.58 W
Jacques Cartier, Mt., Can.	104	48.59 N	66.00 W
Jacquet River, Can. (zhä-kĕ') (jăk'ĕt)	104	47.55 N	66.00 W
Jacuí, Braz. (zhä-kōō-ē')	141a	21.03 S	46.43 W
Jacutinga, Braz. (zhä-kōō-tēn'gä)	141a	21.17 S	46.36 W
Jade B., F.R.G. (yä'dĕ)	166	53.28 N	8.17 E
Jade Buddha, Temple of the (Yufosi) (P. Int.), China	68a	31.14 N	121.26 E
Jadotville, see Likasi			
Jaén, Peru (ĸä-ĕ'n)	142	5.38 S	78.49 W
Jaen, Sp.	170	37.45 N	3.48 W
Jaffa, C., Austl. (jäf'á)	216	36.58 S	139.29 E
Jaffna, Sri Lanka (jäf'ná)	197	9.44 N	80.09 E
Jagüey Grande, Cuba (hä'gwä grän'dä)	134	22.35 N	81.05 W
Jahore Str., Mala.	191b	1.22 N	103.37 E
Jahrom, Iran	192	28.30 N	53.28 E
Jaibo (R.), Cuba (hä-ē'bò)	125	20.10 N	75.20 W
Jaipur, India	196	27.00 N	75.50 E
Jaisaimer, India	196	27.00 N	70.54 E
Jajce, Yugo. (yī'tsĕ)	172	44.20 N	17.19 E
Jajpur, India	196	20.49 N	86.37 E
Jakarta, Indon.	206	6.17 S	106.45 E
Jakobstad, Fin. (yä'kôb-städh)	158	63.33 N	22.31 E
Jalacingo, Mex. (hä-lä-sĭn'gò)	131	19.47 N	97.16 W
Jalālābād, Afg. (jŭ-lä-lä-bäd')	193a	34.25 N	70.27 E
Jalālah al Baḥrīyah, Jabal, (Mts.), Egypt	223b	29.20 N	32.00 E
Jalapa, Guat. (hä-lä'pä)	132	14.38 N	89.58 W
Jalapa de Diaz (San Felipe), Mex. (dä dē-äz') (sán fä-lē'pä)	131	18.06 N	96.33 W
Jalapa del Marqués, Mex. (děl mär-käs')	131	16.30 N	95.29 W
Jalapa Enríquez, Mex. (ĕn-rē'käz)	131	19.32 N	96.53 W
Jaleswar, Nep.	196	26.50 N	85.55 E
Jalgaon, India	196	21.08 N	75.33 E
Jalisco, Mex. (hä-lēs'kō)	130	21.27 N	104.54 W
Jalisco (State), Mex.	128	20.07 N	104.45 W
Jalón (R.), Sp. (hä-lōn')	170	41.22 N	1.46 W
Jalostotitlán, Mex. (hä-lōs-tē-tlän')	130	21.09 N	102.30 W
Jalpa, Mex. (häl'pä)	131	18.12 N	93.06 W
Jalpa, Mex.	130	21.40 N	103.04 W
Jalpan, Mex. (häl'pän)	130	21.13 N	99.31 W
Jaltepec, Mex. (häl'tě-pěk)	131	17.20 N	95.15 W
Jaltipan, Mex. (häl-tě-pän')	131	17.59 N	94.42 W
Jaltocan, Mex. (häl-tô-kän')	130	21.08 N	98.32 W
Jālū, Wāhat (Oasis), Libya	225	28.58 N	21.45 E
Jamaare (R.), Nig.	229	11.50 N	10.10 E
Jamaica, N. A.	129	17.45 N	78.00 W
Jamaica B., NY	55	40.36 N	73.51 W
Jamaica Cay (I.), Ba.	135	22.45 N	75.55 W
Jamālīyah (Neigh.), Egypt	71a	30.03 N	31.16 E
Jamālpur, Bngl.	196	24.56 N	89.58 E
Jamay, Mex. (hä-mī')	130	20.16 N	103.43 W
Jambi, Indon. (mäm'bē)	206	1.45 S	103.28 E
James (R.), Mo.	123	36.51 N	93.22 W
James (R.), NC	127	36.07 N	81.48 W
James (R.), U.S.	108	46.25 N	98.55 W
James (R.), Va.	111	37.35 N	77.50 W
James B., Can. (jämz)	97	53.53 N	80.40 W
Jamesburg, NJ (jämz'bûrg)	112a	40.21 N	74.26 W
Jameson Raid Memorial (P. Int.), S. Afr.	71b	26.11 S	27.49 E
James Pt., Ba.	135	25.20 N	76.30 W
James Ra., Austl.	214	24.15 S	133.30 E
James Ross (I.), Ant.	140	64.20 S	58.20 W
Jamestown, ND	114	46.54 N	98.42 W
Jamestown, NY (jämz'toun)	111	42.05 N	79.15 W
Jamestown, RI	111	41.30 N	71.21 W
Jamestown, S. Afr.	227c	31.07 S	26.49 E
Jamestown Res., ND	114	47.16 N	98.40 W
Jamiltepec, Mex. (hä-mēl-tå-pěk')	131	16.16 N	97.54 W
Jammerbagten (B.), Den.	164	57.20 N	9.28 E
Jammu, India	196	32.50 N	74.52 E
Jammu and Kashmīr (Disputed Reg.), India-Pak. (kásh-mēr')	196	39.10 N	75.05 E
Jāmnagar, India (jäm-nŭ'gŭr)	196	22.33 N	70.03 E
Jamshedpur, India (jäm'shäd-pōōr)	196	22.52 N	86.11 E
Jamundí, Col. (hä-mōō'n-dē')	142a	3.15 N	76.32 W
Jándula (R.), Sp. (hän'dōō-lä)	170	38.28 N	3.52 W
Janesville, Wi. (jänz'vĭl)	115	42.41 N	89.03 W
Janin, Jordon	191a	32.27 N	35.19 E
Jan Mayen (I.), Nor. (yän mī'ĕn)	158	70.59 N	8.05 W
Jánoshalma, Hung. (yä'nôsh-hôl-mö)	167	46.17 N	19.18 E
Janów Lubelski, Pol. (yä'nōōf lû-bĕl'skĭ)	167	50.40 N	22.25 E
Januária, Braz. (zhä-nwä'rē-ä)	143	15.31 S	44.17 W
Japan, Asia (já-pän')	191	36.30 N	133.30 E
Japan, Sea of, Asia (já-pän')	204	40.08 N	132.55 E
Japeri, Braz.	144b	22.38 S	43.40 W
Japurá (R.), Braz. (zhá-pōō-rä')	142	1.30 S	67.54 W
Jarabacoa, Dom. Rep. (ĸä-rä-bä-kō'ä)	125	19.05 N	70.40 W
Jaral del Progreso, Mex. (hä-räl děl prô-grä'sō)	130	20.21 N	101.05 W
Jarama (R.), Sp. (hä-rä'mä)	170	40.35 N	3.30 W
Jarash, Jordan	191a	32.17 N	35.53 E
Jardim Paulista (Neigh.), Braz.	61d	23.35 S	46.40 W
Jardines, Banco (Bk.), Cuba (bä'n-kō-här-dē'näs)	134	21.45 N	81.40 W
Jardines del Pedregal de San Angel, Mex.	60a	19.18 N	99.13 W
Jari (R.), Braz. (zhä-rē')	143	0.28 N	53.00 W
Jarocin, Pol. (yä-rô'tsyĕn)	167	51.58 N	17.31 E
Jaroslaw, Pol. (yá-rôs-wáf)	167	50.01 N	22.41 E
Jargalant, Mong.	201	46.28 N	116.53 E
Jarud Qi, China (jya-lōō-tŭ shyē)	202	44.35 N	120.40 E
Jasenevo (Neigh.), Sov. Un.	66b	55.36 N	37.33 E
Jasin, Mala.	191b	2.19 N	102.26 E

PLACE (Pronounciation)	PAGE	Lat. °'	Long. °'
Jašiūnai, Sov. Un. (dzȧ-shōō-nȧ'yě)	165	54.27 N	25.25 E
Jāsk, Iran (jäsk)	192	25.46 N	57.48 E
Jaslo, Pol. (yäs'wō)	167	49.44 N	21.28 E
Jason B., Mala.	191b	1.53 N	104.14 E
Jasonville, In. (jā'sŭn-vĭl)	110	39.10 N	87.15 W
Jasper, Al. (jăs'pẽr)	126	33.50 N	87.17 W
Jasper, Can.	99	52.53 N	118.05 W
Jasper, Fl.	126	30.30 N	82.56 W
Jasper, In.	110	38.20 N	86.55 W
Jasper, Mn.	114	43.51 N	96.22 W
Jasper, Tx.	125	30.55 N	93.59 W
Jasper Natl. Park, Can.	99	53.09 N	117.45 W
Jászapáti, Hung. (yäs'ô-pä-tē)	167	47.29 N	20.10 E
Jászberény, Hung.	167	47.30 N	19.56 E
Jatate (R.), Mex. (hä-tä-tä')	131	16.30 N	91.29 W
Jatibonico, Cuba (hä-tē-bô-nē'kō)	134	22.00 N	79.15 W
Játiva, Sp. (hä'tē-vä)	171	38.58 N	0.31 W
Jaú, Braz. (zhä-ōō')	144	22.16 S	48.31 W
Jauja, Peru (Kä-ōō'K)	142	11.43 S	75.32 W
Jaumave, Mex. (hou-mä'vå)	130	23.23 N	99.24 W
Jaunjelgava, Sov. Un. (youn'yĕl'gȧ-vȧ)	165	56.37 N	25.06 E
Javari (R.), Col.-Peru (Kȧ-vä-rē)	142	4.25 S	72.07 W
Java Trench, Indon.	206	9.45 S	107.30 E
Jávea, Sp. (hȧ-vā'ä)	171	38.45 N	0.07 E
Jawa (I.), Indon.	206	8.35 S	111.11 E
Jawa, Laut (Java Sea), Indon.	206	5.10 S	110.30 E
Jawor, Pol. (yä'vôr)	166	51.04 N	16.12 E
Jaworzno, Pol. (yä-vôzh'nō)	167	50.11 N	19.18 E
Jaya, Puncak (Pk.), Indon.	207	4.00 S	131.15 E
Jayapura (Sukarnapura), Indon.	207	2.30 S	140.45 W
Jayb, Wādī al (R.), see Ha 'Arava			
Jazīrat Muhammad, Egypt	71a	30.07 N	31.12 E
Jazzīn, Leb.	191a	33.34 N	35.37 E
Jeanerette, La. (jĕn-ēr-ĕt') (zhän-rĕt')	125	29.54 N	91.41 W
Jebba, Nig. (jĕb'ȧ)	224	9.07 N	4.46 E
Jeddore L., Can.	105	48.07 N	55.35 W
Jedlesee (Neigh.), Aus.	66e	48.16 N	16.23 E
Jędrzejów, Pol. (yăN-dzhā'yŏŏf)	167	50.38 N	20.18 E
Jefferson, Ga. (jĕf'ēr-sŭn)	126	34.05 N	83.35 W
Jefferson, Ia.	115	42.10 N	94.22 W
Jefferson, La.	112d	29.57 N	90.04 W
Jefferson, Pa.	57b	39.56 N	80.04 W
Jefferson, Tx.	125	32.47 N	94.21 W
Jefferson, Wi.	115	42.59 N	88.45 W
Jefferson City, Mo.	123	38.34 N	92.10 W
Jefferson, Mt., Or.	116	44.41 N	121.50 W
Jefferson Park (Neigh.), Il.	58a	41.59 N	87.46 W
Jefferson R., Mt.	117	45.37 N	112.22 W
Jeffersontown, Ky. (jĕf'ēr-sŭn-toun)	113h	38.11 N	85.34 W
Jeffersonville, In. (jĕf'ēr-sŭn-vĭl)	113h	38.17 N	85.44 W
Jega, Nig.	229	12.15 N	4.23 E
Jehol (Reg.), China (jē-hōl)	199	42.31 N	118.12 E
Jeib, Wadi el (R.), Jordan-Isr.	161	30.30 N	35.20 E
Jēkabpils, Sov. Un. (yĕk'ab-pĭls)	165	56.29 N	25.50 E
Jelenia Góra, Pol. (yĕ-lĕn'yȧ gōō'rȧ)	166	50.53 N	15.43 E
Jelgava, Sov. Un. (yĕl'gȧ-vȧ)	165	56.39 N	23.40 E
Jellico, Tn. (jĕl'ĭ-kō)	126	36.34 N	84.06 W
Jena, G.D.R. (yā'nä)	166	50.55 N	11.37 E
Jenkins, Ky. (jĕŋ'kĭnz)	127	37.09 N	82.38 W
Jenkintown, Pa. (jĕŋ'kĭn-toun)	112f	40.06 N	75.08 W
Jennings, La. (jĕn'ĭngz)	125	30.14 N	92.40 W
Jennings, Mi.	110	44.20 N	85.20 W
Jennings, Mo.	119e	38.43 N	90.16 W
Jequié, Braz. (zhĕ-kyĕ')	143	13.53 S	40.06 W
Jequitinhonha (R.), Braz. (zhĕ-kē-tēŋ-ō'n-yä)	143	16.47 S	41.19 W
Jérémie, Hai. (zhā-rā-mē')	135	18.40 N	74.10 W
Jeremoabo, Braz. (zhĕ-rā-mō-ä'bō)	143	10.03 S	38.13 W
Jerez de la Frontera, Sp. (Kĕ-rāth' dā lä frōn-tā'rä)	170	36.42 N	6.09 W
Jerez de Los Caballeros, Sp. (Kĕ-rath'dā lōs kä-väl-yā'rôs)	170	38.20 N	6.45 W
Jerez, Punta (Pt.), Mex. (pōō'n-tä-Kĕ-rāz')	131	23.04 N	97.44 W
Jericho, Austl. (jĕr'ĭ-kō)	215	28.38 S	146.24 E
Jericho, NY	55	40.48 N	73.32 W
Jericho, S. Afr. (jĕr-ĭkô)	223d	25.16 N	27.47 E
Jericho, see Arīhā			
Jerome, Az. (jē-rōm')	121	34.45 N	112.10 W
Jerome, Id.	117	42.44 N	114.31 W
Jersey (I.), Eur. (jûr'zĭ)	168	49.13 N	2.07 W
Jersey City, NJ	112a	40.43 N	74.05 W
Jersey Shore, Pa.	111	41.10 N	77.15 W
Jerseyville, Il. (jēr'zē-vĭl)	123	39.07 N	90.18 W
Jerusalem, Isr.-Jordan (jē-rōō'sȧ-lĕm)	191a	31.46 N	35.14 E
Jesup, Ga. (jĕs'ŭp)	127	31.36 N	81.53 W
Jesús Carranza, Mex. (hĕ-sōō's-kär-rä'n-zä)	131	17.26 N	95.01 W
Jesús del Monte (Neigh.)	60b	23.06 N	82.22 W
Jésus, Île (I.), Can.	54b	45.35 N	73.45 W
Jesús María, Peru	60c	12.04 S	77.04 W
Jewel, Or. (jū'ĕl)	118c	45.56 N	123.30 W
Jewel Cave Natl. Mon., SD	114	43.44 N	103.52 W
Jhālawār, India	196	24.29 N	79.09 E
Jhang Maghiāna, Pak.	196	31.21 N	72.19 E
Jhānsi, India (jän'sē)	196	25.29 N	78.32 E
Jhārsuguda, India	196	22.51 N	86.13 E
Jhelum (R.), Pak. (jā'lŭm)	196	31.40 N	71.51 E
Jhenkāri, India	67a	22.46 N	88.18 E
Jhil Kuranga (Neigh.), India	67d	28.40 N	77.17 E
Jiache, China (jyä-chŭ)	200	38.03 N	116.18 E
Jiading, China (jyä-dĭŋ)	201a	31.23 N	121.15 E
Jialing (R.), China (jyä-lĭŋ)	203	30.30 N	106.20 E
Ji'an, China (jyē-än)	203	27.15 N	115.10 E
Ji'an, China	202	41.00 N	126.04 E
Jianchangying, China (jyĕn-chäŋ-yĭŋ)	200	40.09 N	119.47 E
Jiangcun, China (jyän-tsōōn)	201a	23.16 N	113.14 E
Jiangling, China (jyäŋ-lĭŋ)	203	30.30 N	112.10 E
Jiangshanzhen, China (jyäŋ-shän-jŭn)	200	36.39 N	120.31 E
Jiangsu (Prov.), China (jyäŋ-sōō)	199	33.45 N	120.30 E
Jiangwan, China (jyäŋ-wän)	201b	31.18 N	121.29 E
Jiangxi (Prov.), China (jyäŋ-shyē)	199	28.15 N	116.00 E
Jiangyin, China (jyäŋ-yĭn)	200	31.54 N	120.15 E
Jianli, China (jyĕn-lē)	203	29.50 N	112.52 E
Jianning, China (jyĕn-nĭŋ)	203	26.50 N	116.55 E
Jian'ou, China (jyĕn-ō)	203	27.10 N	118.18 E
Jianshi, China (jyĕn-shr)	203	30.40 N	109.45 E
Jiaohe, China (jyou-hŭ)	202	43.40 N	127.20 E
Jiaoxian, China (jyou shyĕn)	200	36.18 N	120.01 E
Jiaozuo, China (jyou-dzwō)	200	35.15 N	113.18 E
Jiashan, China (jyä-shän)	200	32.41 N	118.00 E
Jiaxing, China (jyä-shyĭŋ)	203	30.45 N	120.50 E
Jiayu, China (jyä-yōō)	203	33.00 N	114.00 E
Jiazhou Wan (B.), China (jyä-jō wän)	200	36.10 N	119.55 E
Jicarilla Ind. Res., NM (Kē-kȧ-rēl'yȧ)	121	36.45 N	107.00 W
Jicaron, Isla (I.), Pan. (Kē-kä-rōn')	133	7.14 N	81.41 W
Jiddah, Sau. Ar.	192	21.30 N	39.15 E
Jieshou, China	200	33.17 N	115.20 E
Jieyang, China (jyĕ-yäŋ)	203	23.38 N	116.20 E
Jiggalong, Austl. (jĭg'ȧ-lông)	214	23.20 S	120.45 E
Jiguani, Cuba (Kē-gwä-nē')	135	20.20 N	76.30 W
Jigüey, Bahía (B.), Cuba (bä-ē'ä-Kē'gwā)	134	22.15 N	78.10 W
Jihlava, Czech. (yē'hlȧ-vȧ)	166	49.23 N	15.33 E
Jijel, Alg.	159	36.49 N	5.47 E
Jijia (R.), Rom.	167	47.35 N	27.02 E
Jijiashi, China (jyē-jyä-shr)	200	32.10 N	120.17 E
Jijiga, Eth.	223a	9.15 N	42.48 E
Jijona, Sp. (Kē-hō'nä)	171	38.31 N	0.29 W
Jilf al-Kabīr, Hadabat al (Plat.), Egypt	225	24.09 N	25.29 E
Jilin, China (jyē-lĭn)	202	43.58 N	126.40 E
Jilin (Prov.), China	199	44.20 N	124.50 E
Jiloca (R.), Sp. (Kē-lō'kȧ)	170	41.13 N	1.30 W
Jilotepeque, Guat. (Kē-lô-tĕ-pĕ'kĕ)	132	14.39 N	89.36 W
Jima, Eth.	225	7.41 N	36.52 E
Jimbolia, Rom. (zhĭm-bô'lyä)	173	45.45 N	20.44 E
Jiménez, Mex. (Kē-mā'nāz)	130	24.12 N	98.29 W
Jimenez, Mex.	124	27.09 N	104.55 W
Jiménez, Mex.	124	29.03 N	100.42 W
Jiménez del Téul, Mex. (tĕ-ōō'l)	130	21.28 N	103.51 W
Jimo, China (jyē-mwo)	200	36.22 N	120.28 E
Jim Thorpe, Pa. (jĭm' thôrp')	111	40.50 N	75.45 W
Jinan, China (jyē-nän)	200	36.40 N	117.01 E
Jincheng, China (jyĭn-chŭŋ)	202	35.30 N	112.50 E
Jindřichov Hradec, Czech. (yĕn'd'r-zhĭ-kōōf hrä'dĕts)	166	49.09 N	15.02 E
Jing (R.), China (jyĭŋ)	202	34.40 N	108.20 E
Jing'anji, China (jyĭŋ-än-jē)	200	34.30 N	116.55 E
Jingdezhen, China (jyĭn-dŭ-jŭn)	203	29.18 N	117.18 E
Jingjiang, China (jyĭŋ-jyäŋ)	200	32.02 N	120.15 E
Jingning, China (jyĭŋ-nĭŋ)	202	35.28 N	105.50 E
Jingpo Hu (L.), China (jyĭŋ-pwo hōō)	202	44.10 N	129.00 E
Jingxian, China (jyĭŋ shyĕn)	203	26.32 N	109.40 E
Jingxian, China	200	37.43 N	116.17 E
Jingxing, China (jyĭŋ-shyĭŋ)	202	47.00 N	123.00 E
Jingzhi, China (jyĭŋ-jr)	200	36.19 N	119.23 E
Jinhua, China (jyĭn-hwä)	203	29.10 N	119.42 E
Jining, China (jyē-nĭŋ)	200	35.26 N	116.34 E
Jining, China	202	41.00 N	113.10 E
Jinja, Ug. (jĭn'jä)	231	0.26 N	33.12 E
Jinotega, Nic. (Kē-nô-tā'gä)	132	13.07 N	86.00 W
Jinotepe, Nic. (Kē-nô-tā'pā)	132	11.52 N	86.12 W
Jinqiao, China (jyĭn-chyou)	200	31.46 N	116.46 E
Jinshan, China (jyĭn-shän)	201b	30.53 N	121.09 E
Jinta, China (jyĭn-tä)	198	40.11 N	98.45 E
Jintan, China (jyĭn-tän)	200	31.47 N	119.34 E
Jin Xian, China (jyĭn shyĕn)	200	39.04 N	121.40 E
Jinxiang, China (jyĭn-shyäŋ)	200	35.03 N	116.20 E
Jinyun, China (jyĭn-yōōn)	203	28.40 N	120.08 E
Jinzhai, China (jyĭn-jī)	200	31.41 N	115.51 E
Jinzhou, China (jyĭn-jō)	202	41.00 N	121.00 E
Jinzhou Wan (B.), China (jyĭn-jō wän)	200	39.07 N	121.17 E
Jinzū-Gawa (Strm.), Jap. (jĕn'zōō gä'wä)	205	36.26 N	137.18 E
Jipijapa, Ec. (Kē-pē-hä'pä)	142	1.36 S	80.52 W
Jiquilisco, Sal. (Kē-kē-lē's-kô)	132	13.18 N	88.32 W
Jiquilpan de Juarez, Mex. (Kē-kēl'pän dā hwä'rāz)	130	20.00 N	102.43 W
Jiquipilco, Mex. (hē-kē-pē'l-kô)	131a	19.32 N	99.37 W
Jirjā, Egypt (jĕr'gȧ)	223b	26.20 N	31.51 E
Jitotol, Mex. (Kē-tô-tōl')	131	17.03 N	92.54 W
Jiu (R.), Rom.	173	44.45 N	23.17 E
Jiugang, China	67b	39.49 N	116.27 E
Jiujiang, China (jyô-jyän)	201a	22.50 N	113.02 E
Jiujiang, China	203	29.43 N	116.00 E
Jiuquan, China (jyô-chyän)	198	39.46 N	98.26 E
Jiurongcheng, China (jyô-rôŋ-chŭŋ)	200	37.23 N	122.31 E
Jiushouzhang, China (jyô-shō-jäŋ)	200	35.59 N	115.52 E
Jiuwuqing, China (jyô-wōō-chyĭŋ)	202a	32.39 N	116.51 E
Jiuyongnian, China (jyô-yôŋ-nĭĕn)	200	36.41 N	114.46 E
Jixian, China (jyē shyĕn)	200	35.25 N	114.03 E
Jixian, China	200	37.37 N	115.33 E
Jixian, China	200	40.03 N	117.25 E
Jiyum (R.), China (jyē-yōōm)	200	39.35 N	117.34 E
Jīzān, Sau. Ar.	195	16.54 N	42.29 E
João Pessoa (Paraíba), Braz. (shô-ouN'pĕ-sōō') (pä-rä-ē'bȧ)	143	7.09 S	34.45 W
João Ribeiro, Braz. (zhô-uN-rē-bä'rō)	141a	20.42 S	44.03 W
Jobabo (R.), Cuba (hō-bä'bä)	134	20.50 N	77.15 W
Jock (R.), Can. (jŏk)	95c	45.08 N	75.51 W
Jocotepec, Mex. (jô-kō-tā-pĕk')	130	20.17 N	103.26 W
Jodar, Sp. (hō'där)	170	37.54 N	3.20 W
Jodhpur, India (hŏd'pōōr)	196	26.23 N	73.00 E
Joensuu, Fin. (yô-ĕn'sōō)	165	62.35 N	29.46 E
Joffre, Mt., Can. (jŏ'f'r)	99	50.32 N	115.13 W
Jōga-Shima (I.), Jap. (jō'gä shē'mä)	205a	35.07 N	139.37 E
Jõgeva, Sov. Un. (yû'gĕ-vȧ)	174	58.45 N	26.23 E
Joggins, Can. (jŏ'gĭnz)	102	45.42 N	64.27 W
Johannesburg, S. Afr. (yô-hän'ĕs-bōōrgh)	227b	26.08 S	27.54 E
Johannisthal (Neigh.), G.D.R.	65a	52.26 N	13.30 E
John Carroll University (P. Int.), Oh.	56a	41.29 N	81.32 W
John Day Dam, Or.	116	45.40 N	120.15 W
John Day R., Or. (jŏn'dā)	116	44.46 N	120.15 W
John Day R., Middle Fork, Or.	116	44.53 N	119.04 W
John Day R., North Fork, Or.	116	45.03 N	118.50 W
John F. Kennedy International Arpt., NY	55	40.38 N	73.47 W
John Martin Res., Co. (jŏn mär'tĭn)	122	37.57 N	103.04 W
Johns Hopkins University (P. Int.), Md.	56c	39.20 N	76.37 W
Johnson (R.), Or. (jŏn'sŭn)	118c	45.27 N	122.20 W
Johnsonburg, Pa. (jŏn'sŭn-bûrg)	111	41.30 N	78.40 W
Johnson City, Il. (jŏn'sŭn)	110	37.50 N	88.55 W
Johnson City, NY	111	42.10 N	76.00 W
Johnson City, Tn.	127	36.17 N	82.23 W
Johnston (I.), Oceania (jŏn'stŭn)	208	17.00 N	168.00 W
Johnstone Saint, Can.	98	50.25 N	126.00 W
Johnston Falls, Afr.	231	10.35 S	28.50 E
Johnstown, NY (jonz'toun)	111	43.00 N	74.20 W
Johnstown, Pa.	111	40.20 N	78.50 W
Johor (R.), Mala. (jŭ-hōr')	191b	1.39 N	103.52 E
Johor Bahru, Mala. (bȧ-hōō-rōō')	191b	1.28 N	103.46 E
Johor, Selat (Str.), Asia	67c	1.28 N	103.48 E
Jõhvi, Sov. Un. (yû'vĭ)	174	59.21 N	27.21 E
Joigny, Fr. (zhwän-yē')	168	47.58 N	3.26 E
Joinville, Braz. (zhwăN-vēl')	144	26.18 S	48.47 W
Joinville, Fr.	168	48.28 N	5.05 E
Joinville (I.), Ant.	140	63.00 S	53.30 W
Joinville-le-Pont, Fr.	64c	48.49 N	2.28 E
Jojutla, Mex. (hō-hōō'tlä)	130	18.39 N	99.11 W
Jola, Mex. (Kō'lä)	130	21.08 N	104.26 W
Joliet, Il. (jō-lĭ-ĕt')	113a	41.37 N	88.05 W
Joliette, Can. (zhō-lyĕt')	103	46.01 N	73.30 W
Jolo Phil. (hō-lō)	206	5.59 N	121.05 E
Jolo I., Phil.	206	5.55 N	121.15 E
Jomalig (I.), Phil. (hô-mä'lēg)	207a	14.44 N	122.34 E
Jomulco, Mex. (hô-mōōl'kō)	130	21.08 N	104.24 W
Jonacatepec, Mex. (hō-nä-kä-tā-pĕk')	130	18.39 N	98.46 W
Jonava, Sov. Un. (yō-nä'vȧ)	165	55.05 N	24.15 E
Jones, Phil. (jōnz)	207a	13.56 N	122.05 E
Jones, Phil.	207a	16.35 N	121.39 E
Jonesboro, Ar. (jōnz'bûrō)	123	35.49 N	90.42 W
Jonesboro, La.	125	32.14 N	92.43 W
Jonesville, La. (jōnz'vĭl)	125	31.35 N	91.50 W
Jonesville, Mi.	110	42.00 N	84.45 W
Jong (R.), S.L.	228	8.10 N	12.10 W
Joniškis, Sov. Un. (yô'nĭsh-kĭs)	165	56.14 N	23.36 E
Jönköping, Swe. (yûn'chû-pĭng)	164	57.47 N	14.10 E
Jonquiere, Can. (zhôN-kyâr')	103	48.25 N	71.15 W
Jonuta, Mex. (hô-nōō'tä)	131	18.07 N	92.09 W
Jonzac, Fr. (zhôN-zȧk')	168	45.27 N	0.27 W
Joplin, Mo. (jŏp'lĭn)	123	37.05 N	94.31 W
Jordan, Asia (jôr'dăn)	190	30.15 N	38.00 E
Jordan (R.), Jordan	191a	31.58 N	35.36 E
Jordan R., Ut.	119b	40.42 N	111.56 W
Jorhāt, India (jôr-hät')	193	26.43 N	94.16 E
Jorullo, Vol. de, Mex. (vôl-kä'n-dĕ-hô-rōōl'yō)	130	18.54 N	101.38 W
José C. Paz, Arg.	60d	34.32 S	58.44 W
Joseph Bonaparte, G., Austl. (jō'sĕf bō'nȧ-pärt)	214	13.30 S	128.40 E
Josephburg, Can.	95g	53.45 N	113.06 W
Joseph L., Can. (jō'sĕf lāk)	95g	53.18 N	113.06 W
Joshua Tree Natl. Mon., Can. (jō'shū-ȧ trē)	120	34.02 N	115.53 W
Jos Plat., Nig. (jôs)	229	9.53 N	9.05 E
Jostedalsbreen (Gl.), Nor. (yôstĕ-däls-brĕĕn)	164	61.40 N	6.55 E
Jotunheimen (Mts.), Nor.	164	61.44 N	8.11 E
Joulter's Cays (Is.), Ba. (jōl'tẽrz)	134	25.20 N	78.10 W
Jouy-en-Josas, Fr.	64c	48.46 N	2.10 E
Jouy-le-Chatel, Fr. (zhwē-lĕ-shä-tĕl')	169b	48.40 N	3.07 E
Jovellanos, Cuba (hō-vĕl-yä'nōs)	134	22.50 N	81.10 W
Jōyō, Jap.	205b	34.51 N	135.48 E
J. Percy Priest Res., Tn.	126	36.00 N	86.45 W
Juan Aldama, Mex. (kōōä'n-äl-dȧ'mä)	130	24.16 N	103.21 W
Juan Anchorena (Neigh.), Arg.	60d	34.29 S	58.30 W
Juan de Fuca, Str. of, Wa.-Can. (hwän' dā fōō'kä)	116	48.25 N	124.37 W
Juan de Nova, Île (I.), Afr.	227	17.18 S	43.07 E
Juan Diaz, (R.), Pan. (Kōōä'n-dē'äz)	128a	9.05 N	79.30 W
Juan Fernández, Islas de (Is.), Chile (ĕ's-läs-dĕ-hwän' fĕr-nän'dāth)	140	33.30 S	79.00 W
Juan González Romero, Mex.	60a	19.30 N	99.04 W
Juan L. Lacaze, Ur. (hōōä'n-ĕ'lĕ-lä-kä'zĕ)	141c	34.25 S	57.28 W
Juan Luis, Cayos de (Is.), Cuba (ka-yōs-dĕ-hwän lōō-ēs')	134	22.15 N	82.00 W
Juárez, Arg. (hōōä'rĕz)	144	37.42 S	59.46 W
Juàzeiro, Braz. (zhōōä'zā'rō)	143	9.27 S	40.28 W
Juazeiro do Norte, Braz. (zhōōä'zā'rō-dō-nôr-tĕ)	143	7.16 S	38.57 W
Jūbā, Sud.	225	4.58 N	31.37 E
Jubayl (Byblos), Leb. (jōō-bīl')	191a	34.07 N	35.38 E
Jubba (R.), Som.	223a	1.30 N	42.25 E
Júcar (R.), Sp. (hōō'kär)	170	39.10 N	1.22 W
Júcaro, Cuba (hōō'kȧ-rō)	134	21.40 N	78.50 W
Juchipila, Mex. (hōō-chē-pē'lȧ)	130	21.26 N	103.09 W
Juchitán, Mex. (hōō-chē-tän')	128	16.15 N	95.00 W
Juchitán de Zaragoza, Mex. (hōō-chē-tän' dā thä-rä-gō'thä)	131	16.27 N	95.03 W
Juchitlán, Mex. (hōō-chē-tlän)	130	20.05 N	104.07 W
Jucuapa, Sal. (Kōō-kwä'pä)	132	13.30 N	88.24 W
Judenburg, Aus. (jōō'dĕn-bûrg)	166	47.10 N	14.40 E
Judith R., Mt. (jōō'dĭth)	117	47.20 N	109.36 W
Jugo-Zapad (Neigh.), Sov. Un.	66b	55.40 N	37.32 E

ng-sing; nŋ-baŋk; N-nasalized n; nŏd; cŏmmit; ōld; ôbey; ôrder; oi-boil; fōōd; fŏŏt; ou-out; s-soft; sh-dish; th-thin; pūre; ûnite; ûrn; stŭd; circŭs; ü-as in French tu; '-indeterminate vowel.

PLACE (Pronounciation)	PAGE	Lat. °'	Long. °'
Juhua Dao (I.), China (jyōō-hwä dou)	200	40.30 N	120.47 E
Juigalpa, Nic. (hwē-gäl'pä)	132	12.02 N	85.24 W
Juilly, Fr.	64c	49.01 N	2.42 E
Juist (I.), F.R.G. (yōō'ēst)	163	53.41 N	6.50 E
Juiz de Fora, Braz. (zhōō-ēzh' dā fō'rä)	141a	21.47 S	43.20 W
Jujuy, Arg. (hōō-hwē')	144	24.14 S	65.15 W
Jujuy (Prov.), Arg. (hōō-hwē')	144	23.00 S	65.45 W
Jukskei (R.), S. Afr.	227b	25.58 S	27.58 E
Julesburg, Co. (jōōlz'bûrg)	122	40.59 N	102.16 W
Juliaca, Peru (hōō-lē-ä'kä)	142	15.26 S	70.12 W
Julian Alps (Mts.), Yugo.	172	46.05 N	14.05 E
Julianehåb, Grnld.	94	60.07 N	46.20 W
Jülich, F.R.G. (yü'lēk)	169c	50.55 N	6.22 E
Jullundur, India	196	31.29 N	75.39 E
Julpaiguri, India	196	26.35 N	88.48 E
Jumento Cays (Is.), Ba. (hōō-mĕn'tō)	135	23.05 N	75.40 W
Jumilla, Sp. (hōō-mēl'yä)	170	38.28 N	1.20 W
Jump (R.), Wi. (jŭmp)	115	45.18 N	90.53 W
Jumpingpound Cr., Can. (jŭmp-ĭng-pound)	95e	51.01 N	114.34 W
Jumrah, Indon.	191b	1.48 N	101.04 E
Jumundá (R.), Braz. (zhōō-mōō'n-dä')	143	1.33 S	57.42 W
Junagādh, India (jōō-nä'gŭd)	196	21.33 N	70.25 E
Junayfah, Egypt	223c	30.11 N	32.26 E
Junaynah, Ra's al (Mt.), Egypt	191a	29.02 N	33.58 E
Junction, Tx. (jŭŋk'shŭn)	124	30.29 N	99.48 W
Junction City, Ks.	123	39.01 N	96.49 W
Jundiaí, Braz. (zhōō'n-dyä-ē')	141a	23.12 S	46.52 W
Juneau, Ak. (jōō'nō)	107	58.25 N	134.30 W
Jungfrau (Pk.), Switz. (yōōng'frou)	166	46.30 N	7.59 E
Juniata (Neigh.), Pa.	56b	40.01 N	75.07 W
Junín, Arg. (hōō-nē'n)	141c	34.35 S	60.56 W
Junín, Col.	142a	4.47 N	73.39 W
Juniyah, Leb. (jōō-nē'ē)	191a	33.59 N	35.38 E
Jupiter (R.), Can.	105	49.40 N	63.20 W
Jupiter, Mt., Wa.	118a	47.42 N	123.04 W
Jur (R.), Sud. (jōōr)	225	6.38 N	27.52 E
Jura (I.), Scot. (jōō'rá)	162	56.09 N	6.45 W
Jura (Mts.), Switz. (zhü-rá')	169	46.55 N	6.49 E
Jura, Sd. of, Scot. (jōō'rá)	162	55.45 N	5.55 W
Jurbarkas, Sov. Un. (yōōr-bär'käs)	165	55.06 N	22.50 E
Jūrmala, Sov. Un.	165	56.57 N	23.37 E
Jurong, China (jyōō-roŋ)	200	31.58 N	119.12 E
Jurong, Singapore	67c	1.21 N	103.42 E
Juruá (R.), Braz. (zhōō-rōō-ä')	142	5.27 S	67.39 W
Juruena (R.), Braz. (zhōō-rōōĕ'nä)	143	12.22 S	58.34 W
Justice, Il.	58a	41.45 N	87.50 W
Jutaí (R.), Braz. (zhōō-táy)	142	4.26 S	68.16 W
Jutiapa, Guat. (hōō-tē-ä'pä)	132	14.16 N	89.55 W
Juticalpa, Hond. (hōō-tē-käl'pä)	132	14.35 N	86.17 W
Juventino Rosas, Mex. (kōō-vĕn-tē'nô-rô-säs)	130	20.38 N	101.02 W
Juventud, Isla de la (I.), Cuba	134	21.40 N	82.45 W
Juvisy-sur-Orge, Fr.	64c	48.41 N	2.23 E
Juxian, China (jyōō shyĕn)	200	35.35 N	118.50 E
Juxtahuaca, Mex. (hōōs-tlä-hwä'kä)	130	17.20 N	98.02 W
Juye, China (jyōō-yū)	200	35.25 N	116.05 E
Južna Morava (R.), Yugo. (ū'zhnä mô'rä-vä)	173	42.30 N	22.00 E
Jwālahari (Neigh.), India	67d	28.40 N	77.06 E
Jylland (Reg.), Den.	164	56.04 N	9.00 E
Jyväskylä, Fin. (yû'vĕs-kû-lĕ)	165	62.14 N	25.46 E

K

PLACE (Pronounciation)	PAGE	Lat. °'	Long. °'
Kaabong, Ug.	231	3.31 N	34.08 E
Kaalfontein, S. Afr. (kärl-fōn-tān)	227b	26.02 S	28.16 E
Kaappunt (C.), S. Afr.	226a	34.21 S	18.30 E
Kaarst, F.R.G.	63	51.14 N	6.37 E
Kabaena, Pulau (I.), Indon. (kä-bá-ā'ná)	206	5.35 S	121.07 E
Kabala, S. L. (ká-bá'lá)	224	9.43 N	11.39 W
Kabale, Ug.	231	1.15 S	29.59 E
Kabalega Falls, Ug.	231	2.15 N	31.41 E
Kabalo, Zaire (kä-bä'lō)	231	6.03 S	26.55 E
Kabambare, Zaire (kä-bäm-bä'rā)	226	4.47 S	27.45 E
Kabba, Nig.	229	7.50 N	6.03 E
Kabe, Jap. (kä'bā)	205	34.32 N	132.30 E
Kabel (Neigh.), F.R.G.	63	51.24 N	7.29 E
Kabinakagami (R.), Can.	102	49.00 N	84.15 W
Kabinda, Zaire (kä-bĕn'dä)	230	6.08 S	24.29 E
Kabompo (R.), Zambia (kà-bôm'pō)	230	14.00 S	23.40 E
Kabongo, Zaire (kà-bông'ō)	226	7.58 S	25.10 E
Kabot, Gui.	228	10.48 N	14.57 W
Kaboudia, Ra's (C.), Tun.	160	35.17 N	11.28 E
Kābul, Afg. (kä'bōōl)	196	34.39 N	69.14 E
Kabul (R.), Asia (kä'bōōl)	193	34.44 N	69.43 E
Kabunda, Zaire	231	12.25 S	29.22 E
Kabwe (Broken Hill), Zambia	231	14.27 S	28.27 E
Kachuga, Sov. Un. (kà-chōō-gà)	181	54.09 N	105.43 E
Kadei (R.), Cam.-Cen. Afr. Rep.	229	4.00 N	15.10 E
Kadıköy (Neigh.), Tur.	66f	40.59 N	29.01 E
Kadiyevka, Sov. Un. (kà-dī-yĕf'kà)	175	48.34 N	38.37 E
Kadnikov, Sov. Un. (käd'nē-kôf)	178	59.30 N	40.10 E
Kadoma, Jap.	205b	34.43 N	135.36 E
Kadoma, Zimb.	231	18.21 S	29.55 E
Kaduna, Nig. (kä-dōō'nä)	229	10.33 N	7.27 E
Kaduna (R.), Nig.	229	9.30 N	6.00 E
Kaédi, Mauritania (kä-ā-dē')	228	16.09 N	13.30 W
Kaena Pt., Hi. (kä'ā-nä)	106a	21.33 N	158.19 W
Kaesŏng (Kaijo), Kor. (kä'ē-sŭng) (kī'jō)	204	38.00 N	126.35 E
Kafanchan, Nig.	229	9.36 N	8.17 E
Kafia Kingi, Sud. (kä'fē-à kiŋ'gē)	225	9.17 N	24.28 E
Kafue (R.), Zambia	231	15.45 S	26.30 E
Kafue, Zambia (kä'fōō)	226	15.45 S	28.17 E
Kafue Flats (Pln.), Zambia	231	16.15 S	26.30 E
Kafue Natl. Pk., Zambia	231	15.00 S	25.35 E
Kafwira, Zaire	231	12.10 S	27.33 E
Kagal'nik (R.), Sov. Un. (kä-gäl''nēk)	175	46.58 N	39.25 E
Kagera (R.), Tan. (kä-gā'rá)	231	1.10 S	31.10 E
Kagoshima, Jap. (kä'gô-shē'má)	205	31.35 N	130.31 E
Kagoshima-Wan (B.), Jap. (kä'gô-shē'mä wän)	205	31.24 N	130.39 E
Kagran (Neigh.), Sov. Un.	66a	48.15 N	16.27 E
Kagul, Sov. Un. (ka-gōōl')	175	45.49 N	28.17 E
Kahayan (R.), Indon.	206	1.45 S	113.40 E
Kahemba, Zaire	230	7.17 S	19.00 E
Kahia, Zaire	231	6.21 S	28.24 E
Kahoka, Mo. (ká-hō'ká)	123	40.26 N	91.42 W
Kahoolawe (I), Hi. (kä-hōō-lä'wē)	106a	20.28 N	156.48 W
Kahoué, Mont (Mtn.), Ivory Coast	228	7.06 N	7.15 W
Kahshahpiwi (R.), Can.	115	48.24 N	90.56 W
Kahuku Pt., Hi. (kä-hōō'kōō)	106a	21.50 N	157.50 W
Kahului, Hi.	106a	20.53 N	156.28 W
Kaiang, Mala.	191b	3.00 N	101.47 E
Kaiashk (R.), Can.	102	49.40 N	89.30 W
Kaibab Ind. Res., Az. (kä'ē-bàb)	121	36.55 N	112.45 W
Kaibab Plat, Az.	121	36.30 N	112.10 W
Kaidori, Jap.	69a	35.37 N	139.27 E
Kaidu (R.), China (kī-dōō)	198	42.35 N	84.04 E
Kaieteur Fall, Guy. (kī-ĕ-tōōr')	143	4.48 N	59.24 W
Kaifeng, China (kī-fŭŋ)	200	34.48 N	114.22 E
Kaijo, see Kaesong			
Kai Kecil (I.), Indon.	207	5.45 S	132.40 E
Kai, Kepulauan (Is.), Indon.	207	5.35 S	132.45 E
Kaikyō, Sōya (Str.), Sov. Un. (sô'yà kà-ē'kī-ō)	177	45.45 N	141.20 E
Kailua, Hi. (kä'ē-lōō'ä)	106a	21.18 N	157.43 W
Kailua Kona, Hi.	106a	19.49 N	155.59 W
Kaimana, Indon.	207	3.32 S	133.47 E
Kaimanawa Mts., N.Z.	217	39.10 S	176.00 E
Kainan, Jap. (kä'ē-nān')	205	34.09 N	135.14 E
Kainji L., Nig.	229	10.25 N	4.50 E
Kaisarianí, Grc.	66d	37.58 N	23.47 E
Kaisermühlen (Neigh.), Aus.	66e	48.14 N	16.26 E
Kaiserslautern, F.R.G. (kī-zĕrs-lou'tĕrn)	166	49.26 N	7.46 E
Kaiserwerth (Neigh.), F.R.G.	63	51.18 N	6.44 E
Kaitaia, N. Z. (kä-ē-tä'ē-á)	217	35.30 S	173.28 E
Kaiwi Chan., Hi. (käē-wē)	106a	21.10 N	157.38 W
Kaiyuan, China (kū-yuän)	203	23.42 N	103.20 E
Kaiyuan, China	202	42.30 N	124.00 E
Kaiyuh Mts., Ak. (kī-yōō')	107	64.25 N	157.38 W
Kajaani, Fin. (kä'yá-nē)	158	64.15 N	27.16 E
Kajang, Gunong (Mt.), Mala.	191b	2.47 N	104.05 E
Kajiki, Jap. (kä'jē-kē)	205	31.44 N	130.41 E
Kakhovka, Sov. Un. (kä-kôf'ká)	175	46.46 N	33.32 E
Kakhovskoye (L.), Sov. Un. (ká-kôf'skô-yē)	175	47.21 N	33.33 E
Kākināda, India	193	16.58 N	82.18 E
Kaktovik, Ak. (kăk-tō'vĭk)	107	70.08 N	143.51 W
Kakwa (R.), Can. (kăk'wá)	99	54.00 N	118.55 W
Kalach, Sov. Un. (ká-lách')	179	50.15 N	40.55 E
Kaladan (R.), Bur.	198	21.07 N	93.04 E
Kalahari Des., Bots. (kä-lä-hä'rē)	226	23.00 S	22.03 E
Kalama (R.), Wa.	118c	46.03 N	122.47 W
Kalama, Wa. (ká-lăm'á)	118c	46.01 N	122.50 W
Kalámai, Grc. (kä-lä-mī')	173	37.04 N	22.08 E
Kalamákion, Grc.	66d	37.55 N	23.43 E
Kalamazoo, Mi. (kăl-á-má-zōō')	110	42.20 N	85.40 W
Kalamazoo (R.), Mi.	110	42.35 N	86.00 W
Kalanchak, Sov. Un. (kä-län-chäk')	175	46.17 N	33.14 E
Kalapana, Hi. (kä-lä-pá'nä)	106a	19.25 N	155.00 W
Kalar (Mtn.), Iran	192	31.43 N	51.41 E
Kalāt, Pak. (kŭ-lät')	196	29.05 N	66.36 E
Kalatoa, Pulau (I.), Indon.	206	7.22 S	122.30 E
Kalemie (Albertville), Zaire	231	5.56 S	29.12 E
Kalgan, see Zhangjiakou			
Kalgoorlie, Austl. (kăl-gōōr'lē)	214	30.45 S	121.35 E
Kaliakra, Nos (Pt.), Rom.	161	43.25 N	28.42 E
Kalima, Zaire	231	2.34 S	26.37 E
Kalina (Neigh.), Zaire	71c	4.18 S	15.16 E
Kalinin (Oblast), Sov. Un.	174	56.50 N	33.08 E
Kalinin (Tver), Sov. Un. (kä-lē'nēn) (tvĕr)	174	56.52 N	35.57 E
Kaliningrad (Königsberg), Sov. Un. (kä-lē-nēn'grät) (kû'nēks-bĕrgh)	165	54.42 N	20.32 E
Kaliningrad, Sov. Un. (kä-lē-nēn'grät)	182b	55.55 N	37.49 E
Kalinkovichi, Sov. Un. (kä-lēn-ko-vē'chē)	175	52.07 N	29.19 E
Kalispel Ind. Res., Wa. (kăl-ĭ-spĕl')	116	48.25 N	117.30 W
Kalispell, Mt. (kăl'ĭ-spĕl)	117	48.12 N	114.18 W
Kalisz, Pol. (kä'lēsh)	167	51.45 N	18.05 E
Kaliua, Tan.	231	5.04 S	31.48 E
Kalixälven (R.), Swe.	158	67.12 N	22.00 E
Kālkāji (Neigh.), India	67d	28.33 N	77.16 E
Kalksburg (Neigh.), Aus.	66e	48.08 N	16.15 E
Kalkum, F.R.G.	63	51.18 N	6.46 E
Kallithéa, Grc.	66d	37.57 N	23.42 E
Kalmar, Swe. (käl'mär)	164	56.40 N	16.19 E
Kalmarsund (Sd.), Swe. (käl'mär)	164	56.30 N	16.17 E
Kal'mius (R.), Sov. Un. (käl''myōōs)	175	47.15 N	37.38 E
Kalmthout, Bel.	157a	51.23 N	4.28 E
Kalmyk A. S. S. R., Sov. Un. (kal'mĭk)	179	46.56 N	46.00 E
Kalocsa, Hung. (kä'lô-chä)	167	46.32 N	19.00 E
Kalohi Chan., Hi. (kä-lō'hī)	106a	20.55 N	157.15 W
Kaloko, Zaire	231	6.47 S	25.48 E
Kalomo, Zambia (kä-lō'mō)	231	17.02 S	26.30 E
Kalsubai Mt., India	196	24.43 N	73.47 E
Kaltenkirchen, F.R.G. (käl'tĕn-kēr-kĕn)	157c	53.50 N	9.57 E
Kālu (R.), India	197b	19.18 N	73.14 E
Kaluga (Oblast), Sov. Un.	174	54.10 N	34.30 E
Kaluga, Sov. Un. (kà-lōō'gä)	174	54.29 N	36.12 E
Kalundborg, Den. (kà-lōōn''bôr')	164	55.42 N	11.07 E
Kalush, Sov. Un. (kä'lōōsh)	167	49.02 N	24.24 E
Kalvarija, Sov. Un. (käl-vä-rē'yá)	165	54.24 N	23.17 E
Kalwa, India	197b	19.12 N	72.59 E
Kal'ya, Sov. Un. (käl'yá)	182a	60.17 N	59.58 E
Kalyān, India	197b	19.16 N	73.07 E
Kalyazin, Sov. Un. (käl-yá'zĕn)	174	57.13 N	37.55 E
Kalyma (R.), Sov. Un.	181	66.32 N	152.46 E
Kama (L.), Sov. Un.	178	55.28 N	51.00 E
Kama (R.), Sov. Un. (kä'mä)	178	56.10 N	53.50 E
Kamaishi, Jap. (kä'mä-ē'shē)	204	39.16 N	142.03 E
Kamakura, Jap. (kä'mä-kōō'rä)	205a	35.19 N	139.33 E
Kamarān (I.), P. D. R. of Yem.	192	15.19 N	41.47 E
Kāmārhāti, India	196a	22.41 N	88.23 E
Kamata (Neigh.), Jap.	69a	35.33 N	139.43 E
Kambove, Zaire (käm-bō'vē)	226	10.58 S	26.43 E
Kamchatka (R.), Sov. Un.	181	54.15 N	158.38 E
Kamchatka, P-Ov (Pen.), Sov. Un.	181	55.19 N	157.45 E
Kāmdebpur, India	67a	22.54 N	88.20 E
Kameari (Neigh.), Jap.	69a	35.46 N	139.51 E
Kameido (Neigh.), Jap.	69a	35.42 N	139.50 E
Kamen, F.R.G. (kä'mĕn)	169c	51.35 N	7.40 E
Kamenets-Podol'skiy, Sov. Un. (ká-mā'nĕts pô-dôl'skĭ)	175	48.41 N	26.34 E
Kamenjak, Rt (C.), Yugo. (kä'mĕ-nyäk)	172	44.45 N	13.57 E
Kamenka, Sov. Un. (kä-mĕŋ'ká)	175	48.02 N	28.43 E
Kamenka, Sov. Un.	167	50.06 N	24.20 E
Kamen'-na-Obi, Sov. Un. (kä-mĭny'nŭ ô'bē)	180	53.43 N	81.28 E
Kamensk-Shakhtinskiy, Sov. Un. (kä'mĕnsk shäk'tĭn-skĭ)	175	48.17 N	40.16 E
Kamensk-Ural'skiy, Sov. Un. (kä'mĕnsk ōō-räl'skĭ)	182a	56.27 N	61.55 E
Kamenz, G.D.R. (kä'mĕnts)	166	51.16 N	14.05 E
Kameoka, Jap. (kä'mā-ōkä)	205b	35.01 N	135.35 E
Kāmet (Mt.), India	196	35.50 N	79.42 E
Kamiakatsuka (Neigh.), Jap.	69a	35.46 N	139.39 E
Kamiasao, Jap.	69a	35.35 N	139.30 E
Kamień Pomorski, Pol.	166	53.57 N	14.48 E
Kamiishihara, Jap.	69a	35.39 N	139.32 E
Kamikitazawa (Neigh.), Jap.	69a	35.40 N	139.38 E
Kamikoma, Jap. (kä'mē-kō'mä)	205b	34.45 N	135.50 E
Kamina, Zaire	230	8.44 S	25.00 E
Kaministikwia (R.), Can. (ká-mĭ-nĭ-stĭk'wĭ-á)	115	48.40 N	89.41 W
Kamioyamada, Jap.	69a	35.35 N	139.24 E
Kamitsuruma, Jap.	69a	35.31 N	139.25 E
Kamituga, Zaire	231	3.04 S	28.11 E
Kamloops, Can. (kăm'lōōps)	99	50.40 N	120.20 W
Kamoshida (Neigh.), Jap.	69a	35.34 N	139.30 E
Kampala, Ug. (käm-pä'lä)	231	0.19 N	32.25 E
Kampar (R.), Indon. (käm'pär)	206	0.30 N	101.30 E
Kampene, Zaire	230	3.36 S	26.40 E
Kampenhout, Bel.	157a	50.56 N	4.33 E
Kamp-Lintfort, F.R.G. (kämp-lĕnt'fōrt)	169c	51.30 N	6.34 E
Kampong Kranji, Singapore	67c	1.26 N	103.46 E
Kampong Loyang, Singapore	67c	1.22 N	103.58 E
Kâmpóng Saôm, Kamp.	206	10.40 N	103.50 E
Kampong Tanjong Keling, Singapore	67c	1.18 N	103.42 E
Kâmpóng Thum, Kamp. (kŏm'pŏng-tŏm)	206	12.41 N	104.29 E
Kâmpôt, Kamp. (käm'pōt)	206	10.41 N	104.07 E
Kamp R., Aus. (kämp)	166	48.30 N	15.45 E
Kampuchea, Asia	206	12.15 N	104.00 E
Kamsack, Can. (kăm'săk)	101	51.34 N	101.54 W
Kamskoye (Res.), Sov. Un.	178	59.08 N	56.30 E
Kamskoye Vdkhr. (Res.), Sov. Un.	182a	59.03 N	56.48 E
Kamudilo, Zaire	231	7.42 S	27.18 E
Kamuela, Hi.	106a	20.01 N	155.40 W
Kamuk, Cerro (Mt.), C. R. (sĕ'r-rô-kä-mōō'k)	133	9.18 N	83.02 W
Kamu Misaki (C.), Jap. (kä'mōō mē-sä'kē)	204	43.25 N	139.35 E
Kamyshevatskaya, Sov. Un. (ká-mwĕsh'ĕ-vät'skä-yá)	175	46.24 N	37.58 E
Kamyshin, Sov. Un. (kä-mwēsh'ĭn)	179	50.08 N	45.20 E
Kamyshlov, Sov. Un. (kä-mēsh'lôf)	178	56.50 N	62.32 E
Kan (R.), Sov. Un. (kän)	180	56.30 N	94.17 E
Kanab, Ut. (kăn'ăb)	121	37.00 N	112.30 W
Kanabeki, Sov. Un. (ká-nä'byĕ-kĭ)	182a	57.48 N	57.16 E
Kanab Plat., Az.	121	36.31 N	112.55 W
Kanaga (I.), Ak. (kă-nă'gà)	107a	52.02 N	177.38 W
Kanagawa (Pref.), Jap. (kä'nä-gä'wä)	205a	35.29 N	139.32 E
Kanai, Jap.	69a	35.35 N	139.28 E
Kanā'is, Ra's al (C.), Egypt	161	31.14 N	28.08 E
Kanamachi, Jap. (kä-nä-mä'chē)	205a	35.46 N	139.52 E
Kanamori, Jap.	69a	35.32 N	139.28 E
Kananga (Luluabourg), Zaire (lōō'lōō-a-bōōrg')	230	6.14 S	22.17 E
Kananikol'skoye, Sov. Un. (ká-ná-nĭ-kôl'skô-yĕ)	182a	52.48 N	57.29 E
Kanasín, Mex. (kä-nä-sē'n)	132a	20.54 N	89.31 W
Kanatak, Ak. (kă-nă'tŏk)	107	57.35 N	155.48 W
Kanawha (R.), U. S. (ká-nô'wá)	109	37.55 N	81.50 W
Kanaya, Jap. (kä-nä'yä)	205a	35.10 N	139.49 E
Kanazawa, Jap. (kä'ná-zä'wá)	205	36.34 N	136.38 E
Kānchenjunga (Mtn.), India-Nep. (kĭn-chĭn-jōōn'gá)	196	27.30 N	88.18 E
Kānchipuram, India	197	12.55 N	79.43 E
Kanda Kanda, Zaire (kän'dá kän'dá)	230	6.56 S	23.36 E

ăt; finăl; rāte; senâte; ärm; åsk; sofá; fâre; ch-choose; dh-as th in other; bē; ēvent; bĕt; recĕnt; cratēr; g-gō; gh-guttural g; bĭt; ĭ-short neutral; rīde; ĸ-guttural k as ch in German ich;

PLACE (Pronounciation)	PAGE	Lat. °′	Long. °′
Kandalaksha, Sov. Un. (kȧn-dȧ-lȧk'shȧ)	178	67.10 N	33.05 E
Kandalakshskiy Zaliv (B.), Sov. Un.	178	66.20 N	35.00 E
Kandava, Sov. Un. (kän'dȧ-vȧ)	165	57.03 N	22.45 E
Kandi, Benin (käɴ-dē')	229	11.08 N	2.56 E
Kandiāro, Pak.	196	27.09 N	68.12 E
Kandla, India (kŭnd'lŭ)	196	23.00 N	70.20 E
Kandy, Sri Lanka (kän'dē)	197	7.18 N	80.42 E
Kane, Pa. (kān)	111	41.40 N	78.50 W
Kaneohe, Hi. (kä-nā-ō'hā)	106a	21.25 N	157.47 W
Kaneohe B., Hi.	106a	21.32 N	157.40 W
Kanëv, Sov. Un. (kä-nyôf')	175	49.46 N	31.27 E
Kanevskaya, Sov. Un. (kȧ-nyĕf'skȧ)	175	46.07 N	38.58 E
Kanevskoye Vdkhr. (Res.), Sov. Un.	179	50.10 N	30.40 E
Kangaroo (I.), Austl. (kăŋ-gȧ-rōō')	216	36.05 S	137.05 E
Kangaroo Ground, Austl.	70b	37.41 S	145.13 E
Kangāvar, Iran (kŭŋ'gā-vär)	192	34.37 N	46.45 E
Kangding, China (käŋ-dĭŋ)	198	30.15 N	101.58 E
Kangean, Kepulauan (I.), Indon. (käŋ'gē-än)	206	6.50 S	116.22 E
Kanggye, Kor. (käng'gyĕ)	204	40.55 N	126.40 E
Kanghwa (I.), Kor. (käng'hwä)	204	37.38 N	126.00 E
Kangnŭng, Kor. (käng'nōō ng)	204	37.42 N	128.50 E
Kango, Gabon (käɴ-gō)	230	0.09 N	10.08 E
Kangowa, Zaire	230	9.55 S	22.48 E
Kaningo, Ken.	231	0.49 S	38.32 E
Kanin Nos, Mys (G.), Sov. Un.	178	68.40 N	44.00 E
Kanin, P-Ov. (Pen.), Sov. Un. (kȧ-nēn')	178	68.00 N	45.00 E
Kanjiža, Yugo. (kä'nyē-zhä)	173	46.05 N	20.02 E
Kankakee, Il. (kăŋ-kȧ-kē')	113a	41.07 N	87.53 W
Kankakee (R.), Il.	110	41.15 N	88.15 W
Kankan, Gui. (käɴ-käɴ) (kän-kän')	228	10.23 N	9.18 W
Kannapolis, NC (kăn-ăp'ô-lĭs)	127	35.30 N	80.38 W
Kannoura, Jap. (kän'nō-ōō'rä)	205	33.34 N	134.18 E
Kano, Nig. (kä'nō)	229	12.00 N	8.30 E
Kanonkop (Mtn.), S. Afr.	226a	33.49 S	18.37 E
Kanopolis Res., Ks. (kăn-ŏp'ô-lĭs)	122	38.44 N	98.01 W
Kānpur, India (kän'pûr)	196	26.00 N	82.45 E
Kansas (State), U. S. (kăn'zȧs)	108	38.30 N	99.40 W
Kansas (R.), Ks.	123	39.08 N	95.52 W
Kansas City, Ks.	119f	39.06 N	94.39 W
Kansas City, Mo.	119f	39.05 N	94.35 W
Kansk, Sov. Un.	180	56.14 N	95.43 E
Kansŏng, Kor.	204	38.09 N	128.29 E
Kantang, Thai. (kän'täng')	206	7.26 N	99.28 E
Kantchari, Burkina	228	12.29 N	1.31 E
Kanton (I.), Oceania	208	3.50 S	174.00 E
Kantunilkin, Mex. (kän-tōō-nēl-kē'n)	132a	21.07 N	87.30 W
Kanzaki (R.), Jap.	69b	34.42 N	135.25 E
Kanzhakovskiy Kamen Gora, (Mt.), Sov. Un. (kȧn-zhȧ'kôvs-kēē kȧmĭen)	182a	59.38 N	59.12 E
Kaohsiung, Taiwan (kä-ō-syōōng')	203	22.35 N	120.25 E
Kaolack, Senegal	228	14.09 N	16.04 W
Kaouar (Oasis), Niger	225	19.16 N	13.09 E
Kaoyu Hu (L.), China (kä'ō-yōō'hōō)	203	32.42 N	118.40 E
Kapaa, Hi.	106a	22.06 N	159.20 W
Kapal, Sov. Un. (kȧ-päl')	180	45.13 N	79.08 E
Kapanga, Zaire	230	8.21 S	22.35 E
Kapchagay, Sov. Un.	191	43.55 N	77.45 E
Kapellen, F.R.G.	63	51.25 N	6.35 E
Kapfenberg, Aus. (käp'fĕn-bĕrgh)	166	47.27 N	15.16 E
Kapiri Mposhi, Zambia	231	13.58 S	28.41 E
Kapoeta, Sud.	225	4.45 N	33.35 E
Kaposvár, Hung. (kô'pôsh-vär)	167	46.21 N	17.45 E
Kapotn'a (Neigh.), Sov. Un.	66b	55.38 N	37.48 E
Kapsan, Kor. (käp'sän')	204	40.59 N	128.22 E
Kapuskasing, Can.	97	49.28 N	82.22 W
Kapuskasing (R.), Can.	102	48.55 N	82.55 W
Kapustin Yar, Sov. Un. (kä'pōōs-tĕn yär')	179	48.30 N	45.40 E
Kaputar, Mt., Austl. (kă-pû-tăr)	216	30.11 S	150.11 E
Kapuvár, Hung. (kô'pōō-vär)	166	47.35 N	17.02 E
Kara (R.), Sov. Un.	178	68.30 N	65.20 E
Kara, Sov. Un. (kärȧ)	180	68.42 N	65.30 E
Karabalā', Iraq (kŭr'bȧ-lä)	192	32.31 N	43.58 E
Karabanovo, Sov. Un. (kä'rä-bȧ-nō-vô)	182b	56.19 N	38.43 E
Karabash, Sov. Un. (kó-rȧ-bäsh')	182a	55.27 N	60.14 E
Kara-Bogaz-Gol, Zaliv (B.), Sov. Un. (kȧ-rä' bŭ-gäs')	179	41.30 N	53.40 E
Karachev, Sov. Un. (kȧ-rȧ-chôf')	174	53.08 N	34.54 E
Karāchi, Pak.	196	24.59 N	68.56 E
Karacumy (Des.), Sov. Un.	155	39.08 N	59.53 E
Karaganda, Sov. Un. (kȧ-rȧ-gän'dä)	180	49.42 N	73.18 E
Karaidel, Sov. Un. (kä'rī-dĕl)	182a	55.52 N	56.54 E
Kara-Khobda (R.), Sov. Un. (kä-rȧ κôb'dȧ)	179	50.40 N	55.00 E
Karakoram Pass, India-Pak.	193	35.35 N	77.45 E
Karakoram Ra., India-Pak. (kä'rä kō'rōōm)	198	35.24 N	76.38 E
Karakorum (Ruins), Mong.	198	47.25 N	102.22 E
Karakumy (Des.), Sov. Un. (kara-kum)	176	40.00 N	57.00 E
Karaman, Tur. (kä-rä-män')	179	37.10 N	33.00 E
Karamay, China (kär-äm-ā)	198	45.37 N	84.53 E
Karamea Bight, N.Z. (kȧ-rȧ-mē'ȧ bīt)	217	41.20 S	171.30 E
Kara Sea, see Karskoye More			
Karashahr (Yanqi), China (kä-rä-shä-är) (yän-chyē)	198	42.14 N	86.28 E
Karatsu, Jap. (kä'rȧ-tsōō)	205	33.28 N	129.59 E
Karaul, Sov. Un. (kä-rä-ōōl')	180	70.13 N	83.46 E
Karave, India	67e	19.01 N	73.01 E
Karawanken Mts., Aus.	166	46.32 N	14.07 E
Karcag, Hung. (kär'tsäg)	167	47.18 N	20.58 E
Kardhitsa, Grc.	173	39.23 N	21.57 E
Kärdla, Sov. Un. (kĕrd'lȧ)	165	58.59 N	22.44 E
Karelian (A. S. S. R.), Sov. Un.	176	62.30 N	32.35 E
Karema, Tan.	231	6.49 S	30.26 E
Kargat, Sov. Un. (kär-gät')	180	55.17 N	80.07 E
Karghalik, see Yecheng			
Kargopol', Sov. Un. (kär-gō-pōl'')	178	61.30 N	38.50 E
Kariaí, Grc.	173	40.14 N	24.15 E
Kariba, L., Afr.	231	17.15 S	27.55 E
Karibib, Namibia (kȧr'ȧ-bĭb)	226	21.55 S	15.50 E
Kārikāl, India (kä-rē-käl')	197	10.58 N	79.49 E
Karimata, Pulau-Pulau (Is.), Indon. (kä-rē-mä'tȧ)	206	1.08 S	108.10 E
Karimata, Selat (Karimata Strait), Indon.	206	1.00 S	107.10 E
Karimun Besar (I.), Indon.	191b	1.10 N	103.28 E
Karimunjawa, Kepulauan (Is.), Indon. (kä'rē-mōōn-yä'vä)	206	5.36 S	110.15 E
Karin, Som. (kȧr'ĭn)	223a	10.43 N	45.50 E
Karkaralinsk, Sov. Un. (kär-kär-ä-lĕnsk')	180	49.18 N	75.28 E
Karkar Dūmān (Neigh.), India	67d	28.39 N	77.18 E
Karkar I., Pap. N. Gui. (kär'kär)	207	4.50 S	146.45 E
Karkheh (R.), Iran	192	32.45 N	47.50 E
Karkinitskiy Zaliv (B.), Sov. Un. (kär-kē-net'skĭ-ē zä'lĭf)	175	45.50 N	32.45 E
Karl-Marx-Stadt (Chemnitz), G.D.R.	166	50.48 N	12.53 E
Karlobag, Yugo. (kär-lō-bäg')	172	44.30 N	15.03 E
Karlovac, Yugo. (kär'lô-vȧts)	172	45.29 N	15.16 E
Karlovka, Sov. Un. (kȧr'lôv-kȧ)	175	49.26 N	35.08 E
Karlovo, Bul. (kär'lô-vō)	173	42.39 N	24.48 E
Karlovy Vary, Czech. (kär'lô-vē vä'rē)	166	50.13 N	12.53 E
Karlshamn, Swe. (kärls'häm)	164	56.11 N	14.50 E
Karlskrona, Swe. (kärls'krō-nä)	164	56.10 N	15.33 E
Karlsruhe, F.R.G. (kärls'rōō-ĕ)	166	49.00 N	8.23 E
Karlstad, Swe. (kärl'städ)	164	59.25 N	13.28 E
Karluk, Ak. (kär'lŭk)	107	57.30 N	154.22 W
Karmøy (I.), Nor. (kärm-ûe)	164	59.14 N	5.00 E
Karnap, F.R.G.	63	51.09 N	6.56 E
Karnataka (State), India	197	14.55 N	75.00 E
Karnobat, Bul. (kär-nô'bät)	173	42.39 N	26.59 E
Kärnten (Carinthia) (State), Aus. (kĕrn'tĕn)	166	46.55 N	13.42 E
Karolinenhof (Neigh.), G.D.R.	65a	52.23 N	13.38 E
Karonga, Malawi (kȧ-rōŋ'gȧ)	226	9.52 S	33.57 E
Kárpathos (I.), Grc.	161	35.34 N	27.26 E
Karpinsk, Sov. Un. (kär'pĭnsk)	182a	59.46 N	60.00 E
Kars, Tur. (kärs)	179	40.35 N	43.00 E
Karsakpay, Sov. Un. (kär-säk-pī')	180	47.47 N	67.07 E
Kārsava, Sov. Un. (kär'sä-vä)	174	56.46 N	27.39 E
Karshi, Sov. Un. (kär'shē)	193	38.30 N	66.08 E
Karskiye Vorota, Proliv (Str.), Sov. Un.	180	70.30 N	58.07 E
Karskoye More (Kara Sea), Sov. Un.	180	74.00 N	68.00 E
Kartaly, Sov. Un. (kȧr'tá lē)	182a	53.05 N	60.40 E
Karunagapalli, India	197	9.09 N	76.34 E
Karvina, Czech.	167	49.50 N	18.30 E
Kasaan, Ak.	98	55.32 N	132.24 E
Kasai (Neigh.), Jap.	69a	35.39 N	139.53 E
Kasai (R.), Zaire	230	3.45 S	19.10 E
Kasama, Zambia (kȧ-sä'mȧ)	231	10.13 S	31.12 E
Kasanga, Tan. (kȧ-säŋ'gȧ)	231	8.28 S	31.09 E
Kasaoka, Jap. (kä'sȧ-ō'kȧ)	205	34.33 N	133.29 E
Kasba-Tadla, Mor. (käs'bȧ-täd'lȧ)	224	32.37 N	5.57 W
Kasempa, Zambia (kȧ-sĕm'pȧ)	231	13.27 S	25.50 E
Kasenga, Zaire (kȧ-sĕŋ'gȧ)	231	10.22 S	28.38 E
Kasese, Ug.	231	0.10 N	30.05 E
Kasese, Zaire	231	1.38 S	27.07 E
Kāshān, Iran (kä-shän')	192	33.52 N	51.15 E
Kashgar, see Kashi			
Kashi (Kashgar), China (kä-shr) (käsh-gär)	198	39.29 N	76.00 E
Kashihara, Jap. (kä'shē-hä'rä)	205b	34.31 N	135.48 E
Kashiji Pln. Zambia	230	13.25 S	22.30 E
Kashin, Sov. Un. (kä-shēn')	174	57.20 N	37.38 E
Kashira, Sov. Un. (kä-shē'rȧ)	174	54.49 N	38.11 E
Kashiwa, Jap. (kä'shē-wä)	205a	35.51 N	139.58 E
Kashiwara, Jap.	205b	34.35 N	135.38 E
Kashiwazaki, Jap. (kä'shē-wä-zä'kē)	178	37.06 N	138.17 E
Kāshmar, Iran	195	35.12 N	58.27 E
Kashmir (Disputed Reg.), see Jammu and Kashmir			
Kashmor, Pak.	196	28.33 N	69.34 E
Kashtak, Sov. Un. (käsh'tȧk)	182a	55.18 N	61.25 E
Kasimov, Sov. Un. (kȧ-sē'môf)	174	54.56 N	41.23 E
Kaskanak, Ak. (kăs-kă'năk)	107	60.00 N	158.00 W
Kaskaskia (R.), Il. (kăs-kăs'kĭ-ȧ)	110	39.10 N	88.50 W
Kaskattama (R.), Can. (kăs-kȧ-tă'mȧ)	101	56.28 N	90.55 W
Kaskinen, see Kaskö			
Kaskö (Kaskinen), Fin. (käs'kû) (käs'kē-nĕn)	165	62.24 N	21.18 E
Kasli, Sov. Un. (käs'lĭ)	182a	55.54 N	60.46 E
Kasongo, Zaire (kä-sôŋ'gō)	226	4.31 S	26.42 E
Kásos (I.), Grc.	161	35.20 N	26.55 E
Kassalā, Sud. (kä-sä'lä)	225	15.26 N	36.28 E
Kassándras, Kólpos (G.), Grc.	173	40.10 N	23.35 E
Kassel, F.R.G. (käs'ĕl)	166	51.19 N	9.30 E
Kassinga. Ang.	226	15.05 S	16.15 E
Kasslerfeld (Neigh.), F.R.G.	63	51.26 N	6.45 E
Kasson, Mn. (kăs'ŭn)	115	44.01 N	92.45 W
Kastamonu, Tur. (kä-stȧ-mō'nōō)	179	41.20 N	33.50 E
Kastoría, Grc. (kȧs-tō'rĭ-ȧ)	173	40.28 N	21.17 E
Kasūr, Pak.	196	31.10 N	74.29 E
Kataba, Zambia	230	16.05 S	25.10 E
Katahdin, Mt., Me. (kȧ-tä'dĭn)	104	45.56 N	68.57 W
Katanga (Reg.), Zaire (kȧ-täŋ'gȧ)	226	8.30 S	25.00 E
Katanning, Austl. (kȧ-tăn'ĭng)	214	33.45 S	117.45 E
Katano, Jap.	69b	34.48 N	135.42 E
Katav-Ivonovski, Sov. Un. (kä'tăf ĭ-vä'nôfsk)	182a	54.46 N	58.13 E
Katayama (Neigh.), Jap.	69a	35.46 N	139.34 E
Kateninskiy, Sov. Un. (kȧtyĕ'nĭs-kĭ)	182a	53.12 N	61.05 E
Kateríni, Grc.	173	40.18 N	22.36 E
Katernberg (Neigh.), F.R.G.	63	51.29 N	7.04 E
Katete, Zambia	231	14.05 S	32.07 E
Katherine, Austl. (kăth'ēr-ĭn)	214	14.15 S	132.20 E
Kāthiāwār (Pen.), India (kä'tyȧ-wär')	196	22.10 N	70.20 E
Kathmandu, Nep. (kăt-măn-dōō')	196	27.49 N	85.21 E
Kathryn, Can. (kăth'rĭn)	95e	51.13 N	113.42 W
Kathryn, Ca.	119a	33.42 N	117.45 W
Katihār, India	196	25.39 N	87.39 E
Katiola, Ivory Coast	228	8.08 N	5.06 W
Katmai Natl. Park, Ak. (kăt'mī)	107	58.38 N	155.00 W
Katompi, Zaire	231	6.11 S	26.20 E
Katopa, Zaire	230	2.45 S	25.06 E
Katowice, Pol.	167	50.15 N	19.00 E
Katrineholm, Swe. (kȧ-trē'nĕ-hōlm)	164	59.01 N	16.10 E
Kātrīnā, Jabal (Mtn.), Egypt	225	28.43 N	34.00 E
Katsbakhskiy, Sov. Un. (kȧts-bäk'skĭ)	182a	52.57 N	59.37 E
Katsina, Nig. (kăt'sē-nȧ)	229	13.00 N	7.32 E
Katsura (R.), Jap. (kä'tsōō-rä)	205b	34.55 N	135.43 E
Katsushika (Neigh.), Jap.	69a	35.43 N	139.51 E
Katta-Kurgan, Sov. Un. (kȧ-tȧ-kōōr-gän')	180	39.45 N	66.42 E
Kattegat (Str.), Eur. (kăt'ĕ-gät)	164	56.57 N	11.25 E
Katternberg (Neigh.), F.R.G.	63	51.09 N	7.02 E
Katumba, Zaire	231	7.45 S	25.18 E
Katun' (R.), Sov. Un. (kȧ-tōōn')	180	51.30 N	86.18 E
Katwijkaan Zee, Neth.	157a	52.12 N	4.23 E
Kauai (I.), Hi.	106a	22.09 N	159.15 W
Kauai Chan., Hi. (kä-ōō-ä'ē)	106a	21.35 N	158.52 W
Kaufbeuren, F.R.G. (kouf'boi-rĕn)	166	47.52 N	10.38 E
Kaufman, Tx. (kôf'măn)	125	32.36 N	96.18 W
Kaukauna, Wi. (kô-kô'nȧ)	115	44.17 N	88.15 W
Kaulakahi Chan., Hi. (kä'ōō-lȧ-kä'hē)	106a	22.00 N	159.55 W
Kaulsdorf-Süd (Neigh.), G.D.R.	65a	52.29 N	13.34 E
Kaunakakai, Hi. (kä'ōō-nȧ-kä'kī)	106a	21.06 N	156.59 W
Kaunas (Kovno), Sov. Un. (kou'nȧs) (kôv'nō)	165	54.42 N	23.54 E
Kaura Namoda, Nig.	229	12.35 N	6.35 E
Kavajë, Alb. (kȧ-vä'yŭ)	173	41.11 N	19.36 E
Kavála, Grc. (kä-vä'lä)	173	40.55 N	24.24 E
Kavieng, Pap. N. Gui. (kä-vē-ĕng')	207	2.44 S	151.02 E
Kawagoe, Jap. (kä-wȧ-gō'ā)	205a	35.55 N	139.29 E
Kawaguchi, Jap. (kä-wä-gōō-chē)	205a	35.48 N	139.44 E
Kawaikini (Mtn.), Hi. (kä-wä'ē-kĭ-nī)	106a	22.05 N	159.33 W
Kawanishi, Jap. (kä-wä'nē-shē)	205b	34.49 N	135.26 E
Kawasaki, Jap. (kä-wä-sä'kē)	205a	35.32 N	139.43 E
Kawashima (Neigh.), Jap.	69a	35.28 N	139.35 E
Kawm Umbū, Egypt	223b	24.30 N	32.59 E
Kaxgar (R.), China	198	39.26 N	74.30 E
Kaya, Burkina (kä'yä)	228	13.05 N	1.05 W
Kayan (R.), Indon.	206	1.45 N	115.38 E
Kaycee, Wy. (kā-sē')	117	43.43 N	106.38 W
Kayes, Mali (kāz)	228	14.27 N	11.26 W
Kayseri, Tur. (kī'sĕ-rē)	179	38.45 N	35.20 E
Kaysville, Ut. (kāz'vĭl)	119b	41.02 N	111.56 W
Kazach'ye, Sov. Un.	181	70.46 N	135.47 E
Kazakh S.S.R., Sov. Un. (kȧ-zäk')	176	48.45 N	59.00 E
Kazan', Sov. Un. (kȧ-zän')	178	55.50 N	49.18 E
Kazanka, Sov. Un. (kȧ-zän'kȧ)	175	47.49 N	32.50 E
Kazanlŭk, Bul. (kȧ'zȧn-lĕk)	173	42.47 N	25.23 E
Kazatin, Sov. Un. (kȧ-zä'tēn)	175	49.43 N	28.50 E
Kazbek, Gora (Mt.), Sov. Un. (kȧz-bĕk')	179	42.45 N	44.30 E
Kāzerūn, Iran	192	29.37 N	51.44 E
Kazincbarcika, Hung. (kô'zĭnts-bôr-tsĭ-ko)	167	48.15 N	20.39 E
Kazungula, Zambia	231	17.45 S	25.20 E
Kazusa Kameyama, Jap. (kä-zōō-sä kä-mȧ'yä-mä)	205a	35.14 N	140.06 E
Kazym (R.), Sov. Un. (kä-zēm')	180	63.30 N	67.41 E
Kéa (I.), Grc.	173	37.36 N	24.13 E
Kealaikahiki Chan., Hi. (kā-ä'lä-ē-kä-hē'kē)	106a	20.38 N	157.00 W
Keansburg, NJ (kēnz'bûrg)	112a	40.26 N	74.08 W
Kearney, Ne. (kär'nĭ)	122	40.42 N	99.05 W
Kearny, NJ	112a	40.46 N	74.09 W
Kearsley, Eng.	64b	53.32 N	2.23 W
Keasey, Or. (kēz'ĭ)	118c	45.51 N	123.20 W
Keban Gölü (L.), Tur.	179	38.20 N	39.50 E
Kebayoran (Neigh.), Indon.	68k	6.12 S	106.46 E
Kebnekaise Mt., Swe. (kĕp'nĕ-kȧ-ēs'ĕ)	158	67.53 N	18.10 E
Kecskemét, Hung. (kĕch'kĕ-māt)	167	46.52 N	19.42 E
Kedah State, Mala. (kä'dä)	206	6.00 N	100.31 E
Kédainiai, Sov. Un. (kē-dī'nĭ-ĭ)	165	55.16 N	23.58 E
Kedgwick, Can. (kĕdj'wĭk)	104	47.39 N	67.21 W
Keenbrook, Ca. (kēn'brŏŏk)	119a	34.16 N	117.29 W
Keene, NH (kēn)	111	42.55 N	72.15 W
Keetmanshoop, Namibia (kāt'mȧns-hōp)	226	26.30 S	18.05 E
Keet Seel Ruin, Az. (kēt sēl)	121	36.46 N	110.32 W
Keewatin, Mn. (kē-wä'tĭn)	115	47.24 N	93.03 W
Keewatin, Dist. of, Can.	96	61.26 N	97.54 W
Kefallinía (Cephalonia) (I.), Grc.	173	38.08 N	20.58 E
Kefe, see Feodosiya			
Keffi, Nig. (kĕf'ē)	229	8.51 N	7.52 E
Ke-Ga, Mui (Pt.), Viet.	206	12.58 N	109.50 E
Kei (R.), S. Afr. (kā)	227c	32.57 S	26.50 E
Keila, Sov. Un. (kā'lȧ)	165	59.19 N	24.25 E
Keilor, Austl.	70b	37.43 S	144.50 E
Kei Mouth, S. Afr.	227c	32.40 S	28.23 E
Keiskammahoek, S. Afr. (kās'kämä-hōōk')	227c	32.42 S	27.11 E
Kéita, Bahr (R.), Chad.	229	9.30 N	19.17 E
Keitele (L.), Fin. (kā'tĕ-lĕ)	165	62.50 N	25.40 E
Kekaha, Hi.	106a	21.57 N	159.42 W
Kelafo, Eth.	223a	5.40 N	44.00 E
Kelang, Mala.	191b	3.20 N	101.27 E
Kelang (R.), Mala.	191b	3.00 N	101.40 E
Kelenföld (Neigh.), Hung.	66g	47.28 N	19.03 E
Kelkit (R.), Tur.	161	40.38 N	37.03 E
Keller, Tx. (kĕl'ēr)	119c	32.56 N	97.15 W
Kellinghusen, F.R.G. (kĕ'lĕng-hōō-zĕn)	157c	53.57 N	9.43 E
Kellogg, Id. (kĕl'ŏg)	116	47.32 N	116.07 W

PLACE (Pronounciation)	PAGE	Lat. °'	Long. °'
Kellyville, Austl.	70a	33.43 S	150.57 E
Kelme', Sov. Un. (kĕl-mȧ)	165	55.36 N	22.53 E
Kélo, Chad	229	9.19 N	15.48 E
Kelowna, Can.	99	49.53 N	119.29 W
Kelsey Bay, Can. (kĕl'sē)	98	50.24 N	125.57 W
Kelso, Wa.	118c	46.09 N	122.54 W
Keluang, Mala.	191b	2.01 N	103.19 E
Kelvedon Hatch, Eng.	62	51.40 N	0.16 E
Kem', Sov. Un. (kĕm)	178	65.00 N	34.48 E
Kemah, Tx. (kē'mȧ)	125a	29.32 N	95.01 W
Kemerovo, Sov. Un.	180	55.31 N	86.05 E
Kemi, Fin. (kā'mē)	158	65.48 N	24.38 E
Kemi (R.), Fin.	158	67.02 N	27.50 E
Kemigawa, Jap. (kĕ'mē-gä'wä)	205a	35.38 N	140.07 E
Kemijarvi, Fin. (kā'mē-yĕr-vē)	158	66.48 N	27.21 E
Kemi-joki (L.), Fin.	158	66.37 N	28.13 E
Kemmerer, Wy. (kém'ēr-ēr)	117	41.48 N	110.36 W
Kemminghausen (Neigh.), F.R.G.	63	51.34 N	7.29 E
Kemp (L.), Tx. (kĕmp)	122	33.55 N	99.22 W
Kempen, F.R.G. (kĕm'pĕn)	169c	51.22 N	6.25 E
Kempsey, Austl. (kĕmp'sē)	216	30.59 S	152.50 E
Kempt (L.), Can. (kĕmpt)	104	47.28 N	74.00 W
Kempten, F.R.G. (kĕmp'tĕn)	166	47.44 N	10.17 E
Kempton Park, S. Afr. (kĕmp'tŏn pärk)	227b	26.07 S	28.29 E
Kemsing, Eng.	62	51.18 N	0.14 E
Ken (R.), India	196	25.00 N	79.55 E
Kenai, Ak. (kĕ-nī')	107	60.38 N	151.18 W
Kenai Mts., Ak.	107	60.00 N	150.00 W
Kenai Pen, Ak.	107	64.40 N	150.18 W
Kenberma, Ma.	54a	42.17 N	70.52 W
Kendal, Eng. (kĕn'dȧl)	162	54.20 N	1.48 W
Kendal, S. Afr.	223d	26.03 S	28.58 E
Kendallville, In. (kĕn'dȧl-vĭl)	110	41.25 N	85.20 W
Kenedy, Tx. (kĕn'ĕ-dĭ)	119	28.49 N	97.50 W
Kenema, SL.	228	7.52 N	11.12 W
Kenilworth, Il.	58a	42.05 N	87.43 W
Kenilworth, NJ	55	40.41 N	74.18 W
Kenitra (Port Lyautey), Mor. (kĕ-nē'trȧ)	160	34.21 N	6.34 W
Kenley (Neigh.), Eng.	62	51.19 N	0.06 W
Kenmare, ND (kĕn-mâr')	114	48.41 N	102.05 W
Kenmore, NY (kĕn'mōr)	113c	42.58 N	78.53 W
Kennebec (R.), Me. (kĕn-ē-bĕk')	104	44.23 N	69.48 W
Kennebunk, Me. (kĕn-ē-buŋk')	104	43.24 N	70.33 W
Kennedale, Tx. (kĕn'-ē-dāl)	119c	32.38 N	97.13 W
Kennedy, C., see Canaveral			
Kennedy, Mt., Can.	107	60.25 N	138.50 W
Kenner, La. (kĕn'ēr)	125	29.58 N	90.15 W
Kennett, Mo. (kĕn'ĕt)	123	36.14 N	90.01 W
Kennewick, Wa. (kĕn'ē-wĭk)	116	46.12 N	119.06 W
Kenney Dam, Can.	98	53.37 N	124.58 W
Kennydale, Wa. (kĕn-nē'dāl)	118a	47.31 N	122.12 W
Kénogami, Can. (kĕn-ô'gä-mē)	103	48.26 N	71.14 W
Kenogamissi L., Can.	102	48.15 N	81.31 W
Keno Hill, Can.	107	63.58 N	135.18 W
Kenora, Can. (kē-nō'rȧ)	101	49.47 N	94.29 W
Kenosha, Wi. (kē-nō'shȧ)	113a	42.34 N	87.50 W
Kenova, WV (kē-nō'vȧ)	110	38.20 N	82.35 W
Kensico Res., NY (kĕn'sĭ-kō)	112a	41.08 N	73.45 W
Kensington, Austl.	70a	33.55 S	151.14 E
Kensington, Ca.	58b	37.54 N	122.16 W
Kensington, Md.	56d	39.02 N	77.03 W
Kensington (Neigh.), NY.	55	40.39 N	73.58 W
Kensington (Neigh.), Pa.	56b	39.58 N	75.08 W
Kensington (Neigh.), S. Afr.	71b	26.12 S	28.06 E
Kensington and Chelsea (Neigh.), Eng.	62	51.29 N	0.11 W
Kent, Oh. (kĕnt)	110	41.05 N	81.20 W
Kent, Wa.	118a	47.23 N	122.14 W
Kentani, S. Afr. (kĕnt-änĭ')	227c	32.31 S	28.19 E
Kentland, In. (kĕnt'lȧnd)	110	40.50 N	87.25 W
Kentland, Md.	56d	38.55 N	76.53 W
Kenton, Oh. (kĕn'tŭn)	110	40.40 N	83.35 W
Kent Pen, Can.	96	68.28 N	108.10 W
Kentucky (State), U. S. (kĕn-tŭk'ĭ)	109	37.30 N	87.35 W
Kentucky (L.), U. S.	109	36.20 N	88.50 W
Kentucky (R.), U. S.	109	38.15 N	85.01 W
Kentwood, La. (kĕnt'wo͝od)	125	30.56 N	90.31 W
Kenya, Afr. (kĕn'yȧ)	222	1.00 N	36.53 E
Kenya, Mt., see Kirinyaga			
Kenyon, Mn. (kĕn'yŭn)	115	44.15 N	92.58 W
Keokuk, Ia. (kē'ō-kŭk)	123	40.24 N	91.34 W
Keoma, Can. (kē-ō'mȧ)	95e	51.13 N	113.39 W
Keon Park, Austl.	70b	37.42 S	145.01 E
Kepenkeck L., Can.	105	48.13 N	54.45 W
Kepno, Pol. (kăŋ'pnō)	167	51.17 N	17.59 E
Kerala (State), India	197	16.38 N	76.00 E
Kerang, Austl. (kē-răng')	216	35.32 S	143.58 E
Keratsinion, Grc.	66d	37.58 N	23.37 E
Kerch', Sov. Un. (kĕrch)	175	45.20 N	36.26 E
Kerchenskiy Proliv (Str.) (Kerch Str.), Sov. Un. (kĕr-chĕn'skĭ prô'lĭf)	175	45.08 N	36.35 E
Kerempe Burun (C.), Tur.	179	42.00 N	33.20 E
Keren, Eth.	225	15.46 N	38.28 E
Kerguélen, Îles, Ind. O. (kĕr'gā-lĕn)	232	49.50 S	69.30 E
Kericho, Ken.	231	0.22 S	35.17 E
Kerinci, Gunung (Mtn.), Indon.	206	1.45 S	101.18 E
Keriya (R.), China (kē'rē-yä)	198	37.13 N	81.59 E
Keriya, see Yütian			
Kerkebet, Eth.	195	16.18 N	37.24 E
Kerkenna, Îles (I.), Tun. (kĕr'kĕn-nä)	225	34.49 N	11.37 E
Kerki, Sov. Un. (kĕr'kē)	193	37.52 N	65.15 E
Kérkira, Grc.	173	39.36 N	19.56 E
Kérkira (I.), Grc.	173	39.33 N	19.36 E
Kermadec Is., N. Z. (kēr-măd'ĕk)	208	30.30 S	177.00 E
Kermadec Tonga Trench, Oceania (kēr-măd'ĕk tŏŋ'gȧ)	208	23.00 S	172.30 W
Kermān, Iran (kĕr-män')	192	30.23 N	57.08 E
Kermānshāh, see Bakhtarān			
Kern (R.), Ca.	120	35.31 N	118.37 W
Kern Can., Ca. (kûrn)	120	36.57 N	119.37 W
Kern, South Fork of (R.), Ca.	120	35.40 N	118.15 W
Kérouané, Gui.	228	9.16 N	9.01 W
Kerpen, F.R.G. (kĕr'pĕn)	169c	50.52 N	6.42 E
Kerrobert, Can.	100	51.53 N	109.13 W
Kerrville, Tx. (kûr'vĭl)	124	30.02 N	99.07 W
Kerulen (R.), Mong. (kĕr'o͞o-lĕn)	199	47.52 N	113.22 E
Kesagami L., Can.	103	50.23 N	80.15 W
Kesan, Tur. (kĕ'shán)	173	40.50 N	26.37 E
Keshan, China (kŭ-shän)	202	48.00 N	126.30 E
Kesour, Monts des (Mts.), Alg.	160	32.51 N	0.30 W
Kestell, S. Afr. (kĕs'tĕl)	223d	28.19 S	28.43 E
Keszthely, Hung. (kĕst'hĕl-lĭ)	167	46.46 N	17.12 E
Ket' (R.), Sov. Un. (kyĕt)	180	58.30 N	84.15 E
Keta, Ghana	224	6.00 N	1.00 E
Ketamputih, Indon.	191b	1.25 N	102.19 E
Ketapang, Indon. (kĕ-tȧ-päng')	206	2.00 S	109.57 E
Ketchikan, Ak. (kĕch-ĭ-kăn')	98	55.21 N	131.35 W
Ketrzyn, Pol. (kăŋ't'r-zĭn)	167	54.04 N	21.24 E
Kettering, Eng. (kĕt'ēr-ĭng)	156	52.23 N	0.43 W
Kettering, Oh.	110	39.40 N	84.15 W
Kettle (R.), Can.	99	49.40 N	119.00 W
Kettle (R.), Mn. (kĕt''l)	115	46.20 N	92.57 W
Kettwig, F.R.G. (kĕt'vēg)	169c	51.22 N	6.56 E
Kety, Pol. (kăŋ tĭ)	167	49.54 N	19.16 E
Ketzin, G.D.R. (kĕ'tzēn)	157b	52.29 N	12.51 E
Keuka (L.), NY (kē-ū'kȧ)	111	42.30 N	77.10 W
Kevelaer, F.R.G. (kĕ'fĕ-lär)	169c	51.35 N	6.15 E
Kew, Austl.	70b	37.49 S	145.02 E
Kew, S. Afr.	71b	26.08 S	28.06 E
Kewanee, Il. (kē-wä'nē)	115	41.15 N	89.55 W
Kewaunee, Wi. (kē-wô'nē)	115	44.27 N	87.33 W
Keweenaw B., Mi. (kē'wē-nô)	115	46.59 N	88.15 W
Keweenaw Pen., Mi.	115	47.28 N	88.12 W
Kew Gardens (P. Int.), Eng.	62	51.28 N	0.18 W
Keya Paha (R.), S.D. (kē-yȧ pä'hä)	114	43.11 N	100.10 W
Key Largo (I.), Fl.	127a	25.11 N	80.15 W
Keyport, NJ (kē'pōrt)	112a	40.26 N	74.12 W
Keyport, Wa.	118a	47.42 N	122.38 W
Keyser, WV (kī'sēr)	111	39.25 N	79.00 W
Key West, Fl. (kē wĕst')	127a	24.31 N	81.47 W
Kežmarok, Czech. (kĕzh'mȧ-rôk)	167	49.10 N	20.27 E
Khabarovo, Sov. Un. (kŭ-bȧr-ôvŏ)	180	69.31 N	60.41 E
Khabarovsk, Sov. Un. (кä-bä'rôfsk)	181	48.35 N	135.12 E
Khaïdhárion, Grc.	66d	37.33 N	22.53 E
Khajuri (Neigh.), India	67d	28.43 N	77.16 E
Khakass Aut. Oblast, Sov. Un.	180	52.32 N	89.33 E
Khalándrion, Grc.	66d	38.01 N	23.48 E
Khālāpur, India	197b	18.48 N	73.17 E
Khalkidhikí (Pen.), Grc.	173	40.30 N	23.18 E
Khalkís, Grc. (кȧl'kĭs)	173	38.28 N	23.38 E
Khal'mer-Yu, Sov. Un. (kŭl-myĕr'-yo͞o')	180	67.52 N	64.25 E
Khalturin, Sov. Un. (кäl'to͞o-rēn)	178	58.28 N	49.00 E
Khambhāt, G. of, India	196	21.20 N	72.27 E
Khammam, India	197	17.09 N	80.13 E
Khānābād, Afg.	196	36.43 N	69.11 E
Khānaqīn, Iraq	195	34.21 N	45.22 E
Khandwa, India	196	21.53 N	76.22 E
Khangai Mts., see Hangayn Nuruu			
Khanh-Hung, Viet.	206	9.45 N	105.50 E
Khaniá, Grc. (кä-nē'ȧ)	172a	35.29 N	24.04 E
Khaníon, Kólpos (G.), Grc.	172a	35.35 N	23.55 E
Khanka (L.), Sov. Un. (кän'kȧ)	199	45.09 N	133.28 E
Khānpur, Pak.	196	28.42 N	70.42 E
Khanty-Mansiysk, Sov. Un. (кŭn-te'mŭn-sēsk')	180	61.02 N	69.01 E
Khān Yūnus, Gaza Strip	191a	31.21 N	34.19 E
Kharagpur, India (kŭ-rŭg'po͝or)	196	22.26 N	87.21 E
Khardah, India	67a	22.44 N	88.22 E
Khar'kov (Oblast), Sov. Un.	175	49.33 N	35.55 E
Khar'kov, Sov. Un. (кär'kôf)	175	50.00 N	36.10 E
Kharlovka, Sov. Un.	178	68.47 N	37.20 E
Kharmanli, Bul. (кȧr-män'lē)	173	41.54 N	25.55 E
Khartoum (Al Kharṭūm), Sud.	225	15.34 N	32.36 E
Khāsh, Iran	192	28.08 N	61.08 E
Khāsh (R.), Afg.	192	32.30 N	64.27 E
Khasi Hills, India	196	25.38 N	91.55 E
Khaskovo, Bul. (кȧs'kô-vô)	173	41.56 N	25.32 E
Khatanga, Sov. Un. (кȧ-tän'gȧ)	181	71.48 N	101.47 E
Khatangskiy Zaliv (B.), Sov. Un. (kä-täŋ'g-skē)	181	73.45 N	108.30 E
Khayāla (Neigh.), India	67d	28.40 N	77.06 E
Khemis Miliana, Alg.	159	36.19 N	1.56 E
Kherson (Oblast), Sov. Un.	175	46.32 N	32.55 E
Kherson, Sov. Un. (кĕr-sôn')	175	46.38 N	32.34 E
Khetan (R.), India	196	10.57 N	78.23 E
Khichripur (Neigh.), India	67d	28.37 N	77.19 E
Khiitola, Sov. Un. (khē'tō-lȧ)	165	61.14 N	29.40 E
Khimki, Sov. Un. (кēm'kĭ)	182b	55.54 N	37.27 E
Khiva, Sov. Un. (kē'vȧ)	155	41.15 N	60.30 E
Khíos, Grc. (kē'ôs)	173	38.23 N	26.09 E
Khíos (I.), Grc.	173	38.20 N	25.45 E
Khmel'nik, Sov. Un.	175	49.34 N	27.58 E
Khmel'nitskiy, Sov. Un. (kmĭĕ'lnē'ts-kēē)	179	49.29 N	26.54 E
Khmel'nitskiy (Oblast), Sov. Un. (кmĕl-nēt'skĭ ôb'lást')	175	49.27 N	26.30 E
Kholargós, Grc.	66d	38.00 N	23.48 E
Kholm, Sov. Un. (кôlm)	174	57.09 N	31.07 E
Kholmsk, Sov. Un. (кŭlmsk)	181	47.09 N	142.33 E
Khomeynīshahr, Iran	195	32.41 N	51.31 E
Khopër (R.), Sov. Un. (кô'pĕr)	179	52.00 N	43.00 E
Khor (R.), Sov. Un.	204	47.23 N	135.20 E
Khor, Sov. Un. (кôr')	204	47.50 N	134.52 E
Khóra Sfakíon, Grc.	172a	35.12 N	24.10 E
Khorel, India	67a	22.42 N	88.19 E
Khorog, Sov. Un. (кôr'ôg)	180	37.30 N	71.47 E
Khorog, Sov. Un.	196	37.10 N	71.43 E
Khorol, Sov. Un. (кô'rôl)	175	49.48 N	33.17 E
Khorol (R.), Sov. Un.	175	49.50 N	33.21 E
Khorramābād, Iran	195	33.30 N	48.20 E
Khorramshahr, Iran (kô-ram'shär)	192	30.36 N	48.15 E
Khotin, Sov. Un. (кô'tĕn)	175	48.29 N	26.32 E
Khot'kovo, Sov. Un.	182b	56.15 N	38.00 E
Khoybār, Sau. Ar.	192	25.45 N	39.28 E
Khoyniki, Sov. Un.	175	51.54 N	30.00 E
Khulna, Bngl.	196	22.50 N	89.38 E
Khūryān Mūryān (Is.), Om.	192	17.27 N	56.02 E
Khust, Sov. Un. (кo͞ost)	167	48.10 N	23.18 E
Khvalynsk, Sov. Un. (кvȧ-lĭnsk')	179	52.30 N	48.00 E
Khvoy, Iran	192	38.32 N	45.01 E
Khyber Pass, Pak. (kī'bēr)	193a	34.28 N	71.18 E
Kialwe, Zaire	231	9.22 S	27.08 E
Kiambi, Zaire (kyăm'bē)	231	7.20 S	28.01 E
Kiamichi (R.), Ok. (kyȧ-mē'chē)	123	34.31 N	95.34 W
Kianta (L.), Fin. (kyȧn'tȧ)	178	65.00 N	28.15 E
Kibenga, Zaire	230	7.55 S	17.35 E
Kibiti, Tan.	231	7.44 S	38.57 E
Kibombo, Zaire	231	3.54 S	25.55 E
Kibondo, Tan.	231	3.35 S	30.42 E
Kibouendé, Con.	71c	4.19 S	15.11 E
Kičevo, Yugo. (kē'chĕ-vô)	173	41.30 N	20.59 E
Kichijōji, Jap.	69a	35.42 N	139.35 E
Kickapoo (R.), Wi. (kĭk'ȧ-po͞o)	115	43.20 N	90.55 W
Kicking Horse P., Can.	99	51.25 N	116.10 W
Kidal, Mali (kē-dȧl')	224	18.33 N	1.00 E
Kidderminster, Eng. (kĭd'ēr-mĭn-stēr)	156	52.23 N	2.14 W
Kidderpore (Neigh.), India	67a	22.31 N	88.19 E
Kidd's Beach, S. Afr. (kĭdz)	227c	33.09 S	27.43 E
Kidsgrove, Eng. (kĭdz'grōv)	156	53.05 N	2.30 W
Kiel, F.R.G. (kēl)	166	54.19 N	10.08 E
Kiel, Wi.	115	43.52 N	88.04 W
Kiel B., F.R.G.	166	54.33 N	10.19 E
Kiel Can., see Nord-Ostsee Kan.			
Kielce, Pol. (kyĕl'tsĕ)	167	50.50 N	20.41 E
Kieldrecht, Bel. (kēl'drĕкt)	157a	51.17 N	4.09 E
Kierspe, F.R.G.	63	51.08 N	7.35 E
Kiev (Oblast), Sov. Un. (kē'yĕf) (ôb'lȧst')	175	50.05 N	30.40 E
Kiev, see Kiyev			
Kievskoye Vdkhr. (Res.), Sov. Un.	179	51.00 N	30.20 E
Kiffa, Mauritania (kēf'ȧ)	228	16.37 N	11.24 W
Kigali, Rw. (kē-gä'lē)	226	1.59 S	30.05 E
Kigoma, Tan. (kē-gō'mä)	231	4.57 S	29.38 E
Kii-Suido (Chan.), Jap. (kē so͞o-ē'dō)	205	33.53 N	134.55 E
Kikaiga (I.), Jap.	204	28.25 N	130.10 E
Kikinda, Yugo. (kē'kĕn-dä)	173	45.49 N	20.30 E
Kikládhes (Is.), Grc.	173	37.30 N	24.45 E
Kikwit, Zaire (kē'kwēt)	230	5.02 S	18.49 E
Kil, Swe. (kēl)	164	59.30 N	13.15 E
Kilauea, Hi. (kē-lä-o͞o-ā'ä)	106a	22.12 N	159.25 W
Kilauea Crater, Hi.	106a	19.28 N	155.18 W
Kilbuck Mts., Ak. (kĭl-bŭk)	107	60.05 N	160.00 W
Kilchu, Kor. (kĭl'cho͞o)	204	40.59 N	129.23 E
Kildare, Ire. (kĭl-dâr')	161	53.09 N	7.05 W
Kilembe, Zaire	230	5.42 S	19.55 E
Kilgore, Tx.	125	32.23 N	94.53 W
Kilifi, Ken.	231	3.38 S	39.51 E
Kilimanjaro (Mtn.), Tan. (kyl-ē-măn-jä'rō)	227	3.09 S	37.19 E
Kilimatinde, Tan. (kĭl-ē-mä-tĭn'dȧ)	226	5.48 S	34.58 E
Kilindoni, Tan.	231	7.55 S	39.39 E
Kilingi-Nõmme, Sov. Un. (kē'lĭn-gē-nôm'mĕ)	165	58.08 N	25.03 E
Kilis, Tur. (kē'lēs)	179	36.50 N	37.20 E
Kiliya, Sov. Un. (kē'lyȧ)	175	45.28 N	29.17 E
Kilkenny, Ire. (kĭl-kĕn-ĭ)	162	52.40 N	7.30 W
Kilkis, Grc. (kĭl'kĭs)	173	40.59 N	22.51 E
Killala, Ire. (kĭ-lä'lȧ)	162	54.11 N	9.10 W
Killara, Austl.	70a	33.46 S	151.09 E
Killarney, Ire.	162	52.03 N	9.05 W
Killarney Heights, Austl.	70a	33.46 S	151.13 E
Killdeer, ND (kĭl'dēr)	114	47.22 N	102.45 W
Kilmarnock, Scot. (kĭl-mär'nŭk)	162	55.38 N	4.25 W
Kilokri (Neigh.), India	67d	28.35 N	77.16 E
Kilrush, Ire. (kĭl'rŭsh)	162	52.40 N	9.16 W
Kilwa Kisiwani, Tan.	231	8.58 S	39.30 E
Kilwa Kivinje, Tan.	227	8.43 S	39.18 E
Kim (R.), Cam.	229	5.40 N	11.17 E
Kimamba, Tan.	231	6.47 S	37.08 E
Kimba, Austl. (kĭm'bȧ)	216	33.08 S	136.25 E
Kimball, Ne. (kĭm-bȧl)	114	41.14 N	103.41 W
Kimball, SD	114	43.44 N	98.58 W
Kimberley, Can. (kĭm'bēr-lĭ)	99	49.41 N	115.59 W
Kimberley, S. Afr.	226	28.40 S	24.50 E
Kimi, Cam.	229	6.05 N	11.30 E
Kimry, Sov. Un. (kĭm'rē)	174	56.53 N	37.24 E
Kimvula, Zaire	230	5.44 S	15.58 E
Kinabalu, Gunong (Mtn.), Mala.	206	5.45 N	115.26 E
Kincardine, Can. (kĭn-kär'dĭn)	110	44.10 N	81.15 W
Kinda, Zaire	230	9.18 S	25.04 E
Kindanba, Con.	230	3.44 S	14.31 E
Kinder, La. (kĭn'dēr)	125	30.30 N	92.50 W
Kindersley, Can. (kĭn'dērz-lē)	100	51.27 N	109.10 W
Kindia, Gui. (kĭn'dē-ȧ)	228	10.04 N	12.51 W
Kindu, Zaire	231	2.57 S	25.56 E
Kinel'-Cherkassy, Sov. Un.	178	53.32 N	51.32 E
Kineshma, Sov. Un. (kē-nĕsh'mȧ)	174	57.27 N	41.02 E
King (I.), Austl. (kĭng)	216	39.35 S	143.40 E
Kingaroy, Austl. (kĭŋ'gȧ-roi)	216	26.37 S	151.50 E
King City, Ca. (kĭng sĭ'tĭ)	120	36.12 N	121.08 W
King City, Can.	95d	43.56 N	79.32 W
Kingcome Inlet, Can. (kĭng'kŭm)	98	50.50 N	126.10 W
Kingfisher, Ok. (kĭng'fĭsh-ēr)	122	35.51 N	97.55 W
King George, Mt., Can.	99	50.35 N	115.24 W
King George Sd., Austl. (jôrj)	214	35.17 S	118.30 E
King George's Res., Eng.	62	51.39 N	0.01 W
Kingisepp, Sov. Un. (kĭŋ-gē-sep')	174	59.22 N	28.38 E
King Leopold Ranges, Austl. (lē'ô-pōld)	214	16.25 S	125.00 E
Kingman, Az. (kĭng'mȧn)	121	35.10 N	114.05 W
Kingman, Ks. (kĭng'mȧn)	122	37.38 N	98.07 W
King of Prussia, Pa.	56b	40.05 N	75.23 W

ăt; finȧl; rāte; senȧte; ärm; ȧsk; sofȧ; fâre; ch-choose; dh-as th in other; bē; ēvent; bĕt; recĕnt; cratēr; g-gō; gh-guttural g; bĭt; ĭ-short neutral; rīde; к-guttural k as ch in German ich;

PLACE (Pronounciation)	PAGE	Lat. °'	Long. °'
Kings (R.), Ca.	120	36.28 N	119.43 W
Kingsbury (Neigh.), Eng.	62	51.35 N	0.17 W
Kings Canyon Natl. Park, Ca. (kăn'yŭn)	120	36.52 N	118.53 W
Kingsclere, Eng. (kĭngs-clēr)	156b	51.18 N	1.15 W
Kingscote, Austl. (kĭngz'kŭt)	216	35.45 S	137.32 E
King Sd., Austl.	214	16.50 S	123.35 E
Kingsdown, Eng.	62	51.21 N	0.17 E
Kingsford, Austl.	70a	33.56 S	151.14 E
Kingsgrove, Austl.	70a	33.57 S	151.06 E
Kings Langley, Eng.	62	51.43 N	0.28 W
King's Lynn, Eng. (kĭngz lĭn')	163	52.45 N	0.20 E
Kings Mt., NC	127	35.13 N	81.30 W
Kings Norton, Eng. (nôr'tŭn)	156	52.25 N	1.54 W
Kings Park, NY (kĭngz pärk)	112a	40.53 N	73.16 W
Kings Park, Va.	56d	38.48 N	77.15 W
Kings Pk., Ut.	117	40.46 N	110.20 W
Kings Point, NY	55	40.49 N	73.45 W
Kingsport, Tn. (kĭngz'pōrt)	127	36.33 N	82.36 W
Kingston, Austl. (kĭngz'tŭn)	216	37.52 S	139.52 E
Kingston, Can.	111	44.15 N	76.30 W
Kingston, Jam.	134	18.00 N	76.45 W
Kingston, NY	111	42.00 N	74.00 W
Kingston, Pa.	111	41.15 N	75.50 W
Kingston, Wa.	118a	47.04 N	122.29 W
Kingston upon Hull, Eng.	156	53.45 N	0.25 W
Kingston upon Thames (Neigh.), Eng.	62	51.25 N	0.19 W
Kingstown, Saint Vincent (kĭngz'toun)	133b	13.10 N	61.14 W
Kingstree, SC (kĭngz'trē)	127	33.30 N	79.50 W
Kingsville, Tx. (kĭngz'vĭl)	124	27.32 N	97.52 W
King William I., Can. (kĭng wĭl'yăm)	96	69.25 N	97.00 W
King William's Town, S. Afr. (kĭng-wĭl'-yŭmz-toun)	217c	32.53 S	27.24 E
Kinira (R.), S. Afr.	227c	30.37 S	28.52 E
Kinloch, Mo. (kĭn-lŏk)	119e	38.44 N	90.19 W
Kinnaird, Can. (kĭn-ärd')	99	49.17 N	117.39 W
Kinnairds Hd., Scot. (kĭn-årds'hĕd)	162	57.42 N	3.55 W
Kinomoto, Jap. (kē'nō-mōtō)	205	33.53 N	136.07 E
Kinosaki, Jap. (kē'nō-sä'kē)	205	35.38 N	134.47 E
Kinshasa (Léopoldville), Zaire	230	4.18 S	15.18 E
Kinshasa-Est (Neigh.), Zaire	71c	4.18 S	15.18 E
Kinshasa-Ouest (Neigh.), Zaire	71c	4.20 S	15.15 E
Kinsley, Ks. (kĭnz'lĭ)	122	37.55 N	99.24 W
Kinston, NC (kĭnz'tŭn)	127	35.15 N	77.35 W
Kintamo, Rapides de, Afr.	71c	4.19 S	15.15 E
Kintampo, Ghana (kēn-täm'pō)	228	8.03 N	1.43 W
Kintsana, Con.	71c	4.19 S	15.10 E
Kintyre (Pen), Scot.	162	55.50 N	5.40 W
Kioroshi, see Ōmori			
Kīrthar Ra., Pak. (kĭr-tŭr)	196	27.00 N	67.10 E
Kiowa, Ks. (kī'ô-wȧ)	122	37.01 N	98.30 W
Kiowa, Ok.	123	34.42 N	95.53 W
Kīyose, Jap.	205a	35.47 N	139.32 E
Kiparissiakós Kólpos (G.), Grc.	173	37.28 N	21.15 E
Kiparissía, Grc.	173	37.17 N	21.43 E
Kipawa Lac (L.), Can.	103	46.55 N	79.00 W
Kipembawe, Tan. (kē-pĕm-bä'wȧ)	231	7.39 S	33.24 E
Kipengere Ra., Tan.	231	9.10 S	34.00 E
Kipili, Tan.	231	7.26 S	30.36 E
Kipusha, Zaire	231	11.46 N	27.14 E
Kipushi, Zaire	231	11.46 N	27.14 E
Kirby, Tx. (kŭr'bĭ)	119d	29.29 N	98.23 W
Kirbyville, Tx. (kŭr'bĭ-vĭl)	125	30.39 N	93.54 W
Kirchderne (Neigh.), F.R.G.	63	51.33 N	7.30 E
Kirchende, F.R.G.	63	51.25 N	7.26 E
Kirchhellen, F.R.G.	63	51.36 N	6.55 E
Kirchhellen Heide (For.), F.R.G.	63	51.36 N	6.53 E
Kirchhörde (Neigh.), F.R.G.	63	51.27 N	7.27 E
Kirchlinde (Neigh.), F.R.G.	63	51.32 N	7.22 E
Kirdâsah, Egypt	71a	30.02 N	31.07 E
Kirenga (R.), Sov. Un. (kē-rĕŋ'gȧ)	181	56.30 N	103.18 E
Kirensk, Sov. Un. (kē-rĕnsk')	181	57.47 N	108.22 E
Kirghiz S. S. R., Sov. Un. (kĭr-gēz')	176	41.45 N	74.38 E
Kirghiz Steppe (Plain), Sov. Un.	176	49.28 N	57.07 E
Kirgizskiy Khrebet (Kirgiz) (Mts.), Sov. Un.	193	37.58 N	72.23 E
Kiri, Zaire	230	1.27 S	19.00 E
Kiribati, Oceania	208	1.30 S	173.00 E
Kirin, see Chilung			
Kirinyaga (Kenya) (Mtn.), Ken.	231	0.10 S	37.20 E
Kiritimati (I.), Oceania	209	2.20 N	157.40 W
Kirkby, Eng.	64a	53.29 N	2.54 W
Kirkby-in-Ashfield, Eng. (kŭrk'bē-ĭn-ăsh'fēld)	156	53.06 N	1.16 W
Kirkcaldy, Scot. (kēr-kô'dĭ)	162	56.06 N	3.15 W
Kirkdale (Neigh.), Eng.	64a	53.26 N	2.59 W
Kirkenes, Nor.	158	69.40 N	30.03 E
Kirkham, Eng. (kûrk'ăm)	156	53.47 N	2.53 W
Kirkland, Can.	54b	45.27 N	73.52 W
Kirkland, Wa. (kûrk'lănd)	118a	47.41 N	122.12 W
Kirklareli, Tur. (kērk'lär-ĕ'lē)	173	41.44 N	27.15 E
Kirksville, Mo. (kûrks'vĭl)	123	40.12 N	92.35 W
Kirkūk, Iraq (kĭr-ko͞ok')	192	35.28 N	44.22 E
Kirkwall, Scot. (kûrk'wôl)	162a	58.58 N	2.59 W
Kirkwood, Md.	56d	38.57 N	76.58 W
Kirkwood, Mo. (kûrk'wo͝od)	119e	38.35 N	90.24 W
Kirkwood, S. Afr.	227c	33.26 S	25.24 E
Kirn, F.R.G. (kērn)	166	49.47 N	7.23 E
Kirov, Sov. Un.	174	54.04 N	34.19 E
Kirov, Sov. Un.	178	58.35 N	49.35 E
Kirovabad, Sov. Un. (kē-rŭ-vŭ-bät')	179	40.40 N	46.20 E
Kirovgrad, Sov. Un. (kē'rŭ-vŭ-grad)	182a	57.26 N	60.03 E
Kirovograd, Sov. Un. (kē-rŭ-vŭ-grät')	175	48.33 N	32.17 E
Kirovograd (Oblast), Sov. Un.	175	48.23 N	31.10 E
Kirovsk, Sov. Un. (kē-rôfsk')	182c	59.52 N	30.59 E
Kirovsk, Sov. Un.	178	67.40 N	33.58 E
Kirsanov, Sov. Un. (kēr-sȧ'nôf)	179	52.40 N	42.40 E
Kirsehir, Tur. (kēr-shĕ'hēr)	179	39.10 N	34.00 E
Kirtachi Seybou, Niger	229	12.48 N	2.29 E
Kirton, Eng. (kûr'tŭn)	156	53.29 N	0.35 W

PLACE (Pronounciation)	PAGE	Lat. °'	Long. °'
Kiruna, Swe. (kē-ro͞o'nä)	158	67.49 N	20.08 E
Kirundu, Zaire	231	0.44 S	25.32 E
Kirwan Heights, Pa.	57b	40.22 N	80.06 W
Kirwin Res., Ks. (kûr'wĭn)	122	39.34 N	99.04 W
Kiryū, Jap. (kē'rĭ-o͞o)	205	36.26 N	139.18 E
Kirzhach, Sov. Un. (kēr-zhák')	174	56.08 N	38.53 E
Kisaki, Tan. (kē-sä'kē)	227	7.37 S	37.43 E
Kisangani (Stanleyville), Zaire	230	0.30 S	25.12 E
Kisarazu, Jap. (kē'sȧ-rä'zo͞o)	205a	35.23 N	139.55 E
Kiselëvsk, Sov. Un. (kē-sĭ-lyôfsk')	180	54.05 N	86.19 E
Kishar Bāla, Iran	68h	35.49 N	51.13 E
Kishinëv, Sov. Un. (ke-shē-nyôf')	175	47.02 N	28.52 E
Kishiwada, Jap. (kē'shē-wä'dä)	205	34.25 N	135.18 E
Kishkino, Sov. Un. (kēsh'kĭ-nô)	182b	55.15 N	38.04 E
Kısıklı (Neigh.), Tur.	66f	41.01 N	29.03 E
Kisiwani, Tan.	231	4.08 S	37.57 E
Kiska (I.), Ak. (kĭs'kä)	107a	52.08 N	177.10 E
Kiskatinaw (R.), Can.	99	55.10 N	120.20 W
Kiskittogisu L., Can.	101	54.05 N	99.00 W
Kiskitto L., Can. (kĭs-kĭ'tō)	101	54.16 N	98.34 W
Kiskunfélegyháza, Hung. (kĭsh'ko͝on-fā'lĕd-y'hä'zô)	167	46.42 N	19.52 E
Kiskunhalas, Hung. (kĭsh'ko͝on-hô'lŏsh)	167	46.24 N	19.26 E
Kiskunmajsa, Hung. (kĭsh'ko͝on-mī'shô)	167	46.29 N	19.42 E
Kismaayo, Som.	227	0.18 S	42.30 E
Kiso, Jap.	69a	35.34 N	139.26 E
Kiso-Gawa (Strm.), Jap. (ke'so-ga'wä)	205	35.29 N	137.12 E
Kiso-Sammyaku (Mts.), Jap. (kē'sō säm'myȧ-ko͞o)	205	35.47 N	137.39 E
Kissamos, Grc.	172a	35.13 N	24.11 E
Kissidougou, Gui. (kē'sē-do͞o'go͞o)	228	9.11 N	10.06 W
Kissimmee, Fl. (kĭ-sĭm'ē)	127a	28.17 N	81.25 W
Kissimmee (L.), Fl.	127a	27.58 N	81.17 W
Kissimmee (R.), Fl.	127a	27.45 N	81.07 W
Kistarcsa, Hung.	66g	47.33 N	19.16 E
Kistrand, Nor. (kē'stränd)	158	70.29 N	25.01 E
Kisujszallás, Hung. (kĭsh'o͞o'y'sä'läsh)	167	47.12 N	20.47 E
Kisumu, Ken. (kē'so͞o-mo͞o)	231	0.06 S	34.45 E
Kita, Mali (kē'tȧ)	228	13.03 N	9.29 W
Kita (Neigh.), Jap.	69a	35.45 N	139.44 E
Kitakami Gawa (R.), Jap. (kē'tȧ-kä'mē gä-wä)	204	39.20 N	141.10 E
Kitakyūshū, Jap. (kē'tȧ-kyo͞o'sho͞o')	205	34.15 N	130.23 E
Kitale, Ken.	231	1.01 N	35.00 E
Kitamachi (Neigh.), Jap.	69a	35.46 N	139.39 E
Kitamba (Neigh.), Zaire	71c	4.19 S	15.14 E
Kitatawara, Jap.	69b	34.44 N	135.42 E
Kit Carson, Co.	122	38.46 N	102.48 W
Kitchener, Can. (kĭch'ĕ-nēr)	110	43.25 N	80.35 W
Kitenda, Zaire	230	6.53 S	17.21 E
Kitgum, Ug. (kĭt'go͞om)	225	3.29 N	33.04 E
Kitimat, Can. (kĭ'tĭ-măt)	98	54.03 N	128.33 W
Kitimat (R.), Can.	98	53.50 N	129.00 W
Kitimat Ra., Can.	98	53.30 N	128.50 W
Kitlope (R.), Can. (kĭt'lōp)	98	53.00 N	128.00 W
Kitsuki, Jap. (kĕt'so͞o-kē)	205	33.24 N	131.35 E
Kittanning, Pa. (kĭ-tăn'ĭng)	111	40.50 N	79.30 W
Kittatinny Mts., NJ (kĭ-tŭ-tĭ'nē)	112a	41.16 N	74.44 W
Kittery, Me. (kĭt'ēr-ĭ)	104	43.07 N	70.45 W
Kittsee, Aus.	157e	48.05 N	17.05 E
Kitty Hawk, NC (kĭt'tē hôk)	127	36.04 N	75.42 W
Kitunda, Tan.	231	6.48 S	33.13 E
Kitwe, Zambia	231	12.49 S	38.13 E
Kitzingen, F.R.G. (kĭt'zĭng-ĕn)	166	49.44 N	10.08 E
Kiunga, Ken.	231	1.45 S	41.29 E
Kivu, Lac (L.), Zaire	231	1.45 S	28.55 E
Kími, Grc.	173	38.38 N	24.05 E
Kímolos (I.), Grc. (kē'mô-lôs)	173	36.52 N	24.20 E
Kíthira (I.), Grc.	161	36.15 N	22.56 E
Kíthnos (I.), Grc.	173	37.24 N	24.10 E
Kiyev (Kiev), Sov. Un. (kē'yĕf)	179	50.27 N	30.30 E
Kizel, Sov. Un. (kē'zĕl)	182a	59.05 N	57.42 E
Kizil Irmak (R.), Tur. (kĭz'ĭl ĭr-mäk')	179	40.15 N	34.00 E
Kizil'skoye, Sov. Un. (kĭz'ĭl-skô-yĕ)	182a	52.43 N	58.53 E
Kizlyar, Sov. Un. (kĭz-lyär')	179	44.00 N	46.50 E
Kizu, Jap. (kē'zo͞o)	205b	34.43 N	135.49 E
Kizuki, Jap.	69a	35.34 N	139.40 E
Kizuri, Jap.	69b	34.39 N	135.34 E
Kizyl Arvat, Sov. Un. (kē'zĭl-ŭr-vät')	155	38.55 N	56.33 E
Klaas Smits (R.), S. Afr.	227c	31.45 S	26.33 E
Klaaswaal, Neth.	157a	51.46 N	4.25 E
Kladno, Czech. (kläd'nō)	166	50.10 N	14.05 E
Klagenfurt, Aust. (klä'gĕn-fo͞ort)	166	46.38 N	14.19 E
Klaipéda (Memel), Sov. Un. (klī'pȧ-dȧ) (mā'mĕl)	165	55.43 N	21.10 E
Klamath Falls, Or.	116	42.13 N	121.49 W
Klamath Mts., Ca.	116	42.00 N	123.25 W
Klamath R., Ca.	116	41.40 N	122.25 W
Klarälven (R.), Swe.	164	60.40 N	13.00 E
Klaskanine (R.), Or. (klăs'kȧ-nīn)	118c	46.02 N	123.43 W
Klatovy, Czech. (klá'tô-vē)	166	49.23 N	13.18 E
Klawock, Ak. (klā'wăk)	107	55.32 N	133.10 W
Kledering (Neigh.), Aus.	66e	48.08 N	16.26 E
Kleef, F.R.G.	63	51.11 N	6.56 E
Kleinbeeren, G.D.R.	65a	52.22 N	13.20 E
Kleinebroich, F.R.G.	63	51.12 N	6.35 E
Klein Elandsvlei, S. Afr.	71b	26.09 S	27.39 E
Kleinmachnow, G.D.R. (klīn-mäĸ'nō)	157b	52.22 N	13.12 E
Klein Ziethen, G.D.R.	65a	52.23 N	13.27 E
Klerksdorp, S. Afr. (klĕrks'dôrp)	223d	26.52 S	26.40 E
Klerksraal, S. Afr. (klĕrks'kräl)	223d	26.15 S	27.10 E
Kletnya, Sov. Un. (klyĕt'nyȧ)	174	52.19 N	33.14 E
Kletsk, Sov. Un. (klĕtsk)	174	53.04 N	26.43 E
Kleve, F.R.G. (klĕ'fĕ)	169c	51.47 N	6.09 E
Kley (Neigh.), F.R.G.	63	51.30 N	7.22 E
Klickitat R., Wa.	116	46.01 N	121.07 W
Klimovichi, Sov. Un. (klē-mô-vē'chē)	174	53.37 N	31.21 E

PLACE (Pronounciation)	PAGE	Lat. °'	Long. °'
Klimovsk, Sov. Un. (klĭ'môfsk)	182b	55.21 N	37.32 E
Klin, Sov. Un. (klēn)	174	56.18 N	36.43 E
Klintehamn, Swe. (klēn'tē-häm)	164	57.24 N	18.14 E
Klintsy, Sov. Un. (klĭn'tsĭ)	174	52.46 N	32.14 E
Klip (R.), S. Afr. (klĭp)	223d	27.18 N	29.25 E
Klipgat, S. Afr.	223d	25.26 S	27.57 E
Klippan, Swe. (klyp'pȧn)	164	56.08 N	13.09 E
Klippoortje, S. Afr.	71b	26.17 S	28.14 E
Kliptown, S. Afr.	71b	26.17 S	27.53 E
Ključ, Yugo. (klyo͞och)	172	44.32 N	16.48 E
Kłodzko, Pol. (klôd'skô)	166	50.26 N	16.38 E
Klondike Reg., Ak.-Can. (klŏn'dĭk)	107	64.12 N	142.38 W
Klosterfelde, G.D.R. (klōs'tĕr-fĕl-dĕ)	157b	52.47 N	13.29 E
Klosterneuburg, Aus. (klōs-tĕr-noi'bo͝orgh)	157e	48.19 N	16.20 E
Kluane (L.), Can.	96	61.15 N	138.40 W
Kluane Natl. Pk., Can.	96	60.25 N	137.53 W
Kluczbork, Pol. (klo͞och'bŏrk)	167	50.59 N	18.15 E
Klyaz'ma (R.), Sov. Un. (klyäz'mȧ)	174	55.49 N	39.19 E
Klyuchevskaya (Vol.), Sov. Un. (klyo͞o-chĕfskä'yä)	181	56.13 N	160.00 E
Klyuchi, Sov. Un. (klyo͞o'chĭ)	182a	57.03 N	57.20 E
Knezha, Bul. (knyä'zhȧ)	173	43.27 N	24.03 E
Knife (R.), ND (nīf)	114	47.06 N	102.33 W
Knight Inlet, Can. (nīt)	98	50.41 N	125.40 W
Knightstown, In. (nīts'toun)	110	39.45 N	85.30 W
Knin, Yugo. (knēn)	172	44.02 N	16.14 E
Knittelfeld, Aus.	166	47.13 N	14.50 E
Knob Pk., Phil. (nŏb)	207a	12.30 N	121.20 E
Knockholt, Eng.	62	51.18 N	0.06 E
Knockholt Pound, Eng.	62	51.19 N	0.08 E
Knoppiesfontein, S. Afr.	71b	26.05 S	28.25 E
Knottingley, Eng. (nŏt'ĭng-lĭ)	156	53.42 N	1.14 W
Knott's Berry Farm (P. Int.), Ca.	59	33.50 N	118.00 W
Knotty Ash (Neigh.), Eng.	64a	53.25 N	2.54 W
Knowsley, Eng.	64a	53.27 N	2.51 W
Knowsley Hall (P. Int.), Eng.	64a	53.26 N	2.50 W
Knox, Austl.	70b	37.53 S	145.18 E
Knox, In. (nŏks)	110	41.15 N	86.40 W
Knox, C., Can.	98	54.12 N	133.20 W
Knoxville, Ia. (nŏks'vĭl)	115	41.19 N	93.05 W
Knoxville, Tn.	126	35.58 N	83.55 W
Knutsford, Eng. (nŭts'fērd)	156	53.18 N	2.22 W
Knyszyn, Pol. (knĭ'shĭn)	167	53.16 N	22.59 E
Kobayashi, Jap. (kō'bȧ-yä'shē)	205	31.58 N	130.59 E
Kōbe, Jap. (kō'bĕ)	205b	34.30 N	135.10 E
Kobelyaki, Sov. Un. (kō-bĕl-yä'kē)	175	49.11 N	34.12 E
København (Copenhagen), Den. (kû-b'n-houn')	164	55.43 N	12.27 E
Koblenz, F.R.G. (kō'blĕntz)	166	50.18 N	7.36 E
Kobozha (R.), Sov. Un. (kô-bō'zhȧ)	174	58.55 N	35.18 E
Kobrin, Sov. Un. (kō'brēn')	167	52.13 N	24.23 E
Kobrinskoye, Sov. Un. (kô-brĭn'skô-yĕ)	182c	59.25 N	30.07 E
Kobuk (R.), Ak. (kō'bŭk)	107	66.58 N	158.48 W
Kobuleti, Sov. Un. (kô-bo͞o-lyä'tē)	179	41.50 N	41.40 E
Kočani, Yugo. (kô'chä-nĕ)	173	41.54 N	22.25 E
Kočevje, Yugo. (kô'chāv-ye)	172	45.38 N	14.51 E
Kocher R., F.R.G. (kôĸ'ĕr)	166	49.00 N	9.52 E
Kōchi, Jap. (kō'chē)	205	33.35 N	133.32 E
Kodaira, Jap.	205a	35.43 N	139.29 E
Kodiak, Ak. (kō'dyăk)	107	57.50 N	152.30 W
Kodiak (I.), Ak.	107	57.24 N	153.32 W
Kodok, Sud. (ko'dŏk)	225	9.57 N	32.08 E
Koforidua, Ghana (kō fō-rĭ-do͞o'ȧ)	228	6.03 N	0.17 W
Kōfu, Jap. (kō'fo͞o')	205	35.41 N	138.34 E
Koga, Jap. (kō'gȧ)	205	36.13 N	139.40 E
Kogan (R.), Gui.	228	11.30 N	14.05 W
Koganе, Jap. (kō'gä-nā)	205a	35.50 N	139.56 E
Koganei, Jap. (kō'gä-nā)	205a	35.42 N	139.31 E
Kogarah, Austl.	70a	33.58 S	151.08 E
Køge, Den. (kû'gĕ)	164	55.27 N	12.09 E
Køge Bugt (B.), Den.	164	55.30 N	12.25 E
Kogil'nik (R.), Sov. Un. (kô-gĕl-nĕk')	175	46.08 N	29.10 E
Kogoni, Mali	228	14.44 N	6.02 W
Koh-i Baba Mt., Afg.	196	39.39 N	67.09 E
Kohīma, India (kô-ē'mȧ)	193	25.45 N	94.41 E
Koito (R.), Jap. (kō'ē-tō)	205a	35.19 N	139.58 E
Kŏje (I.), Kor. (kû'jĕ)	204	34.53 N	129.00 E
Kokand, Sov. Un. (kô-känt')	180	40.27 N	71.07 E
Kokchetav, Sov. Un. (kôk'chĕ-täf)	180	53.15 N	69.13 E
Kokemäenjoki (R.), Fin.	165	61.23 N	22.03 E
Kokhma, Sov. Un. (kôĸ'mȧ)	174	56.57 N	41.08 E
Kokkola, Fin. (kô'kô-lȧ)	158	63.47 N	22.58 E
Kokomo, In. (kō'kō-mō)	110	40.30 N	86.20 W
Koko Nor (Qinghai Hu) (L.), China (kō'kô nor) (chyĭŋ-hī ho͞o)	198	37.26 N	98.30 E
Kokopo, Pap. N. Gui. (kô-kō'pō)	207	4.25 S	152.27 E
Koksoak (R.), Can. (kôk'sô-ăk)	97	57.42 N	69.50 W
Kokstad, S. Afr. (kôk'shtät)	227c	30.33 S	29.27 E
Kokubu, Jap. (kō'ko͞o-bo͞o)	205	31.42 N	130.46 E
Kokubunji, Jap.	69a	35.42 N	139.29 E
Kokuou, Jap. (kō'ko͞o-ō'o͞o)	205b	34.34 N	135.39 E
Kola Pen., see Kol'skiy P-Ov.			
Kolār (Kolār Gold Fields), India (kōl-är')	197	13.39 N	78.33 E
Kolárvo, Czech. (kōl-árōvō)	167	47.54 N	17.59 E
Kolbio, Ken.	231	1.10 S	41.15 E
Kol'chugino, Sov. Un. (kôl-cho͞o'gē-nô)	174	56.19 N	39.29 E
Kolda, Sen.	228	12.53 N	14.57 W
Kolding, Den. (kûl'dĭng)	164	55.29 N	9.24 E
Kole, Zaire (kō'lā)	226	3.19 S	22.46 E
Kolguyev (I.), Sov. Un. (kôl-go͞o'yĕf)	178	69.00 N	49.00 E
Kolín, Czech. (kō'lēn)	166	50.01 N	15.11 E
Kolkasrags (Pt.), Sov. Un. (kôl-käs'rȧgz)	165	57.46 N	22.39 E
Köln (Cologne), F.R.G.	169c	50.56 N	6.57 E
Kolno, Pol. (kôw'nô)	167	53.23 N	21.56 E
Koło, Pol. (kô'wô)	167	52.11 N	18.37 E
Kołobrzeg, Pol. (kô-lôb'zhĕk)	166	54.10 N	15.35 E
Kolomenskoje (Neigh.), Sov. Un.	66b	55.40 N	37.41 E

ng-sing; ŋ-baŋk; ɴ-nasalized n; nŏd; cŏmmit; ōld; ôbey; ôrder; oi-boil; fo͞od; fo͝ot; ou-out; s-soft; sh-dish; th-thin; pūre; ûnite; ûrn; stŭd; circŭs; ü-as in French tu; '-indeterminate vowel.

PLACE (Pronounciation)	PAGE	Lat. °′	Long. °′
Kolomna, Sov. Un. (kȧl-ȯm′nȧ)	182b	55.06 N	38.47 E
Kolomyya, Sov. Un. (kō′lô-mē′yȧ)	167	48.32 N	25.04 E
Kolonie Stolp, G.D.R.	65a	52.28 N	13.46 E
Kolp′ (R.), Sov. Un. (kôlp)	174	59.29 N	35.32 E
Kolpashevo, Sov. Un. (kŭl pȧ shô′vȧ)	180	58.16 N	82.43 E
Kolpino, Sov. Un. (kôl′pė-nȯ)	182c	59.45 N	30.37 E
Kolpny, Sov. Un. (kôlp′nyė)	174	52.14 N	36.54 E
Kol′skiy P-Ov. (Kola Pen.), Sov. Un.	178	67.15 N	37.40 E
Kolva (R.), Sov. Un.	178	61.00 N	57.00 E
Kolwezi, Zaire (kōl-wĕ′zē)	231	10.43 S	25.28 E
Kolyberovo, Sov. Un. (kȯ-lĭ-byâ′rô-vô)	182b	55.16 N	38.45 E
Kolyma (R.), Sov. Un.	181	66.30 N	151.45 E
Kolymskiy (Mts.), **see Gydan,** Khrebet			
Kolyvan′, Sov. Un. (kŏl-ė-vän′)	180	55.28 N	82.59 E
Kom (R.), Cam.-Gabon	230	2.15 N	12.05 E
Komadougou Yobé (R.), Niger-Nig.	229	13.20 N	12.45 E
Komadugu Gana (R.), Nig.	229	12.15 N	11.10 E
Komae, Jap.	205a	35.37 N	139.35 E
Komagome (Neigh.), Jap.	69a	35.44 N	139.45 E
Komandorskie Ostrova (Is.), Sov. Un.	93	55.40 N	167.13 E
Komárno, Czech. (kȯ′mär-nȯ)	167	47.46 N	18.08 E
Komarno, Sov. Un.	167	49.38 N	23.43 E
Komárom, Hung. (kȯ′mä-rôm)	167	47.45 N	18.06 E
Komatipoort, S. Afr. (kō-mä′tė-pōrt)	226	25.21 S	32.00 E
Komatsu, Jap. (kō-mät′so͞o)	205	36.23 N	136.26 E
Komatsushima, Jap. (kō-mät′so͞o-shė′mä)	205	34.04 N	134.32 E
Komeshia, Zaire	231	8.01 S	27.07 E
Komga, S. Afr. (kōm′gȧ)	227c	32.36 S	27.54 E
Komi (A.S.S.R.), Sov. Un. (kȯmė)	176	61.31 N	53.15 E
Kommetijie, S. Afr.	226a	34.09 S	18.19 E
Kommunizma, Pik (Pk.), Sov. Un.	198	39.46 N	71.23 E
Komoe (R.), Ivory Coast	228	5.40 N	3.40 W
Komotiní, Grc.	173	41.07 N	25.22 E
Komrat, Sov. Un. (kȯm-rät′)	175	46.17 N	28.38 E
Komsomolets, Sov. Un. (kȯm-sô-mô′lĕts)	182a	53.45 N	63.04 E
Komsomolets Zaliv (B.), Sov. Un.	179	45.40 N	52.00 E
Komsomol′sk-na-Amure, Sov. Un. (kŭm-sŭ-môlsk′nŭ-ŭ-mo͞or′yĭ)	181	50.46 N	137.14 E
Komsomol′skoye, Sov. Un. (kȯm-sô-môl′skȯ-yĕ)	175	48.42 N	28.44 E
Kona, Mali,	228	14.57 N	3.53 W
Konda (R.), Sov. Un. (kȯn′dȧ)	178	60.50 N	64.00 E
Kondas R., Sov. Un. (kȯn′dȧs)	182a	59.30 N	56.28 E
Kondli (Neigh.), India	67d	28.37 N	77.19 E
Kondoa, Tan. (kȯn-dō′ȧ)	226	4.52 S	36.00 E
Kondolole, Zaire,	231	1.20 N	25.58 E
Kong, Ivory Coast (kông)	224	9.05 N	4.41 W
Kongbo, Cen. Afr. Rep.	230	4.44 N	21.23 E
Kongolo, Zaire (kôŋ′gō′lō)	231	5.23 S	27.00 E
Kongsberg, Nor. (kŭngs′bĕrg)	164	59.40 N	9.36 E
Kongsvinger, Nor. (kŭngs′vĭŋ-gēr)	164	60.12 N	12.00 E
Koni, Zaire (kō′nē)	226	10.32 S	27.27 E
Königsberg, see Kaliningrad			
Königsbrunn, F.R.G. (kû′nēgs-bro͞on)	157d	48.16 N	10.53 E
Königshardt (Neigh.), F.R.G.	63	51.33 N	6.51 E
Königs Wusterhausen, G.D.R. (kû′nēgs vo͞os′tĕr-hou-zĕn)	157b	52.18 N	13.38 E
Konin, Pol. (kô′nyĕn)	167	52.11 N	18.17 E
Kónitsa, Grc. (kȯ′nyē′tsȧ)	173	40.03 N	20.46 E
Konjic, Yugo. (kôn′yēts)	173	43.38 N	17.59 E
Konju, Kor.	205	36.21 N	127.05 E
Konkouré (R.), Gui.	228	10.30 N	13.25 W
Konnagar, India	196a	22.41 N	88.22 E
Konohana (Neigh.), Jap.	69b	34.41 N	135.16 E
Kōnoike, Jap.	69b	34.42 N	135.37 E
Konotop, Sov. Un. (kȯ-nȯ-tôp′)	175	51.13 N	33.14 E
Konpienga (R.), Burkina	228	11.15 N	0.35 E
Konqi (R.), China (kȯn-chyē)	198	41.09 N	87.46 E
Końskie, Pol. (koin′′skyĕ)	167	51.12 N	20.26 E
Konstantinovka, Sov. Un. (kȯn-stȧn-tē′nôf-kȧ)	175	48.33 N	37.42 E
Konstanz, F.R.G. (kȯn′shtänts)	166	47.39 N	9.10 E
Kontagora, Nig. (kōn-tȧ-gō′rä)	229	10.24 N	5.28 E
Konya, Tur. (kōn′yȧ)	179	36.55 N	32.25 E
Kootenay (R.), Can.	99	49.45 N	117.05 W
Kootenay L., Can.	99	49.35 N	116.50 W
Kootenay Natl. Park, Can. (ko͞o′tė-nȧ)	96	51.06 N	117.02 W
Kooyong, Austl.	70b	37.50 S	145.02 E
Kōō-zan (Mtn.), Jap. (ko͞o′zän)	205b	34.53 N	135.32 E
Kopervik, Nor. (kô′pĕr-vėk)	164	59.18 N	5.20 E
Kopeysk, Sov. Un. (kȯ-pāsk′)	182a	55.07 N	61.36 E
Köping, Swe. (chû′pĭng)	164	59.32 N	15.58 E
Kopparberg, Swe. (kŏp′pȧr-bĕrgh)	164	59.53 N	15.00 E
Koppeh Dāgh (Mts.), Iran	192	37.28 N	58.29 E
Koppies, S. Afr.	223d	27.15 S	27.35 E
Koprivnica, Yugo. (kô′prēv-nė′tsȧ)	172	46.10 N	16.48 E
Kopychintsy, Sov. Un. (kȯ-pė-chēn′tsĕ)	167	49.06 N	25.55 E
Korçë, Alb. (kȯr′chĕ)	173	40.37 N	20.48 E
Korčula (I.), Yugo. (kȯr′cho͞o-lȧ)	172	42.50 N	17.05 E
Korea B., China-Kor.	204	39.18 N	123.50 E
Korean Arch., Kor.	204	34.05 N	125.35 E
Korea, North, Asia	191	40.00 N	127.00 E
Korea, South, Asia	191	36.30 N	128.00 E
Korea Str., Kor.-Jap.	204	33.30 N	128.30 E
Korets, Sov. Un. (kȯ-rĕts′)	167	50.35 N	27.13 E
Korhogo, Ivory Coast (kȯr-hō′gō)	228	9.27 N	5.38 W
Kōri, Jap.	69b	34.47 N	135.39 E
Koridhallós, Grc.	66d	37.59 N	23.39 E
Korinthiakós Kólpos (G.), Grc.	173	38.15 N	22.33 E
Kórinthos (Corinth), Grc. (kȯ-rėn′thȯs) (kŏr′ĭnth)	173	37.56 N	22.54 E
Kōriyama, Jap. (kō′rė-yä′mä)	204	37.18 N	140.25 E
Korkino, Sov. Un. (kôr′kē-nŭ)	182a	54.53 N	61.25 E
Korla, China (kōr-lä)	198	41.37 N	86.03 E
Körmend, Hung. (kûr′mĕnt)	166	47.02 N	16.36 E
Kornat (I.), Yugo. (kȯr-nät′)	172	43.46 N	15.10 E
Korneuburg, Aus. (kȯr′noi-bo͝orgh)	157e	48.22 N	16.21 E
Koro, Mali	228	14.04 N	3.05 W
Korocha, Sov. Un. (kȯ-rō′chȧ)	175	50.50 N	37.13 E
Korop, Sov. Un. (kō′rôp)	175	51.33 N	33.54 E
Korosten′, Sov. Un. (kô′rȯs-tĕn)	175	50.51 N	28.39 E
Korostyshev, Sov. Un. (kȯ-rôs′tė-shôf)	175	50.19 N	29.05 E
Koro Toro, Chad	229	16.05 N	18.30 E
Korotoyak, Sov. Un. (kȯ′rȯ-tȯ-yȧk′)	175	51.00 N	39.06 E
Korsakov, Sov. Un. (kôr′sȧ-kôf′)	181	46.42 N	143.16 E
Korsnäs, Fin. (kôrs′nĕs)	165	62.51 N	21.17 E
Korsør, Den. (kôrs′ûr′)	159	55.19 N	11.08 E
Kortrijk, Bel.	163	50.49 N	3.10 E
Koryakskiy Khrebet (Mts.), Sov. Un.	181	62.00 N	168.45 E
Koryukovka, Sov. Un. (kôr-yo͞o-kôf′kȧ)	175	51.44 N	32.24 E
Kościan, Pol. (kŭsh′tsyȧn)	166	52.05 N	16.38 E
Kościerzyna, Pol. (kŭsh-tsyĕ-zhē′nȧ)	167	54.08 N	17.59 E
Kosciusko, Ms. (kŏs-ĭ-ŭs′kō)	126	33.04 N	89.35 W
Kosciusko, Mt., Austl.	216	36.26 S	148.20 E
Kosel′sk, Sov. Un. (kô-zĕlsk′)	174	54.01 N	35.49 E
Kosha, Sud.	225	20.49 N	30.27 E
Koshigaya, Jap. (kȯ′shė-gä′yä)	205a	35.53 N	139.48 E
Koshiki-Rettō (Is.), Jap. (kō-shē′kė rȧt′tō)	205	31.51 N	129.40 E
Kosi (R.), India (kȯ′sē)	196	26.00 N	86.20 E
Košice, Czech. (kō′shė-tsĕ′)	167	48.43 N	21.17 E
Kosino, Sov. Un.	66b	55.43 N	37.52 E
Kosmos, S. Afr. (kŏz′mŏs)	227b	25.45 S	27.51 E
Kosmosa, Monument (P. Int.), Sov. Un.	66b	55.49 N	37.38 E
Kosobrodskiy, Sov. Un. (kä-sô′brȯd-skĭ)	182a	54.14 N	60.53 E
Koso Lake, see Hövsgöl Nuur			
Kosovska Mitrovica, Yugo. (kȯ′sȯv-skä′ mė′trȯ-vė-tsä′)	173	42.51 N	20.50 E
Kostajnica, Yugo. (kôs′tä-ė-nē′tsȧ)	172	45.14 N	16.32 E
Koster, S. Afr.	223d	25.52 S	26.52 E
Kostino, Sov. Un. (kôs′tĭ-nô)	182b	55.54 N	37.51 E
Kostroma, Sov. Un. (kȯs-trȯ-mȧ′)	174	57.46 N	40.55 E
Kostroma (Oblast), Sov. Un.	174	57.50 N	41.10 E
Kostrzyn, Pol. (kôst′chėn)	166	52.35 N	14.38 E
Kos′va R., Sov. Un. (kôs′vȧ)	182a	58.44 N	57.08 E
Koszalin, Pol. (kô-shä′lĭn)	166	54.12 N	16.10 E
Köszeg, Hung. (kû′sĕg)	166	47.21 N	16.32 E
Kota, India	196	25.17 N	75.49 E
Kota Baharu, Mala. (kō′tä bä′ro͞o)	206	6.15 N	102.23 E
Kotabaru, Indon.	206	3.22 S	116.15 E
Kota Kinabalu, Mala.	206	5.55 N	116.05 E
Kota Kota, Malawi (kō-tȧ kō-tȧ)	226	12.52 S	34.16 E
Kota Tinggi, Mala.	191b	1.43 N	103.54 E
Kotel, Bul. (kō-tĕl′)	173	42.54 N	26.28 E
Kotel′nich, Sov. Un. (kȯ-tyĕl′nėch)	178	58.15 N	48.20 E
Kotel′nyy (I.), Sov. Un. (kȯ-tyĕl′nė)	181	74.51 N	134.09 E
Kothapur, India	197	16.48 N	74.15 E
Kotka, Fin. (kŏt′kȧ)	165	60.28 N	26.56 E
Kotlas, Sov. Un. (kôt′lȧs)	178	61.10 N	46.50 E
Kotlin, Ostrov (I.), Sov. Un. (ȯs-trôf′ kôt′lĭn)	182c	60.02 N	29.49 E
Kōtō (Neigh.), Jap.	69a	35.41 N	139.48 E
Kotor, Yugo. (kō′tȯr)	173	42.26 N	18.48 E
Kotorosl′ (R.), Sov. Un. (kȯ-tô′rȯsl)	174	57.18 N	39.08 E
Kotor Varoš, Yugo. (kȯ′tȯr vä′rȯsh)	172	44.37 N	17.23 E
Kotovsk, Sov. Un. (kȯ-tôfsk′)	175	47.49 N	29.31 E
Kotte, Sri Lanka	197	6.50 N	80.05 E
Kotto (R.), Cen. Afr. Rep.	225	5.17 N	22.04 E
Kotuy (R.), Sov. Un. (kô-to͞o′)	181	71.00 N	103.15 E
Kotzebue, Ak. (kȯt′sē-bo͞o)	107	66.48 N	162.42 W
Kotzebue Sd., Ak.	107	67.00 N	164.28 W
Koualé, Mali	228	11.24 N	7.01 W
Kouchibouguac Natl. Pk., Can.	104	46.53 N	65.35 W
Koudougou, Burkina (ko͞o-do͞o′go͞o)	228	12.15 N	2.22 W
Kouilou (R.), Con.	230	4.00 S	12.05 E
Koula-Moutou, Gabon	230	1.08 S	12.29 E
Koulikoro, Mali (ko͞o-lė-kō′rȯ)	228	12.53 N	7.33 W
Koulouguidi, Mali	228	13.27 N	17.33 E
Koumra, Chad	229	8.55 N	17.33 E
Koundara, Gui.	228	12.29 N	13.18 W
Koundé, Cen. Afr. Rep. (ko͞on-dā′)	225	6.08 N	14.32 E
Kounradskiy, Sov. Un. (kŭ-o͞on-rät′skē)	180	47.25 N	75.10 E
Kouroussa, Gui. (ko͞o-ro͞o′sä)	228	10.39 N	9.53 W
Koutiala, Mali (ko͞o-tė-ä′lä)	224	12.29 N	5.29 W
Kouvola, Fin. (kō′o͞o-vȯ-lä)	165	60.51 N	26.40 E
Kouzhen, China (kō-jŭn)	200	36.19 N	117.37 E
Kovda (L.), Sov. Un. (kôv′dȧ)	178	66.45 N	32.00 E
Kovel′ Sov. Un. (kō′vĕl)	167	51.13 N	24.45 E
Kovno, see Kaunas			
Kovrov, Sov. Un. (kȯv-rôf′)	174	56.23 N	41.21 E
Kowie, see Port Alfred			
Kowloon, Hong Kong (kō′lo͞on′)	203	22.28 N	114.20 E
Kowloon City, Hong Kong	68c	22.19 N	114.11 E
Kowloon (Jiulong), Hong Kong	68c	22.18 N	114.10 E
Koyuk, Ak. (kȯ-yo͞ok′)	107	65.00 N	161.18 W
Koyukuk (R.), Ak. (kȯ-yo͞o′ko͝ok)	107	66.25 N	153.50 W
Kozáni, Grc.	173	40.16 N	21.51 E
Kozelets, Sov. Un. (kȯzĕ-lyĕts)	175	50.53 N	31.07 E
Kozienice, Pol. (kō-zyĕ-nē′tsĕ)	167	51.34 N	21.35 E
Koźle, Pol. (kôzh′lĕ)	167	50.19 N	18.10 E
Kozloduy, Bul. (kŭz′lȯ-dwē)	173	43.45 N	23.42 E
Kōzu (I.), Jap. (kō′zo͞o)	205	34.16 N	139.03 E
Kozukue (Neigh.), Jap.	69a	35.30 N	139.36 E
Kraai (R.), S. Afr. (krā′ė)	227c	30.50 S	27.03 E
Krabbendijke, Neth.	157a	51.26 N	4.05 E
Krâchéh, Kamp.	206	12.28 N	106.06 E
Kragerö, Nor. (krä′gĕr-û)	164	58.53 N	9.21 E
Kragujevac, Yugo. (krä′go͞o′yĕ-vȧts)	173	44.01 N	20.55 E
Krahenhöhe (Neigh.), F.R.G.	63	51.10 N	7.06 E
Kra, Isth. of, Thai.	206	9.30 S	99.45 E
Kraków, Pol. (krä′ko͝of)	167	50.05 N	20.00 E
Kraljevo, Yugo. (kräl′ye-vô)	159	43.39 N	20.48 E
Kramatorsk, Sov. Un. (krȧ-mä′tôrsk)	175	48.43 N	37.32 E
Kramfors, Swe. (kräm′fȯrs)	164	62.54 N	17.49 E
Krampnitz, G.D.R.	65a	52.28 N	13.04 E
Kranj, Yugo. (krän′)	172	46.16 N	14.23 E
Kranskop, S. Afr. (kränz′kŏp)	227c	28.57 S	30.54 E
Kransnaya Gorka, Sov. Un. (kräs′nȧ-yȧ gôr′ká)	182a	55.13 N	56.43 E
Krāslava, Sov. Un. (kräs′lä-vä)	174	55.53 N	27.12 E
Kraslice, Czech. (kräs′lė-tsĕ)	166	50.19 N	12.30 E
Krasnaya Sloboda, Sov. Un.	179	48.25 N	44.35 E
Kraśnik, Pol. (kräsh′nĭk)	167	50.53 N	22.15 E
Krasnoarmeysk, Sov. Un. (kräs′nȯ-ȧr-maśk′)	182b	56.06 N	38.09 E
Krasnoarmeyskoye, Sov. Un.	175	48.19 N	37.04 E
Krasnodar, Sov. Un. (kräs′nȯ-dȧr)	175	45.03 N	38.55 E
Krasnodarskiy (Oblast) **Province,** Sov. Un. (krȧs-nȯ-där′skĭ ôb′lȧst)	175	47.28 N	38.13 E
Krasnogorsk, Sov. Un.	182b	55.49 N	37.20 E
Krasnogorskiy, Sov. Un. (kräs-nȯ-gôr′skĭ)	182a	54.36 N	61.25 E
Krasnograd, Sov. Un. (kräs′nȯ-grät)	175	49.23 N	35.26 E
Krasnogvardeyskiy, Sov. Un. (krȧ′sno-gvăr-dzyē ės-kēė)	182a	57.17 N	62.05 E
Krasnokamsk, Sov. Un. (kräs-nȯ-kämsk′)	178	58.00 N	55.45 E
Krasnokutsk, Sov. Un. (krȧs-nȯ-ko͞otsk′)	175	50.03 N	35.05 E
Krasnosel′ye, Sov. Un. (kräs′nȯ-sĕl′yĕ)	175	48.44 N	32.24 E
Krasnoslobodsk, Sov. Un. (kräs′nȯ-slȯbôtsk′)	178	54.20 N	43.50 E
Krasnotur′insk, Sov. Un. (krŭs-nŭ-to͞o-rensk′)	182a	59.47 N	60.15 E
Krasnoufimsk, Sov. Un. (krŭs-nŭ-o͞o-fēmsk′)	182a	56.38 N	57.46 E
Krasnoural′sk, Sov. Un. (kräs′nȯ-o͞o-rälsk′)	182a	58.21 N	60.05 E
Krasnousol′skiy, Sov. Un. (kräs-nȯ-o͞o-sôl′skĭ)	182a	53.53 N	56.30 E
Krasnovishersk, Sov. Un. (kräs-nȯ-vėshersk′)	178	60.22 N	57.20 E
Krasnovodsk, Sov. Un. (krȧs-nȯ-vȯtsk′)	179	40.00 N	52.50 E
Krasnoyarsk, Sov. Un. (kräs-nȯ-yȧrsk′)	180	56.13 N	93.12 E
Krasnoye Selo, Sov. Un. (kräs′nŭ-yŭ sâ′lō)	182c	59.44 N	30.06 E
Krasnyj Stroitel′ (Neigh.), Sov. Un.	66b	55.35 N	37.37 E
Krasny Kholm, Sov. Un. (kräs′nė ĸōlm)	174	58.03 N	37.11 E
Krasnystaw, Pol. (kräs-nė-stȧf′)	167	50.59 N	23.11 E
Krasnyy Bor, Sov. Un. (kräs′nė bôr)	182c	59.41 N	30.40 E
Krasnyy Klyuch, Sov. Un. (kräs′nė′klyûch′)	182a	55.24 N	56.43 E
Krasnyy Kut, Sov. Un. (krȧs-nė ko͞ot′)	179	50.50 N	47.00 E
Kratovo, Sov. Un. (krä′tô-vô)	182b	55.35 N	38.10 E
Kratovo, Yugo. (krä′tȯ-vȯ)	173	42.04 N	22.12 E
Kray (Neigh.), F.R.G.	63	51.28 N	7.05 E
Krefeld, F.R.G. (krā′fĕlt)	169c	51.20 N	6.34 E
Kremenchug, Sov. Un. (krĕm′ĕn-cho͞ogh′)	175	49.04 N	33.26 E
Kremenchugskoye (Res.), Sov. Un. (krĕm-ĕn-cho͞ogh′skô-ye)	175	49.20 N	32.45 E
Kremenets, Sov. Un. (krĕ-mĕn-yĕts′)	167	50.06 N	25.43 E
Kreml′ (P. Int.), Sov. Un.	66b	55.45 N	37.37 E
Kremmen, G.D.R. (krĕ′mĕn)	157b	52.45 N	13.02 E
Krempe, F.R.G. (krĕm′pĕ)	157c	53.50 N	9.29 E
Krems, Aus. (krĕms)	166	48.25 N	15.36 E
Krestsy, Sov. Un.	165	58.18 N	32.26 E
Kresttsy, Sov. Un. (krȧst′sė)	174	58.16 N	32.25 E
Kretinga, Sov. Un. (krĕ-tĭŋ′gȧ)	165	55.55 N	21.17 E
Kreuzberg, F.R.G.	63	51.09 N	7.27 E
Kreuzberg (Neigh.), F.R.G.	65a	52.30 N	13.23 E
Kribi, Cam. (krē′bė)	229	2.57 N	9.55 E
Krichëv, Sov. Un. (krē′chôf)	174	53.44 N	31.39 E
Krilon, Mys (Pt.), Sov. Un. (mĭs krĭl′ȯn)	204	45.58 N	142.00 E
Krimpen aan de IJssel, Neth.	157a	51.55 N	4.34 E
Krishna (R.), India	193	16.23 N	75.00 E
Krishnanagar, India	196	23.29 N	88.33 E
Krishnapur, India	67a	22.36 N	88.26 E
Kristiansand, Nor. (krĭs-tyȧn-sän′′)	164	58.09 N	7.59 E
Kristianstad, Swe. (krĭs-tyȧn-städ′)	164	56.02 N	14.09 E
Kristiansund, Nor. (krĭs-tyȧn-so͞on′′)	164	63.07 N	7.49 E
Kristinehamn, Swe. (krės-tē′nĕ-häm′)	164	59.20 N	14.05 E
Kristinestad, Fin. (krĭs-tē′nĕ-städh)	165	62.16 N	21.28 E
Kriva-Palanka, Yugo. (krē-vȧ-pȧ-läŋ′kȧ)	173	42.12 N	22.21 E
Krivoye Ozero, Sov. Un.	175	47.57 N	30.21 E
Krivoy Rog, Sov. Un. (krė-voi′ rȯgh′)	175	47.54 N	33.22 E
Križevci, Yugo. (krē′zhĕv-tsĭ)	172	46.02 N	16.30 E
Krk (I.), Yugo. (k′rk)	172	45.06 N	14.33 E
Krnov, Czech. (k′r′nôf)	167	50.05 N	17.41 E
Krokodil (R.), S. Afr. (krŏ′kŏ-dī)	223d	24.25 S	27.08 E
Krolevets, Sov. Un. (krȯ-lĕ′vyĕts)	175	51.33 N	33.21 E
Kroměříž, Czech. (krô′myĕr-zhēzh)	167	49.18 N	17.23 E
Kromy, Sov. Un. (krȯ′mė)	174	52.44 N	35.41 E
Kronshtadt, Sov. Un. (krōn′shtät)	182c	59.59 N	29.47 E
Kroonstad, S. Afr. (krōn′shtät)	223d	27.40 S	27.15 E
Kropotkin, Sov. Un. (krȧ-pôt′kĭn)	179	45.25 N	40.30 E
Krosno, Pol. (krȯs′nȯ)	167	49.41 N	21.46 E
Krotoszyn, Pol. (krȯ-tō′shĭn)	167	51.41 N	17.25 E
Krško, Yugo. (k′rsh′kȯ)	172	45.58 N	15.30 E
Kruger Natl. Park, S. Afr. (kro͞o′gēr) (krü′gĕr)	226	23.22 S	30.18 E
Krugersdorp, S. Afr. (kro͞o′gĕrz-dȯrp)	227b	26.06 S	27.46 E
Krugersdorp West, S. Afr.	71b	26.06 S	27.45 E
Krujë, Alb. (kro͞o′yȧ)	173	41.32 N	19.49 E
Krummenerl, F.R.G.	63	51.05 N	7.45 E

PLACE (Pronounciation)	PAGE	Lat. °′	Long. °′
Krummensee, G.D.R.	65a	52.36 N	13.42 E
Krung Thep (Bangkok), Thai.	206	13.50 N	100.29 E
Kruševac, Yugo. (krōō'shĕ-vàts)	173	43.34 N	21.21 E
Kruševo, Yugo.	173	41.20 N	21.15 E
Krylatskoje (Neigh.), Sov. Un.	66b	55.45 N	37.26 E
Krylbo, Swe. (krül'bô)	164	60.07 N	16.14 E
Krymskaya, Sov. Un. (krĭm'skà-yà)	175	44.58 N	38.01 E
Krymskaya (Oblast), Sov. Un.	175	45.08 N	34.05 E
Krymskiy P-Ov (Crimea) (Pen.), Sov. Un. (krēm-skĭ pô-lōō-ôs'trôf)	175	45.18 N	33.30 E
Krynki, Pol. (krĭn'kė)	167	53.15 N	23.47 E
Kryukov, Sov. Un. (k'r'yōō-kôf')	175	49.02 N	33.26 E
Ksar Chellala, Alg.	171	35.12 N	2.20 E
Ksar-el-Kebir, Mor.	160	35.01 N	5.48 W
Ksar-es-Souk, Mor.	160	31.58 N	4.25 W
K2 (Godwin Austen), Pak. (gŏd wĭn ôs'tĕn)	198	36.06 N	76.38 E
Kuai (R.), China (kōō-ī)	200	33.30 N	116.56 E
Kuala Klawang, Mala.	191b	2.57 N	102.04 E
Kuala Lumpur, Mala. (kwä'lä lōōm-pōōr')	191b	3.08 N	101.42 E
Kuandian, China (kůän-dĭĕn)	202	40.40 N	124.50 E
Kuba, Sov. Un. (kōō'bä)	179	41.05 N	48.30 E
Kuban' (R.), Sov. Un. (kōō-bàn'')	175	45.10 N	37.55 E
Kuban (R.), Sov. Un.	179	45.20 N	40.05 E
Kuban R., Sov. Un.	161	45.14 N	38.20 E
Kubenskoye (L.), Sov. Un.	178	59.40 N	39.40 E
Kuching, Mala. (kōō'chĭng)	206	1.30 N	110.26 E
Kuchinoerabo (I.), Jap. (kōō'chē nō ĕr'á-bō)	205	30.31 N	129.53 E
Küçükbakkal, Tur.	66f	40.58 N	29.06 E
Kudamatsu, Jap. (kōō'dà-mä'tsōō)	205	34.00 N	131.51 E
Kudap, Indon.	191b	1.14 N	102.30 E
Kudat, Mala. (kōō-dät')	206	6.56 N	116.48 E
Kudbrooke (Neigh.), Eng.	62	51.28 N	0.03 E
Kudirkos Naumietis, Sov. Un. (kōōdĭr-kôs nå'ōō-mĕ'tĭs)	165	54.51 N	23.00 E
Kudymkar, Sov. Un. (kōō-dĭm-kär')	180	58.43 N	54.52 E
Kufstein, Aus. (kōōf'shtīn)	166	47.34 N	12.11 E
Kuhstedt, F.R.G. (kōō'shtĕ)	157c	53.23 N	8.58 E
Kuibyshev, see Kuybyshev			
Kuilsrivier, S. Afr.	226a	33.56 S	18.41 E
Kuito, Ang.	230	12.22 S	16.56 E
Kuji, Jap.	205	33.57 N	131.18 E
Kujū-san (Mt.), Jap. (kōō'jōō-sän')	205	33.07 N	131.14 E
Kukës, Alb. (kōō'kĕs)	173	42.03 N	20.25 E
Kula, Bul. (kōō'là)	173	43.52 N	23.13 E
Kula, Tur.	179	38.32 N	28.30 E
Kula Kangri Mt., China	196	33.11 N	90.36 E
Kular, Khrebet (Mts.), Sov. Un. (kōō-lär')	181	69.00 N	131.45 E
Kuldīga, Sov. Un. (kōōl'dē-gà)	165	56.59 N	21.59 E
Kulebaki, Sov. Un. (kōō-lĕ-bàk'ĭ)	178	55.22 N	42.30 E
Küllenhahn (Neigh.), F.R.G.	63	51.14 N	7.08 E
Kulmbach, F.R.G. (klōōlm'bäĸ)	166	50.07 N	11.28 E
Kulunda, Sov. Un. (kōō-lōōn'dà)	180	52.38 N	74.00 E
Kulundinskoye (L.), Sov. Un.	180	52.45 N	77.18 E
Kum (R.), Kor. (kōōm)	204	36.50 N	127.30 E
Kuma (R.), Sov. Un. (kōō'mä)	179	44.50 N	45.10 E
Kumamoto, Jap. (kōō'mä-mō'tô)	205	32.49 N	130.40 E
Kumano-Nada (Sea), Jap. (kōō-mä'nō nä-dä)	205	34.03 N	136.36 E
Kumanovo, Yugo. (kōō-mä'nô-vô)	173	42.10 N	21.41 E
Kumasi, Ghana (kōō-mä'sė)	228	6.41 N	1.35 W
Kumba, Cam. (kōōm'bà)	229	4.38 N	9.25 E
Kumbakonam, India (kōōm'bŭ-kō'nŭm)	197	10.59 N	79.25 E
Kumkale, Tur.	173	39.59 N	26.10 E
Kumo, Nig.	229	10.03 N	11.13 E
Kumta, India	197	14.19 N	75.28 E
Kumul, see Hami			
Kunashak, Sov. Un. (kû-nä'shák)	182a	55.43 N	61.35 E
Kunashir (Kunashiri) (I.), Sov. Un. (kōō-nŭ-shēr')	199	44.40 N	145.45 E
Kunashiri (I.), see Kunashir			
Kunda, Sov. Un. (kōō'dà)	174	59.30 N	26.28 E
Kundelungu, Plateau des (Plat.), Zaire	222	9.00 S	25.30 E
Kundravy, Sov. Un. (kōōn'drà-vĭ)	182a	54.50 N	60.14 E
Kundur (I.), Indon.	191b	0.49 N	103.20 E
Kunene (Cunene) (R.), Ang.-Namibia	230	17.05 S	12.35 E
Kungälv, Swe. (kŭng'ĕlf)	164	57.53 N	12.01 E
Kungrad, Sov. Un. (kōōn-grät')	155	42.59 N	59.00 E
Kungsbacka, Swe. (kŭngs'bä-kà)	164	57.31 N	12.04 E
Kungur, Sov. Un. (kōōn-gōōr')	182a	57.27 N	56.53 E
Kunitachi, Jap.	69a	35.41 N	139.26 E
Kunlun Shan (Mts.), China (kōōn-lōōn shän)	198	35.26 N	83.09 E
Kunming, China (kōōn-mĭŋ)	203	25.10 N	102.50 E
Kunsan, Kor. (kōōn'sän')	203	35.54 N	126.46 E
Kunshan, China (kōōnshän)	201b	31.23 N	120.57 E
Kuntsëvo, Sov. Un. (kōōn-tsyô'vô)	182b	55.43 N	37.27 E
Kun'ya (R.), Sov. Un. (kōōn'yà)	174	56.45 N	30.53 E
Kun'ya, Sov. Un.	182a	58.42 N	56.47 E
Kuopio, Fin. (kōō-ô'pē-ŏ)	158	62.48 N	28.30 E
Kupa (R.), Yugo.	172	45.32 N	14.50 E
Kupang, Indon.	207	10.14 S	123.37 E
Kupavna, Sov. Un.	182b	55.49 N	38.11 E
Kupferdreh (Neigh.), F.R.G.	63	51.23 N	7.05 E
Kupino, Sov. Un. (kōō-pĭ'nô)	180	54.00 N	77.47 E
Kupiškis, Sov. Un. (kōō-pĭsh'kĭs)	141	55.50 N	24.55 E
Kupyansk, Sov. Un. (kōōp-yänsk')	175	49.44 N	37.38 E
Kuqa, China (kōō-chyä)	198	41.34 N	82.44 E
Kura (R.), Sov. Un. (kōō'rà)	179	41.10 N	45.40 E
Kurashiki, Jap. (kōō'rä-shē'kė)	205	34.37 N	133.44 E
Kuraymah, Sud.	225	18.34 N	31.49 E
Kurayoshi, Jap. (kōō'rà-yō'shė)	205	35.25 N	133.49 E
Kurdistan (Reg.), Tur.-Iran (kûrd'ĭ-stăn)	179	37.40 N	43.30 E
Kurdufān (Prov.), Sud. (kôr-dô-fän')	225	14.08 N	28.39 E
Kŭrdzhali, Bul.	173	41.39 N	25.21 E
Kure, Jap. (kōō'rĕ)	205	34.17 N	132.35 E
Kuressaare, Sov. Un. (kōō'rĕ-sä'rĕ)	165	58.15 N	22.26 E
Kurgan, Sov. Un. (kōōr-găn')	180	55.28 N	65.14 E
Kurgan Tyube, Sov. Un. (kōōr-gän' työō'bĕ)	180	38.00 N	68.49 E
Kurihama, Jap. (kōō-rē-hä'mä)	205a	35.14 N	139.42 E
Kuril Is., Sov. Un. (kōō'rĭl)	181	46.20 N	149.30 E
Ku-ring-gai, Austl.	70a	33.45 S	151.08 E
Kurisches Haff (Bay), Sov. Un.	165	55.10 N	21.08 E
Kurl (Neigh.), F.R.G.	63	51.35 N	7.35 E
Kurla (Neigh.), India	197b	19.03 N	72.53 E
Kurmuk, Sud. (kōōr'mōōk)	225	10.40 N	34.13 E
Kurnell, Austl.	70a	34.01 S	151.13 E
Kurnool, India (kōōr-nōōl')	197	16.00 N	78.04 E
Kuro (I.), Jap. (kōō'rô)	205	30.49 N	129.56 E
Kurrajong, Austl.	211b	33.33 S	150.40 E
Kuršėnai, Sov. Un. (kōōr'shå-nĭ)	155	56.01 N	22.56 E
Kursk (Oblast), Sov. Un. (kōōrsk)	165	51.30 N	35.13 E
Kursk, Sov. Un. (kōōrsk)	165	51.44 N	36.08 E
Kuršumlija, Yugo. (kōōr'shōōm'lĭ-yà)	163	43.08 N	21.18 E
Kūrtī, Sud.	225	18.08 N	31.39 E
Kuruçeşme (Neigh.), Tur.	66f	41.03 N	29.02 E
Kuruman, S. Afr. (kōō-rōō-män')	226	27.25 S	23.30 E
Kurume, Jap.	69a	35.45 N	139.32 E
Kurume, Jap. (kōō'rōō-mĕ)	205	33.10 N	130.30 E
Kururi, Jap. (kōō'rōō-rė)	205a	35.17 N	140.05 E
Kusa, Sov. Un. (kōō'sà)	182a	55.19 N	59.27 E
Kushchëvskaya, Sov. Un.	175	46.34 N	39.40 E
Kushikino, Jap. (kōō'shĭ-kē'nō)	205	31.44 N	130.19 E
Kushimoto, Jap. (kōō'shĭ-mō'tō)	205	33.29 N	135.47 E
Kushiro, Jap. (kōō'shē-rō)	204	43.00 N	144.22 E
Kush-Murun (L.), Sov. Un. (kōōsh-mōō-rōōn')	180	52.30 N	64.15 E
Kushum (R.), Sov. Un. (kōō-shōōm')	179	50.30 N	50.40 E
Kushva, Sov. Un. (kōōsh'và)	182a	58.18 N	59.51 E
Kuskokwim (R.), Ak.	107	61.32 N	160.36 W
Kuskokwim B., Ak. (kŭs'kô-kwĭm)	107	59.25 N	163.14 W
Kuskokwim Mts., Ak.	107	62.08 N	158.00 W
Kuskovak, Ak. (kŭs-kō'văk)	107	60.10 N	162.50 W
Kuskovo (Neigh.), Sov. Un.	66b	55.44 N	37.49 E
Kustanay, Sov. Un. (kōōs-tà-nī')	180	53.10 N	63.39 E
Kūstī, Sud.	225	13.09 N	32.39 E
Kütahya, Tur. (kû-tä'hyà)	179	39.20 N	29.50 E
Kutaisi, Sov. Un. (kōō-tŭ-ē'sē)	179	42.15 N	42.40 E
Kutaradja, Indon.	206	5.30 N	95.20 E
Kutch, Gulf of, India	196	22.45 N	68.33 E
Kutch, Rann of (Swp.), India	196	23.59 N	69.13 E
Kutenholz, F.R.G. (kōō'tĕn-hōlts)	157c	53.29 N	9.20 E
Kutim, Sov. Un. (kōō'tĭm)	182a	60.22 N	58.51 E
Kutina, Yugo. (kōō'tē-nà)	172	45.29 N	16.48 E
Kutno (L.), Sov. Un.	178	65.15 N	31.30 E
Kutno, Pol. (kōōt'nô)	167	52.14 N	19.22 E
Kutulik, Sov. Un. (kōō tōō'lyĭk)	179	53.12 N	102.51 E
Kuty, Sov. Un. (kōō'tė)	167	48.16 N	25.12 E
Kuusamo, Fin. (kōō'sà-mô)	158	65.59 N	29.10 E
Kuvshinovo, Sov. Un. (kōōv-shē'nô-vô)	174	57.01 N	34.09 E
Kuwait, Asia	190	29.00 N	48.45 E
Kuwait, see Al Kuwayt			
Kuwana, Jap. (kōō'wà-nà)	205	35.02 N	136.40 E
Kuybyshev, (Kuibyshev), Sov. Un. (kōō'ē-bĭ-shĭf)	178	53.10 N	50.05 E
Kuybyshevskoye (Res.), Sov. Un.	178	53.40 N	49.00 E
Kuz'minki (Neigh.), Sov. Un.	66b	55.42 N	37.48 E
Kuzneckovo, Sov. Un.	182b	55.29 N	38.22 E
Kuznetsk, Sov. Un. (kōōz-nyĕtsk')	179	53.00 N	46.30 E
Kuznetsk Basin, Sov. Un.	180	57.15 N	86.15 E
Kuznetsovka, Sov. Un. (kōōz-nyĕt'sôf-kà)	182a	54.41 N	56.40 E
Kuznetsovo, Sov. Un. (kōōz-nyĕt-sô'vô)	174	56.39 N	36.55 E
Kuznetsy, Sov. Un.	182b	55.50 N	38.39 E
Kvarner Zaliv (B.), Yugo. (kvär'nĕr)	172	44.41 N	14.05 E
Kvichak, Ak. (vĭc'-hăk)	107	59.00 N	156.48 W
Kwa (R.), Zaire	230	3.00 S	16.45 E
Kwahu Plat., Ghana	228	7.00 N	1.35 W
Kwando (R.), Zambia	230	16.50 S	22.40 E
Kwango (Cuango) (R.), Afr. (kwäng'ō')	230	6.35 S	16.50 E
Kwangwazi, Tan.	231	7.47 S	38.15 E
Kwa-Thema, S. Afr.	71b	26.18 S	28.23 E
Kwekwe, Zimb.	226	18.49 S	29.45 E
Kwenge (R.), Zaire (kwĕŋ'gĕ)	230	6.45 S	18.23 E
Kwidzyń, Pol. (kvē'dzĭn)	167	53.45 N	18.56 E
Kwilu (R.), Zaire (kwē'lōō)	230	3.22 S	17.22 E
Kyakhta, Sov. Un. (kyäĸ'ta)	181	51.00 N	107.30 E
Kyaukpyu, Bur. (chouk'pyoo')	198	19.19 N	93.33 E
Kyayisu (R.), India	196	38.05 N	74.36 E
Kybartai, Sov. Un. (kē'bär-tī')	165	54.40 N	22.46 E
Ky Lam, Viet.	203	15.48 N	108.30 E
Kyn, Sov. Un. (kĭn')	182a	57.52 N	58.42 E
Kynuna, Austl. (kī-nōō'nà)	215	21.30 S	142.12 E
Kyoga, L., Ug.	231	1.30 N	32.45 E
Kyōga-Saki (C.), Jap. (kyō'gä sa'kė)	205	35.46 N	135.14 E
Kyŏngju, Kor. (kyŭng'yōō)	204	35.48 N	129.12 E
Kyōto, Jap. (ky 'tō')	205b	35.00 N	135.46 E
Kyōto (Pref.), Jap.	205b	34.56 N	135.42 E
Kyren, Sov. Un. (kĭ-rĕn')	180	51.46 N	102.13 E
Kyrönjoki (R.), Fin.	165	63.03 N	22.20 E
Kyrya, Sov. Un. (kēr'yà)	182a	59.18 N	59.03 E
Kyshtym, Sov. Un. (kĭsh-tĭm')	182a	55.43 N	60.33 E
Kytlym, Sov. Un. (kĭt'lĭm)	182a	59.30 N	59.15 E
Kyūhōji (Neigh.), Jap.	69b	34.38 N	135.35 E
Kyūshū (I.), Jap. (kyōō'shōō')	205	32.27 N	131.03 E
Kyustendil, Bul. (kyōōs-tĕn-dĭl')	173	42.16 N	22.39 E
Kyzyl, Sov. Un. (kĭ zĭl)	180	51.37 N	93.38 E
Kyzyl Kum, Peski (Des.), Sov. Un. (kĭ zĭl kōōm)	155	42.47 N	64.45 E
Kzyl-Orda, Sov. Un. (kzĕl-ôr'dà)	180	44.58 N	65.45 E

L

PLACE (Pronounciation)	PAGE	Lat. °′	Long. °′
Laa, Aus.	166	48.42 N	16.23 E
Laab im Walde, Aus.	66e	48.09 N	16.11 E
Laaken (Neigh.), F.R.G.	63	51.15 N	7.15 E
La Almunia de Doña Godina, Sp. (lä'äl-mōōn'yä dā dō nyä gô-dē'nä)	170	41.29 N	1.22 W
Laas Caanood, Som.	223a	8.24 N	47.20 E
La Asunción, Ven. (lä ä-sōōn-syōn')	142	11.02 N	63.57 W
La Baie, Can.	103	48.21 N	70.53 W
La Banda, Arg. (lä bän'dä)	144	27.48 S	64.12 W
La Bandera, Chile	61b	33.34 S	70.39 W
La Barca, Mex. (lä bär'kà)	130	20.17 N	102.33 W
Labé, Gui. (là-bā')	228	11.19 N	12.17 W
Labe (R.), see Elbe			
Laberge (L.), Can. (là-bērzh')	96	61.08 N	136.42 W
Laberinto de las Doce Leguas (Is.), Cuba (lä-bä-rēn tô dā läs dō'sā lā'gwäs)	134	20.40 N	78.35 W
Labinsk, Sov. Un.	179	44.30 N	40.40 E
Labis, Mala. (lăb'ĭs)	191b	2.23 N	103.01 E
La Bisbal, Sp. (lä bēs-bäl')	171	41.55 N	3.00 E
Labo, Phil. (lä'bô)	207a	14.11 N	122.49 E
La Boissière, Fr.	64c	48.46 N	1.59 E
Labo, Mt., Phil.	207a	14.00 N	122.47 E
Labouheyre, Fr. (là-bōō-âr')	168	44.14 N	0.58 W
Laboulaye, Arg. (lä-bô'ōō-lä-yĕ)	144	34.01 S	63.10 W
Labrador (Reg.), Can. (lăb'rȧ-dôr)	97	53.05 N	63.30 W
Labrador Sea, Can.	105	50.38 N	55.00 W
Lábrea, Braz. (lä-brā'ä)	142	7.28 S	64.39 W
Labuan, Pulau (I.), Mala. (lä-bōō-än')	206	5.28 N	115.11 E
Labuha, Indon.	207	0.43 S	127.35 E
L'Acadie, Can. (là-kà-dē')	95a	45.18 N	73.22 W
L'Acadie (R.), Can.	95a	45.24 N	73.21 W
La Calera, Chile (lä-kä-lĕ-rä)	141b	32.47 S	71.11 W
La Calera, Col.	142a	4.43 N	73.58 W
Lac Allard, Can.	105	50.38 N	63.28 W
La Canada, Ca. (lä kän-yä'dä)	119a	34.13 N	118.12 W
La Candelaria, Mex.	60a	19.20 N	99.09 W
Lacantum (R.), Mex. (lä-kän-tōō'm)	131	16.13 N	90.52 W
La Carolina, Sp. (lä kä-rô-lē'nä)	170	38.16 N	3.48 W
La Catedral, Cerro (Mtn.), Mex. (sĕ'r-rô-lä-kä-tĕ-drà'l)	131a	19.32 N	99.31 W
Lac-Beauport, Can. (läk-bō-pōr')	95b	46.58 N	71.17 W
Laccadive Sea, Asia	196	9.10 N	75.17 E
Laccadive Is., see Lakshadweep			
Lac Court Oreille Ind. Res., Wi. (lăk kôrt-ô-rĕl) (lak kōōr tô-rā'y')	115	46.04 N	91.18 W
Lac du Flambeau Ind. Res., Wi.	115	46.12 N	89.50 W
La Ceiba, Hond. (lä sĕbä)	132	15.45 N	86.52 W
La Ceja, Col. (lä-sĕ-ĸä)	142a	6.02 N	75.25 W
Lac-Frontière, Can.	97	46.42 N	70.00 W
Lacha (L.), Sov. Un. (là'chä)	178	61.15 N	39.05 E
La Chaux de Fonds, Switz. (lá shō dē-fôɴ')	166	47.07 N	6.47 E
Lach Dera (R.), Som. (läk dä'rä)	223a	0.45 N	41.26 E
L'Achigan (R.), Can. (lä-shē-gäɴ)	95a	45.49 N	73.48 W
Lachine, Can. (lȧ-shēn')	95a	45.26 N	73.40 W
Lachlan (R.), Austl. (läk'lăn)	216	33.54 S	145.15 E
La Chorrera, Pan. (làchôr-rā'rä)	128a	8.54 N	79.47 W
Lachta (Neigh.), Sov. Un.	66a	60.00 N	30.09 E
Lachute, Can. (là-shōōt')	95a	45.39 N	74.20 W
La Ciotat, Fr. (lä syô-tà')	169	43.13 N	5.35 E
La Cisterna, Chile	61b	33.33 S	70.41 W
Lackawanna, NY (lak-à-wŏn'á)	113c	42.49 N	78.50 W
Lac la Biche, Can.	99	54.46 N	112.58 W
La Columna (Mtn.), see Bolivar			
Lacombe, Can.	99	52.28 N	113.44 W
La Concordia, Mex. (lä-kōn-kô'r-dyä)	131	16.07 N	92.40 W
Laconia, NH (là-kō'nĭ-ȧ)	111	43.30 N	71.30 W
La Conner, Wa. (là kŏn'ēr)	118a	48.23 N	122.30 W
La Coruña, Sp. (lä kô-rōō'nyä)	170	43.20 N	8.20 W
La Courneuve, Fr.	64c	48.56 N	2.23 E
Lacreek (L.), SD (lå'krēk)	114	43.04 N	101.46 W
La Cresenta, Ca. (lȧ krĕs'ĕnt-å)	119a	34.14 N	118.13 W
La Cross, Ks. (lȧ-krôs')	122	38.30 N	99.20 W
La Crosse, Wi.	115	43.48 N	91.14 W
La Cruz, Col. (lȧ krōōz')	142	1.37 N	77.00 W
La Cruz, C. R. (lä-krōō'z)	132	11.05 N	85.37 W
Lac Simard, (L.), Can.	103	47.38 N	78.40 W
Lacs, Riviere des (R.), ND (rē-vyĕr' de läk)	114	48.30 N	101.45 W
La Cuesta, C. R. (lä-kwĕ's-tä)	133	8.32 N	82.51 W
La Culebra, Sierra de (Mts.), Sp. (sē-ĕ'r-rä-dĕ-lä-kōō-lĕ-brä)	170	41.52 N	6.21 W
La Cygne, Ks. (là-sēn'y') (lå-sēn')	123	38.20 N	94.45 W
Ladd, Il. (lăd)	110	41.25 N	89.25 W
Ladíspoli, It. (lä-dē's-pô-lē)	171d	41.57 N	12.05 E
Lādīz, Iran	195	28.56 N	61.19 E
Ladner, Can. (lăd'nēr)	118d	49.05 N	123.05 W
Lādnun, India (läd'nōōn)	196	27.45 N	74.20 E
Ladoga, Lake, see Ladozhskoye Ozero			
La Dolorita, Ven.	61a	10.29 N	66.47 W
La Dorado, Col. (lä dô-rä'dä)	142a	5.28 N	74.42 W
Ladozhskoye Ozero (Ladoga, L.), Sov. Un. (là-dôsh'skô-yē ô'zĕ-rō)	165	60.59 N	31.30 E
La Durantaye, Can. (lä dü-räɴ-tā')	95b	46.51 N	70.51 W
Lady Frere, S. Afr. (lā-dē frâ'r')	227c	31.48 S	27.16 E
Lady Grey, S. Afr.	227c	30.44 S	27.17 E
Ladysmith, Can. (lā'dĭ-smĭth)	98	48.58 N	123.49 W
Ladysmith, S. Afr.	227c	28.38 S	29.48 E
Ladysmith, Wi.	115	45.27 N	91.07 W
Lae, Pap. N. Gui. (lä'å)	207	6.15 S	146.57 E
Laerdalsøyri, Nor.	164	61.08 N	7.26 E
Laesø (I.), Den. (lâs'û)	164	57.17 N	10.57 E
La Esperanza, Hond. (lä ĕs-på-rän'zä)	132	14.20 N	88.21 W
La Estrada, Sp. (lä ĕs-trä'dä)	170	42.42 N	8.29 W
Lafa, China (lä'fä)	204	43.49 N	127.19 E
Lafayette, Al.	126	32.52 N	85.25 W

ng-sing; nŋ-baŋk; ɴ-nasalized n; nŏd; cŏmmit; ōld; ôbey; ôrder; oi-boil; fōōd; fŏŏt; ou-out; s-soft; sh-dish; th-thin; pūre; ůnite; ûrn; stŭd; circŭs; ü-as in French tu; '-indeterminate vowel.

PLACE (Pronounciation)	PAGE	Lat. °'	Long. °'
Lafayette, Ca.	118b	37.53 N	122.07 W
Lafayette, Ga. (lă-fâ-yĕt')	126	34.41 N	85.19 W
Lafayette, In.	110	40.25 N	86.55 W
Lafayette, La.	125	30.15 N	92.02 W
La Fayette, RI	112b	41.34 N	71.29 W
Lafayette Hill, Pa.	56b	40.05 N	75.15 W
Laferrere, Arg.	60d	34.45 S	58.35 W
La Ferté-Alais, Fr. (lä-fĕr-tā'ä-lā')	169b	48.29 N	2.19 E
La Ferté-sous-Jouarre, Fr. (lá fĕr-tā'sōō-zhōō-är')	169b	48.56 N	3.07 E
Lafia, Nig.	229	8.30 N	8.30 E
Lafiagi, Nig.	229	8.52 N	5.25 E
Laflèche, Can.	54b	45.30 N	73.28 W
La Flèche, Fr. (là flăsh')	168	47.43 N	0.03 W
La Floresta, Sp.	65e	41.27 N	2.04 E
La Florida, Chile	61b	33.27 S	70.33 W
La Follete, Tn. (lă-fŏl'ĕt)	126	36.23 N	84.07 W
Lafourche, Bay., La. (bă-yōō'lá-fōōrsh')	125	29.25 N	90.15 W
La Frette-sur-Seine, Fr.	64c	48.58 N	2.11 E
La Gaiba, Braz. (lä-gī'bä)	143	17.54 S	57.32 W
Lagan, N. Ire. (lā'găn)	162	54.30 N	6.00 W
Lågan (R.), Nor. (lô'ghĕn)	164	59.15 N	9.47 E
Lagan (R.), Swe.	164	56.34 N	13.25 E
La Garenne-Colombes, Fr.	64c	48.55 N	2.15 E
Lagarto, R., Pan. (lä-gä'r-tô)	128a	9.08 N	80.05 W
Lagartos L., Mex. (lä-gä'r-tôs)	132a	21.32 N	88.15 W
Laghouat, Alg. (lä-gwät')	224	33.45 N	2.49 E
Lagny, Fr. (län-yē')	169b	48.53 N	2.41 E
Lagoa da Prata, Braz. (là-gô'ä-dà-prä'tà)	141a	20.04 S	45.33 W
Lagoa Dourada, Braz. (là-gô'ä-dōō-rä'dä)	141a	20.55 S	44.03 W
Lagogne, Fr. (laN-gōn'y')	168	44.43 N	3.50 E
Lagonay, Phil.	207a	13.44 N	123.31 E
Lagonoy G., Phil. (lä-gô-noi')	207a	13.34 N	123.46 E
Lagos, Nig. (lä'gōs)	229	6.27 N	3.24 E
Lagos, Port. (lä'gôzh)	170	37.08 N	8.43 W
Lagos de Moreno, Mex. (lä'gōs dā mō-rā'nō)	130	21.21 N	101.55 W
La Grand' Combe, Fr. (là grän kaNb')	168	44.12 N	4.03 E
La Grande, Or. (là grănd')	116	45.20 N	118.06 W
La Grande (R.), Can.	97	53.55 N	77.30 W
La Grange, Austl. (lä grānj)	214	18.40 S	122.00 E
La Grange, Ga. (là-grānj')	126	33.01 N	85.00 W
La Grange, Il.	113a	41.49 N	87.53 W
Lagrange, In.	110	41.40 N	85.25 W
La Grange, Ky.	110	38.20 N	85.25 W
La Grange, Mo.	123	40.04 N	91.30 W
Lagrange, Oh.	113d	41.14 N	82.07 W
Lagrange, Tx.	125	29.55 N	96.50 W
La Grange Highlands, Il.	58a	41.48 N	87.53 W
La Grange Park, Il.	58a	41.50 N	87.52 W
La Granja, Chile	61b	33.32 S	70.39 W
La Grita, Ven. (lä grē'tà)	142	8.02 N	71.59 W
La Guaira, Ven. (lä gwä'ē-rä)	143b	10.36 N	66.54 W
La Guardia, Sp. (lä gwär'dē-á)	170	41.55 N	8.48 W
La Guardia Arpt., NY	55	40.46 N	73.53 W
Laguna, Braz. (lä-gōō'nä)	144	28.19 S	48.42 W
Laguna, Cayos (Is.), Cuba (kä'yōs-lä-gōō'nä)	134	22.15 N	82.45 W
Laguna de Bay (L.), Phil. (lä-gōō'nä dā bä'ē)	207a	14.24 N	121.13 E
Laguna Ind. Res., NM	121	35.00 N	107.30 W
Lagunillas, Bol. (lä-gōō-nēl'yäs)	142	19.42 S	63.38 W
Lagunillas, Mex. (lä-gōō-nē'l-yäs)	130	21.34 N	99.41 W
La Habana (Havana), Cuba (lä-ä-bà'nä)	135a	23.08 N	82.23 W
La Habra, Ca. (là hàb'rà)	119a	34.56 N	117.57 W
La Habra Heights, Ca.	59	33.57 N	117.57 W
Lahaina, Hi. (lä-hä'ē-nä)	106a	20.52 N	156.39 W
La Häy-les-Roses, Fr.	64c	48.47 N	2.21 E
Lāhījān, Iran	195	37.12 N	50.01 E
Laholm, Swe. (lä'hôlm)	164	56.30 N	13.00 E
La Honda, Ca. (lā hôn'dà)	118b	37.20 N	122.16 W
Lahore, Pak. (lä-hōr')	196	32.00 N	74.18 E
Lahr, F.R.G. (lär)	166	48.19 N	7.52 E
Lahti, Fin. (lä'tē)	165	60.59 N	27.39 E
Lai, Chad.	229	9.29 N	16.18 E
Lai'an, China (lī-än)	200	32.27 N	118.25 E
Laibin, China (lī-bĭn)	203	23.42 N	109.20 E
Lai, C., Viet.	203	17.08 N	107.30 E
L'Aigle, Fr. (lĕ'gl')	168	48.45 N	0.37 E
Lainate, It.	65c	45.34 N	9.02 E
Lainz (Neigh.), Aus.	66e	48.11 N	16.17 E
Laisamis, Ken.	231	1.36 N	37.48 E
Laiyang, China (läī'yäNg)	200	36.59 N	120.42 E
Laizhou Wan (B.), China (lī-jō wän)	200	37.22 N	119.19 E
Laja, Río de la (R.), Mex. (rē'ō-dĕ-lä-lä'Kä)	130	20.17 N	100.57 W
Lajas, Cuba (lä'häs)	134	22.25 N	80.20 W
Lajeado, Braz. (lä-zhĕä'dô)	144	29.24 S	51.46 W
Lajeado Velho (Neigh.), Braz.	61d	23.32 S	46.23 W
Laje, Ponta da (C.), Port.	65d	38.40 N	9.19 W
Lajes, Braz. (là'zhĕs)	144	27.47 S	50.17 W
Lajinha, Braz. (lä-zhē'nyä)	141a	20.08 S	41.36 W
La Jolla, Ca. (là hoi'yà)	120a	32.51 N	117.16 W
La Jolla Ind. Res., Ca.	120	33.19 N	116.21 W
La Junta, Co. (là hōōn'tà)	122	37.59 N	103.35 W
Lake Arrowhead, Ca.	59	33.52 N	118.05 W
Lake Arthur, La. (är'thŭr)	125	30.06 N	92.40 W
Lake Barcroft, Va.	56d	38.51 N	77.09 W
Lake Barkley (Res.), Tn.	126	36.45 N	88.00 W
Lake Benton, Mn. (bĕn'tŭn)	114	44.15 N	96.17 W
Lake Bluff, Il. (blŭf)	113a	42.17 N	87.50 W
Lake Brown, Austl. (broun)	214	31.03 S	118.30 E
Lake Charles, La. (chärlz')	125	30.15 N	93.14 W
Lake City, Fl.	127	30.09 N	82.40 W
Lake City, Ia.	115	42.14 N	94.43 W
Lake City, Mn.	115	44.28 N	92.19 W
Lake City, SC	127	33.57 N	79.45 W
Lake Cowichan, Can. (kou'ĭ-chăn)	98	48.50 N	124.03 W
Lake Crystal, Mn. (krĭs'tál)	115	44.05 N	94.12 W
Lake Dist., Eng. (lāk)	162	54.25 N	3.20 W
Lake Elmo, Mn. (ĕlmō)	119g	45.00 N	92.53 W
Lake Forest, Il. (fŏr'ĕst)	113a	42.16 N	87.50 W
Lake Fork (R.), Ut.	121	40.30 N	110.25 W
Lake Geneva, Wi. (jĕ-nē'và)	115	42.36 N	88.28 W
Lake Harbour, Can. (här'bēr)	97	62.43 N	69.40 W
Lake Havasu City, Az.	120	34.27 N	114.22 W
Lake June, Tx. (jōōn)	119c	32.43 N	96.45 W
Lakeland, Fl. (lāk'lănd)	127a	28.02 N	81.58 W
Lakeland, Ga.	126	31.02 N	83.02 W
Lakeland, Mn.	119g	44.57 N	92.47 W
Lake Linden, Mi. (lĭn'dĕn)	115	47.11 N	88.26 W
Lake Louise, Can. (lōō-ēz')	99	51.26 N	116.11 W
Lakemba, Austl.	70a	33.55 S	151.05 E
Lake Mills, Ia. (mĭlz')	115	43.25 N	93.32 W
Lakemore, Oh. (lāk-mōr)	113d	41.01 N	81.24 W
Lake Odessa, Mi.	110	42.50 N	85.15 W
Lake Oswego, Or. (ŏs-wē'go)	118c	45.25 N	122.40 W
Lake Placid, NY	111	44.17 N	73.59 W
Lake Point, Ut.	119b	40.41 N	112.16 W
Lakeport, Ca. (lāk'pōrt)	120	39.03 N	122.54 W
Lake Preston, SD (prēs'tŭn)	114	44.21 N	97.23 W
Lake Providence, La. (prŏv'ĭ-dĕns)	125	32.48 N	91.12 W
Lake Red Rock (Res.), Ia.	115	41.30 N	93.15 W
Lake Sharpe (Res.), SD	114	44.30 N	100.00 W
Lakeside, Ca. (lāk'sīd)	120a	32.52 N	116.55 W
Lakeside, S. Afr.	71b	26.06 S	28.09 E
Lake Station, In.	113a	41.34 N	87.15 W
Lake Stevens, Wa.	118a	48.01 N	122.04 W
Lake Success, NY (sŭk-sĕs')	112a	40.46 N	73.43 W
Lakeview, Ca. (lāk-vū')	119a	33.50 N	117.07 W
Lakeview (Neigh.), Il.	58a	41.57 N	87.39 W
Lakeview, Or.	116	42.11 N	120.21 W
Lake Village, Ar.	123	33.20 N	91.17 W
Lake Wales, Fl. (wālz')	127a	27.54 N	81.35 W
Lakewood, Ca. (lāk'wŏŏd)	119a	33.50 N	118.09 W
Lakewood, Co.	122	39.44 N	105.06 W
Lakewood, Oh.	113d	41.29 N	81.48 W
Lakewood, Pa.	111	40.05 N	74.10 W
Lakewood, Wa.	118a	48.09 N	122.13 W
Lakewood Center, Wa.	118a	47.10 N	122.31 W
Lake Worth, Fl. (wûrth')	127a	26.37 N	80.04 W
Lake Worth Village, Tx.	119c	32.49 N	97.26 W
Lake Zürich, Il. (tsü'rĭk)	113a	42.11 N	88.05 W
Lakhdenpokh'ya, Sov. Un. (l'äk-dĭe'npôKyà)	165	61.33 N	30.10 E
Lakhtinskiy, Sov. Un. (lák-tĭn'skĭ)	182c	59.59 N	30.10 E
Lakota, ND (lá-kō'tá)	114	48.04 N	98.21 W
Lakshadweep (State), India	197	10.10 N	72.50 E
Lakshadweep Is. (Laccadive Is.), India	197	11.00 N	73.02 E
Laleham, Eng.	62	51.25 N	0.30 W
La Libertad, Guat. (lä lē-bĕr-tädh')	132	15.31 N	91.44 W
La Libertad, Guat.	132a	16.46 N	90.12 W
La Libertad, Sal.	132	13.29 N	89.20 W
La Ligua, Chile (lä lē'gwä)	141b	32.21 S	71.13 W
La Lisa, Cuba	60b	23.04 N	82.26 W
Lalitpur, Nep.	196	27.23 N	85.24 E
Lalín, Sp. (lä-lē'n)	170	42.40 N	8.05 W
La Línea, Sp. (lä lē'nā-ä)	170	36.11 N	5.22 W
La Louviere, Bel. (là lōō-vyâr')	163	50.30 N	4.10 E
La Luz, Mex. (lä lōōz')	130	21.04 N	101.19 W
Lama-Kara, Togo	228	9.33 N	1.12 E
La Malbaie, Can. (là mál-bā')	103	47.39 N	70.10 W
La Mancha (Mts.), Sp. (lä män'chä)	170	38.55 N	4.20 W
Lamar, Co. (lá-mär')	122	38.04 N	102.44 W
Lamar, Mo.	123	37.28 N	94.15 W
La Marmora, Pta. (Mtn.), It. (lä-mä'r-mô-rä)	174	40.00 N	9.28 E
La Marque, Tx. (lå-märk)	125a	29.23 N	94.58 W
Lamas, Peru (lä'màs)	142	6.24 S	76.41 W
Lamballe, Fr. (läN-bäl')	168	48.29 N	2.36 W
Lambaréné, Gabon (läN-bà-rå-nā')	230	0.42 S	10.13 E
Lambari, Braz. (läm-bà'rē)	141a	21.58 S	45.22 W
Lambayeque, Peru (läm-bä-yā'kå)	142	6.41 S	79.58 W
Lambert, Ms. (lăm'bērt)	126	34.10 N	90.16 W
Lambertville, NJ (lăm'bērt-vĭl)	111	40.20 N	75.00 W
Lambeth (Neigh.), Eng.	62	51.30 N	0.07 W
Lambourne End, Eng.	62	51.38 N	0.08 E
Lambrate (Neigh.), It.	65c	45.29 N	9.15 E
Lambro (R.), It.	65c	45.26 N	9.16 E
Lambton, S. Afr.	71b	26.15 S	28.10 E
Lame Deer, Mt. (lām dēr')	117	45.36 N	106.40 W
Lamego, Port. (lä-mā'gō)	170	41.07 N	7.47 W
La Mesa, Ca. (lä mā'sä)	120a	32.46 N	117.01 W
La Mesa, Col.	142a	4.38 N	74.27 W
Lamesa, Tx.	122	32.44 N	101.54 W
La Mirada, Ca.	59	33.54 N	118.01 W
Lamía, Grc. (lá-mē'á)	173	38.54 N	22.25 E
Lamon B., Phil. (lä-mōn')	207a	14.35 N	121.52 E
La Mora, Chile (lä-mō'rä)	141b	32.28 S	70.56 W
La Mott, Pa.	56b	40.04 N	75.08 W
La Moure, ND (lá mōōr')	114	46.23 N	98.17 W
Lampa (R.), Chile (lá'm-pä)	141b	33.15 S	70.55 W
Lampasas, Tx. (lăm-păs'ás)	124	31.06 N	98.10 W
Lampasas R., Tx.	124	31.18 N	98.08 W
Lampazos, Mex. (läm-pä'zōs)	124	27.03 N	100.30 W
Lampedusa (I.), It. (läm-på-dōō'sä)	174	35.29 N	12.58 E
Lamstedt, F.R.G. (läm'shtĕt)	157c	53.38 N	9.06 E
Lamu, Ken. (lä'mōō)	231	2.16 S	40.54 E
Lamu I., Ken.	231	2.25 S	40.50 E
La Mure, Fr. (là mür')	169	44.55 N	5.50 E
Lan' (R.), Sov. Un. (làn')	174	52.38 N	27.05 E
Lanai (I.), Hi. (lä-nä'ē)	106a	20.48 N	157.06 W
Lanai City, Hi.	106a	20.50 N	156.56 W
Lanak La (P.), China	196	34.40 N	79.50 E
La Nao, Cabo de (C.), Sp. (kà'bô-dĕ-lä-nä'ō)	171	38.43 N	0.14 E
Lanark, Scot. (lăn'árk)	162	55.40 N	3.50 W
Lancashire (Co.), Scot. (lăŋ'ká-shĭr)	156	53.49 N	2.42 W
Lancaster, Can. (lăŋ'kás-tēr)	104	45.15 N	66.06 W
Lancaster, Eng.	162	54.04 N	2.55 W
Lancaster, Ky.	110	37.35 N	84.30 W
Lancaster, Ma.	105a	42.28 N	71.40 W
Lancaster, NH	111	44.25 N	71.30 W
Lancaster, NY	113c	42.54 N	78.42 W
Lancaster, Oh.	110	39.40 N	82.35 W
Lancaster, Pa.	111	40.05 N	76.20 W
Lancaster, Tx.	119c	32.36 N	96.45 W
Lancaster, Wi.	115	42.51 N	90.44 W
Lândana, Ang. (län-dä'nä)	226	5.15 S	12.07 E
Landau, F.R.G. (län'dou)	166	49.13 N	8.07 E
Lander, Wy. (lăn'dēr)	117	42.49 N	108.24 W
Landerneau, Fr. (läN-dĕr-nō')	168	48.28 N	4.14 W
Landes (Plain), Fr. (läNd)	168	44.22 N	0.52 W
Landover, Md.	56d	38.56 N	76.54 W
Landsberg, F.R.G. (länds'bōōrgh)	157d	48.03 N	10.53 E
Lands End Pt., Eng.	162	50.03 N	5.45 W
Landshut, F.R.G. (länts'hōōt)	166	48.32 N	12.09 E
Landskrona, Swe. (làns-krōō'nä)	164	55.51 N	12.47 E
Lane Cove, Austl.	70a	33.49 S	151.10 E
Lanett, Al. (lá-nĕt')	126	32.52 N	85.13 W
Langadhás, Grc.	173	40.44 N	24.10 E
Langat (R.), Mala.	191b	2.46 N	101.33 E
Langdon, Can. (lăng'dŭn)	95e	50.58 N	113.40 W
Langdon, Mn.	119g	44.49 N	92.56 W
Langdon Hills, Eng.	62	51.34 N	0.25 E
L'Ange-Gardien, Can. (läNzh gàr-dyăN')	95b	46.55 N	71.06 W
Langeland (I.), Den.	164	54.52 N	10.46 E
Langenberg, F.R.G.	63	51.21 N	7.09 E
Langenbochum, F.R.G.	63	51.37 N	7.07 E
Langendreer (Neigh.), F.R.G.	63	51.28 N	7.19 E
Langenhorst, F.R.G.	63	51.22 N	7.02 E
Langenthal, Switz.	169	47.11 N	7.50 E
Langenzersdorf, Aus.	157e	48.30 N	16.22 E
Langesund, Nor. (läng'ĕ-sōōn')	164	58.59 N	9.38 E
Langfjorden (Fd.), Nor.	164	62.40 N	7.45 E
Langhorne, Pa. (lăng'hôrn)	112f	40.10 N	74.55 W
Langhorne Acres, Md.	56d	38.51 N	77.16 W
Langia Mts., Ug.	231	3.35 N	33.35 E
Langjökoll (Glacier), Ice. (läng-yû'kōōl)	158	64.40 N	20.31 W
Langla Co. (L.), China (läŋ-lä tswo)	196	30.42 N	80.40 E
Langlade (I.), Saint Pierre & Miquelon	103	46.50 N	56.20 W
Langley, Can. (lăng'lĭ)	118d	49.06 N	122.39 W
Langley, Md.	56d	38.57 N	77.10 W
Langley, SC	127	33.32 N	81.52 W
Langley, Wa.	118a	48.02 N	122.25 W
Langley Ind. Res., Can.	118d	49.12 N	122.31 W
Langley Park, Md.	56d	38.59 N	76.59 W
Langnau, Switz. (läng'nou)	166	46.56 N	7.46 E
Langon, Fr. (läN-gôN')	168	44.34 N	0.16 W
Langres, Fr. (läN'gr')	168	47.53 N	5.20 E
Langres, Plateau de (Plat.), Fr. (plä-tō'dĕ-läN'grĕ)	168	47.39 N	5.00 E
Langsa, Indon. (läng'sà)	206	4.33 N	97.52 E
Lang Son, Viet. (läng'sŏn')	206	21.52 N	106.42 E
Langst-Kierst, F.R.G.	63	51.18 N	6.43 E
L'Anguille (R.), Ar. (läN-gē'y')	123	35.23 N	90.52 W
Langxi, China (läŋ-shyē)	200	31.10 N	119.09 E
Langzhong, China (läŋ-jôŋ)	203	31.40 N	106.05 E
Lanham, Md. (lăn'ăm)	112e	38.58 N	76.54 W
Lanigan, Can. (lăn'ĭ-gán)	100	51.52 N	105.02 W
Lank-Latum, F.R.G.	63	51.18 N	6.41 E
Lankoviri, Nig.	229	9.00 N	11.25 E
Lankwitz (Neigh.), F.R.G.	65a	52.26 N	13.21 E
Lansdale, Pa. (lănz'dāl)	111	40.20 N	75.15 W
Lansdowne, Austl.	70a	33.54 S	150.59 E
Lansdowne, Md.	56c	39.15 N	76.40 W
Lansdowne, Pa.	112f	39.57 N	75.17 W
L'Anse, Mi. (làns)	115	46.43 N	88.28 W
L'Anse and Vieux Desert Ind. Res., Mi.	115	46.41 N	88.12 W
Lansford, Pa. (lănz'fērd)	120	40.50 N	75.50 W
Lansing, Ia.	115	43.22 N	91.16 W
Lansing, Il.	113a	41.34 N	87.33 W
Lansing, Ks.	119f	39.15 N	94.53 W
Lansing, Mi.	110	42.45 N	84.35 W
Lansing (Neigh.), Can.	54c	43.45 N	79.25 W
Lantianchang, China	67b	39.58 N	116.17 E
Lanús, Arg. (lä-nōōs')	144a	34.27 S	58.24 W
Lanusei, It. (lä-nōō-sĕ'y)	172	39.51 N	9.34 E
Lanúvio, It. (lä-nōō'vyô)	171d	41.41 N	12.42 E
Lanzarote I., Can. Is. (län-zá-rō'tä)	224	29.04 N	13.03 W
Lanzhou, China (län-jō)	202	35.55 N	103.55 E
Laoag, Phil. (lä-wäg')	206	18.13 N	120.38 E
Lao Ho (R.), China (lä'ō hō')	199	43.37 N	120.05 E
Laohumiao, China	67b	39.58 N	116.20 E
Laon, Fr. (läN)	168	49.36 N	3.35 E
La Oroya, Peru (lä-ô-rō'yä)	142	11.30 S	76.00 W
Laos, Asia (lā-ōs) (là-ōs')	206	20.15 N	102.00 E
Laoshan Wan (B.), China (lou-shän wän)	200	36.21 N	120.48 E
Lapa (Neigh.), Braz.	61c	22.55 S	43.11 W
La Palma, Pan. (lä-päl'mä)	133	8.25 N	78.07 W
La Palma, Sp.	170	37.24 N	6.36 W
La Palma I., Can. Is.	224	28.42 N	19.03 W
La Pampa (Prov.), Arg.	144	37.25 S	67.00 W
Lapa Rio Negro, Braz. (lä-pä-rē'ō-nĕ'grô)	144	26.12 S	49.56 W
La Paternal (Neigh.), Arg.	60d	34.36 S	58.28 W
La Paz, Arg. (lä päz')	144	30.48 S	59.47 W
La Paz, Bol.	143	16.31 S	68.03 W
La Paz, Hond.	132	14.15 N	87.40 W
La Paz, Mex. (lä-pá'z)	130	23.39 N	100.44 W
La Paz, Mex.	128	24.00 N	110.15 W
Lapeer, Mi. (lá-pēr')	110	43.05 N	83.15 W
La-Penne-sur-Huveaune, Fr. (la-pĕn'sür-ü-vōn')	168a	43.18 N	5.33 E
La Perouse, Austl.	70a	33.59 S	151.14 E
La Piedad Cabadas, Mex. (lä pyä-dhädh' kä-bä'dhäs)	130	20.20 N	102.04 W

ăt; finăl; rāte; senåte; ärm; àsk; sofá; fâre; ch-choose; dh-as th in other; bē; ēvent; bĕt; recĕnt; craftēr; g-gō; gh-guttural g; bĭt; ĭ-short neutral; rīde; K-guttural k as ch in German ich;

PLACE (Pronounciation)	PAGE	Lat. °′	Long. °′
Lapland (Reg.), Eur. (lăp'lănd)	158	68.20 N	22.00 E
La Plata, Arg. (lä plä'tä)	141c	34.54 S	57.57 W
La Plata, Mo. (lȧ plā'tȧ)	123	40.03 N	92.28 W
La Plata Pk., Co.	121	39.00 N	106.25 W
La Playa, Cuba	60b	23.06 N	82.27 W
La Pocatière, Can. (lȧ pô-kȧ-tyår')	104	47.24 N	70.01 W
La Poile B., Can. (lȧ pwäl')	105	47.38 N	58.20 W
La Porte, In. (lȧ pōrt')	110	41.35 N	86.45 W
Laporte, Oh.	113d	41.19 N	82.05 W
La Porte, Tx.	125a	29.40 N	95.01 W
La Porte City, Ia.	115	42.20 N	92.10 W
Lappeenranta, Fin. (lä'pēn-rän'tä)	165	61.04 N	28.08 E
La Prairie, Can. (lȧ-prâ-rē')	95a	45.24 N	73.30 W
Lâpseki, Tur. (läp'sȧ-kē)	173	40.20 N	26.41 E
Laptev Sea, Sov. Un. (läp'tyĭf)	176	75.39 N	120.00 E
La Puebla, Sp. (lä pwā'blä)	171	39.46 N	3.02 E
La Puebla de Montalbán, Sp. (lä pwā'blä dā mōnt-äl-bän')	170	39.54 N	4.21 W
La Puente, Ca. (pwĕn'tē)	119a	34.01 N	117.57 W
La Punta, Peru	60c	12.05 S	77.10 W
Lapusul (R.), Rom. (lä'pōō-shōōl)	167	47.29 N	23.46 E
La Queue-en-Brie, Fr.	64c	48.47 N	2.35 E
La Quiaca, Arg. (lä kē-ä'kä)	144	22.15 S	65.44 W
L'Aquila, It. (lȧ'kē-lä)	172	42.22 N	13.24 E
Lār, Iran (lär)	192	27.31 N	54.12 E
Lara, Austl.	211a	38.02 S	144.24 E
Larache, Mor. (lä-räsh')	224	35.15 N	6.09 W
Laramie (R.), Co.	122	40.56 N	105.55 W
Laramie, Wy. (lăr'ȧ-mĭ)	108	41.20 N	105.40 W
Laranjeiras (Neigh.), Braz.	61c	22.56 S	43.11 W
Larchmont, NY (lärch'mŏnt)	112a	40.56 N	73.46 W
Larch Mtn., Or. (lärch)	118c	45.32 N	122.06 W
Laredo, Sp. (lȧ-rā'dhō)	170	43.24 N	3.24 W
Laredo, Tx.	124	27.31 N	99.29 W
La Reina, Chile	61b	33.27 S	70.33 W
La Réole, Fr. (lȧ rā-ōl')	168	44.37 N	0.03 W
Largeau, Chad (lär-zhō')	229	17.55 N	19.07 E
Largo, Cayo, Cuba (kä'yō-lär'gō)	134	21.40 N	81.30 W
Larimore, ND (lăr'ĭ-mōr)	114	47.53 N	97.38 W
Larino, It. (lä-rē'nô)	172	41.48 N	14.54 E
La Rioja, Arg. (lä rē-ōhä)	144	29.18 S	67.42 W
La Rioja (Prov.), Arg. (lä-rē-ô'kä)	144	28.45 S	68.00 W
Lárisa, Grc. (lä'rē-sȧ)	173	39.38 N	22.25 E
Lārkāma, Pak.	196	27.40 N	68.12 E
Larkspur, Ca.	58b	37.56 N	122.32 W
Lárnakos, Kólpos (B.), Cyprus	191a	36.50 N	33.45 E
Lárnax, Cyprus	191a	34.55 N	33.37 E
Larned, Ks. (lär'nĕd)	122	38.09 N	99.07 W
La Robla, Sp. (lä rōb'lä)	170	42.48 N	5.36 W
La Rochelle, Fr. (lȧ rô-shĕl')	168	46.10 N	1.09 W
La Roche-sur-Yon, Fr. (lȧ rôsh'sûr-yôɴ')	168	46.39 N	1.27 W
La Roda, Sp. (lä rō'dä)	170	39.13 N	2.08 W
La Romona, Dom. Rep. (lä-rä-mô'nä)	135	18.25 N	69.00 W
Larrey Pt., Austl. (lăr'ē)	214	19.15 S	118.15 E
Laruns, Fr. (lȧ-răɴs')	168	42.58 N	0.28 W
Larvik, Nor. (lär'vĕk)	164	59.06 N	10.03 E
La Sabana, Ven. (lä-sä-bȧ'nä)	143b	10.38 N	66.24 W
La Sabina, Cuba (lä-sä-bē'nä)	135a	22.51 N	82.16 W
La Sagra (Mtn.), Sp. (lä sä'grä)	170	37.56 N	2.35 E
La Sal, Ut. (lȧ săl')	121	38.10 N	109.20 W
La Salle, Can. (lȧ săl')	113b	42.14 N	83.06 W
La Salle, Can.	95a	45.26 N	73.39 W
La Salle, Can.	95f	49.41 N	97.16 W
La Salle, Il.	110	41.20 N	89.05 W
Las Animas, Co. (lȧs ă'nĭ-mȧs)	122	38.03 N	103.16 W
La Sarre, Can.	103	48.43 N	79.12 W
Lascahobas, Hai. (läs-kä-ō'bȧs)	135	19.00 N	71.55 W
Las Cruces, Mex. (läs-krōō'sĕs)	131	16.37 N	93.54 W
Las Cruces, NM	121	32.20 N	106.50 W
La Selle, Massif De (Mts.), Hai. (lä'sĕl')	135	18.25 N	72.05 W
La Serena, Chile (lä-sĕ-rĕ'nä)	144	29.55 S	71.24 W
La Seyne, Fr. (lä-sån')	169	43.07 N	5.52 E
Las Flores, Arg. (läs flo'rĕs)	141c	36.01 S	59.07 W
Las Flores, Ven.	61a	10.34 N	66.56 W
Lashio, Bur. (lăsh'ē-ō)	198	22.58 N	98.03 E
Lashkarak, Iran	68h	35.49 N	51.36 E
Las Juntas, C. R. (läs-kōō'n-täs)	132	10.15 N	85.00 W
Las Maismas (Reg.), Sp. (läs-mī's-mäs)	170	37.05 N	6.25 W
Las Minas, Ven.	61a	10.27 N	66.52 W
La Solana, Sp. (lä-sô-lä-nä)	170a	38.56 N	3.13 W
Las Palmas, Pan.	133	8.08 N	81.30 W
Las Palmas de Gran Canaria, Can. Is. (läs päl'mäs)	224	28.07 N	15.28 W
La Spezia, It. (lä-spĕ'zyä)	172	44.07 N	9.48 E
Las Piedras, Ur. (läs-pyĕ'drȧs)	141c	34.42 S	56.08 W
Las Pilas (Vol.), Nic. (läs-pē'läs)	132	12.32 N	86.43 W
Las Rejas, Chile	61b	33.28 S	70.44 W
Las Rosas, Mex. (läs rō thäs)	131	16.24 N	92.23 W
Las Rozas de Madrid, Sp. (läs rō'thas dā mä-dhrēd')	171a	40.29 N	3.53 W
Lassee, Aus.	157e	48.14 N	16.50 E
Lassen Pk., Ca. (lăs'ĕn)	116	40.30 N	121.32 W
Lassen Volcanic Natl. Park, Ca.	116	40.43 N	121.35 W
L'Assomption, Can. (lȧs-sôm-syôɴ)	95a	45.50 N	73.25 W
Lass Qoray, Som.	223a	11.13 N	48.19 E
Las Tablas, Pan. (läs tä'bläs)	133	7.48 N	80.16 W
Last Mountain (L.), Can. (lȧst moun'tĭn)	100	51.05 N	105.10 W
Lastoursville, Gabon (lȧs-tōōr-vēl')	226	1.00 S	12.49 E
Las Tres Virgenes, Vol., Mex. (vē'r-hē-nĕs)	128	26.00 N	111.45 W
Las Tunas (Prov.), Cuba	134	21.05 N	77.00 W
Las Vacas, Mex. (läs-vȧ'käs)	131	16.24 N	95.48 W
Las Vegas, Chile (läs-vĕ'gäs)	141b	30.50 S	70.59 W
Las Vegas, Nv. (läs vā'gäs)	120	36.12 N	115.10 W
Las Vegas, NM	122	35.36 N	105.13 W
Las Vegas, Ven. (läs-vĕ'gäs)	143b	10.26 N	64.08 W
Las Vigas, Mex.	130	19.38 N	97.03 W

PLACE (Pronounciation)	PAGE	Lat. °′	Long. °′
Las Vizcachas, Meseta de (Plat.), Arg. (mĕ-sĕ'tä-dĕ-läs-vēz-kä'chȧs)	144	49.35 S	71.00 W
Latacunga, Ec. (lä-tä-kōōŋ'gä)	142	1.02 S	78.33 W
Latakia, see Al Lādhiqīah			
La Teste-de-Buch, Fr. (lä-tĕst-dĕ-büsh)	168	44.38 N	1.11 W
Lathrop, Mo. (lā'thrŭp)	123	39.32 N	94.21 W
Latimer, Eng.	62	51.41 N	0.33 W
Latium (Reg.), see Lazio			
Latoritsa R., Sov. Un. (lȧ-tô'rī-tsȧ)	167	48.27 N	22.30 E
Latourell, Or. (lȧ-tou'rĕl)	118c	45.32 N	122.13 W
La Tremblade, Fr. (lä-trĕɴ-bläd')	168	45.45 N	1.12 W
Latrobe, Pa. (lȧ-trōb')	111	40.25 N	79.15 W
Lattingtown, NY	55	40.54 N	73.36 W
La Tuque, Can. (lȧ'tük')	97	47.27 N	72.49 W
Lātūr, India (lä-tōōr')	197	18.20 N	76.35 E
Latvian (S. S. R.), Sov. Un.	176	57.28 N	24.29 E
Launceston, Austl. (lôn'sĕs-tŭn)	216	41.35 S	147.22 E
Launceston, Eng. (lôrn'stŏn)	162	50.38 N	4.26 W
La Unión, Chile (lä-ōō-nyô'n)	144	40.15 S	73.04 W
La Unión, Mex. (lä ōōn-nyōn')	130	17.59 N	101.48 W
La Unión, Sal.	132	13.18 N	87.51 W
La Unión, Sp.	171	37.38 N	0.50 W
Laupendahl, F.R.G.	63	51.21 N	6.56 E
Laura, Austl. (lôrȧ)	215	15.40 S	144.45 E
Laura, Sov. Un. (lou'rȧ)	174	57.36 N	27.29 E
Laurel, De. (lô'rĕl)	111	38.30 N	75.40 W
Laurel, Md.	112e	39.06 N	76.51 W
Laurel, Ms.	126	31.42 N	89.07 W
Laurel, Mt.	117	45.41 N	108.45 W
Laurel, Wa.	118d	48.52 N	122.29 W
Laurel Gardens, Pa.	57b	40.31 N	80.01 W
Laurel Hollow, NY	55	40.52 N	73.28 W
Laurelwood, Or. (lô'rĕl-wōōd)	118c	45.25 N	123.05 W
Laurens, SC (lô'rĕnz)	127	34.29 N	82.03 W
Laurentian Highlands (Reg.), Can. (lô'rĕn-tĭ-ăn)	94	49.00 N	74.50 W
Laurentides, Can. (lô'rĕn-tīdz)	95a	45.51 N	73.46 W
Lauria, It. (lou'rē-ä)	172	40.03 N	15.02 E
Laurinburg, NC (lô'rĭn-bûrg)	127	34.45 N	79.27 W
Laurium, Mi. (lô'rĭ-ŭm)	115	47.13 N	88.28 W
Lausanne, Switz. (lō-zȧn')	166	46.32 N	6.35 E
Lautaro, Chile (lou-tä'rô)	144	38.40 S	72.24 W
Laut Kecil, Kepulauan (Is.), Indon.	206	4.44 S	115.43 E
Laut, Pulau (I.), Indon.	206	3.39 S	116.07 E
Lauzon, Can. (lō-zôɴ')	95b	46.50 N	71.10 W
Lava Beds Natl. Mon., Ca. (lä'vȧ bĕds)	116	41.38 N	121.44 W
Lavaca R., Tx. (lȧ-văk'ȧ)	125	29.05 N	96.50 W
Lava Hot Springs, Id.	117	42.37 N	111.58 W
Laval, Can.	95a	45.31 N	73.44 W
Laval, Fr. (lä-väl')	168	48.05 N	0.47 W
Laval-des-Rapides (Neigh.), Can.	54b	45.33 N	73.42 W
Laval-Ouest (Neigh.), Can.	54b	45.33 N	73.52 W
La Vecilla de Curueno, Sp.	170	42.53 N	5.18 W
La Vega, Dom. Rep. (lä-vĕ'gä)	135	19.15 N	70.35 W
La Vega (Neigh.), Ven.	61a	10.28 N	66.57 W
Lavella (I.), Sol. Is.	215	7.50 S	155.45 E
Lavello, It. (lä-vĕl'lô)	172	41.05 N	15.50 E
La Verne, Ca. (lȧ vûrn')	119a	34.06 N	117.46 W
Laverton, Austl. (lā'vēr-tŭn)	214	28.45 S	122.30 E
La Victoria, Peru	60c	12.04 S	77.02 W
La Victoria, Ven. (lä vēk-tō'rē-ä)	143b	10.14 N	67.20 W
Lavonia, Ga. (lȧ-vō'nĭ-ȧ)	126	34.26 N	83.05 W
Lavon Res., Tx.	125	33.06 N	96.20 W
Lavras, Braz. (lä'vräzh)	141a	21.15 S	44.59 W
Lávrion, Grc. (läv'rĭ-ôn)	173	37.44 N	24.05 E
Lawndale, Ca. (lôn'dāl)	119a	33.54 N	118.22 W
Lawndale (Neigh.), Il.	58a	41.51 N	87.43 W
Lawndale (Neigh.), Pa.	56b	40.03 N	75.05 W
Lawnside, NJ	56b	39.52 N	75.03 W
Lawra, Ghana	228	10.39 N	2.52 W
Lawrence, In. (lô'rĕns)	113g	39.59 N	86.01 W
Lawrence, Ks.	123	38.57 N	95.13 W
Lawrence, Ma.	105a	42.42 N	71.09 W
Lawrence, Pa.	113e	40.18 N	80.07 W
Lawrenceburg, In. (lô'rĕns-bûrg)	113f	39.06 N	84.47 W
Lawrenceburg, Ky.	110	38.00 N	85.00 W
Lawrenceburg, Tn.	126	35.13 N	87.20 W
Lawrenceville, Ga. (lô-rĕns-vĭl)	126	33.56 N	83.57 W
Lawrenceville, Il.	110	38.45 N	87.45 W
Lawrenceville, NJ	112a	40.17 N	74.44 W
Lawrenceville (Neigh.), Pa.	57b	40.28 N	79.57 W
Lawrenceville, Va.	127	36.43 N	77.52 W
Lawsonia, Md. (lô-sō'nĭ-ȧ)	111	38.00 N	75.50 W
Lawton, Ok. (lô'tŭn)	122	34.36 N	98.25 W
Lawz, Jabal al (Mtn.), Sau. Ar.	192	28.46 N	35.37 E
Layang Layang, Mala. (lä-yäng' lä-yäng')	191b	1.49 N	103.28 E
Laysan (I.), Hi.	107b	26.00 N	171.00 W
Layton, Ut. (lā'tŭn)	119b	41.04 N	111.58 W
Lazdijai, Sov. Un. (läzh'dē-yī')	165	54.12 N	23.35 E
Lazio (Latium) (Reg.), It. (lä'zyô) (lā't-zēōōm)	172	42.05 N	12.25 E
Lead, SD (lēd)	114	44.22 N	103.47 W
Leader, Can.	100	50.55 N	109.32 W
Leadville, Co. (lĕd'vĭl)	122	39.14 N	106.18 W
Leaf (R.), Ms. (lēf)	126	31.43 N	89.20 W
League City, Tx. (lēg)	125a	29.31 N	95.05 W
Leamington, Can. (lĕm'ĭng-tŭn)	110	42.05 N	82.35 W
Leamington, Eng. (lē'mĭng-tŭn)	162	52.17 N	1.25 W
Leatherhead, Eng. (lĕdh'ēr-hĕd')	156b	51.17 N	0.20 W
Leavenworth, Ks. (lĕv'ĕn-wûrth)	119f	39.19 N	94.54 W
Leavenworth, Wa.	116	47.35 N	120.39 W
Leawood, Ks. (lē'wōōd)	119f	38.58 N	94.37 W
Leba, Pol. (lā'bä)	167	54.45 N	17.34 E
Lebam R., Mala.	191b	1.35 N	104.09 E
Lebango, Con.	230	0.22 N	14.49 E
Lebanon, Asia	192	34.00 N	34.00 E
Lebanon, Il. (lĕb'ȧ-nŭn)	119e	38.36 N	89.49 W
Lebanon, In.	110	40.00 N	86.30 W
Lebanon, Ky.	126	37.32 N	85.15 W

PLACE (Pronounciation)	PAGE	Lat. °′	Long. °′
Lebanon, Mo.	123	37.40 N	92.43 W
Lebanon, NH	111	43.40 N	72.15 W
Lebanon, Oh.	110	39.25 N	84.10 W
Lebanon, Or.	116	44.31 N	122.53 W
Lebanon, Pa.	111	40.20 N	76.20 W
Lebanon, Tn.	126	36.10 N	86.16 W
Lebanon Mts., Leb.	161	33.30 N	35.32 E
Lebedin, Sov. Un. (lyĕ'bĕ-dēn)	175	48.56 N	31.35 E
Lebedin, Sov. Un.	175	50.34 N	34.27 E
Lebedyan', Sov. Un. (lyĕ'bĕ-dyän')	174	53.03 N	39.08 E
Le Blanc, Fr. (lĕ-bläɴ')	168	46.38 N	0.59 E
Le Blanc-Mesnil, Fr.	64c	48.56 N	2.28 E
Leblon (Neigh.), Braz.	61c	22.59 S	43.13 W
Le Borgne, Hai. (lĕ bōrn'y')	135	19.50 N	72.30 W
Lebork, Pol. (lăɴ-bōōrk')	167	54.33 N	17.46 E
Le Bourget, Fr.	64c	48.56 N	2.26 E
Lebrija, Sp. (lå-brē'hä)	170	36.55 N	6.06 W
Lebú, Chile (lĕ-bōō')	144	37.35 S	73.37 W
Lecce, It. (lĕt'chā)	173	40.22 N	18.11 E
Lecco, It. (lĕk'kō)	172	45.52 N	9.28 E
Le Châtelet-en-Brie, Fr. (lĕ-shä-tĕ-lā'ĕɴ-brē')	169b	48.29 N	2.50 E
Leche, Laguna de (L.), Cuba (lä-gōō'nä-dĕ-lĕ'chĕ)	134	22.10 N	78.30 W
Leche, Laguna de la (L.), Mex.	124	27.16 N	102.45 W
Lech R., F.R.G. (lĕk)	166	47.41 N	10.52 E
Lecompte, La.	125	31.06 N	92.25 W
Le Creusot, Fr. (lĕkrû-zō)	168	46.48 N	4.23 E
Ledesma, Sp. (lå-dĕs'mä)	170	41.05 N	5.59 W
Ledsham, Eng.	64a	53.16 N	2.58 W
Leduc, Can. (lĕ-dōōk')	99	53.16 N	113.33 W
Leech (L.), Mn. (lēch)	115	47.06 N	94.16 W
Leeds, Al. (lēdz)	112h	33.33 N	86.33 W
Leeds, Eng.	156	53.48 N	1.33 W
Leeds, ND	114	48.18 N	99.24 W
Leeds and Liverpool Can., Eng. (lĭv'ēr-pōōl)	156	53.36 N	2.38 W
Leegebruch, G.D.R. (lĕh'gĕn-brōōĸ)	157b	52.43 N	13.12 E
Leek, Eng. (lēk)	156	53.06 N	2.01 W
Lee Manor, Va.	56d	38.52 N	77.15 W
Leer, F.R.G. (lâr)	166	53.14 N	7.27 E
Lees, Eng.	64b	53.32 N	2.04 W
Leesburg, Fl. (lēz'bûrg)	127	28.49 N	81.53 W
Leesburg, Va.	111	39.10 N	77.30 W
Lees Ferry, Az.	121	36.55 N	111.45 W
Lees Summit, Mo.	119f	38.55 N	94.23 W
Lee Stocking (I.), Ba.	135	23.45 N	76.05 W
Leesville, La. (lēz'vĭl)	125	31.09 N	93.17 W
Leetonia, Oh. (lē-tō'nĭ-ȧ)	110	40.50 N	80.45 W
Leeuwarden, Neth. (lā'wär-dĕn)	163	52.12 N	5.50 E
Leeuwin, C., Austl. (lōō'wĭn)	214	34.15 S	114.30 E
Leeward Is., N. A. (lē'wērd)	125	12.25 N	62.15 W
Le Francois, Mart.	133b	14.37 N	60.55 W
Lefroy (L.), Austl. (lē-froi')	214	31.30 S	122.00 E
Leganés, Sp. (lå-gä'nås)	171a	40.20 N	3.46 W
Legazpi, Phil. (lå-gäs'pē)	207a	13.09 N	123.44 E
Legge Pk., Austl. (lĕg)	216	41.33 S	148.10 E
Leghorn, see Livorno			
Legnano, It. (lå-nyä'nō)	172	45.35 N	8.53 E
Legnica, Pol. (lĕk-nĭt'sȧ)	166	51.13 N	16.10 E
Leh, India (lā)	196	34.10 N	77.40 E
Le Havre, Fr. (lē ȧv'r')	168	49.31 N	0.07 E
Lehi, Ut. (lē'hī)	121	40.25 N	111.55 W
Lehman Caves Natl. Mon., Nv. (lē'măn)	121	38.54 N	114.08 W
Lehnin, G.D.R. (lĕh'nĕn)	157b	52.19 N	12.45 E
Leião, Port.	65d	38.44 N	9.18 W
Leicester, Eng. (lĕs'tēr)	156	52.37 N	1.08 W
Leicestershire, (Co.), Eng.	156	52.40 N	1.12 W
Leichhardt, Austl.	70a	33.53 S	151.07 E
Leichhardt, (R.), Austl. (līk'härt)	214	18.30 S	139.45 E
Leiden, Neth. (lī'dĕn)	157a	52.09 N	4.29 E
Leigh Creek, Austl. (lē krēk)	216	30.33 S	138.30 E
Leikanger, Nor. (lī'käŋ'gēr)	164	61.11 N	6.51 E
Leimuiden, Neth.	157a	52.13 N	4.40 E
Leine R., F.R.G. (lī'nĕ)	166	51.58 N	9.56 E
Leinster, Ire. (lĕn-stēr)	162	52.45 N	7.19 W
Leipsic, Oh. (līp'sĭk)	110	41.05 N	84.00 W
Leipzig, G.D.R. (līp'tsĭk)	166	51.20 N	12.24 E
Leiria, Port. (lā-rē'ä)	170	39.45 N	8.50 W
Leitchfield, Ky. (lēch'fēld)	126	37.28 N	86.20 W
Leitha (R.), Aus.	157e	48.04 N	16.57 E
Leithe (Neigh.), F.R.G.	63	51.29 N	7.06 E
Leitrim, Can.	95c	45.20 N	75.36 W
Leizhou Bandao (Pen.), China (lā-jō bän-dou)	203	20.42 N	109.10 E
Lékéti, Monts de la (Mts.), Con.	230	2.34 S	14.17 E
Le Kremlin-Bicêtre, Fr.	64c	48.49 N	2.21 E
Leksand, Swe. (lĕk'sänd)	164	60.45 N	14.56 E
Leland, Wa. (lē'lănd)	118a	47.54 N	122.53 W
Leliu, China (lŭ-lĭō)	201a	22.52 N	113.09 E
Le Locle, Switz. (lē lô'kl')	166	47.03 N	6.43 E
Le Maire, Estrecho de (Str.), Arg. (ĕs-trĕ'chô-dĕ-lĕ-mī'rĕ)	144	55.15 S	65.30 W
Le Mans, Fr. (lē män')	168	48.01 N	0.12 E
Le Marin, Mart.	133b	14.28 N	60.55 W
Le Mars, Ia. (lē märz')	114	42.46 N	96.09 W
Lemay, Mo.	119e	38.32 N	90.17 W
Lemdiyya, Alg.	224	36.18 N	2.40 E
Leme, Morro do (Hill), Braz.	61c	22.58 S	43.10 W
Lemery, Phil. (lā-mä-rē')	207a	13.51 S	120.55 E
Le Mesnil-Amelot, Fr.	64c	49.01 N	2.36 E
Le Mesnil-le-Roi, Fr.	64c	48.56 N	2.08 E
Lemesós, Cyprus	191a	34.39 N	33.02 E
Lemhi R., Id.	117	44.40 N	113.27 W
Lemhi Ra. (Mts.), Id. (lĕm'hī)	117	44.35 N	113.33 W
Lemmon, SD (lĕm'ŭn)	114	45.55 N	102.10 W
Le Môle, Hai. (lē mōl')	135	19.50 N	73.20 W
Lemon Grove, Ca. (lĕm'ŭn-grōv)	120a	32.44 N	117.02 W
Lemon Heights, Ca.	59	33.46 N	117.48 W
Lemont, Il. (lē'mŏnt)	113a	41.40 N	87.59 W
Le Moule, Guad. (lē mōōl')	133b	16.19 N	61.22 W

PLACE (Pronounciation)	PAGE	Lat. °′	Long. °′
LeMoyne, Can.	54b	45.31 N	73.29 W
Lempa R., Sal. (lĕm'pä)	132	13.20 N	88.46 W
Lemvig, Den. (lĕm'vĕgh)	164	56.33 N	8.16 E
Lena, Swe. (lī'nä)	164	60.01 N	17.40 E
Lençóes Paulista, Braz. (lĕn-sôns' pou-lēs'tá)	144	22.30 S	48.45 W
Lençóis, Braz. (lĕn-sóis)	143	12.38 S	41.28 W
Lenexa, Ks. (lē'nĕx-ă)	119f	38.58 N	99.44 W
Lenger, Sov. Un. (lyĭn'gyĕr)	155	41.38 N	70.00 E
Lengyandong, China (lŭŋ-yän-dôŋ)	201a	23.12 N	113.21 E
Lenik (R.), Mala.	191b	1.59 N	102.51 E
Leninabad, Sov. Un. (lĕ-nyē-nȧ bät')	180	40.15 N	69.49 E
Lenina, Gora (Hill), Sov. Un.	66b	55.42 N	37.31 E
Leninakan, Sov. Un. (lĕ-nyē-nȧ-kän')	179	40.40 N	43.50 E
Leningrad (Oblast), Sov. Un.	174	59.15 N	30.30 E
Leningrad, Sov. Un. (lyĕ-nĕn-grät')	182c	59.57 N	30.20 E
Leningradskaya, Sov. Un. (lyĕ-nĭn-gräd'skȧ-yȧ)	175	46.19 N	39.23 E
Lenino, Sov. Un. (lyĕ'nĭ-nô)	182b	55.37 N	47.41 E
Leninogorsk, Sov. Un. (lyĕ-nĭn ŭ gôrsk')	180	50.29 N	83.25 E
Leninsk, Sov. Un. (lyĕ-nēnsk')	179	48.40 N	45.10 E
Leninsk-Kuznetski, Sov. Un. (lyĕ-nēnsk'kōōz-nyĕt'skĭ)	180	54.28 N	86.48 E
Lenkoran', Sov. Un. (lĕn-kô-rän')	179	38.52 N	48.58 E
Lennox, Ca.	59	33.56 N	118.21 W
Lennox, SD (lĕn'ŭks)	114	43.22 N	96.53 W
Lenoir, NC (lē-nōr')	127	35.54 N	81.35 W
Lenoir City, Tn.	126	35.47 N	84.16 W
Lenox, Ia.	115	40.51 N	94.29 W
Lenz, S. Afr.	71b	26.19 S	27.49 E
Léo, Upper Volta	228	11.06 N	2.06 W
Leoben, Aus. (lå-ō'bĕn)	166	47.22 N	15.09 E
Léogane, Hai. (lā-ō-gan')	135	18.30 N	72.35 W
Leola, SD (lē-ō'lȧ)	114	45.43 N	99.55 W
Leominster, Ma. (lĕm'ĭn-stēr)	105a	42.32 N	71.45 W
Leon, Ia. (lē'ŏn)	115	40.43 N	93.44 W
León, Mex. (lå-ōn')	130	21.08 N	101.41 W
León, Nic. (lĕ-ō'n)	132	12.28 N	86.53 W
Leon (Reg.), Sp. (lĕ-ō'n)	170	41.18 N	5.50 W
León, Sp. (lĕ-ō'n)	170	42.38 N	5.33 W
Leonforte, It. (lā-ōn-fôr'tä)	172	37.40 N	14.27 E
Leonia, NJ	55	40.52 N	73.59 W
Leon R., Tx. (lē'ōn)	124	31.54 N	98.20 W
Leopoldau (Neigh.), Aus.	66e	48.16 N	16.27 E
Leopold II, L., see **Mai-Ndombe**			
Leopoldina, Braz. (lā-ô-pôl-dē'nä)	141a	21.32 S	42.38 W
Léopold, Mont (Hill), Zaire	71c	4.19 S	15.15 E
Leopoldsburg, Bel.	157a	51.07 N	5.18 E
Leopoldsdorf im Marchfelde, Aus. (lā'ô-pôlts-dôrf')	157e	48.14 N	16.42 E
Leopoldstadt (Neigh.), Aus.	66e	48.13 N	16.23 E
Léopoldville, see **Kinshasa**			
Leovo, Sov. Un. (lå-ō'vô)	175	46.30 N	28.16 E
Lepe, Sp. (lā'pā)	170	37.15 N	7.12 W
Le Pecq, Fr.	64c	48.54 N	2.07 E
Lepel', Sov. Un. (lyĕ-pĕl')	174	54.52 N	28.41 E
Le Perreux-sur-Marne, Fr.	64c	48.51 N	2.30 E
Leping, China (lŭ-pĭŋ)	203	29.02 N	117.12 E
L'Epiphanie, Can. (lā-pē-fä-nē')	95a	45.51 N	73.29 W
Le Plessis-Belleville, Fr. (lĕ-plĕ-sē'bĕl-vēl')	169b	49.05 N	2.46 E
Le Plessis-Bouchard, Fr.	64c	49.00 N	2.14 E
Le Plessis-Trévise, Fr.	64c	48.49 N	2.34 E
Lepontine Alpi (Mts.), Switz. (lĕ-pŏn'tĭn)	166	46.28 N	8.38 E
Le Port-Marly, Fr.	64c	48.53 N	2.06 E
Lepreau, Can. (lē-prō')	104	45.10 N	66.28 W
Le Pré-Saint-Gervais, Fr.	64c	48.53 N	2.25 E
Lepsinsh, Sov. Un.	180	45.32 N	80.47 E
Le Puy, Fr. (lē pwē')	168	45.02 N	3.54 E
Le Raincy, Fr.	64c	48.54 N	2.31 E
Lercara Friddi, It. (lĕr-kä'rä)	172	36.47 N	13.36 E
Lerdo, Mex. (lĕr'dō)	124	25.31 N	103.30 W
Léré, Chad (lā-rā')	225	9.42 N	14.14 E
Léré, Mali	228	15.43 N	4.55 W
Leribe, Leso.	227c	28.53 S	28.02 E
Lérida, Sp. (lā'rē-dhä)	171	41.38 N	0.37 E
Lerma, Mex. (lĕr'mä)	131	19.49 N	90.34 W
Lerma, Mex.	131a	19.17 N	99.30 W
Lerma (R.), Mex.	130	20.14 N	101.50 W
Lerma, Sp. (lĕ'r-mä)	170	42.03 N	3.45 W
Le Roy, NY (lē roi')	111	43.00 N	78.00 W
Lerwick, Scot. (lĕr'ĭk) (lûr'wĭk)	162a	60.08 N	1.27 W
Léry, Can. (lā-rī')	95a	45.21 N	73.49 W
Lery, L., La. (lĕ'rē)	112d	29.48 N	89.45 W
Les Andelys, Fr. (lā-zäɴ-dē-lē')	169b	49.15 N	1.25 E
Les Cayes, Hai.	135	18.15 N	73.45 W
Les Cèdres, Can. (lā-sĕdr'')	95a	45.18 N	74.03 W
Les Clayes-sous-Bois, Fr.	64c	48.49 N	1.59 E
Les Grésillons, Fr.	64c	48.56 N	2.01 E
Lesh (Alessio), Alb. (lĕshĕ) (ä-lā'sē-ō)	173	41.47 N	19.40 E
Leshan, China (lŭ-shän)	203	29.40 N	103.40 E
Lésigny, Fr.	64c	48.45 N	2.37 E
Lésina, Lago di (L.), It. (lä'gō dē lā'zē-nä)	172	41.48 N	15.12 E
Leskovac, Yugo. (lĕs'kō-vȧts)	173	43.00 N	21.58 E
Leslie, Ar. (lĕz'lĭ)	123	35.49 N	92.32 W
Leslie, S. Afr.	223d	26.23 S	28.57 E
Les Lilas, Fr.	64c	48.53 N	2.25 E
Les Loges-en-Josas, Fr.	64c	48.46 N	2.09 E
Lesnoj (Neigh.), Sov. Un.	66a	60.00 N	30.19 E
Lesnoy, Sov. Un. (lĕs'noi)	178	66.45 N	34.45 E
Lesogorsk, Sov. Un. (lyĕs'ō-gôrsk)	204	49.28 N	141.59 E
Lesotho, Afr. (lĕsō'thō)	226	29.45 S	28.07 E
Lesozavodsk, Sov. Un. (lyĕ-sô-zȧ-vôdsk')	204	45.21 N	133.19 E
Les Pavillons-sous-Bois, Fr.	64c	48.55 N	2.30 E
Les Sables-d'Olonne, Fr. (lā sȧ'bl'dô-lŭn')	168	46.30 N	1.47 W
Les Saintes Is., Guad. (lā-săɴt')	133b	15.50 N	61.40 W

PLACE (Pronounciation)	PAGE	Lat. °′	Long. °′
Lesser Khingan Range (Xiao Hinggan Ling), China (shyou hĭŋyän lĭŋ)	199	69.50 N	129.26 E
Lesser Slave (R.), Can.	99	55.15 N	114.30 W
Lesser Slave L., Can. (lĕs'ēr slāv)	99	55.25 N	115.30 W
Lesser Sunda Is., Indon.	206	9.00 S	120.00 E
L'Estaque, Fr. (lĕs-täl)	168a	43.22 N	5.20 E
Lester, Pa.	56b	39.52 N	75.17 W
Les Thilliers-en-Vexin, Fr. (lā-tē-yā'ĕɴ-vē-săɴ')	169b	49.19 N	1.36 E
Le Sueur, Mn. (lē sōōr')	115	44.27 N	93.53 W
Lésvos (I.), Grc.	173	39.15 N	25.40 E
Leszno, Pol. (lĕsh'nô)	166	51.51 N	16.35 E
Letchmore Heath, Eng.	62	51.40 N	0.20 W
Le Teil, Fr. (lē tā'y')	168	44.34 N	4.39 E
Le Temple, Fr.	64c	49.00 N	1.58 E
Lethbridge, Austl.	70a	33.44 S	150.48 E
Lethbridge, Can. (lĕth'brĭj)	99	49.42 N	112.50 W
Le Thillay, Fr.	64c	49.00 N	2.28 E
Letichev, Sov. Un. (lyĕ-tē-chĕf')	175	49.22 N	27.29 E
Leticia, Col. (lē-tē'syȧ)	142	4.04 S	69.57 W
Leting, China (lŭ-tĭŋ)	200	39.26 N	118.53 E
Letmathe, F.R.G. (lĕt'mät-hĕ)	169c	51.22 N	7.37 E
Le Tréport, Fr. (lē-trā'pôr')	168	50.03 N	1.21 E
Leuven (Louvain), Bel.	157a	50.53 N	4.42 E
Levack, Can.	102	46.38 N	81.23 W
Levádhia, Grc.	173	38.25 N	22.51 E
Le Val-d'Albian, Fr.	64c	48.45 N	2.11 E
Levallois-Perret, Fr. (lē-väl-wä'pē-rĕ')	169b	48.53 N	2.17 E
Levanger, Nor. (lĕ-väng'ĕr)	158	63.42 N	11.01 E
Levanna (Mtn.), Fr.-It. (lå-vä'nä)	172	45.25 N	7.14 E
Levenshulme (Neigh.), Eng.	64b	53.27 N	2.10 W
Leveque, C., Austl. (lē-vĕk')	214	16.26 S	123.08 E
Leverkusen, F.R.G. (lĕ'fĕr-kōō-zĕn)	169c	51.01 N	6.59 E
Le Vésinet, Fr.	64c	48.54 N	2.08 E
Levice, Czech. (lā'vĕt-sĕ)	167	48.13 N	18.37 E
Levico, It. (lā'vē-kō)	172	46.02 N	11.20 E
Le Vigan, Fr. (lē vē-gäɴ')	168	43.59 N	3.36 E
Lévis, Can. (lā-vē') (lē'vĭs)	95b	46.49 N	71.11 W
Levittown, NY	55	40.41 N	73.31 W
Levittown, Pa. (lē'vĭt-toun)	112f	40.08 N	74.50 W
Levkás, Grc. (lyĕfkäs')	173	38.49 N	20.43 E
Levkás (I.), Grc.	173	38.42 N	20.22 E
Levoča, Czech. (lā'vô-chȧ)	167	49.03 N	20.38 E
Levy (L.), Fl. (lē'vĭ)	127	29.31 N	82.23 W
Lewes, De. (lōō'ĭs)	111	38.45 N	75.10 W
Lewes, Eng.	162	50.51 N	0.01 E
Lewinsville, Va.	56d	38.54 N	77.12 W
Lewinsville Heights, Va.	56d	38.53 N	77.12 W
Lewis (R.) **East Fk.**, Wa.	118c	45.52 N	122.40 W
Lewisburg, Tn. (lū'ĭs-bûrg)	126	35.27 N	86.47 W
Lewisburg, WV	110	37.50 N	80.20 W
Lewisdale, Md.	56d	38.58 N	76.58 W
Lewisham (Neigh.), Eng.	62	51.27 N	0.01 E
Lewisham, S. Afr.	71b	26.07 S	27.49 E
Lewis Hills, Can.	105	48.48 N	58.30 W
Lewis, I. of, Scot. (lōō'ĭs)	162	58.05 N	6.07 W
Lewisporte, Can. (lū'ĭs-pōrt)	105	49.15 N	55.04 W
Lewis R., Wa.	116	46.05 N	122.09 W
Lewis Ra., Mt. (lū'ĭs)	117	48.05 N	113.06 W
Lewiston, Id. (lū'ĭs-tŭn)	116	46.24 N	116.59 W
Lewiston, Me.	104	44.05 N	70.14 W
Lewiston, NY	113c	43.11 N	79.02 W
Lewiston, Ut.	117	41.58 N	111.51 W
Lewistown, Il. (lū'ĭs-toun)	123	40.23 N	90.06 W
Lewistown, Mt.	117	47.05 N	109.25 W
Lewistown, Pa.	111	40.35 N	77.30 W
L'Étang-la-Ville, Fr.	64c	48.52 N	2.05 E
Lexington, Ky. (lĕk'sĭng-tŭn)	110	38.05 N	84.30 W
Lexington, Ma.	105a	42.27 N	71.14 W
Lexington, Ms.	126	33.08 N	90.02 W
Lexington, Mo.	123	39.11 N	93.52 W
Lexington, Nb.	122	40.46 N	99.44 W
Lexington, NC	127	35.47 N	80.15 W
Lexington, Tn.	126	35.37 N	88.24 W
Lexington, Va.	111	37.45 N	79.20 W
Leybourne, Eng.	62	51.18 N	0.25 E
Leyte (I.), Phil. (lā'tā)	207	10.35 N	125.35 E
Lezajsk, Pol. (lĕ'zhä-ĭsk)	167	50.14 N	22.25 E
Lezha (R.), Sov. Un. (lĕ-zhä')	174	58.59 N	40.27 E
L'gov, Sov. Un. (lgôf)	175	51.42 N	35.15 E
Lhasa, China (läs'ä)	196	29.41 N	91.12 E
L'Hautil, Fr.	64c	49.00 N	2.01 E
Liangxiangzhen, China (lĭäŋ-shyäŋ-jŭn)	202a	39.43 N	116.08 E
Lianjiang, China (lĭĕn-jyäŋ)	203	21.38 N	110.15 E
Lianozovo, Sov. Un. (lĭ-a-nô'zô-vô)	182b	55.54 N	37.36 E
Lianshui, China (lĭĕn-shwā)	200	33.46 N	119.15 E
Lianyungang, China (lĭĕn-yōōn-gäŋ)	200	34.35 N	119.09 E
Liaocheng, China (lĭou-chŭŋ)	200	36.27 N	115.56 E
Liaodong Bandao (Pen.), China (lĭou-dôŋ bän-dou)	200	39.45 N	122.22 E
Liaodong Wan (B.), China (lĭou-dôŋ wäŋ)	202	40.25 N	121.15 E
Liaoning (Prov.), China	199	41.31 N	122.11 E
Liaoyang, China (lyä'ō-yäng')	202	41.18 N	123.10 E
Liaoyuan, China (lĭou-yüän)	202	43.00 N	124.59 E
Liard (R.), Can. (lē-är')	119	59.43 N	126.42 W
Libano, Col. (lē'bȧ-nô)	142a	4.55 N	75.05 W
Libby, Mt. (lĭb'ē)	116	48.27 N	115.35 W
Libenge, Zaire (lē-bĕŋ'gä)	225	3.39 N	18.40 E
Liberal, Ks. (lĭb'ēr-ăl)	122	37.01 N	100.56 W
Liberdade (Neigh.), Braz.	61d	23.35 S	46.37 W
Liberec, Czech. (lē'bĕr-ĕts)	166	50.45 N	15.06 E
Liberia, Afr. (lī-bē'rĭ-ȧ)	222	6.30 N	9.55 W
Liberia, C. R.	132	10.38 N	85.28 W
Libertad, Arg.	60d	34.42 S	58.38 W
Libertad de Orituco, Ven. (lē-bĕr-tä'd-dĕ-ō-rē-tōō'kô)	143b	9.32 N	66.24 W
Liberty, In. (lĭb'ēr-tĭ)	110	39.35 N	84.55 W
Liberty, Mo.	119f	39.15 N	94.25 W
Liberty, Pa.	57b	40.20 N	79.51 W

PLACE (Pronounciation)	PAGE	Lat. °′	Long. °′
Liberty, SC	127	34.47 N	82.41 W
Liberty, Tx.	125	30.03 N	94.46 W
Liberty, Ut.	119b	41.20 N	111.52 W
Liberty B., Wa.	118a	47.43 N	122.41 W
Liberty L., Md.	112e	39.25 N	76.56 W
Liberty Manor, Md.	56c	39.21 N	76.47 W
Libertyville, Il. (lĭb'ēr-tĭ-vĭl)	113a	42.17 N	87.57 W
Libode, S. Afr. (lĭ-bō'dĕ)	227c	31.33 S	29.03 E
Libón, R., Hai.	135	19.30 N	71.45 W
Libourne, Fr. (lē-bōōrn')	168	44.55 N	0.12 W
Library, Pa.	57b	40.18 N	80.02 W
Libres, Mex. (lē'brās)	131	19.26 N	97.41 W
Libreville, Gabon (lē-br'vēl')	230	0.23 N	9.27 E
Liburn, Ga. (lĭb'ûrn)	112c	33.53 N	84.09 W
Libya, Afr. (lĭb'ē-ä)	222	27.38 N	15.00 E
Libyan Des. (Aş Şaḩrā' al Lībīyah), Libya (lĭb'ē-ăn)	225	28.23 N	23.34 E
Libyan Plat., Egypt	161	30.58 N	26.20 E
Licancábur, Cerro (Mtn.), Chile (sĕ'r-rō-lē-kȧn-kȧ'bōōr)	144	22.45 S	67.45 W
Licanten, Chile (lē-kän-tē'n)	141b	34.58 S	72.00 W
Lichfield, Eng. (lĭch'fēld)	156	52.41 N	1.49 W
Lichinga, Moz.	231	13.18 S	35.14 E
Lichtenberg (Neigh.), G.D.R.	65a	51.31 N	13.29 E
Lichtenburg, S. Afr. (lĭk'tĕn-bĕrgh)	223d	26.09 S	26.10 E
Lichtendorf, F.R.G.	63	51.28 N	7.37 E
Lichtenplatz (Neigh.), F.R.G.	63	51.15 N	7.12 E
Lichtenrade (Neigh.), F.R.G.	65a	52.23 N	13.25 E
Lichterfelde (Neigh.), F.R.G.	65a	52.26 N	13.19 E
Lick Cr., In. (lĭk)	113g	39.43 N	86.06 W
Licking (R.), Ky. (lĭk'ĭng)	110	38.30 N	84.10 W
Lida, Sov. Un. (lē'dȧ)	167	53.53 N	25.19 E
Lidcombe, Austl.	70a	33.52 S	151.03 E
Lidgerwood, ND (lĭj'ēr-wood)	114	46.04 N	97.10 W
Lidköping, Swe. (lēt'chû-pĭng)	164	58.31 N	13.06 E
Lido Beach, NY	55	40.35 N	73.38 W
Lido di Roma, It. (lē'dô-dē-rô'mä)	171d	41.19 N	12.17 E
Lidzbark, Pol. (lĭts'bärk)	167	54.07 N	20.36 E
Liebenbergsvlei (R.), S. Afr.	223d	27.35 S	28.25 E
Liebenwalde, G.D.R. (lē'bĕn-väl-dĕ)	157b	52.52 N	13.24 E
Liechou Pan-Tao (Pen.), China	203	20.40 N	109.25 E
Liechtenstein, Eur. (lēk'tĕn-shtīn)	159	47.10 N	10.00 E
Liège, Bel. (lē-āzh')	163	50.40 N	5.30 E
Lienyün, China (lĭan'yün)	199	33.10 N	120.01 E
Lienz, Aus. (lē-ĕnts')	166	46.49 N	12.45 E
Liepāja, Sov. Un. (le'pä-yä')	165	56.31 N	20.59 E
Lier, Bel.	157a	51.08 N	4.34 E
Lierenfeld (Neigh.), F.R.G.	63	51.13 N	6.51 E
Liesing, Aus. (lē'sĭng)	157e	48.09 N	16.17 E
Liestal, Switz. (lēs'täl)	166	47.28 N	7.44 E
Lievre, Rivière du (R.), Can.	111	45.00 N	75.25 W
Lifanga, Zaire	230	0.19 N	21.57 E
Lifou, (I.), N. Cal.	215	21.15 S	167.32 E
Ligao, Phil. (lē-gä'ō)	207a	13.14 N	123.33 E
Lightning Ridge, Austl.	216	29.23 S	147.50 E
Ligonha (R.), Moz. (lē-gō'nyȧ)	227	16.14 S	39.00 E
Ligonier, In. (lĭg-ō-nēr)	110	41.30 N	85.35 W
Ligovo, Sov. Un. (lē'gô-vô)	182c	59.51 N	30.13 E
Liguria (Reg.), It. (lē-gōō-rē-ä)	172	44.24 N	8.27 E
Ligurian Sea, Eur. (lĭ-gū'rĭ-ăn)	172	43.42 N	8.32 E
Lihou Rfs., Austl. (lē-hōō')	215	17.23 S	152.43 E
Lihuang, China (lē'hōōäng)	200	31.32 N	115.46 E
Lihue, Hi. (lē-hōō'ā)	106a	21.59 N	159.23 W
Lihula, Sov. Un. (lē'hōō-lȧ)	165	58.41 N	23.50 E
Liji, China (lē-jyē)	200	33.47 N	117.47 E
Lijiang, China (lē-jyäŋ)	200	27.00 N	100.08 E
Lijin, China (lē-jyĭn)	200	37.30 N	118.15 E
Likasi (Jadotville), Zaire	231	10.59 S	26.44 E
Likhoslavl', Sov. Un. (lyē-kôslävˈ'l)	174	57.07 N	35.27 E
Likhovka, Sov. Un. (lyē-ĸôf'kȧ)	175	48.52 N	33.57 E
Likouala (R.), Con.	230	0.10 S	16.30 E
Lille, Fr. (lēl)	168	50.38 N	3.01 E
Lille Baelt (str.), Den.	164	55.09 N	9.53 E
Lillehammer, Nor. (lēl'ē-häm'mĕr)	164	61.07 N	10.25 E
Lillesand, Nor. (lēl'ē-sän')	164	58.16 N	8.19 E
Lilleström, Nor. (lēl'ĕ-strûm)	164	59.56 N	11.04 E
Lilliwaup, Wa. (lĭl'ĭ-wŏp)	118a	47.28 N	123.07 W
Lillooet, Can. (lĭ'lōō-ĕt)	99	50.30 N	121.55 W
Lillooet (R.), Can.	99	49.50 N	122.10 W
Lilongwe, Malawi (lē-lô-än)	231	13.59 S	33.44 E
Liluāh, India	67a	22.35 N	88.23 E
Lilydale, Austl.	70b	37.45 S	145.21 E
Lilyfield, Austl.	70a	33.52 S	151.10 E
Lima, Oh. (lī'mȧ)	110	40.40 N	84.05 W
Lima, Peru (lē'mä)	142	12.06 S	76.55 W
Lima, Swe.	164	60.54 N	13.24 E
Lima (R.), Port.	170	41.45 N	8.22 W
Lima Duarte, Braz. (dwä'r-tĕ)	141a	21.52 S	43.47 W
Limão (Neigh.), Braz.	61d	23.30 S	46.40 W
Lima Res., Mt.	117	44.45 N	112.15 W
Limay (R.), Arg. (lē-mä'ē)	144	39.50 S	69.15 W
Limbazi, Sov. Un. (lēm'bä-zĭ)	165	57.32 N	24.44 E
Limbdi, India	196	22.37 N	71.52 E
Limbé, Hai.	135	19.45 N	72.30 W
Limburg an der Lahn, F.R.G. (lem-bōōrg')	166	50.22 N	8.03 E
Limefield, Eng.	64b	53.37 N	2.18 W
Limeira, Braz. (lē-mā'rä)	141a	22.34 S	47.24 W
Limestone Bay, Can. (lĭm'stōn)	101	53.50 N	98.50 W
Limfjorden (Fd.), Den.	164	56.55 N	8.56 E
Limmen Bght., Austl. (lĭm'ĕn)	214	14.45 S	136.00 E
Limni, Grc. (lēm'nē)	173	38.47 N	23.22 E
Limnos (I.), Grc.	173	39.58 N	24.48 E
Limoges, Can. (lē-môzh')	95c	45.20 N	75.15 W
Limon, Co. (lī'mŏn)	122	39.15 N	103.41 W
Limón, C. R. (lē-mōn')	133	10.01 N	83.02 W
Limón, Hond. (lē-mō'n)	132	15.53 N	85.34 W
Limón B., Pan.	128a	9.21 N	79.58 W
Limon (R.), Dom. Rep.	135	18.20 N	71.40 W
Limours, Fr. (lē-mōōr')	169b	48.39 N	2.05 E
Limousin, Plateaux du (Plat.), Fr. (plä-tō' dü lē-mōō-zăɴ')	168	45.44 N	1.09 E

PLACE (Pronunciation)	PAGE	Lat. °′	Long. °′
Limoux, Fr. (lē-mo͞o′)	168	43.03 N	2.14 E
Limpopo R., Afr. (lĭm-pō′pō)	226	23.15 S	27.46 E
Linares, Chile (lē-nä′räs)	141b	35.51 S	71.35 W
Linares, Mex.	124	24.53 N	99.34 W
Linares (Prov.), Chile	141b	35.53 S	71.30 W
Linares, Sp. (lē-nä′rēs)	170	38.07 N	3.38 W
Linaro, C., It. (lē-nä′rä)	172	42.02 N	11.53 E
Lince, Peru	60c	12.05 S	77.03 W
Linchuan, China (lĭn-chůän)	203	27.58 N	116.18 E
Lincoln, Arg. (lĭŋ′kŭn)	141c	34.51 S	61.29 W
Lincoln, Can.	95d	43.10 N	79.29 W
Lincoln, Ca.	120	38.51 N	121.19 W
Lincoln, Eng.	156	53.14 N	0.33 W
Lincoln, Il.	123	40.09 N	89.21 W
Lincoln, Ks.	122	39.02 N	98.08 W
Lincoln, Me.	104	45.23 N	68.31 W
Lincoln, Ma.	105a	42.25 N	71.19 W
Lincoln, Ne.	123	40.49 N	96.43 W
Lincoln, Pa.	57b	40.18 N	79.51 W
Lincoln Center (P. Int.), NY	55	40.46 N	73.59 W
Lincoln Heath (Reg.), Eng.	156	53.23 N	0.39 W
Lincolnia Heights, Va.	56d	38.50 N	77.09 W
Lincoln, Mt., Co.	122	39.20 N	106.19 W
Lincoln Park, Mi.	113b	42.14 N	83.11 W
Lincoln Park, NJ	112a	40.56 N	74.18 W
Lincoln Park (P. Int.), Il.	58a	41.56 N	87.38 W
Lincoln Place (Neigh.), Pa.	57b	40.22 N	79.55 W
Lincolnshire (Co.), Eng.	156	53.12 N	0.29 W
Lincolnshire Wolds (Hills), Eng. (woldz′)	162	53.25 N	0.23 W
Lincolnton, NC (lĭŋ′kŭn-tŭn)	127	35.27 N	81.15 W
Lincolnwood, Il.	58a	42.00 N	87.46 W
Linda-a-Velha, Port.	65d	38.43 N	9.14 W
Lindale, Ga. (lĭn′dāl)	126	34.10 N	85.10 W
Lindau, F.R.G. (lĭn′dou)	166	47.33 N	9.40 E
Linden, Al. (lĭn′dĕn)	126	32.16 N	87.47 W
Linden, Ma.	54a	42.26 N	71.02 W
Linden, Mo.	119f	39.13 N	94.35 W
Linden, NJ	112a	40.39 N	74.14 W
Linden (Neigh.), S. Afr.	71b	26.08 S	28.00 E
Lindenberg, G.D.R.	65a	52.36 N	13.31 E
Linden-dahlhausen (Neigh.), F.R.G.	63	51.26 N	7.09 E
Lindenhorst (Neigh.), F.R.G.	63	51.33 N	7.27 E
Lindenhurst, NY (lĭn′dĕn-hûrst)	112a	40.41 N	73.23 W
Lindenwold, NJ (lĭn′dĕn-wôld)	112f	39.50 N	75.00 W
Linderhausen, F.R.G.	63	51.18 N	7.17 E
Lindesberg, Swe. (lĭn′dĕs-bĕrgh)	164	59.37 N	15.14 E
Lindesnes (C.), Nor. (lĭn′ĕs-nĕs)	163	58.00 N	7.05 E
Lindfield, Austl.	70a	33.47 S	151.10 E
Lindho, China	202	40.45 N	107.30 E
Lindi, Tan. (lĭn′dē)	231	10.00 S	39.43 E
Lindian, China (lĭn-dĭĕn)	202	42.08 N	124.59 E
Lindi R., Zaire	225	1.00 N	27.13 E
Lindley, S. Afr. (lĭnd′lē)	223d	27.52 S	27.55 E
Lindow, G.D.R. (lēn′dōv)	157b	52.58 N	12.59 E
Lindsay, Can. (lĭn′zē)	111	44.20 N	78.45 W
Lindsay, Ok.	122	34.50 N	97.38 W
Lindsborg, Ks. (lĭnz′bôrg)	122	38.34 N	97.42 W
Lineville, Al. (līn′vĭl)	126	33.18 N	85.45 W
Linfen, China	202	36.00 N	111.38 E
Linga, Kepulauan (Is.), Indon.	206	0.35 S	105.05 E
Lingao, China (lĭn-gou)	203	19.58 N	109.40 E
Lingayen, Phil. (lĭŋ′gä-yän′)	207a	16.01 N	120.13 E
Lingayen G., Phil.	207a	16.18 N	120.11 E
Lingbi, China (lĭŋ-bē)	200	33.33 N	117.33 E
Lingdianzhen, China	200	31.52 N	121.28 E
Lingen, F.R.G. (lĭŋ′gĕn)	166	52.32 N	7.20 E
Lingling, China (lĭŋ-lĭŋ)	203	26.10 N	111.40 E
Lingshou, China (lĭŋ-shō)	200	38.21 N	114.41 E
Linguère, Senegal (lĭŋ-gĕr′)	228	15.24 N	15.07 W
Lingwu, China	202	38.05 N	106.18 E
Lingyuan, China (lĭŋ-yůän)	202	41.12 N	119.20 E
Linhai, China	203	28.52 N	121.08 E
Linhe, China (lĭn-hŭ)	202	40.49 N	107.45 E
Linhó, Port.	65d	38.46 N	9.23 W
Linhuaiguan, China (lĭn-hwī-gůän)	200	32.55 N	117.38 E
Linhuanj, China (lĭ-hwĭ-jyĕ)	200	33.42 N	116.33 E
Linjiangi, China (lĭn-jyäŋ)	202	41.45 N	127.00 E
Linköping, Swe. (lĭn′chû-pĭng)	164	58.25 N	15.35 E
Linksfield (Neigh.), S. Afr.	71b	26.10 S	28.06 E
Linmeyer, S. Afr.	71b	26.16 S	28.04 E
Linn (Neigh.), F.R.G.	63	51.20 N	6.38 E
Linnhe, Loch (L.), Scot. (lĭn′ē)	162	56.35 N	4.30 W
Linqing, China (lĭn-chyĭŋ)	200	36.49 N	115.42 E
Linqux, China (lĭn-chyo͞o)	200	36.31 N	118.33 E
Lins, Braz. (lē′ns)	143	21.42 S	49.41 W
Linthicum Heights, Md. (lĭn′thĭ-kŭm)	112e	39.12 N	76.39 W
Linton, In. (lĭn′tŭn)	110	39.05 N	87.15 W
Linton, ND	114	46.16 N	100.15 W
Lintorf, F.R.G.	63	51.20 N	6.49 E
Linwu, China (lĭn′wo͞o′)	203	25.20 N	112.30 E
Linxi, China (lĭn-shyē)	202	43.30 N	118.02 E
Linyi, China (lĭn-yē)	200	35.04 N	118.21 E
Linying, China (lĭn′yĭng′)	200	33.48 N	113.56 E
Linz, Aus. (lĭnts)	166	48.18 N	14.18 E
Linzhang, China (lĭn-jäŋ)	200	36.19 N	114.40 E
Līvāni, Sov. Un. (lē′vá-nē)	174	56.24 N	26.12 E
Lipa, Phil. (lē-pä′)	207a	13.55 N	121.10 E
Lipari, It. (lē′pä-rē)	172	38.29 N	15.00 E
Lipari (I.), It.	172	38.32 N	15.04 E
Lipetsk, Sov. Un. (lyē′pĕtsk)	174	52.26 N	39.34 E
Lipetsk, (Oblast), Sov. Un.	174	52.18 N	38.30 E
Liping, China (lē-pĭŋ)	203	26.18 N	109.00 E
Lipno, Pol. (lēp′nô)	167	52.50 N	19.12 E
Lippe (R.), F.R.G. (lĭp′ē)	163	51.36 N	6.45 E
Lippolthausen (Neigh.), F.R.G.	63	51.37 N	7.29 E
Lippstadt, F.R.G. (lĭp′shtät)	166	51.39 N	8.20 E
Lipscomb, Al. (lĭp′skŭm)	112h	33.26 N	86.56 W
Liptsy, Sov. Un. (lyēp′tsē)	175	50.11 N	36.25 E
Lipu, China (lē-po͞o)	203	24.38 N	110.35 E
Lira, Ug.	231	2.15 N	32.54 E
Liri (R.), It. (lē′rē)	172	41.49 N	13.30 E
Liria, Sp. (lē′ryä)	171	39.35 N	0.34 W
Lisala, Zaire (lē-sä′lä)	230	2.09 N	21.31 E
Lisboa (Lisbon), Port. (lēzh-bō′ä) (lĭz′bŭn)	171b	38.42 N	9.05 W
Lisbon, ND	114	46.21 N	97.43 W
Lisbon, Oh.	110	40.45 N	80.50 W
Lisbon, see Lisboa			
Lisbon Falls, Me.	104	43.59 N	70.03 W
Lisburn, N. Ire. (lĭs′bŭrn)	162	54.35 N	6.05 W
Lisburne, C., Ak.	107	68.20 N	165.40 W
Lishi, China (lē-shr)	202	37.32 N	111.12 E
Lishu, China	202	43.12 N	124.18 E
Lishui, China (lĭ′shwĭ′)	200	31.41 N	119.01 E
Lishui, China	203	28.28 N	120.00 E
Lisianski I., Hi.	107b	25.30 N	174.00 W
Lisieux, Fr. (lē-zyû′)	168	49.10 N	0.13 E
Lisiy Nos, Sov. Un. (lĭ′sĭy-nôs)	182c	60.01 N	30.00 E
Liski, Sov. Un. (lyēs′kē)	175	50.56 N	39.28 E
Lisle, Il. (līl)	113a	41.48 N	88.04 W
L'Isle-Adam, Fr. (lēl-ädäɴ′)	169b	49.05 N	2.13 E
Lismore, Austl. (lĭz′môr)	216	28.48 S	153.18 E
Lister, Mt., Ant. (lĭs′tēr)	232	78.05 S	163.00 E
Litani (R.), Lib.	191a	33.28 N	35.42 E
Litchfield, Il. (lĭch′fēld)	123	39.10 N	89.38 W
Litchfield, Mn.	115	45.08 N	94.34 W
Litchfield, Oh.	113d	41.10 N	82.01 W
Litherland, Eng.	64a	53.28 N	2.59 W
Lithgow, Austl. (lĭth′gō)	216	33.23 S	149.31 E
Lithinon Akra (C.), Grc.	172a	34.59 N	24.35 E
Lithonia, Ga. (lĭ-thō′nĭ-ȧ)	112c	33.43 N	84.07 W
Lithuanian S. S. R., Sov. Un. (lĭth-ů-ā-′nĭ-ȧ)	178	55.42 N	23.30 E
Litin, Sov. Un. (lē-tēn)	175	49.16 N	28.11 E
Litókhoron, Grc. (lē′tô-ĸō′rôn)	173	40.05 N	22.29 E
Litoko, Zaire	230	1.13 S	24.47 E
Litoměřice, Czech. (lē′tô-myĕr′zhĭ-tsĕ)	166	50.33 N	14.10 E
Litomyšl, Czech. (lē′tô-mēsh′l)	166	49.52 N	16.14 E
Litoo, Tan.	231	9.45 S	38.24 E
Little (R.), Austl.	211a	37.54 S	144.27 E
Little (R.), Tn.-Mo.	126	36.28 N	89.39 W
Little R., Tx.	125	30.48 N	96.50 W
Little Abaco (I.), Ba. (ä′bä-kō)	134	26.55 N	77.45 W
Little Abitibi (R.), Can.	102	50.15 N	81.30 W
Little America, Ant.	232	78.30 S	161.30 W
Little Andaman I., Andaman & Nicobar Is. (ăn-dȧ-măn′)	206	10.39 N	93.08 E
Little Bahama Bk., Ba. (bȧ-hā′mȧ)	134	26.55 N	78.40 W
Little Belt Mts., Mt. (bĕlt)	117	47.00 N	110.50 W
Little Berkhamsted, Eng.	62	51.45 N	0.08 W
Little Bighorn R., Mt. (bĭg-hôrn)	117	45.08 N	107.30 W
Little Bitterroot R., Mt. (bĭt′ēr-o͞ot)	116	47.45 N	114.45 W
Little Bitter, see Al Buhayrah al Murrah aş Şughrá			
Little Blue R., Mo. (blo͞o)	119f	38.52 N	94.25 W
Little Blue (R.), Ne.	122	40.15 N	98.01 W
Littleborough, Eng. (lĭt′′l-bŭr-ô)	156	53.39 N	2.06 W
Little Burstead, Eng.	62	51.36 N	0.24 E
Little Calumet R., Il. (kăl-ů-mĕt′)	113a	41.38 N	87.38 W
Little Cayman (I.), Cayman Is. (kā′mȧn)	134	19.40 N	80.05 W
Little Chalfont, Eng.	62	51.40 N	0.34 W
Little Colorado (R.), Az. (kŏl-ô-rä′dō)	121	36.05 N	111.35 W
Little Compton, RI (kŏmp′tŏn)	112b	41.31 N	71.07 W
Little Corn I., Nic.	133	12.19 N	82.50 W
Little End, Eng.	62	51.41 N	0.14 E
Little Exuma (I.), Ba. (ĕk-so͞o′mä)	135	23.25 N	75.40 W
Little Falls, Mn. (fôlz)	115	45.58 N	94.23 W
Little Falls, NJ	55	40.53 N	74.14 W
Little Falls, NY	111	43.05 N	74.55 W
Little Ferry, NJ	55	40.51 N	74.03 W
Littlefield, Tx. (lĭt′′l-fēld)	122	33.55 N	102.17 W
Little Fork (R.), Mn. (fôrk)	115	48.24 N	93.30 W
Little Hans Lollick (I.), Vir. Is (U.S.A.) (häns lôl′lĭk)	129c	18.25 N	64.54 W
Little Hulton, Eng.	64b	53.32 N	2.25 W
Little Humboldt R., Nv. (hŭm′bōlt)	116	41.10 N	117.40 W
Little Inagua (I.), Ba. (ē-nä′gwä)	135	21.30 N	73.00 W
Little Isaac (I.), Ba. (ī′zȧk)	134	25.55 N	79.00 W
Little Kanawha (R.), WV (kȧ-nô′wȧ)	110	39.05 N	81.30 W
Little Karroo (Mts.), S. Afr. (kȧ-ro͞o)	226	33.50 S	21.02 E
Little Lever, Eng.	64b	53.34 N	2.22 W
Little Mecatina (R.), Can. (mĕ cȧ tĭ nȧ)	97	52.40 N	62.21 W
Little Miami R., Oh. (mī-ăm′ĭ)	113f	39.19 N	84.15 W
Little Minch (Chan.), Scot.	162	57.35 N	6.45 W
Little Missouri (R.), Ar. (mĭ-so͞o′rĭ)	123	34.15 N	93.54 W
Little Missouri (R.), SD	114	45.46 N	103.48 W
Little Nahant, Ma.	54a	42.25 N	70.56 W
Little Neck (Neigh.), NY	55	40.46 N	73.44 W
Little Pee Dee (R.), SC (pē-dē′)	127	34.35 N	79.21 W
Little Powder R., Wy. (pou′dēr)	117	44.51 N	105.20 W
Little Red (R.), Ar. (rĕd)	123	35.25 N	91.55 W
Little Red R., Ok.	123	33.53 N	94.38 W
Little Rock, Ar. (rôk)	123	34.42 N	92.16 W
Little Sachigo L., Can. (să′chĭ-gō)	101	54.09 N	92.11 W
Little San Salvador (I.), Ba. (săn săl′vȧ-dôr)	135	24.35 N	75.55 W
Little Satilla (R.), Ga. (sȧ-tĭl′ȧ)	114	31.43 N	82.47 W
Little Sioux (R.), Ia. (so͞o)	114	42.22 N	95.47 W
Little Smoky (R.), Can. (smōk′ĭ)	99	55.10 N	116.55 W
Little Snake R., Co. (snāk)	117	40.40 N	108.21 W
Little Stanney, Eng.	64b	53.15 N	2.53 W
Little Sutton, Eng.	64a	53.17 N	2.57 W
Little Tallapoosa (R.), Al. (tăl-ȧ-po͞o′sȧ)	126	32.25 N	85.28 W
Little Tennessee (R.), Tn. (tĕn-ĕ-sē′)	126	35.36 N	84.05 W
Little Thurrock, Eng.	62	51.28 N	0.21 E
Littleton, Co. (lĭt′′l-tŭn)	122	39.34 N	105.01 W
Littleton, Eng.	62	51.24 N	0.28 W
Littleton, Ma.	105a	42.32 N	71.29 W
Littleton, NH	103	44.15 N	71.45 W
Little Wabash (R.), Il. (wô′băsh)	110	38.50 N	88.30 W
Little Warley, Eng.	62	51.35 N	0.19 E
Little Wood R., Id. (wo͝od)	117	43.00 N	114.08 W
Liuhe, China	202	42.10 N	125.38 E
Liuli, Tan.	231	11.05 S	34.38 E
Liulicun, China	67b	39.56 N	116.28 E
Liup'an Shan (Mts.), China	202	36.20 N	105.30 E
Liuwa Pln., Zambia	230	14.30 S	22.40 E
Liuyang, China (lyo͞o′yäng′)	203	28.10 N	113.35 E
Liuyuan, China (lĭô-yůän)	200	36.09 N	114.37 E
Liuzhou, China (lĭô-jō)	203	24.25 N	109.30 E
Lively, Can.	102	46.26 N	81.09 W
Livengood, Ak. (lĭv′ĕn-go͝od)	107	65.30 N	148.35 W
Live Oak, Fl. (līv′ōk)	126	30.15 N	83.00 W
Livermore, Ca. (lĭv′ēr-mōr)	118b	37.41 N	121.46 W
Livermore, Ky.	110	37.30 N	87.05 W
Liverpool, Austl. (lĭv′ēr-po͞ol)	211b	33.55 S	150.56 E
Liverpool, Can.	104	44.02 N	64.41 W
Liverpool, Eng.	156	53.25 N	2.52 W
Liverpool, Tx.	125a	29.18 N	95.17 W
Liverpool B., Can.	107	69.45 N	130.00 W
Liverpool Ra., Austl.	215	31.47 S	31.00 E
Livindo R., Gabon	225	1.09 N	13.30 E
Livingston, Al. (lĭv′ĭng-stŭn)	126	32.35 N	88.09 W
Livingston, Guat.	132	15.50 N	88.45 W
Livingston, Il.	119e	38.58 N	89.51 W
Livingston, Mt.	117	45.40 N	110.35 W
Livingston, NJ	112a	40.47 N	74.20 W
Livingston, Tn.	126	36.23 N	85.20 W
Livingstone, Zambia (lĭv-ĭng-stôn)	231	17.50 S	25.53 E
Livingstone, Chutes de (Livingstone Falls), Con.-Zaire	230	4.50 S	14.30 E
Livingstone Mts., Tan.	231	9.30 S	34.10 E
Livingstonia, Malawi (lĭv-ĭng-stō′nĭ-ȧ)	231	10.36 S	34.07 E
Livno, Yugo. (lēv′nô)	172	43.50 N	17.03 E
Livny, Sov. Un. (lēv′nē)	174	52.28 N	37.36 E
Livonia, Mi. (lĭ-vō-nĭ-ȧ)	113b	42.25 N	83.23 W
Livorno (Leghorn), It. (lē-vôr′nō) (lĕg′hôrn)	172	43.32 N	11.18 E
Livramento, Braz. (lē-vrä-mĕ′n-tô)	144	30.46 S	55.21 W
Livry-Gargan, Fr.	64c	48.56 N	2.33 E
Limoges, Fr.	168	45.50 N	1.15 E
Lixian, China (lē shyĕn)	203	29.42 N	111.40 E
Lixian, China	200	38.30 N	115.38 E
Liyang, China (lē′yäng′)	200	31.30 N	119.29 E
Lizard Pt., Eng. (lĭz′ȧrd)	162	49.55 N	5.09 W
Lizy-sur-Ourcq, Fr. (lēk-sē′sür-o͞ork′)	169b	49.01 N	3.02 E
Ljmuiden, Neth.	157a	52.27 N	4.35 E
Ljubljana, Yugo. (lyo͞o′blyä′na)	172	46.04 N	14.29 E
Ljubuški, Yugo. (lyo͞o′bo͝osh-kē)	172	43.11 N	17.29 E
Ljungan (R.), Swe.	164	62.50 N	13.45 E
Ljungby, Swe. (lyo͝ong′bü)	164	56.49 N	13.56 E
Ljusdal, Swe. (lyo͞os′däl)	164	61.50 N	16.11 E
Ljusnan (R.), Swe.	164	61.55 N	15.33 E
Llandudno, Wales (lăn-düd′nō)	162	53.20 N	3.46 W
Llanelli, Wales (lá-nĕl′ĭ)	162	51.44 N	4.09 W
Llanes, Sp. (lyä′nås)	170	43.25 N	4.41 W
Llano, Tx. (lă′nō) (lyä′nō)	124	30.45 N	98.41 W
Llano R., Tx.	124	30.38 N	99.04 W
Llanos (Reg.), Col.-Ven. (lyá′nōs)	142	4.00 N	71.15 W
Llera, Mex. (lyā′rä)	130	23.16 N	99.03 W
Llerena, Sp. (lyā-rā′nä)	170	38.14 N	6.02 W
Llobregat (R.), Sp. (lyô-brē-gät′)	171	41.55 N	1.55 E
Lloyd L., Can. (loid)	95e	50.52 N	114.13 W
Lloydminster, Can.	102	53.17 N	110.00 W
Lluchmayor, Sp. (lyo͞och-mä-yôr′)	171	39.28 N	2.53 E
Llullaillaco (Vol.), Arg. (lyo͞o-lyī-lyä′kō)	144	24.50 S	68.30 W
Loange (R.), Zaire (lô-äŋ′gä)	230	6.10 S	19.40 E
Lo Aranguiz, Chile	61b	33.23 S	70.40 W
Lobatsi, Bots. (lō-bä′tsē)	226	25.13 S	25.35 E
Lobau (Pln.), Aus.	66e	48.10 N	16.32 E
Lobería, Arg. (lô-bĕ′rē′ä)	144	38.13 S	58.48 W
Lobito, Ang. (lô-bĕ′tō)	230	12.30 S	13.34 E
Lobnya, Sov. Un. (lôb′nyá)	182b	56.01 N	37.29 E
Lobo, Phil.	207a	13.39 N	121.14 E
Lobos, Arg. (lō′bôs)	141c	35.10 S	59.08 W
Lobos, Cayo (I.), Ba. (lō′bôs)	134	22.25 N	77.40 W
Lobos de Tierra (I.), Peru (lô′bō-dĕ-tyĕ′r-rä)	142	6.29 S	80.55 W
Lobos, Isla de (I.), Mex. (ē′s-lä-dĕ-lô′bōs)	131	21.24 N	97.11 W
Lobva, Sov. Un. (lôb′vá)	182a	59.12 N	60.28 E
Lobva R., Sov. Un.	182a	59.14 N	60.17 E
Locarno, Switz. (lô-kär′nō)	166	46.10 N	8.43 E
Lochearn, Md.	56c	39.21 N	76.43 W
Loches, Fr. (lôsh)	168	47.08 N	0.56 E
Lochloosa (L.), Fl. (lŏk-lō′sȧ)	127	29.33 N	82.07 W
Loch Raven Res., Md.	112e	39.28 N	76.38 W
Lockeport, Can.	104	43.42 N	65.07 W
Lockhart, SC (lŏk′härt)	127	34.47 N	81.30 W
Lockhart, Tx.	125	29.54 N	97.40 W
Lock Haven, Pa. (lŏk′hā-vĕn)	111	41.05 N	77.30 W
Lockland, Oh. (lŏk′lănd)	113f	39.14 N	84.27 W
Lockport, Can. (lŏk′pōrt)	95f	50.05 N	96.56 W
Lockport, Il.	113a	41.35 N	88.04 W
Lockport, NY	113c	43.11 N	78.43 W
Lockwillow, S. Afr.	71b	26.17 S	27.50 E
Loc-ninh, Viet. (lōk′nĭng′)	206	12.00 N	106.30 E
Locust Grove, NY	55	40.48 N	73.30 W
Locust Valley, NY	55	40.53 N	73.36 W
Lod, Isr. (lōd)	191a	31.57 N	34.55 E
Lodève, Fr. (lô-dĕv′)	168	43.43 N	3.18 E
Lodeynoye Pole, Sov. Un. (lô-dĕy-nô′yĕ)	165	60.43 N	33.24 E
Lodge Cr., Can. (lŏj)	100	49.20 N	110.20 W
Lodge Cr., Mt.	117	48.51 N	109.30 W
Lodgepole Cr., Wy. (lŏj′pōl)	114	41.22 N	104.48 W
Lodhran, Pak.	196	29.40 N	71.39 E
Lodi, Ca. (lō′dī)	120	38.07 N	121.17 W

ng-sing; nŋ-baŋk; ɴ-nasalized n; nŏd; cŏmmit; ōld; ôbey; ôrder; oi-boil; fo͞od; fo͝ot; ou-out; s-soft; sh-dish; th-thin; pūre; ůnite; ûrn; stŭd; circŭs; ü-as in French tu; ′-indeterminate vowel.

PLACE (Pronounciation)	PAGE	Lat. °'	Long. °'
Lodi, It. (lô'dē)	172	45.18 N	9.30 E
Lodi, NJ	55	40.53 N	74.05 W
Lodi, Oh. (lō'dī)	113d	41.02 N	82.01 W
Lodosa, Sp. (lô-dō'sä)	170	42.27 N	2.04 W
Lodwar, Ken.	231	3.07 N	35.36 E
Łódź, Pol. (wōōdzh)	167	51.46 N	19.13 E
Loeches, Sp. (lô-āch'ĕs)	171a	40.22 N	3.25 W
Loffa (R.), Lib.	228	7.10 N	10.35 W
Lofoten (Is.), Nor. (lô'fō-tĕn)	158	68.26 N	13.42 E
Logan, Oh. (lō'găn)	110	39.35 N	82.25 W
Logan, Ut.	117	41.46 N	111.51 W
Logan, WV	110	37.50 N	82.00 W
Logan, Mt., Can.	96	60.54 N	140.33 W
Logansport, In. (lō'gănz-pōrt)	110	40.45 N	86.25 W
Logan Square (Neigh.), Il.	58a	41.56 N	87.42 W
Lognes, Fr.	64c	48.50 N	2.38 E
Logone (R.), Afr. (lō-gō'nā) (lô-gôn')	229	11.15 N	15.10 E
Logroño, Sp. (lô-grō'nyō)	170	42.28 N	2.25 W
Logrosán, Sp. (lô-grô-sän')	170	39.22 N	5.29 W
Løgstør, Den. (lügh-stûr')	164	56.56 N	9.15 E
Lohausen (Neigh.), F.R.G.	63	51.16 N	6.44 E
Lohberg, F.R.G.	63	51.35 N	6.46 E
Lo Hermida, Chile	61b	33.29 S	70.33 W
Lohheide, F.R.G.	63	51.30 N	6.40 E
Löhme, G.D.R.	65a	52.37 N	13.40 E
Lohmühle, F.R.G.	63	51.31 N	6.40 E
Löhnen, F.R.G.	63	51.36 N	6.39 E
Loir (R.), Fr. (lwår)	168	47.40 N	0.07 E
Loire (R.), Fr.	168	47.19 N	1.11 W
Loja, Ec. (lō'hä)	142	3.49 S	79.13 W
Loja, Sp. (lô'-kä)	170	37.10 N	4.11 W
Loka, Zaire	230	0.20 N	17.57 E
Lokala Drift, Bots. (lô'kä-lá drĭft)	223d	24.00 S	26.38 E
Lokandu, Zaire	231	2.31 S	25.47 E
Lokhvitsa, Sov. Un. (lôĸ-vĕt'sá)	175	50.21 N	33.16 E
Lokichar, Ken.	231	2.23 N	35.39 E
Lokitaung, Ken.	231	4.16 N	35.45 E
Lokofa-Bokolongo, Zaire	230	0.12 N	19.22 E
Lokoja, Nig. (lô-kō'yä)	229	7.47 N	6.45 E
Lokolama, Zaire	230	2.34 S	19.53 E
Lokosso, Burkina	228	10.19 N	3.40 W
Loliondo, Tan.	231	2.03 S	35.37 E
Lolland, Den. (lôl'än')	164	54.41 N	11.00 E
Lolo, Mt.	117	46.45 N	114.05 W
Lol R., Sud. (lōl)	225	9.06 N	28.09 E
Lom, Bul. (lōm)	173	43.48 N	23.15 E
Loma Linda, Ca. (lō'má lĭn'dá)	119a	34.04 N	117.16 W
Loma Mansa (Mtn.), S.L.	228	9.13 N	11.07 W
Lomami (R.), Zaire	230	0.50 S	24.40 E
Lomas Chapultepec (Neigh.), Mex.	60a	19.26 N	99.13 W
Lomas de Zamora, Arg. (lō'mäs dā zä-mō'rä)	144a	34.31 S	58.24 W
Lombard, Il. (lŏm-bärd)	113a	41.53 N	88.01 W
Lombardia (Reg.), It. (lôm-bär-dē'ä)	172	45.20 N	9.30 E
Lombardy, S. Afr.	71b	26.07 S	28.08 E
Lomblen, Pulau (I.), Indon. (lŏm-blĕn')	207	8.08 S	123.45 E
Lombok (I.), Indon. (lŏm-bŏk')	206	9.15 S	116.15 E
Lomé, Togo. (lō-mā') (lō'mā)	228	6.08 N	1.13 E
Lomela, Zaire (lô-mā'lä)	226	2.19 S	23.33 E
Lomela (R.), Zaire	230	0.35 S	21.20 E
Lometa, Tx. (lō-mē'tá)	124	31.10 N	98.25 W
Lomie, Cam. (lô-mē-ā')	229	3.10 N	13.37 E
Lomita, Ca. (lō-mē'tá)	119a	33.48 N	118.20 W
Lommel, Bel.	157a	51.14 N	5.21 E
Lommond, Loch (L.), Scot. (lŏk lō'mŭnd)	162	56.15 N	4.40 W
Lomonosov, Sov. Un. (lô-mô'nô-sof)	182c	59.54 N	29.47 E
Lompoc, Ca. (lŏm-pōk')	120	34.39 N	120.30 W
Lomza, Pol. (lôm'zhá)	167	53.11 N	22.04 E
Lonaconing, Md. (lō-ná-kō'nĭng)	111	39.35 N	78.55 W
London, Can. (lŭn'dŭn)	110	43.00 N	81.20 W
London, Eng.	156b	51.30 N	0.07 W
London, Ky.	126	37.07 N	84.06 W
London, Oh.	110	39.50 N	83.30 W
London Colney, Eng.	62	51.43 N	0.18 W
Londonderry, Can. (lŭn'dŭn-dĕr-ĭ)	104	45.29 N	63.36 W
Londonderry, N. Ire.	162	55.00 N	7.19 W
Londonderry, C., Austl.	214	13.30 S	127.00 E
London Zoo (P. Int.), Eng.	62	51.32 N	0.09 W
Londrina, Braz. (lôn-drē'nä)	143	21.53 S	51.17 W
Lonely (I.), Can. (lōn'lĭ)	110	45.35 N	81.30 W
Lone Pine, Ca.	120	36.36 N	118.03 W
Lone Star, Nic.	133	13.58 N	84.25 W
Long (I.), Ba.	135	23.25 N	75.10 W
Long (I.), Can.	104	44.21 S	66.25 W
Long (L.), ND	114	46.47 N	100.14 W
Long (L.), Wa.	118a	47.29 N	122.36 W
Longa, Ang.	230	14.42 S	18.32 E
Longa (R.), Ang. (lôŋ'gá)	230	10.20 S	13.50 E
Long B., SC	127	33.30 N	78.54 W
Long Beach, Ca. (lông bēch)	119a	33.46 N	118.12 W
Long Beach, NY	112a	40.35 N	73.38 W
Long Branch, NJ (lông branch)	112a	40.18 N	73.59 W
Long Ditton, Eng.	62	51.23 N	0.20 W
Longdon, ND (lông'-dŭn)	114	48.45 N	98.23 W
Long Eaton, Eng. (ē'tŭn)	156	52.54 N	1.16 W
Longfield, Eng.	62	51.24 N	0.18 E
Longford, Ire. (lông'fērd)	162	53.43 N	7.40 W
Longgu, China (lôŋ-gōō)	200	34.52 N	116.48 E
Longhorn, Tx. (lông-hôrn)	119d	29.33 N	98.23 W
Longhua, China	68a	31.09 N	121.26 E
Long I., Ak.	98	54.54 N	132.45 W
Long I., NY (lông)	111	40.50 N	72.50 W
Long I., Pap. N. Gui.	207	5.10 S	147.30 E
Longido, Tan.	231	2.44 S	36.41 E
Long Island City (Neigh.), NY	55	40.45 N	73.56 W
Long Island Sd., Ct.-NY (lông ī'lănd)	111	41.05 N	72.45 W
Longjumeau, Fr. (lôɴ-zhü-mō')	169b	48.42 N	2.17 E
Longkou, China (lôŋ-kō)	200	37.39 N	120.21 E
Long L., Can.	102	49.10 N	86.45 W
Longlac, Can. (lông'lak)	102	49.41 N	86.28 W
Longlake, SD (lông-lāk)	114	45.52 N	99.06 W
Longmont, Co. (lông'mŏnt)	122	40.11 N	105.07 W
Longnor, Eng. (lông'nôr)	156	53.11 N	1.52 W
Long Pine, Ne. (lông pīn)	114	42.31 N	99.42 W
Long Point, Austl.	70a	34.01 S	150.54 E
Long Point B., Can.	111	42.40 N	80.10 W
Long Prairie, Mn. (lông prâr'ĭ)	115	45.58 N	94.49 W
Long Pt., Can.	101	53.02 N	98.40 W
Long Pt., Can.	105	48.48 N	58.46 W
Long Pt., Can.	111	42.35 N	80.05 W
Long Range Mts., Can.	105	48.00 N	58.30 W
Longreach, Austl. (lông'rēch)	215	23.32 S	144.17 E
Long Reach (R.), Can.	104	45.26 N	66.05 W
Long Reef Point, Austl.	70a	33.45 S	151.19 E
Long Rf., Austl.	211b	33.45 S	151.22 E
Longridge, Eng. (lông'rĭj)	156	53.51 N	2.37 W
Longs Pk., Co. (lôngz)	122	40.17 N	105.37 W
Longtansi, China (lôŋ-tä-sz)	200	32.12 N	115.53 E
Longton, Eng. (lông'tŭn)	156	52.59 N	2.08 W
Longueuil, Can. (lôɴ-gû'y')	95a	45.32 N	73.30 W
Longueville, Austl.	70a	33.50 S	151.10 E
Longview, Tx.	125	32.29 N	94.44 W
Longview, Wa. (lông-vū)	118c	46.06 N	123.02 W
Longville, La. (lông'vĭl)	125	30.36 N	93.14 W
Longwy, Fr. (lôɴ-wē')	169	49.32 N	6.14 E
Longxi, China (lôŋ-shyē)	202	35.00 N	104.40 E
Long-xuyen, Viet. (loung' sōō'yĕn)	206	10.31 N	105.28 E
Longzhen, China (lôŋ-jŭn)	181	48.47 N	126.43 E
Longzhou, China (lôŋ-jō)	203	22.20 N	107.02 E
Lonoke, Ar. (lō'nōk)	123	34.48 N	91.52 W
Lons-le-Saunier, Fr. (lôɴ-lē-sō-nyā')	169	46.40 N	5.33 E
Lontue, (R.), Chile (lŏn-tōōĕ')	141b	35.20 S	70.45 W
Looc, Phil. (lô-ŏk')	207a	12.16 N	121.59 E
Loogootee, In.	110	38.40 N	86.55 W
Lookout, C., NC (lŏŏk'out)	127	34.34 N	76.38 W
Lookout Pt. Res., Or.	116	43.51 N	122.38 W
Loolmalasin (Mtn.), Tan.	231	3.03 S	35.46 E
Looma, Can. (ōō'mă)	95g	53.22 N	113.15 W
Loop (Neigh.), Il.	58a	41.53 N	87.38 W
Loop Head, Ire. (lōōp)	162	52.32 N	9.59 W
Loosahatchie (R.), Tn. (lōz-á-hă'chē)	126	35.20 N	89.45 W
Loosdrechtsche Plassen (L.), Neth.	157a	52.11 N	5.09 E
Lopatka, Mys (C.), Sov. Un. (lô-păt'ká)	177	51.00 N	156.52 E
Lopez B., Phil. (lō'pāz)	207a	14.04 N	122.00 E
Lopez, Cap (C.), Gabon	230	0.37 N	8.43 E
Lopez I, Wa.	118a	48.25 N	122.53 W
Lopori (R.), Zaire (lō-pō'rē)	230	1.35 N	20.43 E
Lo Prado Arriba, Chile	61b	33.26 S	70.45 W
Lora, Sp. (lō'rä)	170	37.40 N	5.31 W
Lorain, Oh. (lô-rān')	113d	41.28 N	82.10 W
Loralai, Pak. (lō-rŭ-lī')	196	30.31 N	68.35 E
Lorca, Sp. (lôr'kä)	170	37.39 N	1.40 W
Lord Howe (I.), Austl. (lôrd hou)	215	31.44 S	157.56 W
Lordsburg, NM (lôrdz'bûrg)	121	32.20 N	108.45 W
Lorena, Braz. (lô-rā'ná)	141a	22.45 S	45.07 W
Loreto, Braz. (lô-rā'tō)	143	7.09 S	45.10 W
Loretteville, Can. (lô-rĕt-vĕl')	95b	46.51 N	71.21 W
Lorica, Col. (lō-rē'kä)	142	9.14 N	75.54 W
Lorient, Fr. (lō-rē'äɴ')	168	47.45 N	3.22 W
Lorn, Firth of, Scot. (fûrth ŏv lôrn')	162	56.10 N	6.09 W
Lörrach, F.R.G. (lûr'äĸ)	166	47.36 N	7.38 E
Los Alamitos, Ca. (lōs ăl-á-mē'tōs)	119a	33.48 N	118.04 W
Los Alamos, NM (ăl-á-mōs')	121	35.53 N	106.20 W
Los Altos, Ca. (ăl-tōs')	118b	37.23 N	122.06 W
Los Andes, Chile (ăn'dĕs)	141b	32.44 S	70.36 W
Los Angeles, Ca. (ăŋ'gĕl-ĕs) (ă'jĕl-ĕs)	119a	34.00 N	118.15 W
Los Angeles, Chile (äŋ'hā-lās)	144	37.27 S	72.15 W
Los Angeles Aqueduct, Ca.	120	35.12 N	118.02 W
Los Angeles Arpt., Ca.	59	33.56 N	118.24 W
Los Angeles R., Ca.	119a	33.50 N	118.13 W
Los Bronces, Chile (lôs brō'n-sĕs)	141b	33.09 S	70.18 W
Loscha R., Id. (lōs'chă)	116	46.20 N	115.11 W
Los Chonos, Archipielago de, Chile (är-chē-pyĕ'lä-gô dĕ lôs chô'nôs)	144	44.35 N	76.15 W
Los Cuatro Alamos, Chile	61b	33.32 S	70.44 W
Los Dos Caminos, Ven.	61a	10.31 N	66.50 W
Los Estados, Isla de (I.), Arg. (ē's-lä dĕ lôs ĕs-dôs)	144	54.45 S	64.25 W
Los Gatos, Ca. (gä'tōs)	120	37.13 N	121.59 W
Los Herreras, Mex. (ĕr-rä-räs)	124	25.55 N	99.23 W
Los llanos, Dom. Rep. (lôs ĕ-lä'nōs)	135	18.35 N	69.30 W
Los Indios, Cayos de (Is.), Cuba (kä'vōs dĕ lôs ē'n-dvô's)	134	21.50 N	83.10 W
Lošinj (I.), Yugo.	172	44.35 N	14.34 E
Losino Petrovskiy, Sov. Un.	182b	55.52 N	38.12 E
Los Nietos, Ca. (nyā'tōs)	119a	33.57 N	118.05 W
Los Palacios, Cuba	134	22.35 N	83.15 W
Los Pinos (R.), Co.-NM (pē'nōs)	121	36.58 N	107.35 W
Los Reyes Mex.(rā'yĕs)	130	19.35 N	102.29 W
Los Reyes, Mex.	131a	19.21 N	98.58 W
Los Santos, Pan. (săn'tōs)	133	7.57 N	80.24 W
Los Santos de Maimona Sp. (săn'tōs)	170	38.38 N	6.30 W
Los Teques, Ven. (tĕ'kĕs)	143b	10.22 N	67.04 W
Lost R., Id. (lôst)	117	43.56 N	113.38 W
Lost R, Or.	116	42.07 N	121.30 W
Lost River Mts., Id. (rĭ'vēr)	117	44.23 N	113.48 W
Los Vilos, Chile (vē'lôs)	141b	31.56 S	71.29 W
Lot (R.), Fr. (lôt)	168	44.32 N	1.08 E
Lota, Chile (lō'tä)	144	37.11 S	73.14 W
Lothian, Md. (lōth'ĭăn)	112e	38.50 N	76.38 W
Lotikipi Pln, Ken.	231	4.25 N	34.55 E
Lötschberg Tunnel, Switz.	166	46.26 N	7.54 E
Louangphrabang, Laos (lōō-ăng'prä-băng')	206	19.47 N	102.15 E
Loudon, Tn. (lou'dŭn)	126	35.43 N	84.20 W
Loudonville, Oh. (lou'dŭn-vĭl)	110	40.40 N	82.15 W
Loudun, Fr. (lōō-dŭɴ')	168	47.03 N	0.00
Louga, Senegal (lōō'gä)	228	15.37 N	16.13 W
Loughborough, Eng. (lŭf'bŭr-ō)	156	56.46 N	1.12 W
Loughton, Eng.	62	51.39 N	0.03 E
Louisa, Ky. (lōō'ēz-á)	110	38.05 N	82.40 W
Louisade Arch., Pap. N. Gui. (lōō-ĭs-äd är-kĭ-pĕl-ĭ-gō)	215	10.44 S	153.58 E
Louisburg, NC (lōō'ĭs-bûrg)	127	36.05 N	79.19 W
Louisburg, Can. (lōō'ĭs-bourg)	105	45.55 N	59.58 W
Louiseville, Can.	104	46.17 N	72.58 W
Louisiana, Mo. (lōō-ē-zē-ăn'á)	123	39.24 N	91.03 W
Louisiana (State), U. S.	109	30.50 N	92.50 W
Louis Trichardt, S. Afr. (lōō'ĭs trĭch'art)	226	22.52 S	29.53 E
Louisville, Co. (lōō'ĭs-vĭl) (lōō'ē-vĭl)	122	39.58 N	105.08 W
Louisville, Ga.	127	33.00 N	82.25 W
Louisville, Ky.	113h	38.15 N	85.45 W
Louisville, Ms.	126	33.07 N	89.02 W
Louis XIV, Pte., Can.	97	54.35 N	79.51 W
Loulé, Port. (lō-lā')	170	37.08 N	8.03 W
Louny, Czech. (lō'nē)	166	50.20 N	13.47 E
Loup (R.), Ne. (lōōp)	114	41.17 N	97.58 W
Loup City, Ne.	114	41.15 N	98.59 W
Lourdes, Fr. (lōōrd)	170	43.06 N	0.03 W
Lourenço Marques, see Maputo			
Loures, Port. (lō'rĕzh)	171b	38.49 N	9.10 W
Lousa, Port. (lō'zá)	170	40.05 N	8.12 W
Louth, Eng. (louth)	162	53.27 N	0.02 W
Louvain, see Leuven			
Louveciennes, Fr.	64c	48.52 N	2.07 E
Louviers, Fr. (lōō-vyā')	168	49.13 N	1.11 E
Louvre (P. Int.), Fr.	64c	48.52 N	2.20 E
Louvres, Fr. (lōōv'r')	169b	49.03 N	2.30 E
Lovat', Sov. Un. (lô-vát'y')	174	57.23 N	31.18 E
Lovech, Bul. (lō'vĕts)	173	43.10 N	24.40 E
Lovedale, Pa.	57b	40.17 N	79.52 W
Loveland, Co. (lŭv'lănd)	122	40.24 N	105.04 W
Loveland, Oh.	113	39.16 N	84.15 W
Lovell, Wy. (lŭv'ĕl)	117	44.50 N	108.23 W
Lovelock, Nv. (lŭv'lŏk)	120	40.10 N	118.37 W
Loves Green, Eng.	62	51.43 N	0.24 E
Lovick, Al. (lŭ'vĭk)	112h	33.34 N	86.38 W
Loviisa, Fin. (lô'vē-sá)	165	60.28 N	26.10 E
Low, C., Can. (lō)	97	62.58 N	86.50 W
Lowa, Zaire (lō'wá)	226	1.30 S	27.18 E
Lowell, In.	113a	41.17 N	87.26 W
Lowell, Ma.	105a	42.38 N	71.18 W
Lowell, Mi.	110	42.55 N	85.20 W
Löwenberg, G.D.R. (lû'vĕn-bĕrgh)	157b	52.53 N	13.09 E
Lower Arrow (L.), Can. (ăr'ō)	99	49.40 N	118.80 W
Lower Austria (State), see Niederösterreich			
Lower Broughton (Neigh.), Eng.	64b	53.29 N	2.15 W
Lower Brule Ind. Res., SD (brü'lā)	114	44.15 N	100.21 W
Lower Higham, Eng.	62	51.26 N	0.28 E
Lower Hutt, N.Z. (hŭt)	217	41.55 S	174.55 E
Lower Klamath L., Ca. (klăm'áth)	116	41.55 N	121.50 W
Lower L., Ca.-Nv.	116	41.21 N	119.53 W
Lower Marlboro, Md. (lō'ēr mărl'bōrō)	112e	38.40 N	76.42 W
Lower Monumental Res., Wa.	116	46.45 N	118.50 W
Lower Nazeing, Eng.	62	51.44 N	0.01 E
Lower New York Bay (B.), NY	55	40.33 N	74.02 W
Lower Otay Res., Ca. (ō'tā)	120a	32.37 N	116.46 W
Lower Place, Eng.	64b	53.36 N	2.09 W
Lower Red. (L.), Mn. (rĕd)	115	47.58 N	94.31 W
Lower Saxony (State), see Niedersachsen			
Lowestoft, Eng. (lō'stŏft)	163	52.31 N	1.45 E
Lowicz, Pol. (lô'vĭch)	167	52.06 N	19.57 E
Lowville, NY (lou'vĭl)	111	43.45 N	75.30 W
Loxicha (Santa Catarina), Mex. (lô-zē'chä) (sän-tä kä-tä-rē'nä)	131	16.03 N	96.46 W
Loxton, Austl. (lôks'tŭn)	216	34.25 S	140.38 E
Loyauté, Iles, N. Cal.	215	21.17 S	168.16 E
Loznica, Yugo. (lōz'nē-tsá)	173	44.31 N	19.16 E
Lozorno, Czech.	157e	48.21 N	17.03 E
Lozova, Sov. Un. (lô-zô'vá)	175	48.54 N	36.17 E
Lozovatka, Sov. Un. (lô-zō-vät'kä)	175	48.03 N	33.19 E
Lozovaya, Sov. Un. (lô-zo-vä'yä)	175	48.27 N	38.37 E
Lozoya, Canal de, Sp. (kä-nä'l dĕ lô-thō'yä)	171a	40.36 N	3.41 W
Luachimo, Ang.	230	7.20 S	20.47 E
Lualaba (R.), Zaire (lōō-á-lä'bá)	231	1.00 S	25.45 E
Luama (R.), Zaire (lōō'ä-má)	231	4.17 S	27.45 E
Lu'an, China (lōō-än)	200	31.45 N	116.29 E
Luan (R.), China	202	41.25 N	117.15 E
Luanda, Ang. (lōō-än'dä)	230	8.48 S	13.14 E
Luanguinga (R.), Ang. (lōō-ä-gĭŋ'gá)	226	14.00 S	20.45 E
Luangwa (R.), Zambia (lōō-äŋ'gwá)	231	11.25 S	32.55 E
Luanshya, Zambia	231	13.08 S	28.24 E
Luanxian, China (luän shyĕn)	200	39.47 N	118.40 E
Luao, Ang.	230	10.42 S	22.12 E
Luarca, Sp. (lwä'kä)	170	43.33 N	6.30 W
Lubaczów, Pol. (lōō-bä'chōōf)	177	50.08 N	23.10 E
Lubán, Pol. (lōō'bän')	166	51.08 N	15.17 E
Lubānas Ezers (L.), Sov. Un. (lōō-bä'nás ā'zĕrs)	165	56.48 N	26.30 E
Lubang, Phil. (lōō-băng')	207a	13.49 N	120.07 E
Lubang (Is.), Phil.	207a	13.47 N	119.56 E
Lubango, Ang.	230	14.55 S	13.30 E
Lubao, Phil. (lōō-bä'ō)	207a	14.55 N	120.36 E
Lubartow, Pol. (lōō-bär'tōōf)	167	51.27 N	22.37 E
Lubawa, Pol. (lōō-bä'vä)	167	53.31 N	19.47 E
Lübben, G.D.R. (lüb'ĕn)	166	51.56 N	13.53 E
Lubbock, Tx. (lŭb'ŭk)	122	33.35 N	101.50 W
Lubec, Me. (lū'bĕk)	104	44.49 N	67.01 W
Lübeck, F.R.G. (lü'bĕk)	166	53.53 N	10.42 E
Lübecker Bucht (B.), G.D.R. (lü'bĕ-kĕr bōōĸt)	166	54.10 N	11.20 E
Lubilash (R.), Zaire (lōō-bē-lash'-)	230	7.35 S	23.55 E
Lubin, Pol. (lyōō'bĭn)	166	51.24 N	16.14 E
Lublin, Pol. (lyōō'blĕn')	167	51.14 N	22.33 E
L'ublino (Neigh.), Sov. Un.	66b	55.41 N	37.44 E
Lubny, Sov. Un. (lōōb'nē)	175	50.01 N	33.02 E

PLACE (Pronounciation)	PAGE	Lat. °′	Long. °′
Lubuagan, Phil. (lōō-bwä-gä'n)	207a	17.24 N	121.11 E
Lubudi, Zaire	231	9.57 S	25.58 E
Lubudi (R.), Zaire (lōō-bōō'dē)	231	9.20 S	25.20 E
Lubumbashi (Élisabethville), Zaire	231	11.40 S	27.28 E
Lucano, Ang.	231	11.16 S	21.38 E
Lucca, It. (lōōk'kä)	172	43.51 N	10.29 E
Lucea, Jam.	134	18.25 N	78.10 W
Luce B., Scot. (lūs)	162	54.45 N	4.45 W
Lucena, Phil. (lōō-sā'nä)	207a	13.55 N	121.36 E
Lucena, Sp. (lōō-thā'nä)	170	37.25 N	4.28 W
Lucena del Cid, Sp. (lōō'thā'nä dā thēdh')	171	40.08 N	0.18 W
Lučenec, Czech. (lōō'chā-nyĕts)	167	48.19 N	19.41 E
Lucera, It. (lōō-châ'rä)	172	41.31 N	15.22 E
Luchi, China	203	28.18 N	110.10 E
Luchou, Taiwan	68d	25.05 N	121.28 E
Lucin, Ut. (lů-sĕn')	117	41.23 N	113.59 W
Lucipara, Kepulauan (I.), Indon. (lōō-sē-pä'rå)	207	5.45 S	128.15 E
Luckenwalde, G.D.R. (lōōk-ĕn-väl'dē)	157b	52.05 N	13.10 E
Lucknow, India (lŭk'nou)	196	26.54 N	80.58 E
Luçon, Fr. (lü-sôN')	168	46.27 N	1.12 W
Lucrecia, Cabo (C.), Cuba (kå'bô-lōō-krā'sē-å)	135	21.05 N	75.30 W
Lüda, China (lů-dä)	200	38.54 N	121.35 E
Luda Kamchiya (R.), Bul.	173	42.46 N	27.13 E
Luddesdown, Eng.	62	51.22 N	0.24 E
Lüdenscheid, F.R.G. (lü'dĕn-shīt)	169c	51.13 N	7.38 E
Lüderitz, Namibia (lü'dēr-īts) (lü'dē-rīts)	226	26.35 S	15.15 E
Lüderitz Bucht (B.), Namibia	226	26.35 S	14.30 E
Ludhiāna, India	196	31.00 N	75.52 E
Lüdinghausen, F.R.G. (lü'dĕng-hou-zĕn)	169c	51.46 N	7.27 E
Ludington, Mi. (lŭd'ĭng-tŭn)	110	44.00 N	86.25 W
Ludlow, Eng. (lŭd'lō)	156	52.22 N	2.43 W
Ludlow, Ky.	113f	39.05 N	84.33 W
Ludvika, Swe. (loodh-vē'kå)	164	60.10 N	15.09 E
Ludwigsburg, F.R.G. (lōōt'vēks-bōōrgh)	166	48.53 N	9.14 E
Ludwigsfelde, G.D.R. (lōōd'vēgs-fĕl-dĕ)	157b	52.18 N	13.16 E
Ludwigshafen, F.R.G. (lōōt'vēks-hä'fĕn)	166	49.29 N	8.26 E
Ludwigslust, G.D.R. (lōōt'vēks-lōōst)	166	53.18 N	11.31 E
Ludza, Sov. Un. (lōōd'zå)	174	56.33 N	27.45 E
Luebo, Zaire (lōō-ā'bô)	226	5.15 S	21.22 E
Luena, Ang.	230	11.45 S	19.55 E
Luena, Zaire	231	9.27 S	25.47 E
Lufira (R.), Zaire (lōō-fē'rå)	226	9.32 S	27.15 E
Lufkin, Tx. (lŭf'kĭn)	125	31.21 N	94.43 W
Luga, Sov. Un. (lōō'gå)	174	58.43 N	29.52 E
Luga (R.), Sov. Un.	174	59.00 N	29.25 E
Lugano, Switz. (lōō-gä'nō)	166	46.01 N	8.52 E
Lugarno, Austl.	70a	33.59 S	151.03 E
Lugenda (R.), Moz. (lōō-zhĕn'dä)	231	12.05 S	38.15
Lugnaquilla Mtn., Ire. (lōōk-nå-kwĭ-lå)	162	52.56 N	6.30 W
Lugo, It. (lōō'gô)	172	44.28 N	11.57 E
Lugo, Sp. (lōō'gō)	170	43.01 N	7.32 W
Lugoj, Rom.	173	45.51 N	21.56 E
Lugouqiao, China	67b	39.51 N	116.13 E
Luhe, China (lōō-hŭ)	200	32.22 N	118.50 E
Luhe, see Winsen			
Luiana, Ang.	230	17.23 S	23.03 E
Luilaka (R.), Zaire (lōō-ē-lä'kå)	226	2.18 S	21.15 E
Luimneach, Ire. (lĭm'nåk)	162	52.39 N	8.35 W
Luis Moya, Mex. (lōōē's-mô-yä)	130	22.26 N	102.14 W
Luján, Arg. (lōō'hän')	141c	34.36 S	59.07 W
Luján (R.), Arg.	141c	34.33 S	58.59 W
Lujchow Pen., China	199	20.40 N	100.30 E
Lujia, China (lōō-jyä)	200	31.17 N	120.54 W
Lukanga Swp., Zambia (lōō-käŋ'gå)	231	14.30 S	27.25 E
Lukenie (R.), Zaire (lōō-kå'ynå)	230	3.10 S	19.05 E
Lukolela, Zaire	226	1.03 S	17.01 E
Lukovit, Bul. (lōō'kō-vēt')	173	43.13 N	24.07 E
Łuków, Pol. (wōō'kōōf)	167	51.57 N	22.25 E
Lukuga (R.), Zaire (lōō-kōō'gå)	231	5.50 S	27.35 E
Lule (R.), Swe.	178	66.20 N	20.25 E
Luleå, Swe. (lōō-lĕ-ô)	158	65.39 N	21.52 E
Lüleburgaz, Tur. (lü'lĕ-bōōr-gäs')	173	41.25 N	27.23 E
Luling, Tx. (lū'lĭng)	125	29.41 N	97.38 W
Lulong, China (lōō-lôŋ)	200	39.54 N	118.53 E
Lulonga (R.), Zaire	230	1.00 N	18.37 E
Lulu (I.), Can. (lū'lōō)	118d	49.09 N	123.05 W
Lulua (R.), Zaire (lōō'lōō-å)	230	15.40 N	22.07 E
Luluabourg, see Kananga			
Lulu I, Ak.	96	55.28 N	133.30 W
Lulu I, Can.	98	49.09 N	123.05 W
Lumajangdong Co. (L.), China (lōō-ma-jäŋ-dôŋtswo)	196	34.00 N	81.47 E
Lumber (R.), NC (lŭm'bēr)	127	35.12 N	79.35 W
Lumberton, Ms. (lŭm'bēr-tŭn)	126	31.00 N	89.25 W
Lumberton, NC	127	34.47 N	79.00 W
Luminárias, Braz. (lōō-mē-nå'ryäs)	141a	21.32 S	44.53 W
Lummi (I.), Wa.	118d	48.42 N	122.43 W
Lummi B., Wa. (lŭm'ĭ)	118d	48.47 N	122.44 W
Lummi Island, Wa.	118d	48.44 N	122.42 W
Lumwana, Zambia	230	11.50 S	25.10 E
Lün, Mong.	198	47.58 N	104.52 E
Luna, Phil. (lōō'nå)	207a	16.51 N	120.22 E
Lund, Swe. (lŭnd)	164	55.42 N	13.10 E
Lunda (Reg.), Ang. (lōōn'då)	222	8.53 S	20.00 E
Lundi (R.), Zimb. (lōōn'dē)	226	21.09 S	30.10 E
Lundy (I.), Eng. (lŭn'dē)	162	51.12 N	4.50 W
Lüneberger Heide (Reg.), F.R.G. (lü'nē-bōōr-gēr hī'dē)	166	53.08 N	10.00 E
Lüneburg, F.R.G. (lü'nē-bōōrgh)	166	53.16 N	10.25 E
Lunel, Fr. (lü-nĕl')	168	43.41 N	4.07 E
Lünen, F.R.G. (lü'nĕn)	169c	51.36 N	7.30 E
Lunenburg, Can. (lōō'nĕn-bûrg)	104	44.23 N	64.19 W
Lunenburg, Ma.	105a	42.36 N	71.44 W
Lunéville, Fr. (lü-nå-vel')	169	48.37 N	6.29 E
Lunga (R.), Zambia (lōōŋ'gå)	226	12.58 S	26.18 E
Lungué-Bungo (R), Ang.	230	13.00 S	21.27 E
Lūni (R), India	196	25.20 N	72.00 E
Luninets (R), Sov. Un. (lōō-nēn'yets)	174	52.14 N	26.54 E
Lunsar, S.L.	228	8.41 N	12.32 W
Lunt, Eng.	64a	53.31 N	2.59 W
Luodian, China (lwô-dĭēn)	201a	31.25 N	121.20 E
Luoding, China (lwô-dĭŋ)	203	23.42 N	111.35 E
Luohe, China (lwô-hŭ)	200	33.35 N	114.02 E
Luoyang, China (lwô-yäŋ)	202	34.45 N	112.32 E
Luozhen, China (lwô-jŭn)	200	37.45 N	118.29 E
Luque, Par. (loo'kā)	144	25.18 S	57.17 W
Lūrah (R), Afg.	196	32.10 N	67.20 E
Luray, Va. (lū-rā')	111	38.40 N	78.25 W
Lurgan, N. Ire. (lûr'găn)	162	54.27 N	6.28 W
Lurigancho, Peru	60c	12.02 S	77.01 W
Lúrio, Moz. (lōō'rē-ô)	227	13.17 S	40.29 E
Lúrio (R), Moz.	231	14.00 S	38.45 E
Lurnea, Austl.	70a	33.56 S	150.54 E
Lusaka, Zaire	231	7.10 S	29.27 E
Lusaka, Zambia (lōō-sä'kå)	231	15.25 S	28.17 E
Lusambo, Zaire (lōō-säm'bō)	230	4.58 S	23.27 E
Lusanga, Zaire	226	5.13 S	18.43 E
Lusangi, Zaire	231	4.37 S	27.08 E
Lushai Hills, Bur.	196	28.28 N	92.50 E
Lushan, China	202	33.45 N	113.00 E
Lushiko (R), Zaire	230	6.35 S	19.45 E
Lushoto, Tan. (lōō-shō'tō)	227	4.47 S	38.17 E
Lüshun, China (lü-shŭn)	200	38.49 N	121.15 E
Lusikisiki, S. Afr. (lōō-sē-kē-sē'kē)	227c	31.22 S	29.37 E
Lusk, Wy. (lŭsk)	114	42.46 N	104.27 W
Lutcher, La. (lŭch'ēr)	125	30.03 N	90.43 W
Lütgendortmund (Neigh.), F.R.G.	63	51.30 N	7.21 E
Luton, Eng. (lū'tŭn)	162	51.55 N	0.28 W
Lutsk, Sov. Un. (lōōtsk)	167	50.45 N	25.20 E
Lüttringhausen (Neigh.), F.R.G.	63	51.13 N	7.14 E
Luuq, Som.	223a	3.38 N	42.35 E
Luverne, Al. (lū-vûn')	126	31.42 N	86.15 W
Luverne, Mn.	114	43.40 N	96.13 W
Luvua (R), Zaire (lōō'vōō-å)	231	7.00 S	27.45 E
Luwingu, Zambia	231	10.15 S	29.55 E
Luxapalila Cr., Al. (lŭk-så-pôl'ĭ-lå)	126	33.36 N	88.08 W
Luxembourg, Eur.	154	49.30 N	6.22 E
Luxembourg, Lux. (lŭk-sĕm-bûrg) (lük sän-bōōr') (look-sĕm-bōōrgh)	169	49.38 N	6.30 E
Luxeuil-les-Baines, Fr.	169	47.49 N	6.19 E
Luxomni, Ga. (lŭx'ŏm-nī)	112c	33.54 N	84.07 W
Luxor, see Al Uqşur			
Lu Xun Museum (P. Int.), China	68a	31.16 N	121.28 E
Luya Shan (Mtn.), China	202	38.50 N	111.40 E
Luyi, China (lōō-yē)	200	33.52 N	115.32 E
Luyuan, China	67b	39.54 N	116.27 E
Luz, Braz.	61c	22.48 S	43.05 W
Luz (Neigh.), Port.	65d	38.46 N	9.10 W
Luza (R.), Sov. Un. (lōō'zä)	178	60.30 N	47.10 E
Luzern, Switz. (lōō-tsĕrn)	166	47.03 N	8.18 E
Luzhou, China (lōō-jō)	203	28.58 N	105.25 E
Luziânia, Braz. (lōō-zyå'nēå)	143	16.17 S	47.44 W
Lužniki (Neigh.), Sov. Un.	66b	55.43 N	37.33 E
Luzon (I.), Phil. (lōō-zŏn')	206	17.10 N	119.45 E
Luzon Str., Phil.	203	20.40 N	121.00 E
L'vov, Sov. Un. (l'vōōf)	167	49.51 N	24.01 E
Lyakhovskiye (Is.), Sov. Un. (lya'kô'v-skyĕ)	181	73.45 N	145.15 E
Lyalta, Can.	95e	51.07 N	113.36 W
Lyalya R., Sov. Un. (lyå'lyå)	182a	58.58 N	60.17 E
Lyaskovets, Bul.	173	43.07 N	25.41 E
Lydenburg, S. Afr. (lī'dĕn-bûrg)	226	25.06 S	30.21 E
Lydiate, Eng.	64a	53.32 N	2.57 W
Lye Green, Eng.	62	51.43 N	0.35 W
Lyell, Mt., Ca. (lī'ĕl)	120	37.44 N	119.22 W
Lykens, Pa. (lī'kĕnz)	111	40.35 N	76.45 W
Lyna R., Pol. (lĭn'å)	167	53.56 N	20.30 E
Lynbrook, NY	55	40.39 N	73.41 W
Lynch, Ky. (lĭnch)	126	36.56 N	82.55 W
Lynchburg, Va. (lĭnch'bûrg)	127	37.23 N	79.08 W
Lynch Cove, Wa. (lĭnch)	118a	47.26 N	122.54 W
Lynden, Can. (lĭn'dĕn)	95d	43.14 N	80.08 W
Lynden, Wa.	118d	48.56 N	122.27 W
Lyndhurst, Austl.	211a	38.03 S	145.14 E
Lyndhurst, NJ	55	40.49 N	74.07 W
Lyndhurst, Oh.	56a	41.31 N	81.30 W
Lyndon, Ky. (lĭn'dŭn)	113h	38.15 N	85.36 W
Lyndonville, Vt. (lĭn'dŭn-vĭl)	111	44.35 N	72.00 W
Lyne, Eng.	62	51.23 N	0.33 W
Lynn, Ma. (lĭn)	105a	42.28 N	70.57 W
Lynnewood Gardens, Pa.	56b	40.04 N	75.09 W
Lynnfield, Ma.	54a	42.32 N	71.03 W
Lynn Lake, Can. (lăk)	101	56.51 N	100.30 W
Lynwood, Ca. (lĭn'wŏŏd)	119a	33.56 N	118.13 W
Lyon, Fr. (lē-ôN')	168	45.44 N	4.52 E
Lyons, Ga. (lī'ŭnz)	127	32.08 N	82.19 W
Lyons, Il.	58a	41.49 N	87.50 W
Lyons, Ks.	122	38.20 N	98.11 W
Lyons, Ne.	114	41.57 N	96.28 W
Lyons, NJ	112a	40.41 N	74.33 W
Lyons, NY	111	43.05 N	77.00 W
Lysefjorden (Fd.), Nor.	164	58.59 N	6.35 E
Lysekil, Swe. (lü'sē-kĕl)	164	58.17 N	11.22 E
Lysterfield, Austl.	70b	37.56 S	145.18 E
Lys'va, Sov. Un. (lĭs'vå)	182a	58.07 N	57.47 E
Lytham, Eng. (lĭth'ăm)	156	53.44 N	2.58 W
Lytkarino, Sov. Un.	182b	55.25 N	37.55 E
Lyttelton, S. Afr. (lĭt'l'ton)	227b	25.51 S	28.13 E
Lyuban', Sov. Un. (lyōō'bån)	182c	59.21 N	31.15 E
Lyubar, Sov. Un. (lyōō'bär)	175	49.56 N	27.44 E
Lyubertsy, Sov. Un. (lyōō'bĕr-tsĕ)	182b	55.40 N	37.55 E
Lyubim, Sov. Un. (lyōō-bēm')	174	58.24 N	40.39 E
Lyublino, Sov. Un. (lyōōb'lĭ-nô)	182b	55.41 N	37.45 E
Lyudinovo, Sov. Un. (lū-dē'novō)	174	53.52 N	34.28 E

M

PLACE (Pronounciation)	PAGE	Lat. °′	Long. °′
Ma'ān, Jordan (mä-än')	191a	30.12 N	35.45 E
Maartensdijk, Neth.	157a	52.09 N	5.10 E
Maas (R.), Neth.	169c	51.32 N	6.07 E
Maastricht, Neth. (mäs'trĭKt)	163	50.51 N	5.35 E
Mabaia, Ang.	230	7.13 S	14.03 E
Mabana, Wa. (mä-bä-nä)	118a	48.06 N	122.25 W
Mabank, Tx. (mā'bănk)	125	32.21 N	96.05 W
Mabeskraal, S. Afr.	223d	25.12 S	26.47 E
Mableton, Ga. (mā'b'l-tŭn)	112c	33.49 N	84.34 W
Mabrouk, Mali	224	19.27 N	1.16 W
Mabula, S. Afr. (mä'bōō-la)	223d	24.49 S	27.59 E
Macaé, Braz. (mä-kä-ā')	141a	22.22 S	41.47 W
Macaira (R.), Ven. (mä-kī'rä)	143b	9.37 N	66.16 W
Macalelon, Phil. (mä-kä-lā-lōn')	207a	13.46 N	122.09 E
Macao, Asia	199	22.00 N	113.00 E
Macapá, Braz. (mä-kä-pä')	143	0.08 N	50.02 W
Macau, Braz. (mä-kå'ōō)	143	5.12 S	36.34 W
Macaya, Pico de (Pk.), Hai.	135	18.25 N	74.00 W
Macclesfield, Eng. (măk''lz-fēld)	156	53.15 N	2.07 W
Macclesfield Can., Eng. (măk''lz-fēld)	156	53.14 N	2.07 W
Macdona, Tx. (măk-dō'nå)	119d	29.20 N	98.42 W
Macdonald (I.), Austl. (măk-dŏn'ăld)	214	23.40 S	127.40 E
Macdonnell Ra., Austl. (măk-dŏn'ĕl)	214	23.40 S	131.30 E
MacDowell L., Can. (măk-dou ĕl)	101	52.15 N	92.45 W
Macdui, Ben (Mtn.), Scot. (bĕn măk-dōō'ē)	162	57.06 N	3.45 W
Macedonia, Oh. (măs-ē-dō'nĭ-å)	113d	41.19 N	81.30 E
Macedonia (Reg.), Eur. (măs-ē-dō'nĭ-å)	173	41.05 N	22.15 E
Maceió, Braz. (mä-sâ-yō')	143	9.33 S	35.35 W
Macerata, It. (mä-chå-rä'tä)	172	43.18 N	13.28 E
Macfarlane, L., Austl. (măc'fär-lān)	216	32.10 S	137.00 E
Machache (Mtn.), Leso.	223c	29.22 S	27.53 E
Machado, Braz. (mä-shå-dô)	141a	21.42 S	45.55 W
Machakos, Ken.	231	1.31 S	37.16 E
Machala, Ec. (mä-chå'lä)	142	3.18 S	78.54 W
Machens, Mo. (măk'ĕns)	119e	38.54 N	90.20 W
Machias, Me. (må-chī'ås)	104	44.22 N	67.29 W
Machida, Jap. (mä-chē'dä)	205a	35.32 N	139.28 E
Machilipatnam, India	197	16.22 N	81.10 E
Machu Picchu, Peru (må'chōō-pē'k-chōō)	142	13.07 S	72.34 W
Măcin, Rom. (må-chēn')	175	45.15 N	28.09 E
Macina (Depression), Mali	228	14.50 N	4.40 W
Mackay, Austl. (mă-kī')	215	21.15 S	149.08 E
Mackay, Id. (măk-kā')	117	43.55 N	113.38 W
Mackay (I), Austl. (mă-kī')	214	22.30 S	127.45 E
MacKay (L.), Can. (măk-kā')	96	64.10 N	112.35 W
Mackay (R.), Can.	100	56.50 N	112.30 W
Mackenzie (R.), Can.	96	63.38 N	124.23 W
Mackenzie B., Ak.	107	69.20 N	137.10 W
Mackenzie, Dist. of, Can.	96	63.48 N	125.25 W
Mackenzie Mts., Can. (må-kĕn'zĭ)	96	63.41 N	129.27 W
Mackinac, Str. of, Mi. (măk'ĭ-nô) (măk'ĭ-năk)	110	45.50 N	84.40 W
Mackinaw (R.), Il.	110	40.35 N	89.25 W
Mackinaw City, Mi. (măk'ĭ-nô)	110	45.45 N	84.45 W
Mackinnon Road, Ken.	231	3.44 S	39.03 E
Macleantown, S. Afr. (măk-lān'toun)	227c	32.48 S	27.48 E
Maclear, S. Afr. (må-klēr')	227c	31.06 S	28.23 E
Macleod, Austl.	70b	37.43 S	145.04 E
Macomb, Il. (må-kōōm')	123	40.27 N	90.40 W
Mâcon, Fr. (mä-kôN)	168	46.19 N	4.51 E
Macon, Ga. (mā'kŏn)	126	32.49 N	83.39 W
Macon, Ms.	126	32.07 N	88.31 W
Macon, Mo.	123	39.42 N	92.29 W
Macquarie (R.), Austl.	216	31.43 S	148.04 E
Macquarie Fields, Austl.	70a	33.59 S	150.53 E
Macquarie Is., Austl. (må-kwŏr'ē)	232	54.36 S	158.45 E
Macquarie University (P. Int.), Austl.	70a	33.46 S	151.06 E
Macritchie Res., Singapore	67c	1.21 N	103.50 E
Macuelizo, Hond. (mä-kwē-lē'zô)	132	15.22 N	88.32 W
Macuto, Ven.	61a	10.37 N	66.53 W
Ma'dabā, Jordan	191a	31.43 N	34.47 E
Madagascar, Afr. (măd-å-găs'kår)	222	18.05 S	43.12 E
Madame (I.), Can. (må-dåm')	105	45.33 N	61.02 W
Madanapalle, India	197	13.06 N	78.09 E
Madang, Pap. N. Gui. (mä-däng')	207	5.15 S	145.45 E
Madaoua, Niger (må-dou'å)	224	14.04 N	6.03 E
Madawaska (R.), Can. (măd-å-wŏs'kå)	111	45.20 N	77.25 W
Madeira (R.), Braz.	142	6.48 S	62.43 W
Madeira, Arquipelado da (Is.), Port. (är-kē-pē'lä-gō-dä-mä-dĕý-rä)	224	33.26 N	16.44 W
Madeira, Ilha da (I.), Mad. Is. (mä-dā'rä)	224	32.41 N	16.15 W
Madelia, Mn. (må-dē'lĭ-å)	115	44.03 N	94.23 W
Madeline (I.), Wi. (măd'ĕ-lĭn)	115	46.47 N	91.30 W
Madera, Ca. (må-dā'rå)	120	36.57 N	120.04 W
Madera (Vol.), Nic.	132	11.27 N	85.30 W

PLACE (Pronounciation)	PAGE	Lat. °'	Long. °'
Madgaon, India	197	15.09 N	73.58 E
Madhya Pradesh (State), India (mŭd'vŭ prū-dāsh')	196	22.04 N	77.48 E
Madill, Ok. (mȧ-dĭl')	123	34.04 N	96.45 W
Madīnat ash Sha'b, P.D.R. of Yem.	192	12.45 N	44.00 E
Madingo, Con.	230	4.07 S	11.22 E
Madingou, Con.	230	4.09 S	13.34 E
Madison, Fl. (măd'ĭ-sŭn)	126	30.28 N	83.25 W
Madison, Ga.	126	33.34 N	83.29 W
Madison, Il.	119e	38.40 N	90.09 W
Madison, In.	110	38.45 N	85.25 W
Madison, Ks.	123	38.08 N	96.07 W
Madison, Me.	104	44.47 N	69.52 W
Madison, Mn.	114	44.59 N	96.13 W
Madison, NC	127	36.22 N	79.59 W
Madison, Ne.	114	41.49 N	97.27 W
Madison, NJ	112a	40.46 N	74.25 W
Madison, SD	114	44.01 N	97.08 W
Madison, Wi.	115	43.05 N	89.23 W
Madison Heights, Mi.	57c	42.30 N	83.06 W
Madison R, Mt.	117	45.15 N	111.30 W
Madison Res, Mt.	117	45.25 N	111.28 W
Madisonville, Ky. (măd'ĭ-sŭn-vĭl)	110	37.20 N	87.30 W
Madisonville, La.	119	30.22 N	90.10 W
Madisonville, Tx.	119	30.57 N	95.55 W
Madjori, Burkina	228	11.26 N	1.15 E
Mado Gashi, Ken.	231	0.44 N	39.10 E
Madona, Sov. Un. (mȧ'dō'nȧ)	174	56.50 N	26.14 E
Mad R., Ca. (măd)	116	40.38 N	123.37 W
Madrakah, Ra's al (C.), Om.	192	18.53 N	57.48 E
Madras, India (mȧ-drȧs') (mŭ-drŭs')	197	13.08 N	80.15 E
Madre de Dios, Arch., Chile (mä'drā dā dē-ōs')	144	50.40 S	76.30 W
Madre de Dios, Rio (R.), Bol. (rē'ō-mä'drā dā dē-ōs')	142	12.07 S	68.02 W
Madre del Sur, Sierra (Mts.), Mex. (sē-ĕ'r-rä-mä'drā dĕlsōōr')	130	17.35 N	100.35 W
Madre, Laguna L., Mex. (lä-gōō'nä mä'drā)	119	25.08 N	97.41 W
Madre, Sierra (Mts.), Mex. (sē-ĕ'r-rä-mȧ'drĕ)	130	15.55 N	92.40 W
Madre, Sierra (Mts.), Phil.	207a	16.40 N	122.10 E
Madrid, Ia. (măd'rĭd)	115	41.51 N	93.48 W
Madrid, Sp. (mä-drē'd)	171a	40.26 N	3.42 W
Madridejos, Sp. (mä-dhrē-dhä'hōs)	170	39.29 N	3.32 W
Madrillon, Va.	56d	38.55 N	77.14 W
Madura (I.), Indon. (mȧ-dōō'rä)	206	6.45 S	113.30 E
Madurai, India (mä-dōō'rä)	197	9.57 N	78.04 E
Madureira (Neigh.), Braz.	61c	22.53 S	43.21 W
Madureira, Serra do, (Mtn.), Braz. (sĕ'r-rä-dô-mä-dōō-rā'rȧ)	144b	22.49 S	43.30 W
Maebashi, Jap. (mä-ĕ-bä'shē)	205	36.26 N	139.04 E
Maeno (Neigh.), Jap.	69a	35.46 N	139.42 E
Maestra, Sierra (Mts.), Cuba (sē-ĕ'r-rȧ-mä-ās'trä)	134	20.05 N	77.05 W
Maewo (I.), Vanuatu	215	15.17 S	168.16 E
Mafeking, S. Afr. (mäf'ĕ'kĭng)	226	25.46 S	24.45 E
Mafia (I.), Tan. (mä-fē'ä)	231	7.47 S	40.00 E
Mafra, Braz. (mä'frä)	144	26.21 S	49.59 W
Mafra, Port. (mäf'rȧ)	171b	38.56 N	9.20 W
Magadan, Sov. Un. (mȧ-gȧ-dän')	181	59.39 N	150.43 E
Magadan Oblast, Sov. Un.	181	63.00 N	170.30 E
Magadi, Ken.	231	1.54 S	36.17 E
Magadi (L.), Ken. (mä-gä'dē)	231	1.50 S	36.00 E
Magalhães Bastos (Neigh.), Braz.	61c	22.53 S	43.23 W
Magalies (R), S. Afr. (mä-gä'lyĕs)	227b	25.51 S	27.42 E
Magaliesberg (Mts.), S. Afr.	227b	25.45 S	27.43 E
Magaliesburg, S. Afr.	223d	26.01 S	27.32 E
Magallanes, Phil. (mä-gäl-yä'nās)	207a	12.48 N	123.52 E
Magallanes, Estrecho de (Str.), Arg.-Chile (ĕs-trĕ'chō-dĕ-mä-gäl-yä'nĕs)	144	52.30 S	68.45 W
Magangué, Col. (mä-gän'gā)	142	9.08 N	74.56 W
Magat (R.), Phil. (mä-gät')	207a	16.45 N	121.16 E
Magdalena, Arg. (mäg-dä-lā'nä)	141c	35.05 S	57.32 W
Magdalena, Bol.	142	13.17 S	63.57 W
Magdalena (I.), Chile	144	44.45 S	73.15 W
Magdalena, Mex.	108	30.34 N	110.50 W
Magdalena, NM	121	34.10 N	107.45 W
Magdalena, Bahia (B.), Mex. (bä-ē'ä-mäg-dä-lā'nä)	128	24.30 N	114.00 W
Magdalena Contreras, Mex.	60a	19.18 N	99.17 W
Magdalena del Mar, Peru	60c	12.06 S	77.05 W
Magdalena, Rio (R.), Col.	142	7.45 N	74.04 W
Magdalen Is., Can. (măg'dȧ-lĕn)	105	47.27 N	61.25 W
Magdalen Laver, Eng.	62	51.45 N	0.11 E
Magdeburg, G.D.R. (mäg'dĕ-bōōrgh)	166	52.07 N	11.39 E
Magé, Braz. (mä-zhā')	144b	22.39 S	43.02 W
Magenta, It. (mȧ-jĕn'tȧ)	172	45.26 N	8.53 E
Mageroya (I.), Nor.	158	71.10 N	24.11 E
Maggiore, Lago (L.), It.	172	46.03 N	8.25 E
Maghāghah, Egypt	223b	28.38 N	30.50 E
Maghniyya, Alg.	160	34.52 N	1.40 W
Maghull, Eng.	64a	53.32 N	2.57 W
Maginu, Jap.	69a	35.35 N	139.36 E
Magiscatzin, Mex. (mä-kēs-kät-zēn')	130	22.48 N	98.42 W
Maglaj, Yugo. (mä'glä-ē)	173	44.34 N	18.12 E
Magliana (Neigh.), It.	66c	41.50 N	12.25 E
Maglić, Yugo. (mäg'lēch)	173	43.36 N	20.36 E
Maglie, It. (mäl'yā)	173	40.06 N	18.20 E
Magna, Ut. (măg'nȧ)	119b	40.43 N	112.06 W
Magnitogorsk, Sov. Un. (mȧg-nyē'tô-gôrsk)	182a	53.26 N	59.05 E
Magnolia, Ar. (măg-nō'lĭ-ȧ)	123	33.16 N	93.13 W
Magnolia, Ms.	126	31.08 N	90.27 W
Magnolia, NJ	56b	39.51 N	75.02 W
Magny-en-Vexin, Fr. (mä-nyē'ĕɴ-vĕ-săɴ')	169b	49.09 N	1.45 E
Magny-les-Hameaux, Fr.	64c	48.44 N	2.04 E
Magog, Can. (mȧ-gŏg')	111	45.15 N	72.10 W
Magome (Neigh.), Jap.	69a	35.35 N	139.43 E
Magpie (R.), Can.	102	50.40 N	64.30 W

PLACE (Pronounciation)	PAGE	Lat. °'	Long. °'
Magpie (R.), Can.	115	48.13 N	84.50 W
Magpie Lac (L.), Can.	104	50.55 N	64.39 W
Magrath, Can.	99	49.25 N	112.52 W
Maguanying, China	67b	39.52 N	116.17 E
Magude, Moz. (mä-gōō'dȧ)	226	24.58 S	32.39 E
Magwe, Bur. (mŭg-wā')	198	20.19 N	94.57 E
Mahābād, Iran	179	36.55 N	45.50 E
Mahahi Port, Zaire (mä-hä'gē)	225	2.14 N	31.12 E
Mahajanga, Mad.	227	15.12 S	46.26 E
Mahakam (Strm.), Indon.	206	0.30 S	116.15 E
Mahali Mts., Tan.	231	6.20 S	30.00 E
Mahaly, Mad. (mȧ-hȧl-ē')	227	24.09 S	46.20 E
Mahameru, Gunung (Mtn.), Indon.	206	8.00 S	112.50 E
Mahānadi (R.), India (mŭ-hä-nŭd'ē)	196	20.50 N	84.27 E
Mahanoro, Mad. (mȧ-hȧ-nō'rō)	227	19.57 S	48.47 E
Mahanoy City, Pa. (mä-hȧ-noi')	111	40.50 N	76.10 W
Mahārāshtra (State), India	196	19.06 N	75.00 E
Maḩaţţat al-Hilmīyah (Neigh.), Egypt	71a	30.07 N	31.19 E
Maḩaţţat al Qaţrānah, Jordan	191a	31.15 N	36.04 E
Maḩaţţat 'Aqabat al Hijāzīyah, Jordan	191a	29.45 N	35.55 E
Maḩaţţat ar Ramlah, Jordan	191	29.31 N	35.57 E
Maḩaţţat Jurf ad Darāwīsh, Jordan	191a	30.41 N	35.51 E
Mahavavy (R.), Mad. (mä-hä-vä'vē)	227	17.42 S	46.06 E
Mahaweli (R.), India	196	7.47 N	80.43 E
Mahd adh-Dhahab, Sau. Ar.	195	23.30 N	40.52 E
Mahe, India (mä-ā')	197	11.42 N	75.39 E
Mahenge, Tan. (mä-hĕŋ'gȧ)	231	7.38 S	36.16 E
Mahi (R.), India	196	23.16 N	73.20 E
Māhīm (Neigh.), India	67e	19.03 N	72.49 E
Māhīm Bay, India	197b	19.03 N	72.45 E
Mahlabatini, S. Afr. (mä'lȧ-bȧ-tē'nē)	227c	28.15 S	31.29 E
Mahlow, G.D.R. (mä'lōv)	157b	52.23 N	13.24 E
Mahlsdorf (Neigh.), G.D.R.	65a	52.31 N	13.37 E
Mahlsdorf-Süd (Neigh.), G.D.R.	65a	52.29 N	13.36 E
Mahnomen, Mn. (mô-nō'mĕn)	114	47.18 N	95.58 W
Mahón, Sp. (mä-ōn')	171	39.52 N	4.15 E
Mahone B., Can.	104	44.30 N	64.15 W
Mahone Bay, Can. (mȧ-hōn')	104	44.27 N	64.23 W
Mahopac, L., NY (mā-hō'păk)	112a	41.24 N	73.45 W
Mahrauli (Neigh.), India	67d	28.31 N	77.11 E
Māhul (Neigh.), India	67e	19.01 N	72.53 E
Mahwah, NJ (mȧ-wä')	112a	41.05 N	74.09 W
Maidenhead, Eng. (mād'ĕn-hĕd)	156b	51.30 N	0.44 W
Maidstone, Austl.	70b	37.47 S	144.52 E
Maidstone, Eng.	156b	51.17 N	0.32 E
Maiduguri, Nig. (mä'ē-dȧ-gōō'rē)	229	11.51 N	13.10 E
Maigualida Sierra (Mts.), Ven. (sĕ-ĕ'r-rȧ-mī-gwä'lē-dĕ)	142	6.30 N	65.50 W
Maijdi, Bngl.	196	22.59 N	91.08 E
Maikop, see Maykop			
Main (R.), F.R.G. (mīn)	166	49.49 N	9.20 E
Main Barrier Ra., Austl. (băr''ēr)	216	31.25 S	141.40 E
Mai-Ndombe, Lac (Leopold II, L.), Zaire	226	2.16 S	19.00 E
Maine (State), U. S. (mān)	109	45.25 N	69.50 W
Mainland (I.), Scot. (mān-lănd)	162a	60.19 N	2.40 W
Maintenon, Fr. (mäɴ-tĕ-nôɴ')	169b	48.35 N	1.35 E
Maintirano, Mad. (mä'ēn-tē-rä'nō)	227	18.05 S	44.08 E
Mainz, F.R.G. (mīnts)	166	49.59 N	8.16 E
Maio I., C. V. (mä'yo)	224b	15.15 N	22.50 W
Maipo (R.), Chile (mī'pō)	141b	33.45 S	71.08 W
Maipo (Vol.), Arg.	144	34.08 S	69.51 W
Maipú, Arg. (mī'pōō')	141c	36.51 S	57.54 W
Maipú, Chile	61b	33.31 S	70.46 W
Maiquetía, Ven. (mī-kĕ-tē'ä)	143b	10.37 N	66.56 W
Maisí, Punta (Pt.), Cuba (pōō'n-tä-mī-sē')	135	20.10 N	74.00 W
Maison-Rouge, Fr. (mȧ-zôɴ-rōōzh')	169b	48.34 N	3.09 E
Maisons-Alfort, Fr.	64c	48.48 N	2.26 E
Maisons-Laffitte, Fr.	64c	48.57 N	2.09 E
Maitani, Jap.	69b	34.49 N	135.22 E
Maitland, Austl. (māt'lănd)	216	32.45 S	151.40 E
Maizuru, Jap. (mä-ĭ'zōō-rōō)	205	32.26 N	135.15 E
Majene, Indon.	206	3.34 S	119.00 E
Maji, Eth.	225	6.14 N	35.34 E
Majorca (I.), see Mallorca			
Makah Ind. Res., Wa. (mȧ kī')	116	48.17 N	124.52 W
Makala, Zaire	71c	4.25 S	15.15 E
Makanya, Tan. (mä-kän'yä)	227	4.15 S	37.49 E
Makanza, Zaire	225	1.42 N	19.08 E
Makarska, Yugo. (mȧ'kär-skȧ)	172	43.17 N	17.05 E
Makar'yev, Sov. Un.	178	57.50 N	43.48 E
Makasar, see Ujung Pandang			
Makasar, Selat (Makassar Strait), Indon.	206	2.00 S	118.07 E
Makati, Phil.	68g	14.34 N	121.01 E
Makaw, Zaire	230	3.29 S	18.19 E
Make (I.), Jap. (mä'kȧ)	205	30.43 N	130.49 E
Makeni, S. L.	228	8.53 N	12.03 W
Makeyevka, Sov. Un. (mŭk-yä'ŭf-kȧ)	175	48.03 N	38.00 E
Makgadikgadi Pans (L.), Bots.	223	20.38 S	21.31 E
Makhachkala, Sov. Un. (mäĸ'äch-kä'lä)	179	43.00 N	47.40 E
Makhaleng (R.), Leso.	227c	29.53 S	27.33 E
Makindu, Ken.	231	2.17 S	37.49 E
M'akino, Sov. Un.	66b	55.48 N	37.22 E
Makkah (Mecca), Sau. Ar. (mĕk'ȧ)	192	21.27 N	39.45 E
Makkovik, Can.	97	55.01 N	59.10 W
Makó, Hung. (mô'kō)	167	46.13 N	20.30 E
Makokou, Gabon (mȧ-kō-kōō')	230	0.34 N	12.52 E
Maków Mazowiecki, Pol. (mä'kōov mä-zō-vyĕts'kē)	167	52.51 N	21.07 E
Makuhari, Jap. (mä-kōō-hä'rē)	205a	35.39 N	140.04 E
Makurazaki, Jap. (mä'kōō-rä-zä'kē)	205	31.16 N	130.18 E
Makurdi, Nig.	229	7.45 N	8.32 E
Makushin, Ak. (mȧ-kōō'shĭn)	107	53.57 N	166.28 W
Makushino, Sov. Un. (mȧ-kōō-shēn'ō)	180	55.03 N	67.43 E
Malabar Coast, India (măl'ȧ-bär)	197	11.19 N	75.33 E
Malabar Pt., India	67e	18.57 N	72.47 E
Malabo, Equat. Gui.	230	3.45 N	8.47 E
Malabon, Phil.	207a	14.39 N	120.57 E

PLACE (Pronounciation)	PAGE	Lat. °'	Long. °'
Malacca, Str. of, Asia (mȧ-lăk'ȧ)	206	4.15 N	99.44 E
Malad, Id. (mȧ-läd')	117	42.11 N	112.15 W
Málaga, Col. (mȧ'lä-gȧ)	142	6.41 N	72.46 W
Málaga, Sp.	170	36.45 N	4.25 W
Malagón, Sp. (mä-lä-gōn')	170	39.12 N	3.52 W
Malaita (I.), Sol. Is. (mȧ-lä'ē-tȧ)	215	8.38 S	161.15 E
Malakāl, Sud. (mȧ-lȧ-käl')	225	9.46 N	31.54 E
Malakhovka, Sov. Un. (mȧ-läk'ôf-kȧ)	182b	55.38 N	38.01 E
Malakoff, Fr.	64c	48.49 N	2.19 E
Malakpur (Neigh.), India	67d	28.42 N	77.12 E
Malang, Indon.	206	8.06 S	112.50 E
Malange, Ang. (mä-läŋ-gȧ)	230	9.32 S	16.20 E
Malanville, Benin	224	12.04 N	3.09 E
Malapedia (R.), Can.	104	48.11 N	67.08 W
Mala Punta (Pt.), Pan. (pōō'n-tä-mä'lä)	133	7.32 N	79.44 W
Mälaren (L.), Swe.	164	59.38 N	16.55 E
Malartic, Can.	97	48.07 N	78.11 W
Malaspina Str. Can. (măl-ȧ-spē'nȧ)	98	49.44 N	124.20 W
Malatya, Tur. (mȧ-lä'tyȧ)	179	38.30 N	38.15 E
Malawi, Afr.	222	11.15 S	33.45 E
Malawi, L., see Nyasa, L.			
Malaya (Reg.), Mala. (mȧ-lā'yȧ)	206	3.35 N	101.30 E
Malaya Vishera, Sov. Un. (vē-shä'rä)	174	58.51 N	32.13 E
Malay Pen., Asia (mȧ-lā') (mā'lā)	206	7.46 N	101.06 E
Malaysia, Asia (mȧ-lā'zhȧ)	206	4.10 N	101.22 E
Mal B., Ire. (măl)	162	52.51 N	9.45 W
Malbon, Austl. (măl'bŭn)	214	21.15 S	140.30 E
Malbork, Pol. (mäl'börk)	167	54.02 N	19.04 E
Malcabran (R.), Port. (mäl-kä-brän')	171b	38.47 N	8.46 W
Malden (I.), Oceania	209	4.20 S	154.30 W
Malden, Ma. (môl'dĕn)	105a	42.26 N	71.04 W
Malden, Mo.	123	36.32 N	89.56 W
Maldives, Asia	190	4.30 N	71.30 E
Maldon, Eng. (môrl'dŏn)	156b	51.44 N	0.39 E
Maldonado, Ur. (mäl-dŏ-nä'dō)	144	34.54 S	54.57 W
Maldonado, Punta (Pt.), Mex. (pōō'n-tä)	130	16.18 N	98.34 W
Maléa, Akra (C.), Grc.	173	37.31 N	23.13 E
Mālegaon, India	196	20.35 N	74.30 E
Male Karpaty (Mts.), Czech.	167	48.31 N	17.15 E
Malekula (I.), Vanuatu (mä-lä-kōō'lä)	215	16.44 S	167.45 E
Malema, Moz.	231	14.57 S	37.20 E
Malhão da Estrêla (Mtn.), Sp. (mäl-you'ɴ-dä-ĕs-trĕ'lä)	170	40.20 N	7.38 W
Malheur L., Or. (mȧ-lōōr')	116	43.16 N	118.37 W
Malheur R., Or. (mȧ-lōōr')	116	43.45 N	117.41 W
Mali, Afr.	222	15.45 N	0.15 W
Malibu, Ca. (mă'lĭ-bōō)	119a	34.03 N	118.38 W
Malimba, Monts (Mts.), Zaire	231	7.45 S	29.15 E
Malin, Sov. Un. (mȧ-lēn')	175	50.44 N	29.15 E
Malinalco, Mex. (mä-lē-näl'kō)	130	18.54 N	99.31 W
Malinaltepec, Mex. (mä-lē-näl-tȧ-pĕk')	130	17.01 N	98.41 W
Malindi, Ken. (mä-lēn'dē)	227	3.14 S	40.04 E
Malin Hd., N. Ire.	162	55.23 N	7.24 W
Malino, Sov. Un. (mä'lĭ-nô)	182b	55.07 N	38.12 E
Malinovka, Sov. Un. (mȧ-lē-nôf'kȧ)	175	49.50 N	36.43 E
Malkara, Tur. (mäl'ĸȧ-rȧ)	173	40.51 N	26.52 E
Malko Tŭrnovo, Bul. (mäl'kō-t'r'nō-vȧ)	173	41.59 N	27.28 E
Mallaig, Scot.	162	56.59 N	5.55 W
Mallawī, Egypt (mȧ-lä'wē)	223b	27.43 S	30.49 E
Mallet Creek, Oh. (măl'ĕt)	113d	41.10 N	81.55 W
Mallorca (Majorca) (I.), Sp. (mäl-yô'r-kä)	171	39.18 N	2.22 E
Mallorquinas, Sp.	65e	41.28 N	2.16 E
Mallow, Ire. (măl'ō)	162	52.07 N	9.04 W
Malmédy, Bel. (mȧl-mā-dē')	163	50.25 N	6.01 E
Malmesbury, S. Afr. (mämz'bēr-ĭ)	226	33.30 S	18.35 E
Malmköping, Swe. (mälm'chû'pĭng)	164	59.09 N	16.39 E
Malmö, Swe. (mälm'û)	164	55.36 N	12.58 E
Malmyzh, Sov. Un. (mȧl-mēzh')	181	49.58 N	137.07 E
Malmyzh, Sov. Un.	178	56.30 N	50.48 E
Malnoue, Fr.	64c	48.50 N	2.36 E
Maloarkhangelsk, Sov. Un. (mä'lô-år-käŋ'gĕlsk)	174	52.26 N	36.29 E
Malolos, Phil. (mä-lô'lôs)	207a	14.51 N	120.49 E
Malomal'sk, Sov. Un. (mȧ-lô-mälsk'')	182a	58.47 N	59.55 E
Malone, NY (mȧ-lōn')	111	44.50 N	74.20 W
Malonga, Zaire	230	10.24 S	23.10 E
Maloti Mts., Leso	227c	29.00 S	28.29 E
Maloyaroslavets, Sov. Un. (mä'lō-yä-rô-slä-vyĕts)	174	55.01 N	36.25 E
Malozemel'skaya Tundra (Plains), Sov. Un.	178	67.30 N	50.00 E
Malpas, Eng. (măl'pȧz)	144	53.01 N	2.46 W
Malpelo, Isla de (I.), Col. (mäl-pä'lō)	142	3.55 N	81.30 W
Malpeque B., Can. (môl-pĕk')	104	46.30 N	63.47 W
Malta, Eur.	154	35.52 N	13.30 E
Malta, Mt. (môl'tȧ)	117	48.20 N	107.50 W
Maltahöhe, Namibia (mäl'tä-hö'ĕ)	226	24.45 S	16.45 E
Maltrata, Mex. (mäl-trä'tä)	131	18.48 N	97.16 W
Maluku (Moluccas) (Is.), Indon.	207	2.22 S	128.25 E
Maluku, Laut (Molucca) (Sea), Indon.	207	0.15 N	125.41 E
Malūt, Sud.	225	10.30 N	32.17 E
Mālvan, India	197	16.08 N	73.32 E
Malvern, Ar. (măl'vērn)	123	34.21 N	92.47 W
Malvern (Neigh.), S. Afr.	71b	26.12 S	28.06 E
Malverne, NY	55	40.40 N	73.40 W
Malvern East, S. Afr.	71b	26.12 S	28.08 E
Malyy Anyuy (R.), Sov. Un.	181	67.52 N	164.30 E
Malyy Lyakhovskiye (I.), Sov. Un.	181	74.15 N	142.30 E
Malyy Tamir (I.), Sov. Un.	181	78.10 N	107.30 E
Mamantel, Mex. (mä-män-tĕl')	131	18.36 N	91.06 W
Mamaroneck, NY (măm'ȧ-rō-nĕk)	112a	40.57 N	73.44 W
Mamau, Gui.	224	10.26 N	12.07 W
Mambasa, Zaire,	231	1.21 N	29.03 E
Mamberamo (R.), Indon. (mäm-bȧ-rä'mō)	207	2.30 S	138.00 E
Mamburao, Phil. (mäm-bōō'rä-ō)	207a	13.14 N	120.35 E

PLACE (Pronounciation)	PAGE	Lat. °′	Long. °′
Mamera, Ven.	61a	10.27 N	66.59 W
Mamfe, Cam. (mäm'fĕ)	224	5.46 N	9.17 E
Mamihara, Jap. (mä'mē-hä-rä)	205	32.41 N	131.12 E
Mammoth Cave, Ky. (măm'ŭth)	126	37.10 N	86.04 W
Mammoth Cave Natl. Park, Ky.	126	37.20 N	86.21 W
Mammoth Hot Springs, Wy. (măm'ŭth hôt sprĭngz)	117	44.55 N	110.50 W
Mamnoli, India	197b	19.17 N	73.15 E
Mamoré (R.), Bol. (mä-mô-rā')	142	13.19 S	65.27 W
Mampong, Ghana	228	7.04 N	1.24 W
Mamry, Jezioro (L.), Pol. (mäm'rĭ)	167	54.10 N	21.28 E
Man, Ivory Coast	228	7.24 N	7.33 W
Manacor, Sp. (mä-nä-kôr')	171	39.35 N	3.15 E
Manado, Indon.	207	1.29 N	124.50 E
Managua, Cuba (mä-nä'gwä)	135a	22.58 N	82.17 W
Managua, Nic.	132	12.10 N	86.16 W
Managua, Lago de (L.), Nic. (lä'gô-dĕ)	132	12.28 N	86.10 W
Manakara, Mad. (mä-nä-kä'rŭ)	227	22.17 S	48.06 E
Mananara (R.), Mad. (mä-nä-nä'rŭ)	227	23.15 S	48.15 E
Mananjary, Mad. (mä-nän-zhä'rē)	227	20.16 S	48.13 E
Manáos, see Manaus			
Manas, China (mä-nä-sz)	198	44.30 N	86.00 E
Manas (R.), China	198	45.00 N	85.45 E
Manas Hu (L.), China (mä-nä-sü hōō)	198	45.49 N	86.08 E
Manassas, Va. (mȧ-năs'ȧs)	111	38.45 N	77.30 W
Manaus (Manáos), Braz. (mä-nä'ōōzh)	143	3.01 S	60.00 W
Manayunk (Neigh.), Pa.	56b	40.01 N	75.13 W
Mancelona, Mi. (măn-sē-lō'nȧ)	110	44.50 N	85.05 W
Mancha Real, Sp. (män'chä rā-äl')	170	37.48 N	3.37 W
Manchazh, Sov. Un. (män'chásh)	182a	56.30 N	58.10 E
Manchester, Ct. (măn'chĕs-tēr)	111	41.45 N	72.30 W
Manchester, Eng.	156	53.28 N	2.14 W
Manchester, Ga.	126	32.50 N	84.37 W
Manchester, Ia.	115	42.30 N	91.30 W
Manchester, Ma.	105a	42.35 N	70.47 W
Manchester, Mo.	119e	38.36 N	90.31 W
Manchester, NH	111	43.00 N	71.30 W
Manchester, Oh.	110	38.40 N	83.35 W
Manchester Docks (P. Int.), Eng.	64b	53.28 N	2.17 W
Manchester Ship Canal, Eng.	156	53.20 N	2.40 W
Manchuria (Reg.), China (măn-chōō'rē-ȧ)	199	48.00 N	124.58 E
Mand (R.), Iran	192	28.20 N	52.30 E
Mandal, Nor. (män'däl)	164	58.03 N	7.28 E
Mandalay, Bur. (măn'dȧ-lā)	198	22.00 N	96.08 E
Mandalselva (R.), Nor.	164	58.25 N	7.30 E
Mandaluyong, Phil.	68g	14.35 N	121.02 E
Mandan, ND (măn'dăn)	114	46.49 N	100.54 W
Mandāoli (Neigh.), India	67d	28.38 N	77.18 E
Mandara Mts., Cam.-Nig. (män-dä'rä)	229	10.15 N	13.23 E
Mandau Siak (R.), Indon.	191b	1.03 N	101.25 E
Mandimba, Moz.	231	14.21 S	35.39 E
Mandinga, Pan. (män-dĭŋ'gä)	133	9.32 N	79.04 W
Mandla, India	196	22.43 N	80.23 E
Mándra, Grc. (män'drä)	173	38.06 N	23.32 E
Mandres-les-Roses, Fr.	64c	48.42 N	2.33 E
Mandritsara, Mad. (mȧn-drēt-sä'rȧ)	227	15.49 S	48.47 E
Manduria, It. (män-dōō'rē-ä)	173	40.23 N	17.41 E
Mandve, India	197b	18.47 N	72.52 E
Māndvi, India (mŭnd'vē)	197b	19.29 N	72.53 E
Māndvi, India (mŭnd'vē)	196	22.54 N	69.23 E
Mandvi (Neigh.), India	67e	18.57 N	72.50 E
Mandya, India	197	12.40 N	77.00 E
Manfalūt, Egypt (män-fȧ-loot')	223b	27.18 N	30.59 E
Manfredonia, It. (män-frå-dô'nyä)	172	41.39 N	15.55 E
Manfredónia, Golfo di (G.), It. (gôl-fô-dē)	172	41.34 N	16.05 E
Manga (Reg.), Niger	229	14.00 N	11.50 E
Mangabeiras, Chap. das (Plains), Braz. (shä-pä'däs-däs-mäŋ-gä-bē'ē-räzh)	143	8.05 S	47.32 W
Mangalore, India (mŭŋ-gŭ-lōr')	197	12.53 N	74.52 E
Manganji, Jap.	69a	35.40 N	139.26 E
Mangaratiba, Braz. (män-gä-rä-tē'bȧ)	141a	22.56 S	44.03 W
Mangatarem, Phil. (män'gȧ-tä'rĕm)	207a	15.48 N	120.18 E
Mange, Zaire	230	0.54 N	20.30 E
Mangkalihat, Tandjoeng (C.), Indon. (mäng'kȧ-lē-hät')	206	1.25 N	119.55 E
Mangles, Islas de, Cuba (ē's-läs-dĕ-mäŋ'gläs) (măn'g'lz)	134	22.05 N	83.50 W
Mangoky (R.), Mad. (män-gō'kē)	227	22.02 S	44.11 E
Mangole, Pulau (I.), Indon.	207	1.35 S	126.22 E
Mangualde, Port. (män-gwäl'dĕ)	170	40.38 N	7.44 W
Mangueira, L. da (L.), Braz. (män-gā'ē-rȧ)	144	33.15 S	52.45 W
Mangum, Ok. (măŋ'gŭm)	122	34.52 N	99.31 W
Mangyshlak, P-Ov. (Pen.), Sov. Un.	179	44.30 N	50.40 E
Mangzhangdian, China (mäŋ-jäŋ-dĭĕn)	200	32.07 N	114.44 E
Manhasset, NY	55	40.48 N	73.42 W
Manhattan, Il.	113a	41.25 N	87.29 W
Manhattan, Ks. (măn-hăt'ăn)	123	39.11 N	96.34 W
Manhattan Beach, Ca.	119a	33.53 N	118.24 W
Manhuaçu, Braz. (män-ōōȧ'sōō)	141a	20.17 S	42.01 W
Manhumirim, Braz. (män-ōō-mē-rē'N)	141a	22.02 S	41.57 W
Mania (R.), Mad. (män'yä)	227	19.52 S	46.02 E
Manicoré, Braz. (mä-nē-kō-rā')	143	5.53 S	61.13 W
Manicouagane (R.), Can.	97	50.00 N	68.35 W
Manicouagane, Lac (L.), Can.	97	51.30 N	68.19 W
Manicuare, Ven. (mä-nē-kwä'rĕ)	143b	10.35 N	64.10 W
Manihiki Is., Oceania (mä'nē-hē'kē)	209	9.40 S	158.00 W
Manikuagen, Rivière (R.), Can.	102	49.30 N	68.30 W
Manila, Phil.	207a	14.37 N	121.00 E
Manila B., Phil. (mȧ-nĭl'ȧ)	207a	14.38 N	120.46 E
Manipur (State), India	198	25.00 N	94.00 E
Manique de Baixo, Port.	65d	38.44 N	9.22 W
Manisa, Tur. (mä'nē-sȧ)	179	38.40 N	27.30 E

PLACE (Pronounciation)	PAGE	Lat. °′	Long. °′
Manistee, Mi. (măn-ĭs-tē')	110	44.15 N	86.20 W
Manistee (R.), Mi	110	44.25 N	85.45 W
Manistique, Mi. (măn-ĭs-tēk')	115	45.58 N	86.16 W
Manistique (L.), Mi	115	46.14 N	85.30 W
Manistique (R.), Mi	115	46.05 N	86.09 W
Manitoba (Prov.), Can. (măn-ĭ-tō'bȧ)	96	55.12 N	97.29 W
Manitoba (L.), Can.	101	51.00 N	98.45 W
Manito L., Can. (măn'ĭ-tō)	100	52.45 N	109.45 W
Manitou (I.), Mi. (măn'ĭ-tōō)	115	47.21 N	87.33 W
Manitou (L.), Can.	115	49.21 N	93.01 W
Manitou Is., Mi.	110	45.05 N	86.00 W
Manitoulin I., Can. (măn-ĭ-tōō'lĭn)	110	45.45 N	81.30 W
Manitou Springs, Co.	122	38.51 N	104.58 W
Manitowoc, Wi. (măn-ĭ-tō-wŏk')	115	44.05 N	87.42 W
Manitqueira, Serra da (Mts.), Braz. (sĕr'rä dä män-tē-kā'ē-rȧ)	141a	22.40 S	45.12 W
Maniwaki, Can.	103	46.23 N	76.00 W
Manizales, Col. (mä-nē-zä'lås)	142a	5.05 N	75.31 W
Manjacaze, Moz. (man'yä-kä'zĕ)	226	24.37 S	33.49 E
Mānjra (R.), India	196	18.18 N	77.00 E
Mankato, Ks. (măn-kā'tō)	122	39.45 N	98.12 W
Mankato, Mn.	115	44.10 N	93.59 W
Mankim, Cam.	229	5.01 N	12.00 E
Manlléu, Sp. (män-lyā'ōō)	171	42.00 N	2.16 E
Manly, Austl.	70a	33.48 S	151.17 E
Mannar, Sri Lanka (mȧ-när')	197	9.48 N	80.03 E
Mannar, G. of, India	197	8.47 N	78.33 E
Mannersdorf am Leithagebirge, Aus.	157e	47.58 N	16.36 E
Mannheim, F.R.G. (män'hīm)	166	49.30 N	8.31 E
Manning, Ia. (măn'ĭng)	115	41.53 N	95.04 W
Manning, SC	127	33.41 N	80.12 W
Mannington, WV (măn'ĭng-tŭn)	110	39.30 N	80.55 W
Mannswörth (Neigh.), Aus.	66e	48.09 N	16.31 E
Mannu (R.), It. (mä'n-nōō)	172	39.32 N	9.03 E
Mano (R.), Lib.	228	7.00 N	11.25 W
Man of War B., Ba.	125	21.05 N	74.05 W
Man of War Chan., Ba.	125	22.45 N	76.10 W
Manokwari, Indon. (mȧ-nŏk-wä'rē)	207	0.56 S	134.10 E
Manono, Zaire	231	7.18 S	27.25 E
Manor, Can. (măn'ēr)	101	49.36 N	102.05 W
Manor, Wa.	118c	45.45 N	122.36 W
Manorhaven, NY	55	40.50 N	73.42 W
Manori (Neigh.) India	197b	19.13 N	72.43 E
Manosque, Fr. (mȧ-nōsh')	169	43.51 N	5.48 E
Manotick, Can.	95c	45.13 N	75.41 W
Manresa, Sp. (män-rā'sä)	171	41.44 N	1.52 E
Mansa, Zambia	231	11.12 S	28.53 E
Mansabá, Guinea-Bissau	228	12.18 N	15.15 W
Mansel (I.), Can. (măn'sĕl)	97	61.56 N	81.10 W
Manseriche, Pongo de (Water Gap), Peru (pō'n-gō-dĕ-män-sĕ-rē'chĕ)	142	4.15 S	77.45 W
Mansfield, Eng. (mănz'fēld)	156	53.08 N	1.12 W
Mansfield, La.	125	32.02 N	93.43 W
Mansfield, Oh.	110	40.45 N	82.30 W
Mansfield, Wa.	116	47.48 N	119.39 W
Mansfield, Mt., Vt.	111	44.30 N	72.45 W
Mansfield Woodhouse, Eng. (wŏŏd-hous)	156	53.08 N	1.12 W
Manso (R.), Braz.	143	13.30 S	51.45 W
Manta, Ec. (män'tä)	142	1.03 S	80.16 W
Manteno, Il. (măn-tē-nō)	113a	41.15 N	87.50 W
Manteo, NC	127	35.55 N	75.40 W
Mantes-la-Jolie, Fr. (mäNt-ĕ-lä-zhō-lē')	169b	48.59 N	1.42 E
Manti, Ut. (măn'tī)	121	39.15 N	11.40 W
Mantilla (Neigh.), Cuba	60b	23.04 N	82.20 W
Mantova (Mantua), It. (män'tô-vä) (măn'tŭ-ȧ)	172	45.09 N	10.47 E
Mantua, Cuba (män-tōō'ä)	134	22.20 N	84.15 W
Mantua, Md.	56d	38.51 N	77.15 W
Mantua, Ut. (măn'tŭ-ȧ)	119b	41.30 N	111.57 W
Mantua, see Mantova			
Manuan (L.), Can. (mä-nōō'ȧn)	104	50.36 N	70.50 W
Manuan (R.), Can.	104	50.15 N	70.30 W
Manui, Pulau (Is.), Indon. (mä-nōō'ē)	207	3.35 S	123.38 E
Manus, (I.), Pap. N. Gui. (mä'nōōs)	207	2.22 S	146.22 E
Manvel, Tx. (măn'vel)	125a	29.28 N	95.22 W
Manville, NJ (măn'vĭl)	112a	40.33 N	74.36 W
Manville, RI	112b	41.57 N	71.27 W
Manyal Shīhah, Egypt	71a	29.57 N	31.14 E
Manych (R.), Sov. Un. (mä-nĭch')	179	47.00 N	41.10 E
Manych Dep., Sov. Un.	155	46.32 N	42.44 E
Manych-Gudilo (Lake), Sov. Un.	179	46.40 N	42.50 E
Manzala L., Egypt	223b	31.14 N	32.04 E
Manzanares, Col. (män-sä-nä'rĕs)	142a	5.15 N	75.09 W
Manzanares (R.), Sp. (mänz-nä'rĕs)	171a	40.36 N	3.48 W
Manzanares, Canal del, Sp. (kä-nä'l-dĕl-män-thä-nä'rĕs)	171a	40.20 N	3.38 W
Manzanillo, Cuba (män'zä-nēl'yō)	134	20.20 N	77.05 W
Manzanillo, Mex.	130	19.02 N	104.21 W
Manzanillo, Bahía de (B.), Hai.	135	19.55 N	71.50 W
Manzanillo, Bahía de (B.), Mex. (bä-ē'ä-dĕ-män-zä-nē'l-yō)	130	19.00 N	104.38 W
Manzanillo, Punta (Pt.), Pan.	133	9.40 N	79.33 W
Manzhouli, China (män-jō-lē)	202	49.25 N	117.15 E
Manzovka, Sov. Un. (mȧn-zhô'f-kȧ)	204	44.16 N	132.13 E
Mao, Chad (mä'ō)	229	14.07 N	15.19 E
Mao, Dom. Rep.	135	19.35 N	71.10 W
Maoke, Pegunungan (Mtn.), Indon.	207	4.00 S	138.00 E
Maoming, China	203	21.55 N	110.40 E
Maoniu Shan (Mtn.), China (mou-nĭō shän)	202	32.45 N	104.09 E
Mapastepec, Mex. (ma-päs-tå-pĕk')	131	15.24 N	92.52 W
Mapia, Kepulauan (I.), Indon. (mä'pē-ȧ)	207	0.57 N	134.22 E
Mapimi, Mex. (mä-pē-mē')	124	25.50 N	103.50 W
Mapimi, Bolsón de (Des.), Mex. (bôl-sŏ'n-dĕ-mä-pē'mē)	124	27.27 N	103.20 W
Maple Creek, Can. (mā'p'l) (crēk)	100	49.55 N	109.27 W
Maple Cross, Eng.	62	51.37 N	0.30 W
Maple Grove, Can. (grōv)	95a	45.19 N	73.51 W

PLACE (Pronounciation)	PAGE	Lat. °′	Long. °′
Maple Heights, Oh.	113d	41.25 N	81.34 W
Maple Leaf Gardens (P. Int.), Can.	54c	43.40 N	79.23 W
Maple Shade, NJ (shād)	112f	39.57 N	75.01 W
Maple Valley, Wa. (văl'ē)	118a	47.24 N	122.02 W
Maplewood, Mn. (wŏŏd)	119g	45.00 N	93.03 W
Maplewood, Mo.	119e	38.37 N	90.20 W
Maplewood, NJ	55	40.44 N	74.17 W
Mapocho (R.), Chile	61b	33.25 S	70.47 W
Mapumulo, S. Afr. (mȧ-pä-mōō'lō)	227c	29.12 S	31.05 E
Maputo (Lourenço Marques), Moz.	226	26.50 S	32.30 E
Maqueda Chan.,Phil. (mä-kā'dä)	207a	13.40 N	123.52 E
Maquela do Zombo, Ang. (mȧ-kā'lȧ dōō zôm'bōō)	226	6.08 S	15.15 E
Maquoketa, Ia. (mȧ-kō-kē-tȧ)	115	42.04 N	90.42 W
Maquoketa (R.), Ia.	115	42.08 N	90.40 W
Maracaibo, Ven. (mä-rä-kī'bō)	142	10.38 N	71.45 W
Maracaibo, Lago de (L.), Ven. (lä'gô-dĕ-mä-rä-kī'bō)	142	9.55 N	72.13 W
Maracay, Ven. (mä-rä-käy')	143b	10.15 N	67.35 W
Marādah, Libya	225	29.10 N	19.07 E
Maradi, Niger (mȧ-rà-dē')	229	13.29 N	7.06 E
Marāgheh, Iran	179	37.20 N	46.10 E
Maraisburg, S. Afr.	227b	26.12 S	27.57 E
Marais des Cygnes (R.), Ks.	123	38.30 N	95.30 W
Marajó, Ilha de (I.), Braz. (mä-rä-zhō')	143	0.30 N	50.00 W
Maralal, Ken.	231	1.06 N	36.42 E
Marali, Cen. Afr. Rep.	229	6.01 N	18.24 E
Marand, Iran	195	38.26 N	45.46 E
Maranguape, Braz. (mä-räŋ-gwä'pĕ)	143	3.48 S	38.38 W
Maranhão (State), Braz. (mä-rän-youN)	143	5.15 S	45.52 W
Maranhão see São Luis			
Maranoa (R.), Austl. (mä-rä-nō'ä)	216	27.01 S	148.03 E
Marano di Napoli, It. (mä-rä'nō-dē-nȧ'pô-lē)	171c	40.39 N	14.12 E
Marañón, Rio (R.), Peru (rē'ō-mä-rä-nyōn')	142	4.26 S	75.08 W
Maraoli (Neigh.), India	67e	19.03 N	72.54 E
Marapanim, Braz. (mä-rä-pä-nē'N)	143	0.45 S	47.42 W
Maras, Tur. (mä-räsh')	179	37.40 N	36.50 W
Marathon, Can.	102	48.50 N	86.10 W
Marathon, Fl. (măr'ȧ-thŏn)	127a	24.41 N	81.06 W
Marathon, Oh.	113f	39.09 N	83.59 W
Maravatio, Mex. (mä-rȧ-vä'tē-ō)	130	19.54 N	100.25 W
Marawi, Sud.	225	18.07 N	31.57 E
Marayong, Austl.	70a	33.45 S	150.54 E
Marble Bar, Austl. (märb''l bär)	214	21.15 S	119.15 E
Marble Can., Az. (mär'b'l)	121	36.21 N	111.48 W
Marble Hall, S. Afr. (hâll)	223d	24.59 S	29.19 E
Marblehead, Ma. (mär'b'l-hĕd)	105a	42.30 N	70.51 W
Marburg an der Lahn, F.R.G.	166	50.49 N	8.46 E
Marcala, Hond. (mär-kä-lä)	132	14.08 N	88.01 W
Marca, Ponta da (Pt.), Ang.	230	16.31 S	11.42 E
Marceline, Mo. (mär-sē-lēn')	123	39.42 N	92.56 W
Marche (Reg.), It. (mär'kā)	174	43.35 N	12.33 E
Marchegg, Aus.	157e	48.18 N	16.55 E
Marchena (I.), Ec. (ē's-lä-mär-chĕ'nä)	142	0.29 N	90.31 W
Marchena, Sp. (mär-chä'nä)	170	37.20 N	5.25 W
Marchfeld (Reg.), Aus.	157e	48.14 N	16.37 E
Marco Polo Bridge (P. Int.), China	67b	39.52 N	116.12 E
Marcos Paz, Arg. (mär-kōs' päz)	141c	34.49 S	58.51 W
Marcus (I.), Asia (mär'kŭs)	208	24.00 N	155.00 E
Marcus Hook, Pa. (mär'kŭs hŏŏk)	112f	39.49 N	75.25 W
Marcy, Mt., NY (mär'sē)	111	44.10 N	73.55 W
Mar de Espanha, Braz. (mär-dĕ-ĕs-pä'nyȧ)	141a	21.53 S	43.00 W
Mar del Plata, Arg. (mär dĕl- plä'ta)	144	37.59 S	57.35 W
Mardin, Tur. (mär-dēn')	179	37.25 N	40.40 E
Mare (I.), N. Cal. (mȧ-rā')	215	21.53 S	168.30 E
Maree, Loch (L.), Scot. (mä-rē')	162	57.40 N	5.44 W
Mareil-Marly, Fr.	64c	48.53 N	2.05 E
Marengo, Ia. (mȧ-rĕŋ'gō)	115	41.47 N	92.04 W
Marennes, Fr. (mȧ-rĕn')	168	45.49 N	1.08 W
Marfa, Tx. (mär'fȧ)	124	30.19 N	104.01 W
Marganets, Sov. Un.	175	47.41 N	34.33 E
Margarethenhöhe (Neigh.), F.R.G.	63	51.26 N	6.58 E
Margaretting, Eng.	62	51.41 N	0.25 E
Margarita, Pan. (mär-gōō-rē'tä)	128a	9.20 N	79.55 W
Margarita, Isla de (I.), Ven. (mä-gȧ-rē'tȧ)	143b	11.00 N	64.15 W
Margate, Eng. (mär'gāt)	162	51.21 N	1.17 E
Margate, S. Afr. (mä-gāt')	227c	30.52 S	30.21 E
Margherita Pk., Afr.	231	0.22 N	29.51 E
Marguerite (R.), Can.	104	50.39 N	66.42 W
Mari (A. S. S. R.), Sov. Un. (mä'rē)	178	56.20 N	48.00 E
Maria, Can. (mȧ-rē'ȧ)	104	48.10 N	66.04 W
María Cleofas (I.), Mex. (mä-rē'ä klā'ō-fäs)	130	21.17 N	106.14 W
Mariager, Den. (mä-rē-ägh'ĕr)	164	56.38 N	10.00 E
María Magdalena (I.), Mex. (mä rē'ä mäg-dä-lā'nä)	130	21.25 N	106.23 W
Mariana, Braz. (mä-ryä'nä)	141a	20.23 S	43.24 W
Mariana Is., Oceania (mä-rē-ä'nȧ)	208	17.20 N	145.00 E
Marianao, Cuba (mä-rē-ä-nä'ō)	135a	23.05 N	82.26 W
Mariana Trench, Oceania	208	12.00 N	144.00 E
Marianna, Ar. (mā-rĭ-ăn'ȧ)	123	34.45 N	90.45 W
Marianna, Fl.	126	30.46 N	85.14 W
Marianna, Pa.	113e	40.01 N	80.05 W
Mariano Acosta, Arg. (mä-rēä'nô-ȧ-kŏs'tä)	144a	34.28 S	58.48 W
Mariano Acosta, Arg.	60d	34.40 S	58.50 W
Mariano J. Haedo, Arg.	60d	34.39 S	58.36 W
Mariánské Lázne, Czech. (mär'yán-skĕ'läz'nyĕ)	156	49.58 N	12.42 E
Maria Paula, Braz.	61c	22.54 S	43.02 W
Marías, Islas (Is.), Mex. (mä-rē'äs)	128	21.30 N	106.40 W
Marias R., Mt. (mȧ-rī'ăz)	117	48.15 N	110.50 W
Mariato, Punta (Pt.), Pan.	133	7.17 N	81.09 W
Maribo, Den. (mä'rĕ-bô)	164	54.46 N	11.29 E
Maribor, Yugo. (mä're-bôr)	172	46.33 N	15.37 E

ng-sing; ŋ-baŋk; N-nasalized n; nŏd; cŏmmit; ōld; ôbey; ôrder; oi-boil; fōōd; fŏŏt; ou-out; s-soft; sh-dish; th-thin; pūre; ûnite; ûrn; stŭd; circŭs; ü-as in French tu; '-indeterminate vowel.

PLACE (Pronounciation)	PAGE	Lat. °'	Long. °'
Maribyrnong, Austl.	70b	37.46 S	144.54 E
Maricá, Braz. (mä-rē-kä')	141a	22.55 S	42.49 W
Maricaban (I.), Phil. (mä-rē-kä-bän')	207a	13.40 N	120.44 E
Marico R., S. Afr. (mä'rĭ-cô)	223d	24.53 S	26.22 E
Marie Byrd Land, Ant. (må rē'bûrd')	232	78.00 S	130.00 W
Mariefred, Swe. (mä-rē'ĕ-frĭd)	164	59.17 N	17.09 E
Marie Galante I., Guad. (må-rē' gȧ-läNt')	133b	15.58 N	61.05 W
Mariehamn, Fin. (må-rē'ĕ-häm''n)	164	60.07 N	19.57 E
Mariehamn, see Maarianhamina			
Mariendorf (Neigh.), F.R.G.	65a	52.26 N	13.23 E
Marienfelde (Neigh.), F.R.G.	65a	52.25 N	13.22 E
Mariestad, Swe. (mä-rē'ĕ-städ')	164	58.43 N	13.45 E
Marietta, Ga. (mā-rĭ-ĕt'ȧ)	112c	33.57 N	84.33 W
Marietta, Oh.	110	39.25 N	81.30 W
Marietta, Ok.	123	33.53 N	97.07 W
Marietta, Wa.	118d	48.48 N	122.35 W
Mariinsk, Sov. Un. (må-re'ĭnsk)	180	56.15 N	87.28 E
Marijampole, Sov. Un. (mä-rē-yäm-pô'lě)	165	54.33 N	23.26 E
Marikana, S. Afr. (mă'-rĭ-kä-nȧ)	223d	25.40 S	27.28 E
Marikina, Phil.	68g	14.37 N	121.06 E
Marília, Braz. (mä-rē'lyȧ)	143	22.02 S	49.48 W
Marimba, Ang.	230	8.28 S	17.08 E
Marina del Rey, Ca.	59	33.59 N	118.28 W
Marina del Rey (B.), Ca.	59	33.58 N	118.27 W
Marin City, Ca.	58b	37.52 N	122.21 W
Marinduque I., Phil. (mä-rēn-dōō'kä)	207a	13.14 N	121.45 E
Marine, Il. (mȧ-rēn')	119e	38.48 N	89.47 W
Marine City, Mi.	110	42.45 N	82.30 W
Marine L., Mn.	119g	45.13 N	92.55 W
Marineland of the Pacific (P. Int.), Ca.	59	33.44 N	118.24 W
Marine on Saint Croix, Mn. (äN sĕN krōō-ä)	119g	45.11 N	92.47 W
Marinette, Wi. (mår-ĭ-nĕt')	115	45.04 N	87.40 W
Maringa (R.), Zaire (mä-rĭŋ'gä)	230	1.15 N	20.05 E
Marinha Grande, Port. (mä-rēn'yȧ grän'dě)	170	39.49 N	8.53 W
Marion, Al. (măr'ĭ-ŭn)	126	32.36 N	87.19 W
Marion, Ia.	115	42.01 N	91.39 W
Marion, Il.	110	37.40 N	88.55 W
Marion, In.	110	40.35 N	85.45 W
Marion, Ks.	123	38.21 N	97.02 W
Marion, Ky.	126	37.19 N	88.05 W
Marion, NC	127	35.40 N	82.00 W
Marion, ND	114	46.37 N	98.20 W
Marion, Oh.	110	40.35 N	83.10 W
Marion, SC	127	34.08 N	79.23 W
Marion, Va.	127	36.48 N	81.33 W
Marion (R.), SC	127	33.25 N	80.35 W
Marion Rf., Austl.	215	18.57 S	151.31 E
Mariposa, Chile (mä-rē-pō'sä)	141b	35.33 S	71.21 W
Mariposa Cr., Ca.	120	37.14 N	120.30 W
Mariquita, Col. (mä-rē-kē'tä)	142a	5.13 N	74.52 W
Mariscal Estigarribia, Par. (mä-rēs-käl'ĕs-tē-gär-rē'byä)	143	22.03 S	60.28 W
Marisco, Ponta do (Pt.), Braz. (pô'n-tä-dô-mä-rē's-kö)	144b	23.01 S	43.17 W
Maritime Alps (Mts.), Fr.-It. (mă'rĭ-tīm ălps)	169	44.20 N	7.02 E
Mariveles, Phil.	207a	14.27 N	120.29 E
Marj Uyan, Leb.	191a	33.21 N	35.36 E
Marka, Som.	223a	1.45 N	44.47 E
Marka Kul' (L.), Sov. Un.	198	49.15 N	85.48 E
Markaryd, Swe. (mär'kä-rüd)	164	56.30 N	13.34 E
Marked Tree, Ar. (märkt trē)	123	35.31 N	90.26 W
Marken, I., Neth.	157a	52.26 N	5.08 E
Market Bosworth, Eng. (bŏz'wûrth)	156	52.37 N	1.23 W
Market Deeping, Eng. (dēp'ĭng)	156	52.40 N	0.19 W
Market Drayton, Eng. (drā'tŭn)	156	52.54 N	2.29 W
Market Harborough, Eng. (här'bŭr-ô)	156	52.28 N	0.55 W
Market Rasen, Eng. (rā'zĕn)	156	53.23 N	0.21 W
Markham, Can. (märk'ăm)	95d	43.53 N	79.15 W
Markham, Mt., Ant.	232	82.59 S	159.30 E
Markovka, Sov. Un. (mår-kôf'kȧ)	175	49.32 N	39.34 E
Markovo, Sov. Un. (mär'kô-vô)	181	64.46 N	170.48 E
Markrāna, India	196	27.08 N	74.43 E
Marks, Sov. Un.	179	51.40 N	46.40 E
Marksville, La. (märks'vĭl)	125	31.09 N	92.05 W
Markt Indersdorf, F.R.G. (märkt ēn'dērs-dōrf)	157d	48.22 N	11.23 E
Marktredwitz, F.R.G. (märk-rĕd'vēts)	166	50.02 N	12.05 E
Markt Schwaben, F.R.G. (märkt shvä'bĕn)	157d	48.12 N	11.52 E
Marl, F.R.G. (märl)	169c	51.40 N	7.05 E
Marlboro, NJ	112a	40.18 N	74.15 W
Marlborough, Ma.	105a	42.21 N	71.33 W
Marlette, Mi. (mär-lĕt')	110	43.25 N	83.05 W
Marlin, Tx. (mär'lĭn)	125	31.18 N	96.52 W
Marlinton, WV (mär'lĭn-tŭn)	111	38.15 N	80.10 W
Marlow, Eng. (mär'lō)	156b	51.33 N	0.46 W
Marlow, Ok.	122	34.38 N	97.56 W
Marls, The (Shoals), Ba. (märls)	134	26.30 N	77.15 W
Marly-le-Roi, Fr.	64c	48.52 N	2.05 E
Marmande, Fr. (mår-mäNd')	168	44.30 N	0.10 E
Marmara (I.), Tur. (mär'mȧ-rȧ)	173	40.38 N	27.35 E
Marmara Denizi (Sea), Tur.	179	40.40 N	28.00 E
Marmarth, ND (mär'mårth)	114	46.19 N	103.57 W
Mar Muerto (L.), Mex. (mär-mōōĕ'r-tô)	131	16.13 N	94.22 W
Marne, F.R.G. (mär'nĕ)	157c	53.57 N	9.01 E
Marne (R.), Fr. (märn)	168	49.08 N	3.39 E
Maroa, Ven. (mä-rō'ä)	142	2.43 N	67.37 W
Maroantsetra, Mad. (mȧ-rō-äŋ-tsā'trȧ)	227	15.18 S	49.48 E
Maro Jarapeto (Mtn.), Col. (mä-rô-hä-rä-pĕ'tô)	142a	6.29 N	76.39 W
Marolles-en-Brie, Fr.	64c	48.44 N	2.33 E
Maromokotro (Mtn.), Mad.	227	14.00 S	49.11 E
Marondera, Zimb.	231	18.10 S	31.36 E

PLACE (Pronounciation)	PAGE	Lat. °'	Long. °'
Maroni (R.), Fr. Gu.-Sur. (mȧ-rō'nē)	143	3.02 N	53.54 W
Maro Rf., Hi.	106b	25.15 N	170.00 W
Maroua, Cam. (mär'wä)	229	10.36 N	14.20 E
Maroubra, Austl.	70a	33.57 S	151.16 E
Marple, Eng. (mär'p'l)	157	53.24 N	2.04 W
Marquard, S. Afr.	223d	28.41 S	27.26 E
Marquesas Is., Fr. Polynesia (mär-kĕ'säs)	209	8.50 S	141.00 W
Marquesas Keys (Is.), Fl. (mår-kē'zȧs)	127a	24.37 N	82.15 W
Marquês de Valença, Braz. (mår-kĕ's-dĕ-vä-lĕ'n-sȧ)	141a	22.16 S	43.42 W
Marquette, Can. (mår-kĕt')	95f	50.04 N	97.43 W
Marquette, Mi.	115	46.32 N	87.25 W
Marquez, Tx. (mär-kāz')	125	31.14 N	96.15 W
Marra, Jabal (Mt.), Sud. (jĕb'ĕl mär'ä)	225	13.00 N	23.47 E
Marrakech, Mor. (mȧr-rä'kĕsh)	224	31.38 N	8.00 W
Marree, Austl. (măr'rē)	216	29.38 S	137.55 E
Marrero, La.	112d	29.55 N	90.06 W
Marrickville, Austl.	70a	33.55 S	151.09 E
Marrupa, Moz.	231	13.08 S	37.30 E
Mars, Pa. (märz)	113e	40.42 N	80.01 W
Marsā al Burayqah, Libya	194	30.25 N	19.34 E
Marsabit, Ken.	231	2.20 N	37.59 E
Marsala, It. (mär-sä'lä)	172	37.48 N	12.28 E
Marsā Maṭrūḥ, Egypt	225	31.19 N	27.14 E
Marscheid (Neigh.), F.R.G.	63	51.14 N	7.14 E
Marsden, Eng. (märz'dĕn)	156	53.36 N	1.55 W
Marseille, Fr. (mår-sâ'y')	168a	43.18 N	5.25 E
Marseilles, Il. (mär-sĕlz')	110	41.20 N	88.40 W
Mar, Serra do (Mts.), Braz. (sĕr'rȧ dōō mär')	144	26.30 S	49.15 W
Marsfield, Austl.	70a	33.47 S	151.07 E
Marshall, Il. (mär'shăl)	110	39.20 N	87.40 W
Marshall, Mi.	110	42.20 N	84.55 W
Marshall, Mn.	114	44.28 N	95.49 W
Marshall, Mo.	123	39.07 N	93.12 W
Marshall, Tx.	125	32.33 N	94.22 W
Marshall Is., Pac. Is. Trust Ter.	208	10.00 N	165.00 E
Marshalltown, Ia. (mär'shȧl-toun)	115	42.02 N	92.55 W
Marshallville, Ga. (mär'shȧl-vĭl)	126	32.29 N	83.55 W
Marshfield, Ma. (märsh'fēld)	105a	42.06 N	70.43 W
Marshfield, Mo.	123	37.20 N	92.53 W
Marshfield, Wi.	115	44.40 N	90.10 W
Marsh Harbour, Ba.	134	26.30 N	77.00 W
Mars Hill, In. (märz'hĭl')	113g	39.43 N	86.15 W
Mars Hill, Me.	104	46.34 N	67.54 W
Marstrand, Swe. (mär'stränd)	164	57.54 N	11.33 E
Marsyaty, Sov. Un. (märs'yȧ-tĭ)	182a	60.03 N	60.28 E
Mart, Tx. (märt)	125	31.32 N	96.49 W
Martaban, G. of, Bur. (mär-tŭ-bän')	206	16.34 N	96.58 E
Martapura, Indon.	206	3.19 S	114.45 E
Marten (Neigh.), F.R.G.	63	51.31 N	7.23 E
Marthas Vineyard (I.), Ma. (mär'thȧz vĭn'yȧrd)	107	41.25 N	70.35 W
Martí, Cuba (mär-tē')	134	23.00 N	80.55 W
Martigny, Switz. (mȧr-tē-nyē')	166	46.06 N	7.00 E
Martigues, Fr.	168a	43.24 N	5.05 E
Martin (R.), Al.	126	32.40 N	86.05 W
Martin, Tn. (mär'tĭn)	126	36.20 N	88.45 W
Martina Franca, It. (mär-tē'nä fräŋ'kä)	173	40.43 N	17.21 E
Martinez, Ca. (mär-tē'nĕz)	118b	38.01 N	122.08 W
Martinez, Tx.	119d	29.25 N	98.20 W
Martinique, N. A. (mȧr-tē-nēk')	129	14.50 N	60.40 W
Martin Pt., Ak.	107	70.10 N	142.00 W
Martinsburg, WV (mär'tĭnz-bûrg)	111	39.30 N	78.00 W
Martins Ferry, Oh. (mär'tĭnz)	110	40.05 N	80.45 W
Martinsville, In. (mär'tĭnz-vĭl)	110	39.25 N	86.25 W
Martinsville, Va.	127	36.40 N	79.53 W
Martínez (Neigh.), Arg.	60d	34.29 S	58.30 W
Martos, Sp. (mär'tōs)	170	37.43 N	3.58 W
Martre, Lac la (L.), Can. (läk la märtr)	96	63.24 N	119.58 W
Marugame, Jap. (mä'rōō-gä'mä)	205	34.19 N	133.48 E
Marungu (Mts.), Tan.	231	7.50 S	29.50 E
Marve (Neigh.), India	197b	19.12 N	72.43 E
Marvila (Neigh.), Port.	65d	38.44 N	9.06 W
Marvín, Sp. (mär-vē'n)	170	42.24 N	8.40 W
Marwitz, G.D.R.	65a	52.41 N	13.09 E
Mary, Sov. Un. (mä'rē)	176	37.45 N	61.47 E
Mar'yanskaya, Sov. Un. (mår-yän'skȧ-yȧ)	175	45.04 N	38.39 E
Maryborough, Austl. (mâ'rĭ-bŭr-ô)	216	25.35 S	152.40 E
Maryborough, Austl.	216	37.00 S	143.50 E
Maryland (State), U. S. (mĕr'ĭ-lănd)	109	39.10 N	76.25 W
Maryland Park, Md.	56d	38.53 N	76.54 W
Mary's R., Nv. (mā'rĭz)	116	41.25 N	115.10 W
Marystown, Can. (mâr'ĭz-toun)	105	47.11 N	55.10 W
Marysville, Ca.	120	39.09 N	121.37 W
Marysville, Can.	104	45.59 N	66.35 W
Marysville, Oh.	110	40.15 N	83.25 W
Marysville, Wa.	118a	48.03 N	122.11 W
Maryūṭ (L.), Egypt	223b	31.09 N	30.10 E
Maryville, Il. (mā'rĭ-vĭl)	119e	38.44 N	89.57 W
Maryville, Mo.	123	40.21 N	94.51 W
Maryville, Tn.	126	35.44 N	83.59 W
Marzahn (Neigh.), G.D.R.	65a	52.33 N	13.33 E
Mārzuq, Libya	225	26.00 N	14.09 E
Marzūq, Idehan (Dunes), Libya	225	24.30 N	13.00 E
Masai Steppe (Plat.), Tan.	231	4.30 S	36.40 E
Masaka, Ug.	231	0.20 S	31.44 E
Masalasef, Chad	229	11.43 N	17.08 E
Masalembo-Besar (I.), Indon.	206	5.40 S	114.28 E
Masan, Kor. (mä-sän')	204	35.10 N	128.31 E
Masangwe, Tan.	231	5.28 S	30.05 E
Masasi, Tan. (mä-sä'sē)	231	10.43 S	38.48 E
Masatepe, Nic. (mä-sä-tĕ'pĕ)	132	11.57 N	86.10 W
Masaya, Nic. (mä-sä'yä)	132	11.58 N	86.05 W
Masbate, Phil. (mäs-bä'tä)	207a	12.21 N	123.38 E
Masbate (I), Phil.	207a	12.19 N	123.03 E

PLACE (Pronounciation)	PAGE	Lat. °'	Long. °'
Mascarene Is., Mauritius	232	20.20 S	56.40 E
Mascot, Austl.	70a	33.56 S	151.12 E
Mascot, Tn. (măs'kŏt)	126	36.04 N	83.45 W
Mascota, Mex. (mäs-kō'tä)	130	20.33 N	104.45 W
Mascota (R.), Mex.	130	20.33 N	104.52 W
Mascouche, Can. (mȧs-kōōsh')	95a	45.45 N	73.36 W
Mascouche (R.), Can.	95a	45.44 N	73.45 W
Mascoutah, Il. (măs-kū'tā)	119e	38.29 N	89.48 W
Maseru, Leso. (măz'ēr-ōō)	226	29.09 S	27.11 E
Mashhad, Iran.	192	36.17 N	59.30 E
Mashra'ar-Ragg, Sud.	225	8.28 N	29.15 E
Masi-Manimba, Zaire	230	4.46 S	17.55 E
Masindi, Ug. (mä-sēn'dē)	225	1.44 N	31.43 E
Masjed Soleymān, Iran	192	31.45 N	49.17 E
Mask, Lough (B.), Ire. (lŏk mȧsk)	162	53.35 N	9.23 W
Maslovo, Sov. Un. (mäs'lô-vô)	182a	60.08 N	60.28 E
Mason, Mi. (mā'sŭn)	110	42.35 N	84.25 W
Mason, Oh.	113f	39.22 N	84.18 W
Mason, Tx.	124	30.46 N	99.14 W
Mason City, Ia.	115	43.08 N	93.14 W
Masonville, Va.	56d	38.51 N	77.12 W
Maspeth (Neigh.), NY	55	40.43 N	73.55 W
Masquaro (L.), Can.	105	50.34 N	60.40 W
Massa, It. (mäs'sä)	172	44.02 N	10.08 E
Massachusetts (State), U. S. (măs-ȧ-chōō'sĕts)	109	42.20 N	72.30 W
Massachusetts B., Ma.	104	42.26 N	70.20 W
Massachusetts Institute of Technology (P. Int.), Ma.	54a	42.21 N	71.06 W
Massafra, It. (mäs-sä'frä)	172	40.35 N	17.05 E
Massa Marittima, It.	172	43.03 N	10.55 E
Massapequa, NY	112a	40.41 N	73.28 W
Massaua, see Mitsiwa			
Massena, NY (mă-sē'nȧ)	111	44.55 N	74.55 W
Masset, Can. (măs'ĕt)	96	54.02 N	132.09 W
Masset Inlet, Can.	98	53.42 N	132.20 E
Massif Central (Plat.), Fr. (mȧ-sēf' säN-trȧl')	168	45.12 N	3.02 E
Massillon, Oh. (măs'ĭ-lŏn)	110	40.50 N	81.35 W
Massinga, Moz. (mä-sĭn'gä)	226	23.18 S	35.18 E
Massive, Mt., Co. (măs'ĭv)	121	39.05 N	106.30 W
Masson, Can. (mȧs-sŭn)	95c	45.33 N	75.25 W
Massy, Fr.	64c	48.44 N	2.17 E
Masuda, Jap. (mä-sōō'dȧ)	205	34.42 N	131.53 E
Masuria (Reg.), Pol.	167	53.40 N	21.10 E
Matadi, Zaire (mȧ-tä'dē)	230	5.49 S	13.27 E
Matagalpa, Nic. (mä-tä-gäl'pä)	132	12.52 N	85.57 W
Matagami (L.), Can. (mȧ-tä-gä'mē)	97	50.10 N	78.28 W
Matagorda B., Tx. (măt-ȧ-gôr'dȧ)	125	28.32 N	96.13 W
Matagorda I., Tx.	125	28.13 N	96.27 W
Matam, Senegal (mä-täm')	228	15.40 N	13.15 W
Matamoros, Mex. (mä-tä-mō'rôs)	124	25.32 N	103.13 W
Matamoros, Mex.	125	25.52 N	97.30 W
Matandu (R.), Tan.	231	8.55 S	38.35 E
Matane, Can. (mȧ-tȧn')	104	48.51 N	67.32 W
Matanzas, Cuba (mä-tän'zäs)	134	23.05 N	81.35 W
Matanzas (Prov.), Cuba	134	22.45 N	81.20 W
Matanzas, Bahía (B.), Cuba (bä-ē'ä)	134	23.10 N	81.30 W
Matapalo, Cabo (C.), C. R. (kȧ'bô-mä-tä-pä'lō)	133	8.22 N	83.25 W
Matapédia, Can. (mä-tȧ-pā'dē-ȧ)	104	47.58 N	66.56 W
Matapédia, (L.), Can.	104	48.33 N	67.32 W
Matapédia, (R.), Can.	104	48.10 N	67.10 W
Mataquito (R.), Chile (mä-tä-kē'tô)	141b	35.08 S	71.35 W
Matara, Sri Lanka (mä-tä'rä)	197	5.59 N	80.35 E
Mataram, Indon.	206	8.45 S	116.15 E
Mataró, Sp. (mä-tä-rō')	171	41.33 N	2.27 E
Matatiele, S. Afr. (mä-tä-tyā'lä)	227c	30.21 S	28.49 E
Matawan, NJ	112a	40.24 N	74.13 W
Matawin (R.), Can. (măt ȧ-wĭn)	104	46.46 N	73.25 W
Matehuala, Mex. (mä-tâ-wä'lä)	130	23.38 N	100.39 W
Matera, It. (mä-tå'rä)	172	40.42 N	16.37 E
Mateur, Tun. (mȧ-tûr')	159	37.09 N	9.43 E
Mātherān, India	197b	18.58 N	73.16 E
Matheson, Can.	103	48.35 N	80.33 W
Mathews, L., Ca. (măth ūz)	119a	33.50 N	117.24 W
Mathura, India (mu-tōō'rū)	196	27.39 N	77.39 E
Matias Barbosa, Braz. (mä-tē'äs-bȧr-bô-sä)	139a	21.53 S	43.19 W
Matillas, Laguna (L.), Mex. (lä-gōō'nä-mä-tē'l-yäs)	131	18.02 N	92.36 W
Matina, C. R. (mä-tē'nä)	133	10.06 N	83.20 W
Matiši, Sov. Un. (mä'tē-sē)	165	57.43 N	25.09 E
Matlalcueyetl, Cerra, Mex. (sĕ'r-rä-mä-tläl-kwĕ'yĕtl)	130	19.13 N	98.02 W
Matlock, Eng. (măt'lŏk)	156	53.08 N	1.33 W
Matochkin Shar, Sov. Un. (mä'tŏch-kĭn)	180	73.57 N	56.16 E
Mato Grosso, Braz. (mät'ōō grōs'ōō)	143	15.04 S	59.58 W
Mato Grosso (State), Braz.	143	14.38 S	55.36 W
Mato Grosso, Chapada de (Plain), Braz. (shä-pä'dä-dĕ)	143	13.39 S	55.42 W
Mato Grosso do Sul (State), Braz.	143	20.00 S	56.00 W
Matosinhos, Port.	170	41.10 N	8.48 W
Matrah, Om. (mȧ-trä')	192	23.36 N	58.27 E
Matsubara, Jap.	205b	34.34 N	135.34 E
Matsudo, Jap. (mät'sōō-dô)	205a	35.48 N	139.55 E
Matsue, Jap. (mät'sōō-ĕ)	205	35.29 N	133.04 E
Matsumoto, Jap. (mät'sōō-mō'tô)	205	36.15 N	137.59 E
Matsuyama, Jap. (mät'sōō-yä'mä)	205	33.48 N	132.45 E
Matsuzaka, Jap. (mät'sōō-zä'kä)	205	34.35 N	136.34 E
Mattamuskeet (R.), NC (măt-tȧ-mŭs'kēt)	127	35.34 N	76.03 W
Mattaponi (R.), Va. (măt'ȧ-pōnĭ')	111	37.45 N	77.00 W
Mattawa, Can. (măt'ȧ-wȧ)	103	46.15 N	78.49 W
Matterhorn (Mtn.), Switz. (mät'ēr-hôrn)	166	45.57 N	7.36 E
Matteson, Il. (mătt'ē-sŭn)	113a	41.30 N	87.42 W
Matthew Town, Ba. (măth'ū toun)	135	21.00 N	73.40 W
Mattoon, Il. (mă-tōōn')	110	39.30 N	88.20 W
Maturín, Ven. (mä-tōō-rēn')	142	9.48 N	63.16 W
Mátyásföld (Neigh.), Hung.	66g	47.31 N	19.13 E

PLACE (Pronounciation)	PAGE	Lat. °'	Long. °'
Mátyas-Templom (P. Int.), Hung.	66g	47.30 N	19.02 E
Maúa, Moz	221	13.51 S	37.10 E
Mauá, Braz.	61d	23.40 S	46.27 W
Mauban, Phil. (mä'o͞o-bän')	207a	14.11 N	121.44 E
Maubeuge, Fr. (mô-bûzh')	168	50.18 N	3.57 E
Maud, Oh. (môd)	113f	39.21 N	84.23 W
Mauer, Aus. (mou'ēr)	157e	48.09 N	16.16 E
Mauer (Neigh.), Aus.	66e	48.09 N	16.16 E
Maués, Braz. (mà-wě's)	143	3.34 S	57.30 W
Mau Escarpment (Cliff), Ken.	231	0.45 S	35.50 E
Maui (I.), Hi. (mä'o͞o-ē)	106a	20.52 N	156.02 W
Maule (R.), Chile (má'o͞o-lě)	141b	35.45 S	70.50 W
Maumee, Oh. (mô-mē')	110	41.30 N	83.40 W
Maumee (R.), In.-Oh.	110	41.10 N	84.50 W
Maumee B., Oh.	110	41.50 N	83.20 W
Maun, Bots. (mä-o͞on')	226	19.52 S	23.40 E
Mauna Kea (Vol.), Hi. (mä'o͞o-näkā'ä)	106a	19.52 N	155.30 W
Mauna Loa (Vol.), Hi. (mä'o͞o-nälō'ä)	106a	19.28 N	155.38 W
Maung Nakhon Sawan, Thai.	206	16.00 N	99.52 E
Maurecourt, Fr.	64c	49.00 N	2.04 E
Maurepas L., La. (mō-rē-pä')	125	30.18 N	90.40 W
Mauricie, Pare Natl. de la (Natl. Pk.), Can.	104	46.46 N	73.00 W
Mauritania, Afr. (mô-rẻ-tā'nĭ-à)	222	19.38 N	13.30 W
Mauritius, Afr. (mô-rĭsh'ĭ-ŭs)	232	20.18 S	57.36 E
Maury, Wa. (mô'rĭ)	118a	47.22 N	122.23 W
Mauston, Wi. (môs'tŭn)	115	43.46 N	90.05 W
Maverick, (R.), Az. (mă-vûr'ĭk)	121	33.40 N	109.30 W
Mavinga, Ang.	230	15.50 S	20.21 E
Maxcanú, Mex. (mäs-kä-no͞o')	131	20.35 N	89.59 W
Maxville, Can. (măks'vĭl)	95c	45.17 N	74.52 W
Maxville, Mo.	119e	38.26 N	90.24 W
Maya (R.), Sov. Un. (mä'yä)	181	58.00 N	135.45 E
Mayaguana (I.), Ba.	135	22.25 N	73.00 W
Mayaguana Passage (Str.), Ba.	135	22.20 N	73.25 W
Mayagüez, P. R. (mä-yä-gwāz')	129b	18.12 N	67.10 W
Mayarí, Cuba (mä-yä-rē')	125	20.45 N	75.40 W
Mayari (R.), Cuba	125	20.25 N	75.35 W
Mayas, Montañas (Mts.), Belize (mōntăŋ'äs mä'äs)	132a	16.43 N	89.00 W
Mayd (I.), Som.	223a	11.24 N	46.38 E
Mayen, F.R.G. (mī'ĕn)	166	50.19 N	7.14 E
Mayenne (R.), Fr. (mà-yĕn)	168	48.14 N	0.45 W
Mayfair (Neigh.), Pa.	56b	40.02 N	75.03 W
Mayfair (Neigh.), S. Afr.	71b	26.12 S	28.01 E
Mayfair West (Neigh.), S. Afr.	71b	26.12 S	28.00 E
Mayfield, Ky. (mā'fēld)	126	36.44 N	88.19 W
Mayfield Cr., Ky.	127	36.54 N	88.47 W
Mayfield Heights, Oh.	113d	41.31 N	81.26 W
Mayfield Res., Wa.	116	46.31 N	122.34 W
Maykop (Maikop), Sov. Un. (mī-kôp')	179	44.35 N	40.10 E
Maykor, Sov. Un. (mī-kôr')	182a	59.01 N	55.52 E
Maymyo, Bur. (mī'myō)	198	22.14 N	96.32 E
Maynard, Ma. (mā'nàrd)	105a	42.25 N	71.27 W
Mayne, Can. (mān)	118d	48.51 N	123.18 W
Mayne (I), Can.	118d	48.52 N	123.14 W
Mayo, Can. (mā-yō')	96	63.40 N	135.51 W
Mayo, Fl.	126	30.02 N	83.08 W
Mayo, Md.	112e	38.54 N	76.31 W
Mayodan, NC (mā-yō'dăn)	127	36.25 N	79.59 W
Mayon (Vol.), Phil. (mä-yōn')	207a	13.21 N	123.43 E
Mayotte (I.), France (mà-yôt')	227	13.07 S	45.32 W
May Pen, Jam	134	18.00 N	77.25 W
Mayraira Pt., Phil.	203	18.40 N	120.45 E
Mayran, Laguna de (L.), Mex. (lä-o͞o'nä-dě-mī-rän')	124	25.40 N	102.35 W
Maysville, Ky. (māz'vĭl)	110	38.35 N	83.45 W
Mayumba, Gabon	230	3.25 S	10.39 E
Mayville, NY (mā'vĭl)	111	42.15 N	79.30 W
Mayville, ND	114	47.30 N	97.20 W
Mayville, Wi.	115	43.30 N	88.45 W
Maywood, Ca. (mā'wo͝od)	119a	33.59 N	118.11 W
Maywood, Il.	113a	41.53 N	87.51 W
Maywood, NJ.	55	40.56 N	74.04 W
Mazabuka, Zambia (mä-zä-bo͞o'kä)	231	15.51 S	27.46 E
Mazagão, Braz. (mä-zà-gou'N)	143	0.05 S	51.27 W
Mazapil, Mex. (mä-zä-pēl')	124	24.40 N	101.30 W
Mazara del Vallo, It. (mät-sä'rä dĕl väl'lō)	172	37.40 N	12.37 E
Mazār-i-Sharif, Afg. (mà-zär'-ē-shà-rēf')	196	36.48 N	67.12 E
Mazarrón, Sp. (mä-zär-rō'n)	170	36.37 N	1.29 W
Mazaruni (R.), Guy. (mä-zä-ro͞o'nẻ)	143	5.58 N	59.37 W
Mazatenango, Guat. (mä-zä-tā-näŋ'gō)	132	14.30 N	91.30 W
Mazatla, Mex.	131a	10.30 N	99.24 W
Mazatlán, Mex.	130	23.14 N	106.27 W
Mazatlán (San Juan), Mex. (mä-zä-tlän') (san hwän')	131	17.05 N	95.26 W
Mažeikiai, Sov. Un. (mà-zhā'kẻ-ī)	165	56.19 N	22.24 E
Mazhafah, Jabal (Mts.), Sau. Ar.	191a	28.56 N	35.05 E
Mazilovo (Neigh.), Sov. Un.	66b	55.44 N	37.26 E
Mazoe (R.), Moz.	231	16.40 S	32.50 E
Mazorra, Cuba	60b	23.01 N	82.24 W
Mazzarino, It. (mät-sä-rē'nō)	172	37.16 N	14.15 E
Mbabane, Swaz. (m'bä-bä'nẻ)	226	26.18 S	31.14 E
Mbaiki, Cen. Afr. Rep. (m'bà-ē'kẻ)	229	3.53 N	18.00 E
Mbakana, Montagne de (Mts.), Cam.	229	7.55 N	14.40 E
Mbakaou, Barrage de, Cam.	229	6.10 N	12.55 E
Mbala (Abercorn), Zambia	231	8.50 S	31.22 E
Mbale, Ug.	231	1.05 N	34.10 E
Mbamba Bay, Tan.	231	11.17 S	34.46 E
Mbandaka (Coquilhatville), Zaire	230	0.04 N	18.16 E
Mbanza Congo, Ang.	230	6.30 N	14.10 E
Mbanza-Ngungu, Zaire	230	5.20 S	10.55 E
Mbarara, Ug.	231	0.37 S	30.39 E
Mbasay, Chad	229	7.39 N	15.40 E
Mbeya, Tan.	231	8.54 S	33.27 E
Mbigou, Gabon (m-bē-go͞o')	226	2.07 S	11.30 E
Mbinda, Con.	230	2.00 S	12.55 E
Mbogo, Tan.	231	7.26 S	33.26 E
Mbomou (Bomu) (R.), Cen. Afr. Rep.-Zaire (m'bō'mo͞o)	230	4.50 S	23.35 E
Mbout, Mauritania (m'bo͞o')	224	16.03 N	12.31 W
Mbuji-Mayi (Bakwanga), Zaire	230	6.09 S	23.28 E
McAdam, Can. (măk-ăd'ăm)	104	45.36 N	67.20 W
McAfee, NJ (măk-à'fē)	112a	41.10 N	74.32 W
McAlester, Ok. (măk ăl'ĕs-tēr)	123	34.55 N	95.45 W
McAllen, Tx. (măk-ăl'ĕn)	124	26.12 N	98.14 W
McBride, Can. (măk-brīd')	99	53.18 N	120.10 W
McCalla, Al. (mĕk-kăl'lă)	112h	33.20 N	87.00 W
McCamey, Tx. (mă-kā'mĭ)	124	31.08 N	102.13 W
McCaysville, Ga. (mă-kāz'vĭl)	126	34.57 N	84.21 W
McColl, SC (mà-kôl')	127	34.40 N	79.34 W
McComb, Ms. (mà-kōm')	126	31.14 N	90.27 W
McConaughy, L., Ne. (măk kŏ'nō ĭ')	114	41.24 N	101.40 W
McCook, Il.	58a	41.48 N	87.50 W
McCook, Ne. (mà-ko͝ok')	122	40.13 N	100.37 W
McCormick, SC (mà-kôr'mĭk)	127	33.56 N	82.20 W
McCormick Place (P. Int.), Il.	58a	41.51 N	87.37 W
McDonald, Pa. (măk-dŏn'ăld)	113e	40.22 N	80.13 W
McDonald I, Austl.	232	53.00 S	72.45 E
McDonald L., Can. (măk-dŏn-ăld)	95e	51.12 N	113.53 W
McGehee, Ar. (mà-gē')	123	33.39 N	91.22 W
McGill, Nv. (mà-gĭl')	120	39.25 N	114.47 W
McGill University (P. Int.), Can.	54b	45.30 N	73.35 W
McGowan, Wa. (măk-gou'ăn)	118c	46.15 N	123.55 W
McGrath, Ak. (măk'gràth)	107	62.58 N	155.20 W
McGregor, Can. (măk-grĕg'ēr)	113b	42.08 N	82.58 W
McGregor, Ia.	115	42.58 N	91.12 W
McGregor, Tx	125	31.26 N	97.23 W
McGregor L., Can. (măk-grĕg'ēr)	95c	45.38 N	75.44 W
McGregor (R.), Can.	99	54.10 N	121.00 W
McHenry, Il. (măk-hĕn'rĭ)	113a	42.21 N	88.16 W
Mchinji, Malawi	231	13.42 S	32.50 E
McIntosh, SD (măk'ĭn-tŏsh)	114	45.54 N	101.22 W
McKay (R), Or.	118	45.43 N	123.00 W
McKeesport, Pa. (mà-kez'pōrt)	113e	40.21 N	79.51 W
McKees Rocks, Pa. (mà-kēz' rŏks)	113e	40.29 N	80.05 W
McKenzie, Tn. (mà-kĕn'zĭ)	126	36.07 N	88.30 W
McKenzie R., Or.	116	44.07 N	122.20 W
McKinley, Mt., Ak. (mà-kĭn'lĭ)	107	63.00 N	151.02 W
McKinney, Tx. (mà-kĭn'ĭ)	123	33.12 N	96.35 W
McKnight Village, Pa.	57b	40.31 N	80.00 W
McLaughlin, SD (măk-lŏf'lĭn)	114	45.48 N	100.45 W
McLean, Va. (măc'lān)	112e	38.56 N	77.11 W
McLeansboro, Il. (mà-klānz'bŭr-ō)	110	38.10 N	88.35 W
McLennan, Can. (măk-lĭn'nàn)	96	55.42 N	116.54 W
McLeod (R), Can.	99	53.45 N	115.15 W
McLeod Lake, Can.	98	54.59 N	123.02 W
McLoughlin, Mt., Or. (măk-lŏk'lĭn)	116	42.27 N	122.20 W
McMillan L., Tx. (măk-mĭl'àn)	124	32.40 N	104.09 W
McMillin, Wa. (măk-mĭl'ĭn)	118a	47.08 N	122.14 W
McMinnville, Or. (măk-mĭn'vĭl)	116	45.13 N	123.13 W
McMinnville, Tn.	126	35.41 N	85.47 W
McMurray, Pa.	57b	40.17 N	80.05 W
McMurray, Wa. (măk-mŭr'ĭ)	118a	48.19 N	122.15 W
McNary, Az. (măk-nâr'ẻ)	121	34.10 N	109.55 W
McNary, La.	125	30.58 N	92.32 W
McNary Dam, Or.-Wa.	116	45.57 N	119.15 W
McPherson, Ks. (măk-fŭr's'n)	123	38.21 N	97.41 W
McRae, Ga. (măk-rā')	126	32.02 N	82.55 W
McRoberts, Ky. (măk-rŏb'ērts)	126	37.12 N	82.40 W
Mead, Ks. (mēd)	122	37.17 N	100.21 W
Mead, L., Az.-Nv.	121	36.20 N	114.14 W
Meade Pk., Id.	117	42.19 N	111.16 W
Meadow Lake, Can. (mĕd'ō lāk)	100	54.08 N	108.26 W
Meadowlands, S. Afr.	71b	26.13 S	27.54 E
Meadows, Can. (mĕd'ōz)	95f	50.02 N	97.35 W
Meadville, Pa. (mēd'vĭl)	111	41.40 N	80.10 W
Meaford, Can. (mē'fērd)	110	44.35 N	80.40 W
Mealy Mts., Can. (mē'lē)	97	53.32 N	57.58 W
Meandarra, Austl. (mē-ăn-dă'rà)	216	27.47 S	149.40 E
Meaux, Fr. (mō)	169b	48.58 N	2.53 E
Mecapalapa, Mex. (mā-kä-pä-lä'pä)	131	20.32 N	97.52 W
Mecatina (I.), Can. (mā-kà-tē'nà)	105	50.50 N	58.33 W
Mecatina (R.), Can. (mā-kà-tē'nà)	105	50.50 N	59.45 W
Mecca, see Makkah			
Mechanic Falls, Me. (mẻ-kăn'ĭk)	104	44.05 N	70.23 W
Mechanicsburg, Pa. (mẻ-kăn'ĭks-bûrg)	111	40.15 N	77.00 W
Mechanicsville, Md. (mẻ-kăn'ĭks-vĭl)	112e	38.27 N	76.45 W
Mechanicville, NY (mẻkăn'ĭk-vĭl)	111	42.55 N	73.45 W
Mechelen, Bel.	157a	51.01 N	4.28 E
Méchérial, Mor.	160	33.30 N	0.13 W
Mecicine Bow Ra., Co.-Wy. (mĕd'ĭ-sĭn bō)	122	40.55 N	106.02 W
Meckinghoven, F.R.G.	63	51.37 N	7.19 E
Mecklenburg (Reg.), G.D.R. (mĕk'lĕn-bo͝orgh)	166	53.34 N	12.18 E
Medan, Indon. (mā-dän')	206	3.35 N	98.35 E
Medanosa, Punta (Pt.), Arg. (po͞o'n-tä-mĕ-dä-nō'sä)	144	47.50 S	65.53 W
Medden (R.), Eng. (mĕd'ĕn)	156	53.14 N	1.05 W
Medellín, Col. (må-dhĕl-yēn')	142a	6.15 N	75.34 W
Medellín, Mex. (mĕ-dĕl-yẻ'n)	131	19.03 N	96.08 W
Medenine, Tun. (mā-dē-nēn')	160e	33.22 N	10.33 E
Medfeld, Ma. (mĕd'fēld)	105a	42.11 N	71.19 W
Medford, Ma. (mĕd'fērd)	105a	42.25 N	71.07 W
Medford, NJ	112f	39.54 N	74.50 W
Medford, Ok.	122	36.47 N	97.44 W
Medford, Or.	116	42.19 N	122.52 W
Medford, Wi.	115	45.09 N	90.22 W
Medford Hillside, Ma.	54a	42.24 N	71.07 W
Media, Pa. (mē'dĭ-à)	112f	39.55 N	75.24 W
Medias, Rom. (mĕd-yäsh')	167	46.09 N	24.21 E
Medical Lake, Wa. (mĕd'ĭ-kăl)	116	47.34 N	117.40 W
Medicine Bow R., Wy.	117	41.58 N	106.30 W
Medicine Hat, Can. (mĕd'ĭ-sĭn hăt)	100	50.03 N	110.40 W
Medicine L., Mt. (mĕd'ĭ-sĭn)	117	48.24 N	104.15 W
Medicine Lodge, Ks.	122	37.17 N	98.37 W
Medina, NY (mẻ-dī'nà)	111	43.15 N	78.20 W
Medina, Oh.	113d	41.08 N	81.52 W
Medina del Campo, Sp. (må-dē'nä dĕl käm'pō)	170	41.18 N	4.54 W
Medina de Ríoseco, Sp. (må-dē'nä dā rẻ-ō-sā'kô)	170	41.53 N	5.05 W
Médina Gonassé, Sen.	228	13.08 N	13.45 W
Medina L., Tx.	124	29.36 N	98.47 W
Medina R., Tx.	124	29.45 N	99.13 W
Medina, see Al Madīnah			
Medina Sidonia, Sp. (sẻ-dō'nyä)	170	36.28 N	5.58 W
Medio (R.), Arg. (mĕ'dyô)	141c	33.40 S	60.30 W
Mediterranean Sea, Afr.-Asia-Eur. (mĕd-ĭ-tēr-ā'nẻ-ăn)	160	36.22 N	13.25 E
Medjerda (R.), Tun. (mĕ-jĕr'dà)	159	36.43 N	9.54 E
Mednogorsk, Sov. Un.	180	51.27 N	57.22 E
Medvedista (R.), Sov. Un. (mĕd-vyĕ'dẻ tsá)	179	50.10 N	43.40 E
Medvedkovo (Neigh.), Sov. Un.	66b	55.53 N	37.38 E
Medvezhegorsk, Sov. Un. (mĕd-vyĕzh'yĕ-gôrsk')	178	63.00 N	34.20 E
Medvezh'y (Is.), Sov. Un.	181	71.00 N	161.25 E
Medway, Ma. (mĕd'wā)	105a	42.08 N	71.23 W
Medyn', Sov. Un. (mĕ-dēn')	174	54.58 N	35.53 E
Medzhibozh, Sov. Un. (mĕd-zhẻ-bōzh')	175	49.23 N	27.29 E
Meekatharra, Austl. (mē-kà-thăr'à)	214	26.30 S	118.38 E
Meeker, Co. (mēk'ēr)	121	40.00 N	107.55 W
Meelpaeg L., Can. (mēl'pà-ĕg)	105	48.22 N	56.52 W
Meerane, G.D.R. (mā-rä'nẻ)	166	50.51 N	12.27 E
Meerbusch, F.R.G.	169c	51.15 N	6.41 E
Meerut, India (mē'ro͞ot)	196	28.59 N	77.43 E
Megalópolis, Grc. (mĕg-à lŏ'pō-lĭs)	173	37.22 N	22.08 E
Meganom, M.(C.), Sov. Un. (mĕ-gà-nôm')	175	44.48 N	35.17 E
Mégara, Grc. (mĕg'à-rà)	173	37.59 N	23.21 E
Megget, SC (mĕg'ĕt)	127	32.44 N	80.15 W
Meghelaya (State), India	198	25.30 N	91.30 E
Megler, Wa. (mĕg'lēr)	118c	46.15 N	123.52 W
Meglino (L.), Sov. Un. (må-glē'nô)	174	58.32 N	35.27 E
Meguro (Neigh.), Jap.	69a	35.38 N	139.42 E
Meherrin (R.), Va. (mẻ-hĕr'ĭn)	127	36.40 N	77.49 W
Mehlville, Mo.	119e	38.30 N	90.19 W
Mehpālpur (Neigh.), India	67d	28.33 N	77.08 E
Mehrābād, Iran	68h	35.40 N	51.20 E
Mehram Nagar (Neigh.), India	67d	28.34 N	77.07 E
Mehrow, G.D.R.	65a	52.34 N	13.37 E
Mehrum, F.R.G.	63	51.35 N	6.37 E
Mehsāna, India	196	23.42 N	72.23 E
Mehun-sur-Yévre, Fr. (mĕ-ŭN-sür-yĕvr')	168	47.11 N	2.14 E
Meide, F.R.G.	63	51.11 N	6.55 E
Meiderich (Neigh.), F.R.G.	63	51.28 N	6.46 E
Meidling (Neigh.), Aus.	66e	48.11 N	16.20 E
Meiersberg, F.R.G.	63	51.17 N	6.57 E
Meiji Shrine (P. Int.), Jap.	69a	35.41 N	139.42 E
Meiling Pass, China (mā'lĭng')	203	25.22 N	115.00 E
Meinerzhagen, F.R.G. (mī'nĕrts-hä-gĕn)	169c	51.06 N	7.39 E
Meiningen, G.D.R. (mī'nĭng-ĕn)	166	50.35 N	10.25 E
Meiringen, Switz.	166	46.45 N	8.11 E
Meissen, G.D.R.	166	51.11 N	13.28 E
Meizhu, China (mā-jo͞o)	200	31.17 N	119.12 E
Mejillones, Chile (må-kẻ-lyō'nås)	144	23.07 S	70.31 W
Mekambo, Gabon	230	1.01 N	13.56 E
Mekele, Eth.	225	13.31 N	39.19 E
Meknés, Mor. (mĕk'nĕs) (mĕk-nĕs')	224	33.56 N	5.44 W
Mekong (Lancang) (R.), China (län-tsäŋ)	198	24.45 N	100.31 E
Mekong R., Thai.-Laos	206	17.53 N	103.57 E
Mékrou (R.), Afr.	229	11.35 N	2.25 E
Melaka (Malacca), Mala.	191b	2.11 N	102.15 E
Melaka (State), Mala.	191b	2.19 N	102.09 E
Melbourne, Austl. (mĕl'bŭrn)	211a	37.52 S	145.08 E
Melbourne, Eng.	156	52.49 N	1.26 W
Melbourne, Fl.	127a	28.05 N	80.37 W
Melbourne, Ky.	113f	39.02 N	84.22 W
Melcher, Ia. (mĕl'chēr)	115	41.13 N	93.11 W
Melekess, Sov. Sov. Un. (mĕl-yĕk ĕs)	178	54.20 N	49.30 E
Melenki, Sov. Un. (mĕ-lyĕŋ'kẻ)	174	55.25 N	41.34 E
Melfort, Can. (mĕl'fôrt)	100	52.52 N	104.36 W
Melghir Chott (L.), Alg.	224	33.52 N	5.22 E
Melik, Wadi el (R.), Sud.	225	16.48 N	29.30 E
Melilla (Sp.), Afr. (mā-lēl'yä)	224	35.24 N	3.30 W
Melipilla, Chile (må-lẻ-pē'lyä)	141b	33.40 S	71.12 W
Melita, Can.	101	49.11 N	101.09 W
Melitopol', Sov. Un. (mā-lẻ-tô'pôl-y')	175	46.49 N	35.19 E
Melívoia, Grc.	173	39.42 N	22.47 E
Melkrivier, S. Afr.	223d	24.01 S	28.23 E
Mellen, Wi. (mĕl'ĕn)	115	46.20 N	90.40 W
Mellerud, Swe. (mål'ĕ-ro͞odh)	164	58.43 N	12.25 E
Melling, Eng.	64a	53.30 N	2.56 W
Melmoth, S. Afr.	227c	28.38 S	31.26 E
Melo, Ur. (mā'lō)	144	32.18 S	54.07 W
Melocheville, Can. (mĕ-lôsh-vēl')	95a	45.24 N	73.56 W
Melozha R., Sov. Un. (myĕ'lô-zhà)	182b	56.06 N	38.34 E
Melrose, Ma. (mĕl'rōz)	105a	42.29 N	71.06 W
Melrose, Mn.	115	45.39 N	94.49 W
Melrose Highlands, Ma.	54a	42.28 N	71.04 W
Melrose Park, Il.	113a	41.54 N	87.52 W
Melsetter, Zimb. (mĕl-sĕt'ēr)	226	19.44 S	32.51 E
Meltham, Eng. (mĕl'thăm)	156	53.35 N	1.51 W
Melton, Austl. (mĕl'tŭn)	211a	37.41 S	144.35 E
Melton Mowbray, Eng. (mō'brâ)	156	52.45 N	0.52 W
Melúli (R.), Moz.	231	16.10 S	39.30 E
Melun, Fr. (mē-lŭN')	169b	48.32 N	2.40 E
Melunga, Ang.	230	17.16 S	16.24 E
Melville, Can. (mĕl'vĭl)	100	50.55 N	102.48 W
Melville, La.	119	30.39 N	91.45 W
Melville (I.), Austl.	214	11.30 S	131.12 E
Melville (R.), Can.	97	53.46 N	59.31 W
Melville, C., Austl.	215	14.15 S	145.50 E
Melville Hills, Can.	96	69.18 N	124.57 W
Melville Pen, Can.	97	67.44 N	84.09 W

ng-sing; nŋ-baŋk; N-nasalized n; nŏd; cŏmmit; ōld; ôbey; ôrder; oi-boil; fo͞od; fo͝ot; ou-out; s-soft; sh-dish; th-thin; pūre; ůnite; ûrn; stŭd; circŭs; ü-as in French tu; '-indeterminate vowel.

PLACE (Pronounciation)	PAGE	Lat. °′	Long. °′
Melvindale, Mi. (měl′vĭn-dāl)	113b	42.17 N	83.11 W
Mélykút, Hung. (má′l′kōōt)	167	46.14 N	19.21 E
Memba, Moz. (měm′bá)	227	14.12 N	40.35 E
Memel, S. Afr. (mě′měl)	223d	27.42 S	29.35 E
Memel, see Klaipéda			
Memmingen, F.R.G. (měm′ĭng-ěn)	166	47.59 N	10.10 E
Memo (R.), Ven. (mě′mō)	143b	9.32 N	66.30 W
Memphis, Mo. (měm′fĭs)	123	40.27 N	92.11 W
Memphis, Tn. (měm′fĭs)	126	35.07 N	90.03 W
Memphis, Tx.	122	34.42 N	100.33 W
Memphis (Ruins), Egypt	223b	29.50 N	31.12 E
Memphremagog (L.), Can. (měm′frē-mā′gŏg)	111	45.05 N	72.10 W
Mena, Ar. (mē′ná)	123	34.35 N	94.09 W
Mena, Sov. Un. (mē-ná′)	175	51.31 N	32.14 E
Menangle, Austl.	211b	34.08 S	150.48 E
Menard, Tx. (mě-närd′)	124	30.56 N	99.48 W
Menasha, Wi. (mě-năsh′á)	115	44.12 N	88.29 W
Mende, Fr. (mäND)	168	44.31 N	3.30 E
Menden, F.R.G. (měn′děn)	169c	51.26 N	7.47 E
Menden (Neigh.), F.R.G.	63	51.24 N	6.54 E
Menderes (R).), Tur. (měn′děr-ĕs)	179	37.50 N	28.20 E
Mendes, Braz. (mě′n-dĕs)	144b	22.32 S	43.44 W
Mendocino, C., Ca. (měn′dô-sē′nō)	116	40.25 N	124.22 W
Mendota, Il. (měn-dō′tá)	115	41.34 N	89.06 W
Mendota (L.), Wi.	115	43.09 N	89.41 W
Mendoza, Arg. (měn-dō′sä)	144	32.48 S	68.45 W
Mendoza (Prov.), Arg.	144	35.10 S	69.00 W
Mengcheng, China (mǔŋ-chǔŋ)	200	33.15 N	116.34 E
Mengede (Neigh.), F.R.G.	63	51.34 N	7.23 E
Menglinghausen (Neigh.), F.R.G.	63	51.28 N	7.25 E
Meng Shan (Mts.), China (mǔŋ shän)	200	35.47 N	117.23 E
Mengzi, China	198	23.22 N	103.20 E
Menindee, Austl. (mě-nĭn-dē)	216	32.23 S	142.30 E
Menlo Park, Ca. (měn′lō pärk)	118b	37.27 N	122.11 W
Menlo Park Terrace, NJ	55	40.32 N	74.20 W
Menno, SD (měn′ō)	114	43.14 N	97.34 W
Menominee, Mi. (mě-nŏm′ĭ-nē)	115	45.08 N	87.40 W
Menominee (R.), Mi.-Wi.	115	45.37 N	87.54 W
Menominee Falls, Wi. (fôls)	113a	43.11 N	88.06 W
Menominee Ra, Mi.	115	46.07 N	88.53 W
Menomonee R., Wi.	113a	43.09 N	88.06 W
Menomonie, Wi.	115	44.53 N	91.55 W
Menongue, Ang.	230	14.36 S	17.48 E
Menorca (I.) (Minorca), Sp. (mě-nô′r′-kä)	171	40.05 N	3.58 E
Mentana, It. (měn-tä′nä)	171d	42.02 N	12.40 E
Mentawai, Kepulauan (Is.), Indon. (měn-tä-vī′)	206	1.08 S	98.10 E
Menton, Fr. (mäN-tôN′)	169	43.46 N	7.37 E
Mentone, Austl.	70b	37.59 S	145.05 E
Mentone, Ca. (měn′tōne)	119a	34.05 N	117.08 W
Mentz (R.), S. Afr. (měnts)	227c	33.13 S	25.15 E
Menzel Bourguiba, Tun.	159	37.12 N	9.51 E
Menzelinsk, Sov. Un. (měn′zyĕ-lěnsk′)	178	55.40 N	53.15 E
Menzies, Austl. (měn′zēz)	214	29.45 S	122.15 E
Meogui, Mex. (må-ō′gē)	124	28.17 N	105.28 W
Meopham, Eng.	62	51.22 N	0.22 E
Meopham Station, Eng.	62	51.23 N	0.21 E
Meppel, Neth. (měp′ěl)	163	52.41 N	6.08 E
Meppen, F.R.G. (měp′ěn)	166	52.40 N	7.18 E
Merabéllou, Kólpos (G.), Grc.	172a	35.16 N	25.55 E
Meramec (R.), Mo. (měr′á-měk)	123	38.06 N	91.06 W
Merano, It. (må-rä′nō)	172	46.39 N	11.10 E
Merasheen (I.), Can. (mě′rä-shēn)	105	47.30 N	54.15 W
Merauke, Indon. (må-rou′kä)	207	8.32 S	140.17 E
Meraux, La. (mě-rō′)	108d	29.56 N	89.56 W
Mercader y Millás, Sp.	65e	41.21 N	2.05 E
Mercato San Severino, It. (měr-kä′tō sän sě-vē-rē′nō)	171c	40.34 N	14.38 E
Merced, Ca. (měr-sěd′)	120	37.17 N	120.30 W
Merced (R), Ca.	120	37.25 N	120.31 W
Mercedario, Cerro (Mtn.), Chile (měr-sä-dhä′rě-ō)	141b	31.58 S	70.07 W
Mercedes, Arg. (měr-sä′dhäs)	144	29.04 S	58.01 W
Mercedes, Arg.	141c	34.41 S	59.26 W
Mercedes, Tx.	124	26.09 N	97.55 W
Mercedes, Ur.	141c	33.17 S	58.04 W
Mercedita, Chile (měr-sě-dē′tä)	141b	33.51 S	71.10 W
Mercer Island, Wa. (mûr′sěr)	118a	47.35 N	122.15 W
Mercês, Braz. (mě-sě′s)	141a	21.13 S	43.20 W
Mercês, Port.	65d	38.47 N	9.19 W
Merchong (R), Mala.	191b	3.08 N	103.13 E
Merchtem, Bel.	157a	50.57 N	4.13 E
Mercier, Can.	95a	45.19 N	73.45 W
Mercier-Lacombe, Alg. (měr-syá′ lá-kôNb)	171	35.18 N	0.11 W
Mercy, C., Can.	97	64.48 N	63.22 W
Merdeka Palace (P. Int.), Indon.	68k	6.10 S	106.49 E
Mere, Eng.	64b	53.20 N	2.25 W
Meredale, S. Afr.	71b	26.17 S	27.59 E
Meredith, NH (měr′ě-dĭth)	111	43.35 N	71.35 W
Merefa, Sov. Un. (měr-ě′fä)	175	49.49 N	36.04 E
Merendón, Serranía de (Mts.), Hond. (sěr-rä-ně′á-dä mä-rěn-dōn′)	132	15.01 N	89.05 W
Mereworth, Eng. (mě-rě wûrth)	156b	51.15 N	0.23 E
Mergui, Bur. (měr-gē′)	206	12.29 N	98.39 E
Mergui Arch., Asia	206	12.04 N	97.02 E
Meric (R.), Grc.-Tur.	164	40.43 N	26.19 E
Mérida, Mex.	132a	20.58 N	89.37 W
Mérida, Ven.	142	8.30 N	71.15 W
Mérida, Cordillera de (Mts.), Ven. (mě′rě-dhä)	142	8.30 N	70.45 W
Meriden, Ct. (měr′ĭ-děn)	111	41.30 N	72.50 W
Meridian, Ms. (mě-rĭd-ĭ-án)	126	32.21 N	88.41 W
Meridian, Tx.	125	31.56 N	97.37 W
Mérignac, Fr.	168	44.50 N	0.40 W
Merikarvia, Fin. (mä′rě-kär′vě-á)	165	61.51 N	21.30 E
Mering, F.R.G. (mě′rěng)	157d	48.16 N	11.00 E
Merion Station, Pa.	56b	40.00 N	75.15 W
Meriwether Lewis Natl. Mon., Tn. (měr′ĭ-wĕth-ĕr lōō′ĭs)	126	35.25 N	87.25 W
Merkel, Tx. (mûr′kĕl)	124	32.26 N	100.02 W
Merkiné, Sov. Un. (měr′kĭ-ně)	165	54.09 N	24.10 E
Merksem, Bel.	157a	51.15 N	4.27 E
Merkys R., Sov. Un. (mär′kĭs)	167	54.23 N	25.00 E
Merlo, Arg. (měr-lô)	144a	34.35 S	58.44 W
Merlynston, Austl.	70b	37.43 S	144.58 E
Merri (R.), Austl.	70b	37.48 S	145.01 E
Merriam, Ks. (měr-rĭ-yám)	119f	39.01 N	94.42 W
Merriam, Mn.	119g	44.44 N	93.36 W
Merrick, NY (měr′ĭk)	112a	40.40 N	73.33 W
Merrifield, Va. (měr′ĭ-fěld)	112e	38.50 N	77.12 W
Merrill, Wi. (měr′ĭl)	115	45.11 N	89.42 W
Merrimac, Ma. (měr′ĭ-măk)	105a	45.20 N	71.00 W
Merrimack, NH	105a	42.51 N	71.25 W
Merrimack (R.), Ma.-NH (měr′ĭ-măk)	111	43.10 N	71.30 W
Merrimack R., Ma.	105a	42.49 N	70.44 W
Merrionette Park, Il.	58a	41.41 N	87.42 W
Merritt, Can. (měr′ĭt)	99	50.07 N	120.47 W
Merrylands, Austl.	70a	33.50 S	150.59 E
Merryville, La. (měr′ĭ-vĭl)	125	30.46 N	93.34 W
Mersa Fatma, Eth.	225	14.54 N	40.14 E
Merscheid (Neigh.), F.R.G.	63	51.10 N	7.01 E
Merseburg, G.D.R. (měr′zě-bōōrgh)	166	51.21 N	11.59 E
Mersey (R.), Eng. (mûr′zě)	156	52.52 N	2.04 W
Merseyside (Co.), Eng.	156	53.29 N	2.59 W
Mersin, Tur. (měr-sēn′)	179	37.00 N	34.40 E
Mersing, Mala.	191b	2.25 N	103.51 E
Merta Road, India (mär′tŭ rŏd)	196	26.50 N	73.54 E
Merthyr Tydfil, Wales (mûr′ther tĭd′vĭl)	162	51.46 N	3.30 W
Mértola Almodóvar, Port. (měr-tô-lá-äl-mô-dô′vär)	170	37.39 N	8.04 W
Merton (Neigh.), Eng.	62	51.25 N	0.12 W
Méru, Fr. (må-rü′)	169b	49.14 N	2.08 E
Meru, Ken. (mä′rōō)	225	0.01 N	37.45 E
Merume Mts., Guy. (měr-ü′mě)	143	5.45 N	60.15 W
Meru, Mt., Tan.	231	3.15 S	36.43 E
Merwerde, Kanal (Can.), Neth.	157a	52.15 N	5.01 E
Merwin (L.), Wa. (měr′wĭn)	118c	45.58 N	122.27 W
Merzifon, Tur. (měr′ze-fôn)	179	40.50 N	35.30 E
Merzig, F.R.G. (měr′tsěg)	169	49.27 N	6.54 E
Mesa, Az. (mā′sá)	121	33.25 N	111.50 W
Mesabi Ra., Mn. (mā-sôb′bě)	115	47.17 N	93.04 W
Mesagne, It. (mä-sän′yá)	173	40.34 N	17.51 E
Mesa Verde Natl. Park, Co. (věr′dě)	121	37.22 N	108.27 W
Mescalero Ind. Res., NM (měs-kä-lä′rō)	121	33.10 N	105.45 W
Meščerskij, Sov. Un.	66b	55.40 N	37.25 E
Meshchovsk, Sov. Un. (myěsh′chěfsk)	174	54.17 N	35.19 E
Mesilla, NM (må-sē′yä)	121	32.15 N	106.45 W
Meskine, Chad	229	11.25 N	15.21 E
Mesolóngion, Grc. (mě-sô-lôn′gě-ôn)	173	38.23 N	21.28 E
Mesquita, Braz.	61c	22.48 S	43.26 W
Messina, It. (mě-sē′ná)	172	38.11 N	15.34 E
Messina, S. Afr.	226	22.17 S	30.13 E
Messina, Stretto di (Str.), It. (stě′t-tô dē)	172	38.10 N	15.34 E
Messíni, Grc.	173	37.05 N	22.00 E
Méssiniakós Kólpos (G.), Grc.	173	36.59 N	22.00 E
Messy, Fr.	64c	48.58 N	2.42 E
Mesta (R.), Bul. (měs-stá′)	173	41.42 N	23.40 E
Mestre, It. (měs′trä)	172	45.29 N	12.15 E
Meta (Dept.), Col. (mě′tä)	142a	3.28 N	74.07 W
Meta (R.), Col.	142	4.33 N	72.09 W
Métabetchouane (R.), Can. (mě-tä-bět-chōō-än′)	104	47.45 N	72.00 W
Metairie, La.	125	30.00 N	90.11 W
Metán, Arg. (mě-tá′n)	144	25.32 S	64.51 W
Metangula, Moz.	226	12.42 S	34.48 E
Metapán, Sal. (må-täpän′)	132	14.21 N	89.26 W
Metcalfe, Can. (mět-käf)	95c	45.14 N	75.27 W
Metchosin, Can.	118a	48.22 N	123.33 W
Metepec, Mex. (må-tě-pěk′)	130	18.56 N	98.31 W
Metepec, Mex.	131a	19.15 N	99.36 W
Methow R., Wa. (mět′hou)	116	48.26 N	120.15 W
Methuen, Ma. (mě-thū′ěn)	105a	42.44 N	71.11 W
Metkovic', Yugo. (mět′kô-vĭch)	173	43.02 N	17.40 E
Metlakatla, Ak. (mět-lá-kät′lá)	107	55.08 N	131.35 W
Metropolis, Il. (mě-trŏp′ô-lĭs)	123	37.09 N	88.46 W
Metropolitan Museum of Art (P. Int.), NY	55	40.47 N	73.58 W
Metter, Ga. (mět′ěr)	127	32.21 N	82.05 W
Mettmann, F.R.G. (mět′män)	169c	51.15 N	6.58 E
Metuchen, NJ (mě-tū′chĕn)	112a	40.32 N	74.21 W
Metz, Fr. (mětz)	169	49.08 N	6.10 E
Metztitlán, Mex. (mětz-tět-län)	130	20.36 N	98.45 W
Meuban, Cam.	229	2.27 N	12.41 E
Meudon, Fr.	64c	48.48 N	2.14 E
Meuse (R.), Eur. (mûz) (müz)	168	50.32 N	5.22 E
Mexborough, Eng. (měks′bŭr-ô)	156	53.30 N	1.17 W
Mexia, Tx. (mä-hē′ä)	125	31.32 N	96.29 W
Mexian, China	203	24.20 N	116.10 E
Mexicalcingo, Mex. (mě-kě-käl-sēn′go)	131a	19.13 N	99.34 W
Mexicali, Mex. (måk-sě-kä′lě)	120	32.28 N	115.29 W
Mexican Hat, Ut. (měk′sĭ-kăn hăt)	121	37.10 N	109.55 W
Mexico, Me. (měk′sĭ-kō)	104	44.34 N	70.33 W
Mexico, Mo.	123	39.09 N	91.51 W
Mexico, N. A.	94	23.45 N	104.00 W
Mexico (State), Mex. (måk′sě-kō)	128	19.50 N	99.50 W
Mexico City, Mex. (měk′sĭ-kō)	131a	19.28 N	99.09 W
Mexico, G. of, N. A.	128	25.15 N	93.45 W
Mexticacán, Mex. (měs′tě-kä-kän′)	130	21.12 N	102.43 W
Meyers Chuck, Ak.	98	55.44 N	132.15 W
Meyersdale, Pa. (mī′ěrz-dāl)	111	39.55 N	79.00 W
Meyerton, S. Afr. (mī′ěr-tŭn)	223d	26.35 S	28.01 E
Meymaneh, Afg.	192	35.53 N	64.38 E
Mezen', Sov. Un.	178	65.50 N	44.05 E
Mezen' (R), Sov. Un.	178	65.20 N	44.45 E
Mézenc, Mt., Fr. (mōN-mä-zěN′)	168	44.55 N	4.12 E
Mezha (R.), Sov. Un. (myä′zhá)	174	55.53 N	31.44 E
Mézieres-sur-Seine, Fr. (mä-zyär′sür-sän′)	169b	48.58 N	1.49 E
Mezökövesd, Hung. (mě′zŭ-kŭ′věsht)	167	47.49 N	20.36 E
Mezötur, Hung. (mě′zŭ-tōōr)	167	47.00 N	20.36 E
Mezquital, Mex. (måz-kě-täl′)	130	23.30 N	104.20 W
Mezquital (R.), Mex.	130	23.07 N	104.52 W
Mezquitic, Mex. (måz-kě-těk′)	130	22.25 N	103.43 W
Mezquitic (R.), Mex.	130	22.25 N	103.45 W
Mfangano I., Ken.	231	0.28 S	33.35 E
Mga, Sov. Un. (m′gá)	182c	59.45 N	31.04 E
Mgeni (R.), S. Afr.	227c	29.38 S	30.53 E
Mglin, Sov. Un. (m′glěn′)	174	53.03 N	32.52 W
Mia, Oued (R.), Alg.	160	29.26 N	3.15 E
Miacatlán, Mex. (mě′ä-kä-tlän′)	130	18.42 N	99.17 W
Mia-dong (Neigh.), Kor.	68b	37.37 N	127.01 E
Miahuatlán, Mex. (mě′ä-wä-tlän′)	131	16.20 N	96.38 W
Miajadas, Sp. (mě-ä-hä′däs)	170	39.10 N	5.53 W
Miami, Az.	121	33.20 N	110.55 W
Miami, Fl.	127a	25.45 N	80.11 W
Miami, Ok.	123	36.51 N	94.51 W
Miami, Tx.	122	35.41 N	100.39 W
Miami (R.), Oh.	110	39.20 N	84.45 W
Miami Beach, Fl.	127a	25.47 N	80.07 W
Miami Drainage Can., Fl.	134	26.25 N	80.50 W
Miamisburg, Oh. (mī-ăm′ĭz-bûrg)	110	39.40 N	84.20 W
Miamitown, Oh. (mī-ăm′ĭ-toun)	113f	39.13 N	84.43 W
Mianeh, Iran	192	37.15 N	47.13 E
Miangos, Pulau, (I.), Phil. (myä′n-gäs)	207	5.30 N	127.00 E
Miaodao Qundao (Is.), China (mĭou-dou chyŏon-dou)	200	38.06 N	120.35 E
Miaoli, Taiwan (mě-ou′lĭ)	203	24.30 N	120.48 E
Miaozhen, China (mĭou-jūn)	200	31.44 N	121.28 E
Miass, Sov. Un. (mĭ-äs′)	182a	55.00 N	60.03 E
Miastko, Pol. (my′äst′kô)	166	54.01 N	17.00 E
Michajlovskoje, Sov. Un.	66b	55.35 N	37.35 E
Michalovce, Czech. (mě′Kä-lôf′tsě)	167	48.44 N	21.56 E
Michel Pk., Kan.	98	53.35 N	125.25 W
Michelson, Mt. Ak. (mĭch′ĕl-sŭn)	107	69.11 N	144.12 W
Michendorf, F.R.G. (mĭ′Kĕn-dôrf)	157b	52.19 N	13.02 E
Miches, Dom. Rep. (mě′chěs)	135	19.00 N	69.05 W
Michigan (State), U. S. (mĭsh-′ĭ-gán)	109	45.55 N	87.00 W
Michigan, L., U. S.	109	43.20 N	87.10 W
Michigan City, In.	110	41.40 N	86.55 W
Michikamau (L.), Can.	97	54.11 N	63.21 W
Michillinda, Ca.	59	34.07 N	118.05 W
Michipicoten (I.), Can. (mě-shī-pī-kō′těn)	115	47.49 N	85.50 W
Michipicoten (R.), Can.	115	47.56 N	84.42 W
Michipicoten Harbour, Can.	115	47.58 N	84.58 W
Michoacán (State), Mex.	130	19.15 N	101.30 W
Michurinsk, Sov. Un. (mǐ-chōō-rǐnsk′)	174	52.53 N	40.32 E
Mico, Punta (Pt.), Nic. (pōō′n-tä-mě′kō)	133	11.38 N	83.24 W
Midas, Nv. (mī′dás)	116	41.15 N	116.50 W
Middelfart, Den. (měd′′l-färt)	164	55.30 N	9.45 E
Middle (R.), Can.	98	55.00 N	125.50 W
Middle Andaman I., Andaman & Nicobar Is. (än-dá-män′)	206	12.44 N	93.21 E
Middle Bayou, Tx.	125a	29.38 N	95.06 W
Middle Bight (B.), Ba. (bīt)	134	24.20 N	77.35 W
Middleburg, S. Afr. (mǐd′ĕl-bûrg)	226	31.30 S	25.00 E
Middleburg, S. Afr.	223d	25.47 S	29.30 E
Middleburgh Heights, Oh.	56a	41.22 N	81.48 W
Middlebury, Vt. (mǐd′′l-bĕr-ĭ)	111	44.00 N	73.10 W
Middle Concho, Tx. (kŏn′chō)	124	31.21 N	100.50 W
Middle Loup (R.), Ne. (lōōp)	114	41.49 N	100.20 W
Middleport, Oh. (mǐd′′l-pōrt)	110	39.00 N	82.05 W
Middle River, Md.	112e	39.20 N	76.27 W
Middlesboro, Ky. (mǐd′′lz-bûr-ô)	126	36.36 N	83.42 W
Middlesbrough, Eng. (mǐd′′lz-brŭ)	162	54.35 N	1.18 W
Middlesex, NJ (mǐd′′l-sěks)	112a	40.34 N	74.30 W
Middleton, Can. (mǐd′′l-tŭn)	104	44.57 N	65.04 W
Middleton, Eng.	156	53.04 N	2.12 W
Middleton (I.), Ak.	107	59.35 N	146.35 W
Middletown, Ct.	111	41.35 N	72.40 W
Middletown, De.	111	39.30 N	75.40 W
Middletown, Ma.	105a	42.35 N	71.01 W
Middletown, NY	112a	41.26 N	74.25 W
Middletown, Oh.	110	39.30 N	84.25 W
Middlewich, Eng. (mǐd′′l-wǐch)	156	53.11 N	2.27 W
Middlewit, S. Afr. (mǐd′l′l-wǐt)	223d	24.50 S	27.00 E
Midfield, Al.	112h	33.28 N	86.54 W
Midi, Canal du (R.), Fr. (kä-näl-dü-mě-dě′)	171	43.22 N	1.35 E
Midicine Lodge (R.), Ks.	122	37.20 N	98.57 W
Mid Illovo, S. Afr. (mǐd Ǐl′ô-vō)	227c	29.59 S	30.32 E
Midland, Can. (mǐd′lánd)	111	44.45 N	79.50 W
Midland, Mi.	110	43.40 N	84.20 W
Midland, Tx.	124	32.05 N	102.05 W
Midland Beach (Neigh.), NY	55	40.34 N	74.05 W
Midlothian, Il.	58a	41.38 N	87.42 W
Midvale, Ut. (mǐd′vāl)	119b	40.37 N	111.54 W
Midway, Al. (mǐd′wā)	126	32.03 N	85.30 W
Midway, S. Afr.	71b	26.17 S	27.51 E
Midway City, Ca.	59	33.45 N	118.00 W
Midway Is., Pac. O.	208	28.00 N	179.00 W
Midwest, Wy. (mǐd-wěst′)	117	43.25 N	106.15 W
Midye, Tur. (měd′yě)	179	41.35 N	28.10 E
Midzyrzecz, Pol. (myän-dzŭ′zhěch)	166	52.26 N	15.35 E
Mielec, Pol. (myě′lěts)	167	50.17 N	21.27 E
Mier, Mex. (myěr)	124	26.26 N	99.08 W
Mieres, Sp. (myä′räs)	170	43.14 N	5.45 W
Mier y Noriega, Mex. (myär′ě nô-rě-ä′gä)	130	22.28 N	100.08 W
Miguel Auza, Mex. (mě-gě′l-ä-ōō′zä)	130	24.17 N	103.27 W
Miguel Pereira, Braz. (pě-rä′rä)	144b	22.27 S	43.28 W

PLACE (Pronunciation)	PAGE	Lat. °′	Long. °′		PLACE (Pronunciation)	PAGE	Lat. °′	Long. °′		PLACE (Pronunciation)	PAGE	Lat. °′	Long. °′
Mijares (R.), Sp. (mē-hä′räs)	171	40.05 N	0.42 W		Minami (Neigh.), Jap.	68e	34.58 N	135.45 E		Mirando City, Tx. (mĭr-án′dō)	124	27.25 N	99.03 W
Mikage, Jap. (mē′ká-gå)	205b	34.42 N	135.15 E		Minamisenju (Neigh.), Jap.	69a	35.44 N	139.48 E		Mira Por Vos Islets (Is.), Ba.	135	22.05 N	74.30 W
Mikawa-Wan (B.), Jap.					Minas, Cuba (mē′näs)	134	21.03 N	77.35 W		(mē′rä pŏr vōs)	135	22.05 N	74.30 W
(mē′kä-wä wän)	205	34.43 N	137.09 E		Minas, Indon.	191b	0.52 N	101.29 E		Mira Por Vos Pass (Str.), Ba.	135	22.10 N	74.35 W
Mikhaylov, Sov. Un.	174	54.14 N	39.03 E		Minas, Ur. (mē′näs)	144	34.18 S	55.12 W		Mirbât, Om.	192	16.58 N	54.42 E
Mikhaylovka, Sov. Un.					Minas Basin, Can. (mī′nás)	104	45.20 N	64.00 W		Mirebalais, Hai. (mēr-bá-lē′)	135	18.50 N	72:05 W
(mē-kä′ĕ-laf-kȧ)	175	47.16 N	35.12 E		Minas Chan., Can.	104	45.15 N	64.45 W		Mirecourt, Fr. (mēr-kōōr′)	169	48.20 N	6.08 E
Mikhaylovka, Sov. Un.	182a	55.35 N	55.57 E		Minas de Oro, Hond.					Mirfield, Eng. (mûr′fĕld)	156	53.41 N	1.42 W
Mikhaylovka, Sov. Un.	182c	59.20 N	30.21 E		(mē′näs-dĕ-dĕ-ō-rô)	132	14.52 N	87.19 W		Mirgorod, Sov. Un.	175	49.56 N	33.36 E
Mikhaylovka, Sov. Un.	179	50.05 N	43.10 E		Minas de Riotinto, Sp.					Miri, Mala. (mē′rē)	206	4.13 N	113.56 E
Mikhnëvo, Sov. Un. (mĭk-nyô′vō)	182b	55.08 N	37.57 E		(mē′näs dä rē-ō-tēn′tō)	170	37.43 N	6.35 W		Mirim, L., Braz.-Ur. (mē-rēN′)	144	33.00 S	53.15 W
Miki, Jap. (mē′kĕ)	205b	34.47 N	134.59 E		Minas Gerais (State), Braz.					Mírina, Grc.	173	39.52 N	25.01 E
Mikindani, Tan. (mē-kĕn-dä′nĕ)	231	10.17 S	40.07 E		(mē′näzh-zhē-rá′ēs)	143	17.45 S	43.50 W		Miropol′ye, Sov. Un. (mē-rō-pôl′yĕ)	175	51.02 N	35.13 E
Mikkeli, Fin. (mĕk′ĕ-lĭ)	165	61.42 N	27.14 E		Minas Nova, Braz.					Mîrpur Khâs, Pak. (mēr′pōōr ĸäs)	196	25.36 N	69.10 E
Míkonos (I.), Grc.	173	37.26 N	25.30 E		(mē′näzh nō′väzh)	143	17.20 S	42.19 W		Mirzâpur, India (mēr′zä-pōōr)	196	25.12 N	82.38 E
Mikulov, Czech. (mĭ′kōō-lôf)	166	48.47 N	16.39 E		Minas, Sierra de las (Mts.), Guat.					Mirzâpur, India	67a	22.50 N	88.24 E
Mikumi, Tan.	231	7.24 S	36.59 E		(syĕr′rä dä läs mē′näs)	132	15.08 N	90.25 W		Misailovo, Sov. Un.	66b	55.34 N	37.49 E
Mikuni, Jap. (mē′kōō-nē)	205	36.09 N	136.14 E		Minatare (L.), Ne. (mĭn′á-târ)	114	41.56 N	103.07 W		Misantla, Mex. (mē-sän′tlä)	131	19.55 N	96.49 W
Mikuni-Sammyaku (Mts.), Jap.					Minatitlan, Mex. (mē-nä-tē-tlän′)	131	17.59 N	94.33 W		Miscou (I.), Can. (mĭs′kō)	104	47.58 N	64.35 W
(säm′myä-kōō)	205	36.51 N	138.38 E		Minatitlan, Mex.	130	19.21 N	104.02 W		Miscou Pt., Can.	104	48.04 N	64.32 W
Mikura (I.), Jap. (mē′kōō-rä)	205	33.53 N	139.26 E		Minato, Jap. (mē′nä-tō)	205a	35.13 N	139.52 E		Miseno, C., It. (mē-zĕ′nō)	171c	40.33 N	14.12 E
Milaca, Mn. (mē-lǎk′á)	115	45.45 N	93.41 W		Minato (Neigh.), Jap.	69a	35.39 N	139.45 E		Misery, Mt., Saint Kitts-Nevis			
Milan, Mi. (mī′lǎn)	110	42.05 N	83.40 W		Minato (Neigh.), Jap.	69b	34.39 N	135.26 E		(mĭz′rē-ĭ)	133b	17.28 N	62.47 W
Milan, Mo.	123	40.13 N	93.07 W		Minch, The (Chan.), Scot.	162	58.04 N	6.04 W		Mishan, China (mĭ′shäN)	204	45.32 N	132.19 E
Milan, Tn.	126	35.54 N	88.47 W		Mindanao (I.), Phil. (mĭn-dä-nou′)	207	7.30 N	125.10 E		Mishawaka, In. (mĭsh-á-wôk′á)	110	41.45 N	86.15 W
Milan, see Milano					Mindanao Sea, Phil.	207	8.55 N	124.00 E		Mishina, Jap. (mē′shē-mä)	205	35.09 N	138.56 E
Milano (Milan), It. (mē-lä′nō)	172	45.29 N	9.12 E		Minden, F.R.G. (mĭn′dĕn)	166	52.17 N	8.58 E		Misiones (Prov.), Arg. (mē-syō′näs)	144	27.00 S	54.30 W
Milås, Tur. (mē′läs)	179	37.10 N	27.25 E		Minden, La.	125	32.36 N	93.19 W		Miskito, Cayos (Is.), Nic.	133	14.34 N	82.30 W
Milazzo, It. (mē-låt′sô)	172	38.13 N	15.17 E		Minden, Ne.	122	40.30 N	98.54 W		Miskolc, Hung. ·(mĭsh′kôlts)	167	48.07 N	20.50 E
Milbank, SD (mĭl′bäɴk)	114	45.13 N	96.38 W		Mindoro (I.), Phil. (mĭn-dô′rō)	207a	13.04 N	121.06 E		Misr al-Qadîmah (Old Cairo) (Neigh.),			
Mildura, Austl. (mĭl-dū′rá)	216	34.10 S	142.18 E		Mindoro Str., Phil.	207a	12.28 N	120.33 E		Egypt	71a	30.00 N	31.14 E
Miles City, Mt. (mīlz)	117	46.24 N	105.50 W		Mindyak, Sov. Un. (mĕn′dyák)	182a	54.01 N	58.48 E		Misool (I.), Pulau, Indon. (mē-sōōl′)	207	2.00 S	130.05 E
Milford, Ct. (mĭl′fĕrd)	111	41.15 N	73.05 W		Mineola, NY (mĭn-ē-ō′lá)	112a	40.43 N	73.38 W		Misquah Hills, Mn. (mĭs-kwä′ hĭlz)	115	47.50 N	90.30 W
Milford, De.	111	38.55 N	75.25 W		Mineola, Tx.	125	32.39 N	95.31 W		Misr al Jadîdah (Ruins), Egypt	223b	30.06 N	31.35 E
Milford, Md.	56c	39.21 N	76.44 W		Mineral del Chico, Mex.					Misr al-Jadîdah (Heliopolis) (Neigh.),			
Milford, Ma.	105a	42.09 N	71.31 W		(mē-nä-räl′dĕl chē′kô)	130	20.13 N	98.46 W		Egypt	225	32.23 N	14.58 E
Milford, Mi.	113b	42.35 N	83.36 W		Mineral del Monte, Mex.					Misrâtah, Libya	225	32.23 N	14.58 E
Milford, NH	111	42.50 N	71.40 W		(mē-nä-räl dĕl mōn′tĕ)	130	20.18 N	98.39 W		Missinaibi L., Can.	102	48.23 N	83.40 W
Milford, Oh.	113f	39.11 N	84.18 W		Mineral′nyye Vody, Sov. Un.	179	44.10 N	43.15 E		Missinaibi (R.), Can. (mĭs′ĭn-ä′ĕ-bē)	97	50.27 N	83.01 W
Milford, Ut.	121	38.20 N	113.05 W		Mineral Point, Wi. (mĭn′ēr-ál)	115	42.50 N	90.10 W		Mission, Ks. (mĭsh′ủn)	119f	39.02 N	94.39 W
Miling, Austl. (mĭl′′ng)	214	30.30 S	116.25 E		Mineral Wells, Tx. (mĭn′ēr-ál wĕlz)	124	32.48 N	98.06 W		Mission, Tx.	124	26.14 N	98.19 W
Milipitas, Ca. (mĭl-ĭ-pĭ′tás)	118b	37.26 N	121.54 W		Minerva, Oh. (mĭ-nur′vá)	110	40.45 N	81.10 W		Mission City, Can. (sĭ′tĭ)	118d	49.08 N	112.18 W
Milk R., Can.-U.S.	117	48.25 N	108.45 W		Minervino, It. (mē-nĕr-vē′nō)	172	41.07 N	16.05 E		Mississagi (R.), Can.	102	46.35 N	83.30 W
Milk River, Can. (mĭlk)	99	49.09 N	112.05 W		Mineyama, Jap. (mē-nĕ-yä′mä)	205	35.38 N	135.05 E		Mississauga, Can.	95d	43.34 N	79.37 W
Millau, Fr. (mē-yō′)	168	44.06 N	3.04 E		Mingan, Can.	104	50.18 N	64.02 W		Mississinewa (R.), In.			
Millbourne, Pa.	56b	39.58 N	75.15 W		Mingechaur (R.), Sov. Un.	179	41.00 N	47.20 E		(mĭs-ĭ-sĭn′ĕ-wä)	110	40.30 N	85.45 W
Millbrae, Ca. (mĭl′brā)	118b	37.36 N	122.23 W		Mingenew, Austl. (mĭn′gĕ-nů)	214	29.15 S	115.45 E		Mississippi (State), U.S. (mĭs-ĭ-sĭp′ĕ)	109	32.30 N	89.45 W
Millburn, NJ	55	40.44 N	74.20 W		Mingo Junction, Oh. (mĭg′gō)	110	40.15 N	80.40 W		Mississippi (L.), Can.	111	45.05 N	76.15 W
Millbury, Ma. (mĭl′bĕr-ĭ)	105a	42.11 N	71.46 W		Minho (Reg.), Port. (mēn yōō)	170	41.32 N	8.13 W		Mississippi (R.), U.S.	109	31.50 N	91.30 W
Mill Cr., Ca. (mĭl)	95g	53.13 N	113.25 W		Minho, Rio (R.), Port. (rē′ō mē′n-yô)	170	41.28 N	9.05 W		Mississippi Sd., Ms.	126	34.16 N	89.10 W
Mill Cr., Ca.	120	40.07 N	121.55 W		Minho (R.), Jam.	134	17.55 N	77.20 W		Missoula, Mt. (mĭ-zōō′lá)	117	46.25 N	114.00 W
Milledgeville, Ga. (mĭl′ĕj-vĭl)	126	33.05 N	83.15 W		Ministík L., Can. (mĭ-nĭs′tĭk)	95g	53.23 N	113.05 W		Missouri (State), U.S. (mĭ-sōō′rĕ)	109	38.00 N	93.40 W
Mille Îles, R. des, Can.					Minna, Nig. (mĭn′ä)	229	9.37 N	6.33 E		Missouri (R.), U.S.	109	40.40 N	96.00 W
(rē-vyâr′ dä mĭl′ĭl′)	95a	45.41 N	73.40 W		Minneapolis, Ks. (mĭn-ē-ăp′ô-lĭs)	123	39.07 N	97.41 W		Missouri City, Tx.	125a	29.37 N	95.32 W
Mille Lac Ind. Res., Mn. (mĭl lǎk′)	115	46.14 N	94.13 W		Minneapolis, Mn.	119g	44.58 N	93.15 W		Missouri Coteau, (Plat.), U.S.	108	47.30 N	101.00 W
Mille Lacs (L.), Mn.	115	46.25 N	93.22 W		Minnedosa, Can. (mĭn-ē-dō′sá)	101	50.14 N	99.51 W		Missouri Valley, Ia.	114	41.35 N	95.53 W
Mille Lacs, Lac des (L.), Can.					Minneota, Mn. (mĭn-ē-ō′tá)	114	44.34 N	95.59 W		Mist, Or. (mĭst)	118c	46.00 N	123.15 W
(läk dĕ mēl läks)	115	48.52 N	90.53 W		Minnesota (State), U.S.					Mistassibi (R.), Can. (mĭs-tȧ-sĭ′bē)	104	49.44 N	69.58 W
Millen, Ga. (mĭl′ĕn)	127	32.47 N	81.55 W		(mĭn-ē-sō′tá)	109	46.10 N	90.20 W		Mistassini, Can. (mĭs-tȧ-sĭ′nē)	104	48.56 N	71.55 W
Miller, SD (mĭl′ēr)	114	44.31 N	99.00 W		Minnesota (R), Mn.	114	45.04 N	96.03 W		Mistassini (R.), Can.	97	50.48 N	73.30 W
Millerovo, Sov. Un. (mĭl′ĕ-rô-vô)	175	48.58 N	40.27 E		Minnetonka (L.), Mn. (mĭn-ē-tôn′ká)	115	44.52 N	93.34 W		Mistassini (R.), Can.	104	50.02 N	72.38 W
Millersburg, Ky. (mĭl′ērz-bûrg)	103	38.15 N	84.10 W		Minnie Maud Cr., Ut. (mĭn′ĭmŏd′)	121	39.50 N	110.30 W		Mistelbach, Aust. (mĭs′tĕl-bäk)	166	48.34 N	16.33 E
Millersburg, Oh.	103	40.35 N	81.55 W		Minnitaki L., Can. (mĭ′nĭ-tä′kĕ)	101	49.58 N	92.00 W		Misteriosa, L., Mex. (mēs-tē-ryō′sä)	132a	18.05 N	90.15 W
Millersburg, Pa.	111	40.35 N	76.55 W		Minô, Jap. (mē′nō)	205b	34.49 N	135.28 E		Mistretta, It. (mē-strĕt′tä)	172	37.54 N	14.22 E
Millers Ferry Lake (Res.), Al.	126	32.10 N	87.15 W		Mino (R.), Jap.	205b	34.56 N	135.06 E		Mitaka, Jap.	205a	35.42 N	139.34 E
Millerton, Ca. (mĭl′ēr-tǔn)	104	46.56 N	65.40 W		Miño (R.), Sp. (mē′nyō)	170	42.28 N	7.48 W		Mita, Punta de (Pt.), Mex.			
Millertown, Can. (mĭl′ēr-toun)	105	48.49 N	56.32 W		Minonk, Il. (mĭ′nŏnk)	110	40.55 N	89.00 W		(pōō′n-tä-dĕ-mē′tä)	130	20.44 N	105.34 W
Mill Green, Eng.	62	51.41 N	0.22 E		Minooka, Il. (mĭ-nōō′ká)	113a	41.27 N	88.15 W		Mitcham, Austl.	70b	37.49 S	145.12 E
Mill Hill (Neigh.), Eng.	62	51.37 N	0.13 W		Minorca (I.), see Menorca					Mitcham (Neigh.), Eng.	62	51.24 N	0.10 W
Millicent, Austl. (mĭl-ĭ-sĕnt)	216	37.30 S	140.20 E		Minot, ND (mĭ′nŏt)	114	48.13 N	101.16 W		Mitchell, Il. (mĭch′ĕl)	119e	38.46 N	90.05 W
Millinocket, Me. (mĭl-ĭ-nŏk′ĕt)	104	45.40 N	68.44 W		Minsk, Sov. Un. (mēnsk)	174	53.54 N	27.35 E		Mitchell, In.	110	38.45 N	86.25 W
Millis, Ma. (mĭl-ĭs)	105a	42.10 N	71.22 W		Minsk (Oblast), Sov. Un.	174	53.50 N	27.43 E		Mitchell, Ne.	114	41.56 N	103.49 W
Mill Neck, NY	55	40.52 N	73.34 W		Mińsk Mazowiecki, Pol.					Mitchell, SD	114	43.42 N	98.01 W
Millstadt, Il. (mĭl′stät)	119e	38.27 N	90.06 W		(mēn′sk mä-zô-vyĕt′skĭ)	167	52.10 N	21.35 E		Mitchell (R.), Austl.	215	15.30 S	142.15 E
Millstone (R.), NJ (mĭl′stōn)	112a	40.27 N	74.38 W		Minsterley, Eng. (mĭnstēr-lĕ)	156	52.38 N	2.55 W		Mitchell, Mt., NC	127	35.47 N	82.15 W
Millstream, Austl. (mĭl′strēm)	214	21.45 S	117.10 E		Mintard, F.R.G.	63	51.22 N	6.54 E		Mît Ghamr, Egypt	223b	30.43 N	31.20 E
Milltown, Can. (mĭl′toun)	104	45.13 N	67.19 W		Minto, Austl.	70a	34.01 S	150.51 E		Mitilíni, Grc.	173	39.09 N	26.35 E
Millvale, Pa.	57b	40.29 N	79.58 W		Minto, Can.	104	46.05 N	66.05 W		Mitla P., Egypt	191a	30.03 N	32.40 E
Mill Valley, Cal. (mĭl)	118b	37.54 N	122.32 W		Minto (L.), Can.	97	57.18 N	75.50 W		Mito, Jap. (mē′tō)	205	36.20 N	140.23 E
Millwood Res., Ar.	123	33.00 N	94.00 W		Minturno, It. (mēn-tōōr′nō)	172	41.17 N	13.44 E		Mitsiwa (Massaua), Eth.	225	15.40 N	39.19 E
Milly-la-Forêt, Fr. (mē-yē′-la-fŏ-rē′)	169b	48.24 N	2.28 E		Minûf, Egypt (mē-nōōf′)	223b	30.28 N	30.55 E		Mitsu, Jap. (mē′sōō)	205	34.21 N	132.49 E
Milmont Park, Pa.	56b	39.53 N	75.20 W		Minusinsk, Sov. Un. (mē-nōō-sěnsk′)	180	53.47 N	91.45 E		Mitte (Neigh.), G.D.R.	65a	52.31 N	13.24 E
Milnerton, S. Afr. (mĭl′nēr-tǔn)	226a	33.52 S	18.30 E		Min′yar, Sov. Un. (mĕn′yȧr)	182	55.06 N	57.33 E		Mittelland (Can.), G.D.R.			
Milnor, ND (mĭl′nēr)	114	46.17 N	97.29 W		Miquelon L., Can. (mĭ′kĕ-lŏn)	95g	53.16 N	112.55 W		(mĭt′ĕl-länd)	166	52.18 N	10.42 E
Milnrow, Eng.	64b	53.37 N	2.06 W		Miquelon (I.), Can., Saint Pierre & Miquelon,					Mittenwalde, G.D.R. (mĭt-tĕn-väl-dĕ)	157b	52.16 N	13.33 E
Milo, Me.	104	44.16 N	69.01 W		(mĭk-ē-lôn′)	105	47.00 N	56.40 W		Mittweida, G.D.R. (mĭt-vī′dä)	166	50.59 N	12.58 E
Milo (I.), see Mílos					Miquihuana, Mex. (mē-kē-wä′nä)	130	23.36 N	99.45 W		Mitumba, Monts (Mts.), Zaire	231	10.50 S	27.00 E
Milon-la-Chapelle, Fr.	64c	48.44 N	2.03 E		Miquon, Pa.	56b	40.04 N	75.16 W		Mityayevo, Sov. Un. (mĭt-yä′yĕ-vô)	182a	60.17 N	61.02 E
Mílos, (Milo) (I.), Grc. (mē′lōs)	173	36.45 N	24.35 E		Mira (R.), Port. (mē′rä)	170	37.29 N	8.15 W		Miura, Jap.	205a	35.08 N	139.37 E
Mílpa Alta, Mex. (mē′l-pä-ä′l-tä)	131a	19.11 N	99.01 W		Miracema, Braz. (mē-rä-sē′mä)	141a	21.24 S	42.10 W		Mius (R.), Sov. Un. (mē-ōōs′)	175	47.30 N	38.48 W
Milspe, F.R.G.	63	51.18 N	7.21 E		Mirador, Braz. (mē-rä-dōr′)	143	6.19 S	44.12 W		Miwa, Jap. (mē′wä)	205b	34.32 N	135.51 E
Milton, Can.	95d	43.31 N	79.53 W		Miraflores, Col. (mē-rä-flō′räs)	142	5.10 N	73.13 W		Mixcoac (Neigh.), Mex.	60a	19.23 N	99.12 W
Milton, Fl. (mĭl′tǔn)	126	30.37 N	87.02 W		Miraflores, Peru	142	16.19 S	71.20 W		Mixico, Guat. (mēs′kō)	132	14.37 N	90.37 W
Milton, Ma.	105a	42.15 N	71.05 W		Miraflores Locks, Pan.	128a	9.00 N	79.35 W		Mixquiahuala, Mex. (mēs-kē-wä′lä)	130	20.12 N	99.13 W
Milton, Pa.	111	41.00 N	76.50 W		Miragoâne, Hai. (mē-rä-gwän′)	135	18.25 N	73.05 W		Mixteco (R.), Mex. (mēs-tā′kō)	130	17.45 N	98.10 W
Milton, Ut.	119b	41.04 N	111.44 W		Miraí, Braz. (mē-rä-ē′)	141a	21.13 S	42.36 W		Miyake (I.), Jap. (mē′yä-kå)	205	34.06 N	139.21 E
Milton, Wa.	118a	47.15 N	122.20 W		Mira Loma, Ca. (mĭ′rá lō′má)	119a	34.01 N	117.32 W		Miyake, Jap. (mē′yä-kĕ)	205b	34.35 N	135.34 E
Milton, Wi.	115	42.45 N	89.00 W		Miramar, Fr.	168	43.33 N	6.15 E		Miyakonojō, Jap. (mē′yä-kō′nō-jō)	205	31.42 N	131.03 E
Milton-Freewater, Or.	116	45.57 N	118.25 W		Miramar (Neigh.), Cuba	60b	23.07 N	82.25 W		Miyazaki, Jap. (mē′yä-zä′kē)	205	31.55 N	131.27 E
Milvale, Pa. (mĭl′vál)	57b	40.29 N	79.58 W		Miramas, Fr.	168	43.35 N	5.00 E		Miyoshi, Jap. (mē-yō′shē)	205	34.48 N	132.49 E
Milville, NJ (mĭl′vĭl)	111	39.25 N	75.00 W		Miramichi B., Can. (mĭr′á-mē′shē)	104	47.08 N	65.08 W		Mizdah, Libya (mĕz′dä)	160	31.29 N	13.09 E
Milwaukee, Wi. (mĭl-wô′kĕ)	113a	43.02 N	87.55 W		Miranda, Austl.	70a	34.02 S	151.06 E		Mizil, Rom. (mĕ′zĕl)	173	45.01 N	26.30 E
Milwaukee, Wi.	113a	43.03 N	87.55 W		Miranda, Can. (mē-rä′n-dä)	142a	3.57 N	76.11 W		Mizonokuchi, see Takatsu			
Milwaukee R., Wi.	113a	43.10 N	87.56 W		Miranda, Ven.	143b	10.09 N	68.24 W		Mizonuma, Jap.	69a	35.48 N	139.36 E
Mimiapan, Mex. (mē-myä-pän′)	131a	19.26 N	99.28 W		Miranda (State), Ven.	143b	10.17 N	66.41 W		Mizoram (Union Ter.), India	196	23.25 N	92.45 E
Mimoso do Sul, Braz.					Miranda de Ebro, Port.					Mizue (Neigh.), Jap.	69a	35.41 N	139.54 E
(mē-mō′sō-dô-sōō′l)	141a	21.03 S	41.21 W		(mē-rän′dä ĕ-brō-dwĕ′rō)	170	41.30 N	6.17 W		Mizuho (Neigh.), Jap.	69a	35.36 N	139.21 E
Min (R.), China (mēn)	203	26.03 N	118.30 E		Miranda de Ebro, Sp.					Mjölby, Swe. (myûl′bü)	164	58.20 N	15.09 E
Min (R.), China	203	28.00 N	104.00 E		(mē-rä′n-dä-dĕ-ē′brō)	170	42.42 N	2.59 W		Mjörn (L.), Swe.	164	57.55 N	12.22 E
Mina (R.), Alg. (mē′nä)	171	35.24 N	0.51 E		Mirandela, Port. (mē-rän-dä′lá)	170	41.28 N	7.10 W		Mjösa, Nor. (myûsä)	164	60.41 N	11.25 E
Minago (R.), Can. (mĭ-nä′gō)	101	54.25 N	98.45 W										
Minakuchi, Jap. (mē′nä-kōō′chē)	205	34.59 N	136.06 E										

PLACE (Pronounciation)	PAGE	Lat. °'	Long. °'
Mkalama, Tan.	226	4.07 S	34.38 E
Mkomazi (R.), S. Afr.	227c	30.10 S	30.30 E
Mkushi, Zambia	231	13.40 S	29.20 E
Mkwaja, Tan.	231	5.47 S	38.51 E
Mladá Boleslav, Czech. (mlä'dä bô'lĕ-sláf)	166	50.26 N	14.52 E
Mlala Hills, Tan.	231	6.47 S	31.45 E
Mlanje Mts., Malawi	231	15.55 S	35.30 E
Mlawa, Pol. (mwä'vá)	167	53.07 N	20.25 E
Mlazi (R.), S. Afr.	227c	29.52 S	30.42 E
Mljet (I.), Yugo. (mlyĕt)	173	42.40 N	17.45 E
Mmabatho, Boph.	222	25.42 S	25.43 E
Mnevniki (Neigh.), Sov. Un.	66b	55.45 N	37.28 E
Mo (R.), Togo	228	9.05 N	0.55 E
Moa (R.), S. L.	228	7.40 N	11.15 W
Moab, Ut. (mō'ăb)	121	38.35 N	109.35 W
Moanda, Gabon	226	1.37 S	13.09 E
Moapa River Ind. Res., Nv. (mō-ăp'á)	120	36.44 N	115.01 W
Moa, Pulau (I.), Indon.	207	8.30 S	128.30 E
Moar L., Can. (môr)	101	52.00 N	95.09 W
Moba, Nig.	71d	6.27 N	3.28 E
Mobaye, Cen. Afr. Rep. (mô-bä'y')	230	4.19 N	21.11 E
Mobayi-Mbongo, Zaire	225	4.14 N	21.11 E
Moberly, Mo. (mō'bẽr-lĭ)	123	39.24 N	92.25 W
Moberly (R.), Can.	99	55.40 N	121.15 W
Mobile, Al. (mô-bēl')	126	30.42 N	88.03 W
Mobile B., Al.	126	30.26 N	87.56 W
Mobile (R.), Al.	126	31.15 N	88.00 W
Mobridge, SD (mō'brĭj)	114	45.32 N	100.26 W
Moca, Dom. Rep. (mô'kä)	135	19.25 N	70.35 W
Moçambique, Moz. (mō-säN-bē'kĕ)	231	15.03 S	40.42 E
Moçâmedes, Ang. (mô-zá-mĕ-dĕs)	230	15.10 S	12.09 E
Moçâmedes (Reg.), Ang.	226	16.00 S	12.15 E
Mocha, Yemen (mō'kä)	192	13.11 N	43.20 E
Mochitlán, Mex. (mō-chē-tlän')	130	17.10 N	99.19 W
Mochudi, Bots. (mō-chōō'dê)	226	24.13 S	26.07 E
Mocímboa da Praia, Moz. (mô-sē'ĕm-bô-á prä'ēá)	231	11.20 S	40.21 E
Moclips, Wa.	116	47.14 N	124.13 W
Mococa, Braz. (mô-kô'ká)	141a	21.29 S	46.58 W
Môco, Serra (Mts.), Arg.	230	12.25 S	15.10 E
Moctezuma, Mex. (môk'tā-zōō'mä)	130	22.44 N	101.06 W
Mocuba, Moz.	231	16.50 S	36.59 E
Modderbee, S. Afr.	71b	26.10 S	28.24 E
Modderfontein, S. Afr.	227b	26.06 S	28.10 E
Modena, It. (mô'dĕ-nä)	172	44.38 N	10.54 E
Modesto, Ca. (mô-dĕs'tō)	120	37.39 N	121.00 W
Modica, It. (mô-dē-kä)	159	36.50 N	14.43 E
Modjeska, Ca.	59	33.43 N	117.37 W
Mödling, Aust. (mûd'lĭng)	157e	48.06 N	16.17 E
Moelv, Nor.	164	60.55 N	10.40 E
Moengo, Sur.	143	5.43 N	54.19 W
Moenkopi, Az.	121	36.07 N	111.13 W
Moers, F.R.G. (mûrs)	169c	51.27 N	6.38 E
Moffat Tun., Co. (môf'ăt)	122	39.52 N	106.20 W
Mofolo, S. Afr.	71b	26.14 S	27.53 E
Mogadore, Oh. (mŏg-á-dōr')	113d	41.04 N	81.23 E
Mogaung, Bur. (mô-gä'ōōng)	198	25.30 N	96.52 E
Mogi das Cruzes, Braz. (mô-gê-däs-krōō'sĕs)	141a	23.33 S	46.10 W
Mogi-Guaçu (R.), Braz. (mô-gê-gwá'sōō)	141a	22.06 S	47.12 W
Mogilëv, Sov. Un. (mô-gē-lyôf')	174	53.53 N	30.22 E
Mogilëv (Oblast), Sov. Un. (mô-gē-lyôf')	174	53.28 N	30.15 E
Mogilëv-Podol'skiy, Sov. Un. (mô-gê-lyôf') (pô-dôl'skĭ)	175	48.27 N	27.51 E
Mogilno, Pol. (mô-gēl'nō)	167	52.38 N	17.58 W
Mogi-Mirim, Braz. (mô-gē-mē-rē'N)	141a	22.26 S	46.57 W
Mogincual, Moz.	231	15.35 S	40.25 E
Mogok, Bur. (mô-gōk')	198	23.14 N	96.38 E
Mogollon, NM (mō-gô-yōn')	121	33.25 N	108.45 W
Mogollon, Plat., Az. (mō-gô-yōn')	121	34.26 N	111.17 W
Mogol R., S. Afr. (mô-gŏl)	223d	24.12 S	27.55 E
Moguer, Sp. (mô-gĕr')	170	37.15 N	6.50 W
Mohács, Hung. (mô'hâch)	167	45.59 N	18.38 E
Mohale's Hoek, Leso.	227c	30.09 S	27.28 E
Mohall, ND (mō'hôl)	114	48.46 N	101.29 W
Mohammadia, Alg.	171	35.35 N	0.05 E
Mohave (L.), Nv. (mô-hä'vä)	120	35.23 N	114.40 W
Mohawk (R.), NY (mō'hôk)	111	43.15 N	75.20 W
Mohe, China (mwo-hŭ)	199	53.33 N	122.30 E
Moheli (I.), Comoros (mô-â-lē') (mô-hä'lê)	227	12.23 S	43.38 E
Mohenjo-Dero (Ruins), Pak.	196	27.20 N	68.10 E
Mohili (Neigh.), India	67e	19.06 N	72.53 E
Mõisaküla, Sov. Un. (mẽẽ'sá-kü'lá)	165	58.07 N	25.12 E
Moisie (R.), Can. (mwá-zē')	105	50.35 N	66.25 W
Moissac, Fr. (mwä-sák')	168	44.07 N	1.05 E
Moita, Port. (mô-ē'tá)	171b	38.39 N	9.00 W
Mojave, Ca.	120	35.06 N	118.09 W
Mojave (R.), Ca. (mô-hä'vä)	120	34.46 N	117.24 W
Mojave Desert, Ca.	120	35.05 N	117.30 W
Mokelumne (R.), Ca. (mō-kê-lŭm'nê)	120	38.30 N	120.17 W
Mokhotlong, Leso.	227c	29.18 S	29.06 E
Mokp'o, Kor. (môk'pō')	204	34.50 N	126.30 E
Moksha (R.), Sov. Un. (môk-shä')	178	54.40 N	43.20 E
Mol, Bel.	157a	51.21 N	5.09 E
Molat (I.), Yugo. (mô'lät)	172	44.15 N	14.40 E
Moldavia (Reg.), Rom.	167	47.20 N	27.12 E
Moldavian S. S. R., Sov. Un.	176	48.00 N	28.00 E
Molde, Nor. (môl'dĕ)	164	62.44 N	7.15 E
Moldova R., Rom.	167	47.17 N	26.27 E
Moldoveanu (Mtn.), Rom.	173	45.33 N	24.38 E
Molepolole, Bots. (mō-lā-pô-lō'lā)	226	24.15 S	25.33 W
Molfetta, It. (môl-fĕt'tä)	172	41.11 N	16.38 E
Molina, Chile (mō-lē'nä)	141b	35.07 S	71.17 W
Molina de Aragón, Sp. (mô-lē'nä dĕ ä-rä-gô'n)	170	41.40 N	1.54 W
Molina de Segura, Sp. (mô-lē'nä dĕ sĕ-gōō'rä)	170	38.03 N	1.07 W
Moline, Il. (mô-lēn')	115	41.31 N	90.34 W
Molino de Rosas, Mex.	60a	19.22 N	99.13 W
Moliro, Zaire	231	8.13 S	30.34 E
Moliterno, It. (mōl-ê-tĕr'nō)	172	40.13 N	15.54 W
Molins de Rey, Sp.	65e	41.25 N	2.01 E
Möllen, F.R.G.	63	51.35 N	6.42 E
Mollendo, Peru (mô-lyĕn'dō)	142	17.02 S	71.59 W
Moller, Port, Ak. (pōrt mōl'ẽr)	107	56.18 N	161.30 W
Mölndal, Swe. (mûln'däl)	164	57.39 N	12.01 E
Molochnaya (R.), Sov. Un. (mô-lôch'ná-yá) (rē-kä')	175	47.05 N	35.22 E
Molochnoye, Ozero (L.), Sov. Un. (ô'zē-rô mô-lôch'nô-yĕ)	175	46.35 N	35.32 E
Molodechno, Sov. Un. (mô-lô-dĕch'nô)	174	54.18 N	26.57 E
Molodechno (Oblast), Sov. Un.	174	54.27 N	27.38 E
Molody Tud, Sov. Un. (mō-lō-dô'ē tōō'd)	182b	55.17 N	37.31 E
Mologa (R.), Sov. Un. (mô-lô'gá)	174	58.05 N	35.43 E
Molokai (I.), Hi. (mō-lô kä'ē)	106a	21.15 N	157.05 E
Molokcha R., Sov. Un. (mô'lôk-chä)	182b	56.15 N	38.29 E
Molopo (R.), S. Afr. (mō-lō-pô)	226	27.45 S	20.45 E
Molson L., Can. (mōl'sŭn)	101	54.12 N	96.45 W
Molteno, S. Afr. (môl-tā'nô)	227c	31.24 S	26.23 E
Moma, Moz.	231	16.44 S	39.14 E
Mombasa, Ken. (mōm-bä'sä)	231	4.03 N	39.40 E
Mombetsu, Jap. (mōm'bĕt-sōō')	204	44.21 N	142.48 E
Momboyo (R.), Zaire	230	0.20 S	19.20 E
Momence, Il. (mô-mĕns')	113a	41.09 N	87.40 W
Momostenango, Guat. (mô-mŏs-tā-näŋ'gô)	132	15.02 N	91.25 W
Momotombo, Nic.	132	12.25 N	86.43 W
Mompog Pass, Phil. (mŏm-pŏg')	207a	13.35 N	122.09 E
Mompos, Col. (mōm-pōs')	142	8.05 N	74.30 W
Møn (I.), Den. (mûn)	164	54.54 N	12.30 E
Monaca, Pa. (mŏ-nă'kō)	113e	40.41 N	80.17 W
Monaco, Eur. (mŏn'á-kō)	159	43.43 N	7.47 E
Monaghan, Ire. (mŏ'á-găn)	162	54.16 N	7.20 W
Mona Pass, N.A. (mō'nä)	129	18.00 N	68.10 W
Monarch Mtn., Can. (mŏn'ẽrk)	98	51.41 N	125.53 W
Monashee Mts., Can. (mŏ-nă'shē)	99	50.30 N	118.30 W
Monastir, Tun. (mōn-ás-tēr')	159	35.49 N	10.56 E
Monastir, see Bitola			
Monastyrishche, Sov. Un. (mô-nás-tē-rēsh'chå)	175	48.57 N	29.53 E
Monastyrshchina, Sov. Un. (mô-nás-tẽrsh'chĭ-ná)	174	54.19 N	31.49 E
Moncada, Sp.	65e	41.29 N	2.11 E
Monçao, Braz. (mon-souN')	143	3.39 S	45.23 W
Moncayo (Mtn.), Sp. (môn-kä'yō)	170	41.44 N	1.48 W
Monchegorsk, Sov. Un. (mōn'chĕ-gôrsk)	178	69.00 N	33.35 E
Mönchengladbach, F.R.G. (mûn'кĕn gläd'bäк)	169c	51.12 N	6.28 E
Moncique, Serra de (Mts.), Port. (sĕr'rä dä môn-chē'kĕ)	170	37.22 N	8.37 W
Monclova, Mex. (môn-klō'vä)	124	26.53 N	101.25 W
Moncton, Can. (mŭŋk'tŭn)	104	46.06 N	64.47 W
Mondego, Cabo (C.), Port. (ká'bō môn-dā'gōō)	170	40.12 N	8.55 W
Mondêgo (R.), Port. (môn-dĕ'gō)	170	40.10 N	8.36 W
Mondeor, S. Afr.	71b	26.17 S	28.00 E
Mondombe, Zaire (môn-dôm'bå)	226	0.45 S	23.06 E
Mondoñedo, Sp. (môn-dô-nyā'dō)	170	43.35 N	7.18 W
Mondovì, It. (mōn-dô'vē')	172	44.23 N	7.53 E
Mondovi, Wi. (mŏn-dō'vĭ)	115	44.35 N	91.42 W
Monee, Il. (mŏ-nĭ)	113a	41.25 N	87.45 W
Monessen, Pa. (mŏ'nĕs'sĕn)	113e	40.09 N	79.53 W
Monett, Mo. (mô-nĕt')	123	36.55 N	93.55 W
Monforte de Lemos, Sp. (môn-fôr'tä dĕ lĕ'môs)	170	42.30 N	7.30 W
Monga, Chad.	229	4.12 N	22.49 E
Mongala R., Zaire (mōn-gál'á)	225	3.20 N	21.30 E
Mongalla, Sud.	225	5.11 N	31.46 E
Mongat, Sp.	65e	41.28 N	2.17 E
Monghyr, India (mŏn-gēr')	196	25.23 N	86.34 E
Mongo, Chad	194	12.11 N	18.42 E
Mongo (R.), S.L.	228	9.50 N	11.50 W
Mongolia, Asia (mŏŋ-gō'lĭ-á)	190	46.00 N	100.00 E
Mongos, Chaîne des (Mts.), Cen. Afr. Rep.	225	8.04 N	21.59 E
Mongoumba, Cen. Afr. Rep. (mŏŋ-gōōm'bá)	230	3.38 N	18.36 E
Mongu, Zambia (mŏŋ-gōō')	230	15.15 S	23.09 E
Monken Hadley (Neigh.), Eng.	62	51.40 N	0.11 W
Monkey Bay, Malawi	231	14.05 S	34.55 E
Monkey River, Belize (mŭŋ'kĭ)	132a	16.22 N	88.33 W
Monkland, Can. (mŭngk-lănd)	95c	45.12 N	74.52 W
Monkoto, Zaire (mōn-kō'tō)	230	1.38 S	20.39 E
Monmouth, Il. (mŏn'mŭth)(mŏn'mouth)	123	40.54 N	90.38 W
Monmouth Junction, NJ (mŏn'mouth jŭngk'shŭn)	112a	40.23 N	74.33 W
Monmouth Mtn., Can. (mŏn'mŭth)	98	51.00 N	123.47 W
Mono (L.), Can. (mō'nō)	120	38.04 N	119.00 W
Mono (R.), Togo	228	7.20 N	1.25 E
Monon, In. (mō'nŏn)	110	40.55 N	86.55 W
Monongah, WV (mō-nŏŋ'gá)	111	39.25 N	80.10 W
Monongahela, Pa. (mô-nŏn-gá-hē'lá)	113e	40.11 N	79.55 W
Monongahela (R.), Pa.	57b	40.27 N	80.00 W
Monongahela (R.), WV	111	39.30 N	80.10 W
Monopoli, It. (mô-nô'pô-lê)	173	40.55 N	17.17 E
Monóvar, Sp. (mô-nō'vär)	171	38.26 N	0.50 W
Monreale, It. (mōn-rå-ä'lā)	172	38.04 N	13.15 E
Monroe, Ga. (mŭn-rō')	126	33.47 N	83.43 W
Monroe, La.	125	32.30 N	92.06 W
Monroe, Mi.	110	41.55 N	83.25 W
Monroe, NC	127	34.58 N	80.34 W
Monroe, NY	112a	41.19 N	74.11 W
Monroe, Ut.	121	38.35 N	112.10 W
Monroe, Wa.	118a	47.52 N	121.58 W
Monroe, Wi.	115	42.35 N	89.40 W
Monroe (L.), Fl.	127	28.50 N	81.15 W
Monroe City, Mo.	123	39.38 N	91.41 W
Monroeville, Al. (mŭn-rō'vĭl)	126	31.33 N	87.19 W
Monròvia, Ca. (mŏn-rō'vĭ-á)	119a	34.09 N	118.00 W
Monrovia, Lib.	228	6.18 N	10.47 W
Mons, Bel. (môN')	163	50.29 N	3.55 E
Monson, Me. (mŏn'sŭn)	104	45.17 N	69.28 W
Mönsterås, Swe. (mŭn'stĕr-ôs)	164	57.04 N	16.24 E
Montagh Ata (Mt.), China	198	38.26 N	75.23 E
Montagne Tremblante Prov. Pk., Can.	109	46.30 N	75.51 W
Montague, Can. (mŏn'tá-gū)	105	46.10 N	62.39 W
Montague, Mi.	110	43.30 N	86.25 W
Montague (I.), Ak.	107	60.10 N	147.00 W
Montalbán, Ven. (mōnt-äl-bän)	143b	10.14 N	68.19 W
Montalbancito, Ven.	61a	10.28 N	66.59 W
Montalcone, It. (mōn-täl-kô'nē)	172	45.49 N	13.30 E
Montalegre, Port. (mōn-tä-lā'grĕ)	170	41.49 N	7.48 W
Montana (State), U.S. (mŏn-tăn'á)	108	47.10 N	111.50 W
Montánchez, Sp. (môn-tän'chåth)	170	39.18 N	6.09 W
Montara, Ca.	58b	37.33 N	122.31 W
Montargis, Fr. (môN-tàr-zhē')	168	47.59 N	2.42 E
Montataire, Fr. (môN-tá-târ)	169b	49.15 N	2.26 E
Montauban, Fr. (môN-tô-bäN')	168	44.01 N	1.22 E
Montauk, NY	111	41.03 N	71.57 W
Montauk Pt., NY (mŏn-tôk')	111	41.05 N	71.55 W
Montbanch, Sp. (mônt-bän'ch)	171	41.20 N	1.08 E
Montbard, Fr. (môN-bàr')	168	47.40 N	4.19 E
Montbéliard, Fr. (môN-bā-lyàr')	169	47.32 N	6.45 E
Mont Belvieu, Tx. (mŏnt bĕl'vū)	125a	29.51 N	94.53 W
Montbrison, Fr. (môN-brē-zoN')	168	45.38 N	4.06 E
Montceau, Fr. (môN-sō')	168	46.39 N	4.22 E
Montclair, Ca.	59	34.06 N	117.41 W
Montclair, NJ (mŏnt-klâr')	112a	40.49 N	74.13 W
Mont-de-Marsan, Fr. (môN-dē-màr-säN')	168	43.54 N	0.32 W
Montdidier, Fr. (môN-dē-dyā')	168	49.42 N	2.33 E
Monte, Arg. (mŏ'n-tĕ)	141c	35.25 S	58.49 W
Monteagudo, Bol. (mōn'tå-ä-gōō'dhō)	142	19.49 S	63.48 W
Montebello, Ca. (mŏn-tē-bĕl'ō)	119a	34.01 N	118.06 W
Montebello, Can.	95c	45.40 N	74.56 W
Monte Bello (Is.), Austl.	214	20.30 S	114.10 E
Monte Caseros, Arg. (mŏ'n-tĕ-kä-sĕ'rôs)	144	30.16 S	57.39 W
Monte Chingolo (Neigh.), Arg.	60d	34.45 S	58.20 W
Mont Ecillos, Cord. de (Mts.), Hond. (kôr-dĕl-yĕ'rä dĕ mô'nt ĕ-sĕ'l-yōs)	132	14.19 N	87.52 W
Monte Cristi, Dom. Rep. (mŏ'n-tĕ-krē's-tē)	135	19.50 N	71.40 W
Montecristo, I. di, It. (mōn'tå-krēs'tō)	172	42.20 N	10.19 E
Monte Escobedo, Mex. (mōn'tå ĕs-kô-bā'dhō)	130	22.18 N	103.34 W
Monteforte Irpino, It. (môn-tĕ-fô'r-tĕ ē'r-pē'nō)	171c	40.39 N	14.42 E
Montefrío, Sp. (mōn-tå-frē'ō)	170	37.20 N	4.02 W
Montego Bay, Jam. (mŏn-tē'gō)	134	18.30 N	77.55 W
Monte Grande, Arg. (mŏ'n-tĕ grän'dĕ)	144a	34.34 S	58.28 W
Montelavar, Port. (mōn-tĕ-là-vär')	171b	38.51 N	9.20 W
Montélimar, Fr. (môN-tā-lē-mär')	168	44.33 N	4.47 E
Montellano, Sp. (mōn-tå-lyä'nō)	170	37.00 N	5.34 W
Montello, Wi. (mŏn-tĕl'ō)	115	43.47 N	89.20 W
Montemorelos, Mex. (mōn'tå-mō-rā'lōs)	124	25.14 N	99.50 W
Montemor-o-Novo, Port. (mōN-tĕ-môr'ōō-nō'vōō)	170	38.39 N	8.11 W
Montenegro (Reg.), **see Crna Gora**			
Montepuez, Moz.	231	13.07 S	39.00 E
Montepulciano, It. (môn'tå-pōōl-chä'nō)	172	43.05 N	11.48 E
Montereau-faut-Yonne, Fr. (môN-t'rō'fō-yôn')	168	48.24 N	2.57 E
Monterey, Ca. (mŏn-tĕ-rā')	120	36.36 N	121.53 W
Monterey, Tn.	126	36.06 N	85.15 W
Monterey B., Ca.	120	36.48 N	122.01 W
Monterey Park, Ca.	119a	34.04 N	118.08 W
Montería, Col. (mōn-tā-rā'ä)	142	8.47 N	75.57 W
Monteros, Arg. (môn-tĕ'rôs)	144	27.14 S	65.29 W
Monterotondo, It. (môn-tĕ-rô-tô'n-dō)	171d	42.03 N	12.39 E
Monterrey, Mex. (mōn-tĕr-rā')	124	25.43 N	100.19 W
Montesano, Wa. (mŏn-tē-sä'nō)	116	46.59 N	123.35 W
Monte Sant' Angelo, It. (mô'n-tĕ sän ä'n-gzhĕ-lô)	172	41.43 N	15.59 E
Montes Claros, Braz. (môn-tĕs-klä'rôs)	143	16.44 S	43.41 W
Montespaccato (Neigh.), It.	66c	41.54 N	12.23 E
Montevallo, Al. (mŏn-tē-văl'ō)	126	33.05 N	86.49 W
Montevarchi, It. (mōn-tå-vär'kē)	172	43.30 N	11.45 E
Monteverde Nuovo (Neigh.), It.	66c	41.51 N	12.27 E
Montevideo, Ur. (mōn'tå-vē-dhā'ō)	141c	34.50 S	56.10 W
Monte Vista, Co. (mŏn'tĕ vĭs'tá)	121	37.35 N	106.10 W
Montezuma, Ga. (mŏn-tē-zōō'má)	126	32.17 N	84.00 W
Montezuma Castle Natl. Mon., Az.	121	34.38 N	111.50 W
Montfermeil, Fr.	64c	48.54 N	2.34 E
Montflorit, Sp.	65e	41.29 N	2.08 E
Montfoort, Neth.	157a	52.02 N	4.56 E
Montfor-l'Amaury, Fr. (môN-fôr'lä-mō-rē')	169b	48.47 N	1.49 E
Montfort, Fr. (mōn-fôr)	168	48.09 N	1.58 W
Montgeron, Fr.	64c	48.42 N	2.27 E
Montgomery, Al. (mŏnt-gŭm'ẽr-ĭ)	126	32.23 N	86.17 W
Montgomery, WV	110	38.10 N	81.25 W
Montgomery City, Mo.	123	38.58 N	91.29 W
Montgomery Knolls, Md.	56c	39.14 N	76.48 W
Monticello, Ar. (mŏn-tĭ-sĕl'ō)	123	33.38 N	91.47 W
Monticello, Fl.	126	30.32 N	83.53 W
Monticello, Ga.	126	33.00 N	83.11 W
Monticello, Ia.	115	42.14 N	91.13 W
Monticello, Il.	110	40.05 N	88.35 W

PLACE (Pronounciation)	PAGE	Lat. °′	Long. °′
Monticello, In.	110	40.40 N	86.50 W
Monticello, Ky.	126	36.47 N	84.50 W
Monticello, Me.	104	46.19 N	67.53 W
Monticello, Mn.	115	45.18 N	93.48 W
Monticello, NY	111	41.35 N	74.40 W
Monticello, Ut.	121	37.55 N	109.25 W
Montigny-le-Bretonneux, Fr.	64c	48.46 N	2.02 E
Montigny-lés-Cormeilles, Fr.	64c	48.59 N	2.12 E
Montijo, Port. (môn-tē′zhō)	171b	38.42 N	8.58 W
Montijo, Sp. (môn-tē′hō)	170	38.55 N	6.35 W
Montijo, Bahia (B.), Pan. (bä-ē′ä môn-tē′hō)	133	7.36 N	81.11 W
Mont-Joli, Can. (môɴ zhō-lē′)	104	48.35 N	68.11 W
Montjuich, Castillo de (P. Int.), Sp.	65e	41.22 N	2.10 E
Montluçon, Fr. (môɴ-lü-sôɴ′)	168	46.20 N	2.35 E
Montmagny, Can. (môɴ-mán-yē′)	95b	46.59 N	70.33 W
Montmagny, Fr.	64c	48.58 N	2.21 E
Montmartre (Neigh.), Fr.	64c	48.53 N	2.21 E
Montmorency, Austl.	70b	37.43 S	145.07 E
Montmorency, Fr. (môɴ′mô-räɴ-sē′)	169b	48.59 N	2.19 E
Montmorency (R.), Can. (mŏnt-mô-rĕn′sĭ)	95b	47.30 N	71.10 W
Montmorillon, Fr. (môɴ′mô-rē-yôɴ′)	168	46.26 N	0.50 E
Montone (R.), It. (môn-tô′nĕ)	172	44.03 N	11.45 E
Montoro, Sp. (môn-tō′rô)	170	38.01 N	4.22 W
Montpelier, Id.	117	42.19 N	111.19 W
Montpelier, In. (mŏnt-pēl′yẽr)	110	40.35 N	85.20 W
Montpelier, Oh.	110	41.35 N	84.35 W
Montpelier, Vt.	111	44.20 N	72.35 W
Montpellier, Fr. (môɴ-pĕ-lyā′)	168	43.38 N	3.53 E
Montréal, Can. (mŏn-trē-ôl′)	95a	45.30 N	73.35 W
Montreal (R.), Can.	103	47.50 N	80.30 W
Montreal (R.), Can.	102	47.15 N	84.20 W
Montreal L., Can.	100	54.20 N	105.40 W
Montréal-Nord, Can.	95a	45.36 N	73.38 W
Montréal-Ouest, Can.	54b	45.27 N	73.39 W
Montreuil, Fr.	64c	48.52 N	2.27 E
Montreux, Switz. (môn-trû′)	166	46.26 N	6.52 E
Montrose, Austl.	70b	37.49 S	145.21 E
Montrose, Ca. (mŏnt-rōz)	119a	34.13 N	118.13 W
Montrose, Co. (mŏn-trōz′)	121	38.30 N	107.55 W
Montrose, Oh.	113d	41.08 N	81.38 W
Montrose, Pa. (mŏnt-rōz′)	111	41.50 N	75.50 W
Montrose, Scot.	162	56.45 N	2.25 W
Montrose Hill, Pa.	57b	40.30 N	79.51 W
Montrouge, Fr.	64c	48.49 N	2.19 E
Mont-Royal, Can.	95a	47.31 N	73.39 W
Mont Saint Martin, Fr. (môɴ sáɴ mär-táɴ′)	169	49.34 N	6.13 E
Montserrat, N.A. (mŏnt-sĕ-răt′)	129	16.48 N	63.15 W
Monts, Pointe des (Pt.), Can. (pwăɴt′ dā môɴ′)	104	49.19 N	67.22 W
Montvale, NJ (mŏnt-vāl′)	112a	41.02 N	74.01 W
Monywa, Bur. (mŏn′yōō-wȧ)	206	22.02 N	95.16 E
Monza, It. (mōn′tsä)	172	45.34 N	9.17 E
Monzón, Sp. (mōn-thōn′)	171	41.54 N	1.09 E
Moóca (Neigh.), Braz.	61d	23.33 S	46.35 W
Moody, Tx. (mōō′dĭ)	125	31.18 N	97.20 W
Mooi (R.), S. Afr. (mō′ĭ)	223d	26.34 S	27.03 E
Mooi (R.), S. Afr.	227c	29.00 S	30.15 E
Mooirivier, S. Afr.	227c	29.14 S	29.59 E
Moolap, Austl.	211a	38.11 S	144.26 E
Moonachie, NJ	55	40.50 N	74.03 W
Moonta, Austl. (mōōn′tȧ)	216	34.05 S	137.42 E
Moora, Austl. (mōōr′ȧ)	214	30.35 S	116.12 E
Moorabbin, Austl.	70b	37.56 S	145.02 E
Moorcroft, Wy. (mōr′krôft)	117	44.17 N	104.59 W
Moore (L.), Austl. (mōr)	214	29.50 S	128.12 E
Moorebank, Austl.	70a	33.56 S	150.56 E
Moorenweis, F.R.G. (mō′rĕn-vīz)	157d	48.10 N	11.05 E
Moore Res., Vt.-NH	111	44.20 N	72.10 W
Moorestown, NJ (morz′toun)	112f	39.58 N	74.56 W
Mooresville, In. (mōrz′vĭl)	113g	39.37 N	86.22 W
Mooresville, NC	127	35.34 N	80.48 W
Moorhead, Mn. (mōr′hĕd)	114	46.52 N	96.44 W
Moorhead, Ms.	126	33.25 N	90.30 W
Moorland (Plain), see Landes			
Mooroolbark, Austl.	70b	37.47 S	145.19 E
Moorside, Eng.	64b	53.34 N	2.04 W
Moose (L.), Can. (mōōs)	96	54.14 N	99.28 W
Moose (R.), Can.	97	51.01 N	80.42 W
Moose Creek, Can.	95c	45.16 N	74.58 W
Moosehead, Me. (mōōs′hĕd)	104	45.37 N	69.15 W
Moose I., Can.	101	51.50 N	97.09 W
Moose Jaw, Can. (mōōs jô)	100	50.23 N	105.32 W
Moose Jaw (Cr.), Can.	100	50.34 N	105.17 W
Moose Lake, Can.	101	53.40 N	100.28 W
Moose Mtn., Can.	101	49.45 N	102.37 W
Moose Mtn. Cr., Can.	100	49.12 N	102.10 W
Moosilauke (Mtn.), NH (mōō-sĭ-lä′kē)	111	44.00 N	71.50 W
Moosinning, F.R.G. (mō′zē-nĕng)	157d	48.17 N	11.51 E
Moosomin, Can. (mōō′sō-mĭn)	101	50.07 N	101.40 W
Moosonee, Can. (mōō′sō-nē)	97	51.20 N	80.44 W
Mopti, Mali (mŏp′tē)	228	14.30 N	4.12 W
Moquegua, Peru (mô-kā′gwä)	142	17.15 S	70.54 W
Mór, Hung. (mōr)	167	47.51 N	18.14 E
Mora, India	197b	18.54 N	72.56 E
Mora, Mn. (mō′rȧ)	115	45.52 N	93.18 W
Mora, NM	122	35.58 N	105.17 W
Mora, Sp. (mō-rä)	170	39.42 N	3.45 W
Mora, Swe. (mō′rä)	164	61.00 N	14.29 E
Morādābād, India (mô-rä-dä-bäd′)	196	28.57 N	78.48 E
Morales, Guat. (mô-rä′lēs)	132	15.29 N	88.46 W
Moramanga, Mad. (mō-rä-mäŋ′gä)	227	18.48 S	48.09 E
Morangis, Fr.	64c	48.42 N	2.20 E
Morant Pt., Jam. (mô-rănt′)	135	17.55 N	76.10 W
Morata de Tajuña, Sp. (mô-rä′tä dā tä-hōō′nyä)	171a	40.14 N	3.27 W
Moratuwa, Sri Lanka	197	6.35 N	79.59 E
Morava (Moravia) (Prov.), Czech. (mô′rä-vä)(mô-rā′vĭ-ȧ)	167	49.21 N	16.57 E
Morava R., Czech.	166	49.53 N	16.53 E
Moravia, see Morava			
Morawhanna, Guy. (mô-rȧ-hwä′nȧ)	143	8.12 N	59.33 W
Moray Firth, Scot. (mŭr′å)	162	57.41 N	3.55 W
Mörbylånga, Swe. (mûr′bü-lôŋ′gå)	164	56.32 N	16.23 E
Morden, Can. (môr′dĕn)	101	49.11 N	98.05 W
Mordialloc, Austl. (môr-dĭ-ăl′ŏk)	211a	38.00 S	145.05 E
Mordvin, (A.S.S.R.), Sov. Un.	178	54.18 N	43.50 E
Moreau (R.), SD (mô-rō′)	114	45.13 N	102.22 W
More, Ben (Mtn.), Scot. (bĕn môr)	162	58.09 N	5.01 W
Moree, Austl. (mō′rē)	216	29.20 S	149.50 E
Morehead, Ky.	110	38.10 N	83.25 W
Morehead City, NC (mōr′hĕd)	127	34.43 N	76.43 W
Morehouse, Mo. (mōr′hous)	123	36.49 N	89.41 W
Morelia, Mex. (mô-rā′lyä)	130	19.43 N	101.12 W
Morella, Sp. (mô-rāl′yä)	171	40.38 N	0.07 W
Morelos, Mex. (mô-rā′lōs)	130	22.46 N	102.36 W
Morelos, Mex.	131a	19.41 N	99.29 W
Morelos, Mex.	124	28.24 N	100.51 W
Morelos (Neigh.), Mex.	60a	19.27 N	99.07 W
Morelos, R., Mex.	124	25.27 N	99.35 W
Morena, Sierra (Mt.), Ca. (syĕr′rä mô-rā′nä)	118b	37.24 N	122.19 W
Morena, Sierra (Mts.), Sp. (syĕr′rä mô-rā′nä)	170	38.15 N	5.45 W
Morenci, Az. (mô-rĕn′sĭ)	121	33.05 N	109.25 W
Morenci, Mi.	110	41.50 N	84.50 W
Moreno, Arg. (mô-rĕ′nō)	144a	34.39 S	58.47 W
Moreno, Ca.	119a	33.55 N	117.09 W
Mores (I.), Ba. (mōrz)	134	26.20 N	77.35 W
Moresby (I.), Can. (mōrz′bĭ)	118b	48.43 N	123.15 W
Moresby I., Can.	96	52.50 N	131.55 W
Moreton, Eng.	64a	53.24 N	3.07 W
Moreton B., Austl. (môr′tŭn)	216	27.12 S	153.10 E
Moreton (I.), Austl. (môr′tŭn)	216	26.53 S	152.42 E
Morewood, Can. (mōr′wood)	95c	45.11 N	75.17 W
Morgan, Mt. (môr′găn)	117	48.55 N	107.56 W
Morgan, Ut.	117	41.04 N	111.42 W
Morgan City, La.	125	29.41 N	91.11 W
Morganfield, Ky. (môr′găn-fēld)	110	37.40 N	87.55 W
Morgan's Bay, S. Afr.	227c	32.42 S	28.19 E
Morganton, NC (môr′găn-tŭn)	127	35.44 N	81.42 W
Morgantown, WV (môr′găn-toun)	111	39.40 N	79.55 W
Morga Ra, Afg.	193a	34.02 N	70.38 E
Morgenzon, S. Afr. (môr′gănt-sŏn)	223d	26.44 S	29.39 E
Moriac, Austl.	211a	38.15 S	14.12 E
Morice L., Can.	98	54.00 N	127.37 W
Moriguchi, Jap. (mō′rē-gōō′chē)	205b	34.44 N	135.34 E
Morinville, Can. (mō′rĭn-vĭl)	95g	53.48 N	113.39 W
Morioka, Jap. (mō′rē-ō′kȧ)	204	39.40 N	141.21 E
Morivione (Neigh.), It.	65c	45.26 N	9.12 E
Morkoka (R.), Sov. Un. (môr-kô′kȧ)	181	65.35 N	111.00 E
Morlaix, Fr. (mōr-lĕ′)	168	48.36 N	3.48 W
Morley, Can. (mōr′lē)	95e	51.10 N	114.51 W
Morley Green, Eng.	64b	53.20 N	2.16 W
Mormant, Fr.	169	48.35 N	2.54 E
Morne Diablotin, Mt. Dominica (môrn dē-ȧ-blô-tăɴ′)	133b	15.31 N	61.24 W
Morne Gimie, Mt., Saint Lucia (môrn′ zhē-mē′)	133b	13.53 N	61.03 W
Morningside, Md.	56d	38.50 N	76.53 W
Mornington, Austl.	211a	38.13 S	145.02 E
Morobe, Pap. N. Gui.	207	8.03 S	147.45 E
Morocco, Afr. (mô-rŏk′ō)	222	32.00 N	7.00 W
Morogoro, Tan. (mō-rō-gō′rō)	231	6.49 S	37.40 E
Moroleón, Mex. (mô-rō-lā-ōn′)	130	20.07 N	101.15 W
Morombe, Mad. (mōō-rōōm′bā)	227	21.39 S	43.34 E
Morón, Arg. (mo-rō′n)	144a	34.24 S	58.37 W
Morón, Cuba (mô-rōn′)	134	22.05 N	78.35 W
Morón, Ven. (mô-rō′n)	143b	10.29 N	68.11 W
Morondava, Mad. (mō-rōn-dä′vȧ)	227	20.17 S	44.18 E
Morón de la Frontera, Sp. (mô-rōn′dā lä frōn-tā′rä)	170	37.08 N	5.20 W
Morongo Ind. Res., Ca. (mō-rôŋ′gō)	120	33.54 N	116.47 W
Moroni, Comoros	226	11.41 S	43.16 E
Moroni, Ut. (mō-rō′nĭ)	121	39.30 N	111.40 W
Morotai (I.), Indon. (mō-rō-tä′ē)	207	2.12 N	128.30 E
Moroto, Ug.	231	2.32 N	34.39 E
Morozovsk, Sov. Un.	179	48.20 N	41.50 E
Morrill, Ne. (mŏr′ĭl)	114	41.59 N	103.54 W
Morrilton, Ar. (mŏr′ĭl-tŭn)	123	35.09 N	92.42 W
Morrinhos, Braz. (mô-rēn′yōzh)	143	17.45 S	48.56 W
Morris, Can. (mŏr′ĭs)	101	49.21 N	97.22 W
Morris, Il.	110	41.20 N	88.25 W
Morris, Mn.	114	45.35 N	95.53 W
Morris (R.), Can.	101	49.30 N	97.30 W
Morrison, Il. (mŏr′ĭ-sŭn)	115	41.48 N	89.58 W
Morris Plains, NJ (mŏr′ĭs pláns)	112a	40.49 N	74.29 W
Morris Res., Ca.	119a	34.11 N	117.49 W
Morristown, NJ (mŏr′rĭs-toun)	112a	40.48 N	74.29 W
Morristown, Tn.	126	36.10 N	83.18 W
Morrisville, Pa. (mŏr′ĭs-vĭl)	112f	40.12 N	74.46 W
Morro, Castillo del (P. Int.), Cuba	60b	23.09 N	82.21 W
Morro do Chapéu, Braz. (môr-ōō dōō-shä-pĕ′ōō)	143	11.34 S	41.03 W
Morrow, Oh. (mŏr′ō)	113f	39.21 N	84.07 W
Mors (I.), Den.	164	56.46 N	8.38 E
Mörsenbroich (Neigh.), F.R.G.	63	51.15 N	6.48 E
Morshansk, Sov. Un. (môr-shànsk′)	179	53.25 N	41.35 E
Mortara, It. (môr-tä′rä)	172	45.13 N	8.47 E
Morteros, Arg. (môr-tĕ′tôs)	144	30.47 S	62.00 W
Mortes, Rio das (R.), Braz. (rē′o-däs-mô′r-tĕs)	141a	21.04 S	44.29 W
Mortlake, Austl.	70a	33.51 S	151.07 E
Mortlake (Neigh.), Eng.	62	51.28 N	0.16 W
Morton, Pa.	56b	39.55 N	75.20 W
Morton Grove, Il.	58a	42.02 N	87.47 W
Morton Ind. Res., Mn. (mŏr′tŭn)	115	44.35 N	94.48 W
Mortsel, Bel. (môr-sĕl′)	157a	51.10 N	4.28 E
Morvan (Mts.), Fr. (mōr-väɴ′)	168	47.11 N	4.10 E
Morzhovets (I.), Sov. Un. (mōr′zhô-vyĕts′)	178	66.40 N	42.30 E
Mosal'sk, Sov. Un. (mō-zȧlsk′)	174	54.27 N	34.57 E
Moscavide, Port.	65d	38.47 N	9.06 W
Moscow, Id. (mŏs′kō)	116	46.44 N	116.57 W
Moscow, see Moskva			
Moscow Can., see Imeni Moskvy, Kanal			
Mosel R., F.R.G. (mō′sĕl) (mô-zĕl′)	166	49.49 N	7.00 E
Moses Lake, Wa.	116	47.08 N	119.15 W
Moses L., Wa. (mō′zĕz)	116	47.09 N	119.30 W
Moses R., S. Afr.	223d	25.17 S	29.04 E
Moshchnyy (Is.), Sov. Un. (môsh′chnĭ)	165	59.56 N	28.07 E
Moshi, Tan. (mō′shē)	231	3.21 S	37.20 E
Mosiøen, Nor.	158	65.50 N	13.10 E
Moskháton, Grc.	66d	37.57 N	23.41 E
Moskva (Moscow), Sov. Un. (mŏs-kvä′)	182b	55.45 N	37.37 E
Moskva (Oblast), Sov. Un.	174	55.38 N	36.48 E
Moskva (R.), Sov. Un.	174	55.50 N	37.05 E
Mosman, Austl.	70a	33.49 S	151.14 E
Mosonmagyaróvár, Hung.	167	47.51 N	17.16 E
Mosquitos, Costa de, Nic. (kôs-tä-dĕ-mōs-kē′tō)	133	12.05 N	83.49 W
Mosquitos, Gulfo de los (G.), Pan. (gōō′l-fô-dĕ-lôs-mōs-kē′tōs)	133	9.17 N	80.59 W
Moss, Nor. (môs)	164	59.29 N	10.39 E
Moss Bank, Eng.	64a	53.29 N	2.44 W
Moss Beach, Ca. (môs bēch)	118b	37.32 N	122.31 W
Moss Crest (Mtn.), Va.	56d	38.55 N	77.15 W
Mosselbaai, S. Afr. (mô′sŭl bā)	226	34.06 S	22.23 E
Mossendjo, Con.	230	2.57 S	12.44 E
Mossley, Eng. (môs′lĭ)	156	53.31 N	2.02 W
Mossley Hill (Neigh.), Eng.	64a	53.23 N	2.55 W
Mossoró, Braz. (mō-sô-rōō′)	143	5.13 S	37.14 W
Moss Point, Ms. (môs)	126	30.25 N	88.32 W
Most, Czech. (môst)	166	50.32 N	13.37 E
Mostaganem, Alg. (mŏs′tä-gȧ-nĕm′)	224	36.04 N	0.11 E
Mostar, Yugo. (môs′tär)	173	43.20 N	17.51 E
Móstoles, Sp. (môs-tō′lās)	171a	40.19 N	3.52 W
Mostoos Hills, Can. (mŏs′tōōs)	100	54.50 N	108.45 W
Mosvatnet, Nor.	164	59.55 N	7.50 E
Motagua R., Guat. (mō-tä′gwä)	132	15.29 N	88.39 W
Motala, Swe. (mō-tô′lä)	164	58.34 N	15.00 E
Motherwell, Scot. (mŭdh′ẽr-wĕl)	162	55.45 N	4.05 W
Motril, Sp. (mô-trēl′)	170	36.44 N	3.32 W
Mottingham (Neigh.), Eng.	62	51.26 N	0.03 E
Motul, Mex. (mō-tōō′l)	132a	21.07 N	89.14 W
Mouaskar, Alg.	224	35.25 N	0.08 E
Mouchoir Bk., Ba. (mōō-shwär′)	135	21.35 N	70.40 W
Mouchoir Passage (Str.), Ba.	135	21.05 N	71.05 W
Moudjéria, Mauritania	228	17.53 N	12.20 W
Moudon, Switz.	169	46.40 N	6.47 E
Mouila, Gabon,	230	1.52 S	11.01 E
Mouille Pt., S. Afr.	226a	33.54 S	18.19 E
Moulins, Fr. (mōō-lăɴ′)	168	46.34 N	3.19 E
Moulmein, Bur. (mōl-mān′)	206	16.30 N	97.39 E
Moulouya, Oued (R.), Mor. (mōō-lōō′yȧ)	160	34.07 N	3.27 W
Moultrie, Ga. (mōl′trĭ)	126	31.10 N	83.48 W
Moultrie (Dam), SC	127	33.12 N	80.00 W
Mound City, Mo.	123	40.08 N	95.13 W
Mound City (Mound), Il.	123	37.06 N	89.13 W
Mound City Group Natl. Mon., Oh.	110	39.25 N	83.00 W
Moundon, Chad	229	8.34 N	16.05 E
Moundsville, WV (moundz′vĭl)	110	39.50 N	80.50 W
Mountain Brook, Al. (moun′tĭn brŏŏk)	112h	33.30 N	86.45 W
Mountain Creek L., Tx.	119c	32.43 N	97.03 W
Mountain Grove, Mo. (grōv)	123	37.07 N	92.16 W
Mountain Home, Id. (hōm)	116	43.08 N	115.43 W
Mountain Park, Can. (pärk)	99	52.55 N	117.14 W
Mountain View, Ca. (moun′tĭn vū)	118b	37.25 N	122.07 W
Mountain View, Mo.	123	36.59 N	91.46 W
Mount Airy, NC (âr′ĭ)	127	36.28 N	80.37 W
Mount Athos (Reg.), see Áyion Óros			
Mount Ayliff, S. Afr. (ā′lĭf)	227c	30.48 S	29.24 E
Mount Ayr, Ia. (âr)	115	40.43 N	94.06 W
Mount Baldy, Ca.	59	34.14 N	117.40 W
Mount, C., Lib.	228	6.47 N	11.20 W
Mount Carmel, Il. (kär′mĕl)	110	38.25 N	87.45 W
Mount Carmel, Pa.	111	40.50 N	76.25 W
Mount Caroll, Il.	115	42.05 N	89.55 W
Mount Clemens, Mi. (klĕm′ĕnz)	113b	42.36 N	82.52 W
Mount Dennis (Neigh.), Can.	54c	43.42 N	79.30 W
Mount Desert (I.), Me. (dē-zûrt′)	104	44.15 N	68.08 W
Mount Dora, Fl. (dō′rȧ)	127a	28.45 N	81.38 W
Mount Druitt, Austl.	70a	33.46 S	150.49 E
Mount Duneed, Austl.	211a	38.15 S	144.20 E
Mount Eliza, Austl.	211a	38.11 S	145.05 E
Mount Ephraim, NJ	56b	39.53 N	75.06 W
Mountevideo, Mn. (mŏn′tȧ-vĕ-dhā′ō)	114	44.56 N	95.42 W
Mount Fletcher, S. Afr. (flĕ′chẽr)	227c	30.42 S	28.32 E
Mount Forest, Can. (fŏr′ĕst)	110	44.00 N	80.45 W
Mount Frere, S. Afr. (frâr′)	227c	30.54 S	29.02 E
Mount Gambier, Austl. (găm′bēr)	216	37.30 S	140.53 E
Mount Gilead, Oh. (gĭl′ĕăd)	110	40.30 N	82.50 W
Mount Greenwood (Neigh.), Il.	58a	41.42 N	87.43 W
Mount Healthy, Oh. (hĕlth′ē)	113f	39.14 N	84.32 W
Mount Hebron, Md.	56c	39.18 N	76.50 W
Mount Holly, NJ (hŏl′ĭ)	112f	39.59 N	74.47 W
Mount Hope, Can.	95d	43.09 N	79.55 W
Mount Hope, NJ (hōp)	112a	40.55 N	74.32 W
Mount Hope, WV	110	37.55 N	81.10 W
Mount Isa, Austl. (ī′zȧ)	214	21.00 S	139.45 E
Mount Kisco, NY (kĭs′kō)	112a	41.12 N	73.44 W
Mountlake Terrace, Wa. (mount lāk tĕr′ĭs)	118a	47.48 N	122.19 W
Mount Lebanon, Pa. (lĕb′ȧ-nŭn)	113e	40.22 N	80.03 W
Mount Magnet, Austl. (măg-nĕt)	214	28.00 S	118.00 E
Mount Martha, Austl.	211a	38.17 S	145.01 E
Mount Morgan, Austl. (môr-găn)	215	23.42 S	150.45 E
Mount Moriac, Austl.	211a	38.13 S	144.12 E

PLACE (Pronunciation)	PAGE	Lat. °′	Long. °′
Mount Morris, Mi. (mĭr'ĭs)	110	43.10 N	83.45 W
Mount Morris, NY	111	42.45 N	77.50 W
Mountnessing, Eng.	62	51.39 N	0.21 E
Mount Olive, NC (ŏl'ĭv)	127	35.11 N	78.05 W
Mount Oliver, Pa.	57b	40.28 N	79.59 W
Mount Peale, Ut.	121	38.26 N	109.16 W
Mount Pleasant, Ia. (plĕz'ănt)	115	40.59 N	91.34 W
Mount Pleasant, Mi.	110	43.35 N	84.45 W
Mount Pleasant, SC	127	32.46 N	79.51 W
Mount Pleasant, Tn.	126	35.31 N	87.12 W
Mount Pleasant, Tx.	123	33.10 N	94.56 W
Mount Pleasant, Ut.	121	39.35 N	111.20 W
Mount Pritchard, Austl.	70a	33.54 S	150.54 E
Mount Prospect, Il. (prŏs'pĕkt)	113a	42.03 N	87.56 W
Mount Rainier, Md.	56d	38.56 N	76.58 W
Mount Rainier Natl. Park, Wa. (rå-nēr')	116	46.47 N	121.17 W
Mount Revelstoke Natl. Park, Can. (rĕv'ĕl-stōk)	96	51.22 N	120.15 W
Mount Savage, Md. (săv'åj)	111	39.45 N	78.55 W
Mount Shasta, Ca. (shăs'tȧ)	116	41.18 N	122.17 W
Mount Sterling, Il. (stûr'lĭng)	123	39.59 N	90.44 W
Mount Sterling, Ky.	110	38.05 N	84.00 W
Mount Stewart, Can. (stū'ărt)	115	46.22 N	62.52 W
Mount Union, Pa. (ūn'yŭn)	111	40.25 N	77.50 W
Mount Vernon, Il. (vûr'nŭn)	110	38.20 N	88.50 W
Mount Vernon, In.	110	37.55 N	87.50 W
Mount Vernon, Mo.	123	37.09 N	93.48 W
Mount Vernon, NY	112a	40.55 N	73.51 W
Mount Vernon, Oh.	110	40.25 N	82.30 W
Mount Vernon, Pa.	57b	40.17 N	79.48 W
Mount Vernon, Va.	112e	38.43 N	77.06 W
Mount Vernon, Wa.	118a	48.25 N	122.20 W
Mount Washington (Neigh.), Md.	56c	39.22 N	76.40 W
Mount Washington Summit, Md.	56c	39.23 N	76.40 W
Mount Waverley, Austl.	70b	37.53 S	145.08 E
Moura, Braz. (mō'rȧ)	143	1.33 S	61.38 W
Moura, Port.	170	38.08 N	7.28 W
Mourenx, Fr. (mo͞o-rän)	168	43.24 N	0.40 W
Mourne, Mts., N. Ire. (môrn)	162	54.10 N	6.09 W
Moussoro, Chad	229	13.39 N	16.29 E
Moûtiers, Fr. (mo͞o-tyâr')	169	45.31 N	6.34 E
Mowbullan, Mt., Austl. (mō'bo͝o-lăn)	216	26.50 S	151.34 E
Moyahua, Mex. (mô-yä'wä)	130	21.16 N	103.10 W
Moyale, Ken. (mô-yä'lä)	225	3.28 N	39.04 E
Moyamba, S.L. (mô-yäm'bä)	228	8.10 N	12.26 W
Moyen Atlas (Mts.), Mor.	160	32.49 N	5.28 W
Moyeuvre-Grande, Fr.	169	49.15 N	6.26 E
Moyie R., Id. (moi'yē)	116	38.50 N	116.10 W
Moylan, Pa.	56b	39.54 N	75.23 W
Moyobamba, Peru (mō-yō-bäm'bä)	142	6.12 S	76.56 W
Moyuta, Guat. (mô-ē-o͞o'tä)	132	14.01 N	90.05 W
Moyyero (R.), Sov. Un.	181	67.15 N	104.10 E
Mozambique, Afr. (mō-zăm-bēk')	222	20.15 S	33.53 E
Mozambique Chan., Afr. (mō-zăm-bek')	227	24.00 S	38.00 E
Mozdok, Sov. Un. (môz-dôk')	179	43.45 N	44.35 E
Mozhaysk, Sov. Un. (mô-zhäysk')	174	55.31 N	36.02 E
Mozhayskiy, Sov. Un. (mô-zhäy'skĭ)	182c	59.42 N	30.08 E
Mozyr', Sov. Un. (mô-zür')	175	52.03 N	29.14 E
Mpanda, Tan.	231	6.22 S	31.02 E
Mpika, Zambia	231	11.54 S	31.26 E
Mpimbe, Malawi	231	15.18 S	35.04 E
Mporokoso, Zambia ('m-pō-rō-kō'sō)	231	9.23 S	30.05 E
Mpwapwa, Tan. ('m-pwä'pwä)	231	6.21 S	36.29 E
Mqanduli, S. Afr. ('m-kän'do͞o-lē)	227c	31.50 S	28.42 E
Mragowo, Pol. (mräŋ'gô-vô)	167	53.52 N	21.18 E
M'Sila, Alg. (m'sē'lä)	224	35.47 N	4.34 E
Msta (R.), Sov. Un. (m'stä')	174	58.33 N	32.08 E
Mstislavl', Sov. Un. (m'stē-slävl')	174	54.01 N	31.42 E
Mtakataka, Malawi	231	14.12 S	34.32 E
Mtamvuna (R.), S. Afr.	227c	30.43 S	29.53 E
Mtata (R.), S. Afr.	227c	31.48 S	29.03 E
Mt. Nimba Natl. Pk., Gui.-Ivory Coast	228	7.35 N	8.10 W
Mtsensk, Sov. Un. (m'tsĕnsk)	174	53.17 N	36.33 E
Mtwara, Tan.	231	10.16 S	40.11 E
Muang Khon Kaen, Thai.	206	16.37 N	102.41 E
Muang Lamphum, Thai.	206	18.40 N	98.59 E
Muar (R.), Mala.	191b	2.18 N	102.43 E
Mubende, Ug.	231	0.35 N	31.23 E
Mubi, Nig.	229	10.18 N	13.20 E
Mucacata, Moz.	231	13.20 S	39.59 E
Much, F.R.G. (mo͞oĸ)	169c	50.54 N	7.24 E
Muchinga Mts., Zambia	231	12.40 S	30.50 E
Much Wenlock, Eng. (mŭch wĕn'lŏk)	156	52.35 N	2.33 W
Muckalee Cr., Ga. (mŭk'ă lē)	126	31.55 N	84.10 W
Mucking, Eng.	62	51.30 N	0.26 E
Muckleshoot Ind. Res., Wa. (mŭck''l-sho͞ot)	118a	47.21 N	122.04 W
Mucubela, Moz.	231	16.55 S	37.52 E
Mucugê, Braz. (mo͞o-ko͞o-zhĕ')	143	13.02 S	41.19 W
Mud (L.), Mi. (mŭd)	115	46.12 N	84.32 W
Mud (L.), Nv.	120	40.28 N	119.11 W
Mudan (R.), China (mo͞o-dän)	202	45.30 N	129.40 E
Mudanjiang, China (mo͞o-dän-jyäŋ)	202	44.28 N	129.38 E
Muddy (R.), Nv. (mŭd'ĭ)	120	36.56 N	114.42 W
Muddy Boggy Cr., Ok. (mud'ĭ bôg'ĭ)	123	34.42 N	96.11 W
Muddy Cr., Ut. (mŭd'ĭ)	121	38.45 N	111.10 W
Mudgee, Austl. (mŭ-jē)	216	32.47 S	149.10 E
Mudjatik (R.), Can.	100	56.23 N	107.40 W
Mufulira, Zambia	231	12.33 S	28.14 E
Muğla, Tur. (mo͞og'lä)	179	37.10 N	28.20 E
Mühileiten, Aus.	66e	48.10 N	16.34 E
Mühldorf, F.R.G. (mül-dôrf)	166	48.15 N	12.33 E
Mühlenbeck, G.D.R.	65a	52.40 N	13.22 E
Mühlhausen, G.D.R. (mül'hou-zĕn)	166	51.13 N	10.25 E
Muhu (I.), Sov. Un. (mo͞o'ho͞o)	165	58.41 N	22.55 E
Mui Ron, C., Viet.	203	18.05 N	106.45 E
Muir Woods Natl. Mon., Ca. (mūr)	120	37.54 N	123.22 W
Muizenberg, S. Afr. (mwĭz-ĕn-bûrg')	226a	34.07 S	18.28 E
Mujāhidpur (Neigh.), India	67d	28.34 N	77.13 E
Mukachëvo, Sov. Un. (mo͞o-kȧ-chyô'vô)	167	48.25 N	22.43 E
Mukhtuya, Sov. Un. (mo͞ok-to͞o'yȧ)	181	61.00 N	113.00 E
Mukilteo, Wa. (mū-kĭl-tā'ō)	118a	47.57 N	122.18 W
Muko, Jap. (mo͞o'kô)	205b	34.57 N	135.43 E
Muko (R.), Jap. (mo͞o'kô)	205b	34.52 N	135.17 E
Mukutawa (R.), Can.	101	53.10 N	97.28 W
Mukwonago, Wi. (mū-kwō-nȧ'gō)	113a	42.52 N	88.19 W
Mula, Al. (mŭl'gȧ)	112h	33.33 N	86.59 W
Mula, Sp. (mo͞o'lä)	170	38.05 N	1.12 W
Mulde R., G.D.R. (mo͞ol'dĕ)	166	50.30 N	12.30 E
Muleros, Mex. (mo͞o-lā'rōs)	130	23.44 N	104.00 W
Muleshoe, Tx.	122	34.13 N	102.43 W
Mulgrave, Can. (mŭl'grāv)	105	45.37 N	61.23 W
Mulgrave (I.), Austl.	215	10.08 S	142.14 E
Mulhacén, (Mtn.), Sp.	170	37.04 N	3.18 W
Mülheim, F.R.G. (mül'hīm)	169c	51.25 N	6.53 E
Mülheim an der Ruhr, F.R.G.	63	51.24 N	6.54 E
Mulhouse, Fr. (mü-lo͞oz')	169	47.46 N	7.20 E
Muling, China (mo͞o-lĭŋ)	202	44.32 N	130.18 E
Muling (R.), China	202	44.40 N	130.30 E
Mullan, Id. (mŭl'ăn)	116	47.26 N	115.50 W
Müller, Pegunungan (Mts.), Indon. (mül'ēr)	206	0.22 N	113.05 E
Mullingar, Ire. (mŭl-ĭn-gär)	162	53.31 N	7.26 W
Mullins, SC (mŭl'ĭnz)	127	34.11 N	79.13 W
Mullins River, Belize	132a	17.08 N	88.18 W
Mull, I. of, Scot. (mŭl)	162	56.40 N	6.19 W
Multān, Pak. (mo͞o-tän')	196	30.17 N	71.13 E
Multnomah Chan., Or. (mŭl nō mȧ)	118c	45.41 N	122.53 W
Mulumbe, Monts (Mts.), Zaire	231	8.47 S	27.20 E
Mulvane, Ks. (mŭl-vān')	123	37.30 N	97.13 W
Mumbwa, Zambia (mo͞om'bwä)	231	14.59 S	27.04 E
Mumias, Ken.	231	0.20 N	34.29 E
Muna, Mex. (mo͞o'nȧ)	132a	20.28 N	89.42 W
Münchehofe, G.D.R.	65a	52.30 N	13.40 E
München (Munich), F.R.G. (mün'kĕn)	157d	48.08 N	11.35 E
Muncie, In. (mŭn'sĭ)	110	40.10 N	85.30 W
Mundelein, Il. (mŭn-dē-lĭn')	113a	42.16 N	88.00 W
Mündelheim (Neigh.), F.R.G.	63	51.21 N	6.41 E
Mundonueva, Pico de (Pk.), Col. (pē'kô-dĕ-mo͞o'n-dô-nwĕ'vä)	142a	4.18 N	74.12 W
Muneco, Cerro (Mtn.), Mex. (sĕ'r-rô-mo͞o-nĕ'kō)	131a	19.13 N	99.20 W
Mungana, Austl. (mŭn-găn'ȧ)	215	17.15 S	144.18 E
Mungbere, Zaire	231	2.38 N	28.30 E
Munger, Mn. (mŭn'gēr)	119h	46.48 N	92.20 W
Mungindi, Austl. (mŭn-gĭn'dē)	216	32.00 S	148.45 E
Munhall, Pa. (mŭn'hôl)	113e	40.24 N	79.53 W
Munhango, Ang. (mo͞on-häŋ'gȧ)	226	12.15 S	18.55 E
Munich, see **München**			
Munirka (Neigh.), India	67d	28.34 N	77.10 E
Munising, Mi. (mū'nĭ-sĭng)	115	46.24 N	86.41 W
Munku Sardyk (Mtn.), Sov. Un.-Mong. (mo͞on'ko͞o sär-dĭk')	180	51.45 N	100.30 E
Muñoz, Phil. (mo͞on-nyōth')	207a	15.44 N	120.53 E
Munro (Neigh.), Arg.	60d	34.32 S	58.31 W
Münster, F.R.G. (mün'stĕr)	169c	51.57 N	7.38 E
Munster, In. (mŭn'stēr)	113a	41.34 N	87.31 W
Munster, Ire. (mŭn-stēr)	162	52.30 N	9.24 W
Muntok, Indon. (mo͞on-tŏk')	206	2.05 S	105.11 E
Munzi Freire, Braz. (mo͞o-nē'z-frā'rĕ)	141a	20.29 S	41.25 W
Muong Sing, Laos (mo͞o'ông-sĭng')	206	21.06 N	101.17 E
Muping, China (mo͞o-pĭŋ)	200	37.23 N	121.36 E
Muqdisho, Som.	223a	2.08 N	45.22 E
Muqui, Braz. (mo͞o-ko͞oē)	141a	20.56 S	41.20 W
Muradiye, Tur. (mo͞o-rä'dē-yĕ)	179	39.00 N	43.40 E
Murat, Fr. (mü-rä')	168	45.05 N	2.56 E
Murat (R.), Tur. (mo͞o-rät')	179	38.50 N	40.40 E
Murayama, Jap.	69a	35.45 N	139.23 E
Murchison (R.), Austl. (mûr'chĭ-sŭn)	214	26.45 S	116.15 E
Murcia, Sp. (mo͞or'thyä)	170	38.00 N	1.10 W
Murcia (Reg.), Sp.	170	38.35 N	1.51 W
Murdo, SD (mûr'dô)	114	43.53 N	100.42 W
Mureş R., Rom. (mo͞o'rĕsh)	167	46.02 N	21.50 E
Muret, Fr. (mü-rĕ')	168	43.28 N	1.17 E
Murfreesboro, Tn. (mûr'frēz-bŭr-ô)	126	35.50 N	86.19 W
Murgab (R.), Sov. Un. (mo͞or-gäb')	143	37.07 N	62.32 E
Muriaé, Braz. (mo͞o-ryȧ-ĕ')	141a	21.10 S	42.21 W
Muriaé (R.), Braz.	141a	21.20 S	41.40 W
Murino, Sov. Un. (mo͞o'rĭ-nô)	182c	60.03 N	30.28 E
Müritz (L.), G.D.R. (mür'its)	166	53.20 N	12.33 E
Murku Sardyk (Pk.), Sov. Un.-Mong.	198	51.56 N	100.21 E
Murmansk, Sov. Un. (mo͞or-mänsk')	178	69.00 N	33.20 E
Murom, Sov. Un. (mo͞o'rôm)	178	55.30 N	42.00 W
Muroran, Jap. (mo͞o'rō-rän)	204	42.21 N	141.05 E
Muros, Sp. (mo͞o'rōs)	170	42.48 N	9.00 W
Muroto-Zaki (Pt.), Jap. (mo͞o'rô-tō zä'kē)	205	33.14 N	134.12 E
Murphy, Mo. (mŭr'fĭ)	119e	38.29 N	90.29 W
Murphy, NC	126	35.05 N	84.00 W
Murphysboro, Il. (mûr'fĭz-bŭr-ô)	123	37.46 N	89.21 W
Mur R., Aus. (mo͞or)	166	47.10 N	14.08 E
Murray, Ky. (mŭr'ĭ)	126	36.39 N	88.17 W
Murray, Ut.	119b	40.40 N	111.53 W
Murray (R.), Can.	99	55.00 N	121.00 W
Murray (R.), SC (mŭr'ĭ)	127	34.07 N	81.18 W
Murray Bridge, Austl.	216	35.10 S	139.35 E
Murray Harbour, Can.	104	46.00 N	62.31 W
Murray R., Austl.	216	34.20 S	142.21 E
Murray Reg., Austl. (mŭ'rē)	215	33.20 S	142.30 E
Murrumbidgee (R.), Austl. (mŭr-ŭm-bĭd'jē)	216	34.30 S	145.20 E
Murrupula, Moz.	231	15.27 S	38.47 E
Murshidābād, India (mo͞or'shē-dä-bäd')	196	24.08 N	87.11 E
Murska Sobota, Yugo. (mo͞or'skä sô'bô-tä)	172	46.40 N	16.14 E
Murtal, Port.	65d	38.42 N	9.22 W
Muruasigar (Mtn.), Ken.	231	3.08 N	35.02 E
Murwāra, India	196	23.54 N	80.23 E
Murwillumbah, Austl. (mŭr-wĭl'lŭm-bŭ)	216	28.15 S	153.30 E
Mürz R., Aus. (mürts)	166	47.30 N	15.21 E
Murzzuschlag, Aus. (mürts'tso͞o-shlägh)	166	47.37 N	15.41 E
Mus, Tur. (mo͞osh)	179	38.55 N	41.30 E
Musala (Mtn.), Bul.	173	42.05 N	23.24 E
Musan, Kor. (mo͞o'sän)	204	41.11 N	129.10 E
Musashino, Jap. (mo͞o-sä'shē-nō)	205a	35.43 N	139.35 E
Muscat, Om. (mŭs-kăt')	192	23.23 N	58.30 E
Muscatine, Ia. (mŭs-kȧ-tēn)	115	41.26 N	91.00 W
Muscat & Oman, see **Oman**			
Muscle Shoals, Al. (mŭs''l shōlz)	126	34.44 N	87.38 W
Musgrave Ra., Austl. (mŭs'grāv)	214	26.15 S	131.15 E
Mushie, Zaire (mŭsh'ē)	226	3.04 S	16.50 E
Mushin, Nig.	229	6.32 N	3.22 E
Musi (Strm.), Indon. (mo͞o'sē)	206	2.40 S	103.42 E
Musinga, Alto (Ht.), Col. (ä'l-tô-mo͞o-sē'n-gä)	142a	6.40 N	76.13 W
Muskego L., Wi. (mŭs-kē'gō)	113a	42.53 N	88.10 W
Muskegon, Mi. (mŭs-kē'gŭn)	110	43.15 N	86.20 W
Muskegon (R.), Mi.	110	43.20 N	85.55 W
Muskegon Heights, Mi.	110	43.10 N	86.20 W
Muskingum (R.), Oh. (mŭs-kĭŋ'gŭm)	110	39.45 N	81.55 W
Muskogee, Ok. (mŭs-kō'gē)	123	35.44 N	95.21 W
Muskoka (L.), Can. (mŭs-kō'kȧ)	111	45.00 N	79.30 W
Musoma, Tan.	231	1.30 S	33.48 E
Mussau I., Pap. N. Gui. (mo͞o-sä'o͞o)	207	1.30 S	149.32 E
Musselshell R., Mt. (mŭs''l-shĕl)	117	46.25 N	108.20 W
Mussende, Ang.	230	10.32 S	16.05 E
Mussuma, Ang.	230	14.14 S	21.59 E
Mustafakemalpasa, Tur.	179	40.05 N	28.30 E
Mustang Bayou, Tx.	125a	29.22 N	95.12 W
Mustang Cr., Tx. (mŭs'tăng)	122	36.22 N	102.46 W
Mustang I., Tx.	125	27.43 N	97.00 W
Mustique I., Saint Vincent (mŭs-tēk')	133b	12.53 N	61.03 W
Musturud, Egypt	71a	30.08 N	31.17 E
Mustvee, Sov. Un. (mo͞ost'vē-ĕ)	165	38.50 N	26.54 E
Musu Dan (C.), Kor. (mo͞o'so͞o dȧn)	199	40.51 N	130.00 E
Musu Dan (Pt.), Kor. (mo͞o'so͞o dȧn)	204	40.48 N	129.50 E
Muswellbrook, Austl. (mŭs'wŭnl-bro͝ok)	216	32.15 S	150.50 E
Mutare, Zimb.	226	18.49 S	32.39 E
Mutombo Mukulu, Zaire (mo͞o-tôm'bō mo͞o-ko͞o'lo͞o)	226	8.12 S	23.56 E
Mutsu Wan (B.), Jap. (mo͞ot'so͞o wän)	204	41.20 N	140.55 E
Mutton Bay, Can. (mŭt''n)	105	50.48 N	59.02 W
Mutum, Braz. (mo͞o-to͞o'm)	141a	19.48 S	41.24 W
Muyun-Kum, Peski (Des.), Sov. Un. (mo͞o-yo͞on'ko͞om')	180	44.30 N	70.00 E
Muzaffargarh, Pak.	196	30.09 N	71.15 E
Muzaffarpur, India	196	26.13 N	85.20 E
Muzon, C., Ak.	98	54.41 N	132.44 W
Muzquiz, Mex. (mo͞oz'kēz)	124	27.53 N	101.31 W
Muztagata (Mtn.), China	198	38.20 N	75.28 E
Mvomero, Tan.	231	6.20 S	37.25 E
Mvoti (R.), S. Afr.	227c	29.18 S	30.52 E
Mwanza, Tan. (mwän'zä)	231	2.31 S	32.54 E
Mwaya, Tan. (mwä'yä)	226	9.19 S	33.51 E
Mwenga, Zaire	231	3.02 S	28.26 E
Mweru (L.), Zaire-Zambia	231	8.50 S	28.50 E
Mwingi, Ken.	231	0.56 S	38.04 E
Myingyan, Bur. (myĭng-yŭn')	198	21.37 N	95.26 E
Myitkyina, Bur. (myĭ'chē-nȧ)	198	25.33 N	97.25 E
Myjava, Czech. (mûē'yȧ-vä)	167	48.45 N	17.33 E
Mymensingh, Bngl.	196	24.48 N	90.28 E
Mynämäki, Fin.	165	60.41 N	21.58 E
Myohyang San (Mtn.), Kor. (myō'hyang)	204	40.00 N	126.12 E
Mýrdalsjökull (Gl.), Ice. (mür'däls-yû'ko͞ol)	158	63.34 N	18.04 W
Myrtle Beach, SC (mûr't'l)	127	33.42 N	78.53 W
Myrtle Point, Or.	116	43.04 N	124.08 W
Mysen, Nor.	164	59.32 N	11.16 E
Myshikino, Sov. Un. (mēsh'kē-nô)	174	57.48 N	38.21 E
Mysore, India (mī-sōr')	197	12.31 N	76.42 E
Mysovka, Sov. Un. (mē' sôf-kȧ)	165	55.11 N	21.17 E
Mystic, Ia. (mĭs'tĭk)	115	40.47 N	92.54 W
Mytishchi, Sov. Un. (mē-tēsh'chĭ)	182b	55.55 N	37.46 E
Mziha, Tan.	231	5.54 S	37.47 E
Mzimba, Malawi ('m-zĭm'bä)	231	11.52 S	33.34 E
Mzimkulu (R.), S. Afr.	227c	30.12 S	29.57 E
Mzimvubu (R.), S. Afr.	227c	31.22 S	29.20 E
Mzsvingo, Zimb.	226	20.07 S	30.47 E
Mzuzu, Malawi	231	11.30 S	34.10 E

N

PLACE (Pronunciation)	PAGE	Lat. °′	Long. °′
Naab R., F.R.G. näp)	166	49.38 N	12.15 E
Naaldwijk, Neth.	157a	52.00 N	4.11 E
Naalehu, Hi.	106a	19.00 N	155.35 W
Naantali, Fin. (nän'tȧ-lē)	165	60.29 N	22.03 E
Nabberu (L.), Austl. (năb'ēr-o͞o)	214	26.05 S	120.35 E
Nabeul, Tun. (nā-bûl')	224	36.34 N	10.45 E
Nabiswera, Ug.	231	1.28 N	32.16 E

PLACE (Pronounciation)	PAGE	Lat. °'	Long. °'
Naboomspruit, S. Afr.	223d	24.32 S	28.43 E
Nābulus, Jordan	191a	32.13 N	35.16 E
Nacala, Moz. (nä-kä'lä)	231	14.34 S	40.41 E
Nacaome, Hond. (nä-kä-ō'mä)	132	13.32 N	87.28 W
Naceur, Bou Mt., Mor.	160	33.50 N	3.55 W
Na Cham, Viet. (nä chäm')	203	22.02 N	106.30 E
Naches R., Wa. (năch'ĕz)	116	46.51 N	121.03 W
Náchod, Czech. (näk'ôt)	166	50.25 N	16.08 E
Nächstebreck (Neigh.), F.R.G.	63	51.18 N	7.14 E
Nacimiento (R.), Ca. (nà-sĭ-myĕn'tô)	120	35.50 N	121.00 W
Nacogdoches, Tx. (năk'ô-dō'chĕz)	125	31.36 N	94.40 W
Nadadores, Mex. (nä-dä-dō'rās)	124	27.04 N	101.36 W
Nadiād, India	196	22.45 N	72.51 E
Nadir, Vir. Is. (U.S.A.)	129c	18.19 N	64.53 W
Nădlac, Rom.	173	46.09 N	20.52 E
Nad Nisou, see Jablonec			
Nad Váhom, see Nové Mesto			
Nadvornaya, Sov. Un. (näd-vôr'nà-yà)	167	48.37 N	24.35 E
Nadym (R.), Sov. Un. (nà'dĭm)	180	64.30 N	72.48 E
Naestved, Den. (nĕst'vĭdh)	164	55.14 N	11.46 E
Nafada, Nig.	229	11.08 N	11.20 E
Nafishah, Egypt	223c	30.34 N	32.15 E
Nafūd ad Dahy (Des.), Sau. Ar.	193	22.15 N	44.15 E
Naga, Phil. (nä'gä)	207a	13.37 N	123.12 E
Naga (I.), Jap.	205	32.09 N	130.16 E
Nagahama, Jap. (nä'gä-hä'mä)	205	33.32 N	132.29 E
Nagahama, Jap.	205	35.23 N	136.16 E
Nagaland (State), India	198	25.47 N	94.15 E
Nagano, Jap. (nä'gä-nô)	205	36.42 N	138.12 E
Nagao, Jap.	69b	34.50 N	135.43 E
Nagaoka, Jap. (nä'gà-ō'kà)	205	37.22 N	138.49 E
Nagaoka, Jap.	205b	34.54 N	135.42 E
Nāgappattinam, India	197	10.48 N	79.51 E
Nagarote, Nic. (nä-gä-rô'tĕ)	132	12.17 N	86.35 W
Nagasaki, Jap. (nä'gà-sä'kē)	205	32.48 N	129.53 E
Nagata (Neigh.), Jap.	69b	34.40 N	135.09 E
Nagatino (Neigh.), Sov. Un.	66b	55.41 N	37.41 E
Nagatsuta (Neigh.), Jap.	69a	35.32 N	139.30 E
Nāgaur, India	196	27.19 N	73.41 E
Nagaybakskiy, Sov. Un. (nà-gày-bäk'skĭ)	182a	53.33 N	59.33 E
Nagcarlan, Phil. (näg-kär-län')	207a	14.07 N	121.24 E
Nag, Co (L.), China	196	31.38 N	91.18 E
Nāgercoil, India	197	8.15 N	77.29 E
Nagorno Karabakh (Reg.), Sov. Un. (nu-gôr'nŭ-kŭ-rŭ-bäk')	179	40.10 N	46.50 E
Nagoya, Jap. (nä'gō'yà)	205	35.09 N	136.53 E
Nāgpur, India (näg'pōōr)	196	21.12 N	79.09 E
Nagua, Dom. Rep. (nà'gwä)	135	19.20 N	69.40 W
Nagykanizsa, Hung. (nôd'y'kô'nē-shô)	166	46.27 N	17.00 E
Nagykōrös, Hung. (nôd'y'kŭ-rūsh)	167	47.02 N	19.46 E
Nagytarcsa, Hung.	66g	47.32 N	19.17 E
Naha, Jap. (nä'hä)	199	26.02 N	127.43 E
Nahanni Natl. Pk., Can.	96	62.10 N	125.15 W
Nahant, Ma. (nà-hănt)	105a	42.26 N	70.55 W
Nahant B., Ma.	54a	42.27 N	70.55 W
Nahariyya, Isr.	191a	33.01 N	35.06 E
Nahaut, Ma.	54a	42.25 N	70.55 W
Nahmer, F.R.G.	63	51.20 N	7.35 E
Nahr al Khābur (R.), Syr.	179	35.50 N	41.00 E
Nahuel Huapi (L.), Arg. (nä'wĕl wä'pē)	144	41.00 S	71.30 W
Nahuizalco, Sal. (nä-wē-zäl'kō)	132	13.50 N	89.43 W
Nāhyā, Egypt	71a	30.03 N	31.07 E
Naic, Phil. (nä-ēk)	207a	14.20 N	120.46 E
Naica, Mex. (nä-ē'kä)	124	27.53 N	105.30 W
Naiguatá, Ven. (nī-gwä-tà')	143b	10.37 N	66.44 W
Naiguata, Pico (Mtn.), Ven. (pē'kô)	143b	10.32 N	66.44 W
Naihāti, India	196a	22.54 N	88.25 E
Nain, Can. (nīn)	97	56.29 N	61.52 W
Nā'īn, Iran	195	32.52 N	53.05 E
Nairn, Scot. (nârn)	162	57.35 N	3.54 W
Nairobi, Ken. (nī-rō'bē)	231	1.17 S	36.49 E
Naivasha, Ken. (nī-vä'shà)	227	0.47 S	36.29 E
Najd (Des.), Sau. Ar.	192	25.18 N	42.38 E
Naj 'Hammādī, Egypt (näg'hä-mä'dē)	223b	26.02 N	32.12 E
Najin, Kor. (nä'jĭn)	204	42.04 N	130.35 E
Najran (Des.), Sau. Ar. (nŭj-rän')	192	17.29 N	45.30 E
Naju, Kor. (nä'jōō')	204	35.02 N	126.42 E
Najusa (R.), Cuba (nä-hōō'sä)	134	21.55 N	77.55 W
Naka (R.), Jap.	69a	35.39 N	139.51 E
Nakadorishima (I.), Jap. (nä'kä'dô'rē-shē'mä)	202	33.00 N	128.20 E
Nakagyō (Neigh.), Jap.	68e	35.01 N	135.45 E
Nakajima, Jap.	69a	35.26 N	139.56 E
Nakanobu (Neigh.), Jap.	69a	35.36 N	139.43 E
Nakatsu, Jap. (nä'käts-ōō)	205	33.34 N	131.10 E
Nakhichevan, Sov. Un. (nà-kē-chĕ-vàn')	179	39.10 N	45.30 E
Nakhodka, Sov. Un. (nŭ-kôt'kŭ)	181	43.03 N	133.08 E
Nakhon Ratchasima, Thai.	206	14.56 N	102.14 E
Nakhon Sawan, Thai.	206	15.42 N	100.06 E
Nakhon Si Thammarat, Thai.	206	8.27 N	99.58 E
Nakskov, Den. (näk'skou)	164	54.51 N	11.06 E
Nakto nad Notecia, Pol. (näk'wō näd nō-tĕ'chōn)	167	53.10 N	17.35 E
Naktong (R.), Kor. (näk'tŭng)	204	36.10 N	128.30 E
Nal'chik, Sov. Un. (nàl-chĕk')	179	43.30 N	43.35 E
Nalón (R.), Sp. (nä-lōn')	170	43.15 N	5.38 W
Nālūt, Libya (nä-lōōt')	224	31.51 N	10.49 E
Namakan (L.), Mn. (nă'mà-kàn)	115	48.20 N	92.43 W
Namak, Daryacheh-ye (L.), Iran	192	34.58 N	51.33 E
Namakzār-e Shāhdād (L.), Iran (nŭ-mŭk-zär')	192	31.00 N	58.30 E
Namamugi (Neigh.), Jap.	69a	35.29 N	139.41 E
Namangan, Sov. Un. (nà-màn-gän')	180	41.08 N	71.59 E
Namao, Can.	95g	53.43 N	113.30 W
Namatanai, Pa. N. Gui. (nä'mä-tà-nä'ē)	207	3.43 S	152.26 E
Nambe Pueblo Ind. Res., NM (näm'bā pwĕb'lô)	121	35.52 N	105.39 W
Nambour, Austl. (năm'bōōr)	216	26.48 S	153.00 E
Nam Co (L.), China (näm tswo)	196	30.30 N	91.10 E
Nam-Dinh, Viet. (näm dēnk')	206	20.30 N	106.10 E
Nametil, Moz.	231	15.43 S	39.21 E
Namhae (I.), Kor. (näm'hī')	204	34.23 N	128.05 E
Namib (Des.), Namibia (nä-mēb')	226	18.45 S	12.45 E
Namibia, Afr.	222	19.30 S	16.13 E
Namoi (R.), Austl. (năm'oi)	216	30.10 S	148.43 E
Namous, Oued en (R.), Alg. (nà-mōōs')	160	31.48 N	00.19 W
Nampa, Id. (năm'pà)	116	43.35 N	116.35 W
Namp'o, Kor.	202	38.47 N	125.28 E
Nampuecha, Moz.	231	13.59 S	40.18 E
Nampula, Moz.	231	15.07 S	39.15 E
Namsos, Nor. (näm'sôs)	158	64.28 N	11.14 E
Namu, Can.	98	51.03 N	127.50 W
Namuli, Serra (Mts.), Moz.	231	15.05 S	37.05 E
Namur, Bel. (nà-mür')	163	50.29 N	4.55 E
Namutoni, Namibia (nà-mōō-tō'nē)	226	18.45 S	17.00 E
Nan (R.), Thai	206	18.11 N	100.29 E
Nanacamilpa, Mex. (nä-nä-kä-mē'l-pä)	131a	19.30 N	98.33 W
Nanaimo, Can. (nà-nī'mō)	98	49.10 N	123.56 W
Nanam, Kor. (nä'nän')	204	41.38 N	129.37 E
Nanao, Jap. (nä'nä-ō)	205	37.03 N	136.59 E
Nan'ao Dao, China (nän-ou dou)	203	23.30 N	117.30 E
Nancefield, S. Afr.	71b	26.17 S	27.53 E
Nanchang, China (nän-chäŋ)	203	28.38 N	115.48 E
Nanchangshan Dao (I.), China (nän-chäŋ-shän dou)	200	37.56 N	120.42 E
Nancheng, China (nän-chäŋ)	203	26.50 N	116.40 E
Nanchong, China (nän-chôŋ)	203	30.45 N	106.05 E
Nancy, Fr. (näN-sē')	169	48.42 N	6.11 E
Nancy Cr., Ga. (năn'cē)	112c	33.51 N	84.25 W
Nanda Devi (Mt.), India (nän'dä dā'vē)	196	30.30 N	80.25 E
Nānded, India	196	19.13 N	77.21 E
Nandurbār, India	196	21.29 N	74.13 E
Nandyāl, India	197	15.54 N	78.09 E
Nanga Parbat, Pak.	196	35.20 N	74.35 E
Nangi, India	196a	22.30 N	88.14 E
Nangis, Fr. (näN-zhē')	169b	48.33 N	3.01 E
Nangong, China (nän-gôŋ)	200	37.22 N	115.22 E
Nangweshi, Zambia	230	16.26 S	23.17 E
Nanhuangcheng Dao (I.), China (nän-hŭäŋ-chŭŋ dou)	200	38.22 N	120.54 E
Nanhui, China	201b	31.03 N	121.45 E
Nani Dinh, Viet.	203	20.25 N	106.08 E
Nani Hu (L.), China (näN'yi' hōō)	200	31.12 N	119.05 E
Naniwa (Neigh.), Jap.	69b	34.39 N	135.30 E
Nanjing, China (nän-jyĭŋ)	200	32.04 N	118.46 E
Nanjuma (R.), China (nän-jyōō-mä)	200	39.37 N	115.45 E
Nanle, China (nän-lŭ)	200	36.03 N	115.13 E
Nan Ling (Mts.), China	203	25.15 N	111.40 E
Nanliu (R.), China (nän-lĭō)	203	22.00 N	109.18 E
Nannine, Austl. (nă-nēn')	214	25.50 S	118.30 E
Nanning, China (nän'nĭng')	203	22.56 N	108.10 E
Nānole (Neigh.), India	67e	19.01 N	72.55 E
Nanpan (R.), China (nän-pän)	203	24.50 N	105.30 E
Nanping, China (nän-pĭŋ)	203	26.40 N	118.05 E
Nansei-shotō (Ryukyu Islands), Jap.	199	27.30 N	127.00 E
Nansemond, Va. (năn'sē-mŭnd)	112g	36.46 N	76.32 W
Nansemond R., Va.	112g	36.50 N	76.34 W
Nantai Zan (Mtn.), Jap. (nän-täē zän)	205	36.47 N	139.28 E
Nanterre, Fr.	64c	48.53 N	2.12 E
Nantes, Fr. (näNt')	168	47.13 N	1.37 W
Nanteuil-le-Haudouin, Fr. (näN-tû-lĕ-ō-dwăN')	169b	49.08 N	2.49 E
Nanticoke, Pa. (năn'tĭ-kōk)	111	41.10 N	76.00 W
Nantong, China (nän-tôŋ)	200	32.02 N	120.51 E
Nantong, China	200	32.08 N	121.06 E
Nantouillet, Fr.	64c	49.00 N	2.42 E
Nantucket (I.), Ma. (năn-tŭk'ĕt)	111	41.15 N	70.05 W
Nantwich, Eng. (nănt'wĭch)	156	53.04 N	2.31 W
Nanxiang, China (nän-shyäŋ)	201b	31.17 N	121.17 E
Nanxiong, China (nän-shôŋ)	203	25.10 N	114.20 E
Nanyang, China	202	33.00 N	112.42 E
Nanyang, Hu (L.), China (nän-yäŋ hōō)	200	35.14 N	116.24 E
Nanyuan, China (nän-yŭän)	202a	39.48 N	116.24 E
Naoābād, India	67a	22.28 N	88.27 E
Naolinco, Mex. (nä-o-lēŋ'kō)	131	19.39 N	96.50 W
Naopukuria, India	67a	22.55 N	88.16 E
Náousa, Grc. (nä'ōō-sà)	173	40.38 N	22.05 E
Naozhou Dao (I.), China (nou-jō dou)	203	20.58 N	110.58 E
Napa, Ca. (năp'à)	120	38.20 N	122.17 W
Napanee, Can. (năp'à-nē)	111	44.15 N	77.00 W
Naperville, Il. (nā'pēr-vĭl)	113a	41.46 N	88.09 W
Napier, N.Z. (nā'pĭ-ēr)	217	39.30 S	177.00 E
Napierville, Can. (nā'pĭ-ē-vĭl)	95a	45.11 N	73.24 W
Naples, Fl. (nā'p'lz)	127a	26.07 N	81.46 W
Naples, see Napoli			
Napo (R.), Peru (nä'pō)	142	1.49 S	74.20 W
Napoleon, Oh. (nà-pō'lē-ŭn)	110	41.20 N	84.10 W
Napoleonville, La. (nà-pō'lē-ŭn-vĭl)	125	29.56 N	91.03 W
Napoli (Naples), It. (nä'pô-lē)	171c	40.37 N	14.12 E
Napoli, Golfo de (G.), It. (gôl-fô-dē)	171c	40.29 N	14.08 E
Nappanee, In. (năp'à-nē)	110	41.30 N	86.00 W
Nara, Jap. (nä'rä)	205b	34.41 N	135.50 E
Nara, Mali	224	15.09 N	7.27 W
Nara (Pref.), Jap.	205b	34.36 N	135.49 E
Nara (R.), Sov. Un.	174	55.05 N	37.16 E
Naracoorte, Austl. (nă-rà-kōōn'tē)	216	36.50 S	140.50 E
Narashino, Jap.	205a	35.41 N	140.01 E
Naraspur, India	197	16.32 N	81.43 E
Nārāyanpāra, India	67a	22.54 N	88.19 E
Narbèrth, Pa. (när'bûrth)	112f	40.01 N	75.17 W
Narbonne, Fr. (nár-bōn')	168	43.12 N	3.00 E
Nardò, It. (när-dō')	173	40.11 N	18.02 E
Nare, Col. (nä'rĕ)	142a	6.12 N	74.37 W
Narew R., Pol. (när'ĕf)	167	52.43 N	21.19 E
Narmada (R.), India	196	22.17 N	74.45 E
Naroch' (L.), Sov. Un. (nä'rôch)	174	54.51 N	27.00 E
Narodnaya, Gora (Mtn.), Sov. Un. (nà-rôd'nà-yà)	178	65.10 N	60.10 E
Naro-Fominsk, Sov. Un. (nä'rô-mēnsk')	174	55.23 N	36.43 E
Narrabeen, Austl. (năr-à-bĭn)	211b	33.44 S	151.18 E
Narragansett, RI (năr-ă-găn'sĕt)	112b	41.26 N	71.27 W
Narragansett B., RI	111	41.20 N	71.15 W
Narrandera, Austl. (nà-ràn-dē'rà)	216	34.40 S	146.40 E
Narraweena, Austl.	70a	33.45 S	151.16 E
Narre Warren North, Austl.	70b	37.59 S	145.19 E
Narrogin, Austl. (năr'ô-gĭn)	214	33.00 S	117.15 E
Naruo, Jap.	69b	34.43 N	135.23 E
Narva, Sov. Un. (nàr'và)	174	59.24 N	28.12 E
Narvacan, Phil. (när-vä-kän')	207a	17.27 N	120.29 E
Narva Jõesuu, Sov. Un. (nàr'và ōō-ô-ă'sōō-ōō)	174	59.26 N	28.02 E
Narvik, Nor. (när'vĕk)	158	68.21 N	17.18 E
Narvskiy Zaliv (B.), Sov. Un. (nàr'vskĭ zä'lĭf)	165	59.35 N	27.25 E
Nar'yan-Mar, Sov. Un. (när'yàn mär')	178	67.42 N	53.30 E
Naryilco, Austl. (năr-ĭl'kō)	216	28.40 S	141.50 E
Narym, Sov. Un. (nä-rēm')	180	58.47 N	82.05 E
Naryn (R.), Sov. Un. (nŭ-rĭn')	193	41.46 N	73.00 E
Naseby, Eng. (nāz'bĭ)	156	52.23 N	0.59 W
Nashua, Mo. (năsh'ŭ-à)	119f	39.18 N	94.34 W
Nashua, NH	105a	42.47 N	71.23 W
Nashville, Ar. (năsh'vĭl)	123	33.56 N	93.50 W
Nashville, Ga.	126	31.12 N	83.15 W
Nashville, Il.	123	38.21 N	89.42 W
Nashville, Mi.	110	42.35 N	85.50 W
Nashville, Tn.	126	36.10 N	86.48 W
Nashwauk, Mn. (năsh'wôk)	115	47.21 N	93.12 W
Našice, Yugo. (nä'shē-tsĕ)	173	45.29 N	18.06 E
Nasielsk, Pol. (nä'syĕlsk)	167	52.35 N	20.50 E
Näsijärvi (L.), Fin. (nĕ'sē-yĕr'vē)	178	61.42 N	24.05 E
Nāsik, India (nä'sĭk)	196	20.02 N	73.49 E
Nāṣir, Sud. (nä-zēr')	225	8.30 N	33.06 E
Nasirabād, India	196	26.13 N	74.48 E
Nāṣir, Buḥayrat, see Nasser, L.			
Naskaupi (R.), Can. (näs'kô-pĭ)	97	53.59 N	61.10 W
'Nasondoye, Zaire	230	10.22 S	25.06 E
Nass (R.), Can. (năs)	98	55.00 N	129.30 W
Nassau, Ba. (năs'ô)	134	25.05 N	77.20 W
Nassenheide, G.D.R. (nä'sĕn-hī-dĕ)	157b	52.49 N	13.13 E
Nasser, L. (Nāṣir, Buḥayrat), Egypt	223b	23.50 N	32.50 E
Nässjö, Swe. (nĕs'shû)	164	57.39 N	14.39 E
Nasugbu, Phil. (nà-sōōg-bōō')	207a	14.05 N	120.37 E
Nasworthy L., Tx. (năz'wûr-thē)	124	31.17 N	100.30 W
Natá, Pan. (nä-tà')	133	8.20 N	80.30 W
Natagaima, Col. (nä-tä-gī'mä)	142a	3.38 N	75.07 W
Nātāgarh, India	67a	22.42 N	88.25 E
Natal, Braz. (nä-täl')	143	6.00 S	35.13 W
Natal (Prov.), S. Afr. (nà-täl')	226	28.50 S	30.07 E
Natalspruit, S. Afr.	71b	26.19 S	28.09 E
Natashquan, Can. (nä-tăsh'kwän)	105	50.11 N	61.49 W
Natashquan (R.), Can.	105	50.35 N	61.35 W
Natchez, Ms. (năch'ĕz)	126	1.35 N	91.20 W
Natchitoches, La. (năk'ĭ-tŏsh)(nàch-ĭ-tōsh')	125	31.46 N	93.06 W
Natick, Ma. (nā'tĭk)	105a	42.17 N	71.21 W
National Area (Reg.), Sov. Un.	181	66.30 N	170.30 E
National Bison Ra. (Mts.), Mt. (năsh'ŭn-ăl bī's'n)	117	47.18 N	113.58 W
National City, Ca.	120a	32.38 N	117.01 W
National Park, Pa.	56b	39.51 N	75.12 W
Natitingou, Benin	228	10.19 N	1.22 E
Natividade, Braz. (nä-tē-vē-dä'dĕ)	143	11.43 S	47.34 W
Natrona Hts., Pa. (nā'trŏ nà)	113e	40.38 N	79.43 W
Natron, L., Tan. (nā'trŏn)	231	2.17 S	36.10 E
Naṭrūn, Wādī an, Egypt	223b	30.33 N	30.12 E
Natuna Besar (I.), Indon.	206	4.00 N	106.50 E
Natural Bridges Natl. Mon., Ut. (năt'ŭ-răl brĭj'ĕs)	121	37.20 N	110.20 W
Naturaliste, C., Austl. (năt-ŭ-rà-lĭst')	214	33.30 S	115.10 E
Naucalpan, Mex. (nä'ōō-käl-pà'n)	131a	19.28 N	99.14 W
Nauchampatepetl (Mtn.), Mex. (näōō-chäm-pä-tē'pĕtl)	131	19.32 N	97.09 W
Nauen, G.D.R. (nou'ĕn)	157b	52.36 N	12.53 E
Naugatuck, Ct. (nô'gà-tŭk)	111	41.25 N	73.05 W
Naujan, Phil. (nä-ōō-hän')	207a	13.19 N	121.17 E
Naumburg, G.D.R. (noum'bōōrgh)	166	51.10 N	11.50 E
Naupada (Neigh.), India	67e	19.04 N	72.50 E
Nauru, Oceania	208	0.30 S	167.00 E
Nautla, Mex. (nä-ōōt'lä)	131	20.14 N	96.44 W
Nava, Mex. (nä'vä)	124	28.25 N	100.44 W
Nava del Rey, Sp. (nä-vä dĕl rā'ē)	170	41.22 N	5.04 W
Navahermosa, Sp. (nä-vä-ĕr-mō'sä)	170	39.39 N	4.28 W
Navajas, Cuba (nä-vä-häs')	134	22.40 N	81.20 W
Navajo Ind. Res., Az.-NM (năv'à-hō)	121	36.31 N	109.24 W
Navajo Natl. Mon., Az.	121	36.43 N	110.39 W
Navajo Res., NM	121	36.57 N	107.26 W
Navalcarnero, Sp. (nä-väl'kär-nā'rō)	171a	40.17 N	4.05 W
Navalmoral de la Mata, Sp. (nä-väl'mōräl' dā lä mä'tä)	170	39.53 N	5.32 W
Navan, Can. (nă'vàn)	95c	45.25 N	75.26 W
Navarino (I.), Chile (nä-vä-rē'nō)	144	55.30 S	68.15 W
Navarra (Reg.), Sp. (nä-vär'rä)	170	42.40 N	1.35 W
Navarro, Arg. (nä-vá'r-rō)	141c	35.00 S	59.16 W
Navasota, Tx. (năv-à-sō'tà)	125	30.24 N	96.05 W
Navasota R., Tx.	125	31.03 N	96.11 W
Navassa (I.), N.A. (nà-văs'à)	135	18.25 N	75.15 W
Navestock, Eng.	62	51.39 N	0.13 E
Navestock Side, Eng.	62	51.39 N	0.16 E
Navia (R.), Sp. (nä-vē'ä)	170	43.10 N	6.45 W
Navidad, Chile (nä-vē-dä'd)	141b	34.57 S	71.51 W
Navidad Bk., Ba. (nä-vē-dädh')	135	20.05 N	69.00 W

PLACE (Pronounciation)	PAGE	Lat. °'	Long. °'
Navidade do Carangola, Braz. (nä-vē-dä'dô-kä-rän-gô'la)	141a	21.04 S	41.58 W
Navojoa, Mex. (nä-vô-kô'ä)	128	27.00 N	109.40 W
Navotas, Phil.	68g	14.40 N	120.57 E
Návplion, Grc.	173	37.33 N	22.46 E
Nawābshāh, Pak. (nȧ-wäb'shä)	196	26.20 N	68.30 E
Náxos (I.), Grc. (nák'sôs)	173	37.15 N	25.20 E
Nayābās, India	67d	28.45 N	77.19 E
Nayarit (State), Mex. (nä-yä-rēt')	128	22.00 N	105.15 W
Nayarit, Sierra de (Mts.), Mex. (sē-ĕ'r-rä-dĕ)	130	23.20 N	105.07 W
Naye, Senegal	228	14.25 N	12.12 W
Naylor, Md. (nā'lōr)	112e	38.43 N	76.46 W
Nazaré, Braz. (nä-zä-rĕ')	143	13.04 S	38.49 W
Nazaré da Mata, Braz. (dä-mä-tä)	143	7.46 S	35.13 W
Nazaré, Port. (nä-zä-rā')	170	39.38 N	9.04 W
Nazas, Mex. (nä'zäs)	124	25.14 N	104.08 W
Nazas, R., Mex.	124	25.08 N	104.20 W
Nazerat, Isr.	191a	32.43 N	35.19 E
Nazilli, Tur. (nȧ-zĭ-lē')	179	37.40 N	28.10 E
Naziya R., Sov. Un. (nȧ-zē'yȧ)	182c	59.48 N	31.18 E
Nazko (R.), Can.	98	52.35 N	123.10 W
Nazlat as-Sammān, Egypt	71a	29.59 N	31.08 E
Nazlat Khalīfah, Egypt	71a	30.01 N	31.10 E
Ndalatando, Ang.	230	9.18 S	14.54 E
Ndali, Benin	229	9.51 N	2.43 E
Ndélé, Cen. Afr. Rep. (n'dā-lā')	225	8.21 N	20.43 E
Ndikiniméki, Cam.	229	4.46 N	10.50 E
N'Djamena, Chad	229	12.07 N	15.03 E
Ndjili (Neigh.), Zaire	71c	4.20 S	15.22 E
Ndjolé, Gabon (n'dzhô-lā')	226	0.15 S	10.45 E
Ndola, Zambia (n'dō'lä)	231	12.58 S	28.38 E
Ndoto Mts., Ken.	231	1.55 N	37.05 E
Ndrhamcha, Sebkha de (L.), Mauritania	228	18.50 N	15.15 W
Nduye, Zaire	231	1.50 N	29.01 E
Neagh Lough (L.), N. Ire. (lŏk nā)	162	54.40 N	6.47 W
Néa Ionía, Grc.	66d	38.02 N	23.45 E
Néa Liósia, Grc.	66d	38.02 N	23.42 E
Néa Páfos, Cyprus	191a	34.46 N	32.27 E
Neapean (R.), Austl.	211b	33.40 S	150.39 E
Neápolis, Grc. (nå-ŏp' ô-lĭs)	173	36.35 N	23.08 E
Neápolis, Grc.	172a	35.17 N	25.37 E
Near Is., Ak. (nēr)	107a	52.20 N	172.40 E
Near North Side (Neigh.), Il.	58a	41.54 N	87.38 W
Néa Smírni, Grc.	66d	37.57 N	23.43 E
Neath, Wales (nēth)	162	51.41 N	3.50 W
Nebine Cr., Austl. (nĕ-bēne')	216	27.50 S	147.00 E
Nebit-Dag, Sov. Un. (nyĕ-bēt'däg')	179	39.30 N	54.20 E
Nebraska (State), U.S. (nē-brăs'kȧ)	108	41.45 N	101.30 W
Nebraska City, Ne.	123	40.40 N	95.50 W
Nechako (R.), Can.	98	52.45 N	124.55 W
Nechako Plat., Can. (nĭ-chă'kō)	98	54.00 N	124.30 W
Nechako Ra., Can.	98	53.20 N	124.30 W
Nechako Res., Can.	98	53.25 N	125.10 W
Neches R., Tx. (nĕch'ĕz)	125	31.03 N	94.40 W
Neckar R., F.R.G. (nĕk'är)	166	49.16 N	9.06 E
Necker I., Hi.	106b	24.00 N	164.00 W
Necochea, Arg. (nā-kô-chā'ä)	144	38.30 S	58.45 W
Nedlitz (Neigh.), G.D.R.	65a	52.26 N	13.03 E
Nedrigaylov, Sov. Un. (nĕ-drĭ-gī'lôf)	175	50.49 N	33.52 E
Needham, Ma. (nēd'ăm)	105a	42.17 N	71.14 W
Needham Heights, Ma.	54a	41.28 N	71.14 W
Needles, Ca. (nē'd'lz)	120	34.51 N	114.39 W
Neenah, Wi. (nē'nȧ)	115	44.10 N	88.30 W
Neepawa, Can.	101	50.13 N	99.29 W
Nee Res., Co. (nee)	122	38.26 N	102.56 W
Nee Soon, Singapore	67c	1.24 N	103.49 E
Negareyama, Jap. (nå'gä-rå-yä'mä)	205a	35.52 N	139.54 E
Negaunee, Mi. (nē-gô'nē)	115	46.30 N	87.37 W
Negeri Sembilan (State), Mala. (nă'grē-sĕm-bē-län')	191b	2.46 N	101.54 E
Negev (Des.), Isr. (nĕ'gĕv)	191a	30.34 N	34.43 E
Negombo, Sri Lanka	197	7.39 N	79.49 E
Negotin, Yugo. (nĕ'gô-tēn)	173	44.13 N	22.33 E
Negro (R.), Arg.	144	39.50 S	65.00 W
Negro (R.), Ur.	141c	33.17 S	58.18 W
Negro, Cerro (Mt.), Pan. (sĕ'r»rô-nā'grô)	133	8.44 N	80.37 W
Negro R., Nic.	132	13.01 N	87.10 W
Negro, Rio (R.), Braz. (rē'ō nā'grōō)	142	0.18 S	63.21 W
Negros (I.), Phil. (nā'grōs)	206	9.50 N	121.45 E
Neguá, Col. (nā-gwá')	142a	5.51 N	76.36 W
Nehalem R., Or. (nē-hăl'ĕm)	116	45.52 N	123.37 W
Nehaus an der Oste, F.R.G. (noi'houz)(ôz'tē)	157c	53.48 N	9.02 E
Nehbandān, Iran	195	31.32 N	60.02 E
Nehe, China (nŭ-hŭ)	202	48.23 N	124.58 E
Neheim-Hüsten, F.R.G. (nĕ'hīm)	169c	51.28 N	7.58 E
Neiba, Dom. Rep. (nå-ē'bä)	135	18.30 N	71.20 W
Neiba, Bahai de (B.), Dom. Rep. (bä-ä'ē-dĕ)	135	18.10 N	71.00 W
Neiba, Sierra de (Mts.), Dom. Rep. (sē-ĕr'rä-dĕ)	135	18.40 N	71.40 W
Neihart, Mt. (nī'härt)	117	46.54 N	110.39 W
Neijiang, China (nā-jyäŋ)	203	29.38 N	105.01 E
Neillsville, Wi. (nēlz'vĭl)	115	44.35 N	90.37 W
Nei Monggol (Inner Monglia)(Aut. Reg.), China (nā-mŭŋ-gol)	198	40.15 N	105.00 E
Neiqiu, China (nā-chyō)	200	37.17 N	114.32 E
Neira, Col. (nā'rä)	142a	5.10 N	75.32 W
Neisse (R.), Pol. (nēs)	166	51.30 N	15.00 E
Neiva, Col. (nå-ē'vä)(nā'vä)	142a	2.55 N	75.16 W
Neixiang, China (nā-shyäŋ)	202	33.00 N	111.38 E
Nekemte, Eth.	225	9.09 N	36.29 E
Nekoosa, Wi. (nē-kōō'sȧ)	115	44.19 N	89.54 W
Neksø, Den. (nĕk'sû)	164	55.05 N	15.05 E
Neligh, Ne. (nē'lĭg)	114	42.06 N	98.02 W
Nel'kan, Sov. Un. (nĕl-kän')	181	57.45 N	136.36 E
Nellore, India (nĕl-lōr')	197	14.28 N	79.59 E
Nel'ma, Sov. Un. (nĕl-mä')	204	47.34 N	139.05 E
Nelson, Can. (nĕl'sŭn)	99	49.29 N	117.17 W
Nelson, Eng.	156	53.50 N	2.13 W
Nelson, N.Z.	217	41.15 S	173.22 E
Nelson (I.), Ak.	107	60.38 N	164.42 W
Nelson (R.), Can.	101	56.50 N	93.40 W
Nelson, C., Austl.	216	38.29 S	141.20 E
Nelson Cr., Nv.	120	40.22 N	114.43 W
Nelsonville, Oh. (nĕl'sŭn-vĭl)	110	39.30 N	82.15 W
Néma, Mauritania (nā'mä)	228	16.37 N	7.15 W
Nemadji R., Wi. (nē-măd'jē)	119h	46.33 N	92.16 W
Neman, Sov. Un. (ŋĕ'-man)	165	55.02 N	22.01 E
Neman R., Sov. Un.	167	53.28 N	24.45 E
Nematābād, Iran	68h	35.38 N	51.12 E
Nembe, Nig.	229	4.35 N	6.26 E
Nemčinovka, Sov. Un.	66b	55.43 N	37.23 E
Nemeiban L., Can. (nĕ-mĕ'bȧn)	100	55.20 N	105.20 W
Nemirov, Sov. Un. (nyå-mē'rôf)	175	48.56 N	28.51 E
Nemours, Fr.	168	48.16 N	2.41 E
Nemuro, Jap. (nä'mōō-rō)	204	43.13 N	145.10 E
Nemuro Str., Jap.	204	43.07 N	145.10 E
Nen (R.), China (nŭn)	199	47.07 N	123.28 E
Nen (R.), Eng. (nĕn)	156	52.32 N	0.19 W
Nenagh, Ire. (nē'nȧ)	162	52.50 N	8.05 W
Nenana, Ak. (nå-nä'nȧ)	107	64.28 N	149.18 W
Nenikyul', Sov. Un. (nĕ-nyē'kyûl)	182c	59.26 N	30.40 E
Nenjiang, China (nŭn-jyäŋ)	202	49.02 N	125.15 E
Neodesha, Ks. (nē-ō-dĕ-shô')	123	37.24 N	95.41 W
Néon Psikhikón, Grc.	66d	38.00 N	23.47 E
Neosho, Mo.	123	36.51 N	94.22 W
Neosho (R.), Ks. (nē-ō'shō)	123	38.07 N	95.40 W
Nepal, Asia (nĕ-pôl')	190	28.45 N	83.00 E
Nephi, Ut. (nē'fī)	121	39.40 N	111.50 W
Nepisiguit (R.), Can. (nĭ-pĭ'sĭ-kwĭt)	104	47.25 N	66.28 W
Nepomuceno, Braz. (nĕ-pô-mōō-sĕ'no)	141a	21.15 S	45.13 W
Nera (R.), It. (nā'rä)	172	42.45 N	12.54 E
Nérac, Fr. (nā-räk')	168	44.08 N	0.19 E
Nerchinsk, Sov. Un. (nyĕr' chĕnsk)	181	51.47 N	116.17 E
Nerchinskiy Khrebet (Mts.), Sov. Un.	181	50.30 N	118.30 E
Nerchinskiy Zavod, Sov. Un. (nyĕr'chĕn-skĭzȧ-vôt')	181	51.35 N	119.46 E
Nerekhta, Sov. Un. (nyĕ-rĕĸ'tȧ)	174	57.29 N	40.34 E
Neretva (R.), Yugo. (nĕ'rĕt-vȧ)	173	43.08 N	17.50 E
Nerja, Sp. (nĕr'hä)	170	36.45 N	3.53 W
Nerl' (R.), Sov. Un. (nyĕrl)	174	56.59 N	37.57 E
Nerskaya R., Sov. Un. (nyĕr'skȧ-yȧ)	182b	55.31 N	38.46 E
Nerussa (R.), Sov. Un. (nyå-rōō'sȧ)	174	52.24 N	34.20 E
Ness, Eng.	64a	53.17 N	3.03 W
Ness City, Ks. (nĕs)	122	38.27 N	99.55 W
Ness, Loch (L.), Scot. (lŏĸ nĕs)	162	37.23 N	4.20 W
Nesterov, Sov. Un. (nyĕs-tā'rôf)	165	54.39 N	22.38 E
Nesterov, Sov. Un. (ŋĕs'-tzhyé-rôf)	167	50.03 N	23.58 E
Neston, Eng.	64a	53.18 N	3.04 W
Néstos (R.), Grc. (nās'tōs)	173	41.25 N	24.12 E
Nesvizh, Sov. Un. (nyĕs'vēsh)	174	53.13 N	26.44 E
Netanya, Isr.	191a	32.19 N	34.52 E
Netcong, NJ (nĕt'cŏnj)	112a	40.54 N	74.42 W
Netherlands, Eur. (nĕdh'ĕr-lăndz)	154	53.01 N	3.57 E
Netherlands Guiana, see Suriname			
Netherton, Eng.	64a	53.30 N	2.58 W
Nette (Neigh.), F.R.G.	63	51.33 N	7.25 E
Nettilling (L.), Can.	97	66.30 N	70.40 W
Nett Lake Ind. Res., Mn. (nĕt lāk)	115	48.23 N	93.19 W
Nettuno, It. (nĕt-tōō'nô)	171d	41.28 N	12.40 E
Neubeckum, F.R.G. (noi'bĕ-kōōm)	169c	51.48 N	8.01 E
Neubrandenburg, G.D.R. (noi-brän'dĕn-bōōrgh)	166	53.33 N	13.16 E
Neuburg, F.R.G. (noi'bōōrgh)	166	48.43 N	11.12 E
Neuchâtel, Switz. (nû-shȧ-tĕl')	166	47.00 N	6.52 E
Neuchatel, Lac de (L.), Switz.	166	46.48 N	6.53 E
Neudorf (Neigh.), F.R.G.	63	51.25 N	6.47 E
Neuenhagen, G.D.R. (noi'ĕn-hä-gĕn)	157b	52.31 N	13.41 E
Neuenhagen bei Berlin, G.D.R.	65a	52.32 N	13.41 E
Neuenhof (Neigh.), F.R.G.	63	51.10 N	7.13 E
Neuenkamp (Neigh.), F.R.G.	63	51.26 N	6.44 E
Neuenrade, F.R.G. (noi'ĕn-rä-dĕ)	169c	51.17 N	7.47 E
Neu-Erlaa (Neigh.), Aus.	66e	48.08 N	16.19 E
Neu Fahrland, G.D.R.	65a	52.26 N	13.03 E
Neufchâtel-en-Bray, Fr. (nû-shä-tĕl'ĕɴ-brā')	168	49.43 N	1.25 E
Neuilly-sur-Marne, Fr.	64c	48.51 N	2.32 E
Neuilly-sur-Seine, Fr.	64c	48.53 N	2.16 E
Neukirchen-Vluyn, F.R.G.	63	51.27 N	6.33 E
Neulengbach, Aus.	157e	48.13 N	15.55 E
Neumarkt, F.R.G. (noi'märkt)	166	49.17 N	11.30 E
Neumünster, F.R.G. (noi'münstēr)	166	54.04 N	10.00 E
Neunkirchen, Aust. (noin'kĭrĸ-ĕn)	166	47.43 N	16.05 E
Neunkirchen, F.R.G.	169	49.21 N	7.20 E
Neuquén, Arg. (nĕ-ōō-kān')	144	38.52 S	68.12 W
Neuquen (Prov.), Arg.	144	39.40 S	70.45 W
Neuquén (R.), Arg.	144	38.45 S	69.00 W
Neuruppin, G.D.R. (noi'rōō-pēn)	157b	52.55 N	12.48 E
Neuse (R.), NC (nūz)	127	36.12 N	78.50 W
Neusiedler See (L.), Aus. (noi-zēd'lēr)	166	47.54 N	16.31 E
Neuss, F.R.G. (nois)	169c	51.12 N	6.41 E
Neusserweyhe (Neigh.), F.R.G.	63	51.13 N	6.39 E
Neustadt, F.R.G. (noi'shtät)	166	49.21 N	8.08 E
Neustadt bei Coburg, F.R.G. (bī kō'bōōrgh)	166	50.20 N	11.09 E
Neustadt in Holstein, F.R.G.	166	54.06 N	10.50 E
Neustift am Walde (Neigh.), Aus.	66e	48.15 N	16.18 E
Neustrelitz, G.D.R. (noi-strā'lĭts)	166	53.21 N	13.05 E
Neutral Hills, Can. (nū'trăl)	100	52.10 N	110.50 W
Neu Ulm, F.R.G. (noi ōō lm')	166	48.23 N	10.01 E
Neuva Pompeya (Neigh.), Arg.	60d	34.39 S	58.25 W
Neuville, Can. (nū'vĭl)	95b	46.39 N	71.35 W
Neuville-sur-Oise, Fr.	64c	49.01 N	2.04 E
Neuwaldegg (Neigh.), Aus.	66e	48.14 N	16.17 E
Neuwied, F.R.G. (noi'vēdt)	166	50.26 N	7.28 E
Neva (R.), Sov. Un. (nyĕ-vä')	182c	59.49 N	30.54 E
Nevada, Ia. (nē-vä'dȧ)	115	42.01 N	93.27 W
Nevada, Mo.	123	37.49 N	94.21 W
Nevada (State), U.S. (nĕ vȧ'dȧ)	108	39.30 N	117.00 W
Nevada City, Ca.	120	39.16 N	120.01 W
Nevada, Sierra (Mts.), Sp. (syĕr'rä nā-vä'dhä)	170	37.01 N	3.28 W
Nevada, Sierra (Mts.), U.S. (sē-ĕ'r-rä nē-vä'dȧ)	108	39.20 N	120.05 W
Nevado, Cerro el (Mtn.), Col. (sĕ'r-rô-ĕl-nĕ-vä'dô)	142a	4.02 N	74.08 W
Nevado de Colima (Mtn.), Mex. (nȧ-vä'dhō dä kō-lē'mä)	130	19.34 N	103.39 W
Neva Stantsiya, Sov. Un. (nyĕ-vä' stän'tsĭ-yȧ)	162c	59.53 N	30.30 E
Nevel', Sov. Un. (nyĕ'vĕl)	174	56.03 N	29.57 E
Neveri (R.), Ven. (nĕ-vĕ-rē)	143b	10.13 N	64.18 W
Nevers, Fr. (nē-vâr')	168	46.59 N	3.10 E
Neves, Braz.	61c	22.51 S	43.06 W
Neve, Serra da (Mts.), Ang.	230	13.40 S	13.20 E
Nevesinje, Yugo. (nĕ-vĕ'sĕn-yĕ)	173	43.15 N	18.08 E
Neviges, F.R.G.	63	51.19 N	7.05 E
Neville I., Pa.	57b	40.31 N	80.08 W
Nevis, Ben (Mtn.), Scot. (bĕn)	162	56.47 N	5.00 W
Nevis I., Saint Kitts-Nevis (nē'vĭs)	133b	17.05 N	62.38 W
Nevis Pk., Saint Kitts-Nevis	133b	17.11 N	62.33 W
Nevşehir, Tur. (nĕv-shĕ'hĕr)	179	38.40 N	34.35 E
Nev'yansk, Sov. Un. (nĕv-yänsk')	182a	57.29 N	60.14 E
New (R.), Va. (nū)	127	37.20 N	80.35 W
Newabāgam, India	67a	22.48 N	88.24 E
New Addington (Neigh.), Eng.	62	51.21 N	0.01 W
Newala, Tan.	231	10.56 S	39.18 E
New Albany, In. (nû ôl'bȧ-nĭ)	113h	38.17 N	85.49 W
New Albany, Ms.	126	34.28 N	39.00 W
New Amsterdam, Guy. (ăm'stēr-dăm)	143	6.14 N	57.30 W
Newark, Ca. (nū'ērk)	118b	37.32 N	122.02 W
Newark, De. (nōō'ärk)	111	39.40 N	75.45 W
Newark, Eng. (nū'ērk)	156	53.04 N	0.49 W
Newark, NJ (nōō'ûrk)	112a	40.44 N	74.10 W
Newark, NY (nū'ērk)	111	43.05 N	77.10 W
Newark, Oh.	110	40.05 N	82.25 W
Newaygo, Mi. (nū'wā-go)	110	43.25 N	85.50 W
New Bedford, Ma. (bĕd'fērd)	111	41.35 N	70.55 W
Newberg, Or. (nū'bûrg)	110	45.17 N	122.58 W
New Bern, NC (bûrn)	127	35.05 N	77.05 W
Newbern, Tn.	126	36.05 N	89.12 W
Newberry, Mi. (nū'bĕr-ĭ)	115	46.22 N	85.31 W
Newberry, SC	127	34.15 N	81.40 W
New Boston, Mi. (bôs'tŭn)	113b	42.10 N	83.24 W
New Boston, Oh.	110	38.45 N	82.55 W
New Braunfels, Tx. (nū broun'fĕls)	124	29.43 N	98.07 W
New Brighton, Eng.	64a	53.26 N	3.03 W
New Brighton, Mn. (brī'tŭn)	119g	45.04 N	93.12 W
New Brighton, Pa.	113e	40.34 N	80.18 W
New Brighton (Neigh.), NY	55	40.38 N	74.06 W
New Britain, Ct. (brĭt''n)	111	41.40 N	72.45 W
New Britain (I.), Pap. N. Gui.	207	6.45 S	149.38 E
New Brunswick, NJ (brŭnz'wĭk)	112a	40.29 N	74.27 W
New Brunswick (Prov.), Can.	97	47.14 N	66.30 W
Newburg, In.	110	38.00 N	87.25 W
Newburg, Mo.	123	37.54 N	91.53 W
Newburgh, NY	111	41.30 N	74.00 W
Newburgh Heights, Oh.	113d	41.27 N	81.40 W
Newbury, Eng. (nū'bēr-ĭ)	162	51.24 N	1.26 W
Newbury, Ma.	105a	42.48 N	70.52 W
Newburyport, Ma. (nū'bēr-ĭ-pōrt)	105a	42.48 N	70.53 W
New Caledonia, Oceania	215	21.28 S	164.40 E
New Canaan, Ct. (kā-nȧn)	112a	41.06 N	73.30 W
New Carlisle, Can. (kär-lĭl')	104	48.01 N	65.20 W
New Carrollton, Md.	56d	35.58 N	76.53 W
Newcastle, Austl. (nū-kȧs''l)	216	33.00 S	151.55 E
Newcastle, Can.	104	47.00 N	65.34 W
New Castle, De.	111	39.40 N	75.35 W
Newcastle, Eng. (nû-kȧs''l) (nû-käs''l)	156	53.01 N	2.14 W
New Castle, In.	110	39.55 N	82.25 W
New Castle, Oh.	110	40.20 N	82.10 W
New Castle, Pa.	110	41.00 N	80.25 W
Newcastle, Tx.	122	33.13 N	98.44 W
Newcastle, Wy.	114	43.51 N	104.11 W
Newcastle upon Tyne, Eng.	162	55.00 N	1.45 W
Newcastle Waters, Austl. (wô'tērz)	214	17.10 S	133.25 E
Newclare (Neigh.), S. Afr.	71b	26.11 S	27.58 E
Newcomerstown, Oh. (nū'kŭm-ērz-toun)	110	40.15 N	81.40 W
New Croton Res., NY (krō'tôn)	112a	41.15 N	73.47 W
New Delhi, India (dĕl'hī)	196	28.43 N	77.18 E
Newell, SD (nū'ĕl)	114	44.43 N	103.26 W
New Eltham (Neigh.), Eng.	62	51.26 N	0.04 E
New England Ra., Austl. (nû ĭŋ'glănd)	215	29.32 S	152.30 E
Newenham, C., Ak. (nū-ĕn-hăm)	107	58.40 N	162.32 W
Newfane, NY (nū-fān)	113c	43.17 N	78.44 W
New Ferry, Eng.	64a	53.22 N	2.59 W
Newfoundland (Prov.), Can. (nū-fŭn'lănd')(nū'fŭnd-lănd) (nû'found-lănd')	97a	48.15 N	56.53 W
Newgate, Can. (nû'gāt)	99	49.01 N	115.10 W
Newgate Street, Eng.	62	51.44 N	0.07 W
New Georgia (I.), Sol. Is. (jôr'jĭ-ȧ)	215	8.08 S	158.00 E
New Glasgow, Can. (glȧs'gō)	115	45.35 N	62.36 W
New Guinea (I.), Asia (gĭne)	207	5.45 S	140.00 E
Newhalem, Wa. (nū hā'lŭm)	116	48.44 N	121.11 W
Newham (Neigh.), Eng.	62	51.32 N	0.03 E
New Hampshire (State), U. S. (hămp'shĭr)	109	43.55 N	71.40 W
New Hampton, Ia. (hămp'tŭn)	115	43.03 N	92.20 W
New Hanover, S. Afr. (hăn'ôvĕr)	227c	29.23 S	30.32 E
New Hanover (I.), Pap. N. Gui.	207	2.37 S	150.15 E
New Harmony, In. (nū här'mô-nĭ)	110	38.10 N	87.55 W
New Haven, Ct. (hā'vĕn)	111	41.20 N	72.55 W
Newhaven, Eng.	163	50.45 N	0.10 E
New Haven, In. (nū hāv''n)	110	41.05 N	85.00 W
New Hebrides (Is.), Vanuatu	215	16.00 S	167.00 E

PLACE (Pronounciation)	PAGE	Lat. °'	Long. °'
New Hey, Eng.	64b	50.36 N	2.06 W
New Holland, Eng. (hŏl'ănd)	156	53.42 N	0.21 W
New Holland, NC	127	35.27 N	76.14 W
New Hope Mtn., Al. (hōp)	112h	33.23 N	86.45 W
New Hudson, Mi. (hŭd'sŭn)	113b	42.30 N	83.36 W
New Hyde Park, NY	55	40.44 N	73.41 W
New Hythe, Eng.	62	51.19 N	0.27 E
New Iberia, La. (ī-bē'rĭ-ȧ)	125	30.00 N	91.50 W
Newington, Can. (nū'ĕng-tŏn)	95c	45.07 N	75.00 W
New Ireland (I.), Pap. N. Gui. (īr'lănd)	207	3.15 S	152.30 E
New Jersey (State), U. S. (jûr'zĭ)	109	40.30 N	74.50 W
New Kensington, Pa. (kĕn'zĭng-tŭn)	113e	40.34 N	79.35 W
Newkirk, Ok. (nū'kûrk)	123	36.52 N	97.03 W
New Kowloon (Xinjiulong), China	68c	22.20 N	114.10 E
New Lagos (Neigh.), Nig.	71d	6.30 N	3.22 E
New Lenox, Il. (lĕn'ŭk)	113a	41.31 N	87.58 W
New Lexington, Oh. (lĕk'sĭng-tŭn)	110	39.40 N	82.10 W
New Lisbon, Wi. (lĭz'bŭn)	115	43.52 N	90.11 W
New Liskeard, Can.	103	47.30 N	79.40 W
New London, Ct. (lŭn'dŭn)	111	41.20 N	72.05 W
New London, Wi.	115	44.24 N	88.45 W
New Madrid, Mo. (măd'rĭd)	123	36.34 N	89.31 W
Newman (L.), Fl.	127	29.41 N	82.13 W
Newman's Grove, Ne. (nū'măn grōv)	114	41.46 N	97.44 W
Newmarket, Can. (nū'mär-kĕt)	111	44.00 N	79.30 W
Newmarket, S. Afr.	71b	26.17 S	28.08 E
New Martinsville, WV (mär'tĭnz-vĭl)	110	39.35 N	80.50 W
New Meadows, Id.	116	44.58 N	116.20 W
New Mexico (State), U. S. (mĕk'sĭ-kō)	108	34.30 N	107.10 W
New Milford, NJ	55	40.56 N	74.01 W
New Mills, Eng. (mĭlz)	156	53.22 N	2.00 W
New Munster, Wi. (mŭn'stēr)	113a	42.35 N	88.13 W
Newnan, Ga. (nū'năn)	126	33.22 N	84.47 W
New Norfolk, Austl. (nôr'fŏk)	216	42.50 S	147.17 E
New Orleans, La. (ôr'lē-ănz)	112d	30.00 N	90.05 W
New Philadelphia, Oh. (fĭl-ȧ-dĕl'fĭ-ȧ)	110	40.30 N	81.30 W
New Plymouth, N. Z. (plĭm'ŭth)	217	39.04 S	174.13 E
Newport, Ar. (nū'pōrt)	123	35.35 N	91.16 W
Newport, Austl.	70b	37.51 S	144.53 E
Newport, Austl.	211b	33.39 S	151.19 E
Newport, Eng. (nū-pôrt)	162	50.41 N	1.25 W
Newport, Eng.	156	52.46 N	2.22 W
Newport, Ky.	113f	39.05 N	84.30 W
Newport, Me.	104	44.49 N	69.20 W
Newport, Mn.	119g	44.52 N	92.59 W
Newport, NH	111	43.20 N	72.10 W
Newport, Or.	116	44.39 N	124.02 W
Newport, RI	112b	41.29 N	71.16 W
Newport, Tn.	126	35.55 N	83.12 W
Newport, Vt.	111	44.55 N	72.15 W
Newport, Wales	162	51.36 N	3.05 W
Newport, Wa.	116	48.12 N	117.01 W
Newport Beach, Ca. (bēch)	119a	33.36 N	117.55 W
Newport News, Va.	112g	36.59 N	76.24 W
New Prague, Mn. (nū prāg)	115	44.33 N	93.35 W
New Providence (I.), Ba. (prŏv'ĭ-dĕns)	134	25.00 N	77.25 W
New Redruth, S. Afr.	71b	26.16 S	28.07 E
New Richmond, Oh. (rĭch'mŭnd)	110	38.55 N	84.15 W
New Richmond, Wi.	115	45.07 N	92.34 W
New Roads, La. (rōds)	125	30.42 N	91.26 W
New Rochelle, NY (rū-shĕl')	112a	40.55 N	73.47 W
New Rockford, ND (rŏk'fŏrd)	114	47.40 N	99.08 W
New Ross, Ire. (rôs)	166	52.25 N	6.55 W
New Sarepta, Can.	95g	53.17 N	113.09 W
New Siberian Is., see Novosibirskiye O-va			
New Smyrna Beach, Fl. (smûr'nȧ)	127	29.00 N	80.57 W
New South Wales (State), Austl. (wālz)	215	32.45 S	146.14 E
Newton, Can. (nū'tŭn)	95f	49.56 N	98.04 W
Newton, Eng.	156	53.27 N	2.37 W
Newton, Ia.	115	41.42 N	93.04 W
Newton, Il.	110	39.00 N	88.10 W
Newton, Ks.	123	38.03 N	97.22 W
Newton, Ma.	105a	42.21 N	71.13 W
Newton, Ms.	126	32.18 N	89.10 W
Newton, NJ	112a	41.03 N	74.45 W
Newton, NC	127	35.40 N	81.19 W
Newton, Tx.	125	30.47 N	93.45 W
Newton (Neigh.), Austl.	70a	33.54 S	151.11 E
Newton Brook (Neigh.), Can.	54c	43.48 N	79.24 W
Newton Highlands, Ma.	54a	41.19 N	71.13 W
Newton Lower Falls, Ma.	54a	42.19 N	71.23 W
Newtonsville, Oh. (nū'tŭnz-vĭl)	113f	39.11 N	84.04 W
Newton Upper Falls, Ma.	54a	42.19 N	71.13 W
Newtonville, Ma.	54a	42.21 N	71.13 W
Newtown, ND (nū'toun)	114	47.57 N	102.25 W
Newtown, Oh.	113f	39.08 N	84.22 W
Newtown, Pa.	112f	40.13 N	74.56 W
Newtownards, Ire. (nu-t'n-ardz')	162	54.35 N	5.39 W
New Ulm, Mn. (ŭlm)	115	44.18 N	94.27 W
New Utrecht (Neigh.), NY	55	40.36 N	73.59 W
New Waterford, Can. (wô'tēr-fērd)	105	46.15 N	60.05 W
New Westminster, Can. (wĕst'mĭn-stēr)	118d	49.12 N	122.55 W
New York, NY (yôrk)	112a	40.40 N	73.58 W
New York (State), U. S.	109	42.45 N	78.05 W
New Zealand, Oceania (zē'lănd)	215a	42.00 S	175.00 E
Nexapa (R.), Mex. (nĕks-ä'pä)	130	18.32 N	98.29 W
Neya-gawa, Jap. (nā'yä gä'wä)	205b	34.47 N	135.38 E
Neyshābūr, Iran	192	36.06 N	58.45 E
Neyva R., Sov. Un. (nēy'vȧ)	182a	57.39 N	60.37 E
Nezhin, Sov. Un. (nyĕzh'ēn)	175	50.03 N	31.52 E
Nez Perce, Id. (nĕz' pûrs')	116	46.16 N	116.15 W
Ngami (R.), Bots. (n'gä'mē)	226	20.56 S	22.31 E
Ngamouéri, Con.	71c	4.14 S	15.14 E
Ngangerabeli Pln., Ken.	231	1.20 S	40.10 E

PLACE (Pronounciation)	PAGE	Lat. °'	Long. °'
Ngangla Ringco (L.), China (ŋäŋ-lä rĭŋ-tswo)	196	31.42 N	82.53 E
Ngaoundéré, Cam. (n'gōn-dȧ-rā')	229	7.19 N	13.35 E
Ngarimbi, Tan.	231	8.28 S	38.36 E
Ngoko (R.), Afr.	230	1.55 N	15.53 E
Ngol-Kedju Hill, Cam.	229	6.20 N	9.45 E
Ngombe, Zaire	71c	4.24 S	15.11 E
Ngong, Ken. ('n-gông)	227	1.27 S	36.39 E
Ngounié (R.), Gabon	230	1.15 S	10.43 E
Ngoywa, Tan.	231	5.56 S	32.48 E
Ngqeleni, S. Afr. ('ng-kĕ-lā'nē)	227c	31.41 S	29.04 E
Nguigmi, Niger ('n-gēg'mē)	229	14.15 N	13.07 E
Ngunza, Ang.	230	11.13 S	13.50 E
Ngurore, Nig.	229	9.18 N	12.14 E
Nguru, Nig. ('n-gōō'rōō)	224	12.53 N	10.26 E
Nguru Mts., Tan.	231	6.10 S	37.35 E
Nha-trang, Viet. (nyä-träng')	206	12.08 N	108.56 E
Niafounke, Mali	224	16.03 N	4.17 W
Niagara, Wi. (nī-ăg'ȧ-rȧ)	115	45.45 N	88.05 W
Niagara Falls, Can.	113c	43.05 N	79.05 W
Niagara Falls, NY	113c	43.06 N	79.02 W
Niagara-on-the-Lake, Can.	95d	43.16 N	79.05 W
Niagara R., U. S.-Can.	113c	43.12 N	79.03 W
Niakaramandougou, Ivory Coast	228	8.40 N	5.17 W
Niamey, Niger (nē-ä-mā')	229	13.31 N	2.07 E
Niamtougou, Togo	228	9.46 N	1.06 E
Niangara, Zaire (nē-äŋ-gȧ'rȧ)	231	3.42 N	27.52 E
Niangua (R.), Mo. (nī-ăŋ'gwȧ)	123	37.30 N	93.05 W
Nias, Pulau (I.), Indon. (nē'äs')	206	0.58 N	97.43 E
Nibe, Den. (nē'bĕ)	164	56.57 N	9.36 E
Nicaragua, N. A. (nĭk-ȧ-rä'gwȧ)	128	12.45 N	86.15 W
Nicaragua, Lago de (L.), Nic. (lä'gō dĕ)	132	11.45 N	85.28 W
Nicastro, It. (nē-käs'trō)	172	38.39 N	16.15 E
Nicchehabin, Punta (Pt.), Mex. (pōō'n-tä-nĕk-chĕ-ä-bē'n)	132a	19.50 N	87.20 W
Nice, Fr. (nēs)	169	43.42 N	7.21 E
Nicheng, China (nē-chŭŋ)	201b	30.54 N	121.48 E
Nichicun (L.), Can. (nĭch'ĭ-kŭn)	97	53.07 N	72.10 W
Nicholas Chan., Ba. (nĭk'ô-lȧs)	134	23.30 N	80.20 W
Nicholasville, Ky. (nĭk'ô-lȧs-vĭl)	110	37.55 N	84.35 W
Nicobar Is., Andaman & Nicobar Is. (nĭk-ô-bär')	206	8.28 N	94.04 E
Nicolai Mtn., Or. (nē-cō lī')	118c	46.05 N	123.27 W
Nicolás Romero, Mex. (nē-kô-lá's rô-mĕ'rô)	131a	19.38 N	99.20 W
Nicolet, L., Mi. (nĭ'kŏ-lĕt)	119k	46.22 N	84.14 W
Nicolls Town, Ba.	134	25.10 N	78.00 W
Nicols, Mn. (nĭk'ĕls)	119g	44.50 N	93.12 W
Nicomeki (R.), Can.	118d	49.04 N	122.47 W
Nicosia, Cyprus (nē-kô-sē'ȧ)	161	35.10 N	33.22 E
Nicoya, C. R. (nē-kō'yä)	132	10.08 N	85.27 W
Nicoya, Golfo de (G.), C. R. (gôl-fô-dĕ)	132	10.03 N	85.04 W
Nicoya, Pen. de, C. R.	132	10.05 N	86.00 W
Nidaros, see Trondheim			
Nidzica, Pol. (nĕ-jēt'sȧ)	167	53.21 N	20.30 E
Niederaden (Neigh.), F.R.G.	63	51.36 N	7.34 E
Niederbonsfeld, F.R.G.	63	51.23 N	7.08 E
Niederdonk, F.R.G.	63	51.14 N	6.41 E
Niederelfringhausen, F.R.G.	63	51.21 N	7.10 E
Niedere Tauern (Mts.), Aus.	166	47.15 N	13.41 E
Niederkrüchten, F.R.G. (nē'dĕr-krük-tĕn)	169c	51.12 N	6.14 E
Nieder-Neuendorf, G.D.R.	65a	52.37 N	13.12 E
Niederösterreich (Lower Austria) (State), Aus.	157e	48.24 N	16.20 E
Niedersachsen (Lower Saxony) (State), F.R.G. (nē'dĕr-zäĸ-sĕn)	166	52.52 N	8.27 E
Niederschöneweide (Neigh.), G.D.R.	65a	52.27 N	13.31 E
Niederschönhausen (Neigh.), G.D.R.	65a	52.35 N	13.23 E
Niélé, Ivory Coast	228	10.12 N	5.38 W
Niellim, Chad	229	9.42 N	17.49 E
Niemeyer (Neigh.), Braz.	61c	23.00 S	43.15 W
Nienburg, F.R.G. (nē'ĕn-bōōrgh)	166	52.40 N	9.15 E
Niénokoué, Mont (Mtn.), Ivory Coast	228	5.26 N	7.10 W
Nierst, F.R.G.	63	51.19 N	6.43 E
Nietverdiend, S. Afr.	223d	25.02 S	26.10 E
Nieuw Nickerie, Sur. (nē-nē'kĕ-rē')	143	5.51 N	57.00 W
Nieves, Mex. (nyā'vȧs)	130	24.00 N	102.57 W
Niğde, Tur. (nĭg'dĕ)	179	37.55 N	34.40 E
Nigel, S. Afr. (nī'jĕl)	223d	26.26 S	28.27 E
Niger, Afr. (nī'jēr)	222	18.02 N	8.30 E
Niger (R.), Afr.	229	5.33 N	6.33 E
Niger Delta, Nig.	229	4.45 N	5.20 E
Nigeria, Afr. (nī-jē'rĭ-ȧ)	222	8.57 N	6.30 E
Nihoa (I.), Hi.	106b	23.15 N	161.30 W
Nihonbashi (Neigh.), Jap.	69a	35.41 N	139.47 E
Nii (I.), Jap. (nē)	205	34.26 N	139.23 E
Niigata, Jap. (nē'ē-gä'tȧ)	204	37.47 N	139.04 E
Niihau (I.), Hi. (nē'ē-ha'ōō)	106a	21.50 N	160.05 W
Niimi, Jap. (nē'mē)	205	34.59 N	133.28 E
Niiza, Jap.	205a	35.48 N	139.34 E
Nijmegen, Neth. (nī'mā-gĕn)	163	51.50 N	5.52 E
Nikaidō, Jap. (nē'kī-dô)	205b	34.36 N	135.48 E
Nikitinka, Sov. Un. (nē-kĭ'tĭn-kȧ)	174	55.33 N	33.19 E
Nikkō, Jap. (nēk'kō)	205	36.44 N	139.35 E
Nikolayev, Sov. Un. (nē-kô-lä'yĕf)	175	46.58 N	32.02 E
Nikolayev (Oblast), Sov. Un. (ôb'låst)	175	47.27 N	31.25 E
Nikolayevka, Sov. Un. (nē-kô-lä'yĕf-kȧ)	182c	59.29 N	29.48 E
Nikolayevka, Sov. Un.	204	48.37 N	134.09 E
Nikolayevskiy, Sov. Un.	179	50.00 N	45.30 E
Nikolayevsk-na-Amure, Sov. Un.	181	53.18 N	140.49 E
Nikolo-Chovanskoje, Sov. Un.	66b	55.36 N	37.27 E
Nikol'sk, Sov. Un. (nē-kôlsk')	178	59.30 N	45.40 E
Nikol'skoye, Sov. Un. (nē-kôl'skô-yĕ)	182c	59.27 N	30.00 E
Nikopol, Bul. (nē'kô-pŏl')	173	43.41 N	24.52 E
Nikopol', Sov. Un.	175	47.36 N	34.24 E
Nikšić, Yugo. (nēk'shĕch)	173	42.45 N	18.57 E
Nilahue (R.), Chile (nē-lä'wĕ)	141b	36.36 S	71.50 W
Nile (R.), Afr. (nīl)	225	19.15 N	32.30 E

PLACE (Pronounciation)	PAGE	Lat. °'	Long. °'
Niles, Il.	58a	42.01 N	87.49 W
Niles, Mi. (nīlz)	110	41.50 N	86.15 W
Niles, Oh.	110	41.15 N	80.45 W
Nileshwar, India	197	12.08 N	74.14 E
Nilgani, India	67a	22.46 N	88.26 E
Nilgiri Hills, India	197	17.05 N	76.22 E
Nilópolis, Braz. (nē-lô'pō-lĕs)	144b	22.48 S	43.25 W
Nimba, Mont (Mtn.), Ivory Coast (nĭm'bȧ)	224	7.40 N	8.33 W
Nimba Mts., Gui.-Ivory Coast	228	7.30 N	8.35 W
Nimrod Res., Ar. (nĭm'rŏd)	123	34.58 N	93.46 W
Nimule, Sud. (nē-mōō'lȧ)	225	3.38 N	32.12 E
Ninda, Ang.	230	14.47 S	21.24 E
Nine Ashes, Eng.	62	51.42 N	0.18 E
Ninety Mile Bch., Austl.	216	38.20 S	147.30 E
Nineveh (Ruins), Iraq (nĭn'ē-vȧ)	179	36.30 N	43.10 E
Ning'an, China (nĭŋ-än)	202	44.20 N	129.20 E
Ningbo, China (nĭŋ-bwo)	203	29.56 N	121.30 E
Ningde, China (nĭŋ-dŭ)	203	26.38 N	119.33 E
Ninghai, China (nĭng'hī')	203	29.20 N	121.20 E
Ninghe, China (nĭŋ-hŭ)	200	39.20 N	167.50 E
Ningjin, China (nĭŋ-jyĭn)	200	37.39 N	116.47 E
Ningjin, China	200	37.37 N	114.55 E
Ningming, China	203	22.22 N	107.06 E
Ningwu, China (nĭng'wōō')	202	39.00 N	112.12 E
Ningxia Huizu (Aut. Reg.), China (nĭŋ-shyä)	198	37.10 N	106.00 E
Ningyang, China (nĭng'yäng')	200	35.46 N	116.48 E
Ninh Binh, Viet. (nĕn bĕnk')	203	20.22 N	106.00 E
Ninigo Group (Is.), Pap. N. Gui.	207	1.15 S	143.30 E
Ninnescah (R.), Ks. (nĭn'ĕs-kä)	122	37.37 N	98.31 W
Nioaque, Braz. (nēô-ä'-kĕ)	143	21.14 S	55.41 W
Niobrara (R.), Ne. (nī-ô-brâr'ȧ)	114	42.46 N	98.46 W
Niokolo Koba, Parc Natl. du (Natl. Pk.), Senegal	228	13.05 N	13.00 W
Nīl, Nahr an-, see Nile (R.)			
Nīmach, India	196	24.32 N	74.51 E
Nioro du Sahel, Mali (nē-ō'rō)	228	15.15 N	9.35 W
Nipawin, Can.	100	53.22 N	104.00 W
Nipe, Bahía de (B.), Cuba (bä-ē'ä-dĕ-nē'pä)	135	20.50 N	75.30 W
Nipe, Sierra de (Mts.), Cuba (sē-ĕ'r-rȧ-dĕ)	135	20.20 N	75.50 W
Nipigon, Can. (nĭp'ĭ-gŏn)	110	48.58 N	88.17 W
Nipigon B., Can.	115	48.56 N	88.00 W
Nipigon (L.), Can.	102	49.37 N	89.55 W
Nipisiguit (R.), Can. (nĭ-pĭ'sĭ-kwĭt)	104	47.26 N	66.15 W
Nipissing (L.), Can. (nĭp'ĭ-sĭng)	103	45.59 N	80.19 W
Niquero, Cuba (nē-kā'rō)	134	20.00 N	77.35 W
Nirmali, India	196	26.30 N	86.43 E
Nîmes, Fr. (nēm)	168	43.49 N	4.22 E
Niš, Yugo. (nēsh)	173	43.18 N	21.55 E
Nisa, Port. (nē'sȧ)	170	39.32 N	7.41 W
Nišava (R.), Yugo. (nē'shȧ-vȧ)	173	43.17 N	22.17 E
Nishi, Jap.	69b	34.41 N	135.30 E
Nishinari (Neigh.), Jap.	69b	34.38 N	135.28 E
Nishino (I.), Jap. (nēsh'ē-nô)	205	36.06 N	132.49 E
Nishinomiya, Jap. (nēsh'ē-nô-mē'yȧ)	205b	34.44 N	135.21 E
Nishinoomote, Jap. (nēsh'ē-nô-mō'tō)	205	30.44 N	130.59 E
Nishio, Jap. (nēsh'ē-ô)	205	34.50 N	137.01 E
Nishionmiya, Jap.	69b	34.43 N	135.20 E
Nishiyodogawa (Neigh.), Jap.	69b	34.42 N	135.27 E
Niska L., Can. (nĭs'kȧ)	100	55.35 N	108.38 W
Nisko, Pol. (nēs'kô)	167	50.30 N	22.07 E
Nisku, Can. (nĭs-kū')	95g	53.21 N	113.33 W
Nisqually R., Wa. (nĭs-kwôl'ĭ)	116	46.51 N	122.33 W
Nissan (R.), Swe.	164	57.06 N	13.22 E
Nisser (L.), Nor. (nĭs'ĕr)	164	59.14 N	8.35 E
Nissum Fd., Den.	164	56.24 N	7.35 E
Niterói, Braz. (nē-tĕ-rô'ĭ)	144b	22.53 S	43.07 W
Nith (R.), Scot. (nĭth)	162	55.13 N	3.55 W
Nitra, Czech. (nē'trȧ)	167	48.18 N	18.04 E
Nitra R., Czech.	167	48.13 N	18.14 E
Nitro, WV (nī'trō)	110	38.25 N	81.50 W
Niue, Oceania (nĭ'ōō)	209	19.50 S	167.00 W
Nivelles, Bel. (nē'vĕl')	163	50.33 N	4.17 E
Níkaia, Grc.	66d	37.58 N	23.39 E
Nízke Tatry (Mts.), Czech.	167	48.57 N	19.18 E
Nixon, Tx. (nĭk'sŭn)	125	29.16 N	97.48 W
Nizāmābād, India	196	18.48 N	78.07 E
Nizhne-Angarsk, Sov. Un. (nyēzh'nyĭ-ŭngärsk')	181	55.49 N	108.46 E
Nizhne-Chirskaya, Sov. Un. (nyĭ-ŭn-gärsk')	179	48.20 N	42.50 E
Nizhne-Kolymsk, Sov. Un. (kô-lēmsk')	181	68.32 N	160.56 E
Nizhneudinsk, Sov. Un. (nĕzh'nyĭ-ōōdēnsk')	180	54.58 N	99.15 E
Nizhniye Sergi, Sov. Un. (nyĕzh' nyē sĕr'gē)	182a	56.41 N	59.19 E
Nizhniye Serogozy, Sov. Un. (nyĕzh'nyĭ sĕ-rô-gô'zĭ)	175	46.51 N	34.25 E
Nizhniy Tagil, Sov. Un. (tŭgĕl')	182a	57.54 N	59.59 E
Nizhnyaya (Lower) Tunguska (R.), Sov. Un. (tōōn-gōōs'kȧ)	180	64.13 N	91.30 E
Nizhnyaya Kur'ya, Sov. Un. (nyĕ'zhnyȧ-yȧ koōr'yȧ)	182a	58.01 N	56.00 E
Nizhnyaya Salda, Sov. Un. (nyĕ'zhnya'ya säl'da')	182a	58.05 N	60.43 E
Nizhnyaya Taymyra (R.), Sov. Un.	180	72.30 N	95.18 E
Nizhnyaya Tura, Sov. Un. (tōō'rȧ)	182a	58.38 N	59.50 E
Nizhnyaya Us'va, Sov. Un. (ōō'vȧ)	182a	59.05 N	58.53 E
Njombe, Tan.	231	9.20 S	34.46 E
Njurunda, Swe. (nyōō-rōōn'dȧ)	164	62.15 N	17.24 E
Nkala Mission, Zambia	231	15.55 S	26.00 E
Nkandla, S. Afr. ('n-känd'lä)	227c	28.40 S	31.06 E
Nkawkaw, Ghana	228	6.33 N	0.47 W
Noākhāli, Bngl.	196	22.52 N	91.08 E
Noatak, Ak. (nō-ȧ'tȧk)	107	67.22 N	163.28 W
Noatak (R.), Ak.	107	67.58 N	162.15 W
Nobeoka, Jap. (nō-bȧ-ō'kȧ)	205	32.36 N	131.41 E

ng-sing; ŋ-baŋk; ɴ-nasalized n; nŏd; cŏmmit; ōld; ôbey; ôrder; oi-boil; fōōd; fŏŏt; ou-out; s-soft; sh-dish; th-thin; pūre; ûnite; ûrn; stŭd; circŭs; ü-as in French tu; '-indeterminate vowel.

PLACE (Pronounciation)	PAGE	Lat. °'	Long. °'
Noblesville, In. (nō'bl'z-vĭl)	110	40.00 N	86.00 W
Nobleton, Can. (nō'bl'tŭn)	95d	43.54 N	79.39 W
Noborito, Jap.	69a	35.37 N	139.34 E
Nocera Inferiore, It. (ĕn-fĕ-ryô'rē)	171c	40.30 N	14.38 E
Nochistlán, Mex. (nô-chēs-tlän')	130	21.23 N	102.52 W
Nochixtlón (Asunción), Mex. (ä-sōōn-syōn')	131	17.28 N	97.12 W
Nogales, Az. (nô-gä'lĕs)	121	31.20 N	110.55 W
Nogales, Mex. (nō-gä'lĕs)	131	18.49 N	97.09 W
Nogales, Mex.	128	31.15 N	111.00 W
Nogal Val., Som. (nŏ'găl)	223a	8.30 N	47.50 E
Nogaysk, Sov. Un. (nō-gīsk')	175	46.43 N	36.21 E
Nogent-le-Roi, Fr. (nō-zhôn-lĕ-rwä')	169b	48.39 N	1.32 E
Nogent-le-Rotrou, Fr. (rō-trōō')	168	48.22 N	0.47 E
Nogent-sur-Marne, Fr.	64c	48.50 N	2.29 E
Noginsk, Sov. Un. (nô-gēnsk')	182b	55.52 N	38.28 E
Noguera Pallares (R.), Sp.	171	42.18 N	1.03 E
Noirmoutier, Île de (I.), Fr. (nwȧr-mōō-tyā')	168	47.03 N	3.08 W
Noisy-le-Grand, Fr.	64c	48.51 N	2.33 E
Noisy-le-Roi, Fr.	64c	48.51 N	2.04 E
Noisy-le-Sec, Fr.	64c	48.53 N	2.28 E
Nojimā-Zaki (Pt.), Jap. (nō'jē-mä zä-kē)	205	35.54 N	139.48 E
Nokomis, Il. (nō-kō'mĭs)	110	39.15 N	89.10 W
Nola, It. (nô'lä)	171c	40.41 N	14.32 E
Nolinsk, Sov. Un. (nō-lēnsk')	178	57.32 N	49.50 E
Noma Misaki (C.), Jap. (nō'mä mē'sä-kē)	205	31.25 N	130.09 E
Nombre de Dios, Mex. (nôm-brĕ-dĕ-dyō's)	130	23.50 N	104.14 W
Nombre de Dios, Pan. (nô'm-brĕ)	133	9.34 N	79.28 W
Nome, Ak. (nōm)	107	64.30 N	165.20 W
Nonacho (L.), Can.	96	61.48 N	111.20 W
Nonantum, Ma.	54a	42.20 N	71.12 W
Nong'an, China (nôŋ-än)	202	44.25 N	125.10 E
Nongoma, S. Afr. (nōn-gō'mȧ)	226	27.48 S	31.45 E
Nooksack, Wa. (no͝ok'săk)	118d	48.55 N	122.19 W
Nooksack (R.), Wa.	118d	48.54 N	122.31 W
Noordwijk aan Zee, Neth.	157a	52.14 N	4.25 E
Noordzee, Kanal, (Can.), Neth.	157a	52.27 N	4.42 E
Nootka (I.), Can. (nōōt'kȧ)	96	49.32 N	126.42 W
Nootka Sd., Can.	98	49.33 N	126.38 W
Nóqui, Ang. (nô-kē')	230	5.51 S	13.25 E
Nor (R.), China (nou')	204	46.55 N	132.45 E
Nora, In. (nō'rä)	113g	39.54 N	86.08 W
Nora, Swe.	164	59.32 N	14.56 E
Noranda, Can.	103	48.15 N	79.01 W
Norbeck, Md. (nôr'bĕk)	112e	39.06 N	77.05 W
Norborne, Mo. (nôr'bôrn)	123	39.17 N	93.39 W
Norco, Ca. (nôr'kô)	119a	33.57 N	117.33 W
Norcross, Ga. (nôr'krôs)	112c	33.56 N	84.13 W
Nordegg, Can. (nûr'dĕg)	99	52.28 N	116.04 W
Norden, Eng.	64b	53.38 N	2.13 W
Norden, F.R.G. (nôr'dĕn)	166	53.35 N	7.14 E
Norderney I., F.R.G. (nōr'dĕr-nĕy)	166	53.45 N	6.58 E
Nord Fd., Nor. (nô'fyôr)	164	61.50 N	5.35 E
Nordhausen, G.D.R. (nôrt'hau-zĕn)	166	51.30 N	10.48 E
Nordhorn, F.R.G. (nôrt'hôrn)	166	52.26 N	7.05 E
Nordland, Wa. (nôrd'lȧnd)	118a	48.03 N	122.41 W
Nördlingen, F.R.G. (nûrt'lĭng-ĕn)	166	48.51 N	10.30 E
Nord-Ostsee Kan. (Kiel) Can., F.R.G. (nörd-özt-zā) (kēl)	166	54.03 N	9.23 E
Nordrhein-Westfalen (North Rhine-Westphalia) (State), F.R.G. (nörd'hīn-vĕst-fä-lĕn)	166	50.50 N	6.53 E
Nord, Riviere du, Can. (rēv-yĕr' dü nōr)	95a	45.45 N	74.02 W
Nordvik, Sov. Un. (nôrd'vĕk)	181	73.57 N	111.15 E
Nore R., Ire. (nōr)	162	52.34 N	7.15 W
Norf, F.R.G.	63	51.09 N	6.43 E
Norfield, Ms. (nôr'fēld)	126	31.24 N	90.25 W
Norfolk, Ma. (nôr'fŏk)	105a	42.07 N	71.19 W
Norfolk, Ne.	114	42.10 N	97.25 W
Norfolk, Oceania	208	27.10 S	166.50 E
Norfolk, Va.	112g	36.55 N	76.15 W
Norfork, L., Ar.	123	36.25 N	92.09 W
Noria, Mex. (nō'rē-ȧ)	130	23.04 N	106.20 W
Noril'sk, Sov. Un. (nô rēlsk')	180	69.00 N	87.11 E
Normal, Il. (nôr'măl)	110	40.35 N	89.00 W
Norman, Ok. (nôr'măn)	123	35.13 N	97.25 W
Norman (R.), Austl.	215	18.27 S	141.29 E
Normandie (Reg.), Fr. (nōr-män-dē')	168	49.02 N	0.17 E
Normandie, Collines de (Hills), Fr. (kō-lēn'dĕ-nōr-män-dē')	168	48.46 N	0.50 W
Normandy Heights, Md.	56c	39.17 N	76.48 W
Normanhurst, Austl.	70a	33.43 S	151.06 E
Norman, L., NC	127	35.30 N	80.53 W
Normanton, Austl. (nôr'măn-tŭn)	215	17.45 S	141.10 E
Normanton, Eng.	156	53.40 N	1.21 W
Norman Wells, Can.	96	65.26 N	127.00 W
Nornalup, Austl. (nôr-năl'ŭp)	214	35.00 S	117.00 E
Norra Dellen (L.), Swe.	164	61.57 N	16.25 E
Nørresundby, Den. (nû-rĕ-so͞on'bü)	164	57.04 N	9.55 E
Norridge, Il.	58a	41.57 N	87.49 W
Norris, Tn. (nŏr'ĭs)	126	36.09 N	84.05 W
Norris (R.), Tn.	126	36.17 N	84.10 W
Norristown, Pa. (nŏr'ĭs-town)	112f	40.07 N	75.21 W
Norrköping, Swe. (nôr'chûp'ĭng)	164	58.37 N	16.10 E
Norrtälje, Swe. (nôr-tĕl'yĕ)	164	59.47 N	18.39 E
Norseman, Austl. (nôrs'măn)	214	32.15 S	122.00 E
Norte, Punta (Pt.), Arg. (po͞o'n-tä-nōr'tĕ)	141c	36.17 S	56.46 W
Norte, Serra do (Mts.), Braz. (sĕ'r-rä-dô-nôr'te)	143	12.04 S	59.08 W
North Abington, Ma.	54a	42.08 N	70.57 W
North Adams, Ma. (ăd'ămz)	111	42.40 N	73.05 W
Northam, Austl. (nôr-dhăm)	214	31.50 S	116.45 E
Northam, S. Afr. (nôr'thăm)	223d	24.52 S	27.16 E
North America (ȧ-mĕr'ĭ-kȧ)	94		
North American Basin, Atl. O. (ȧ-mĕr'ĭ-kăn)	129	23.45 N	62.45 W
Northampton, Austl. (nôr-thămp'tŭn)	214	28.22 S	114.45 E
Northampton, Eng. (nôrth-ămp'tŭn)	162	52.14 N	0.56 W
Northampton, Ma.	111	42.20 N	72.45 W
Northampton, Pa.	111	40.45 N	75.30 W
Northamptonshire (Co.), Eng.	156	52.25 N	0.47 W
North Andaman I., Andaman & Nicobar Is. (ăn-dȧ-măn')	206	13.15 N	93.30 E
North Andover, Ma. (ăn'dô-vēr)	105a	42.42 N	71.07 W
North Arlington, NJ	55	40.47 N	74.08 W
North Arm, Can. (ärm)	118d	49.13 N	123.01 W
North Atlanta, Ga. (ăt-lăn'tȧ)	112c	33.52 N	84.20 W
North Attleboro, Ma. (ăt''l-bŭr-ô)	112b	41.59 N	71.18 W
North Auburn, Austl.	70a	33.50 S	151.02 E
North Baltimore, Oh. (bôl'tĭ-môr)	110	41.10 N	83.40 W
North Balwyn, Austl.	70b	37.48 S	145.05 E
North Barnaby, Md.	56d	38.49 N	76.57 W
North Barrackpore, India	67a	22.46 N	88.22 E
North Basque, Tx. (băsk)	124	31.56 N	98.01 W
North Battleford, Can. (băt''l-fērd)	100	52.47 N	108.17 W
North Bay, Can.	103	46.13 N	79.26 W
North Beach (Neigh.), Ca.	58b	37.48 N	122.25 W
North Bellmore, NY	55	40.41 N	73.32 W
North Bend, Or. (bĕnd)	116	43.23 N	124.13 W
North Bergen, NJ	55	40.48 N	74.01 W
North Berwick, Me. (bûr'wĭk)	104	43.18 N	70.46 W
North Bight, Ba. (bĭt)	134	24.30 N	77.40 W
North Bimini (I.), Ba. (bĭ'mĭ-nē)	134	25.45 N	79.20 W
North Borneo (Reg.), see Sabah			
Northborough, Ma. (nôrth'bûr-ô)	105a	42.19 N	71.39 W
North Box Hill, Austl.	70b	37.48 S	145.07 E
North Braddock, Pa.	57b	40.24 N	79.52 W
Northbridge, Austl.	70a	33.49 S	151.13 E
Northbridge, Ma. (nôrth'brĭj)	105a	42.09 N	71.39 W
North C., Can.	105c	47.02 N	60.25 W
North C., N.Z.	217	34.31 S	173.02 E
North Caicos (I.), Turks & Caicos (kī'kôs)	135	21.55 N	72.00 W
North Caldwell, NJ	55	40.52 N	74.16 W
North Carolina (State), U. S. (kăr-ô-lī'nȧ)	109	35.40 N	81.30 W
North Cascades Natl. Pk., Wa.	99	48.50 N	120.50 W
North Cat Cay (I.), Ba.	134	25.35 N	79.20 W
North Chan, N. Ire.-Scot.	162	55.15 N	7.56 W
North Chan (B.), Can. (chăn)	110	46.10 N	83.20 W
North Charleston, SC (chärlz'tŭn)	127	32.49 N	79.57 W
North Chicago, Il. (shĭ-kô'gō)	113a	42.19 N	87.51 W
Northcliff (Neigh.), S. Afr.	71b	26.09 S	27.58 E
North College Hill, Oh. (kŏl'ĕj hĭl)	113f	39.13 N	84.33 W
North Concho, Tx. (kŏn'chō)	124	31.40 N	100.48 W
North Cooking Lake, Can. (ko͝ok'ĭng lāk)	95g	53.28 N	112.57 W
Northcote, Austl.	70b	37.46 S	145.00 E
North Dakota (State), U. S. (dȧ-kō'tȧ)	108	47.20 N	101.55 W
North Downs, Eng. (dounz)	162	51.11 N	0.01 W
North Downs (Plat.), Eng.	62	51.10 N	0.10 E
North Dum-Dum, India	196a	22.38 N	88.23 E
Northeast C., Ak. (nôrth-ēst)	107	63.15 N	169.04 W
Northeast Providence Chan., Ba. (prŏv'ĭ-dĕns)	134	25.45 N	77.00 W
Northeast Pt., Ba.	135	21.25 N	73.00 W
Northeast Pt., Ba.	135	22.45 N	73.50 W
Northeim, F.R.G. (nôrt'hīm)	166	51.42 N	9.59 E
North Elbow Cays (Is.), Ba.	134	23.55 N	80.30 W
North Englewood, Md.	56d	38.55 N	76.55 W
Northern Cheyenne Ind. Res., Mt.	117	45.32 N	106.43 W
Northern Dvina (R.), see Severnaya Dvina			
Northern Ireland, U. K. (īr'lănd)	162	54.48 N	7.00 W
Northern Land (Is.), see Severnaya Zemlya			
Northern Territory, Austl.	214	18.15 S	133.00 E
North Essendon, Austl.	70b	37.45 S	144.54 E
Northfield, Il.	58a	42.06 N	87.46 W
Northfield, Mn. (nôrth'fēld)	115	44.28 N	93.11 W
North Fitzroy, Austl.	70b	37.47 S	144.59 E
Northfleet, Eng.	62	51.27 N	0.21 E
North Flinders, Ra., Austl. (flĭn'dērz)	216	31.55 S	138.45 E
North Foreland, Eng. (dōr'lȧnd)	163	51.20 N	1.30 E
North Franklin Mt., Tx. (frăŋ'klĭn)	124	31.55 N	106.30 W
North Frisian Is., Den.	164	55.16 N	8.15 E
North Gamboa, Pan. (gäm-bô'ä)	128a	9.07 N	79.40 W
North Germiston, S. Afr.	71b	26.14 S	28.09 E
North Gower, Can. (gŏw'ēr)	95c	45.08 N	75.43 W
North Haledon, NJ	55	40.58 N	74.11 W
North Hanover, Ma.	54a	42.09 N	70.52 W
North Hills, NY	55	40.47 N	73.41 W
North Hollywood, Ca. (hŏl'ē-wo͝od)	119a	34.10 N	118.23 W
North I., Ca.	120a	32.39 N	117.14 W
North I., N. Z.	217	37.20 S	173.30 E
North Judson, In. (jŭd'sŭn)	110	41.15 N	86.50 W
North Kamloops, Can. (kăm'lo͞ops)	99	50.41 N	120.22 W
North Kansas City, Mo. (kăn'zȧs)	119f	39.08 N	94.34 W
North Kingstown, RI	112b	41.34 N	71.26 W
Northlake, Il.	58a	41.55 N	87.54 W
North Little Rock, Ar. (lĭt''l rŏk)	123	34.46 N	92.13 W
North Loup (R.), Ne. (lo͞op)	114	42.05 N	100.10 W
North Manchester, In. (măn'chĕs-tēr)	110	41.00 N	85.45 W
North Manly, Austl.	70a	33.46 S	151.16 E
Northmead, Austl.	70a	33.47 S	151.00 E
Northmead, S. Afr.	71b	26.10 S	28.20 E
North Merrick, NY	55	40.41 N	73.34 W
Northmoor, Mo. (nôth'mo͞or)	119f	39.10 N	94.37 W
North Moose L., Can.	101	54.09 N	100.20 W
North Mount Lofty Ranges, Austl.	216	33.50 S	138.30 E
North Ockendon (Neigh.), Eng.	62	51.32 N	0.18 E
North Ogden, Ut. (ŏg'dĕn)	119b	41.18 N	111.58 W
North Ogden Pk., Ut.	119b	41.23 N	111.59 W
North Olmsted, Oh. (ōlm-stĕd)	113d	41.25 N	81.55 W
North Parramatta, Austl.	70a	33.48 S	151.00 E
North Pease (R.), Tx. (pēz)	122	34.19 N	100.58 W
North Pender (I.), Can. (pĕn'dēr)	118d	48.48 N	123.16 W
North Philadelphia (Neigh.), Pa.	56b	39.58 N	75.09 W
North Plains, Or. (plānz)	118c	45.36 N	123.00 W
North Platte, Ne. (plăt)	114	41.08 N	100.45 W
North Platte, (R.), U. S.	108	41.20 N	102.40 W
North Point, Hong Kong	68c	22.17 N	114.12 E
Northport, Al. (nôrth'pōrt)	126	33.12 N	87.35 W
Northport, NY	112a	40.53 N	73.20 W
Northport, Wa.	116	48.53 N	117.47 W
North Pt., Barb.	133b	13.22 N	59.36 W
North Pt., Mi.	110	45.00 N	83.20 W
North Quincy, Ma.	54a	42.17 N	71.01 W
North Randolph, Ma.	54a	42.12 N	71.04 W
North Reading, Ma. (rĕd'ĭng)	105a	42.34 N	71.04 W
North Rhine-Westphalia (State), see Nordrhein-Westfalen			
North Richland Hills, Tx.	119c	32.50 N	97.13 W
North Richmond, Ca.	58b	37.57 N	122.22 W
Northridge, Ca. (nôrth'ridj)	119a	34.14 N	118.32 W
North Ridgeville, Oh. (rĭj-vĭl)	113d	41.23 N	82.01 W
North Riverside, Il.	58a	41.51 N	87.49 W
North Royalton, Oh. (roi'ăl-tŭn)	113d	41.19 N	81.44 W
North Ryde, Austl.	70a	33.48 S	151.07 E
North Saint Paul, Mn. (sānt pôl')	115g	45.01 N	92.59 W
North Saskatchewan (R.), Can. (săn-kăch'ē-wän)	100	52.40 N	106.45 W
North Sea, Eur.	158	56.09 N	3.16 E
North Side (Neigh.), Pa.	57b	40.28 N	80.01 W
North Skunk (R.), Ia. (skŭnk)	115	41.39 N	92.46 W
North Springfield, Va.	56d	38.48 N	77.13 W
North Stradbroke I., Austl. (străd'brōk)	215	27.45 S	154.18 E
North Sydney, Austl.	70a	33.50 S	151.13 E
North Sydney, Can. (sĭd'nē)	105	46.13 N	60.15 W
North Taranaki Bight, N. Z. (tȧ-rȧ-nä'kĭ bĭt)	217	38.40 S	174.00 E
North Tarrytown, NY (tăr'ĭ-toun)	112a	41.05 N	73.52 W
North Thompson (R.), Can.	99	50.50 N	120.10 W
North Tonawanda, NY (tŏn-ȧ-wŏn'dȧ)	113c	43.02 N	78.53 W
North Truchas Pks. (Mts.), NM (tro͞o'chäs)	205	37.18 N	137.03 E
North Twillingate (I.), Can. (twĭl'ĭn-gāt)	121	35.58 N	105.37 W
North Uist (I.), Scot. (ū'ĭst)	162	57.37 N	7.22 W
Northumberland, NH	111	44.30 N	71.30 W
Northumberland, Is., Austl.	215	21.42 S	151.30 E
Northumberland Str., Can. (nôr thŭm'bēr-lȧnd)	104	46.25 N	64.20 W
North Umpqua R., Or. (ŭmp'kwȧ)	116	43.20 N	122.50 W
North Valley Stream, NY	55	40.41 N	73.41 W
North Vancouver, Can. (văn-ko͞o'vēr)	118d	49.19 N	123.04 W
North Vernon, In. (vûr'nŭn)	110	39.05 N	85.45 W
North Versailles, Pa.	57b	40.22 N	79.48 W
Northville, Mi. (nôrth-vĭl)	113b	42.26 N	83.28 W
North Wales, Pa. (wālz)	112f	40.12 N	75.16 W
North Weald Bassett, Eng.	62	51.43 N	0.10 E
North West C., Austl. (nôrth'wĕst)	214	21.50 S	112.25 E
Northwest Cape Fear, (R.), NC (căp fēr)	127	34.34 N	79.46 W
Northwestern University (P. Int.), Il.	58a	42.04 N	87.40 W
North West Gander (R.), Can. (găn'dēr)	105	48.40 N	55.15 W
Northwest Har., Md.	56c	39.16 N	76.35 W
Northwest Highlands, Scot.	162	56.50 N	5.20 W
Northwest Providence Chan., Ba. (prŏv'ĭ-dĕns)	134	26.15 N	78.45 W
Northwest Territories, Can. (tĕr'ĭ-tō'rĭs)	96	64.42 N	119.09 W
North Weymouth, Ma.	54a	42.15 N	70.57 W
Northwich, Eng. (nôrth'wĭch)	163	53.15 N	2.31 W
North Wilkesboro, NC (wĭlks'bûrô)	127	36.08 N	81.10 W
North Wilmington, Ma.	54a	42.34 N	71.10 W
Northwood, Ia. (nôrth'wo͝od)	115	43.26 N	93.13 W
Northwood, ND	114	47.44 N	97.36 W
Northwood (Neigh.), Eng.	62	51.37 N	0.25 W
North Wood Cr., Wy.	117	44.02 N	107.37 W
North Yamhill (R.), Or. (yăm' hĭl)	118c	45.22 N	123.21 W
North York, Can.	95d	43.47 N	79.25 W
North York Moors, Eng. (yôrk mo͞orz')	162	54.20 N	0.40 W
North Yorkshire (Co.), Eng.	156	53.50 N	1.10 W
Norton, Ks. (nôr'tŭn)	122	39.40 N	99.54 W
Norton, Ma.	112b	41.58 N	71.08 W
Norton, Va.	127	36.54 N	82.36 W
Norton B., Ak.	107	64.22 N	162.18 W
Norton Heath, Eng.	62	51.43 N	0.19 E
Norton Res., Ma.	112b	42.01 N	71.07 W
Norton Sd., Ak.	107	63.48 N	164.50 W
Norval, Can. (nôr'vȧl)	95d	43.39 N	79.52 W
Norwalk, Ca. (nôr'wôk)	119a	33.54 N	118.05 W
Norwalk, Ct.	112a	41.06 N	73.25 W
Norwalk, Oh.	110	41.15 N	82.35 W
Norway, Eur. (nôr'wā)	154	63.48 N	11.17 E
Norway, Me.	104	44.11 N	70.35 W
Norway, Mi.	115	45.47 N	87.55 W
Norway House, Can.	101	53.59 N	97.50 W
Norwegian Sea, Eur. (nôr-wē'jăn)	158	66.54 N	1.43 E
Norwell, Ma. (nôr'wĕl)	105a	42.10 N	70.47 W
Norwich, Ct. (nôr'wĭch)	111	41.20 N	72.00 W
Norwich, Eng.	163	52.40 N	1.15 E
Norwich, NY	111	42.35 N	75.30 W
Norwood, Ma. (nôr'wo͝od)	105a	42.11 N	71.13 W
Norwood, NC	127	35.15 N	80.08 W
Norwood, Oh.	113f	39.10 N	84.27 W
Norwood, Pa.	56b	39.53 N	75.18 W
Norwood Park (Neigh.), Il.	58a	41.59 N	87.48 W
Nose (Neigh.), Jap.	69b	34.49 N	135.09 E
Nose Cr., Can. (nōz)	95e	51.09 N	114.02 W
Noshiro, Jap. (nō'shē-rō)	204	40.09 N	140.02 E

ăt; finăl; rāte; senāte; ärm; ȧsk; sofȧ; fâre; ch-choose; dh-as th in other; bē; ēvent; bĕt; recĕnt; cratēr; g-gō; gh-guttural g; bĭt; ĭ-short neutral; rīde; ĸ-guttural k as ch in German ich;

PLACE (Pronounciation)	PAGE	Lat. °′	Long. °′
Nosovka, Sov. Un. (nô'sôf-kȧ)	175	50.54 N	31.35 E
Nossa Senhora do Ó (Neigh.), Braz.	61d	23.30 S	46.41 W
Nossob (R.), Namibia (nŏ'sŏb)	226	24.15 S	19.10 E
Noteć R., Pol. (nô'tĕcn)	166	52.50 N	16.19 E
Noto, It. (nô'tô)	159	36.49 N	15.08 E
Notodden, Nor. (nōt'ôd'n)	164	59.35 N	9.15 E
Noto-Hantō (Pen.), Jap. (nô'tō hän'tō)	205	37.18 N	137.03 E
Notre-Dame (P. Int.), Fr.	64c	48.51 N	2.21 E
Notre Dame B., Can. (nō't'r dȧm')	105	49.45 N	55.15 W
Notre-Dame-des-Victoires (Neigh.), Can.	54b	45.35 N	73.34 W
Notre-Dame-du-Lac, Can.	104	47.37 N	68.51 W
Notre Dame, Monts (Mts.), Can.	104	46.35 N	70.35 W
Nottawasaga B., Can. (nŏt'ȧ-wȧ-sä'gȧ)	110	44.45 N	80.35 W
Nottaway (R.), Can. (nŏt'ȧ-wā)	97	50.58 N	78.02 W
Nottingham, Eng. (nŏt'ĭng-ăm)	156	52.58 N	1.09 W
Nottingham, Pa.	56b	40.07 N	74.58 W
Nottingham I., Can.	97	62.58 N	78.53 W
Nottingham Park, Il.	58a	41.46 N	87.48 W
Nottinghamshire (Co.), Eng.	156	53.03 N	1.05 W
Notting Hill, Austl.	70b	37.54 S	145.08 E
Nottoway, (R.), Va. (nôt'ȧ-wā)	127	36.53 N	77.47 W
Notukeu Cr., Can.	100	49.55 N	106.30 W
Nouadnibou, Mauritania	224	21.02 N	17.09 W
Nouakchott, Mauritania	228	18.06 N	15.57 W
Nouamrhar, Mauritania	228	19.22 N	16.31 W
Noumea, N. Cal. (nōō-mā'ä)	215	22.18 S	166.48 E
Nouvelle, Can. (nōō-vĕl')	104	48.09 N	66.22 W
Nouvelle-France, Cap de (C.), Can.	97	62.03 N	74.00 W
Nouzonville, Fr. (nōō-zôɴ-vēl')	168	49.51 N	4.43 E
Nova Cachoeirinha (Neigh.), Braz.	61d	23.28 S	46.40 W
Nova Cruz, Braz. (nō'vȧ-krōō'z)	143	6.22 S	35.20 W
Nova Friburgo, Braz. (frê-bōōr'gōō)	141a	22.18 S	42.31 W
Nova Gaia, Ang.	230	10.09 S	17.31 E
Nova Iguaçu, Braz. (nō'vä-ē-gwä-sōō')	144b	22.45 S	43.27 W
Nova Lima, Braz. (lē'mä)	141a	19.59 S	43.51 W
Nova Lisboa, see Huambo			
Nova Mambone, Moz. (nō'vȧ-mȧm-bō'nĕ)	226	21.04 S	35.13 E
Novara, It. (nô-vä'rä)	172	45.24 N	8.38 E
Nova Resende, Braz.	141a	21.12 S	46.25 W
Nova Scotia (Prov.), Can. (skō'shȧ)	97	44.28 N	65.00 W
Novate Milanese, It.	65c	45.32 N	9.08 E
Nova Varoš, Yugo. (nô'vȧ vä'rôsh)	173	43.24 N	19.53 E
Novaya Ladoga, Sov. Un. (nô'vȧ-ya lȧ-dô-gȧ)	165	60.06 N	32.16 E
Novaya Lyalya, Sov. Un. (lyȧ'lyȧ)	182a	59.03 N	60.36 E
Novaya Odessa, Sov. Un. (ô-dĕs'ä)	175	47.18 N	31.48 E
Novaya Praga, Sov. Un. (prä'gȧ)	175	48.34 N	32.54 E
Novaya Sibir (I.), Sov. Un. (sĕ-bēr')	181	75.42 N	150.00 E
Novaya Vodolaga, Sov. Un. (vô-dôl'ȧ-gȧ)	175	49.43 N	35.51 E
Novaya Zemlya (I.), Sov. Un. (zĕm-lyȧ')	180	72.00 N	54.46 E
Nova Zagora, Bul. (zä'gô-rȧ)	173	42.30 N	26.01 E
Novelda, Sp. (nō-vĕl'dȧ)	171	38.22 N	0.46 W
Nové Mesto nad Váhom, Czech. (nô'vĕ myĕs'tō)	167	48.44 N	17.47 E
Nové Zámky, Czech. (zȧm'kĕ)	167	47.58 N	18.10 E
Novgorod, Sov. Un. (nôv'gô-rŏt)	174	58.32 N	31.16 E
Novgorod (Oblast), Sov. Un.	174	58.27 N	31.55 E
Novgorod-Severskiy, Sov. Un.	175	52.01 N	33.14 E
Novi, Mi. (nō'vī)	113b	42.29 N	83.28 W
Novigrad, Yugo. (nō'vĭ grȧd)	172	44.09 N	15.34 E
Novi Ligure, It. (nô'vē)	172	44.43 N	8.48 E
Novinger, Mo. (nŏv'ĭn-jēr)	123	40.14 N	92.43 W
Novi Pazar, Bul. (pä-zär')	173	43.22 N	27.26 E
Novi Pazar, Yugo. (pȧ-zär')	173	43.08 N	20.30 E
Novi Sad, Yugo. (säd')	173	45.15 N	19.53 E
Novoarchangel'skoje, Sov. Un.	66b	55.55 N	37.33 E
Novoasbest, Sov. Un. (nô-vô-äs-bĕst')	182a	57.43 N	60.14 E
Novoaydar, Sov. Un. (nô'vô-ī-där')	175	48.57 N	39.01 E
Novocherkassk, Sov. Un. (nô'vô-chĕr-kȧsk')	175	47.25 N	40.04 E
Novochovrino (Neigh.), Sov. Un.	66b	55.52 N	37.30 E
Novogirejevo (Neigh.), Sov. Un.	66b	55.45 N	37.49 E
Novogrudok, Sov. Un. (nô-vô-grōō'dôk)	167	53.35 N	25.51 E
Novo-Kazalinsk, Sov. Un. (nô-vŭ-kŭ-zȧ-lyênsk')	176	45.47 N	62.00 E
Novokuznetsk (Stalinsk), Sov. Un. (nō'vô-kōō'z-nyĕ'tsk) (stá'lênsk)	180	53.43 N	86.59 E
Novoladozhskiy Kanal (Can.), Sov. Un. (nô-vô-lä'dôzh-skĭ kȧ-näl')	182c	59.54 N	31.19 E
Novo Mesto, Yugo. (nôvô mâs'tô)	172	45.48 N	15.13 E
Novomirgorod, Sov. Un. (nô'vô-mēr'gô-rôt)	175	48.46 N	31.44 E
Novomoskovsk, Sov. Un. (nô'vô-môs-kôfsk')	174	54.06 N	38.08 E
Novomoskovsk, Sov. Un.	175	48.37 N	35.12 E
Novonikol'skiy, Sov. Un. (nô'vô-nyĭ-kôl'skĭ)	182a	52.28 N	57.12 E
Novorossiysk, Sov. Un. (nô'vô-rô-sēsk')	175	44.43 N	37.48 E
Novorzhev, Sov. Un. (nô'vô-rzhêv')	174	57.01 N	29.17 E
Novo-Selo, Bul. (nô'vô-sĕ'lô)	173	44.09 N	22.46 E
Novosibirsk, Sov. Un. (nô'vô-sê-bērsk')	180	55.09 N	82.58 E
Novosibirskiye O-va (New Siberian Is.), Sov. Un. (no'vŭ-sĭ-bĭr'skē-ē)	181	76.45 N	140.30 E
Novosil', Sov. Un. (nô'vô-sĭl)	174	52.58 N	37.03 E
Novosokol'niki, Sov. Un. (nô'vô-sô-kôl'nē-kē)	174	56.18 N	30.07 E
Novotatishchevskiy, Sov. Un. (nô'vô-tȧ-tyĭsh'chĕv-skĭ)	182a	53.22 N	60.24 E
Novoukrainka, Sov. Un.	175	48.18 N	31.33 E
Novouzensk, Sov. Un. (nô-vô-ōō-zĕnsk')	179	50.40 N	48.08 E

PLACE (Pronounciation)	PAGE	Lat. °′	Long. °′
Novozybkov, Sov. Un. (nô'vô-zēp'kôf)	174	52.31 N	31.54 E
Nový Jičín, Czech. (nô'vē yē'chēn)	167	49.36 N	18.02 E
Novyy Bug, Sov. Un. (bōōk)	175	47.43 N	32.33 E
Novyy Oskol, Sov. Un. (ôs-kôl')	175	50.46 N	37.53 E
Novyy Port, Sov. Un. (nô'vē)	180	67.19 N	72.28 E
Nowa Sól, Pol. (nô'vȧ sŭl')	166	51.49 N	15.41 E
Nowata, Ok. (nô-wä'tȧ)	123	36.42 N	95.38 W
Nowra, Austl. (nou'rȧ)	216	34.55 S	150.45 E
Nowy Dwór Mazowiecki, Pol. (nô'vĭ dvōōr mä-zo-vyĕts'ke)	167	52.26 N	20.46 E
Nowy Sacz, Pol. (nô'vē sôɴch')	167	49.36 N	20.42 E
Nowy Targ, Pol. (tärk')	167	49.29 N	20.02 E
Noxon Res., Mt.	116	47.50 N	115.40 W
Noxubee (R.), Ms. (nŏks'ŭ-bē)	126	33.20 N	88.55 W
Noya, Sp. (no'yä)	170	42.46 N	8.50 W
Noyes I., Ak. (noiz)	98	55.30 N	133.40 W
Nozaki, Jap. (nō'zä-kē)	205b	34.43 N	135.39 E
Nozuta, Jap.	69a	35.35 N	139.27 E
No. 1, Canal, Arg.	141c	36.43 S	58.14 W
No. 9, Canal, Arg.	141c	36.22 S	58.19 W
No. 12, Canal, Arg.	141c	36.47 S	57.20 W
Nqamakwe, S. Afr. ('n-gä-mä'kwȧ)	227c	32.13 S	27.57 E
Nqutu, S. Afr. ('n-kōō'tōō)	227c	28.17 S	30.41 E
Nsawam, Ghana	228	5.50 N	0.20 W
Nsouélé, Con.	71c	4.12 S	15.11 E
Nsukka, Nig.	229	6.52 N	7.24 E
Ntshoni (Mtn.), S. Afr.	227c	29.34 S	30.03 E
Ntwetwe Pan (Salt Flat), Bots.	226	20.00 S	24.18 E
Nu (Salween) (R.), China (nōō)	198	30.08 N	96.38 E
Nubah, Jibāl an-(Mts.), Sud.	225	12.22 N	30.39 E
Nubian Des., Sud. (nōō'bĭ-ăn)	225	21.13 N	33.09 E
Nudo Coropuna (Mt.), Peru (nōō'dô kō-rō-pōō'nä)	142	15.53 S	72.04 W
Nudo de Pasco (Mt.), Peru (dĕ pás'kô)	142	10.34 S	76.12 W
Nueces R., Tx. (nû-ā'sås)	124	28.20 N	98.08 W
Nueltin (L.), Can. (nwĕl'tin)	96	60.14 N	101.00 W
Nueva Armenia, Hond. (nwä'vä är-mā'nē-ȧ)	132	15.47 N	86.32 W
Nueva Atzacoalco, Mex.	60a	19.29 N	99.05 W
Nueva Chicago (Neigh.), Arg.	60d	34.40 S	58.30 W
Nueva Coronela, Cuba	60b	23.04 N	82.28 W
Nueva Esparta (State), Ven. (nwĕ'vä ĕs-pä'r-tä)	143b	10.50 N	64.35 W
Nueva Gerona, Cuba (κĕ-rô'nä)	134	21.55 N	82.45 W
Nueva Palmira, Ur. (päl-mē'rä)	141c	33.53 S	58.23 W
Nueva Rosita, Mex. (nōōĕ'vä rô-sē'tä)	108	27.55 N	101.10 W
Nueva San Salvador (Santa Tecla), Sal. (sän' säl-vȧ-dōr) (sän'tä tĕ'klä)	132	13.41 N	89.16 W
Nueve de Julio, Arg. (nwā'vå dä hōō'lyô)	141c	35.26 S	60.51 W
Nuevitas, Cuba (nwä-vē'täs)	134	21.35 N	77.15 W
Nuevitas, Bahía de, Cuba (bä-ē'ä dĕ nwä-vē'täs)	134	21.30 N	77.05 W
Nuevo, Ca. (nwä'vō)	119a	33.48 N	117.09 W
Nuevo Laredo, Mex. (lä-rā'dhō)	124	27.29 N	99.30 W
Nuevo Leon (State), Mex. (lå-ōn')	128	26.00 N	100.00 W
Nuevo San Juan, Pan. (nwĕ'vô sän κōō-ä'n)	128a	9.14 N	79.43 W
Nugumanovo, Sov. Un. (nû-gû-mä'nô-vô)	182a	55.28 N	61.50 E
Nulato, Ak. (nōō-lä'tō)	107	64.40 N	158.18 W
Nullagine, Austl. (nŭ-lă'jēn)	214	22.00 S	120.07 E
Nullarbor Plain (Reg.), Austl. (nŭ-lär'bôr)	214	31.45 S	126.30 E
Numabin B., Can. (nōō-mä'bĭn)	100	56.30 N	103.08 W
Numansdorp, Neth.	157a	51.43 N	4.25 E
Numazu, Jap. (nōō'mä-zōō)	205	35.06 N	138.55 E
Numfoor, Pulau (I.), Indon.	207	1.20 S	134.48 E
Nun (R.), Nig.	229	5.05 N	6.10 E
Nunawading, Austl.	70b	37.49 S	145.10 E
Nuneaton, Eng. (nŭn'ē-tŭn)	156	52.31 N	1.28 W
Nunivak (I.), Ak. (nōō'nĭ-văk)	107	60.25 N	167.42 W
Nunkiní, Mex. (nōōn-kē-nē')	132a	20.19 N	90.14 W
Ñuñoa, Chile	61b	33.28 S	70.36 W
Nunyama, Sov. Un. (nûn-yä'mȧ)	107	65.49 N	170.32 W
Nuoro, It. (nwô'rō)	172	40.29 N	9.20 E
Nura (R.), Sov. Un. (nōō'rä)	180	49.48 N	73.54 E
Nurata, Sov. Un. (nōōr'ät'ȧ)	180	40.33 N	65.28 E
Nürnberg, F.R.G. (nürn'bĕrgh)	166	49.28 N	11.07 E
Nurse Cay (I.), Ba.	135	22.30 N	75.50 W
Nusabyin, Tur. (nōō'sĭ-bēn)	179	37.05 N	41.10 E
Nushagak (R.), Ak. (nū-shȧ-găk')	107	59.28 N	157.40 W
Nushan Hu (L.), China (nū'shän hōō)	200	32.50 N	117.59 E
Nushki, Pak. (nŭsh'kē)	193	29.30 N	66.02 E
Nussdorf (Neigh.), Aus.	66e	48.15 N	16.22 E
Nuthe R., G.D.R. (nōō'tĕ)	157b	52.15 N	13.11 E
Nutley, NJ (nŭt'lē)	112a	40.49 N	74.09 W
Nutter Fort, WV (nŭt'ēr fôrt)	111	39.15 N	80.15 W
Nutwood, Il. (nŭt'wŏŏd)	119e	39.05 N	90.34 W
Nuwaybi 'al Muzayyinah, Egypt	191a	28.59 N	34.40 E
Nuweland, S. Afr.	226a	33.58 S	18.28 E
Nyack, NY (nī'ăk)	112a	41.05 N	73.55 W
Nyaiqêntanglha Shan (Mts.), China (nyä-ĭn-chyūn-täŋ-lä shän)	198	29.55 N	88.08 E
Nyakanazi, Tan.	231	3.00 S	31.15 E
Nyala, Sud.	225	12.00 N	24.52 E
Nyanga (R.), Gabon	230	2.45 S	10.30 E
Nyanza, Rw.	231	2.21 S	29.45 E
Nyasa, L. (Malawi, L.), Afr. (nyä'sä)	231	10.45 S	34.30 E
Nyazepetrovsk, Sov. Un. (nyä'zĕ-pĕ-trôvsk')	182a	56.04 N	59.38 E
Nyborg, Den. (nü'bôr'')	164	55.20 N	10.45 E
Nybro, Swe. (nü'brô)	164	56.44 N	15.56 E
Nyeri, Ken.	231	0.25 S	36.57 E
Nyika Plat, Malawi	231	10.30 S	35.50 E
Nyíregyháza, Hung. (nyē'rĕd-y'hä'zä)	167	47.58 N	21.45 E
Nykøbing, Den. (nü'kû-bĭng)	164	56.46 N	8.47 E

PLACE (Pronounciation)	PAGE	Lat. °′	Long. °′
Nykøbing, Den.	164	54.45 N	11.54 E
Nykøbing Sjaelland, Den.	164	55.55 N	11.37 E
Nyköping, Swe. (nü'chû-pĭng)	164	58.46 N	16.58 E
Nylstroom, S. Afr. (nĭl'strōm)	223d	24.42 S	28.25 E
Nymagee, Austl. (nī-mȧ-gē')	216	32.17 S	146.18 E
Nymburk, Czech. (nĕm'bŏŏrk)	166	50.12 N	15.03 E
Nynäshamn, Swe. (nü-nĕs-häm'n)	164	58.53 N	17.55 E
Nyngan, Austl. (nĭŋ'gȧn)	216	31.31 S	147.25 E
Nyong (R.), Cam. (nyông)	229	3.40 N	10.25 E
Nyou, Burkina	228	12.46 N	1.56 W
Nyrány, Czech. (nĕr-zhä'nĕ)	166	49.43 N	13.13 E
Nysa, Pol. (nē'sȧ)	167	50.29 N	17.20 E
Nystad, see Uusikaupunki			
Nytva, Sov. Un.	178	58.00 N	55.10 E
Nyungwe, Malawi	231	10.16 S	34.07 E
Nyunzu, Zaire	231	5.57 S	28.01 E
Nyuya (R.), Sov. Un. (nyōō'yȧ)	181	60.30 N	111.45 E
Nzega, Tan.	231	4.13 S	33.11 E
Nzérékoré, Gui.	228	7.45 N	8.49 W
Nzeto, Ang.	230	7.14 S	12.52 E
Nzi (R.), Ivory Coast	228	7.00 N	4.27 W

O

PLACE (Pronounciation)	PAGE	Lat. °′	Long. °′
Oahe Dam, SD (ō-ȧ-hē)	114	44.28 N	100.34 W
Oahe Res., SD	114	45.20 N	100.00 W
Oahu (I.), Hi. (ō-ä'hōō) (ō-ä'hü)	106a	21.38 N	157.48 W
Oak Bay, Can.	98	48.27 N	123.18 W
Oak Bluff, Can. (ōk blŭf)	95f	49.47 N	97.21 W
Oak Creek, Co. (ōk krēk')	117	40.20 N	106.50 W
Oakdale, Ca. (ōk'dāl)	120	37.45 N	120.52 W
Oakdale, Ky.	110	38.15 N	85.50 W
Oakdale, La.	125	30.49 N	92.40 W
Oakdale, Pa.	113e	40.24 N	80.11 W
Oakengates, Eng. (ōk'ĕn-gāts)	156	52.41 N	2.27 W
Oakes, ND (ōks)	114	46.10 N	98.50 W
Oakfield, Me. (ōk'fēld)	104	46.08 N	68.10 W
Oakford, Pa. (ōk'fōrd)	112f	40.08 N	74.58 W
Oak Forest, Il.	58a	41.36 N	87.45 W
Oak Grove, Or. (grōv)	118c	45.25 N	122.38 W
Oakham, Eng. (ōk'ăm)	156	52.40 N	0.38 W
Oakharbor, Oh. (ōk'här'bēr)	110	41.30 N	83.05 W
Oak Harbor, Wa.	118a	48.18 N	122.39 W
Oakland, Ca. (ōk'lănd)	118b	37.48 N	122.16 W
Oakland, Md.	56d	38.52 N	76.55 W
Oakland, Ne.	114	41.50 N	96.28 W
Oakland (Neigh.), Pa.	57b	40.26 N	79.58 W
Oakland City, In.	110	38.20 N	87.20 W
Oakland Gardens (Neigh.), NY	55	40.45 N	73.45 W
Oaklawn, Il. (ōk'lôn)	113a	41.43 N	87.45 W
Oakleigh, Austl. (ōk'lå)	211a	37.54 S	145.05 E
Oakleigh South, Austl.	70b	37.56 S	145.05 E
Oakley, Id. (ōk'lĭ)	117	42.15 N	135.53 W
Oakley, Ks.	122	39.08 N	100.49 W
Oakman, Al. (ōk'măn)	126	33.42 N	87.20 W
Oakmont, Pa. (ōk'mōnt)	113e	40.31 N	79.50 W
Oak Mtn., Al.	112h	33.22 N	86.42 W
Oak Park, Il. (pärk)	113a	41.53 N	87.48 W
Oak Park, Mi.	57c	42.28 N	83.11 W
Oak Point, Wa.	118c	46.11 N	123.11 W
Oak Ridge, Tn. (rĭj)	126	36.01 N	84.15 W
Oak View, Md.	56d	39.01 N	76.59 W
Oakview, NJ	56b	39.51 N	75.09 W
Oakville, Can. (ōk'vĭl)	95d	43.27 N	79.40 W
Oakville, Can.	95f	49.56 N	97.58 W
Oakville, Mo.	119e	38.27 N	90.18 W
Oakville Cr., Can.	95d	43.34 N	79.54 W
Oakwood, Oh.	56a	41.06 N	84.23 W
Oakwood, Tx. (ōk'wŏŏd)	125	31.36 N	95.48 W
Oatley, Austl.	70a	33.59 S	151.05 E
Oatman, Az. (ōt'măn)	121	34.00 N	114.25 W
Oaxaca (State), Mex. (wä-hä'kä)	128	16.45 N	97.00 W
Oaxaca de Juárez, Mex. (κōōá'rĕz)	131	17.03 N	96.42 W
Oaxaca, Sierra de (Mts.), Mex. (sē-ĕ'r-rä dĕ)	131	16.15 N	97.25 W
Ob' (R.), Sov. Un.	180	62.15 N	67.00 E
Oba, Can. (ō'bȧ)	102	48.58 N	84.09 W
Obama, Jap. (ō'bȧ-mä)	205	35.29 N	135.44 E
Oban, Scot. (ō'băn)	162	56.25 N	5.35 W
Oban Hills, Nig.	229	5.35 N	8.30 E
O'Bannon, Ky. (ō-băn'nŏn)	113h	38.17 N	85.30 W
Obatogamau (L.), Can. (ō-bȧ-tō'găm-ô)	103	49.38 N	74.10 W
Oberbauer, F.R.G.	63	51.17 N	7.26 E
Oberbonsfeld, F.R.G.	63	51.22 N	7.08 E
Oberelfringhausen, F.R.G.	63	51.20 N	7.11 E
Oberhaan, F.R.G.	63	51.13 N	7.02 E
Oberhausen, F.R.G. (ō'bĕr-hou'zĕn)	169c	51.27 N	6.51 E
Ober-Kassel (Neigh.), F.R.G.	63	51.14 N	6.46 E
Ober-kirchbach, Aus.	66e	48.17 N	16.12 E
Oberlaa (Neigh.), Aus.	66e	48.08 N	16.24 E
Oberlin, Ks. (o'bēr-lĭn)	122	39.49 N	100.30 W
Oberlin, Oh.	110	41.15 N	82.15 W
Oberösterreich (Prov.), Aus.	166	48.05 N	13.15 E
Oberroth, F.R.G. (ō'bĕr-rōt)	157d	48.19 N	11.20 E
Ober Sankt Veit (Neigh.), Aus.	66e	48.11 N	16.16 E
Oberschöneweide (Neigh.), G.D.R.	65a	52.28 N	13.31 E
Oberwengern, F.R.G.	63	51.23 N	7.22 E

ng-sing; ŋ-baŋk; ɴ-nasalized n; nŏd; cŏmmit; ōld; ôbey; ôrder; oi-boil; fōōd; fŏŏt; ou-out; s-soft; sh-dish; th-thin; pūre; ûnite; ûrn; stŭd; circŭs; ü-as in French tu; '-indeterminate vowel.

PLACE (Pronounciation)	PAGE	Lat. °'	Long. °'
Obgruiten, F.R.G.	63	51.13 N	7.01 E
Óbidos, Braz. (ō'bē-dōōzh)	143	1.57 S	55.32 W
Obihiro, Jap. (ō'bē-hē'rō)	204	42.55 N	142.50 E
Obi, Kepulauan (Is.), Indon. (ō'bē)	207	1.25 S	128.15 E
Obion (R.), Tn.	126	36.10 N	89.25 W
Obion (R.), **North Fk.**, Tn. (ō-bī'ŏn)	126	35.49 N	89.06 W
Obi, Pulau (I.), Indon.	207	1.30 S	127.45 E
Obitochnaya, Kosa (C.), Sov. Un. (kô-sä' ô-bē-tôch'na-ya)	175	46.32 N	36.07 E
Obitsu (R.), Jap. (ō'bēt'sōō)	205a	35.19 N	140.03 E
Obock, Djibouti (ō-bŏk')	223a	11.55 N	43.15 E
Obol' (R.), Sov. Un. (ô-bōl')	174	55.24 N	29.24 E
Oboyan, Sov. Un. (ô-bô-yän')	175	51.14 N	36.16 E
Obskaya Guba (B.), Sov. Un.	180	67.13 N	73.45 E
Obu (Neigh.), Jap.	69b	34.44 N	135.09 E
Obuasi, Ghana	228	6.14 N	1.39 W
Obukhov, Sov. Un. (ō'bōō-kôf)	175	50.07 N	30.36 E
Obukhovo, Sov. Un.	182b	55.50 N	38.17 E
Očakovo (Neigh.), Sov. Un.	66b	55.41 N	37.27 E
Ocala, Fl. (ô-kä'lȧ)	127	29.11 N	82.09 W
Ocampo, Mex. (ô-käm'pō)	130	22.49 N	99.23 W
Ocaña, Col. (ô-kän'yä)	142	8.15 N	73.37 W
Ocaña, Sp. (ô-kä'n-yä)	170	39.58 N	3.31 W
Occidental, Cordillera (Mts.), Col. (kôr-dēl-yĕ'rä ôk-sē-dēn-täl')	142a	5.05 N	76.04 W
Occidental, Cordillera (Mts.), Peru	142	10.12 S	76.58 W
Occidental, Grand Erg (Dunes), Alg.	224	29.30 N	00.45 W
Occidental, Sierra Madre (Mts.), Mex. (sē-ĕ'r-rä-mä'drĕ-ôk-sē-dēn-tä'l)	128	29.30 N	107.30 W
Ocean Beach, Ca. (ō'shăn bēch)	120a	32.44 N	117.14 W
Ocean Bight (B.), Ba.	125	21.15 N	73.15 W
Ocean City, Md.	111	38.20 N	75.10 W
Ocean City, NJ	111	39.15 N	74.35 W
Ocean Falls, Can. (Fôls)	98	52.21 N	127.40 W
Ocean Grove, Austl.	211a	38.16 S	144.32 E
Ocean Grove, NJ (grōv)	111	40.10 N	74.00 W
Oceanside, Ca. (ō'shăn-sīd)	120	33.11 N	117.22 W
Oceanside, NY	112a	40.38 N	73.39 W
Ocean Springs, Ms. (sprĭngs)	126	30.25 N	88.49 W
Ocenele Mari, Rom.	173	45.05 N	24.17 E
Ochakov, Sov. Un. (ô-chä'kôf)	175	46.38 N	31.33 E
Ochiai (Neigh.), Jap.	69a	35.43 N	139.42 E
Ochlockonee R., Fl.-Ga. (ŏk-lô-kō'nē)	126	30.10 N	84.38 W
Ocilla, Ga. (ô-sĭl'ȧ)	126	31.36 N	83.15 W
Ockelbo, Swe. (ôk'ĕl-bō)	164	60.54 N	16.35 E
Ockham, Eng.	62	51.18 N	0.27 W
Ocmulgee (R.), Ga.	127	32.25 N	83.30 W
Ocmulgee Natl. Mon., Ga. (ôk-mŭl'gē)	126	32.45 N	83.28 W
Ocna-Sibiului, Rom. (ôck'nȧ-sē-byōō-lōō-ē)	173	45.52 N	24.04 E
Ocoa, Bahai de (B.), Dom. Rep. (bä-ä'ē-ô-kō'ä)	135	18.20 N	70.40 W
Ococingo, Mex. (ô-kô-sē'n-gô)	131	17.03 N	92.18 W
Ocom, L., Mex. (ô-kō'm)	132a	19.26 N	88.18 W
Oconee, (R.), Ga. (ô-kō'nē)	126	32.45 N	83.00 W
Oconomowoc, Wi. (ô-kŏn'ô-mô-wŏk')	115	43.06 N	88.24 W
Oconto, Wi. (ô-kŏn'tō)	115	44.54 N	87.55 W
Oconto (R.), Wi.	115	45.08 N	88.24 W
Oconto Falls, Wi.	115	44.53 N	88.11 W
Ocós, Guat. (ô-kōs')	132	14.31 N	92.12 W
Ocotal, Nic. (ō-kô-täl')	132	13.36 N	86.31 W
Ocotepeque, Hond. (ô-kō-tå-pā'kå)	132	14.25 N	89.13 W
Ocotlán, Mex. (ō-kō-tlän')	130	20.19 N	102.44 W
Ocotlán de Morelos, Mex. (dā mô-rā'lōs)	131	16.46 N	96.41 W
Ocozocoautla, Mex. (ô-kō'zō-kwä-ōō'tlä)	131	16.44 N	93.22 W
Ocumare del Tuy, Ven. (ō-kōō-mä'ra del twē')	143b	10.07 N	66.47 W
Oda, Ghana	228	5.55 N	0.59 W
Odawara, Jap. (ō'dȧ-wä'rä)	205	35.15 N	139.10 E
Odda, Nor. (ôdh-ȧ)	164	60.04 N	6.30 E
Odebolt, Ia. (ō'dē-bōlt)	114	42.20 N	95.14 W
Odemira, Port. (ō-dȧ-mē'rȧ)	170	37.35 N	8.40 W
Ödemiş, Tur. (û'dĕ-mēsh)	179	38.12 N	28.00 E
Odendaalsrus, S. Afr. (ō'dĕn-däls-rûs')	223d	27.52 S	26.41 E
Odense, Den. (ō'dhĕn-sĕ)	164	55.24 N	10.20 E
Odenton, Md. (ō'dĕn-tŭn)	112e	39.05 N	76.43 W
Odenwald (For.), F.R.G. (ō'dĕn-väld)	166	49.39 N	8.55 E
Oderhaff (L.), G.D.R.	166	53.47 N	14.02 E
Oder R., G.D.R. (ō'dẽr)	166	52.40 N	14.19 E
Odessa, Sov. Un. (ô-dĕs'sä)	175	46.28 N	30.44 E
Odessa, Tx. (ô-dĕs'ȧ)	124	31.52 N	120.21 W
Odessa, Wa.	116	47.20 N	118.42 W
Odessa (Oblast), Sov. Un.	175	46.05 N	29.48 E
Odiel (R.), Sp. (ō-dē-ĕl')	170	37.47 N	6.42 W
Odienné, Ivory Coast (ō-dē-ĕn-nā')	228	9.30 N	7.34 W
Odiham, Eng. (ŏd'ē-ăm)	156b	51.14 N	0.56 W
Odintsovo, Sov. Un. (ô-dēn'tsô-vô)	182b	55.40 N	37.16 E
Odiongan, Phil. (ō-dē-ôŋ'gän)	207a	12.24 N	121.59 E
Odivelas, Port. (ō-dē-vä'lyäs)	171b	38.47 N	9.11 W
Odobesti, Rom. (ō-dō-bĕsh't')	167	45.46 N	27.08 E
O'Donnell, Tx. (ō-dŏn'ĕl)	122	32.59 N	101.51 W
Odorhei, Rom. (ō-dôr-hā')	167	46.18 N	25.17 E
Odra R., Pol. (ô'drȧ)	167	50.28 N	17.55 E
Oeiras, Braz. (wå-ē-räzh')	143	7.05 S	42.01 W
Oeirás, Port. (ô-ē'y-rȧ's)	171b	38.42 N	9.18 W
Oella, Md.	56c	39.16 N	76.47 W
Oelwein, Ia. (ōl'wīn)	115	42.40 N	91.56 W
Oespel (Neigh.), F.R.G.	63	51.30 N	7.23 E
Oestrich, F.R.G.	63	51.22 N	7.38 E
Oestrich (Neigh.), F.R.G.	63	51.34 N	7.22 E
Oestrum, F.R.G.	63	51.25 N	6.40 E
O'Fallon, Il. (ō-făl'ŭn)	119e	38.36 N	89.55 W
O'Fallon Cr., Mt.	117	46.25 N	104.47 W
Ofanto (R.), It. (ō-fän'tō)	172	41.08 N	15.33 E
Offa, Nig.	229	8.09 N	4.44 E
Offenbach, F.R.G. (ôf'ĕn-bäk)	166	50.06 N	8.50 E
Offenburg, F.R.G. (ôf'ĕn-bōōrgh)	166	48.28 N	7.57 E

PLACE (Pronounciation)	PAGE	Lat. °'	Long. °'
Ofin, Nig.	71d	6.33 N	3.30 E
Ofuna, Jap. (ō'fōō-nä)	205a	35.21 N	139.32 E
Ogaden Plat., Eth.	223a	6.45 N	44.53 E
Ogaki, Jap.	205	35.21 N	136.36 E
Ogallala, Ne. (ō-gä-lä'lä)	114	41.08 N	101.44 W
Ogawa, Jap.	69a	35.44 N	139.28 E
Ogbomosho, Nig. (ŏg-bô-mō'shō)	229	8.08 N	4.15 E
Ogden, Ia. (ŏg'dĕn)	115	42.10 N	94.20 W
Ogden, Ut.	119b	41.14 N	111.58 W
Ogden Pk., Ut.	119b	41.11 N	111.51 W
Ogden R., Ut.	119b	41.16 N	111.54 W
Ogdensburg, NJ (ŏg'dĕnz-bûrg)	112a	41.05 N	74.36 W
Ogdensburg, NY	111	44.40 N	75.30 W
Ogeechee, (R.), Ga. (ô-gē'chē)	127	32.35 N	81.50 W
Ogies, S. Afr.	223d	26.03 S	29.04 E
Ogilvie Mts., Can. (ō'g'l-vĭ)	96	64.45 N	138.10 W
Oglesby, Il. (ō'g'lz-bĭ)	110	41.20 N	89.00 W
Oglio (R.), It. (ōl'yō)	172	45.15 N	10.19 E
Ōgo, Jap. (ō'gō)	205b	34.49 N	135.06 E
Ogooué (R.), Gabon	230	0.50 S	9.20 E
Ogou (R.), Togo	228	8.05 N	1.30 E
Ogoyo, Nig.	71d	6.26 N	3.29 E
Ogudnëvo, Sov. Un. (ôg-ōōd-nyô'vô)	182b	56.04 N	38.17 E
Ogudu, Nig.	71d	6.34 N	3.24 E
Ogulin, Yugo. (ō-gōō-lēn')	172	45.17 N	15.11 E
Ogwashi-Uku, Nig.	229	6.10 N	6.31 E
O'Higgins (Prov.), Chile (ô-kē'gēns)	141b	34.17 S	70.52 W
Ohio, (State), U. S. (ō'hī'ō)	109	40.30 N	83.15 W
Ohio R., U. S.	110	37.25 N	88.05 W
Ohoopee (R.), Ga. (ô-hōō'pe-mc)	127	32.32 N	82.38 W
Ohře (R.), Czech. (ōr'zhĕ)	166	50.08 N	12.45 E
Ohrid, Yugo. (ō'ĸrēd)	173	41.08 N	20.46 E
Ohrid, L., Alb.-Yugo.	173	40.58 N	20.35 E
Ōi, Jap. (oi')	205a	35.51 N	139.31 E
Oi-Gawa (Strm.), Jap. (ō'ē-gä'wȧ)	205	35.09 N	138.05 E
Oil City, Pa. (oil sĭ'tĭ)	111	41.25 N	79.40 W
Oirschot, Neth.	157a	51.30 N	5.20 E
Oise (R.), Fr. (wäz)	168	49.30 N	2.56 E
Oisterwijk, Neth.	157a	51.34 N	5.13 E
Oita, Jap. (ō'ē-tä)	205	33.14 N	131.38 E
Oji, Jap. (ō'jē)	205b	34.36 N	135.43 E
Ojinaga, Mex. (ō-ĸē-nä'gä)	124	29.34 N	104.26 W
Ojitlán (San Lucas), Mex. (ōkē-tlän') (sän-lōō'käs)	131	18.04 N	96.23 W
Ojo Caliente, Mex. (ōĸō käl-yĕn'tå)	130	21.50 N	100.43 W
Ojocaliente, Mex. (ô-ĸô-kä-lyĕ'n-tĕ)	130	22.39 N	102.15 W
Ojo del Toro, Pico (Pk.), Cuba (pē'kô-ô-ĸô-dĕl-tô'rô)	134	19.55 N	77.25 W
Oka, Can. (ō-kä)	95a	45.28 N	74.05 W
Oka (R.), Sov. Un. (ô-kȧ')	178	55.10 N	42.10 E
Oka (R.), Sov. Un. (ô-kä')	179	52.10 N	35.20 E
Oka (R.), Sov. Un. (ô-kä')	180	53.28 N	101.09 E
Okahandja, Namibia	226	21.50 S	16.45 E
Okanagan L., Can.	99	50.00 N	119.28 W
Okanagan (R.), Can. (ō'kȧ-näg'ăn)	99	49.06 N	119.43 W
Okano (R.), Gabon (ô'kä'nō)	224	0.15 N	11.08 E
Okanogan, Wa.	116	48.20 N	119.34 W
Okanogan R., Wa.	116	48.36 N	119.33 W
Okatibbee (R.), Ms. (ō'kä-tĭb'ē)	126	32.37 N	88.54 W
Okatoma Cr., Ms. (ô-kȧ-tō'mă)	126	31.43 N	89.34 W
Okavango (Cubango) (R.), Ang. Namibia	226	17.10 S	18.20 E
Okavango Swp., Bots.	226	19.30 S	23.02 E
Okaya, Jap. (ō'kȧ-yȧ)	205	36.04 N	138.01 E
Okayama, Jap. (ō'kȧ-yä'mȧ)	205	34.39 N	133.54 E
Okazaki, Jap. (ō'kȧ-zä'kē)	205	34.58 N	137.09 E
Okeechobee, Fl. (ō-kē-chō'bē)	127	27.15 N	80.50 W
Okeechobee, L., Fl.	127a	27.00 N	80.49 W
O'Keefe Centre (P. Int.), Can.	54c	43.37 N	79.22 W
Okeene, Ok. (ō-kēn')	122	36.06 N	98.19 W
Okefenokee Swp., Ga. (ō'kē-fē-nō'kē)	127	30.54 N	82.20 W
Okemah, Ok. (ō-kē'mä)	123	35.26 N	96.18 W
Okene, Nig.	229	7.33 N	6.15 E
Oke Ogbe, Nig.	71d	6.24 N	3.23 E
Okha, Sov. Un. (ŭ-ĸä')	181	53.44 N	143.12 E
Okhotino, Sov. Un. (ô-ĸô'tĭ-nô)	182b	56.14 N	38.24 E
Okhotsk, Sov. Un. (ô-ĸôtsk')	181	59.28 N	143.32 E
Okhotsk, Sea of, Asia (ô-kôtsk')	191	56.45 N	146.00 E
Oki Guntō (Arch.), Jap. (ō'kē gōōn'tō')	205	36.17 N	133.05 E
Okinawa (I.), Jap. (ō'kē-nä'wȧ)	204	26.30 N	128.30 E
Okinawa Guntō (Is.), Jap. (gōōn'tō')	204	26.50 N	127.25 E
Okino (I.), Jap. (ō'kē-nō)	205	36.22 N	133.27 E
Ōkino Erabu (I.), Jap. (ō-kē'nō-å-rä'bōō)	204	27.18 N	129.00 E
Oklahoma (State), U. S. (ō-klȧ-hō'mȧ)	108	36.00 N	98.20 W
Oklahoma City, Ok.	123	35.27 N	97.32 W
Oklawaha (R.), Fl. (ŏk-lȧ-wô'hô)	127	29.13 N	82.00 W
Okmulgee, Ok. (ŏk-mŭl'gē)	123	35.37 N	95.58 W
Okolona, Ky. (ō-kô-lō'nȧ)	113h	38.08 N	85.41 W
Okolona, Ms.	126	33.59 N	88.43 W
Okushiri (I.), Jap. (ō'koo-shē'rē)	204	42.12 N	139.30 E
Okuta, Nig.	229	9.14 N	3.15 E
Olalla, Wa. (ō-lä'lȧ)	118a	47.26 N	122.33 W
Olanchito, Hond. (ō'län-chē'tô)	132	15.28 N	86.35 W
Öland (I.), Swe. (û-länd')	164	57.03 N	17.15 E
Olathe, Ks. (ô-lā'thē)	119f	38.53 N	94.49 W
Olavarría, Arg. (ō-lä-vär-rē'ä)	144	36.49 N	60.15 W
Olawa, Pol (ô-lä'vȧ)	167	50.57 N	17.18 E
Olazoago, Arg. (ô-läz-kôä'gô)	141c	35.14 S	60.37 W
Olbia, It. (ô'l-byä)	172	40.55 N	9.28 E
Olching, F.R.G. (ôl'ĸĕng)	157d	48.13 N	11.21 E
Old Bahama Chan., N. A. (bȧ-hā'mȧ)	134	22.45 N	78.30 W
Old Bight, Ba.	135	24.15 N	75.20 W
Old Bridge, NJ (brĭj)	112a	40.24 N	74.22 W
Old Brookville, NY	55	40.49 N	73.36 W
Old Crow, Can. (crō)	96	67.51 N	139.58 W
Oldenburg, F.R.G. (ôl'dĕn-bōōrgh)	166	53.09 N	8.13 E
Old Forge, Pa. (fôrj)	111	41.20 N	75.50 W

PLACE (Pronounciation)	PAGE	Lat. °'	Long. °'
Oldham, Eng. (ōld'ăm)	156	53.32 N	2.07 W
Oldham Pond (L.), Ma.	54a	42.03 N	70.51 W
Old Harbor, Ak. (här'bẽr)	107	57.18 N	153.20 W
Old Head of Kinsale, Ire. (ōld hĕd ŏv kĭn-sāl)	162	51.35 N	8.35 W
Old Malden (Neigh.), Eng.	62	51.23 N	0.15 W
Old North Church (P. Int.), Ma.	54a	42.22 N	71.03 W
Old R, Tx.	125a	29.54 N	94.52 W
Olds, Can. (ōldz)	99	51.47 N	114.06 W
Old Tate, Bots.	226	21.18 S	27.43 E
Old Town, Me. (toun)	104	44.55 N	68.42 W
Old Westbury, NY	55	40.47 N	73.37 W
Old Windsor, Eng.	62	51.28 N	0.35 W
Old Wives L., Can. (wīvz)	100	50.56 N	106.00 W
Olean, NY (ō-lē-ăn')	111	42.05 N	78.25 W
Olecko, Pol. (ō-lĕt'skō)	167	54.02 N	22.29 E
Olekma (R.), Sov. Un. (ô-lyĕk-mȧ')	181	55.41 N	120.33 E
Olëkminsk, Sov. Un. (ô-lyĕk-mĕnsk')	181	60.39 N	120.40 E
Olenëk (R.), Sov. Un. (ô-lyĕ-nyôk')	181	70.18 N	121.15 E
Oléron Île, d' (I.), Fr. (ēl' dō lā-rôɴ')	168	45.52 N	1.58 W
Oleśnica, Pol. (ô-lĕsh-nĭ'tsȧ)	167	51.13 N	17.24 E
Olfen, F.R.G. (ōl'fĕn)	169c	51.43 N	7.22 E
Ol'ga, Sov. Un. (ôl'gȧ)	181	43.48 N	135.44 E
Ol'gi, Zaliv (B.), Sov. Un. (zä'lĭf ôl'gĭ)	204	43.43 N	135.25 E
Ol'gopol, Sov. Un. (ôl-gô-pôl'y')	175	48.11 N	29.28 E
Olhão, Port. (ôl-youɴ')	170	37.02 N	7.54 W
Olievenhoutpoort, S. Afr.	227b	25.58 S	27.55 E
Olifants (R.), S. Afr. (ŏl'ĭ-fănts)	226	23.58 S	31.00 E
Ólimbos, Grc.	173	40.03 N	22.22 E
Ólimbos (Mtn.), Cyprus	191a	34.56 N	32.52 E
Olinalá, Mex. (ô-lē-nä-lä')	130	17.47 N	98.51 W
Olinda, Austl.	70b	37.51 S	145.22 E
Olinda, Braz. (ô-lē'n-dä)	143	8.00 S	34.58 W
Olinda, Braz.	61c	22.49 S	43.25 W
Oliva, Sp. (ô-lē'vä)	171	38.54 N	0.07 W
Oliva de la Frontera, Sp. (ô-lē'vä dā)	170	38.33 N	6.55 W
Olivais (Neigh.), Port.	65d	38.46 N	9.06 W
Olive Hill, Ky. (ŏl'ĭv)	110	38.15 N	83.10 W
Oliveira, Braz. (ô-lē-vā'rä)	141a	20.42 S	44.49 W
Olive Mount (Neigh.), Eng.	64a	53.24 N	2.55 W
Olivenza, Sp. (ô-lē-vĕn'thä)	170	38.42 N	7.06 W
Oliver, Can. (ŏ'lĭ-vẽr)	99	49.11 N	119.33 W
Oliver, Can.	95g	53.38 N	113.21 W
Oliver, Wi. (ŏ'lĭvẽr)	119h	46.39 N	92.12 W
Oliver L., Can.	95g	53.19 N	113.00 W
Olivia, Mn. (ō-lĭv'ē-ȧ)	106	44.46 N	95.00 W
Olivos, Arg. (ôlē'vōs)	144a	34.15 S	58.29 W
Ollagüe, Chile (ô-lyä'gå)	142	21.17 S	68.17 W
Ollerton, Eng. (ôl'ẽr-tŭn)	156	53.12 N	1.02 W
Olmos Park, Tx. (ōl'mŭs pärk')	119d	29.27 N	98.32 W
Olmsted, Oh.	56a	41.24 N	81.44 W
Olmsted Falls, Oh.	56a	41.22 N	81.55 W
Olney, Il. (ŏl'nĭ)	110	38.45 N	88.05 W
Olney, Or. (ŏl'nē)	118c	46.06 N	123.45 W
Olney, Tx.	122	33.24 N	98.43 W
Olney (Neigh.), Pa.	56b	40.02 N	75.08 W
Olomane (R.), Can. (ō'lō mȧ'nē)	105	51.05 N	60.50 W
Olomouc, Czech. (ô'lô-mōts)	167	49.37 N	17.15 E
Olonets, Sov. Un. (ô-lô'nĕts)	165	60.58 N	32.54 E
Olongapo, Phil.	207a	14.49 S	120.17 E
Oloron, Gave d' (Strm.), Fr. (gäv-dō-lō-rôɴ')	168	43.21 N	0.44 W
Oloron-Sainte Marie, Fr. (ō-lō-rôɴt'săɴt mȧ-rē')	168	43.11 N	1.37 W
Olot, Sp. (ô-lōt')	171	42.09 N	2.30 E
Olpe, F.R.G. (ōl'pĕ)	169c	51.02 N	7.51 E
Ol'shanka, Sov. Un. (ôl'shäŋ-kȧ)	175	48.14 N	30.52 E
Ol'shany, Sov. Un. (ôl'shȧn-ē)	175	50.02 N	35.54 E
Olsnitz, G.D.R. (ōlz'nētz)	166	50.25 N	12.11 E
Olsztyn, Pol. (ôl'shtĭn)	167	53.47 N	20.28 E
Olten, Switz. (ôl'tĕn)	166	47.20 N	7.53 E
Oltenita, Rom. (ôl-tä'nĭ-tsȧ)	173	44.05 N	26.39 E
Oltul (R.), Rom.	161	44.09 N	24.40 E
Olvera, Sp. (ôl-vĕ'rä)	170	36.55 N	7.16 W
Olympia, Wa. (ō-lĭm'pĭ-ȧ)	116	47.02 N	122.52 W
Olympic Mts., Wa.	116	47.54 N	123.58 W
Olympic Natl. Park, Wa. (ô-lĭm'pĭk)	116	47.54 N	123.00 W
Olympieion (P. Int.), Grc.	66d	37.58 N	23.44 E
Olympus Mt., Wa. (ô-lĭm'pŭs)	116	47.43 N	123.30 W
Olyphant, Pa. (ŏl'ĭ-fănt)	111	41.30 N	75.40 W
Olyutorskiy, Mys (C.), Sov. Un. (ŭl-yōō'tŏr-skē)	181	59.49 N	167.16 E
Omae-Zaki (Pt.), Jap. (ō'mä-å zä'kē)	205	34.37 N	138.15 E
Omagh, N. Ire. (ō'mä)	162	54.35 N	7.25 W
Omaha, Ne. (ō'mȧ-hä)	114	41.18 N	95.57 W
Omaha Ind. Res., Ne.	114	42.09 N	96.08 W
Oman, Asia	190	20.00 N	57.45 E
Oman, G. of, Asia	192	24.24 N	58.58 E
Omaruru, Namibia (ō-mä-rōō'rōō)	226	21.25 S	16.50 E
Omboué, Gabon	230	1.34 S	9.15 E
Ombrone (R.), It. (ôm-brō'nä)	172	42.48 N	11.18 E
Omdurman (Umm Durmān), **Sud**	225	15.45 N	32.30 E
Omealca, Mex. (ōmā-äl'kō)	131	18.44 N	96.45 W
Ometepec, Mex. (ô-mä-tå-pĕk')	130	16.41 N	98.27 W
Om Hajer, Eth.	225	14.06 N	36.46 E
Omineca (R.), Can. (ō-mĭ-nĕk'ȧ)	98	55.10 N	125.45 W
Omineca Mts., Can.	98	56.00 N	125.00 W
Ōmiya, Jap. (ō'mē-yȧ)	205a	35.54 S	139.38 E
Omoa, Hond. (ô-mō'rä)	132	15.43 N	88.03 W
Omoko, Nig.	229	5.20 N	6.39 E
Omolon (R.), Sov. Un. (ō'mō)	181	67.43 N	159.15 E
Omo R., Eth. (ō'mō)	225	5.54 N	36.09 E
Ōmori (Kioroshi), Jap. (ō'mô-rē)(kē'ô-rō-shē)	205a	35.50 N	140.09 E
Omotepe, Isla de (I.), Nic. (ē's-lä-dĕ-ō-mô-tā'pȧ)	132	11.32 N	85.30 W
Omro, Wi. (ŏm'rō)	115	44.01 N	89.46 W
Omsk, Sov. Un. (ômsk)	180	55.12 N	73.19 E
Ōmura, Jap. (ō'mōō-rȧ)	205	32.56 N	129.57 E
Ōmuta, Jap. (ō-mōō-tȧ)	205	33.02 N	130.28 E
Omutninsk, Sov. Un. (ō'mōō-tnēnsk)	178	58.38 N	52.10 E
Onawa, Ia. (ŏn-ȧ-wȧ)	114	42.02 N	96.05 W

ăt; finăl; rāte; senåte; ärm; ȧsk; sofȧ; fâre; ch-choose; dh-as th in other; bē; ē̇vent; bĕt; recĕnt; cratẽr; g-gō; gh-guttural g; bĭt; ĭ-short neutral; rīde; ĸ-guttural k as ch in German ich;

PLACE (Pronounciation)	PAGE	Lat. °'	Long. °'
Onaway, Mi.	110	45.25 N	84.10 W
Once (Neigh.), Arg.	60d	34.36 S	58.24 W
Oncócua, Ang.	230	16.34 S	13.28 E
Onda, Sp. (ōn'dä)	171	39.58 N	0.13 W
Ondava (R.), Czech. (ōn'då-vå)	167	48.51 N	21.40 E
Ondo, Nig.	229	7.04 N	4.47 E
Öndörhaan, Mong.	202	47.20 N	110.40 E
Onega, Sov. Un. (ô-nyĕ'gå)	178	63.50 N	38.08 E
Onega, L., see Onezhskoye Ozero			
Onega (R.), Sov. Un.	178	63.20 N	39.20 E
Oneida, NY (ô-nī'dȧ)	111	43.05 N	75.40 W
Oneida, (L.), NY	111	43.10 N	76.00 W
O'Neill, Ne. (ō-nēl')	114	42.28 N	98.38 W
Onekotan (I.), Sov. Un. (ŭ-nyĕ-kŭ-tän')	181	49.45 N	153.45 E
Oneonta, NY (ō-nē-ŏn'tȧ)	111	42.25 N	75.05 W
Onezhskaja Guba (B.), Sov. Un.	178	64.30 N	36.00 E
Onezhskiy, P-Ov. (Pen.), Sov. Un.	178	64.30 N	37.40 E
Onezhskoye Ozero (Onega, L.), Sov. Un. (ô-năsh'skô-yĕ ô'zĕ-rô)	178	62.02 N	34.35 E
Ongiin Hiid, Mong.	198	46.00 N	102.46 E
Ongole, India	197	15.36 N	80.03 E
Onilahy (R.), Mad.	227	23.41 S	45.00 E
Onitsha, Nig. (ô-nĭt'shå)	229	6.09 N	6.47 W
Onomichi, Jap. (ō'nô-mē'chē)	205	34.27 N	133.12 E
Onon (R.), Sov. Un. (ô'nôn)	181	50.33 N	114.18 E
Onon (R.), Sov. Un. (ô'nôn)	181	48.30 N	110.38 E
Onoto, Ven. (ô-nō'tô)	143b	9.38 N	65.03 W
Onslow, Austl. (ŏnz'lō)	214	21.53 S	115.00 E
Onslow B, NC (ŏnz'lō)	127	34.22 N	77.35 W
Ontake San (Mtn.), Jap. (ôn'tä-kå sän)	205	35.55 N	137.29 E
Ontario, Ca. (ŏn-tā'rĭ-ō)	119a	34.04 N	117.39 W
Ontario, Or.	116	44.02 N	116.57 W
Ontario (Prov.), Can.	97	50.47 N	88.50 W
Ontario, L., U. S.-Can.	109	43.35 N	79.05 W
Ontario Science Centre (P. Int.), Can.	54c	43.43 N	79.21 W
Onteniente, Sp. (ōn-tå-nyĕn'tä)	171	38.48 N	0.35 W
Ontonagon, Mi. (ŏn-tô-năg'ŏn)	115	46.50 N	89.20 W
Onuki, Jap. (ō'nōō-kē)	205a	35.17 N	139.51 E
Oodnadatta, Austl. (ōōd'nȧ-dȧ'tȧ)	214	27.38 S	135.40 E
Ooldea Station, Austl. (ōōl-dā'ä)	214	30.35 S	132.08 E
Oologah Res., Ok.	123	36.43 N	95.32 W
Ooltgensplaat, Neth.	157a	51.41 N	4.19 E
Ōmori (Neigh.), Jap.	69a	35.34 N	139.44 E
Ōsaka-wan (B.), Jap.	69b	34.30 N	135.18 E
Oostanaula (R.), Ga. (ōō-stȧ-nô'lȧ)	126	34.25 N	85.10 W
Oostende, Bel. (ōst-ĕn'dē)	163	51.14 N	2.55 E
Oosterhout, Neth.	157a	51.38 N	4.52 E
Ooster Schelde (R.), Neth.	163	51.40 N	3.40 E
Ootsa L., Can.	98	53.49 N	126.18 W
Ōyodo (Neigh.), Jap.	69b	34.43 N	135.30 E
Opalaca, Sierra de (Mts.), Hond. (sē-sĕ'r-rä-dĕ-ô-pä-lä'kä)	132	14.30 N	88.29 W
Opasquia, Can. (ō-păs'kwē-ȧ)	101	53.16 N	93.53 W
Opatow, Pol. (ô-pä'tōōf)	167	50.47 N	21.25 E
Opava, Czech. (ō'pä-vä)	167	49.56 N	17.52 E
Opelika, Al. (ŏp-ē-lī'kȧ)	126	32.39 N	85.23 W
Opelousas, La. (ŏp-ē-lōō'sȧs)	125	30.33 N	92.04 W
Opeongo (L.), Can. (ŏp-ē-ôŋ'gō)	111	45.40 N	78.20 W
Opheim, Mt. (ō-fīm')	117	48.51 N	106.19 W
Ophir, Ak. (ō'fēr)	107	63.10 N	156.28 W
Ophir, Mt., Mala.	191b	2.22 N	102.37 E
Ophirton (Neigh.), S. Afr.	71b	26.14 S	28.01 E
Opico, Sal. (ô-pē'kō)	132	13.50 N	89.23 W
Opinaca (R.), Can. (ŏp-ĭ-nä'kȧ)	97	52.28 N	77.40 W
Opladen, F.R.G. (ōp'lä-dĕn)	169c	51.04 N	7.00 E
Opobo, Nig.	229	4.34 N	7.27 E
Opochka, Sov. Un. (ō-pôch'kȧ)	174	56.43 N	28.39 E
Opoczno, Pol. (ô-pôch'nô)	167	51.22 N	20.18 E
Opole, Pol. (ô-pôl'ä)	167	50.42 N	17.55 E
Opole Lubelskie, Pol. (ō-pō'lĕ lōō-bĕl'skyĕ)	167	51.09 N	21.58 E
Oposhnya, Sov. Un. (ô-pôsh'nyȧ)	175	49.57 N	34.34 E
Opp, Al. (ŏp)	126	31.18 N	86.15 W
Oppdal, Nor. (ôp'däl)	164	62.37 N	9.41 E
Opportunity, Wa. (ŏp-ŏr tū'nĭ tĭ)	116	47.37 N	117.20 W
Oppum (Neigh.), F.R.G.	63	51.19 N	6.37 E
Oquirrh Mts., Ut. (ō'kwēr)	119b	40.38 N	112.11 W
Oradea, Rom. (ô-räd'yä)	167	47.02 N	21.55 E
Oradell, NJ	55	40.57 N	74.02 W
Oran (Wahran), Alg. (ō-rän)(ô-räɴ')	160	35.46 N	0.45 W
Orán, Arg. (ō-rä'n)	144	23.13 S	64.17 W
Oran, Mo. (ôr'ȧn)	123	37.05 N	89.39 W
Orange, Austl. (ŏr'ĕnj)	216	33.15 S	149.08 E
Orange, Ca.	119a	33.48 N	117.51 W
Orange, Ct.	111	41.15 N	73.00 W
Orange, Fr. (ô-raɴzh')	168	44.08 N	4.48 E
Orange, NJ	112a	40.46 N	74.14 W
Orange, Tx.	122	30.07 N	93.44 W
Orange (L.), Fl.	127	29.30 N	82.12 W
Orange (R.), Namibia-S. Afr.	226	29.15 S	17.30 E
Orangeburg, SC (ŏr'ĕnj-bûrg)	127	33.30 N	80.50 W
Orange, Cabo (C.), Braz. (kȧ-bô-rȧ'n-zhĕ)	143	4.25 N	51.30 W
Orange Cay (I.), Ba. (ŏr-ĕnj kē)	134	24.55 N	79.05 W
Orange City, Ia.	114	43.01 N	96.06 W
Orange Free State (Prov.), S. Afr.	226	28.15 S	26.00 E
Orange Grove (Neigh.), S. Afr.	71b	26.10 S	28.05 E
Orangeville, Can. (ŏr'ĕnj-vĭl)	95d	43.55 N	80.06 W
Orangeville, S. Afr.	223d	27.05 S	28.13 E
Orange Walk, Belize (wôl''k)	132a	18.09 N	88.32 W
Orani, Phil. (ō-rä'nē)	207a	14.47 N	120.32 E
Oranienburg, G.D.R. (ō-rä'nē-ĕn-bōōrgh)	157b	52.45 N	13.14 E
Oranjemund, Namibia	226	28.33 S	16.20 E
Oran, Sebkhan d' (L.), Alg.	171	35.28 N	0.28 W
Orăştie, Rom. (ô-rûsh'tyå)	173	45.50 N	23.14 E
Oraşul-Stalin, see Braşov			
Orbetello, It. (ôr-bȧ-tĕl'lō)	172	42.27 N	11.15 E
Orbigo (R.), Sp. (ôr-bē'gō)	170	42.30 N	5.55 W
Orbost, Austl. (ôr'bŭst)	216	37.43 S	148.20 E
Orcas (I.), Wa. (ôr'kȧs)	118d	48.43 N	122.52 W
Orchard Farm, Mo. (ôr'chẽrd färm)	119e	38.53 N	90.27 W
Orchard Park, NY	113c	42.46 N	78.46 W
Orchards, Wa. (ôr'chẽdz)	118c	45.40 N	122.33 W
Orchilla I., Ven. (ôr-kĭl-ȧ)	142	11.47 N	66.34 W
Ord, Ne. (ôrd)	114	41.35 N	98.57 W
Ord (R.), Austl.	214	17.30 S	128.40 E
Orda, Sov. Un. (ôr'dȧ)	182a	56.50 N	57.12 E
Ordenes, Sp. (ōr'då-nās)	170	43.46 N	8.24 W
Ordos Des., China	202	39.12 N	108.10 E
Ord Pk., Az.	121	33.55 N	109.40 W
Ordu, Tur. (ôr'dōō)	179	41.00 N	37.50 E
Ordway, Co. (ôrd'wā)	122	38.11 N	103.46 W
Ordzhonikidze, Sov. Un. (ora ghō nī kĭd ze)	179	43.05 N	44.35 E
Örebro, Swe. (û'rĕ-brō)	164	59.16 N	15.11 E
Oredezh R., Sov. Un. (ô'rĕ-dĕzh)	182c	59.23 N	30.21 E
Oregon, Il.	115	42.01 N	89.21 W
Oregon (State), U.S.	108	43.40 N	121.50 W
Oregon Caves Natl. Mon., Or. (cāvz)	116	42.05 N	123.13 W
Oregon City, Or.	118c	45.21 N	122.36 W
Öregrund, Swe. (û-rĕ-grōōnd)	164	60.20 N	18.26 E
Orekhov, Sov. Un. (ôr-yĕ'ĸôf)	175	47.34 N	35.51 E
Orekhovo, Bul.	173	43.43 N	23.59 E
Orekhovo-Zuyevo, Sov. Un. (ôr-yĕ'ĸô-vô zōō'yĕ-vô)	174	55.46 N	39.00 E
Orël, Sov. Un. (ôr-yôl')	174	52.54 N	36.03 E
Orël (Oblast), Sov. Un.	174	52.35 N	36.08 E
Orel' (R.), Sov. Un.	175	49.08 N	34.55 E
Oreland, Pa.	56b	40.07 N	75.11 W
Orem, Ut. (ō'rĕm)	121	40.15 N	111.50 W
Ore Mts., see Erzgebirge			
Orenburg, Sov. Un. (ô'rĕn-bōōrg)	179	51.50 N	55.05 E
Orense, Sp. (ô-rĕn'sā)	170	42.20 N	7.52 W
Orfanoú, Kólpos (G.), Grc.	173	40.40 N	23.55 E
Organos, Sierra de los (Mts.), Cuba (sē-ĕ'r-rȧ-dĕ-lôs-ŏ'r-gä-nôs)	134	22.20 N	84.10 W
Organ Pipe Cactus Natl. Mon., Az. (ôr'gȧn pīp kăk'tŭs)	121	32.14 N	113.05 W
Orgãos, Serra das (Mtn.), Braz. (sĕ'r-rä-däs-ôr-gouɴ's)	141a	22.30 S	43.01 W
Orgeyev, Sov. Un. (ôr-gyĕ'yĕf)	175	47.27 N	28.49 E
Orhon (R.), Mong.	198	48.33 N	103.07 E
Oriental, Cordillera (Mts.), Bol. (kôr-dĕl-yĕ'rä ō-rē-ĕn-täl')	142	14.00 S	68.33 W
Oriental, Cordillera (Mts.), Col. (kôr-dĕl-yĕ'rä)	142a	3.30 N	74.27 W
Oriental, Cordillera (Mts.), Dom. Rep. (kôr-dĕl-yĕ'rä-ô-ryĕ'n-täl)	135	18.55 N	69.40 W
Oriental, Sierra Madre, (Mts.), Mex. (sē-ĕ'r-rä-mä'drĕ-ô-ryĕ'n-täl')	128	25.30 N	100.45 W
Orihuela, Sp. (ō'rē-wā'lä)	171	38.04 N	0.55 W
Orillia, Can. (ô-rĭl'ĭ-ȧ)	111	44.35 N	79.25 W
Orin, Wy.	117	42.40 N	105.10 W
Orinda, Ca.	118b	37.53 N	122.11 W
Orinoco, Rio (R.), Ven. (rē'ō-ō-rĭ-nō'kô)	142	8.32 N	63.13 W
Orion, Phil. (ō-rē-ōn')	207a	14.37 N	120.34 E
Orissa (State), India (ō-rĭs'ȧ)	196	25.09 N	83.50 E
Oristano, It. (ô-rēs-tä'nō)	172	39.53 N	8.38 E
Oristano, Golfo di (G.), It. (gôl-fô-dē-ô-rēs-tä'nō)	172	39.53 N	8.12 E
Orituco (R.), Ven. (ô-rē-tōō'kō)	143b	9.37 N	66.25 W
Oriuco, (R.), Ven. (ô-rēōō'kō)	143b	9.36 N	66.25 W
Orivesi (L.), Fin.	165	62.15 N	29.55 E
Orizaba, Mex. (ô-rē-zä'bä)	131	18.52 N	97.05 W
Orkanger, Nor.	164	63.19 N	9.54 W
Orkla (R.), Nor. (ôr'klȧ)	164	62.55 N	9.50 E
Orkney, S. Afr. (ôrk'nĭ)	223d	26.58 S	26.39 E
Orkney (Is.), Scot.	162a	59.01 N	2.08 W
Orlando, Fl. (ôr-lăn'dō)	127a	28.32 N	81.22 W
Orlando, S. Afr. (ôr-lăn-dô)	227b	26.15 S	27.56 E
Orlando West Extension, S. Afr.	71b	26.15 S	27.54 E
Orland Park, Il. (ôr-lăn')	113a	41.38 N	87.52 W
Orleans, Can. (ôr-lå-äɴ')	95c	45.28 N	75.31 W
Orléans, Fr. (ôr-lå-äɴ')	168	47.55 N	1.56 E
Orleans, In. (ôr-lēnz')	110	38.40 N	86.25 W
Orléans, Île d' (I.), Can.	95b	46.56 N	70.57 W
Orléansville, see Ech Cheliff			
Orly, Fr.	64c	48.45 N	2.24 E
Ormond, Austl.	70b	37.54 S	145.03 E
Ormond Beach, Fl. (ôr'mŏnd)	127	29.15 N	81.05 W
Ørmskirk, Eng. (ôrms'kĕrk)	156	53.34 N	2.53 W
Ormstown, Can. (ôrms'toun)	95a	45.07 N	74.00 W
Orneta, Pol. (ôr-nyĕ'tä)	167	54.07 N	20.10 E
Ornö (I.), Swe.	164	59.02 N	18.35 E
Örnsköldsvik, Swe. (ûrn'skôlts-vēk)	158	63.10 N	18.32 E
Orobie, Alpi (Mts.), It. (äl'pē-ô-rō'byĕ)	172	46.05 N	9.47 E
Orocué, Col. (ô-rô-kwā')	142	4.48 N	71.26 W
Oron, Nig.	229	4.48 N	8.14 E
Oro, Rio del (R.), Mex. (rē'ō dĕl ō'rō)	130	18.04 N	100.59 W
Oro, Rio del (R.), Mex.	114	26.04 N	105.40 W
Orosei, Golfo di (G.), It. (gôl-fô-dē-ô-rô-sā'ē)	172	40.12 N	9.45 E
Orosháza, Hung. (ô-rôsh-hä'sô)	167	46.33 N	20.31 E
Orosi Vol., C. R. (ō-rō'sē)	132	11.00 N	85.30 W
Oroville, Ca. (ŏr'ô-vĭl)	120	39.29 N	121.34 W
Oroville, Wa.	116	48.55 N	119.25 W
Orpington (Neigh.), Eng.	62	51.23 N	0.06 E
Orrville, Oh. (ôr'vĭl)	110	40.45 N	81.50 W
Orsa, Swe. (ōr'sä)	164	61.08 N	14.35 E
Orsay, Fr.	64c	48.48 N	2.11 E
Orsett, Eng.	62	51.31 N	0.22 E
Orsha, Sov. Un. (ôr'shȧ)	174	54.29 N	30.28 E
Orsk, Sov. Un. (ôrsk)	179	51.15 N	58.50 E
Orsova, Rom. (ôr'shô-vä)	173	44.43 N	22.26 E
Orsoy, F.R.G.	63	51.31 N	6.41 E
Ortega, Col. (ôr-tĕ'gä)	142a	3.56 N	75.12 W
Ortegal, Cabo (C.), Sp. (kȧ'bô-ôr-tå-gäl')	170	43.46 N	8.15 W
Orth, Aus.	157e	48.09 N	16.42 E
Orthez, Fr. (ôr-tĕz')	171	43.29 N	0.43 W
Ortigueira, Sp. (ôr-tē-gā'ē-rä)	170	43.40 N	7.50 W
Orting, Wa. (ôrt'ĭng)	118a	47.06 N	122.12 W
Ortona, It. (ôr-tō'nä)	172	42.22 N	14.22 E
Ortonville, Mn. (ôr-tŭn-vĭl)	114	45.18 N	96.26 W
Oruba, Nig.	71d	6.35 N	3.25 E
Orūmīyeh, Iran	192	37.30 N	45.15 E
Orūmīyeh, Daryacheh-ye (L.), Iran	192	38.01 N	45.17 E
Oruro, Bol. (ô-rōō'rō)	142	17.57 S	66.59 W
Orvieto, It. (ôr-vyå'tō)	172	42.43 N	12.08 E
Oryu-dong (Neigh.), Kor.	68b	37.29 N	126.51 E
Osa, Sov. Un. (ō'sȧ)	178	57.18 N	55.25 E
Osage, Ia. (ō'sāj)	115	43.16 N	92.49 W
Osage, NJ	56b	39.51 N	75.01 W
Osage (R.), Mo.	123	38.10 N	93.12 W
Osage City, Ks. (ō'sāj sĭ'tĭ)	123	38.28 N	95.53 W
Ōsaka, Jap. (ō'sä-kä)	205b	34.40 N	135.27 E
Ōsaka (Pref.), Jap.	205b	34.45 N	135.36 E
Osaka Castle (P. Int.), Jap.	69b	34.41 N	135.32 E
Ōsaka-Wan (B.), Jap. (wän)	205	34.34 N	135.16 E
Osakis, Mn. (ô-sā'kĭs)	115	45.51 N	95.09 W
Osakis (L.), Mn.	115	45.55 N	94.55 W
Osa, Pen. de, C. R. (ō'sä)	133	8.30 N	83.25 W
Osasco, Braz.	61d	23.32 S	46.46 W
Osawatomie, Ks. (ŏs-ȧ-wăt'ō-mē)	123	38.29 N	94.57 W
Osborne, Ks. (ŏz'bŭrn)	122	39.25 N	98.42 W
Osceola, Ar. (ŏs-ē-ō'lȧ)	123	35.42 N	89.58 W
Osceola, Ia.	115	41.04 N	93.45 W
Osceola, Mo.	123	38.02 N	93.41 W
Osceola, Ne.	114	41.11 N	97.34 W
Osceola, Tn.	123	35.42 N	89.58 W
Oscoda, Mi. (ŏs-kō'dȧ)	110	44.25 N	83.20 W
Osëtr (R.), Sov. Un. (ô'sĕt'r)	174	54.27 N	38.15 E
Osgood, In. (ŏz'gŏŏd)	110	39.10 N	85.20 W
Osgoode, Can.	95c	45.09 N	75.37 W
Osh, Sov. Un. (ôsh)	180	40.28 N	72.47 E
Oshawa, Can. (ŏsh'ȧ-wȧ)	111	43.50 N	78.50 W
Ōshima (I.), Jap. (ō'shē'mä)	205	34.47 N	139.35 E
Oshkosh, Ne. (ŏsh'kŏsh)	114	41.24 N	102.22 W
Oshkosh, Wi.	115	44.01 N	88.35 W
Oshmyany, Sov. Un. (ôsh-myä'nĭ)	165	54.27 N	25.55 E
Oshodi, Nig.	71d	6.34 N	3.21 E
Oshogbo, Nig.	229	7.47 N	4.34 E
Osijek, Yugo. (ôs'ĭ-yĕk)	173	45.33 N	18.48 E
Osinniki, Sov. Un. (ŭ-sē'nyĭ-kē)	180	53.29 N	85.19 E
Oskaloosa, Ia. (ŏs-kȧ-lōō'sȧ)	115	41.16 N	92.40 W
Oskarshamn, Swe. (ôs'kärs-häm'n)	164	57.16 N	16.24 E
Oskarström, Swe. (ôs'kärs-strûm)	164	56.48 N	12.55 E
Oskol (R.), Sov. Un. (ôs-kôl')	175	51.00 N	37.41 E
Oslo, Nor. (ôs'lō)	164	59.56 N	10.41 E
Oslofjorden (Fd.), Nor.	164	59.03 N	10.35 E
Osmaniye, Tur.	179	37.10 N	36.30 E
Osnabrück, F.R.G. (ôs-nä-brük')	166	52.16 N	8.05 E
Osorno, Chile (ô-sō'r-nō)	144	40.42 S	73.13 W
Osorun, Nig.	71d	6.33 N	3.29 E
Osøyra, Nor.	164	60.24 N	5.22 E
Osprey Reef (I.), Austl. (ŏs'prå)	215	14.00 S	146.45 E
Ossa, Mt., Austl. (ŏsȧ)	216	41.45 S	146.05 E
Ossenberg, F.R.G.	63	51.34 N	6.35 E
Osseo, Mn. (ŏs'sē-ō)	119g	45.07 N	93.24 W
Ossining, NY (ŏs'ĭ-nĭng)	112a	41.09 N	73.51 W
Ossipee, NH (ŏs'ĭ-pē)	104	43.42 N	71.08 W
Ossjøen (L.), Nor. (ôs-syûĕn)	164	61.20 N	12.00 E
Ossum-Bösinghoven, F.R.G.	63	51.18 N	6.39 E
Ostankino (Neigh.), Sov. Un.	66b	55.49 N	37.37 E
Ostashkov, Sov. Un. (ôs-täsh'kôf)	174	57.07 N	33.04 E
Ost-Berlin, G.D.R.	65a	52.30 N	13.25 E
Oster, Sov. Un. (ōs'tĕr)	175	50.55 N	30.52 E
Osterdalälven (R.), Swe.	164	61.40 N	13.00 E
Oster Fd., Nor. (ûs'tĕr fyôr')	175	60.40 N	5.25 E
Osterfeld (Neigh.), F.R.G.	63	51.30 N	6.53 E
Östersund, Swe. (ûs'tĕr-sōōnd)	164	63.09 N	14.49 E
Östhammar, Swe. (ûst'häm'är)	164	60.16 N	18.21 E
Ostrava, Czech.	167	49.51 N	18.18 E
Ostróda, Pol. (ôs'trōōt-ȧ)	167	53.41 N	19.58 E
Ostróg, Sov. Un. (ōs-trôk')	175	50.21 N	26.40 E
Ostrogozhsk, Sov. Un. (ōs-tr-gôzhk')	175	50.53 N	39.03 E
Ostrołęka, Pol. (ôs-trô-woɴ'kȧ)	167	53.04 N	21.35 E
Ostropol', Sov. Un. (ôs-trô-pôl')	175	49.48 N	27.32 E
Ostrov, Sov. Un. (ôs-trôf')	174	57.21 N	28.22 E
Ostrov, Sov. Un.	66b	55.35 N	37.51 E
Ostrowiec Świetokrzyski, Pol. (ôs-trō'vyĕts shvyĕɴ-tō-kzhĭ'ske)	167	50.55 N	21.24 E
Ostrów Lubelski, Pol. (ôs'trōōf lōō'bĕl-skĭ)	167	51.32 N	22.49 E
Ostrów Mazowiecka, Pol. (mä-zō-vyĕt'skä)	167	52.47 N	21.54 E
Ostrów Wielkopolski, Pol. (ôs'trōōf vyĕl-kō-pōl'skĕ)	167	51.38 N	17.49 E
Ostrzeszów, Pol. (ôs-tzhä'shōōf)	167	51.26 N	17.56 E
Ostuni, It. (ôs-tōō'nē)	173	40.44 N	17.35 E
Osum (R.), Alb. (ō'sōōm)	173	40.37 N	20.00 E
Ōsumi-Guntō (Arch.), Jap. (ō'sōō-mē gōōn'tō)	205	30.34 N	130.30 E
Ōsumi Kaikyō (Van Diemen)(Str.), Jap. (kä'ē-kyō)(văn dē'mĕn)	205	31.02 N	130.10 E
Osuna, Sp. (ô-sōō'nä)	170	37.18 N	5.05 W
Osveya, Sov. Un. (ôs'vĕ-yȧ)	174	56.00 N	28.08 E
Oswaldtwistle, Eng. (ŏz-wȧld-twĭs''l)	156	53.44 N	2.23 W
Oswegatchie (R.), NY (ŏs-wē-găch'ĭ)	111	44.15 N	75.20 W
Oswego, Ks. (ŏs-wē'gō)	123	37.10 N	95.08 W
Oswego, NY	111	43.25 N	76.30 W
Oświęcim, Pol. (ôsh-vyăɴ'tsyĭm)	167	50.02 N	19.17 E
Otapää, Sov. Un. (ō'tĕ-pâ)	174	58.03 N	26.31 E
Otaru, Jap. (ō'tȧ-rōō)	204	43.07 N	141.00 E
Otavalo, Ec. (ōtä-vä'lō)	142	0.14 N	78.16 W
Otavi, Namibia (ô-tä'vē)	226	19.35 S	17.20 E
Otay, Ca. (ō'tā)	120a	32.36 N	117.04 W
Otford, Eng.	62	51.19 N	0.12 E
Othonoí (I.), Grc.	173	39.51 N	19.26 E

ng-sing; ŋ-baŋk; ɴ-nasalized n; nŏd; cŏmmit; ōld; ôbey; ôrder; oi-boil; fōōd; fŏŏt; ou-out; s-soft; sh-dish; th-thin; pūre; ůnite; ûrn; stŭd; circŭs; ü-as in French tu; '-indeterminate vowel.

PLACE (Pronounciation)	PAGE	Lat. °′	Long. °′
Óthris, Óros (Mts.), Grc.	173	39.00 N	22.15 E
Oti (R.), Ghana	228	9.00 N	0.10 E
Otish, Mts., Can. (ô-tĭsh')	97	52.15 N	70.20 W
Otjiwarongo, Namibia (ŏt-jē-wȧ-rôn'gō)	226	20.20 S	16.25 E
Otočac, Yugo. (ō'tô-chȧts)	172	44.53 N	15.15 E
Otra (R.), Nor.	164	59.13 N	7.20 E
Otradnoye, Sov. Un. (ô-trȧ'd-nôyĕ)	182	59.46 N	30.50 E
Otranto, It. (ō'trän-tô) (ô-trän'tō)	173	40.07 N	18.30 E
Otranto, Strait of, It.-Alb.	173	40.30 N	18.45 E
Otra R., Sov. Un. (ôt'rȧ)	182b	55.22 N	38.20 E
Otsego, Mi. (ŏt-sē'gō)	110	42.25 N	85.45 W
Otsu, Jap. (ō'tsōō)	205b	35.00 N	135.54 E
Otta (L.), Nor. (ôt'tȧ)	164	61.53 N	8.40 E
Ottakring (Neigh.), Aus.	66e	48.12 N	16.19 E
Ottavia (Neigh.), It.	66c	41.58 N	12.24 E
Ottawa, Can. (ŏt'ȧ-wȧ)	95c	45.25 N	75.43 W
Ottawa, Il.	110	41.20 N	88.50 W
Ottawa, Ks.	123	38.37 N	95.16 W
Ottawa, Oh.	110	41.00 N	84.00 W
Ottawa (R.), Can.	97	46.05 N	77.20 W
Ottawa Is., Can.	97	59.50 N	81.00 W
Otter Cr., Ut. (ŏt'ēr)	121	38.20 N	111.55 W
Otter Cr., Vt.	111	44.05 N	73.15 W
Otter Pt., Can.	118a	48.21 N	123.50 W
Ottershaw, Eng.	62	51.22 N	0.32 W
Otter Tail (L.), Mn.	114	46.21 N	95.52 W
Otterville, Il. (ŏt'ēr-vĭl)	119e	39.03 N	90.24 W
Ottery, S. Afr. (ŏt'ēr-ĭ)	226a	34.02 S	18.31 E
Ottumwa, Ia. (ô-tŭm'wȧ)	115	41.00 N	92.26 W
Otukpa, Nig.	229	7.09 N	7.41 E
Otumba, Mex. (ô-tŭm'bä)	131a	19.41 N	98.46 W
Otway, C., Austl. (ŏt'wā)	216	38.55 S	153.40 E
Otway, Seno (B.), Chile (sĕ'nō-ô't-wā'y)	144	53.00 S	73.00 W
Otwock, Pol. (ôt'vôtsk)	167	52.05 N	21.18 E
Ouachita, (R.), U. S.	109	33.25 N	92.30 W
Ouachita Mts., Ok. (wŏsh'ĭ-tô)	123	34.29 N	95.01 W
Ouaddaï (Reg.), Chad (wä-dī')	225	13.04 N	20.00 E
Ouagadougou, Burkina (wä'gȧ-dōō'gōō)	228	12.22 N	1.31 W
Ouahigouya, Burkina (wä-ē-gōō'yä)	228	13.35 N	2.25 W
Oualâta, Mauritania (wä-lä'tä)	224	17.11 N	6.50 W
Ouallene, Alg. (wäl-lân')	224	24.43 N	1.15 E
Ouanaminthe, Hai.	135	19.35 N	71.45 W
Ouanda Djallé, Cen. Afr. Rep. (wän'dȧ jä' lā')	225	8.56 N	22.46 E
Ouarane (Dunes), Mauritania	224	20.44 N	10.27 W
Ouarkoye, Burkina	228	12.05 N	3.40 W
Ouassel (R.), Alg.	171	35.30 N	1.55 E
Oubangui (Ubangi) (R.), Afr. (ōō-bäŋ'gē)	230	4.30 N	20.35 E
Oude Rijn (R.), Neth.	157a	52.09 N	4.33 E
Oudewater, Neth.	157a	52.01 N	4.52 E
Oud-Gastel, Neth.	157a	51.35 N	4.27 E
Oudtshoorn, S. Afr. (outs'hōrn)	226	33.33 S	23.36 E
Oued Rhiou, Alg.	171	35.55 N	0.57 E
Oued Tlelat, Alg.	171	35.33 N	0.28 W
Ouellé, Ivory-Coast	228	7.18 N	4.01 W
Ouenzé (Neigh.), Con.	71c	4.14 S	15.17 E
Ouessant, I. d', Fr. (ēl-dwĕ-säN')	168	48.28 N	5.00 W
Ouesso, Con.	230	1.37 N	16.04 E
Ouest, Pt., Hai.	135	19.00 N	73.25 W
Ouezzane, Mor. (wĕ-zan')	224	34.48 N	5.40 W
Ouham (R.), Cen. Afr. Rep.-Chad	229	8.30 N	17.50 E
Ouidah, Benin (wē-dä')	224	6.25 N	2.05 E
Oujda, Mor.	224	34.41 N	1.45 W
Oulins, Fr. (ōō-lăN')	169b	48.52 N	1.27 E
Oullins, Fr. (ōō-lăN')	168	45.44 N	4.46 E
Oulu, Fin. (ō'lōō)	158	64.58 N	25.43 E
Oulujärvi, (L.), Fin.	158	64.20 N	25.48 E
Oum Chalouba, Chad (ōōm shä-lōō'bä)	225	15.48 N	20.30 E
Oum Hadjer, Chad.	229	13.18 N	19.41 E
Ounas (R.), Fin. (ō'nȧs)	158	67.46 N	24.40 E
Oundle, Eng. (ôn'd'l)	156	52.28 N	0.28 W
Ounianga Kébir, Chad (ōō-nē-äŋ'gȧ kē-bēr')	225	19.04 N	20.22 E
Ouray, Co. (ōō-rā')	123	38.00 N	107.40 W
Ourinhos, Braz. (ôōō-rē'nyōs)	143	23.04 S	49.45 W
Ourique, Port. (ō-rē'kĕ)	170	37.39 N	8.10 W
Ouro Fino, Braz. (ōŭ-rô-fē'nō)	141a	22.18 S	46.21 W
Ouro Prêto, Braz. (ō'rōō prä'tōō)	141a	20.24 S	43.30 W
Outardes, Rivière aux. (R.), Can.	105	50.53 N	68.50 W
Outer (I.), Wi. (out'ēr)	115	47.03 N	90.20 W
Outer Brass (I.), Vir. Is.(U. S. A.) (bräs)	129c	18.24 N	64.58 W
Outer Hebrides (Is.), Scot.	162	57.20 N	7.50 W
Outjo, Namibia (ōt'yō)	226	20.05 S	17.10 E
Outlook, Can.	100	51.31 N	107.05 W
Outremont, Can. (ōō-trē-môN')	95a	45.31 N	73.36 W
Ouyen, Austl. (ōō-ĕn)	216	35.05 S	142.10 E
Ovalle, Chile (ō-väl'yä)	144	30.43 S	71.16 W
Ovando, Bahía de (B.), Cuba (bä-ē'ä-dĕ-ô-vä'n-dō)	135	20.10 N	74.05 W
Ovar, Port. (ô-vär')	170	40.52 N	8.38 W
Overbrook (Neigh.), Pa.	56b	39.58 N	75.16 W
Overbrook (Neigh.), Pa.	57b	40.24 N	79.59 W
Overijse, Bel.	157a	50.46 N	4.32 E
Overland, Mo. (ō-vēr-lȧnd)	119e	38.42 N	90.22 W
Overland Park, Ks.	119f	38.59 N	94.40 W
Overlea, Md. (ō'vēr-lā)(ō'vēr-lē)	112e	39.21 N	76.31 W
Övertornea, Swe.	158	66.19 N	23.31 E
Ovidiopol', Sov. Un. (ô-vē-dē-ô'pôl')	175	46.15 N	03.28 E
Oviedo, Dom. Rep. (ô-vyĕ'dō)	135	17.50 N	71.25 W
Oviedo, Sp. (ō-vē-ā'dhō)	170	43.22 N	5.50 W
Ovruch, Sov. Un. (ôv'rōōch)	175	51.19 N	28.51 E
Owada, Jap. (ō'wä-dȧ)	205a	35.49 N	139.33 E
Owambo (Reg.), Namibia	226	18.10 S	15.00 E
Owando, Con.	230	0.29 S	15.55 E
Owasco (L.), NY (ō-wăsk'kō)	111	42.50 N	76.30 W
Owase, Jap. (ō'wä-shĕ)	205	34.03 N	136.12 E
Óbuda (Neigh.), Hung.	66g	47.33 N	19.02 E
Owego, NY (ō-wē'gō)	111	42.05 N	76.15 W
Owen, Wi. (ō'ĕn)	115	44.56 N	90.35 W
Owens (L.), Ca. (ō'ĕnz)	120	36.27 N	117.45 W
Owens (R.), Ca.	120	37.13 N	118.20 W
Owensboro, Ky. (ō'ĕnz-bŭr-ô)	110	37.45 N	87.05 W
Owen Sound, Can. (ō'ĕn)	110	44.30 N	80.55 W
Owen Stanley Ra., Pap. N. Gui (stăn'lē)	207	9.00 S	147.30 E
Owensville, In. (ō'ĕnz-vĭl)	110	38.15 N	87.40 W
Owensville, Mo.	123	38.20 N	91.29 W
Owensville, Oh.	113f	39.08 N	84.07 W
Owenton, Ky. (ō'ĕn-tŭn)	110	38.35 N	84.55 W
Owerri, Nig. (ō-wĕr'ē)	224	5.26 N	7.04 E
Owings Mill, Md. (ōwĭngz mĭl)	112e	39.25 N	76.50 W
Owl Cr., Wy. (oul)	117	43.45 N	108.46 W
Owo, Nig.	229	7.15 N	5.37 E
Oworonsoki, Nig.	71d	6.33 N	3.24 E
Owosso, Mi. (ō-wŏs'ō)	110	43.00 N	84.15 W
Owyhee Mts., Id. (ô-wī'hē)	116	43.15 N	116.48 W
Owyhee R., Or.	116	43.04 N	117.45 W
Owyhee Res., Or.	116	43.27 N	117.30 W
Owyhee R., South Fork, Id.	116	42.07 N	116.43 W
Oxbow, Can.	101	49.12 N	102.11 W
Oxchuc, Mex. (ôs-chōōk')	131	16.47 N	92.24 W
Oxford, Al. (ŏks'fērd)	126	33.38 N	80.46 W
Oxford, Can. (ŏks'fērd)	103	45.44 N	63.52 W
Oxford, Eng.	156b	51.43 N	1.16 W
Oxford, Ma.	105a	42.07 N	71.52 W
Oxford, Mi.	110	42.50 N	83.15 W
Oxford, Ms.	126	34.22 N	89.30 W
Oxford, NC	127	36.17 N	78.35 W
Oxford, Oh.	110	39.30 N	84.45 W
Oxford Falls, Austl.	70a	33.44 S	151.15 E
Oxford L., Can.	101	54.51 N	95.37 W
Oxfordshire (CO.), Eng.	156b	51.36 N	1.30 W
Oxkutzcab, Mex. (ôx-kōō'tz-käb)	132a	20.18 N	89.22 W
Oxmoor, Al. (ŏks'mōōr)	112h	33.25 N	86.52 W
Oxnard, Ca. (ŏks'närd)	120	34.08 N	119.12 W
Oxon Hill, Md. (ŏks'ōn hĭl)	112e	38.48 N	77.00 W
Oxshott, Eng.	62	51.20 N	0.21 W
Oxtotepec, Mex. (ôx-tô-tĕ'pĕk)	131a	19.10 N	99.04 W
Oyama, Jap.	69a	35.36 N	139.22 E
Oyapock (R.), Braz.-Fr. Gu. (ō-yȧ-pŏk')	143	2.45 N	52.15 W
Oyem, Gabon (ô-yĕm)(ō-yăN')	230	1.37 N	11.35 E
Øyeren (L.), Nor. (ûĭĕrĕn)	164	59.50 N	11.25 E
Oymyakon, Sov. Un. (oi-myŭ-kôn')	181	63.14 N	142.58 E
Oyo, Nig. (ō'yō)	229	7.51 N	3.56 E
Oyonnax, Fr. (ô-yô-nȧks')	169	46.16 N	5.40 E
Oyster Bay, NY	112a	40.52 N	73.32 W
Oyster Bay Cove, NY	55	40.52 N	73.31 W
Oyster Bayou, Tx.	125a	29.41 N	94.33 W
Oyster Cr., Tx. (ois'tēr)	125a	29.13 N	95.29 W
Ozama (R.), Dom. Rep. (ô-zä'mä)	135	18.45 N	69.55 W
Ozamiz, Phil. (ô-zä'mēz)	207	8.06 N	123.43 E
Ozark, Al. (ō'zärk)	126	31.28 N	85.28 W
Ozark, Ar.	123	35.29 N	93.49 W
Ozark Plat, Mo.	123	36.37 N	93.56 W
Ozarks, L. of the, Mo. (ō'zärksz)	123	38.06 N	93.26 W
Ozëry, Sov. Un. (ô-zyô'rē)	174	54.53 N	38.31 E
Ozgol, Iran	68h	35.47 N	51.30 E
Ozieri, It.	172	40.38 N	8.53 E
Ozoir-la-Ferrière, Fr.	64c	48.46 N	2.40 E
Ozone Park (Neigh.), NY	55	40.40 N	73.51 W
Ozorkow, Pol. (ô-zôr'kōōf)	167	51.58 N	19.20 E
Ozuluama, Mex. (ō'zōō-lōō-ä'mä)	131	21.34 N	97.52 W
Ozumba, Mex. (ô-zōō'm-bä)	131a	19.02 N	98.48 W

P

PLACE (Pronounciation)	PAGE	Lat. °′	Long. °′
Paarl, S. Afr. (pärl)	226	33.45 S	18.55 E
Paarlshoop (Neigh.), S. Afr.	71b	26.13 S	27.59 E
Paauilo, Hi. (pä-ä-ōō'ē-lō)	106a	20.03 N	155.25 W
Pabianice, Pol. (pä-byȧ-nē'tsĕ)	167	51.40 N	19.29 E
Pacaás Novos, Massiço de (Mts.), Braz. (mä-sē'sô-dĕ-pä-kȧ's-nô'vōs)	142	11.03 S	64.02 W
Pacaraima, Serra (Mts.), Braz.-Ven. (sĕr'rȧ pä-kä-rä-ē'mȧ)	142	3.45 N	62.30 W
Pacasmayo, Peru (pä-käs-mä'yō)	142	7.24 S	79.30 W
Pachuca, Mex. (pä-chōō'kä)	131	20.07 N	98.43 W
Pacific, Wa. (pȧ-sĭf'ĭk)	118a	47.16 N	122.15 W
Pacifica, Ca. (pȧ-sĭf'ĭ-kä)	118b	37.38 N	122.29 W
Pacific Beach, Ca.	120a	32.47 N	117.22 W
Pacific Grove, Ca.	120	36.37 N	121.54 W
Pacific O.,	208	0	170.00 W
Pacific Palisades (Neigh.), Ca.	59	34.03 N	118.32 W
Pacific Ra., Can.	98	51.00 N	125.30 W
Pacific Rim Natl. Pk., Can.	98	49.00 N	126.00 W
Paço de Arcos, Port.	65d	38.42 N	9.17 W
Pacolet (R.), SC (pă'cō-lĕt)	127	34.55 N	81.49 W
Pacy-sur-Eure, Fr. (pä-sē-sür-ûr')	169b	49.01 N	1.24 E
Padang, Indon. (pä-däng')	206	1.01 S	100.28 E
Padang Endau, Mala.	191b	2.39 N	103.38 E
Padang, Palau (I.), Indon.	191b	1.12 N	102.21 E
Paddington (Neigh.), Eng.	62	51.31 N	0.10 W
Paden City, WV (pā'dĕn)	110	39.30 N	80.55 W
Paderborn, F.R.G. (pä-dēr-bôrn')	166	51.43 N	8.46 E
Paderno Dugnano, It.	65c	45.34 N	9.10 E
Padibe, Ug.	231	3.28 N	32.50 E
Padiham, Eng. (păd'ĭ-hăm)	156	53.48 N	2.19 W
Padilla, Mex. (pä-dēl'yä)	130	24.00 N	98.45 W
Padilla B., Wa. (pä-dēl'lȧ)	118a	48.31 N	122.34 W
Padova (Padua), It. (pä'dô-vä)(păd'ū-ȧ)	172	45.24 N	11.53 E
Padre I., Tx. (pä'drā)	125	27.09 N	97.15 W
Padre Miguel (Neigh.), Braz.	61c	22.53 S	43.26 W
Padstow, Austl.	70a	33.57 S	151.02 E
Padua, see Padova			
Paducah, Ky. (pȧ-dū'kȧ)	126	37.05 N	88.36 W
Paducah, Tx.	122	34.01 N	100.18 W
Paektu San (Mt.), China-Kor. (pâk'tōō-sän')	204	42.00 N	128.03 E
Pag (I.), Yugo (päg)	172	44.30 N	14.48 E
Pagai Selatan, Pulau (I.), Indon.	206	2.48 S	100.22 E
Pagai Utara, Pulau (I.), Indon.	206	2.45 S	100.02 E
Pagasitikós Kólpos (G.), Grc.	173	39.15 N	23.00 E
Page, Az.	123	36.57 N	111.27 W
Pagosa Springs, Co. (pȧ-gō'sȧ)	123	37.15 N	107.05 W
Pagote, India	67e	18.54 N	72.59 E
Pahala, Hi. (pä-hä'lä)	106a	19.11 N	155.28 W
Pahang (State), Mala.	191b	3.02 N	102.57 E
Pahang R., Mala.	206	3.39 N	102.41 E
Pahokee, Fl. (pȧ-hō'kē)	127a	26.45 N	80.40 W
Paide, Sov. Un. (pī'dĕ)	165	58.54 N	25.30 E
Päijänne (L.), Fin. (pĕ'ē-yĕn-nĕ)	165e	61.38 N	25.05 E
Pailolo Chan., Hi. (pä-ē-lō'lō)	106a	21.05 N	156.41 W
Paine, Chile (pī'nĕ)	141b	33.49 S	70.44 W
Painesville, Oh. (pānz'vĭl)	110	41.40 N	81.15 W
Painted Des., Az. (pānt'ĕd)	123	36.15 N	111.35 W
Painted Rock Res., Az.	123	33.00 N	113.05 W
Paintsville, Ky. (pānts'vĭl)	110	37.50 N	82.50 W
Paisley, Austl.	70b	37.51 S	144.51 E
Paisley, Scot. (pāz'lĭ)	162	55.50 N	4.30 W
Paita, Peru (pä-ē'tä)	142	5.11 S	81.12 W
Pai T'ou Shan (Mts.), Korea	202	40.30 N	127.20 E
Paiute Ind. Res., Ut.	123	38.17 N	113.50 W
Pajápan, Mex. (pä-hä'pän)	131	18.16 N	94.41 W
Pakanbaru, Indon.	206	0.43 N	101.15 E
Pakhra R., Sov. Un. (päκ'rá)	182b	55.29 N	37.51 E
Pakistan, Asia	190	28.00 N	67.30 E
Pakistan East, see Bangladesh			
Pakokku, Bur. (pȧ-kŏk'kōō)	206	21.29 N	95.00 E
Paks, Hung. (pŏksh)	167	46.38 N	18.53 E
Pala, Chad	229	9.22 N	14.54 E
Palacios, Tx. (pä-lä'syōs)	125	28.42 N	96.12 W
Palagruža (Is.), Yugo (pä'lä-grōō'zhä)	172	42.20 N	16.23 E
Palaión Fáliron, Grc.	66d	37.55 N	23.41 E
Palaiseau, Fr. (pȧ-lĕ-zō')	169b	48.44 N	2.16 E
Palana, Sov. Un.	181	59.07 N	159.58 E
Palanan B., Phil. (pä-lä'nän)	207a	17.14 N	122.35 E
Palanan Pt., Phil.	207a	17.12 N	122.40 E
Pālanpur, India (pä'lŭn-pōōr)	196	24.08 N	73.29 E
Palapye, Bots (pȧ-läp'yĕ)	226	22.34 S	27.28 E
Palatine, Il. (păl'ȧ-tīn)	113a	42.07 N	88.03 W
Palatka, Fl. (pȧ-lăt'kȧ)	127	29.39 N	81.40 W
Palauig, Phil. (pá-lou'ĕg)	207a	15.27 N	119.54 E
Palau Is., Pac. Is. Trust. Ter. (pä-lä'ōō)	207	7.15 N	134.30 E
Palawan (I.), Phil. (pä-lä'wȧn)	206	9.50 N	117.38 E
Pālayankottai, India	197	8.50 N	77.50 E
Paldiski, Sov. Un. (päl'dĭ-skĭ)	165	59.22 N	24.04 E
Palembang, Indon. (pä-lĕm-bäng')	206	2.57 S	104.40 E
Palencia, Guat. (pä-lĕn'sē-ȧ)	132	14.40 N	90.22 W
Palencia, Sp. (pä-lĕ'n-syä)	170	42.02 N	4.32 W
Palenque, Mex. (pä-lĕŋ'kā)	131	17.34 N	91.58 W
Palenque, Punta (Pt.), Dom. Rep. (pōō'n-tä)	135	18.10 N	70.10 W
Palermo, Col. (pä-lĕr'mô)	142a	2.53 N	75.26 W
Palermo, It.	172	38.08 N	13.24 E
Palermo (Neigh.), Arg.	60d	34.35 S	58.25 W
Palestine, Tx.	125	31.46 N	95.38 W
Palestine (Reg.), Asia (păl'ĕs-tīn)	191a	31.33 N	35.00 E
Paletwa, Bur. (pŭ-lĕt'wä)	198	21.19 N	92.52 E
Palghāt, India	197	10.49 N	76.40 E
Pāli, India	196	25.53 N	73.18 E
Palimé, Togo	228	6.54 N	0.38 E
Palín, Guat. (pä-lēn')	132	14.42 N	90.42 W
Palisade, Nv. (păl-ĭ-sād')	116	40.39 N	116.11 W
Palisades Park, NJ	55	40.51 N	74.00 W
Palizada, Mex. (pä-lē-zä'dä)	131	18.17 N	92.04 W
Palk Str., India (pôk)	196	10.00 N	79.23 E
Pallejá, Sp.	65e	41.25 N	2.00 E
Palma, Braz. (päl'mä)	141a	21.23 S	42.18 W
Palma, Sp.	171	39.35 N	2.38 E
Palma, Ba, de (B.), Sp. (bä-ē'ä-dĕ)	171	39.24 N	2.37 E
Palma del Rio, Sp. (dĕl rē'ō)	170	37.43 N	5.19 W
Palmar de Cariaco, Ven.	61a	10.34 N	66.55 W
Palmares, Braz. (päl-mȧ'rĕs)	143	8.46 S	35.28 W
Palmas, Braz. (päl'mäs)	144	26.20 S	51.56 W
Palmas, C., Lib.	228	4.22 N	7.44 W
Palma Soriano, Cuba (sô-ré-ä'nō)	135	20.15 N	76.00 W
Palm Beach, Fl. (päm bēch')	127a	26.43 N	80.03 W
Palmeira dos Índios, Braz. (pä-mä'rä-dôs-ē'n-dyôs)	143	9.26 S	36.33 W
Palmeirinhas, Ponta das (Pt.), Arg.	230	9.05 S	13.00 E
Palmela, Port. (päl-mä'lä)	171b	38.34 N	8.54 W
Palmer, Ak. (päm'ēr)	107	61.38 N	149.15 W

PLACE (Pronunciation)	PAGE	Lat. °′	Long. °′
Palmer, Wa.	118a	47.19 N	121.53 W
Palmer Park, Md.	56d	38.55 N	76.52 W
Palmerston North, N. Z. (päm'ẽr-stŭn)	217	40.20 N	175.35 W
Palmerville, Austl. (päm'ẽr-vĭl)	215	16.08 S	144.15 E
Palmetto, Fl. (pȧl-mĕt'ô)	127a	27.32 N	82.34 W
Palmetto Pt., Ba.	135	21.15 N	73.25 W
Palmi, It. (päl'mē)	172	38.21 N	15.54 E
Palmira, Col. (päl-mē'rä)	142a	3.33 N	76.17 W
Palmira, Cuba	134	22.15 N	80.25 W
Palmyra, Mo. (păl-mī'rȧ)	123	39.45 N	91.32 W
Palmyra, NJ	112f	40.01 N	75.00 W
Palmyra (I.), Oceania	209	6.00 N	162.20 W
Palmyra (Ruins), Syr.	192	34.25 N	38.28 E
Palmyras Pt., India	196	20.42 N	87.45 E
Palmyre, Syr.	155	30.35 N	37.58 E
Palo Alto, Ca. (pä'lō äl'tō)	118b	37.27 N	122.09 W
Paloduro Cr., Tx. (pā-lō-dōō'rō)	122	36.16 N	101.12 W
Paloh, Mala.	191b	2.11 N	103.12 E
Paloma, L., Mex. (pä-lō'mä)	124	26.53 N	104.02 W
Palomar Park, Ca.	58b	37.29 N	122.16 W
Palomo, Cerro el (Mtn.), Chile (sĕ'r-rô-ĕl-pä-lô'mô)	141b	34.36 S	70.20 W
Palos, Cabo de (C.), Sp. (kȧ'bô-dĕ-pä'lôs)	171	39.38 N	0.43 W
Palos Heights, Il.	58a	41.40 N	87.48 W
Palos Hills, Il.	58a	41.41 N	87.49 W
Palos Park, Il.	58a	41.40 N	87.50 W
Palos Verdes Estates, Ca. (pă'lŭs vûr'dĭs)	119a	33.48 N	118.24 W
Palouse, Wa. (pȧ-lōōz')	116	46.54 N	117.04 W
Palouse Hills, Wa.	116	46.48 N	117.47 W
Palouse R., Wa.	116	47.02 N	117.35 W
Palu, Tur. (pä-loo')	179	38.55 N	40.10 E
Paluan, Phil. (pä-lōō'än)	207a	13.25 N	120.29 E
Pamamushir (I.), Sov. Un.	181	50.42 N	153.45 E
Pamiers, Fr. (pȧ-myā')	168	43.07 N	1.34 E
Pamirs (Plat), Sov. Un.	193	38.14 N	72.27 E
Pamlico R., NC (păm'lĭ-kō)	127	35.25 N	76.59 W
Pamlico Sd., NC	127	35.10 N	76.10 W
Pampa, Tx. (păm'pȧ)	122	35.32 N	100.56 W
Pampa de Castillo (Plat), Arg. (pä'm-pä-dĕ-käs-tē'l-yô)	144	45.30 S	67.30 W
Pampana (R.), S. L.	228	8.35 N	11.55 W
Pampanga (R.), Phil. (päm-päŋ'gä)	207a	15.20 N	120.48 E
Pampas (Reg.), Arg. (päm'päs)	144	37.00 S	64.30 W
Pampilhosa do Botão, Port. (päm-pē-lyō'sȧ-dô-bō-to'uN)	170	40.21 N	8.32 W
Pamplona, Col. (päm-plō'nä)	142	7.19 N	72.41 W
Pamplona, Sp. (päm-plô'nä)	170	42.49 N	1.39 W
Pamunkey (R.), Va. (pȧ-mŭŋ'kĭ)	111	37.40 N	77.20 W
Pana, Il. (pā'nȧ)	110	39.25 N	89.05 W
Panabá, Mex. (pä-nä-bä')	132a	21.18 N	88.15 W
Panagyurishte, Bul. (pȧ-nȧ-gyōō'rĕsh-tĕ)	173	42.30 N	24.11 E
Panaji (Panjim) India,	197	15.33 N	73.52 E
Panamá, N.A. (păn-ȧ-mä')	129	8.35 N	81.08 W
Panamá, B. de, Pan.	133	8.50 N	79.08 W
Panama City, Fl. (păn-ȧ mä' sĭ'tĭ)	126	30.08 N	85.39 W
Panamá, G. de, Pan.	129	7.45 N	79.20 W
Panamá, Istmo de, Pan.	129	9.00 N	81.00 W
Panamint Ra., Ca. (păn-ȧ-mĭnt')	120	36.40 N	117.30 W
Panaria (Is.), It. (pä-nä'rē-a)	172	38.37 N	15.05 E
Panaro (R.), It. (pä-nä'rô)	172	44.47 N	11.06 E
Panay (I.), Phil. (pä-nī')	206	11.15 N	121.38 E
Pančevo, Yugo. (pȧn'chĕ-vô)	173	44.52 N	20.42 E
Pānchghara, India	67a	22.44 N	88.16 E
Panch'iao, Taiwan	68d	25.01 N	121.27 E
Panchor, Mala.	191b	2.10 N	103.43 E
Pānchur, India	196a	22.31 N	88.17 E
Panda, Zaire (pän'dä')	226	10.59 S	27.24 E
Pandar-e Pahlavī, Iran	179	37.30 N	49.30 E
Pan de Guajaibon (Mtn.), Cuba (pän dā gwä-jȧ-bōn')	134	22.50 N	83.20 W
Pandu, Zaire	230	5.00 N	19.15 E
Panevėžys, Sov. Un. (pä'nyĕ-vāzh'ēs)	165	55.44 N	24.21 E
Panfilov, Sov. Un. (pŭn-fē'lôf)	180	44.12 N	79.58 E
Panga, Zaire (päŋ'gä)	231	1.51 N	26.25 E
Pangani, Tan. (pän-gä'nē)	227	5.28 S	38.58 E
Pangani (R.), Tan.	231	4.40 S	37.45 E
Pangkalpinang, Indon. (päng-käl'pē-näng')	206	2.11 S	106.04 E
Pangnirtung, Can.	97	66.08 N	65.26 W
Panguitch, Ut. (păn'gwĭch)	123	37.50 N	112.30 W
Panimávida, Chile (pä-nē-mȧ'vē-dä)	141b	36.44 S	71.26 W
Pānināti, India	196a	22.42 N	88.23 E
Panje, India	67e	18.54 N	72.57 E
Panjim, see Panaji			
Pankow (Neigh.), G.D.R.	65a	52.34 N	13.24 E
Panshi, China (pän-shē)	202	42.50 N	126.48 E
Pan Si Pan (Mtn.), Viet.	203	22.25 N	103.50 E
Pantar, Pulau (I.), Indon. (pän'tär)	207	8.40 N	123.45 E
Pantelleria (I.), It. (pän-tĕl-lȧ-rē'ä)	159	36.43 N	11.59 E
Pantepec, Mex. (pän-tȧ-pĕk')	131	17.11 N	93.04 W
Pantheon (P. Int.), It.	66c	41.55 N	12.29 E
Pantitlán, Mex.	60a	19.25 N	99.05 W
Pantjoran (Neigh.), Indon.	68k	6.14 S	106.50 E
Panuco, Mex. (pä'nōō-kô)	130	22.04 N	98.11 W
Pánuco, Mex. (pä'nōō-kô)	130	29.47 N	105.55 W
Panuco (R.), Mex.	130	21.59 N	98.20 W
Pánuco de Coronado, Mex. (pä'nōō-kô dā kō-rô-nä'dhō)	124	24.33 N	104.20 W
Panvel, India	197b	18.59 N	73.06 E
Panyu, China (pä-yōō)	201a	22.56 N	113.22 E
Panzós, Guat. (pä-zós')	132	15.26 N	89.40 W
Pao, (R.), Ven. (pȧ'ō)	143b	9.52 N	67.57 W
Paola, Ks. (pā-ō'lȧ)	123	38.34 N	94.51 W
Paoli, In. (pā-ō'lĭ)	110	38.35 N	86.30 W
Paoli, Pa.	112f	40.03 N	75.29 W
Paonia, Co. (pā-ō'nyȧ)	121	38.50 N	107.40 W
Paoting, China	202	42.04 N	125.00 E
Pápa, Hung. (pä'pô)	167	47.18 N	17.27 E
Papagayo (R.), Mex. (pä-pä-gä'yō)	130	16.52 N	99.41 W
Papagayo, Golfo del (G.), C. R. (gôl-fô-dĕl-pä-pä-gȧ'yō)	132	10.44 N	85.56 W
Papagayo, Laguna (L.), Mex. (lä-ōō-nä)	130	16.44 N	99.44 W
Papago Ind. Res., Az. (pä'pä'gō)	121	32.33 N	112.12 W
Papantla de Olarte, Mex. (pä-pän'tlä dā-ô-lä'r-tĕ)	128	20.30 N	97.15 W
Papatoapan (R.), Mex. (pä-pä-tô-ä-pȧ'n)	131	18.00 N	96.22 W
Papelón, Ven.	61a	10.27 N	66.47 W
Papenburg, F.R.G. (päp'ĕn-bōōrgh)	166	53.05 N	7.23 E
Papinas, Arg. (pä-pē'näs)	141c	35.30 S	57.19 W
Papineauville, Can. (pä-pē-nō'vēl)	95c	45.38 N	75.01 W
Papua, Gulf of, Pap. N. Gui. (păp-ōō-ȧ)	207	8.20 S	144.45 E
Papua New Guinea, Oceania (păp-ōō-ȧ)(gĭne)	207	7.00 S	142.15 E
Papudo, Chile (pä-pōō'dô)	141b	32.30 S	71.25 W
Paquequer Pequeno, Braz. (pä-kĕ-kĕ'r-pĕ-kĕ'nô)	144b	22.19 S	43.02 W
Pará (State), Braz. (pä-rä')	143	4.45 S	53.30 W
Pará (R.), Braz. (pä-rä')	141a	20.21 S	44.38 W
Para (R.), Sov. Un.	174	53.45 N	40.58 E
Paracale, Phil. (pä-rä-kä'lå)	207a	14.17 N	122.47 E
Paracambi, Braz. (pä-rä-kȧ'm-bē)	144b	22.36 S	43.43 W
Paracatu, Braz. (pä-rä-kä-tōō')	143	17.17 S	46.43 W
Paraćin, Yugo. (pȧ'rä-chēn)	173	43.51 N	21.26 E
Para de Minas, Braz. (pä-rä-dĕ-mē'näs)	141a	19.52 S	44.37 W
Paradise (I.), Ba.	134	25.05 N	77.20 W
Paradise Valley, Ny. (păr'ȧ-dīs)	116	41.28 N	117.32 W
Parados, Cerro de los (Mtn.), Col. (sĕ'r-rô-dĕ-lôs-pä-rä'dôs)	142a	5.44 N	75.13 W
Paragould, Ar. (păr'ȧ-gōōld)	123	36.03 N	90.29 W
Paraguaçu (R.), Braz. (pä-rä-gwä-zōō')	143	12.25 S	39.46 W
Paraguaná, Pen. de (Pen.), Ven. (pĕ-nē'ng-sōō-lä-dĕ-pä-rä-gwä-nȧ')	142	12.00 N	69.55 W
Paraguay, S. A. (păr'ȧ-gwā)	140	24.00 S	57.00 W
Paraguay, Rio (R.), S.A. (rē'ō-pä-rä-gwä'y)	143	21.12 S	57.31 W
Paraíba (State), Braz. (pä-rä-ē'bä)	143	7.11 S	37.05 W
Paraíba (R.), Braz.	141a	23.02 S	45.43 W
Paraíba do Sul, Braz. (dô-sōō'l)	141a	22.10 S	43.18 W
Paraíba, see João Pessoa			
Paraibuna, Braz. (pä-rä-ē-bōō'nä)	141a	23.23 S	45.38 W
Paraíso, C. R.	133	9.50 N	83.53 W
Paraíso, Mex.	131	18.24 N	93.11 W
Paraiso, Pan. (pä-rä-ē'sō)	128a	9.02 N	79.38 W
Paraisópolis, Braz. (pä-rä-ē-sô'pō-lēs)	141a	22.35 S	45.45 W
Paraitinga, Braz. (pä-rä-ē-tē'n-gä)	141a	23.15 S	45.24 W
Parakou, Benim (pȧ-rȧ-kōō')	229	9.21 N	2.37 E
Paramaribo, Sur. (pȧ-rȧ-mȧ'rē-bō)	143	5.50 N	55.15 W
Paramatta, Austl. (păr-ȧ-măt'ȧ)	211b	33.49 S	150.59 E
Paramillo (Mtn.), Col. (pä-rä-mē'l-yō)	142a	7.06 N	75.55 W
Paramount, Ca.	59	33.53 N	118.09 W
Paramus, NJ	112a	40.56 N	74.04 W
Paramushir (I.), Sov. Un.	181	50.45 N	154.00 E
Paran (R.), Isr.	191a	30.05 N	34.50 E
Paraná, Arg. (pä-rä-nä')	144	31.44 S	60.29 W
Paraná (State), Braz.	144	24.25 S	52.00 W
Paraná (R.), Braz.	143	13.05 S	47.11 W
Paranaguá, Braz. (pä-rä'nä-gwä')	143	25.39 S	48.42 W
Paranaíba, Braz. (pä-rä-nȧ-ē'bȧ)	143	19.43 S	51.13 W
Paranaíba (R.), Braz.	143	18.58 S	50.44 W
Parana Ibicuy (R.), Arg. (ē-bē-kōō'ē)	141c	33.27 S	59.26 W
Paranam, Sur.	143	5.39 N	55.13 W
Paranápanema (R.), Braz. (pä-rä-nȧ'pä-nē-mä)	144	22.28 S	52.15 W
Parañaque, Phil.	68g	14.30 N	120.59 E
Paraná, Rio (R.), Arg.	144	32.15 S	60.55 W
Paraopeda (R.), Braz. (pä-rä-o-pĕ'dä)	141a	20.09 S	44.14 W
Parapara, Ven. (pä-rä-pä-rä)	143b	9.44 N	67.17 W
Pará, Rio do (R.), Braz. (rē'ō-dô-pä-rä')	143	1.09 S	48.48 W
Pará, see Belém			
Parati, Braz. (pä-rätē)	141a	23.14 S	44.43 W
Paray-le-Monial, Fr. (pȧ-rĕ'lĕ-mō-nyäl')	168	46.27 N	4.14 E
Pārbati (R.), India	196	24.50 N	76.44 E
Parcel Is., China	206	16.40 N	113.00 E
Parchim, G.D.R. (par'kĭm)	166	53.25 N	11.52 E
Parczew, Pol. (pär'chĕf)	167	51.38 N	22.53 E
Pardo (R.), Braz. (pär'dō)	143	15.25 S	39.40 W
Pardo (R.), Braz.	141a	21.32 S	46.40 W
Pardubice, Czech. (pär'dōō-bĭt-sĕ)	166	50.02 N	15.47 E
Parecis, Serra dos (Mts.), Braz. (sĕr'rȧ dōs pä-rä-sēzh')	143	13.45 S	59.28 W
Paredes de Nava, Sp (pä-rā'dås dā nä'vä)	170	42.10 N	4.41 W
Paredón, Mex.	124	25.56 N	100.58 W
Parent, Can.	103	47.59 N	74.30 W
Parent, Lac (L.), Can.	103	48.40 N	77.00 W
Pare Pare, Indon.	206	4.01 S	119.38 E
Pargolovo, Sov. Un. (pár-gô'lô vô)	182c	60.04 N	30.18 E
Pari (Neigh.), Braz.	61d	23.32 S	46.37 W
Paria (R.), Az.-Ut.	121	37.07 N	111.51 W
Paria, Golfo de (G.), Ven. (gôl-fô-dĕ-br-pä-rē-ä)	142	10.33 N	62.14 W
Paricutín, Vol., Mex. (pä-rē-kōō-tē'n)	130	19.27 N	102.14 W
Parida, Rio de la (R.), Mex. (rē'ō-dĕ-lä-pä-rē'dä)	124	26.23 N	104.40 W
Parima, Serra (Mts.), Braz.-Ven. (sĕr'rȧ pä-rē'mȧ)	142	3.45 N	64.00 W
Pariñas, Punta (Pt.), Peru (pōō'n-tä-pä-rē'n-yäs)	142	4.30 S	81.23 W
Parintins, Braz. (pä-rĭn-tĭNzh')	143	2.34 S	56.30 W
Paris, Ar. (păr'ĭs)	119	35.17 N	93.43 W
Paris, Can.	110	43.15 N	80.23 W
Paris, Fr. (pȧ-rē')	169b	48.51 N	2.20 E
Paris, Il.	110	39.35 N	87.40 W
Paris, Ky.	110	38.15 N	84.15 W
Paris, Mo.	123	39.27 N	91.59 W
Paris, Tn.	126	36.16 N	88.20 W
Paris, Tx.	123	33.39 N	95.33 W
Paris-le-Bourget, Aéroport de (Arpt.), Fr.	64c	49.00 N	2.25 E
Paris-Orly, Aéroport de (Arpt.), Fr.	64c	48.45 N	2.25 E
Parita, Golfo de (G.), Pan. (gôl-fô-dĕ-pä-rē'tä)	133	8.06 N	80.10 W
Park City, Ut.	117	40.39 N	111.33 W
Parkdene, S. Afr.	71b	26.14 S	28.16 E
Parker, SD (pär'kẽr)	114	43.24 N	97.10 W
Parker Dam, Az.-Ca.	123	34.20 N	114.00 W
Parkersburg, WV (pär'kẽrz-bûrg)	110	39.15 N	81.35 W
Parkes, Austl. (pärks)	216	33.10 S	148.10 E
Park Falls, Wi. (pärk)	115	45.55 N	90.29 W
Park Forest, Il.	113a	41.29 N	87.41 W
Parkgate, Eng.	64a	53.18 N	3.05 W
Parkhill Gardens, S. Afr.	71b	26.14 S	28.11 E
Parkland, Wa. (pärk'lȧnd)	118a	47.09 N	122.26 W
Parklawn, Va.	56d	38.50 N	77.09 W
Parklea, Austl.	70a	33.44 S	150.57 E
Park Orchards, Austl.	70b	37.46 S	145.13 E
Park Ra., Co.	117	40.54 N	106.40 W
Park Rapids, Mn.	115	46.53 N	95.05 W
Park Ridge, Il.	113a	42.00 N	87.50 W
Park Ridge Manor, Il.	58a	42.02 N	87.50 W
Park River, ND	114	48.22 N	97.43 W
Parkrose, Or. (pärk'rōz)	118c	45.33 N	122.33 W
Park Rynie, S. Afr.	227c	30.22 S	30.43 E
Parkston, SD (pärks'tŭn)	114	43.22 N	97.59 W
Park Town (Neigh.), S. Afr.	71b	26.11 S	28.03 E
Parktown North (Neigh.), S. Afr.	71b	26.09 S	28.02 E
Park View, NM (vū)	121	36.45 N	106.30 W
Parkview, Pa.	57b	40.30 N	79.56 W
Parkville, Md.	112e	39.22 N	76.32 W
Parkville, Mo.	119f	39.12 N	94.41 W
Parkwood, Md.	56d	39.01 N	77.05 W
Parla, Sp. (pär'lä)	171a	40.14 N	3.46 W
Parliament, Houses of (P. Int.), Eng.	62	51.30 N	0.07 W
Parma, It. (pär'mä)	172	44.48 N	10.20 E
Parma, Oh.	113d	41.23 N	81.44 W
Parma Heights, Oh.	113d	41.23 N	81.36 W
Parnaguá, Braz. (pär-nä-gwȧ')	143	9.52 S	44.27 W
Parnaíba, Braz. (pär-nä-ē'bä)	143	3.00 S	41.42 W
Parnaíba (R.), Braz.	143	3.57 S	42.30 W
Parnassós (Mtn.), Grc.	173	38.36 N	22.35 E
Parndorf, Aus.	157e	48.00 N	16.52 E
Pärnu, Sov. Un. (pĕr'nōō)	165	58.24 N	24.29 E
Pärnu (R.), Sov. Un.	165	58.40 N	25.05 E
Pärnu Laht (B.), Sov. Un. (läKt)	165	58.15 N	24.17 E
Paro, Bhu. (pä'rô)	196	27.30 N	89.30 E
Paroo (R.), Austl. (pä'rōō)	216	29.40 S	144.24 E
Paropamisus (Mts.), Afg.	192	34.45 N	63.58 E
Páros, Grc. (pä'rôs) (pā'rŏs)	173	37.05 N	25.14 E
Páros (I.), Grc.	173	37.11 N	25.00 E
Parow, S. Afr. (pă'rō)	226a	33.54 S	18.36 E
Parowan, Ut. (păr'ô-wăn)	121	37.50 N	112.50 W
Parral, Chile (pär-rä'l)	144	36.07 S	71.47 W
Parral, R., Mex.	124	27.25 N	105.08 W
Parramatta, Austl.	70a	33.49 S	151.00 E
Parramatta (R.), Aust. (păr-ȧ-măt'ȧ)	211b	33.42 S	150.58 E
Parras, Mex. (pär-räs')	124	25.28 N	102.08 W
Parrita, C. R. (pär-rē'tä)	133	9.32 N	84.17 W
Parrsboro, Can. (pärz'bŭr-ô)	104	45.24 N	64.20 W
Parry (I.), Can. (păr'ĭ)	110	45.15 N	80.00 W
Parry Is., Can.	94	75.30 N	110.00 W
Parry, Mt., Can.	98	52.53 N	128.45 W
Parry Sound, Can.	111	45.20 N	80.00 W
Parsnip (R.), Can. (pärs'nĭp)	98	54.45 N	122.20 W
Parsons, Ks. (pär's'nz)	123	37.20 N	95.16 W
Parsons, WV	111	39.05 N	79.40 W
Parthenay, Fr. (pȧr-t'nĕ')	168	46.39 N	0.16 W
Partington, Eng.	64b	53.25 N	2.26 W
Partinico, It. (pär-tē'nē-kô)	172	38.02 N	13.11 E
Partizansk, Sov. Un.	204	43.15 N	133.19 E
Parys, S. Afr. (pȧ-rīs')	223d	26.53 S	27.28 E
Pasadena, Ca. (păs-ȧ-dē'nȧ)	119a	34.09 N	118.09 W
Pasadena, Md.	112e	39.06 N	76.35 W
Pasadena, Tx.	125a	29.43 N	95.13 W
Pasay, Phil.	68g	14.33 N	121.00 E
Pascagoula, Ms. (păs-kȧ-gōō'lȧ)	126	30.22 N	88.33 W
Pascagoula (R.), Ms.	126	30.52 N	88.48 W
Paşcani, Rom. (päsh-kän')	167	47.46 N	26.42 E
Pasco, Wa. (păs'kō)	116	46.13 N	119.04 W
Pascoe Vale, Austl.	70b	37.44 S	144.56 E
Pasewalk, G.D.R. (pä'zĕ-välk)	166	53.31 N	14.01 E
Pashiya, Sov. Un. (pä'shĭ-yȧ)	182a	58.27 N	58.17 E
Pashkovo, Sov. Un. (pȧsh-kô'vô)	204	48.52 N	131.09 E
Pashkovskaya, Sov. Un. (pȧsh-kôf'skȧ-yȧ)	175	45.29 N	39.04 E
Pasig, Phil.	207a	14.34 N	121.05 E
Pasión, Rio de la (R.), Guat. (rē'ō-dĕ-lä-pä-syōn')	132a	16.31 N	90.11 W
Pasir Gudang, Mala.	67c	1.27 N	103.53 E
Pasir Panjang, Singapore	67c	1.17 N	103.47 E
Pasir Puteh, Mala.	67c	1.26 N	103.56 E
Paso de los Libres, Arg. (pä-sô-dĕ-lôs-lē'brĕs)	144	29.33 S	57.05 W
Paso de los Toros, Ur. (tō'rôs)	141c	32.43 S	56.33 W
Paso del Rey, Arg.	60d	34.39 S	58.45 W
Paso Robles, Ca. (pä'sō rō'blĕs)	120	35.38 N	120.44 W
Pasquia Hills, Can. (păs'kwē-ȧ)	102	53.13 N	102.37 W
Passaic, NJ (pă-sā'ĭk)	112a	40.52 N	74.08 W
Passaic R., NJ	112a	40.42 N	74.26 W
Passamaquoddy B., Can. (păs'ȧ-mȧ-kwŏd'ĭ)	104	45.06 N	66.59 W
Passa Tempo, Braz. (pä's-sä-tĕ'm-pô)	141a	21.40 S	44.29 W
Passau, F.R.G. (päs'ou)	166	48.34 N	13.27 E

PLACE (Pronunciation)	PAGE	Lat. °′	Long. °′
Pass Christian, Ms. (pȧs krĭs'tyĕn)	126	30.20 N	89.15 W
Passero, C., It. (päs-sĕ'rô)	159	36.34 N	15.13 E
Passo Fundo, Braz. (pä'sō fōōn'dōō)	144	28.16 S	52.13 W
Passos, Braz. (pä's-sōs)	141a	20.45 S	46.37 W
Pastaza (R.), Peru (päs-tä'zä)	142	3.05 S	76.18 W
Pasto, Col. (päs'tō)	142	1.15 N	77.19 W
Pastora, Mex. (päs-tô-rä)	130	22.08 N	100.04 W
Pasuruan, Indon.	206	7.45 S	112.50 E
Pasvalys, Sov. Un. (päs-vä-lēs')	165	56.04 N	24.23 E
Patagonia (Reg.), Arg. (păt-ȧ-gō'nĭ-ȧ)	144	46.45 S	69.30 W
Pātālganga (R.), India	197b	18.52 N	73.08 E
Patapsco R., Md. (pȧ-tăps'kō)	112e	39.12 N	76.30 W
Paternò, It. (pä-tĕr-nô')	172	37.25 N	14.58 E
Paterson, NJ (păt'ēr-sŭn)	112a	40.55 N	74.10 W
Pathfinder Res., Wy. (păth'fīn-dēr)	117	42.22 N	107.10 W
Patiāla, India (pŭt-ē-ä'lŭ)	196	30.25 N	76.28 E
Pati do Alferes, Braz. (pä-tē-dô-al-fĕ'rĕs)	144a	22.25 S	43.25 W
Patna, India (pŭt'nŭ)	196	25.33 N	85.18 E
Patnanongan, Phil. (pät-nä-nôŋ'gän)	207a	14.50 N	122.25 E
Patoka (R.), Ind. (pȧ-tō'kȧ)	110	38.25 N	87.25 W
Patom Plat., Sov. Un.	181	59.30 N	115.00 E
Patos, Braz. (pä'tōzh)	143	7.03 S	37.14 W
Patos, Wa. (pä'tōs)	118d	48.47 N	122.57 W
Patos de Minas, Braz. (dĕ-mē'näzh)	143	18.39 S	46.31 W
Patos, Lago dos (L.), Braz. (lä'gō-ȧ dozh pä'tōzh)	144	31.15 S	51.30 W
Pátrai (Patras), Grc. (pä-trī') (pä-träs')	173	38.15 N	21.48 E
Patraïkós Kólpos (G.), Grc.	173	38.16 N	21.19 E
Patras, see Pátrai			
Patrocínio, Braz. (pä-trō-sē'nē-ōō)	143	18.48 S	46.47 W
Pattani, Thai. (păt'ȧ-nē)	206	6.56 N	101.13 E
Patten, Me. (păt''n)	104	45.59 N	68.27 W
Patterson, La. (păt'ēr-sŭn)	125	29.41 N	91.20 W
Patton, Pa.	111	40.40 N	78.45 W
Patuca, Punta (Pt.), Hond. (pōō'n-tä-pä-tōō'kä)	133	15.23 N	84.05 W
Patuca R., Hond.	133	15.22 N	84.31 W
Patuxent (R.), Md. (pȧ-tŭk'sĕnt)	111	39.10 N	77.10 W
Pátzcuaro, Mex. (päts'kwä-rô)	130	19.30 N	101.36 W
Pátzcuaro, Lago de (L.), Mex. (lä'gô-dĕ)	130	19.36 N	101.38 W
Patzicia, Guat. (pät-zē'syä)	132	14.36 N	90.57 W
Patzún, Guat. (pät-zōōn')	132	14.40 N	91.00 W
Pau, Fr. (pō)	168	43.18 N	0.23 W
Pau, Gave de (Strm.), Fr. (gäv-dĕ)	168	43.33 N	0.51 W
Paulding, Oh. (pôl'dĭng)	110	41.05 N	84.35 W
Paulinenaue, G.D.R. (pou'lē-nĕ-nou-ĕ)	157b	52.40 N	12.43 E
Paulis, see Isiro			
Paulistana, Braz. (pä'ōō-lēs-tä-nä)	143	8.13 S	41.06 W
Paulo Afonso, Salto (falls), Braz. (säl-tô-pou'lōō äf-fôn'sōō)	143	9.33 S	38.32 W
Paul Roux, S. Afr. (pôrl rōō)	223d	28.18 S	27.57 E
Paulsboro, NJ (pôlz'bē-rô)	112f	39.50 N	75.16 W
Pauls Valley, Ok. (pôlz văl'ē)	123	34.43 N	97.13 W
Pavarandocito, Col. (pä-vä-rän-dô-sē'tô)	142a	7.18 N	76.32 W
Pavda, Sov. Un. (päv'da)	182a	59.16 N	59.32 E
Pavia, It. (pä-vē'ä)	172	45.12 N	9.11 E
Pavlodar, Sov. Un. (páv-lô-där')	180	52.17 N	77.23 E
Pavlo'f B., Ak. (păv-lôf)	107	55.20 N	161.20 W
Pavlograd, Sov. Un. (páv-lô-grát')	175	48.32 N	35.52 E
Pavlovsk, Sov. Un. (páv-lôfsk')	175	50.28 N	40.05 E
Pavlovsk, Sov. Un.	182c	59.41 N	30.27 E
Pavlovskiy Posad, Sov. Un. (páv-lôf'skĭ pô-sát')	182b	55.47 N	38.39 E
Pavuna, Braz. (pä-vōō'nȧ)	144b	22.48 S	43.21 W
Päwesin, G.D.R. (pă'vĕ-zēn)	157b	52.31 N	12.44 E
Pawhuska, Ok. (pô-hŭs'kȧ)	123	36.41 N	96.20 W
Pawnee, Ok. (pô-nē')	123	36.20 N	96.47 W
Pawnee (R.), Ks.	122	38.18 N	99.42 W
Pawnee City, Ne.	123	40.08 N	96.09 W
Paw Paw, Mi. (pô'pô)	110	42.15 N	85.55 W
Paw Paw (R.), Mi.	115	42.14 N	86.21 W
Pawtucket, RI (pô-tŭk'ĕt)	112b	41.53 N	71.23 W
Paxoi (I.), Grc.	173	39.14 N	20.15 E
Paxton, Il. (păks'tŭn)	110	40.35 N	88.00 W
Paya Lebar, Singapore	67c	1.22 N	103.53 E
Payette, Id. (pȧ-ĕt')	116	44.05 N	116.55 W
Payette R., Id.	116	43.57 N	116.26 W
Payette R., North Fork, Id.	116	44.35 N	116.10 W
Payette R., South Fork, Id.	116	44.07 N	115.43 W
Pay-Khoy, Khrebet (Mts.), Sov. Un.	178	68.08 N	63.04 E
Payne (L.), Can. (pān)	97	59.22 N	73.16 W
Paynesville, Mn. (pānz'vĭl)	115	45.23 N	94.43 W
Paynesville, S. Afr.	71b	26.14 S	28.28 E
Payo Obispo, see Cuidad Chetumal			
Paysandú, Ur. (pī-sän-dōō')	144	32.16 S	57.55 W
Payson, Ut. (pā's'n)	121	40.05 N	111.45 W
Pazardzhik, Bul. (pä-zár-dzhek')	173	42.10 N	24.22 E
Pazin, Yugo. (pä'zēn)	172	45.14 N	13.57 E
Peabody, Ks. (pē'bŏd-ĭ)	123	38.09 N	97.09 W
Peabody, Ma.	105a	42.32 N	70.56 W
Peabody Institute (P. Int.), Md.	56c	39.18 N	76.37 W
Peace (R.), Can.	99	55.40 N	118.30 W
Peace Cr., Fl. (pēs)	127a	27.16 N	81.53 W
Peace Dale, RI (dāl)	112b	41.27 N	71.30 W
Peace River, Can. (rĭv'ēr)	99	56.14 N	117.17 W
Peacock Hills, Can. (pē-kŏk' hĭlz)	96	66.08 N	109.55 W
Peak Hill, Austl.	214	25.38 S	118.50 E
Peakhurst, Austl.	70a	33.58 S	151.04 E
Peak, The (Mt.), Eng. (pēk)	156	53.23 N	1.52 W
Pearl (R.), La.-Ms. (pûrl)	126	31.06 N	89.44 W
Pearland, Tx. (pûrl'ănd)	125a	29.34 N	95.17 W
Pearl Harbor, Hi.	106a	21.20 N	157.53 W
Pearsall, Tx. (pēr'sôl)	124	28.53 N	99.06 W
Pearse I., Can. (pērs)	98	54.51 N	130.21 W
Pearston, S. Afr. (pē'ērstŏn)	227c	32.36 S	25.09 E
Peary Land (Reg.), Grnld. (pēr'ĭ)	93	82.00 N	40.00 W
Pease (R.), Tx. (pēz)	122	34.07 N	99.53 W
Peason, La. (pēz''n)	125	31.25 N	93.19 W
Pebane, Moz. (pĕ-bä'nĕ)	231	17.10 S	38.08 E
Peć, Yugo. (pĕch)	173	42.39 N	20.18 E
Pecan Bay, Tx. (pē-kăn')	124	32.04 N	99.15 W
Peçanha, Braz. (pā-kän'yȧ)	143	18.37 S	42.26 W
Pecatonica (R.), Il. (pĕk-ȧ-tŏn-ĭ-kȧ)	115	42.21 N	89.28 W
Pechenga, Sov. Un. (pyĕ'chĕŋ-gà)	178	69.30 N	31.10 E
Pechincha (Neigh.), Braz.	61c	22.56 S	43.21 W
Pechora (R.), Sov. Un.	178	66.00 N	52.30 E
Pechora Basin, Sov. Un. (pyĕ-chô'rȧ)	180	67.55 N	58.37 E
Pechorskaya Guba (B.), Sov. Un.	178	68.40 N	55.00 E
Pecos, NM (pā'kôs)	121	35.29 N	105.41 W
Pecos, Tx.	124	31.26 N	103.30 W
Pecos (R.), U.S.	108	31.10 N	103.10 W
Pécs, Hung. (pāch)	167	46.04 N	18.15 E
Peddie, S. Afr.	227c	33.13 S	27.09 E
Pededze (R.), Sov. Un. (pä'dĕd-zĕ)	174	57.18 N	27.13 E
Pedley, Ca. (pĕd'lē)	119a	33.59 N	117.29 W
Pedra Azul, Braz. (pā'drä-zōō'l)	143	16.03 S	41.13 W
Pedreiras, Braz. (pĕ-drā'räs)	143	4.30 S	44.31 W
Pedro Antonio Santos (Sta. Cruz Chico), Mex. (pā'drô än-tō'nē-ô sän'tōs) (sän'tä krōōz' chē'kô)	132a	18.55 N	88.13 W
Pedro Betancourt, Cuba (bā-täŋ-kōrt')	134	22.40 N	81.15 W
Pedro de Valdivia, Chile (pĕ'drô-dĕ-väl-dē'vē-ä)	144	22.32 S	69.55 W
Pedro do Rio, Braz. (dô-rē'rô)	144b	22.20 S	43.09 W
Pedro II, Braz. (pā'drōō sā-gōōn'dōō)	143	4.20 S	41.27 W
Pedro Juan Caballero, Par. (hōōà'n-kä-bäl-yē'rō)	143	22.40 S	55.42 W
Pedro Miguel, Pan. (mē-gāl')	128a	9.01 N	79.36 W
Pedro Miguel Locks, Pan. (mē-gāl')	128a	9.01 N	79.36 W
Pedro, Pt., Sri Lanka (pē'drô)	197	9.50 N	80.14 E
Peebinga, Austl. (pē-bĭng'ȧ)	216	34.43 S	140.55 E
Peebles, Scot. (pē'b'lz)	162	55.40 N	3.15 W
Pee Dee (R.), NC-SC (pē-dē')	127	34.01 N	79.26 W
Peekskill, NY (pēks'kĭl)	112a	41.17 N	73.55 W
Pegasus B., N.Z. (pĕg'ȧ-sŭs)	217	43.18 S	173.25 E
Pegnitz R., F.R.G. (pĕgh-nēts)	166	49.38 N	11.40 E
Pego, Sp. (pā'gō)	171	38.50 N	0.09 W
Pegu, Bur. (pĕ-gōō')	206	17.17 N	96.29 E
Peguis Ind. Res., Can.	101	51.20 N	97.35 W
Pegu Yoma (Mt.), Bur. (pĕ-gōō'yō'mä)	198	19.16 N	95.59 E
Pehčevo, Yugo. (pĕĸ'chĕ-vô)	173	41.42 N	22.57 E
Pehladpur (Neigh.), India	67d	28.35 N	77.06 E
Peigan Ind. Res., Can.	99	49.35 N	113.40 W
Peipus, L., see Chudskoye Ozero			
Peit'ou, Taiwan	68d	25.08 N	121.29 E
Pekin, Il. (pē'kĭn)	110	40.35 N	89.30 W
Peking, see Beijing			
Pelagie, Isole I., It.	160	35.46 N	12.32 E
Pélagos (I.), Grc.	173	39.17 N	24.05 E
Pelahatchee, Ms. (pĕl-ȧ-hăch'ē)	126	32.17 N	89.48 W
Pelat, Mt., Fr. (pē-lȧ')	169	44.16 N	6.43 E
Peleduy, Sov. Un. (pyĕl-yĭ-dōō'ē)	181	59.50 N	112.47 E
Pelee I., Can. (pē'lē)	110	41.45 N	82.30 W
Pelee, Mt. (Vol.), Mart. (pē-lā')	133b	14.49 N	61.10 W
Pelee, Pt., Can.	110	41.55 N	82.30 W
Pelequén, Chile (pĕ-lĕ-kĕ'n)	141b	34.26 S	71.52 W
Pelew (Is.), see Palau			
Pelham, Ga. (pĕl'hăm)	126	31.07 N	84.10 W
Pelham, NH	105a	42.43 N	71.22 W
Pelham, NY	55	40.55 N	73.49 W
Pelham Manor, NY	55	40.54 N	73.48 W
Pelican (L.), Mn.	115	46.36 N	94.00 W
Pelican B., Can.	101	52.45 N	100.20 W
Pelican Hbr., Ba. (pĕl'ĭ-kăn)	134	26.20 N	76.45 W
Pelican Rapids, Mn. (pĕl'ĭ-kăn)	114	46.34 N	96.05 W
Pella, Ia. (pĕl'ȧ)	115	41.25 N	92.50 W
Pell-Worm I., F.R.G. (pĕl'vôrm)	166	54.33 N	8.25 E
Pelly (L.), Can.	96	66.08 N	102.57 W
Pelly (R.), Can.	96	62.20 N	113.26 W
Pelly B., Can. (pĕl'ĭ)	96	68.57 N	91.05 W
Pelly Crossing, Can.	107	62.50 N	136.50 W
Pelly Mts., Can.	96	61.50 N	133.05 W
Peloncillo Mts., Az. (pĕl-ôn-sĭl'lō)	121	32.40 N	109.20 W
Peloponnisos (Reg.), Grc.	173	37.28 N	22.14 E
Pelotas, Braz. (pā-lō'tăzh)	144	31.45 S	52.18 W
Pelton, Can. (pĕl'tŭn)	113b	42.15 N	82.57 W
Pelym (R.), Sov. Un.	178	60.20 N	63.05 E
Pelzer, SC (pĕl'zēr)	127	34.38 N	82.30 W
Pemanggil (I.), Mala.	191b	2.37 N	104.41 E
Pematangsiantar, Indon.	206	2.58 N	99.03 E
Pemba, Moz. (pĕm'bȧ)	231	12.58 S	40.30 E
Pemba, Zambia	226	15.29 S	27.22 E
Pemba (I.), Tan	231	5.20 S	39.57 E
Pemba Chan., Afr.	231	5.10 S	39.30 E
Pembina, ND (pĕm'bĭ-nȧ)	114	48.58 N	97.15 W
Pembina (R.), Can.	101	49.08 N	98.20 W
Pembina (R.), Can.	99	53.05 N	114.30 W
Pembroke, Can. (pĕm' brŏk)	111	45.50 N	77.00 W
Pembroke, Ma. (pĕm'brŏk)	105a	42.05 N	70.49 W
Pembroke, Wales	162	51.40 N	5.00 W
Pen, India	197b	18.44 N	73.06 E
Penafiel, Port. (pā-nȧ-fyĕl')	170	41.12 N	8.19 W
Peñafiel, Sp. (pā-nyä-fyĕl')	170	41.38 N	4.08 W
Peña Grande (Neigh.), Sp.	65b	40.29 N	3.44 W
Peñalara (Mtn.), Sp. (pā-nyä-lä'rä)	170	40.52 N	3.57 W
Pena Nevada, Cerro, Mex.	130	23.47 N	99.52 W
Peñaranda de Bracamonte, Sp. (pā-nyä-rän'dä dā brä-kä-mōn'tå)	170	40.54 N	5.11 W
Peñarroya-Peublonuevo, Sp. (pĕn-yär-rô'yä-pwĕ'blô-nwĕ'vô)	170	38.18 N	5.18 W
Peñas, Cabo de (C.), Sp. (kȧ'bô-dĕ-pā'nyäs)	170	43.42 N	6.12 W
Penasco R., Tx. (pā-näs'kō)	124	32.50 N	104.45 W
Penas, Golfo de, Chile (gôl-fô-dĕ-pĕ'n-äs)	144	47.15 S	77.30 W
Pendembu, S. L. (pĕn-dĕm'bōō)	228	8.06 N	10.42 W
Pender, Ne. (pĕn'dēr)	114	42.08 N	96.43 W
Penderisco (R.), Col. (pĕn-dĕ-rē's-kô)	142a	6.30 N	76.21 W
Pendjari, Parc Natl. de la (Natl. Pk.), Benin	228	11.25 N	1.30 E
Pendlebury, Eng.	64b	53.31 N	2.20 W
Pendleton, Or. (pĕn'd'l-tŭn)	116	45.41 N	118.47 W
Pend Oreille L., Id. (pŏn-dô-rā') (pĕn-dô-rĕl')	116	48.09 N	116.38 W
Pend Oreille R., Wa.	116	48.44 N	117.20 W
Penedo, Braz. (pā-nā'dōō)	143	10.17 S	36.28 W
Penetanguishene, Can. (pĕn'ē-tăŋ-gĭ-shēn')	111	44.45 N	79.55 W
Pengcheng, China (pŭŋ-chŭŋ)	200	36.24 N	114.11 E
Penglai, China (pŭŋ-lī)	200	37.49 N	120.45 E
Penha (Neigh.), Braz.	61c	22.49 S	43.17 W
Penha de França (Neigh.), Braz.	61d	23.32 S	46.32 W
Peniche, Port. (pĕ-nē'chȧ)	170	39.22 N	9.24 W
Peninsula, Oh. (pĕn-ĭn'sū-lȧ)	113d	41.14 N	81.32 W
Penistone, Eng. (pĕn'ĭ-stŭn)	156	53.31 N	1.38 W
Penjamillo, Mex. (pĕn-hä-mēl'yō)	130	20.06 N	101.56 W
Penjamo, Mex. (pān'hä-mō)	130	20.27 N	101.43 W
Penk (R.), Eng. (pĕnk)	156	52.41 N	2.10 W
Penkridge, Eng. (pĕnk'rĭj)	156	52.43 N	2.07 W
Pennant Hills, Austl.	70a	33.44 S	151.04 E
Penne, It. (pĕn'nā)	172	42.28 N	13.57 E
Penner (R.), India (pĕn'ēr)	196	14.43 N	79.09 E
Penn Hills, Pa.	57b	40.28 N	79.53 W
Pennines (Mts.), Eng. (pĕn-īn')	162	54.30 N	2.10 W
Pennines, Alpes (Mts.), Switz.	166	46.02 N	7.07 E
Pennsauken, NJ.	56b	39.58 N	75.04 W
Pennsboro, WV (pĕnz'bŭr-ô)	110	39.10 N	81.00 W
Penns Grove, NJ (pĕnz grōv)	112f	39.44 N	75.28 W
Pennsylvania (State), U. S. (pĕn-sĭl-vā'nĭ-ȧ)	109	41.00 N	78.10 W
Penn Valley, Pa.	56b	40.01 N	75.16 W
Penn Wynne, Pa.	56b	39.59 N	75.16 W
Penn Yan, NY (pĕn yăn')	111	42.40 N	77.00 W
Pennycutaway (R.), Can.	101	56.10 N	93.25 W
Peno (L.), Sov. Un. (pā'nô)	174	56.55 N	32.28 E
Penobscot (R.), Me.	104	45.00 N	68.36 W
Penobscot B., Me. (pē-nŏb'skŏt)	104	44.20 N	69.00 W
Penong, Austl. (pē-nông')	214	32.00 S	133.00 E
Penonormé, Pan. (pā-nō-nō-mā')	133	8.32 N	80.21 W
Penrith, Austl.	211b	33.45 S	150.42 E
Pensacola, Fl. (pĕn-sȧ-kō'lȧ)	126	30.25 N	87.13 W
Pensacola Dam, Ok.	123	36.27 N	95.02 W
Pensby, Eng.	64a	53.21 N	3.06 W
Pensilvania, Col. (pĕn-sĕl-vȧ'nyä)	142a	5.31 N	75.05 W
Pentagon (P. Int.), Va.	56d	38.52 N	77.03 W
Pentecost (I.), Vanuatu (pĕn'tē-kŏst)	215	16.05 S	168.28 E
Penticton, Can.	99	49.30 N	119.35 W
Pentland Firth, Scot. (pĕnt'lănd)	162a	58.44 N	3.25 W
Penza, Sov. Un. (pĕn'zȧ)	179	53.10 N	45.00 E
Penzance, Eng. (pĕn-zăns')	162	50.07 N	5.40 W
Penzberg, F.R.G. (pĕnts'bĕrgh)	166	47.43 N	11.21 E
Penzhina (R.), Sov. Un. (pyĭn-zē-nŭ)	181	62.15 N	166.30 E
Penzhino, Sov. Un.	181	63.42 N	168.00 E
Penzhinskay'a Guba (B.), Sov. Un.	181	60.30 N	161.30 E
Penzing (Neigh.), Aus.	66e	48.12 N	16.18 E
Peoria, Il. (pē-ō'rĭ-ȧ)	110	40.45 N	89.35 W
Peotillos, Mex. (pā-ō-tel'yōs)	130	22.30 N	100.39 W
Peotone, Il. (pē'ō-tōn)	113a	41.20 N	87.47 W
Pepacton Res., NY (pĕp-ăc'tŭn)	111	42.05 N	74.40 W
Pepe, Cabo (C.), Cuba (kä'bô-pĕ'pĕ)	134	21.30 N	83.10 W
Pepperell, Ma. (pĕp'ēr-ĕl)	105a	42.40 N	71.36 W
Peqin, Alb. (pĕ-kēn')	173	41.03 N	19.48 E
Pequannock, NJ	55	40.57 N	74.18 W
Perales (R.), Sp. (pā-rä'lās)	171	40.24 N	4.07 W
Perales de Tajuña, Sp. (dā tä-hōō'nyä)	171a	40.14 N	3.22 W
Percé, Can. (pĕr'sā')	104	48.31 N	64.13 W
Perche, Collines du (Hills), Fr.	168	48.25 N	0.40 E
Perchtoldsdorf, Aus. (pĕrk'tôlts-dôrf)	157e	48.07 N	16.17 E
Perdekop, S. Afr.	223d	27.11 S	29.38 E
Perdido (R.), Al.-Fl. (pĕr-dī'dō)	126	30.45 N	87.38 W
Perdido, Mt., Sp. (pĕr-dē'dō)	171	42.40 N	0.00 W
Perdões, Braz. (pĕr-dô'ĕs)	141a	21.05 S	45.05 W
Pereira, Col. (pā-rā'rä)	142a	4.49 N	75.42 W
Perekop, Sov. Un. (pĕr-ā-kôp')	175	46.08 N	33.39 E
Pere Marquette, Mi.	110	43.55 N	86.10 W
Pereshchepino, Sov. Un. (pā'răsh-chē'pē-nô)	175	49.02 N	35.19 E
Pereslavl'-Zalesskiy, Sov. Un. (pā-rā-slav''l zȧ-lyĕs'kĭ)	174	56.43 N	38.52 E
Pereyaslav, Sov. Un. (pĕ-rā-yäs'läv)	175	50.05 N	31.25 E
Pergamino, Arg. (pĕr-gä-mē'nō)	141c	33.53 S	60.36 W
Perham, Mn. (pēr'hăm)	114	46.37 N	95.35 W
Peribonca (R.), Can. (pĕr-ĭ-bŏŋ'kȧ)	103	49.10 N	71.20 W
Périgueux, Fr. (pā-rē-gû')	168	45.12 N	0.43 E
Perija, Sierra de (Mts.), Col. (sē-ĕ'r-rȧ-dĕ-pĕ-rē'ĸä)	142	9.25 N	73.30 W
Peristérion, Grc.	66d	38.01 N	23.42 E
Perivale (Neigh.), Eng.	62	51.32 N	0.19 W
Perkam, Tandjung (C.), Indon.	207	1.20 S	138.45 E
Perkins, Can. (pĕr'kĕns)	95c	45.37 N	75.37 W
Perlas, Arch. de Las, Pan. (är-chē-pyĕ'lä-gō-dĕ-läs-pĕr'läs)	133	8.29 N	79.15 W
Perlas, Laguna las (L.), Nic. (lä-gōō'nä-dĕ-läs)	133	12.34 N	83.19 W
Perleberg, G.D.R. (pĕr'lĕ-bĕrg)	166	53.06 N	11.51 E
Perm', Sov. Un. (pĕrm)	182a	58.00 N	56.15 E
Pernambuco (State), Braz. (pĕr-näm-bōō'kō)	143	8.08 S	38.54 W
Pernambuco, see Recife			
Pernik, Bul. (pĕr-nēk')	173	42.36 N	23.04 E
Péronne, Fr. (pā-rŏn')	168	49.57 N	2.49 E
Perote, Mex. (pĕ-rō'tĕ)	131	19.33 N	97.13 W
Perouse Str., Jap.-Sov. Un.	204	45.45 N	141.38 E
Perovo, Sov. Un. (pâ'rô-vô)	182b	55.43 N	37.47 E
Perpignan, Fr. (pĕr-pē-nyäN')	168	42.42 N	2.48 E
Perris, Ca. (pĕr'ĭs)	119a	33.46 N	117.14 W

ăt; finăl; rāte; senåte; ärm; ȧsk; sofȧ; fâre; ch-choose; dh-as th in other; bē; ēvent; bĕt; recĕnt; cratēr; g-gō; gh-guttural g; bĭt; ĭ-short neutral; rīde; ĸ-guttural k as ch in German ich;

PLACE (Pronunciation)	PAGE	Lat. °'	Long. °'
Perros, Bahía (B.), Cuba (bä-ē'ä-pä'rōs)	134	22.25 N	78.35 W
Perrot Île (I.), Can. (pĕr'ŭt)	95a	45.23 N	73.57 W
Perry, Fl. (pĕr'ĭ)	126	30.06 N	83.35 W
Perry, Ga.	126	32.27 N	83.44 W
Perry, Ia.	115	41.49 N	94.40 W
Perry, NY	111	42.45 N	78.00 W
Perry, Ok.	123	36.17 N	97.18 W
Perry, Ut.	119b	41.27 N	112.02 W
Perry Hall, Md.	112e	39.24 N	76.29 W
Perrymont, Pa.	57b	40.33 N	80.02 W
Perryopolis, Pa. (pĕ-rē-ŏ'pô-lĭs)	113e	40.05 N	79.45 W
Perrysburg, Oh. (pĕr ĭz-bûrg)	110	41.35 N	83.35 W
Perryton, Tx. (pĕr'ĭ-tŭn)	122	36.23 N	100.48 W
Perryville, Ak. (pĕr-ĭ-vĭl)	107	55.58 N	159.28 W
Perryville, Mo.	123	37.41 N	89.52 W
Persan, Fr. (pĕr-säN')	169b	49.09 N	2.15 E
Persepolis (Ruins), Iran (pĕr-sĕp'o-lĭs)	155	30.15 N	53.08 E
Persian G., Asia (pûr'zhăn)	192	27.38 N	50.30 E
Persia, see Iran			
Perth, Austl. (pûrth)	214	31.50 S	116.10 E
Perth, Can.	111	44.40 N	76.15 W
Perth, Scot.	162	56.24 N	3.25 W
Perth Amboy, NJ (äm'boi)	112a	40.31 N	74.16 W
Pertuis, Fr. (pĕr-tüē')	169	43.43 N	5.29 E
Peru, Il. (pē-rōō')	110	41.20 N	89.10 W
Peru, In.	110	40.45 N	86.00 W
Peru, S. A.	140	10.00 S	75.00 W
Perugia, It. (pā-rōō'jä)	172	43.08 N	12.24 E
Peruque, Mo. (pē rō'kē)	119e	38.52 N	90.36 W
Pervomaysk, Sov. Un. (pĕr-vô-mĭsk')	175	48.04 N	30.52 E
Pervoural'sk, Sov. Un. (pĕr-vô-ōō-rálsk')	182a	56.54 N	59.58 E
Pervyy Kuril'skiy Proliv (Str.), Sov. Un.	181	51.43 N	154.32 E
Perwenitz, G.D.R.	65a	52.40 N	13.01 E
Pesaro, It. (pā'zä-rō)	172	43.54 N	12.55 E
Pescado (R.), Ven. (pĕs-kä'dō)	143b	9.33 N	65.32 W
Pescara, It. (pās-kä'rä)	172	42.26 N	14.15 E
Pescara (R.), It.	172	42.18 N	13.22 E
Peschanyy, Mys (C.), Sov. Un.	179	43.10 N	51.20 E
Pescia, It. (pā'shä)	172	43.53 N	11.42 E
Peshāwar, Pak. (pĕ-shä'wŭr)	193a	34.01 N	71.34 E
Peshtera, Bul.	173	42.03 N	24.19 E
Peshtigo (R.), Wi.	115	45.15 N	88.14 W
Peshtigo, Wi. (pĕsh'tē-gō)	115	45.03 N	87.46 W
Pesing, Indon.	68k	6.10 S	106.45 E
Peski, Sov. Un. (pyås'kĭ)	182b	55.13 N	38.48 E
Pêso da Régua, Port. (pā-sōō-dä-rā'gwä)	170	41.09 N	7.47 W
Pespire, Hond. (pās-pē'rå)	132	13.35 N	87.20 W
Pesqueria, R., Mex. (pās-kå-rē'ä)	124	25.55 N	100.25 W
Pessac, Fr.	168	44.48 N	0.38 W
Pesterzsébet (Neigh.), Hung.	66g	47.26 N	19.07 E
Pestlorinc (Neigh.), Hung.	66g	47.26 N	19.12 E
Pestújhely (Neigh.), Hung.	66g	47.32 N	19.07 E
Petacalco, Bahía de (B.), Mex. (bä-ē'ä-dĕ-pĕ-tä-käl'kô)	130	17.55 N	102.00 W
Petah Tiqwa, Isr.	191a	32.05 N	34.53 E
Petaluma, Ca. (pĕt-á-lōō'má)	120	38.15 N	122.38 W
Petare, Ven. (pĕ-tä'rĕ)	143b	10.28 N	66.48 W
Petatlán, Mex. (pā-tä-tlän')	130	17.31 N	101.17 W
Petawawa, Can.	103	45.54 N	77.17 W
Petén, Laguna de (L.), Guat. (lä-gōō'nä-dĕ-på-tān')	132a	17.05 N	89.54 W
Petenwell Res., Wi.	115	44.10 N	89.55 W
Peterborough, Austl.	216	32.53 S	138.58 E
Peterborough, Can. (pē'tēr-bŭr-ô)	111	44.20 N	78.20 W
Peterborough, Eng.	156	52.35 N	0.14 W
Peterhead, Scot. (pē-tēr-hĕd')	162	57.36 N	3.47 W
Peter Pond L., Can. (pŏnd)	100	55.55 N	108.44 W
Peter Pt., Can.	111	43.50 N	77.00 W
Petersburg, Ak. (pē'tērz-bûrg)	107	56.52 N	133.10 W
Petersburg, Il.	123	40.01 N	89.51 W
Petersburg, In.	110	38.30 N	87.15 W
Petersburg, Ky.	113f	39.04 N	84.52 W
Petersburg, Va.	127	37.12 N	77.30 W
Peters Creek (R.), Pa.	57b	40.18 N	79.52 W
Petershagen, G.D.R. (pĕ'tĕrs-hä-gĕn)	157b	52.32 N	13.46 E
Petersham, Austl.	70a	33.54 S	151.09 E
Petershausen, F.R.G. (pĕ'tĕrs-hou-zĕn)	157d	48.25 N	11.29 E
Pétionville, Hai.	135	18.30 N	72.20 W
Petit, S. Afr.	71b	26.06 S	28.22 E
Petitcodiac, Can. (pē-tē-kō-dyák')	104	45.56 N	65.10 W
Petite Terre I., Guad. (pē-tēt'târ')	133b	16.12 N	61.00 W
Petit Goâve, Hai. (pē-tē' gō-áv')	135	18.25 N	72.50 W
Petit Jean Cr., Ar. (pē-tē'zhäN')	123	35.05 N	93.55 W
Petit Loango, Gabon	230	2.16 S	9.35 E
Petlalcingo, Mex. (pĕ-tläl-sĕŋ'gō)	131	18.05 N	97.53 W
Peto, Mex. (pĕ'tô)	132a	20.07 N	88.49 W
Petorca, Chile (pā-tōr'kå)	141	32.14 S	70.55 W
Petoskey, Mi. (pē-tŏs-kĭ)	110	45.25 N	84.55 W
Petra, Jordan	191a	30.21 N	35.25 E
Petra Velikogo, Zaliv (B.), Sov. Un. (zä'lĭf pĕt-rä' vĕ-lĭ'kô-vô)	204	42.40 N	131.50 E
Petrich, Bul. (pā'trĭch)	173	41.24 N	23.13 E
Petrified Forest Natl. Park, Az. (pĕt'rĭ-fīd fôr'ĕst)	121	34.58 N	109.35 W
Petrikov, Sov. Un. (pyĕ'trē-kô-v)	175	52.09 N	28.30 E
Petrikovka, Sov. Un. (pyĕ'trē-kôf-kä)	175	48.43 N	34.29 E
Petrinja, Yugo. (pā'trēn-yà)	172	45.25 N	16.17 E
Petrodvorets, Sov. Un. (pyĕ-trô-dvô-ryĕts')	182c	59.53 N	29.55 E
Petrokrepost', Sov. Un. (pyĕ'trô-krē-pôst)	182c	59.56 N	31.03 E
Petrolia, Can. (pē-trō'lĭ-á)	110	42.50 N	82.10 W
Petrolina, Braz. (pĕ-trō-lē'nä)	143	9.18 S	40.28 W
Petronell, Aus.	157e	48.07 N	16.52 E
Petropavlovka, Sov. Un. (pyĕ'trô-päv'lôf-kä)	175	48.24 N	36.23 E
Petropavlovka, Sov. Un.	182a	54.10 N	59.50 E
Petropavlovsk, Sov. Un. (pyĕ-trô-päv'lôfsk)	180	54.44 N	69.07 E
Petropavlovsk-Kamchatskiy, Sov. Un. (käm-chät'skĭ)	181	53.13 N	158.56 E
Petrópolis, Braz. (pĕ-trô-pō-lēzh')	144b	22.31 S	43.10 W
Petroşani, Rom.	173	45.24 N	23.24 E
Petrovsk, Sov. Un. (pyĕ-trôfsk')	179	52.20 N	45.15 E
Petrovskaya, Sov. Un. (pyĕ-trôf'ská-yá)	175	45.25 N	37.50 E
Petrovsko-Razumovskoje (Neigh.), Sov. Un.	66b	55.50 N	37.34 E
Petrovskoye, Sov. Un.	179	45.20 N	43.00 E
Petrovsk-Zabaykal'skiy, Sov. Un. (pyĕ-trôfskzä-bī-käl'skĭ)	181	51.13 N	109.08 E
Petrozavodsk, Sov. Un. (pyā'trô-zá-vôtsk')	165	61.46 N	34.25 E
Petrus Steyn, S. Afr. (pā'trōōs stān')	223d	27.40 S	28.09 E
Petseri, Sov. Un. (pĕt'sĕ-rē)	174	57.48 N	27.33 E
Pewaukee, Wi. (pĭ-wô'kē)	113a	43.05 N	88.15 W
Pewaukee L., Wi.	113a	43.03 N	88.18 W
Pewee Valley, Ky. (pe wē)	113h	38.19 N	85.29 W
Peza (R.), Sov. Un. (pyå'zá)	178	65.35 N	46.50 E
Pézenas, Fr. (pā-zē-nä')	168	43.26 N	3.24 E
Pforzheim, F.R.G. (pfôrts'hīm)	166	48.52 N	8.43 E
Phalodi, India	196	27.13 N	72.22 E
Phan-thiet, Viet. (p'hän')	206	11.30 N	108.43 E
Pharsalus, see Fársala			
Phelps Corner, Md.	56d	38.48 N	76.58 W
Phenix City, Al. (fē'nĭks)	126	32.29 N	85.00 W
Philadelphia, Ms. (fĭl-á-dĕl'phĭ-á)	126	32.45 N	89.07 W
Philadelphia, Pa.	112f	40.00 N	75.13 W
Philip, SD (fĭl'ĭp)	114	44.03 N	101.35 W
Philippeville, see Skikda			
Philippines, Asia (fĭl'ĭ-pēnz)	191	14.25 N	125.00 E
Philippine Sea, Asia (fĭl'ĭ-pēn)	208	16.00 N	133.00 E
Philippine Trench, Phil.	207	10.30 N	127.15 E
Philippopolis, see Plovdiv			
Philipsburg, Pa. (fĭl'lĭps-bērg)	111	40.55 N	78.10 W
Philipsburg, Wy.	117	46.19 N	113.19 W
Phillip (I.), Austl. (fĭl'ĭp)	216	38.32 S	145.10 E
Phillip Chan., Indon.	191b	1.04 N	103.40 E
Phillipi, WV (fĭ-lĭp'ĭ)	111	39.10 N	80.00 W
Phillips, Wi. (fĭl'ĭps)	115	45.41 N	90.24 W
Phillipsburg, Ks. (fĭl'lĭps-bērg)	122	39.44 N	99.19 W
Phillipsburg, NJ	111	40.45 N	75.10 W
Phinga, India	67a	22.41 N	88.25 E
Phitsanulok, Thai.	206	16.51 N	100.15 E
Phnum Pénh, Kamp. (nŏm'pĕn')	206	11.39 N	104.53 E
Phoenix, Az. (fē'nĭks)	121	33.30 N	112.00 W
Phoenix, Md.	112e	39.31 N	76.40 W
Phoenix Is., Oceania	208	4.00 S	174.00 W
Phoenixville, Pa. (fē'nĭks-vĭl)	112f	40.08 N	75.31 W
Phra Nakhon Si Ayutthaya, Thai.	206	14.16 N	100.37 E
Phu Bia (Pk.), Laos	206	19.36 N	103.00 E
Phuket, Thai.	206	7.57 N	98.19 E
Phu-Quoc, Dao (I.), Kamp.	206	10.13 N	104.00 E
Phu-tho-hoa, Viet.	68m	10.46 N	106.39 E
Pi (R.), China (bē)	200	32.06 N	116.31 E
Piacenza, It. (pyä-chĕnt'sä)	172	45.02 N	9.42 E
Pianosa (I.), It. (pyä-nō'sä)	172	42.13 N	15.45 E
Piatra-Neamţ, Rom. (pyä'trá-nå-ämts')	167	46.54 N	26.24 E
Piauí (State), Braz. (pyou'ē)	143	7.40 S	42.25 W
Piauí, Serra do (Mts.), Braz. (sĕr'rá dōō pyou'ē)	143	10.45 S	44.36 W
Piave (R.), It. (pyä'vā)	172	45.45 N	12.15 E
Piazza Armerina, It. (pyät'sä är-må-rē'nä)	172	37.23 N	14.26 E
Pibor R., Sud. (pē'bôr)	225	7.21 N	32.54 E
Pic (R.), Can. (pēk)	115	48.48 N	86.28 W
Picara Pt. (U. S. A.), Vir. Is. (pē-kä'rä)	129c	18.23 N	64.57 W
Picayune, Ms. (pĭk'á yōōn)	126	30.32 N	89.41 W
Picher, Ok. (pĭch'ēr)	123	36.58 N	94.49 W
Pichilemu, Chile (pē-chē-lĕ'mōō)	141b	34.22 S	72.01 W
Pichucalco, Mex. (pē-chōō-käl'kô)	131	17.34 N	93.06 W
Pichucalco (R.), Mex.	131	17.40 N	93.02 W
Pickerel (L.), Can. (pĭk'ēr-ĕl)	115	48.35 N	91.10 W
Pickwick (R.), Tn. (pĭk'wĭck)	126	35.04 N	88.05 W
Pico, Ca. (pē'kô)	119a	34.01 N	118.05 W
Pico de Aneto (Mtn.), Sp. (pē'kō-dĕ-ä-nĕ'tô)	171	42.35 N	0.38 E
Pico I., Açores (pē'kōō)	224a	38.16 N	28.49 W
Pico Rivera, Ca.	119a	34.01 N	118.05 W
Picos, Braz. (pē'kōzh)	143	7.13 S	41.23 W
Picton, Austl. (pĭk'tŭn)	211b	34.11 S	150.37 E
Picton, Can.	103	44.00 N	77.15 W
Pictou, Can. (pĭk-tōō')	104	45.41 N	62.43 W
Pidálion, Akrotírion (C.), Cyprus	191a	34.50 N	34.05 E
Pidurutalagala Mt., Sri Lanka (pē'dōō-rōō-tä'lá-gä'lá)	197	7.00 N	80.46 E
Pie (I.), Can. (pī)	115	48.10 N	89.07 W
Piedade, Braz. (pyä-dä'dĕ)	141a	23.42 S	47.25 W
Piedade do Baruel, Braz.	61d	23.37 S	46.18 W
Piedmont, Al. (pēd'mŏnt)	126	33.54 N	85.36 W
Piedmont, Ca.	118b	37.50 N	122.14 W
Piedmont, Mo.	123	37.09 N	90.42 W
Piedmont, SC	127	34.40 N	82.27 W
Piedmont, WV	111	39.30 N	79.05 W
Piedrabuena, Sp. (pyā-drä-bwā'nä)	170	39.01 N	4.10 W
Piedras Negras, Mex. (pyā'dräs nā'gräs)	124	28.41 N	100.33 W
Piedras, Punta (Pt.), Arg. (pōō'n-tä-pyĕ'dräs)	141c	35.25 S	57.10 W
Pieksämäki, Fin. (pyĕk'sĕ-mĕ-kē)	165	62.18 N	27.14 E
Piemonte (Reg.), It. (pyĕ-mô'n-tĕ)	172	44.30 N	7.42 E
Pienaars R., S. Afr.	223d	25.13 S	28.05 E
Pienaarsrivier, S. Afr.	223d	25.12 S	28.18 E
Pierce, Ne. (pērs)	114	42.11 N	97.33 W
Pierce, WV	111	39.15 N	79.30 W
Piermont, NY (pēr'mŏnt)	112a	41.03 N	73.55 W
Pierre, SD (pēr)	114	44.22 N	100.20 W
Pierrefitte-sur-Seine, Fr.	64c	48.58 N	2.22 E
Pierrefonds, Can.	95a	45.29 N	73.52 W
Pieštany, Czech. (pyĕsh'tyà-nûĭ)	167	48.36 N	17.48 E
Pietermaritzburg, S. Afr. (pē-tēr-má-rĭts-bûrg)	227c	29.36 S	30.23 E
Pietersburg, S. Afr. (pē'tērz-bûrg)	223d	23.56 S	29.30 E
Pietersfield, S. Afr.	71b	26.14 S	28.26 E
Piet Retief, S. Afr. (pēt rĕ-tēf')	226	27.00 S	30.58 E
Pietrosul Pk., Rom.	167	47.35 N	24.49 E
Pieve di Cadore, It. (pyā'vå dē kä-dō'rå)	172	46.26 N	12.22 E
Pigeon (R.), Can.-Mn. (pĭj'ŭn)	115	48.05 N	90.13 W
Pigeon L., Can.	99	53.00 N	114.00 W
Pigeon Lake, Can.	95f	49.57 N	97.36 W
Piggott, Ar. (pĭg-ŭt)	123	36.22 N	90.10 W
Pijijiapan, Mex. (pēKē-kē-ä'pän)	131	15.40 N	93.12 W
Pijnacker, Neth.	157a	52.01 N	4.25 E
Pikes Pk., Co. (pīks)	122	38.49 N	105.03 W
Pikesville, Md.	56c	39.23 N	76.44 W
Pikeville, Ky. (pīk'vĭl)	127	37.28 N	82.31 W
Pikou, China (pē-kō)	200	39.25 N	122.19 E
Pikwitonei, Can. (pĭk'wĭ-tōn)	101	55.35 N	97.09 W
Pila, Pol. (pē'là)	166	53.09 N	16.44 E
Pilansberg, S. Afr. (pĭ'ăns'bûrg)	223d	25.08 S	26.55 E
Pilar, Arg. (pē'lär)	141c	34.27 S	58.55 W
Pilar, Par.	144	27.00 S	58.15 W
Pilar de Goiás, Braz. (dĕ-gô'yà's)	143	14.47 S	49.33 W
Pilchuck (R.), Wa.	118a	48.03 N	121.58 W
Pilchuck Cr., Wa. (pĭl'chŭck)	118a	48.19 N	122.11 W
Pilchuck Mtn., Wa.	118a	48.03 N	121.48 W
Pilcomayo (R.), Par. (pēl-cō-mī'ō)	144	24.45 S	69.15 W
Pilgrim Gardens, NJ	56b	39.57 N	75.19 W
Pilgrims Hatch, Eng.	62	51.38 N	0.17 E
Pili, Phil. (pē'lē)	207a	13.34 N	123.17 E
Pilica R., Pol. (pē-lēt'sä)	167	51.00 N	19.48 E
Pillar Pt., Can. (pĭl'ár)	118a	48.14 N	124.06 W
Pillar Rocks, Wa.	118c	46.16 N	123.35 W
Pilón (R.), Mex. (pē-lōn')	130	24.13 N	99.03 W
Pilot Point, Tx. (pī'lŭt)	123	33.24 N	97.00 W
Pilsen, see Plzeň			
Piltene, Sov. Un. (pĭl'tē-nĕ)	165	57.17 N	21.40 E
Pimal, Cerra (Mtn.), Mex. (sĕ'r-rä-pē-mäl')	130	22.58 N	104.19 W
Pimba, Austl. (pĭm'bá)	214	31.15 S	146.50 E
Pimville (Neigh.), S. Afr. (pĭm'vĭl)	227b	26.17 S	27.54 E
Pinacate, Cerro (Mtn.), Mex. (sĕ'r-rô-pē-nä-kä'tĕ)	128	31.45 N	113.30 W
Pinamalayan, Phil. (pē-nä-mä-lä'yän)	207a	13.04 N	121.31 E
Pinang, see George Town			
Pinarbasi, Tur. (pē'när-bä'shĭ)	179	38.50 N	36.10 E
Pinar del Río, Cuba (pē-när' dĕl rē'ō)	134	22.25 N	83.35 W
Pinar del Río (Prov.), Cuba	134	22.45 N	83.25 W
Pinatubo (Mtn.), Phil. (pē-nä-tōō'bō)	207a	15.09 N	120.19 E
Pincher Creek, Can. (pĭn'chēr krēk)	99	49.29 N	113.57 W
Pinckneyville, Il. (pĭnk'nĭ-vĭl)	123	38.06 N	89.22 W
Pińczów, Pol. (pēn''chōōf)	167	50.32 N	20.33 E
Pindamonhangaba, Braz. (pē'n-dä-mōnyä'n-gä-bä)	141a	22.56 S	45.26 W
Pinder Pt., Ba.	134	26.35 N	78.35 W
Píndhos Oros (Mts.), Grc.	173	39.48 N	21.19 E
Pindiga, Nig.	229	9.59 N	10.54 E
Pine (R.), Can. (pīn)	98	55.30 N	122.20 W
Pine (R.), Wi.	115	45.50 N	88.37 W
Pine Bluff, Ar. (pīn blŭf)	123	34.13 N	92.01 W
Pine Brook, NJ	55	40.52 N	74.20 W
Pine City, Mn. (pīn)	115	45.50 N	93.01 W
Pine Cr., Nv.	120	40.15 N	116.17 W
Pine Creek, Austl.	214	13.45 S	132.00 E
Pinecrest, Va.	56d	38.50 N	77.09 W
Pine Falls, Can.	101	50.35 N	96.15 W
Pine Forest Ra., Nv.	116	41.35 N	118.45 W
Pinega, Sov. Un. (pē-nyĕ'gá)	178	64.40 N	43.30 E
Pinega (R.), Sov. Un.	178	64.10 N	42.30 E
Pine Grove, Can.	54c	43.48 N	79.35 W
Pine Hill, NJ (pīn hĭl)	112f	39.47 N	74.59 W
Pinehurst, Ma.	54a	42.32 N	71.14 W
Pine Is., Fl.	127a	24.48 N	81.32 W
Pine Island Sd., Fl.	127a	26.32 N	82.30 W
Pine Lake Estates, Ga. (låk ĕs-tāts')	112c	33.47 N	84.13 W
Pinelands, S. Afr. (pīn'lănds)	226a	33.57 S	18.30 E
Pine Lawn, Mo. (lôn)	119e	38.42 N	90.17 W
Pine Pass, Can.	98	55.22 N	122.40 W
Pine Ridge, Va.	56d	38.52 N	77.14 W
Pine Ridge Ind. Res., SD (rĭj)	114	43.33 N	102.13 W
Pinerolo, It. (pē-nā-rô'lō)	172	44.47 N	7.18 E
Pines, Lake o' the, Tx.	125	32.50 N	94.40 W
Pinetown, S. Afr. (pīn'toun)	227c	29.47 S	30.52 E
Pine View Res., Ut. (vū)	119b	41.17 N	111.54 W
Pineville, Ky. (pīn'vĭl)	126	36.48 N	83.43 W
Pineville, La.	125	31.20 N	92.25 W
Ping (R.), Thai.	206	17.54 N	98.29 E
Pingding, China (pĭŋ-dĭŋ)	202	37.50 N	113.30 E
Pingdu, China (pĭŋ-dōō)	200	36.46 N	119.57 E
Pingfang, China	67b	39.56 N	116.33 E
Pinggir, Indon.	191b	1.05 N	101.12 E
Pinghe, China (pĭŋ-hŭ)	203	24.30 N	117.02 E
Pingle, China (pĭŋ-lŭ)	203	24.30 N	110.22 E
Pingliang, China (pĭng'lyäng')	202	35.12 N	106.50 E
Pingquan, China (pĭŋ-chyůän)	202	40.58 N	118.40 E
Pingtan, China (pĭŋ-tän)	203	25.30 N	119.45 E
Pingtan Dao (I.), China (pĭŋ-tän dou)	203	25.40 N	119.45 E
P'ingtung, Taiwan	203	22.40 N	120.35 E
Pingwu, China (pĭŋ-wōō)	202	32.20 N	104.40 E
Pingxiang, China (pĭŋ-shyäŋ)	203	27.40 N	113.50 E
Pingyi, China (pĭŋ-yē)	200	35.30 N	117.38 E
Pingyuan, China (pĭŋ-yůän)	200	37.11 N	116.26 E
Pingzhou, China (pĭŋ-jō)	201a	23.01 N	113.11 E
Pinhal, Braz. (pē-nyá'l)	141a	22.11 S	46.43 W
Pinhal Novo, Port. (nô vōō)	171b	38.38 N	8.54 W
Pinheiros (R.), Braz.	61d	23.32 S	46.44 W

PLACE (Pronounciation)	PAGE	Lat. °′	Long. °′
Pinhel, Port. (pēn-yĕl')	170	40.45 N	7.03 W
Piniós (R.), Grc.	173	40.33 N	21.40 E
Pini, Pulau (I.), Indon.	206	0.07 S	98.38 E
Pinnacles Natl. Mon., Ca. (pĭn'ȧ-k'lz)	120	36.30 N	121.00 W
Pinneberg, F.R.G. (pĭn'ĕ-bĕrg)	157c	53.40 N	9.48 E
Pinner (Neigh.), Eng.	62	51.36 N	0.23 W
Pinole, Ca. (pĭ-nō'lē)	118b	38.01 N	122.17 W
Pinos-Puente, Sp. (pwān'tā)	170	37.15 N	3.43 W
Pinotepa Nacional, Mex. (pē-nô-tā'pä nä-syô-näl')	130	16.21 N	98.04 W
Pins, Ile des, N. Cal.	215	22.44 S	167.44 E
Pinsk, Sov. Un. (pēn'sk)	167	52.07 N	26.05 E
Pinta (I.), Ec.	142	0.41 N	90.47 W
Pintendre, Can. (pĕn-tändr')	95b	46.45 N	71.07 W
Pinto, Sp. (pēn'tō)	171a	40.14 N	3.42 W
Pinto Butte, Can. (pĭn'tō)	100	49.22 N	107.25 W
Pioche, Nv. (pī-ō'chē)	121	37.56 N	114.28 W
Piombino, It. (pyôm-bē'nō)	172	42.56 N	10.33 E
Pioneer Mts., Mt. (pī'ô-nēr')	117	45.23 N	112.51 W
Piotrków Trybunalski, Pol. (pyōtr'kōov trĭ-bōō-nal'skē)	167	51.23 N	19.44 E
Piper, Al. (pī'pēr)	126	33.04 N	87.00 W
Piper, Ks.	119f	39.09 N	94.51 W
Pipéri (I.), Grc. (pē'per-ē)	173	39.19 N	24.20 E
Pipe Spring Natl. Mon., Az. (pīp spring)	121	36.50 N	112.45 W
Pipestone, Mn. (pīp'stōn)	114	44.00 N	96.19 W
Pipestone Natl. Mon., Mn.	114	44.03 N	96.24 W
Pipmaucan, Rés., Can. (pĭp-mä-kän')	104	49.45 N	70.00 W
Piqua, Oh. (pĭk'wȧ)	110	40.10 N	84.15 W
Piracaia, Braz. (pē-rä-kȧ'yä)	141a	23.04 S	46.20 W
Piracicaba, Braz. (pē-rä-sē-kä'bä)	141a	22.43 S	47.39 W
Piraeus (Piraiévs), Grc.	66d	37.57 N	23.38 E
Piraí, Braz. (pē-rä-ē')	141a	22.38 S	43.54 W
Piraíba (R.), Braz. (pä-rä-ē'bä)	141a	21.38 S	41.29 W
Piramida, Gol'tsy (Mtn.), Sov. Un.	180	54.00 N	96.00 E
Pirámide de Cuicuilco (P. Int.), Mex.	60a	19.18 N	99.11 W
Piran, Yugo. (pē-rä'n)	172	45.31 N	13.34 E
Piranga, Braz. (pē-rä'n-gä)	141a	20.41 S	43.17 W
Pirapetinga, Braz. (pē-rä-pĕ-tē'n-gä)	141a	21.40 S	42.20 W
Pirapora, Braz. (pē-rá-pō'rȧ)	143	17.39 S	44.54 W
Pirassununga, Braz. (pē-rä-sōō-nōō'n-gä)	141a	22.00 S	47.24 W
Pirenópolis, Braz. (pē-rĕ-nô'pō-lēs)	143	15.56 S	48.49 W
Pírgos, Grc.	173	37.51 N	21.28 E
Piritu, Laguna de (L.), Ven. (lä-gōō'nä-dĕ-pē-rē'tōō)	143b	10.00 N	64.57 W
Pirmasens, F.R.G. (pĭr-mä-zĕns')	166	49.12 N	7.34 E
Pirna, G.D.R. (pĭr'nä)	166	50.57 N	13.56 E
Pirot, Yugo. (pē'rōt)	173	43.09 N	22.35 E
Pirtleville, Az. (pûr't'l-vĭl)	121	31.25 N	109.35 W
Piru, Indon. (pē-rōō')	207	3.15 S	128.25 E
Piryatin, Sov. Un. (pēr-yä-tēn')	175	50.13 N	32.31 E
Pisa, It. (pē'sä)	172	43.52 N	10.24 E
Pisagua, Chile (pē-sä'gwä)	142	18.43 S	70.12 W
Piscataway, Md. (pĭs-kȧ-tă-wā)	112e	38.42 N	76.59 W
Piscataway, NJ	112a	40.35 N	74.27 W
Pisco, Peru (pēs'kō)	142	13.43 S	76.07 W
Pisco, Bahia de (B.), Peru (bä-ē'ä-dĕ)	142	13.43 S	77.48 W
Piseco (L.), NY (pĭ-sā'kô)	111	43.25 N	74.35 W
Pisek, Czech. (pē'sĕk)	166	49.18 N	14.08 E
Pisticci, It. (pēs-tē'chē)	172	40.24 N	16.34 E
Pistoia, It. (pēs-tô'yä)	172	43.57 N	11.54 E
Pisuerga (R.), Sp. (pē-swĕr'gä)	170	41.48 N	4.28 W
Pitalito, Col. (pē-tä-lē'tō)	142	1.45 N	75.09 W
Pitampura Kālan (Neigh.), India	67d	28.42 N	77.08 E
Pitcairn, Oceania	209	25.04 S	130.05 W
Pitcairn, Pa. (pĭt'kârn)	113e	40.29 N	79.47 W
Pitch' (R.), Sov. Un. (p'tĕch)	174	53.17 N	28.16 E
Piteå, Swe. (pē'tē-ô')	158	65.21 N	21.10 E
Pitealven (R.), Swe.	158	66.08 N	18.51 E
Pitesti, Rom. (pē-tĕsht'')	173	44.51 N	24.51 E
Pithara, Austl. (pĭt'ărȧ)	214	30.27 S	116.45 E
Pithiviers, Fr. (pē-tē-vyā')	168	48.12 N	2.14 E
Pitman, NJ (pĭt'mȧn)	112f	39.44 N	75.08 W
Pitons du Carbet, Mt., Mart.	133b	14.40 N	61.05 W
Pit R., Ca. (pĭt)	116	40.58 N	121.42 W
Pitseng, Leso.	227c	29.03 S	28.13 E
Pitt (R.), Can.	118d	49.19 N	122.39 W
Pitt I., Can.	98	53.35 N	129.45 W
Pittsburg, Ca. (pĭts'bûrg)	118b	38.01 N	121.52 W
Pittsburg, Ks.	123	37.25 N	94.43 W
Pittsburg, Tx.	123	32.00 N	94.57 W
Pittsburgh, Pa.	113e	40.26 N	80.01 W
Pittsfield, IL. (pĭts'fēld)	123	39.37 N	90.47 W
Pittsfield, Me.	104	44.45 N	69.44 W
Pittsfield, Ma.	111	42.25 N	73.15 W
Pittston, Pa. (pĭts'tŭn)	111	41.20 N	75.50 W
Piūi, Braz. (pē-ōō'ē)	141a	20.27 S	45.57 W
Piura, Peru (pē-ōō'rä)	142	5.13 S	80.46 W
Piya, Sov. Un. (pē'yȧ)	182a	58.34 N	61.12 E
Placentia, Ca. (plă-sĕn'shĭ-ȧ)	119a	33.52 N	117.50 W
Placentia, Can.	105	47.15 N	53.58 W
Placentia B., Can.	105	47.14 N	54.30 W
Placerville, Ca. (plăs'ēr-vĭl)	120	38.43 N	120.47 W
Placetas, Cuba (plä-thā'täs)	134	22.10 N	79.40 W
Placid (L.), NY (plăs'ĭd)	111	44.20 N	74.00 W
Plain City, Ut. (plān)	119b	41.18 N	112.06 W
Plainfield, Il. (plān'fēld)	113a	41.37 N	88.12 W
Plainfield, In.	113g	39.42 N	86.23 W
Plainfield, NJ	112a	40.38 N	74.25 W
Plainview, Ar. (plān'vū)	123	34.59 N	93.15 W
Plainview, Mn.	115	44.09 N	93.12 W
Plainview, Ne.	114	42.20 N	97.47 W
Plainview, NY	112a	40.47 N	73.28 W
Plainview, Tx.	122	34.11 N	101.42 W
Plainwell, Mi. (plan'wĕl)	110	42.25 N	85.40 W
Plaisance, Can. (plĕ-zäns')	95c	45.37 N	75.07 W
Plana or Flat Cays (Is.), Ba. (plä'nä)	135	22.35 N	73.35 W
Plandome Manor, NY	55	40.49 N	73.42 W
Planegg, F.R.G. (plä'nĕg)	157b	48.06 N	11.27 E
Plano, Tx. (plā'nō)	123	33.01 N	96.42 W
Plantagenet, Can. (plän-täzh-nĕ')	95c	45.33 N	75.00 W
Plant City, Fl. (plȧnt sĭ'tĭ)	127a	28.00 N	82.07 W
Plaquemine, La. (plăk'mēn')	125	30.17 N	91.14 W
Plasencia, Sp. (plä-sĕn'thē-ä)	170	40.02 N	6.07 W
Plast, Sov. Un. (plȧst)	182a	54.22 N	60.48 E
Plaster Rock, Can. (plȧs'tēr rŏk)	104	46.54 N	67.24 W
Plastun, Sov. Un. (plȧs-tōōn')	204	44.41 N	136.08 E
Platani (R.), It. (plä-tä'nē)	172	37.26 N	13.28 E
Plata, R. de la (R.), Arg.-Urg. (dālä plä'tä)	144	34.35 S	58.15 W
Plateforme, Pte., Hai.	135	19.35 N	73.50 W
Platinum, Ak. (plăt'ĭ-nŭm)	107	59.00 N	161.27 W
Plato, Col. (plä'tō)	142	9.49 N	74.48 W
Platón Sánchéz, Mex. (plä-tōn' sän'chĕz)	130	21.14 N	98.20 W
Platt, Eng.	62	51.17 N	0.20 E
Platte, SD (plăt)	114	43.22 N	98.51 W
Platte (R.), Mo.	123	40.09 N	94.40 W
Platte (R.), U. S.	108	40.50 N	100.40 W
Platteville, Wi. (plăt'vĭl)	115	42.44 N	90.31 W
Plattsburg, Mo. (plăts'bûrg)	123	39.33 N	94.26 W
Plattsburg, NY	111	44.40 N	73.30 W
Plattsmouth, Ne. (plăts'mŭth)	114	41.00 N	95.53 W
Plauen, G.D.R. (plou'ĕn)	166	50.30 N	12.08 E
Playa de Guanabo, Cuba (plä-yä-dĕ-gwä-nä'bô)	135a	23.10 N	82.07 W
Playa del Rey (Neigh.), Ca.	59	33.58 N	118.26 W
Playa de Santa Fe, Cuba (sä'n-tä-fĕ')	135a	23.05 N	82.31 W
Playas (L.), NM (plä'yȧs)	121	31.50 N	108.30 W
Playa Vicente, Mex. (vē-sĕn'tā)	131	17.49 N	95.49 W
Playa Vicente (R.), Mex.	131	17.36 N	96.13 W
Playgreen L., Can. (plā'grēn)	101	54.00 N	98.10 W
Plaza de Toros Monumental (P. Int.), Sp.	65e	41.24 N	2.11 E
Pleasant (L.), NY (plĕz'ănt)	111	43.25 N	74.25 W
Pleasant Grove, Al.	112h	33.29 N	86.57 W
Pleasant Hill, Ca.	118b	37.57 N	122.04 W
Pleasant Hill, Mo.	123	38.46 N	94.18 W
Pleasant Hills, Pa.	57b	40.20 N	79.58 W
Pleasanton, Ca. (plĕz'ăn-tŭn)	118b	37.40 N	121.53 W
Pleasanton, Ks.	123	38.10 N	94.41 W
Pleasanton, Tx.	124	28.58 N	98.30 W
Pleasant Plain, Oh. (plĕz'ănt)	113f	39.17 N	84.06 W
Pleasant Ridge, Mi.	113b	42.28 N	83.09 W
Pleasant View, Ut. (plĕz'ănt vū)	119b	41.20 N	112.02 W
Pleasantville, Md.	56c	39.11 N	76.38 W
Pleasantville, NY (plĕz'ănt-vĭl)	112a	41.08 N	73.47 W
Pleasure Ridge Park, Ky. (plĕzh'ēr rĭj)	113h	38.09 N	85.49 W
Plenty, Bay of, N. Z. (plĕn'tē)	217	37.30 S	177.10 E
Plentywood, Mt. (plĕn'tē-wŏŏd)	117	48.47 N	104.38 W
Ples, Sov. Un. (plyĕs)	174	57.26 N	41.29 E
Pleshcheyevo (L.), Sov. Un. (plĕsh-chā'yĕ-vô)	174	56.50 N	38.22 E
Plessisville, Can. (plĕ-sē'vēl')	104	46.12 N	71.47 W
Pleszew, Pol. (plĕ'zhĕf)	167	51.54 N	17.48 E
Plettenberg, F.R.G. (plĕ'tĕn-bĕrgh)	169c	51.13 N	7.53 E
Pleven, Bul. (plĕ'vĕn)	173	43.24 N	24.26 E
Pljevlja, Yugo. (plĕv'lyä)	173	43.20 N	19.21 E
Plock, Pol. (pwôtsk)	167	52.32 N	19.44 E
Ploërmel, Fr. (plô-ĕr-mĕl')	168	47.56 N	2.25 W
Ploieşti, Rom. (plô-yĕsht'')	173	44.56 N	26.01 E
Plomárion, Grc. (plō-mä'rĭ-ŏn)	173	38.51 N	26.24 E
Plomb du Cantal (Mt.), Fr. (plôn'dükän-täl')	168	45.30 N	2.49 E
Plonge, Lac la (L.), Can. (plōnzh)	100	55.08 N	107.25 W
Plovdiv (Philippopolis), Bul. (plôv'dĭf) (fĭl-ĭp-ŏp'ô-lĭs)	173	42.09 N	24.43 E
Pluma Hidalgo, Mex. (plōō'mä ē-dăl'gō)	131	15.54 N	96.23 W
Plumpton, Austl.	70a	33.45 S	150.50 E
Plunge, Sov. Un. (plōōn'gä)	165	55.56 N	21.45 E
Plymouth, Eng. (plĭm'ŭth)	162	50.25 N	4.14 W
Plymouth, In.	110	41.20 N	86.20 W
Plymouth, Ma.	111	42.00 N	70.45 W
Plymouth, Mi.	113b	42.23 N	83.27 W
Plymouth, Montserrat	133b	16.43 N	62.12 W
Plymouth, NH	111	43.50 N	71.40 W
Plymouth, NC	127	35.50 N	76.44 W
Plymouth, Pa.	111	41.15 N	75.55 W
Plymouth, Wi.	115	43.45 N	87.59 W
Plyussa (R.), Sov. Un. (plyōō'sȧ)	174	58.33 N	28.30 E
Plzeň (Pilsen), Czech.	166	49.46 N	13.25 E
Pô, Burkina	228	11.10 N	1.09 W
Po (R.), It.	172	44.57 N	12.38 E
Poá, Braz.	61d	23.32 S	46.20 W
Pobé, Benin (pô-bā')	229	6.58 N	2.41 E
Pocahontas, Ar. (pō-kȧ-hŏn'tȧs)	123	36.15 N	91.01 W
Pocahontas, Ia.	115	42.43 N	94.41 W
Pocatello, Id. (pō-kȧ-tĕl'ō)	117	42.54 N	112.30 W
Pochëp, Sov. Un. (pô-chĕp')	174	52.56 N	32.27 E
Pochinok, Sov. Un. (pô-chē'nôk)	174	54.14 N	32.27 E
Pochinski, Sov. Un.	178	54.40 N	44.50 E
Pochotitán, Mex. (pô-chô-tē-tá'n)	130	21.37 N	104.33 W
Pochutla (San Pedro), Mex. (pô-chōō'tlä) (sän pā'drō)	131	15.46 N	96.28 W
Pocomoke City, Md. (pō-kō-mōk')	111	38.05 N	75.35 W
Pocono Mts., Pa. (pō-cō'nō)	111	41.10 N	75.05 W
Poços de Caldas, Braz. (pō-sôs-dĕ-käl'dȧs)	141a	21.48 S	46.34 W
Poder, Senegal (pô-dôr')	224	16.35 N	15.04 W
Podkamennaya (Stony) (R.) Tunguska, Sov. Un.	180	61.43 N	93.45 E
Podol'sk, Sov. Un. (pô-dôl''sk)	182b	55.26 N	37.33 E
Podvolochisk, Sov. Un.	175	49.32 N	26.16 E
Poggibonsi, It. (pôd-jē-bôn'sē)	172	43.27 N	11.12 E
Pogodino, Sov. Un. (pô-gô'dē-nō)	174	54.17 N	31.00 E
P'ohang, Kor.	204	35.57 N	129.23 E
Point Cook, Austl.	70b	37.56 S	144.45 E
Pointe-à-Pitre, Guad. (pwănt' á pē-tr')	133b	16.15 N	61.32 W
Pointe-aux-Trembles, Can. (pōō-änt' ō-tränbl)	95a	45.39 N	73.30 W
Pointe Claire, Can. (pōō-änt' klĕr)	95a	45.27 N	73.48 W
Pointe-des-Cascades, Can. (kăs-kădz')	95a	45.19 N	73.58 W
Pointe Fortune, Can. (fôr'tūn)	95a	45.34 N	74.23 W
Pointe-Gatineau, Can. (pōō-änt'gä-tē-nō')	95c	45.28 N	75.42 W
Pointe Noire, Con.	230	4.48 S	11.51 E
Point Hope, Ak. (hōp)	107	68.18 N	166.38 W
Point Pleasant, Md.	56c	39.11 N	76.35 W
Point Pleasant, WV (plĕz'ănt)	110	38.50 N	82.10 W
Point Roberts, Wa. (rŏb'ērts)	118d	48.59 N	123.04 W
Poissy, Fr. (pwȧ-sē')	169b	48.55 N	2.02 E
Poitiers, Fr. (pwȧ-tyā')	168	46.35 N	0.18 E
Pokaran, India (pō'kŭr-ŭn)	196	27.00 N	72.05 E
Pokrov, Sov. Un. (pô-krôf)	174	55.56 N	39.09 E
Pokrovsko-Strešnevo (Neigh.), Sov. Un.	66b	55.49 N	37.29 E
Pokrovskoye, Sov. Un. (pô-krôf'skô-yĕ)	175	47.27 N	38.54 E
Pola (R.), Sov. Un. (pō'lä)	174	54.44 N	31.53 E
Pola de Laviana, Sp. (dĕ-lä-vyä'nä)	170	43.15 N	5.29 W
Pola de Siero, Sp.	170	43.24 N	5.39 W
Poland, Eur. (pō'lănd)	154	52.37 N	17.01 E
Polangui, Phil. (pô-läŋ'gē)	207a	13.18 N	123.29 E
Polazna, Sov. Un. (pô'lȧz-nȧ)	182a	58.18 N	56.25 E
Polessk, Sov. Un. (pô'lĕsk)	165	54.50 N	21.14 E
Poles'ye (Pripyat Marshes), Sov. Un.	179	52.10 N	27.30 E
Polevskoy, Sov. Un. (pô-lĕ'vs-kô'ē)	182a	56.28 N	60.14 E
Polgár, Hung. (pôl'gär)	167	47.54 N	21.10 E
Policastro, Golfo di (G.), It.	172	41.00 N	13.23 E
Poligny, Fr. (pō-lē-nyē')	169	46.48 N	5.42 E
Polikhnitos, Grc.	173	39.05 N	26.11 E
Polillo, Phil. (pô-lēl'yō)	207a	14.42 N	121.56 W
Polillo Is., Phil.	207a	15.05 N	122.15 E
Polillo Str., Phil.	207a	15.02 N	121.40 E
Polist' (R.), Sov. Un. (pô'lĭst)	174	57.42 N	31.02 E
Polistena, It. (pō-lēs-tā'nä)	172	40.25 N	16.05 E
Poliyiros, Grc.	173	40.23 N	23.27 E
Polkan, Gol'tsy (Mtn.), Sov. Un.	180	60.18 N	92.08 E
Pollensa, Sp. (pōl-yĕn'sä)	171	39.50 N	3.00 E
Polochic R., Guat. (pō-lô-chēk')	132	15.19 N	89.45 W
Polonnoye, Sov. Un. (pô'lô-nô-yĕ)	175	50.07 N	27.31 E
Polotsk, Sov. Un. (pô'lôtsk)	174	55.30 N	28.48 E
Polpaico, Chile (pôl-pá'y-kô)	141b	33.10 S	70.53 W
Polson, Mt. (pōl'sŭn)	117	47.40 N	114.10 W
Polsum, F.R.G.	63	51.37 N	7.03 E
Poltava, Sov. Un. (pôl-tä'vä)	175	49.35 N	34.33 E
Poltava (Oblast), Sov. Un.	175	49.53 N	32.58 E
Põltsamaa, Sov. Un. (pŏlt'sȧ-mä)	174	58.39 N	26.00 E
Põltsamaa (R.), Sov. Un.	174	58.35 N	25.55 E
Polunochnoye, Sov. Un. (pô-lōō-nô'ch-nô-yĕ)	182a	60.52 N	60.27 E
Poluy (R.), Sov. Un. (pôl'wē)	180	65.45 N	68.15 E
Polyakovka, Sov. Un. (pŭl-yä'kôv-kȧ)	182a	54.38 N	59.42 E
Polyarnyy, Sov. Un. (pŭl-yär'nē)	178	69.10 N	33.30 E
Pomba (R.), Braz. (pô'm-bȧ)	141a	21.28 S	42.28 W
Pomerania (Reg.), Pol. (pŏm-ē-rā'nĭ-ȧ)	166	53.50 N	15.20 E
Pomeranian B., G.D.R. (pō'mē-rä-ny-än)	164	54.10 N	14.20 E
Pomeroy, S. Afr. (pŏm'ēr-roi)	227c	28.36 S	30.26 E
Pomeroy, Wa. (pŏm'ēr-oi)	116	46.28 N	117.35 W
Pomezia, It. (pô-mĕ't-zyä)	171d	41.41 N	12.31 E
Pomigliano d' Arco, It. (pô-mē-lyä'nô-d-ä'r-kô)	171c	40.39 N	14.23 E
Pomme de Terre, Mn. (pŏm dē tĕr')	114	45.22 N	95.52 W
Pomona, Ca. (pō-mō'nȧ)	119a	34.04 N	117.45 W
Pomona Estates, S. Afr.	71b	26.06 S	28.15 E
Pomorie, Bul.	173	42.24 N	27.41 E
Pompano Beach, Fl. (pŏm'pȧ-nô)	127a	26.12 N	80.07 W
Pompeii Ruins, It.	171c	40.31 N	14.29 E
Pomponne, Fr.	64c	48.53 N	2.41 E
Pompton Lakes, NJ (pŏmp'tŏn)	112a	41.01 N	74.16 W
Pompton Plains, NJ	55	40.58 N	74.18 W
Pomuch, Mex. (pô-mōō'ch)	132a	20.12 N	90.10 W
Ponca, Ne. (pŏn'kȧ)	114	42.34 N	96.43 W
Ponca City, Ok.	123	36.42 N	97.07 W
Ponce, P. R. (pōn'sä)	129b	18.01 N	66.43 W
Ponders End (Neigh.), Eng.	62	51.39 N	0.03 W
Pondicherry, India (pŏn-dĭ-shĕr'ē)	197	11.58 N	79.48 E
Pondicherry (State), India	197	11.50 N	74.50 E
Ponferrada, Sp. (pōn-fĕr-rä'dhä)	170	42.33 N	6.38 W
Ponoka, Can. (pŏ-nō'kȧ)	99	52.42 N	113.35 W
Ponoy, Sov. Un.	178	66.58 N	41.00 E
Ponoy (R.), Sov. Un.	178	65.50 N	38.40 E
Ponta Delgada, Açores (pōn'tȧ dĕl-gä'dȧ)	224a	37.40 N	25.45 W
Ponta Grossa, Braz. (grō'sȧ)	144	25.09 S	50.05 W
Pont-à-Mousson, Fr. (pôn'tȧ-mōōsôn')	169	48.55 N	6.02 E
Ponta Porã, Braz.	143	22.30 S	55.31 W
Pontarlier, Fr. (pôn'tár-lyā')	169	46.53 N	6.22 E
Pont-Audemer, Fr. (pôn'tōd'mâr')	168	49.23 N	0.28 E
Pontault-Combault, Fr.	64c	48.47 N	2.36 E
Pontcarré, Fr. (pôn-kȧ-rā')	169b	48.48 N	2.42 E
Pontchartrain L., La. (pôn-shȧr-trăn')	125	30.10 N	90.10 W
Pontedera, It. (pōn-tā-dā'rä)	172	43.37 N	10.37 E
Ponte de Sor, Port. (pōŋ'tĕ dā sōr')	170	39.14 N	8.03 W
Pontefract, Eng. (pŏn'tē-frăkt)	156	53.41 N	1.18 W
Ponte Nova, Braz. (pô'n-tĕ-nô'vȧ)	141a	20.26 S	42.52 W
Pontevedra, Arg.	60d	34.46 S	58.43 W
Pontevedra, Sp. (pōn-tĕ-vĕ-drä)	170	42.28 N	8.38 W
Ponthierville, see Ubundi			
Pontiac, Il. (pŏn'tĭ-ăk)	110	40.55 N	88.35 W
Pontiac, Mi.	113b	42.37 N	83.17 W

PLACE (Pronounciation)	PAGE	Lat. °'	Long. °'
Pontianak, Indon. (pôn-tê-ä'nak)	206	0.04 S	109.20 E
Pontian Kechil, Mala.	191b	1.29 N	103.24 E
Pontic Mts., Turk.	179	41.20 N	34.30 E
Pontinha (Neigh.), Port.	65d	38.46 N	9.11 W
Pontivy, Fr. (pôN-tê-vē')	168	48.05 N	2.57 W
Pont-l'Abbé, Fr. (pôN-lȧ-bā')	168	47.53 N	4.12 W
Pontoise, Fr. (pôN-twȧz')	169b	49.03 N	2.05 E
Pontonnyy, Sov. Un. (pôn'tôn-nyĭ)	182c	59.47 N	30.39 E
Pontotoc, Ms. (pŏn-tō-tŏk')	126	34.11 N	88.59 W
Pontremoli, It. (pôn-trĕm'ô-lē)	172	44.21 N	9.50 E
Ponziane, Isole (I.), It. (ē'sō-lĕ)	172	40.55 N	12.58 E
Poole, Eng. (po͞ol)	162	50.43 N	2.00 W
Poolesville, Md. (poolĕs-vĭl)	112e	39.08 N	77.26 W
Pooley I., Can. (po͞o'lē)	98	52.44 N	128.16 W
Poopó, Lago de (L.), Bol. (lä'gô-dĕ-pō-ō-pō')	142	18.16 S	67.57 W
Popayán, Col. (pō-pä-yän')	142	2.21 N	76.43 W
Poplar, Mt. (pŏp'lẽr)	117	48.08 N	105.10 W
Poplar (Neigh.), Eng.	62	51.31 N	0.01 W
Poplar Bluff, Mo. (blŭf)	123	36.43 N	90.22 W
Poplar Heights, Va.	56d	38.53 N	77.12 W
Poplar Plains, Ky. (plāns)	110	38.20 N	83.40 W
Poplar Point, Can.	95f	50.04 N	97.57 W
Poplar R., Mt.	117	48.34 N	105.20 W
Poplar R., West Fork, Mt.	117	48.59 N	106.06 W
Poplarville, Ms. (pŏp'lẽr-vĭl)	126	30.50 N	89.33 W
Popocatépetl Volcán (Vol.), Mex. (pô-pô-kä-tā'pĕ't'l)	131a	19.01 N	98.38 W
Popokabaka, Zaire (pō'pō-kȧ-bä'kȧ)	230	5.42 S	16.35 E
Popovka, Sov. Un. (pô'pôf-kȧ)	175	50.03 N	33.41 E
Popovka, Sov. Un.	175	51.13 N	33.08 E
Popovo, Bul. (pô'pô-vō)	173	43.23 N	26.17 E
Porbandar, India (pōr-bŭn'dŭr)	196	21.44 N	69.40 E
Porce (R.), Col. (pôr-sĕ)	142a	7.11 N	74.55 W
Porcher I., Can. (pôr'kẽr)	98	53.57 N	130.30 W
Porcuna, Sp. (pôr-ko͞o'nä)	170	37.54 N	4.10 W
Porcupine (R.), Ak.	107	67.00 N	143.25 W
Porcupine (R.), Can.	96	67.38 N	140.07 W
Porcupine Cr., Mt. (pôr'kū-pīn)	117	46.38 N	107.04 W
Porcupine Cr., Mt.	117	48.27 N	106.24 W
Porcupine Hills, Can.	101	52.30 N	101.45 W
Pordenone, It. (pōr-dā-nō'nā)	172	45.58 N	12.38 E
Poreč, Yugo. (pô'rĕch)	172	45.13 N	13.37 E
Pori, Fin. (pô'rē)	165	61.29 N	21.45 E
Poriúncula, Braz. (po-rēo͞o'n-ko͞o-lä)	141a	20.58 S	42.02 W
Porkhov, Sov. Un. (pôr'Kôf)	174	57.46 N	29.33 E
Porlamar, Ven. (pôr-lä-mär')	142	11.00 N	63.55 W
Pornic, Fr. (pôr-nēk')	168	47.08 N	2.07 W
Poronaysk, Sov. Un. (pô'rô-nīsk)	181	49.21 N	143.23 E
Porrentruy, Switz. (pô-räN-trüē')	166	47.25 N	7.02 E
Porsgrunn, Nor. (pôrs'gro͞on')	164	59.09 N	9.36 E
Portachuelo, Bol. (pôrt-ä-chwā'lô)	142	17.20 S	63.12 W
Portage, Pa. (pôr'tāj)	111	40.25 N	78.35 W
Portage, Wi.	115	43.33 N	89.29 W
Portage Des Sioux, Mo. (dē so͞o)	119e	38.56 N	90.21 W
Portage-la-Prairie, Can. (lä-prā'rĭ)	95f	49.57 N	98.25 W
Port Alberni, Can. (pōr äl-bẽr-nē')	98	49.14 N	124.48 W
Portalegre, Port. (pôr-tä-lā'grĕ)	170	39.18 N	7.26 W
Portales, NM (pôr-tä'lĕs)	122	34.10 N	103.11 W
Port Alfred (Kowie), S. Afr. (kou'ĭ)	227c	33.36 S	26.55 E
Port Alice, Can. (ăl'ĭs)	98	50.23 N	127.27 W
Port Allegany, Pa. (ăl-ē-gā'nĭ)	111	41.50 N	78.10 W
Port Angeles, Wa. (ăn'jē-lĕs)	116	48.07 N	123.26 W
Port Antonio, Jam.	135	18.10 N	76.25 W
Portarlington, Austl.	211a	38.07 S	144.39 E
Port Arthur, Tx.	125	29.52 N	93.59 W
Port Augusta, Austl. (ô-gŭs'tă)	216	32.28 S	137.50 E
Port au Port B., Can. (pōr'tō pōr')	105	48.41 N	58.45 W
Port-au-Prince, Hai. (prăNs')	135	18.35 N	72.20 W
Port Austin, Mi. (ôs'tĭn)	110	44.00 N	83.00 W
Port aux Basques, Can.	105	47.36 N	59.09 W
Port Blair, Andaman & Nicobar Is. (blâr)	206	12.07 N	92.45 E
Port Bolivar, Tx. (bŏl'ĭ-vȧr)	125a	29.22 N	94.46 W
Port Borden, Can. (bôr'dĕn)	104	46.15 N	63.42 W
Port-Bouët, Ivory Coast	224	5.24 N	3.56 W
Port-Cartier, Can.	104	50.01 N	66.53 W
Port Chester, NY (chĕs'tẽr)	112a	40.59 N	73.40 W
Port Chicago, Ca. (shĭ-kô'gō)	118b	38.03 N	122.01 W
Port Clinton, Oh. (klĭn'tŭn)	110	41.30 N	83.00 W
Port Colborne, Can.	103	42.53 N	79.13 W
Port Coquitlam, Can. (kô-kwĭt'lăm)	118d	49.16 N	122.46 W
Port Credit, Can. (krĕd'ĭt)	95d	43.33 N	79.35 W
Port-de-Bouc, Fr. (pôr-dĕ-bo͝ok')	168a	43.24 N	5.00 E
Port de Paix, Hai. (pĕ)	135	19.55 N	72.50 W
Port Dickson, Mala. (dĭk'sŭn)	191b	2.33 N	101.49 E
Port Discovery (B.), Wa. (dĭs-kŭv'ẽr-ĭ)	118a	48.05 N	122.55 W
Port Edward, S. Afr. (ĕd'wẽrd)	227c	31.04 S	30.14 E
Port Elgin, Can. (ĕl'jĭn)	104	46.03 N	64.05 W
Port Elizabeth, S. Afr. (ē-lĭz'ȧ-bĕth)	227c	33.57 S	25.37 E
Porterdale, Ga. (pōr'tẽr-dāl)	126	33.34 N	83.53 W
Porterville, Ca. (pōr'tẽr-vĭl)	120	36.03 N	119.05 W
Portezuelo de Tupungato (Vol.), Arg.-Chile (pôr-tĕ-zwĕ-lô-dĕ-to͞o-po͞o'n-gä-tô)	144	33.30 S	69.52 W
Port Francqui, see Ilebo			
Port Gamble, Wa. (găm'bŭl)	118a	47.52 N	122.36 W
Port Gamble Ind. Res., Wa.	118a	47.54 N	122.33 W
Port-Gentil, Gabon (zhäN-tē')	230	0.43 S	8.47 E
Port Gibson, Ms.	126	31.56 N	90.57 W
Port Harcourt, Nig. (här'kŭrt)	229	4.43 N	7.05 E
Port Hardy, Can. (här'dĭ)	98	50.43 N	127.29 W
Port Hawkesbury, Can.	105	45.37 N	61.21 W
Port Hedland, Austl. (hĕd'lănd)	214	20.30 S	118.30 E
Porthill, Id.	116	49.00 N	116.30 W
Port Hood, Can. (ho͝od)	105	46.01 N	61.32 W
Port Hope, Can. (hōp)	111	43.55 N	78.10 W
Port Huron, Mi. (hū'rŏn)	110	43.00 N	82.30 W
Portici, It. (pôr'tē-chē)	171c	40.34 N	14.20 E
Portillo, Chile (pôr-tē'l-yô)	141b	32.51 S	70.09 W
Portimão, Port. (pôr-tē-mo'uN)	170	37.09 N	8.34 W

PLACE (Pronounciation)	PAGE	Lat. °'	Long. °'
Port Jervis, NY (jûr'vĭs)	112a	41.22 N	74.41 W
Portland, Austl. (pōrt'lănd)	216	38.20 S	142.40 E
Portland, In.	110	40.25 N	85.00 W
Portland, Me.	104	43.40 N	70.16 W
Portland, Mi.	110	42.50 N	85.00 W
Portland, Or.	118c	45.31 N	122.41 W
Portland, Tx.	125	27.53 N	97.20 W
Portland Bight (B.), Jam.	134	17.45 N	77.05 W
Portland Can., Ak.	98	55.10 N	130.08 W
Portland Inlet, Can.	98	54.50 N	130.15 W
Portland Pt., Jam	134	17.40 N	77.20 W
Port Lavaca, Tx. (lȧ-vä'kȧ)	125	28.36 N	96.38 W
Port Lincoln, Austl. (lĭŋ-kŭn)	216	34.39 S	135.50 E
Port Ludlow, Wa. (lŭd'lō)	118a	47.26 N	122.41 W
Port Lyautey, see Kenitra			
Port Macquarie, Austl. (mȧ-kwŏ'rĭ)	216	31.25 S	152.45 E
Port Madison Ind. Res., Wa. (măd'ĭ-sŭn)	118a	47.46 N	122.38 W
Port Maria, Jam. (mȧ-rī'ȧ)	134	18.20 N	76.55 W
Port Melbourne, Austl.	70b	37.51 S	144.56 E
Port-Menier, Can. (mē-nyā')	104	49.49 N	64.20 W
Port Moody, Can. (mo͞od'ĭ)	118d	49.17 N	122.51 W
Port Moresby, Pap. N. Gui. (mōrz'bē)	207	9.34 S	147.20 E
Port Neches, Tx. (nĕch'ĕz)	125	29.59 N	93.57 W
Port Nelson, Can. (nĕl'sŭn)	101	57.03 N	92.36 W
Portneuf-Sur-Mer, Can. (pôr-nûf'sür mĕr)	104	48.36 N	69.06 W
Port Nolloth, S. Afr. (nŏl'ŏth)	226	29.10 S	17.00 E
Porto, Port. (pōr'to͞o)	170	41.10 N	8.38 W
Porto Acre, Braz. (ä'krĕ)	142	9.38 S	67.34 W
Porto Alegre, Braz. (ä-lā'grĕ)	144	29.58 S	51.11 W
Porto Alexandre, Ang. (ȧ-lĕ-zhän'drĕ)	230	15.49 S	11.53 E
Porto Amboim, Ang.	230	11.01 S	13.45 E
Portobelo, Pan. (pôr'tô-bā'lô)	133	9.32 N	79.40 W
Pôrto de Pedras, Braz. (pā'dräzh)	143	9.09 S	35.20 W
Pôrto Feliz, Braz. (fĕ-lē's)	141a	23.12 S	47.30 W
Portoferraio, It. (pōr'tô-fĕr-rä'yō)	172	42.47 N	10.20 E
Port of Spain, Trin. (spān)	143	10.44 N	61.24 W
Portogruaro, It. (pôr'tô-gro͞o-ä'rō)	172	45.48 N	12.49 E
Portola, Ca. (pôr'tō-lȧ)	120	39.47 N	120.29 W
Pôrto Mendes, Braz. (mĕ'n-dĕs)	143	24.41 S	54.13 W
Pôrto Murtinho, Braz. (mo͞or-tēn'yo͞o)	143	21.43 S	57.43 W
Pôrto Nacional, Braz. (nȧ-syô-näl')	143	10.43 S	48.14 W
Porto Novo, Benin (pōr'tô-nō'vō)	229	6.29 N	2.37 E
Port Orchard, Wa. (ôr'chẽrd)	118a	47.32 N	122.38 W
Port Orchard (B.), Wa.	118a	47.40 N	122.39 W
Porto Salvo, Port.	65d	38.43 N	9.18 W
Porto Santo, Ilha de (I.), Mad. Is. (säN'to͞o)	224	32.41 N	16.15 W
Pôrto Seguro, Braz. (sā-go͞o'ro͞o)	143	16.26 S	38.59 W
Porto Torres, It. (tôr'rĕs)	172	40.49 N	8.25 E
Porto-Vecchio, Fr. (vĕk'ē-ô)	172	41.36 N	9.17 E
Pôrto Velho, Braz. (vāl'yo͞o)	142	8.45 S	63.43 W
Portoviejo, Ec. (pôr-tô-vyā'hō)	142	1.11 S	80.28 W
Port Phillip B., Austl. (fĭl'ĭp)	216	37.57 S	144.50 E
Port Pirie, Austl. (pĭ'rē)	216	33.10 S	138.00 E
Port Radium, Can. (rā'dē-ŭm)	96	66.06 N	118.03 W
Port Reading, NJ	55	40.34 N	74.16 W
Port Royal (B.), Jam. (roi'ăl)	134	17.50 N	76.45 W
Port Said, see Būr Sa'īd			
Port Saint Johns, S. Afr. (sånt jŏnz)	227c	31.37 S	29.32 E
Port Shepstone, S. Afr. (shĕps'tŭn)	227c	30.45 S	30.23 E
Portsmouth, Dominica	133b	15.33 N	61.28 W
Portsmouth, Eng. (pôrts'mŭth)	162	50.45 N	1.03 W
Portsmouth, NH	111	43.05 N	70.50 W
Portsmouth, Oh.	110	38.45 N	83.00 W
Portsmouth, Va.	112g	36.50 N	76.19 W
Port Sulphur, La. (sŭl'fẽr)	126	29.28 N	89.41 W
Port Sunlight, Eng.	64a	53.21 N	2.59 W
Port Susan (B.), Wa. (sū-zăn')	118a	48.11 N	122.25 W
Port Tampa, Fl. (tăm'pȧ)	127a	27.50 N	82.30 W
Port Townsend, Wa. (tounz'ĕnd)	118a	48.07 N	122.46 W
Port Townsend (B.), Wa.	118a	48.05 N	122.47 W
Portugal, Eur. (pōr'tu-găl)	154	38.15 N	8.08 W
Portugalete, Sp. (pōr-to͞o-gä-lā'tā)	170	43.18 N	3.05 W
Portuguese East Africa, see Mozambique			
Portuguese India, see Gôa, Daman & Diu			
Portuguese West Africa, see Angola			
Port Vendres, Fr. (pôr văN'dr')	168	42.32 N	3.07 E
Port Vue, Pa.	57b	40.20 N	79.52 W
Port Wakefield, Austl. (wāk'fēld)	216	34.12 S	138.10 E
Port Washington, NY (wôsh'ĭng-tŭn)	112a	40.49 N	73.42 W
Port Washington, Wi.	115	43.24 N	87.52 W
Posadas, Arg. (pō-sä'dhäs)	144	27.32 S	55.56 W
Posadas, Sp. (pô-sä-däs)	170	37.48 N	5.09 W
Poshekhon 'ye Volodarsk, Sov. Un. (pô-shyĕ'Kôn-yĕ vôl'ô-dȧrsk)	174	58.31 N	39.07 E
Poso, Danau (L.), Indon. (pō'sō)	206	2.00 S	119.40 E
Pospelokova, Sov. Un. (pôs-pyĕl'kô-vȧ)	182a	59.25 N	60.50 E
Possession Sd., Wa. (pŏ-zĕsh-ŭn)	118a	47.59 N	122.17 W
Possum Kingdom Res., Tx. (pŏs'ŭm kĭng'dŭm)	124	32.58 N	98.12 W
Post, Tx. (pōst)	122	33.12 N	101.21 W
Postojna, Yugo. (pōs-tôynȧ)	172	45.45 N	14.13 E
Pos'yet, Sov. Un. (pos-yĕt')	204	42.27 N	130.47 E
Potawatomi Ind. Res., Ks. (pŏt-ȧ-wä'tō mē)	123	39.30 N	96.11 W
Potchefstroom, S. Afr. (pŏch'ĕf-strōm)	223d	26.42 S	27.06 E
Poteau, Ok. (pō-tō')	123	35.03 N	94.37 W
Poteet, Tx. (pō-tēt)	124	29.05 N	98.35 W
Potenza, It. (pô-tĕnt'sä)	172	40.39 N	15.49 E
Potenza (R.), It.	172	43.09 N	13.00 E
Potgietersrus, S. Afr. (pôt-Kē'tẽrs-rûs)	223d	24.09 S	29.04 E
Potholes Res., Wa.	116	47.00 N	119.20 W

PLACE (Pronounciation)	PAGE	Lat. °'	Long. °'
Poti, Sov. Un. (pô'tē)	179	42.10 N	41.40 E
Potiskum, Nig.	229	11.43 N	11.05 E
Potomac, Md. (pō-tō'măk)	112e	39.01 N	77.13 W
Potomac (R.), Va. (pō-tō'măk)	111	38.15 N	76.55 W
Poto Poto (Neigh.), Con.	71c	4.15 S	15.18 E
Potosí, Bol. (pō-tô-sē')	142	19.42 S	65.42 W
Potosi, Mo. (pŏ-tō'sĭ)	123	37.56 N	90.46 W
Potosí, R., Mex. (pō-tō-sē')	124	25.04 N	99.36 W
Potrerillos, Hond. (pō-trȧ-rēl'yôs)	132	15.13 N	87.58 W
Potsdam, G.D.R. (pôts'däm)	157b	52.24 N	13.04 E
Potsdam, NY (pŏts'dăm)	111	44.40 N	75.00 W
Potsdam (Dist.), G.D.R. (pôts'dăm)	157b	52.31 N	12.45 E
Pottenstein, Aus.	157e	47.58 N	16.06 E
Potters Bar, Eng. (pŏt'ẽz bär)	156b	51.41 N	0.12 W
Potter Street, Eng.	62	51.46 N	0.08 E
Pottstown, Pa. (pŏts'toun)	111	40.15 N	75.40 W
Pottsville, Pa. (pŏts'vĭl)	111	40.40 N	76.15 W
Poughkeepsie, NY (pŏ-kĭp'sē)	111	41.45 N	73.55 W
Poulsbo, Wa. (pōlz'bo͞o)	118a	47.44 N	122.38 W
Poulton-le-Fylde, Eng. (pōl'tŭn-lē-fīld')	156	53.52 N	2.59 W
Pouso Alegre, Braz. (pō'zo͞o ä-lā'grĕ)	141a	22.13 S	45.56 W
Póvoa de Varzim, Port. (pō-vō'ȧ dā vär'zēN)	170	41.23 N	8.44 W
Powder R., Mt.-Wy. (pou'dẽr)	117	45.18 N	105.37 W
Powder R., Or.	116	44.55 N	117.35 W
Powder River, Wy.	117	43.06 N	106.55 W
Powder R., South Fk., Wy.	117	43.13 N	106.54 W
Powell, Wy. (pou'ĕl)	117	44.44 N	108.44 W
Powell L., Can.	98	50.10 N	124.13 W
Powell, L., Ut.	121	37.26 N	110.25 W
Powell Pt., Ba.	125	24.50 N	76.20 W
Powell Res., Ky.-Tn.	126	36.30 N	83.35 W
Powell River, Can.	98	49.52 N	124.33 W
Poyang Hu (L.), China (pwo-yän-ho͞o)	203	29.20 N	116.28 E
Poygan (R.), Wi. (poi'gȧn)	115	44.10 N	89.05 W
Poyle, Eng.	62	51.28 N	0.31 W
Poynton, Eng.	64b	53.21 N	2.07 W
Požarevac, Yugo. (pô'zhȧ'rĕ-vȧts)	173	44.38 N	21.12 E
Poznań, Pol. (pôz'năn')	166	52.24 N	16.55 E
Pozoblanco, Sp. (pô-thō-blăŋ'kō)	170	38.23 N	4.50 W
Pozo Rica, Mex. (pô-zô-rē'kä)	131	20.32 N	97.25 W
Pozos, Mex. (pô'zōs)	130	22.05 N	100.50 W
Pozuelo de Alarcón, Sp. (pô-thwā'lō dā ä-lär-kōn')	171a	40.27 N	3.49 W
Pozzuoli, It. (pôt-swô'lē)	171c	40.34 N	14.08 E
Pra (R.), Ghana (prȧ)	228	5.45 N	1.35 W
Pra (R.), Sov. Un.	174	55.00 N	40.13 E
Prachin Buri, Thai. (prä'chēn)	206	13.59 N	101.15 E
Pradera, Col. (prä-dĕ'rä)	142a	3.24 N	76.13 W
Prades, Fr. (prȧd)	168	42.37 N	2.23 E
Prado, Col. (prä'dô)	142a	3.44 N	74.55 W
Prado Churubusco, Mex.	60a	19.21 N	99.07 W
Prado, Museo del (P. Int.), Sp.	65b	40.25 N	3.41 W
Prado Res., Ca. (prä'dō)	119a	33.45 N	117.40 W
Prados, Braz. (prȧ'dôs)	141a	21.05 S	44.04 W
Prague, see Praha			
Praha (Prague), Czech. (prä'hȧ) (präg)	166	50.05 N	14.26 E
Prahran, Austl.	70b	37.51 S	144.59 E
Praia, C. V. (prä'yȧ)	224b	15.00 N	23.30 W
Praia da Cruz Quebrada, Port.	65d	38.42 N	9.14 W
Praia Funda, Ponta da (Pt.), Braz. (pôn'tä-dȧ-prä'yȧ-fo͞o'n-dä)	144b	23.04 S	43.34 W
Prairie du Chien, Wi. (prâ'rĭ do͞o shēn')	115	43.02 N	91.10 W
Prairie Grove, Can. (prâ'rĭ grōv)	95f	49.48 N	96.57 W
Prairie Island Ind. Res., Mn.	115	44.42 N	92.32 W
Prairies, R. des, Can. (rē-vyâr' dā prâ-rē')	95a	45.40 N	73.34 W
Pratas (Dongsha Dao) (I.), China (dôŋ-shä dou)	203	20.40 N	116.30 E
Prat del Llobregat, Sp.	65e	41.20 N	2.06 E
Prato, It. (prä'tō)	172	43.53 N	11.03 E
Pratt, Ks. (prăt)	122	37.37 N	98.43 W
Pratt's Bottom (Neigh.), Eng.	62	51.20 N	0.07 E
Prattville, Al. (prăt'vĭl)	126	32.28 N	86.27 W
Pravdinsk, Sov. Un.	165	54.26 N	20.11 E
Pravdinskiy, Sov. Un. (prȧv-dĕn'skĭ)	182b	56.03 N	37.52 E
Pravia, Sp. (prä'vē-ä)	170	43.30 N	6.08 W
Pregolya (R.), Sov. Un. (prĕ-gô'lă)	165	54.37 N	20.50 E
Premont, Tx. (prē-mŏnt')	124	27.20 N	98.07 W
Prenton, Eng.	64a	53.22 N	3.03 W
Prenzlau, G.D.R. (prĕnts'lou)	166	53.19 N	13.52 E
Prenzlauer Berg (Neigh.), G.D.R.	65a	52.32 N	13.26 E
Přerov, Czech. (przhĕ'rôf)	167	49.28 N	17.28 E
Presa Aleman (L.), Mex. (prä'sä-lĕ-mȧ'n)	131	18.20 N	96.35 W
Presa de Infiernillo (Res.), Mex.	131	18.50 N	101.50 W
Prescot, Eng. (prĕs'kŭt)	156	53.25 N	2.48 W
Prescott, Az. (prĕs'kŏt)	121	34.30 N	112.30 W
Prescott, Ar.	123	33.47 N	93.23 W
Prescott, Can. (prĕs'kŭt)	111	44.45 N	75.35 W
Prescott, Wi. (prĕs'kŏt)	119g	44.45 N	92.48 W
Presho, SD (prĕsh'ō)	114	43.56 N	100.04 W
Presidencia Rogue Sáenz Peña, Arg. (prĕ-sē-dĕ'n-sēä-rô'kĕ-sȧ'ĕnz-pĕ'n-yȧ)	144	26.52 S	60.15 W
Presidente Epitácio, Braz. (prä-sē-dĕn'tĕ ā-pē-tä'syo͞o)	143	21.56 S	52.01 W
Presidente Roosevelt, (Estacgao) (P. Int.), Braz.	61d	23.33 S	46.36 W
Presidio, Tx. (prĕ-sĭ'dĭ-ô)	124	29.33 N	104.23 W
Presidio of San Francisco (P. Int.), Ca.	58b	37.48 N	122.28 W
Presidio, Rio del (R.), Mex. (rē'ō-dĕl-prĕ-sē'dyô)	130	23.54 N	105.44 W
Prešov, Czech. (prĕ'shôf)	167	49.00 N	21.18 E
Prespa, L., Alb.-Yugo. (prĕs'pä)	173	40.49 N	20.50 E
Prespuntal (R.), Ven. (prĕs-po͞on-täl')	143b	9.55 N	64.32 W
Presque Isle, Me. (prĕsk'ēl')	104	46.41 N	68.03 W
Pressbaum, Aus.	157e	48.12 N	16.06 E

PLACE (Pronounciation)	PAGE	Lat. °′	Long. °′
Prestea, Ghana	228	5.27 N	2.08 W
Preston, Austl.	70b	37.45 S	145.01 E
Preston, Eng. (prĕs'tŭn)	144	53.46 N	2.42 W
Preston, Id. (pres'tŭn)	117	42.05 N	111.54 W
Preston, Mn. (prĕs'tŭn)	115	43.42 N	92.06 W
Preston, Wa.	118a	47.31 N	121.56 W
Prestonburg, Ky. (prĕs'tŭn-bûrg)	110	37.35 N	82.50 W
Prestwich, Eng. (prĕst'wĭch)	144	53.32 N	2.17 W
Pretoria, S. Afr. (prė-tō'rĭ-ȧ)	227b	25.43 S	28.16 E
Pretoria North, S. Afr. (prĕ-tô'rĭ-ȧ no͞ord)	227b	25.41 S	28.11 E
Préveza, Grc. (prĕ'vå-zä)	173	38.58 N	20.44 E
Pribilof (Is.), Ak. (prĭ'bĭ-lof)	107	57.00 N	169.20 W
Priboj, Yugo. (prē'boi)	173	43.33 N	19.33 E
Price (R.), Ut.	121	39.21 N	110.35 W
Price, Ut. (prīs)	121	39.35 N	110.50 W
Priddis, Can. (prĭd'dĭs)	95e	50.53 N	114.20 W
Priddis Cr., Can.	95e	50.56 N	114.32 W
Priego, Sp. (prė-ā'gō)	170	37.27 N	4.13 W
Prienai, Sov. Un. (prė-ĕn'ī)	165	54.38 N	23.56 E
Prieska, S. Afr. (prė-ĕs'kȧ)	226	29.40 S	22.50 E
Priest L., Id. (prēst)	116	48.30 N	116.43 W
Priest Rapids Dam, Wa.	116	46.39 N	119.55 W
Priest Rapids Res., Wa.	116	46.42 N	119.58 W
Priiskovaya, Sov. Un. (prĭ-ēs'kô-vȧ-yȧ)	182a	60.50 N	58.55 E
Prijedor, Yugo. (prē'yĕ-dȯr)	172	44.58 N	16.43 E
Prijepolje, Yugo. (prė'yĕ-pȯ'lyĕ)	173	43.22 N	19.41 E
Prilep, Yugo. (prē'lĕp)	173	41.20 N	21.35 E
Priluki, Sov. Un. (prė-lo͞o'kė)	175	50.36 N	32.21 E
Primorsk, Sov. Un. (prē-môrsk')	165	60.24 N	28.35 E
Primorsko-Akhtarskaya, Sov. Un. (prē-môr'skô äĸ-tär'skĭ-ė)	175	46.03 N	38.09 E
Primos, Pa.	56b	39.55 N	75.18 W
Primrose, S. Afr.	227b	26.11 S	28.11 E
Primrose L., Can.	100	54.55 N	109.45 W
Prince Albert, Can. (prĭns ăl'bērt)	100	53.12 N	105.46 W
Prince Albert Natl. Park, Can.	96	54.10 N	105.25 W
Prince Albert Sd., Can.	97	70.23 N	116.57 W
Prince Charles I., Can. (chärlz)	97	67.41 N	74.10 W
Prince Edward I. (Prov.), Can.	97	46.45 N	63.10 W
Prince Edward Is., S. Afr.	232	46.36 S	37.57 E
Prince Edward Natl. Park, Can. (ĕd'wērd)	104	46.33 N	63.35 W
Prince Edward Pen., Can.	111	44.00 N	77.15 W
Prince Frederick, Md. (prĭnce frĕdērĭk)	112e	38.33 N	76.35 W
Prince George, Can. (jôrj)	98	53.51 N	122.57 W
Prince of Wales (I.), Ak.	98	55.47 N	132.50 W
Prince of Wales (I.), Austl.	215	10.47 S	142.15 E
Prince of Wales, C., Ak. (wālz)	107	65.48 N	169.08 W
Prince Rupert, Can. (roo'pērt)	98	54.19 N	130.19 W
Princes Risborough, Eng. (prĭns'ĕz rĭz'brŭ)	156b	51.41 N	0.51 W
Princess Charlotte B., Austl. (shär'lŏt)	215	13.45 S	144.15 E
Princess Martha Coast, Ant. (mär'thȧ)	232	72.00 S	5.00 W
Princess Royal Chan., Can. (roi'ăl)	98	53.10 N	128.37 W
Princess Royal I., Can.	98	52.57 N	128.49 W
Princeton, Can. (prĭns'tŭn)	99	49.27 N	120.31 W
Princeton, IL.	110	41.20 N	89.25 W
Princeton, In.	110	38.20 N	87.35 W
Princeton, Ky.	126	37.07 N	87.52 W
Princeton, Mi.	115	46.16 N	87.33 W
Princeton, Mn.	115	45.34 N	93.36 W
Princeton, Mo.	123	40.23 N	93.34 W
Princeton, NJ	112a	40.21 N	74.40 W
Princeton, WV	127	37.21 N	81.05 W
Princeton, Wi.	115	43.50 N	89.09 W
Prince William Sd., Ak. (wĭl'yăm)	107	60.40 N	147.10 W
Principe Chan., Can. (prĭn'sĭ-pē)	98	53.28 N	129.45 W
Prineville, Or. (prīn'vĭl)	116	44.17 N	120.48 W
Prineville Res., Or.	116	44.07 N	120.45 W
Prinzapolca, Nic. (prēn-zä-pōl'kä)	133	13.18 N	83.35 W
Prinzapolca R., Nic.	133	13.23 N	84.23 W
Prior Lake, Mn. (prī'ēr)	119g	44.43 N	93.26 W
Priozërsk, Sov. Un. (prĭ-ô'zĕrsk)	165	61.03 N	30.08 E
Pripyat (Pripet) (R.), Sov. Un. (prē'pyät)	179	51.50 N	29.45 E
Pripyat Marshes, see Poles'ye			
Priština, Yugo. (prēsh'tĭ-nä)	173	42.39 N	21.12 E
Pritchard, Al. (prĭt'chârd)	126	30.44 N	87.04 W
Pritzwalk, G.D.R. (prēts'välk)	166	53.09 N	12.12 E
Privas, Fr. (prē-väs')	168	44.44 N	4.37 E
Privol'noye, Sov. Un. (prė'vôl-nô-yĕ)	175	47.30 N	32.21 E
Príncipe (I.), Afr. (prēn'sė-pĕ)	230	1.37 N	7.25 E
Prizren, Yugo. (prē'zrĕn)	173	42.11 N	20.45 E
Procida, It. (prô'chė-dă)	171c	40.31 N	14.02 E
Procida, I. di, It.	171c	40.32 N	13.57 E
Proctor, Mn. (prŏk'tēr)	119h	46.45 N	92.14 W
Proctor, Vt.	111	43.40 N	73.00 W
Proebstel, Wa. (prōb'stĕl)	118c	45.40 N	122.29 W
Proenca-a-Nova, Port. (prȯ-ān'sȧ-ä-nō'vȧ)	170	39.44 N	7.55 W
Progreso, Hond. (prȯ-grĕ'sȯ)	132	15.28 N	87.49 W
Progreso, Mex. (prȯ-grā'sō)	131	21.14 N	89.39 W
Progreso, Mex.	124	27.29 N	101.05 W
Prokop'yevsk, Sov. Un.	180	53.52 N	86.38 E
Prokuplje, Yugo. (prô'ko͝op'l-yĕ)	173	43.16 N	21.40 E
Prome (Pye), Bur.	206	18.46 N	95.15 E
Pronya (R.), Sov. Un. (prô'nyä)	174	54.08 N	30.58 E
Pronya (R.), Sov. Un.	174	54.08 N	39.30 E
Propriá, Braz. (prō-prė-ä')	143	10.17 S	36.47 W
Prospect, Austl.	70a	33.48 S	150.56 E
Prospect, Ky. (prŏs'pĕkt)	113h	38.21 N	85.36 W
Prospect Heights, Il.	58a	42.06 N	87.56 W
Prospect Park, NJ	55	40.56 N	74.10 W
Prospect Park, Pa. (prŏs'pĕkt pärk)	112f	39.53 N	75.18 W
Prosser, Wa. (prŏs'ēr)	116	46.10 N	119.46 W
Prostějov, Czech. (prôs'tyĕ-yôf)	167	49.28 N	17.08 E
Protea, S. Afr.	71b	26.17 S	27.51 E
Protection (I.), Wa. (prȯ-tĕk'shŭn)	118a	48.07 N	122.56 W
Protoka (R.), Sov. Un. (prôt'ȯ-kȧ)	174	55.00 N	36.42 E
Provadiya, Bul. (prō-väd'ė-yȧ)	173	43.13 N	27.28 E
Providence, Ky. (prŏv'ĭ-dĕns)	110	37.25 N	87.45 W
Providence, RI	112b	41.50 N	71.23 W
Providence, Ut.	117	41.42 N	111.50 W
Providencia, Chile	61b	33.26 S	70.37 W
Providencia, Isla de (I.), Col.	133	13.21 N	80.55 W
Providenciales (I.), Turks & Caicos Is. (prō-vė-dĕn-sė-ä'lås) (prŏ-vĭ-dĕn'shȧlz)	125	21.50 N	72.15 W
Provideniya, Sov. Un. (prȯ-vĭ-dă'nĭ-yȧ)	107	64.30 N	172.54 W
Provincetown, Ma.	111	42.03 N	70.11 W
Provo, Ut. (prō'vō)	121	40.15 N	111.40 W
Prozor, Yugo. (prȯ'zôr)	172	43.48 N	17.59 E
Prudence I., RI (pro͞o'dĕns)	112b	41.38 N	71.20 W
Prudhoe B., Ak.	107	70.40 N	147.25 W
Prudnik, Pol. (pro͝od'nĭk)	167	50.19 N	17.34 E
Prussia (Reg.), G.D.R. (prŭsh'ȧ)	166	50.43 N	8.35 E
Pruszków, Pol. (pro͝osh'ko͝of)	167	52.09 N	20.50 E
Prut (R.), Sov. Un. (pro͞ot)	175	48.05 N	27.07 E
Pryor, Ok. (prī'ēr)	123	36.16 N	95.19 W
Prypeć (R.), Sov. Un.	179	51.50 N	25.35 E
Przasnysz, Pol.	167	51.05 N	19.53 E
Przemyśl, Pol. (pzhĕ'mĭsh'l)	167	49.47 N	22.45 E
Przheval'sk, Sov. Un. (p'r-zhĭ-välsk')	180	42.25 N	78.18 E
Psará (I.), Grc. (psä'rȧ)	173	38.39 N	25.26 E
Psël (R.), Sov. Un. (psĕl)	175	49.45 N	33.42 E
Pskov, Sov. Un. (pskôf)	174	57.48 N	28.19 E
Pskov (Oblast), Sov. Un.	174	57.33 N	29.05 E
Pskovskoye Ozero (L.), Sov. Un. (p'skôv'skȯ'yĕ ȯzė-rȯ)	174	58.05 N	28.15 E
Ptuj, Yugo. (pto͞o'ė)	172	46.24 N	15.54 E
Pucheng, China (po͞o'chĕng')	203	28.02 N	118.25 E
Pucheng, China (po͞o-chŭŋ)	200	35.43 N	115.22 E
Puck, Pol. (po͝otsk)	167	54.43 N	18.23 E
Puddington, Eng.	64a	53.15 N	3.00 W
Pudog, China	198	33.29 N	79.26 E
Pudozh, Sov. Un. (po͞o'dȯzh)	178	61.50 N	36.50 E
Puebla, Mex. (pwā'blä)	130	19.02 N	98.11 W
Puebla (State), Mex.	130	19.00 N	97.45 W
Puebla de Don Fadrique, Sp. (pwĕ'blä dā dōn fä-drē'kā)	170	37.55 N	2.55 W
Pueblo, Co. (pwā'blō)	122	38.15 N	104.36 W
Pueblo Libre, Peru	60c	12.08 S	77.05 W
Pueblo Nuevo, Mex. (nwā'vȯ)	130	23.23 N	105.21 W
Pueblo Nuevo (Neigh.), Sp.	65b	40.26 N	3.39 W
Pueblo Viejo, Mex. (vyā'hȯ)	131	17.23 N	93.46 W
Puente Alto, Chile (pwĕ'n-tĕ ȧl'tȯ)	141b	33.36 S	70.34 W
Puenteareas, Sp. (pwĕn-tā-ä-rā'äs)	170	42.09 N	8.23 W
Puentedeume, Sp. (pwĕn-tå-dhå-o͞o'må)	170	43.28 N	8.09 W
Puente-Genil, Sp. (pwĕn'tå-hå-nēl')	170	37.25 N	4.18 W
Puerco (R.), NM (pwĕr'kō)	121	35.15 N	107.05 W
Puerto Aisén, Chile (pwĕ'r-tō ä'y-sĕ'n)	144	45.28 S	72.44 W
Puerto Angel, Mex. (pwĕ'r-tō äŋ'hål)	131	15.42 N	96.32 W
Puerto Armuelles, Pan. (pwe'r-tȯ är-mo͞o-ā'lyās)	133	8.18 N	82.52 W
Puerto Barrios, Guat. (pwĕ'r-tȯ bär'rė-ōs)	132	15.43 N	88.36 W
Puerto Bermúdez, Peru (pwĕ'r-tō bĕr-mo͞o'dāz)	142	10.17 S	74.57 W
Puerto Berrío, Col. (pwĕ'r-tō bĕr-rē'ō)	142a	6.29 N	74.27 W
Puerto Cabello, Ven. (pwĕ'r-tō kä-bĕl'yō)	143b	10.28 N	68.01 W
Puerto Cabezas, Nic. (pwĕ'r-tȯ kä-bā'zäs)	133	14.01 N	83.26 W
Puerto Casado, Par. (pwĕ'r-tō kä-sä'dō)	144	22.16 S	57.57 W
Puerto Castilla, Hond. (pwĕ'r-tȯ käs-tēl'yō)	132	16.01 N	86.01 W
Puerto Chicama, Peru (pwĕ'r-tō chē-kä'mä)	142	7.46 S	79.18 W
Puerto Columbia, Col. (pwĕr'tȯ kȯ-lȯm'bė-ȧ)	142	11.08 N	75.09 W
Puerto Cortés, C. R. (pwĕ'r-tȯ kȯr-tās')	133	9.00 N	83.37 W
Puerto Cortés, Hond. (pwĕ'r-tȯ kȯr-tās')	132	15.48 N	87.57 W
Puerto Cumarebo, Ven. (pwĕ'r-tō ko͞o-mä-rĕ'bȯ)	142	11.25 N	69.17 W
Puerto de Luna, NM (pwĕr'tȯ då lo͞o'nä)	122	34.49 N	104.36 W
Puerto de Nutrias, Ven. (pwĕ'r-tō dĕ no͞o-trė-äs')	142	8.02 N	69.19 W
Puerto Deseado, Arg. (pwĕ'r-tō dā-så-ä'dhō)	144	47.38 S	66.00 W
Puerto de Somport (P.), Fr.-Sp.	171	42.51 N	0.25 W
Puerto Eten, Peru (pwĕ'r-tō ĕ-tĕ'n)	142	6.59 S	79.51 W
Puerto Jimenez, C. R. (pwĕ'r-tȯ ĸė-mĕ'nĕz)	133	8.35 N	83.23 W
Puerto La Cruz, Ven. (pwĕ'r-tō lä kro͞o'z)	143b	10.14 N	64.38 W
Puertollano, Sp. (pwĕ-tȯl-yä'nō)	170	38.41 N	4.05 W
Puerto Madryn, Arg. (pwĕ'r-tō mä-drĕn')	144	42.45 S	65.01 W
Puerto Maldonado, Peru (pwĕ'r-tō mäl-dō-nä'dȯ)	142	12.43 S	69.01 W
Puerto Mexico, see Coatzacoalcos			
Puerto Miniso, Mex. (pwĕ'r-tō mē-nė'sȯ)	130	16.06 N	98.02 W
Puerto Montt, Chile (pwĕ'r-tō mȯ'nt)	144	41.29 S	73.00 W
Puerto Natales, Chile (pwĕ'r-tō nä-tȧ'lĕs)	144	51.48 S	72.01 W
Puerto Niño, Col. (pwĕ'r-tō nė'n-yô)	142a	5.57 N	74.36 W
Puerto Padre, Cuba (pwĕ'r-tō pä'drā)	134	21.10 N	76.40 W
Puerto Peñasco, Mex. (pwĕ'r-tȯ pĕn-yä's-kȯ)	128	31.39 N	113.15 W
Puerto Pinasco, Par. (pwĕ'r-tō pē-nȧ's-kȯ)	144	22.31 S	57.50 W
Puerto Píritu, Ven. (pwĕ'r-tō pē'rē-to͞o)	143b	10.05 N	65.04 W
Puerto Plata, Dom. Rep. (pwĕ'r-tȯ plä'tä)	135	19.50 N	70.40 W
Puerto Princesa, Phil. (pwĕr-tȯ prėn-sā'sä)	206	9.45 N	118.41 E
Puerto Rico, N. A. (pwĕr'tȯ rē'kō)	129	18.16 N	66.50 W
Puerto Rico Trench, N. A.	129	19.45 N	66.30 W
Puerto Salgar, Col. (pwĕ'r-tō säl-gär')	142a	5.30 N	74.39 W
Puerto Santa Cruz, Arg. (pwĕ'r-tō sän'tä kro͞oz')	144	50.04 S	68.32 W
Puerto Suárez, Bol. (pwĕ'r-tō swä'råz)	143	18.55 S	57.39 W
Puerto Tejada, Col. (pwĕ'r-tō tĕ-ĸä'dä)	142a	3.13 N	76.23 W
Puerto Vallarta, Mex. (pwĕ'r-tō väl-yär'tä)	130	20.36 N	105.13 W
Puerto Varas, Chile (pwĕ'r-tō vä'räs)	144	41.16 S	73.03 W
Puerto Wilches, Col. (pwĕ'r-tō vēl'c-hĕs)	142	7.19 N	73.54 W
Pugachëv, Sov. Un. (po͞o'gȧ-chyôf)	179	52.00 N	48.40 E
Puget, Wa. (pū'jĕt)	118c	46.10 N	123.23 W
Puget Sd., Wa.	116	47.49 N	122.26 W
Puglia (Apulia) (Reg.), It. (po͞o'lyä) (ä-po͞o'lyä)	172	41.13 N	16.10 E
Pukaskwa Natl. Pk., Can.	102	48.22 N	85.55 W
Pukeashun Mtn., Can.	99	51.12 N	119.14 W
Pukin (R.), Mala.	191b	2.53 N	102.54 E
Pula, Yugo. (po͞o'lä)	172	44.52 N	13.55 E
Pulacayo, Bol. (po͞o-lä-kä'yō)	142	20.12 N	66.33 W
Pulaski, Tn. (pů-lăs'kĭ)	126	35.11 N	87.03 W
Pulaski, Va.	127	37.00 N	81.45 W
Pulawy, Pol. (po͞o-wä'vė)	167	51.24 N	21.59 E
Pulizat (R.), India	196	13.58 N	79.52 E
Pullman, Wa. (po͝ol'măn)	116	46.44 N	117.10 W
Pullman (Neigh.), Il.	58a	41.43 N	87.36 W
Pulog (Mtn.), Phil. (po͞o'lȯg)	207a	16.38 N	120.53 E
Pultusk, Pol. (po͞ol'to͝osk)	158	52.40 N	21.09 E
Puma Yumco (L.), China (po͞o-mä yo͞om-tswo)	196	28.30 N	90.10 E
Pumphrey, Md.	56c	39.13 N	76.38 W
Pumpkin Cr., Mt. (pŭmp'kĭn)	117	45.47 N	105.35 W
Punakha, Bhu. (po͞o-nŭk'ŭ)	196	27.45 N	89.59 E
Punata, Bol. (po͞o-nä'tä)	142	17.43 S	65.43 W
Punchbowl, Austl.	70a	33.56 S	151.03 E
Pune, India	196	18.38 N	73.53 E
Punggol, Singapore	67c	1.25 N	103.55 E
Punjab (State), India (pŭn'jäb')	196	31.00 N	75.30 E
Puno, Peru (po͞o'nȯ)	142	15.58 S	7.02 W
Punta Arenas, Chile (po͞o'n-tä-rĕ'näs)	144	53.09 S	70.48 W
Punta Brava, Cuba	60b	23.01 N	82.30 W
Punta de Piedras, Ven. (po͞o'n-tä dĕ pyĕ'dräs)	143b	10.54 N	64.06 W
Punta Gorda, Belize (po͝on'tä gôr'dä)	132	16.07 N	88.50 W
Punta Gorda, Fl. (pŭn'tȧ gôr'dȧ)	127a	26.55 N	82.02 W
Punta Gorda, Rio (R.), Nic. (po͞o'n-tä gȯ'r-dä)	133	11.34 N	84.13 W
Punta Indio, Can., Arg. (po͞o'n-tä- ė'n-dyȯ)	141c	34.56 S	57.20 W
Puntarenas, C. R. (po͝ont-ä-rā'näs)	133	9.59 N	84.49 W
Punto Fijo, Ven. (po͞o'n-tȯ fē'ĸô)	142	11.48 N	70.14 W
Punxsutawney, Pa. (pŭnk-sŭ-tô'nė)	111	40.55 N	79.00 W
Puquio, Peru (po͞o'kyȯ)	142	14.43 S	74.02 W
Pur (R.), Sov. Un.	180	65.30 N	77.30 E
Purcell, Ok. (pûr-sĕl')	123	35.01 N	97.22 W
Purcell Mts., Can. (pûr-sĕl')	99	50.00 N	116.30 W
Purdy, Wa. (pûr'dē)	118a	47.23 N	122.37 W
Purépero, Mex. (po͞o-rā'på-rō)	130	19.56 N	102.02 W
Purfleet, Eng.	62	51.29 N	0.15 E
Purgatoire (R.), Colo. (pûr-gȧ-twär')	122	37.25 N	103.53 W
Puri, India (po͝o'rė)	196	19.52 N	85.51 E
Purial, Sierra de (Mts.), Cuba (sē-ĕ'r-rȧ-dĕ-po͞o-rė-äl')	135	20.15 N	74.40 W
Purificacion, Col. (po͞o-rė-fė-kä-syōn')	142a	3.52 N	74.54 W
Purificación, Mex. (po͞o-rē-fė-kä-syȯ'n)	130	19.44 N	104.38 W
Purificación (R.), Mex.	130	19.30 N	104.54 W
Purkersdorf, Aus.	157e	48.13 N	16.11 E
Purley (Neigh.), Eng.	62	51.20 N	0.07 W
Puruandiro, Mex. (po͞o-ro͞o-än'dė-rō)	130	20.04 N	101.33 W
Purús (R.), Braz. (po͞o-ro͞o's)	142	6.45 S	64.34 W
Pusan, Kor.	204	35.08 N	129.05 E
Pushkin, Sov. Un. (po͝osh'kĭn)	182c	59.43 N	30.25 E
Pushkino, Sov. Un. (po͝osh'kė-nȯ)	182b	56.01 N	37.51 E
Pustoshka, Sov. Un. (pûs-tôsh'kȧ)	174	56.20 N	29.33 E
Pustunich, Mex. (po͞os-to͞o'nėch)	131	19.10 N	90.29 W
Putaendo, Chile (po͞o-tä-ĕn-dȯ)	141b	32.37 S	70.42 W
Puteaux, Fr. (pü-tō')	169b	48.52 N	2.12 E
Putfontein, S. Afr. (po͝ot'fŏn-tān)	227b	26.08 S	28.24 E
Puth Kalān (Neigh.), India	67d	28.43 N	77.05 E
Putian, China (po͞o-tĭĕn)	203	25.40 N	119.02 E
Putilkovo, Sov. Un.	66b	55.52 N	37.23 E
Putivl', Sov. Un. (po͞o-tēv'l')	175	51.22 N	33.24 E
Putla de Guerrero, Mex. (po͞o'tlä-dĕ-gĕr-rĕ'rō)	131	17.03 N	97.55 W
Putnam, Ct. (pŭt'năm)	111	41.55 N	71.55 W
Putney (Neigh.), Eng.	62	51.28 N	0.13 W
Putorana, Gory (Mts.), Sov. Un.	180	68.45 N	93.15 E
Pütt, F.R.G.	63	51.11 N	6.59 E
Puttalam, Sri Lanka	197	8.02 N	79.44 E
Putumayo (R.), Col.-Peru (po͞o-to͞o-mä'yō)	142	1.02 S	73.50 W
Putung, Tandjung (C.), Indon.	206	3.35 S	111.50 E
Puulavesi (L.), Fin.	165	61.49 N	27.10 E

ăt; finăl; rāte; senåte; ärm; ȧsk; sofȧ; fâre; ch-choose; dh-as th in other; bē; ėvent; bĕt; recĕnt; cratēr; g-gō; gh-guttural g; bĭt; ĭ-short neutral; rīde; ĸ-guttural k as ch in German ich;

PLACE (Pronounciation)	PAGE	Lat. °′	Long. °′
Puyallup, Wa. (pū-ăl'ŭp)	118a	47.12 N	122.18 W
Puyang, China (pōō-yäŋ)	200	35.42 N	114.58 E
Pweto, Zaire (pwā'tō)	226	8.29 S	28.58 E
Pyasina (R.), Sov. Un. (pyă-sē'nà)	180	72.45 N	87.37 E
Pyatigorsk, Sov. Un. (pyá-tē-gôrsk')	179	44.00 N	43.00 E
Pye, see Prome			
Pyhäjärvi (L.), Fin.	165	60.57 N	21.50 E
Pyinmana, Bur. (pyēn-mä'nŭ)	198	19.47 N	96.15 E
Pymatuning Res., Pa. (pī-mà-tŭn'ĭng)	110	41.40 N	80.30 W
Pymble, Austl.	70a	33.45 S	151.09 E
Pyŏnggang, Kor. (pyŭng'gäng')	204	38.21 N	127.18 E
P'yŏngyang, Kor.	204	39.03 N	125.48 E
Pyramid (L.), Nv. (pĭ'rá-mĭd)	120	40.02 N	119.50 W
Pyramid Lake Ind. Res., Nv.	120	40.17 N	119.52 W
Pyramids, Egypt	223b	29.53 N	31.10 E
Pyrenees (Mts.), Fr.-Sp. (pĭr-e-nēz')	171	43.00 N	0.05 E
Pyrford, Eng.	62	51.19 N	0.30 W
Pyrzyce, Pol. (pĕzhĭ'tsĕ)	166	53.09 N	14.53 E

Q

PLACE (Pronounciation)	PAGE	Lat. °′	Long. °′
Qal'at Bishah, Sau. Ar.	192	20.01 N	42.30 E
Qallābāt, Sud.	225	12.55 N	36.12 E
Qana el Suweis (Suez Can.), Egypt	223c	30.53 N	32.21 E
Qandahār, Afg.	193	31.43 N	65.58 E
Qandala, Som.	195	11.28 N	49.52 E
Qārah (Oasis), Egypt	161	29.28 N	26.29 E
Qareh Sū (R.), Iran	179	38.50 N	47.10 E
Qarqan, see Qiemo			
Qarqan (R.), China	198	38.55 N	87.15 E
Qārūn, Birket (L.) Egypt	223b	29.34 N	30.34 E
Qasr al-Burayqah, Libya	225	30.25 N	19.20 E
Qasr al-Farāfirah, Egypt	225	27.04 N	28.13 E
Qaşr Banī Walīd, Libya	225	31.45 N	14.04 E
Qaşr-e Fīrūzeh, Iran	68h	35.40 N	51.32 E
Qasrel-Boukhari, Alg.	160	35.50 N	2.48 E
Qatar, Asia (kä'tàr)	190	25.00 N	52.45 E
Qaţţārah, Munkhafaḑ (Dep.), Egypt	225	30.07 N	27.30 E
Qāyen, Iran	192	33.45 N	59.08 E
Qazvīn, Iran	195	36.16 N	50.00 E
Qeshm, Iran	192	26.51 N	56.10 E
Qeshm (I.), Iran	192	26.52 N	56.15 E
Qezel Owzan, Iran	192	37.00 N	48.23 E
Qezel Owzan, (R.), Iran	179	37.00 N	47.35 E
Qezi'ot, Egypt-Isr.	191a	30.53 N	34.28 E
Qianwei, China (chyĕn-wā)	200	40.11 N	120.05 E
Qi'anzhen, China (chyē-än-jŭn)	200	32.16 N	120.59 E
Qibao, China (chyē-bou)	201b	31.06 N	121.16 E
Qiblīyah, Jabal al Jalālat al (Plat.), Egypt	191a	28.49 N	32.21 E
Qiemo (Qargan), China (chyär-chyän)	198	38.02 N	85.16 E
Qieshikou, China	67b	39.59 N	116.24 E
Qifţ, Egypt (kĕft)	223b	25.58 N	32.52 E
Qijiang, China (chyē-jyäŋ)	203	29.05 N	106.40 E
Qikou, China (chyē-kō)	200	38.37 N	117.33 E
Qilian Shan (Mts.), China (chyē-lĭĕn shän)	198	38.43 N	98.00 E
Qiliping, China (chyē-lē-pĭŋ)	200	31.28 N	114.41 E
Qinā, Egypt (kä'nà)	223b	26.10 N	32.48 E
Qinā, Wādī, Egypt	223b	26.38 N	32.53 E
Qindao (Tsingtao), China (chyĭn-dou)	200	36.05 N	120.10 E
Qing'an, China (chyĭŋ-än)	202	46.50 N	127.30 E
Qingcheng, China (chyĭŋ-chŭŋ)	200	37.12 N	117.43 E
Qingfeng, China (chyĭŋ-fŭŋ)	200	35.52 N	115.05 E
Qinghai (Prov.), China (chyĭŋ-hī)	198	36.14 N	95.30 E
Qinghai Hu (L.), **see Koko Nor**			
Qinghe, China (chyĭŋ-hŭ)	202a	40.08 N	116.16 E
Qinghuayuan, China	67b	40.00 N	116.19 E
Qingjiang, China (chyĭŋ-jyäŋ)	203	28.00 N	115.30 E
Qingjiang, China	200	33.34 N	118.58 E
Qingliu, China (chyĭŋ-lĭō)	203	26.15 N	116.50 E
Qingningsi, China (chyĭŋ-nĭŋ-sz)	201b	31.16 N	121.33 E
Qingping, China (chyĭŋ-pĭŋ)	200	36.46 N	116.03 E
Qingpu, China (chyĭŋ-pōō)	201b	31.08 N	121.06 E
Qingxian, China (chyĭŋ shyĕn)	200	38.37 N	116.48 E
Qingyang, China (chyĭŋ-yäŋ)	200	36.02 N	107.42 E
Qingyuan, China (chyĭŋ-yōän)	203	23.43 N	113.10 E
Qingyuan, China	202	42.05 N	125.00 E
Qingyun, China (chyĭŋ-yōōn)	200	37.52 N	117.26 E
Qingyundian, China (chĭŋ-yōōn-dĭĕn)	202a	39.41 N	116.31 E
Qinhuangdao, China (chyĭn-huaŋ-dou)	200	39.57 N	119.34 E
Qin Ling (Mts.), China (chyĭn lĭŋ)	191	33.25 N	108.58 E
Qin Ling (Mts.), China	202	33.35 N	108.25 E
Qinyang, China (chyĭn-yäŋ)	202	35.00 N	112.55 E
Qinzhou, China (chyĭn-jō)	203	22.00 N	108.35 E
Qionghai, China (chyôŋ-hī)	203	19.10 N	110.28 E
Qiqian, China (chyē-chyĕn)	199	52.23 N	121.04 E
Qiqihar, China	202	47.18 N	124.00 E
Qiryat Gat, Isr.	191a	31.38 N	34.36 E
Qiryat Shemona, Isr.	191a	33.12 N	35.34 E
Qitai, China (chyē-tī)	198	44.07 N	89.04 E
Qiuxian, China (chyō shyĕn)	200	36.43 N	115.13 E
Qixian, China (chyē-shyĕn),	200	34.33 N	114.47 E
Qixian, China	200	35.36 N	114.13 E
Qiyang, China (chyē-yäŋ)	203	26.40 N	112.00 E
Qolleh-ye, Damāvand (Mtn.), Iran	179	36.05 N	52.05 E
Qom, Iran	192	34.28 N	50.53 E
Quabbin Res., Ma. (kwā'bĭn)	111	42.20 N	72.10 W
Quachita, L., Ar. (kwä shĭ'tō)	123	34.47 N	93.37 W
Quadra, Boca de, Str., Ak. (bōk'ă dĕ kwŏd'rá)	98	55.08 N	130.50 W
Quadra I., Can.	98	50.08 N	125.16 W
Quadraro (Neigh.), It.	66c	41.51 N	12.33 E
Quahran, see Oran			
Quakers Hill, Austl.	70a	33.43 S	150.53 E
Quakertown, Pa. (kwā'kēr-toun)	111	40.30 N	75.20 W
Quamdo, China (chyäm-dwō)	198	31.06 N	96.30 E
Quanah, Tx. (kwä'nà)	122	34.19 N	99.43 W
Quang Ngai, Viet. (kwäng n'gä'ē)	203	15.05 N	108.58 E
Quang Ngai (Mtn.), Viet.	203	15.10 N	108.20 E
Quanjiao, China (chyuän-jyou)	200	32.06 N	118.17 E
Quanzhou, China (chyuän-jō)	203	24.58 N	118.40 E
Quanzhou, China	203	25.58 N	111.02 E
Qu'Appelle (R.), Can.	100	50.35 N	103.25 W
Qu'Appelle Dam, Can.	100	51.00 N	106.25 W
Quartu Sant' Elena It. (kwär-tōō' sänt a'lå-nä)	172	39.16 N	9.12 E
Quartzsite, Az.	121	33.40 N	114.13 W
Quatsino Sd, Can. (kwŏt-sē'nō)	98	50.25 N	128.10 W
Qūchān, Iran	195	37.06 N	58.30 E
Qudi, China	200	37.06 N	117.15 E
Québec, Can. (kwē-bĕk') (kå-bĕk')	95b	46.49 N	71.13 W
Quebec (Prov.), Can.	97	51.07 N	70.25 W
Quedlinburg, G.D.R. (kvĕd'lĕn-bōōrgh)	166	51.45 N	11.10 E
Qued-Zem, Mor. (wĕd-zĕm')	224	33.05 N	5.49 W
Queen Bess, Mt., Can.	98	51.16 N	124.34 W
Queen Charlotte Is., Can. (kwēn shär'lŏt)	98	53.30 N	132.25 W
Queen Charlotte Ra., Can.	98	53.00 N	132.00 W
Queen Charlotte Sd., Can.	98	51.30 N	129.30 W
Queen Charlotte Str., Can. (strāt)	98	50.40 N	127.25 W
Queen Elizabeth Is., Can. (ē-lĭz'á-bĕth)	94	78.20 N	110.00 W
Queen Maud G., Can. (mäd)	96	68.27 N	102.55 W
Queen Maud Land, Ant.	232	75.00 S	10.00 E
Queen Maud Mts., Ant.	232	85.00 S	179.00 W
Queens Chan., Austl. (kwēnz)	214	14.25 S	129.10 E
Queenscliff, Austl.	211a	38.16 S	144.39 E
Queensland (state), Austl. (kwēnz'lănd)	215	22.45 S	141.01 E
Queenstown, Austl. (kwēnz'toun)	216	42.00 S	145.40 E
Queenstown, S. Afr.	227c	31.54 S	26.53 E
Queimados, Braz. (kā-mà'dôs)	144b	22.42 S	43.34 W
Quela, Ang.	230	9.16 S	17.02 E
Quelimane, Moz. (kā-lē-mä'nĕ)	216	17.48 S	37.05 E
Quelpart (I.), **see Cheju**			
Queluz, Port.	65d	38.45 N	9.15 W
Quemado de Güines, Cuba (kā-mä'dhä-dē-gwē'nĕs)	134	22.45 N	80.20 W
Quemoy (Chinmen), Taiwan	203	24.30 N	118.20 E
Quemoy (I.), Taiwan	203	24.35 N	118.45 E
Quepos, C.R. (kā'pôs)	133	9.26 N	84.10 W
Quepos, Punta (Pt.), C.R. (pōō'n-tä)	133	9.23 N	84.20 W
Querenburg (Neigh.), F.R.G.	63	51.27 N	7.16 E
Querétaro, Mex. (kå-rā'tä-rō)	130	20.37 N	100.25 W
Querétaro (State), Mex.	130	21.00 N	100.00 W
Quesada, Sp. (kā-sä'dhä)	170	37.51 N	3.04 W
Quesnel, Can. (kā-nĕl')	98	52.59 N	122.30 W
Quesnel L., Can.	99	52.32 N	121.05 W
Quesnel (R.), Can.	98	52.15 N	122.00 W
Quetame, Col. (kĕ-tä'mĕ)	142a	4.20 N	73.50 W
Quetta, Pak. (kwĕt'ä)	196	30.19 N	67.01 E
Quezaltenango, Guat. (kå-zäl'tå-näŋ'gō)	132	14.50 N	91.30 W
Quezaltepeque, Guat. (kå-zäl'tå-pā'kå)	132	14.39 N	89.26 W
Quezaltepeque, Sal. (kĕ-zäl'tĕ'pĕ-kĕ)	132	13.50 N	89.17 W
Quezon City, Phil. (kā-zōn)	207a	14.40 N	121.02 E
Qufu, China (chyōō-fōō)	200	35.37 N	116.54 E
Quibdo, Col. (kēb'dō)	142a	5.42 N	76.41 W
Quiberon, Fr. (kē-bē-rôN')	168	47.29 N	3.08 W
Quiçama, Parque Nacional de (Natl. Pk.), Ang.	230	10.00 S	13.25 E
Quiché, Guat. (kē-shā')	132	15.05 N	91.08 W
Quicksborn, F.R.G. (kvēks'bōrn)	157c	53.44 N	9.54 E
Quilcene, Wa. (kwĭl-sēn')	118a	47.50 N	122.53 W
Quilimari, Chile (kē-lē-mä'rē)	141b	32.06 S	71.28 W
Quillan, Fr. (kē-yäN')	168	43.53 N	2.13 E
Quillota, Chile (kēl-yō'tä)	141b	32.52 S	71.14 W
Quilmes, Arg. (kēl'mās)	144b	34.43 S	58.16 W
Quilon, India (kwē-lōn')	197	8.58 N	76.16 E
Quilpie, Austl. (kwĭl'pē)	216	26.34 S	149.20 E
Quilpué, Chile (kēl-pōō ĕ')	141b	33.03 S	71.22 W
Quimbaya, Col. (kēm-bä'yä)	142a	4.38 N	75.46 W
Quimbele, Ang.	230	6.28 S	16.13 E
Quimbonge, Ang.	230	8.36 S	18.30 E
Quimper, Fr. (kăN-pĕr')	168	47.59 N	4.04 W
Quinalt R., Wa.	116	47.23 N	124.10 W
Quinault Ind. Res., Wa.	116	47.27 N	124.34 W
Quincy, Fl. (kwĭn'sē)	126	30.35 N	84.35 W
Quincy, Il.	123	39.55 N	91.23 W
Quincy, Ma.	105a	42.15 N	71.00 W
Quincy, Mi.	110	42.00 N	84.50 W
Quincy, Or.	118c	46.08 N	123.10 W
Quincy B., Ma.	54a	42.17 N	70.58 W
Qui-nhon, Viet. (kwĭnyŏn)	206	13.51 N	109.03 E
Quinn R., Nv. (kwĭn)	116	41.42 N	117.45 W
Quintanar de la Orden, Sp. (kēn-tä-när')	170	39.36 N	3.02 W
Quintana Roo (State), Mex. (rô'ô)	132a	19.30 N	88.30 W
Quinta Normal, Chile	61b	33.27 S	70.42 W
Quintero, Chile (kēn-tē'rô)	141b	32.48 S	71.30 W
Quinto Romano (Neigh.), It.	65c	45.29 N	9.05 E
Quionga, Moz.	231	10.37 S	40.30 E
Quiroga, Mex. (kē-rō'gä)	130	19.39 N	101.30 W
Quiroga, Sp. (kē-rō'gä)	170	42.28 N	7.18 W
Quitaúna, Braz.	61d	23.31 S	46.47 W
Quitman, Ga. (kwĭt'măn)	126	30.46 N	83.35 W
Quitman, Ms.	126	33.02 N	88.43 W
Quito, Ec. (kē'tō)	142	0.17 S	78.32 W
Quixadá, Braz. (kē-shä-dä')	143	4.58 S	38.58 W
Qulūşanā, Egypt (kōō-lōōs'nä)	223b	28.22 N	30.44 E
Qumbu, S. Afr. (kōōm'bōō)	227c	31.10 S	28.48 E
Quorn, Austl. (kwôrn)	216	32.20 S	138.00 E
Qurayyah, Wādī (R.), Egypt	191a	30.08 N	34.27 E
Qūş, Egypt (kōōs)	223b	25.53 N	32.48 E
Qutang, China (chyōō-täŋ)	200	32.33 N	120.07 E
Quthing, Leso.	227c	30.35 S	27.42 E
Quvea (I.), N. Cal.	215	20.43 S	166.48 E
Quxian, China (chyōō-shyĕn)	203	28.58 N	118.58 E
Quxian, China	203	30.40 N	106.48 E
Quzhou, China (chyoô-jō)	200	36.47 N	114.58 E
Quzvīn, Iran	192	36.10 N	49.59 E

R

PLACE (Pronounciation)	PAGE	Lat. °′	Long. °′
Raab R., Aus. (räp)	166	46.55 N	15.55 E
Raadt (Neigh.), F.R.G.	63	51.24 N	6.56 E
Raahe, Fin. (rä'ĕ)	158	64.39 N	24.22 E
Raasdorf, Aus.	66e	48.15 N	16.34 E
Rab (I.), Yugo. (räb)	172	44.45 N	14.40 E
Raba, Indon.	206	8.32 S	118.49 E
Raba R., Hung.	167	47.28 N	17.12 E
Rabat, Mor. (rá-bät')	224	33.59 N	6.47 W
Rabaul, Pap. N. Gui. (rä'boul)	207	4.15 S	152.19 E
Rābigh, Sau. Ar.	195	22.48 N	39.01 E
Raby, Eng.	64a	53.19 N	3.02 W
Raccoon (R.), Ia. (ră-kōōn')	115	42.07 N	94.45 W
Raccoon Cay (I.), Ba.	135	22.25 N	75.50 W
Race, C., Can. (rās)	105	46.40 N	53.10 W
Raceview, S. Afr.	71b	26.17 S	28.08 E
Rachado, C., Mala.	191b	2.26 N	101.29 E
Racibórz, Pol. (rä-chē'bōōzh)	167	50.06 N	18.14 E
Racine, Wi. (rá-sēn')	113a	42.43 N	87.49 W
Raco, Mi. (rá cō)	119k	46.22 N	84.43 W
Rădăuti, Rom.'(rû-dû-ōōts'')	167	47.53 N	25.55 E
Radcliffe, Eng. (răd'klĭf)	156	53.34 N	2.20 W
Radevormwald, F.R.G. (rä'dĕ-fōrm-väld)	169c	51.12 N	7.22 E
Radford, Va. (răd'fērd)	127	37.06 N	81.33 W
Rādhanpur, India	196	23.57 N	71.38 E
Radium, S. Afr. (rā'dĭ-ŭm)	223d	25.06 S	28.18 E
Radlett, Eng.	62	51.42 N	0.20 W
Radnor, Pa.	56b	40.02 N	75.21 W
Radom, Pol. (rä'dôm)	167	51.24 N	21.11 E
Radomir, Bul. (rä'dô-mēr)	173	42.33 N	22.58 E
Radomsko, Pol. (rä-dôm'skô)	167	51.04 N	19.27 E
Radomyshl, Sov. Un. (rä-dô-mēsh''l)	175	50.30 N	29.13 E
Radoviš, Yugo. (rä-dô-vēsh)	173	41.39 N	22.28 E
Radul', Sov. Un. (rá'dōōl)	175	51.52 N	30.46 E
Radviliškis, Sov. Un. (räd'vē-lēsh'kēs)	165	55.49 N	23.31 E
Radwah, Jabal (Mtn.), Sau. Ar.	192	24.44 N	38.14 E
Radzyń Podlaski, Pol. (räd'zēn-y' pŭd-lä'skĭ)	167	51.49 N	22.40 E
Raeford, NC (rā'fērd)	127	34.57 N	79.15 W
Raesfeld, F.R.G. (răz'fĕld)	169c	51.46 N	6.50 E
Raeside, Austl. (rā'sīd)	214	29.20 S	122.30 E
Rae Str., Can. (rā)	96	68.40 N	95.03 W
Rafaela, Arg. (rä-fä-å'lä)	144	31.15 S	61.21 W
Rafael Castillo, Arg.	60d	34.42 S	58.37 W
Rafah, Egypt (rä'fä)	191a	31.14 N	34.12 E
Rafaï, Cen. Afr. Rep. (rä-fī')	225	4.59 N	23.58 E
Rafḩā, Sau. Ar.	192	29.43 N	43.13 E
Rafsanjān, Iran	192	30.45 N	56.30 E
Raft R., Id. (răft)	117	42.20 N	113.17 W
Ragay, Phil. (rä-gī')	207a	13.49 N	122.45 E
Ragay G., Phil.	207a	13.44 N	122.38 E
Ragga, Egypt	179	36.00 N	39.00 E
Ragunda, Swe. (rä-gōōn'dä)	164	63.07 N	16.24 E
Ragusa, It. (rä-gōō'sä)	159	36.58 N	14.41 E
Ragusa, see Dubrovnik			
Rahm (Neigh.), F.R.G.	63	51.21 N	6.47 E
Rahnsdorf (Neigh.), G.D.R.	65a	52.26 N	13.42 E
Rahway, NJ (rô'wā)	112a	40.37 N	74.16 W
Rāichūr, India (rä'ē-chōōr')	197	16.23 N	77.18 E
Raigarh, India (rī'gŭr)	196	21.57 N	83.32 E
Rainbow Bridge Natl. Mon., Ut. (rān'bō)	121	37.05 N	111.00 W
Rainbow City, Pan.	128a	9.20 N	79.23 W
Rainford, Eng.	64a	53.30 N	2.48 W
Rainhill, Eng.	64a	53.26 N	2.46 W
Rainhill Stoops, Eng.	64a	53.24 N	2.45 W
Rainier, Or.	118c	46.05 N	122.56 W
Rainier, Mt., Wa. (rā-nēr')	116	46.52 N	121.46 W
Rainy (L.), Can.-Mn. (rān'ē)	101	48.43 N	94.29 W
Rainy (R.), Can.-Mn.	101	48.50 N	94.41 W
Rainy River, Can.	101	48.43 N	94.29 W
Raipur, India (rū'jŭ-bōō-rē')	196	21.25 N	81.37 E
Raisin (R.), Mi. (rā'zĭn)	110	42.00 N	83.35 W
Raitan, NJ (rā-tăn)	112a	40.34 N	74.40 W
Rājahmundry, India (räj-ŭ-mŭn'drē)	197	17.03 N	81.51 E
Rajang (Strm.), Mala.	206	2.10 N	113.30 E

ng-sing; ŋ-baŋk; N-nasalized n; nŏd; cŏmmit; ōld; ôbey; ôrder; oi-boil; fōōd; fŏŏt; ou-out; s-soft; sh-dish; th-thin; pūre; ůnite; ûrn; stŭd; circŭs; ü-as in French tu; '-indeterminate vowel.

PLACE (Pronunciation)	PAGE	Lat. °'	Long. °'
Rājapālaiyam, India	196	9.30 N	77.33 E
Rājasthān (State), India (rä'jŭs-tän)	196	31.20 N	72.00 E
Rājkot, India (räj'kōt)	196	22.20 N	70.48 E
Rājpur, India	196a	22.24 N	88.25 E
Rājpur (Neigh.), India	67d	28.41 N	77.12 E
Rājshāhi, Bngl.	196	24.26 S	88.39 E
Rakhov, Sov. Un. (rä'Kôf)	167	48.02 N	24.13 E
Rakh'ya, Sov. Un. (räk'yȧ)	182c	60.06 N	30.50 E
Rakitnoye, Sov. Un. (rȧ-kēt'nô-yĕ)	175	50.51 N	35.53 E
Rákoscsaba (Neigh.), Hung.	66g	47.29 N	19.17 E
Rákoshegy (Neigh.), Hung.	66g	47.28 N	19.14 E
Rákoskeresztúr (Neigh.), Hung.	66g	47.29 N	19.15 E
Rákosliget (Neigh.), Hung.	66g	47.30 N	19.16 E
Rákospalota (Neigh.), Hung.	66g	47.34 N	19.08 E
Rákosszentmihály (Neigh.), Hung.	66g	47.32 N	19.11 E
Rakovnik, Czech. (rä'kôk-nyēk)	166	50.07 N	13.45 E
Rakvere, Sov. Un. (rȧk'vĕ-rĕ)	174	59.22 N	26.14 E
Raleigh, NC	127	35.45 N	78.39 W
Raleigh, B., NC	127	34.50 N	76.15 W
Ram (R.), Can.	99	52.10 N	115.05 W
Rama, Nic. (rä'mä)	133	12.11 N	84.14 W
Ramallo, Arg. (rä-mä'l-yô)	141c	33.28 S	60.02 W
Ramanāthapuram, India	197	9.13 N	78.52 E
Rambouillet, Fr. (räN-bōō-yĕ')	169b	48.39 N	1.49 E
Rame Hd, S. Afr.	227c	31.48 S	29.22 E
Ramenka (Neigh.), Sov. Un.	66b	55.41 N	37.30 E
Ramenskoye, Sov. Un. (rá'mĕn-skô-yĕ)	182b	55.34 N	38.15 E
Ramlat as Sab'atayn (Reg.), Sau. Ar.	192	16.08 N	45.15 E
Ramm, Jabal (Mts.), Jordan	191a	29.37 N	35.32 E
Ramos, Mex. (rä'mōs)	130	22.46 N	101.52 W
Ramos (R.), Nig.	229	5.10 N	5.40 E
Ramos Arizpe, Mex. (ä-rēz'pȧ)	124	25.33 N	100.57 W
Rampart, Ak. (răm'pärt)	107	65.28 N	150.18 W
Rampo Mts., NJ-NY (răm'pō)	112a	41.06 N	72.12 W
Rāmpur, India (räm'pōōr)	196	28.53 N	79.03 E
Ramree I., Bur. (räm'rē')	206	19.01 N	93.23 E
Ramsayville, Can. (răm'zē vĭl)	95c	45.23 N	75.34 W
Ramsbottom, Eng. (rămz'bŏt-ŭm)	156	53.39 N	2.20 W
Ramsden Heath, Eng.	62	51.38 N	0.28 E
Ramsey, Isle of Man (răm'zē)	162	54.20 N	4.25 W
Ramsey, NJ	112a	41.03 N	74.09 W
Ramsey L., Can.	102	47.15 N	82.16 W
Ramsgate, Austl.	70a	33.59 S	151.08 E
Ramsgate, Eng. (rămz'gāt)	163	51.19 N	1.20 E
Ramsjö, Swe. (räm'shû)	164	62.11 N	15.44 E
Ramu (R.), Pap. N. Gui. (rä'mōō)	207	5.35 S	145.16 E
Rancagua, Chile (rän-kä'gwä)	141b	34.10 S	70.43 W
Rance (R.), Fr. (räNs)	168	48.17 N	2.30 W
Rānchī, India (rän'chē)	196	23.24 N	85.18 E
Ranchleigh, Md.	56c	39.22 N	76.40 W
Rancho Boyeros, Cuba (rä'n-chô-bô-yĕ'rôs)	135a	23.00 N	82.23 W
Rancho Palos Verdes, Ca.	59	33.45 N	118.24 W
Randallstown, Md. (răn'dȧlz-toun)	112e	39.22 N	76.48 W
Randburg, S. Afr.	71b	26.06 S	27.59 E
Randers, Den. (rän'ĕrs)	164	56.28 N	10.03 E
Randfontein, S. Afr. (rănt'fŏn-tān)	227b	26.10 S	27.42 E
Randleman, NC (răn'd'l-măn)	127	35.49 N	79.50 W
Randolph, Ma. (răn'dŏlf)	105a	42.10 N	71.03 W
Randolph, Ne.	114	42.22 N	97.22 W
Randolph, Vt.	111	43.55 N	72.40 W
Random I., Can. (răn'dŭm)	105	48.12 N	53.25 W
Randsfjorden (Fd.), Nor.	164	60.35 N	10.10 E
Randwick, Austl.	70a	33.55 S	151.15 E
Ranérou, Senegal	228	15.18 N	13.58 W
Rangeley, Me. (rānj'lē)	104	44.56 N	70.38 W
Rangeley (L.), Me.	104	45.00 N	70.25 W
Ranger, Tx. (rān'jēr)	124	32.26 N	98.41 W
Rangia, India	196	26.32 N	91.39 E
Rangoon, Bur. (răŋ-gōōn')	206	16.46 N	96.09 E
Rangpur, Bngl. (rŭng'pōōr)	196	25.48 N	89.19 E
Rangsang (I.), Indon. (räng'säng')	191b	0.53 N	103.05 E
Rangsdorf, G.D.R. (rängs'dōrf)	157b	52.17 N	13.25 E
Ranholas, Port.	65d	38.47 N	9.22 W
Rānīganj, India (rä-nē-gŭnj')	196	23.40 N	87.08 E
Rankin, Pa.	57b	40.25 N	79.53 W
Rankin Inlet, Can. (răŋ'kĕn)	96	62.45 N	94.27 W
Ranova (R.), Sov. Un. (rä'nô-vȧ)	174	53.55 N	40.03 E
Ransomville, NY (răn'sum-vĭl)	113c	43.15 N	78.54 W
Rantau, Mala.	191b	2.35 N	101.58 E
Rantelkomboa, Bulu (Mtn.), Indon.	206	3.22 S	119.50 E
Rantoul, Il. (răn-tōōl')	110	40.25 N	88.05 W
Raoyang, China (rou-yäŋ)	200	38.16 N	115.45 E
Rapallo, It. (rä-päl'lô)	172	44.21 N	9.14 E
Rapa Nui (Easter) (I.), Chile (rä'pä nōō'ē) (ēs'tēr)	209	26.50 S	109.00 W
Rapel (R.), Chile (rä-pål')	141b	34.05 S	71.30 W
Rapid (R.), Mn. (răp'ĭd)	115	48.21 N	94.50 W
Rapid City, SD	114	44.06 N	103.14 W
Rapla, Sov. Un. (räp'lȧ)	165	59.02 N	24.46 E
Rappahannock (R.), Va. (răp'ȧ-hăn'ŭk)	111	38.20 N	75.25 W
Raquette (L.), NY (răk'ĕt)	111	43.50 N	74.35 W
Rara Mazowiecka, Pol. (rä'rä mä-zō-vyĕts'kä)	167	51.46 N	20.17 E
Raritan R., NJ (răr'ĭ-tăn)	112a	40.32 N	74.27 W
Rarotonga, Cook Is. (rä'rô-tŏŋ'gȧ)	209	20.40 S	163.00 W
Ra's an Naqb, Jordan	191a	30.00 N	35.29 E
Ras Dashen Terara (Mtn.), Eth. (räs dä-shän')	225	12.49 N	38.14 E
Raseiniai, Sov. Un. (rä-syā'nyī)	165	55.23 N	23.04 E
Ra's Fartak (C.), P. D. R. of Yem.	192	15.43 N	52.17 E
Rashayya, Leb.	191a	33.30 N	35.50 E
Rashīd (Rosetta), Egypt (rȧ-shēd') (rô-zĕt'ȧ)	223b	31.22 N	30.25 E
Rashīd, Masabb (R. Mth.), Egypt	223b	31.30 N	29.58 E
Rashkina, Sov. Un. (rȧsh'kĭ-nȧ)	182a	59.57 N	61.30 E
Rashkov, Sov. Un. (räsh'kôf)	175	47.55 N	28.51 E
Rasht, Iran	192	37.13 N	49.45 E
Raška, Yugo. (räsh'kȧ)	173	43.16 N	20.40 E
Ras Kuh Mt., Pak.	196	34.03 N	65.10 E

PLACE (Pronunciation)	PAGE	Lat. °'	Long. °'
Rasskazovo, Sov. Un. (räs-kä'sô-vô)	179	52.40 N	41.40 E
Rastatt, F.R.G. (rä-shtät)	166	48.51 N	8.12 E
Rastes, Sov. Un. (rȧs'tĕs)	182a	59.24 N	58.49 E
Rastunovo, Sov. Un. (rȧs-tōō'nô-vô)	182b	55.15 N	37.50 E
Ras Uarc (C.), Mor.	170	35.28 N	2.58 W
Ratangarh, India (rŭ-tŭn'gŭr)	196	28.10 N	74.30 E
Ratcliff, Tx. (răt'klĭf)	125	31.22 N	95.09 W
Rath (Neigh.), F.R.G.	63	51.17 N	6.49 E
Rathenow, G.D.R. (rä'tĕ-nō)	166	52.36 N	12.20 E
Rathlin I., Ire. (răth-lĭn)	162	55.18 N	6.13 W
Rathmecke, F.R.G.	63	51.15 N	7.38 E
Ratingen, F.R.G. (rä'tĕn-gĕn)	169	51.18 N	6.51 E
Rat Is., Ak. (răt)	107a	51.35 N	176.48 E
Ratlām, India	196	23.19 N	75.05 E
Ratnāgiri, India	197	17.04 N	73.24 E
Raton, NM (rȧ-tōn')	122	36.52 N	104.26 W
Rattlesnake Cr., Or. (răt''l snāk)	116	42.38 N	117.39 W
Rättvik, Swe. (rĕt'vēk)	164	60.54 N	15.07 E
Rauch, Arg. (rȧ'ōōch)	141c	36.47 S	59.05 W
Raufoss, Nor. (rou'fōs)	164	60.44 N	10.30 E
Raúl Soares, Braz. (rä-ōō'l-sôȧ'rĕs)	141a	20.05 S	42.28 W
Rauma, Fin. (rä'ōō-mȧ)	165	61.07 N	21.31 E
Rauna, Sov. Un. (råū'nȧ)	165	57.21 N	25.31 E
Raurkela, India	196	22.15 N	84.53 E
Rautalampi, Fin. (rä'ōō-tĕ-läm'pô)	165	62.39 N	26.25 E
Rava-Russkaya, Sov. Un. (rä'vȧ rōōs'kȧ-yȧ)	167	50.14 N	23.40 E
Ravenna, It. (rä-vĕn'nä)	172	44.27 N	12.13 E
Ravenna, Ne. (rȧ-vĕn'ȧ)	114	41.20 N	98.50 W
Ravenna, Oh.	110	41.10 N	81.20 W
Ravensburg, F.R.G. (rä'vĕns-bōōrgh)	166	47.48 N	9.35 E
Ravensdale, Wa. (rā'vĕnz-dāl)	118a	47.22 N	121.58 W
Ravensthorpe, Austl. (rā'vĕns-thôrp)	214	33.30 S	120.20 E
Ravenswood, S. Afr.	71b	26.11 S	28.15 E
Ravenswood, WV (rā'vĕnz-wŏŏd)	110	38.55 N	81.50 W
Ravensworth, Va.	56d	38.48 N	77.13 W
Ravenwood, Va.	56d	38.52 N	77.09 W
Rāwalpindi, Pak. (rä-wŭl-pēn'dē)	196	33.40 N	73.10 E
Rawāndūz, Iraq	192	36.37 N	44.30 E
Rawicz, Pol. (rä'vēch)	166	51.36 N	16.51 E
Rawlina, Austl. (rôr-lēnȧ)	214	31.13 S	125.45 E
Rawlins, Wy. (rô'lĭnz)	117	41.46 N	107.15 W
Rawson, Arg. (rô'sŭn)	144	43.16 S	65.09 W
Rawson, Arg.	141c	34.36 S	60.03 W
Rawtenstall, Eng. (rô'tĕn-stôl)	156	53.42 N	2.17 W
Raya, Bukit (Mtn.), Indon.	206	0.45 S	112.11 E
Ray, C., Can. (rā)	105	47.40 N	59.18 W
Raychikinsk, Sov. Un. (rī'chĭ-kēnsk)	181	49.52 N	129.17 E
Rayleigh, Eng. (rā'lē)	156b	51.35 N	0.36 E
Raymond, Can. (rā'mŭnd)	99	49.27 N	112.39 W
Raymond, Wa.	116	46.41 N	123.42 W
Raymondville, Tx. (rā'mŭnd-vĭl)	122	26.30 N	97.46 W
Ray Mts., Ak.	107a	65.40 N	151.45 W
Rayne, La. (rān)	125	30.12 N	92.15 W
Rayón, Mex. (rä-yōn')	130	21.49 N	99.39 W
Rayton, S. Afr. (rā'tŭn)	227b	25.45 S	28.33 E
Raytown, Mo. (rā'toun)	119f	39.01 N	94.48 W
Rayville, La. (rā-vĭl)	125	32.28 N	91.46 W
Razdel'naya, Sov. Un. (räz-dĕl'nä-yȧ)	175	46.47 N	30.08 E
Razdol'noye, Sov. Un. (räz-dôl'nô-yĕ)	204	43.38 N	131.58 E
Razgrad, Bul.	173	43.32 N	26.32 E
Razlog, Bul. (räz'lôk)	173	41.54 N	23.32 E
Razorback Mtn., Can. (rā'zēr-băk)	98	51.35 N	124.42 W
Raz, Pte. du (Pt.), Fr. (pwăNt dü rä)	168	48.02 N	4.43 W
Rea (R.), Eng. (rē)	156	52.25 N	2.31 W
Reaburn, Can. (rā'bûrn)	95f	50.06 N	97.53 W
Reading, Eng. (rĕd'ĭng)	156b	51.25 N	0.58 W
Reading, Ma.	105a	42.32 N	71.07 W
Reading, Mi.	110	41.45 N	84.45 W
Reading, Oh.	113f	39.14 N	84.26 W
Reading, Pa.	111	40.20 N	75.55 W
Readville (Neigh.), Ma.	54a	42.14 N	71.08 W
Realengo, Braz. (rē-ä-län-gô)	144b	23.50 S	43.25 W
Real Felipe, Castillo (P. Int.), Peru	60c	12.04 S	77.09 W
Rebel Hill, Pa.	56b	40.04 N	75.20 W
Rebiana (Oasis), Libya	225	24.10 N	22.03 E
Rebun (I.), Jap. (rē'bōōn)	204	45.25 N	140.54 E
Recanati, It. (rā-kä-nä'tē)	172	43.25 N	13.35 E
Recherche, Arch. of the, Austl. (rē-shârsh')	214	34.17 S	122.30 E
Rechitsa, Sov. Un. (ryĕ'chĕt-sȧ)	174	52.22 N	30.24 E
Recife (Pernambuco), Braz. (rȧ-sē'fĕ) (pĕr-näm-bōō'kō)	143	8.09 S	34.59 W
Recife, Kapp (C.), S. Afr. (rȧ-sē'fĕ)	227c	34.03 S	25.43 E
Recklinghausen, F.R.G.	63	51.36 N	7.13 E
Recklinghausen-Süd (Neigh.), F.R.G.	63	51.34 N	7.13 E
Reconquista, Arg. (rā-kôn-kēs'tä)	144	29.01 S	59.41 W
Reconquista (R.), Arg.	60d	34.27 S	58.36 W
Rector, Ar. (rĕk'tēr)	123	36.16 N	90.21 W
Red (Basin), see Szechwan			
Red (R.), Can.-U.S. (rĕd)	101	49.11 N	97.18 W
Red (R.), North Fk., Tx.	122	35.20 N	100.08 W
Red (R.), Tn.	126	36.35 N	86.55 W
Red (R.), U.S.	109	31.40 N	92.55 W
Red (R.), Viet.	206	22.25 N	103.50 E
Redan, Ga. (rē-dăn') (rĕd'ăn)	112c	33.44 N	84.09 W
Red Bank, NJ (băngk)	112a	40.21 N	74.06 W
Red Bank National Park, NJ.	56b	39.52 N	75.10 W
Red Bluff, Ca. (blŭf)	118	40.10 N	122.14 W
Red Bluff Res., Tx.	124	32.03 N	103.52 W
Redbridge (Neigh.), Eng.	62	51.34 N	0.05 E
Redby, Mn. (rĕd'bē)	115	47.52 N	94.55 W
Red Cedar (R.), Wi. (sē'dēr)	115	45.03 N	91.48 W
Redcliff, Can. (rĕd'clĭf)	100	50.05 N	110.47 W
Redcliffe, Austl. (rĕd'clĭf)	207	27.20 S	153.12 E
Red Cliff Ind. Res., Wi.	115	46.48 N	91.22 W
Red Cloud, Ne. (kloud)	122	40.06 N	98.32 W
Red Deer, Can. (dēr)	99	52.16 N	113.48 W
Red Deer (R.), Can.	99	52.05 N	113.00 W

PLACE (Pronunciation)	PAGE	Lat. °'	Long. °'
Red Deer (R.), Can.	100	52.55 N	102.10 W
Red Deer L., Can.	101	52.58 N	101.28 W
Reddick, Il. (rĕd'dĭk)	113a	41.06 N	88.16 W
Redding, Ca. (rĕd'ĭng)	116	40.36 N	122.25 W
Reddish, Eng.	64b	53.26 N	2.09 W
Redenção da Serra, Braz. (rĕ-dĕn-souN-dä-sĕ'r-rä)	141a	23.17 S	45.31 W
Redfield, SD (rĕd'fēld)	114	44.53 N	98.30 W
Red Fish Bar, Tx.	125a	29.29 N	94.53 W
Redford (Neigh.), Mi.	57c	42.25 N	83.16 W
Redford Township, Mi.	57c	42.25 N	83.16 W
Red Hill, Ca.	59	33.45 N	117.48 W
Red Indian L., Can. (ĭn'dĭ-ăn)	105	48.40 N	56.50 W
Redklinghausen, F.R.G. (rĕk'lĭng-hou-zĕn)	169c	51.36 N	7.13 E
Red Lake, Can. (lāk)	101	51.02 N	93.49 W
Red Lake (R.), Mn.	114	48.02 N	96.04 W
Red Lake Falls, Mn. (lāk fôls)	114	47.52 N	96.17 W
Red Lake Ind. Res., Mn.	114	48.09 N	95.55 W
Redlands, Ca. (rĕd'lăndz)	119a	34.04 N	117.11 W
Red Lion, Pa. (lī'ŭn)	111	39.55 N	76.30 W
Red Lodge, Mt.	117	45.13 N	107.16 W
Redmond, Wa. (rĕd'mŭnd)	118a	47.40 N	122.07 W
Rednitz R., F.R.G. (rĕd'nētz)	166	49.10 N	11.00 E
Red Oak, Ia. (ōk)	114	41.00 N	95.12 W
Redon, Fr. (rē-dôN')	168	47.42 N	2.03 W
Redonda I., Antigua (rĕ-dŏn'dȧ)	133b	16.55 N	62.28 W
Redonda, Isla, Braz. (ē's-lä-rĕ-dô'n-dä)	144b	23.05 S	43.11 W
Redondela, Sp. (rā-dhôn-dā'lä)	170	42.16 N	8.34 W
Redondo, Port. (rā-dôn'dōō)	170	38.40 N	7.32 W
Redondo, Wa. (rē-dŏn'dō)	118a	47.21 N	122.19 W
Redondo Beach, Ca.	119a	33.50 N	118.23 W
Red Pass, Can. (pȧs)	99	52.59 N	118.59 W
Red Rock Cr., Mt.	117	44.54 N	112.44 W
Red R., Prairie Dog Town Fk., Tx. (prā'rĭ)	122	34.54 N	101.31 W
Red R., Salt Fk., Tx.	122	35.04 N	100.31 W
Red Sea, Afr.-Asia	225	23.15 N	37.00 E
Redstone, Can. (rĕd'stōn)	98	52.08 N	123.42 W
Red Sucker L., Can. (sŭk'ēr)	101	54.09 N	93.40 W
Redwater Cr., Mt.	117	47.37 N	105.25 W
Red Willow Cr., Ne.	122	40.34 N	100.48 W
Red Wing, Mn.	115	44.34 N	92.35 W
Redwood City, Ca. (rĕd' wŏŏd)	118b	37.29 N	122.13 W
Redwood Falls, Mn.	115	44.32 N	95.06 W
Reed City, Mi. (rēd)	110	43.50 N	85.35 W
Reed L., Can.	101	54.37 N	100.30 W
Reedley, Ca. (rēd'lē)	120	36.37 N	119.27 W
Reedsburg, Wi. (rēdz'bûrg)	115	43.32 N	90.01 W
Reedsport, Or. (rēdz'pôrt)	116	43.42 N	124.08 W
Reelfoot (R.), Tn. (rēl'fŏŏt)	126	36.18 N	89.20 W
Ree, Lough (B.), Ire. (lŏK'rē')	162	53.30 N	7.45 W
Rees, F.R.G. (rēz)	169c	51.46 N	6.25 E
Reeves, Mt., Austl. (rēv's)	216	33.50 S	149.56 E
Reform, Al. (rē-fôrm')	126	33.23 N	88.00 W
Refugio, Tx. (rā-fōō'hyō) (rē-fū'jō)	125	28.18 N	97.15 W
Rega (R.), Pol. (rĕ-gä)	166	53.48 N	15.30 E
Regen R., F.R.G. (rā'ghĕn)	166	49.09 N	12.21 E
Regensburg, F.R.G. (rā'ghĕns-bōōrgh)	166	49.02 N	12.06 E
Regents Park, Austl.	70a	33.53 S	151.02 E
Regent's Park (P. Int.), Eng.	62	51.32 N	0.09 W
Reggane, Alg.	224	27.08 N	0.06 E
Reggio, La. (rĕg'jĭ-ō)	112d	29.50 N	89.46 W
Reggio di Calabria, It. (rĕ'jô dē kä-lä'brē-ä)	172	38.07 N	15.42 E
Reggio nell' Emilia, It.	172	44.43 N	10.34 E
Reghin, Rom. (rā-gēn')	167	46.47 N	24.44 E
Regina, Can. (rē-jī'nȧ)	100	50.25 N	104.39 W
Regla, Cuba (rāg'lä)	135a	23.08 N	82.20 W
Regnitz (R.), F.R.G. (rĕg'nētz)	166	49.50 N	10.55 E
Rego Park (Neigh.), NY	55	40.44 N	73.52 W
Reguengos de Monsaraz, Port. (rā-gĕŋ'gōzh dā mōn-sä-räzh')	170	38.26 N	7.30 W
Reh, F.R.G.	63	51.22 N	7.33 E
Rehoboth, Namibia	226	23.10 S	17.15 E
Rehovot, Isr.	191a	31.53 N	34.49 E
Reichenbach, G.D.R. (rī'kĕn-bäK)	166	50.36 N	12.18 E
Reidsville, NC (rēdz'vĭl)	127	36.20 N	79.37 W
Reigate, Eng. (rī'gāt)	156b	51.12 N	0.12 W
Ré, Ile de (I.), Fr. (ēl dē rā')	168	46.10 N	1.53 W
Reims, Fr. (răNs)	168	49.16 N	4.00 E
Reina Adelaida, Arch., Chile (är-chē'pyē'lȧ-gô-rā'nä-ä-dē-lī'dä)	144	52.00 S	74.15 W
Reinbeck, Ia. (rīn'bĕk)	115	42.22 N	92.34 W
Reindeer (L.), Can. (rān'dēr)	96	57.36 N	101.23 W
Reindeer (R.), Can.	100	55.45 N	103.30 W
Reindeer I., Can.	101	52.25 N	98.00 W
Reindeer L., Can.	101	57.15 N	102.40 W
Reinosa, Sp. (rā-ē-nō'sä)	170	43.01 N	4.08 W
Reisholz (Neigh.), F.R.G.	63	51.11 N	6.52 E
Reistertown, Md. (rēs'tēr-toun)	112e	39.28 N	76.50 W
Reitz, S. Afr.	223d	27.48 S	28.25 E
Rema, Jabal (Mtn.), Yemen	192	14.13 N	44.38 E
Rembau, Mala.	191b	2.36 N	102.06 E
Remedios, Col. (rĕ-mĕ'dyôs)	142a	7.03 N	74.42 W
Remedios, Cuba (rā-mā'dhē-ōs)	134	22.30 N	79.35 W
Remedios, Pan. (rĕ-mĕ'dyōs)	133	8.14 N	81.46 W
Remedios de Escalada (Neigh.), Arg.	60d	34.43 S	58.23 W
Remiremont, Fr. (rē-mēr-môN')	169	48.01 N	6.35 E
Rempang I., Indon.	191b	0.51 N	104.04 E
Remscheid, F.R.G. (rĕm'shīt)	169c	51.10 N	7.11 E
Rena, Nor.	164	61.08 N	11.17 E
Renca, Chile	61b	33.24 S	70.44 W
Renca, Cerro (Mtn.), Chile	61b	33.23 S	70.43 W
Rendova (I.), Sol. Is. (rĕn'dô-vȧ)	215	8.38 S	156.26 E
Rendsburg, F.R.G. (rĕnts'bōōrgh)	166	54.19 N	9.39 E
Renfrew, Can. (rĕn'frōō)	111	45.30 N	76.30 W
Rengam, Mala. (rĕn'gäm')	191b	1.53 N	103.24 E
Rengo, Chile (rĕn'gō)	141b	34.22 S	70.50 W
Reni, Sov. Un. (ran')	175	45.26 N	28.18 E

PLACE (Pronounciation)	PAGE	Lat. °′	Long. °′
Renmark, Austl. (rĕn′märk)	216	34.10 S	140.50 E
Rennel (I.), Sol. Is. (rĕn-nĕl′)	215	11.50 S	160.38 E
Rennes, Fr. (rĕn)	168	48.07 N	1.02 W
Rennselaer, NY (rĕn′sē-lâr)	111	42.40 N	73.45 W
Reno, Nv. (rē′nō)	120	39.32 N	119.49 W
Reno (R.), It. (rā′nȯ)	172	44.10 N	10.55 E
Renovo, Pa. (rė-nō′vō)	111	41.20 N	77.50 W
Renqiu, China (rŭn-chyȯ)	200	38.44 N	116.05 E
Rensselaer, In. (rĕn′sē-lâr)	110	41.00 N	87.10 W
Rentchler, Il. (rĕnt′chlĕr)	119e	38.30 N	89.52 W
Renton, Wa. (rĕn′tŭn)	118a	47.29 N	122.13 W
Renville, Mn. (rĕn′vĭl)	115	44.44 N	95.13 W
Repentigny, Can.	95a	45.47 N	73.26 W
Republic, Al. (rė-pŭb′lĭk)	112h	33.37 N	86.54 W
Republic, Wa.	116	48.38 N	118.44 W
Republican (R.), Ks.	123	39.40 N	97.40 W
Republican (R.), **South Fk.,** Co. (rė-pŭb′lĭ-kăn)	122	39.35 N	102.28 W
Repulse B., Austl. (rė-pŭls′)	215	20.56 S	149.22 E
Requena, Sp. (rā̇-kā′nä)	170	39.29 N	1.03 W
Reseda (Neigh.), Ca.	59	34.12 N	118.31 W
Resende, Braz. (rĕ-sĕ′n-dĕ)	141a	22.30 S	44.26 W
Resende Costa, Braz. (kôs-tä)	141a	20.55 S	44.12 W
Reservoir, Austl.	70b	37.43 S	145.00 E
Reshetilovka, Sov. Un. (ryĕ′ shĕ-tė-lôf-kȧ)	175	49.34 N	34.04 E
Resistencia, Arg. (rā-sės-tĕn′syä)	144	27.24 S	58.54 W
Resiţa, Rom. (rā̇′shė-tȧ)	173	45.18 N	21.56 E
Resolute, Can. (rĕz-ȯ-lūt′)	94	74.41 N	95.00 W
Resolution (I.), Can. (rĕz-ȯ-lū′shŭn)	97	61.30 N	63.58 W
Resolution I., N.Z. (rĕz-ŏ̤l-ûshûn)	217	45.43 S	166.20 E
Resse (Neigh.), F.R.G.	63	51.34 N	7.07 E
Restigouche (R.), Can. (rĕs-tė-go͞osh′)	104	47.35 N	67.35 W
Restrepo, Col. (rĕs-trĕ′pȯ)	142a	3.49 N	76.31 W
Restrepo, Col.	142a	4.16 N	73.32 W
Retalhuleu, Guat. (rā-täl-o͞o-lān′)	132	14.31 N	91.41 W
Rethel, Fr. (r-tl′)	168	49.34 N	4.20 E
Réthimnon, Grc.	172a	35.21 N	24.30 E
Retie, Bel.	157a	51.16 N	5.08 E
Retiro, Parque del (P. Int.), Sp.	65b	40.25 N	3.41 W
Retsil, Wa. (rĕt′sĭl)	118a	47.33 N	122.37 W
Reunion, Afr. (rā-ü-nyôn′)	232	21.06 S	55.36 E
Reus, Sp. (rā′o͞os)	171	41.08 N	1.05 E
Reusrath, F.R.G.	63	51.06 N	6.57 E
Reutlingen, F.R.G. (roit′lĭng-ĕn)	166	48.29 N	9.14 E
Reutov, Sov. Un. (rĕ-o͞o′ôf)	182b	55.45 N	37.52 E
Reval, see Tallinn			
Revda, Sov. Un. (ryâv′dȧ)	182a	56.48 N	59.57 E
Revelstoke, Can. (rĕv′ĕl-stōk)	99	51.59 N	118.12 W
Reventazon, R., C.R. (rā̇-vĕn-tä-zōn′)	133	10.10 N	83.30 W
Revere, Ma. (rė-vēr′)	105a	42.24 N	71.01 W
Revesby, Austl.	70a	33.57 S	151.01 E
Revillagigedo Chan, Ak. (rĕ-vĭl′ȧ-gĭ-gē′dō)	98	55.10 N	131.13 W
Revillagigedo I., Ak.	98	55.35 N	131.23 W
Revillagigedo, Islas (I.), Mex. (ė′s-läs-rĕ-vėl-yä-hė′gĕ-dȯ)	128	18.45 N	111.00 W
Revin, Fr. (rē-văɴ)	168	49.56 N	4.34 E
Rewa, India (rā′wä)	196	24.41 N	81.11 E
Rewāri, India	196	28.19 N	76.39 E
Rexburg, Id. (rĕks′bûrg)	117	43.50 N	111.48 W
Rey, Iran	68h	35.35 N	51.25 E
Reyes, Bol. (rā′yĕs)	142	14.19 S	67.16 W
Reyes, Pt., Ca.	120	38.00 N	123.00 W
Rey, Isla del (I.), Pan. (ė′s-lä-dĕl-rā′ė)	133	8.20 N	78.40 W
Reykjanes (C.), Ice. (rā′kyȧ-nĕs)	154	63.37 N	24.33 W
Reykjavik, Ice. (rā′kyȧ-vĕk)	158	64.09 N	21.39 W
Rey, L., Mex. (rā)	124	27.00 N	103.33 W
Reynosa, Mex. (rā-ė-nō′sä)	124	26.05 N	98.21 W
Rēzekne, Sov. Un. (rā̇′zĕk-nĕ)	174	56.31 N	27.19 E
Rezh, Sov. Un. (rĕzh′)	182a	57.22 N	61.23 E
Rezina, Sov. Un. (ryĕzh′ĕ-nĭ)	175	47.44 N	28.56 E
Rhaetien Alps (Mts.), It.	172	46.22 N	10.33 E
Rheinberg, F.R.G. (rīn′bĕrgh)	169c	51.33 N	6.37 E
Rheine, F.R.G. (rī′nĕ)	166	52.16 N	7.26 E
Rheinen, F.R.G.	63	51.27 N	7.38 E
Rheinhausen, F.R.G.	63	51.24 N	6.44 E
Rhein-Herne-Kanal (Can.), F.R.G.	63	51.27 N	6.47 E
Rheinkamp, F.R.G.	63	51.30 N	6.37 E
Rheinland-Pfalz (Rhineland-Palatinate) (State), F.R.G.	166	50.05 N	6.40 E
Rhein R., F.R.G. (rīn)	166	50.34 N	7.21 E
Rheydt, F.R.G. (rĕ′yt)	169c	51.10 N	6.28 E
Rhine (R.), Eur.	154	50.34 N	7.21 E
Rhinelander, Wi. (rīn′lăn-dĕr)	115	45.39 N	89.25 W
Rhin Kanal (Can.), G.D.R. (rēn kä-näl′)	157b	52.47 N	12.40 E
Rhin R., G.D.R. (rēn)	157b	52.52 N	12.49 E
Rhiou (R.), Alg.	171	35.45 N	1.18 E
Rho, It.	65c	45.32 N	9.02 E
Rhode Island (State), U.S. (rōd ī′lȧnd)	109	41.35 N	71.40 W
Rhode I., RI	112b	41.31 N	71.14 W
Rhodes, Austl.	70a	33.50 S	151.05 E
Rhodes, Eng.	64b	53.33 N	2.14 W
Rhodes, S. Afr. (rȯdz)	227c	30.48 S	27.56 E
Rhodon, Fr.	64c	48.43 N	2.04 E
Rhodope Mts., Bul. (rô′dȯ-pĕ)	173	42.00 N	24.08 E
Rhondda, Wales (rŏn′dhȧ)	162	51.40 N	3.40 W
Rhône (R.), Fr. (rōn)	168	45.14 N	4.53 E
Rhoon, Neth.	157a	51.52 N	4.24 E
Rhum (I.), Scot. (rŭm)	162	57.00 N	6.20 W
Riachão, Braz. (rė-ä-chouɴ′)	143	7.15 S	46.30 W
Rialto, Ca. (rē-ăl′tō)	119a	34.06 N	117.23 W
Riau (Prov.), Indon.	191b	0.56 N	101.25 E
Riau, Kepulauan (I.), Indon.	206	0.30 N	104.55 E
Riau, Selat (Str.), Indon.	191b	0.40 N	104.27 E
Riaza (R.), Sp. (rė-ä′thä)	170	41.25 N	3.25 W
Ribadavia, Sp. (rē-bä-dhä′vė-ä)	170	42.18 N	8.06 W
Ribadeo, Sp. (rē-bä-dhā′ō)	170	37.32 N	7.05 W
Ribadesella, Sp. (rē′bä-dā-sāl′yä)	170	43.30 N	5.02 W
Ribauè, Moz.	231	14.57 S	38.17 E
Ribe, Den. (rē′bĕ)	164	55.20 N	8.45 E
Ribeirão Prêto, Braz. (rė-bā-rouɴ-prĕ′tô)	141a	21.11 S	47.47 W
Ribera, NM (rē-bĕ′rä)	122	35.23 N	105.27 W
Riberalta, Bol. (rē-bā̇-räl′tä)	142	11.06 S	66.02 W
Rib Lake, Wi. (rĭb lāk)	115	45.20 N	90.11 W
Rice, Ca. (rīs)	120	34.05 N	114.50 W
Rice (L.), Can.	111	44.05 N	78.10 W
Rice L., Mn.	119g	45.10 N	93.09 W
Rice Lake, Wi.	115	45.30 N	91.44 W
Richards I., Can. (rĭch′ērds)	107	69.45 N	135.30 W
Richards Landing, Can. (lănd′ĭng)	119k	46.18 N	84.02 W
Richardson, Tx. (rĭch′ērd-sŭn)	119c	32.56 N	96.44 W
Richardson, Wa.	118a	48.27 N	122.54 W
Richardson Mts., Can.	96	66.58 N	136.19 W
Richardson Mts., N.Z.	217	44.50 S	168.30 E
Richardson Park, De. (pärk)	111	39.45 N	75.35 W
Richelieu (R.), Can. (rēsh′lyû′)	111	45.05 N	73.25 W
Richfield, Mn.	119g	44.53 N	93.17 W
Richfield, Oh.	113d	41.14 N	81.38 W
Richfield, Ut.	121	38.45 N	112.05 W
Richford, Vt. (rĭch′fērd)	111	45.00 N	72.35 W
Rich Hill, Mo. (rĭch hĭl)	123	38.05 N	94.21 W
Richibucto, Can. (rĭ-chĭ-bŭk′tō)	104	46.41 N	64.52 W
Richland, Ga. (rĭch′lănd)	126	32.05 N	84.40 W
Richland, Wa.	116	46.17 N	119.19 W
Richland Center, Wi. (sĕn′tēr)	115	43.20 N	90.25 W
Richmond, Austl. (rĭch′mŭnd)	215	20.47 S	143.14 E
Richmond, Austl.	70b	37.49 S	145.00 E
Richmond, Austl.	211b	33.36 S	150.45 E
Richmond, Ca.	118b	37.56 N	122.21 W
Richmond, Can.	95c	45.12 N	75.49 W
Richmond, Can.	104	45.40 N	72.07 W
Richmond, Il.	113a	42.29 N	88.18 W
Richmond, In.	110	39.50 N	85.00 W
Richmond, Ky.	110	37.45 N	84.20 W
Richmond, Mo.	123	39.16 N	93.58 W
Richmond, S. Afr.	227c	29.52 S	30.17 E
Richmond, Tx.	125	29.35 N	95.45 W
Richmond, Ut.	117	41.55 N	111.50 W
Richmond, Va.	111	37.35 N	77.30 W
Richmond (Neigh.), Eng.	62	51.28 N	0.18 W
Richmond (Neigh.), NJ	56b	39.59 N	75.06 W
Richmond Beach, Wa.	118a	47.47 N	122.23 W
Richmond Heights, Mo.	119e	38.38 N	90.20 W
Richmond Heights, Oh.	56a	41.33 N	81.29 W
Richmond Highlands, Wa.	118a	47.46 N	122.22 W
Richmond Hill, Can. (hĭl)	95d	43.53 N	79.26 W
Richmond Hill (Neigh.), NY	55	40.42 N	73.49 W
Richmondtown Restoration (P. Int.), NY	55	40.34 N	74.09 W
Richmond Valley (Neigh.), NY	55	40.31 N	74.13 W
Richton, Ms. (rĭch′tŭn)	126	31.20 N	89.54 W
Richwood, WV (rĭch′wo͝od)	110	38.10 N	80.30 W
Ricketts Pt., Austl.	70b	38.00 S	145.02 E
Rickmansworth, Eng.	62	51.39 N	0.29 W
Ridderkerk, Neth.	157a	51.52 N	4.35 E
Rideau (R.), Can.	95c	45.17 N	75.41 W
Rideau L., Can. (rė-dō′)	111	44.40 N	76.20 W
Ridge, Eng.	62	51.41 N	0.15 W
Ridgefield, Ct. (rij′fēld)	112a	41.16 N	73.30 W
Ridgefield, NJ	55	40.50 N	74.00 W
Ridgefield, Wa.	118c	45.49 N	122.40 W
Ridgefield Park, NJ	55	40.51 N	74.01 W
Ridgeway, Can. (rĭj′wā)	113c	42.53 N	79.02 W
Ridgewood, NJ (ridj′wo͝od)	112a	40.59 N	74.08 W
Ridgewood (Neigh.), NY	55	40.42 N	73.53 W
Ridgway, Pa.	111	41.25 N	78.40 W
Riding Mountain Natl. Park, Can. (rīd′ĭng)	96	50.59 N	99.19 W
Riding Mtn., Can. (rīd′ĭng)	101	50.37 N	99.37 W
Riding Rocks (Is.), Ba.	134	25.20 N	79.10 W
Ridley Park, Pa.	56b	39.53 N	75.19 W
Riebeek-Oos, S. Afr.	227c	33.14 S	26.09 E
Ried, Aus. (rēd)	166	48.13 N	13.30 E
Riemke (Neigh.), F.R.G.	63	51.30 N	7.13 E
Riesa, G.D.R. (rē′zȧ)	166	51.17 N	13.17 E
Rieti, It. (rė-ā′tē)	172	42.25 N	12.51 E
Rietvlei, S. Afr.	71b	26.18 S	28.03 E
Rievleidam (L.), S. Afr.	227b	25.52 S	28.18 E
Rifle, Co. (rī′f′l)	121	39.35 N	107.50 W
Riga, G. of, Sov. Un.	165	57.56 N	23.05 E
Rigaud, Can. (rė-gō′)	95a	45.29 N	74.18 W
Rigby, Id. (rĭg′bė)	117	43.40 N	111.55 W
Rigeley, WV (rĭj′lė)	111	39.40 N	78.45 W
Rigolet, Can. (rĭg-ō-lā′)	97	54.10 N	58.40 W
Riihimäki, Fin.	165	60.44 N	24.44 E
Rijeka (Fiume), Yugo. (rĭ-yĕ′kä)	172	45.22 N	14.24 E
Rijkevorsel, Bel.	157a	51.21 N	4.46 E
Rijswijk, Neth.	157a	52.03 N	4.19 E
Rika R., Sov. Un. (rė′kȧ)	167	48.21 N	23.37 E
Rima (R.), Nig.	229	13.30 N	5.50 E
Rimavska Sobota, Czech. (rē′mȧf-skȧ sô′bȯ-tȧ)	167	48.25 N	20.01 E
Rimbo, Swe. (rēm′bo͞o)	164	59.45 N	18.22 E
Rimini, It. (rē′mė-nē)	172	44.03 N	12.33 E
Rimouski, Can. (rė-mo͞os′kė)	104	48.27 N	68.32 W
Rinc n de Romos, Mex. (rėn-kōn dā rô-mōs′)	130	22.13 N	102.21 W
Rincón, Cuba	60b	22.57 N	82.25 W
Ringkøbing, Den. (rĭng′kûb-ĭng)	164	56.06 N	8.14 E
Ringkøbing Fd., Den.	164	55.55 N	8.04 E
Ringsted, Den. (rĭng′stĕdh)	164	55.27 N	11.49 E
Ringvassøya (I.), Nor. (rĭng′väs-ûė)	158	69.58 N	16.43 E
Ringwood, Austl.	211a	37.49 S	145.14 E
Ringwood North, Austl.	70b	37.48 S	145.14 E
Rinjani, Gunung (Mtn.), Indon.	206	8.39 S	116.22 E
Rio Abajo, Pan. (rė′ō-ä-bä′ᴋȯ)	128a	9.01 N	78.30 W
Rio Balsas, Mex. (rė′ō-bäl-säs)	130	17.59 N	99.45 W
Riobamba, Ec. (rē′ō-bäm-bä)	142	1.45 S	78.37 W
Rio Bonito, Braz. (rē′o͞o bō-nē′to͞o)	141a	22.44 S	42.38 W
Rio Branco, Braz. (rē′o͞o brän′ko͞o)	142	9.57 S	67.50 W
Rio Branco (Ter.), Braz.	143	2.35 N	61.25 W
Rio Casca, Braz. (rē′ō-kȧ′s-kä)	141a	20.15 S	42.39 W
Rio Chico, Ven. (rė′ō chė′kŏ)	143b	10.20 N	65.58 W
Rio Claro, Braz. (rē′o͞o klä′ro͞o)	141a	21.25 S	47.33 W
Rio Comprido (Neigh.), Braz.	61c	22.55 S	43.12 W
Rio das Flores, Braz. (rē′ō-däs-flô-rĕs)	141a	22.10 S	43.35 W
Rio de Janeiro, Braz. (rē′o͞o dā zhä-nā̇′ė-ro͞o)	144b	22.50 S	43.20 W
Rio de Janeiro (State), Braz.	143	22.27 S	42.43 W
Rio de Mouro, Port.	65d	38.46 N	9.20 W
Rio Frío, Mex. (rė′ō-frē′ȯ)	131a	19.21 N	98.40 W
Rīga, Sov. Un. (rē′gȧ)	165	56.55 N	24.05 E
Rīgān, Iran	192	28.45 N	58.55 E
Rīgestān (Reg.), Afr.	192	30.53 N	64.42 E
Rio Grande, Braz. (rē′o͞o grän′dĕ)	144	31.04 S	52.14 W
Rio Grande, Mex. (rē′ō grän′dā)	130	23.51 N	102.59 W
Rio Grande (R.), Co. (rē′o͞o grän′dĕ)	121	37.44 N	106.51 W
Riogrande, Tx. (rē′ō grȧn-dā)	124	26.23 N	98.48 W
Rio Grande do Norte (State), Braz. (rē′o͞o grän′dĕ do͞o nôr′tĕ)	143	5.26 S	37.20 W
Rio Grande do Sul (State), Braz. (rē′o͞o grän′dĕ-dȯ-so͞o′l)	144	29.00 S	54.00 W
Riom, Fr. (rė-ôɴ′)	168	45.54 N	3.08 E
Rio Muni (Prov.), Equat. Gui. (rē′ō mo͞o′nė)	222	1.47 N	8.33 E
Rio Negro, Embalse del (Res.), Ur. (ĕm-bä′l-sĕ-dĕl-rė′ō-nĕ′grō)	144	32.45 S	55.50 W
Rionero, It. (rē-ō-nā′rȯ)	172	40.55 N	15.42 E
Rio Novo, Braz. (rē′ō-nô′vȯ)	141a	21.30 S	43.08 W
Rio Pardo de Minas, Braz. (rē′ō pär′dō-dĕ-mē′näs)	143	15.43 S	42.24 W
Rio Pombo, Braz. (rē′ō pôm′bä)	141a	21.17 S	43.09 W
Rio Sorocaba, Represado (Res.), Braz. (rĕ-prĕ-sä-dȯ-rē′ō-sȯ-rō-kä′bä)	141a	23.37 S	47.19 W
Rio Verde, Braz. (vĕr′dĕ)	143	17.47 S	50.49 W
Ripley, Eng. (rĭp′lė)	156	53.03 N	1.24 W
Ripley, Eng.	62	51.18 N	0.29 W
Ripley, Ms.	126	34.44 N	88.55 W
Ripley, Tn.	126	35.44 N	89.34 W
Ripoll, Sp. (rė-pōl′′)	171	42.10 N	2.10 E
Ripon, Wi. (rĭp′ŏn)	115	43.49 N	88.50 W
Ripon (I.), Austl.	214	20.05 S	118.10 E
Ripon Falls, Ug.	225	0.38 N	33.02 E
Rîmnicu-Sărat, Rom.	173	45.24 N	27.06 E
Rîmnicu-Vilcea, Rom.	173	45.07 N	24.22 E
Risaralda (Dept.), Col.	142a	6.45 S	76.00 W
Risdon, Austl. (rĭz′dŭn)	215	42.37 S	147.32 E
Rishiri (I.), Jap. (rē-shē′rē)	204	45.10 N	141.08 E
Rishon le Ziyyon, Isr.	191a	31.57 N	34.48 E
Rishra, India	196a	22.42 N	88.22 E
Rising Sun, In. (rīz′ĭng sŭn)	110	38.55 N	84.55 W
Risle (R.), Fr.	168	49.12 N	0.43 E
Risor, Nor. (rēs′ûr)	164	58.44 N	9.10 E
Ritacuva, Alto (Mtn.), Col. (ä′l-tȯ-rē-tä-ko͞o′vä)	142	6.22 N	72.13 W
Ritchie, Va.	56d	38.52 N	76.52 W
Rithāla (Neigh.), India	67d	28.43 N	77.06 E
Rittman, Oh. (rĭt′năn)	113d	40.58 N	81.47 W
Ritzville, Wa. (rīts′vĭl)	116	47.08 N	118.23 W
Riva, Dom. Rep. (rē′vä)	135	19.10 N	69.55 W
Riva, It. (rė′vä)	172	45.54 N	10.49 E
Riva, Md. (ri′vă)	112e	38.57 N	76.36 W
Rivas, Nic. (rē′väs)	132	11.25 N	85.51 W
Rive-de-Gier, Fr. (rēv-dē-zhė-ā′)	168	45.32 N	4.37 E
Rivera, Ur. (rė-vā′rä)	144	30.52 S	55.32 W
River Cess, Lib. (rĭv′ēr sĕs)	224	5.46 N	9.52 W
Riverdale, Il. (rĭv′ēr dāl)	113a	41.38 N	87.36 W
Riverdale, Md.	56d	38.58 N	76.55 W
Riverdale, Ut.	119b	41.11 N	112.00 W
Riverdale (Neigh.), NY	55	40.54 N	73.54 W
River Edge, NJ	55	40.56 N	74.02 W
River Falls, Al.	126	31.20 N	86.25 W
River Falls, Wi.	115	44.48 N	92.38 W
River Forest, Il.	58a	41.53 N	87.49 W
River Grove, Il.	58a	41.56 N	87.50 W
Riverhead, Eng.	62	51.17 N	0.10 E
Riverhead, NY (rĭv′ēr hĕd)	111	40.55 N	72.40 W
Riverina (Reg.), Austl. (rĭv-ēr-ē′nä)	216	34.55 S	144.30 E
River Jordan, Can. (jôr′dăn)	118a	48.25 N	124.03 W
River Oaks, Tx. (ōkz)	119c	32.47 N	97.24 W
River Rouge, Mi. (ro͞ozh)	113b	42.16 N	83.09 W
Rivers, Can.	101	50.01 N	100.15 W
Riverside, Ca. (rĭv′ēr-sīd)	119a	33.59 N	117.21 W
Riverside, Il.	58a	41.50 N	87.49 W
Riverside, NJ	112f	40.02 N	74.58 W
Rivers Inlet, Can.	98	51.45 N	127.15 W
Riverstone, Austl.	211b	33.41 S	150.52 E
Riverton, Va.	111	39.00 N	78.15 W
Riverton, Wy.	117	43.02 N	108.24 W
Rivesaltes, Fr. (rēv′zält′)	168	42.48 N	2.48 E
Riviera Beach, Fl. (rĭv-ĭ-ēr′ȧ bēch)	127a	26.46 N	80.04 W
Riviera Beach, Md.	112e	39.10 N	76.32 W
Rivie′re Beaudette, Can. (bō-dĕt′)	95a	45.14 N	74.20 W
Rivière-du-Loup, Can. (rė-vyâr′ dü lo͞o′)	104	47.50 N	69.32 W
Rivière Que Barre, Can. (rēv-yĕr′ kē-bär)	95g	53.47 N	113.51 W
Rivière-Trois-Pistoles, Can. (trwä′pės-tȯl′)	104	48.07 N	69.10 W
Rímac, Peru	60c	12.02 S	77.03 W
Rímac (R.), Peru	60c	12.02 S	77.09 W
Río Branco, Ur. (rĭȯ brăncȯ)	144	32.33 S	53.29 W
Río Cuarto, Arg. (rē′ō kwär′tō)	144	33.05 S	64.15 W
Río de Jesús, Pan. (rė′ō-dĕ-ᴋĕ-so͞o′s)	133	7.54 N	80.59 W
Río Dercero, Arg. (rė′ō dĕr-sĕ′rȯ)	144	32.12 S	63.59 W
Río Gallegos, Arg. (rē′ō gä-lā′gōs)	144	51.43 S	69.15 W

PLACE (Pronounciation)	PAGE	Lat. °′	Long. °′
Río Grande, Ven.	61a	10.35 N	66.57 W
Ríohacha, Col. (rē′ō-ä′chä)	142	11.30 N	72.54 W
Río Hato, Pan. (rḗ′ō-ä′tô)	133	8.19 N	80.11 W
Ríonegro, Col. (rḗ′ō-nĕ′grō)	142a	6.09 N	75.22 W
Río Negro (Dept.), Ur. (rē′ō-nĕ′grō)	141c	32.48 S	57.45 W
Río Negro (Prov.), Arg. (rē′ō nā′grō)	144	40.15 S	68.15 W
Ríosucio, Col. (rē′ō-so͞o′syô)	142a	5.25 N	75.41 W
Ríoverde, Mex. (rē′ō-vĕr′dā)	130	21.54 N	99.59 W
Riyadh (Ar Rīyāḑ), Sau. Ar.	192	24.31 N	46.47 E
Rize, Tur. (rē′zĕ)	179	41.00 N	40.30 E
Rizhao, China (rĕ-jou)	200	35.27 N	119.28 E
Rizzuto, C., It. (rēt-so͞o′tô)	173	38.53 N	17.05 E
Rjukan, Nor. (ryo͞o′kän)	164	59.53 N	8.30 E
Roanne, Fr. (rō-än′)	168	46.02 N	4.04 E
Roanoke, Al. (rō′á-nōk)	126	33.08 N	85.21 W
Roanoke, Va.	127	37.16 N	79.55 W
Roanoke (R.), NC-Va.	127	36.17 N	77.22 W
Roanoke (Staunton) (R.), Va.	127	37.05 N	79.20 W
Roanoke Rapids, NC	127	36.25 N	77.40 W
Roanoke Rapids, L., NC	127	36.28 N	77.37 W
Roan Plat., Co. (rōn)	121	39.25 N	108.50 W
Roatan, Hond. (rō-ä-tän′)	132	16.18 N	86.33 W
Roatan I., Hond.	132	16.19 N	86.46 W
Robbeneiland (I.), S. Afr.	226a	33.48 S	18.22 E
Robbins, Il. (rŏb′ĭnz)	113a	41.39 N	87.42 W
Robbinsdale, Mn. (rŏb′ĭnz-dāl)	119g	45.03 N	93.22 W
Robe, Wa. (rōb)	118a	48.06 N	121.50 W
Robertsham (Neigh.), S. Afr.	71b	26.15 S	28.00 E
Roberts, Mt., Austl. (rŏb′ērts)	215	32.05 S	152.30 E
Robertson, Lac (L.), Can.	105	51.00 N	59.10 W
Robertsport, Lib. (rŏb′ērts-pōrt)	228	6.45 N	11.22 W
Roberts, Pt., Wa. (rŏb′ērts)	118d	48.58 N	123.05 W
Roberval, Can. (rŏb′ēr-văl) (rô-bĕr-vál′)	97	48.32 N	72.15 W
Robinson, Il. (rŏb′ĭn-sŭn)	110	39.00 N	87.45 W
Robinson, S. Afr.	71b	26.09 S	27.43 E
Robinson's, Can.	105	48.16 N	58.50 W
Robinvale, Austl. (rŏb-ĭn′vāl)	216	34.45 S	142.45 E
Roblin, Can.	101	51.15 N	101.25 W
Robson, Mt., Can. (rŏb′sŭn)	99	53.07 N	119.09 W
Robstown, Tx. (rŏbz′toun)	125	27.46 N	97.41 W
Roca, Cabo da (C.), Port. (ká′bō-dä-rô′kă)	171b	38.47 N	9.30 W
Rocas, Atol das (Atoll), Braz. (ä-tôl-däs-rō′kás)	143	3.50 S	33.46 W
Rocedos São Pedro E São Paulo, (I.), Braz. (rô-zĕ′dôs-souɴ-pĕ′drô-ĕ-souɴ-päo͞o-lô)	140	1.50 N	30.00 W
Rocha, Ur. (rō′chás)	144	34.26 S	54.14 W
Rocha Miranda (Neigh.), Braz.	61c	22.52 S	43.22 W
Rocha Sobrinho, Braz.	61c	22.47 S	43.25 W
Rochdale, Eng. (rŏch′dāl)	156	53.37 N	2.09 W
Roche à Bateau, Hai. (rôsh á bá-tō′)	135	18.10 N	74.00 W
Rochefort, Fr. (rôsh-fŏr′)	168	45.55 N	0.57 W
Rochelle, Il. (rô-shĕl′)	115	41.53 N	89.06 W
Rochelle Park, NJ	55	40.55 N	74.04 W
Rochester, In. (rŏch′ĕs-tēr)	110	41.05 N	86.20 W
Rochester, Mi.	113b	42.41 N	83.09 W
Rochester, Mn.	115	44.01 N	92.30 W
Rochester, NH	111	43.20 N	71.00 W
Rochester, NY	111	43.15 N	77.35 W
Rochester, Pa.	113e	40.42 N	80.16 W
Rock (R.), Ia.	114	43.17 N	96.13 W
Rock (R.), Il.	115	41.40 N	89.52 W
Rock (R.), Or.	118c	45.34 N	122.52 W
Rock (R.), Or.	118c	45.52 N	123.14 W
Rockaway, NJ (rŏck′á-wā)	112a	40.54 N	74.30 W
Rockaway Park (Neigh.), NY	55	40.35 N	73.50 W
Rockaway Point (Neigh.), NY	55	40.33 N	73.55 W
Rockbank, Austl.	211a	37.44 S	144.40 E
Rockcliffe Park, Can. (rok′klĭf pärk)	95c	45.27 N	75.40 W
Rock Cr., Can. (rŏk)	100	49.01 N	107.00 W
Rock Cr., Il.	113a	41.16 N	87.54 W
Rock Cr., Mt.	117	46.25 N	113.40 W
Rock Cr., Or.	116	45.30 N	120.06 W
Rock Cr., Wa.	116	47.09 N	117.50 W
Rock Creek Park (P. Int.), DC.	56d	38.58 N	77.03 W
Rockdale, Austl., Egypt	71a	33.57 S	151.08 E
Rockdale, Md.	112e	39.22 N	76.49 W
Rockdale, Tx. (rŏk′dāl)	125	30.39 N	97.00 W
Rockefeller Center (P. Int.), NY	55	40.45 N	74.00 W
Rock Falls, Il. (rŏk fôlz)	115	41.45 N	89.42 W
Rock Ferry, Eng.	64a	53.22 N	3.00 W
Rockford, Il. (rŏk′fērd)	115	42.16 N	89.07 W
Rockhampton, Austl. (rŏk-hămp′tŭn)	215	23.26 S	150.29 E
Rockhill, SC (rŏk′hĭl)	127	34.55 N	81.01 W
Rockingham, NC (rŏk′ĭng-hăm)	127	34.54 N	79.45 W
Rockingham For., Eng. (rok′ĭng-hăm)	156	52.29 N	0.43 W
Rock Island, Il.	115	41.31 N	90.37 W
Rock Island Dam, Wa. (ī lănd)	116	47.17 N	120.33 W
Rockland, Can. (rŏk′lănd)	95c	45.33 N	75.17 W
Rockland, Me.	104	44.06 N	69.09 W
Rockland, Ma.	105a	42.07 N	70.55 W
Rockland Res., Austl.	216	36.55 S	142.20 E
Rockledge, Pa.	56b	40.03 N	75.05 W
Rockmart, Ga. (rŏk′märt)	126	33.58 N	85.00 W
Rockmont, Wi. (rŏk′mŏnt)	119h	46.34 N	91.54 W
Rockport, In. (rŏk′pōrt)	110	38.20 N	87.00 W
Rockport, Ma.	105a	42.39 N	70.37 W
Rockport, Mo.	123	40.25 N	95.30 W
Rockport, Tx.	125	28.03 N	97.03 W
Rock Rapids, Ia. (răp′ĭdz)	114	43.26 N	96.10 W
Rock Sd., Ba.	135	24.50 N	76.05 W
Rocksprings, Tx. (rŏk sprĭngs)	124	30.02 N	100.12 W
Rock Springs, Wy.	117	41.35 N	109.13 W
Rockstone, Guy. (rŏk′stôn)	143	5.55 N	57.27 W
Rock Valley, Ia. (văl′ĭ)	114	43.13 N	96.17 W
Rockville, In. (rŏk′vĭl)	110	39.45 N	87.15 W
Rockville, Md.	112e	39.05 N	77.11 W
Rockville Centre, NY (sĕn′tēr)	112a	40.39 N	73.39 W
Rockwall, Tx. (rŏk′wôl)	123	32.55 N	96.23 W
Rockwell City, Ia. (rŏk′wĕl)	115	42.22 N	94.37 W
Rockwood, Can. (rŏk-wo͝od)	95d	43.37 N	80.08 W
Rockwood, Me.	104	45.39 N	69.45 W
Rockwood, Tn.	126	35.51 N	84.41 W
Rocky (R.), Oh.	56a	41.30 N	81.49 W
Rocky Boys Ind. Res., Mt.	117	48.08 N	109.34 W
Rocky Ford, Co.	122	38.02 N	103.43 W
Rocky Hbr., Hong Kong	68c	22.20 N	114.19 E
Rocky Hill, NJ (hĭl)	112a	40.24 N	74.38 W
Rocky Island L., Can.	102	46.56 N	83.04 W
Rocky Mount, NC	127	35.55 N	77.47 W
Rocky Mountain House, Can.	99	52.22 N	114.55 W
Rocky Mountain Natl. Park, Co.	122	40.29 N	106.06 W
Rocky Mts., N.A.	94	50.00 N	114.00 W
Rocky R., East Br., Oh.	113d	41.13 N	81.43 W
Rocky River, Oh.	56a	41.30 N	81.40 W
Rocky River, Oh.	113d	41.29 N	81.51 W
Rocky R., West Br., Oh.	113d	41.17 N	81.54 W
Rocquencourt, Fr.	64c	48.50 N	2.07 E
Rodas, Cuba (rō′dhás)	135	22.20 N	80.35 W
Roden (R.), Eng. (rō′dĕn)	156	52.49 N	2.38 W
Rodeo, Ca. (rō′dḗō)	118b	38.02 N	122.16 W
Rodeo, Mex. (rô-dā′ō)	124	25.12 N	104.34 W
Roderick I., Can. (rŏd′ĕ-rĭk)	98	52.40 N	128.22 W
Rodez, Fr. (rô-dĕz′)	168	44.22 N	2.34 E
Rōdhos, Grc.	161	36.24 N	28.15 E
Ródhos (I.), Grc.	161	36.00 N	28.29 E
Rodniki, Sov. Un. (rôd′nḗ-kḗ)	174	57.08 N	41.48 E
Rodonit, Kep I (C.), Alb.	173	41.38 N	19.01 E
Rodosto, see Tekirdağ			
Roebling, NJ (rōb′lĭng)	112f	40.07 N	74.48 W
Roebourne, Austl. (rō′bŭrn)	214	20.50 S	117.15 E
Roebuck, B. Austl. (rō′bŭck)	214	18.15 S	121.10 E
Roedtan, S. Afr.	223d	24.37 S	29.08 E
Roehampton (Neigh.), Eng.	62	51.27 N	0.14 W
Roeselare, Bel.	163	50.55 N	3.05 E
Roesiger (L.), Wa. (rōz′ĭ-gēr)	118a	47.59 N	121.56 W
Roes Welcome Sd., Can. (rōz)	97	64.10 N	87.23 W
Rogachëv, Sov. Un. (rôg′á-chyôf)	174	53.07 N	30.04 E
Rogans Hill, Austl.	70a	33.44 S	151.01 E
Rogatica, Yugo. (rô-gä′tḗ-tsä)	173	43.46 N	19.00 E
Rogatin, Sov. Un. (rô-gä′tĭn)	167	49.22 N	24.37 E
Rogers, Ar. (rŏj-ērz)	123	36.19 N	94.07 W
Rogers City, Mi.	110	45.30 N	83.50 W
Rogers Park (Neigh.), Il.	58a	42.01 N	87.40 W
Rogersville, Tn.	126	36.21 N	83.00 W
Rognac, Fr. (rŏn-yäk′)	168a	43.29 N	5.15 E
Rogoaguado (L.), Bol. (rō′gō-ä-gwä-dō)	142	12.42 S	66.46 W
Rogovskaya, Sov. Un. (rô-gôf′ská-yá)	175	45.43 N	38.42 E
Rogózno, Pol. (rô′gôzh-nô)	166	52.44 N	16.53 E
Rogue R., Or. (rōg)	116	42.32 N	124.13 W
Rohdenhaus, F.R.G.	63	51.18 N	7.01 E
Röhlinghausen (Neigh.), F.R.G.	63	51.36 N	7.14 E
Rohrbeck, G.D.R.	65a	52.32 N	13.02 E
Roissy, Fr.	64c	48.47 N	2.39 E
Roissy-en-France, Fr.	64c	49.00 N	2.31 E
Rojas, Arg. (rō′häs)	141c	34.11 S	60.42 W
Rojo, Cabo (C.), Mex. (rō′hō)	131	21.35 N	97.16 W
Rojo, Cabo (C.), P. R. (rō′hō)	129b	17.55 N	67.14 W
Rokel (R.), S. L.	228	9.00 N	11.55 W
Rokkō-Zan (Mtn.), Jap. (rôk′kō zän)	205b	34.46 N	135.16 E
Roksana, S. Afr.	71b	26.07 S	28.04 E
Rokugō (Neigh.), Jap.	69a	35.33 N	139.43 E
Rokycany, Czech. (rô′kĭ′tsá-nĭ)	166	49.44 N	13.37 E
Roldanillo, Col. (rôl-dä-nē′l-yō)	142a	4.24 N	76.09 W
Rolla, Mo.	123	37.56 N	91.45 W
Rolla, ND	114	48.52 N	99.32 W
Rolleville, Ba.	135	23.40 N	76.00 W
Rolling Acres, Md.	56c	39.17 N	76.52 W
Röllinghausen (Neigh.), F.R.G.	63	51.31 N	7.08 E
Rolling Hills, Ca.	59	33.46 N	118.21 W
Roma, Austl. (rō′má)	216	26.30 S	148.48 E
Roma, Leso.	227c	29.28 S	27.43 E
Roma (Rome), It. (rō′mä) (rōm)	171d	41.52 N	12.37 E
Romaine (R.), Can. (rô-mĕn′)	105	51.22 N	63.23 W
Romainville, Fr.	64c	48.53 N	2.26 E
Roman, Rom. (rō′män)	167	46.56 N	26.57 E
Romania, Eur. (rō-mā′nḗ-á)	154	46.18 N	22.53 E
Romano, C., Fl. (rō-mā′nō)	127a	25.48 N	82.00 W
Romano, Cayo (I.), Cuba (kä′yō-rô-má′nô)	134	22.15 N	78.00 W
Romanovo, Sov. Un. (rô-mä′nô-vô)	182a	59.09 N	61.24 E
Romans, Fr. (rô-mäɴ′)	168	45.04 N	4.49 E
Romblon, Phil. (rōm-blōn′)	207a	12.34 N	122.16 E
Romblon I., Phil.	207a	12.33 N	122.17 E
Rome, Ga. (rōm)	126	34.14 N	85.10 W
Rome, NY	111	43.15 N	75.25 W
Romeo, Mi. (rō′mḗ-ō)	110	42.50 N	83.00 W
Rome, see Roma			
Romford, Eng. (rŭm′fērd)	156b	51.35 N	0.11 E
Romiley, Eng.	64b	53.25 N	2.05 W
Romilly-sur-Seine, Fr. (rô-mḗ-yē′sür-sān′)	168	48.32 N	3.41 E
Romita, Mex. (rō-mē′tä)	130	20.53 N	101.32 W
Romny, Sov. Un. (rôm′nĭ)	175	50.46 N	33.31 E
Rømø (I.), Den. (rûm′û)	164	55.08 N	8.17 E
Romoland, Ca. (rŏ′mō′lănd)	119a	33.44 N	117.11 W
Romorantin-Lanthenay, Fr. (rô-mô-räɴ-täɴ′)	168	47.24 N	1.46 E
Rompin, Mala.	191b	2.42 N	102.30 E
Rompin (R.), Mala.	191b	2.54 N	103.10 E
Romsdalsfjorden (Fd.), Nor.	164	62.40 N	7.05 W
Romulus, Mi. (rom′ū lŭs)	113b	42.14 N	83.24 W
Ronaldsay, North (I.), Scot.	162	59.21 N	2.23 W
Ronaldsay, South (I.), Scot. (rŏn′ăld-s′ā)	162	59.48 N	2.55 W
Ronan, Mt. (rō′năn)	117	47.28 N	114.03 W
Roncador, Serra do (Mts.), Braz. (sĕr′rá do͞o rôn-kä-dôr′)	143	12.44 S	52.19 W
Roncesvalles, Sp. (rôn-sĕs-vä′l-yĕs)	170	43.00 N	1.17 W
Ronceverte, WV (rŏn′sḗ-vûrt)	110	37.45 N	80.30 W
Ronda, Sp. (rōn′dä)	170	37.45 N	5.10 W
Ronda, Sierra de (Mts.), Sp.	170	36.35 N	5.03 W
Rondebult, S. Afr.	71b	26.18 S	28.14 E
Rondônia (Ter.), Braz.	142	10.15 S	63.07 W
Ronge, Lac la (L.), Can. (rŏnzh)	100	55.10 N	105.00 W
Rongjiang, China (rôŋ-jyäŋ)	203	25.52 N	108.45 E
Rongxian, China	203	22.50 N	110.32 E
Rønne, Den. (rûn′ĕ)	164	55.08 N	14.46 E
Ronneby, Swe. (rōn′ĕ-bü)	164	56.13 N	15.17 E
Ronne Ice Shelf, Ant.	232	77.30 S	38.00 W
Ronsdorf (Neigh.), F.R.G.	63	51.14 N	7.12 E
Ront Ra. (Mts.), Co. (rŏnt)	122	40.59 N	105.29 W
Roodepoort, S. Afr. (rō′dĕ-pōrt)	227b	26.10 S	27.52 E
Roodhouse, Il. (ro͞od′hous)	123	39.29 N	90.21 W
Rooiberg, S. Afr.	223d	24.46 S	27.42 E
Roosendaal, Neth. (rō′zĕn-däl)	157a	51.32 N	4.27 E
Roosevelt, NY	55	40.41 N	73.36 W
Roosevelt, Ut. (rōz′′vĕlt)	121	40.20 N	110.00 W
Roosevelt (R.), Az.	121	33.45 N	111.00 W
Roosevelt (R.), Braz. (rô′sĕ-vĕlt)	143	9.22 S	60.28 W
Roosevelt I., Ant.	232	79.30 S	168.00 W
Root R., Wi.	113a	42.49 N	87.54 W
Rooty Hill, Austl.	70a	33.46 S	150.50 E
Roper (R.), Austl. (rōp′ēr)	214	14.50 S	134.00 E
Ropsha, Sov. Un. (rôp′shá)	182c	59.44 N	29.53 E
Roque Pérez, Arg. (rô′kĕ-pĕ′rĕz)	141c	35.23 S	59.22 W
Roques, Islas los (Is.), Ven.	142	21.25 N	67.40 W
Roraima (Ter.), Braz. (rô′rīy-mă)	142	2.00 N	62.15 W
Roraima, Mtn., Ven.-Guy. (rô-rä-ē′mä)	143	5.12 N	60.52 W
Røros, Nor. (rûr′ôs)	164	62.36 N	11.25 E
Ros′ (R.), Sov. Un. (rôs)	175	49.40 N	30.22 E
Rosales, Mex. (rō-zä′lās)	124	28.15 N	100.43 W
Rosales, Phil. (rô-sä′lĕs)	207a	15.54 N	120.38 E
Rosa, Monte (Mt.), It. (mōn′tā rō′zä)	166	45.56 N	7.51 E
Rosamorada, Mex. (rō′zä-mō-rä′dhä)	130	22.06 N	105.16 W
Rosanna, Austl.	70b	37.45 S	145.04 E
Rosaria, Laguna (L.), Mex. (lä-go͞o′nä-rô-sá′ryä)	131	17.50 N	93.51 W
Rosario, Arg. (rô-zä′rḗ-ō)	141c	32.58 S	60.42 W
Rosario, Braz. (rô-zä′rḗ-o͞o)	143	2.49 S	44.15 W
Rosario, Mex.	124	26.31 N	105.40 W
Rosario, Mex.	130	22.58 N	105.54 W
Rosario, Phil.	207a	13.49 N	121.13 W
Rosario, Ur.	141c	34.19 S	57.24 E
Rosario, Cayo (I.), Cuba (kä′yō-rô-sä′ryō)	134	21.40 N	81.55 W
Rosário do Sul, Braz. (rô-zä′rḗ-o͞o-dô-so͞o′l)	144	30.17 S	54.52 W
Rosário Oeste, Braz. (ō′ĕst′ĕ)	143	14.47 S	56.20 W
Rosario Str., Wa.	118a	48.27 N	122.45 W
Rosas, Golfo de (G.), Sp. (gôl-fô-dĕ-rō′zäs)	171	42.10 N	3.20 E
Rosbach, F.R.G. (rōz′bäĸ)	169c	50.47 N	7.38 E
Roscoe, Tx. (rôs′kō)	124	32.26 N	100.38 W
Roseau, Dominica	133b	15.17 N	61.23 W
Roseau, Mn. (rô-zō′)	114	48.52 N	95.47 W
Roseau (R.), Mn.	114	48.52 N	96.11 W
Rosebank (Neigh.), S. Afr.	71b	26.09 S	28.02 E
Roseberg, Or. (rōz′bûrg)	116	43.13 N	123.30 W
Rosebery (Neigh.), Austl.	70a	33.55 S	151.12 E
Rosebud (R.), Can. (rōz′bŭd)	99	51.20 N	112.20 W
Rosebud Cr., Mt.	117	45.48 N	106.34 W
Rosebud Ind. Res., SD	114	43.13 N	100.42 W
Rosedale, Ms.	126	33.49 N	90.56 W
Rosedale, Wa.	118a	47.20 N	122.39 W
Rosedale (Neigh.), Can.	54c	43.41 N	79.22 W
Rosedale (Neigh.), NY	55	40.39 N	73.45 W
Roseires Res., Sud.	224	11.15 N	34.45 E
Roseland (Neigh.), Il.	58a	41.42 N	87.38 W
Roselle, Il. (rō-zĕl′)	113a	41.59 N	88.05 W
Roselle, NJ	55	40.40 N	74.16 W
Rosemead, Ca.	59	34.04 N	118.03 W
Rosemere, Can. (rōz′mēr)	95a	45.38 N	73.48 W
Rosemont, Il.	58a	41.59 N	87.52 W
Rosemont, Pa.	56b	40.01 N	75.19 W
Rosemount, Mn. (rōz′mount)	119g	44.44 N	93.08 W
Rosendal, S. Afr. (rô-sĕn′täl)	223d	28.32 S	27.56 E
Roseneath, S. Afr.	71b	26.17 S	28.11 E
Rosenheim, F.R.G. (rō′zĕn-hīm)	166	47.52 N	12.06 E
Rosenthal (Neigh.), G.D.R.	65a	52.36 N	13.23 E
Rosetown, Can. (rōz′toun)	100	51.33 N	108.00 W
Rose Tree, Pa.	56b	39.56 N	75.23 W
Rosetta, see Rashīd,			
Rosettenville (Neigh.), S. Afr.	227b	26.15 S	28.04 E
Roseville, Austl.	70a	33.47 S	151.11 E
Roseville, Ca. (rōz′vĭl)	120	38.44 N	121.19 W
Roseville, Mi.	113b	42.30 N	82.55 W
Roseville, Mn.	119g	45.01 N	93.10 W
Rosiclare, Il. (rōz′y-klâr)	110	37.30 N	88.15 W
Rosignol, Guy. (rŏs-ĭg-nćl)	143	6.16 N	57.37 W
Roșiori-de-Vede, Rom. (rô-shôr′ḗ dĕ vĕ-dĕ)	173	44.06 N	25.00 E
Roskilde, Den. (rôs′kḗl-dĕ)	164	55.39 N	12.04 E
Roslavl′, Sov. Un. (rôs′läv′l)	174	53.56 N	32.52 E
Roslyn, NY	55	40.48 N	73.39 W
Roslyn, Wa. (rŏz′lĭn)	116	47.14 N	121.00 W
Roslyn Estates, NY	55	40.47 N	73.40 W
Roslyn Heights, NY	55	40.47 N	73.39 W
Rosny-sous-Bois, Fr.	64c	48.53 N	2.29 E
Rosovka, Sov. Un.	175	47.14 N	36.35 E
Rösrath, F.R.G. (rûz′rät)	169c	50.53 N	7.11 E
Ross, Oh. (rôs)	113f	39.19 N	84.39 W
Rossano, It. (rô-sä′nō)	172	39.34 N	16.38 E
Rossan Pt., Ire.	162	54.45 N	8.30 W
Ross Cr., Can.	95g	53.50 N	113.08 W
Ross Dam, Wa.	116	48.40 N	121.07 W
Rosseau (L.), Can. (rôs-sō′)	103	45.15 N	79.30 W
Rossel (I.), Pap. N. Gui. (rô-sĕl′)	215	11.31 S	154.00 E

PLACE (Pronounciation)	PAGE	Lat. °'	Long. °'
Rosser, Can. (rôs'sẽr)	95f	49.59 N	97.27 W
Ross I., Can.	101	54.14 N	97.45 W
Rossignol, L., Can.	104	44.10 N	65.10 W
Rossland, Can. (rôs'lănd)	99	49.05 N	118.48 W
Rossmore, Austl.	70a	33.57 S	150.46 E
Rosso, Mauritania	228	16.30 N	15.49 W
Rossosh', Sov. Un. (rôs'sŭsh)	175	50.12 N	39.32 E
Rossouw, S. Afr.	227c	31.12 S	27.18 E
Ross Sea, Ant.	232	76.00 S	178.00 W
Ross Shelf Ice, Ant.	232	81.30 S	175.00 W
Rossvatnet (L.), Nor.	158	65.36 N	13.08 E
Rossville, Ga. (rôs'vĭl)	126	34.57 N	85.22 W
Rossville, Md.	56c	39.20 N	76.29 W
Rosthern, Can.	100	52.41 N	106.25 W
Rostherne, Eng.	64b	53.21 N	2.23 W
Rostock, G.D.R. (rôs'tŭk)	166	54.04 N	12.06 E
Rostov, Sov. Un.	174	57.13 N	39.23 E
Rostov (Oblast), Sov. Un.	175	47.38 N	39.15 E
Rostov-na-Donu, Sov. Un. (rôstôv-nå-dô-no͞o)	179	47.16 N	39.47 E
Roswell, Ga. (rŏz'wĕl)	126	34.02 N	84.21 W
Roswell, NM	122	33.23 N	104.32 W
Rosyln, Pa.	56b	40.07 N	75.08 W
Rotan, Tx. (rô-tăn')	122	32.51 N	100.27 W
Rothenburg, F.R.G.	166	49.20 N	10.10 E
Rotherham, Eng. (rŏdh'ẽr-ăm)	156	53.26 N	1.21 W
Rothesay, Can. (rôth'så)	104	45.23 N	66.00 W
Rothesay, Scot.	162	55.50 N	3.14 W
Roth-neusiedl (Neigh.), Aus.	66e	48.08 N	16.23 E
Rothwell, Eng.	156	53.44 N	1.30 W
Roti, Pulau (I.), Indon. (rō'tē)	206	10.30 S	122.52 E
Roto, Austl. (rō'tô)	216	33.07 S	145.30 E
Rotorua, N.Z.	217	38.07 S	176.17 E
Rotterdam, Neth. (rôt'ẽr-däm')	157a	51.55 N	4.27 E
Rottweil, F.R.G. (rōt'vīl)	166	48.10 N	8.36 E
Roubaix, Fr. (ro͞o-bĕ')	168	50.42 N	3.10 E
Rouen, Fr. (ro͞o-äN')	168	49.25 N	1.05 E
Rouge (R.), Can. (ro͞ozh)	95d	43.53 N	79.21 W
Rouge (R.), Can.	103	46.40 N	74.50 W
Rouge, R., Mi.	113b	42.30 N	83.15 W
Rough River Res., Ky.	110	37.45 N	86.10 W
Round Lake, Il.	113a	42.21 N	88.05 W
Round Pd., Can.	105	48.15 N	55.57 W
Round Rock, Tx.	125	30.31 N	97.41 W
Round Top (Mtn.), Or. (tŏp)	118c	45.41 N	123.22 W
Roundup, Mt. (round'ŭp)	117	46.25 N	108.35 W
Rousay (I.), Scot. (ro͞o'zå)	162a	59.10 N	3.04 W
Rouyn, Can. (ro͞on)	97	48.22 N	79.03 W
Rovaniemi, Fin. (rô'vá-nyĕ'mĭ)	158	66.29 N	25.45 E
Rovato, It. (rô-vä'tō)	172	45.33 N	10.00 E
Roven'ki, Sov. Un. (rô-vĕn'kĭ')	175	48.06 N	39.44 E
Roven'ki, Sov. Un.	175	49.54 N	38.54 E
Rovereto, It. (rō-vå-rā'tô)	172	45.53 N	11.05 E
Rovigo, It. (rô-vē'gô)	172	45.05 N	11.48 E
Rovinj, Yugo. (rô'ēn')	172	45.05 N	13.40 E
Rovira, Col. (rô-vē'rä)	142a	4.14 N	75.13 W
Rovno, Sov. Un. (rôv'nô)	167	50.37 N	26.17 E
Rovno (Oblast), Sov. Un.	175	50.55 N	27.00 E
Rovnoye, Sov. Un. (rôv'nô-yĕ)	175	48.11 N	31.46 E
Rovuma (Ruvuma) (R.), Moz.-Tan.	231	10.50 S	39.50 E
Rowland Heights, Ca.	59	33.59 N	117.54 W
Rowley, Ma. (rou'lē)	105a	42.43 N	70.53 W
Rowville, Austl.	70b	37.56 S	145.14 E
Roxana, Il. (rŏks'ăn-ná)	119e	38.51 N	90.05 W
Roxas, Phil. (rô-xäs)	206	11.30 N	122.47 E
Roxboro, Can.	54b	45.31 N	73.48 W
Roxboro, NC (rŏks' bŭr-ô)	127	36.22 N	78.58 W
Roxborough (Neigh.), Pa.	56b	40.02 N	75.13 W
Roxbury (Neigh.), NY	55	40.34 N	73.54 W
Roxo, Cap (C.), Senegal	228	12.20 N	16.43 W
Roy, NM (roi)	122	35.54 N	104.09 W
Roy, Ut.	119b	41.10 N	112.02 W
Royal (I.), Ba.	134	25.30 N	76.50 W
Royal Albert Hall (P. Int.), Eng.	62	51.30 N	0.11 W
Royal Can., Ire. (roi-ăl)	162	53.28 N	6.45 W
Royal Natal Natl. Pk., S. Afr. (roi'ăl)	227c	28.35 S	28.54 E
Royal Naval College (P. Int.), Eng.	62	51.29 N	0.01 W
Royal Oak, Can. (roi'ăl ōk)	118a	48.30 N	123.24 W
Royal Oak, Mi.	113b	42.29 N	83.09 W
Royal Oak Township, Mi.	57c	42.27 N	83.10 W
Royal Ontario Museum (P. Int.), Can.	54c	43.40 N	79.24 W
Royalton, Mi. (roi'ăl-tŭn)	110	42.00 N	86.25 W
Royan, Fr. (rwä-yäN')	168	45.40 N	1.02 W
Roye, Fr. (rwä)	168	49.43 N	2.40 E
Royersford, Pa. (rô' yẽrz-fẽrd)	112f	40.11 N	75.32 W
Royston, Ga. (roiz'tŭn)	126	34.15 N	83.06 W
Royton, Eng. (roi'tŭn)	156	53.34 N	2.07 W
Rozay-en-Brie, Fr. (rô-zā-ĕN-brē')	169b	48.41 N	2.57 E
Rozelle, Austl.	70a	33.52 S	151.10 E
Rozhaya R., Sov. Un. (rô'zhá-yá)	182b	55.20 N	37.37 E
Rožňava, Czech. (rôzh'nyá-vá)	167	48.39 N	20.32 E
Rtishchevo, Sov. Un. ('r-tĭsh'chĕ-vô)	179	52.15 N	43.40 E
Ru (R.), China (ro͞o)	200	33.07 N	114.18 E
Ruacana Falls, Ang.-Namibia	226	17.15 S	14.45 E
Ruaha Natl. Pk., Tan.	231	7.15 S	34.50 E
Ruapehu (Vol.), N.Z. (ro͞o-á-pā'ho͞o)	217	39.15 S	175.37 E
Rubeho Mts., Tan.	231	6.45 S	36.15 E
Rubidoux, Ca.	119a	33.59 N	117.24 W
Rubondo I., Tan.	231	2.10 S	31.55 E
Rubtsovsk, Sov. Un.	180	51.31 N	81.17 E
Ruby, Ak. (ro͞o'bē)	107	64.38 N	155.22 W
Ruby (L.), Nv.	120	40.11 N	115.20 W
Ruby Mts., Nv.	120	40.11 N	115.36 W
Ruby R., Mt.	117	45.06 N	112.10 W
Rüdersdorf, G.D.R.	65a	52.29 N	13.47 E
Rudge Ramos, Braz.	61d	23.41 S	46.34 W
Rüdinghausen (Neigh.), F.D.R.	63	51.27 N	7.25 E
Rudkøbing, Den. (ro͞odh'kûb-ĭng)	164	54.56 N	10.44 E
Rüdnitz, G.D.R. (rüd'nētz)	157b	52.44 N	13.38 E
Rudolf, L., Ken.-Eth. (ro͞o'dŏlf)	231	3.30 N	36.05 E
Rudolstadt, G.D.R. (ro͞o'dôl-shtät)	163	50.46 N	13.30 E
Rudow (Neigh.), F.R.G.	65a	52.25 N	13.30 E
Rueil-Malmaison, Fr.	64c	48.53 N	2.11 E
Rufā'ah, Sud. (ro͞o-fä'ä)	225	14.52 N	33.30 E
Ruffec, Fr. (rü-fĕk')	168	46.03 N	0.11 E
Rufiji (R.), Tan. (ro͞o-fē'jē)	231	8.00 S	39.20 E
Rufisque, Senegal (rü-fēsk')	228	14.43 N	17.17 W
Rufunsa, Zambia	231	15.05 S	29.40 E
Rufus Woods, Wa.	116	48.02 N	119.33 W
Rugao, China (ro͞o-gou)	200	32.24 N	120.33 E
Rugby, Eng. (rŭg'bē)	156	52.22 N	1.15 W
Rugby, ND	114	48.22 N	100.00 W
Rugeley, Eng. (ro͞oj'lē)	156	52.46 N	1.56 W
Rügen (Pen.), G.D.R. (rü'ghĕn)	166	54.28 N	13.47 E
Rüggeberg, F.R.G.	63	51.16 N	7.22 E
Ruhlsdorf, G.D.R.	65a	52.23 N	13.16 E
Ruhnu-Saar (I.), Sov. Un. (ro͞ono͞o-sâ'âr)	165	57.46 N	23.15 E
Ruhrort (Neigh.), F.R.G.	63	51.26 N	6.45 E
Ruhr R., F.R.G. (ro͞or)	166	51.18 N	8.17 E
Rui'an, China (rwā-än)	203	27.48 N	120.40 E
Ruislip (Neigh.), Eng.	62	51.34 N	0.25 W
Ruiz, Mex. (ro͞oē'z)	130	21.55 N	105.09 W
Ruiz, Nevado del (Pk.), Col. (nĕ-vá'dô-dĕl-ro͞oē'z)	142a	4.52 N	75.20 W
Rūjiena, Sov. Un. (ro͞o'yĭ-ā-nà)	165	57.54 N	25.19 E
Ruki (R.), Zaire	230	0.05 S	18.55 E
Rukwa, L., Tan. (ro͞ok-wä')	231	8.00 S	32.25 E
Rum (R.), Mn. (rŭm)	115	45.52 N	93.45 W
Ruma, Yugo. (ro͞o'má)	173	45.00 N	19.53 E
Rum'ancevo, Sov. Un.	66b	55.38 N	37.26 E
Rumbek, Sud. (rŭm'bĕk)	225	6.52 N	29.43 E
Rum Cay (I.), Ba.	135	23.40 N	74.50 W
Rumelihisari (Neigh.), Tur.	66f	41.05 N	29.03 E
Rumeln-Kaldenhausen, F.R.G.	63	51.24 N	6.40 E
Rumford, Me. (rŭm'fẽrd)	104	44.32 N	70.35 W
Rummah, Wādī ar (R.), Sau. Ar.	192	26.17 N	41.45 E
Rummānah, Egypt	191a	31.01 N	32.39 E
Rummelsburg (Neigh.)	65a	52.30 N	13.29 E
Rummenohl, F.R.G.	63	51.17 N	7.32 E
Runan, China (ro͞o-nän)	200	32.59 N	114.22 E
Runcorn, Eng. (rŭŋ'kôrn)	156	53.20 N	2.44 W
Runnemede, NJ	56b	39.51 N	75.04 W
Runnymede (P. Int.), Eng.	62	51.26 N	0.34 W
Ruo (R.), China (rwô)	198	41.15 N	100.46 E
Rupat, Palau (I.), Indon. (ro͞o'pät)	191b	1.55 N	101.35 E
Rupat, Selat (Str.), Indon.	191b	1.55 N	101.17 E
Rupert, Id. (ro͞o'pẽrt)	117	42.36 N	113.41 W
Rupert, Rivière de (R.), Can.	97	51.35 N	76.30 W
Rural Ridge, Pa.	57b	40.35 N	79.50 W
Ruse (Russe), Bul. (ro͞o'sĕ) (ro͞o'sĕ)	173	43.50 N	25.59 E
Rushan, China (ro͞o-shän)	200	36.54 N	121.31 E
Rush City, Mn.	115	45.40 N	92.59 W
Rusholme (Neigh.), Eng.	64b	53.27 N	2.12 W
Rushville, Il. (rŭsh'vĭl)	123	40.08 N	90.34 W
Rushville, In.	110	39.35 N	85.30 W
Rushville, Ne.	114	42.43 N	102.27 W
Rusizi (R.), Zaire	231	3.00 S	29.05 E
Rusk, Tx. (rŭsk)	125	31.49 N	95.09 W
Ruskin, Can. (rŭs'kĭn)	118d	49.10 N	122.25 W
Russ (R.), Aus.	157e	48.12 N	16.55 E
Russas, Braz. (ro͞o's-säs)	143	4.48 S	37.50 W
Russel L., Can.	101	56.15 N	101.30 W
Russell, Ca.	118b	37.39 N	122.08 W
Russell, Can. (rŭs'ĕl)	101	50.47 N	101.15 W
Russell, Can.	95c	45.15 N	75.22 W
Russell, Ks.	122	38.51 N	98.51 W
Russell, Ky.	110	38.30 N	82.45 W
Russell Gardens, NY	55	40.47 N	73.43 W
Russell Is., Sol. Is.	215	9.16 S	158.30 E
Russellville, Al. (rŭs'ĕl-vĭl)	126	34.29 N	87.44 W
Russellville, Ar.	123	35.16 N	93.08 W
Russelville, Ky.	126	36.48 N	86.51 W
Russe, see Ruse			
Russian (R.), Ca. (rŭsh'ăn)	120	38.59 N	123.10 W
Russian S. F. S. R., Sov. Un.	176	61.00 N	60.00 E
Rustenburg, S. Afr. (rŭs'tĕn-bûrg)	223d	25.40 S	26.15 E
Ruston, La. (rŭs'tŭn)	125	32.32 N	92.39 W
Ruston, Wa.	118a	47.18 N	122.30 W
Rusville, S. Afr.	71b	26.10 S	28.18 E
Rutchenkovo, Sov. Un. (ro͞o-chĕn'kô-vô)	175	47.54 N	37.36 E
Rute, Sp. (ro͞o'tā)	170	37.20 N	4.34 W
Ruth, Nv. (ro͞oth)	120	39.17 N	115.00 W
Ruthenia (Reg.), Sov. Un.	167	48.25 N	23.00 E
Rutherford, NJ	55	40.49 N	74.07 W
Rutherfordton, NC (rŭdh'ẽr-fẽrd-tŭn)	127	35.23 N	81.58 W
Rutland, Vt.	111	43.35 N	72.55 W
Rutledge, Md. (rŭt'lĕdj)	112e	39.34 N	76.33 W
Rutledge, Pa.	56b	39.54 N	75.20 W
Rutog, China (ro͞o-tô-gŭ)	196	33.42 N	79.56 E
Rutshuru, Zaire (ro͞ot-sho͞o'ro͞o)	231	1.11 S	29.27 E
Rüttenscheid (Neigh.), F.R.G.	63	51.26 N	7.00 E
Ruvo, It. (ro͞o'vô)	172	41.07 N	16.32 E
Ruvuma (Rovuma) (R.), Moz.-Tan.	231	10.50 S	39.50 E
Ruza, Sov. Un. (ro͞o'zá)	174	55.42 N	36.12 E
Ruzhany, Sov. Un. (ro͞o-zhän'ĭ)	167	52.49 N	24.54 E
Rwanda, Afr.	222	2.10 S	29.37 E
Ryabovo, Sov. Un. (ryä'bô-vô)	182c	59.24 N	31.08 E
Ryarsh, Eng.	62	51.19 N	0.24 E
Ryazan', Sov. Un. (ryä-zän'')	174	54.37 N	39.43 E
Ryazan' (Oblast), Sov. Un.	174	54.10 N	39.37 E
Ryazhsk, Sov. Un. (ryäzh'sk')	174	53.43 N	40.04 E
Rybachiy, P-Ov. (Pen.), Sov. Un.	178	69.50 N	33.20 E
Rybatskoye, see Andropov	182c	59.50 N	30.31 E
Rybinsk, see Andropov			
Rybinskoye Vdkhr. (Res.), Sov. Un.	174	58.23 N	38.15 E
Rybnik, Pol. (rĭb'nĕk)	167	50.06 N	18.37 E
Rybnitsa, Sov. Un. (rĭb'nĕt-sá)	175	47.45 N	29.02 E
Rydal, Pa.	56b	40.06 N	75.06 W
Rydalmere, Austl.	70a	33.49 S	151.02 E
Ryde, Austl.	70a	33.49 S	151.06 E
Ryde, Eng. (rīd)	162	50.43 N	1.16 W
Rye, NY (rī)	112a	40.58 N	73.42 W
Ryl'sk, Sov. Un. (rĕl''sk)	175	51.33 N	34.42 E
Rynfield, S. Afr.	71b	26.09 S	28.20 E
Ryōtsu, Jap. (ryōt'so͞o)	204	38.02 N	138.23 E
Rypin, Pol. (rĭ'pĕn)	167	53.04 N	19.25 E
Ryukyu, see Nansei-shotō			
Rzeszów, Pol. (zhå-sho͞of)	167	50.02 N	22.00 E
Rzhev, Sov. Un. ('r-zhĕf)	174	56.16 N	34.17 E
Rzhishchëv, Sov. Un. ('r-zhĭsh'chĕf)	175	49.58 N	31.05 E

S

PLACE (Pronounciation)	PAGE	Lat. °'	Long. °'
Saale R., G.D.R. (sä-lĕ)	166	51.14 N	11.52 E
Saalfeld, G.D.R. (säl'fĕlt)	166	50.38 N	11.20 E
Saarbrücken, F.R.G. (zähr'brü-kĕn)	166	49.15 N	7.01 E
Saaremaa (Ezel) (I.), Sov. Un. (sä'rĕ-mä)	165	58.28 N	21.30 E
Saarland (State), F.R.G.	166	49.25 N	6.50 E
Saarn (Neigh.), F.R.G.	63	51.24 N	6.53 E
Saarnberg (Neigh.), F.R.G.	63	51.25 N	6.53 E
Saavedra, Arg. (sä-ä-vā'drä)	144	37.45 S	62.23 W
Šabac, Yugo. (shä'bàts)	173	44.45 N	19.49 E
Sabadell, Sp. (sä-bä-dhål')	171	41.32 N	2.07 E
Sabah (Reg.), Mala.	206	5.10 N	116.25 E
Saba I., Neth. Antilles (sä'bä)	133b	17.39 N	63.20 W
Sabana, Arch. de, Cuba (är-chē-pyĕ'lä-gô dĕ sä-bä'nä)	134	23.05 N	80.00 W
Sabana de la Mar, Dom. Rep. (sä-bä'nä dā lä mär')	135	19.05 N	69.30 W
Sabana de Uchire, Ven. (sä-bä'nä dĕ o͞o-chē'rĕ)	143b	10.02 N	65.32 W
Sabanagrande, Hond. (sä-bä'nä-grä'n-dĕ)	132	13.47 N	87.16 W
Sabanalarga, Col. (sä-bá'nä-lär'gä)	142	10.38 N	75.02 W
Sabana, R., Pan. (sä-bä'nä)	133	8.40 N	78.02 W
Sabanas Páramo (Mtn.), Col. (sä-bá'näs pá'rä-mô)	142a	6.28 N	76.08 W
Sabancuy, Mex. (sä-bäŋ-kwē')	131	18.58 N	91.09 W
Sabang, Indon. (sä'bäng)	206	5.52 N	95.26 E
Sabaudia, It. (sá-bou'dē-ä)	174	41.19 N	13.00 E
Sabetha, Ks. (sá-bĕth'á)	123	39.54 N	95.49 W
Sabhā, Libya	194	27.03 S	14.26 E
Sabi (R.), Zimb. (sä'bē)	226	20.18 S	32.07 E
Sabile, Sov. Un. (sá'bē-lĕ)	165	57.03 N	22.34 E
Sabinal, Tx. (sá-bī'nál)	124	29.19 N	99.27 W
Sabinal, Cayo (I.), Cuba (kä'yō sä-bē-näl')	134	21.40 N	77.20 W
Sabinas, Mex.	128	28.05 N	102.30 W
Sabinas, R., Mex. (sä-bē'näs)	124	26.37 N	99.52 W
Sabinas, Rio (R.), **Mex.** (rē'ō sä-bē'näs)	124	27.25 N	100.33 W
Sabinas Hidalgo, Mex. (ē-däl'gō)	124	26.30 N	100.10 W
Sabine, Tx. (sá-bēn')	125	29.44 N	93.54 W
Sabine (R.), U.S.	109	31.35 N	94.00 W
Sabine L., La.-Tx.	125	29.53 N	93.41 W
Sabine, Mt., Ant.	232	72.05 S	169.10 E
Sablayan, Phil. (säb-lä-yän')	207a	12.49 N	120.47 E
Sable, C., Can. (sā'b'l)	104	43.25 N	65.24 W
Sable, C., Fl.	127a	25.12 N	81.10 W
Sables, Rivière aux (R.), Can.	103	49.00 N	70.20 W
Sablé-sur-Sarthe, Fr. (säb-lā-sür-särt')	168	47.50 N	0.17 W
Sablya, Gora (Mtn.), Sov. Un.	178	64.50 N	59.00 E
Sàbor (R.), Port. (sä-bōr')	170	41.18 N	6.54 W
Saburovo (Neigh.), Sov. Un.	66b	55.38 N	37.42 E
Sabzevār, Iran	195	36.13 N	57.42 E
Sac (R.), Mo. (sôk)	123	38.11 N	93.45 W
Sacandaga Res., NY (săk-ăn-dâ'gá)	111	43.10 N	74.15 W
Sacavém, Port. (sä-kä-vĕN')	171b	38.47 N	9.06 W
Sacavém (R.), Port.	165b	38.52 N	9.06 W
Sac City, Ia. (sŏk)	115	42.25 N	95.00 W
Sachigo L., Can. (săch'ĭ-gō)	101	53.49 N	92.08 W
Sachsen (Reg.), G.D.R. (zäK'sĕn)	166	50.45 N	12.17 E
Sacketts Harbor, NY (săk'ĕts)	111	43.55 N	76.05 W
Sackville, Can. (săk'vĭl)	104	45.54 N	64.22 W
Saco, Me. (sô'kô)	104	43.30 N	70.28 W
Saco (R.), Braz. (sä'kô)	144b	22.20 S	43.26 W
Saco (R.), Me.	104	43.53 N	70.46 W
Sacra Famalia do Tinguá, Braz. (sä-krä fä-mä'lyä dō tĕn-gwá')	144b	22.29 S	43.36 W
Sacramento, Ca. (săk-rá-mĕn'tō)	120	38.35 N	121.30 W
Sacramento, Mex.	124	25.45 N	103.22 W
Sacramento, Mex.	124	27.05 N	101.45 W
Sacramento (R.), Ca.	120	40.20 N	122.07 W
Sacré-Cœur (P. Int.), Fr.	64c	48.53 N	2.21 E
Sacrow (Neigh.), G.D.R.	65a	52.26 N	13.06 E
Şa'dah, Yemen	192	16.50 N	43.45 E
Saddle Brook, NJ	55	40.54 N	74.06 W
Saddle Lake Ind. Res., Can.	99	54.00 N	111.40 W
Saddle Mtn., Or. (săd''l)	118c	45.58 N	123.40 W
Saddle Rock, NY	55	40.48 N	73.45 W
Sadiya, India (sŭ-dē'yä)	193	27.53 N	95.35 E
Sado (I.), Jap. (sä'dō)	204	38.05 N	138.26 E
Sado (R.), Port. (sä'do͞o)	170	38.15 N	8.20 W
Saeby, Den. (sĕ'bü)	164	57.21 N	10.29 E
Saeki, Jap. (sä'å-kē)	205	32.56 N	131.51 E
Safdar Jang's Tomb (P. Int.), India	67d	28.36 N	77.13 E
Safford, Az. (săf'fẽrd)	121	32.50 N	109.45 W

PLACE (Pronounciation)	PAGE	Lat. °'	Long. °'
Safi (Asfi), Mor. (sä'fē) (äs'fē)	224	32.24 N	9.09 W
Safid Rud (R.), Iran	179	36.50 N	49.40 E
Saga, Jap. (sä'gä)	205	33.15 N	130.18 E
Sagamihara, Jap.	69a	35.32 N	139.23 E
Sagami-Nada (Sea), Jap. (sä'gä'mē nä-dä)	205	35.06 N	139.24 E
Sagamore Hills, Oh. (săg'ȧ-môr hĭlz)	113d	41.19 N	81.34 W
Saganaga (L.), Can.-Mn. (sä-gȧ-nä'gȧ)	115	48.13 N	91.17 W
Sāgar, India	196	23.55 N	78.45 E
Saguache Cr., Co.	111	38.05 N	106.40 W
Saginaw, Mi. (săg'ĭ-nô)	110	43.25 N	84.00 W
Saginaw, Mn.	119h	46.51 N	92.26 W
Saginaw, Tx.	119c	32.52 N	97.22 W
Saginaw B., Mi.	110	43.50 N	83.40 W
Sagiz (R.), Sov. Un. (sä'gēz)	179	48.30 N	56.10 E
Saguache, Co. (sȧ-wăch') (sȧ-gwä'chē)	111	38.05 N	106.10 W
Sagua de Tánamo, Cuba (sä-gwä dē tá'nä-mō)	135	20.40 N	75.15 W
Sagua la Grande, Cuba (sä-gwä lä grä'n-dě)	134	22.45 N	80.05 W
Saguaro Natl. Mon., Az. (säg-wä'rō)	121	32.12 N	110.40 W
Saguenay (R.), Can. (săg-ē-nā')	102	48.20 N	70.15 W
Sagunto, Sp. (sä-gōōn'tō)	171	39.40 N	0.17 W
Sahara Des., Afr. (sȧ-hä'rȧ)	222	23.44 N	1.40 W
Saharan Atlas (Mts.), Mor.-Alg.	160	32.51 N	1.02 W
Sahāranpur, India (sŭ-hä'rŭn-pōōr')	196	29.58 N	77.41 E
Sahara Village, Ut. (sȧ-hä'rȧ)	119b	41.06 N	111.58 W
Sāhiwāl, Pak.	196	30.43 N	73.04 E
Sahuayo de Dias, Mex.	130	20.03 N	102.43 W
Saigon, see Ho Chi Minh City			
Saijō, Jap. (sä'ē-jô)	205	33.55 N	133.13 E
Saimaa, Fin. (sä'ĭ-mä)	165	61.24 N	28.45 E
Sain Alto, Mex. (sä-ēn' äl'tō)	130	23.35 N	103.13 W
Saint Adolphe, Can. (sånt a'dŏlf) (săN' tȧ-dôlf')	95f	49.40 N	97.07 W
Saint Afrique, Fr. (săN' tȧ-frēk')	168	43.58 N	2.52 E
Saint Albans, Austl. (sånt ôl'bănz)	211a	37.44 S	144.47 E
Saint Albans, Eng.	156b	51.44 N	0.20 W
Saint Albans, Vt.	111	44.50 N	73.05 W
Saint Albans, WV	110	38.20 N	81.50 W
Saint Albans (Neigh.), NY	55	40.42 N	73.46 W
Saint Albans Cathedral (P. Int.), Eng.	62	51.45 N	0.20 W
Saint Albert, Can. (sånt ăl'bērt)	95g	53.38 N	113.38 W
Saint Amand-MontRond, Fr. (săN't ȧ-mäN' môN-rôN')	168	46.44 N	2.28 E
Saint André, Cap (C.), Mad.	227	16.15 S	44.31 E
Saint André-Est., Can.	95a	45.33 N	74.19 W
Saint Andrew, B., Fl.	126	30.20 N	85.45 W
Saint Andrews, Can.	104	45.05 N	67.03 W
Saint Andrews, Scot.	162	56.20 N	2.40 W
Saint Andrew's Chan., Can. (ăn'drōōz)	105	46.06 N	60.28 W
Saint Anicet, Can. (sěNt ä-nē-sě')	95a	45.07 N	74.23 W
Saint Ann, Mo. (sånt ăn')	119e	38.44 N	90.23 W
Saint Anne, Il.	113a	41.01 N	87.44 W
Saint Anne of the Congo (P. Int.), Con.	71c	4.16 S	15.17 E
Saint Anns B., Can. (ănz)	105	46.20 N	60.30 W
Saint Ann's Bay, Jam.	134	18.25 N	77.15 W
Saint Anselme, Can. (săN' täN-sělm')	95b	46.37 N	70.58 W
Saint Anthony, Can. (săN ăn'thô-nē)	105	51.24 N	55.35 W
Saint Anthony, Id. (sånt ăn'thō-nē)	117	43.59 N	111.42 W
Saint Antoine-de-Tilly, Can.	95b	46.00 N	71.31 W
Saint Apollinaire, Can. (săN' tȧ-pôl-ē-nâr')	95b	46.36 N	71.30 W
Saint Arnoult-en-Yvelines, Fr. (săN-tär-nōō'ěN-nēv-lēn')	169b	48.33 N	1.55 E
Saint Augustin-de-Québec, Can. (sěn tō-gūs-tēn')	95b	46.45 N	71.27 W
Saint Augustin-Deux-Montagnes, Can.	95a	45.38 N	73.59 W
Saint Augustine, Fl. (sånt ô'gŭs-tēn)	127	29.53 N	81.21 W
Saint Barthelemy I., Guad.	133b	17.55 N	62.32 W
Saint Bees Hd., Eng. (sånt bēz' hĕd)	162	54.30 N	3.40 W
Saint Benoit, Can. (sěN bě-nōō-ä')	95a	45.34 N	74.05 W
Saint Bernard, La. (bēr-närd')	112d	29.52 N	89.52 W
Saint Bernard, Oh.	113f	39.10 N	84.30 W
Saint-Brice-sous-Forêt, Fr.	64c	49.00 N	2.21 E
Saint Bride Mt., Can. (sånt brīd)	99	51.30 N	115.57 W
Saint Brieuc, Fr. (săN' brēs')	168	48.32 N	2.47 W
Saint Bruno, Can. (brū'nō)	95a	45.31 N	73.40 W
Saint Canut, Can. (săN' kȧ-nū')	95a	45.43 N	74.04 W
Saint Casimir, Can. (kȧ-zē-mēr')	104	46.45 N	72.34 W
Saint Catharines, Can. (kăth'ȧ-rĭnz)	95d	43.10 N	79.14 W
Saint Catherine, Mt., Grenada	133b	12.10 N	62.42 W
Saint Chamas, Fr. (săN-shä-mä')	168a	43.32 N	5.03 E
Saint Chamond, Fr. (săN' shȧ-môN')	168	45.30 N	4.17 E
Saint Charles, Can. (sånt shärlz')	95b	46.47 N	70.57 W
Saint Charles, Il. (sånt chärlz')	113a	41.55 N	88.19 W
Saint Charles, Mi.	110	43.20 N	84.10 W
Saint Charles, Mn.	115	43.56 N	92.05 W
Saint Charles, Mo.	119e	38.47 N	90.29 W
Saint Charles, Lac (L.), Can.	95b	46.56 N	71.21 W
Saint Christopher-Nevis, N.A.	129	17.24 N	63.30 W
Saint Christopher-Nevis (I.), Saint Christopher-Nevis	129	17.24 N	63.30 W
Saint Clair, Mi. (sånt klâr)	110	42.55 N	82.30 W
Saint Clair (L.), Can.-Mi.	110	42.25 N	82.30 W
Saint Clair (R.), Can.-Mi.	110	42.45 N	82.25 W
Saint Clair Shores, Mi.	113b	42.30 N	82.54 W
Saint Claude, Fr. (săN' klōd')	169	46.24 N	5.53 E
Saint Clet, Can. (săNt' klā')	95a	45.22 N	74.21 W
Saint Cloud, Fl. (sånt kloud')	127a	28.13 N	81.17 W
Saint-Cloud, Fr.	64c	48.51 N	2.13 E
Saint Cloud, Mn.	115	45.33 N	94.08 W
Saint Constant, Can. (kōn'stȧnt)	95a	45.23 N	73.34 W
Saint Croix (I.), Vir. Is. (U.S.A.) (sånt kroi')	129b	17.40 N	64.43 W
Saint Croix (R.), Can.-Me. (kroi')	104	45.28 N	67.32 W
Saint Croix I., S. Afr. (săN krwă)	227c	33.48 S	25.45 E
Saint Croix Ind. Res., Wi.	115	45.40 N	92.21 W
Saint Croix R., Mn.-Wi. (sånt kroi')	115	45.00 N	92.44 W
Saint-Cyr-l'Ecole, Fr.	64c	48.48 N	2.04 E
Saint Damien-de-Buckland, Can. (sånt dā'mē-ĕn)	95b	46.37 N	70.39 W
Saint David, Can. (dā'vĭd)	95b	46.47 N	71.11 W
Saint Davids, Pa.	56b	40.02 N	75.22 W
Saint David's Hd., Wales	162	51.54 N	5.25 W
Saint-Denis, Fr. (săN'dē-nē')	169b	48.26 N	2.22 E
Saint Dié, Fr. (dē-ā')	169	48.18 N	6.55 E
Saint Dizier, Fr. (dē-zyā')	168	48.49 N	4.55 E
Saint Dominique, Can. (sěN dō-mē-nēk')	95a	45.19 N	74.09 W
Sainte Anne, Can. (săNt'ȧn') (sånt ăn')	104	46.55 N	71.46 W
Sainte Anne, Guad.	133b	16.15 N	61.23 W
Sainte-Anne (R.), Can.	95b	47.07 N	70.50 W
Sainte Anne-de-Beaupré, Can. (dē bō-prā')	95b	47.02 N	70.56 W
Sainte Anne-des-Plaines, Can. (dā plěN)	95a	45.46 N	73.49 W
Sainte Barbe, Can. (sånt bärb')	95a	45.14 N	74.12 W
Sainte Claire, Can.	95b	46.36 N	70.52 W
Sainte-Dorothée (Neigh.), Can.	54b	45.32 N	73.49 W
Saint Edouard-de-Napierville, Can. (sěN-tē-dōō-är')	95a	45.14 N	73.31 W
Sainte Euphémie, Can. (sěNt û-fē-mē')	95b	46.47 N	70.27 W
Sainte Famille, Can. (săN't fȧ-mē'y')	95b	46.58 N	70.58 W
Sainte Felicite, Can.	104	48.54 N	67.20 W
Sainte Foy, Can. (săNt fwä)	95b	46.47 N	71.18 W
Sainte-Geneviève, Can.	54b	45.29 N	73.52 W
Sainte Genevieve, Mo. (sånt jĕn'ē-vēv)	123	37.58 N	90.02 W
Sainte-Hélène, Île (I.), Can.	54b	45.31 N	73.32 W
Sainte Justine-de-Newton, Can. (sånt jūs-tēn')	95a	45.22 N	74.22 W
Saint Elias, Mt., Can. (sånt ē-lī'ȧs)	107	60.25 N	141.00 W
Sainte-Marie-aux-Mines, Fr. (săN'tē-mä-rē'ō-mēn')	169	48.14 N	7.08 E
Sainte Marie-Beauce, Can. (săNt'mȧ-rē')	104	46.27 N	71.03 W
Sainte Marie, Cap (C.), Mad.	227	25.31 S	45.00 E
Sainte Martine, Can.	95a	45.14 N	73.37 W
Sainte Pétronille, Can. (sěNt pět-rō-nēl')	95b	46.51 N	71.08 W
Sainte Rose, Guad.	133b	16.19 N	61.45 W
Sainte-Rose (Neigh.), Can.	54b	45.36 N	73.47 W
Saintes, Fr.	168	45.44 N	0.41 W
Sainte Scholastique, Can. (skô-lȧs-tēk')	95a	45.39 N	74.05 W
Saint Étienne, Fr.	168	45.26 N	4.22 E
Saint Etienne-de-Lauzon, Can. (săN' tā-tyĕn')	95b	46.39 N	71.19 W
Saint Eustache, Can. (săN' tû-stȧsh')	95a	45.34 N	73.54 W
Saint Eustache, Can.	95f	49.58 N	97.47 W
Saint Eustatius I., Neth. Antilles (sånt u-stā'shŭs)	133b	17.32 N	62.45 W
Saint Félicien, Can. (săN fā-lē-syăN')	105	48.39 N	72.28 W
Saint Féréol, Can. (fa-rā-ôl')	95b	47.07 N	70.52 W
Saint Florent-sur-Cher, Fr. (săN' flō-räN'sür-shâr')	168	46.58 N	2.15 E
Saint Flour, Fr. (săN flōōr')	168	45.02 N	3.09 E
Saint Francis L., Can. (săN frăn'sĭs)	111	45.00 N	74.20 W
Saint Francis (R.), Ar.	123	35.56 N	90.27 W
Saint François, Can. (săN'fräN-swä')	95b	47.01 N	70.49 W
Saint François de Boundji, Con.	223	1.03 S	15.22 E
Saint Francois Xavier, Can.	95f	49.55 N	97.32 W
Saint Gaudens, Fr. (gō-dăNs')	168	43.07 N	0.43 E
Saint George, Austl. (sånt jôrj')	216	28.02 S	148.40 E
Saint George, Can. (săN jôrj')	104	45.08 N	66.49 W
Saint George, Can. (săN'zhôrzh')	95d	43.14 N	80.15 W
Saint George, SC (sånt jôrj')	127	33.11 N	80.35 W
Saint George, Ut.	121	37.05 N	113.40 W
Saint George, C., Can.	105	48.28 N	59.15 W
Saint George, C., Fl.	126	29.30 N	85.20 W
Saint George (I.), Ak.	107	56.30 N	169.40 W
Saint George (Neigh.), NY	55	40.39 N	74.05 W
Saint George's, Can. (jôrj'ĕs)	105	48.26 N	58.29 W
Saint Georges, Fr. Gu.	143	3.48 N	51.47 W
Saint Georges, Grenada	133b	12.02 N	61.57 W
Saint Georges B., Can.	105	45.49 N	61.45 W
Saint George's B., Can.	105	48.20 N	59.00 W
Saint George's Chan., Eng.-Ire. (jôr-jĕz)	162	51.45 N	6.30 W
Saint Germain-en-Laye, Fr. (săN' zhěr-măN-äN-lā')	169b	48.53 N	2.05 E
Saint Gervais, Can. (zhěr-vě')	95b	46.43 N	70.53 W
Saint Girons, Fr. (zhē-rôN')	168	42.58 N	1.08 E
Saint-Gratien, Fr.	64c	48.58 N	2.17 E
Saint Gregory, Mt., Can. (sånt grĕg'ēr-ē)	105	49.19 N	58.13 W
Saint Helena, Atl. O.	222	16.01 S	5.16 W
Saint Helenabaai (B.), Afr.	226	32.25 S	17.15 E
Saint Helens, Eng. (sånt hěl'ěnz)	156	53.27 N	2.44 W
Saint Helens, Or. (hěl'ěnz)	118c	45.52 N	122.49 W
Saint Helens, Mt., Wa.	116	46.13 N	122.10 W
Saint Helier, Jersey (hyěl'yēr)	168	49.12 N	2.06 W
Saint Henri, Can. (săN' hěn'rē)	95b	46.41 N	71.04 W
Saint Hubert, Can.	95a	45.29 N	73.24 W
Saint Hyacinthe, Can. (săN' tē-ä-săNt') (sånt hī'ȧ-sĭnth)	111	45.35 N	72.55 W
Saint-Ignace, Can.	104	46.42 N	70.30 W
Saint Ignace, Mi. (sånt ĭg'nȧs)	115	45.51 N	84.39 W
Saint Ignace (I.), Can. (săN' ĭg'nȧs)	115	48.47 N	88.14 W
Saint Irenee, Can. (săN' tē-rā-nā')	104	47.34 N	70.15 W
Saint Isidore-de-Laprairie, Can. (săN' tē-zē-dōr') (sånt ĭz'ĭ-dôr)	95a	45.18 N	73.41 W
Saint Isidore-de-Prescott, Can. (săN' ĭz'ĭ-dôr-prěs-kŏt)	95c	45.23 N	74.54 W
Saint Isidore-Dorchester, Can. (dôr-chěs'tēr)	95b	46.35 N	71.05 W
Saint Ives, Austl.	70a	33.44 S	151.10 E
Saint Jacob, Il. (jā-kŏb)	119e	38.43 N	89.46 W
Saint James, Mn. (sånt jāmz')	115	43.58 N	94.37 W
Saint James, Mo.	113	37.59 N	91.37 W
Saint James, C., Can.	98	51.58 N	131.00 W
Saint Janvier, Can. (săN' zhän-vyā')	95a	45.43 N	73.56 W
Saint Jean, Can. (săN' zhäN')	111	45.20 N	73.15 W
Saint Jean, Can.	95b	46.55 N	70.54 W
Saint Jean-Chrysostome, Can. (krĭ-zōs-tōm')	95b	46.43 N	71.12 W
Saint Jean-d'Angely, Fr. (däN-zhå-lē')	168	45.56 N	0.33 W
Saint Jean-de-Luz, Fr. (dē lūz')	168	43.23 N	1.40 W
Saint Jean, Lac (L.), Can.	103	48.35 N	72.00 W
Saint Jérôme, Can. (sånt jě-rōm') (săN zhā-rōm')	95a	45.47 N	74.00 W
Saint Joachim-de-Montmorency, Can. (sånt jō'ȧ-kĭm)	95b	47.04 N	70.51 W
Saint John, Can. (sånt jŏn)	104	45.16 N	66.03 W
Saint John, In.	113a	41.27 N	87.29 W
Saint John, Ks.	122	37.59 N	98.44 W
Saint John, ND	114	48.57 N	99.42 W
Saint John B., Can.	105	50.54 N	57.08 W
Saint John, C., Can.	105	50.00 N	55.32 W
Saint John I., Can.	105	50.49 N	57.14 W
Saint John (I.), Vir. Is. (U.S.A.)	129b	18.16 N	64.48 W
Saint John (R.), Can.	104	46.39 N	67.40 W
Saint John (R.), N.A.	97	45.15 N	67.40 W
Saint Johns, Antigua	133b	17.07 N	61.50 W
Saint Johns, Az. (jŏnz)	121	34.30 N	109.25 W
Saint John's, Can. (jŏns)	105	47.34 N	52.43 W
Saint Johns, Mi.	110	43.05 N	84.35 W
Saint Johns (R.), Fl.	127	29.54 N	81.32 W
Saint Johnsburg, NY	57a	43.05 N	78.53 W
Saint Johnsbury, Vt. (jŏnz'bĕr-ē)	111	44.25 N	72.00 W
Saint John's University (P. Int.), NY	55	40.43 N	73.48 W
Saint Joseph, Can. (jō'zhûf)	104	46.17 N	70.52 W
Saint Joseph, Dominica	133b	15.25 N	61.26 W
Saint Joseph, Mi.	110	42.05 N	86.30 W
Saint Joseph, Mo. (sånt jō-sěf)	123	39.44 N	94.49 W
Saint Joseph (I.), Can.	110	46.15 N	83.55 W
Saint Joseph (L.), Can. (jō'zhûf)	97	51.31 N	90.40 W
Saint Joseph (R.), Mi. (sånt jō'sěf)	110	41.45 N	85.50 W
Saint Joseph, B., Fl. (jō'zhûf)	126	29.48 N	85.26 W
Saint Joseph-de-Beauce, Can. (sěN zhō-zěf'dē bōs)	103	46.18 N	70.52 W
Saint Joseph-du-Lac, Can. (sěN zhō-zěf' dü läk)	95a	45.32 N	74.00 W
Saint Joseph I., Tx. (sånt jō-sěf)	125	27.58 N	96.50 W
Saint Junien, Fr. (săN'zhü-nyăN')	168	45.53 N	0.54 E
Saint Kilda, Austl.	70b	37.52 S	144.59 E
Saint Kilda (I.), Scot. (kĭl'dȧ)	162	57.10 N	8.32 W
Saint Kitts (I.), Saint Kitts-Nevis (sånt kĭtts)	129	17.24 N	63.30 W
Saint Lambert, Can. (săN' läN-běr') (sånt lăm'bērt)	95a	45.29 N	73.29 W
Saint Lambert-de-Lévis, Can.	95b	46.35 N	71.12 W
Saint Laurent, Can. (săN'lō-rän)	95a	45.31 N	73.41 W
Saint Laurent, Fr. Gu.	143	5.27 N	53.56 W
Saint Laurent-d'Orleans, Can.	95b	46.52 N	71.00 W
Saint Lawrence, Can. (sånt lô'rěns)	105	46.55 N	55.23 W
Saint Lawrence (I.), Ak. (sånt lô'rěns)	107	63.10 N	172.12 W
Saint Lawrence, Gulf of, Can.	105	48.00 N	62.00 W
Saint Lawrence R. (Fleuve Saint-Laurent), Can.-U.S.	97	48.24 N	69.30 W
Saint Lazare, Can. (săN'lȧ-zár')	95b	46.39 N	70.48 W
Saint Lazare-de-Vaudreuil, Can.	95a	45.24 N	74.08 W
Saint Léger-en-Yvelines, Fr. (săN-lā-zhē'ěN-nēv-lēn')	169b	48.43 N	1.45 E
Saint Leonard, Can. (sånt lěn'ȧrd)	104	47.10 N	67.56 W
Saint Léonard, Can.	95a	45.36 N	73.35 W
Saint Leonard, Md.	112e	38.29 N	76.31 W
Saint-Lô, Fr. (săN'lō')	168	49.08 N	1.07 W
Saint Louis, Mi. (sånt lōō'ĭs)	110	43.25 N	84.35 W
Saint Louis, Mo. (sånt lōō'ĭs) (lōō'ē)	119e	38.39 N	90.15 W
Saint-Louis, Senegal	228	16.02 N	16.30 W
Saint Louis (R.), Mn. (sånt lōō'ĭs)	115	46.57 N	92.58 W
Saint Louis-de-Gonzague, Can. (săN' lōō ē')	95a	45.13 N	74.00 W
Saint Louis, Lac (L.), Can. (săN' lōō ē')	95a	45.24 N	73.51 W
Saint Louis Park, Mn.	119g	44.56 N	93.21 W
Saint Lucia, N. A.	129	13.54 N	60.40 W
Saint Lucia Chan., N. A. (lū'shĭ-ȧ)	133b	14.15 N	61.00 W
Saint Lucie Can., Fl. (lū'sē)	127a	26.57 N	80.25 W
Saint Magnus B., Scot. (măg'nŭs)	162a	60.25 N	2.09 W
Saint Malo, Fr. (săN' mȧ-lō')	168	48.40 N	2.02 W
Saint Malo, Golfe de (G.), Fr. (gôlf-dē-săN-mä-lō')	168	48.50 N	2.49 W
Saint-Mandé, Fr.	64c	48.50 N	2.25 E
Saint Marc, Hai. (săN' mȧrk')	135	19.10 N	72.40 W
Saint-Marc, Canal de (Chan.), Hai.	135	19.05 N	73.15 W
Saint Marcellin, Fr. (mär-sē-lăN')	169	45.08 N	5.15 E
Saint Margarets, Md.	112e	39.02 N	76.30 W
Saint Maries, Id. (sånt mā'rēs)	116	47.18 N	116.34 W
Saint Martin I., Guad.-Neth-Antilles (mär'tĭn)	133b	18.06 N	62.54 W
Saint Martins, Can. (mär'tĭnz)	104	45.21 N	65.32 W
Saint Martinville, La. (mär'tĭn-vĭl)	125	30.08 N	91.50 W
Saint Mary, C., Gam.	228	13.28 N	16.40 W
Saint Mary (R.), Can. (mā'rē)	99	49.25 N	113.00 W
Saint Mary (Res.), Can.	99	49.30 N	113.00 W
Saint Mary Cray (Neigh.), Eng.	62	51.23 N	0.07 E
Saint Marylebone (Neigh.), Eng.	62	51.31 N	0.10 W
Saint Marys, Austl. (mā'rēz)	216	41.40 S	148.10 E
Saint Marys, Austl.	70a	33.47 S	150.47 E
Saint Marys, Can.	110	43.15 N	81.10 W
Saint Marys, Ga.	127	30.43 N	81.35 W
Saint Mary's, Ks.	123	39.12 N	96.03 W

PLACE (Pronounciation)	PAGE	Lat. °'	Long. °'
Saint Mary's, Oh.	110	40.30 N	84.25 W
Saint Marys, Pa.	111	41.25 N	78.30 W
Saint Marys, WV	110	39.20 N	81.15 W
Saint Mary's B., Can.	104	44.20 N	66.10 W
Saint Mary's B., Can.	105	46.50 N	53.47 W
Saint Marys Is., Can.	105	50.19 N	59.17 W
Saint Marys R., Can.-U.S.	119k	46.27 N	84.33 W
Saint Marys (R.), Ga.-Fl.	127	30.37 N	82.05 W
Saint Mathew, SC (măth'ū)	127	33.40 N	80.46 W
Saint Matthew (I.), Ak.	107	60.25 N	172.10 W
Saint Matthews, Ky. (măth'ūz)	113h	38.15 N	85.39 W
Saint Maur-des-Fossés, Fr.	169b	48.48 N	2.29 E
Saint-Maurice, Fr.	64c	48.49 N	2.25 E
Saint Maurice (R.), Can. (săN' mō-rēs') (sånt mô'rĭs)	104	47.20 N	72.55 W
Saint-Mesmes, Fr.	64c	48.59 N	2.42 E
Saint Michael, Ak. (sånt mī'kĕl)	107	63.22 N	162.20 W
Saint Michel, Can. (săN'mē-shĕl')	95b	46.52 N	70.54 W
Saint-Michel, Can.	54b	45.35 N	73.35 W
Saint Michel-de-l'Atalaye, Hai.	135	19.25 N	72.20 W
Saint Michel-de-Napierville, Can.	95a	45.14 N	73.34 W
Saint Mihiel, Fr. (săN' mē-yĕl')	169	48.53 N	5.30 E
Saint Moritz, Switz. (sånt mō'rĭts) (zăŋkt mō'rēts)	166	46.31 N	9.50 E
Saint Nazaire, Fr. (săN'nà-zâr')	168	47.18 N	2.13 W
Saint Nérée, Can. (nā-rā')	95b	46.43 N	70.43 W
Saint Nicolas, Can. (ne-kô-lä')	95b	46.42 N	71.32 W
Saint Nicolas, Cap (C.), Hai.	135	19.45 N	73.35 W
Saint-Nom-la-Bretèche, Fr.	64c	48.51 N	2.01 E
Saint Omer, Fr. (săN'tô-mâr')	168	50.44 N	2.16 E
Saint-Ouen, Fr.	64c	48.54 N	2.20 E
Saint Pancras (Neigh.), Eng.	62	51.32 N	0.07 W
Saint Pascal, Can. (sĕN pă-skăl')	104	47.32 N	69.48 W
Saint Paul, Can. (sånt pôl')	99	53.59 N	111.17 W
Saint Paul, Mn.	119g	44.57 N	93.05 W
Saint Paul, Ne.	114	41.13 N	98.28 W
Saint Paul (I.), Ak.	107	57.10 N	170.20 W
Saint Paul (R.), Lib.	228	7.10 N	10.00 W
Saint Paul I, Can.	105	47.15 N	60.10 W
Saint Paul, Île (I.), Ind. O.	232	38.43 S	77.31 E
Saint Paul Park, Mn. (pärk)	119g	44.51 N	93.00 W
Saint Pauls, NC (pôls)	127	34.47 N	78.57 W
Saint Paul's Cathedral (P. Int.), Eng.	62	51.31 N	0.06 W
Saint Paul's Cray (Neigh.), Eng.	62	51.24 N	0.07 E
Saint Peter, Mn. (pē tēr)	115	44.20 N	93.56 W
Saint Peter Port, Guernsey	168	49.27 N	2.35 W
Saint Petersburg, Fl. (pē'tērz-bûrg)	127a	27.47 N	82.38 W
Saint Philémon, Can. (sĕN fēl-mōN')	95b	46.41 N	70.28 W
Saint Philippe-d'Argenteuil, Can. (săN'fe-lēp')	95a	45.20 N	73.28 W
Saint Philippe-de-Lapairie, Can.	95a	45.38 N	74.25 W
Saint-Pierre, Can.	54b	45.27 N	73.39 W
Saint Pierre, Mart. (săN'pyâr')	133b	14.45 N	61.12 W
Saint Pierre (I.), Saint Pierre & Miquelon	105	46.47 N	56.11 W
Saint Pierre-d'Orléans, Can.	95b	46.53 N	71.04 W
Saint Pierre, Lac (L.), Can.	104	46.07 N	72.45 W
Saint Pierre & Miquelon, N. A.	105	46.53 N	56.40 W
Saint Pierre-Montmagny, Can.	95b	46.55 N	70.37 W
Saint Placide, Can. (plås'ĭd)	95a	45.32 N	74.11 W
Saint Pol-de-Léon, Fr. (săN-pô'dĕ-lā-ôN')	168	48.41 N	4.00 W
Saint Pölten, Aus. (zăŋkt-pûl'tĕn)	166	48.12 N	15.38 E
Saint-Prix, Fr.	64c	49.01 N	2.16 E
Saint Quentin, Fr. (săN'kăN-tăN')	168	49.52 N	3.16 E
Saint Raphaël, Can. (rä-fà-él')	95b	46.48 N	70.46 W
Saint Raymond, Can. (săN' rā-môN') (sånt rā'mŭnd)	104	46.50 N	71.51 W
Saint Rédempteur, Can. (săN rā-dăNp-tûr')	95b	46.42 N	71.18 W
Saint Rémi, Can. (sĕN rē-mē')	95a	45.15 N	73.36 W
Saint-Rémy-lès-Chevreuse, Fr.	64c	48.42 N	2.04 E
Saint Romuald-d'Etchemin, Can. (sĕN rō'mōō-äl)	95b	46.45 N	71.14 W
Saint Siméon, Can.	104	47.51 N	69.55 W
Saint Stanislas-de-Kostka, Can. (sĕN stä-nēs-läz' dĕ kōst'kä)	95a	45.11 N	74.08 W
Saint Stephen, Can. (stē'vĕn)	104	45.12 N	66.17 W
Saint Sulpice, Can.	95a	45.50 N	73.21 W
Saint Thérèse-de-Blainville, Can. (tĕ-rĕz' dĕ blĕN-vēl')	95a	45.38 N	73.51 W
Saint-Thibault-des-Vignes, Fr.	64c	48.52 N	2.41 E
Saint Thomas, Can. (tŏm'ăs)	110	42.45 N	81.15 W
Saint Thomas (I.), Vir. Is. (U.S.A.)	129c	18.22 N	64.57 W
Saint Thomas Hbr., Vir. Is. (U.S.A.) (tŏm'ăs)	129c	18.19 N	64.56 W
Saint Thomas, see Charlotte Amalie			
Saint Timothée, Can. (tē-mô-tā')	95a	45.17 N	74.03 W
Saint Tropez, Fr. (trô-pē')	169	43.15 N	6.42 E
Saint Valentin, Can. (văl-ĕn-tīn)	95a	45.07 N	73.19 W
Saint Valéry-sur-Somme, Fr. (vá-lā-rē')	168	50.10 N	1.39 E
Saint Vallier, Can. (väl-yā')	95b	46.54 N	70.49 W
Saint Veit, Aus. (zăŋkt vīt')	166	46.46 N	14.20 E
Saint Victor, Can. (vĭk'tēr)	104	46.09 N	70.56 W
Saint Vincent and the Grenadines, N. A.	129	13.20 N	60.50 W
Saint-Vincent-de-Paul (Neigh.) Can.	54b	45.37 N	73.39 W
Saint Vincent, G., Austl. (vĭn'sĕnt)	216	34.55 S	138.00 E
Saint Vincent Pass, N. A.	133b	13.35 N	61.10 W
Saint Walburg, Can.	100	53.39 N	109.12 W
Saint Yrieix-la-Perche, Fr. (ē-rē-ĕ)	168	45.30 N	1.08 E
Saitama (Pref.), Jap. (sī'tä-mä)	205a	35.52 N	139.40 E
Saitbaba, Sov. Un. (sá-ēt'bá-bà)	182a	54.06 N	56.42 E
Saïda, Alg. (sä'ē-dä)	224	34.51 N	00.07 E
Sajama, Nevada (Pk.), Bol. (nĕ-vá'dä-sä-hä'mä)	142	18.13 S	68.53 W
Sakai, Jap. (sä'kä-ē)	205b	34.34 N	135.28 E
Sakaiminato, Jap.	205	35.33 N	133.15 E
Sakākah, Sau. Ar.	192	29.58 N	40.03 E
Sakakawea, Lake, ND	114	47.49 N	101.58 W
Sakania, Zaire (sá-kä'nĭ-á)	231	12.45 S	28.34 E

PLACE (Pronounciation)	PAGE	Lat. °'	Long. °'
Sakarya (R.), Tur. (sá-kär'yá)	179	40.10 N	31.00 E
Sakata, Jap. (sä'kä-tä)	204	38.56 N	139.57 E
Sakchu, Kor. (säk'chōō)	204	40.29 N	125.09 E
Sakhalin (I.), Sov. Un. (sá-ká-lēn')	181	51.52 N	144.15 E
Sakiai, Sov. Un. (shä'kĭ-ī)	165	54.59 N	23.05 E
Sakishima-Gunto (Is.), Jap. (sä'kē-shē'ma gōōn'tō')	203	24.25 N	125.00 E
Sakmara (R.), Sov. Un.	179	52.00 N	56.10 E
Sakomet R., RI (sä-kō'mĕt)	112b	41.32 N	71.11 W
Sakurai, Jap.	205b	34.31 N	135.51 E
Sakwaso L., Can. (sá-kwá'sō)	101	53.01 N	91.55 W
Sal (R.), Sov. Un. (sál)	179	47.20 N	42.10 E
Sala, Swe. (sô'lä)	164	59.56 N	16.34 E
Sala Consilina, It. (sä'lä kôn-sē-lē'nä)	172	40.24 N	15.38 E
Salada, Laguna (L.), Mex. (lä-gōō'nä-sä-lä'dä)	120	32.34 N	115.45 W
Saladillo, Arg. (sä-lä-dēl'yô)	141c	35.38 S	59.48 W
Salado, Hong. (sä-lä'dhō)	132	15.44 N	87.03 W
Salado (R.), Arg. (sä-lä'dô)	144	26.05 S	63.35 W
Salado (R.), Arg.	141c	35.53 S	58.12 W
Salado (R.), Mex. (sä-lä'dô)	131	18.30 N	97.29 W
Salado Cr., Tx.	119d	29.23 N	98.25 W
Salado de los Nadadores Rio (R.), Mex. (dĕ-lôs-nä-dä-dô'rĕs)	124	27.26 N	101.35 W
Salado, Rio (R.), Mex. (rē'ō)	124	26.55 N	99.36 W
Salal, Chad	229	14.51 N	17.13 E
Salamá, Guat. (sä-lä'mä)	132	15.06 N	90.19 W
Salamá, Hond. (sä-lä-má')	132	14.43 N	86.30 W
Salamanca, Chile (sä-lä-mä'n-kä)	141b	31.48 S	70.57 W
Salamanca, Mex.	130	20.36 N	101.10 W
Salamanca, NY (sál-à-măŋ'kà)	111	42.10 N	78.45 W
Salamanca, Sp. (sä-lä-mä'n-kà)	170	40.54 N	5.42 W
Salamat, Bahr (R.), Chad. (bär sä-lä-mät')	225	10.06 N	19.16 E
Salamina, Col. (sä-lä-mē'-nä)	142a	5.25 N	75.29 W
Salamis, Grc. (săl'á-mĭs)	173	37.58 N	23.30 E
Salat-la-Canada, Fr.	168	44.52 N	1.13 E
Salaverry, Peru (sä-lä-vă'rē)	142	8.16 S	78.54 W
Salawati (I.), Indon. (sä-lä-wä'tē)	207	1.22 N	130.15 E
Salawe, Tan.	231	3.19 S	32.52 E
Sala-y-Gómez I. Chile	209	26.50 S	105.50 W
Sal, Cay (I.), Ba. (kē sål)	134	23.45 N	80.25 W
Salcedo, Dom. Rep. (säl-sä'dō)	135	19.25 N	70.30 W
Saldaña (R.), Col. (säl-dá'n-yä)	142a	3.42 N	75.16 W
Saldanha, S. Afr.	226	32.55 S	18.05 E
Saldus, Sov. Un. (sál'dōōs)	165	56.39 N	22.30 E
Sale, Austl. (sāl)	216	38.10 S	147.07 E
Sale, Eng.	156	53.24 N	2.20 W
Salé, Mor. (sá-lā')	224	34.09 N	6.42 W
Sale (R.), Can. (sál'rē-vyâr')	95f	49.44 N	97.11 W
Salekhard, Sov. Un. (sŭ-lyĭ-kärt)	178	66.35 N	66.50 E
Salem, Il. (sā'lĕm)	110	38.40 N	89.00 W
Salem, India	197	11.39 N	78.11 E
Salem, In.	110	38.35 N	86.00 W
Salem, Ma.	105a	42.31 N	70.54 W
Salem, Mo.	123	37.36 N	91.33 W
Salem, NH	105a	42.46 N	71.16 W
Salem, NJ	111	39.35 N	75.30 W
Salem, Oh.	110	40.55 N	80.50 W
Salem, Or.	116	44.55 N	123.03 W
Salem, S. Afr.	227c	33.29 S	26.30 E
Salem, SD	114	43.43 N	97.23 W
Salem, Va.	127	37.16 N	80.05 W
Salem, WV	110	39.15 N	80.35 W
Salemi, It. (sä-lĕ'mē)	172	37.49 N	12.48 E
Salerno, It. (sä-lĕr'nô)	171c	40.27 N	14.46 E
Salerno, Golfo di (G.), It. (gôl-fô-dē)	172	40.30 N	14.40 E
Salford, Eng. (săl'fērd)	156	53.26 N	2.19 W
Salgir (R.), Sov. Un. (sál'gĕr)	175	45.25 N	34.22 E
Salgótarján, Hung. (shôl'gô-tôr-yän)	167	48.06 N	19.50 E
Sal. I., C. V. Is. (säal)	224b	16.45 N	22.39 W
Salida, Co. (sá-lī'dá)	122	38.31 N	106.01 W
Salies-de-Béan, Fr.	168	43.27 N	0.58 W
Salima, Malawi	231	13.47 S	34.26 E
Salina (I.), It. (sä-lē'nä)	172	38.35 N	14.48 E
Salina, Ks. (sá-lī'ná)	123	38.50 N	97.37 W
Salina, Ut.	121	39.00 N	111.55 W
Salina Cruz, Mex. (sä-lē'nä krōōz')	131	16.10 N	95.12 W
Salina Pt., Ba.	135	22.10 N	74.20 W
Salinas, Ca. (sá-lē'nás)	120	36.41 N	121.40 W
Salinas, Mex.	130	22.38 N	101.42 W
Salinas, P. R.	129b	17.58 N	66.16 W
Salinas (R.), Ca.	120	36.33 N	121.29 W
Salinas (R.), Mex. (sä-lē'näs)	131	16.15 N	90.31 W
Salinas, Bahia de (B.), Nic.-C. R. (bä-ē'ä-dĕ-sá-lē'nás)	132	11.05 N	85.55 W
Salinas, Cape, Sp. (sä-lēnäs)	171	39.14 N	1.02 E
Salinas Victoria, Mex. (sä-lē'näs vēk-tō'rē-ä)	124	25.59 N	100.19 W
Saline (R.), Ak. (sá-lēn')	123	34.06 N	92.30 W
Saline (R.), Ks.	122	39.05 N	99.43 W
Salins-les-Bains, Fr. (sá-lăN'-lā-băN')	169	46.55 N	5.54 E
Salisbury, Can.	104	46.03 N	65.05 W
Salisbury, Eng. (sôlz'bē-rē)	162	50.35 N	1.51 W
Salisbury, Md.	111	38.20 N	75.40 W
Salisbury, Mo.	123	39.24 N	92.47 W
Salisbury, NC	127	35.40 N	80.29 W
Salisbury, see Harare			
Salisbury (I.), Can.	97	63.36 N	76.20 W
Salisbury Plain, Eng.	162	51.15 N	1.52 W
Salkehatchie (R.), SC (sô-kē-hăch'ē)	127	33.09 N	81.10 W
Salkhia, India	67a	22.35 N	88.21 E
Sallisaw, Ok. (săl'ĭ-sô)	123	35.27 N	94.48 W
Salmon, Id. (săm'ŭn)	117	45.11 N	113.54 W
Salmon (R.), Can.	104	46.19 N	65.36 W
Salmon (R.), Can.	98	54.00 N	123.50 W
Salmon (R.), Id.	116	45.30 N	115.45 W
Salmon (R.), Middle Fork, Id.	116	44.54 N	114.50 W
Salmon (R.), NY	111	44.35 N	74.15 W
Salmon (R.), South Fork, Id.	116	44.51 N	115.47 W

PLACE (Pronounciation)	PAGE	Lat. °'	Long. °'
Salmon (R.), Wa.	118c	45.44 N	122.36 W
Salmon Arm, Can.	99	50.42 N	119.16 W
Salmon Falls (R.), Id.	116	42.22 N	114.53 W
Salmon Gums, Austl. (gŭmz)	214	33.00 S	122.00 E
Salmon River Mts., Id.	116	44.15 N	115.44 W
Salon-de-Provence, Fr. (sá-lôN-dĕ-prô-văNs')	169	43.48 N	5.09 E
Salonta, Rom. (sä-lôn'tä)	167	46.46 N	21.38 E
Salop (Co.), Eng.	156	52.36 N	2.45 W
Saloum (R.), Senegal	228	14.10 N	15.45 W
Salsette I., India	197b	19.12 N	72.52 E
Sal'sk, Sov. Un. (sälsk)	179	46.30 N	41.20 E
Salt, (R.), Az. (sôlt)	121	33.28 N	111.35 W
Salt (R.), Mo.	123	39.54 N	92.11 W
Salta, Arg. (säl'tä)	144	24.50 S	65.16 W
Salta (Prov.), Arg.	144	25.15 S	65.00 W
Saltair, Ut. (sôlt'âr)	119b	40.46 N	112.09 W
Salt Cay (I.), Turks & Caicos Is.	135	21.20 N	71.15 W
Salt Cr., Il. (sôlt)	113a	42.01 N	88.01 W
Saltillo, Mex. (säl-tēl'yo-mc)	124	25.24 N	100.59 W
Salt Lake City, Ut. (sôlt lāk sĭ'tĭ)	119b	40.45 N	111.52 W
Salto, Arg. (säl'tō)	141c	34.17 S	60.15 W
Salto, Ur.	144	31.18 S	57.45 W
Salto (R.), Mex.	130	22.16 N	99.18 W
Salto Grande, Braz. (grän'dā)	143	22.57 S	49.58 W
Salton Sea, Ca. (sôlt'ŭn)	120	33.28 N	115.43 W
Salto, Serra do (Mtn.), Braz. (sĕ'r-rä-dô)	141a	20.26 S	43.28 W
Saltpond, Ghana	224	5.16 N	1.07 W
Salt River Ind. Res., Az. (sôlt rĭv'ēr)	121	33.40 N	112.01 W
Saltsjöbaden, Swe. (sält'shû-bäd'ĕn)	164	59.15 N	18.20 E
Saltspring I, Can. (sält'sprĭng)	98	48.47 N	123.30 W
Saltville, Va. (sôlt'vĭl)	127	36.50 N	81.45 W
Saltykovka, Sov. Un. (sál-tē'kôf-ká)	182b	55.45 N	37.56 E
Saluda, SC (sá-lōō'dá)	127	34.02 N	81.46 W
Saluda (R.), SC	127	34.07 N	81.48 W
Salud, Mt., Pan. (sä-lōō'th)	128a	9.14 N	79.42 W
Saluzzo, It. (sä-lōōt'sō)	172	44.39 N	7.31 E
Salvador (Bahia), Braz. (säl-vä-dōr') (bä-ē'ä)	143	12.59 S	38.27 W
Salvador L., La.	125	29.45 N	90.20 W
Salvador Pt., Ba.	134	24.30 N	77.45 W
Salvatierra, Mex. (säl-vä-tyĕr'rä)	130	20.13 N	100.52 W
Salwā Baḥrī, Egypt	223b	24.43 N	32.58 E
Salween R., Bur. (sál-wēn')	198	26.46 N	98.19 E
Sal'yany, Sov. Un.	179	39.40 N	49.10 E
Salzburg, Aus. (sälts'bōōrgh)	166	47.48 N	13.04 E
Salzburg (State), Aus.	166	47.30 N	13.18 E
Salzwedel, G.D.R. (sälts-vā'dĕl)	166	52.51 N	11.10 E
Samāika (Neigh.), India	67d	28.32 N	77.05 E
Samālūt, Egypt (sä-mä-lōōt')	223b	28.17 N	30.43 E
Samaná, Dom. Rep. (sä-mä-nä')	135	19.15 N	69.25 W
Samana Cabo (C.), Dom. Rep. (ká'bô)	135	19.20 N	69.00 W
Samana or Atwood Cay (I.), Ba.	135	23.05 N	73.45 W
Samar (I.), Phil. (sä'mär)	207	11.30 N	126.07 E
Samara (R.), Sov. Un. (sá-mä'rá)	175	48.47 N	35.30 E
Samara (R.), Sov. Un.	179	52.50 N	50.35 E
Samarai, Pap. N. Gui. (sä-mä-rä'ē)	207	10.45 S	150.49 E
Samarkand, Sov. Un. (sá-már-känt')	180	39.42 N	67.00 E
Sāmarrā', Iraq	195	34.12 N	43.52 E
Samba, Zaire	231	4.38 S	26.22 E
Sambalpur, India (sŭm'bŭl-pōōr)	196	21.30 N	84.05 E
Sāmbhar (R.), India	196	27.00 N	74.58 E
Sambor, Sov. Un. (säm'bôr)	167	49.31 N	23.12 E
Samborombón (R.), Arg.	141c	35.20 S	57.52 W
Samborombón, Bahia (B.), Arg. (bä-ē'ä-säm-bô-rôm-bô'n)	141c	35.57 S	57.05 W
Sambre (R.), Bel. (säN'br')	163	50.20 N	4.15 E
Sambungo, Ang.	230	8.39 S	20.43 E
Sammamish (R.), Wa.	118a	47.43 N	122.08 W
Sammamish, L., Wa. (sá-măm'ĭsh)	118a	47.35 N	122.02 W
Samoa (I.), Oceania	208	15.00 S	170.00 W
Samokov, Bul. (sä'mô-kôf)	173	42.20 N	23.33 E
Samora Correia, Port. (sä-mō'rä-kôr-rē'yä)	171b	38.55 N	8.52 W
Samorovo, Sov. Un. (sá-má-rô'vô)	180	60.47 N	69.13 E
Sámos (I.), Grc. (să'mŏs)	173	37.53 N	26.35 E
Samothráki (I.), Grc.	173	40.23 N	25.10 E
Sampaloc Pt., Phil. (säm-pä'lôk)	207a	14.43 N	119.56 E
Sam Rayburn Res, Tx.	125	31.10 N	94.15 W
Samsø (I.), Den. (säm'sû)	164	55.49 N	10.47 E
Samson, Al. (săm'sŭn)	126	31.06 N	86.02 W
Samsu, Kor. (säm'sōō')	204	41.12 N	128.00 E
Samsun, Tur. (sàm'sōōn')	179	41.20 N	36.05 E
Samtredia, Sov. Un. (sám'trĕ-dē)	179	42.18 N	42.25 E
Samuel (I.), Can. (sàm'ū-ĕl)	118d	48.50 N	123.10 W
Samur (R.), Sov. Un. (sä-mōōr')	179	41.40 N	47.20 E
San, Mali (sän)	228	13.18 N	4.54 W
Şan'ā', Yemen (sän'ä)	192	15.17 N	44.05 E
Sanaga (R.), Cam. (sä-nä'gä)	229	4.10 N	10.40 E
San Ambrosio, Isla (I.), Chile (ē's-lä-dĕ-sän äm-brō'zē-ō)	140	26.40 S	80.00 W
Sanana, Pulau (I.), Indon.	207	2.15 S	126.38 E
Sanandaj, Iran	192	36.44 N	46.43 E
San Andreas, Ca. (săn ăn'drē-ăs)	120	38.10 N	120.42 W
San Andreas (L.), Ca.	118b	37.36 N	122.26 W
San Andrés, Col. (sän-än-drĕ's)	142a	6.57 N	75.41 W
San Andrés, Mex. (sän-än-drās')	131a	19.15 N	99.10 W
San Andrés (L.), see Petén, Laguna de			
San Andrés de Giles, Arg. (sän-än-drĕ's-dĕ-gē'lĕs)	141c	34.26 S	59.28 W
San Andres I., Col.	133	12.32 N	81.34 W
San Andres, Laguna de (L.), Mex.	131	22.40 N	97.50 W
San Andres Mts., NM	121	33.45 N	106.40 W
San Andres, Mts., U. S. (săn ăn'drē-ăs)	108	33.00 N	106.40 W
San Andrés Totoltepec, Mex.	60a	19.15 N	99.10 W
San Andrés Tuxtla, Mex. (sän-än-drā's-tōōs'tlä)	131	18.27 N	95.12 W
San Angelo, Tx. (săn ăn-jē-lō)	124	31.28 N	100.22 W

ng-sing; ŋ-baŋk; N-nasalized n; nŏd; cŏmmit; ōld; ôbey; ôrder; oi-boil; fōōd; fŏŏt; ou-out; s-soft; sh-dish; th-thin; pūre; ûnite; ûrn; stŭd; circŭs; ü-as in French tu; '-indeterminate vowel.

PLACE (Pronounciation)	PAGE	Lat. °'	Long. °'
San Antioco, I. di, It. (ē'sō-lä-dē-sän-än-tyō'kô)	172	39.00 N	8.25 E
San Antonio, Chile (sän-àn-tô'nyō)	141b	33.34 S	71.36 W
San Antonio, Col.	142a	2.57 N	75.06 W
San Antonio, Col.	142a	3.55 N	75.28 W
San Antonio, Phil.	207a	14.57 N	120.05 E
San Antonio, Tx. (săn ăn-tō'nē-ō)	119d	29.25 N	98.30 W
San Antonio (R.), Ca.	120	36.00 N	121.13 W
San Antonio Abad, Sp. (sän än-tō'nyô ä-bädh')	171	38.59 N	1.17 E
San Antonio B., Tx.	125	28.20 N	97.08 W
San Antonio, Cabo (C.), Cuba (kä'bô-sän-än-tō'nyô)	134	21.55 N	84.55 W
San Antonio de Areco, Arg. (dā ä-rā'kô)	141c	34.16 S	59.30 W
San Antonio de Galipán, Ven.	61a	10.33 N	66.53 W
San Antonio de las Vegas, Cuba (sän än-tō'nyô-dē-läs-vē'gäs)	135a	22.51 N	82.16 W
San Antonio de los Baños, Cuba (dā lōs bän'yōs)	135a	22.54 N	82.30 W
San Antonio de los Cobres, Arg. (dā lōs kō'brās)	144	24.15 S	66.29 W
San Antônio de Pádua, Braz. (dĕ-pá'dwä)	141a	21.32 S	42.09 W
San Antonio de Tamanaco, Ven. (sän-än-tô-nyō-dē-tà-mä-nà'kô)	143b	9.42 N	66.03 W
San Antonio Heights, Ca.	59	34.10 N	117.40 W
San Antonio Oeste, Arg. (sän-nä-tō'nyō ô-ĕs'tā)	144	40.49 S	64.56 W
San Antonio Pk., Ca. (săn ăn-tō'nĭ-ō)	119a	34.17 N	117.39 W
San Antonio R., Tx.	124	29.00 N	97.58 W
Sanarate, Guat. (sä-nä-rä'tĕ)	132	14.47 N	90.12 W
San Augustine, Tx. (săn ô'gŭs-tēn)	125	31.33 N	94.08 W
San Bartolo, Mex. (sän bär-tō'lô)	131a	19.36 N	99.43 W
San Bartolo, Mex.	124	24.43 N	103.12 W
San Bartolomé de la Cuadra, Sp.	65e	41.26 N	2.02 E
San Bartolomeo, It. (bär-tô-lô-mā'ô)	172	41.25 N	15.04 E
San Baudilio de Llobregat, Sp.	65e	41.21 N	2.03 E
San Benedetto del Tronto, It. (bā'nā-dĕt'tô dĕl trōn'tô)	172	42.58 N	13.54 E
San Benito, Tx. (săn bĕ-nē'tô)	125	26.07 N	97.37 W
San Benito (R.), Ca.	120	36.40 N	121.20 W
San Bernardino, Ca. (bûr-när-dē'nô)	119a	34.07 N	117.19 W
San Bernardino Mts., Ca.	120	34.05 N	116.23 W
San Bernardo, Chile (sän bĕr-när'dô)	141b	33.35 S	70.42 W
San Blas, Mex. (sän bläs')	130	21.33 N	105.19 W
San Blas, C., Fl.	126	29.38 N	85.38 W
San Blas, Cord. de (Mts.), Pan. (kôr-dĕl-yĕ'rä-dĕ)	133	9.17 N	78.20 W
San Blas,Golfo de (G.), Pan.	133	9.33 N	78.42 W
San Blas, Punta (Pt.), Pan.	133	9.35 N	78.55 W
San Bruno, Ca. (săn brū-nō)	118b	37.38 N	122.25 W
San Buenaventura, Mex. (bwā'nà-vĕn-tōō'rá)	124	27.07 N	101.30 W
San Carlos, Ca. (săn kär'lōs)	118b	37.30 N	122.15 W
San Carlos, Chile (sän-kà'r-lōs)	144	36.23 S	71.58 W
San Carlos, Col.	142a	6.11 N	74.58 W
San Carlos, Equat. Gui.	230	3.27 N	8.33 E
San Carlos, Mex. (sän ĸär'lōs)	131	17.49 N	92.33 W
San Carlos, Mex.	124	24.36 N	98.52 W
San Carlos, Nic. (sän-kä'r-lôs)	133	11.08 N	84.48 W
San Carlos, Phil.	207a	15.56 N	120.20 E
San Carlos, Ven.	142	9.36 N	68.35 W
San Carlos de Bariloche, Arg. (sän-kà'r lōs-dĕ-bä-rē' lô'chĕ)	144	41.15 S	71.26 W
San Carlos Ind. Res, Az. (săn kär'lōs)	121	33.27 N	110.15 W
San Carlos R., C. R.	133	10.36 N	84.18 W
San Carlos Res, Az.	121	33.05 N	110.29 W
San Casimiro, Ven. (kä-sē-mē'rô)	143b	10.01 N	67.02 W
San Cataldo, It. (kä-täl'dō)	172	37.30 N	13.59 E
Sánchez, Dom. Rep. (sän'chĕz)	135	19.15 N	69.40 W
Sanchez, Río de los (R.), Mex. (rē'ō-dĕ-lôs)	130	20.31 N	102.29 W
Sánchez Román (Tlaltenango), Mex. (rô-mà'n) (tlä'l-tĕ-nän-gô)	130	21.48 N	103.20 W
Sanchung, Taiwan	68d	25.04 N	121.29 E
San Clemente, Sp. (sän klā-mĕn'tā)	170	39.25 N	2.24 W
San Clemente (I.), Ca.	120	33.02 N	118.36 W
San Clemente de Llobregat, Sp.	65e	41.20 N	2.00 E
San Cristobal, Dom. Rep. (krēs-tô'bäl)	135	18.25 N	70.05 W
San Cristóbal, Guat.	132	15.22 N	90.26 W
San Cristóbal, Ven.	142	7.43 N	72.15 W
San Cristobal (I.), Ec.	142	1.05 S	89.15 W
San Cristobal (I.), Sol. Is.	215	10.47 S	162.17 E
Sancti Spíritus, Cuba (säŋk'tē spē'rē-tōōs)	134	21.55 N	79.25 W
Sancti Spiritus (Prov.), Cuba	134	22.05 N	79.20 W
San Cugat del Vallés, Sp.	65e	41.28 N	2.05 E
Sancy, Puy de (Pk.), Fr. (pwē-dĕ-säɴ-sē')	168	45.30 N	2.53 E
Sand (I.), Or. (sănd)	118c	46.16 N	124.01 W
Sand (I.), Wi.	115	46.03 N	91.09 W
Sand (R.), S. Afr.	223d	28.09 S	26.46 E
Sand (R.), S. Afr.	227c	28.30 S	29.30 E
Sanda, Jap. (sän'dä)	205b	34.53 N	135.14 E
Sandakan, Mala. (sàn-dä'kàn)	206	5.51 N	118.03 E
Sanday (I.), Scot. (sănd'ā)	162a	59.17 N	2.25 W
Sandbach, Scot. (sănd'băch)	156	53.08 N	2.22 W
Sandefjord, Nor. (sän'dĕ-fyôr')	164	59.09 N	10.14 E
San de Fuca, Wa. (de-fōō-cä)	118a	48.14 N	122.44 W
Sanders, Az.	121	35.13 N	109.20 W
Sanderson, Tx. (săn'dĕr-sŭn)	124	30.09 N	102.24 W
Sanderstead (Neigh.), Eng.	62	51.20 N	0.05 W
Sandersville, Ga. (săn'dĕrz-vĭl)	126	32.57 N	82.50 W
Sandhammar, C., Swe. (sänt'häm-màr)	164	55.24 N	14.37 E
Sand Hills (Reg.), Ne. (sănd)	114	41.57 N	101.29 W
Sand Hook, NJ (sănd hŏŏk)	112a	40.29 N	74.05 W
Sandhurst, Eng. (sănd'hûrst)	156b	51.20 N	0.48 W
San Diego, Ca. (săn dē-ā'gô)	120a	32.43 N	117.10 W
San Diego, Tx.	122	27.47 N	98.13 W
San Diego (R.), Ca.	120	32.53 N	116.57 W
San Diego de la Unión, Mex. (sän dē-ā-gô dā lä ōō-nyōn')	130	21.27 N	100.52 W
Sandies Cr., Tx. (sănd'ēz)	125	29.13 N	97.34 W
San Dimas, Ca. (săn dē-màs)	119a	34.07 N	117.49 W
San Dimas, Mex. (dē-mäs')	122	24.08 N	105.57 W
Sandnes, Nor. (sänd'nĕs)	164	58.52 N	5.44 E
Sandoa, Zaire (sän-dō'à)	226	9.39 S	23.00 E
Sandomierz, Pol. (sàn-dô'myĕzh)	167	50.39 N	21.45 E
San Doná di Piave, It. (sän dô nà' dē pyä'vē)	172	45.38 N	12.34 E
Sandoway, Bur. (sän-dô-wī')	198	18.24 N	94.28 E
Sandpoint, Id. (sănd point)	116	48.17 N	116.34 W
Sandringham, Austl. (săn'drĭng-ăm)	211a	37.57 S	145.01 E
Sandringham (Neigh.), S. Afr.	71b	26.09 S	28.07 E
Sandrio, It. (sä'n-dryô)	172	46.11 N	9.53 E
Sands Point, NY	55	40.51 N	73.43 W
Sand Springs, Ok. (sănd sprĭnz)	123	36.08 N	96.06 W
Sandstone, Austl. (sănd'stōn)	214	28.00 S	119.25 E
Sandstone, Mn.	113	46.08 N	92.53 W
Sanduo, China (sän-dwô)	200	32.49 N	119.39 E
Sandusky, Al. (săn-dŭs'kē)	112h	33.32 N	86.50 W
Sandusky, Mi.	110	43.25 N	82.50 W
Sandusky, Oh.	110	41.25 N	82.45 W
Sandusky (R.), Oh.	110	41.10 N	83.20 W
Sandwich, Il. (sănd'wĭch)	110	42.35 N	88.53 W
Sandy, Or. (sănd'ē)	118c	45.24 N	122.16 W
Sandy, Ut.	119b	40.36 N	111.53 W
Sandy C., Austl.	216	24.25 S	153.10 E
Sandy Cr., Wy.	117	42.08 N	109.35 W
Sandy (R.), Or.	118c	45.28 N	122.17 W
Sandy Hook, Ct. (hŏŏk)	112a	41.25 N	73.17 W
Sandy L., Can.	95g	53.46 N	113.58 W
Sandy L., Can.	101	53.00 N	93.07 W
Sandy L., Can.	105	49.16 N	57.00 W
Sandy Point, Tx.	125a	29.22 N	95.27 W
Sandy Pt., Wa.	118d	48.48 N	122.42 W
Sandy Springs, Ga. (springz)	112c	33.55 N	84.23 W
San Enrique, Arg. (sän-ĕn-rē'kĕ)	141c	35.47 S	60.22 W
San Estanislao, Par. (ĕs-tä-nēs-lá'ô)	144	24.38 S	56.20 W
San Esteban, Hond. (ĕs-tĕ'bän)	132	15.13 N	85.53 W
San Fabian, Phil. (fä-byä'n)	207a	16.14 N	120.28 E
San Felipe, Chile (fĕ-lē'pā)	141b	32.45 S	70.43 W
San Felipe, Mex. (fĕ-lē'pĕ)	130	21.29 N	101.13 W
San Felipe, Mex.	130	22.21 N	105.26 W
San Felipe, Ven. (fĕ-lē'pĕ)	142	10.13 N	68.45 W
San Felipe, Cayos de (Is.), Cuba (kä'yōs-dĕ-sän-fĕ-lē'pĕ)	134	22.00 N	83.30 W
San Felipe, Cr., Ca. (săn fē-lēp'ā)	120	33.10 N	116.03 W
San Felipe Terremotos, Mex.	60a	19.22 N	99.04 W
San Felíu de Guixols, Sp. (sän fā-lē'ōō dā gē-hôls)	171	41.45 N	3.01 E
San Felíu de Llobregat, Sp.	65e	41.23 N	2.03 E
San Félix, Isla (I.), Chile (ē's-lä-dĕ-sän fā-lēks')	140	26.20 S	80.10 W
San Fernanda, Sp. (fĕr-nä'n-dä)	170	36.28 N	6.13 W
San Fernando, Arg. (fĕr-nä'n-dô)	144a	34.11 S	58.34 W
San Fernando, Ca. (fĕr-nän'dô)	119a	34.17 N	118.27 W
San Fernando, Chile	141b	36.36 S	70.58 W
San Fernando, Mex. (fĕr-nän'dô)	124	24.52 N	98.10 W
San Fernando, Phil. (sän fĕr-nä'n-dô)	207a	16.38 N	120.19 E
San Fernando de Apure, Ven. (sän-fĕr-nä'n-dō-dĕ-ä-pōō'rā)	142	7.46 N	67.29 W
San Fernando de Atabapo, Ven. (dĕ-ä-tä-bä'pô)	142	3.58 N	67.41 W
San Fernando de Henares, Sp. (dĕ-ā-nä'rās)	171a	40.23 N	3.31 W
San Fernando R., Mex. (sän fĕr-nän'dô)	124	25.07 N	98.25 W
Sånfjället (Mtn.), Swe.	164	62.19 N	13.30 E
Sanford, Can. (săn'fērd)	95f	49.41 N	97.27 W
Sanford, Fl. (săn'fôrd)	127a	28.46 N	80.18 W
Sanford, Me. (săn'fērd)	104	43.26 N	70.47 W
Sanford, NC	127	35.26 N	79.10 W
San Francisco, Arg. (sän frän'sĭs'kô)	144	31.23 S	62.09 W
San Francisco, Ca.	118b	37.45 N	122.26 W
San Francisco, Sal.	132	13.48 N	88.11 W
San Francisco (R.), NM	121	33.35 N	108.55 W
San Francisco B., Ca. (săn frăn'sĭs'kô)	118b	37.45 N	122.21 W
San Francisco Culhuacán, Mex.	60a	19.20 N	99.06 W
San Francisco del Oro, Mex. (dĕl ō'rō)	128	27.00 N	106.37 W
San Francisco del Rincón, Mex. (dĕl rēn-kōn')	130	21.01 N	101.51 W
San Francisco de Macaira, Ven. (dĕ-mä-kī'rä)	143b	9.58 N	66.17 W
San Francisco de Macoris, Dom. Rep. (dā-mä-kō'rēs)	135	19.20 N	70.15 W
San Francisco de Paula, Cuba (dā pou'lä)	135a	23.04 N	82.18 W
San Francisco el Grande, Iglesia de (P. Int.), Sp.	65b	40.25 N	3.43 W
San Francisco, see Ixhuatán			
San Gabriel, Ca. (săn gä-brē-ĕl') (gă'brē-ĕl)	119a	34.06 N	118.06 W
San Gabriel Chilac, Mex. (sän-gä-brē-ĕl-chē-läk')	130	18.19 N	97.22 W
San Gabriel Mts, Ca.	119a	34.17 N	118.03 W
San Gabriel R., Ca.	119a	33.47 N	118.06 W
San Gabriel Res., Ca.	119a	34.14 N	117.48 W
Sangamon (R.), Il. (săn'gà-mŭn)	123	40.08 N	90.08 W
Sangenjaya (Neigh.), Jap.	69a	35.38 N	139.40 E
Sanger, Ca. (săng'ēr)	120	36.42 N	119.33 W
Sangerhausen, G.D.R. (säng'ĕr-hou-zĕn)	166	51.28 N	11.17 E
Sangha (R.), Afr.	229	2.40 N	16.10 E
Sangihe Pulau (I.), Indon. (säŋ'gē-ē)	207	3.30 N	125.30 E
San Gil, Col. (sän-ĸē'l)	142	6.32 N	73.13 W
San Giovanni in Fiore, It. (sän jô-vän'nē ēn fyō'rā)	172	39.15 N	16.40 E
San Giuseppe Vesuviano, It. (sän-zhēōō-sĕ'p-pĕ-vĕ-sōō-vyà'nô)	171c	40.36 N	14.31 E
Sangju, Kor. (säng'jōō')	204	36.20 N	128.07 E
Sāngli, India	197	16.56 N	74.38 E
Sangmélima, Cam.	229	2.56 N	11.59 E
San Gorgonio Mt., Ca. (săn gôr-gō'nĭ-ō)	119a	34.06 N	116.50 W
Sangre De Cristo Ra., U. S. (săng'grē-de-krēs-tō)	108	37.45 N	105.50 W
San Gregoria, Ca. (săn grē-gôr'ā)	118b	37.20 N	122.23 W
San Gregorio Atlapulco, Mex.	60a	19.15 N	99.03 W
Sangro (R.), It. (säŋ'grô)	172	41.38 N	13.56 E
Sangüesa, Sp. (sän-gwĕ'sä)	170	42.36 N	1.15 W
Sanhe, China (sän-hŭ)	200	39.59 N	117.06 E
Sanibel I., Fl. (săn'ĭ-bĕl)	127a	26.26 N	82.15 W
San Ignacio, Belize	132a	17.11 N	89.04 W
San Ildefonso, C. Phil. (sän-ēl-dĕ-fōn-sô)	207a	16.03 N	122.10 E
San Ildefonso o la Granja, Sp. (ō lä grän'khä)	170	40.54 N	4.02 W
San Ildefonso, see Villa Alta			
San Isidro, Arg. (ē-sē'drô)	144a	34.13 S	58.31 W
San Isidro, C.R.	133	9.24 N	83.43 W
San Isidro, Peru	60c	12.07 S	77.03 W
San Jacinto, Ca. (săn jȧ-sĭn'tô)	119a	33.47 N	116.57 W
San Jacinto, Phil. (sän hä-sēn'tô)	207a	12.33 N	123.43 E
San Jacinto (R.), West Fork, Tx.	125	30.35 N	95.37 W
San Jacinto R., Ca. (săn jȧ-sĭn'tô)	119a	33.44 N	117.14 W
San Jacinto R., Tx.	125	30.25 N	95.05 W
San Javier, Chile (sän-hà-vē'ĕr)	141b	35.35 S	71.43 W
San Jerónimo, Mex.	131a	19.31 N	98.46 W
San Jerónimo de Juárez, Mex. (hā-rō'nē-mô dā hwä'rāz)	130	17.08 N	100.30 W
San Jerónimo Lídice, Mex.	60a	19.20 N	99.13 W
San Joaquin, Ven.	143b	10.16 N	67.47 W
San Joaquin (R.), Ca. (săn hwä-kēn')	120	37.10 N	120.51 W
San Joaquin Valley, Ca.	120	36.45 N	120.30 W
San Jorge, Golfo (G.), Arg. (gôl-fô-sän-ĸô'r-ĸĕ)	144	46.15 S	66.45 W
San José, Bol. (sän hō-sā')	143	17.54 S	60.42 W
San Jose, Ca. (săn hō-zā')	118b	37.20 N	121.54 W
San Jose, C. R. (sän hō-sā')	133	9.57 N	84.05 W
San José, Guat.	132	13.56 N	90.49 W
San Jose, Phil.	207a	12.22 N	121.04 E
San Jose, Phil.	207a	15.49 N	120.57 E
San José, Ur. (hô-sĕ')	141c	34.20 S	56.43 W
San Jose (I.), Mex. (ĸô-sĕ')	128	25.00 N	110.35 W
San Jose (R.), NM (săn hô-zā')	121	35.15 N	108.10 W
San José de Feliciano, Arg. (dā lä ĕs-kē'nà)	144	30.26 S	58.44 W
San José de Galipán, Ven.	61a	10.35 N	66.54 W
San José de Gauribe, Ven. (sän-hô-sĕ'dĕ-gàōō-rē'bĕ)	143b	9.51 N	65.49 W
San Jose de las Lajas, Cuba (sän-ĸô-sĕ'dĕ-läs-la'käs)	135a	22.58 N	82.10 W
San José (Dept.), Ur.	141c	34.17 S	56.23 W
San Jose, Isla de (I.), Pan. (ē's-lä-dĕ-sän hô-sā')	133	8.17 N	79.20 W
San José Iturbide, Mex. (ē-tōōr-bē'dĕ)	130	21.00 N	100.24 W
San José (R.), Ur. (sän-hô-sĕ')	141c	34.05 S	56.47 W
San Juan, Arg. (hwän')	144	31.36 S	68.29 W
San Juan, Col. (hōōà'n)	142a	3.23 N	73.48 W
San Juan, Dom. Rep. (sän hwän')	135	18.50 N	71.15 W
San Juan, Phil.	207a	16.41 N	120.20 E
San Juan, P. R. (sän hwän')	129b	18.30 N	66.10 W
San Juan (Prov.), Arg.	144	31.00 S	69.30 W
San Juan (R.), Mex. (sän-hōō-än')	131	18.10 N	95.23 W
San Juan (R.), Ut.	121	37.10 N	110.30 W
San Juan Bautista, Par. (sän hwän' bou-tēs'tä)	144	26.48 S	57.09 W
San Juan, Cabezas de (C.), P. R.	129b	18.29 N	65.30 W
San Juan, Cabo (C.), Equat. Gui.	230	1.08 N	9.23 E
San Juan Capistrano, Mex. (sän-hōō-än' kä-pēs-trä'nô)	130	22.41 N	104.07 W
San Juan Cr., Ca. (săn hwän')	120	35.24 N	120.12 W
San Juan de Aragón, Mex.	60a	19.28 N	99.05 W
San Juan de Aragón, Bosque (P. Int.), Mex.	60a	19.28 N	99.04 W
San Juan de Aragón, Zoologico de (P. Int.), Mex.	60a	19.28 N	99.05 W
San Juan de Dios, Ven.	61a	10.35 N	66.57 W
San Juan de Guadalupe, Mex. (sän hwan dā gwä-dhä-lōō'pā)	124	24.37 N	102.43 W
San Juan del Monte, Phil.	68g	14.36 N	121.02 E
San Juan del Norte (Greytown), Nic. (dĕl nôr-tā) (grā'toun)	133	10.55 N	83.44 W
San Juan del Norte Bahia de (B.), Nic. (bä-ē'ä-dĕ-sän hwän dĕl nôr'tā)	133	11.12 N	83.40 W
San Juan de los Lagos, Mex. (sän-hōō-än'dā lōs lä'gôs)	130	21.15 N	102.18 W
San Juan de los Lagos (R.), Mex. (dā lōs lä'gôs)	130	21.13 N	102.12 W
San Juan de los Morros, Ven. (dĕ-lôs-mô'r-rôs)	143b	9.54 N	67.22 W
San Juan del Rio, Mex. (dĕl rē'ô)	130	20.21 N	99.59 W
San Juan del Rio, Mex. (sän hwän del rē'ô)	124	24.47 N	104.29 W
San Juan del Sur, Nic. (dĕl sōōr)	132	11.15 N	85.53 W
San Juan de Sabinas, Mex. (dĕ-sä-bē'näs)	124	27.56 N	101.23 W
San Juan Despí, Sp.	65e	41.22 N	2.04 E
San Juan Evangelista, Mex. (sän-hōō-ä'n-ĕ-väŋ-kĕ-lēs'ta')	131	17.57 N	95.08 W
San Juan I., Wa.	118a	48.28 N	123.08 W
San Juan Is., Can. (săn hwän)	118d	48.49 N	123.14 W
San Juan Ixtenco, Mex. (ēx-tĕ'n-kô)	131	19.14 N	97.52 W
San Juan Martinez, Cuba (sän kōō ä'n-mär-tē'nĕz)	134	22.15 N	83.50 W

PLACE (Pronounciation)	PAGE	Lat. °'	Long. °'
San Juan Mts., Co. (san hwän')	121	37.50 N	107.30 W
San Juan, Pico (Pk.), Cuba (pē'kô-sän-kōōá'n)	134	21.55 N	80.00 W
San Juan R., Nic.	133	10.58 N	84.18 W
San Juan, Rio (R.), Mex. (rē'ō-sän-hwän)	124	25.35 N	99.15 W
San Juan, see **Guichicovi**			
San Juan, see **Mazatlán**			
San Julián, Arg. (sän hōō-lyá'n)	144	49.17 S	68.02 W
San Justo, Arg. (hōōs'tō)	144a	34.25 S	58.33 W
San Justo Desvern, Sp.	65e	41.23 N	2.05 E
Sankanbiriwa (Mtn.), S. L.	228	8.56 N	10.48 W
Sankarani R., Gui.-Mali (sän'kä-rä'nē)	228	11.10 N	8.35 W
Sankt Gallen, Switz.	166	47.25 N	9.22 E
Sankuru (R.), Zaire (sän-kōō'rōō)	230	4.00 S	22.35 E
San Lazaro, C., Mex. (sän-lá'zä-rō)	128	24.58 N	113.30 W
San Leandro, Ca. (săn lē-ăn'drō)	118b	37.43 N	122.10 W
San Lorenzo, Arg. (sän lō-rĕn'zō)	141c	32.46 S	60.44 W
San Lorenzo, Ca. (săn lō-rĕn'zō)	118b	37.41 N	122.08 W
San Lorenzo, Hond. (sän lō-rĕn'zō)	132	13.24 N	87.24 W
San Lorenzo de El Escorial, Sp. (sän lōrĕn'tho dĕl ĕs-kō-rē-äl')	171a	40.36 N	4.09 W
San Lorenzo Tezonco, Mex.	60a	19.18 N	99.04 W
Sanlúcar de Barrameda, Sp. (sän-lōō'kär)	170	36.46 N	6.21 W
San Lucas, Bol. (lōō'kås)	142	20.12 S	65.06 W
San Lucas, C., Mex.	128	22.45 N	109.45 W
San Lucas, see **Ojitlán**			
San Luis, Arg. (lōō-ēs')	144	33.16 S	66.15 W
San Luis, Col. (lōōē's)	142a	6.03 N	74.57 W
San Luis, Cuba	135	20.15 N	75.50 W
San Luis, Guat.	132	14.38 N	89.42 W
San Luis (Neigh.), Cuba	60b	23.05 N	82.20 W
San Luis (Prov.), Arg.	144	32.45 S	66.00 W
San Luis (State), Mex.	128	22.45 N	101.45 W
San Luis de la Paz, Mex. (då lä päz')	130	21.17 N	100.32 W
San Luis del Cordero, Mex. (dĕl kôr-dā'rō)	124	25.25 N	104.20 W
San Luis Obispo, Ca. (ō-bĭs'pō)	120	35.18 N	120.40 W
San Luis Obispo, B., Ca.	120	35.07 N	121.05 W
San Luis Potosi, Mex. (pō-tō-sē')	130	22.08 N	100.58 W
San Luis Potosí (State), Mex.	128	22.45 N	101.45 W
San Luis Rey (R.), Ca. (rā'ē)	120	33.22 N	117.06 W
San Luis Tlaxialtemalco, Mex.	60a	19.15 N	99.03 W
San Manuel, Az. (săn măn'ū-ĕl)	121	32.30 N	110.45 W
San Marcial, NM (săn mår-shäl')	121	33.40 N	107.00 W
San Marco, It. (sän mär'kō)	172	41.53 N	15.50 E
San Marcos, Guat. (mär'kōs)	132	14.57 N	91.49 W
San Marcos, Mex.	130	16.46 N	99.23 W
San Marcos, Tx. (săn mär'kōs)	124	29.53 N	97.56 W
San Marcos de Colón, Hond. (sän-mä'r-kōs-dĕ-kō-lō'n)	132	13.17 N	86.50 W
San Marcos R., Tx.	124	30.08 N	98.15 W
San Marcos, Universidad de (P. Int.), Peru	60c	12.03 S	77.05 W
San Maria (Vol.), Guat. (sän-mä-rē'ä)	132	14.45 N	91.33 W
San Maria di Léuca, C., It. (dē-lĕ'ōō-kä)	173	39.47 N	18.20 E
San Marino, Ca. (săn mĕr-ē'nō)	119a	34.07 N	118.06 W
San Marino, Eur.	159	43.40 N	13.00 E
San Marino, San Marino (sän mä-rē'nō)	172	44.55 N	12.26 E
San Martin Chalchicuautla, Mex. (sän mär-tē'n chäl-chē-kwä-ōō'tlä)	130	21.22 N	98.39 W
San Martin de la Vega, Sp. (sän mär ten' då lä vā'gä)	171a	40.12 N	3.34 W
San Martín, Col. (sän mår-tē'n)	142a	3.42 N	73.44 W
San Martín, Mex. (mär-tē'n)	131	18.36 N	95.11 W
San Martín (L.), Arg.-Chile	144	48.15 S	72.30 W
San Martín Hidalgo, Mex. (sän mär-tē'n-ē-däl'gō)	130	20.27 N	103.55 W
San Mateo, Ca. (săn mä-tā'ō)	118b	37.34 N	122.20 W
San Mateo (Etlatongo), Mex. (sän-mä-tĕ'ō) (ĕ-tlä-tô'n-gō)	131	16.59 N	97.04 W
San Mateo, Sp. (sän mä-tā'ō)	171	40.26 N	0.09 E
San Mateo, Ven. (sän mà-tĕ'ō)	143b	9.45 N	64.34 W
San Matías, Golfo (G.), Arg. (sän mä-tē'äs)	144	41.30 S	63.45 W
Sanmen Wan (B.), China	203	29.00 N	122.15 E
San Miguel, Arg. (sän mē-gĕ'l)	144a	34.17 S	58.43 W
San Miguel, Chile	61b	33.30 S	70.40 W
San Miguel, Mex. (sän mē-gål')	131	18.18 N	97.09 W
San Miguel, Pan.	133	8.26 N	78.55 W
San Miguel, Peru	60c	12.06 S	77.06 W
San Miguel, Phil. (sän mē-gĕl')	207a	15.09 N	120.56 E
San Miguel, Sal. (sän mē-gål')	132	13.28 N	88.11 W
San Miguel, Ven. (sän mē-gĕ'l)	143b	9.56 N	64.58 W
San Miguel (I.), Ca.	120	34.03 N	120.23 W
San Miguel (R.), Bol. (sän-mē-gĕl')	142	13.34 S	63.58 W
San Miguel (R.), Co. (săn mē-gĕl')	121	38.15 N	108.40 W
San Miguel (R.), Mex. (sän mē-gål')	131	15.27 N	92.00 W
San Miguel (Vol.), Sal.	132	13.27 N	88.17 W
San Miguel B., Phil.	207a	13.55 N	123.12 E
San Miguel, Bahia (B.), Pan. (bä-ē'ä-sän mē-gål')	133	8.17 N	78.26 W
San Miguel de Allende, Mex. (då ä-lyĕn'då)	130	20.54 N	100.44 W
San Miguel del Padrón, Cuba	60b	23.05 N	82.19 W
San Miguel el Alto, Mex. (ĕl äl'tō)	130	21.03 N	102.26 W
San Miguel, see **Sola de Vega**			
San Miguel, see **Talea de Castro**			
Sannār, Sud.	225	13.34 N	33.32 E
San Narcisco, Phil. (sän när-sē'sō)	207a	15.01 N	120.05 E
San Narcisco, Phil.	207a	13.34 N	122.33 E
San Nicolás, Arg. (sän nē-kō-lá's)	141c	33.20 S	60.14 W
San Nicolas, Phil. (nē-kō-läs')	207a	16.05 N	120.45 E
San Nicolas (I.), Ca. (săn nĭ'kō-là)	120	33.14 N	119.10 W
San Nicolás (R.), Mex.	130	19.40 N	105.08 W
Sanniquellie, Ivory Coast	228	7.22 N	8.43 W
Sannois, Fr.	64c	48.58 N	2.15 E
Sannūr, Wādī, Egypt	223b	28.48 N	31.12 E
Sanok, Pol. (sä'nōk)	167	49.31 N	22.13 E
San Pablo, Ca. (săn păb'lō)	118b	37.58 N	122.21 W
San Pablo, Phil. (sän-pä-blō)	207a	14.05 N	121.20 E
San Pablo, Ven. (sän-pá'blō)	143b	9.46 N	65.04 W
San Pablo B., Ca. (săn păb'lō)	118b	38.04 N	122.25 W
San Pablo R., Pan. (sän päb'lō)	133	8.12 N	81.12 W
San Pablo Res, Ca.	118b	37.55 N	122.12 W
San Pascual, Phil. (päs-kwäl')	207a	13.08 N	122.59 E
San Pedro, Arg. (sän pē'drō)	144	24.15 S	64.15 W
San Pedro, Arg.	141c	33.41 S	59.42 W
San Pedro, Ca. (săn pē'drō)	119a	33.44 N	118.17 W
San Pedro, Chile (sän pĕ'drō)	141b	33.54 S	71.27 W
San Pedro, Mex. (sän pā'drō)	131	18.38 N	92.25 W
San Pedro, Par. (sän-pĕ'drō)	144	24.13 S	57.00 W
San Pedro, Sal. (sän pā'drō)	132	13.49 N	88.58 W
San Pedro (R.), Az.	121	32.48 N	110.37 W
San Pedro (R.), Cuba (sän-pĕ'drō)	134	21.05 N	78.15 W
San Pedro (R.), Mex. (sän pā'drō)	130	22.08 N	104.59 W
San Pedro B., Ca. (săn pē'drō)	119a	33.42 N	118.12 W
San Pedro de las Colonias, Mex. (dĕ-läs-kō-lō'nyäs)	124	25.47 N	102.58 W
San Pedro de Macorís, Dom. Rep. (sän-pĕ'drō-då mä-kō-rēs')	135	18.30 N	69.30 W
San Pedro Lagunillas, Mex. (sän pā'drō lä-gōō-nēl'yäs)	130	21.12 N	104.47 W
San Pedro R., Guat. (sän pä'drō)	132a	17.11 N	90.23 W
San Pedro R., Mex.	124	27.56 N	105.50 W
San Pedro, Rio de (R.), Mex. (rē'ō-dĕ-sän-pĕ'drō)	131	18.23 N	92.13 W
San Pedro, Rio de (R.), Mex.	130	21.51 N	102.24 W
San Pedro, see **Amusgos**			
San Pedro, see **Pochutla**			
San Pedro Sula, Hond. (sän pā'drō sōō'lä)	132	15.29 N	88.01 W
San Pedro Xalostoc, Mex.	60a	19.32 N	99.05 W
San Pedro y San Pablo, see **Teposcolula**			
San Pedro Zacatenco, Mex.	60a	19.31 N	99.08 W
San Pietro, I. di, It. (ē'sō-lä-dē-sän pyä'trō)	172	39.09 N	8.15 E
San Pietro in Vaticano (P. Int.), It.	66c	41.54 N	12.28 E
San Quentin, Ca. (săn kwĕn-tĕn')	118b	37.57 N	122.29 W
San Quintin, Phil. (sän kēn-tēn')	207a	15.59 N	120.47 E
San R, Pol.	167	50.33 N	22.12 E
San Rafael, Arg. (sän rä-fä-ĕl')	144	34.30 S	68.13 W
San Rafael, Ca. (săn rà-fĕl)	118b	37.58 N	122.31 W
San Rafael, Col. (sän-rä-fä-ĕ'l)	142a	6.18 N	75.02 W
San Rafael (R.), Ut. (săn rà-fĕl')	121	39.05 N	110.50 W
San Rafael, Cabo (C.), Dom. Rep. (kà'bō)	135	19.00 N	68.50 W
San Ramon, Ca. (săn rä-mōn')	118b	37.47 N	122.59 W
San Ramōn, C. R.	133	10.07 N	84.30 W
San Remo, It. (sän rā'mō)	172	43.48 N	7.46 E
San Roman, C., Ven. (sän-rô-mä'n)	129	12.00 N	69.45 W
San Roque, Col. (sän-rō'kĕ)	142a	6.29 N	75.00 W
San Roque, Sp.	170	36.13 N	5.23 W
San Saba, Tx. (săn să'bá)	124	31.12 N	98.43 W
San Saba R., Tx.	124	30.58 N	99.12 W
San Salvador, Sal. (sän säl-vä-dōr')	132	13.45 N	89.11 W
San Salvador (I.), Ec.	142	0.14 S	90.50 W
San Salvador (R.), Ur. (sän-säl-vä-dō'r)	141c	33.42 S	58.04 W
San Salvador (Watling) (I.), Ba. (săn săl'và-dôr)	135	24.05 N	74.30 W
Sansanné-Mango, Togo (sän-sà-nā' mäɴ'gō)	228	10.21 N	0.28 E
San Sebastian, Can. Is. (sän så-bås-tyän')	224	28.09 N	17.11 W
San Sebastián, Sp.	170	43.19 N	1.59 W
San Sebastián, Ven. (sän-sĕ-bäs-tyá'n)	143b	9.58 N	67.11 W
San Sebastián de los Reyes, Sp. (sän sā-bäs-tyän'då lōs rā'yĕs)	171a	40.33 N	3.38 W
San Severo, It. (sän sĕ-vâ'rō)	172	41.43 N	15.24 E
Sanshui, China (sän-shwā)	199	23.14 N	112.51 E
San Simon (R.), Az. (săn sī-mōn')	121	32.45 N	109.30 W
San Siro (Neigh.), It.	65c	45.29 S	9.07 E
Sanssouci, Schloss (P. Int.), Sp.	65a	52.24 N	13.02 E
Santa Ana, Ca. (săn'tà ăn'à)	119a	33.45 N	117.52 W
Santa Ana, Mex. (sän'tä ä'nä)	130	19.18 N	98.10 W
Santa Ana, Sal.	132	14.02 N	89.35 W
Santa Ana Mts., Ca.	119a	33.44 N	117.36 W
Santa Ana R., Ca.	119a	33.41 N	117.57 W
Santa Anna, Tx.	124	31.44 N	99.18 W
Santa Anna, Cochilha de (Mts.), Braz. (kô-chē'lä dĕ sän-tä-nä)	144	30.30 S	56.30 W
Santa Antão (I.), C. V. Is. (sä-tä-á'n-zhĕ-lō)	224b	17.20 N	26.05 W
Santa Bárbara, Braz. (sän-tä-bä'r-bä-rä)	141a	19.57 S	43.25 W
Santa Barbara, Ca. (săn'tà bär'bá-rà)	120	34.26 N	119.43 W
Santa Barbara, Hond. (sän'tà bär'bá-rá)	132	14.52 N	88.20 W
Santa Bárbara, Mex.	124	26.48 N	105.50 W
Santa Barbara (I.), Ca.	120	33.30 N	118.44 W
Santa Barbara (Is.), Ca.	120	33.45 N	119.46 W
Santa Barbara Chan., Ca.	120	34.15 N	120.00 W
Santa Branca, Braz. (sän-tä-brä'ɴ-kä)	139a	23.25 S	45.52 W
Santa Catalina (I.), Ca.	120	33.29 N	118.37 W
Santa Catalina, Cerro de (Mt.), Pan. (sĕ'r-rō-dĕ-sän-tä-kä-tä-lē'nä)	133	8.39 N	81.36 W
Santa Catalina, G. of, Ca. (săn'tà kă-tà-lē'nà)	120	33.00 N	117.58 W
Santa Catarina, Mex. (sän'tä kä-tä-rē'nä)	124	25.41 N	100.27 W
Santa Catarina (R.), Mex.	130	16.31 N	98.39 W
Santa Catarina (State), Braz. (sän-tä-kä-tä-rē'nà)	144	27.15 S	50.30 W
Santa Catarina, see **Loxicha**			
Santa Catarina, see **Yosonotú**			
Santa Clara, Ca. (săn'tà klâr'à)	116b	37.21 N	121.56 W
Santa Clara, Cuba (sän't klä'rä)	134	22.25 N	80.00 W
Santa Clara, Mex.	124	24.29 N	103.22 W
Santa Clara, Ur.	144	32.46 S	54.51 W
Santa Clara (R.), Ca. (săn'tà klă'rà)	120	34.22 N	118.53 W
Santa Clara, (Vol.), Nic.	132	12.44 N	87.00 W
Santa Clara, Bahía de (B.), Cuba (bä-ē'ä-dĕ-sän-tä-klä-rä)	134	23.05 N	80.50 W
Santa Clara, Sierra, (Mts.), Mex. (sē-ĕ'r-rä-sän'tà klä'rä)	128	27.30 N	113.50 W
Santa Coloma de Cervelló, Sp.	65e	41.22 N	2.01 E
Santa Coloma de Gramanet, Sp.	65e	41.27 N	2.13 E
Santa Cruz, Bol. (sän'tà krōōz')	142	17.45 S	63.03 W
Santa Cruz, Braz. (sän-tä-krōō's)	144	29.43 S	52.15 W
Santa Cruz, Braz.	144b	22.55 S	43.41 W
Santa Cruz, Ca.	120	36.59 N	122.02 W
Santa Cruz, Chile	141b	34.38 S	71.21 W
Santa Cruz, C. R.	132	10.16 N	85.37 W
Santa Cruz, Mex.	124	25.50 N	105.25 W
Santa Cruz, Phil.	203a	13.28 N	122.02 E
Santa Cruz, Phil.	203a	14.17 N	121.25 E
Santa Cruz, Phil.	203a	15.46 N	119.53 E
Santa Cruz (Prov.), Arg.	144	48.00 S	70.00 W
Santa Cruz (I.), Ec. (sän-tä-krōō'z)	142	0.38 S	90.20 W
Santa Cruz (R.), Arg. (sän'tà krōōz')	144	50.05 S	66.30 W
Santa Cruz (R.), Az. (săn'tà krōōz')	121	32.30 N	111.30 W
Santa Cruz Barillas, Guat. (sän-tä-krōō'z-bä-rē'l-yäs)	132	15.47 N	91.22 W
Santa Cruz Chico, see **Pedro Antonio Santos**			
Santa Cruz del Sur, Cuba (sän-tä-krōō's-dĕl-sōō'r)	134	20.45 N	78.00 W
Santa Cruz de Tenerife, Can. Is. (sän'tä krōōz då tā-nå-rē'få)	224	28.07 N	15.27 W
Santa Cruz Is., Sol. Is.	215	10.58 S	166.47 E
Santa Cruz Meyehualco, Mex.	60a	19.20 N	99.03 W
Santa Cruz Mts., Ca. (săn'tà krōōz')	118b	37.30 N	122.19 W
Santa Domingo, Cay (I.), Ba.	135	21.50 N	75.45 W
Santa Eduviges, Chile	61b	33.33 S	70.39 W
Santa Elena del Gomero, Chile	61b	33.29 S	70.46 W
Santa Eugenia de Ribeira, Sp. (sän-tä-ĕōō-hĕ'nyä-dĕ-rē-bĕ'y-rä)	170	42.34 N	8.55 W
Santa Eulalia del Rio, Sp. (sän'tä å-ōō-lä'lē-ä dĕl rē'ō)	171	38.58 N	1.29 E
Santa Fe, Arg. (sän'tä fā')	144	31.33 S	60.45 W
Santa Fe, Cuba (sän-tä-fĕ')	134	21.45 N	82.40 W
Santa Fé, Cuba	60b	23.05 N	82.31 W
Santa Fe, Mex.	60a	19.23 N	99.14 W
Santa Fe, NM (săn'tà fā')	121	35.10 N	106.00 W
Santa Fe, Sp. (sän'tä-fā')	170	37.12 N	3.43 W
Santa Fe (Prov.), Arg. (sän'tä fā')	144	32.00 S	61.15 W
Santa Filomena, Braz. (sän-tä-fē-lō-mĕ'nä)	143	9.09 S	44.45 W
Santa Genoveva, (Mtn.), Mex. (sän-tä-hĕ-nō-vĕ'vä)	128	23.30 N	110.00 W
Santai, China (san-tī)	203	31.02 N	105.02 E
Santa Inés, Ven. (sän'tä ē-nĕ's)	143b	9.54 N	64.21 W
Santa Inés (I.), Chile (sän'tä ē-nās')	144	53.45 S	74.15 W
Santa Isabel (I.), Sol. Is.	215	7.57 S	159.28 E
Santa Lucia, Cuba (sän'tä lōō-sē'ä)	134	21.50 N	77.30 W
Santa Lucia, Ur. (sän-tä-lōō-sē'ä)	141c	34.27 S	56.23 W
Santa Lucia, Ven.	143b	10.18 N	66.40 W
Santa Lucia B., Cuba (sän'tà lōō-sē'ä)	134	22.55 N	84.20 W
Santa Lucia (R.), Ur. (sän-tä-lōō-sē'ä)	141c	34.19 S	56.13 W
Santa Magarita (I.), Mex. (sän'tà mär-gä-rē'tà)	128	24.15 N	112.00 W
Santa Maria, Braz. (sän'tà mä-rē'à)	144	29.40 S	54.00 W
Santa Maria, Ca. (săn-tà mà-rē'à)	120	34.57 N	120.28 W
Santa Maria, It. (sän-tä mä-rē'ä)	172	41.05 N	14.15 E
Santa Maria, Phil. (sän-tä-mä-rē'ä)	207a	14.48 N	120.57 E
Santa Maria (R.), Mex. (sän'tà mä-rē'ä)	130	21.33 N	100.17 W
Santa Maria, C, Ba.	135	23.45 N	75.30 W
Santa Maria, Cabo de (C.), Port. (kà'bō-dĕ-sän-tä-mä-rē'ä)	170	36.58 N	7.54 W
Santa Maria, Cayo (I.), Cuba (kä'yō-săn'tà mà-rē'à)	134	22.40 N	79.00 W
Santa Maria de los Angeles, Mex. (dĕ-lôs-á'n-hĕ-lĕs)	130	22.10 N	103.34 W
Santa Maria de Ocotán, Mex. (sän'tä-mä-rē'ä-dĕ-ō-kō-tá'n)	130	22.56 N	104.30 W
Santa Maria I., Açores (sän-tä-mä-rē'ä)	224a	37.09 N	26.02 W
Santa Maria Madalena, Braz. (sän-tä-mà-rē'ä-mà-dà-lĕ-nä)	141a	22.00 S	42.00 W
Santa Maria, see **Huazolotitlán**			
Santa María del Oro, Mex. (sän'tä-mä-rē'ä-dĕl-ô-rō)	130	21.21 N	104.35 W
Santa María del Rio, Mex. (sän'tà mä-rē'ä dĕl rē'ō)	130	21.46 N	100.43 W
Santa María del Rosario, Cuba	60b	23.04 N	82.15 W
Santa María Tulpetlac, Mex.	60a	19.34 N	99.03 W
Santa Marta, Col. (sän'tà mär'tà)	142	11.15 N	74.13 W
Santa Marta, Peru	60c	12.02 S	76.56 W
Santa Marta, Cabo de (C.), Ang.	230	13.52 S	12.25 E
Santa Martha Acatitla, Mex.	60a	19.22 N	99.01 W
Santa Monica, Ca. (săn'tà mŏn'ĭ-kà)	119a	34.01 N	118.29 W
Santa Mónica (Neigh.), Ven.	61a	10.29 N	66.53 W
Santa Monica B., Ca.	59	33.54 N	118.25 W
Santa Monica Mts., Ca.	119a	34.08 N	118.38 W
Santana (R.), Braz. (sän-tä'nä)	144b	22.33 S	43.37 W
Santander, Col. (sän-tän-dĕr')	142a	3.00 N	76.25 W
Santander, Sp. (sän-tän-dâr')	170	43.27 N	3.50 W
Sant' Antimo, It.	171c	40.40 N	14.11 E
Santañy, Sp. (sän-tän'yē)	171	39.21 N	3.08 E
Santa Paula, Ca. (săn'tà pô'là)	120	34.24 N	119.05 W
Santarém, Braz. (sän-tä-rĕɴ')	143	2.28 S	54.37 W
Santarém, Port.	170	39.18 N	8.48 W

ng-sing; ŋ-baŋk; ɴ-nasalized n; nŏd; cŏmmit; ōld; ôbey; ôrder; oi-boil; fōōd; fŏŏt; ou-out; s-soft; sh-dish; th-thin; pūre; ůnite; ûrn; stŭd; circŭs; ü-as in French tu; '-indeterminate vowel.

PLACE (Pronounciation)	PAGE	Lat. °′	Long. °′
Santaren Chan., Ba. (săn-tȧ-rĕn')	134	24.15 N	79.30 W
Santa Rita, NM (săn'tȧ rē'tȧ)	121	32.45 N	108.05 W
Santa Rita do Passo Quatro, Braz. (sän-tä-rē'tä-dô-kwä'trô)	141a	21.43 S	47.27 W
Santa Rita do Sapucai, Braz. (sä-pōō-kà'ē)	141a	22.15 S	45.41 W
Santa Rosa, Arg. (sän-tä-rô-sä)	144	36.45 S	64.10 W
Santa Rosa, Ca. (săn'tȧ rō'zȧ)	120	38.27 N	122.42 W
Santa Rosa, Col. (sän-tä-rô-sä)	142a	6.38 N	75.26 W
Santa Rosa, Ec.	142	3.29 S	78.55 W
Santa Rosa, Guat. (sän'tȧ rō'sȧ)	132	14.21 N	90.16 W
Santa Rosa, Hond.	132	14.45 N	88.51 W
Santa Rosa, NM (săn'tȧ rō'sȧ)	122	34.55 N	104.41 W
Santa Rosa, Ven. (sän-tä-rô-sä)	143b	9.37 N	64.10 W
Santa Rosa de Cabal, Col. (sän-tä-rô-sä-dĕ-kä-bä'l)	142a	4.53 N	75.38 W
Santa Rosa de Huechuraba, Chile	61b	33.21 S	70.41 W
Santa Rosa de Locobe, Chile	61b	33.26 S	70.33 W
Santa Rosa de Viterbo, Braz. (sän-tä-rô-sȧ-dĕ-vē-tĕr'-bô)	141a	21.30 S	47.21 W
Santa Rosa Ind. Res., Ca. (săn'tȧ rō'zȧ')	120	33.28 N	116.50 W
Santa Rosalia, see Ciudad Camargo			
Santa Rosalía, Mex. (sän'tȧ rô-zä'lē-ȧ)	128	27.13 N	112.15 W
Santa Rosa Mts., Nv. (săn'tȧ rō'zȧ)	116	41.33 N	117.50 W
Santa Susana, Ca. (săn'tȧ sōō-zä'nȧ)	119a	34.16 N	118.42 W
Santa Tecla, see Nueva San Salvador			
Santa Teresa, Arg. (sän-tä-tĕ-rĕ'sä)	141c	33.27 S	60.47 W
Santa Teresa, Ven.	143b	10.14 N	66.40 W
Santa Teresa de lo Ovalle, Chile	61b	33.23 S	70.47 W
Santa Ursula Coapa, Mex.	60a	19.17 N	99.11 W
Santa Vitória do Palmar, Braz. (sän-tä-vē-tō'ryä-dô-päl-mär)	144	33.30 S	53.16 W
Santa Ynez (R.), Ca. (săn'tȧ ē-nĕz')	120	34.40 N	120.20 W
Santa Ysabel Ind. Res., Ca. (săn-tȧ ĭ-zȧ-bĕl')	120	33.05 N	116.46 W
Santee, Ca. (săn tē')	120a	32.50 N	116.58 W
Santee (R.), SC	127	33.27 N	80.02 W
Santeny, Fr.	64c	48.43 N	2.34 E
Sant' Eufemia, Golfo di (G.), It. (gôl-fô-dē-sän-tĕ'ōō-fē'myä)	172	38.53 N	15.53 E
Santiago, Braz. (sän-tyȧ'gô)	144	29.05 S	54.46 W
Santiago, Chile (sän-tē-ä'gô)	141b	33.26 S	70.40 W
Santiago, Pan.	133	8.07 N	80.58 W
Santiago, Phli. (sän-tyä'gô)	207a	16.42 N	121.33 E
Santiago (Prov.), Chile (sän-tyȧ'gō)	141b	33.28 S	70.55 W
Santiago (I.), Phil.	207a	16.29 N	120.03 E
Santiago Acahualtepec, Mex.	60a	19.21 N	99.01 W
Santiago de Compostela, Sp.	170	42.52 N	8.32 W
Santiago de Cuba, Cuba (sän-tyȧ'gô-dā kōō'bä)	135	20.00 N	75.50 W
Santiago de Cuba (Prov.), Cuba	135	20.20 N	76.05 W
Santiago de las Vegas, Cuba (sän-tyȧ'gô-dĕ-läs-vĕ'gäs)	135a	22.58 N	82.23 W
Santiago del Estero, Arg. (sän-tē-ä'gō-dĕl ĕs-tä'rō)	144	27.50 S	64.14 W
Santiago del Estero (Prov.), Arg. (sän-tē-ä'gō-dĕl ĕs-tä-rō)	144	27.15 S	63.30 W
Santiago de los Cabelleros, Dom. Rep. (sän-tyȧ'gô-dā lōs kä-bä-yä'rôs)	135	19.30 N	70.45 W
Santiago Mts., Tx. (sän-tē-ä'gô)	124	30.00 N	103.30 W
Santiago Res., Ca.	119a	33.47 N	117.42 W
Santiago, Rio Grande de (R.), Mex. (rē'o-grä'n-dĕ-dĕ-sän-tyä'gô)	130	21.15 N	104.05 W
Santiago Rodriguez, Dom. Rep. (sän-tyȧ'gô-rô-drē'gĕz)	135	19.30 N	71.25 W
Santiago, see Zacatepec			
Santiago Tepalcatlalpan, Mex.	60a	19.15 N	99.08 W
Santiago Tuxtla, Mex. (sän-tyȧ'gô-tōō'x-tlä)	131	18.28 N	95.18 W
Santiaguillo, Laguna de (L.), Mex. (lä-oō'nä-dĕ-sän-tē-ä-gēl'yō)	124	24.51 N	104.43 W
Santiam R., Or. (săn'tyăm)	116	44.42 N	122.26 W
Santissimo (Neigh.), Braz.	61c	22.53 S	43.31 W
Santisteban del Puerto, Sp. (sän'tē stå-bän'dĕl pwĕr'tô)	170	38.15 N	3.12 W
Santo Amaro, Braz. (sän'tōō ä-mä'rōō)	143	12.32 S	38.33 W
Santo Amaro (Neigh.), Braz.	61d	23.39 S	46.42 W
Santo Amaro de Campos, Braz. (sän-tō-ä-mä'rô-dĕ-kȧm'pôs)	141a	22.01 S	41.05 W
Santo André, Braz. (sän-tô-än-drĕ')	141a	23.40 S	46.31 W
Santo Angelo, Braz. (sän-tō-ȧ'n-zhĕ-lô)	144	28.16 S	53.59 W
Santo Antônio do Monte, Braz. (sän-tō-än-tō'nyô-dô-môn'tĕ)	141a	20.06 S	45.18 W
Santo Domingo, Cuba (sän'tô-dōmĭn'gô)	134	22.35 N	80.20 W
Santo Domingo, Dom. Rep. (sän'tô dô-mĭn'gô)	135	18.30 N	69.55 W
Santo Domingo, Nic. (sän-tô-dô-mē'n-gō)	132	12.15 N	84.56 W
Santo Domingo de la Caizada, Sp. (dā lä käl-thä'dä)	170	42.27 N	2.55 W
Santo Domingo, see Zanatepec			
Santoña, Sp. (sän-tō'nyä)	170	43.25 N	3.27 W
Sant' Onofrio (Neigh.), It.	66c	41.56 N	12.25 E
Santos, Braz. (sän'tozh)	141a	23.58 S	46.20 W
Santos Dumont, Braz. (sän'tôs-dōō-mô'nt)	141a	21.28 S	43.33 W
Santo Tomé, Arg. (sän-tô-tô-mĕ')	144	28.32 S	56.04 W
Sanuki, Jap. (sä'nōō-kĕ)	205a	35.16 N	139.53 E
San Urbano, Arg. (sän-ōōr-bä'nô)	141c	33.39 S	61.28 W
San Valentin, M. (Mtn.), Chile (sän-vä-lĕn-tē'n)	144	46.41 S	73.30 W
San Vicente, Arg. (sän-vē-sĕn'tĕ)	141c	35.00 S	58.26 W
San Vicente, Chile	141b	34.25 S	71.06 W
San Vicente, Sal. (sän vē-sĕn'tȧ)	132	13.41 N	88.43 W
San Vicente de Alcántara, Sp. (sän vē-thĕn'tȧ dā äl-kän'tä-rä)	170	39.24 N	7.08 W

PLACE (Pronounciation)	PAGE	Lat. °′	Long. °′
San Vicente dels Horts, Sp.	65e	41.24 N	2.01 E
San Vito al Tagliamento, It. (san vē'tô)	172	45.53 N	12.52 E
San Xavier Ind. Res., Az. (x-ä'vĭēr)	121	32.07 N	111.12 W
San Ysidro, Ca. (sän ysĭ-drō')	120a	32.33 N	117.02 W
Sanyuanli, China (sän-yůän-lē)	202a	23.11 N	113.16 E
São Bernado do Campo, Braz. (souN-bĕr-när'dô-dô-kä'm-pô)	141a	23.44 S	46.33 W
São Borja, Braz. (souN-bôr-zhä)	144	28.44 S	55.59 W
São Caetano do Sul, Braz.	61d	23.36 S	46.34 W
São Carlos, Braz. (souN kär'lōzh)	141a	22.02 S	47.54 W
São Cristovão, Braz. (souN-krēs-tō-vouN)	143	11.04 S	37.11 W
São Cristóvão (Neigh.), Braz.	61c	22.54 S	43.14 W
São Fidélis, Braz. (souN-fē-dĕ'lēs)	141a	21.41 S	41.45 W
São Francisco, Braz. (souN frăN-sēsh'kōō)	143	15.59 S	44.42 W
São Francisco do Sul, Braz. (souN frăN-sēsh'kōō-dô-sōō'l)	144	26.15 S	48.42 W
São Francisco, Rio (R.), Braz. (rē'ô-sän-frän-sē's-kô)	143	8.56 S	40.20 W
São Gabriel, Braz. (souN'gä-brē-ĕl')	144	30.28 S	54.11 W
São Geraldo, Braz. (souN-zhĕ-rä'l-dô)	141a	21.01 S	42.49 W
São Gonçalo, Braz. (souN'gōŋ-sä'lōō)	144b	22.55 S	43.04 W
São Gonçalo do Sapucaí, Braz. (souN-gôn-sä'lō-dô-sä-pōō-kī')	141a	21.55 S	45.34 W
São Hill, Tan.	231	8.20 S	35.12 E
Sao Joao, Guinea-Bissau	228	11.32 N	15.26 W
São João da Barra, Braz. (souN-zhôuN-dä-bä'rä)	144b	21.40 S	41.03 W
São João da Boa Vista, Braz. (souN-zhôuN-dä-bôä-vē's-tä)	141a	21.58 S	46.45 W
São João del Rei, Braz. (souN zhô-ouN'dĕl-rā)	141a	21.08 S	44.14 W
São João de Meriti, Braz. (souN-zhôuN-dĕ-mĕ-rē-tē)	144b	22.47 S	43.22 W
São João do Arguaia, Braz. (souN zhô-ouN'dô-ä-rä-gwä'yä)	141	5.29 S	48.44 W
São João dos Lampas, Port. (souN' zhô-ouN' dōzh län-päzh')	171b	38.52 N	9.24 W
São João Nepomuceno, Braz. (souN-zhôuN-nĕ-pô-mōō-sĕ-nō)	141a	21.33 S	43.00 W
São Jorge I., Açores (souN zhôr'zhĕ)	224a	38.28 N	27.34 W
São José do Rio Pardo, Braz. (souN-zhô-sĕ'dô-rē'ô-pá'r-dō)	141a	21.36 S	46.50 W
São José do Rio Prêto, Braz. (souN zhô-zĕ'dô-re'ô-prē-tō)	143	20.57 S	49.12 W
São José dos Campos, Braz. (souN zhô-zä'dōzh käN pōzh')	141a	23.12 S	45.53 W
São Julião da Barra, Port.	65d	38.40 N	9.21 W
São Leopoldo, Braz. (souN-lĕ-ô-pôl'dô)	144	29.46 S	51.09 W
São Luis (Maranhão), Braz. (souN-lōōē's-mä-rän-youN')	143	2.31 S	43.14 W
São Luis do Paraitinga, Braz. (souN-lōōē's-dô-pä-rä-ē-tē'n-gä)	141a	23.15 S	44.18 W
São Manuel (R.) Braz.	143	8.28 S	57.07 E
São Mateus, Braz. (souN mä-tā'ōōzh)	143	18.44 S	39.45 W
São Mateus, Braz.	61c	22.49 S	43.23 W
São Miguel Arcanjo, Braz. (souN-mē-gĕ'l-ár-kän-zhō)	141a	23.54 S	47.59 W
São Miguel I., Açores	224a	37.59 N	26.38 W
São Miguel Paulista (Neigh.), Braz.	61d	23.30 S	46.26 W
Saona (I.), Dom. Rep. (sä-ô'nä)	135	18.10 N	68.55 W
Saône (R.), Ra. (sōn)	168	46.27 N	4.58 E
São Nicolau, Ang.	230	14.15 S	12.21 E
São Nicolau, C. V. (souN' nē-kô-louN')	224b	16.19 N	25.19 W
São Paulo, Braz. (souN' pou'lōō)	141a	23.34 S	46.38 W
São Paulo (State), Braz. (souN pou'lōō)	143	21.45 S	50.47 W
São Paulo de Olivença, Braz. (souN'pou'lōōdå ô-lē-vĕn'sȧ)	142	3.32 S	68.46 W
São Pedro, Braz. (souN-pĕ'drô)	141a	22.34 S	47.54 W
São Pedro de Aldeia, Braz. (souN-pĕ'drô-dĕ-äl-dĕ'yä)	141a	22.50 S	42.04 W
São Raimundo Nonato, Braz. (souN' rī-mōō'n-do nô-nä'tōō)	143	9.09 S	42.32 W
São Roque, Braz. (souN' rō'kĕ)	141a	23.32 S	47.08 W
São Roque, Cabo de (C.), Braz. (kä'bo-dĕ-souN' rō'kĕ)	143	5.06 S	35.11 W
São Sebastião, Braz. (souN sȧ-bäs-tē-ouN')	141a	23.48 S	45.25 W
São Sebastião do Paraíso, Braz. (souN-sĕ-bäs-tē-ouN-dô-pä-rä-ē'sō)	141a	20.54 S	46.58 W
São Sebastião, Ilha de (I.), Braz. (ēl'yȧ dȧ souN' sȧ-bäs-tē-ouN')	141a	23.52 S	45.22 W
São Simão, Braz. (souN-sē-mouN)	141a	21.30 S	47.33 W
São Tiago I., C. V. (souN tē-ä'gōō)	224b	15.09 N	24.45 W
São Tomé, São Tomé & Príncipe (souN tô-mă')	230	0.20 N	6.44 E
São Tomé (I.), São Tomé & Príncipe	230	0.20 N	7.00 E
São Tomé, Cabo de (C.), Braz. (kä'bō-dĕ-souN-tô-mĕ')	141a	22.00 S	40.00 W
Sao Tome & Principe, Afr. (prēn'sē-pĕ)	222	1.00 N	6.00 E
Saoura, Oued (R.), Alg.	160	29.39 N	1.42 W
São Vicente, Braz. (souN ve-se'n-tĕ)	141a	23.57 S	46.25 W
Sao Vincente I., C. V. (souN vē-sĕn'tå)	224b	16.51 N	24.35 W
São Vinente, Cabo de (C.), Port. (kȧ'bō-dĕ-sän-vē-sĕ'n-tĕ)	170	37.03 N	9.31 W
Sapele, Nig. (sä-pä'lā)	229	5.54 N	5.41 E
Sapitwa (Mtn.), Malawi	231	15.58 S	35.38 E
Sapozhok, Sov. Un. (sä-pô-zhôk')	174	53.58 N	40.44 E
Sapporo, Jap. (säp-pô'rô)	204	43.02 N	141.29 E
Sapronovo, Sov. Un. (säp-rô'nô-vô)	182b	55.13 N	38.25 E
Sapucaia, Braz. (sä-pōō-kä'yȧ)	141a	22.01 S	42.54 W
Sapucaí (R.), Braz. (sä-pōō-kȧ-ē')	141a	21.07 S	45.53 W

PLACE (Pronounciation)	PAGE	Lat. °′	Long. °′
Sapucaí Mirim (R.), Braz. (sä-pōō-kä-ē'mē-rēN)	141a	21.06 S	47.03 W
Sapulpa, Ok. (sȧ-pŭl'pȧ)	123	36.01 N	96.05 W
Sâqiyat Makkī, Egypt	71a	30.00 N	31.13 E
Saqqez, Iran	195	36.14 N	46.16 E
Saquarema, Braz. (sä-kwä-rĕ-mä)	141a	22.56 S	42.32 W
Sara, Wa. (sä'rä)	118c	45.45 N	122.42 W
Sara, Bahr (R.), Chad-Cen. Afr. Rep. (bär)	225	8.19 N	17.44 E
Sarajas de Madrid (Neigh.), Sp.	65b	40.28 N	3.35 W
Sarajevo, Yugo. (sä-rä-yĕv'ô) (sȧ-rä'ya-vô)	173	43.15 N	18.26 E
Sarakhs, Iran	195	36.32 N	61.11 E
Sarana, Sov. Un. (sá-rä'ná)	182a	56.31 N	57.44 E
Saranac L., NY (săr'ȧ-năk)	111	44.15 N	74.20 W
Saranac Lake, NY	111	44.20 N	74.05 W
Sarandi, Arg. (sä-rän'dē)	144a	34.36 S	58.21 W
Sarandi Grande, Ur. (sä-rän'dē-grän'dĕ)	141c	33.42 S	56.21 W
Sārangpur, India	196	23.39 N	76.32 E
Saranley, Som.	223a	2.28 N	42.15 E
Saransk, Sov. Un. (sá-ränsk')	178	54.10 N	45.10 E
Sarany, Sov. Un. (sȧ-rá'nĭ)	182a	58.33 N	58.48 E
Sara Pk., Nig.	229	9.37 N	9.25 E
Sarapul, Sov. Un. (sä-räpōōl')	178	56.28 N	53.50 E
Sarasota, Fl. (săr-ȧ-sōtȧ)	127a	27.27 N	82.30 W
Saratoga, Tx. (săr-ȧ-tō'gȧ)	125	30.17 N	94.31 W
Saratoga, Wa.	118a	48.04 N	122.29 W
Saratoga Pass, Wa.	118a	48.09 N	122.33 W
Saratoga Springs, NY (sprĭngz)	111	43.05 N	74.50 W
Saratov, Sov. Un. (sá rä'tôf)	179	51.30 N	45.30 E
Saravane, Laos	203	15.48 N	106.40 E
Sarawak (Reg.), Mala. (sȧ-rä'wäk)	206	2.30 N	112.45 E
Sárbogárd, Hung. (shär'bô-gärd)	167	46.53 N	18.38 E
Sarcee Ind. Res., Can. (sär'sē)	95e	50.58 N	114.23 W
Sarcelles, Fr.	64c	49.00 N	2.23 E
Sardalas, Libya	224	25.59 N	10.33 E
Sardinia (I.), It. (sär-dĭn'ĭȧ)	172	40.08 N	9.05 E
Sardis, Ms. (sär'dĭs)	126	34.26 N	89.55 W
Sargent, Ne. (sär'jĕnt)	114	41.40 N	99.38 W
Sarh (Fort-Archambault), Chad. (är-chaN-bō')	229	9.09 N	18.23 E
Sarikamis, Tur.	179	40.30 N	42.40 E
Sariñena, Sp. (sä-rēn-yĕ'nä)	171	41.46 N	0.11 W
Sariwŏn, Korea (sä'rē-wŭn')	202	38.40 N	125.45 E
Sark (I.), Guernsey (särk)	168	49.28 N	2.22 W
Şarkoy, Tur. (shär'kû-ē)	173	40.39 N	27.07 E
Sarmiento, Monte (Mt.), Chile (mô'n-tĕ-sär-myĕn'tō)	144	54.28 S	70.40 W
Sarnia, Can. (sär'nē-ȧ)	110	43.00 N	82.25 W
Sarno, It. (sä'r-nô)	171c	40.35 N	14.38 E
Sarny, Sov. Un. (sär'nē)	167	51.17 N	26.39 E
Saronikós Kólpos (G.), Grc.	173	37.51 N	23.30 E
Saros Körfezi (G.), Tur. (sä'rôs)	173	40.30 N	26.20 E
Sárospatak, Hung. (shä'rôsh-pô'tôk)	167	48.19 N	21.35 E
Šar Planina (Mts.), Yugo. (shär plä'nē-na)	173	42.07 N	21.54 E
Sarpsborg, Nor. (särps'bôrg)	164	59.17 N	11.07 E
Sarratt, Eng.	62	51.41 N	0.29 W
Sarrebourg, Fr. (sär-bōōr')	169	48.44 N	7.02 E
Sarreguemines, Fr. (sär-gē-mēn')	169	49.06 N	7.05 E
Sarria, Sp. (sär'ē-ä)	170	42.14 N	7.17 W
Sarstun R., Guat. (särs-tōō'n)	132	15.50 N	89.26 W
Sartène, Fr. (sär-tĕn')	172	41.36 N	8.59 E
Sarthe (R.), Fr. (särt)	168	47.44 N	0.32 W
Sartrouville, Fr.	64c	48.57 N	2.10 E
Sárvár, Hung. (shär'vär)	166	47.14 N	16.55 E
Saryche, Mys (C.), Sov. Un. (mĭs sȧ-rēch')	179	44.25 N	33.00 E
Sary-Ishikotrau, Peski (Des.), Sov. Un. (sä'rē ē' shĕ-kô-trou)	180	46.12 N	75.30 E
Sarysu (R.), Sov. Un. (sä'rē-sōō)	180	47.47 N	69.14 E
Sasarām, India (sŭs-ŭ-räm')	196	25.00 N	84.00 E
Sasayama, Jap. (sä'sä-yä'mä)	205	35.05 N	135.14 E
Sasebo, Jap. (sä'sȧ-bô)	205	33.12 N	129.43 E
Sashalom (Neigh.), Hung.	66g	47.31 N	19.11 E
Sašice, Czech.	166	49.14 N	13.31 E
Saskatchewan (Prov.), Can.	96	54.46 N	107.40 W
Saskatchewan (R.), Can. (săs-kăch'ē-wăn)	100	53.45 N	103.20 W
Saskatoon, Can. (săs-kȧ-tōōn')	100	52.07 N	106.38 W
Sasolburg, S. Afr.	223d	26.52 S	27.47 E
Sasovo, Sov. Un. (sás'ô-vô)	178	54.20 N	42.00 E
Saspamco, Tx. (săs-păm'cō)	119d	29.13 N	98.18 W
Sassafras, Austl.	70b	37.52 S	145.21 E
Sassandra, Ivory Coast	228	4.58 N	6.05 W
Sassandra (R.), Ivory Coast (sás-sän'drá)	228	5.35 N	6.25 W
Sassari, It. (säs'sä-rē)	172	40.44 N	8.33 E
Sassnitz, G.D.R. (säs'nĕts)	166	54.31 N	13.37 E
Satadougou, Mali (sä-tä-dōō-goō')	228	12.21 N	10.07 W
Säter, Swe. (sĕ'tĕr)	164	60.21 N	15.50 E
Sātghara, India	67a	22.44 N	88.21 E
Satilla (R.), Ga. (sȧ-tĭl'ȧ)	127	31.15 N	82.13 W
Satka, Sov. Un. (sät'kȧ)	182a	55.03 N	59.02 E
Sátoraljaujhely, Hung. (shä'tô-rô-lyô-ōō'yĕl')	167	48.24 N	21.40 E
Satu-Mare, Rom. (sä'tōō-má'rĕ)	167	47.50 N	22.53 E
Saturna, Can. (sä-tûr'ná)	118d	48.48 N	123.12 W
Saturna (I.), Can.	118d	48.47 N	123.03 W
Sauda, Nor.	164	59.40 N	6.21 E
Saudárkrókur, Ice.	158	65.41 N	19.38 W
Saudi Arabia, Asia (sá-ōō'dĭ á-rä'bĭ-ȧ)	190	22.40 N	46.00 E
Sauerlach, F.R.G. (zou'ĕr-läK)	157d	47.58 N	11.39 E
Saugatuck, Mi. (sô'gȧ-tŭk)	110	42.40 N	86.10 W
Saugeer (R.), Can. (sô'gēr)	110	44.20 N	81.20 W
Saugerties, NY (sô'gēr-tēz)	111	42.05 N	73.55 W
Saugus, Ma. (sô'gŭs)	105a	42.28 N	71.01 W
Sauk (R.), Mn. (sôk)	115	45.30 N	94.45 W
Sauk Centre, Mn.	115	45.43 N	94.58 W
Sauk City, Wi.	115	43.16 N	89.45 W

PLACE (Pronounciation)	PAGE	Lat. °′	Long. °′
Sauk Rapids, Mn. (răp'ĭd)	115	45.35 N	94.08 W
Sault Sainte Marie, Can.	102	46.31 N	84.20 W
Sault Sainte Marie, Mi. (so͞o sănt må-rē')	119k	46.29 N	84.21 W
Saumatre, Etang (L.), Hai.	135	18.40 N	72.10 W
Saunders L., Can. (săn'dẽrs)	95g	53.18 N	113.25 W
Saurimo, Ang.	230	9.39 S	20.24 E
Sausalito, Ca. (sô-så-lē'tō)	118b	37.51 N	122.29 W
Sausset-les-Pins, Fr. (sō-sĕ'lā-păN')	168a	43.20 N	5.08 E
Saútar, Ang.	230	11.06 S	18.27 E
Sauvie I., Or. (sô'vē)	118c	45.43 N	123.49 W
Sava (R.), Yugo. (sä'vä)	173	44.50 N	17.00 E
Savage, Md. (să'vĕj)	112e	39.07 N	76.49 W
Savage, Mn.	119g	44.47 N	93.20 W
Savalan (Mtn.), Iran	179	38.20 N	48.00 E
Savalen (L.), Nor.	164	62.19 N	10.15 E
Savalou, Benin	229	7.56 N	1.58 E
Savanna, Il. (så-văn'å)	115	42.05 N	90.09 W
Savannah, Ga. (så-văn'å)	127	32.04 N	81.07 W
Savannah, Mo.	115	39.58 N	94.49 W
Savannah, Tn.	126	35.13 N	88.14 W
Savannah (R.), Ga.-SC	127	33.11 N	81.51 W
Savannakhét, Indo China	206	16.33 N	104.45 E
Savanna la Mar, Jam. (så-văn'å lå mär')	134	18.10 N	78.10 W
Sávara R., Czech.	166	49.36 N	15.24 E
Savé, Benin (så-vā')	224	8.09 N	2.03 E
Save (R.), Fr.	168	43.32 N	0.50 E
Save, Rio (R.), Moz. (rē'ō-sä'vĕ)	226	21.28 S	34.14 E
Sāveh, Iran	195	35.01 N	50.20 E
Saverne, Fr. (så-vĕrn')	169	48.40 N	7.22 E
Savigliano, It. (sä-vēl-yä'nô)	172	44.38 N	7.42 E
Savigny-sur-Orge, Fr.	169b	48.41 N	2.22 E
Savona, It. (sä-nō'nä)	172	44.19 N	8.28 E
Savonlinna, Fin. (sá'vôn-lēn'nà)	165	61.53 N	28.49 E
Savran', Sov. Un. (säv-rän')	175	48.07 N	30.09 E
Sawahlunto, Indon.	206	0.37 S	100.50 E
Sawākin, Sud.	225	19.02 N	37.19 E
Sawda, Jabal as (Mts.), Libya	225	28.14 N	13.46 E
Sawhāj, Egypt	223b	26.34 N	31.40 E
Sawknah, Libya	225	29.04 N	15.53 E
Sawu, Laut (Savu Sea), Indon.	206	9.15 S	122.15 E
Sawu, Pulau (I.), Indon.	206	10.15 S	122.00 E
Sawyer, (L.), Wa. (sô'yẽr)	118a	47.20 N	122.02 W
Say, Niger (sä'ē)	224	13.09 N	2.16 E
Sayan Khrebet (Mts.), Sov. Un. (sŭ-yän')	180	51.30 N	90.00 E
Saydā (Sidon), Leb. (sä'ē-dä) (sī'dŏn)	191a	33.34 N	35.23 E
Sayhūt, P. D. R. of Yem.	192	15.23 N	51.28 E
Sayre, Ok. (sā'ẽr)	122	35.19 N	99.40 W
Sayre, Pa.	111	41.55 N	76.30 W
Sayreton, Al. (sā'ẽr-tŭn)	112h	33.34 N	86.51 W
Sayreville, NJ (sâr'vĭl)	112a	40.28 N	74.21 W
Sayr Usa, Mong.	198	44.15 N	107.00 E
Sayula, Mex. (sä-yo͞o'lä)	131	17.51 N	94.56 W
Sayula, Mex.	130	19.50 N	101.33 W
Sayula, Luguna de (L.), Mex. (lä-go͞o'nä-dĕ)	130	20.00 N	103.33 W
Say'un, P.D.R. of Yem.	192	16.00 N	48.59 E
Sayville, NY (sā'vĭl)	111	40.45 N	73.10 W
Saywūn, P.D.R. of Yem.	195	15.56 N	48.47 E
Sazanit (I.), Alb.	173	40.30 N	19.17 E
Sazhino, Sov. Un. (sáz-hē'nô)	182a	56.20 N	58.15 E
Scäffle, Swe.	164	59.10 N	12.55 E
Scala, Teatro alla (P. Int.), It.	65c	45.28 N	9.11 E
Scandinavian Pen., Eur.	190	62.00 N	14.00 E
Scanlon, Mn. (skăn'lôn)	119h	46.27 N	92.26 W
Scappoose, Or. (skă-po͞os')	118c	45.46 N	122.53 W
Scappoose (R.), Or.	118c	45.47 N	122.57 W
Scarborough, Can. (skär'bẽr-ô)	95d	43.45 N	79.12 W
Scarborough, Eng. (skär'bŭr-ô)	162	54.16 N	0.19 W
Scarsdale, NY (skärz'dāl)	112a	41.01 N	73.47 W
Scarth Hill, Eng.	64a	53.33 N	2.52 W
Scatari I, Can. (skăt'á-rē)	103	46.00 N	59.44 W
Sceaux, Fr.	64c	48.47 N	2.17 E
Schaerbeek, Bel. (skär'bāk)	157a	50.33 N	4.23 E
Schaffhausen, Switz. (shäf'hou-zĕn)	166	47.42 N	8.38 E
Schalksmühle, F.R.G.	63	51.14 N	7.31 E
Schapenrust, S. Afr.	71b	26.16 S	28.22 E
Scharl, F.R.G.	63	51.06 N	7.40 E
Scharnhorst (Neigh.), F.R.G.	63	51.32 N	7.32 E
Schefferville, Can.	97	54.52 N	67.01 W
Scheiblingstein, Aus.	66e	48.16 N	16.13 E
Schelde, R., Bel.	163	51.04 N	3.55 E
Schenectady, NY (skĕ-nĕk'tá-dē)	111	42.50 N	73.55 W
Scheveningen, Neth.	157a	52.06 N	4.15 E
Schiedam, Neth.	157a	51.55 N	4.23 E
Schildow, G.D.R.	65a	52.38 N	13.23 E
Schiller Park, Il.	58a	41.58 N	87.52 W
Schiltigheim, Fr. (shĕl'tegh-hīm)	169	48.48 N	7.47 E
Schio, It. (skē'ô)	172	45.43 N	11.23 E
Schleswig, F.R.G. (shĕls'vēgh)	166	54.32 N	9.32 E
Schleswig-Holstein (State), F.R.G. (shlĕs'vēgh-hōl'shtīn)	166	54.40 N	9.10 E
Schmalkalden, G.D.R. (shmäl'käl-dĕn)	166	50.41 N	10.25 E
Schneider, In. (schnīd'ẽr)	113a	41.12 N	87.26 W
Schofield, Wi. (skō'fēld)	115	44.52 N	89.37 W
Schöller, F.R.G.	63	51.14 N	7.01 E
Scholven (Neigh.), F.R.G.	63	51.36 N	7.01 E
Schönbrunn, Schloss (P. Int.), Aus.	66e	48.11 N	16.19 E
Schönebeck, G.D.R. (shû'nĕ-bergh)	166	52.01 N	11.44 E
Schönebeck (Neigh.), F.R.G.	63	51.28 N	6.56 E
Schöneberg (Neigh.), F.R.G.	65a	52.29 N	13.21 E
Schönefeld, G.D.R.	65a	52.23 N	13.30 E
Schöneiche, G.D.R.	65a	52.28 N	13.41 E
Schönerlinde, G.D.R.	65a	52.39 N	13.27 E
Schonnebeck (Neigh.), F.R.G.	63	51.29 N	7.04 E
Schönow, G.D.R.	65a	52.40 N	13.32 E
Schönwalde, G.D.R.	65a	52.37 N	13.07 E
Schoonhoven, Neth.	157a	51.56 N	4.51 E
Schramberg, F.R.G. (shräm'bĕrgh)	166	48.14 N	8.24 E
Schreiber, Can.	102	48.50 N	87.10 W
Schroon (L.), NY (skro͞on)	111	43.50 N	73.50 W
Schultzendorf, G.D.R. (sho͞ol'tzĕn-dōrf)	157b	52.21 N	13.55 E
Schumacher, Can.	102	48.30 N	81.30 W
Schüren (Neigh.), F.R.G.	63	51.30 N	7.32 E
Schuyler, Ne. (slī'lẽr)	114	41.28 N	97.05 W
Schuylkill (R.), Pa. (sko͞ol'kĭl)	112	40.10 N	75.31 W
Schuylkill-Haven, Pa. (sko͞ol'kĭl hā-vĕn)	111	40.35 N	76.10 W
Schwabach, F.R.G. (shvä'bäk)	166	49.19 N	11.02 E
Schwäbische Alb (Mts.), F.R.G. (shvă'bē-shĕ älb)	166	48.11 N	9.09 E
Schwäbisch Gmünd, F.R.G. (shvă'bēsh gmünd)	166	48.47 N	9.49 E
Schwäbisch Hall, F.R.G. (häl)	166	49.08 N	9.44 E
Schwafheim, F.R.G.	63	51.25 N	6.39 E
Schwandorf, F.R.G. (shvän'dôrf)	166	49.19 N	12.08 E
Schwanebeck, G.D.R.	65a	52.37 N	13.32 E
Schwanenwerder (Neigh.), F.R.G.	65a	52.27 N	13.10 E
Schwaner, Pegunungan Mts., Indon. (skvän'ẽr)	206	1.05 S	112.30 E
Schwarzenberg, F.R.G.	63	51.24 N	6.42 E
Schwarzwald (For.), F.R.G. (shvärts'väld)	166	47.54 N	7.57 E
Schwaz, Aus.	166	47.20 N	11.45 E
Schwechat, Aus. (shvĕk'át)	157e	48.09 N	16.29 E
Schwedt, G.D.R. (shvĕt)	166	53.04 N	14.17 E
Schweflinghausen, F.R.G.	63	51.16 N	7.25 E
Schweinfurt, F.R.G. (shvīn'fo͝ort)	166	50.03 N	10.14 E
Schwelm, F.R.G. (shvĕlm)	169c	51.17 N	7.18 E
Schwenke, F.R.G.	63	51.11 N	7.26 E
Schwerin, G.D.R. (shvĕ-rēn')	166	53.36 N	11.25 E
Schwerin (Neigh.), F.R.G.	63	51.33 N	7.20 E
Schweriner See (L.), G.D.R. (shvĕ'rē-nĕr zā)	166	53.40 N	11.06 E
Schwerte, F.R.G. (shvĕr'tĕ)	169c	51.26 N	7.34 E
Schwielowsee (L.), G.D.R. (shvē'lōv zā)	157b	52.20 N	12.52 E
Schwyz, Switz. (schēts)	166	47.01 N	8.38 E
Sciacca, It. (shē-äk'kä)	172	37.30 N	13.09 E
Science and Industry, Museum of (P. Int.), Il.	58a	41.47 N	87.35 W
Scilly, Isles of (Is.), Eng. (sĭl'ē)	162	49.56 N	6.50 W
Scioto (R.), Oh. (sī-ō'tō)	110	39.10 N	82.55 W
Scituate, Ma. (sĭt'ū-āt)	105a	42.12 N	70.45 W
Scobey, Mt. (skō'bē)	117	48.48 N	105.29 W
Scoggin, Or. (skŏ'gĭn)	118c	45.28 N	123.14 W
Scoresby, Austl.	70b	37.54 S	145.14 E
Scotch (R.), Can. (skŏch)	95c	45.21 N	74.56 W
Scotia, Ca. (skō'shå)	116	40.29 N	124.06 W
Scotland, SD	114	43.08 N	97.43 W
Scotland, U. K. (skŏt'lånd)	162	57.05 N	5.10 W
Scotland Neck, NC (nĕk)	127	36.06 N	77.25 W
Scotstown, Can. (skŏts'toun)	111	45.35 N	71.15 W
Scott Air Force Base, Il.	119e	38.33 N	89.52 W
Scottburgh, S. Afr. (skŏt'bŭr-ô)	227c	30.18 S	30.42 E
Scott, C., Can. (skŏt)	96	50.47 N	128.26 W
Scott City, Ks.	122	38.28 N	100.54 W
Scottdale, Ga. (skŏt'dāl)	112c	33.47 N	84.16 W
Scott Is., Ant.	232	67.00 S	178.00 E
Scott, Mt., Or.	118c	45.27 N	122.33 W
Scott, Mt., Or.	116	42.55 N	122.00 W
Scott Ra., Ant.	232	68.00 S	55.00 E
Scottsbluff, Ne. (skŏts'blŭf)	114	41.52 N	103.40 W
Scotts Bluff Natl. Mon., Ne.	114	41.45 N	103.47 W
Scottsboro, Al. (skŏts'bŭro)	101	34.40 N	86.03 W
Scottsburg, In. (skŏts'bûrg)	110	38.40 N	85.50 W
Scottsdale, Austl. (skŏts'dāl)	216	41.12 S	147.37 E
Scottsville, Ky. (skŏts'vĭl)	101	36.45 N	86.10 W
Scott Township, Pa.	57b	40.24 N	80.06 W
Scottville, Mi.	110	44.00 N	86.20 W
Scranton, Pa. (skrăn'tŭn)	111	41.45 N	75.45 W
Scugog (L.), Can. (skū'gŏg)	111	44.05 N	78.55 W
Scunthorpe, Eng. (skŭn'thôrp)	156	53.36 N	0.38 W
Scutari, L., Alb. (sko͞o'tä-rē)	173	42.14 N	19.33 E
Scutari, see Shkodër			
Seabeck, Wa. (sē'bĕck)	128a	47.38 N	122.50 W
Sea Bright, NJ (sē brīt)	112a	40.22 N	73.58 W
Seabrook, Md.	56d	38.58 N	76.51 W
Seabrook, Tx. (sē'bro͝ok)	125	29.34 N	95.01 W
Sea Cliff, NY	55	40.51 N	73.38 W
Seacombe, Eng.	64a	53.25 N	3.01 W
Seaford, De. (sē'fẽrd)	111	38.35 N	75.40 W
Seaford, NY	55	40.40 N	73.30 W
Seaforth, Austl.	70a	33.48 S	151.15 E
Seaforth, Eng.	64a	53.28 N	3.01 W
Seagraves, Tx. (sē'grāvs)	122	32.51 N	102.38 W
Sea, Is., Ga.-SC (sē)	127	31.21 N	81.05 W
Seal, Eng.	62	51.17 N	0.14 E
Seal (R.), Can.	96	59.08 N	96.37 W
Seal Beach, Ca.	119a	33.44 N	118.06 W
Seal Cays (Is.), Ba.	135	22.40 N	75.55 W
Seal Cays (Is.), Turks & Caicos Is.	135	21.10 N	71.45 W
Seal I., S. Afr. (sēl)	226a	34.07 S	18.36 E
Seal Rocks (Rocks), Ca.	58b	37.47 N	122.31 W
Sealy, Tx. (sē'lē)	125	29.46 N	96.10 W
Searcy, Ar. (sûr'sē)	123	35.13 N	91.43 W
Searles (L.), Ca. (sûrl's)	120	35.44 N	117.22 W
Searsport, Me. (sērz'pōrt)	104	44.28 N	68.55 W
Seaside, Or. (sē'sīd)	116	45.59 N	123.55 W
Seat Pleasant, Md.	56d	38.53 N	76.52 W
Seattle, Wa. (sē-ăt''l)	118a	47.36 N	122.20 W
Sebaco, Nic. (sĕ-bä'kô)	132	12.50 N	86.03 W
Sebago, Me. (sĕ-bā'gō)	104	43.52 N	70.20 W
Sebastion Vizcaino, Bahia (B.), Mex. (bä-ē'ä-sĕ-bäs-tyô'n-vēs-kä-ē'nô)	128	28.45 N	115.15 W
Sebastopol, Ca. (sē-bás'tô-pôl)	120	38.27 N	122.50 W
Sebderat, Eth.	225	15.30 N	36.45 E
Sébé (R.), Gabon	230	0.45 S	13.30 E
Sebeş, Rom.	173	45.58 N	23.34 E
Sebewaing, Mi. (se'bē-wăng)	110	43.45 N	83.25 W
Sebezh, Sov. Un. (syĕ'bĕzh)	174	56.16 N	28.29 E
Sebinkarahisar, Tur.	179	40.15 N	38.10 E
Sebnitz, G.D.R. (zĕb'nēts)	166	51.01 N	14.16 E
Sebou, Oued (R.), Mor.	160	34.23 N	5.18 W
Sebree, Ky. (sē-brē')	110	37.35 N	87.30 W
Sebring, Fl. (sē'brĭng)	127a	27.30 N	81.26 W
Sebring, Oh.	110	40.55 N	81.05 W
Secane, Pa.	56b	39.55 N	75.18 W
Secaucus, NJ	55	40.47 N	74.04 W
Secchia (R.), It. (sĕ'kyä)	172	44.25 N	10.25 E
Seco (R.), Mex. (sĕ'kō)	131	18.11 N	93.18 W
Sedalia, Mo.	123	38.42 N	93.12 W
Sedan, Fr. (sē-däN)	168	49.49 N	4.55 E
Sedan, Ks. (sē-dăn')	123	37.07 N	96.08 W
Sedom, Isr.	191a	31.04 N	35.24 E
Sedro Woolley, Wa. (sē'drô-wo͝ol'ē)	118a	48.30 N	122.14 W
Šeduva, Sov. Un. (shĕ'do͞o-vá)	165	55.46 N	23.45 E
Seeberg, G.D.R.	65a	52.33 N	13.41 E
Seeburg, G.D.R.	65a	52.31 N	13.07 E
Seefeld, G.D.R.	65a	52.37 N	13.40 E
Seekoevlei (L.), S. Afr. (zā'ko͞of-lī)	226a	34.04 S	18.33 E
Seer Green, Eng.	62	51.37 N	0.36 W
Seestall, F.R.G. (zā'shtäl)	157d	47.58 N	10.52 E
Sefrou, Mor. (sē-fro͞o')	160	33.49 N	4.46 W
Sefton, Eng.	64a	53.30 N	2.58 W
Seg (L.), Sov. Un. (syĕgh)	178	64.00 N	33.30 E
Segamat, Mala. (sā'gá-mát)	191b	2.30 N	102.49 E
Segang, China (sŭ-gäŋ)	200	31.59 N	114.13 E
Segbana, Benin	229	10.56 N	3.42 E
Segorbe, Sp. (sĕ-gôr-bĕ)	171	39.50 N	0.30 W
Ségou, Mali (sā-go͞o')	228	13.27 N	6.16 W
Segovia, Col. (sĕ-gô'vēä)	142a	7.08 N	74.42 W
Segovia, Sp. (sā-gō'vē-ä)	170	40.58 N	4.05 W
Segovia (R.), see Coco			
Segre (R.), Sp. (sā'grā)	171	41.54 N	1.10 E
Seguam (I.), Ak. (sē'gwäm)	107a	52.16 N	172.10 W
Seguam Pass., Ak.	107a	52.20 N	173.00 W
Séguédine, Niger	229	20.12 N	12.59 E
Séguéla, Ivory Coast (sā-gā-lä')	228	7.57 N	6.40 W
Seguin, Tx. (sĕ-gēn')	124	29.35 N	97.58 W
Segula (I.), Ak. (sē-gū'lá)	107a	52.08 N	178.35 E
Segura (R.), Sp.	170	38.24 N	2.12 W
Segura (R.), Sp. (så-go͞o'rä)	171	38.07 N	0.33 W
Segura, Sierra de (Mts.), Sp. (sē-ĕ'r-rä-dĕ)	170	38.05 N	2.45 W
Sehwān, Pak.	196	26.33 N	67.51 E
Seibeeshiden, Jap.	69a	35.34 N	139.22 E
Seibo, Dom. Rep. (sĕ'y-bō)	135	18.45 N	69.05 W
Seiling, Ok.	122	36.09 N	98.56 W
Seinäjoki, Fin. (sâ'ē-nĕ-yô'kē)	165	62.47 N	22.50 E
Seine (R.), Can. (sån)	102	49.04 N	91.00 W
Seine (R.), Can. (sån)	95f	49.48 N	96.30 W
Seine (R.), Fr.	168	49.21 N	1.17 E
Seine, Baie de la (B.), Fr. (bī dē lä sån)	168	49.37 N	0.53 W
Seio do Venus (Mtn.), Braz. (sĕ-yô-dô-vĕ'no͞os)	144b	22.28 S	43.12 W
Seixal, Port. (så-ē-shäl')	171b	38.38 N	9.06 W
Sekenke, Tan.	231	4.16 S	34.10 E
Sekondi-Takoradi, Ghana (sĕ-kôn'dē tä-kō-rä'dē)	228	4.59 N	1.43 W
Sekota, Eth.	225	12.47 N	38.59 E
Selangor (State), Mala. (sâ-län'gōr)	191b	2.53 N	101.29 E
Selanovtsi, Bul. (sål'á-nôv-tsĭ)	173	43.42 N	24.05 E
Selaru I., Indon.	207	8.30 S	130.30 E
Selatan, Tandjung (C.), Indon. (så-lä'tän)	206	4.09 S	114.40 E
Selawik, Ak. (sē-lá-wĭk)	107	66.30 N	160.09 W
Selayar, Pulau (I.), Indon.	206	6.15 S	121.15 E
Selbecke (Neigh.), F.R.G.	63	51.20 N	7.28 E
Selbusjøen (L.), Nor. (sĕl'bo͞o)	164	63.18 N	11.55 E
Selby, Eng. (sĕl'bē)	156	53.47 N	1.03 W
Selby (Neigh.), S. Afr.	71b	26.13 S	28.02 E
Seldovia, Ak. (sĕl-dō'vē-å)	107	59.26 N	151.42 W
Selection Park, S. Afr.	71b	26.18 S	28.27 E
Selemdzha (R.), Sov. Un. (så-lĕmt-zhä')	181	52.28 N	131.50 E
Selenga (R.), Sov. Un. (sĕ lĕŋ gä')	181	51.00 N	106.40 E
Selenge, Mong.	198	49.04 N	102.23 E
Selennyakh (R.), Sov. Un. (sĕl-yĭn-yäk)	181	67.42 N	141.45 E
Sélestat, Fr. (sĕ-lē-stä')	169	48.16 N	7.27 E
Selibaby, Mauritania (så-lē-bá-bē')	224	15.21 N	12.11 W
Seliger (L.), Sov. Un. (sĕl'lē-gĕr)	174	57.14 N	33.18 E
Selizharovo, Sov. Un. (så'lē-zhä'rô-vô)	174	56.51 N	33.28 E
Selkirk, Can. (sĕl'kûrk)	101	50.09 N	96.52 W
Selkirk Mts., Can.	96	51.00 N	117.40 W
Selleck, Wa. (sĕl'ĕck)	118a	47.22 N	121.52 W
Sellersburg, In. (sĕl'ẽrs-bûrg)	113h	38.25 N	85.45 W
Sellya Khskaya, Guba (B.), Sov. Un. (sĕl-yäk'skâ-yá)	181	72.30 N	136.00 E
Selma, Al. (sĕl'må)	126	32.25 N	87.00 W
Selma, Ca.	120	36.34 N	119.37 W
Selma, NC	127	35.33 N	78.16 W
Selma, Tx.	119d	29.33 N	98.19 W
Selmer, Tn.	126	35.11 N	88.36 W
Selsingen, F.R.G. (zĕl'zĕn-gĕn)	157c	53.22 N	9.13 E
Seltar, Singapore	67c	1.25 N	103.53 E
Selway R., Id. (sĕl'wå)	116	46.07 N	115.12 W
Selwyn (L.), Can. (sĕl'wĭn)	96	59.41 N	104.30 W
Seman (R.), Alb.	173	40.48 N	19.53 E
Semarang, Indon. (sĕ-mä'räng)	206	7.03 S	110.27 E
Semarinda, Indon.	206	0.30 S	117.10 E
Sembawang, Singapore	67c	1.27 N	103.50 E
Semendria, see Smederevo			
Semënovka, Sov. Un. (sĕ-myôn'ôf-kå)	175	52.10 N	32.34 E
Semeru, Gunung (Mtn.), Indon.	206	8.06 S	112.55 E
Semiahmoo Ind. Res., Can.	118d	49.01 N	122.43 W
Semiahmoo Spit, Wa. (sĕm'ĭ-á-mo͞o)	118d	48.59 N	122.52 W

ng-sing; ŋ-baŋk; N-nasalized n; nŏd; cŏmmit; ōld; ôbey; ôrder; oi-boil; fo͞od; fo͝ot; ou-out; s-soft; sh-dish; th-thin; pūre; ůnite; ûrn; stŭd; circŭs; ü-as in French tu; '-indeterminate vowel.

PLACE (Pronunciation)	PAGE	Lat. °'	Long. °'
Semichi Is., Ak. (sē-mē'chī)	107a	52.40 N	174.50 W
Seminoe Res., Wy. (sĕm'ĭ nô)	117	42.08 N	107.10 W
Seminole, Ok. (sĕm'ĭ-nōl)	123	35.13 N	96.41 W
Seminole, Tx.	124	32.43 N	102.39 W
Seminole Ind. Res., Fl.	127a	26.19 N	81.11 W
Seminole Ind. Res., Fl.	127a	27.05 N	81.25 W
Seminole, L., Fl.-Ga.	126	30.57 N	84.46 W
Semipalatinsk, Sov. Un. (sĕ'mē-pá-lá-tyēnsk')	180	50.28 N	80.29 E
Semisopochnoi (I.), Ak. (sĕ-mē-sá-pōsh' noi)	107a	51.45 N	179.25 W
Semiyarskoye, Sov. Un. (sĕ'mē-yär'skô-yĕ)	180	51.03 N	78.28 E
Semliki R., Ug.-Zaire (sĕm'lē-kē)	225	0.45 N	29.36 E
Semlin, see Zemun			
Semmering P., Aus. (sĕm'ĕr-ĭng)	166	47.39 N	15.50 E
Semnān, Iran	179	35.30 N	53.30 E
Senador Pompeu, Braz. (sĕ-nä-dōr-pôm-pĕ'ōō)	143	5.34 S	39.18 W
Senatobia, Ms. (sĕ-ná-tō'bē-á)	126	34.36 N	89.56 W
Send, Eng.	62	51.17 N	0.31 W
Sendai, Jap. (sĕn-dī')	204	38.18 N	141.02 E
Seneca, Ks. (sĕn'ĕ-ká)	123	39.49 N	96.03 W
Seneca, Md.	112e	39.04 N	77.20 W
Seneca, SC	126	34.40 N	82.58 W
Seneca (L.), NY	111	42.30 N	76.55 W
Seneca Falls, NY	111	42.55 N	76.55 W
Senegal, Afr. (sĕn-ĕ-gôl')	222	14.53 N	14.58 W
Sénégal (R.), Afr.	228	16.00 N	14.00 W
Senekal, S. Afr. (sĕn'ĕ-kál)	223d	28.20 S	27.37 E
Senftenberg, G.D.R. (zĕnf'tĕn-bĕrgh)	166	51.32 N	14.00 E
Sengunyane (R.), Leso	227c	29.35 S	28.08 E
Senhor do Bonfim, Braz. (sĕn-yôr dô bôN-fē'N)	143	5.21 S	40.09 W
Senigallia, It. (sā-nē-gäl'lyä)	172	43.42 N	13.16 E
Senj, Yugo. (sĕn')	172	44.58 N	14.55 E
Senja (I.), Nor. (sĕnyä)	158	69.28 N	16.10 E
Senlis, Fr. (säN-lēs')	169b	49.13 N	2.35 E
Sennar Dam, Sud.	225	13.38 N	33.38 E
Senneterre, Can.	97	48.20 N	77.22 W
Senno, Sov. Un. (syĕ'nô)	174	54.48 N	29.43 E
Senriyama, Jap.	69b	34.47 N	135.30 E
Sens, Fr. (säNs)	168	48.05 N	3.18 E
Sensuntepeque, Sal. (sĕn-sōōn-tā-pā'kā)	132	13.53 N	88.34 W
Senta, Yugo. (sĕn'tä)	173	45.54 N	20.05 E
Sentosa (I.), Singapore	67c	1.15 N	103.50 E
Senzaki, Jap. (sĕn'zä-kē)	205	34.22 N	131.09 E
Seoul, see Sŏul			
Sepang, Mala.	191b	2.43 N	101.45 E
Sepetiba, Baia de (B.), Braz. (bäē'ä dĕ sā-pā-tē'bá)	144b	23.01 S	43.42 W
Sepik (R.), Pap. N. Gui. (sĕp-ĕk')	207	4.07 S	142.40 E
Septentrional, Cordillera (Mts.), Dom. Rep. (kôr-dēl-yĕ'rä sĕp-tĕn-tryô-nä'l)	135	19.50 N	71.15 W
Septeuil, Fr. (sĕ-tû')	169b	48.53 N	1.40 E
Sept-Îles, Can. (sĕ-tēl')	104	50.12 N	66.23 W
Sequatchie (R.), Tn. (sē-kwăch'ē)	126	35.33 N	85.14 W
Sequim, Wa. (sē'kwĭm)	118a	48.05 N	123.07 W
Sequim B., Wa.	118a	48.04 N	122.58 W
Sequoia Natl. Park, Ca. (sē-kwoi'á)	120	36.34 N	118.37 W
Seragoon Hbr., Singapore	67c	1.23 N	103.57 E
Seraing, Bel. (sē-răN')	163	50.38 N	5.28 E
Seram (I.), Indon.	207	2.45 S	129.30 E
Serāmpore, India	196a	22.44 N	88.21 E
Serang, Indon. (sā-räng')	206	6.13 S	106.10 E
Seranggung, Indon.	191b	0.49 N	104.11 E
Serangoon, Singapore	67c	1.22 N	103.54 E
Serbia (Reg.), see Srbija			
Serdobsk, Sov. Un. (sĕr-dôpsk')	179	52.30 N	44.20 E
Serebr'anyj Bor (Neigh.), Sov. Un.	66b	55.48 N	37.30 E
Sered', Czech.	167	48.17 N	17.43 E
Seredina-Buda, Sov. Un. (sĕ-rā-dē'ná-bōō'dá)	175	52.11 N	34.03 E
Seremban, Mala. (sĕr-ĕm-bän')	191b	2.44 N	101.57 E
Serengeti Natl. Pk., Tan.	231	2.20 S	34.50 E
Serengeti Pln., Tan.	231	2.40 S	34.55 E
Serenje, Zambia (sē-rĕn'yē)	226	13.12 S	30.49 E
Seres, see Sérrai			
Seret, Czech.	167	48.17 N	17.43 E
Seret R., Sov. Un. (sĕr'ĕt)	167	49.45 N	25.30 E
Sergeya Kirova (I.), Sov. Un. (sĕr-gyĕ'yá kē'rô-vá)	180	77.30 N	86.10 E
Sergipe (State), Braz. (sĕr-zhē'pĕ)	143	10.27 S	37.04 W
Sergiyevsk, Sov. Un.	178	53.58 N	51.00 E
Sérifos, Grc.	173	37.10 N	24.32 E
Sérifos (I.), Grc.	173	37.42 N	24.17 E
Serodino, Arg. (sĕ-rô-dē'nō)	141c	32.36 S	60.56 W
Seropédica, Braz. (sĕ-rô-pĕ'dē-kä)	144b	22.44 S	43.43 W
Serov, Sov. Un. (syĕ-rôf')	182a	59.36 N	60.30 E
Serowe, Bots. (sĕ-rō'wĕ)	226	22.18 S	26.39 E
Serpa, Port. (sĕr-pä)	170	37.56 N	7.38 W
Serpukhov, Sov. Un. (syĕr'pōō-Kôf)	174	54.53 N	37.27 E
Sérrai (Seres), Grc. (sĕr'rĕ) (sĕr'ĕs)	173	41.06 N	23.36 E
Serranias Del Burro, Mex. (sĕr-rä-nē'äs dĕl bōō'r-rô)	124	29.39 N	102.07 W
Serrinha, Braz. (sĕr-rēn'yá)	143	11.43 S	38.49 W
Serta, Port. (sĕr'tá)	170	39.48 N	8.01 W
Sertânia, Braz. (sĕr-tá'nyä)	143	8.28 S	37.13 W
Sertãozinho, Braz. (sĕr-touN-zē'n-yô)	141a	21.10 S	47.58 W
Serting (R.), Mala.	191b	3.01 N	102.32 E
Seruí, Braz. (sĕ-rōō-ē')	144b	22.40 S	43.08 W
Servon, Fr.	64c	48.43 N	2.35 E
Sese Is., Ug.	231	0.30 S	32.30 E
Sesia (R.), It. (sāz'yä)	172	45.33 N	8.25 E
Sesimbra, Port. (sĕ-sē'm-brä)	171b	38.27 N	9.06 W
Sesmyl (R.), S. Afr.	227b	25.51 S	28.06 E
Sesto San Giovanni, It.	65c	45.32 N	9.14 E
Sestri Levante, It. (sĕs'trē lĕ-vän'tä)	172	44.15 N	9.24 E
Sestroretsk, Sov. Un. (sĕs-trô-rĕtsk)	182c	60.06 N	29.58 E
Sestroretskiy Razliv, Ozero (L.), Sov. Un. (ô'zĕ-rô sĕs-trô' rĕts-kĭ-räz'lĭf)	182c	60.05 N	30.07 E
Seta, Jap. (sē'tä)	205b	34.58 N	135.56 W
Setagaya (Neigh.), Jap.	69a	35.39 N	139.40 E
Séte, Fr. (sĕt)	168	43.24 N	3.42 E
Sete Lagoas, Braz. (sĕ-tĕ lä-gô'äs)	143	19.23 S	43.58 W
Sete Pontes, Braz.	61c	22.51 S	43.05 W
Seto, Jap. (sē'tō)	205	35.11 N	137.07 E
Seto-Naikai (Sea), Jap. (sĕ'tô nī'kī)	205	33.50 N	132.25 E
Seton Hall University (P. Int.), NY	55	40.45 N	74.15 W
Settat, Mor. (sĕt-ät') (sē-tá')	224	33.02 N	7.30 W
Sette-Cama, Gabon. (sĕ-tē-kä-mä')	226	2.29 S	9.40 E
Settecamini (Neigh.), It.	66c	41.56 N	12.37 E
Settimo Milanese, It.	65c	45.29 N	9.03 E
Settlement Pt., Ba. (sĕt'l-mĕnt)	134	26.40 N	79.00 W
Settlers, S. Afr. (sĕt'lĕrs)	223d	24.57 S	28.33 E
Settsu, Jap.	205b	34.46 N	135.33 E
Setúbal, Port. (sá-tōō'bäl)	171b	30.32 N	8.54 W
Setúbal, B. de, Port. (bä-ē'ä)	170	38.27 N	9.08 W
Seul, Lac (L.), Can. (lák sûl)	101	50.20 N	92.30 W
Sevan (L.), Sov. Un. (syĭ-vän')	179	40.10 N	45.20 E
Sevastopol' (Akhiar), Sov. Un. (syĕ-vás-tô'pôl'') (äK'yár)	175	44.34 N	33.34 E
Seven Hills, Austl.	70a	33.46 S	150.57 E
Seven Hills, Oh.	56a	41.22 N	81.41 W
Seven Is., see Shichitō			
Seven Kings (Neigh.), Eng.	62	51.34 N	0.05 E
Sevenoaks, Eng. (sĕ-vĕn-ôks')	156b	51.16 N	0.12 E
Severka R., Sov. Un. (sá'vĕr-ká)	182b	55.11 N	38.41 E
Severn (R.), Can. (sĕv'ĕrn)	97	55.21 N	88.42 W
Severna Park, Md. (sĕv'ĕrn-á)	112e	39.04 N	76.33 W
Severnaya Dvina (Northern Dvina) (R.), Sov. Un.	178	63.00 N	42.40 E
Severnaya Zemlya (Northern Land) (Is.), Sov. Un. (sĕ-vyĭr-nī'u zĭ-m'lyä')	177	79.33 N	101.15 E
Severoural'sk, Sov. Un. (sĕ-vyĭ-rŭ-ōō-rälsk')	182a	60.08 N	59.53 E
Sevier (L.), Ut. (sē-vēr')	121	38.55 N	113.10 W
Sevier R., Ut.	121	39.25 N	112.20 W
Sevier R., East Fork, Ut.	121	37.45 N	112.10 W
Sevilla, Col. (sĕ-vē'l-yä)	142a	4.16 N	75.56 W
Sevilla, Sp. (sā-vēl'yä)	170	37.29 N	5.58 W
Seville, Oh. (sĕ'vĭl)	113d	41.01 N	81.45 W
Sevlievo, Bul. (sĕv'lyĕ-vô)	173	41.02 N	25.05 E
Sevran, Fr.	64c	48.56 N	2.32 E
Sèvres, Fr.	64c	48.49 N	2.12 E
Sevsk, Sov. Un. (syĕfsk)	174	52.08 N	34.28 E
Seward, Ak. (sū'ărd)	107	60.18 N	149.28 W
Seward, Ne.	123	40.55 N	97.06 W
Seward Pen., Ak.	107	65.40 N	164.00 W
Sewell, Chile (sĕ'ōō-ĕl)	144	34.01 S	70.18 W
Sewickley, Pa. (sē-wĭk'lē)	113e	40.33 N	80.11 W
Seybaplaya, Mex. (sā-ē-bä-plä'yä)	131	19.38 N	90.40 W
Seychelles, Afr. (sā-shĕl')	224	5.20 S	55.10 E
Seydisfjördur, Ice. (sā'dēs-fyûr-dōōr)	158	65.21 N	14.08 W
Seyé, Mex. (sĕ-yĕ')	132a	20.51 N	89.22 W
Seyhan (R.), Tur.	161	37.28 N	35.40 E
Seylac, Som.	223a	11.19 N	43.20 E
Seym (R.), Sov. Un. (sĕym)	175	51.23 N	33.22 E
Seymour, In. (sē'mōr)	103	38.55 N	85.55 W
Seymour, Ia.	115	40.41 N	93.03 W
Seymour, S. Afr. (sē'môr)	227c	32.33 S	26.48 E
Seymour, Tx.	122	33.35 N	99.16 W
Sezela, S. Afr.	227c	30.33 S	30.37 E
Sezze, It. (sĕt'sā)	172	41.32 N	13.30 E
Sfax, Tun. (sfäks)	224	34.51 N	10.45 E
Sfîntu-Gheorghe, Rom.	173	45.53 N	25.49 E
's-Gravenhage (The Hague), Neth. ('s Krä'vĕn-hä'Kĕ) (hāg)	157a	52.05 N	4.16 E
Sha (R.), China (shä)	199	33.33 N	114.30 E
Shaanxi (Prov.), China (shän-shyĕ)	198	35.30 N	109.10 E
Shabeelle (R.), Som.	223a	1.38 N	43.50 E
Shablykino, Sov. Un. (sháb-lē'kĭ-nô)	182b	56.22 N	38.37 E
Shache (Yarkand), China (shä-chŭ)	198	38.15 N	77.15 E
Shackleton Shelf Ice, Ant. (shăk''l-tŭn)	232	65.00 S	100.00 E
Shades Cr., Al. (shādz)	112h	33.20 N	86.55 W
Shades Mtn., Al.	112h	33.22 N	86.51 W
Shagamu, Nig.	229	6.51 N	3.39 E
Shāhdara (Neigh.), India	67d	28.40 N	77.18 E
Shāhjahānpur, India (shä-jŭ-hän'pōōr)	196	27.58 N	79.58 E
Shah Mosque (P. Int.), Iran	68h	35.40 N	51.25 E
Shahrezā, Iran (shä-rä'zā)	192	31.47 N	51.47 E
Shajing, China (shä-jyĭŋ)	201a	22.44 N	113.48 E
Shakarpur Khās (Neigh.), India	67d	28.38 N	77.17 E
Shaker Hts., Oh. (shā'kĕr)	113d	41.28 N	81.34 W
Shakhty, Sov. Un. (shäK'tē)	175	47.41 N	40.11 E
Shaki, Nig.	229	8.39 N	3.25 E
Shakopee, Mn. (shăk'ō-pe)	119g	44.48 N	93.31 W
Shakūrpur (Neigh.), India	67d	28.41 N	77.09 E
Shala L., Eth. (shä'lá)	225	7.34 N	39.00 E
Shambe, Sud. (shäm'bā)	225	7.08 N	30.46 E
Shām, Jabal ash (Mtn.), Om.	192	23.01 N	57.45 E
Shammar, Jabal (Mts.), Sau. Ar. (jĕb'ĕl shŭm'ár)	192	27.13 N	40.16 E
Shamokin, Pa. (shá-mō'kĭn)	111	40.45 N	76.30 W
Shamrock, Tx. (shăm'rŏk)	122	35.14 N	100.12 W
Shamva, Zimb (shäm'vá)	226	17.18 S	31.35 E
Shandī, Sud.	225	16.44 N	33.29 E
Shandon, Oh. (shăn-dŭn)	113f	39.20 N	84.13 W
Shandong (Prov.), China (shän-dôŋ)	199	36.08 N	117.09 E
Shandong, Bandao (Pen.), China (shän-dôŋ bän-dou)	202	37.00 N	120.10 E
Shangcai, China (shäŋ-tsī)	200	33.16 N	114.16 E
Shangcheng, China (shäŋ-chŭŋ)	200	31.47 N	115.22 E
Shangdu, China (shäŋ-dōō)	202	41.38 N	113.22 E
Shanghai, China (shăng'hī')	201b	31.14 N	121.27 E
Shanghai-Shi (Mun.), China (shäŋ-hī shr)	199	31.30 N	121.45 E
Shanghe, China (shäŋ-hŭ)	200	37.18 N	117.10 E
Shanglin, China (shäŋ-lĭn)	200	38.20 N	116.05 E
Shangqiu, China (shäŋ-chyô)	200	34.24 N	115.39 E
Shangrao, China (shäŋ-rou)	203	28.25 N	117.58 E
Shangzhi, China (shäŋ-jr)	202	45.18 N	127.52 E
Shanhaiguan, China	200	40.01 N	119.45 E
Shannon, Al. (shăn'ŭn)	112h	33.23 N	86.52 W
Shannon (R.), Ire. (shăn'ŏn)	162	52.30 N	9.58 W
Shanshan, China (shän'shán')	198	42.51 N	89.53 E
Shantar (I.), Sov. Un. (shän'tär)	181	55.13 N	138.42 E
Shantou (Swatow), China (shän-tō)	203	23.20 N	116.40 E
Shanxi (Prov.), China (shän-shyē)	199	37.30 N	112.00 E
Shan Xian, China (shän shyĕn)	200	34.47 N	116.04 E
Shaobo, China (shou-bwo)	200	32.33 N	119.30 E
Shaobo Hu (L.), China (shou-bwo hōō)	200	32.07 N	119.13 E
Shaoguan, China (shou-gŭän)	203	24.58 N	113.42 E
Shaoxing, China (shou-shyĭŋ)	203	30.00 N	120.40 E
Shapki, Sov. Un. (shäp'kĭ)	182c	59.36 N	31.11 E
Shaqrā', P.D.R. of Yem.	195	13.21 N	45.42 E
Shark B., Austl. (shärk)	214	25.30 S	113.00 E
Sharon, Ma. (shăr'ŏn)	105a	42.07 N	71.11 W
Sharon, Pa.	110	41.15 N	80.30 W
Sharon Hill, Pa.	56b	39.55 N	75.16 W
Sharon Springs, Ks.	122	38.51 N	101.45 W
Sharonville, Oh. (shăr'ŏn vĭl)	113f	39.16 N	84.24 W
Sharpsburg, Pa. (shärps'bûrg)	113e	40.30 N	79.54 W
Sharps Hill, Pa.	57b	40.30 N	79.56 W
Sharr, Jabal (Mtn.), Sau. Ar.	192	28.00 N	36.07 E
Shashi, China (shä-shē)	203	30.20 N	112.18 E
Shasta L., Ca. (shăs'tá)	116	40.51 N	122.32 W
Shasta, Mt., Ca.	116	41.35 N	122.12 W
Shatsk, Sov. Un. (shátsk)	178	54.00 N	41.40 E
Shattuck, Ok. (shăt'ŭk)	122	36.16 N	99.53 W
Shaunavon, Can.	100	49.40 N	108.25 W
Shaw, Eng.	64b	53.35 N	2.06 W
Shaw, Ms. (shô)	126	33.36 N	90.44 W
Shawano, Wi. (shá-wô'nô)	115	44.41 N	88.13 W
Shawinigan, Can.	97	46.32 N	72.46 W
Shawnee, Ks. (shô-nē')	119f	39.01 N	94.43 W
Shawnee, Ok.	123	35.20 N	96.54 W
Shawneetown, Il. (shô'nē-toun)	110	37.40 N	88.05 W
Shayang, China	203	31.00 N	112.38 E
Shchara (R.), Sov. Un. (sh-chä'rá)	167	53.17 N	25.12 E
Shchëlkovo, Sov. Un. (shchĕl'kô-vô)	182b	55.55 N	38.00 E
Shchëtovo, Sov. Un. (shchĕ'tô-vô)	175	48.11 N	39.13 E
Shchigry, Sov. Un. (shchē'grē)	175	51.52 N	36.54 E
Shchors, Sov. Un. (shchôrs)	175	51.38 N	31.58 E
Shchuch'ye Ozero, Sov. Un. (shchōōch'yĕ ô'zĕ-rō)	182a	56.31 N	56.35 E
Sheakhala, India	196a	22.47 N	88.10 E
Shebele R., Eth. (shā'bá-lē)	223a	6.07 N	43.10 E
Sheboygan, Wi. (shē-boi'găn)	115	43.45 N	87.44 W
Sheboygan Falls, Wi.	115	43.43 N	87.51 W
Shechem (Ruins), Jordan	191a	32.15 N	35.22 E
Shedandoah, Pa.	111	40.50 N	76.15 W
Shediac, Can. (shĕ'dē-ăk)	104	46.13 N	64.32 W
Shedin Pk., Can. (shĕd'ĭn)	98	55.55 N	127.32 W
Sheepshead Bay (Neigh.), NY	55	40.35 N	73.56 W
Sheerness, Eng. (shēr'nĕs)	156b	51.26 N	0.46 E
Sheffield, Al. (shĕf'fēld)	126	35.42 N	87.42 W
Sheffield, Can.	95d	43.20 N	80.13 W
Sheffield, Eng.	156	53.23 N	1.28 W
Sheffield, Oh.	113d	41.26 N	82.05 W
Sheffield Lake, Oh.	113d	41.30 N	82.03 W
Sheksna (R.), Sov. Un. (shĕks'ná)	178	59.50 N	38.40 E
Shelagskiy, Mys (C.), Sov. Un. (shĭ-läg'skē)	181	70.08 N	170.52 E
Shelbina, Ar. (shĕl-bī'ná)	123	39.41 N	92.03 W
Shelburn, In. (shĕl'bŭrn)	110	39.10 N	87.30 W
Shelburne, Can.	104	43.46 N	65.19 W
Shelburne, Can.	111	44.04 N	80.12 W
Shelby, In. (shĕl'bē)	113a	41.12 N	87.21 W
Shelby, Mi.	110	43.35 N	86.20 W
Shelby, Ms.	126	33.56 N	90.44 W
Shelby, Mt.	117	48.35 N	111.55 W
Shelby, NC	127	35.16 N	81.35 W
Shelby, Oh.	110	40.50 N	82.40 W
Shelbyville, Il. (shĕl'bē-vĭl)	110	39.20 N	88.45 W
Shelbyville, In.	110	39.30 N	85.45 W
Shelbyville, Ky.	110	38.10 N	85.15 W
Shelbyville, Tn.	126	35.30 N	86.28 W
Shelbyville Res., Il.	192	39.30 N	88.45 W
Sheldon, Ia. (shĕl'dŭn)	114	43.10 N	95.50 W
Sheldon, Tx.	125a	29.52 N	95.07 W
Shelekhova, Zaliv (B.), Sov. Un.	181	60.00 N	156.00 E
Shelikof Str., Ak. (shĕ'lē-kôf)	107	57.56 N	154.20 W
Shellbrook, Can.	100	53.15 N	106.22 W
Shelley, Id. (shĕl'lē)	117	43.24 N	112.06 W
Shellow Bowells, Eng.	62	51.45 N	0.20 E
Shellrock (R.), Ia. (shĕl'rŏk)	115	43.25 N	93.19 W
Shelon' (R.), Sov. Un. (shá'lôn)	174	57.50 N	29.40 E
Shelter, Port (B.), China	68c	22.21 N	114.17 E
Shelton, Ct. (shĕl'tŭn)	111	41.15 N	73.05 W
Shelton, Ne.	122	40.46 N	98.41 W
Shelton, Wa.	116	47.14 N	123.05 W
Shemakha, Sov. Un. (shĕ-má-kä')	182a	56.16 N	59.19 E
Shemakha, Sov. Un.	179	40.35 N	48.40 E
Shenandoah, Ia. (shĕn-ăn-dō'á)	123	40.46 N	95.23 W
Shenandoah, Va.	111	38.30 N	78.30 W
Shenandoah (R.), Va.	111	38.55 N	78.05 W
Shenandoah Natl. Park., Va.	111	38.35 N	78.25 W
Shendam, Nig.	229	8.53 N	9.32 E
Shenfield, Eng.	62	51.38 N	0.19 E
Shengfang, China (shengfäng)	200	39.05 N	116.40 E
Shenkursk, Sov. Un. (shĕn-kōōrsk')	182	62.10 N	43.08 E
Shenmu, China	202	38.55 N	110.35 E
Shenqiu, China	200	33.11 N	115.06 E
Shenxian, China (shŭn shyän)	200	38.02 N	115.33 E
Shenxian, China (shŭn shyĕn)	200	36.14 N	115.38 E
Shenyang, China (shŭn-yäŋ)	202	41.45 N	123.22 E
Shenze, China (shŭn-dzŭ)	200	38.12 N	115.12 E

PLACE (Pronounciation)	PAGE	Lat. °'	Long. °'
Sheopur, India	196	25.37 N	78.10 E
Shepard, Can. (shĕ'pärd)	95e	50.57 N	113.55 W
Shepetovka, Sov. Un. (shĕ-pĕ-tôf'ka)	175	50.10 N	27.01 E
Shepparton, Austl. (shĕp'ăr-tŭn)	216	36.15 S	145.25 E
Shepperton, Eng.	62	51.24 N	0.27 W
Sherborn, Ma. (shûr'bŭrn)	105a	42.15 N	71.22 W
Sherbro I., S. L.	228	7.30 N	12.55 W
Sherbrooke, Can.	111	45.24 N	71.54 W
Sherburn, Eng. (shûr'bŭrn)	156	53.47 N	1.15 W
Shereshevo, Sov. Un. (shĕ-rĕ-shĕ-vô)	167	52.31 N	24.08 E
Sheridan, Ar. (shĕr'ĭ-dăn)	123	34.19 N	92.21 W
Sheridan, Or.	116	45.06 N	123.22 W
Sheridan, Wy.	117	44.48 N	106.56 W
Sherman, Tx. (shĕr'măn)	123	33.39 N	96.37 W
Sherman Oaks (Neigh.), Ca.	59	34.09 N	118.26 W
Sherna R., Sov. Un. (shĕr'na)	182b	56.08 N	38.45 E
Sherridon, Can.	101	55.10 N	101.10 W
's Hertogenbosch, Neth. (sĕr-tō'ghĕn-bôs)	157a	51.41 N	5.19 E
Sherwood, Or.	118c	45.21 N	122.50 W
Sherwood For., Eng.	156	53.11 N	1.07 W
Sherwood Park, Can.	99	53.31 N	113.19 W
Shetland (Is.), Scot. (shĕt'lănd)	162a	60.35 N	2.10 W
Sheva, India	67e	18.56 N	72.57 E
Shevchenko, Sov. Un.	192	44.00 N	51.10 E
Shewa Gimira, Eth.	225	7.13 N	35.49 E
Shexian, China (shŭ shyĕn)	200	36.34 N	113.42 E
Sheyang (R.), China (she-yäŋ)	200	33.42 N	119.40 E
Sheyenne (R.), ND (shī-ĕn')	114	46.42 N	97.52 W
Shi (R.), China (shr)	200	31.58 N	115.50 E
Shi (R.), China	200	32.09 N	114.11 E
Shiawassee (R.), Mi. (shī-á-wôs'ē)	110	43.15 N	84.05 W
Shibām, P. D. R. of Yem. (shē'bäm)	192	16.02 N	48.40 E
Shibīn al Kawn, Egypt (shē-bēn'ĕl kōm')	223b	30.31 N	31.01 E
Shibīn al Qanāṭir, Egypt (ká-nä'tĕr)	223b	30.18 N	31.21 E
Shibuya (Neigh.), Jap.	69a	35.40 N	139.42 E
Shichitō (Seven Is.), Jap. (shē'chē-tō)	205	34.18 N	139.28 E
Shicun, China (shr-tsōōn)	200	33.47 N	117.18 E
Shields R., Mt. (shēldz)	117	45.54 N	110.40 W
Shifnal, Eng. (shĭf'năl)	156	52.40 N	2.22 W
Shihlin, Taiwan	68d	25.05 N	121.31 E
Shijian, China (shr-jyĕn)	200	31.27 N	117.51 E
Shijiazhuang, China (shr-jyä-jŭäŋ)	200	38.04 N	114.31 E
Shijiu Hu (L.), China (shr-jyō hōō)	200	31.29 N	119.07 E
Shijōnawate, Jap.	69b	34.45 N	135.39 E
Shikārpur, Pak.	196	27.51 N	68.52 E
Shiki, Jap. (shē'kē)	205a	35.50 N	139.35 E
Shikoku (I.), Jap. (shē'kō'kōō)	205	33.43 N	133.33 E
Shilibao, China	67b	39.55 N	116.29 E
Shilka (R.), Sov. Un. (shĭl'ka)	181	53.00 N	118.45 E
Shilla (Mt.), India	196	37.18 N	78.17 E
Shillong, India (shēl-lông')	196	25.39 N	91.58 E
Shiloh, Il. (shī'lō)	119e	38.34 N	89.54 W
Shilong, China (shr-lôŋ)	203	23.05 N	113.58 E
Shilou, China	201a	22.58 N	113.29 E
Shimabara, Jap. (shē'mä-bä'rä)	205	32.46 N	130.22 E
Shimada, Jap. (shē'mä-dä)	205	34.49 N	138.13 E
Shimber Berris (Mtn.), Som	223a	10.40 N	47.23 E
Shimizu, Jap. (shē'mē-zōō)	205	35.00 N	138.29 E
Shimminato, Jap. (shēm'mē'nä-tô)	205	36.47 N	137.05 E
Shimoda, Jap. (shē'mô-dá)	205	34.41 N	138.58 E
Shimoga, India	197	13.59 N	75.38 E
Shimohōya, Jap.	69a	35.45 N	139.34 E
Shimoigusa (Neigh.), Jap.	69a	35.43 N	139.37 E
Shimomizo, Jap.	69a	35.31 N	139.23 E
Shimoni, Ken.	231	4.39 S	39.23 E
Shimonoseki, Jap. (shē'mô-nō-sĕ'kē) (shē-mô-nô'sĕ-kĭ)	205	33.58 N	130.55 E
Shimo-Saga, Jap. (shē'mô sä'gä)	205b	35.01 N	135.41 E
Shimoshakujii (Neigh.), Jap.	69a	35.45 N	139.37 E
Shimotsuruma, Jap.	69a	35.29 N	139.28 E
Shimoyugi, Jap.	69a	35.38 N	139.23 E
Shinagawa-Wan (B.), Jap. (shē'nä-gä'wä wän)	205a	35.37 N	139.49 E
Shinano-Gawa (Strm.), Jap. (shē-nä'nô gä'wä)	205	36.43 N	138.22 E
Shinbārī, Egypt	71a	30.07 N	31.09 E
Shīndand, Afg.	195	33.18 N	62.08 E
Shingū, Jap. (shĭn'gōō)	205	33.43 N	135.59 E
Shinji (L.), Jap. (shĭn'jē)	205	35.23 N	133.05 E
Shinjuku (Neigh.), Jap.	69a	35.41 N	139.42 E
Shinkolobwe, Zaire	231	11.02 S	26.35 E
Shin, Loch (L.), Scot. (lŏĸ shĭn)	162	58.08 N	4.02 W
Shinyanga, Tan. (shĭn-yäŋ'gä)	225	3.40 S	33.26 E
Shiono Misaki (C.), Jap. (shē-ô'nô mē'sä-kē)	204	33.20 N	136.10 E
Shīrāz, Iran (shē-räz')	192	29.32 N	52.27 E
Shipai, China (shr-pī)	201a	23.07 N	113.23 E
Ship Channel Cay (I.), Ba. (shĭp chă-nĕl kē)	134	24.50 N	76.50 W
Shipley, Eng. (shĭp'lē)	156	53.50 N	1.47 W
Shippegan, Can. (shĭ'pē-găn)	104	47.45 N	64.42 W
Shippegan I., Can.	104	47.50 N	64.38 W
Shippenburg, Pa. (shĭp'ĕn bûrg)	111	40.00 N	77.30 W
Shipshaw (R.), Can. (shĭp'shô)	104	48.50 N	71.03 W
Shiqma (R.), Isr.	191a	31.31 N	34.40 E
Shirane-san (Mtn.), Jap. (shē'rä'nā-sän')	205	35.44 N	138.14 E
Shira Saki (C.), Jap. (shē'rä sä'kē)	204	41.25 N	142.10 E
Shirati, Tan. (shē-rä'tē)	226	1.15 S	34.02 E
Shīrāz, Iran	195	29.36 N	52.32 E
Shire (R.), Malawi (shē'rā)	231	16.20 S	35.05 E
Shirley, Ma. (shûr'lē)	105a	42.33 N	71.39 W
Shirokoye, Sov. Un. (shē'rô-kô-yĕ)	175	47.40 N	33.18 E
Shishaldin Vol., Ak. (shī-shăl'dĭn)	107a	54.48 N	164.00 W
Shively, Ky. (shīv'lē)	113h	38.11 N	85.47 W
Shivpuri, India	196	25.31 N	77.46 E
Shivta, Horvot (Ruins), Isr.	191a	30.54 N	34.36 E
Shivwits (Shebit) Ind. Res., Ut. (shĭv'wĭts) (shĕ'bĭt)	121	37.10 N	113.50 W
Shivwits Plat, Az.	121	36.13 N	113.42 W

PLACE (Pronounciation)	PAGE	Lat. °'	Long. °'
Shiwan, China (shr-wän)	201a	23.01 N	113.04 E
Shiwan Dashan (Mts.), China (shr-wän dä-shän)	203	22.10 N	107.30 E
Shizuki, Jap. (shĭ'zōō-kē)	205	34.29 N	134.51 E
Shizuoka, Jap. (shē'zōō'ōká)	205	34.58 N	138.24 E
Shklov, Sov. Un. (shklôf)	174	54.11 N	30.23 E
Shkodër (Scutari), Alb. (shkô'dûr) (skōō'tärē)	173	42.04 N	19.30 E
Shkotovo, Sov. Un. (shkô'tô-vô)	204	43.15 N	132.21 E
Shoal Cr., Il. (shōl)	123	38.37 N	89.25 W
Shoal L., Can.	101	49.32 N	95.00 W
Shoals, In. (shōlz)	110	38.40 N	86.45 W
Shōdai, Jap.	69b	34.51 N	135.42 E
Shōdo (I.), Jap. (shō'dō)	205	34.27 N	134.27 E
Shogunle, Nig.	71d	6.35 N	3.21 E
Sholāpur, India (shō'lä-pōōr)	197	17.42 N	75.51 E
Shomolu, Nig.	71d	6.32 N	3.23 E
Shoreham, Eng.	62	51.20 N	0.11 E
Shorewood, Wi. (shōr'wŏŏd)	113a	43.05 N	87.54 W
Shoshone, Id. (shô-shōn'tē)	117	42.56 N	114.24 W
Shoshone L., Wy.	117	44.17 N	110.50 W
Shoshone R., Wy.	117	44.20 N	109.28 W
Shoshoni, Wy.	117	43.14 N	108.05 W
Shostka, Sov. Un. (shôst'ka)	175	51.51 N	33.31 E
Shougouang, China (shō-gŭäŋ)	200	36.53 N	118.45 E
Shouxian, China (shō shyĕn)	200	32.36 N	116.45 E
Shpola, Sov. Un. (shpô'la)	175	49.01 N	31.36 E
Shreveport, La. (shrēv'pôrt)	125	32.30 N	93.46 W
Shrewsbury, Eng. (shrōōz'bĕr-ĭ)	156	52.43 N	2.44 W
Shrewsbury, Ma.	105a	42.18 N	71.43 W
Shroud Cay (I.) (shroud), Ba.	134	24.20 N	76.40 W
Shu (R.), China (shōō)	200	34.47 N	118.27 E
Shuangcheng, China (shŭäŋ-chŭŋ)	202	45.18 N	126.18 E
Shuanghe, China (shŭäŋ-hŭ)	200	31.33 N	116.48 E
Shuangliao, China	199	43.37 N	123.30 E
Shuangyang, China	202	43.28 N	125.45 E
Shubrā al-Khaymah, Egypt	71a	30.06 N	31.15 E
Shuhedun, China (shōō-hŭ-dōōn)	200	31.33 N	117.01 E
Shuiye, China (shwā-yŭ)	200	36.08 N	114.07 E
Shule (R.), China (shōō-lŭ)	198	40.53 N	94.55 E
Shullsburg, Wi. (shŭlz'bûrg)	115	42.35 N	90.16 W
Shumagin (Is.), Ak. (shōō'mä-gĕn)	107	55.22 N	159.20 W
Shumen, Bul.	173	43.15 N	26.54 E
Shunde, China (shōōn-dŭ)	201a	22.50 N	113.15 E
Shungnak, Ak. (shŭng'nak)	107	66.55 N	157.20 W
Shunut, 'Gora (Mt.), Sov. Un. (gá-rä shōō'nōōt)	182a	56.33 N	59.45 E
Shunyi, China (shōōn-yē)	202a	40.09 N	116.38 E
Shuqrah, P. D. R. of Yem.	192	13.32 N	46.02 E
Shūrāb (R.), Iran (shōō räb)	192	31.08 N	55.30 E
Shuri, Jap. (shōō'rē)	204	26.10 N	127.48 E
Shur R., Iran (shōōr)	179	35.40 N	50.10 E
Shurugwi, Zimb	226	19.34 S	30.03 E
Shūshtar, Iran (shōōsh'tŭr)	192	31.50 N	48.46 E
Shuswap L., Can. (shōōs'wŏp)	99	50.57 N	119.15 W
Shuya, Sov. Un. (shōō'yá)	174	56.52 N	41.23 E
Shuyang, China (shōō yäng)	200	34.09 N	118.47 E
Shweba, Bur.	203	22.23 N	96.13 E
Shyaulyay, see Šiauliai			
Siak Ketjil (R.), Indon.	191b	1.01 N	101.45 E
Siaksriinderapura, Indon. (sē-äks'rĭ ĕn'drá-pōō'rä)	191b	0.48 N	102.05 E
Siālkot, Pak. (sē-äl'kōt)	196	32.39 N	74.30 E
Šiátista, Grc. (syä'tĭs-ta)	173	40.15 N	21.32 E
Šiauliai (Shyaulyay), Sov. Un. (shē-ou'lē-ī)	165	55.57 N	23.19 E
Siau, Pulau (I.), Indon.	207	2.40 N	126.00 E
Sibay, Sov. Un. (sē'báy)	182a	52.41 N	58.40 E
Šibenik, Yugo. (shē-bā'nĕk)	172	43.44 N	15.55 E
Siberia (Reg.), Asia	190	57.00 N	97.00 E
Siberut, Pulau (I.), Indon. (sē'bā-rōōt)	206	1.22 S	99.45 E
Sibī, Pak.	196	29.41 N	67.52 E
Sibiti, Con. (sē-bē-tē')	230	3.41 S	13.21 E
Sibiu, Rom. (sē-bĭ-ōō')	173	45.47 N	24.09 E
Sibley, Ia. (sĭb'lē)	114	43.24 N	95.33 W
Sibolga, Indon. (sē-bō'gä)	206	1.45 N	98.45 E
Sibpur, India	67a	22.34 N	88.19 E
Sibsāgar, India (sēb-sŭ'gŭr)	193	26.47 N	94.45 E
Sibutu I., Phil.	206	4.40 N	119.30 E
Sibuyan (I.), Phil. (sē-bōō-yän')	207a	12.19 N	122.25 E
Sibuyan Sea, Phil.	206	12.43 N	122.38 E
Sichuan (Prov.), China (sz-chŭän)	198	31.20 N	103.00 E
Sicily (I.), It. (sĭs'ĭ-lē)	159	37.38 N	13.30 E
Sickingmühle, F.R.G.	63	51.42 N	7.07 E
Sico R., Hond. (sē-kô)	132	15.32 N	85.42 W
Sicuaní, Peru (sē-kwä'nē)	142	14.12 S	71.12 W
Sidamo (Prov.), Eth. (sē-dä'mô)	223	5.08 N	37.45 E
Sidao, China	67b	39.51 N	116.26 E
Sidcup (Neigh.), Eng.	62	51.25 N	0.06 E
Siderno Marina, It. (sē-dĕr'nô mä-rē'nä)	172	38.18 N	16.19 E
Sidhirókastron, Grc.	173	41.13 N	23.27 E
Sidi Aïssa, Alg.	171	35.53 N	3.44 E
Sīdī Barrānī, Egypt	194	31.36 N	25.55 E
Sidi bel Abbès, Alg. (sē'dē-bĕl á-bĕs')	224	35.15 N	0.43 W
Sidi Ifni, Mor. (ēf'nē)	224	29.22 N	10.15 W
Sidley, Mt., Ant. (sĭd'lē)	232	77.25 S	129.00 W
Sidney, Can.	98	48.39 N	123.24 W
Sidney, Mt. (sĭd'nē)	117	47.43 N	104.07 W
Sidney, Ne.	114	41.10 N	103.00 W
Sidney, Oh.	110	40.20 N	84.10 W
Sidney Lanier, L., Ga. (lăn'yēr)	126	34.27 N	83.56 W
Sido, Mali	228	11.40 N	7.36 W
Sidon, see Saydā			
Sidr, Wādī (R.), Egypt	191a	29.43 N	32.58 E
Siedlce, Pol. (syĕd''l-tsĕ)	167	52.09 N	22.20 E
Siegburg, F.R.G. (zēg'bōōrgh)	169c	50.48 N	7.13 E
Siegen, F.R.G. (zē'ghĕn)	169c	50.52 N	8.01 E
Sieghartskirchen, Aus.	157e	48.16 N	16.00 E
Siemensstadt (Neigh.), F.R.G.	65a	52.32 N	13.17 E

PLACE (Pronounciation)	PAGE	Lat. °'	Long. °'
Siemiatycze, Pol. (syĕm'yä'tē-chĕ)	167	52.26 N	22.52 E
Siemionówka, Pol. (sĕĕ-mĕō'nôf-kä)	167	52.53 N	23.50 E
Siem Reap, Kamp. (syĕm'rä'äp)	206	13.32 N	103.54 E
Siena, It. (sē-ĕn'ä)	172	43.19 N	11.21 E
Sieradz, Pol. (syĕ'rädz)	167	51.35 N	18.45 E
Sierpc, Pol. (syĕrpts)	167	52.51 N	19.42 E
Sierra Blanca, Tx. (sē-ĕ'rá blaŋ-kä)	124	31.10 N	105.20 W
Sierra Blanca Pk., NM (blăn'ká)	121	33.25 N	105.50 W
Sierra Leone, Afr. (sē-ĕr'rä lā-ō'nā)	222	8.48 N	12.30 W
Sierra Madre, Ca. (mä'drē)	119a	34.10 N	118.03 W
Sierra Mojada, Mex. (sē-ĕ'r-rä-mô-ĸä'dä)	124	27.22 N	103.42 W
Sigean, Fr. (sē-zhŏɴ')	168	43.02 N	2.56 E
Sigeurney, Ia. (sē-gûr-nĭ)	115	41.16 N	92.10 W
Sighetu Marmatiei, Rom.	167	47.57 N	23.55 E
Sighisoara, Rom. (sē-gē-shwä'rá)	167	46.11 N	24.48 E
Siglufjördur, Ice.	158	66.06 N	18.45 W
Signakhi, Sov. Un.	179	41.45 N	45.50 E
Signal Hill, Ca. (sĭg'năl hĭl)	119a	33.48 N	118.11 W
Sigsig, Ec. (sēg-sēg')	142	3.04 S	78.44 W
Sigtuna, Swe. (sēgh-tōō'ná)	164	59.40 N	17.39 E
Siguanea, Ensenada de la (B.), Cuba (ĕn-sĕ-nä-dä-dĕ-lä-sē-gwä-nā'ä)	134	21.45 N	83.15 W
Siguatepeque, Hond. (sē-gwá'tē-pĕ-kē)	132	14.33 N	87.51 W
Sigüenza, Sp. (sē-gwĕ'n-zä)	170	41.03 N	2.38 W
Siguiri, Gui. (sē-gē-rē')	228	11.25 N	9.10 W
Sihong, China (sz-hôŋ)	200	33.25 N	118.13 E
Siirt, Tur. (sĭ-ērt')	179	38.00 N	42.00 E
Sikalongo, Zambia	231	16.46 S	27.07 E
Sikasso, Mali (sē-käs'sō)	228	11.19 N	5.40 W
Sikeston, Mo. (sīks'tŭn)	123	36.50 N	89.35 W
Sikhote Alin', Khrebet (Mts.), Sov. Un. (se-ĸō'ta a-lēn')	181	45.00 N	135.45 E
Sikinos (I.), Grc. (sĭ'kĭ-nōs)	173	36.45 N	24.55 E
Sikkim (State), India	196	27.42 N	88.25 E
Siklós, Hung. (sĭ'klōsh)	167	45.51 N	18.18 E
Sil (R.), Sp. (sē'l)	170	42.20 N	7.13 W
Silāmpur (Neigh.), India	67d	28.40 N	77.16 E
Silang, Phil. (sē-läng')	207a	14.14 N	120.58 E
Silao, Mex. (sē-lä'ō)	130	20.56 N	101.25 W
Silchar, India (sĭl-chär')	196	24.52 N	92.50 E
Silent Valley, S. Afr. (sī'lĕnt vă'lē)	223d	24.32 S	26.40 E
Siler City, NC (sī'lĕr)	127	35.45 N	79.29 W
Silesia (Reg.), Pol. (sĭ-lē'shá)	167	50.58 N	16.53 E
Silifke, Tur.	179	36.20 N	34.00 E
Siling Co (L.), China	196	32.05 N	89.10 E
Silistra, Bul. (sē-lēs'trá)	161	44.01 N	27.13 E
Siljan (R.), Swe. (sēl'yän)	164	60.48 N	14.28 E
Silkeborg, Den. (sĭl'kĕ-bôr')	164	56.10 N	9.33 E
Sillery, Can. (sēl'-re')	95b	46.46 N	71.15 W
Siloam Springs, Ar. (sĭ-lōm)	123	36.10 N	94.32 W
Siloana Plns., Zambia	230	16.55 S	23.10 E
Silocayoápan, Mex. (sē-lô-kä-yô-á'pän)	130	17.29 N	98.09 W
Silsbee, Tx. (sĭlz' bē)	125	30.19 N	94.09 W
Şilschede, F.R.G.	63	51.21 N	7.19 E
Šilutė, Sov. Un. (shĭ-lōō'tā)	165	55.23 N	21.26 E
Silva Jardim, Braz. (sē'l-vä-zhär-dēɴ)	141a	22.40 S	42.24 W
Silvana, Wa. (sĭ-văn'ă)	118a	48.12 N	122.16 W
Silvânia, Braz. (sēl-vá'nyä)	143	16.43 S	48.33 W
Silvassa, India	196	20.10 N	73.00 E
Silver (L.), Mo.	123	39.38 N	93.12 W
Silverado, Ca. (sĭl-vēr-ä'dō)	118a	33.45 N	117.40 W
Silver Bank Passage (Str.), Ba.	135	20.40 N	70.20 W
Silver Bay, Mn.	115	47.24 N	91.07 W
Silver Bk., Ba.	135	20.40 N	69.40 W
Silver City, NM (sĭl'vēr sĭ'tĭ)	121	32.45 N	108.20 W
Silver City, Pan.	133	9.20 N	79.54 W
Silver Cr., Az.	121	34.30 N	110.05 W
Silver Cr., In.	113h	38.20 N	85.45 W
Silver Creek, NY (crēk)	111	42.35 N	79.10 W
Silver Cr., Muddy Fk., In.	113h	38.26 N	85.52 W
Silverdale, Wa. (sĭl'vēr-dāl)	118a	49.39 N	122.42 W
Silver Hill, Md.	56d	38.51 N	76.57 W
Silver L., Wi.	113a	42.35 N	88.08 W
Silver Lake, Ma.	54a	42.00 N	70.48 W
Silver Lake, Wi. (lăk)	113a	42.33 N	88.10 W
Silver Spring, Md. (sprĭng)	112e	39.00 N	77.00 W
Silver Star Mtn., Wa.	118c	45.45 N	122.15 W
Silverthrone Mtn., Can. (sĭl'vēr-thrōn)	98	51.31 N	126.06 W
Silverton, Co. (sĭl'vēr-tŭn)	121	37.50 N	107.40 W
Silverton, Oh.	113f	39.12 N	84.24 W
Silverton, Or.	116	45.02 N	122.46 W
Silverton, S. Afr.	227b	25.45 S	28.13 E
Silves, Port. (sēl'vĕzh)	170	37.15 N	8.24 W
Silvies R., Or. (sĭl'vēz)	116	43.44 N	119.15 W
Sim, Sov. Un. (sĭm)	182a	55.00 N	57.42 E
Simao, China (sz-mou)	198	22.56 N	101.07 E
Simba, Zaire	230	0.36 N	22.55 E
Simcoe, Can. (sĭm'kō)	111	42.50 N	80.20 W
Simcoe (L.), Can.	111	44.30 N	79.20 W
Simeulue, Pulau (I.), Indon.	206	2.27 N	95.30 E
Simferopol' (Akmechet), Sov. Un. (sēm-fĕ-rô'pôl') (ák-mĕch'ĕt)	175	44.58 N	34.04 E
Simi (I.), Grc.	161	36.27 N	27.41 E
Similk Beach, Wa. (sē'mĭlk)	118a	48.27 N	122.35 W
Simla, India (sĭm'lá)	196	31.09 N	77.15 E
Simla (Neigh.), India	67a	22.35 N	88.22 E
Simleul-Silvaniei, Rom. (shēm-lä'ōōl-sēl-vä'nyĕ-ē)	167	47.14 N	22.46 E
Simms Pt., Ba.	134	25.00 N	77.40 W
Simojovel, Mex. (sē-mō-hô-vĕl')	131	17.12 N	92.43 W
Simonésia, Braz. (sē-mō-nĕ'syä)	141a	20.04 S	41.53 W
Simonette (R.), Can. (sī-mŏn-ĕt')	99	54.15 N	118.00 W
Simonstad, S. Afr.	226a	34.11 S	18.25 E
Simood Sound, Can.	98	50.45 N	126.25 W
Simplon P., Switz. (sĭm'plŏn) (săɴ-plôɴ')	166	46.13 N	7.53 E
Simpson (I.), Can.	115	48.43 N	87.44 W
Simpson Des., Austl. (sĭmp-sŭn)	214	24.40 S	136.40 E

ng-sing; ŋ-baŋk; ɴ-nasalized n; nŏd; cŏmmit; ōld; ôbey; ôrder; oi-boil; fōōd; fŏŏt; ou-out; s-soft; sh-dish; th-thin; pūre; ûnite; ûrn; stŭd; circŭs; ü-as in French tu; '-indeterminate vowel.

PLACE (Pronounciation)	PAGE	Lat. °′	Long. °′
Sim R., Sov. Un.	182a	55.00 N	57.42 E
Simrishamn, Swe. (sēm'rēs-häm'n)	164	55.35 N	14.19 E
Sims Bayou, Tx. (sĭmz bī-yōō')	125a	29.37 N	95.23 W
Simushir (I.), Sov. Un. (se-mōō'shēr)	199	47.15 N	150.47 E
Sinaia, Rom. (sĭ-nä'yȧ)	173	45.20 N	25.30 E
Sinai Pen., Egypt (sī'nī)	225	29.24 N	33.29 E
Sinaloa (State), Mex. (sē-nä-lô-ä)	128	25.15 N	107.45 W
Sinan, China (sz-nän)	203	27.50 N	108.30 E
Sinanju, Kor. (sĭ'nän-jōō')	204	39.39 N	125.41 E
Sinap, Tur.	179	42.00 N	35.05 E
Sincé, Col. (sēn'sā)	142	9.15 N	75.14 W
Sincelejo, Col. (sēn-sā-lā'hō)	142	9.12 N	75.30 W
Sinclair Inlet, Wa. (sĭn-klâr')	118a	47.31 N	122.41 W
Sinclair Mills, Can.	98	54.02 N	121.41 W
Sindi, Sov. Un. (sēn'dē)	165	58.20 N	24.40 E
Sinel'nikovo, Sov. Un. (sē'nye-brl-nē'kô'vô)	175	49.19 N	35.33 E
Sines, Port. (sē'nāzh)	170	37.57 N	8.50 W
Singapore, Singapore (sĭn'gȧ-pōr')	191b	1.18 N	103.52 E
Singapore, Asia	191b	1.22 N	103.45 E
Singapore Str., Indon.	191b	1.14 N	104.20 E
Singlewell or Ifield, Eng.	62	51.25 N	0.23 E
Singu, Bur. (sĭn'gŭ)	198	22.37 N	96.04 E
Siniye Lipyagi, Sov. Un. (sēn'ē lēp'yä-gē)	175	51.24 N	38.29 E
Sinj, Yugo. (sēn')	172	43.42 N	16.39 E
Sinjah, Sud.	225	13.09 N	33.52 E
Sinkāt, Sud.	195	18.50 N	36.50 E
Sinking (Aut. Reg.), see Xinjiang			
Sin'kovo, Sov. Un. (sĭn-kô'vô)	182b	56.23 N	37.19 E
Sinnamary, Fr. Gu.	143	5.15 N	57.52 W
Sinni (R.), It. (sēn'nē)	172	40.05 N	16.15 E
Sinnūris, Egypt	223b	29.25 N	30.52 E
Sino, Pedra de (Mtn.), Braz. (pě'drä-dô-sē'nô)	144b	22.27 S	43.02 W
Sino-Soviet Friendship, Palace of (P. Int.), China	68a	31.14 N	121.25 E
Sint Niklaas, Bel.	157a	51.10 N	4.07 E
Sinton, Tx. (sĭn'tŭn)	125	28.03 N	97.30 W
Sintra, Port. (sēn'trȧ)	171b	38.48 N	9.23 W
Sint Truiden, Bel.	125a	50.49 N	5.14 E
Sinŭiju, Kor. (sĭ'nōōĭ-jōō)	204	40.04 N	124.33 E
Sinyavino, Sov. Un. (sĭn-yä'vĭ-nô)	182c	59.50 N	31.07 E
Sinyaya (R.), Sov. Un. (sēn'yȧ-yȧ)	174	56.40 N	28.20 E
Sinyukha (R.), Sov. Un. (sē'nyōō-kȧ)	175	48.34 N	30.49 E
Sīdī Barrānī, Egypt	225	31.41 N	26.09 E
Sion, Switz. (sē'ôn)	166	46.15 N	7.17 E
Sioux City, Ia. (sōō sĭ'tĭ)	114	42.30 N	96.25 W
Sioux Falls, SD (fôlz)	114	43.33 N	96.43 W
Sioux Lookout, Can.	101	50.06 N	91.55 W
Sipí, Col. (sē-pē')	142a	4.39 N	76.38 W
Siping, China (sz-pĭŋ)	202	43.05 N	124.24 E
Sipiwesk, Can.	96	55.27 N	97.24 W
Sipsey (R.), Al. (sĭp'sē)	126	33.26 N	87.42 W
Sipura, Pulau (I.), Indon.	206	2.15 S	99.33 E
Siqueros, Mex. (sē-kā'rōs)	130	23.19 N	106.14 W
Siquia, R., Nic. (sē-kē'ä)	133	12.23 N	84.36 W
Siracusa, It. (sē-rä-koo'sä)	159	37.02 N	15.19 E
Sirājganj, Bngl. (sĭ-räj'gŭnj)	196	24.23 N	89.43 E
Sirama, Sal. (Sē-rä-mä)	132	13.23 N	87.55 W
Sir Douglas, Mt., Can. (sûr dŭg'lăs)	99	50.44 N	115.20 W
Sir Edward Pellew Group (Is.), Austl. (pĕl'ū)	214	15.15 S	137.15 E
Siret, Rom.	167	47.58 N	26.01 E
Siret (R.), Rom.	167	46.10 N	27.18 E
Sirhān, Wadi (R.), Sau. Ar.	192	31.02 N	37.16 E
Sirsa, India	196	29.39 N	75.02 E
Sir Sandford, Mt., Can. (sûr sănd'fērd)	99	51.40 N	117.52 W
Sirvintos, Sov. Un. (shēr'vĭn-tôs)	165	55.02 N	24.59 E
Sir Wilfrid Laurier, Mt., Can. (sûr wĭl'frĭd lôr'yēr)	99	52.47 N	119.45 W
Sisak, Yugo. (sē'sȧk)	172	45.29 N	16.20 E
Sisal, Mex. (sē-säl')	131	21.09 N	90.03 W
Sishui, China (sz-shwā)	200	35.40 N	117.17 E
Sisquoc (R.), Ca. (sĭs'kwŏk)	120	34.47 N	120.13 W
Sisseton, SD (sĭs'tŭn)	114	45.39 N	97.04 W
Sistān, Daryacheh-ye (L.), Iran-Afg.	192	31.45 N	61.15 E
Sisteron, Fr. (sēst'rôn)	169	44.10 N	5.55 E
Sisterville, WV (sĭs'tēr-vĭl)	110	39.30 N	81.00 W
Sitía, Grc. (sē'tĭ-ȧ)	172a	35.09 N	26.10 E
Sitka, Ak. (sĭt'kȧ)	107	57.08 N	135.18 W
Sittingbourne, Eng. (sĭt-ĭng-bôrn)	156b	51.20 N	0.44 E
Sittwe, Bur.	206	20.09 N	92.54 E
Sivas, Tur. (sē'väs)	179	39.50 N	36.50 E
Sivash (L.), Sov. Un. (sē'vȧsh)	175	45.55 N	34.42 E
Siverek, Tur. (sē'vě-rěk)	179	37.50 N	39.20 E
Siverskaya, Sov. Un. (sē'věr-skȧ-yȧ)	165	59.17 N	30.03 E
Siwah (Oasis), Egypt (sē'wä)	225	29.33 N	25.11 E
Sídheros, Ákra (C.), Grc.	172a	35.19 N	26.20 E
Sífnos (I.), Grc.	173	36.58 N	24.30 E
Síros (I.), Grc.	173	37.23 N	24.55 E
Síwah, Egypt	194	29.12 N	25.31 E
Sixaola R., C. R. (sē-kä-ō'lä) (sĕk-sȧ-ō'lä)	133	9.31 N	83.07 W
Sixian, China (sz shyěn)	200	33.29 N	116.57 E
Sixth Cataract, Sud.	225	16.26 N	32.44 E
Siyang, China (sz-yäŋ)	200	33.43 N	118.42 E
Sjaelland (I.), Den. (shĕl'lán')	164	55.34 N	11.35 E
Sjenica, Yugo. (syě'nē-tsȧ)	173	43.15 N	20.02 E
Skadovsk, Sov. Un. (skä'dôfsk)	175	46.08 N	32.54 E
Skagen, Den. (skä'ghěn)	164	57.43 N	10.32 E
Skagerrak (Str.), Eur. (skä-ghě-räk')	164	57.43 N	8.28 E
Skagit B., Wa. (skăg'ĭt)	118a	48.20 N	122.32 W
Skagit R., Wa.	116	48.29 N	121.52 W
Skagway, Ak. (skăg-wā)	107	59.30 N	135.28 W
Skälderviken (B.), Swe.	164	56.20 N	12.25 E
Skalistyy, Golets (Mtn.), Sov. Un.	181	57.28 N	119.48 E
Skamania, Wa. (skȧ-mā'nĭ-ȧ)	118c	45.37 N	112.03 W
Skamokawa, Wa.	118c	46.16 N	123.27 W
Skanderborg, Den. (skän-ěr-bôr')	164	56.04 N	9.55 E
Skaneateles, NY (skăn-ē-ăt'lĕs)	111	42.55 N	76.25 W
Skaneateles (L.), NY	111	42.50 N	76.20 W
Skänninge, Swe. (shěn'ĭng-ě)	164	58.24 N	15.02 E
Skanör-Falsterbo, Swe. (skän'ûr)	164	55.24 N	12.49 E
Skara, Swe. (skä'rȧ)	164	58.25 N	13.24 E
Skeena (R.), Can. (skē'nȧ)	98	54.10 N	129.40 W
Skeena Mts., Can.	98	56.00 N	128.00 W
Skeerpoort, S. Afr.	227b	25.49 S	27.45 E
Skeerpoort (R.), S. Afr.	227b	25.58 S	27.41 E
Skeldon, Guy. (skěl'dŭn)	143	5.49 N	57.15 W
Skellefteå, Swe. (shěl'ěf-tē-a')	158	64.47 N	20.48 E
Skellefteälven (R.), Swe.	158	62.25 N	19.28 E
Skelmersdale, Eng.	64a	53.33 N	2.48 W
Skhodnya, Sov. Un. (skôd'nyȧ)	182b	55.57 N	37.21 E
Skhodnya R., Sov. Un.	182b	55.55 N	37.16 E
Skíathos (I.), Grc. (skē'ȧ-thôs)	173	39.15 N	23.25 E
Skibbereen, Ire. (skĭb'ēr-ēn)	162	51.32 N	9.25 W
Skidegate Inlet, Can. (skĭ'-dē-gāt')	98	53.15 N	132.00 W
Skidmore, Tx. (skĭd'môr)	125	28.16 N	97.40 W
Skien, Nor. (skē'ěn)	164	59.13 N	9.35 E
Skierniewice, Pol. (skyěr-nyě-vēt'sě)	167	51.58 N	20.13 E
Skihist Mtn., Can.	98	50.11 N	121.54 W
Skikda (Philippeville), Alg.	160	36.58 N	6.51 E
Skilpadfontein, S. Afr.	223d	25.02 S	28.50 E
Skíros, Grc.	173	38.53 N	24.32 E
Skiros (I.), Grc.	173	38.50 N	24.43 E
Skive, Den. (skē'vě)	164	56.34 N	8.56 E
Skjálfandafljót (R.), Ice. (skyäl'fänd-ô)	158	65.24 N	16.40 W
Skjerstad, Nor. (skyěr-städ)	158	67.12 N	15.37 E
Škofja Loka, Yugo. (shkôf'yȧ lō'kȧ)	172	46.10 N	14.20 E
Skokie, Il. (skō'kē)	113a	42.02 N	87.45 W
Skokomish Ind. Res., Wa. (Skō-kō'mĭsh)	118a	47.22 N	123.07 W
Skole, Sov. Un. (skô'lě)	167	49.03 N	23.32 E
Skópelos (I.), Grc. (skô'pȧ-lôs)	173	39.04 N	23.31 E
Skopin, Sov. Un. (skô'pēn)	174	53.49 N	39.35 E
Skopje, Yugo. (skôp'yě)	173	42.02 N	21.26 E
Skövde, Swe. (shûv'dě)	164	58.25 N	13.48 E
Skovorodino, Sov. Un. (skô'vô-rô'dĭ-nô)	181	53.53 N	123.56 E
Skowhegan, Me. (skou-hē'gȧn)	104	44.45 N	69.27 W
Skradin, Yugo. (skrä'děn)	172	43.49 N	17.58 E
Skreia, Nor. (skrā'ȧ)	164	60.40 N	10.55 E
Skudeneshavn, Nor. (skōō'dě-nes-houn')	164	59.10 N	5.19 E
Skuilte, S. Afr.	71b	26.07 S	28.19 E
Skull Valley Ind. Res., Ut. (skŭl)	121	40.25 N	112.50 W
Skuna, (R.), Ms. (skû'nȧ)	126	33.57 N	89.36 W
Skunk (R.), Ia. (skŭnk)	115	41.12 N	92.14 W
Skuodas, Sov. Un. (skwô'dȧs)	165	56.16 N	21.32 E
Skurup, Swe. (skû'rōōp)	164	55.29 N	13.27 E
Skvira, Sov. Un. (skvē'rȧ)	175	49.43 N	29.41 E
Skwierzyna, Pol. (skvē-ěr'zhĭ-nȧ)	166	52.35 N	15.30 E
Skye, I. of, Scot. (skī)	162	57.25 N	6.17 W
Skykomish (R.), Wa. (skī'kō-mĭsh)	118a	47.50 N	121.55 W
Skyring, Seno (B.), Chile (sě'nô-s-krē'ng)	144	52.35 S	72.30 W
Slade Green (Neigh.), Eng.	62	51.28 N	0.12 E
Slagese, Den.	164	55.25 N	11.19 E
Slamet, Gunung (Mtn.), Indon. (slä'mět)	206	7.15 S	109.15 E
Slănic, Rom. (slû'nēk)	173	45.13 N	25.56 E
Slate (I.), Can. (slāt)	115	48.38 N	87.14 W
Slater, Mo. (slāt'ēr)	123	39.13 N	93.03 W
Slatina, Rom. (slä'tē-nä)	173	44.26 N	24.21 E
Slaton, Tx. (slā'tŭn)	122	33.26 N	101.38 W
Slattocks, Eng.	64b	53.35 N	2.10 W
Slave (R.), Can. (slāv)	96	59.40 N	111.21 W
Slavgorod, Sov. Un. (sláf'gô-rôt)	180	52.58 N	78.43 E
Slavonija (Reg.), Yugo. (slä-vô'nē-yä)	173	45.29 N	17.31 E
Slavonska Požega, Yugo. (slä-vôn'skä pô'zhě-gä)	172	45.18 N	17.42 E
Slavonski Brod, Yugo. (skä-vôn'skē brôd)	173	45.10 N	18.01 E
Slavuta, Sov. Un. (slá-vōō'tȧ)	175	50.18 N	27.01 E
Slavyansk, Sov. Un. (sláv'yänsk')	175	48.52 N	37.34 E
Slavyanskaya, Sov. Un. (sláv-yán'skȧ-yȧ)	175	45.14 N	38.09 E
Slayton, Mn. (slā'tŭn)	114	44.00 N	95.44 W
Sleaford, Eng. (slē'fērd)	156	53.00 N	0.25 W
Sleepy Eye, Mn. (slēp'ĭ ī)	115	44.17 N	94.44 W
Sleepy Hollow, Ca.	59	33.57 N	117.47 W
Slidell, La. (slī-děl')	125	30.17 N	89.47 W
Sliedrecht, Neth.	157a	51.49 N	4.46 E
Sligo, Ire. (slī'gō)	162	54.17 N	8.19 W
Slite, Swe. (slē'tě)	164	57.41 N	18.47 E
Sliven, Bul. (slē'věn)	173	42.41 N	26.20 E
Sloan, NY	57a	42.54 N	78.47 W
Sloatsburg, NY (slōts'bŭrg)	112a	41.09 N	74.11 W
Slobodka, Sov. Un. (slô'bôd-kȧ)	165	54.34 N	26.12 E
Slobodskoy, Sov. Un. (slô'bôt-skoi)	178	58.48 N	50.02 E
Sloka, Sov. Un. (slô'kȧ)	165	56.57 N	23.37 E
Slonim, Sov. Un. (swō'něm)	167	53.05 N	25.19 E
Slough, Eng. (slou)	156b	51.29 N	0.36 E
Slovakia (Prov.), see Slovensko			
Slovenija (Reg.), Yugo. (slô-vě'nē-yä)	172	45.58 N	14.43 E
Slovensko (Slovakia) (Prov.), Czech. (slô-věn'skô) (slô-vȧk'ĭȧ)	167	48.40 N	19.00 E
Sluch' (R.), Sov. Un.	167	50.56 N	26.48 E
Slunj, Yugo. (slōōn')	172	45.08 N	15.46 E
Slupsk, Pol. (swōōpsk)	167	54.28 N	17.02 E
Slutsk, Sov. Un. (slōōtsk)	174	53.02 N	27.34 E
Slyne Head, Ire. (slīn)	162	53.25 N	10.05 W
Smackover, Ar. (smăk'ô-vēr)	123	33.22 N	92.42 W
Smederevo (Semedria), Yugo. (smě'de-rě-vô) (sě-měn'drĭ-ȧ)	173	44.39 N	20.54 E
Smederevska Palanka, Yugo. (smě-dě-rěv'skä pä-län'kä)	173	44.21 N	21.00 E
Smedjebacken, Swe. (smĭ'tyě-bä-kěn)	164	60.09 N	15.19 E
Smela, Sov. Un. (smyā'lȧ)	175	49.14 N	31.52 E
Smeloye, Sov. Un. (smyā'lô-ě)	175	50.55 N	33.36 E
Smethport, Pa. (směth'pōrt)	111	41.50 N	78.25 W
Smethwick (Warley), Eng.	156	52.31 N	2.04 W
Smiltene, Sov. Un. (smēl'tě-ně)	174	57.26 N	25.57 E
Smith, Can. (smĭth)	99	55.10 N	114.02 W
Smith (I.), Wa.	118a	48.20 N	122.53 W
Smith Center, Ks. (sěn'tēr)	122	39.45 N	98.46 W
Smithers, Can. (smĭth'ērs)	98	54.47 N	127.10 W
Smithfield, Austl.	70a	33.51 S	150.57 E
Smithfield, NC (smĭth'fēld)	127	35.30 N	78.21 W
Smithfield, Ut.	117	41.50 N	111.49 W
Smithland, Ky. (smĭth'lănd)	110	37.10 N	88.25 W
Smith Mountain Lake (Res.), Va.	127	37.00 N	79.45 W
Smith Point, Tx.	125a	29.32 N	94.45 W
Smith R., Mt.	117	47.00 N	111.20 W
Smiths Falls, Can. (smĭths)	103	44.55 N	76.05 W
Smithton, Austl. (smĭth'tŭn)	216	40.55 S	145.12 E
Smithton, Il.	119e	38.24 N	89.59 W
Smithville, Tx. (smĭth'vĭl)	125	30.00 N	97.08 W
Smitswinkelvlakte, S. Afr.	226a	34.16 S	18.25 E
Smoke Creek Des., Nv. (smōk crēk)	120	40.28 N	119.40 W
Smoky (R.), Can. (smōk'ĭ)	99	55.30 N	117.30 W
Smoky Hill (R.), Ks. (smōk'ĭ hĭl)	123	38.40 N	97.32 W
Smøla (I.), Nor. (smûlä)	164	63.16 N	7.40 E
Smolensk, Sov. Un. (smô-lyěnsk')	174	54.46 N	32.03 E
Smolensk (Oblast), Sov. Un.	174	55.00 N	32.18 E
Smyadovo, Bul.	173	43.04 N	27.00 E
Smyrna, De. (smûr'nȧ)	111	39.20 N	75.35 W
Smyrna, Ga.	112c	33.53 N	84.31 W
Snag, Can. (snăg)	107	62.18 N	140.30 W
Snake (R.), Mn. (snāk)	115	45.58 N	93.20 W
Snake (R.), Wa.	116	46.35 N	117.20 W
Snake Ra., Nv.	121	39.20 N	114.15 W
Snake R., Henrys Fork, Id.	117	43.52 N	111.55 W
Snake River Pln., Id.	117	43.08 N	114.46 W
Snap Pt., Ba.	134	23.45 N	77.30 W
Sneffels Pk., Co. (snĕf'ĕlz)	121	38.00 N	107.50 W
Snelgrove, Can. (snēl'grōv)	95d	43.44 N	79.50 W
Sniardwy, Jezioro (L.), Pol. (snyärt'vĭ)	167	53.46 N	21.59 E
Snodland, Eng.	62	51.20 N	0.27 E
Snøhetta (Mtn.), Nor. (snû-hěttä)	164	62.18 N	9.12 E
Snohomish (R.), Wa.	118a	47.53 N	122.04 W
Snohomish, Wa. (snô-hō'mĭsh)	118a	47.55 N	122.05 W
Snoqualmie, Wa. (snō qwäl'mē)	118a	47.32 N	121.50 W
Snoqualmie R., Wa.	116	47.32 N	121.53 W
Snov (R.), Sov. Un. (snôf)	175	51.38 N	31.38 E
Snowden, Pa.	57b	40.16 N	79.58 W
Snowdon (Mtn.), Wales	162	53.05 N	4.04 W
Snow Hill, Md. (hĭl)	111	38.15 N	75.20 W
Snow Lake, Can.	101	54.50 N	100.10 W
Snowy Mts., Austl. (snō'ē)	215	36.17 S	148.30 E
Snyder, Ok. (snī'dēr)	122	34.40 N	98.57 W
Snyder, Tx.	124	32.48 N	100.53 W
Soar (R.), Eng. (sōr)	156	52.44 N	1.09 W
Sobat R., Sud. (sō'bȧt)	225	9.04 N	32.02 E
Sobinka, Sov. Un. (sô-bĭŋ'kȧ)	174	55.59 N	40.02 E
Sobo Zan (Mt.), Jap. (sô'bô zän)	205	32.47 N	131.27 E
Sobral, Braz. (sô-brä'l)	143	3.39 S	40.16 W
Sochaczew, Pol. (sô-кä'chěf)	167	52.14 N	20.18 E
Sochi, Sov. Un. (sôch'ĭ)	179	43.35 N	39.50 E
Society Is., Fr. Polynesia (sô-sī'ě-tē)	209	15.00 S	157.30 W
Socoltenango, Mex. (sô-kôl-tě-näŋ'gō)	131	16.17 N	92.20 W
Socorro, Braz. (sô-kô'r-rō)	141a	22.35 S	46.32 W
Socorro, Col. (sô-kôr'rō)	142	6.23 N	73.19 W
Socorro, NM	121	34.05 N	106.55 W
Socotra I., P. D. R. of Yem. (sô-kō'trȧ)	223a	13.00 N	52.30 E
Socúellamos, Sp. (sô-kōō-āl'yä-mōs)	170	39.18 N	2.48 W
Soda (L.), Ca. (sō'dȧ)	120	35.12 N	116.25 W
Soda Pk., Wa.	118c	45.53 N	122.04 W
Soda Springs, Id. (sprĭngz)	117	42.39 N	111.37 W
Söderhamn, Swe. (sû-děr-häm''n)	164	61.20 N	17.00 E
Söderköping, Swe.	164	58.30 N	16.14 E
Södertälje, Swe. (sû-děr-těl'yě)	164	59.12 N	17.35 E
Sodingen (Neigh.), F.R.G.	63	51.32 N	7.15 E
Sodo, Eth.	225	7.03 N	37.46 E
Sodpur, India	67a	22.42 N	88.23 E
Södra Dellen (L.), Swe.	164	61.45 N	16.30 E
Soest, F.R.G. (zōst)	166	51.35 N	8.05 E
Soeurs, Île des (I.), Can.	54b	45.28 N	73.33 W
Sofia, see Sofiya			
Sofiya (Sofia), Bul. (sô'fē-yȧ) (sô'fē-ȧ)	173	42.43 N	23.20 E
Sofiyevka, Sov. Un. (sô-fē'yěf-kȧ)	175	48.03 N	33.53 E
Soga, Jap. (sô'gä)	205a	35.35 N	140.08 E
Sogamoso, Col. (sô-gä-mô'sō)	142	5.42 N	72.51 W
Sognafjorden (Fd.), Nor.	164	61.09 N	5.30 E
Sogozha (R.), Sov. Un. (sô'gô-zhȧ)	174	58.35 N	39.08 E
Soissons, Fr. (swä-sôn')	168	49.23 N	3.17 E
Soisy-sous-Montmorency, Fr.	64c	48.59 N	2.18 E
Sōka, Jap. (sō'kä)	205a	35.50 N	139.49 E
Sokal', Sov. Un. (sô'käl')	167	50.28 N	24.20 E
Soke, Tur. (sû'kě)	179	37.40 N	27.10 E
Sokodé, Togo (sô-kô-dā')	228	8.59 N	1.08 E
Sokolka, Pol. (sô-kōōl'kȧ)	167	53.23 N	23.30 E
Sokol'niki (Neigh.), Sov. Un.	66b	55.48 N	37.41 E
Sokolo, Mali (sô-kô-lō')	224	14.51 N	6.09 W
Sokone, Senegal	228	13.53 N	16.22 W
Sokoto, Nig. (sō'kô-tō)	229	13.04 N	5.16 E
Sokotów Podlaski, Pol. (sô-kô-wōōf' pŭd-lä'skĭ)	167	52.24 N	22.15 E
Sola de Vega (San Miguel), Mex. (sō'lä dā vā'gä) (sän mē-gāl')	131	16.31 N	96.58 W
Solander, C., Austl.	211b	34.03 S	151.16 E
Solano, Phil. (sō-lä'nō)	207a	16.31 N	121.11 E
Sölderholz (Neigh.), F.R.G.	63	51.29 N	7.35 E
Soledad, Col. (sō-lě-dä'd)	142	10.47 N	75.00 W
Soledad Díez Gutierrez, Mex. (sô-lā-dhädh'dē'äz gōō-tyā'rěz)	130	22.19 N	100.54 W
Soleduck R., Wa. (sōl'dŭk)	116	47.59 N	124.28 W
Solentiname, Islas de (Is.), Nic. (ē's-läs-dě-sô-lěn-tē-nä'mȧ)	132	11.15 N	85.16 W
Solheim, S. Afr.	71b	26.11 S	28.10 E

ăt; finăl; rāte; senāte; ärm; ȧsk; sofȧ; fâre; ch-choose; dh-as th in other; bē; ēvent; bět; recěnt; cratēr; g-gō; gh-guttural g; bĭt; ĭ-short neutral; rīde; к-guttural k as ch in German ich;

PLACE (Pronunciation)	PAGE	Lat. °′	Long. °′
Solihull, Eng. (sō'lĭ-hŭl)	156	52.25 N	1.46 W
Solikamsk, Sov. Un. (sô-lē-kȧmsk')	182a	59.38 N	56.48 E
Sol'-Iletsk, Sov. Un.	179	51.10 N	55.05 E
Solimões, Rio (R.), Braz. (rē'ō-sô-lē-mô'ĕs)	142	2.45 S	67.44 W
Solingen, F.R.G. (zô'lĭng-ĕn)	169c	51.10 N	7.05 E
Sollefteå, Swe. (sôl-lĕf'tē-ô)	164	63.06 N	17.17 E
Sóller, Sp. (sō'lyĕr)	171	39.45 N	2.40 E
Solncevo, Sov. Un.	66b	55.39 N	37.24 E
Sologne (Reg.), Fr. (sō-lōn'yĕ)	168	47.36 N	1.53 E
Solola, Guat. (sō-lō'lä)	132	14.45 N	91.12 W
Solomon Is., Oceania (sŏ'lō-mŭn)	208	7.00 S	160.00 E
Solomon R., Ks.	122	39.24 N	98.19 W
Solomon R. North Fk., Ks.	122	39.34 N	99.52 W
Solomon R., South Fk., Ks.	122	39.19 N	99.52 W
Solon, China (swo-lo͞on)	202	47.32 N	121.18 E
Solon, Oh. (sō'lŭn)	113d	41.23 N	81.26 W
Solothurn, Switz. (zô'lō-tho͞orn)	166	47.13 N	7.30 E
Solovetskiye (I.), Sov. Un.	178	65.10 N	35.40 E
Šolta (I.), Yugo. (shôl'tä)	172	43.20 N	16.15 E
Soltau, F.R.G. (sôl'tou)	166	53.00 N	9.50 E
Sol'tsy, Sov. Un. (sôl'tsē)	174	58.04 N	30.13 E
Solvay, NY (sŏl'vā)	111	43.05 N	76.10 W
Sölvesborg, Swe. (sûl'vĕs-bôrg)	164	56.04 N	14.35 E
Sol'vychegodsk, Sov. Un. (sôl'vē-chĕ-gôtsk')	178	61.18 N	46.58 E
Solway Firth, Eng.-Scot. (sŏl'wā fûrth')	162	54.42 N	3.55 W
Solwezi, Zambia	231	12.11 S	26.25 E
Somalia, Afr. (sō-ma'lē-ȧ)	222	3.28 N	44.47 E
Somanga, Tan.	231	8.24 S	39.17 E
Sombor, Yugo. (sôm'bôr)	173	45.45 N	19.10 E
Sombrerete, Mex. (sōm-brā-rā'tā)	130	23.38 N	103.37 W
Sombrero, Cayo (C.), Ven. (kä-yô-sôm-brĕ'rô)	143b	10.52 N	68.12 W
Somerdale, NJ	56b	39.51 N	75.01 W
Somerset, Ky. (sŭm'ēr-sĕt)	126	37.05 N	84.35 W
Somerset, Md.	56d	38.58 N	77.05 W
Somerset, Ma.	112b	41.46 N	71.05 W
Somerset, Pa.	111	40.00 N	79.05 W
Somerset, Tx.	119d	29.13 N	98.39 W
Somerset East, S. Afr.	227c	32.44 S	25.36 E
Somersworth, NH (sŭm'ērz-wûrth)	104	43.16 N	70.53 W
Somerton, Az. (sŭm'ēr-tŭn)	120	32.36 N	114.43 W
Somerton (Neigh.), Pa.	56b	40.06 N	75.01 W
Somerville, Ma. (sŭm'ēr-vĭl)	105a	42.23 N	71.06 W
Somerville, NJ	112a	40.34 N	74.37 W
Somerville, Tn.	126	35.14 N	89.21 W
Somerville, Tx.	125	30.21 N	96.31 W
Somesul R., Rom. (sô-mā'sho͞ol)	167	47.43 N	23.09 E
Somma Vesuviana, It. (sôm'mä vā-zo͞o-vē-ä'nä)	171c	40.38 N	14.27 E
Somme (R.), Fr. (sŏm)	168	50.02 N	2.04 E
Sommerberg, F.R.G.	63	51.27 N	7.32 E
Sommerfeld, G.D.R. (zō'mĕr-fĕld)	157b	52.48 N	13.02 E
Sommerville, Austl.	211a	38.14 S	145.10 E
Somoto, Nic. (sô-mō'tō)	132	13.28 N	86.37 W
Somuncurá, Meseta de (Plat.), Arg. (mĕ-sĕ'tä-dĕ-sô-mo͞o'n-ko͞o-rá')	144	41.15 S	68.00 W
Son (R.), India (sōn)	196	24.40 N	82.35 E
Soná, Pan. (sō'nä)	133	8.00 N	81.19 W
Sonari, India	67e	18.52 N	72.59 E
Sŏnchŏn, Kor. (sŭn'shŭn)	204	39.49 N	124.56 E
Sondags (R.), S. Afr.	227c	33.17 S	25.14 E
Sønderborg, Den. (sûn''er-bôrgh)	164	54.55 N	9.47 E
Sondershausen, G.D.R. (zōn'dērz-hou'zĕn)	166	51.17 N	10.45 E
Song Ca (R.), Viet.	203	19.15 N	105.00 E
Songea, Tan. (sôn-gā'ȧ)	231	10.41 S	35.39 E
Songhua (R.), **see Sungari**			
Songjiang, China (sôŋ-jyäŋ)	201b	31.01 N	121.14 E
Sŏngjin, Kor. (sŭng'jĭn')	204	40.38 N	129.10 E
Songkhla, Thai. (sông'ĸlä')	206	7.09 N	100.34 E
Songwe, Zaire	231	12.25 S	29.40 E
Sonneberg, G.D.R. (sôn'ē-bĕrgh)	166	50.20 N	11.14 E
Sonora, Ca. (sō-nō'rȧ)	120	37.58 N	120.22 W
Sonora, Tx.	124	30.33 N	100.38 W
Sonora (State), Mex.	128	29.45 N	111.15 W
Sonora (R.), Mex.	128	28.45 N	111.35 W
Sonora Pk., Ca.	120	38.22 N	119.39 W
Sonseca, Sp. (sôn-sā'kä)	170	39.41 N	3.56 W
Sonsón, Col. (sôn-sōn')	142a	5.42 N	75.28 W
Sonsonate, Sal. (sōn-sō-nä'tā)	132	13.46 N	89.43 W
Sonsorol Is., Pac. Is. Trust Ter. (sŏn-sô-rōl')	207	5.03 N	132.33 E
Sooke Basin, Can. (so͝ok)	118a	48.21 N	123.47 W
Soo Locks, Can.-U. S. (so͞o lŏks)	119	46.30 N	84.30 W
Sopetrán, Col. (sō-pĕ-trä'n)	142a	6.30 N	75.44 W
Sopot, Pol. (sô'pôt)	164	54.26 N	18.25 E
Sopron, Hung. (shŏp'rôn)	166	47.41 N	16.36 E
Sora, It. (sō'rä)	172	41.43 N	13.37 E
Sorbas, Sp. (sôr'bäs)	170	37.05 N	2.07 W
Sorbonne (P. Int.), Fr.	64c	48.51 N	2.21 E
Sordo (R.), Mex. (sô'r-dō)	131	16.39 N	97.33 W
Sorel, Can. (sô-rĕl')	103	46.01 N	73.07 W
Sorell, C., Austl.	216	42.10 S	144.50 E
Soresina, It. (sō-rā-zē'nä)	172	45.17 N	9.51 E
Soria, Sp. (sō'rē-ä)	170	41.46 N	2.28 W
Soriano (Dept.), Ur. (sō-rēä'nō)	141c	33.25 S	58.00 W
Sorocaba, Braz. (sô-rô-kä'bȧ)	141a	23.29 S	47.27 W
Soroki, Sov. Un. (sô-rō'kē)	175	48.09 N	28.17 E
Sorong, Indon. (sō-rông')	207	1.00 S	131.20 E
Sorot' (R.), Sov. Un. (sō-rō'tzh)	174	57.08 N	29.23 E
Soroti, Ug. (sō-rō'tē)	231	1.43 N	33.37 E
Sørøya (I.), Nor.	158	70.37 N	20.58 E
Sorraia (R.), Port. (sôr-rī'ä)	170	38.55 N	8.42 W
Sorrento, It. (sôr-rĕn'tō)	171c	40.23 N	14.23 E
Sorsogon, Phil. (sôr-sōgōn')	207	12.51 N	124.02 E
Sortavala, Sov. Un. (sôr'tä-vä-lä)	165	61.43 N	30.40 E
Sŏsan, Korea (sŭ'sän)	202	36.40 N	126.25 E
Sosenki, Sov. Un.	66b	55.34 N	37.26 E
Sosna (R.), Sov. Un. (sôs'nȧ)	175	50.33 N	38.15 E

PLACE (Pronunciation)	PAGE	Lat. °′	Long. °′
Sosnitsa, Sov. Un. (sôs-nē'tsȧ)	175	51.30 N	32.29 E
Sosnogorsk, Sov. Un.	180	63.13 N	54.09 E
Sosnowiec, Pol. (sôs-nô'vyĕts)	167	50.17 N	19.10 E
Sosunova, Mys (Pt.), Sov. Un. (mĭs sō'so͞o-nôf'ȧ)	204	46.28 N	138.06 E
Sos'va (R.), Sov. Un. (sôs'vȧ)	178	63.10 N	63.30 E
Sos'va R., Sov. Un. (sôs'vȧ)	182a	59.55 N	60.40 E
Sota (R.), Benin	229	11.10 N	3.20 E
Sota la Marina, Mex. (sô-tä-lä-mä-rē'nä)	130	22.45 N	98.11 W
Soteapan, Mex. (sō-tȧ-ä'pän)	131	18.14 N	94.51 W
Soto la Marina, Rio (R.), Mex. (rē'ō-so'tō lä mä-rē'nä)	130	23.55 N	98.30 W
Sotuta, Mex. (sô-to͞o'tä)	132a	20.35 N	89.00 W
Souanké, Con.	230	2.05 N	14.03 E
Soublette, Ven. (sō-o͞o-blĕ'tĕ)	143b	9.55 N	66.06 W
Souflion, Grc.	173	41.12 N	26.17 E
Soufriere, Saint Lucia (so͞o-frē-âr')	133b	13.50 N	61.03 W
Soufrière (Vol.), Montserrat	133b	16.43 N	62.10 W
Soufriere, Mt., Saint Vincent	133b	13.19 N	61.12 W
Sŏul (Seoul), Kor.	204	37.35 N	127.03 E
Soulanges, Can.	54b	45.20 N	74.15 W
Sounding Cr., Can. (soun'dĭng)	100	51.35 N	111.00 W
Souq Ahras, Alg.	159	36.23 N	8.00 E
Sources, Mt. aux, Leso.-S. Afr. (môɴ'tō so͞ors')	223c	28.47 S	29.04 E
Soure, Port. (sōr-ĕ)	170	40.04 N	8.37 W
Souris, Can. (so͞o'rē')	105	46.20 N	62.17 W
Souris, Can.	101	49.38 N	100.15 W
Souris (R.), Can.	101	49.10 N	102.00 W
Sourlake, Tx. (sour'lāk)	125	30.09 N	94.24 W
Sousse, Tun. (so͞os)	224	36.00 N	10.39 E
South (R.), NC	127	34.49 N	78.33 W
South Africa, Afr.	222	28.00 S	24.50 E
Southall (Neigh.), Eng.	62	51.31 N	0.23 W
South Amboy, NJ (south'ăm'boi)	112a	40.28 N	74.17 W
South America	138		
Southampton, Eng. (south-ămp'tŭn)	162	50.54 N	1.30 W
Southampton, NY	111	40.53 N	72.24 W
Southampton I., Can.	97	64.38 N	84.00 W
South Andaman I., Andaman & Nicobar Is. (ăn-dȧ-măn')	206	11.57 N	93.24 E
South Australia (State), Austl. (ôs-trā'lĭ-ȧ)	214	29.45 S	132.00 E
South B., Ba.	135	20.55 N	73.35 W
South Bend, In. (bĕnd)	110	41.40 N	86.20 W
South Bend, Wa. (bĕnd)	116	46.39 N	123.48 W
South Bight (B.), Ba.	134	24.20 N	77.35 W
South Bimini (I.), Ba. (bē'mē-nē)	134	25.40 N	79.20 W
Southborough, Ma. (south'bŭr-ô)	105a	42.18 N	71.33 W
South Boston, Va. (bôs'tŭn)	127	36.41 N	78.55 W
South Boston (Neigh.), Ma.	54a	42.20 N	71.03 W
Southbridge, Ma. (south'brĭj)	111	42.05 N	72.00 W
South Brooklyn (Neigh.), NY	55	40.41 N	73.59 W
South Caicos (I.), Turks & Caicos (kī'kōs)	135	21.30 N	71.35 W
South Carolina (State), U. S. (kăr-ô-lī'nȧ)	109	34.15 N	81.10 W
South Cave, Eng. (cāv)	156	53.45 N	0.35 W
South Charleston, WV (chärlz'tŭn)	110	38.20 N	81.40 W
South Chicago (Neigh.), Il.	58a	41.44 N	87.33 W
South China Sea, Asia (chī'nȧ)	206	15.23 N	114.12 E
South Cr., Austl.	211b	33.43 S	167.00 E
Southcrest, S. Afr.	71b	26.15 S	28.07 E
South Dakota (State), U. S. (dȧ-kō'tȧ)	108	44.20 N	101.55 W
South Darenth, Eng.	62	51.24 N	0.15 E
South Downs, Eng. (dounz)	162	50.55 N	1.13 W
South Dum-Dum, India	196a	22.36 N	88.25 E
Southeast Asia Treaty Organization Headquarters (P. Int.), Thai	68f	13.45 N	100.31 E
Southeast, C., Austl.	215	43.47 S	146.03 E
Southend-on-Sea, Eng. (south-ĕnd')	156b	51.33 N	0.41 E
Southern Alps (Mts.), N. Z. (sŭ-thûrn ălps)	217	43.35 S	170.00 E
Southern California, University of (P. Int.), Ca.	59	34.02 N	118.17 W
Southern Cross, Austl.	214	31.13 S	119.30 E
Southern Indian (L.), Can. (sŭth'ērn ĭn'dĭ-ăn)	99	56.46 N	98.57 W
Southern Pines, NC (sŭth'ērn pīnz)	127	35.10 N	79.23 W
Southern Ute Ind. Res., Co. (ūt)	121	37.05 N	108.23 W
Southern Yemen, see Yemen, People's Democratic Republic of			
South Euclid, Oh. (ū'klĭd)	113d	41.30 N	81.34 W
Southfield, Mi.	57c	42.29 N	83.17 W
Southfleet, Eng.	62	51.25 N	0.19 E
South Fox (I.), Mi. (fŏks)	110	45.25 N	85.55 W
South Gate, Ca. (gāt)	119a	33.57 N	118.13 W
Southgate (Neigh.), Eng.	62	51.38 N	0.08 W
South Georgia (I.), Falk Is. (jôr'jȧ)	140	54.00 S	37.00 W
South Germiston, S. Afr.	71b	26.15 S	28.10 E
South Green, Eng.	62	51.37 N	0.26 E
South Haven, Mi. (hāv''n)	110	42.25 N	86.15 W
South Head (C.), Austl.	70a	33.50 S	151.17 E
South Hempstead, NY	55	40.41 N	73.37 W
South Hill, Va.	127	36.44 N	78.08 W
South Hills (Neigh.), S. Afr.	71b	26.15 S	28.05 E
South I., N. Z.	217	42.40 S	169.00 E
South Indian Lake, Can.	101	56.50 N	99.00 W
Southington, Ct. (sŭdh'ĭng-tŭn)	111	41.35 N	72.55 W
South Loup (R.), Ne. (lo͞op)	114	41.21 N	100.08 W
South Lynnfield, Ma.	54a	42.31 N	71.00 W
South Media, Pa.	56b	39.54 N	75.23 W
South Melbourne, Austl.	70b	37.50 S	144.57 E
South Merrimack, NH (mĕr'ĭ-măk)	105a	42.47 N	71.36 W
South Milwaukee, Wi. (mĭl-wô'kē)	113a	42.55 N	87.52 W
South Mimms, Eng.	62	51.42 N	0.14 W
South Moose L., Can.	101	53.51 N	100.20 W
South Nation (R.), Can. (nā'shŭn)	95c	45.12 N	75.07 W
South Negril Pt., Jam. (nå-grēl')	134	18.15 N	78.25 W

PLACE (Pronunciation)	PAGE	Lat. °′	Long. °′
South Ockendon, Eng.	62	51.32 N	0.18 E
South Ogden, Ut. (ŏg'dĕn)	119b	41.12 N	111.58 W
South Orange, NJ	55	40.45 N	74.15 W
South Orkney Is., B. A. T.	232	57.00 S	45.00 W
South Oxhey, Eng.	62	51.38 N	0.23 W
South Paris, Me. (păr'ĭs)	104	44.13 N	70.32 W
South Park, Ky. (pärk)	113h	38.06 N	85.43 W
South Pasadena, Ca. (păs-ȧ-dē'nȧ)	119a	34.06 N	118.08 W
South Pease (R.), Tx. (pēz)	121	33.54 N	100.45 W
South Pender (I.), Can. (pĕn'dēr)	118d	48.45 N	123.09 W
South Philadelphia (Neigh.), Pa.	56b	39.56 N	75.10 W
South Pittsburgh, Tn. (pĭs'bûrg)	126	35.00 N	85.42 W
South Platte (R.), U. S. (plăt)	108	40.40 N	102.40 W
South Porcupine, Can.	102	48.28 N	81.13 W
Southport, Austl. (south'pōrt)	216	27.57 S	153.27 E
Southport, Eng. (south'pôrt)	156	53.38 N	3.00 W
Southport, In.	113g	39.40 N	86.07 W
Southport, NC	127	35.55 N	78.02 W
South Portland, Me. (pōrt-lănd)	104	43.37 N	70.15 W
South Prairie, Wa. (prā'rĭ)	118a	47.08 N	122.06 W
South Pt., Barb.	133b	13.00 N	59.43 W
South Pt., Mi.	110	44.50 N	83.20 W
South R., Ga.	112c	33.40 N	84.15 W
South Range, Wi. (rānj)	119h	46.37 N	91.59 W
South River, NJ (rĭv'ēr)	112a	40.27 N	74.23 W
South Saint Paul, Mn.	119g	44.54 N	93.02 W
South Salt Lake, Ut. (sôlt lāk)	119b	40.44 N	111.53 W
South Sandwich Is., Falk. Is. (sănd'wĭch)	140	58.00 S	27.00 W
South Sandwich Trench, S. A.-Ant.	140	55.00 S	27.00 W
South San Francisco, Ca. (săn frăn-sĭs'kô)	118d	37.39 N	122.24 W
South San Francisco, Ca.	58b	37.39 N	122.24 W
South San Jose Hills, Ca.	59	34.01 N	117.55 W
South Saskatchewan (R.), Can. (sās-kach'ē-wän)	100	53.15 N	105.05 W
South Shetland Is., B. A. T.	232	62.00 S	70.00 W
South Shields, Eng. (shēldz)	162	55.00 N	1.22 W
South Shore (Neigh.), Il.	58a	41.46 N	87.35 W
South Side (Neigh.), Pa.	57b	40.26 N	79.58 W
South Sioux City, Ne. (so͞o sĭt'ē)	114	42.48 N	96.26 W
South Taranaki Bight, N. Z. (tä-rä-nä'kē)	217	39.35 S	173.50 E
South Thompson (R.), Can. (tŏmp'sŭn)	99	50.41 N	120.21 W
Southton, Tx. (south'tŭn)	119d	29.18 N	98.26 W
South Uist (I.), Scot. (ū'ĭst)	162	57.15 N	7.24 W
South Umpqua R., Or. (ŭmp'kwå)	116	43.00 N	122.54 W
South Walpole, Ma.	54a	42.06 N	71.16 W
South Waltham, Ma.	54a	42.22 N	71.15 W
Southwark (Neigh.), Eng.	62	51.30 N	0.06 W
South Weald, Eng.	62	51.37 N	0.16 E
Southwell, Eng. (south'wĕl)	156	53.04 N	0.56 W
South West Africa, see Namibia			
South Westbury, NY	55	40.45 N	73.35 W
Southwest Miramichi (R.), Can. (mĭr ȧ-mē'shē)	104	46.35 N	66.17 W
Southwest Pt., Ba.	134	25.50 N	77.10 W
Southwest Pt., Ba.	135	23.55 N	74.30 W
South Weymouth, Ma.	54a	42.10 N	70.57 W
South Whittier, Ca.	59	33.56 N	118.03 W
South Yorkshire (Co.), Eng.	156	53.29 N	1.35 W
Sovetsk (Tilsit), Sov. Un. (sô-vyĕtsk')	165	55.04 N	21.54 E
Sovetskaya Gavan', Sov. Un. (sŭ-vyĕt'skī-u gä'vŭn')	181	48.59 N	140.14 E
Soviet Union, Eur.-Asia (sō-vĭ-ĕt')	190	60.30 N	64.00 E
Sow (R.), Eng. (sou)	156	52.45 N	2.12 W
Soweto (Neigh.), S. Afr.	71b	26.14 S	27.54 E
Sōya Misaki (C.), Jap. (sō'yȧ mē'sä-kē)	204	45.35 N	141.25 E
Soyo, Ang	230	6.10 S	12.25 E
Sozh (R.), Sov. Un. (sôzh)	174	52.17 N	31.00 E
Sozopol, Bul. (sôz'ō-pôl')	173	42.18 N	27.50 E
Spa, Bel. (spä)	163	50.30 N	5.50 E
Spain, Eur. (spān)	154	40.15 N	4.30 W
Spalding, Ne. (spôl'dĭng)	114	41.43 N	98.23 W
Spanaway, Wa. (spăn'ȧ-wā)	118a	47.06 N	122.26 W
Spandau (Neigh.), F.R.G.	65a	52.32 N	13.12 E
Spangler, Pa. (spăng'lēr)	111	40.40 N	78.50 W
Spanish Fork, Ut. (spăn'ĭsh fôrk)	121	40.10 N	111.40 W
Spanish Town, Jam.	134	18.00 N	76.55 W
Sparks, Nv. (spärks)	120	39.34 N	119.45 W
Sparrows Point, Md. (spăr'ōz)	112e	39.13 N	76.29 W
Sparta, Ga. (spär'tȧ)	126	33.16 N	82.59 W
Sparta, Il.	123	38.07 N	89.42 W
Sparta, Mi.	110	43.10 N	85.45 W
Sparta, Tn.	126	35.54 N	85.26 W
Sparta, Wi.	115	43.56 N	90.50 W
Sparta Mts., NJ	112a	41.00 N	74.38 W
Spartanburg, SC (spär'tăn-bûrg)	127	34.57 N	82.13 W
Sparta, see Spárti			
Spartel (C.), Mor. (spär-tĕl')	170	35.48 N	5.50 W
Spárti, Grc. (Sparta)	173	37.07 N	22.28 E
Spartivento, C., It. (spär-tē-vĕn'tō)	172	37.55 N	16.09 E
Spartivento, C., It.	172	38.54 N	8.52 E
Spas-Demensk, Sov. Un. (spȧs dyĕ-mĕnsk')	174	54.24 N	34.02 E
Spas-Klepiki, Sov. Un. (spȧs klĕp'ē-kē)	174	55.09 N	40.11 E
Spassk-Ryazanskiy, Sov. Un. (ryä-zän'skĭ)	174	54.24 N	40.21 E
Spassk-Dal'niy, Sov. Un. (spŭsk'däl'nyē)	181	44.30 N	133.00 E
Spátha, Ákra (C.), Grc.	172a	35.42 N	24.45 E
Spaulding, Al. (spôl'dĭng)	112h	33.27 N	86.50 W
Spear, C., Can. (spēr)	105	47.32 N	52.32 W
Spearfish, SD (spēr'fĭsh)	114	44.28 N	103.52 W
Speed, In. (spēd)	113h	38.25 N	85.45 W
Speedway, In. (spēd'wā)	113g	39.47 N	86.14 W
Speichersee (L.), F.R.G.	157d	48.12 N	11.47 E
Speke (Neigh.), Eng.	64b	53.21 N	2.51 W
Speldorf (Neigh.), F.R.G.	63	51.25 N	6.52 E

ng-sing; ŋ-baŋk; ɴ-nasalized n; nŏd; cŏmmit; ōld; ôbey; ôrder; oi-boil; fo͞od; fo͝ot; ou-out; s-soft; sh-dish; th-thin; pūre; ůnite; ûrn; stŭd; circŭs; ü-as in French tu; '-indeterminate vowel.

PLACE (Pronunciation)	PAGE	Lat. °'	Long. °'
Spellen, F.R.G.	63	51.37 N	6.37 E
Spencer, In. (spĕn'sẽr)	110	39.15 N	86.45 W
Spencer, Ia.	115	43.09 N	95.08 W
Spencer, NC	127	35.43 N	80.25 W
Spencer, WV	110	38.55 N	81.20 W
Spencer G., Austl. (spĕn'sẽr)	216	34.20 S	136.55 E
Sperenberg, G.D.R. (shpĕ'rĕn-bĕrgh)	157b	52.09 N	13.22 E
Sperkhiós (R.), Grc.	173	38.54 N	22.02 E
Spey (L.), Scot. (spā)	162	57.25 N	3.29 W
Speyer, F.R.G. (shpī'ẽr)	166	49.18 N	8.26 E
Sphinx (Pyramid), Egypt (sfĭnks)	223b	29.57 N	31.08 E
Spijkenisse, Neth.	157a	51.51 N	4.18 E
Spinazzola, It. (spē-nät'zô-lä)	172	40.58 N	16.05 E
Spirit Lake, Id. (spĭr'ĭt)	116	47.58 N	116.51 W
Spirit Lake, Ia. (lāk)	115	43.25 N	95.08 W
Spišská Nová Ves, Czech. (spēsh'skä nō'vä vĕs)	167	48.56 N	20.35 E
Spitsbergen (Is.), see Svalbard			
Spittal, Aus. (shpē-täl')	166	46.48 N	13.28 E
Split, Yugo. (splēt)	172	43.30 N	16.28 E
Split L., Can.	101	56.08 N	96.15 W
Spokane, Wa. (spōkăn')	116	47.39 N	117.25 W
Spokane R., Wa.	116	47.47 N	118.00 W
Spoleto, It. (spô-lā'tō)	172	42.44 N	12.44 E
Spoon (R.), Il. (spo͞on)	123	40.36 N	90.22 W
Spooner, Wi. (spo͞on'ẽr)	115	45.50 N	91.53 W
Sporádhes (Is.), Grc.	173	38.55 N	24.05 E
Sportswood, Austl.	70b	37.50 S	144.53 E
Spotswood, NJ (spŏtz'wo͝od)	112a	40.23 N	74.22 W
Sprague R., Or. (sprāg)	116	42.30 N	121.42 W
Spratly (I.), China (sprăt'lē)	206	8.38 N	11.54 E
Spray, NC (sprā)	127	36.30 N	79.44 W
Spree R., G.D.R. (shprā)	166	51.53 N	14.08 E
Spremberg, G.D.R. (shprĕm'bĕrgh)	166	51.35 N	14.23 E
Spring (R.), Ar.	123	36.25 N	91.35 W
Springbok, S. Afr. (sprĭng'bŏk)	226	29.35 S	17.55 E
Spring, Cr., Nv. (sprĭng)	120	40.18 N	117.45 W
Spring Cr., Tx.	125	30.03 N	95.43 W
Spring Cr., Tx.	124	31.08 N	100.50 W
Springdale, Ar. (sprĭng'dāl)	123	36.10 N	94.07 W
Springdale, Can.	105	49.30 N	56.05 W
Springdale, Pa.	113e	40.33 N	79.46 W
Springer, NM (sprĭng'ẽr)	122	36.21 N	104.37 W
Springerville, Az.	121	34.08 N	109.17 W
Springfield, Co. (sprĭng'fēld)	122	37.24 N	102.04 W
Springfield, Il.	123	39.46 N	89.37 W
Springfield, Ky.	110	37.35 N	85.10 W
Springfield, Ma.	111	42.05 N	72.35 W
Springfield, Mn.	115	44.14 N	94.59 W
Springfield, Mo.	123	37.13 N	93.17 W
Springfield, NJ	55	40.43 N	74.19 W
Springfield, Oh.	110	39.55 N	83.50 W
Springfield, Or.	116	44.01 N	123.02 W
Springfield, Pa.	56b	39.55 N	75.24 W
Springfield, Tn.	126	36.30 N	86.53 W
Springfield, Vt.	111	43.20 N	72.35 W
Springfield, Va.	56d	38.45 N	77.13 W
Springfontein, S. Afr. (sprĭng'fôn-tīn)	226	30.16 S	25.45 E
Springhill, Can. (sprĭng-hĭl')	105	45.39 N	64.03 W
Spring Mill, Pa.	56b	40.04 N	75.17 W
Spring Mts., Nv.	120	36.18 N	115.49 W
Springs, S. Afr. (sprĭngs)	227b	26.16 S	28.27 E
Springstein, Can. (sprĭng'stīn)	95f	49.49 N	97.29 W
Springton Res., Pa. (sprĭng-tŭn)	112f	39.57 N	75.26 W
Springvale, Austl.	211a	37.57 S	145.09 E
Springvale South, Austl.	70b	37.58 S	145.09 E
Spring Valley, Ca.	120a	32.46 N	117.01 W
Springvalley, Il. (sprĭng-văl'ĭ)	110	41.20 N	89.15 W
Spring Valley, Mn.	115	43.41 N	92.26 W
Spring Valley, NY	112a	41.07 N	74.03 W
Springville, Ut. (sprĭng-vĭl)	121	40.10 N	111.40 W
Springwood, Austl.	211b	33.42 S	150.34 E
Sprockhövel, F.R.G.	63	51.22 N	7.15 E
Spruce Grove, Can. (spro͞os grōv)	95g	53.32 N	113.55 W
Spur, Tx. (spûr)	122	33.29 N	100.51 W
Squam (L.), NH (skwôm)	111	43.45 N	71.30 W
Squamish, Can. (skwō'mĭsh)	98	49.42 N	123.09 W
Squamish (R.), Can.	98	50.10 N	124.30 W
Squillace, Gulfo di (G.), It. (go͞o'l-fô-dē skwēl-lä'chå)	172	38.44 N	16.47 E
Squirrel Hill (Neigh.), Pa.	57b	40.26 N	79.55 W
Squirrel's Heath (Neigh.)	62	51.35 N	0.13 E
Srbija (Serbia) (Reg.), Yugo. (sr bē-yä) (sẽr'bē-ä)	173	44.05 N	20.35 E
Srbobran, Yugo. (s'r'bô-brän')	173	45.32 N	19.50 E
Sredne-Kolymsk, Sov. Un. (s'rĕd'nyĕ kô-lēmsk')	181	67.49 N	154.55 E
Sredne Rogatka, Sov. Un. (s'rĕd'nȧ-ya) (rô gär'tkȧ)	182c	59.49 N	30.20 E
Sredniy Ik (R.), Sov. Un. (srĕd'nĭ ĭk)	182a	55.46 N	58.50 E
Sredniy Ural (Mts.), Sov. Un. (o͞o'răl)	182a	57.47 N	59.00 E
Śrem, Pol. (shrĕm)	167	52.06 N	17.01 E
Sremska Karlovci, Yugo. (srĕm'skē kär'lov-tsē)	173	45.10 N	19.57 E
Sremska Mitrovica, Yugo. (srĕm'skä mē'trô-vē-tsä')	173	44.59 N	19.39 E
Sretensk, Sov. Un. (s'rĕ'tĕnsk)	181	52.13 N	117.39 E
Sri Lanka (Ceylon), Asia	190	8.45 N	82.30 E
Srīnagar, India (srē-nŭg'ŭr)	196	34.11 N	74.49 E
Sroda, Pol. (shrô'dȧ)	167	52.14 N	17.17 E
Staaken (Neigh.), G.D.R.	65a	52.32 N	13.08 E
Stabroek, Bel.	157a	51.20 N	4.21 E
Stade, F.R.G. (shtä'dĕ)	157c	53.36 N	9.28 E
Städjan (Mtn.), Swe. (stĕd'yän)	164	61.53 N	12.50 E
Stadlau (Neigh.), Aus.	66e	48.14 N	16.28 E
Stafford, Eng. (stăf'fẽrd)	156	52.48 N	2.06 W
Stafford, Ks.	122	37.58 N	98.37 W
Staffordshire (Co.), Eng.	156	52.45 N	2.00 W
Stahnsdorf, G.D.R. (shtäns'dôrf)	157b	52.22 N	13.10 E
Staines, Eng.	62	51.26 N	0.13 W
Stains, Fr.	64c	48.57 N	2.23 E
Stalinabad, see Dushanbe			
Stalingrad, see Volgograd			
Stalino, see Donetsk			
Stalin, see Varna			
Stalinsk, see Novokuznetsk			
Stalybridge, Eng. (stā'lē-brĭj)	156	53.29 N	2.03 W
Stambaugh, Mi. (stăm'bô)	115	46.03 N	88.38 W
Stamford, Ct. (stăm'fẽrd)	112a	41.03 N	73.32 W
Stamford, Eng.	156	52.39 N	0.28 W
Stamford, Tx.	122	32.57 N	99.48 W
Stammersdorf, Aus. (shtäm'ẽrs-dôrf)	157e	48.19 N	16.25 E
Stamps, Ar. (stămps)	123	33.22 N	93.31 W
Stanberry, Mo. (stan'bĕr-ē)	123	40.12 N	94.34 W
Standerton, S. Afr. (stăn'dẽr-tŭn)	223d	26.57 S	29.17 E
Standing Rock Ind. Res., ND (stănd'ĭng rŏk)	114	47.07 N	101.05 W
Standish, Eng. (stăn'dĭsh)	156	53.36 N	2.39 W
Stanford, Ky. (stăn'fẽrd)	126	37.29 N	84.40 W
Stanford le Hope, Eng.	62	51.31 N	0.26 E
Stanford Rivers, Eng.	62	51.41 N	0.13 E
Stanger, S. Afr. (stăŋ-ger)	227c	29.22 S	31.18 E
Staniard Creek, Ba.	134	24.50 N	77.55 W
Stanislaus (R.), Ca. (stăn'ĭs-lô)	120	38.10 N	120.16 W
Stanley, Can. (stăn'lē)	104	46.17 N	66.44 W
Stanley, Falk. Is.	144	51.46 S	57.59 W
Stanley, Hong Kong	68c	22.13 N	114.12 E
Stanley, ND	114	48.20 N	102.25 W
Stanley, Wi.	115	44.56 N	90.56 W
Stanley Mound (Hill), Hong Kong	68c	22.14 N	114.12 E
Stanley Pool (L.), Zaire	229	4.07 S	15.40 E
Stanley Res., India (stăn'lē)	196	12.07 N	77.27 E
Stanleyville, see Kisangani			
Stanlow, Eng.	64a	53.17 N	2.52 W
Stanmore (Neigh.), Eng.	62	51.37 N	0.19 W
Stann Creek, Belize (stăn krēk)	132a	17.01 N	88.14 W
Stanovoy Khrebet (Mts.), Sov. Un. (stŭn-ȧ-voi')	181	56.12 N	127.12 E
Stansted, Eng.	62	51.20 N	0.18 E
Stanton, Ca. (stăn'tŭn)	119a	33.48 N	118.00 W
Stanton, Ne.	114	41.57 N	97.15 W
Stanton, Tx.	124	32.08 N	101.46 W
Stanwell, Eng.	62	51.27 N	0.29 W
Stanwell Moor, Eng.	62	51.28 N	0.30 W
Stanwood, Wa. (stăn'wo͝od)	118a	48.14 N	122.23 W
Stapleford Abbots, Eng.	62	51.38 N	0.10 E
Stapleford Tawney, Eng.	62	51.40 N	0.11 E
Staples, Mn. (stā'p'lz)	115	46.21 N	94.48 W
Stapleton, Al.	126	30.45 N	87.48 W
Stara Planina (Balkan Mts.), Bul.	154	42.50 N	24.45 E
Staraya Kupavna, Sov. Un. (stä'rȧ-yȧ kû-päf'nȧ)	182b	55.48 N	38.10 E
Staraya Russa, Sov. Un. (stä'rȧ-yȧ ro͞osȧ)	174	57.58 N	31.21 E
Stara Zagora, Bul. (zä'gô-rȧ)	173	42.26 N	25.37 E
Starbuck, Can. (stär'bŭk)	95f	49.46 N	97.36 W
Stargard Szczeciński, Pol. (shtär'gärt shchĕ-chyn'skē)	166	53.19 N	15.03 E
Staritsa, Sov. Un. (stä'rē-tsȧ)	174	56.29 N	34.58 E
Starke, Fl. (stärk)	127	29.55 N	82.07 W
Starkville, Co. (stärk'vĭl)	122	37.06 N	104.34 W
Starkville, Ms.	126	33.27 N	88.47 W
Starnberg, F.R.G. (shtärn-bĕrgh)	157d	47.59 N	11.20 E
Starnberger See (L.), F.R.G.	166	47.58 N	11.30 E
Starobel'sk, Sov. Un. (stä-rô-byĕlsk')	175	49.19 N	38.57 E
Starodub, Sov. Un. (stä-rô-dro͞op')	174	52.25 N	32.49 E
Starogard Gdański, Pol. (stä'rô-grad gdĕn'skē)	167	53.58 N	18.33 E
Staro-Konstantinov, Sov. Un. (stä'rô kôn-stȧn-tē'nôf)	175	49.45 N	27.12 E
Staro-Minskaya, Sov. Un. (stä'rô mĭn'skȧ-yȧ)	175	46.19 N	38.51 E
Staro-Shcherbinovskaya, Sov. Un.	175	46.38 N	38.38 E
Staro-Subkhangulovo, Sov. Un. (stäro-so͞ob-kan-go͞o'lōvō)	182a	53.08 N	57.24 E
Staroutkinsk, Sov. Un. (stȧ-rô-o͞ot'kĭnsk)	182a	57.14 N	59.21 E
Staroverovka, Sov. Un.	175	49.31 N	35.48 E
Start Pt., Eng. (stårt)	162	50.14 N	3.34 W
Stary Sacz, Pol. (stä-rē sônch')	167	49.32 N	20.36 E
Staryy Oskol, Sov. Un. (stä'rē ôs-kôl')	175	51.18 N	37.51 E
Stassfurt, G.D.R. (shtäs'fo͞ort)	166	51.52 N	11.35 E
Staszów, Pol. (stä'sho͞of)	167	50.32 N	21.13 E
State College, Pa. (stāt kŏl'ĕj)	111	40.50 N	77.55 W
State Line, Mn. (līn)	119h	46.36 N	92.18 W
Staten I., NY (stăt'ĕn)	112a	40.35 N	74.10 W
Statesboro, Ga. (stāts'bŭr-ô)	127	32.26 N	81.47 W
Statesville, NC (stāts'vĭl)	127	34.45 N	80.54 W
Statue of Liberty National Monument (P. Int.), NY	55	40.41 N	74.03 W
Staunton, Il. (stôn'tŭn)	119e	39.01 N	89.47 W
Staunton, Va.	111	38.10 N	79.05 W
Stavanger, Nor. (stä'väng'ẽr)	164	58.59 N	5.44 E
Stave (R.), Can. (stāv)	118d	49.12 N	122.24 W
Staveley, Eng. (stāv'lē)	156	53.17 N	1.21 W
Stavenisse, Neth.	157a	51.35 N	3.59 E
Stavropol', Sov. Un.	179	45.05 N	41.50 E
Stawno, Pol. (swav'nō)	166	54.21 N	16.38 E
Steamboat Springs, Co. (stēm'bōt')	122	40.30 N	106.48 W
Steblëv, Sov. Un. (styĕp'lyôf)	175	49.23 N	31.03 E
Steel (R.), Can. (stēl)	115	49.08 N	86.55 W
Steelton, Pa. (stēl'tŭn)	111	40.15 N	76.45 W
Steenbergen, Neth.	157a	51.35 N	4.18 E
Steens Mts., Or. (stēnz)	116	42.15 N	118.52 W
Steep Pt., Austl. (stēp)	214	26.15 N	112.05 E
Stefaniee, L., see Chew Bahir			
Steger, Il. (stē'gẽr)	113a	41.28 N	87.38 W
Steglitz (Neigh.), F.R.G.	65a	52.28 N	13.19 E
Steiermark (Styria) (State), Aus. (shtī'ẽr-märk)	166	47.22 N	14.40 E
Steinbach, Can.	96	49.32 N	96.41 W
Steinkjer, Nor. (stēĭn-kyĕr)	158	64.00 N	11.19 E
Steinstücken (Neigh.), G.D.R.	65a	52.23 N	13.08 E
Stella, Wa. (stĕl'ȧ)	118c	46.11 N	123.12 W
Stellarton, Can. (stĕl'ȧr-tŭn)	104	45.34 N	62.40 W
Stendal, G.D.R (shtĕn'däl)	166	52.37 N	11.51 E
Stepanakert, Sov. Un. (styĕ'pän-ȧ-kĕrt)	179	39.50 N	46.40 E
Stephens, Port, Austl. (stē'fĕns)	216	32.43 S	152.55 E
Stephenville, Can. (stē'vĕn-vĭl)	105	48.33 N	58.35 W
Stepney (Neigh.), Eng.	62	51.31 N	0.02 W
Stepnyak, Sov. Un. (styĭp-nyäk')	180	52.37 N	70.43 E
Sterkrade, F.R.G. (shtĕr'krädĕ)	169c	51.31 N	6.51 E
Sterkrade (Neigh.), F.R.G.	63	51.31 N	6.51 E
Sterkstroom, S. Afr.	227c	31.33 S	26.36 E
Sterling, Co. (stûr'lĭng)	122	40.38 N	103.14 W
Sterling, Il.	115	41.48 N	89.42 W
Sterling, Ks.	122	38.11 N	98.11 W
Sterling, Ma.	105a	42.26 N	71.41 W
Sterling, Tx.	124	31.53 N	100.58 W
Sterling Park, Ca.	58b	37.41 N	122.26 W
Sterlitamak, Sov. Un. (styĕr'lē-ta-mák')	182a	53.38 N	55.56 E
Šternberk, Czech. (shtĕrn'bĕrk)	167	49.44 N	17.18 E
Stettin, see Szczecin			
Stettler, Can.	99	52.19 N	112.43 W
Steubenville, Oh. (stū'bĕn-vĭl)	110	40.20 N	80.40 W
Stevens (L.), Wa. (stē'vĕnz)	118a	47.59 N	122.06 W
Stevens Point, Wi.	115	44.30 N	89.35 W
Stevensville, Mt. (stē'vĕnz-vĭl)	117	46.31 N	114.03 E
Stewart (R.), Can. (stū'ērt)	96	63.27 N	138.48 W
Stewart I., N. Z.	217	46.56 S	167.40 E
Stewart Manor, NY	55	40.43 N	73.41 W
Stewiacke, Can. (stū'wē-ăk)	104	45.08 N	63.21 W
Steynsrus, S. Afr. (stīns'ro͞os)	223d	27.58 S	27.33 E
Steyr, Aus. (shtīr)	166	48.03 N	14.24 E
Stickney, Il.	58a	41.49 N	87.47 W
Stiepel (Neigh.), F.R.G.	63	51.25 N	7.15 E
Stif, Alg.	224	36.18 N	5.21 E
Stikine (R.), Can. (stĭ-kēn')	96	58.17 N	130.10 W
Stikine Ranges, Can.	96	59.05 N	130.00 W
Stillaguamish (R.), South Fk. Wa. (stĭl-ȧ-gwä'mĭsh)	118a	48.05 N	121.59 W
Stillaguamish (R.), Wa.	118a	48.11 N	122.18 W
Stillwater, Mn. (stĭl'wô-tẽr)	119g	45.04 N	92.48 W
Stillwater, Mt.	117	45.23 N	109.45 W
Stillwater, Ok.	123	36.06 N	97.03 W
Stillwater R., Mt.	116	48.47 N	114.40 W
Stillwater Ra., Nv.	120	39.43 N	118.11 W
Stintonville, S. Afr.	71b	26.14 S	28.13 E
Štip, Yugo. (shtĭp)	173	41.43 N	22.07 E
Stirling, Scot. (stûr'lĭng)	162	56.05 N	3.59 W
Stittsville, Can. (stĭts'vĭl)	95c	45.15 N	75.54 W
Stjördalshalsen, Nor. (styûr-däls-hälsĕn)	164	63.26 N	11.00 E
Stockbridge Munsee Ind. Res., Wi. (stŏk'brĭdj mŭn-sē)	115	44.49 N	89.00 W
Stockerau, Aus. (shtô'kĕ-rou)	157e	48.24 N	16.13 E
Stockholm, Me. (stŏk'hōlm)	104	47.05 N	68.08 W
Stockholm, Swe. (stôk'hôlm)	164	59.23 N	18.00 E
Stockport, Eng. (stŏk'pôrt)	156	53.24 N	2.09 W
Stockton, Ca. (stŏk'tŭn)	120	37.56 N	121.16 W
Stockton, Eng.	162	54.35 N	1.25 W
Stockton, Ks.	122	39.26 N	99.16 W
Stockton (I.), Wi.	115	46.56 N	90.25 W
Stockton Plat., Tx.	124	30.34 N	102.35 W
Stockton Res., Mo.	123	37.40 N	93.45 W
Stockum (Neigh.), F.R.G.	63	51.28 N	7.22 E
Stöde, Swe. (stû'dĕ)	164	62.26 N	16.35 E
Stoke D'Abernon, Eng.	62	51.19 N	0.23 W
Stoke Newington (Neigh.), Eng.	62	51.34 N	0.05 W
Stoke-on-Trent, Eng. (stōk-ŏn-trĕnt)	156	53.01 N	2.12 W
Stoke Poges, Eng.	62	51.33 N	0.35 W
Stokhod (R.), Sov. Un. (stô-kôd)	167	51.24 N	25.20 E
Stolac, Yugo. (stô'làts)	173	43.03 N	17.59 E
Stolbovy (Is.), Sov. Un. (stôl-bô-voi')	181	73.43 N	133.05 E
Stolin, Sov. Un. (stô'lĕn)	167	51.54 N	26.52 E
Stolpe, G.D.R.	65a	52.40 N	13.16 E
Stömstad, Swe.	164	58.58 N	11.09 E
Stondon Massey, Eng.	62	51.41 N	0.18 E
Stone, Eng.	62	51.27 N	0.16 E
Stone, Eng.	156	52.54 N	2.09 W
Stoneham, Can. (stōn'ȧm)	95b	46.59 N	71.22 W
Stoneham, Ma.	105a	42.30 N	71.05 W
Stonehaven, Scot. (stōn'hā-v'n)	162	56.57 N	2.09 W
Stone Mountain, Ga. (stōn)	112c	33.49 N	84.10 W
Stone Park, Il.	58a	41.45 N	87.53 W
Stonewall, Can. (stōn'wôl)	95f	50.09 N	97.21 W
Stonewall, Ms.	126	32.08 N	88.44 W
Stoney Creek, Can. (stō'nē)	95d	43.13 N	79.45 W
Stonington, Ct. (stōn'ĭng-tŭn)	111	41.20 N	71.55 W
Stony Cr., Ca. (stō'nē)	120	39.28 N	122.35 W
Stony Indian Res., Can.	95e	51.10 N	114.45 W
Stony Mountain, Can.	95f	50.05 N	97.13 W
Stony Plain, Can. (stō'nē plān)	95g	53.02 N	114.00 W
Stony Plain Ind. Res., Can.	95g	53.29 N	113.48 W
Stony Point, NY	112a	41.13 N	73.58 W
Stony Run, Md.	56c	39.11 N	76.42 W
Storå (R.), Den.	164	56.22 N	8.35 E
Stora Lule (R.), Swe. (sto͞o'rä lo͞o'lĕ)	178	67.00 N	19.30 E
Stora Sotra (I.), Nor.	164	60.24 N	4.35 E
Stord (I.), Nor. (stôrd)	164	59.54 N	5.15 E
Store Baelt (Str.), Den.	164	55.25 N	10.50 E
Storeton, Eng.	64a	53.21 N	3.03 W
Storfjorden (Fd.), Nor.	164	62.17 N	6.19 E
Stormberg (Mts.), S. Afr. (stôrm'bûrg)	227c	31.28 S	26.35 E
Storm Lake, Ia.	115	42.39 N	95.12 W
Stormy Pt., Vir. Is. (U.S.A.) (stôr'mē)	129c	18.22 N	65.01 W
Stornoway, Scot. (stôr'nô-wā)	162	58.13 N	6.21 W

ăt; finăl; rāte; senåte; ärm; ȧsk; sofȧ; fâre; ch-choose; dh-as th in other; bē; ēvent; bĕt; recĕnt; cratẽr; g-gō; gh-guttural g; bĭt; ĭ-short neutral; rīde; ĸ-guttural k as ch in German ich;

PLACE (Pronounciation)	PAGE	Lat. °′	Long. °′
Storozhinets, Sov. Un. (stô-rō'zhĕn-yĕts)	167	48.10 N	25.44 E
Störsjo, Swe. (stôr'shû)	164	62.49 N	13.08 E
Störsjoen (L.), Nor. (stôr-syûĕn)	164	61.32 N	11.30 E
Störsjon (L.), Swe.	164	63.06 N	14.00 E
Storvik, Swe. (stôr'vĕk)	164	60.37 N	16.31 E
Stoughton, Ma. (stō'tŭn)	105a	42.07 N	71.06 W
Stoughton, Wi.	115	42.54 N	89.15 W
Stour (R.), Eng. (stour)	163	52.09 N	0.29 E
Stourbridge, Eng. (stour'brĭj)	156	52.27 N	2.08 W
Stow, Ma. (stō)	105a	42.56 N	71.31 W
Stow, Oh.	113d	41.09 N	81.26 W
Stowe Township, Pa.	57b	40.29 N	80.04 W
Straatsdrif, S. Afr.	223d	25.19 S	26.22 E
Strabane, N. Ire. (stră-băn')	162	54.59 N	7.27 W
Straelen, F.R.G. (shtră'lĕn)	169c	51.26 N	6.16 E
Strahan, Austl. (strā'ăn)	215	42.08 S	145.28 E
Strakonice, Czech. (strä'kô-nyē-tsĕ)	166	49.18 N	13.52 E
Straldzha, Bul. (sträl'dzhȧ)	173	42.37 N	26.44 E
Stralsund, G.D.R. (shräl'sōōnt)	166	54.18 N	13.04 E
Strangford, Lough (B.), Ire. (lŏk străng'fērd)	162	54.30 N	5.34 W
Strängnäs, Swe. (strĕng'nĕs)	164	59.23 N	16.59 E
Stranraer, Scot. (străn-rär')	162	54.55 N	5.05 W
Strasbourg, Fr. (stràs-bōōr')	169	48.36 N	7.49 E
Stratford, Can. (străt'fērd)	110	43.20 N	81.05 W
Stratford, Ct.	111	41.10 N	73.05 W
Stratford, Wi.	115	44.16 N	90.02 W
Stratford-upon-Avon, Eng.	162	52.13 N	1.41 W
Strathcona Prov. Pk., Can.	98	49.40 N	125.50 W
Strathfield, Austl.	70a	33.52 S	151.06 E
Strathmoor (Neigh.), Mi.	57c	42.23 N	83.11 W
Straubing, F.R.G. (strou'bĭng)	166	48.52 N	12.36 E
Strauch, F.R.G.	63	51.09 N	6.56 E
Strausberg, G.D.R. (strous'bĕrgh)	166	52.35 N	13.50 E
Strawberry (R.), Ut.	121	40.05 N	110.55 W
Strawberry Mts., Or. (strô'bĕr'ĭ)	116	44.19 N	119.20 W
Strawberry Point, Ca.	58b	37.54 N	122.31 W
Strawn, Tx. (strôn)	124	32.38 N	98.28 W
Streatham (Neigh.), Eng.	62	51.26 N	0.08 W
Streator, Il. (strē'tēr)	110	41.05 N	88.50 W
Streeter, ND	114	46.40 N	99.22 W
Streetsville, Can. (strētz'vĭl)	95d	43.34 N	79.43 W
Strehaia, Rom. (strĕ-ĸä'yȧ)	173	44.37 N	23.13 E
Strel'na, Sov. Un. (strĕl'nȧ)	182c	59.52 N	30.01 E
Stretford, Eng. (strĕt'fērd)	156	53.25 N	2.19 W
Strickland (R.), Pap. N. Gui. (strĭk'lănd)	207	6.15 S	142.00 E
Strijen, Neth.	157a	51.44 N	4.23 E
Stromboli (Vol.), It. (strŏm'bô-lē)	172	38.46 N	15.16 E
Stromyn, Sov. Un. (strô'mĭn)	182b	56.02 N	38.29 E
Strong (R.), Ms. (strông)	126	32.03 N	89.42 W
Strongsville, Oh. (strôngz'vĭl)	113d	41.19 N	81.50 W
Stronsay (I.), Scot. (strŏn'sā)	162a	59.09 N	2.35 W
Stroudsburg, Pa. (stroudz'bûrg)	111	41.00 N	75.15 W
Strubenvale, S. Afr.	71b	26.16 S	28.28 E
Struer, Den.	164	56.29 N	8.34 E
Strugi Krasnyye, Sov. Un. (strōō'gĭ krä's-ny'yĕ)	174	58.14 N	29.10 E
Struisbelt, S. Afr.	71b	26.19 S	28.29 E
Struma (R.), Bul. (strōō'mȧ)	173	41.55 N	23.05 E
Strumica, Yugo. (strōō'mĭ-tsȧ)	173	41.26 N	22.38 E
Strümp, F.R.G.	63	51.17 N	6.40 E
Strunino, Sov. Un.	182b	56.23 N	38.34 E
Struthers, Oh. (strŭdh'ērz)	110	41.00 N	80.35 W
Struvenhütten, F.R.G. (shtrōō'vĕn-hü-tĕn)	157c	53.52 N	10.04 E
Strydpoortberge (Mts.), S. Afr.	223d	24.08 N	29.18 E
Stryy, Sov. Un. (strē')	167	49.16 N	23.51 E
Strzelce Opolskie, Pol. (stzhĕl'tsĕ o-pŏl'skyĕ)	167	50.31 N	18.20 E
Strzelin, Pol. (stzhĕ-lĭn)	167	50.48 N	17.06 E
Strzelno, Pol. (stzhål'nô)	167	52.37 N	18.10 E
Stuart, Fl. (stū'ērt)	127a	27.10 N	80.14 W
Stuart, Ia.	115	41.31 N	94.20 W
Stuart (I.), Ak.	107	63.25 N	162.45 W
Stuart (I.), Wa.	118d	48.42 N	123.10 W
Stuart L., Can.	98	54.32 N	124.35 W
Stuart Ra., Austl.	214	29.00 S	134.30 E
Stung Treng, Kamp. (stōōng'trĕng')	206	13.36 N	106.00 E
Stupava, Czech.	157e	48.17 N	17.02 E
Stupsk, Pol. (swōōpsk)	167	54.28 N	17.02 E
Sturgeon (R.), Can.	95g	53.41 N	113.46 W
Sturgeon (R.), Mi.	115	46.43 N	88.43 W
Sturgeon B., Can.	101	52.00 N	98.00 W
Sturgeon Bay, Wi.	115	44.50 N	87.22 W
Sturgeon Falls, Can.	97	46.19 N	79.49 W
Sturgis, Ky.	110	37.35 N	88.00 W
Sturgis, Mi.	110	41.45 N	85.25 W
Sturgis, SD	114	44.25 N	103.31 W
Sturt Cr., Austl.	214	19.40 S	127.40 E
Sturtevant, Wi. (stŭr'tē-vănt)	113a	42.42 N	87.54 W
Stutterheim, S. Afr. (stŭrt'ēr-hĭm)	227c	32.34 S	27.27 E
Stuttgart, Ar. (stŭt'gärt)	123	34.30 N	91.33 W
Stuttgart, F.R.G. (shtōōt'gärt)	166	48.48 N	9.15 E
Styal, Eng.	64b	53.21 N	2.15 W
Stykkisholmur, Ice.	158	65.00 N	21.48 W
Styria, see Steiermark			
Styr' R., Sov. Un. (stēr)	167	51.44 N	26.07 E
Styrum (Neigh.), F.R.G.	63	51.27 N	6.51 E
Suao, Taiwan (sōō'ou)	203	24.35 N	121.45 E
Subarnarakha (R.), India	196	22.38 N	86.26 E
Subata, Sov. Un. (sōō'bȧ-tȧ)	165	56.02 N	25.54 E
Subic, Phil. (sōō'bĭk)	207a	14.52 N	120.15 E
Subic B., Phil.	207a	14.41 N	120.11 E
Subotica, Yugo. (sōō'bô'tē-tsȧ)	173	46.06 N	19.41 E
Subugo (Mtn.), Ken.	231	1.40 S	35.49 E
Succasunna, NJ (sŭk'kȧ-sŭn'nȧ)	112a	40.52 N	74.37 W
Suceava, Rom. (sōō-chȧ-ä'vȧ)	167	47.39 N	26.17 E
Suceava R., Rom.	167	47.45 N	26.10 E
Sucha, Pol. (sōō'ĸȧ)	167	49.44 N	19.40 E
Suchiapa, Mex. (sōō-chē-ä'pä)	131	16.38 N	93.08 W
Suchiapa (R.), Mex.	131	16.27 N	93.26 W
Suchitoto, Sal. (sōō-chē-tō'tō)	132	13.58 N	89.03 W
Sucia Is., Wa. (soū'sē-ȧ)	118d	48.46 N	122.54 W
Sucio (R.), Col. (sōō'syô)	142a	6.55 N	76.15 W
Suck, Ire. (sŭk)	162	53.34 N	8.16 W
Sucre, Bol. (sōō'krā)	142	19.06 S	65.16 W
Sucre (State), Ven. (sōō'krĕ)	143b	10.18 N	65.12 W
Sucy-en-Brie, Fr.	64c	48.46 N	2.32 E
Suda, Sov. Un. (sōō'dȧ)	182a	56.58 N	56.45 E
Suda (R.), Sov. Un. (sōō'dȧ)	174	59.24 N	36.40 E
Sudair, Sau. Ar. (sŭ-dä'ēr)	192	25.48 N	46.28 E
Sudalsvatnet (L.), Nor.	164	59.35 N	6.59 E
Sudan, Afr.	222	14.00 N	28.00 E
Sudan (Reg.), Afr. (sōō-dän')	229	15.00 N	7.00 E
Sudberg (Neigh.), F.R.G.	63	51.11 N	7.08 E
Sudbury, Can. (sŭd'bēr-ē)	97	46.28 N	81.00 W
Sudbury, Ma.	105a	42.23 N	71.25 W
Sud, Canal du (Chan.), Hai.	135	18.40 N	73.15 W
Suderwich (Neigh.), F.R.G.	63	51.37 N	7.15 E
Sudetes (Mts.), Czech.	166	50.41 N	15.37 E
Sudogda, Sov. Un. (sōō'dôk-dȧ)	174	55.57 N	40.29 E
Sudost' (R.), Sov. Un. (sōō-dôst')	174	52.43 N	33.13 E
Sud, Rivière du, Can. (rē-vyâr'dü süd')	95b	46.56 N	70.35 W
Sudzha, Sov. Un. (sōōd'zhȧ)	175	51.14 N	35.11 E
Sueca, Sp. (swā'kä)	171	39.12 N	0.18 W
Suemez I., Ak.	98	55.17 N	133.21 W
Suez Can., see Qana el Suweis			
Suez, G. of, Egypt (sōō-ĕz')	223c	29.53 N	32.33 E
Suez, see As Suways			
Suffern, NY (sŭf'fērn)	112a	41.07 N	74.09 W
Suffolk, Va. (sŭf'ŭk)	112g	36.43 N	76.35 W
Sugandha, India	67a	22.54 N	88.20 E
Sugar (Cr.), In.	110	39.55 N	87.10 W
Sugar City, Co.	122	38.12 N	103.42 W
Sugar Cr., Il. (shōōg'ēr)	123	40.14 N	89.28 W
Sugar Creek, Mo.	119f	39.07 N	94.27 W
Sugar I., Mi.	119k	46.31 N	84.12 W
Sugarloaf Pt., Austl. (sōōgēr'lōf)	216	32.19 S	153.04 E
Suggi L., Can.	101	54.22 N	102.47 W
Suginami (Neigh.), Jap.	69a	35.42 N	139.38 E
Sūhānak, Iran	68h	35.48 N	51.32 E
Suhaymī, Wādī as (R.), Egypt	191a	29.48 N	33.12 E
Sühbaatar, Mong	181	50.18 N	106.31 E
Suhl, G.D.R. (zōōl)	166	50.37 N	10.41 E
Suichuan (Mtn.), China	203	26.25 N	114.10 E
Suide, China (swā-dü)	202	37.32 N	110.12 E
Suifenhe, China (swā-fŭn-hŭ)	181	44.47 N	131.13 E
Suihua, China,	202	46.38 N	126.50 E
Suining, China (sōō'ē-nĭng')	200	33.54 N	117.57 E
Suipacha, Arg. (swē-pä'chȧ)	141c	34.45 S	59.43 W
Suiping, China (swā-pĭŋ)	200	33.09 N	113.58 E
Suir R., Ire. (sūr)	162	52.20 N	7.32 W
Suisun B., Ca. (sōōē-sōōn')	118b	38.07 N	122.02 W
Suita, Jap. (sōō'ē-tä)	205b	34.45 N	135.32 E
Suitland, Md. (sōōt'lănd)	112e	38.51 N	76.57 W
Suixian, China (swā shyĕn)	203	31.42 N	113.20 E
Suiyüan (Reg.), China (swā-yüĕn)	198	41.31 N	107.04 E
Suizhong, China (swā-jŏŋ)	200	40.22 N	120.20 E
Sukabumi, Indon.	206	6.52 S	106.56 E
Sukadana, Indon.	206	1.15 S	110.30 E
Sukagawa, Jap. (sōō'kä-gä'wä)	205	37.08 N	140.07 E
Sukarnapura, see Jayapura			
Sukhinichi, Sov. Un. (sōō'ĸē'nē-chē)	174	54.07 N	35.18 E
Sukhona (R.), Sov. Un. (sōō-ĸô'nȧ)	178	59.30 N	42.20 E
Sukhoy Log, Sov. Un. (sōō'kôy lôg)	182a	56.55 N	62.03 E
Sukhumi, Sov. Un. (sōō-kōōm')	179	43.00 N	41.00 E
Sukkur, Pak. (sŭk'ŭr)	196	27.49 N	68.50 E
Sukkwan I., Ak.	98	55.05 N	132.45 W
Suksun, Sov. Un. (sōōk'sōōn)	182a	57.08 N	57.22 E
Sukumo, Jap. (sōō'kōō-mô)	205	32.58 N	132.45 E
Sukunka (R.), Can.	99	55.00 N	121.50 W
Sula (R.), Sov. Un. (sōō-lȧ')	175	50.36 N	33.13 E
Sulaco R., Hond. (sōō-lä'kō)	132	14.55 N	87.31 W
Sulaimān Ra., Pak. (sōō-lä-ē-män')	196	29.47 N	69.10 E
Sulak (R.), Sov. Un. (sōō-lák')	179	43.30 N	47.00 E
Sula, Kepulauan (I.), Indon.	207	2.20 S	125.20 E
Sulawesi (I.), see Celebes			
Suleya, Sov. Un. (sōō-lē'ya)	182a	55.12 N	58.52 E
Sulfeld, F.R.G. (zōō'fĕld)	157c	53.48 N	10.13 E
Sūlgan, Iran	68h	35.49 N	51.15 E
Sulina, Rom. (sōō-lē'nȧ)	175	45.08 N	29.38 E
Sulitelma (Mtn.), Nor.-Swe. (sōō-lē-tyĕl'mȧ)	158	67.03 N	16.35 E
Sullana, Peru (sōō-lyä'nä)	142	4.57 N	80.47 W
Sulligent, Al. (sŭl'ĭ-jĕnt)	126	33.52 N	88.06 W
Sullivan, Il. (sŭl'ĭ-văn)	110	41.35 N	88.35 W
Sullivan, In.	110	39.05 N	87.20 W
Sullivan, Mo.	123	38.13 N	91.09 W
Sulmona, It. (sōōl-mō'nä)	172	42.02 N	13.58 E
Sulphur, Ok. (sŭl'fŭr)	123	34.31 N	96.58 W
Sulphur (R.), Tx.	123	33.26 N	95.06 W
Sulphur Springs, Tx. (sprĭngz)	123	33.09 N	95.36 W
Sultan, Wa. (sŭl'tăn)	118a	47.52 N	121.49 W
Sultan (R.), Wa.	118a	47.55 N	121.49 W
Sultepec, Mex. (sōōl-tȧ-pĕk')	130	18.50 N	99.51 W
Sulu Arch., Phil. (sōō'lōō)	206	5.52 N	122.00 E
Suluntah, Libya	161	32.39 N	21.49 E
Sulūq, Libya	194	31.39 N	20.15 E
Sulu Sea, Phil.	206	8.25 N	119.00 E
Suma, Jap. (sōō'mä)	205b	34.39 N	135.08 E
Suma (Neigh.), Jap.	69b	34.39 N	135.08 E
Sumas, Wa. (sū'mȧs)	118d	49.00 N	122.16 W
Sumatera (I.), see Sumatra			
Sumatra (Sumatera) (I.), Indon. (sōō-mä'trȧ)	206	2.06 N	99.40 E
Sumba (I.), Indon. (sŭm'bȧ)	206	9.52 S	119.00 E
Sumba, Ile (I.), Zaire	230	1.44 N	19.32 E
Sumbawa (I.), Indon. (sōōm-bä'wä)	206	9.00 S	118.18 E
Sumbawa-Besar, Indon.	206	8.32 S	117.20 E
Sumbawanga, Tan.	231	7.58 S	31.37 E
Sümeg, Hung. (shü'mĕg)	167	46.59 N	17.19 E
Sumida (R.), Jap. (sōō'mē-dä)	205	36.01 N	139.24 E
Sumidouro, Braz. (sōō-mē-dō'rōō)	141a	22.04 S	42.41 W
Sumiyoshi, Jap. (sōō'mē-yō'shē)	205b	34.43 N	135.16 E
Sumiyoshi (Neigh.), Jap.	69b	34.36 N	135.31 E
Summer L., Or. (sŭm'ēr)	116	42.50 N	120.35 W
Summerland, Can. (sŭ'mēr-lănd)	99	49.39 N	117.33 W
Summerseat, Eng.	64b	53.38 N	2.19 W
Summerside, Can. (sŭm'ēr-sīd)	104	46.25 N	63.47 W
Summerton, SC (sŭm'ēr-tŭn)	127	33.37 N	80.22 W
Summerville, SC (sŭm'ēr-vĭl)	127	33.00 N	80.10 W
Summit, Il. (sŭm'mĭt)	113a	41.47 N	87.48 W
Summit, NJ	112a	40.43 N	74.21 W
Summit Lake Ind. Res., Nv.	116	41.35 N	119.30 W
Summit Park, Md.	56c	39.23 N	76.41 W
Summit Pk., Co.	121	37.20 N	106.40 W
Sumner, Wa. (sŭm'nēr)	118a	47.12 N	122.14 W
Šumperk, Czech. (shōōm'pĕrk)	166	49.57 N	17.02 E
Sumrall, Ms. (sŭm'rôl)	126	31.25 N	89.34 W
Sumter, SC (sŭm'tēr)	127	33.55 N	80.21 W
Sumy, Sov. Un. (sōō'mĭ)	175	50.54 N	34.47 E
Sumy (Oblast), Sov. Un.	175	51.02 N	34.05 E
Sunburst, Mt.	117	48.53 N	111.55 W
Sunbury, Eng.	62	51.25 N	0.26 W
Sunbury, Pa. (sŭn'bēr-ē)	111	40.50 N	76.45 W
Sundance, Wy. (sŭn'dăns)	117	44.24 N	104.27 W
Sundarbans (Swp.), Bngl.-India (sōōn'dēr-bŭns)	196	21.50 N	89.00 E
Sunda Selat (Str.), Indon.	206	5.45 S	106.15 E
Sunday Str., Austl. (sŭn'dā)	214	15.50 S	122.45 E
Sundbyberg, Swe. (sōōn'bü-bĕrgh)	164	59.24 N	17.56 E
Sunderland, Eng. (sŭn'dēr-lănd)	162	54.55 N	1.25 W
Sunderland, Md.	112e	38.41 N	76.36 W
Sundridge, Eng.	62	51.17 N	0.18 E
Sundsvall, Swe. (sōōnds'väl)	164	62.24 N	19.19 E
Sunflower, (R.), Ms. (sŭn-flou'ēr)	126	32.57 N	90.40 W
Sungari (Songhua) (R.), China (sōŋ-hwä)	199	46.09 N	127.53 E
Sungari Res., China	202	42.55 N	127.50 E
Sungurlu, Tur. (sōōn'gōōr-lōō')	179	40.08 N	34.20 E
Sun Kosi (R.), Nep.	196	27.13 N	85.52 E
Sunland, Ca. (sŭn-lănd)	119a	34.16 N	118.18 W
Sunne, Swe. (sōōn'ĕ)	164	59.51 N	13.07 E
Sunninghill, Eng. (sŭnĭng'hĭl)	156b	51.23 N	0.40 W
Sunnymead, Ca. (sŭn'ĭ-mēd)	119a	33.56 N	117.15 W
Sunnyside, Ut.	121	39.35 N	110.20 W
Sunnyside, Wa.	116	46.19 N	120.00 W
Sunnyvale, Ca. (sŭn-nē-vāl)	118b	37.23 N	122.02 W
Sunol, Ca. (sōō'nŭl)	118b	37.36 N	122.53 W
Sun R., Mt. (sŭn)	117	47.34 N	111.53 W
Sunset, Ut. (sŭn-sĕt)	119b	41.08 N	112.02 W
Sunset Beach, Ca.	59	33.43 N	118.04 W
Sunset Crater Natl. Mon., Az. (krā'tēr)	121	35.20 N	111.30 W
Sunshine, Austl.	211a	37.47 S	144.50 E
Suntar, Sov. Un. (sōōn-tár')	181	62.14 N	117.49 E
Sunyani, Ghana	228	7.20 N	2.20 W
Suoyarvi, Sov. Un. (sōō'ô-yĕr'vē)	165	62.12 N	32.29 E
Superior, Az. (su-pē'rĭ-ēr)	121	33.15 N	111.10 W
Superior, Ne.	122	40.04 N	98.05 W
Superior, Wi.	119h	46.44 N	92.06 W
Superior, Wy.	117	41.45 N	108.57 W
Superior, L., Can.-U.S.	97	47.38 N	89.20 W
Superior, Laguna (L.), Mex. (lä-gōō'nȧ sōō-pä-rē-ōr')	131	16.20 N	94.55 W
Superior Village, Wi.	119h	46.38 N	92.07 W
Sup'ung Res., Kor.-China (sōō'pōōng)	204	40.35 N	126.00 E
Suqian, China (sōō-chyĕn)	200	33.57 N	118.17 E
Suquamish, Wa. (sōō-gwä'mĭsh)	118a	47.44 N	122.34 W
Şūr (Tyre), Leb. (sōōr) (tīr)	191a	33.16 N	35.13 E
Şūr, Om.	192	22.23 N	59.28 E
Sura (Neigh.), India	67a	22.33 N	88.25 E
Surabaya, Indon.	206	7.23 S	112.45 E
Surakarta, Indon.	206	7.35 S	110.45 E
Surany, Czech. (shōō'rȧ-nû')	167	48.05 N	18.11 E
Surat, Austl. (sŭ-răt)	216	27.18 S	149.00 E
Surat, India (sōō'rŭt)	196	21.08 N	73.22 E
Surat Thani, Thai.	206	8.59 N	99.14 E
Surazh, Sov. Un. (sōō-ràzh')	174	53.02 N	32.27 E
Surazh, Sov. Un.	174	55.24 N	30.46 E
Surbiton (Neigh.), Eng.	62	51.24 N	0.18 W
Surco, Peru	60c	12.09 S	77.01 W
Suresnes, Fr.	64c	48.52 N	2.14 E
Surgères, Fr. (sür-zhâr')	168	46.06 N	0.51 W
Surgut, Sov. Un. (sōōr-gōōt')	180	61.18 N	73.38 E
Suriname, S.A. (sōō-rē-näm')	140	4.00 N	56.00 W
Surquillo, Peru	60c	12.07 S	77.02 W
Sūrmaq, Iran	195	31.03 N	52.48 E
Surt, Libya	225	31.14 N	16.37 E
Surt, Khalīj (G.), Afr.	161	31.30 N	18.28 E
Suruga-Wan (B.), Jap. (sōō'rōō-gä wän)	205	34.52 N	138.36 E
Suru-Lere (Neigh.), Nig.	71d	6.31 N	3.22 E
Susa, It. (sōō'sä)	172	45.01 N	7.09 E
Susa, Jap.	205	34.40 N	131.39 E
Sušak (I.), Yugo.	172	42.45 N	16.30 E
Susaki, Jap. (sōō'sä-kē)	205	33.23 N	133.16 E
Susak, Otok (I.), Yugo. (sōō'shȧk)	172	44.31 N	14.15 E
Susitna, Ak. (sōō-sĭt'nȧ)	107	61.28 N	150.28 W
Susitna (R.), Ak.	107	62.00 N	150.28 W
Susong, China (sōō-sôŋ)	203	30.18 N	116.08 E
Susquehanna, Pa. (sŭs'kwē-hăn'ȧ)	111	41.55 N	73.55 W
Susquehanna (R.), Pa.	111	39.50 N	76.20 W
Sussex, Can. (sŭs'ĕks)	104	45.43 N	65.31 W
Sussex, NJ	112a	41.12 N	74.36 W
Sussex, Wi.	113a	43.08 N	88.12 W
Sutherland, Austl. (sŭdh'ēr-lănd)	211b	34.02 S	151.04 E
Sutherland, S. Afr. (sŭ'thēr-lănd)	226	32.25 S	20.40 E
Sutlej (R.), Pak.-India (sŭt'lĕj)	196	30.15 N	72.25 E
Sutton, Eng. (sut''n)	156b	51.21 N	0.12 W
Sutton, Ma.	105a	42.09 N	71.46 W
Sutton-at-Hone, Eng.	62	51.25 N	0.14 E

ng-sing; ŋ-baŋk; ɴ-nasalized n; nŏd; cŏmmit; ōld; ôbey; ôrder; oi-boil; fōōd; fŏŏt; ou-out; s-soft; sh-dish; th-thin; pūre; ûnite; ûrn; stŭd; circŭs; ü-as in French tu; '-indeterminate vowel.

PLACE (Pronounciation)	PAGE	Lat. °′	Long. °′
Sutton Coldfield, Eng. (kōld′fēld)	156	52.34 N	1.49 W
Sutton-in-Ashfield, Eng. (ĭn-ăsh′fēld)	156	53.07 N	1.15 W
Suurbekom, S. Afr.	71b	26.19 S	27.44 E
Suurberge (Mts.), S. Afr.	227c	33.15 S	25.32 E
Suwa, Jap. (sōō′wä)	205	36.03 N	138.08 E
Suwanee L., Can.	101	56.08 N	100.10 W
Suwannee (R.), Fl.-Ga. (sōō-wô′nē)	126	29.42 N	83.00 W
Suwatki, Pol. (sōō-vou′kē)	167	54.05 N	22.58 E
Suways al Ḥulwah, Tur′at as (Can.), Egypt	223c	30.15 N	32.20 E
Suxian, China (sōō shyĕn)	200	33.37 N	117.51 E
Suzdal′, Sov. Un. (sōōz′dal)	174	56.26 N	40.29 E
Suzhou, China (sōō-jō)	200	31.19 N	120.37 E
Suzuki-shinden, Jap.	69a	35.43 N	139.31 E
Suzu Misaki (C.), Jap. (sōō′zōō mē′sä-kē)	204	37.30 N	137.35 E
Svalbard (Spitsbergen) (Is.), Eur. (sväl′bärt) (spĭts′bûr-gĕn)	176	77.00 N	20.00 E
Svaneke, Den. (svä′nĕ-kĕ)	164	55.08 N	15.07 E
Svatovo, Sov. Un. (svä′tô-vô)	175	49.23 N	38.10 E
Svedala, Swe. (svĕ′dä-lä)	164	55.29 N	13.11 E
Sveg, Swe.	164	62.03 N	14.22 E
Svelvik, Nor. (svĕl′vĕk)	164	59.37 N	10.18 E
Svenčionys, Sov. Un.	165	55.09 N	26.09 E
Svendborg, Den. (svĕn-bôrgh)	164	55.05 N	10.35 E
Svensen, Or. (svĕn′sĕn)	118c	46.10 N	123.39 W
Sverdlovsk, Sov. Un. (svĕrd-lôfsk′)	182a	56.51 N	60.36 E
Svetlaya, Sov. Un. (svyĕt′lȧ-yȧ)	204	46.09 N	137.53 E
Svilajnac, Yugo. (svē′lȧ-ē-näts)	173	44.12 N	21.14 E
Svilengrad, Bul. (svĕl′ĕn-grȧt)	173	41.44 N	26.11 E
Svir′ (R.), Sov. Un.	178	60.55 N	33.40 E
Svir Kanal (Can.), Sov. Un. (kȧ-näl′)	165	60.10 N	32.40 E
Svishtov, Bul. (svĕsh′tôf)	173	43.36 N	25.21 E
Svisloch′ (R.), Sov. Un. (svēs′lôk)	174	53.38 N	28.10 E
Svitavy, Czech.	166	49.46 N	16.28 E
Svitsa (R.), Sov. Un. (svĭ-tsä)	167	49.09 N	24.10 E
Svobodnyy, Sov. Un. (svô-bôd′nĭ)	181	51.28 N	128.28 E
Svolvaer, Nor. (svôl′vĕr)	158	68.15 N	14.29 E
Svyatoy Nos, Mys (C.), Sov. Un. (svyŭ′toi nôs)	181	72.18 N	139.28 E
Swadlincote, Eng. (swŏd′lĭn-kôt)	156	52.46 N	1.33 W
Swain Rfs., Austl. (swān)	215	22.12 S	152.08 E
Swainsboro, Ga. (swānz′bŭr-ô)	127	32.37 N	82.21 W
Swakopmund, Namibia (svä′kôp-mōōnt) (swȧ′kôp-mōōnd)	226	22.40 S	14.30 E
Swallowfield, Eng. (swŏl′ô-fēld)	156b	51.21 N	0.58 W
Swampscott, Ma. (swômp′skŏt)	105a	42.28 N	70.55 W
Swan (R.), Austl.	214	31.30 S	126.30 E
Swan (R.), Can.	101	51.58 N	101.45 W
Swan Acres, Pa.	57b	40.33 N	80.02 W
Swan Hill, Austl.	216	35.20 S	143.30 E
Swan Hills, Can. (hĭlz)	99	54.52 N	115.45 W
Swan, I., Austl. (swŏn)	211a	38.15 S	144.41 E
Swan L., Can.	101	52.30 N	100.45 W
Swanland (Reg.), Austl. (swŏn′lănd)	214	31.45 S	119.15 E
Swanley, Eng.	62	51.24 N	0.12 E
Swan R., Mt.	117	47.50 N	113.40 W
Swan Ra., Mt.	117	47.50 N	113.40 W
Swan River, Can. (swŏn rĭv′ẽr)	101	52.06 N	101.16 W
Swanscombe, Eng.	62	51.26 N	0.18 E
Swansea, Il. (swŏn′sē)	119e	38.32 N	89.59 W
Swansea, Ma.	112b	41.45 N	71.09 W
Swansea, Wales	162	51.37 N	3.59 W
Swansea (Neigh.), Can.	54c	43.38 N	79.28 W
Swanson Res., Ne. (swŏn′sŭn)	122	40.13 N	101.30 W
Swartberg (Mtn.), S. Afr.	227c	30.08 S	29.34 E
Swarthmore, Pa.	56b	39.54 N	75.21 W
Swartkop (Mtn.), S. Afr.	226a	34.13 S	18.27 E
Swartruggens, S. Afr.	223d	25.59 S	26.40 E
Swartspruit, S. Afr.	227b	25.44 S	28.01 E
Swatow, see Shantou			
Swaziland, Afr. (Swä′zē-lănd)	226	26.45 S	31.30 E
Sweden, Eur. (swē′dĕn)	154	60.10 N	14.10 E
Swedesboro, NJ (swēdz′bē-rō)	112f	39.45 N	75.22 W
Sweetwater, Tn. (swēt′wô-tẽr)	126	35.36 N	84.29 W
Sweetwater, Tx.	124	32.28 N	100.25 W
Sweetwater (L.), ND	114	48.15 N	98.35 W
Sweetwater R., Wy.	117	42.19 N	108.35 W
Sweetwater Res., Ca.	120a	32.42 N	116.54 W
Świebodziec, Pol. (shvyĕn-bo′jĕts)	166	52.16 N	15.36 E
Świdnica, Pol. (shvĭd-nē′tsä)	166	50.50 N	16.30 E
Świdwin, Pol. (shvĭd′vĭn)	166	53.46 N	15.48 E
Świebodzin, Pol. (shvyăn-bôd′jĕn)	166	50.51 N	16.17 E
Świecie, Pol. (shvyăn′tsyĕ)	167	53.23 N	18.26 E
Świętokrzyskie Góry (Mts.), Pol. (shvyĕn-tô-kzhĭ′skyĕ gōō′rĭ)	167	50.57 N	21.02 E
Swift (R.), Eng.	156	52.26 N	1.08 W
Swift (R.), Me. (swĭft)	104	44.42 N	70.40 E
Swift Current, Can. (swĭft kûr′ĕnt)	100	50.17 N	107.50 W
Swift Res., Wa.	116	46.03 N	122.10 W
Swindle I., Can.	98	52.32 N	128.35 W
Swindon, Eng. (swĭn′dŭn)	162	51.35 N	1.55 W
Swinomish Ind. Res., Wa. (swĭ-nō′mĭsh)	118a	48.25 N	122.27 W
Świnoujście, Pol. (shvĭ-nĭ-ô-wēsh′chyĕ)	166	53.56 N	14.14 E
Swinton, Eng. (swĭn′tŭn)	156	53.30 N	1.19 W
Swinton, Eng.	64b	53.31 N	2.20 W
Swissvale, Pa. (swĭs′vāl)	113e	40.25 N	79.53 W
Switzerland, Eur. (swĭt′zẽr-lănd)	154	46.30 N	7.43 E
Syas′ (R.), Sov. Un. (syäs)	174	59.28 N	33.24 E
Sycamore, Il. (sĭk′ȧ-mōr)	115	42.00 N	88.42 W
Sychëvka, Sov. Un. (sē-chôf′kȧ)	174	55.52 N	34.18 E
Sydenham, Austl.	70b	37.42 S	144.46 E
Sydenham (Neigh.), Eng	62	51.26 N	0.03 W
Sydenham (Neigh.), S. Afr.	71b	26.09 S	28.06 E
Sydney, Austl. (sĭd′nē)	211b	33.55 S	151.17 E
Sydney, Can.	103	46.09 N	60.11 W
Sydney Mines, Can.	103	46.14 N	60.14 W
Syktyvkar, Sov. Un. (sük-tüf′kär)	178	61.35 N	50.40 E
Sylacauga, Al. (sĭl-ȧ-kô′gȧ)	126	33.10 N	86.15 W
Sylarna (Mtn.), Swe.	164	63.00 N	12.10 E
Sylt I., F.R.G. (sĭlt)	166	54.55 N	8.30 E
Sylvania, Austl.	70a	34.01 S	151.07 E
Sylvania, Ga. (sĭl-vā′nĭ-ȧ)	127	32.44 N	81.40 W
Sylvania Heights, Austl.	70a	34.02 S	151.06 E
Sylvester, Ga. (sĭl-vĕs′tẽr)	126	31.32 N	83.50 W
Syndal, Austl.	70b	37.53 S	145.09 E
Syosset, NY	55	40.50 N	73.30 W
Syracuse, Ks. (sĭr′ȧ-kūs)	122	37.59 N	101.44 W
Syracuse, NY	111	43.05 N	76.10 W
Syracuse, Ut.	119b	41.06 N	112.04 W
Syr-Dar′ya (R.), Sov. Un.	176	44.15 N	65.45 E
Syria, Asia (sĭr′ĭ-ȧ)	190	35.00 N	37.15 E
Syrian Des. (Bādiyat ash Shām), Asia (sĭr′ĭ-ăn)	192	32.03 N	39.30 E
Sysert′, Sov. Un. (sē′sĕrt)	182a	56.30 N	60.48 E
Syso′la (R.), Sov. Un.	178	60.50 N	50.40 E
Syukunosho, Jap.	69b	34.50 N	135.32 E
Syzran′, Sov. Un. (sĕz-rän′)	179	53.10 N	48.10 E
Szamotuty, Pol. (shȧ-mô-tōō′wē)	166	52.36 N	16.34 E
Szarvas, Hung. (sôr′vôsh)	167	46.51 N	20.36 E
Szczebrzeszyn, Pol. (shchĕ-bzhȧ′shĕn)	167	50.41 N	22.58 E
Szczecin (Stettin), Pol. (shchĕ′tsĭn) (shtĕ-tēn′)	166	53.25 N	14.35 E
Szczecinek, Pol. (shchĕ′tsĭ-nĕk)	166	53.41 N	16.42 E
Szczuczyn, Pol. (shchōō′chĕn)	167	53.32 N	22.17 E
Szczytno, Pol. (shchĭt′nô)	167	53.33 N	21.00 E
Szechwan Basin (Red), China	198	30.45 N	104.40 E
Szeged, Hung. (sĕ′gĕd)	167	46.15 N	20.12 E
Székesfehérvár, Hung. (sā′kĕsh-fĕ′hãr-vär)	167	47.12 N	18.26 E
Szekszárd, Hung. (sĕk′särd)	167	46.19 N	18.42 E
Szentendre, Hung. (sĕnt′ĕn-drĕ)	167	47.40 N	19.07 E
Szentes, Hung. (sĕn′tĕsh)	167	46.38 N	20.18 E
Szigetvar, Hung. (sĕ′gĕt-vär)	167	46.05 N	17.50 E
Szolnok, Hung. (sôl′nôk)	167	47.11 N	20.12 E
Szombathely, Hung. (sôm′bôt-hĕl′)	166	47.13 N	16.35 E
Szprotawa, Pol. (shprō-tä′vä)	166	51.34 N	15.29 E
Szydlowiec, Pol. (shid-wô′vyets)	167	51.13 N	20.53 E

T

PLACE (Pronounciation)	PAGE	Lat. °′	Long. °′
Taal (L.), Phil. (tä-äl′)	207a	13.58 N	121.06 E
Tabaco, Phil. (tä-bä′kō)	207a	13.27 N	123.40 E
Tabankulu, S. Afr. (tä-bän-kōō′la)	227c	30.56 S	29.19 E
Tabasara, Serrania de (Ra.), Pan. (sĕr-rä-nē′ä dā tä-bä-sä′rä)	133	8.29 N	81.22 W
Tabasco, Mex. (tä-bäs′kō)	130	21.47 N	103.04 W
Tabasco (State), Mex.	131	18.10 N	83.00 W
Taber, Can.	99	49.47 N	112.08 W
Tablas (I.), Phil. (tä′bläs)	207a	12.26 N	112.15 E
Tablas Str., Phil.	207a	12.17 N	121.41 E
Table B., S. Afr. (tā′b′l)	226a	33.41 S	18.27 E
Table Mt., S. Afr.	226a	33.58 S	18.26 E
Table Rock Lake, Mo.	123	36.37 N	93.29 W
Tabligbo, Togo	228	6.35 N	1.30 E
Taboão da Serra, Braz.	61d	23.38 S	46.46 W
Taboga (I.), Pan. (tä-bō′gä)	128a	8.48 N	79.35 W
Taboguilla (I.), Pan. (tä-bô-gē′l-yä)	128a	8.48 N	79.31 W
Taboleiro (Plat.), Braz. (tä-bô-lä′rô)	143	9.34 S	39.22 W
Tábor, Czech. (tä′bôr)	166	49.25 N	14.40 E
Tabora, Tan. (tä-bō′rä)	231	5.01 S	32.48 E
Tabou, Ivory Coast (tȧ-bōō′)	228	4.25 N	7.21 W
Tabrīz, Iran (tȧ-brēz′)	192	38.00 N	46.13 E
Tabuaeran (I.), Oceania	209	3.52 N	159.20 W
Tacámbaro (R.), Mex. (tä-käm′bä-rō)	130	18.55 N	101.25 W
Tacambaro de Codallos, Mex. (dā kô-däl′yōs)	130	19.12 N	101.28 W
Tacaná (Vol.), Mex.-Guat. (tä-kä-nä′)	132	15.09 N	92.07 W
Tacarigua, Laguna de la (L.), Ven. (lä-gōō′nä-dĕ-lä-tä-kä-rē′gwä)	143b	10.18 N	65.43 W
Tacheng, China (tä-chŭŋ)	198	46.50 N	83.24 E
Tachie (R.), Can.	98	54.30 N	125.00 W
Tachikawa, Jap.	69a	35.42 N	139.25 E
Tacloban, Phil. (tä-klō′bän)	207	11.06 N	124.58 E
Tacna, Peru (täk′nä)	142	18.34 S	70.16 W
Tacoma, Wa. (tȧ-kō′mȧ)	118a	47.14 N	122.27 W
Taconic Ra., NY (tȧ-kŏn′ĭk)	111	41.55 N	73.40 W
Tacony (Neigh.), Pa.	56b	40.02 N	75.03 W
Tacotalpa, Mex. (tä-kô-täl′pä)	131	17.37 N	92.51 W
Tacotalpa (R.), Mex.	131	17.24 N	92.38 W
Tacuarembó, Ur. (tä-kwä-rĕm′bô)	144	31.44 S	55.56 W
Tacuba (Neigh.), Mex.	60a	19.28 N	99.12 W
Tacubaya (Neigh.), Mex.	60a	19.25 N	99.12 W
Tademaït, Plat. du, Alg. (tä-dē-mä′ēt)	224	28.00 N	2.15 E
Tadio, Lagune (Lagoon), Ivory Coast	228	5.20 N	5.25 W
Tadjoura, Djibouti (tȧd-zhōō′rȧ)	223a	11.48 N	42.54 E
Tadley, Eng. (tăd′lē)	156b	51.19 N	1.08 W
Tadó, Col. (tä-dō′)	142a	5.15 N	76.30 W
Tadotsu, Jap. (tä′dô-tsōō)	205	34.14 N	133.43 E
Tadoussac, Can. (tȧ-dōō-sȧk′)	103	48.09 N	69.43 W
Tadworth, Eng.	62	51.17 N	0.14 W
Taebaek Sanmaek (Mts.), Kor. (tī-bĭk′ sän-mĭk′)	204	37.20 N	128.50 E
Taedong R., Kor. (tī-dŏng)	204	38.38 N	124.32 E
Taegu, Kor. (tī′gōō′)	204	35.49 N	128.41 E
Taejŏn, Kor.	204	36.20 N	127.26 E
Tafalla, Sp. (tä-fäl′yä)	170	42.30 N	1.42 W
Tafna (R.), Alg. (täf′nä)	171	35.28 N	1.00 W
Taft, Ca. (tȧft)	120	35.09 N	119.27 W
Tagama (Reg.), Niger	229	15050 N	6.30 E
Taganrog, Sov. Un. (tȧ-gȧn-rôk′)	175	47.13 N	38.44 E
Taganrogskiy Zaliv (B.), Sov. Un. (tȧ-gȧn-rôk′skĭ zä′lĭf)	175	46.55 N	38.17 E
Tagula (I.), Pap. N. Gui. (tä′gōō-lȧ)	215	11.45 S	153.46 E
Tagus (R.), Port.	170	39.23 N	8.01 W
Tagus (Tajo) (R.), Sp. (tā′gŭs)	170	39.40 N	5.07 W
Tahan, Gunong (Pk.), Mala.	206	4.33 N	101.52 E
Tahat (Mtn.) Alg. (tä-hät′)	224	23.22 N	5.21 E
Tahiti (I.), Fr. Polynesia (tä-hē′tē) (tä′ē-tē′)	209	17.30 S	149.30 W
Tahkuna Nina, Sov. Un. (tȧh-kōō′nȧ nē′nȧ)	165	59.08 N	22.03 E
Tahlequah, Ok. (tă-lĕ-kwä′)	123	35.54 N	94.58 W
Tahoe (L.), Ca.-Nv. (tä′hō)	120	39.09 N	120.18 W
Tahoua, Niger (tä′ōō-ä)	229	14.54 N	5.16 E
Ṭahṭā, Egypt (tä′tä)	223b	26.48 N	31.29 E
Tahtsa (L.), Can. (tŏt′-sȧ-pĕk)	98	53.33 N	127.47 W
Tahuya, Wa. (tȧ-hū-yä′)	118a	47.23 N	123.03 W
Tahuya (R.), Wa.	118a	47.28 N	122.55 W
Tai′an, China (tī-än)	200	36.13 N	117.08 E
Taibai Shan (Mtn.), China (tī-bī shän)	202	33.42 N	107.25 E
Taibus Qi, China (tī-bōō-sz chyē)	202	41.52 N	115.25 E
Taicang, China (tī-tsäŋ)	201b	31.26 N	121.06 E
T′aichung, Taiwan (tī′chōōng)	203	24.10 N	120.42 E
Tai′erzhuang, China (tī-är-jūäŋ)	200	34.34 N	117.44 E
Taigu, China (tī-gōō)	202	37.25 N	112.35 E
Taihang Shan (Mts.), China (tī-häŋ shän)	202	35.45 N	112.00 E
Taihe, China (tī-hŭ)	200	33.10 N	115.38 E
Tai Hu (L.), China (tī hōō)	200	31.13 N	120.00 E
Tailagoin (Reg.), Mong. (tī′lȧ-gän′ kä′rä)	198	43.39 N	105.54 E
Tailai, China (tī-lī)	202	46.20 N	123.10 E
Tailem Bend, Austl. (tā-lĕm)	216	35.15 S	139.30 E
Taimyr, P-Ov (Pen.), see Taymyr			
T′ainan, Taiwan (tī′nan′)	203	23.08 N	120.18 E
Tainaron, Akra (C.), Grc.	161	36.20 N	21.20 E
Taining, China (tī′nĭng′)	203	26.58 N	117.15 E
T′aipei, Taiwan (tī′pā′)	203	25.02 N	121.38 E
Taipei Institute of Technology (P. Int.), Taiwan	68d	25.02 N	121.32 E
Taiping, Mala.	206	4.56 N	100.39 E
Taiping, Ling (Mtn.), China (lĭŋ tī-pĭŋ)	202	47.03 N	120.30 E
Tai Po Tsai, China	68c	22.21 N	114.15 E
Taira, see Iwaki			
Taisha, Jap. (tī′shä)	205	35.23 N	132.40 E
Taishan, China (tī-shän)	203	22.15 N	112.50 E
Tai Shan (Mtn.), China (tī shän)	200	36.16 N	117.05 E
Taishet, see Tayshet			
Taitao, Peninsula de, Chile (pĕ-nē′ng-sōō-lä-dĕ-tä-ē-tä′ō)	144	46.20 S	77.15 W
Taitō (Neigh.), Jap.	69a	35.43 N	139.47 E
T′aitung, Taiwan (tī′tōōng′)	203	22.45 N	121.02 E
Taiwan (Formosa), Asia (tī-wän) (fôr-mō′sȧ)	191	23.30 N	122.20 E
Taiwan Normal University (P. Int.), Taiwan	68d	25.02 N	121.31 E
Taiwan Str., Asia	203	24.30 N	120.00 E
Tai Wan Tau, China	68c	22.18 N	114.17 E
Tai Wan Tsun, China	68c	22.19 N	114.12 E
Taínaron, Akra (C.), Grc.	173	37.45 N	22.00 E
Taixian, China (tī shyĕn)	200	32.31 N	119.54 E
Taixing, China (tī-shyĭŋ)	200	32.12 N	119.58 E
Taiyanggong, China	67b	39.58 N	116.25 E
Taiyuan, China (tī-yūän)	202	37.32 N	112.38 E
Taizhou, China (tī-jō)	200	32.23 N	119.41 E
Ta′izz, Yemen	195	13.38 N	44.04 E
Tajano de Morais, Braz. (tĕ-zhä′nô-dĕ-mô-rä′ĕs)	141a	22.05 S	42.04 W
Tajik (S.S.R.), Sov. Un.	176	39.22 N	69.30 E
Tajninka, Sov. Un.	66b	55.54 N	37.45 E
Tajo (R.), **see Tagus**			
Tajrīsh, Iran	68h	35.48 N	51.25 E
Tajumulco (Vol.), Guat. (tä-hōō-mōōl′kō)	132	15.03 N	91.53 W
Tajuña (R.), Sp. (tä-kōō′n-yä)	170	40.23 N	2.36 W
Tājūrā′, Libya	160	32.56 N	13.24 W
Tak, Thai.	206	16.57 N	99.12 E
Taka (I.), Jap. (tä′kä)	205	30.47 N	130.23 E
Takada, Jap. (tä′kȧ-dä)	205	37.08 N	138.30 E
Takahashi, Jap. (tä′kä′hä-shĭ)′	205	34.47 N	133.35 E
Takaishi, Jap.	205b	34.32 N	135.27 E
Takamatsu, Jap. (tä′kä′mä-tsōō′)	205	34.20 N	134.02 E
Takamori, Jap. (tä′kä′mô-rē′)	205	32.50 N	131.08 E
Takaoka, Jap. (ta′kä′ô-kä′)	205	36.45 N	136.59 E
Takapuna, N.A.	217	36.48 S	174.47 E
Takarazuka, Jap. (tä′kä-rä-zōō′kä)	205b	34.48 N	135.22 E
Takasaki, Jap. (tä′kät′sōō-kē′)	205	36.20 N	139.00 E
Takatsu (Mizonokuchi), Jap. (tä-kät′sōō) (mē′zō-nō-kōō′chē)	205a	35.36 N	139.37 E
Takatsuki, Jap. (tä′kät′sōō-kē′)	205b	34.51 N	135.38 E
Takaungu, Ken. (tä′kä′ōōŋ-gōō′)	197	3.41 S	39.48 E
Takayama, Jap. (tä′kä′yä′mä)	205	36.11 N	137.16 E
Takefu, Jap. (tä′kĕ-fōō)	205	35.57 N	136.09 E
Takenotsuka (Neigh.), Jap.	69a	35.48 N	139.48 E
Takla L., Can.	98	55.25 N	125.53 W
Takla Makan (Des.), China (mä-kän′)	198	39.22 N	82.34 E
Takoma Park, Md. (tä′kōmȧ pärk)	112e	38.59 N	77.00 W
Takum, Nig.	229	7.17 N	9.59 E
Tala, Mex. (tä′lä)	130	20.39 N	103.42 W
Talagante, Chile (tä-lä-gá′n-tĕ)	141b	33.39 S	70.54 W
Talanga, Hond. (tä-lä′n-gä)	132	14.21 N	87.09 W
Talara, Peru (tä-lä′rä)	142	4.32 S	81.17 W
Talasea, Pap. N. Gui. (tä-lä-sā′ä)	207	5.20 S	150.00 E
Talata Mafara, Nig.	229	12.35 N	6.04 E

PLACE (Pronounciation)	PAGE	Lat. °′	Long. °′
Talaud, Kepulauan (Is.), Indon. (tä-lout′)	207	4.17 N	127.30 E
Talavera de la Reina, Sp. (tä-lä-vā′rä dā lä rȧ-ē′nä)	170	39.58 N	4.51 W
Talawdī, Sud.	225	10.41 N	30.21 E
Talca, Chile (täl′kä)	141b	35.25 S	71.39 W
Talca (Prov.), Chile	141b	35.23 S	71.15 W
Talcahuano, Chile (täl-kä-wä′nō)	144	36.41 S	73.05 W
Talca, Punta (Pt.), Chile (pōō′n-tä-täl′kä)	139b	33.25 S	71.42 W
Taldom, Sov. Un. (täl-dôm)	174	56.44 N	37.33 E
Taldy-Kurgan, Sov. Un. (tål′dĭ-kŏŏr-gän′)	180	45.03 N	77.18 E
Talea de Castro (San Miguel), Mex. (tä′lȧ-ä dā käs′trō)	131	17.22 N	96.14 W
Talibu, Pulau (I.), Indon.	207	1.30 S	125.00 E
Talim (I.), Phil. (tä-lēm′)	207a	14.21 N	121.14 E
Talisay, Phil. (tä-lē′sī)	207a	14.08 N	122.56 E
Talkeetna, Ak. (tål-kēt′nȧ)	107	62.18 N	150.02 W
Talkheh Rūd (R.), Iran	179	38.00 N	46.50 E
Talladega, Al. (tăl-ȧ-dē′gȧ)	126	33.25 N	86.06 W
Tallahassee, Fl. (tăl-ȧ-hăs′ė)	126	30.25 N	84.17 W
Tallahatchie (R.), Ms. (tal-ȧ hăch′ė)	126	34.21 N	90.03 W
Tallapoosa, Ga. (tăl-ȧ-pōō′sȧ)	126	33.44 N	85.15 W
Tallapoosa (R.), Al.	126	32.22 N	86.08 W
Tallassee, Al. (tăl′ȧ-sė)	126	32.30 N	85.54 W
Tallinn (Reval), Sov. Un. (tål′lėn) (rā′väl)	165	59.26 N	24.44 E
Tallmadge, Oh. (tăl′mĭj)	113d	41.06 N	81.26 W
Tallulah, La. (tă-lōō′lȧ)	125	32.25 N	91.13 W
Tally Ho, Austl.	70b	37.52 S	145.09 E
Talmanca, Cord. de (Mts.), C. R. (kôr-dēl-yĕ′rä-dĕ-täl-mä′n-kä)	133	9.37 N	83.55 W
Tal′noye, Sov. Un. (tål′nô-yĕ)	175	48.52 N	30.43 E
Talo (Mt.), Eth.	225	10.45 N	37.55 E
Taloje Budrukh, India	197b	19.05 N	73.05 E
Talpa de Allende, Mex. (täl′pä dā äl-yĕn′dȧ)	130	20.25 N	104.48 W
Talsi, Sov. Un. (tal′sĭ)	165	57.16 N	22.35 E
Taltal, Chile (täl-täl′)	144	25.26 S	70.32 W
Taly, Sov. Un. (täl′ĭ)	175	49.51 N	40.07 E
Tama, Ia. (tā′mä)	115	41.57 N	92.36 W
Tama (R.), Jap.	69a	35.32 N	139.47 E
Tama (R.), Jap.	205a	35.38 N	139.35 E
Tamagawa (Neigh.), Jap.	69a	35.37 N	139.39 E
Tama-kyūryō (Hills), Jap.	69a	35.35 N	139.30 E
Tamale, Ghana (tä-mä′lȧ)	228	9.25 N	0.50 W
Taman′, Sov. Un. (tȧ-män′′)	175	45.13 N	36.46 E
Tamaná, Cerro (Mtn.), Col. (sĕ′r-rô-tä-mä-nȧ′)	142a	5.06 N	76.10 W
Tamanaco (R.), Ven. (tä-mä-nä′kō)	143b	9.32 N	66.00 W
Tamaqua, Pa. (tȧ-mô′kwă)	111	40.45 N	75.50 W
Tamar (R.), Eng. (tā′mär)	162	50.35 N	4.15 W
Tamarite de Litera, Sp. (tä-mä-rē′tā)	171	41.52 N	0.24 E
Tamaulipas (State), Mex. (tä-mä-ōō-lē′päs′)	130	23.45 N	98.30 W
Tamazula de Gordiano, Mex. (tä-mä-zōō′lä dā gôr-dė-ä′nô)	130	19.44 N	103.09 W
Tamazulapan del Progreso, Mex. (tä-mä-zōō-lä′päm-dĕl-prô-grĕ-sō)	131	17.41 N	97.34 W
Tamazunchale, Mex. (tä-mä-zōōn-chä′lȧ)	130	21.16 N	98.46 W
Tambacounda, Senegal (täm-bä-kōōn′dä)	228	13.47 N	13.40 W
Tambador, Serra do (Mts.), Braz. (sĕ′r-rä-dô-täm′bä-dōr)	143	10.33 S	41.16 W
Tambelan, Kepulauan (Is.), Indon. (täm-bȧ-län′)	206	0.38 N	107.38 E
Tambo, Austl. (tăm′bō)	216	24.50 S	146.15 E
Tambov, Sov. Un. (tȧm-bôf′)	179	52.45 N	41.10 E
Tambov (Oblast), Sov. Un.	174	52.50 N	40.42 E
Tambre (R.), Sp. (täm′brā)	170	42.59 N	8.33 W
Tambura, Sud. (täm-bōō′rä)	225	5.34 N	27.30 E
Tame (R.), Eng. (tām)	156	52.41 N	1.42 W
Tâmega (R.), Port. (tȧ-mā′gȧ)	170	41.30 N	7.45 W
Tamenghest, Alg.	224	22.34 N	5.34 E
Tamenghest, Oued (R.), Alg.	224	22.15 N	2.51 E
Tamesí (R.), Mex. (tä-mĕ-sė′)	130	22.36 N	98.32 W
Tamgak, Monts (Mtn.), Niger (tam-gäk′)	229	18.40 N	8.40 E
Tamgue, Massif du (Mtn.), Gui.	228	12.15 N	12.35 W
Tamiahua, Mex. (tä-myä-wä)	131	21.17 N	97.26 W
Tamiahua, Laguna (L.), Mex. (lä-gōō′nä-tä-myä-wä)	131	21.38 N	97.33 W
Tamiami, Can., Fl. (tă-mī-ăm′ĭ)	127a	25.52 N	80.08 W
Tamil Nadu (State), India	197	11.30 N	78.00 E
Tammisaari, see Ekenäs			
Tampa, Fl. (tăm′pȧ)	127a	27.57 N	82.25 W
Tampa B., Fl.	127a	27.35 N	82.38 W
Tampere, Fin. (tȧm′pĕ-rĕ)	158	61.21 N	23.39 E
Tampico, Mex. (täm-pē′kō)	131	22.14 N	97.51 W
Tampico Alto, Mex. (täm-pē′kō äl′tō)	131	22.07 N	97.48 W
Tampin, Mala.	191b	2.28 N	102.15 E
Tamuín, Mex. (tä-mōō-ė′n)	130	22.04 N	98.47 W
Tamworth, Austl. (tăm′wûrth)	216	31.01 S	151.00 E
Tamworth, Eng.	156	52.58 N	1.41 W
Tana (I.), Vanuatu	215	19.32 S	169.27 E
Tana (R.), Ken. (tä′nä)	231	2.00 S	40.15 E
Tana (R.), Nor.-Fin.	158	69.20 N	24.54 E
Tanabe, Jap. (tä-nä′bā)	205	33.45 N	135.21 E
Tanabe, Jap.	205b	34.49 N	135.46 E
Tanacross, Ak. (tă′nȧ-crōs)	107	63.20 N	143.30 W
Tanaga (I.), Ak. (tä-nä′gä)	107a	51.28 N	178.10 W
Tanahbala, Pulau (I.), Indon. (tȧ-nä-bä′lä)	206	0.30 S	98.22 E
Tanahmasa, Pulau (I.), Indon. (tȧ-nä-mä′sä)	206	0.03 S	97.30 E
Tanakpur, India (tăn′ăk-pōōr)	196	29.10 N	80.07 E
Tana L., Eth.	225	12.09 N	36.41 E
Tanami, Austl. (tȧ-nā′mė)	214	19.45 S	129.50 E
Tanana, Ak. (tă′nȧ-nô)	107	65.18 N	152.20 W

PLACE (Pronounciation)	PAGE	Lat. °′	Long. °′
Tanana (R.), Ak.	107	64.26 N	148.40 W
Tanaro (R.), It. (tä-nä′rô)	172	44.45 N	8.02 E
Tanashi, Jap.	205a	35.44 N	139.34 E
Tan-binh, Viet.	68m	10.48 N	106.40 E
Tanbu, China (tän-bōō)	201a	23.20 N	113.06 E
Tancheng, China (tän-chŭŋ)	200	34.37 N	118.22 E
Tanchŏn, Kor. (tän′chŭn)	204	40.29 N	128.50 E
Tancítaro, Mex. (tän-sē′tä-rō)	130	19.16 N	102.24 W
Tancítaro, Cerro de, Mex. (sĕ′r-rô-dĕ)	130	19.24 N	102.19 W
Tancoco, Mex. (tän-kō′kō)	131	21.16 N	99.45 W
Tandil, Arg. (tän-dēl′)	132	36.16 S	59.01 W
Tandil, Sierra del (Mts.), Arg.	132	38.40 S	59.40 W
Tanega (I.), Jap. (tä′nȧ-gä′)	205	30.36 N	131.11 E
Tanezrouft (Reg.), Alg. (tä′nĕz-rŏŏft)	224	24.17 N	0.30 W
Tang (R.), China (täŋ)	200	33.38 N	117.29 E
Tang (R.), China	200	39.13 N	114.45 E
Tanga, Tan. (tăŋ′gȧ)	231	5.04 S	39.06 E
Tangancícuaro, Mex. (täŋ-gän-sē′kwa»um rô)	130	19.52 N	102.13 W
Tanganyika, L., Afr.	231	5.15 S	29.40 E
Tanger (Tangier), Mor. (tăn-jēr′)	224	35.52 N	5.55 W
Tangermünde, G.D.R. (täŋ′ĕr-mün′de)	166	52.33 N	11.58 E
Tanggu, China (täŋ-gōō)	200	39.04 N	117.41 E
Tanggula Shan (Mts.), China (täŋ-gōō-lä shän)	198	33.15 N	89.07 E
Tangho, China	202	32.40 N	112.50 E
Tangier, see Tanger			
Tangipahoa R., La. (tăn′jė-pȧ-hō′ȧ)	125	30.48 N	90.28 W
Tangra Yumco (L.), China (täŋ-rä yōōm-tswo)	196	30.50 N	85.40 E
T′angshan, China	200	39.38 N	118.11 E
Tangxian, China (täŋ shyĕn)	200	38.09 N	115.00 E
Tangzha, China (täŋ-jä)	200	32.06 N	120.48 E
Tanimbar, Kepulauan (Is.), Indon.	207	8.00 S	132.00 E
Tanjong (C.), Mala.	191b	1.53 N	102.29 E
Tanjong Piai (I.), Mala.	191b	1.16 N	103.11 E
Tanjong Ramunia (C.), Mala.	191b	1.27 N	104.44 E
Tanjungbalai, Indon. (tän′jông-bä′lȧ)	191b	1.00 N	103.26 E
Tanjungkarand, Indon.	206	5.16 S	105.06 E
Tanjungpandan, Indon.	206	2.47 S	107.51 E
Tanjungpinang, Indon. (tän′jŏng-pē′näng)	191b	0.55 N	104.29 E
Tanjungpriok (Neigh.), Indon.	68k	6.06 S	106.53 E
Tannu-Ola (Mts.), Sov. Un.	177	51.00 N	94.00 E
Tannūrah, Ra′s al (C.), Sau. Ar.	192	26.45 N	49.59 E
Tano (R.), Ghana	228	5.40 N	2.30 W
Tan-qui-dong, Viet.	68m	10.44 N	106.43 E
Tanquijo, Arrecife (Reef), Mex. (är-rĕ-sē′fĕ-tän-kė′kô)	131	21.07 N	97.16 W
Tanshui Ho (R.), Taiwan	68d	25.08 N	121.27 E
Tan Son Nhut, Viet.	68m	10.49 N	106.40 E
Ţanţā, Egypt (tän′tä)	223b	30.50 N	31.00 E
Tan-thoi-nhut, Viet.	68m	10.50 N	106.36 E
Tan-thuan-dong, Viet.	68m	10.45 N	106.44 E
Tantoyuca, Mex. (tän-tō-yōō′kä)	130	21.22 N	98.13 W
Tanyang, Kor.	204	36.53 N	128.20 E
Tanzania, Afr.	222	6.48 S	33.58 E
Tao (R.), China (tou)	202	35.30 N	103.40 E
Tao′an, China (tou-än)	202	45.15 N	122.45 E
Tao′er (R.), China (tou-är)	202	45.40 N	122.00 E
Taormina, It. (tä-ôr-mē′nä)	172	37.53 N	15.18 E
Taos, NM (tä′ȯs)	121	36.25 N	105.35 W
Taoudenni, Mali (tä′ōō-dĕ-nė′)	224	22.57 N	3.37 W
Taoussa, Mali	228	16.55 N	0.35 W
Taoyuan, China (tou-yüän)	203	29.00 N	111.15 E
Tapa, Sov. Un. (tȧ′pȧ)	165	59.16 N	25.56 E
Tapachula, Mex.	132	14.55 N	92.20 W
Tapajós (R.), Braz. (tä-pä-zhô′s)	143	3.27 S	55.33 W
Tapalque, Arg. (tä-päl-kĕ′)	141c	36.22 S	60.05 W
Tapanatepec, Mex. (tä-pä-nä-tĕ-pĕk)	131	16.22 N	94.19 W
Tāpi (R.), India	196	21.33 N	74.30 E
Tapiales, Arg.	60d	34.44 S	58.30 W
Tappi Saki (C.), Jap. (täp′pė sä′kė)	204	41.05 N	139.40 E
Tapps (L.), Wa. (tăpz)	118a	47.20 N	122.12 W
Tapsiā (Neigh.), India	67a	22.32 N	88.22 E
Taqātu′ Hayyā, Sud.	225	18.10 N	36.17 E
Taquara (Neigh.), Braz.	61c	22.55 S	43.21 W
Taquara, Serra de (Mts.), Braz. (sĕ′r-rä-dĕ-tä-kwä′rä)	143	15.28 S	54.33 W
Taquari (R.), Braz. (tä-kwä′rĭ)	143	18.35 S	56.50 W
Tar (R.), NC (tär)	127	35.58 N	78.06 W
Tara, Sov. Un. (tä′rȧ)	180	56.58 N	74.13 E
Tara (I.), Phil. (tä′rä)	207a	12.18 N	120.28 E
Tara (R.), Sov. Un. (tä′rȧ)	180	56.32 N	76.13 E
Ţarābulus (Tripoli), Leb. (tȧ-rä′bōō-lōōs)	191a	34.25 N	35.50 E
Tarābulus (Tripoli), Libya	225	32.50 N	13.13 E
Tarābulus (Tripolitania) (Prov.), Libya	225	31.00 N	12.26 E
Tarakan, Indon.	206	3.17 N	118.04 E
Tarancón, Sp. (tä-rän-kōn′)	170	40.01 N	3.00 W
Taranto, It. (tä′rän-tô)	172	40.30 N	17.15 E
Taranto, Golfo di (G.), It. (gȯl-fȯ-dē tä′rän-tô)	172	40.03 N	17.10 E
Tarapoto, Peru (tä-rä-pȯ′tō)	142	6.29 S	76.26 W
Tarare, Fr. (tȧ-rär′)	168	45.55 N	4.23 E
Tarascon, Fr. (tȧ-rȧs-kôɴ′)	168	42.53 N	1.35 E
Tarascon, Fr. (tä-räs-kôɴ)	168	43.47 N	4.41 E
Tarashcha, Sov. Un. (tä′rȧsh-chȧ)	175	49.34 N	30.52 E
Tarasht, Iran	68h	35.42 N	51.21 E
Tarata, Bol. (tä-rä′tä)	142	17.43 S	66.00 W
Taravo (R.), Fr.	172	41.54 N	8.58 E
Tarazit, Massif de (Mts.), Niger	229	20.05 N	7.35 E
Tarazona, Sp. (tä-rä-thō′nä)	170	41.54 N	1.45 W
Tarazona de la Mancha, Sp. (tä-rä-zȯ′nä-dĕ-lä-mä′n-chä)	170	39.13 N	1.50 W
Tarbat Ness (Hd.), Scot. (tȧr′bȧt)	162	57.51 N	3.50 W
Tarbes, Fr. (tȧrb)	168	43.04 N	0.05 E
Tarbock Green, Eng.	64a	53.23 N	2.49 W
Tarboro, NC (tär′bŭr-ȯ)	127	35.53 N	77.34 W
Tarbū, Libya	225	26.07 N	15.49 E

PLACE (Pronounciation)	PAGE	Lat. °′	Long. °′
Taredo (Neigh.), India	67e	19.58 N	72.49 E
Taree, Austl. (tă-rē′)	216	31.52 S	152.21 E
Tarentum, Pa. (tȧ-rĕn′tŭm)	113e	40.36 N	79.44 W
Tarfa, Wādī at, Egypt	223b	28.14 N	31.00 E
Tarfaya, Mor.	224	27.58 N	12.55 W
Tarhūnah, Libya	194	32.26 N	13.38 E
Tarija, Bol. (tär-rē′hä)	142	21.42 S	64.52 W
Tarīm, P. D. R. of Yem. (tȧ-rĭm′)	192	16.13 N	49.08 E
Tarim (R.), China (tȧ-rĭm′)	198	40.45 N	85.39 E
Tarim Basin, China (tȧ-rĭm′)	198	39.52 N	82.34 E
Tarkastad, S. Afr.	227c	32.01 S	26.18 E
Tarkhankut, Mys (C.), Sov. Un. (mĭs tȧr-ĸän′kŏŏt)	175	45.18 N	32.08 E
Tarkio, Mo. (tär′kĭ-ō)	123	40.27 N	95.22 W
Tarks (R.), S. Afr. (tä′kȧ)	227c	32.15 S	26.00 E
Tarkwa, Ghana (tärk′wä)	228	5.19 N	1.59 W
Tarlac, Phil. (tär′läk)	207	15.29 N	120.36 E
Tarlton, S. Afr. (tärl′tŭn)	227b	26.05 S	27.38 E
Tarma, Peru (tär′mä)	142	11.26 S	75.40 W
Tarn (R.), Fr. (tärn)	168	44.03 N	2.41 E
Tàrnava Mica R., Rom. (tĕr-nä′vȧ mē′kŏ)	169	46.17 N	24.20 E
Tarnów, Pol. (tär′nŏŏf)	169	50.02 N	21.00 E
Taro (R.), It. (tä′rō)	172	44.41 N	10.03 E
Taroudant, Mor. (tȧ-rōō-dänt′)	224	30.39 N	8.52 W
Tarpon Springs, Fl. (tär′pŏn)	127a	28.07 N	82.44 W
Tarporley, Eng. (tär′pēr-lė)	156	53.09 N	2.40 W
Tarpum B., Ba. (tär′pŭm)	135	25.05 N	76.20 W
Tarquinia (Corneto), It. (tär-kwē′nė-ä) (kôr-nā′tô)	172	42.16 N	11.46 E
Tarragona, Sp. (tär-rä-gō′nä)	171	41.05 N	1.15 E
Tarrant, Al. (tăr′ănt)	112h	33.35 N	86.46 W
Tarrasa, Sp. (tär-rä′sä)	171	41.34 N	2.01 E
Tárrega, Sp. (tä rȧ-gä)	171	41.40 N	1.09 E
Tarrejón de Ardoz, Sp. (tär-rĕ-ĸȯ′n-dĕ-är-dȯz)	171a	40.28 N	3.29 W
Tarrytown, NY (tär′ĭ-toun)	112a	41.04 N	73.52 W
Tarsus, Tur. (tȧr′sŏŏs) (tär′sŭs)	179	37.00 N	34.50 E
Tartagal, Arg. (tär-tä-gȧ′l)	144	23.31 S	63.47 W
Tartu (Dorpat), Sov. Un. (tär′tŏŏ) (dôr′pät)	174	58.23 N	26.44 E
Ţarţūs, Egypt	161	34.54 N	35.59 E
Tarumi, Jap. (tä′rōō-mė)	205b	34.38 N	135.04 E
Tarusa, Sov. Un. (tä-rōōs′ȧ)	174	54.43 N	37.11 E
Tarzana, Ca. (tär-ză′ȧ)	119a	34.10 N	118.32 W
Tashauz, Sov. Un. (tŭ-shŭ-ōōs′)	155	41.50 N	59.45 E
Tashkent, Sov. Un. (tȧsh′kĕnt)	180	41.23 N	69.04 E
Tasman B., N. Z. (tăz′măn)	217	40.50 S	173.20 E
Tasmania (State), Austl. (tăz-mā′nĭ-ȧ)	216	38.20 S	146.30 E
Tasmania (I.), Austl.	215	41.28 S	142.30 E
Tasman Pen, Austl.	216	43.00 S	148.30 E
Tasman Sea, Oceania	208	29.30 S	155.00 E
Tasquillo, Mex. (täs-kē′lyō)	130	20.34 N	99.21 W
Tassili-n-Ajjer (Plat.), Alg. (tȧs′ė-lė ä′jĕr)	224	25.40 N	6.57 E
Tatar (A. S. S. R.), Sov. Un. (tȧ-tär′)	178	55.30 N	51.00 E
Tatarsk, Sov. Un. (tȧ-tärsk′)	180	55.15 N	75.00 E
Tatar Str., Sov. Un.	181	51.00 N	141.45 E
Tate Gallery (P. Int.), Eng.	62	51.29 N	0.08 W
Tater Hill (Mtn.), Or. (tāt′ēr hĭl)	118c	45.47 N	123.02 W
Tateyama, Jap. (tä′tė-yä′mä)	205	35.04 N	139.52 E
Tathong Chan., Asia	68c	22.15 N	114.15 E
Tatlow, Mt., Can.	98	51.23 N	123.52 W
Tatsfield, Eng.	62	51.18 N	0.02 E
Tatuí, Braz. (tä-tōō-ē′)	141a	23.21 S	47.49 W
Tau, Nor.	164	59.05 N	5.59 E
Taubaté, Braz. (tou-bȧ-tā′)	141a	23.03 S	45.32 W
Tauern Tun, Aus.	166	47.12 N	13.17 E
Taung, S. Afr. (tä′ŏŏng)	226	27.25 S	24.47 E
Taunton, Ma. (tän′tŭn)	112b	41.54 N	71.03 W
Taunton R., RI	112b	41.50 N	71.02 W
Taupo, L., N. Z. (tä′ōō-pō)	217	38.42 S	175.55 E
Taurage, Sov. Un. (tou′rȧ-gā)	165	55.15 N	22.18 E
Taurus Mts., see Toros Dağlari			
Tauste, Sp. (tä-ōōs′tȧ)	170	41.55 N	1.15 W
Tavda, Sov. Un. (tȧv-dȧ′)	180	58.00 N	64.44 E
Tavda (R.), Sov. Un.	178	59.20 N	63.28 E
Taverny, Fr. (tȧ-vēr-nē′)	169b	49.02 N	2.13 E
Taviche, Mex. (tä-vė′chĕ)	131	16.43 N	96.35 W
Tavira, Port. (tä-vē′rȧ)	170	37.09 N	7.42 W
Tavistock, NJ	56b	39.53 N	75.02 W
Tavoy, Bur.	206	14.04 N	98.19 E
Tavşanli, Tur. (tȧv′shän-lĭ)	179	39.30 N	29.30 E
Tawakoni (L.), Tx.	125	32.51 N	95.59 W
Tawaramoto, Jap. (tä′wä-rä-mȯ-tȯ)	205b	34.33 N	135.48 E
Tawas City, Mi.	110	44.15 N	83.30 W
Tawas Pt., Mi. (tô′wȧs)	110	44.15 N	83.25 W
Tawitawi Group (Is.), Phil. (tä′wė-tä′wė)	206	4.52 N	120.35 E
Tawkar, Sud.	225	18.28 N	37.46 E
Taxco de Alarcón, Mex. (täs′kō dĕ ä-lär-kȯ′n)	130	18.34 N	99.37 W
Tay (R.), Scot.	162	56.35 N	3.37 W
Tayabas B., Phil. (tä-yä′bäs)	207a	13.44 N	121.40 E
Tayga, Sov. Un. (tī′gä)	180	56.12 N	85.47 E
Taygonos, Mys (Taigonos) (C.), Sov. Un.	181	60.37 N	160.17 E
Tay, Loch (L.), Scot.	162	56.25 N	5.07 W
Taylor, Mi.	57c	42.13 N	83.16 W
Taylor, Tx.	125	30.35 N	97.25 W
Taylor, Mt., NM	121	35.20 N	107.40 W
Taylorville, Il. (tā′lēr-vĭl)	110	39.30 N	89.20 W
Taymā, Sua. Ar.	192	27.45 N	38.55 E
Taymyr (Taimyr) (L.), Sov. Un. (tī-mĭr′)	181	74.13 N	100.45 E
Taymyr, P-Ov (Taimyr) (Pen.), Sov. Un.	180	75.15 N	95.00 E
Táyros, Grc.	66d	37.58 N	23.42 E
Tayshet (Taishet), Sov. Un. (tī-shĕt′)	180	56.09 N	97.49 E
Taytay, Phil (tī-tī)	180	10.37 N	119.10 E
Taytay, Phil.	68g	14.34 N	121.08 E
Tayung, Phil. (tā-yōōng′)	207a	16.01 N	120.45 E

PLACE (Pronounciation)	PAGE	Lat. °′	Long. °′
Taz (R.), Sov. Un. (táz)	180	67.15 N	80.45 E
Taza, Mor. (tä'zä)	224	34.08 N	4.00 W
Tazovskoye, Sov. Un.	180	66.58 N	78.28 E
Tbessa, Alg.	224	35.27 N	8.13 E
Tbilisi, Sov. Un. ('tbĭl-yē'sē)	179	41.40 N	44.45 E
Tchibanga, Gabon (chē-bäŋ'gä)	230	2.51 S	11.02 E
Tchien, Lib.	228	6.04 N	8.08 W
Tchigai, Plat. du (Plat.), Chad-Niger	229	21.20 N	14.50 E
Tczew, Pol. (t'chĕf')	167	54.06 N	18.48 E
Teabo, Mex. (tĕ-ä'bô)	132a	20.25 N	89.14 W
Teague, Tx.	125	31.39 N	96.16 W
Teaneck, NJ	55	40.53 N	74.01 W
Teapa, Mex. (tā-ä'pä)	131	17.35 N	92.56 W
Tebing Tinggi (I.), Indon. (teb'ĭng-tĭng'gä)	191b	0.54 N	102.39 E
Tebukbetung, Indon.	206	5.30 S	105.04 E
Tecalitlán, Mex. (tā-kä-lē-tlän')	130	19.28 N	103.17 W
Techiman, Ghana	228	7.35 N	1.56 W
Tecoanapa, Mex. (tāk-wä-nä-pä')	130	16.33 N	98.46 W
Tecoh, Mex. (tĕ-kô)	132a	20.46 N	89.27 W
Tecolotlán, Mex. (tā-kô-lô-tlän')	130	20.13 N	103.57 W
Tecolutla, Mex. (tā-kô-lōō'tlä)	131	20.33 N	97.00 W
Tecolutla (R.), Mex.	131	20.16 N	97.14 W
Tecomán, Mex. (tā-kô-män')	130	18.53 N	103.53 W
Tecómitl, Mex. (tĕ-kŏ'mētl)	131a	19.13 N	98.59 W
Tecozautla, Mex. (tā'kô-zä-ōō'tlä)	130	20.33 N	99.38 W
Tecpan de Galeana, Mex. (tĕk-pän' dā gä-lā-ä'nä)	130	17.13 N	100.41 W
Tecpatán, Mex. (tĕk-pä-tá'n)	131	17.08 N	93.18 W
Tecuala, Mex. (tĕ-kwä-lä)	130	22.24 N	105.29 W
Tecuci, Rom. (ta-kōōch')	167	45.51 N	27.30 E
Tecumseh, Can. (tē-kŭm'sē)	113b	42.19 N	82.53 W
Tecumseh, Mi.	110	42.00 N	84.00 W
Tecumseh, Ne.	124	40.21 N	96.09 W
Tecumseh, Ok.	123	35.18 N	96.55 W
Teddington (Neigh.), Eng.	62	51.25 N	0.20 W
Tees (R.), Eng. (tēz)	162	54.40 N	2.10 W
Tefé, Braz. (tĕf-ā')	142	3.27 S	64.43 W
Teganuna (L.), Jap. (tā'gä-nōō'nä)	205a	35.50 N	140.02 E
Tegel (Neigh.), F.R.G.	65a	52.35 N	13.17 E
Tegeler See (L.), G.D.R.	65a	52.35 N	13.15 E
Tegucigalpa, Hond. (tā-gōō-sē-gäl'pä)	132	14.08 N	87.15 W
Tehachapi Mts., Ca. (tē-hă-shā'pĭ)	120	34.50 N	118.55 W
Tehar (Neigh.), India	67d	28.38 N	77.07 E
Tehentlo L., Can.	98	55.11 N	125.00 W
Tehrān, Iran (tē-hrän')	192	35.45 N	51.30 E
Tehuacan, Mex. (tā-wä-kän')	131	18.27 N	97.23 W
Tehuantepec (Sto. Domingo), Mex. (tå-wän-tå-pĕk') (sän-tô dô-mē'n-gô)	131	16.20 N	95.14 W
Tehuantepec (R.), Mex.	131	16.30 N	95.23 W
Tehuantepec, Golfo de (G.), Mex. (gôl-fô dĕ)	128	15.45 N	95.00 W
Tehuantepec, Istmo de (Isth.), Mex. (ē'st-mô dĕ)	131	17.55 N	94.35 W
Tehuehuetla Arroyo (R.), Mex. (tĕ-wĕ-wĕ'tlä ar-rô-yô)	130	17.54 N	100.26 W
Tehuitzingo, Mex. (tå-wē-tzĭŋ'gō)	130	18.21 N	98.16 W
Tejeda, Sierra de (Mts.), Sp. (sē-ĕ'r-rä dĕ tĕ-kĕ'dä)	170	36.55 N	5.57 W
Tejúpan (Santiago), Mex. (tĕ-kōō-pä'n) (sän-tyä'gô)	131	17.39 N	97.34 W
Tejúpan, Punta (Pt.), Mex. (pōō'n-tä)	130	18.19 N	103.30 W
Tejupilco de Hidalgo, Mex. (tå-hōō-pēl'kô dā ē-dhäl'gō)	130	18.52 N	100.07 W
Tekamah, Ne. (tē-kā'mȧ)	114	41.46 N	96.13 W
Tekax de Alvaro Obregon, Mex. (tĕ-kä'x dĕ ä'l-vä-rô-brĕ-gô'n)	132a	20.12 N	89.11 W
Tekeze (R.), Eth.	225	13.38 N	38.00 E
Tekirdağ (Rodosto), Tur. (tĕ-kēr'dägh')	173	41.00 N	27.28 E
Tekit, Mex. (tĕ-kē't)	132a	20.35 N	89.18 W
Tekoa, Wa. (tē-kō'ȧ)	116	47.15 N	117.03 W
Tekstil'ščiki (Neigh.), Sov. Un.	66b	55.42 N	37.44 E
Tela, Hond. (tā'lä)	132	15.45 N	87.25 W
Tela, India	67d	28.44 N	77.20 E
Tela, Bahia de (B.), Hond. (bä-ē'ä dĕ)	132	15.53 N	87.29 W
Telapa Burok, Gunong (Mt.), Mala.	191b	2.51 N	102.04 E
Telavi, Sov. Un.	179	42.00 N	45.20 E
Tel Aviv-Yafo, Isr. (tĕl-ä-vēv'já'fá)	191a	32.03 N	34.46 E
Telegraph Creek, Can. (tĕl'ē-gráf)	96	57.59 N	131.22 W
Teleneshty, Sov. Un. (tyĕ-le-nĕsht'i)	175	47.31 N	28.22 E
Telescope Pk., Ca. (tĕl'ē skōp)	120	36.12 N	117.05 W
Telesung, Indon.	191b	1.07 N	102.53 E
Telica (Vol.), Nic. (tā-lē'kä)	132	12.38 N	86.52 W
Telimélé, Gui.	228	10.54 N	13.02 W
Tell City, In. (tĕl)	110	38.00 N	86.45 W
Teller, Ak. (tĕl'ēr)	107	65.17 N	166.28 W
Tello, Col. (tĕ'l-yô)	142a	3.05 N	75.08 W
Telluride, Co. (tĕl'ū-rīd)	121	37.55 N	107.50 W
Telok Datok, Mala.	191b	2.51 N	101.33 E
Teloloapan, Mex. (tā'lô-lô-ä'pän)	130	18.19 N	99.54 W
Tel'pos-Iz, Gora (Mtn.), Sov. Un. (tyĕl'pôs-ēz')	178	63.50 N	59.20 E
Telšiai, Sov. Un. (tĕl'sha'ē)	165	55.59 N	22.17 E
Teltow, G.D.R. (tĕl'tō)	157b	52.24 N	13.12 E
Teltower Hochfläche (Plat.), G.D.R.	65a	52.22 N	13.20 E
Teluklecak, Indon.	191b	1.53 N	101.45 E
Tema, Ghana	228	5.38 N	0.01 E
Temascalcingo, Mex. (tā'mäs-käl-sĭŋ'gō)	130	19.55 N	100.00 W
Temascaltepec, Mex. (tā'mäs-käl-tå pĕk)	130	19.00 N	100.03 W
Temax, Mex. (tĕ'mäx)	132a	21.10 N	88.51 W
Temir, Sov. Un. (tyĕ'mĭr)	179	49.10 N	57.15 E
Temir-Tau, Sov. Un.	180	50.08 N	73.13 E
Témiscaming, Can. (tē-mĭs'kȧ-mĭng)	103	46.40 N	78.50 W
Temiscouata (L.), Can. (tĕ'mĭs-kōō-ä'tä)	104	47.40 N	68.50 W
Temoaya, Mex. (tĕ-mô-a-um-yä)	131a	19.28 N	99.36 W
Tempelhof (Neigh.), F.R.G.	65a	52.28 N	13.23 E
Temperley, Arg. (tĕ'm-pĕr-lä)	144a	34.32 S	58.24 W
Tempio Pausania, It. (tĕm'pē-ō pou-sä'nē-ä)	172	40.55 N	9.05 E
Temple, Tx. (tĕm'p'l)	125	31.06 N	97.20 W
Temple City, Ca.	119a	34.07 N	118.02 W
Temple Hills, Md.	56d	38.49 N	76.57 W
Temple of Heaven (P. Int.), China	67b	39.53 N	116.25 E
Templestowe, Austl.	70b	37.45 S	145.07 E
Templeton, Can. (tĕm'p'l-tŭn)	95c	45.29 N	75.37 W
Temple University (P. Int.), Pa.	56b	39.59 N	75.09 W
Templin, G.D.R. (tĕm-plēn')	166	53.08 N	13.30 E
Tempoal (R.), Mex. (tĕm-pô-ä'l)	130	21.38 N	98.23 W
Temryuk, Sov. Un. (tyĕm-ryōōk')	175	45.17 N	37.21 E
Temuco, Chile (tā-mōō'kō)	144	38.46 S	72.38 W
Temyasovo, Sov. Un. (tĕm-yä'sô-vô)	182a	53.00 N	58.06 E
Tenabó, Mex. (tĕ-nä-bŏ')	132a	20.05 N	90.11 W
Tenafly, NJ	55	40.56 N	73.58 W
Tenāli, India	197	16.10 N	80.32 E
Tenamaxtlán, Mex. (tā'nä-mäs-tlän')	130	20.13 N	104.06 W
Tenancingo, Mex. (tå-nän-sēŋ'gō)	130	18.54 N	99.36 W
Tenango, Mex. (tå-näŋ'gō)	131a	19.09 N	98.51 W
Tenasserim, Bur. (tĕn-ăs'ēr-ĭm)	206	12.09 N	99.01 E
Tenderovskaya Kosa (C.), Sov. Un. (tĕn-dĕ-fôf'skȧ-yȧ kô-sä')	175	46.12 N	31.17 E
Ténéré (Des.), Niger	229	19.23 N	10.15 E
Tenerife I., Can. Is. (tå-nå-rē'få) (tĕn-ēr-ĭf')	224	28.41 N	17.02 W
Ténès, Alg. (tā-nĕs')	159	36.28 N	1.22 E
Tengiz (L.), Sov. Un. (tyĭn-gēz')	180	50.45 N	68.39 E
Tengxian, China (tŭŋ shyĕn)	200	35.07 N	117.08 E
Tenjin, Jap. (tĕn'jēn)	205b	34.54 N	135.04 E
Tenke, Zaire (tĕŋ'kå)	231	11.26 S	26.45 E
Tenkiller Ferry Res., Ok. (tĕn-kĭl'ēr)	123	35.42 N	94.47 W
Tenkodogo, Burkina (tĕŋ-kô-dō'gô)	228	11.47 N	0.22 W
Tenmile (R.), Wa. (tĕn mīl)	118d	48.52 N	122.32 W
Tennant Creek, Austl. (tĕn'ănt)	214	19.45 S	134.00 E
Tennessee (State), U. S. (tĕn-ĕ-sē')	109	35.50 N	88.00 W
Tennessee (L.), U. S.	109	35.35 N	88.20 W
Tennessee (R.), U. S.	126	35.10 N	88.20 W
Tennille, Ga. (tĕn'ĭl)	126	32.55 N	86.50 W
Tennōji (Neigh.), Jap.	69b	34.39 N	135.31 E
Teno (R.), Chile (tĕ'nô)	141b	34.55 S	71.00 W
Tenora, Austl. (tĕn-ôrȧ)	216	34.23 S	147.33 E
Tenosique, Mex. (tā-nō-sē'kå)	131	17.27 N	91.25 W
Tenri, Jap.	205b	34.36 N	135.50 E
Tenryū-Gawa (Strm.), Jap. (tĕn'ryōō'gä'wä)	205	35.16 N	137.54 E
Tensas R., La. (tĕn'sô)	125	31.54 N	91.30 W
Tensaw (R.), Al. (tĕn'sô)	126	30.45 N	87.52 W
Tenterfield, Austl. (tĕn'tēr-fēld)	216	29.00 S	152.06 E
Ten Thousand, Is., Fl. (tĕn thou'zănd)	127a	25.45 N	81.35 W
Teocaltiche, Mex. (tā'ô-käl-tē'chå)	130	21.27 N	102.38 W
Teocelo, Mex. (tā-ô-sā'lō)	131	19.22 N	96.57 W
Teocuitatlán de Corona, Mex. (tā'ô-kwē'tä-tlän' dā kô-rō'nä)	130	20.06 N	103.22 W
Teófilo Otoni, Braz. (tē-ō'fē-lō-tô'nē)	143	17.49 S	41.18 W
Teoloyucan, Mex. (tā'ô-lô-yōō'kän)	130	19.43 N	99.12 W
Teopisca, Mex. (tā-ô-pēs'kä)	131	16.30 N	92.33 W
Teotihuacán,, Mex. (tĕ-ô-tē-wá-ká'n)	131a	19.40 N	98.52 W
Teotitlán del Camino, Mex. (tā-ô-tē-tlän' dĕl kä-mē'nô)	131	18.07 N	97.04 W
Tepalcatepec, Mex. (tā'päl-kä-tå'pĕk)	130	19.11 N	102.51 W
Tepalcatepec (R.), Mex.	130	18.54 N	102.25 W
Tepalcates, Mex.	60a	19.23 N	99.04 W
Tepalcingo, Mex. (tā-päl-sēŋ'gô)	130	18.34 N	98.49 W
Tepatitlan de Morelos, Mex. (tā-pä-tē-tlän' dā mô-rä'los)	130	20.15 N	102.47 W
Tepeaca, Mex. (tā-på-ä'kä)	131	18.57 N	97.54 W
Tepecoacuilco de Trujano, Mex. (tā'på-kō'ä-kwēl'kō dā trōō-hä'nō)	130	19.15 N	99.29 W
Tepeji del Rio, Mex. (tā-på-ĸe' dĕl rē'ō)	130	19.55 N	99.22 W
Tepelmeme, Mex. (tā'pĕl-mā'må)	131	17.51 N	97.23 W
Tepepan, Mex.	60a	19.16 N	99.08 W
Tepetlaoxtoc, Mex. (tā'på-tlä'ôs-tōk')	131a	19.34 N	98.49 W
Tepezala, Mex. (tā-på-zä-lä')	130	22.12 N	102.12 W
Tepic, Mex. (tā-pēk')	130	21.32 N	104.53 W
Teplaya Gora, Sov. Un. (tyôp'lȧ-yȧ gô-rȧ)	182a	58.32 N	59.08 W
Teplice Sanov, Czech. (tĕp'li-tsĕ shä'nôf)	166	50.39 N	13.50 E
Teposcolula (San Pedro y San Pablo), Mex. (tā-pôs-kô-lōō'lä) (sän pā'drō ē sän pä'blō)	131	17.33 N	97.29 W
Tequendama, Salto de (Falls), Col. (sä'l-tô dĕ tĕ-kĕn-dä'mä)	142a	4.34 N	74.18 W
Tequila, Mex. (tā-kē'lä)	130	20.53 N	103.48 W
Tequisistlán (R.), Mex. (tĕ-kē-sēs-tlá'n)	131	16.20 N	95.40 W
Tequisquiapan, Mex. (tå-kēs-kē-ä'pän)	130	20.33 N	99.57 W
Ter (R.), Sp. (tĕr)	171	42.04 N	2.52 E
Téra, Niger	228	14.01 N	0.45 E
Tera (R.), Sp. (tā'rä)	170	42.05 N	6.24 W
Teramo, It. (tā'rä-mô)	172	42.40 N	13.41 E
Terborg, Neth. (tĕr-bôrg)	169c	51.55 N	6.23 E
Tercan, Tur. (tĕr'jän)	179	39.40 N	40.12 E
Terceira I., Acores (tĕr-sā'rä)	224a	38.49 N	26.36 W
Terebovlya, Sov. Un. (tĕ-rĕ'bôv-lyȧ)	167	49.18 N	25.43 E
Terek (R.), Sov. Un.	179	43.30 N	45.10 E
Terenkul', Sov. Un. (tĕ-rĕn'kōōl)	182a	55.38 N	62.18 E
Teresina, Braz. (tĕr-å-sē'nȧ)	143	5.04 S	42.42 W
Teresópolis, Braz. (tĕr-å-sō'pō-lēzh)	144b	22.25 S	42.59 W
Teriberka, Sov. Un. (tyĕr-ē-byôr'kȧ)	178	69.00 N	35.15 E
Terme, Tur. (tĕr'mĕ)	179	41.05 N	42.00 E
Termez, Sov. Un. (tyĕr'mĕz)	193	37.19 N	67.20 E
Terminal I., Ca.	59	33.45 N	118.15 W
Termini, It. (tĕr'mē-nē)	172	37.58 N	13.39 E
Términos, Laguna de (L.), Mex. (lä-gōō'nä dĕ ĕ'r-mē-nôs)	131	18.37 N	91.32 W
Termoli, It. (tĕr'mô-lē)	172	42.00 N	15.01 E
Tern (R.), Eng. (tûrn)	156	52.49 N	2.31 W
Ternate, Indon. (tĕr-nä'tä)	207	0.52 N	127.25 E
Terni, It. (tĕr'nē)	172	42.38 N	12.41 E
Ternopol', Sov. Un. (tĕr-nō-pŏl')	167	49.32 N	25.36 E
Terpeniya, Mys (C.), Sov. Un.	181	48.44 N	144.42 E
Terpeniya, Zaliv (B.), Sov. Un. (zä'lĭf tĕr-pä'nĭ-yȧ)	204	49.10 N	143.05 E
Terrace, Can. (tĕr'ĭs)	98	54.31 N	128.35 W
Terracina, It. (tĕr-rä-chē'nä)	172	41.18 N	13.14 E
Terra Nova Natl. Park, Can.	105	48.37 N	54.15 W
Terrebonne, Can. (tĕr-bŏn')	95a	45.42 N	73.38 W
Terrebonne B., La.	125	28.55 N	90.30 W
Terre Haute, In. (tĕr-ē hōt')	110	39.25 N	87.25 W
Terrell, Tx. (tĕr'ĕl)	125	32.44 N	96.15 W
Terrell, Wa.	118d	48.53 N	122.44 W
Terrell Hills, Tx. (tĕr'ĕl hĭlz)	119d	29.28 N	98.27 W
Terschelligng (I.), Neth. (tĕr-sĸĕl'ĭng)	163	53.25 N	5.12 E
Teruel, Sp. (tå-rōō-ĕl')	170	40.20 N	1.05 W
Tešanj, Yugo. (tĕ'shän')	173	44.36 N	17.59 E
Teschendorf, G.D.R. (tĕ'shĕn-dŏrf)	157b	52.51 N	13.10 E
Tesecheacan, Mex. (tĕ-sĕ-chē-ä-kä'n)	131	18.10 N	95.41 W
Teshekpuk (L.), Ak. (tē-shĕk'pŭk)	107	70.18 N	152.36 W
Teshio Dake (Mt.), Jap. (tĕsh'ē-ō-dä'kä)	204	44.00 N	142.50 E
Teshio Gawa (R.), Jap. (tĕsh'ē-ô gä'wä)	204	44.53 N	144.55 E
Tesiin Gol (R.), Mong.	198	50.14 N	94.30 E
Teslin, Can. (tĕs-lĭn)	107	60.10 N	132.30 W
Teslin (L.), Can.	96	60.12 N	132.08 W
Teslin (R.), Can.	96	61.18 N	134.14 W
Tessalon, Can.	102	46.20 N	83.35 W
Tessaoua, Niger (tĕs-sä'ōō-ä)	224	13.53 N	7.53 E
Tessenderlo, Bel.	157a	51.04 N	5.08 E
Test (R.), Eng. (tĕst)	162	51.10 N	2.20 W
Testa del Gargano (Pt.), It. (tās'tä dĕl gär-gä'nō)	172	41.48 N	16.13 E
Tetachuck L., Can.	98	53.20 N	125.50 W
Tete, Moz. (tā'tĕ)	231	16.13 S	33.35 E
Tête Jaune Cache, Can. (tĕt'zhōn-kăsh)	99	52.57 N	119.26 W
Tetepiskaw, Lac (L.), Can.	102	51.02 N	69.23 W
Teterboro, NJ	55	40.52 N	74.03 W
Teterev (R.), Sov. Un. (tyĕ'tyĕ-rĕf)	175	50.35 N	29.18 E
Teterow, G.D.R. (tā'tĕ-rō)	166	53.46 N	12.33 E
Teteven, Bul. (tĕt'ĕ-ven')	174	42.57 N	24.15 E
Teton R., Mt. (tē'tŏn)	117	47.54 N	111.37 W
Tetouan, Mor.	224	35.42 N	5.34 W
Tetovo, Yugo. (tā'tô-vô)	173	42.01 N	21.00 E
Tetyukhe-Pristan, Sov. Un. (tĕt-yōō'ĸĕ prĭ-stän')	204	44.21 N	135.44 E
Tetyushi, Sov. Un. (tyt-yōō'shĭ)	178	54.58 N	48.40 E
Teupitz, G.D.R. (toi'pĕtz)	157b	42.08 N	13.37 E
Tevere (Tiber) (R.), It.	66c	41.49 N	12.25 E
Tevere (Tiber) (R.), It. (tå'vå-rä) (tī'bēr)	172	42.30 N	12.14 E
Teverya, Isr.	191a	32.48 N	35.32 E
Tewksbury, Ma. (tūks'bĕr-ĭ)	105a	42.37 N	71.14 W
Texada I., Can.	98	49.40 N	124.24 W
Texarkana, Ar. (tĕk-sär-kän'ȧ)	123	33.26 N	94.02 W
Texarkana, Tx.	123	33.26 N	94.04 W
Texas (State), U. S.	108	31.00 N	101.00 W
Texas City, Tx.	125a	29.23 N	94.54 W
Texcaltitlán, Mex. (tās-käl'tē-tlän')	130	18.54 N	99.51 W
Texcoco, Mex. (tās-kō'kō)	131a	19.31 N	98.53 W
Texel (I.), Neth. (tĕk'sĕl)	163	53.10 N	4.45 E
Texistepec, Mex. (tĕk-sēs-tā-pĕk')	131	17.51 N	94.46 W
Texiutlán, Mex. (tå-zē-ōō-tlän')	131	19.48 N	97.21 W
Texmelucan, Mex. (tās-må-lōō'kän)	131a	19.17 N	98.26 W
Texoma, L., Ok. (tĕk'ō-mä)	123	34.03 N	96.28 W
Texontepec, Mex. (tå-zōn-tå-pĕk')	130	19.52 N	98.48 W
Texontepec de Aldama, Mex. (dā äl-dä'mä)	130	20.19 N	99.19 W
Teyateyaneng, Leso.	227c	29.11 S	27.43 E
Teykovo, Sov. Un. (tĕy-kô-vô)	174	56.52 N	40.34 E
Tezpur, India	196	26.42 N	92.52 E
Tha-anne (R.), Can.	96	60.50 N	96.56 W
Thabana Ntlenyana (Mtn.), Leso.	227c	29.28 S	29.17 E
Thabazimbi, S. Afr.	223d	24.36 S	27.22 E
Thailand, Asia	190	16.30 N	101.00 E
Thailand, G. of, Asia	206	11.37 N	100.46 E
Thākurpukur, India	67a	22.28 N	88.19 E
Thale Luang (L.), Thai.	206	7.51 N	99.39 E
Thame, Eng. (tām)	156b	51.43 N	0.59 W
Thames (R.), Can. (tĕmz)	110	42.40 N	81.45 W
Thames (R.), Eng.	163	51.26 N	0.54 E
Thames Ditton, Eng.	62	51.23 N	0.21 W
Thāmit, Wadi (R.), Libya	161	30.39 N	16.23 E
Thāna, India (thä'nŭ)	197b	19.13 N	72.58 E
Thāna Cr., India	197b	19.03 N	72.58 E
Thanh-Hoa, Viet. (tän'hō'ä)	203	19.46 N	105.42 E
Thanjāvūr, India	197	10.51 N	79.11 E
Thann, Fr. (tän)	169	47.49 N	7.05 E
Thaon-les-Vosges, Fr. (tä-ŏN-lā-vōzh')	169	48.16 N	6.24 E
Thargomindah, Austl. (thár'gō-mĭn'dȧ)	216	27.58 S	143.57 E
Thásos (I.), Grc. (thă'sōs)	173	40.41 N	24.53 E
Thatch Cay (I.), Vir. Is. (U. S. A.) (thăch)	129c	18.22 N	64.53 W
Thatto Heath, Eng.	64a	53.26 N	2.45 W
Thaya R., Aus.-Czech. (tä'yȧ)	166	48.48 N	15.40 E
Thayer, Mo. (thâ'ēr)	123	36.30 N	91.34 W
The Basin, Austl.	70b	37.51 S	145.19 E
Thebes (Ruins), Egypt (thēbz)	223b	25.47 N	32.39 E
Thebes, see Thivai			
The Brothers (Mtn.), Wa. (brŭth'ērs)	118a	47.39 N	123.08 W

PLACE (Pronounciation)	PAGE	Lat. °'	Long. °'
The Capital (P. Int.), DC	56d	38.53 N	77.00 W
The Coteau (Hills), Can.	100	51.10 N	107.30 W
The Dalles, Or. (dălz)	116	45.36 N	121.10 W
The Father (Mtn.), Pap. N. Gui.	207	5.05 S	151.30 E
The Hague, see 's Gravenhage			
Thelum, Pak.	196	32.59 N	73.43 E
The Narrows (Str.), NY	55	40.37 N	74.03 W
The Oaks, Austl.	211b	34.04 S	150.36 E
Theodore, Austl. (thēŏ'dôr)	216	24.51 S	150.09 E
Theodore Roosevelt Dam, Az. (thē-ô-dôr rōō-sȧ-vĕlt)	121	33.46 N	111.25 W
Theodore Roosevelt Natl. Park, ND	114	47.20 N	103.42 W
Theológos, Grc.	173	40.37 N	24.41 E
The Oval (P. Int.), Eng.	62	51.29 N	0.07 W
The Pas, Can. (pä)	101	53.50 N	101.15 W
The Rajah (Mtn.), Can.	99	53.15 N	118.31 W
Thermopolis, Wy. (thēr-mŏp'ô-lĭs)	117	43.38 N	108.11 W
The Round Mtn., Austl.	216	30.17 S	152.19 E
The Sound (Str.), Austl.	70a	33.49 S	151.17 E
Thessalía (Reg.), Grc.	173	39.50 N	22.09 E
Thessalon, Can.	97	46.11 N	83.37 W
Thessaloníki, Grc. (thĕs-sȧ-lô-nē'kē)	173	40.38 N	22.59 E
Thetford Mines, Can. (thĕt'fērd mīns)	104	46.05 N	71.20 W
The Twins (Mtn.), Leso.-S. Afr. (twĭnz)	227c	30.09 S	28.29 E
Theunissen, S. Afr.	223d	28.25 S	26.44 E
Theydon Bois, Eng.	62	51.40 N	0.06 E
Thiais, Fr.	64c	48.46 N	2.23 E
Thibaudeau, Can. (tĭ'bō-dō')	101	57.05 N	94.08 W
Thibodaux, La. (tē-bô-dō')	125	29.48 N	90.48 W
Thief (L.), Mn. (thēf)	114	48.32 N	95.46 W
Thief (R.), Mn.	114	48.18 N	96.07 E
Thief Rivers Falls, Mn. (thēf rĭv'ēr fôlz)	114	48.07 N	96.11 W
Thier, F.R.G.	63	51.05 N	7.22 E
Thiers, Fr. (tyâr)	168	45.51 N	3.32 E
Thiès, Senegal (tē-ĕs')	228	14.48 N	16.56 W
Thika, Ken.	231	1.03 S	37.05 E
Thimbu, Bhu.	196	27.33 N	89.42 E
Thingvallavatn (L.), Ice.	158	64.12 N	20.22 W
Thionville, Fr. (tyôN-vēl')	169	49.23 N	6.31 E
Third Cataract, Sud.	225	19.53 N	30.11 E
Thisted, Den. (tēs'tĕdh)	164	56.57 N	8.38 E
Thistilfjördur (Fd.), Ice.	158	66.29 N	14.59 W
Thistle (I.), Austl. (thĭs''l)	216	34.55 S	136.11 E
Thistletown (Neigh.), Can.	54c	43.44 N	79.33 W
Thívai (Thebes), Grc.	173	38.20 N	23.18 E
Thjórsá (R.), Ice. (tyûr'sȧ)	158	64.23 N	19.18 W
Thohoyandou, Venda	222	23.00 S	30.29 E
Tholen, Neth.	157a	51.32 N	4.11 E
Thomas, Ok. (tŏm'ăs)	122	35.44 N	98.43 W
Thomas, WV	111	39.15 N	79.30 W
Thomaston, Ga. (tŏm'ăs-tŭn)	126	32.51 N	84.17 W
Thomaston, NY	55	40.47 N	73.43 W
Thomastown, Austl.	70b	37.41 S	145.01 E
Thomasville, Al. (tŏm'ăs-vĭl)	126	31.55 N	87.43 W
Thomasville, NC	127	35.52 N	80.05 W
Thomlinson, Mt., Can.	98	55.33 N	127.29 W
Thompson, Can.	101	55.48 N	97.59 W
Thompson (R.), Can.	99	50.15 N	121.20 W
Thompson (R.), Mo.	123	40.32 N	93.49 W
Thompson Falls, Mt.	116	47.35 N	115.20 W
Thomson, Ga. (tŏm'sŭn)	127	33.28 N	82.29 W
Thomson (R.) Austl. (tŏm-sŏn)	215	29.30 S	143.07 E
Thomson's Falls, Ken.	231	0.02 N	36.22 E
Thon Buri (Neigh.), Thai.	68f	13.43 N	100.29 E
Thong, Eng.	62	51.24 N	0.24 E
Thong Hoe, Singapore	67c	1.25 N	103.42 E
Thong-tay-hoi, Viet.	68m	10.50 N	106.39 E
Thonon-les-Bains, Fr. (tô-nôN'lā-băN')	169	46.22 N	6.27 E
Thorigny-sur-Marne, Fr.	64c	48.53 N	2.42 E
Thórisvatn (L.), Ice.	158	64.02 N	19.09 W
Thornbury, Austl.	70b	37.45 S	145.00 E
Thorne, Eng. (thôrn)	156	53.37 N	0.58 W
Thornhill, S. Afr.	71b	26.07 S	28.09 E
Thornleigh, Austl.	70a	33.44 S	151.05 E
Thornton, Eng.	64a	53.30 N	3.00 W
Thornton Hough, Eng.	64a	53.19 N	3.03 W
Thornton-le-Moors, Eng.	64a	53.16 N	2.50 W
Thorntown, In. (thôrn'tŭn)	110	40.05 N	86.35 W
Thornwood Common, Eng.	62	51.43 N	0.08 E
Thorold, Can. (thō'rōld)	95d	43.13 N	79.12 W
Thouars, Fr. (tōō-är')	168	47.00 N,	0.17 W
Thousand Is., NY-Can. (thou'zănd)	111	44.15 N	76.10 W
Thrace (Reg.), Grc.-Tur. (thrās)	173	41.20 N	26.07 E
Thrapston, Eng. (thrăp'stŭn)	156	52.23 N	0.32 W
Three Forks, Mt. (thrē fôrks)	117	45.56 N	111.35 W
Three Oaks, Mi. (thrē ōks)	110	41.50 N	86.40 W
Three Points, C., Ghana	228	4.45 N	2.06 W
Three Rivers, Mi.	110	42.00 N	83.40 W
Thule, Grnld.	75	76.34 N	68.47 W
Thun, Switz. (tōōn)	166	46.46 N	7.34 E
Thunder B., Can. (thŭn'dēr)	115	48.29 N	88.52 W
Thunder Bay, Can.	102	48.28 N	89.12 W
Thunder Hills, Can.	100	54.30 N	106.00 W
Thunersee (L.) Switz.	166	46.40 N	7.30 E
Thurber, Tx. (thûr'bēr)	124	32.30 N	98.23 W
Thüringen (Thuringia) (former state or region), G.D.R. (tü'rĭng-ĕn)	166	51.07 N	10.45 E
Thurles, Ire. (thûrlz)	162	52.44 N	7.45 W
Thurrock, Eng. (thŭ'rŏk)	156b	51.28 N	0.19 E
Thursday (I.), Austl. (thûrz-dā)	215	10.17 S	142.23 E
Thurso, Can. (thŭn'sô)	95c	45.36 N	75.15 W
Thurso, Scot.	162	58.35 N	3.40 W
Thurston Pen. Ant. (thûrs'tŭn)	232	71.20 S	98.00 W
Thysville, Zaire (tēs-vēl')	226	5.08 S	14.58 E
Tiandong, China (tĭĕn-dôŋ)	203	23.32 N	107.10 E
Tianjin, China	200	39.08 N	117.14 E
Tianjin Shi (Mun.), China (tĭĕn-jyĭn shr)	200	39.30 N	117.13 E
Tianmen, China (tĭĕn-mŭn)	203	30.40 N	113.10 E
Tianshui, China (tĭĕn-shwā)	202	34.25 N	105.40 E
Tibagi, Braz. (tē'bȧ-zhē)	144	24.40 S	50.35 W
Tibasti, Sarir (Des.), Chad	225	24.00 N	16.30 E
Tibati, Cam.	229	6.27 N	12.38 E
Tiber (R.), see Tevere			
Tibesti Massif (Mts.), Chad	225	20.40 N	17.48 E
Tibet (Aut. Reg.), see Xizang			
Tibet, Plat. of, China (tĭ-bĕt')	198	32.22 N	83.30 E
Tibleşului, Munţii (Mts.), Rom	167	47.41 N	24.05 E
Tibnīn, Leb.	191a	33.12 N	35.23 E
Tiburon, Ca. (tē-bōō-rōn')	118b	37.53 N	122.27 W
Tiburon, Ca.	58b	36.04 N	119.19 W
Tiburon, Hai.	135	18.35 N	74.25 W
Tiburón (I.), Mex.	128	28.45 N	113.10 W
Tiburon, Cabo (C.), Pan. (kȧ'bô)	133	8.42 N	77.19 W
Tiburon I., Ca.	118b	37.52 N	122.26 W
Ticaco Pass, Phil. (tē-kä-kō)	207a	12.38 N	123.50 E
Ticao I., Phil. (tē-kä'ō)	207a	12.40 N	123.30 E
Tickhill, Eng. (tĭk'ĭl)	156	53.26 N	1.06 W
Ticonderoga, NY (tī-kŏn-dēr-ō'gȧ)	111	43.50 N	73.30 W
Ticul, Mex. (tē-kōō'l)	132a	20.22 N	89.32 W
Tidaholm, Swe. (tē'dȧ-hōlm)	164	58.11 N	13.53 E
Tideswell, Eng. (tīdz'wĕl)	156	53.17 N	1.47 W
Tidikelt (Reg.), Alg. (tē-dē-kĕlt')	224	25.53 N	2.11 E
Tidjikdja, Mauritania (tē-jĭk'jä)	228	18.33 N	11.25 W
Tiefenbroich, F.R.G.	63	51.18 N	6.49 E
Tieling, China (tĭĕ-lĭŋ)	202	42.18 N	123.50 E
Tielmes, Sp. (tyâl-màs')	171a	40.15 N	3.20 W
Tienen, Bel. (Brussels In.)	157	50.49 N	4.58 E
Tienshan Hu (L.), China (dĭän'shän'hōō)	200	31.08 N	120.30 E
Tien Shan (Mts.), Sov. Un.-China	198	42.00 N	78.46 E
Tiergarten (Neigh.), F.R.G.	65a	52.31 N	13.21 E
Tiergarten (P. Int.), F.R.G.	65a	52.30 N	13.21 E
Tierp, Swe. (tyĕrp)	164	60.21 N	17.28 E
Tierpoort, S. Afr.	227b	25.53 N	28.26 E
Tierra Blanca, Mex. (tyĕ'r-rä-blä'n-kä)	131	18.28 N	96.19 W
Tierra del Fuego (Reg.), Chile-Arg. (tyĕr'rä dĕl fwā'gō)	144	53.50 S	68.45 W
Tiétar (R.), Sp. (tē-ā'tär)	170	39.56 N	5.44 W
Tietê, Braz. (tyā-tā')	141a	23.08 S	47.42 W
Tieté, (R.), Braz.	143	20.46 S	50.46 W
Tietê (R.), Braz.	61d	23.29 S	46.51 W
Tiffin, Oh. (tĭf'ĭn)	110	41.10 N	83.15 W
Tifton, Ga. (tĭf'tŭn)	126	31.25 N	83.34 W
Tigard, Or. (tī'gärd)	118c	45.25 N	122.46 W
Tignish, Can. (tĭg'nĭsh)	104	46.57 N	64.02 W
Tigoda (R.), Sov. Un. (tē'gô-dȧ)	182c	59.29 N	31.15 E
Tigre, Arg. (tē'grĕ)	144	34.09 S	58.35 W
Tigre (R.), Peru	142	2.20 S	75.41 W
Tigres, Península dos (Pen.), Ang. (pĕ-nē'ŋ-sōō-lä-dôs-tē'grĕs)	226	16.30 S	11.45 E
Tigris (R.), Asia	192	34.45 N	44.10 E
Tihert, Alg.	224	35.28 N	1.15 E
Tihuatlán, Mex. (tē-wä-tlän')	131	20.43 N	97.34 W
Tijuana, Mex. (tē-hwä'nä)	120a	32.32 N	117.02 W
Tijuca, Pico da (Mtn.), Braz. (pē'kō-dä-tē-zhōō'kȧ)	144b	22.56 S	43.17 W
Tikal (Ruins), Guat. (tē-käl')	132a	17.16 N	89.49 W
Tikhoretsk, Sov. Un. (tē-Kôr-yĕtsk')	179	45.55 N	40.05 E
Tikhvin, Sov. Un. (tēK-vēn')	174	59.36 N	33.38 E
Tikrīt, Iraq	192	34.36 N	43.31 E
Tiksi, Sov. Un. (tĕk-sē')	181	71.42 N	128.32 E
Tilburg, Neth. (tĭl'bûrg)	157a	51.33 N	5.05 E
Tilbury, Eng.	62	51.28 N	0.23 E
Tilemsi, Vallée du (Val.), Mali	228	17.50 N	0.25 E
Tilichiki, Sov. Un. (tyĭ-le-chĭ-kē)	181	60.49 N	166.14 E
Tiligul (R.), Sov. Un. (tē'lĭ-gûl)	175	47.25 N	30.27 E
Tilimsen, Alg.	224	34.53 N	1.21 W
Tillabéry, Niger (tē-yȧ-bā-rē')	224	14.14 N	1.30 E
Tillamook, Or. (tĭl'ȧ-mōōk)	116	45.27 N	123.50 W
Tillamook B., Or.	116	45.32 N	124.26 W
Tillberga, Swe. (tēl-bĕr'ghȧ)	164	59.40 N	16.34 E
Tillsonburg, Can. (tĭl'sŭn-bûrg)	103	42.50 N	80.50 W
Tilsit, see Sovetsk			
Tim, Sov. Un. (tēm)	175	51.39 N	37.07 E
Timaru, N.Z. (tĭm'ȧ-rōō)	217	44.26 S	171.17 E
Timashevskaya, Sov. Un. (tēmä-shĕfs-kȧ'yȧ)	175	45.47 N	38.57 E
Timbalier B., La. (tĭm'bȧ-lēr)	125	28.55 N	90.14 W
Timber, Or. (tĭm'bēr)	118c	45.43 N	123.17 W
Timberview, Md.	56c	39.13 N	76.45 W
Timbo, Gui. (tĭm'bō)	224	10.41 N	11.51 W
Timbuktu, see Tombouctou			
Times Square (P. Int.), NY	55	40.45 N	74.00 W
Timétrine Monts (Mts.), Mali.	228	19.50 N	0.30 W
Timimoun, Alg. (tē-mē-mōōn')	224	29.14 N	0.22 E
Timiris, Cap (C.), Mauritania	228	19.23 N	16.32 W
Timis (R.), Rom.	173	45.28 N	21.06 E
Timiskaming Station, Can. (tē-mĭs'kȧ-mĭng)	97	46.41 N	79.01 W
Timişoara, Rom.	173	45.44 N	21.21 E
Timmins, Can. (tĭm'ĭnz)	97	48.25 N	81.22 W
Timmonsville, SC (tĭm'ŭnz-vĭl)	127	34.09 N	79.55 W
Timor (I.), Indon. (tē-mōr')	207	10.08 S	125.00 E
Timor Sea, Asia	208	12.40 S	125.00 E
Timpanogos Cave Natl. Mon., Ut. (tĭ-măn'ō-gŏz)	121	40.25 N	111.45 W
Timperley, Eng.	64b	53.24 N	2.19 W
Timpson, Tx. (tĭmp'sŭn)	125	31.55 N	94.24 W
Timpton (R.), Sov. Un. (tēmp'tôn)	181	57.15 N	126.35 E
Timsâh (L.), Egypt (tĭm'sä)	223c	30.34 N	32.22 E
Tina (R.), S. Afr. (tē'nȧ)	227c	30.50 S	28.44 E
Tinaguillo, Ven. (tē-nä-gē'l-yō)	143b	9.55 N	68.18 W
Tina, Monte (Mtn.), Dom. Rep. (mô'n-tĕ-tē'nȧ)	135	18.50 N	70.40 W
Tindouf, Alg. (tēn-dōōf')	224	27.43 N	7.44 W
Tinggi, Palau (I.), Mala.	191b	2.16 N	104.16 E
Tinghert, Plat. du, Alg.	224	27.30 N	7.30 E
Tingi Mts., S. L.	228	9.00 N	10.50 W
Ting Kau, Hong Kong	68c	22.23 N	114.04 E
Tinglin, China	201b	30.53 N	121.18 E
Tingo María, Peru (tē'ngô-mä-rē'ä)	142	9.15 S	76.04 W
Tingréla, Ivory Coast	228	10.29 N	6.24 W
Tingsryd, Swe. (tĭngs'rüd)	164	56.32 N	14.58 E
Tingtzu Wan (B.), China (dĭng'tze wän)	200	36.33 N	121.06 E
Tinguindio Paracho, Mex. (tēn'kē'n-dyō-pärä-chô)	130	19.38 N	102.02 W
Tinguiririca (R.), Chile (tē'n-gē-rē-rē'kä)	141b	36.48 S	70.45 W
Tinley Park, Il. (tĭn'lē)	113a	41.34 N	87.47 W
Tinnoset, Nor. (tĕn'nôs'sĕt)	164	59.44 N	9.00 E
Tinnsjø, Nor. (tĭnnsyû)	164	59.55 N	8.49 E
Tinogasta, Arg. (tē-nô-gäs'tä)	144	28.07 S	67.30 W
Tinsukia, India (tin-sōō'kĭ-ȧ)	193	27.18 N	95.29 W
Tintic, Ut. (tĭn'tĭk)	121	39.55 N	112.15 W
Tioga (Neigh.), Pa.	56b	40.00 N	75.10 W
Tīh, Jabal at (Mts.), Egypt	191a	29.23 N	34.05 E
Tioman (I.), Mala.	191b	2.25 N	104.30 E
Tīnah, Khalīj at (G.), Egypt	191a	31.06 N	32.42 E
Tio, Pic de (Pk.), Gui.	228	8.55 N	8.55 W
Tipitapa, Nic. (tē-pē-tä'pä)	132	12.14 N	86.05 W
Tipitapa R., Nic.	132	12.13 N	85.57 W
Tippah Cr., (R.), Ms. (tĭp'pȧ)	126	34.43 N	88.15 W
Tippecanoe (R.), In. (tĭp-ē-kȧ-nōō')	110	40.55 N	86.45 W
Tipperary, Ire. (tĭ-pē-râ'rē)	162	52.28 N	8.13 W
Tippo Bay, Ms. (tĭp'ō bīōō')	123	33.35 N	90.06 W
Tipton, In.	110	40.15 N	86.00 W
Tipton, Ia.	115	41.46 N	91.10 W
Tirane, Alb. (tē-rä'nä)	173	41.48 N	19.50 E
Tirano, It. (tē-rä'nō)	172	46.12 N	10.09 E
Tiraspol', Sov. Un. (tē-räs'pôl')	175	46.52 N	29.38 E
Tire, Tur. (tē'rĕ)	179	38.05 N	27.48 E
Tiree (I.), Scot. (tī-rē')	162	56.34 N	6.30 W
Tires, Port.	65d	38.43 N	9.21 W
Tirich Mir (Mt.), Pak.	196	36.50 N	71.48 E
Tirlyanskiy, Sov. Un. (tĭr-lyän'skĭ)	182a	54.13 N	58.37 E
Tirol (State), Aus. (tē-rōl')	166	47.13 N	11.10 E
Tîrgovişte, Rom.	173	44.54 N	25.29 E
Tîrgu-Jiu, Rom.	173	45.02 N	23.17 E
Tîrgu-Mureş, Rom.	167	46.33 N	24.35 E
Tîrgu Neamt, Rom.	167	47.14 N	26.23 E
Tîrgu-Ocna, Rom.	167	46.18 N	26.38 E
Tîrgu-Secuiesc, Rom.	167	46.04 N	26.06 E
Tirso (R.), It. (tēr'sô)	172	40.15 N	9.03 E
Tiruchchirāppalli, India (tĭr'ōō-chĭ-rä'pȧ-lĭ)	197	10.49 N	78.48 E
Tirunelveli, India	197	8.53 N	77.43 E
Tiruppur, India	197	11.11 N	77.08 E
Tisa (R.), Hung.-Yugo. (tē'sȧ)	173	45.50 N	20.13 E
Tisdale, Can. (tĭz'dāl)	100	52.51 N	104.04 W
Tista (R.), India	196	26.03 N	88.52 E
Titāgarh, India	196a	22.44 N	88.23 E
Titicaca, Lago (L.), Bol.-Peru (lä'gō-tē-tē-kä'kä)	142	16.12 S	70.33 W
Titiribí, Col. (tē-tē-rē-bē')	142a	6.05 N	75.47 W
Titograd, Yugo.	173	42.25 N	20.42 E
Tito, Lagh (R.), Ken.	231	2.25 N	39.05 E
Titovo Užice, Yugo. (tē'tô-vô ōō'zhē-tsĕ)	173	43.51 N	19.53 E
Titov Veles, Yugo. (tē'tôv vĕ'lĕs)	173	41.42 N	21.50 E
Titterstone Clee Hill, Eng. (klē)	156	52.24 N	2.37 W
Titule, Zaire	230	3.17 N	25.32 E
Titusville, Fl. (tī'tŭs-vĭl)	127a	28.37 N	80.44 W
Titusville, Pa.	111	40.40 N	79.40 W
Titz, F.R.G. (tētz)	169c	51.00 N	6.26 E
Tiu Keng Wan, China	68c	22.18 N	114.15 E
Tiverton, RI (tĭv'ēr-tun)	112b	41.38 N	71.11 W
Tivoli, It. (tē'vô-lē)	171d	41.38 N	12.48 E
Tínos (I.), Grc.	173	37.45 N	25.12 E
Tîrnăveni, Rom.	167	46.19 N	24.18 E
Tírnavos, Grc.	173	39.50 N	22.14 E
Tixkokob, Mex. (tēx-kō-kō'b)	132a	21.01 N	89.23 W
Tixtla de Guerrero, Mex. (tē'x-tlä-dĕ-gĕr-rē'rô)	130	17.36 N	99.24 W
Tizapán, Mex.	60a	19.20 N	99.13 W
Tizard Bk. and Rf., China (tĭz'ȧrd)	206	10.51 N	113.20 E
Tizimín, Mex. (tē-zē-mē'n)	132a	21.08 N	88.10 W
Tizi-Ouzou, Alg. (tē'zē-ōō-zōō')	224	36.44 N	4.04 E
Tiznados (R.), Ven. (tēz-nä'dôs)	143b	9.53 N	67.49 W
Tiznit, Mor. (tēz-nēt)	224	29.52 N	9.39 W
Tlacolula de Matamoros, Mex. (tlä-kō-lōō'lä dā mätä-mō'rôs)	131	16.56 N	96.29 W
Tlacotálpan, Mex. (tlä-kō-täl'pän)	131	18.39 N	95.40 W
Tlacotepec, Mex. (tlä-kō-tâ-pĕ'k)	130	17.46 N	99.57 W
Tlacotepec, Mex.	130	19.11 N	99.41 W
Tlacotepec, Mex.	131	18.41 N	97.40 W
Tláhuac, Mex. (tlä-wäk')	131a	19.16 N	99.00 W
Tlajomulco de Zúñiga, Mex. (tlä-hô-mōō'l-ko-dĕ-zōō'n-yē-gä)	130	20.30 N	103.27 W
Tlalchapa, Mex. (tläl-chä'pä)	130	18.26 N	100.29 W
Tlalixcoyan, Mex. (tlä-lēs'kô-yän')	131	18.53 N	96.04 W
Tlalmanalco, Mex. (tläl-mä-nä'l-kô)	131a	19.12 N	98.48 W
Tlalnepantia, Mex. (tläl-nĕ-pȧ'n-tyä)	131a	19.32 N	99.13 W
Tlalnepantla, Mex. (tläl-nȧ-pän'tlä)	131a	18.59 N	99.01 W
Tlalpan, Mex. (täl-pä'n)	131a	19.17 N	99.10 W
Tlalpujahua, Mex. (tläl-pōō-Kä'wä)	130	19.15 N	100.10 W
Tlaltenango, see Sánchez Román			
Tlaltenco, Mex.	60a	19.17 N	99.01 W
Tlapa, Mex. (tlä'pä)	130	17.30 N	98.09 W
Tlapacoyan, Mex. (tlä-pä-kô-yä'n)	131	19.57 N	97.11 W
Tlapaneco (R.), Mex. (tlä-pänĕ'kô)	130	17.59 N	98.44 W
Tlapehuala, Mex. (tlä-pȧ-wä'lä)	130	18.17 N	100.30 W
Tlaquepaque, Mex. (tlä-kĕ-pä'kĕ)	130	20.39 N	103.17 W
Tlatlaya, Mex. (tlä-tlä'yä)	130	18.36 N	100.14 W
Tlaxcala, Mex. (tläs-kä'lä)	130	19.16 N	98.14 W
Tlaxcala (State), Mex.	130	19.30 N	98.15 W
Tlaxco, Mex. (tläs'kō)	130	19.37 N	98.06 W
Tlaxiaco Sta. María Asunción, Mex. (tläk-sē-ä'kō sän'tä mä-rē'ä ä-sōōn-syōn')	131	17.16 N	95.41 W

PLACE (Pronounciation)	PAGE	Lat. °′	Long. °′
Tlayacapan, Mex. (tlä-yä-kä-pä'n)	131a	18.57 N	99.00 W
Tlevak Str., Ak.	98	53.03 N	132.58 W
Tlumach, Sov. Un. (t'lû-mäch')	167	48.47 N	25.00 E
Toa (R.), Cuba (tō'ä)	135	20.25 N	74.35 W
Toamasina, Mad.	227	18.14 S	49.25 E
Toana Ra. (Mts.), Nv. (tō-á-nō')	117	40.45 N	114.11 W
Toar, Cuchillas de (Mtn.), Cuba (kōō-chē'l-lyäs-dĕ-tô-ä'r)	135	18.20 N	74.50 W
Tobago (I.), N. A. (tô-bā'gō)	129	11.15 N	60.30 W
Toba Inlet, Can.	98	50.20 N	124.50 W
Tobarra, Sp. (tô-bär'rä)	170	38.37 N	1.42 W
Tobol (R.), Sov. Un. (tô-bôl')	180	56.02 N	65.30 E
Tobol'sk, Sov. Un. (tô-bôlsk')	180	58.09 N	68.28 E
Tocaima, Col. (tô-kä'y-mä)	142a	4.28 N	74.38 W
Tocantinópolis, Braz. (tô-kän-tē-nō'pō-lēs)	143	6.27 S	47.18 W
Tocantins (R.), Braz. (tō-kän-tēns')	143	3.28 S	49.22 W
Toccoa, Ga. (tŏk'ô-á)	126	34.35 N	83.20 W
Toccoa (R.), Ga.	126	34.53 N	84.24 W
Tochigi, Jap. (tō'chē-gĭ)	205	36.25 N	139.45 E
Tocoa, Hond. (tô-kô'ä)	132	15.37 N	86.01 W
Tocopilla, Chile (tō-kô-pēl'yä)	144	22.03 S	70.08 W
Tocuyo de la Costa, Ven. (tô-kōō'yō-dĕ-lä-kôs'tä)	143b	11.03 N	68.24 W
Toda, Jap.	205d	35.48 N	139.42 E
Todmorden, Eng. (tŏd'môr-dĕn)	156	53.43 N	2.05 W
Toécé, Burkina	228	11.50 N	1.16 W
Tofino, Can. (tō-fē'nō)	98	49.09 N	125.54 W
Töfsingdalens (Natl. Park), Swe.	164	62.09 N	13.05 E
Togane, Jap. (tō'gä-nä)	205	35.29 N	140.16 E
Togian, Kepulauan (Is.), Indon.	206	0.20 S	122.00 E
Togo, Afr. (tō'gō)	222	8.00 N	0.52 E
Toguzak R., Sov. Un. (tô'gōō-zák)	182a	53.40 N	61.42 E
Tohopekaliga (L.), Fl. (tō'hô-pē'kà-lī'gá)	127a	28.16 N	81.09 W
Toijala, Fin. (toi'yá-lá)	165	61.11 N	21.46 E
Toi-Misaki (C.), Jap. (toi mē'sä-kē)	205	31.20 N	131.20 E
Toiyabe Ra., Nv. (toi'yă-bē)	120	38.59 N	117.22 W
Tokachi Gawa (R.), Jap. (tô-kä'chē gä'wä)	204	43.10 N	142.30 E
Tokaj, Hung. (tô'kô-ê)	167	48.06 N	21.24 E
Tokara Guntō (Is.), Jap. (tô-kä'rä gōōn'tō')	204	29.45 N	129.15 E
Tokara Kaikyo (Str.), Jap. (tō'kä'rä kī'kyō)	204	30.20 N	129.50 E
Tokat, Tur. (tô-kät')	179	40.20 N	36.30 E
Tokelau Is., Oceania (tō-kē-lä'ōō)	208	8.00 S	176.00 W
Tokmak, Sov. Un. (tŏk'mák)	180	42.44 N	75.41 E
Tokorozawa, Jap. (tô'kô-rô-zä'wä)	205a	35.47 N	139.29 E
Toksu Palace (P. Int.), Kor.	68b	37.35 N	126.58 E
Tokuno (I.), Jap. (tô-kōō'nō)	204	27.42 N	129.25 E
Tokushima, Jap. (tō'kōō'shē-mä)	205	34.06 N	134.31 E
Tokuyama, Jap. (tō'kōō'yä-mä)	205	34.04 N	131.49 E
Tōkyō, Jap. (tō'kē-ō)	205a	35.41 N	139.44 E
Tōkyō (Pref.), Jap.	205a	35.42 N	139.40 E
Tōkyō-Wan (B.), Jap. (tō'kyō wän)	205a	35.56 N	139.56 E
Tolbukhin, Bul.	173	43.33 N	27.52 E
Tolcayuca, Mex. (tôl-kä-yōō'kä)	130	19.55 N	98.54 W
Toledo, Ia. (tô-lē'dō)	115	41.59 N	92.35 W
Toledo, Oh.	110	41.40 N	83.35 W
Toledo, Or.	116	44.37 N	123.58 W
Toledo, Sp. (tô-lĕ'dō)	170	39.53 N	4.02 W
Toledo Bend Res., La.-Tx.	109	31.30 N	93.30 W
Toledo, Montes de (Mts.), Sp. (mô'n-tĕs-dĕ-tô-lĕ'dô)	170	39.33 N	4.40 W
Toliara, Mad.	227	20.16 S	43.44 E
Tolima (Dept.), Col. (tô-lē'mä)	142a	4.07 N	75.20 W
Tolimán, Mex. (tô-lê-män')	130	20.54 N	99.54 W
Tolima, Nevado del (Pk.), Col. (nĕ-vä-dô-dĕl-tô-lē'mä)	142a	4.40 N	75.20 W
Tollesbury, Eng. (tōl'z-bĕrĭ)	156b	51.46 N	0.49 E
Tollygunge (Neigh.), India	67a	22.30 N	88.21 E
Tolmezzo, It. (tôl-mĕt'zô)	172	46.25 N	13.03 E
Tolmin, Yugo. (tôl'mēn)	172	46.12 N	13.45 E
Tolna, Hung. (tôl'nô)	167	46.25 N	18.47 E
Tolosa, Sp. (tô-lō'sä)	170	43.10 N	2.05 W
Tolo, Teluk (B.), Indon. (tō'lō)	206	2.00 S	122.06 E
Tolt (R.), Wa. (tōlt)	118a	47.13 N	121.49 W
Toluca, Il. (tô-lōō'ká)	110	41.00 N	89.10 W
Toluca, Mex. (tô-lōō'kä)	131a	19.17 N	99.40 W
Toluca, Nevado de (Mtn.), Mex. (nĕ-vä-dô-dĕ-tô-lōō'kä)	131a	19.09 N	99.42 W
Tolworth (Neigh.), Eng.	62	51.23 N	0.17 W
Tolyatti, Sov. Un.	178	53.30 N	49.10 E
Tom' (R.), Sov. Un.	180	55.33 N	85.00 E
Tomah, Wi. (tō'má)	115	43.58 N	90.31 W
Tomahawk, Wi. (tŏm'á-hôk)	115	45.27 N	89.44 W
Tomakovka, Sov. Un. (tô-mä'kôf-kà)	175	47.49 N	34.43 E
Tomar, Port. (tō-mär')	170	39.36 N	8.26 W
Tomashevka, Sov. Un. (tô-mä'shĕf-kà)	167	51.34 N	23.37 E
Tomaszow Lubelski, Pol. (tô-mä'shōōf lōō-bĕl'skĭ)	167	50.20 N	23.27 E
Tomaszów Mazowiecki, Pol. (tô-mä'shōōf mä-zô'vyĕt-skĭ)	167	51.33 N	20.00 E
Tomatlán, Mex. (tô-mä-tlä'n)	130	19.54 N	105.14 W
Tomatlán (R.), Mex.	130	19.56 N	105.14 W
Tombadonkéa, Gui.	228	11.00 N	14.23 W
Tombador, Serra do (Mts.), Braz. (sĕr'rá dōō tōm-bä-dôr')	143	11.31 S	57.33 W
Tombigbee (R.), Al. (tŏm-bĭg'bē)	126	31.45 N	88.02 W
Tombos, Braz. (tô'm-bôs)	141a	20.53 S	42.00 W
Tombouctou (Timbuktu), Mali (tôm-bōōk-tōō')	228	16.46 N	3.01 W
Tombs of the Caliphs (P Int.), Egypt	71a	30.03 N	31.17 E
Tombstone, Az. (tōōm'stōn)	121	31.40 N	110.00 W
Tomelilla, Swe. (tô'mĕ-lēl-lä)	164	55.34 N	13.55 E
Tomelloso, Sp. (tō-māl-lyō'sō)	170	39.09 N	3.02 W
Tomini, Teluk (B.), Indon. (tô-mē'nē)	206	0.10 N	121.00 E
Tommot, Sov. Un. (tôm-môt')	181	59.13 N	126.22 E
Tomsk, Sov. Un. (tŏmsk)	180	56.29 N	84.57 E
Tonalá, Mex. (tō-nä-lä')	131	16.05 N	93.45 W
Tonala, Mex.	130	20.38 N	103.14 W
Tonalá (R.), Mex.	131	18.05 N	94.08 W
Tonawanda, NY (tôn-á-wŏn'dá)	113c	43.01 N	78.53 W
Tonawanda Cr., NY	113c	43.05 N	78.43 W
Tonawanda, Town of, NY	57a	42.59 N	78.52 W
Tonbei, China (tôŋ-bā)	202	48.00 N	126.48 E
Tonbridge, Eng. (tŭn-brij)	156b	51.11 N	0.17 E
Tonda, Jap. (tôn'dä)	205b	34.51 N	135.38 E
Tondabayashi, Jap. (tôn-dä-bä'yä-shē)	205b	34.29 N	135.36 E
Tondano, Indon. (tôn-dä'nō)	207	1.15 N	124.50 E
Tønder, Den. (tûn'nĕr)	164	54.47 N	8.49 E
Tondlá, Mex.	131	16.04 N	93.57 W
Tone (R.), Jap. (tō'nē)	205a	35.55 N	139.57 E
Tone-Gawa (Strm.), Jap. (tô'nē gä'wa)	205	36.12 N	139.19 E
Tonekābon, Iran	179	36.40 N	51.00 E
Tonga, Oceania (tŏŋ'gá)	208	18.50 S	175.20 W
Tong'an, China (tôŋ-än)	203	24.48 N	118.02 E
Tongguan, China (tôŋ-gūän)	202	34.48 N	110.25 E
Tonghe, China (tôŋ-hŭ)	202	45.58 N	128.40 E
Tonghua, China (tôŋ-hwä)	202	41.43 N	125.50 E
Tongjiang, China (tôŋ-jyäŋ)	199	47.38 N	132.54 E
Tongliao, China (tôŋ-lĭou)	202	43.30 N	122.15 E
Tongo, Cam.	229	5.11 N	14.00 E
Tongoy, Chile (tōn-goi')	144	30.16 S	71.29 W
Tongren, China (tôŋ-rŭn)	203	27.45 N	109.12 E
Tongshan, China (tôŋ-shän)	200	34.27 N	116.27 E
Tongtian (R.), China (tôŋ-tĭĕn)	198	34.11 N	96.08 E
Tongue of Arabat (Spit), see Arabatskaya Strelka			
Tongue of the Ocean (Chan.), Ba. (tŭng ŏv thē ōshŭn)	134	24.05 N	77.20 W
Tongue R., Mt. (tŭng)	117	45.08 N	106.40 W
Tongxian, China (tôŋ shyĕn)	202a	39.55 N	116.40 E
Tonj R., Sud. (tônj)	225	6.18 N	28.33 E
Tonk, India (Tŏŋk)	196	26.13 N	75.45 E
Tonkawa, Ok. (tŏŋ kà-wô)	123	36.42 N	97.19 W
Tonkin, Gulf of, Viet. (tôn-kăn')	203	20.30 N	108.10 E
Tonle Sap (L.), Kamp. (tôn'lā säp')	206	13.03 N	102.49 E
Tonneins, Fr. (tô-năn')	168	44.24 N	0.18 E
Tönning, F.R.G. (tû'nĕng)	166	54.20 N	8.55 E
Tonopah, Nv. (tō-nô-pä')	120	38.04 N	117.15 W
Tönsberg, Nor. (tûns'bĕrgh)	164	59.19 N	10.25 E
Tönsholt, F.R.G.	63	51.38 N	6.58 E
Tonto (R.), Mex. (tōn'tō)	131	18.15 N	96.13 W
Tonto Cr., Az.	121	34.05 N	111.15 W
Tonto Natl. Mon., Az. (tôn'tô)	121	33.33 N	111.08 W
Tooele, Ut. (tōō-ĕl ē)	119b	40.33 N	112.17 W
Toohsien, China	203	25.30 N	111.32 W
Toongabbie, Austl.	70a	33.47 S	150.57 E
Toot Hill, Eng.	62	51.42 N	0.12 E
Toowoomba, Austl. (tōō wōōm'bá)	216	23.72 S	152.10 E
Topanga, Ca. (tō'păn-gá)	119a	34.05 N	118.36 W
Topeka, Ks. (tô-pē'ká)	123	39.02 N	95.41 W
Topilejo, Mex. (tô-pē-lĕ'hô)	131a	19.12 N	99.09 W
Topkapi (Neigh.), Tur.	66f	41.02 N	28.54 E
Topkapi Müzesi (P. Int.), Tur.	66f	41.00 N	28.59 E
T'oplyj Stan (Neigh.), Sov. Un.	66b	55.37 N	37.30 E
Topock, Az.	121	34.40 N	114.20 W
Top of Hebers, Eng.	64b	53.34 N	2.12 W
Topol'čany, Czech. (tô-pôl'chä-nü)	167	48.38 N	18.10 E
Topolobampo, Mex. (tō-pō-lô-bä'm-pô)	128	25.45 N	109.00 W
Topolovgrad, Bul.	173	42.05 N	26.19 E
Toppenish, Wa. (tôp'ĕn-ĭsh)	116	46.22 N	120.00 W
Toppings, Eng.	64b	53.37 N	2.25 W
Tora, Île (I.), Mauritania	228	19.50 N	16.45 W
Torbat-e Heydarīyeh, Iran	195	35.16 N	59.13 E
Torbat-e Jām, Iran	195	35.14 N	60.36 E
Torbay, Can. (tôr-bā')	105	47.40 N	52.43 W
Torbay, see Torquay			
Torbreck, Mt., Austl. (tōr-brĕk)	216	37.05 S	146.55 E
Torch (L.), Mi. (tôrch)	110	45.00 N	85.30 W
Torcy, Fr.	64c	48.51 N	2.39 E
Tor di Quinto (Neigh.), It.	66c	41.56 N	12.28 E
Töreboda, Swe. (tū'rē-bō'dä)	164	58.44 N	14.04 E
Torhout, Bel.	163	51.01 N	3.04 E
Toribío, Col. (tô-rē-bē'ô)	142a	2.58 N	76.14 W
Toride, Jap. (tô'rē-dä)	205a	35.54 N	104.04 E
Torino (Turin), It. (tô-rē'no) (tū'rĭn)	172	45.05 N	7.44 E
Tormes (R.), Sp. (tōr'mās)	170	41.12 N	6.15 W
Torneälven (R.), Swe.	158	67.29 N	22.05 E
Torneträsk (L.), Swe. (tôr'nĕ trĕsk)	152	68.10 N	20.36 E
Torngat Mts., Can.	97	59.18 N	64.35 W
Tornio, Fin. (tôr'nĭ-ô)	158	65.55 N	24.09 E
Toro, Lac (L.), Can.	104	46.53 N	73.46 W
Toronto, Can. (tô-rŏn'tō)	95d	43.40 N	79.23 W
Toronto, Oh.	110	40.30 N	80.35 W
Toronto, L., Mex. (lä'gô-tô-rô'n-tō)	124	27.35 N	105.37 W
Toropets, Sov. Un. (tô'rô-pyĕts)	174	56.31 N	31.37 E
Toros Dağlari (Taurus Mts.), Tur. (tô'rŭs)	179	37.00 N	32.40 E
Torote (R.), Sp. (tô-rō'tä)	171a	40.36 N	3.24 W
Tor Pignatara (Neigh.), It.	66c	41.52 N	12.32 E
Torquay (Torbay), Eng. (tôr-kē')	162	50.30 N	3.26 W
Torra, Cerro (Mtn.), Col. (sĕ'r-rô-tō'r-rä)	142a	4.41 N	76.22 W
Torrance, Ca. (tŏr'rănc)	119a	33.50 N	118.20 W
Torre Annunziata, It. (tôr'rä ä-nōōn-tsē-ä'tä)	171c	40.31 N	14.27 E
Torreblanca, Sp.	171	40.18 N	0.12 E
Torre del Greco, It. (tôr'rā dĕl grā'kô)	171c	40.32 N	14.23 E
Torrejoncillo, Sp. (tôr'rā-hôn-thē'lyō)	170	39.54 N	6.26 W
Torrelavega, Sp. (tôr-rā'lä-vä'gä)	170	43.22 N	4.02 W
Torrellas de Llobregat, Sp.	65e	41.21 N	1.59 E
Torre Maggiore, It. (tôr'rä mäd-jō'rā)	172	40.41 N	15.18 E
Torrens, L., Austl. (tŏr-ĕns)	216	30.07 S	137.40 E
Torrente, Sp. (tôr-rĕn'tā)	171	39.25 N	0.28 W
Torreon, Mex. (tôr-rå-ōn')	124	25.32 N	103.26 W
Torres Is., Vanuatu (tôr'rĕs) (tŏr'ĕz)	215	13.18 S	165.59 E
Torres Martinez Ind. Res., Ca. (tôr'ĕz mär-tē'nĕz)	120	33.33 N	116.21 W
Torres Novas, Port. (tôr'rĕzh nō'väzh)	170	39.28 N	8.37 W
Torres Str., Austl. (tôr'rĕs)	207	10.30 S	141.30 E
Torres Vedras, Port. (tôr'rĕsh vă'dräzh)	170	39.08 N	9.18 W
Torrevieja, Sp. (tôr-rā-vyā'hä)	171	37.58 N	0.40 W
Torrijos, Phil. (tôr-rē'hōs)	207a	13.19 N	122.06 E
Torrington, Ct. (tŏr'ĭng-tŭn)	111	41.50 N	73.10 W
Torrington, Wy.	114	42.04 N	104.11 W
Torro, Sp. (tô'r-rō)	170	41.27 N	5.23 W
Tor Sapienza (Neigh.), It.	66c	41.54 N	12.35 E
Torsby, Swe. (tôrs'bü)	164	60.07 N	12.56 E
Torshälla, Swe. (tôrs'hĕl-ä)	164	59.26 N	16.21 E
Tórshavn, Faer. (tôrs-houn')	158	62.00 N	6.55 W
Tortola (I.), Vir. Is. (Br.) (tôr-tō'lä)	129b	18.34 N	64.40 W
Tortona, It. (tôr-tō'nä)	172	44.52 N	8.52 W
Tortosa, Sp. (tôr-tō'sä)	171	40.59 N	0.33 E
Tortosa, Cabo de (C.), Sp. (ká'bô-dĕ-tôr-tō-sä)	171	40.42 N	0.55 E
Tortue, Canal de la (Chan.), Hai. (tôr-tü')	135	20.05 N	73.20 W
Tortue, Ile de la (I.), Hai.	135	20.10 N	73.00 W
Tortue, Rivière de la (R.), Can. (lä tōr-tü')	95a	45.12 N	73.32 W
Tortuga, Isla la (I.), Ven. (ē's-lä-lä-tôr-tōō'gä)	143b	10.55 N	65.18 W
Tortuguitas, Arg.	60d	34.28 S	58.45 W
Toruń, Pol. (tō'rōōn')	167	53.01 N	18.37 E
Tõrva, Sov. Un. (t'r'vá)	174	58.02 N	25.56 E
Torzhok, Sov. Un. (tôr'zhôk)	174	57.03 N	34.53 E
Tosa-Wan (B.), Jap. (tō'sä wän)	205	33.14 N	133.39 E
Toscana (Reg.), It. (tôs-kä'nä)	172	43.23 N	11.08 E
Toshima (Neigh.), Jap.	69a	35.44 N	139.43 E
Tosna R., Sov. Un.	182c	59.38 N	30.52 E
Tosno, Sov. Un. (tôs'nô)	182c	59.32 N	30.52 E
Tostado, Arg. (tôs-tä'dō)	144	29.10 S	61.43 W
Tosya, Tur. (tôz'yá)	179	41.00 N	34.00 E
Totana, Sp. (tō-tä-nä)	170	37.45 N	1.28 W
Tot'ma, Sov. Un. (tôt'má)	178	60.00 N	42.20 E
Totness, Sur.	143	5.51 N	56.17 W
Totonicapán, Guat. (tôtō-nē-kä'pän)	132	14.55 N	91.20 W
Totoras, Arg. (tô-tô'räs)	141c	32.33 S	61.13 W
Totowa, NJ	55	40.54 N	74.13 W
Totsuka, Jap. (tōt'sōō-kä)	205	35.24 N	139.32 E
Tottenham, Eng. (tŏt'ĕn-ám)	156b	51.35 N	0.06 W
Tottenville (Neigh.), NY	55	40.31 N	74.15 W
Totteridge (Neigh.), Eng.	62	51.38 N	0.12 W
Tottington, Eng.	64b	53.37 N	2.20 W
Tottori, Jap. (tô'tô-rē)	205	35.30 N	134.15 E
Touba, Ivory Coast	228	8.17 N	7.41 W
Touba, Senegal	228	14.51 N	15.53 W
Toubkal Jebel (Mtn.), Mor.	224	31.15 N	7.46 W
Tougan, Burkina	228	13.04 N	3.04 W
Touggourt, Alg. (tōō-gōōrt') (tōō-gōōr')	224	33.09 N	6.07 E
Touil, Oued (R.), Alg. (tōō-ēl')	160	34.42 N	21.6 E
Toul, Fr. (tōōl)	169	48.39 N	5.51 E
Toulnustouc (R.), Can.	104	50.23 N	67.55 W
Toulon, Fr. (tōō-lôn')	169	43.09 N	5.54 E
Toulouse, Fr. (tōō-lōōz')	168	43.37 N	1.27 E
Toungoo, Bur. (tō-ōōŋ-gōō')	206	19.00 N	96.29 E
Tourane, see Da Nang			
Tourcoing, Fr. (tōōr-kwăn')	168	50.44 N	3.06 E
Tournan-en-Brie, Fr. (tōōr-nän-ĕn-brē')	169b	48.45 N	2.47 E
Tours, Fr. (tōōr)	168	47.23 N	0.39 E
Touside, Pic (Pk.), Chad (tōō-sē-dā')	225	21.10 N	16.30 E
Toussus-le-Noble, Fr.	64c	48.45 N	2.07 E
Tovdalselva (R.), Nor. (tôv-däls-ĕlvá)	164	58.23 N	8.16 E
Towaco, NJ	55	40.56 N	74.21 W
Towanda, Pa. (tô-wän'dá)	111	41.45 N	76.30 W
Tower Hamlets (Neigh.), Eng.	62	51.32 N	0.03 W
Tower of London (P. Int.), Eng.	62	51.30 N	0.05 W
Towers of Silence (P. Int.), India	67e	18.58 N	72.48 E
Town Bluff L., Tx.	125	30.52 N	94.30 W
Towner, ND (tou'nĕr)	114	48.21 N	100.24 W
Town Reach (Str.), Asia	67c	1.28 N	103.44 E
Townsend, Ma. (toun'zĕnd)	105a	42.41 N	71.42 W
Townsend, Mt.	117	46.19 N	111.35 W
Townsend, Mt., Wa.	118a	47.52 N	123.03 W
Townsville, Austl. (tounz'vĭl)	143	19.18 S	146.50 E
Towson, Md. (tou'sŭn)	112e	39.24 N	76.36 W
Towuti, Danau (L.), Indon. (tô-wōō'tē)	206	3.00 S	121.45 E
Toxkan (R.), China	198	40.34 N	77.15 E
Toyah, Tx. (tō'yá)	124	31.19 N	103.46 W
Toyama, Jap. (tō'yä-mä)	205	36.42 N	137.14 E
Toyama-Wan (B.), Jap.	205	36.58 N	137.16 E
Toyoda, Jap.	69a	35.39 N	139.23 E
Toyohashi, Jap. (tō'yô-hä'shē)	205	34.44 N	137.21 E
Toyonaka, Jap. (tō'yô-nä'kà)	205b	34.47 N	135.28 E
Tozeur, Tun. (tô-zûr')	160	33.59 N	8.11 E
Traar (Neigh.), F.R.G.	63	51.23 N	6.36 E
Trabzon, Tur. (tráb'zôn)	179	41.00 N	39.45 E
Tracy, Ca. (trā'sē)	120	37.45 N	121.27 W
Tracy, Can.	104	46.00 N	73.13 W
Tracy, Mn.	114	44.13 N	95.37 W
Tracy City, Tn.	126	35.15 N	85.44 W
Trafalgar, Cabo (C.), Sp. (ká'bô-trä-fäl-gä'r)	170	36.10 N	6.02 W
Trafaria, Port.	65d	38.40 N	9.14 W
Trafford Park, Eng.	64b	53.28 N	2.20 W
Trafonomby (Mtn.), Mad.	227	24.32 S	46.35 E
Trail, Can. (trāl)	99	49.06 N	117.42 W
Traisen (R.), Aus.	157e	48.15 N	15.55 E
Traiskirchen, Aus.	157e	48.01 N	16.18 E
Trakai, Sov. Un. (trá-kāy)	165	54.38 N	24.59 E
Trakiszki, Pol. (trà-kē'-sh-kē)	167	54.16 N	23.07 E

PLACE (Pronounciation)	PAGE	Lat. °′	Long. °′
Tralee, Ire. (trȧ-lē′)	162	52.16 N	9.20 W
Tranas, Swe. (trän′ôs)	164	58.03 N	14.56 E
Trancoso, Port. (träŋ-kō′so͞o)	170	40.46 N	7.23 W
Trangan, Pulau (I.), Indon. (träŋ′gän)	207	6.52 S	133.30 E
Trani, It. (trä′nē)	172	41.15 N	16.25 E
Tranmere, Eng.	64a	53.23 N	3.01 W
Transcaucasia (Reg.), Sov. Un.	155	41.17 N	44.30 E
Trans Himalayas (Mts.), see Gangdisê Shan			
Transvaal (Prov.), S. Afr. (trăns-väl′)	226	24.21 S	28.18 E
Transylvania (Reg.), Rom. (trăn-sĭl-vā′nĭ-ȧ)	167	46.30 N	22.35 E
Transylvanian Alps (Mts.), see Carpaţii Meridionali			
Trapani, It. (trä′pä-nē)	172	38.02 N	12.34 E
Trappes, Fr. (tráp)	169b	48.47 N	2.01 E
Traralgon, Austl. (trȧ′răl-gŏn)	216	38.15 S	146.33 E
Trarza (Reg.), Mauritania	228	17.35 N	15.15 W
Trasimeno, Lago (L.), Ir. (lä′gō trä-sē-mä′nō)	172	43.00 N	12.12 E
Trás-os-Montes (Mts.), Port. (träzh′ōzh mōn′tāzh)	170	41.33 N	7.13 W
Traun R., Aus. (troun)	166	48.10 N	14.15 E
Traunstein, F.R.G. (troun′stīn)	166	47.52 N	12.38 E
Traverse City, Mi.	110	44.45 N	85.40 W
Traverse, L., Mn.-SD (trăv′ẽrs)	114	45.46 N	96.53 W
Travnik, Yugo. (träv′nēk)	172	44.13 N	17.43 E
Treasure I., Ca. (trĕzh′ẽr)	118b	37.49 N	122.22 W
Trebbin, G.D.R. (trĕ′bēn)	157b	52.13 N	13.13 E
Třebič, Czech. (t′rzhĕ′bēch)	166	49.13 N	15.53 E
Trebinje, Yugo. (trå′bēn-yĕ)	173	42.43 N	18.21 E
Trebisov, Czech. (trĕ′bē-shôf)	167	48.36 N	21.32 E
Třeboň, Czech. (t′rzhĕ′bôn′)	166	49.00 N	14.48 E
Tregrosse Is., Austl. (trē-grōs′)	215	18.08 S	150.53 E
Treinta y Tres, Ur. (trå-ēn′tä ē trās′)	144	33.14 S	54.17 W
Trélazé, Fr. (trā-lá-zā′)	168	47.27 N	0.32 W
Trelew, Arg. (trē′lū)	144	43.15 S	65.25 W
Trelleborg, Swe.	164	55.24 N	13.07 E
Tremblay-lès-Gonnesse, Fr.	64c	48.59 N	2.34 E
Tremiti, Isole (Is.), It. (ē′sō-lĕ trā-mē′tē)	172	42.07 N	16.33 E
Tremont (Neigh.), NY	55	40.51 N	73.55 W
Trenčín, Czech. (trĕn′chēn)	167	48.52 N	18.02 E
Trenque Lauquén, Arg. (trĕn′kĕ-lá′o͞o-kĕ′n)	144	35.50 S	62.44 W
Trent (R.), Can. (trĕnt)	103	44.15 N	77.55 W
Trent and Mersey Can., Eng. (trĕnt) (mûr zē)	156	53.11 N	2.24 W
Trentino-Alto Adige (Reg.), It.	172	46.16 N	10.47 E
Trento, It. (trĕn′tô)	172	46.04 N	11.07 E
Trenton, Can. (trĕn′tŭn)	97	44.05 N	77.35 W
Trenton, Can.	105	45.37 N	62.38 W
Trenton, Mi.	113b	42.08 N	83.12 W
Trenton, Mo.	123	40.05 N	93.36 W
Trenton, NJ	112a	40.13 N	74.46 W
Trenton, Tn.	126	35.57 N	88.55 W
Trepassey, Can. (trē-păs′ē)	105	46.44 N	53.22 W
Trepassey B., Can.	105	46.40 N	53.20 W
Treptow (Neigh.), G.D.R.	65a	52.29 N	13.29 E
Tres Arroyos, Arg. (trās′är-rō′yōs)	144	38.18 S	60.16 W
Três Coracoes, Braz. (trĕ′s kō-rä-zô′ēs)	141a	21.41 S	45.14 W
Tres Cumbres, Mex. (trĕ′s ko͞o′m-brĕs)	131a	19.03 N	99.14 W
Três Lagoas, Braz. (trĕ′s lä-gô′äs)	143	20.48 S	51.42 W
Três Marias, Represa (Res.), Braz. (rē-prā′sä trĕs′ mä-rē′äs)	143	18.15 S	45.30 W
Tres Morros, Alto de (Mtn.), Col. (á′l-tō dĕ trĕ′s mô′r-rôs)	142a	7.08 N	76.10 W
Três Pontas, Braz. (trĕ′pô′n-täs)	141a	21.22 S	45.30 W
Três Pontas, Cabo das (C.), Ang.	230	10.23 S	13.32 E
Três Rios, Braz. (trĕ′s rē′ōs)	141a	22.07 S	43.13 W
Très-Saint Rédempteur, Can. (săN rā-dăNp-tûr′)	95a	45.26 N	74.23 W
Tressancourt, Fr.	64c	48.55 N	2.00 E
Treuenbrietzen, G.D.R. (troi′ĕn-brē-tzĕn)	157b	52.06 N	12.52 E
Treviglio, It. (trā-vē′lyô)	172	45.30 N	9.34 E
Treviso, It. (trĕ-vē′sō)	172	45.39 N	12.15 E
Triangle, The (Reg.), Asia	198	26.00 N	98.00 E
Trichardt, S. Afr. (trĭ-kärt′)	223	26.32 N	29.16 E
Triel-sur-Seine, Fr.	64c	48.59 N	2.00 E
Trieste, It. (trē-ĕs′tā)	172	45.39 N	13.48 E
Trigueros, Sp. (trē-gā′rōs)	170	37.23 N	6.50 W
Trikala, Grc.	173	39.33 N	21.49 E
Trikora, Puncak (Pk.), Indon.	207	4.15 S	138.45 E
Trim Cr., Il. (trĭm)	113a	41.19 N	87.39 W
Trincomalee, Sri Lanka (trĭŋ-kō-mȧ-lē′)	197	8.39 N	81.12 E
Tring, Eng. (trĭng)	156b	51.46 N	0.40 W
Trinidad, Bol. (trē-nē-dhädh′)	142	14.48 S	64.43 W
Trinidad, Col. (trĭn′ĭdăd)	122	37.11 N	104.31 W
Trinidad, Cuba (trē-nē-dhädh′)	134	21.50 N	80.00 W
Trinidad, Ur.	141c	33.29 S	56.55 W
Trinidad (I.), Trin. (trĭn′ĭ-dăd)	143	10.00 N	61.00 W
Trinidad and Tobago, N. A. (trĭn′ĭ-dăd) (tô-bā′gō)	129	11.00 N	61.00 W
Trinidade, Ilha da (I.), Braz. (ē′lä dā trē-nē-dä-dĕ)	140	21.00 S	32.00 W
Trinidad R., Pan.	128a	8.55 N	80.01 W
Trinidad, Sierra de (Mts.), Cuba (sē-ĕ′r-rá dĕ trē-nē-dä′d)	134	21.50 N	79.55 W
Trinitaria, Mex. (trē-nē-tä′ryä)	131	16.09 N	92.04 W
Trinité, Mart.	133b	14.47 N	61.00 W
Trinity, Can. (trĭn′ĭ-tē)	105	48.59 N	53.55 W
Trinity, Tx.	125	30.52 N	95.27 W
Trinity (Is.), Ak.	107	56.25 N	153.15 W
Trinity (R.), East Fk., Tx.	122	33.24 N	96.42 W
Trinity (R.), West Fk., Tx.	123	33.22 N	98.26 W
Trinity B., Can.	105	48.00 N	53.40 W
Trinity R., Ca.	116	40.50 N	123.20 W
Trinity R., Tx.	125	30.50 N	95.09 W

PLACE (Pronounciation)	PAGE	Lat. °′	Long. °′
Trino, It. (trē′nô)	172	45.11 N	8.16 E
Trion, Ga. (trī′ŏn)	126	34.32 N	85.18 W
Trípolis, Grc. (trĭ′pô-lĭs)	173	37.32 N	22.32 E
Tripoli, see Ţarābulus			
Tripolitania (Prov.), see Tarābulus			
Tripp, SD (trĭp)	114	43.13 N	97.58 W
Tripura (State), India	196	24.00 N	92.00 E
Tristan da Cunha Is., Alt. O. (três-tän′dä ko͞on′yá)	232	35.30 S	12.15 W
Triste, Golfo (G.), Ven. (gôl-fô trē′s-tĕ)	143b	10.40 N	68.05 W
Triticus Res., NY (trī tĭ-cŭs)	112a	41.20 N	73.36 W
Trivandrum, India (trē-vŭn′drŭm)	197	8.34 N	76.58 E
Trnava, Czech. (t′r′nȧ-vȧ)	167	48.22 N	17.34 E
Trobriand Is., Pap. N. Gui. (trō-brē-ănd′)	207	8.25 S	151.45 E
Trogir, Yugo. (trô′gēr)	172	43.32 N	16.17 E
Troice-Lykovo (Neigh.), Sov. Un.	66b	55.47 N	37.24 E
Trois-Rivières, Can. (trwä′rē-vyâ′)	97	46.21 N	72.35 W
Troitsk, Sov. Un. (trô′ētsk)	182a	54.06 N	61.34 E
Troitsko-Pechorsk, Sov. Un. (trô′ĭtsk-ō-pyĕ-chôrsk′)	180	62.18 N	56.07 E
Troitskoye, Sov. Un.	175	47.39 N	30.16 E
Trollhättan, Swe. (trôl′hĕt-ĕn)	164	58.17 N	12.17 E
Trollheim (Mts.), Nor. (trôll-hĕĭm)	164	62.48 N	9.05 E
Trombay (Neigh.), India	67e	19.02 N	72.57 E
Tromsö, Nor. (trôm′sû)	158	69.38 N	19.12 E
Trona, Ca. (trō′nȧ)	120	35.49 N	117.20 W
Tronador, Cerro (Mtn.), Arg. (sĕ′r-rô trō-nä′dôr)	144	41.17 S	71.56 W
Troncoso, Mex. (trôn-kô′sō)	130	22.43 N	102.22 W
Trondheim, Nor. (trôn′hâm)	164	63.25 N	11.35 E
Tropar′ovo (Neigh.), Sov. Un.	66b	55.39 N	37.29 E
Trosa, Swe. (trō′sä)	164	58.54 N	17.25 E
Trottiscliffe, Eng.	62	51.19 N	0.21 E
Trout (L.), Can.	97	51.16 N	92.46 W
Trout (L.), Can.	96	61.10 N	121.30 W
Trout Cr., Or.	116	42.18 N	118.31 W
Troutdale, Or. (trout′dāl)	118c	45.32 N	122.23 W
Trout L., Can.	101	51.13 N	93.20 W
Trout Lake, Mi.	115	46.20 N	85.02 W
Trouville, Fr. (tro͞o-vēl′)	168	49.23 N	0.05 E
Troy, Al. (troi)	126	31.47 N	85.46 W
Troy, Il.	119e	38.44 N	89.53 W
Troy, Ks.	123	39.46 N	95.07 W
Troy, Mo.	123	38.56 N	99.57 W
Troy, Mt.	116	48.28 N	115.56 W
Troy, NY	111	42.45 N	73.45 W
Troy, NC	127	35.21 N	79.58 W
Troy, Oh.	110	40.00 N	84.10 W
Troyes Fr. (trwä)	168	48.18 N	4.03 E
Troy Ruins, Tur.	173	39.59 N	26.14 E
Troyville (Neigh.), S. Afr.	71b	26.12 S	28.04 E
Trstenik, Yugo. (t′r′stĕ-nêk)	173	43.36 N	20.00 E
Trst, see Trieste			
Trubchëvsk, Sov. Un. (tro͞op′chĕfsk)	174	52.36 N	32.46 E
Trucial States, see United Arab Emirates			
Truckee, Ca. (trŭk′ē)	120	39.20 N	120.12 W
Truckee (R.), Ca.-Nv.	120	39.25 N	120.07 W
Truganina, Austl.	211a	37.49 N	144.44 E
Trujillo, Col. (tro͞o-ĸē′l-yō)	142a	4.10 N	76.20 W
Trujillo, Hond. (tro͞o-ĸēl′yō)	132	15.55 N	85.58 W
Trujillo, Peru	142	8.08 S	79.00 W
Trujillo, Sp. (tro͞o-ĸē′l-yô)	170	39.27 N	5.50 W
Trujillo, Ven.	142	9.15 N	70.28 W
Trujillo (R.), Mex.	130	23.12 N	103.10 W
Trujin, L., Dom. Rep. (tro͞o-ĸēn′)	135	17.45 N	71.25 W
Trumann, Ar. (tro͞o′măn)	123	35.41 N	90.31 W
Trŭn, Bul. (trŭn)	173	42.49 N	22.39 E
Truro, Can. (tro͞o′rō)	104	45.22 N	63.16 W
Truro, Eng.	162	50.17 N	5.05 W
Trussville, Al. (trŭs′vĭl)	112h	33.37 N	86.37 W
Trust Territory of the Pacific Islands, Pac. O.	208	10.00 N	155.00 E
Truth or Consequences, NM (tro͞oth ŏr kŏn′sē-kwĕn-sĭs)	121	33.10 N	107.20 W
Trutnov, Czech. (tro͞ot′nôf)	166	50.36 N	15.36 E
Trzcianka, Pol. (tchyän′kȧ)	166	53.02 N	16.27 E
Trzebiatow, Pol. (tchĕ-byä′to͞o-v)	166	54.03 N	15.16 E
Tsaidam Basin, China (tsī-däm)	198	37.19 N	94.08 E
Tsala Apopka (R.), Fl. (tsä′lȧ ă-pŏp′kȧ)	127	28.57 N	82.11 W
Tsast Bogd (Mt.), Mong.	198	46.44 N	92.34 E
Tsavo Natl. Pk., Ken.	231	2.35 S	38.45 E
Tsawwassen Ind. Res., Can.	118d	49.03 N	123.11 W
Tselinograd, Sov. Un. (tsĕ′lē-nô-grä′d)	180	51.10 N	71.43 E
Tsentral′nyy-Kospashskiy, Sov. Un. (tsĕn-träl′nyĭ-kôs-pàsh′skĭ)	182a	59.03 N	57.48 E
Tshela, Zaire (tshä′lȧ)	230	4.59 S	12.56 E
Tshikapa, Zaire (tshē-kä′pä)	230	6.25 S	20.48 E
Tshofa, Zaire	230	5.14 S	25.15 E
Tshuapa (R.), Zaire	230	10.15 S	21.25 E
Tsiafajovona (Mtn.), Mad.	227	19.17 S	47.27 E
Tsimlyanskiy (Res.), Sov. Un. (tsym-lyä′ns-kēē)	179	47.50 N	43.40 E
Tsing I., China	68c	22.21 N	114.05 E
Tsin Shui Wan (B.), Hong Kong	68c	22.13 N	114.10 E
Tsiribihina (R.), Mad. (tsē′rē-bē-hē-nä′)	227	19.45 S	43.30 E
Tsitsa (R.), S. Afr. (tsē′tsȧ)	227c	31.28 S	28.53 E
Tsolo, S. Afr. (tsō′lō)	227c	31.19 S	28.47 E
Tsomo, S. Afr.	227c	32.03 S	27.49 E
Tsomo (R.), S. Afr.	227c	31.53 S	27.48 E
Tsu, Jap. (tso͞o)	205	34.42 N	136.31 E
Tsuchiura, Jap. (tso͞o′chē-o͞o-rä)	205	36.04 N	140.09 E
Tsuda, Jap. (tso͞o′dä)	205b	34.48 N	135.43 E
Tsugaru Kaikyō (Str.), Jap. (tso͞o′gä-ro͞o kī′kyō)	204	41.25 N	140.20 E
Tsukumono (Neigh.), Jap.	69b	34.50 N	135.11 E
Tsumeb, Namibia (tso͞o′mĕb)	226	19.10 S	17.45 E
Tsunashima, Jap. (tso͞o′nä-shē′mä)	205a	35.32 N	139.37 E

PLACE (Pronounciation)	PAGE	Lat. °′	Long. °′
Tsunashima (Neigh.), Jap.	69a	35.32 N	139.38 E
Tsuruga, Jap. (tso͞o′ro͞o-gä)	205	35.39 N	136.04 E
Tsurugi San (Mtn.), Jap. (tso͞o′ro͞o-gē sän)	205	33.52 N	134.07 E
Tsurumi (R.), Jap.	69a	35.29 N	139.41 E
Tsuruoka, Jap. (tso͞o′ro͞o-ō′kä)	204	38.43 N	139.51 E
Tsurusaki, Jap. (tso͞o′ro͞o-sä′kē)	205	33.15 N	131.42 E
Tsu Shima (I.), Jap. (tso͞o shē′mä)	205	34.28 N	129.30 E
Tsushima Kaikyō (Str.), Asia (tso͞o′shē-mä kī′kyō)	205	33.52 N	129.30 E
Tsuwano, Jap. (tso͞o′wȧ-nō′)	205	34.28 N	131.47 E
Tsu Wan (Quanwan), China	68c	22.22 N	114.07 E
Tsuyama, Jap. (tso͞o′yä-mä′)	205	35.05 N	134.00 E
Tua (R.), Port. (to͞o′ä)	170	41.23 N	7.18 W
Tualatin (R.), Or. (to͞o′ȧ-lȧ-tĭn)	118c	45.25 N	122.54 W
Tuamoto, Îles, Fr. Polynesia (to͞o-ä-mō′to͞o)	209	19.00 S	141.20 W
Tuapse, Sov. Un. (to͞o′áp-sĕ)	179	44.00 N	39.10 E
Tuareg (Reg.), Alg.	224	21.26 N	2.51 E
Tubarão, Braz. (to͞o-bä-rouN′)	144	28.23 N	48.56 W
Tübingen, F.R.G. (tü′bĭng-ĕn)	166	48.33 N	9.05 E
Tubinskiy, Sov. Un. (tû bĭn′skĭ)	182a	52.53 N	58.15 E
Tubruq, Libya	225	32.03 N	24.04 E
Tucacas, Ven. (to͞o-kä′käs)	143b	10.48 N	68.20 W
Tuckahoe, NY	55	40.57 N	73.50 W
Tucker, Ga. (tŭk′ẽr)	112c	33.51 N	84.13 W
Tucson, Az. (to͞o-sŏn′)	121	32.15 N	111.00 W
Tucumán, Arg. (to͞o-ko͞o-män′)	144	26.52 S	65.08 W
Tucumán (Prov.), Arg.	144	26.30 S	65.30 W
Tucumcari, NM (to͞o′kŭm-kâr-ē)	122	35.11 N	103.43 W
Tucupita, Ven. (to͞o-ko͞o-pē′tä)	142	9.00 N	62.09 W
Tucuruí, Braz. (to͞o-ko͞o-to͞o-ē′)	143	3.34 S	49.44 W
Tudela, Sp. (to͞o-dhā′lä)	170	42.03 N	1.37 W
Tugaloo (R.), Ga.-SC (tŭg′ȧ-lo͞o)	126	34.35 N	83.05 W
Tugela (R.), S. Afr. (to͞o-gel′ȧ)	227c	28.50 S	30.52 E
Tugela Ferry, S. Afr.	227c	28.44 S	30.27 E
Tug Fork (R.), WV (tŭg)	110	37.50 N	82.30 W
Tuguegarao, Phil. (to͞o-gā-gȧ-rä′ō)	207a	17.37 N	121.44 E
Tuhai (R.), China (to͞o-hī)	200	37.05 N	116.56 E
Tuinplaas, S. Afr.	223d	24.54 S	28.46 E
Tujunga, Ca. (to͞o-jŭŋ′gȧ)	119a	34.15 N	118.16 W
Tukan, Sov. Un. (to͞o′kån)	182a	53.52 N	57.25 E
Tukangbesi, Kepulauan (Is.), Indon.	207	6.00 S	124.15 E
Tūkrah, Libya	225	32.34 N	20.47 E
Tuktoyaktuk, Can. (to͞ok-tō-yăk′to͞ok)	96	69.32 N	132.37 W
Tukums, Sov. Un. (to͞o′ko͞oms)	165	56.57 N	23.09 E
Tukuyu, Tan. (to͞o-ko͞o′yȧ)	226	9.13 S	33.43 E
Tukwila, Wa. (tŭk′wĭ-lȧ)	118a	47.28 N	122.16 W
Tula, Mex. (to͞o′lä)	130	20.04 N	99.22 W
Tula, Sov. Un. (to͞o′lȧ)	174	54.12 N	37.37 E
Tula (Oblast), Sov. Un.	174	53.45 N	37.19 E
Tula (R.), Mex. (to͞o′lä)	130	20.40 N	99.27 W
Tulagai (I.), Sol. Is. (to͞o-lä′gē)	215	9.15 S	160.17 E
Tulalip, Wa. (tū-lă′lĭp)	118a	48.04 N	122.18 W
Tulalip Ind. Res., Wa.	118a	48.06 N	122.16 W
Tulancingo, Mex. (to͞o-län-sĭŋ′gō)	130	20.04 N	98.24 W
Tulangbawang (R.), Indon.	206	4.17 S	105.00 E
Tulare, Ca. (to͞o-lä′rȧ) (tul-âr′)	120	36.12 N	119.22 W
Tulare Basin, Ca.	120	35.57 N	120.18 W
Tularosa, NM (to͞o-lȧ-rō′zȧ)	121	33.05 N	106.05 W
Tulcán, Ec. (to͞ol-kän′)	142	0.44 N	77.52 W
Tulcea, Rom. (to͞ol′chȧ)	175	45.10 N	28.47 E
Tul′chin, Sov. Un. (to͞ol′chĕn)	175	48.42 N	28.53 E
Tulcingo, Mex. (to͞ol-sĭŋ′gō)	130	18.03 N	98.27 W
Tule (R.), Ca. (to͞o′lå)	120	36.08 N	118.50 W
Tule River Ind. Res., Ca. (to͞o′lå)	120	36.05 N	118.35 W
Tuli, Zimb. (to͞o′lē)	226	20.58 S	29.12 E
Tulia, Tx. (to͞o′lĭ-ȧ)	122	34.32 N	101.46 W
Tulijá (R.), Mex. (to͞o-lē-ĸá′)	131	17.28 N	92.11 W
Tulik Vol., Ak. (to͞o′lĭk)	107a	53.28 N	168.10 W
Tūlkarm, Jordan (to͞ol kärm)	191a	32.19 N	35.02 E
Tullahoma, Tn. (tŭl-ȧ-hō′mȧ)	126	35.21 N	86.12 W
Tullamarine, Austl.	70b	37.41 S	144.52 E
Tullamore, Ire. (tŭl-ȧ-môr′)	162	53.15 N	7.29 W
Tulle, Fr. (tül)	168	45.15 N	1.45 E
Tulln, Aus. (to͞oln)	157e	48.21 N	16.04 E
Tullner Feld (Reg.), Aus.	157e	48.20 N	15.59 E
Tulpetlac, Mex. (to͞ol-på-tlåk′)	131a	19.33 N	99.04 W
Tulsa, Ok. (tŭl′sȧ)	123	36.08 N	95.58 W
Tuluá, Col. (to͞o-lo͞o-á′)	142a	4.06 N	76.12 W
Tulum, Mex. (to͞o-lo͞o′m)	132a	20.17 N	87.26 W
Tulun, Sov. Un. (to͞o-lo͞on′)	180	54.29 N	100.43 E
Tumaco, Col. (to͞o-mä′kô)	142	1.41 N	78.44 W
Tuma R., Nic. (to͞o′mä)	132	13.07 N	85.32 W
Tumba, Lac (L.), Zaire (to͞om′bä)	230	0.50 S	17.45 E
Tumbes, Peru (to͞o′m-bĕs)	142	3.39 S	80.27 W
Tumbiscatío, Mex. (to͞om-bē-skä-tē′ō)	130	18.32 N	102.23 W
Tumbo (I.), Can.	118d	48.49 N	123.04 W
Tumen, China (to͞o-mŭn)	202	43.00 N	129.50 E
Tumen (R.), China	204	42.08 N	128.40 E
Tumeremo, Ven. (to͞o-må-rä′mō)	143	7.15 N	61.28 W
Tumkūr, India	197	13.22 N	77.05 E
Tumuacacori Natl. Mon., Az. (to͞o-mä-kä′kå-rē)	121	31.36 N	110.20 W
Tumuc-Humac Mts., S. A. (to͞o-mo͞ok′o͞o-mäk′)	143	2.15 N	54.50 W
Tunas de Zaza, Cuba (to͞o′näs dā zä′zä)	134	21.40 N	79.35 W
Tunbridge Wells, Eng. (tŭn′brĭj welz′)	162	51.05 N	0.09 E
Tundra (Reg.), Sov. Un.	180	70.45 N	84.00 E
Tunduru, Tan.	231	11.07 S	37.21 E
Tungabhadra Res., India	196	15.26 N	75.57 E
Tungpa, China (to͞ong-bä)	200	35.56 N	116.19 E
Tuni, India	197	17.29 N	82.38 E
Tunica, Ms. (tū′nĭ-kȧ)	126	34.41 N	90.23 W
Tunis, Tun. (tū′nĭs)	224	36.59 N	10.06 E
Tunis, Golfe de (G.), Tun.	159	37.06 N	10.43 E
Tunisia, Afr. (tu-nĭzh′ē-ȧ)	222	35.00 N	10.11 E
Tunja, Col. (to͞o′n-há)	142	5.32 N	73.19 W

PLACE (Pronounciation)	PAGE	Lat. °′	Long. °′
Tunkhannock, Pa. (tŭnk-hăn′ŭk)	111	41.35 N	75.55 W
Tunnel (R.), Wa. (tŭn′ĕl)	118a	47.48 N	123.04 W
Tuoji Dao (I.), China (twô-jyē dou)	200	38.11 N	120.45 E
Tuolumne (R.), Ca. (twô-lŭm′nē)	120	37.35 N	120.37 W
Tuostakh (R.), Sov. Un.	181	67.09 N	137.30 E
Tupã, Braz. (tōō-pá)	143	21.47 S	50.33 W
Tupelo, Ms. (tū′pĕ-lō)	126	34.14 N	88.43 W
Tupinambaranas, Ilha (I.), Braz. (ē′lä-tōō-pē-näɴ-bä-rä′näs)	143	3.04 S	58.09 W
Tupiza, Bol. (tōō-pē′zä)	142	21.26 S	65.43 W
Tupper Lake, NY (tŭp′ēr)	111	44.15 N	74.25 W
Tuquerres, Col. (tōō-kĕ′r-rĕs)	142	1.12 N	77.44 W
Tura, Sov. Un. (tōōr′á)	180	64.08 N	99.58 E
Turbio (R.), Mex. (tōōr-byô)	130	20.28 N	101.40 W
Turbo, Col. (tōō′bō)	142	8.02 N	76.43 W
Turda, Rom. (tōōr′dá)	167	46.35 N	23.47 E
Turfan Depression, China	198	42.16 N	90.00 E
Turffontein (Neigh.), S. Afr.	71b	26.15 S	28.02 E
Turgay, Sov. Un. (tōōr′gī)	180	49.42 N	63.39 E
Turgayka (R.), Sov. Un. (tōōr-gī′kă)	155	49.44 N	66.15 E
Tŭrgovishte, Bul.	173	43.14 N	26.36 E
Turgutlu, Tur.	179	38.30 N	27.20 E
Türi, Sov. Un. (tü′rĭ)	165	58.49 N	25.29 E
Turia (R.), Sp. (tōō′ryä)	170	40.12 N	1.18 W
Turicato, Mex. (tōō-rē-kä′tō)	130	19.03 N	101.24 W
Turiguano (I.), Cuba (tōō-rē-gwä′nō)	134	22.20 N	78.35 W
Turin, see Torino			
Turka, Sov. Un. (tōōr′ká)	167	49.10 N	23.02 E
Turkestan, Sov. Un. (tûr-kĕ-stăn′) (tōōr-kĕ-stan′)	180	42.40 N	65.00 E
Turkestan (Reg.), Sov. Un.	176	43.27 N	62.14 E
Turkey, Eur.-Asia	190	38.45 N	32.00 E
Turkey (R.), Ia. (tûrk′ē)	115	43.20 N	92.16 W
Turkmen (S. S. R.), Sov. Un. (tōōrk-mĕn′)	176	40.46 N	56.01 E
Turks (Is.), Turks & Caicos Is. (tûrks)	129	21.40 N	71.45 W
Turks I. Pass, Turks & Caicos Is.	135	21.15 N	71.25 W
Turku (Åbo), Fin. (tōōr′kōō) (ô′bô)	165	60.28 N	22.12 E
Turlock, Ca. (tûr′lŏk)	120	37.30 N	120.51 W
Turneffe (I.), Belize	132a	17.25 N	87.43 W
Turner, Ks. (tûr′nēr)	119f	39.05 N	94.42 W
Turner Sd., Ba.	134	24.20 N	78.05 W
Turners Pen, S.L.	228	7.20 N	12.40 W
Turnhout, Bel. (tŭrn-hout′)	157a	51.19 N	4.58 E
Turnov, Czech. (tōōr′nôf)	166	50.36 N	15.12 E
Turnu-Măgurel, Rom.	173a	43.54 N	24.49 E
Turpan, China (tōō-är-pän)	198	43.06 N	88.41 E
Turquino, Pico de (Pk.), Cuba (pē′kō dā tōōr-kē′nō)	134	20.00 N	76.50 W
Turramurra, Austl.	70a	33.44 S	151.08 E
Turrialba, C. R. (tōōr-ryä′l-bä)	133	9.54 N	83.41 W
Turtkul′, Sov. Un. (tōōrt-kōōl′)	155	41.28 N	61.02 E
Turtle (R.), Can.	101	49.20 N	92.30 W
Turtle B., Tx.	125a	29.48 N	94.38 W
Turtle Cr., SD	114	44.40 N	98.53 W
Turtle Creek, Pa.	57b	40.25 N	79.49 W
Turtle Mountain Ind. Res., ND	114	48.45 N	99.57 W
Turtle Mts., ND	114	48.57 N	100.11 W
Turukhansk, Sov. Un. (tōō-rōō-Känsk′)	180	66.03 N	88.39 E
Turya R., Sov. Un. (tōōr′yá)	167	51.18 N	24.55 E
Tuscaloosa, Al. (tŭs-ká-lōō′sá)	126	33.10 N	87.35 W
Tuscarora, Nv. (tŭs-ká-rō′rá)	116	41.18 N	116.15 W
Tuscarora Ind. Res., NY	113c	43.10 N	78.51 W
Tuscola, Il. (tŭs-kō-lá)	110	39.50 N	88.20 W
Tuscumbia, Al. (tŭs-kŭm′bĭ-á)	126	34.41 N	87.42 W
Tushino, Sov. Un. (tōō′shĭ-nô)	182b	55.51 N	37.24 E
Tuskegee, Al. (tŭs-kē′gē)	126	32.25 N	85.40 W
Tustin, Ca. (tŭs′tĭn)	119a	33.44 N	117.49 W
Tutayev, Sov. Un. (tōō-tá-yĕf′)	174	57.53 N	39.34 E
Tutbury, Eng. (tŭt′bēr-ē)	156	52.52 N	1.51 W
Tuticorin, India (tōō-tē-kō-rĭn′)	197	8.51 N	78.09 E
Tutitlan, Mex. (tōō-tē-tlä′n)	131a	19.38 N	99.10 W
Tutóia, Braz. (tōō-tō′yá)	143	2.42 S	42.21 W
Tutrakan, Bul.	173	44.02 N	26.36 E
Tuttle Creek Res., Ks.	123	39.30 N	96.38 W
Tuttlingen, F.R.G. (tōōt′lĭng-ĕn)	166	47.58 N	8.50 E
Tutwiler, Ms. (tŭt′wĭ-lēr)	126	34.01 N	90.25 W
Tuva Aut. Oblast, Sov. Un.	180	51.15 N	90.45 E
Tuvalu, Oceania	208	5.20 S	174.00 E
Tuwayq, Jabal (Mts.), Sau. Ar.	192	20.45 N	46.30 E
Tuxedo, Md.	56d	38.55 N	76.55 W
Tuxedo Park, NY (tŭk-sē′dō pärk)	112a	41.11 N	74.11 W
Tuxford, Eng. (tŭks′fērd)	156	53.14 N	0.54 W
Tuxpan, Mex. (tōōs′pän)	130	19.34 N	103.22 W
Tuxpan, Mex.	131	20.57 N	97.26 W
Túxpan (R.), Mex. (tōōs′pän)	131	20.55 N	97.52 W
Túxpan, Arrecife (Rf.), Mex. (är-rē-sē′fē-tōō′x-pä′n)	131	21.01 N	97.12 W
Tuxtepec, Mex. (tōōs-tá-pĕk′)	131	18.06 N	96.09 W
Tuxtla Gutiérrez, Mex. (tōōs′tlä gōō-tyâr′rĕs)	131	16.44 N	93.08 W
Tuy, Sp.	158	42.07 N	8.49 W
Tuy (R.), Ven. (tōō′ē)	143b	10.15 N	66.03 W
Tuyra R., Pan. (tōō-ē′rá)	133	7.55 N	77.37 W
Tuz Gölü (L.), Tur.	179	39.00 N	33.30 E
Tuzigoot Natl. Mon., Az.	121	34.40 N	111.52 W
Tuzla, Yugo. (tōōz′lá)	173	44.33 N	18.46 E
Tvedestrand, Nor. (tvĭ′dhĕ-stränd)	164	58.39 N	8.54 E
Tveitsund, Nor. (tvåt′sōōnd)	164	59.03 N	8.29 E
Tver, see Kalinin			
Tvertsa (L.), Sov. Un. (tvĕr′tsá)	154	56.58 N	35.22 E
Tweed (R.), Scot. (twēd)	162	55.32 N	2.35 W
Tweeling, S. Afr. (twē′lĭng)	223d	27.34 S	28.31 E
Twelvemile Cr., NY (twĕlv′mīl)	113c	43.13 N	78.58 W
Twenty Mile Cr., Can. (twĕn′tĭ mīl)	95d	43.09 N	79.49 W
Twickenham, Eng. (twĭk′′n-ăm)	156b	51.26 N	0.20 W
Twillingate, Can. (twĭl′ĭn-gāt)	105	49.39 N	54.46 W
Twin Bridges, Mt. (twĭn brĭ-jĕz)	117	45.34 N	112.17 W
Twin Falls, Id. (fôls)	117	42.33 N	114.29 W
Twinsburg, Oh. (twĭnz′bûrg)	113d	41.19 N	81.26 W
Twitchell Res., Ca.	120	34.50 N	120.10 W

PLACE (Pronounciation)	PAGE	Lat. °′	Long. °′
Two Butte Cr., Co. (tōō būt)	122	37.39 N	102.45 W
Two Harbors, Mn.	115	47.00 N	91.42 W
Two Prairie Bay, Ar. (prâ′rĭ bī ōō′)	123	34.48 N	92.07 W
Two Rivers, Wi. (rĭv′ērz)	115	44.09 N	87.36 W
Tyabb, Austl.	211a	38.16 S	145.11 E
Tyachev, Sov. Un. (tyä′chĕf)	167	48.01 N	23.42 E
Tyasmin (R.), Sov. Un. (tyȧs-mĭn′)	175	49.14 N	32.23 E
Tylden, S. Afr. (tĭl-dĕn)	227c	32.08 S	27.06 E
Tyldesley, Eng. (tĭldz′lē)	156	53.32 N	2.28 W
Tyler, Mn. (tī′lēr)	114	44.18 N	96.08 W
Tyler, Tx.	125	32.21 N	95.19 W
Tyler Park, Va.	56d	38.52 N	77.12 W
Tylertown, Ms. (tī′lēr-toun)	126	31.08 N	90.06 W
Tyndall, SD (tĭn′dál)	114	42.58 N	97.52 W
Tyndinskiy, Sov. Un.	181	55.22 N	124.45 E
Tyne (R.), Eng. (tīn)	162	54.59 N	1.56 W
Tynemouth, Eng. (tīn′mŭth)	162	55.04 N	1.39 W
Tynest, Nor. (tün′sĕt)	164	62.17 N	10.45 E
Tyngsboro, Ma. (tĭnj-bûr′ô)	105a	42.40 N	71.27 W
Tyre, see Şūr			
Tyrifjorden (Fd.), Nor.	164	60.03 N	10.25 E
Tyrone, NM (tī′rōn)	121	32.40 N	108.20 W
Tyrone, Pa.	111	40.40 N	78.15 W
Tyrrell, L., Austl. (tĭr′ĕll)	216	35.12 S	143.00 E
Tyrrhenian Sea, It. (tĭr-rē′nĭ-án)	159	40.10 N	12.15 E
Tysons Corner, Va.	56d	38.55 N	77.14 W
Tyub-Karagan, Mys (C.), Sov. Un.	179	44.30 N	50.10 E
Tyukalinsk, Sov. Un. (tyōō-ká-lĭnsk′)	180	56.03 N	71.43 E
Tyukyan (R.), Sov. Un. (työōk′yán)	181	65.42 N	116.09 E
Tyuleniy (I.), Sov. Un.	179	44.30 N	48.00 E
Tyumen′, Sov. Un. (työō-mĕn′)	180	57.02 N	65.28 E
Tyura-Tam, Sov. Un.	180	46.00 N	63.15 E
Tzucacab, Mex. (tzōō-kä-kä′b)	132a	20.06 N	89.03 W

U

PLACE (Pronounciation)	PAGE	Lat. °′	Long. °′
Uarc, Ras (C.), Mor.	160	35.31 N	2.45 W
Uaupés, Braz. (wä-ōō′pās)	142	0.02 S	67.03 W
Ubá, Braz. (ōō-bá′)	141a	21.08 S	42.55 W
Ubangi (Oubangui) (R.), Afr. (ōō-bäŋ′gē)	230	4.30 N	20.35 E
Ubatuba, Braz. (ōō-bá-tōō′bá)	141a	23.25 S	45.06 W
Ubeda, Sp. (ōō′bā-dä)	170	38.01 N	3.23 W
Uberaba, Braz. (ōō-bā-rä′bá)	143	19.47 S	47.47 W
Uberlândia, Braz. (ōō-bĕr-lä′n-dyä)	143	18.54 S	48.11 W
Ubombo, S. Afr. (ōō-bôm′bô)	226	27.33 S	32.13 E
Ubon Ratchathani, Thai. (ōō′bŭn rä′chätá-nē)	206	15.15 N	104.52 E
Ubort′ (R.), Sov. Un. (ōō-bôrt′)	175	51.18 N	27.43 E
Ubrique, Sp. (ōō-brē′kā)	170	36.43 N	5.36 W
Ubundi (Ponthierville), Zaire	231	00.21 S	25.29 E
Ucayali (R.), Peru (ōō′kä-yä′lē)	142	8.58 S	74.13 W
Uccle, Bel. (ü′kl′)	157a	50.48 N	4.17 E
Uchaly, Sov. Un. (ū-chä′lĭ)	182a	54.22 N	59.28 E
Uch-Aral, Sov. Un. (ōōch′á-ral′)	180	46.14 N	80.58 E
Uchiko, Jap. (ōō′chē-kō)	205	33.30 N	132.39 E
Uchinoura, Jap. (ōō′chē-nō-ōō′rá)	205	31.16 N	131.03 E
Uchinskoye Vdkhr. (Res.), Sov. Un. (ōōch-ĕn′skô-yĕ vô-dô-Krá-nĭ′lĭ-shchĕ)	182b	56.08 N	37.44 E
Uchiura-Wan (B.), Jap. (ōō′chē-ōō′rä wän)	204	42.20 N	140.44 E
Uchur (R.), Sov. Un. (ōō-chōōr′)	181	58.27 N	131.34 E
Ückendorf (Neigh.), F.R.G.	63	51.30 N	7.07 E
Uda (R.), Sov. Un. (ōō′dá)	181	52.28 N	110.51 E
Uda (R.), Sov. Un.	181	53.54 N	131.29 E
Udaipur, India (ōō-dŭ′ē-pōōr)	196	24.41 N	73.41 E
Uday (R.), Sov. Un. (ōō-dī′)	175	50.45 N	32.13 E
Uddevalla, Swe. (ŏŏd′dĕ-väl-á)	164	58.21 N	11.55 E
Udine, It. (ōō′dē-nā)	172	46.05 N	13.14 E
Udmurt (A. S. S. R.), Sov. Un.	180	57.00 N	53.00 E
Udon Thani, Thai.	206	17.31 N	102.51 E
Udskaya Guba (B.), Sov. Un.	143	55.00 N	136.30 E
Ueda, Jap. (wä′dä)	205	36.26 N	138.16 E
Uedesheim (Neigh.), F.R.G.	63	51.10 N	6.48 E
Uekermünde, G.D.R. (ü′kĕr-mün-dĕ)	166	53.43 N	14.01 E
Uele R., Zaire (wä′lå)	230	3.55 N	23.30 E
Uerdingen (Neigh.), F.R.G.	63	51.21 N	6.39 E
Ufa, Sov. Un. (ōō′fa)	182a	54.45 N	55.57 E
Ufa (R.), Sov. Un.	178	56.00 N	57.05 E
Ugab (R.), Namibia (ōō′gäb)	226	21.10 S	14.00 E
Ugalla (R.), Tan. (ōō-gä′lä)	231	6.15 S	32.30 E
Uganda, Afr. (ōō-gän′dä) (ū-găn′dá)	222	2.00 N	32.28 E
Ugashik L., Ak. (ōō′gá-shēk)	107	57.36 N	157.10 W
Ugie, S. Afr. (ōō′jē)	227c	31.13 S	28.14 E
Uglegorsk, Sov. Un. (ōō-glĭ-gôrsk)	181	49.00 N	142.31 E
Ugleural′sk, Sov. Un. (ōōg-lĕ-ōō-rálsk′)	182a	58.58 N	57.35 E
Uglich, Sov. Un. (ōōg-lēch′)	174	57.33 N	38.19 E
Uglitskiy, Sov. Un. (ōōg-lĭt′skĭ)	182a	53.50 N	60.18 E
Uglovka, Sov. Un. (ōōg-lôf′ká)	174	58.14 N	33.24 E
Ugra (R.), Sov. Un. (ōōg′rá)	174	54.43 N	34.20 E
Ugŭrchin, Bul.	173	43.06 N	24.23 E
Uhrichsville, Oh. (ū′rĭks-vĭl)	110	40.25 N	81.20 W
Uiju, Kor. (ōō′ējōō)	204	40.09 N	124.33 E
Uil (R.), Sov. Un. (ōō-ēl′)	179	49.30 N	55.10 E
Uinkaret Plat., Az. (ū-ĭn′kâr-ĕt)	121	36.43 N	113.15 W
Uinskoye, Sov. Un. (ōō-ĭn′skô-yĕ)	182a	56.53 N	56.25 E
Uinta (R.), Ut. (ū-ĭn′tá)	121	40.25 N	109.55 W

PLACE (Pronounciation)	PAGE	Lat. °′	Long. °′
Uintah, Ut. (ū-ĭn′tȧ)	119b	41.09 N	111.56 W
Uintah and Ouray Ind. Res., Ut.	121	39.55 N	109.20 W
Uitenhage, S. Afr.	227c	33.46 S	25.26 E
Uithoorn, Neth.	157a	52.13 N	4.49 E
Uíge, Ang.	230	7.37 S	15.03 E
Uji, Jap. (ōō′jē)	205b	34.53 N	135.49 E
Ujiji, Tan. (ōō-jē′jē)	231	4.55 S	29.41 E
Ujjain, India (ōō-jŭēn)	196	23.18 N	75.37 E
Ujung Pandang (Makasar), Indon.	206	5.08 S	119.28 E
Ukerewe I., Tan.	231	2.00 S	32.40 E
Ukhta, Sov. Un. (ōōk′tá)	178	65.22 N	31.30 E
Ukhta, Sov. Un.	180	63.08 N	53.42 E
Ukiah, Ca. (ū-kī′á)	120	35.09 N	122.12 W
Ukita (Neigh.), Jap.	69a	35.40 N	139.52 E
Ukmerge, Sov. Un. (ōōk′mĕr-ghå)	165	55.16 N	24.45 E
Ukrainian (S. S. R.), Sov. Un.	176	49.15 N	30.15 E
Uku (I.), Jap. (ōōk′ōō)	205	33.18 N	129.02 E
Ulan Batar, (Ulaanbaatar) Mong.	198	47.56 N	107.00 E
Ulanhad, see Chifeng			
Ulan-Ude, Sov. Un. (ōō′län ōō′dȧ)	181	51.59 N	107.41 E
Ulchin, Kor. (ōōl′chĕn′)	204	36.57 N	129.26 E
Ulcinj (Dulcigno), Yugo. (ōōl′tsĕn′)	173	41.56 N	19.15 E
Ulhās (R.), India	197b	19.13 N	73.03 E
Ulhāsnagar, India	197b	19.10 N	73.07 E
Uliastay, Mong.	198	47.49 N	97.00 E
Ulindi (R.), Zaire (ōō-lĭn′dē)	230	1.55 S	26.17 E
Ulla, Sov. Un. (ōōl′á)	174	55.14 N	29.15 E
Ulla (R.), Sov. Un.	174	54.58 N	29.03 E
Ulla (R.), Sp. (ōō′lä)	170	42.45 N	8.33 W
Üllendahl (Neigh.), F.R.G.	63	51.19 N	7.18 E
Ullŭng (I.), Kor. (ōōl′lōōng′)	204	37.29 N	130.50 E
Ulm, F.R.G. (ōōlm)	166	48.24 N	9.59 E
Ulmer, Mt., Ant. (ŭl′mûr′)	232	77.30 S	86.00 W
Ulricehamn, Swe. (ōōl-rē′sĕ-häm)	164	57.49 N	13.23 E
Ulsan, Kor. (ōōl′sän′)	204	35.35 N	129.22 E
Ulster (Reg.), Ire.-N. Ire. (ŭl′stēr)	162	54.41 N	7.10 W
Ulua R., Hond. (ōō-lōō′á)	132	15.49 N	87.45 W
Ulubāria, India	196a	22.27 N	88.09 E
Uluguru Mts., Tan.	231	7.15 S	37.30 E
Ulukişla, Tur. (ōō-lōō-kēsh′lá)	179	36.40 N	34.30 E
Ulunga, Sov. Un. (ōō-lōōn′gá)	204	46.16 N	136.29 E
Ulungur (R.), China (ōō-lōōn-gûr)	198	46.31 N	149.00 E
Ulu-Telyak, Sov. Un. (ōō lōō′tĕlyăk)	182a	54.54 N	57.01 E
Ulverstone, Austl. (ŭl′vēr-stŭn)	216	41.20 S	146.22 E
Ul′yanovka, Sov. Un. (ōō-lyä′nôf-ká)	182c	59.38 N	30.47 E
Ul′yanovsk, Sov. Un. (ōō-lyä′nôfsk)	178	54.20 N	48.05 E
Ulysses, Ks. (ū-lĭs′ēz)	122	37.34 N	101.25 W
Ulzangom, Mong.	198	50.23 N	92.14 E
Ülzen, F.R.G. (ült′sĕn)	166	52.58 N	10.34 E
Umán, Mex. (ōō-män′)	131	20.52 N	89.44 W
Umań, Sov. Un. (ōō-mán′)	175	48.44 N	30.13 E
Umatilla Ind. Res., Or. (ū-má-tĭl′á)	116	45.38 N	118.35 W
Umberpāda, India	197b	19.28 N	73.04 E
Umbria (Reg.), It. (ŭm′brĭ-á)	172	42.53 N	12.22 E
Umeå, Swe. (ōō′mĕ-ô)	158	63.48 N	20.29 E
Umeälven (R.), Swe.	158	64.57 N	18.51 E
Umhlatuzi (R.), S. Afr. (ōōm′hlá-tōō′zĭ)	227c	28.47 S	31.17 E
Umiat, Ak. (ōō′mĭ-ăt)	107	69.20 N	152.28 W
Umkomaas, S. Afr. (ōōm-kō′mäs)	227c	30.12 S	30.48 E
Umm Durmān, see Omdurman			
Umnak (I.), Ak. (ōōm′nák)	107a	53.10 N	169.08 W
Umnak Pass, Ak.	107a	53.10 N	168.04 W
Umniati (R.), Zimb.	226	17.08 S	29.11 E
Umpqua R., Or. (ŭmp′kwá)	116	43.42 N	123.50 W
Umtata, Trans. (ōōm-tä′tä)	227c	31.36 S	28.47 E
Umtentweni, S. Afr.	227c	30.41 S	30.29 E
Umzimkulu, S. Afr. (ōōm-zĕm-kōō′lōō)	227c	30.12 S	29.53 E
Umzinto, S. Afr. (ōōm-zĭn′tô)	227c	30.19 S	30.41 E
Una (R.), Yugo. (ōō′ná)	172	44.38 N	16.10 E
Unalakleet, Ak. (ū-ná-lák′lēt)	107	63.50 N	160.42 W
Unalaska, Ak. (ū-ná-lás′ká)	107a	53.30 N	166.20 W
Unare (R.), Ven.	143b	9.45 N	65.12 W
Unare, Laguna de (L.), Ven. (lä-gōō′nä-de-ōō-ná′rĕ)	143b	10.07 N	65.23 W
Unayzah, Sau Ar.	192	25.50 N	44.02 E
Uncas, Can. (ŭŋ′kȧs)	95g	53.30 N	113.02 W
Uncia, Bol. (ōōn′sē-ä)	142	18.28 S	66.32 W
Uncompahgre (R.), Co.	121	38.20 N	107.45 W
Uncompahgre Pk., Co. (ŭn-kŭm-pä′grē)	121	38.00 N	107.30 W
Uncompahgre Plat., Co.	121	38.40 N	108.40 W
Underberg, S. Afr. (ŭn′dēr-bûrg)	227c	29.51 S	29.32 E
Undo, Eth.	225	6.37 N	38.29 E
Unecha, Sov. Un. (ōō-nĕ′chá)	174	32.51 N	32.44 E
Ungava B., Can. (ŭŋ-gá′vá)	97	59.46 N	67.18 W
Ungava, Péninsule d′ (Pen.), Can.	97	59.55 N	74.00 W
União da Vitória, Braz. (ōō-nē-ouɴ′ dá vē-tō′ryä)	144	26.17 S	51.13 W
Unidad Sante Fe, Mex.	60a	19.23 N	99.15 W
Unije (I.), Yugo. (ōō′nē-yĕ)	172	44.39 N	14.10 E
Unimak (I.), Ak. (ōō-nē-mák′)	107a	54.30 N	163.35 W
Unimak Pass, Ak.	107a	54.22 N	165.22 W
Union, Ms. (ūn′yŭn)	126	32.35 N	89.07 W
Union, Mo.	123	38.28 N	90.59 W
Union, NC	127	34.42 N	81.40 W
Union, NJ	55	40.42 N	74.16 W
Union, Or.	116	45.13 N	117.52 W
Union City, Ca.	118b	37.36 N	122.01 W
Union City, Ind.	110	40.10 N	85.00 W
Union City, Mi.	110	42.00 N	85.10 W
Union City, NJ	55	40.46 N	74.02 W
Union City, Pa.	111	41.50 N	79.50 W
Union City, Tn.	126	36.25 N	89.04 W
Uniondale, NY	55	40.43 N	73.36 W
Union de Reyes, Cuba (ōō-nyō′n-dĕ-rĕ-vĕ′s)	134	22.45 N	81.30 W
Union de San Antonio, Mex. (sän än-tō′nyō)	130	21.07 N	101.56 W
Union de Tula, Mex. (tōō′lä)	130	19.57 N	104.14 W

ăt; finăl; rāte; senāte; ärm; ȧsk; sofȧ; fâre; ch-choose; dh-as th in other; bē; ēvent; bĕt; recĕnt; cratēr; g-gō; gh-guttural g; bĭt; ĭ-short neutral; rīde; ĸ-guttural k as ch in German ich;

PLACE (Pronounciation)	PAGE	Lat. °'	Long. °'
Union Grove, Wi. (ūn-yŭn grōv)	113a	42.41 N	88.03 W
Unión Hidalgo, Mex. (ē-dä'lgô)	131	16.29 N	94.51 W
Union Point, Ga.	126	33.37 N	83.08 W
Union Springs Al. (sprĭngz)	126	32.08 N	85.43 W
Uniontown, Al. (ūn'yŭn-toun)	126	32.26 N	87.30 W
Uniontown, Oh.	113d	40.58 N	81.25 W
Uniontown, Pa.	111	39.55 N	79.45 W
Unionville, Mo. (ūn'yŭn-vĭl)	123	40.28 N	92.58 W
Unisan, Phil. (o͞o-nē'sän)	207a	13.50 N	121.59 E
Unitas, Mts., U. S. (ū-nĭ'tăs)	108	40.35 N	111.00 W
United Arab Emirates, Asia	190	24.00 N	54.00 E
United Arab Republic, see Egypt			
United Kingdom, Eur.	158	56.30 N	1.40 W
United Nations Headquarters (P. Int.), NY	55	40.45 N	73.58 W
United Pueblo Ind. Res., NM (u-nīt'ĕd pōō-ĕb'lō) (pwā'blō)	121	35.30 N	107.00 W
United States, N. A.	94	38.00 N	110.00 W
Unity, Can.	100	52.27 N	109.10 W
Universal, In. (ū-nĭ-vûr'sal)	110	39.35 N	87.30 W
University City, Mo. (ū'nĭ-vûr'sĭ-tĭ)	119e	38.40 N	90.19 W
University Heights, Oh.	56a	41.30 N	81.32 W
University Park, Md.	56d	38.58 N	76.57 W
University Park, Tx.	119c	32.51 N	96.48 W
Unna, F.R.G. (o͞o'nä)	169c	51.32 N	7.41 E
Unst (I.), Scot. (o͞onst)	162a	60.50 N	1.24 W
Unterhaching, F.R.G. (o͞on'tĕr-hä-kĕng)	157d	48.03 N	11.38 E
Untermauerbach, Aus.	66e	48.14 N	16.12 E
Unye, Tur. (ün'yĕ)	179	41.00 N	37.10 E
Unzha (R.), Sov. Un. (o͞on'zhà)	178	57.45 N	44.10 E
Upa (R.), Sov. Un. (o͞o'pà)	174	53.54 N	36.48 E
Upanda, Sierra do (Mts.), Ang. (sē-ĕ'r-rä-dô-o͞o-pä'n-dä)	222	13.15 S	14.15 E
Upata, Ven. (o͞o-pä'tä)	142	7.58 N	62.27 W
Upemba, Parc Natl. de l' (Natl. Pk.), Zaire	231	9.10 S	26.15 E
Up Holland, Eng.	64a	53.33 N	2.44 W
Upington, S. Afr. (ŭp'ĭng-tŭn)	226	28.25 S	21.15 E
Upland, Ca. (ŭp'lănd)	119a	34.06 N	117.38 W
Upland, Pa.	56b	39.51 N	75.23 W
Upolu Pt., Hi. (o͞o-pô'lo͞o)	106a	20.15 N	155.48 W
Upper Arrow L., Can. (ăr'ō)	99	50.30 N	117.55 W
Upper Brookville, NY	55	40.51 N	73.34 W
Upper Darby, Pa. (där'bĭ)	112f	39.58 N	75.16 W
Upper de Lacs (R.), ND (dē lăk)	114	48.58 N	101.55 W
Upper Ferntree Gully, Austl.	70b	37.54 S	145.19 E
Upper Kapuas Mts., Mala.	206	1.45 N	112.06 E
Upper L., Nv. (ŭp'ēr)	116	41.42 N	119.59 W
Upper Marlboro, Md. (ûpēr märl'bōrô)	112e	38.49 N	76.46 W
Upper Mill, Wa. (mĭl)	118a	47.11 N	121.55 W
Upper New York B., NY	55	40.41 N	74.03 W
Upper Red L., Mn. (rĕd)	115	48.14 N	94.53 W
Upper Saint Clair, Pa.	57b	40.21 N	80.05 W
Upper Sandusky, Oh. (săn-dŭs'kē)	110	40.50 N	83.20 W
Upper San Leandro Res., Ca. (ŭp'ēr săn lē-ăn'drô)	118b	37.47 N	122.04 W
Upper Tooting (Neigh.), Eng.	62	51.26 N	0.10 W
Upper Volta, see Burkina Faso			
Uppingham, Eng. (ŭp'ĭng-ăm)	156	52.35 N	0.43 W
Uppsala, Swe. (o͞op'sà-lä)	164	59.53 N	17.39 E
Upton, Eng.	62	51.30 N	0.35 W
Uptown, Ma. (ŭp'toun)	105a	42.10 N	71.36 W
Uptown (Neigh.), Il.	58a	41.58 N	87.40 W
Upwey, Austl.	70b	37.54 S	145.20 E
Uraga, Jap. (o͞o'rà-gä')	205a	35.15 N	139.43 E
Uraga-Kaikyō (Str.), Jap. (o͞o'rä-gä kī'kyō)	205a	35.11 N	139.44 W
Ural (R.), Sov. Un. (o͞o-räl') (ū-rôl)	179	49.50 N	51.30 E
Urals (Mts.), Sov. Un.	176	56.28 N	58.13 E
Ural'sk, Sov. Un. (o͞o-rálsk')	179	51.15 N	51.10 E
Uran, India (o͞o-rän')	197b	18.53 N	72.46 E
Uranium City, Can.	96	59.34 N	108.59 W
Urawa, Jap. (o͞o'rä-wä')	205a	35.52 N	139.39 E
Urayasu, Jap. (o͞o'rä-yä'so͞o)	205a	35.40 N	139.54 E
Urazovo, Sov. Un. (o͞o-rà'zô-vô)	175	50.08 N	38.03 E
Urbana, Il. (ûr-băn'à)	110	40.10 N	88.15 W
Urbana, Oh.	110	40.05 N	83.50 W
Urbino, It. (o͞or-bē'nô)	172	43.43 N	12.37 E
Urda, Sov. Un. (o͞or'dà)	179	48.50 N	47.30 E
Urdaneta, Phil. (o͞or-dä-nä'tä)	207a	15.59 N	120.34 E
Urdinarrain, Arg. (o͞or-dē-när-rāē'n)	141c	32.43 S	58.53 W
Urdzhar, Sov. Un. (o͞ord-zhär')	180	47.28 N	82.00 E
Urfa, Tur. (o͞or'fà)	179	37.20 N	38.45 E
Urgench, Sov. Un. (o͞or-gĕnch')	155	41.32 N	60.33 E
Uritsk, Sov. Un. (o͞o'rĭtsk)	182c	59.50 N	30.11 E
Urla, Tur. (o͞or'là)	173	38.20 N	26.44 E
Urman, Sov. Un. (o͞or'màn)	182a	54.53 N	56.52 E
Urmi (R.), Sov. Un. (o͞or'mē)	204	48.50 N	134.00 E
Urmston, Eng.	64b	53.27 N	2.21 W
Uromi, Nig.	229	6.44 N	6.18 E
Urrao, Col. (o͞or-rà'ô)	142a	6.19 N	76.11 W
Urshel'skiy, Sov. Un. (o͞or-shĕl'skēē)	174	55.50 N	40.11 E
Ursus, Pol.	167	52.12 N	20.53 E
Urubamba (R.), Peru (o͞o-ro͞o-bäm'bä)	142	11.48 S	72.34 W
Uruguaiana, Braz. (o͞o-ro͞o-gwī-ä'nà)	144	29.45 S	57.00 W
Uruguay, S. A. (o͞o-ro͞o-gwī') (ū'ro͞o-gwā)	140	32.45 S	56.00 W
Uruguay, Rio (R.), Braz. (rē'ō-o͞o-ro͞o-gwī)	144	27.05 S	55.15 W
Ürümqi, China (ū-rŭm-chyē)	198	43.49 N	87.43 E
Urup (I.), Sov. Un. (o͞o'ro͞op')	181	46.08 N	149.00 E
Uryupinsk, Sov. Un. (o͞or'yo͞o-pēn-sk')	179	50.50 N	42.00 E
Urziceni, Rom. (o͞o-zē-chĕn'')	173	44.45 N	26.42 E
Usa, Jap.	204	33.31 N	131.22 E
Usa (R.), Sov. Un. (o͞o'sà)	178	66.00 N	58.20 E
Uşak, Tur. (o͞o'shàk)	179	39.50 N	29.15 E
Usakos, Namibia (o͞o-sä'kōs)	226	22.00 S	15.40 E

PLACE (Pronounciation)	PAGE	Lat. °'	Long. °'
Usambara Mts., Tan.	231	4.40 S	38.25 E
Usangu Flats (Pln.), Tan.	231	8.10 S	34.00 E
Ushaki, Sov. Un. (o͞o'shá-kĭ)	182c	59.28 N	31.00 E
Ushakovskoye, Sov. Un. (o͞o-shá-kôv'skô-yĕ)	182a	56.18 N	62.23 E
Ushashi, Tan.	231	2.00 S	33.57 E
Ushiku, Jap. (o͞o'shē-ko͞o)	205a	35.24 N	140.09 E
Ushimado, Jap. (o͞o'shē-mä'dō)	205	34.37 N	134.09 E
Ushuaia, Arg. (o͞o-sho͞o-ī'ä)	144	54.46 S	68.24 W
Üsküdar, Tur.	179	40.55 N	29.00 E
Usman', Sov. Un. (o͞os-man')	174	52.03 N	39.40 E
Usmānpur (Neigh.), India	67d	28.41 N	77.15 E
Usol'ye, Sov. Un. (o͞o-sô'lyĕ)	182a	59.24 N	56.40 E
Usol'ye-Sibirskoye, Sov. Un. (o͞o-sô'lyĕsĭ' bēr'skô-yĕ)	180	52.44 N	103.46 E
Uspallata P., Arg.-Chile (o͞os-pä-lyä'tä)	144	32.47 S	70.08 W
Uspanapa (R.), Mex. (o͞os-pä-nä'pä)	131	17.43 N	94.14 W
Ussel, Fr. (üs'ĕl)	168	45.33 N	2.17 E
Ussuri (R.), China (o͞o-so͞o'rē)	199	46.30 N	133.56 E
Ussuriysk, Sov. Un.	181	43.48 N	132.09 E
Ust'-Bol'sheretsk, Sov. Un.	181	52.41 N	157.00 E
Ustica, I. di, It. (ē'sō-lä-dē-o͞os'tē-kä)	172	38.43 N	12.11 E
Ustinovka, Sov. Un. (o͞os-tē'nôf-kä)	175	47.59 N	32.31 E
Ústí, Czech. (o͞os'tē)	166	50.39 N	14.02 E
Ust'-Izhora, Sov. Un. (o͞ost-ĕz'hô-rà)	182c	59.49 N	30.35 E
Ustka, Pol. (o͞ost'kà)	166	54.34 N	16.52 E
Ust'-Kamchatsk, Sov. Un.	181	56.13 N	162.18 E
Ust'-Kamenogorsk, Sov. Un.	180	49.58 N	80.43 E
Ust'-Katav, Sov. Un. (o͞ost kà'táf)	182a	54.55 N	58.12 E
Ust'-Kishert', Sov. Un. (o͞ost kē'shĕrt)	182a	57.21 N	57.13 E
Ust'-Kulom, Sov. Un. (ko͝o'lŭm)	178	61.38 N	54.00 E
Ust'-Maya, Sov. Un. (mà'yà)	181	60.33 N	134.43 E
Ust' Olenëk, Sov. Un.	181	72.52 N	120.15 E
Ust-Ordynskiy, Sov. Un. (o͞ost-ôr-dyēnsk'ĭ)	181	52.47 N	104.39 E
Ust' Penzhino, Sov. Un.	181	63.00 N	165.10 E
Ust' Port, Sov. Un. (o͞ost'pôrt')	180	69.20 N	83.41 E
Ust'-Tsil'ma, Sov. Un. (tsĭl'mà)	178	65.25 N	52.10 E
Ust'-Tyrma, Sov. Un. (tur'mà)	181	50.27 N	131.17 E
Ust'Uls, Sov. Un. (o͞ols)	182a	60.35 N	58.32 E
Ust'-Urt, Plato (Plat.), Sov. Un. (o͞ort)	176	44.03 N	54.58 E
Ustyuzhna, Sov. Un. (yo͞ozh'nà)	174	58.49 N	36.19 E
Usu, China (ū-so͞o)	198	44.28 N	84.07 E
Usuki, Jap. (o͞o'so͞o-kē')	205	33.06 N	131.47 E
Usulutan, Sal. (o͞o-so͞o-lä-tän')	132	13.22 N	88.25 W
Usumacinta (R.), Mex. (o͞o'so͞o-mä-sēn'tō)	131	18.24 N	92.30 W
Us'va, Sov. Un. (o͞os'và)	182a	58.41 N	57.38 E
Utah (State), U. S. (ū'tô)	108	39.25 N	112.40 W
Utah (L.), Ut.	121	40.10 N	111.55 W
Utan, India	197b	19.27 N	72.43 E
Ute Mtn. Ind. Res., NM	121	36.57 N	108.34 W
Utena, Sov. Un. (o͞o'tā-nä)	165	55.32 N	25.40 E
Utete, Tan. (o͞o-tā'tå)	227	8.05 S	38.47 E
Utfort, F.R.G.	63	51.28 N	6.38 E
Utica, In. (ū'tĭ-kà)	113h	38.20 N	85.39 W
Utica, NY	111	43.05 N	75.10 W
Utiel, Sp. (o͞o-tyål')	170	39.34 N	1.13 W
Utika, Mi. (ū'tĭ-kà)	113b	42.37 N	83.02 W
Utik L., Can.	101	55.16 N	96.00 W
Utikuma L., Can.	100	55.50 N	115.25 W
Utila I., Hond. (o͞o-tē'lä)	132	16.07 N	87.05 W
Utinga, Braz.	61d	23.38 S	46.32 W
Uto, Jap. (o͞o'tō')	205	32.43 N	130.39 E
Utrecht, Neth. (ū'trĕkt) (ü'trĕkt)	157a	52.05 N	5.06 E
Utrera, Sp. (o͞o-trā'rä)	170	37.12 N	5.48 W
Utsunomiya, Jap. (o͞ot'so͞o-nô-mē-yà')	205	36.35 N	139.52 E
Uttaradit, Thai.	206	17.47 N	100.10 E
Uttarpara-Kotrung, India	196a	22.40 N	88.21 E
Uttar Pradesh (State), India (o͞ot-tär-prä-dēsh)	196	27.00 N	80.00 E
Uttoxeter, Eng. (ŭt-tôk'sē-tēr)	156	52.54 N	1.52 W
Utuado, P. R. (o͞o-to͞o-ä'dhō)	129b	18.16 N	66.40 W
Uusikaupunki (Nystad), Fin. (o͞o'sĭ-kou'po͝on-kĭ) (nü'städh)	165	60.48 N	21.24 E
Uvalde, Tx. (ū-văl'dē)	124	29.14 N	99.47 W
Uvel'skiy, Sov. Un. (o͞o-vyĕl'skĭ)	182a	54.27 N	60.22 E
Uvinza, Tan.	231	5.06 S	30.22 E
Uvira, Zaire (o͞o-vē'rä)	226	3.28 S	29.03 E
Uvod' (R.), Sov. Un. (o͞o-vôd')	174	56.52 N	41.03 E
Uvongo Beach, S. Afr.	227c	30.49 S	30.23 E
Uvs Nuur (L.), Mong.	198	50.29 N	93.32 E
Uwajima, Jap. (o͞o-wä'jē-mä)	205	33.12 N	132.35 E
Uxbridge, Ma. (ŭks'brĭj)	105a	42.05 N	71.38 W
Uxbridge (Neigh.), Eng.	62	51.33 N	0.29 W
Uxmal (Ruins), Mex. (o͞o'x-mä'l)	132a	20.22 N	89.44 W
Uyama, Jap.	69b	34.50 N	135.41 E
Uy R., Sov. Un. (o͞oy)	182a	54.05 N	62.11 E
Uyskoye, Sov. Un. (ûy'skô-yĕ)	182a	54.22 N	60.01 E
Uyuni, Bol. (o͞o-yo͞o'nē)	142	20.28 S	66.45 W
Uyuni, Salar de (Salt Flat), Bol. (sä-lär-dē)	142	20.58 S	67.09 W
Uzbek S. S. R., Sov. Un. (o͞oz-bĕk')	176	42.42 N	60.00 E
Uzen, Bol'shoy (R.), Sov. Un.	179	49.50 N	49.35 E
Uzh (R.), Sov. Un. (o͞ozh)	175	51.07 N	29.05 E
Uzhgorod, Sov. Un. (o͞ozh'gô-rôt)	167	48.38 N	22.18 E
Uzunköpru, Tur. (o͞o'zo͞on'kû-prü)	173	41.17 N	26.42 E

V

PLACE (Pronounciation)	PAGE	Lat. °'	Long. °'
Vaal (R.), S. Afr. (väl)	226	28.15 S	24.30 E
Vaaldam (L.), S. Afr.	223d	26.58 S	28.37 E
Vaalplaas, S. Afr.	223d	25.39 S	28.56 E
Vaalwater, S. Afr.	223d	24.17 S	28.08 E
Vaasa, Fin. (vä'sà)	165	63.06 N	21.39 E
Vác, Hung. (väts)	167	47.46 N	19.10 E
Vache, Île À (I.), Hai. (väsh)	135	18.05 N	73.40 W
Vadsø, Nor. (vädh'sû)	158	70.08 N	29.52 E
Vadstena, Swe. (väd'stĭ'nà)	164	58.27 N	14.53 E
Vaduz, Liech. (vä'do͞ots)	166	47.10 N	9.32 E
Vaga (R.), Sov. Un. (va'gà)	178	61.55 N	42.30 E
Vah R., Czech. (väĸ)	167	48.07 N	17.52 E
Vaigai (R.), India	196	10.20 N	78.13 E
Vaires-sur-Marne, Fr.	64c	48.52 N	2.39 E
Vakh (R.), Sov. Un. (vàĸ)	180	61.30 N	81.33 E
Valachia (Reg.), Rom.	173	44.45 N	24.17 E
Valcanuta (Neigh.), It.	66c	41.53 N	12.25 E
Valcartier-Village, Can. (väl-kärt-yē'vē-läzh')	95b	46.56 N	71.28 W
Valdai Hills, Sov. Un. (vál-dī' gô'rĭ)	174	57.50 N	32.35 E
Valday (Valdai), Sov. Un. (vál-dī')	174	57.58 N	33.13 E
Valdecañas, Embalse de (Res.), Sp.	170	39.15 N	5.30 W
Valdemārpils, Sov. Un.	165	57.22 N	22.34 E
Valdemorillo, Sp. (väl-då-mô-rēl'yō)	171a	40.30 N	4.04 W
Valdepeñas, Sp. (väl-då-pān'yäs)	170	38.46 N	3.22 W
Valderaduey (R.), Sp. (väl-dĕ-rä-dwĕ'y)	170	41.39 N	5.35 W
Valdés, Pen., Arg. (väl-dĕ's)	144	42.15 S	63.15 W
Valdez, Ak. (văl'dēz)	107	61.10 N	146.18 W
Valdilecha, Sp. (väl-dē-lā'chä)	171a	40.17 N	3.19 W
Valdivia, Chile (väl-dē'vä)	144	39.47 S	73.13 W
Valdivia, Col. (väl-dē'vēä)	142a	7.10 N	75.26 W
Val-d' Or., Can.	103	48.03 N	77.50 W
Valdosta, Ga. (văl-dŏs'tà)	126	30.50 N	83.18 W
Valdoviño, Sp. (väl-dô-vē'nō)	170	43.36 N	8.05 W
Vale, Or. (vāl)	116	43.59 N	117.14 W
Valença, Braz. (vä-lĕɴ'sà)	143	13.43 S	38.58 W
Valença, Port.	170	42.03 N	8.36 W
Valence, Fr. (vä-lĕɴs)	168	44.56 N	4.54 E
Valencia, Sp. (vä-lĕn'thē-ä)	171	39.26 N	0.23 W
Valencia, Ven. (vä-lĕn'syä)	143b	10.11 N	68.00 W
Valencia (Reg.), Sp. (vä-lĕn'thē-ä)	171	39.08 N	0.43 W
Valencia de Alcántara, Sp.	170	39.34 N	7.13 W
Valencia I., Ire. (vá-lĕn'shá)	162	51.55 N	10.26 W
Valencia, Lago de (L.), Ven.	143b	10.11 N	67.45 W
Valenciennes, Fr. (vá-läɴ-syĕn')	168	50.24 N	3.36 E
Valentine, Ne. (vá läɴ-tē-nyē')	114	42.52 N	100.34 W
Valentín Alsina (Neigh.), Arg.	60d	34.40 S	58.25 W
Valera, Ven. (vä-lē'rä)	142	9.12 N	70.45 W
Valerianovsk, Sov. Un. (vá-lĕ-rĭ-ä'nôvsk)	182a	58.47 N	59.34 E
Valérien, Mont (Hill), Fr.	64c	48.53 N	2.13 E
Valga, Sov. Un. (väl'gá)	174	57.47 N	26.03 E
Valhalla, S. Afr. (vál-hăl-á)	227b	25.49 S	28.09 E
Valier, Mt. (vă-lēr')	117	48.17 N	112.14 W
Valjevo, Yugo. (väl'yå-vô)	173	44.17 N	19.57 E
Valki, Sov. Un. (väl'kē)	175	49.49 N	35.40 E
Valladolid, Mex. (väl-yä-dhō-lēdh')	132a	20.39 N	88.13 W
Valladolid, Sp. (väl-yä-dhō-lēdh')	170	41.41 N	4.41 W
Vall de Uxó, Sp. (väl-dē-o͞ox-ó')	171	39.50 N	0.15 W
Valldoreix, Sp.	65e	41.28 N	2.04 E
Valle, Arroyo del, Ca. (ä-rō'yō dĕl väl'yå)	120	37.36 N	121.43 W
Vallecas, Sp. (väl-yä'käs)	171a	40.23 N	3.37 W
Vallecas (Neigh.), Sp.	65b	40.23 N	3.37 W
Valle de Allende, Mex. (väl'yā dā äl-yĕn'då)	124	26.55 N	105.25 W
Valle de Bravo, Mex. (brä'vô)	130	19.12 N	100.07 W
Valle de Guanape, Ven. (vä'l-yĕ-dĕ-gwä-nä'pĕ)	143b	9.54 N	65.41 W
Valle de la Pascua, Ven. (lä-pä's-ko͞oä)	142	9.12 N	65.08 W
Valle del Cauca, Col. (vä'l-yĕ del kou'ĸä)	142a	4.03 N	76.13 W
Valle de Santiago, Mex. (sän-tē-ä'gô)	130	20.23 N	101.11 W
Valledupar, Col. (do͞o-pär')	142	10.13 N	73.39 W
Valle Grande, Bol. (grän'dā)	142	18.27 S	64.03 W
Vallejo, Ca. (vä-yä'hō) (vă-lā'hō)	118b	38.06 N	122.15 W
Vallejo, Sierra de (Mts.), Mex. (sē-ĕ'r-rä-dĕ-väl-yĕ'ĸô)	130	21.00 N	105.10 W
Vallenar, Chile (väl-yå-när')	144	28.39 S	70.52 W
Valletta, Malta (väl-lĕt'ä)	160	35.50 N	14.29 E
Valle Vista, Ca. (väl'yà vĭs'tà)	119a	33.45 N	116.53 W
Valley City, ND	114	46.55 N	97.59 W
Valley City, Oh. (văl'ĭ)	113d	41.14 N	81.56 W
Valleydale, Ca.	59	34.06 N	117.56 W
Valley Falls, Ks.	123	39.25 N	95.26 W
Valleyfield, Can. (văl'ē-fēld)	95a	45.16 N	74.09 W
Valley Mede, Md.	56c	39.17 N	76.50 W
Valley Park, Mo. (văl'ē pärk)	119e	38.33 N	90.30 W
Valley Stream, NY (văl'ĭ strēm)	112a	40.39 N	73.42 W
Valli di Comácchio (L.), It. (vä'lē-dē-kô-má'chyô)	172	44.38 N	12.15 E
Vallière, Hai. (väl-yâr')	135	19.30 N	71.55 W
Vallimanca (R.), Arg. (väl-yē-mä'n-kä)	141c	36.21 S	60.55 W
Valls, Sp. (väls)	171	41.15 N	1.15 E
Valmiera, Sov. Un. (vál'myĕ-rá)	165	57.34 N	25.54 E
Valognes, Fr. (vá-lôn'y')	168	49.32 N	1.30 W
Valona, see Vlorë			
Valparaíso, Chile (väl'pä-rä-ē'sô)	141b	33.02 S	71.32 W
Valparaiso, In. (văl-pá-rā'zō)	110	41.25 N	87.05 W
Valparaiso, Mex.	130	22.49 N	103.33 W
Valpariso (Prov.), Chile	141b	32.58 S	71.23 W
Valréas, Fr. (vál-rà-ä')	168	45.25 N	4.56 E
Vals (R.), S. Afr.	223d	27.32 S	26.51 E
Valsbaai (False Bay), S. Afr.	226a	34.14 S	18.35 E

ng-sing; ŋ-baŋk; ɴ-nasalized n; nŏd; cŏmmit; ōld; ôbey; ôrder; oi-boil; fo͞od; fo͝ot; ou-out; s-soft; sh-dish; th-thin; pūre; ůnite; ûrn; stŭd; circŭs; ü-as in French tu; '-indeterminate vowel.

PLACE (Pronounciation)	PAGE	Lat. °′	Long. °′
Vals, Tandjung (C.), Indon.	207	8.30 s	137.15 E
Valuyevo, Sov. Un. (vå-lo͞o′yĕ-vô)	182b	55.34 N	37.21 E
Valuyki, Sov. Un. (vå-lo͞o-ē′kė)	175	50.14 N	38.04 E
Valverde del Camino, Sp. (väl-vĕr-dĕ-dĕl-kä-mė′nō)	170	37.34 N	6.44 W
Vambanād (R.), India	196	10.00 N	76.03 E
Vammala, Fin.	165	61.19 N	22.51 E
Van, Tur. (vån)	179	38.04 N	43.10 E
Van Buren, Ar. (văn bū′rĕn)	123	35.26 N	94.20 W
Van Buren, Me.	104	47.09 N	67.58 W
Vanceburg, Ky. (văns′bûrg)	110	38.35 N	83.20 W
Vancouver, Can. (văn-ko͞o′vẽr)	118d	49.16 N	123.06 W
Vancouver, Wa.	118c	45.37 N	122.40 W
Vancouver I., Can.	98	49.50 N	125.05 W
Vancouver Island Ra., Can.	98	49.25 N	125.25 W
Vandalia, Il. (văn-dā′lĭ-ȧ)	110	39.00 N	89.00 W
Vandalia, Mo.	123	39.19 N	91.30 W
Vanderbijlpark, S. Afr.	223d	26.43 s	27.50 E
Vanderhoof, Can.	98	54.01 N	124.01 W
Van Diemen (Str.), **see Ōsumi Kaikyō**			
Van Diemen, C., Austl. (văndē′mĕn)	214	11.05 s	130.15 E
Van Diemen G., Austl.	214	11.50 s	131.30 E
Vandreuil, Can. (vô-drû′y′)	95a	45.24 N	74.02 W
Vanegas, Mex. (vä-nĕ′gäs)	130	23.54 N	100.54 W
Vänern (L.), Swe.	164	58.52 N	13.17 E
Vänersborg, Swe. (vĕ′nẽrs-bôr′)	164	58.24 N	12.15 E
Vanga, Ken. (väŋ′gä)	227	4.38 s	39.10 E
Vangani, India	197b	19.07 N	73.15 E
Van Gölü (L.), Tur.	179	38.45 N	43.00 E
Van Horn, Tx.	124	31.03 N	104.50 W
Vanier, Can.	95c	45.27 N	75.39 W
Vaniköy (Neigh.), Tur.	66f	41.04 N	29.04 E
Van Lear, Ky. (văn lēr′)	110	37.45 N	82.50 W
Vannes, Fr. (vån)	168	47.42 N	2.46 W
Van Nuys, Ca. (văn nīz′)	119a	34.11 N	118.27 W
Van Rees, Pegunungan (Mtn.), Indon.	207	2.30 s	138.45 E
Vantaan (R.), Fin.	165	60.25 N	24.43 E
Vanuatu, Oceania	215	16.02 s	169.15 E
Vanves, Fr.	64c	48.50 N	2.18 E
Van Wert, Oh. (văn wûrt′)	110	40.50 N	84.35 W
Vanzago, It.	65c	45.32 N	9.00 E
Vara, Swe. (vä′rä)	164	58.17 N	12.55 E
Varaklāni, Sov. Un.	172	56.38 N	26.46 E
Varallo, It. (vä-räl′lô)	172	45.44 N	8.14 E
Vārānasi (Benares), India	196	25.25 N	83.00 E
Varanerfjorden (Fd.), Nor.	158	70.05 N	30.20 E
Varano, Lago di (L.), It. (lä′gō-dē-vä-rä′nō)	172	41.52 N	15.55 E
Varaždin, Yugo. (vä′räzh′dėn)	172	46.17 N	16.20 E
Varazze, It. (vä-rät′sā)	172	44.23 N	8.34 E
Varberg, Swe. (vär′bĕrg)	164	57.06 N	12.16 E
Vardar (R.), Yugo. (vär′där)	173	41.40 N	21.50 E
Vardø, Nor. (värd′û)	158	70.23 N	30.15 E
Varėna, Sov. Un. (vä-rā′nå)	165	54.16 N	24.35 E
Varennes, Can. (vå-rĕn′)	95a	45.41 N	73.27 W
Varěs, Yugo. (vä′rĕsh)	173	44.10 N	18.20 E
Varese, It. (vä-rā′så)	172	45.45 N	8.49 E
Vargem Grande (Neigh.), Braz.	61c	22.59 s	43.29 W
Varginha, Braz. (vär-zhė′n-yä)	141a	21.33 s	45.25 W
Varkaus, Fin. (vär′kous)	165	62.19 N	27.51 E
Varlamovo, Sov. Un. (vár-lå′mô-vô)	182a	54.37 N	60.41 E
Varna (Stalin), Bul. (vär′nȧ) (stä′lĭn)	173	43.14 N	27.58 E
Varna, Sov. Un.	182a	53.22 N	60.59 E
Värnamo, Swe. (vĕr′nå-mô)	164	57.11 N	13.45 E
Varnsdorf, Czech. (värns′dôrf)	166	50.54 N	14.36 E
Varnville, SC (värn′vĭl)	127	32.49 N	81.05 W
Várpalota (P. Int.), Hung.	66g	47.30 N	19.02 E
Vars, Can. (värz)	95c	45.21 N	75.21 W
Varvaropolye, Sov. Un. (vår′vår′ô-pô-lyĕ)	175	48.38 N	38.37 E
Vasa, India	197b	19.20 N	72.47 E
Vascongadas (Reg.), Sp. (väs-kôn-gä′däs)	170	42.35 N	2.46 W
Vashka (R.), Sov. Un.	178	63.20 N	47.50 E
Vashon, Wa. (văsh′ŭn)	118a	47.27 N	122.28 W
Vashon Heights, Wa. (hītz)	118a	47.30 N	122.28 W
Vashon I., Wa.	118a	47.27 N	122.27 W
Vasiljevskij, Ostrov (I.), Sov. Un.	66a	59.56 N	30.15 E
Vasil′kov, Sov. Un. (vå-sėl′-kôf′)	175	50.10 N	30.22 E
Vaslui, Rom. (vås-lo͞o′ė)	167	46.39 N	27.49 E
Vassar, Mi. (văs′ẽr)	110	43.25 N	83.35 W
Vassouras, Braz. (väs-sō′räzh)	144b	22.25 s	43.40 W
Västerås, Swe. (vĕs′tĕr-ôs)	164	59.39 N	16.30 E
Västerdalälven (R.), Swe.	164	61.06 N	13.10 E
Västervik, Swe. (vĕs′tĕr-vēk)	164	57.45 N	16.35 E
Vasto, It. (väs′tô)	172	42.06 N	12.42 E
Vasyugan (R.), Sov. Un. (vås-yo͞o-gån′)	180	58.52 N	77.30 E
Vatican City (Città del Vaticano), Eur. (văt′ĭ-kăn sĭt′ė) (chē-tá′del vä-tė-kä′nô)	171d	41.54 N	12.22 E
Vaticano, C., It. (vä-tė-kä′nô)	172	38.38 N	15.52 E
Vatnajökull (Gl.), Ice. (vät′nå-yû-ko͞ol)	158	64.34 N	16.41 W
Vatomandry, Mad. (vä-to͞o-män′drē)	227	18.53 s	48.13 E
Vatra Dornei, Rom. (vät′rå dôr′nå′)	167	47.22 N	25.20 E
Vättern (L.), Swe.	164	58.15 N	14.24 E
Vattholma, Swe.	164	60.01 N	17.40 E
Vaucluse, Austl.	70a	33.51 s	151.17 E
Vaugh, Wa. (vôn)	118a	47.21 N	122.47 W
Vaughan, Can.	95d	43.47 N	79.36 W
Vaughn, NM	122	34.37 N	105.13 W
Vauhallan, Fr.	64c	48.44 N	2.12 E
Vaujours, Fr.	64c	48.56 N	2.35 E
Vaupés (R.), Col. (vå′o͞o-pĕ′s)	142	1.18 N	71.14 W
Vaxholm, Swe. (väks′hôlm)	164	59.26 N	18.19 E
Växjo, Swe. (vĕks′shû)	164	56.53 N	14.46 E
Vaygach (I.), Sov. Un. (vī-gȧch′)	178	70.00 N	59.00 E
Veadeiros, Chapadas dos (Mts.), Braz. (shä-pä′däs-dôs-vĕ-ȧ-dā′rōs)	143	15.20 s	48.43 W
Vedea (R.), Rom. (vå′dyȧ)	173	44.25 N	24.45 E
Vedia, Arg. (vĕ′dyä)	141c	34.29 s	61.30 W
Veedersburg, In. (vē′dẽrz-bûrg)	110	40.05 N	87.15 W
Vega (I.), Nor.	158	65.38 N	10.51 E
Vega de Alatorre, Mex. (vā′gä dā ä-lä-tōr′rå)	131	20.02 N	96.39 W
Vega Real (Mts.), Dom. Rep. (vĕ′gä-rĕ-ä′l)	135	19.30 N	71.05 W
Vegreville, Can.	100	53.30 N	112.03 W
Vehār L., India	197b	19.11 N	72.52 E
Veinticinco de Mayo, Arg. (vå-ēn′tė-sēn′kō dā mä′yō)	141c	35.26 s	60.09 W
Vejer de la Frontera, Sp.	170	36.15 N	5.58 W
Vejle, Den. (vī′lĕ)	164	55.41 N	9.29 E
Velbert, F.R.G. (fĕl′bĕrt)	169c	51.20 N	7.03 E
Velebit (Mts.), Yugo. (vā′lĕ-bėt)	172	44.25 N	15.23 E
Velen, F.R.G. (fĕ′lĕn)	169c	51.54 N	7.00 E
Vélez-Málaga, Sp. (vā′lāth-mä′lä-gä)	170	36.48 N	4.05 W
Vélez-Rubio, Sp. (ro͞o′bė-ô)	170	37.38 N	2.05 W
Velika Kapela (Mts.), Yugo. (vĕ′lė-kä kä-pĕ′lä)	172	45.03 N	15.20 E
Velika Morava (R.), Yugo. (mô′rä-vä)	173	44.20 N	21.10 E
Velikaya (R.), Sov. Un. (vå-lē′kȧ-yȧ)	174	57.25 N	28.07 E
Velikiy Bychkov, Sov. Un. (vĕ-lē′kē bo͝och-kôf′)	167	47.59 N	24.01 E
Velikiye Luki, Sov. Un. (vyē-lē′-kyė lo͞o′ke)	174	56.19 N	30.32 E
Velikiy Ustyug, Sov. Un. (vå-lē′kĭ o͞os-tyo͝og′)	178	60.45 N	46.38 E
Veliko Tŭrnovo, Bul.	173	43.06 N	25.38 E
Velikoye, Sov. Un. (vå-lē′kô-yĕ)	174	57.21 N	39.45 E
Velikoye (L.), Sov. Un.	174	57.00 N	36.53 E
Veli Lošinj, Yugo (lô′shėn′)	172	44.30 N	14.29 E
Velizh, Sov. Un. (vå′lėzh)	174	55.37 N	31.11 E
Velke Meziřičí, Czech. (vĕl′kā mĕzh′′r-zhyĭ-chĭ)	166	49.21 N	16.01 E
Vella (I.), Sol. Is. (vāl′yä)	215	8.00 s	156.42 E
Velletri, It. (vĕl-lā′trē)	171d	41.42 N	12.48 E
Vellore, India (vĕl-lōr′)	197	12.57 N	79.09 E
Vels, Sov. Un. (vĕls)	182a	60.35 N	58.47 E
Vel′sk, Sov. Un. (vĕlsk)	178	61.00 N	42.18 E
Velten, G.D.R. (fel′tĕn)	157b	52.41 N	13.11 E
Velya R., Sov. Un. (vĕl′yȧ)	182b	56.23 N	37.54 E
Venadillo, Col. (vĕ-nä-dē′l-yō)	142a	4.43 N	74.55 W
Venado, Mex. (vå-mä′dō)	130	22.54 N	101.07 W
Venado Tuerto, Arg. (vĕ-nä′dô-to͞oĕ′r-tô)	144	33.28 s	61.47 W
Vendôome, Fr. (väɴ-dōm′)	168	47.46 N	1.05 E
Veneto (Reg.), It. (vĕ-nĕ′tô)	172	45.58 N	11.24 E
Venëv, Sov. Un. (vĕn-ĕf′)	174	54.19 N	38.14 E
Venezia (Venice), It. (vå-nāt′sė-ä)	172	45.25 N	12.18 E
Venezuela, S.A. (vĕn-ė-zwē′lȧ)	140	8.00 N	65.00 W
Venezuela, Golfo de (G.), Ven. (gôl-fô-dĕ)	142	11.34 N	71.02 W
Veniaminof, Mt., Ak.	107	56.12 N	159.20 W
Venice, Ca. (vĕn′ĭs)	119a	33.59 N	118.28 W
Venice, Il.	119e	38.40 N	90.10 W
Venice, see Venezia			
Venice (Neigh.), Ca.	59	34.00 N	118.29 W
Venice, Gulf of (G.), It.	172	45.23 N	13.00 E
Venlo, Neth.	169c	51.22 N	6.11 E
Vennhausen (Neigh.), F.R.G.	63	51.13 N	6.51 E
Venta (R.), Sov. Un. (vĕn′tȧ)	165	57.05 N	21.45 E
Ventana, Sierra de la (Mts.), Arg. (sē-ĕ-rä-dĕ-lä-vĕn-tȧ′nä)	144	38.00 s	63.00 W
Ventersburg, S. Afr. (vĕn-tẽrs′bûrg)	223d	28.06 s	27.10 E
Ventersdorp, S. Afr. (vĕn-tẽrs′dôrp)	223d	26.20 s	26.48 E
Venterspos Location, S. Afr.	71b	26.18 s	27.42 E
Ventimiglia, It. (vĕn-tė-mēl′yä)	172	43.46 N	7.37 E
Ventnor, NJ (vĕnt′nẽr)	111	39.20 N	74.25 W
Ventspils, Sov. Un. (vĕnt′spėls)	165	57.24 N	21.41 E
Ventuari (R.), Ven. (vĕn-to͞oȧ′rē)	142	4.47 N	65.56 W
Ventura, Ca. (vĕn-to͞o′rȧ)	120	34.18 N	119.18 W
Venukovsky, Sov. Un. (vĕ-no͞o′kôv-skĭ)	182b	55.10 N	37.26 E
Venustiano Carranza, Mex. (vĕ-no͞os-tyä′nō-kär-rä′n-zä)	130	19.44 N	103.48 W
Venustiano Carranzo, Mex. (kär-rä′n-zô)	131	16.21 N	92.36 W
Vera, Arg. (vĕ-rä)	144	29.22 s	60.09 W
Vera, Sp. (vā′rä)	170	37.18 N	1.53 W
Veracruz, Mex.	131	19.13 N	96.07 W
Vera Cruz, (State), Mex. (vā-rä-kro͞oz′)	128	20.30 N	97.15 W
Verāval, India (vĕr′vŭ-väl)	196	20.59 N	70.49 E
Verberg (Neigh.), F.R.G.	63	51.22 N	6.36 E
Vercelli, It. (vĕr-chĕl′lė)	172	45.18 N	8.27 E
Verchères, Can. (vĕr-shâr′)	95a	45.46 N	73.21 W
Verde (I.), Phil. (vĕr′då)	207a	13.34 N	121.11 E
Verde (R.), Az. (vûrd)	121	34.04 N	111.40 W
Verde (R.), Mex.	130	21.48 N	99.50 W
Verde (R.), Mex.	131	16.05 N	97.44 W
Verde (R.), Mex.	130	20.50 N	103.00 W
Verde, Cap (C.), Ba.	135	22.50 N	75.00 W
Verde, Cay (I.), Ba.	135	22.00 N	75.05 W
Verde Island Pass., Phil. (vĕr′dē)	207a	13.36 N	120.39 E
Verdemont, Ca. (vûr′dė-mŏnt)	119a	34.12 N	117.22 W
Verden, F.R.G. (fĕr′dĕn)	166	52.55 N	9.15 E
Verdigris (R.), Ok. (vûr′dė-grēs)	123	36.50 N	95.29 W
Verdun, Can. (vĕr′dŭɴ′)	95a	45.27 N	73.34 W
Verdun, Fr. (vâr-dûɴ′)	168	49.09 N	5.21 E
Verdun, Fr.	171	43.48 N	1.10 E
Vereeniging, S. Afr. (vĕ-rā′nĭ-gĭng)	223d	26.40 s	27.56 E
Verena, S. Afr. (vĕr-ėn ȧ)	223d	25.30 s	29.02 E
Vereya, Sov. Un. (vĕ-rå′yȧ)	174	55.21 N	36.08 E
Verga, NJ	56b	39.52 N	75.10 W
Vergara, Sp. (vĕr-gä′rä)	170	43.08 N	2.23 W
Verín, Sp. (vå-rēn′)	170	41.56 N	7.26 W
Verkhne-Kamchatsk, Sov. Un. (vyĕrk′nyĕ kȧm-chatsk′)	181	54.42 N	158.41 E
Verkhne Neyvinskiy, Sov. Un. (nā-vĭn′skĭ)	182a	57.17 N	60.10 E
Verkhne Ural′sk, Sov. Un. (o͞o-ralsk′)	182a	53.53 N	50.15 E
Verkhneye, Sov. Un. (vyĕrĸ′nĕ-yĕ)	175	48.53 N	38.29 E
Verkhniy Avzyan, Sov. Un. (vyĕrk′nyĕ ȧv-zyȧn′)	182a	53.32 N	57.30 E
Verkhniye Kigi, Sov. Un. (vyĕrk′nĭ-yĕ kĭ′gĭ)	182a	55.23 N	58.37 E
Verkhniy Ufaley, Sov. Un. (o͞o-fȧ′lā)	182a	56.04 N	60.15 E
Verkhnyaya Pyshma, Sov. Un. (vyĕrk′nyä-yä po͞osh′mȧ)	182a	56.57 N	60.37 E
Verkhnyaya Salda, Sov. Un. (säl′dȧ)	182a	58.03 N	60.33 E
Verkhnyaya Tunguska (Angara), (R.), Sov. Un. (to͞on-go͞os′kȧ)	180	58.13 N	97.00 E
Verkhnyaya Tura, Sov. Un. (to͞o′rȧ)	182a	58.22 N	59.51 E
Verkhnyaya Yayva, Sov. Un. (yäy′vȧ)	182a	59.28 N	59.38 E
Verkhotur′ye, Sov. Un. (vyĕr-kô-to͞or′yĕ)	182a	58.52 N	60.47 E
Verkhoyansk, Sov. Un. (vyĕr-ĸô-yänsk′)	181	67.43 N	133.33 E
Verkhoyanskiy Khrebet (Mts.), Sov. Un. (vyĕr-ĸô-yänskĭ)	181	67.45 N	128.00 E
Vermilion, Can. (vẽr-mĭl′yŭn)	99	53.22 N	110.51 W
Vermilion (L.), Mn.	115	47.49 N	92.35 W
Vermilion (R.), Can.	104	47.30 N	73.15 W
Vermilion (R.), Can.	99	53.30 N	111.00 W
Vermilion (R.), Il.	110	41.05 N	89.00 W
Vermilion (R.), Mn.	115	48.09 N	92.31 W
Vermilion Hills, Can.	100	50.43 N	106.50 W
Vermilion Ra, Mn.	115	47.55 N	91.59 W
Vermillion, SD	114	42.46 N	96.56 W
Vermillion (R.), SD	114	43.54 N	97.14 W
Vermillion B., La.	125	29.47 N	92.00 W
Vermont, Austl.	70b	37.50 s	145.12 E
Vermont (State), U.S. (vẽr-mŏnt′)	109	43.50 N	72.50 W
Vernal, Ut. (vûr′nȧl)	117	40.29 N	109.40 W
Verneuk Pan (L.), S. Afr. (vĕr-nŭk′)	226	30.10 s	21.46 E
Vernon, Ca. (vŭr′nŭn)	119a	34.01 N	118.12 W
Vernon, Can. (vĕr-nôɴ′)	99	50.18 N	119.15 W
Vernon, Can.	95c	45.10 N	75.27 W
Vernon, In. (vûr′nŭn)	110	39.00 N	85.40 W
Vernon, NJ	112a	39.00 N	85.40 W
Vernon, Tx.	122	34.09 N	99.16 W
Vernonia, Or. (vûr-nō′nyȧ)	118c	45.52 N	123.12 W
Vero Beach, Fl. (vē′rô)	127a	27.36 N	80.25 W
Véroia, Grc.	173	40.30 N	22.13 E
Verona, It. (vā-rō′nä)	172	45.28 N	11.02 E
Verona, NJ	55	40.50 N	74.12 W
Verona, Pa.	57b	40.30 N	79.50 W
Verrières-le-Buisson, Fr.	64c	48.45 N	2.16 E
Versailles, Fr. (vĕr-sī′y′)	169b	48.48 N	2.07 E
Versailles, Ky. (vẽr-sālz′)	110	38.05 N	84.45 W
Versailles, Mo.	123	38.27 N	92.52 W
Versailles, Pa.	57b	40.21 N	79.51 W
Versailles (Neigh.), Arg.	60d	34.38 s	58.31 W
Versailles, Château de (P. Int.), Fr.	64c	48.48 N	2.07 E
Vert, Cap (C.), Senegal	228	14.43 N	17.30 W
Verulam, S. Afr. (vĕ-ro͞o-lăm)	227c	29.39 s	31.08 E
Verulamium (P. Int.), Eng.	62	51.45 N	0.22 W
Verviers, Bel. (vĕr-vyā′)	163	50.35 N	5.57 E
Vesëloye, Sov. Un. (vĕ-syô′lô-yĕ)	175	46.59 N	34.56 E
Vesijärvi (L.), Fin.	165	61.09 N	25.10 E
Vesn′aki (Neigh.), Sov. Un.	66b	55.44 N	37.49 E
Vesoul, Fr. (vē-so͞ol′)	169	47.38 N	6.11 E
Vestavia Hills, Al.	112h	33.26 N	86.46 W
Vesterålen (Is.), Nor. (vĕs′tẽr ô′lĕn)	158	68.54 N	14.03 E
Vestfjord, Nor.	158	67.33 N	12.59 E
Vestmannaeyjar, Ice. (vĕst′män-ä-ā′yär)	158	63.12 N	20.17 W
Vesuvio, (Mtn.), It. (vĕ-so͞o′vyä)	171c	40.35 N	14.26 E
Ves′yegonsk, Sov. Un. (vĕ-syĕ-gônsk′)	174	58.42 N	37.09 E
Veszprem, Hung. (vĕs′prām)	167	47.05 N	17.53 E
Vészto, Hung. (vĕs′tû)	167	46.55 N	21.18 E
Vetka, Sov. Un. (vyĕt′kȧ)	174	52.36 N	31.05 E
Vetlanda, Swe. (vĕt-län′dä)	164	57.26 N	15.05 E
Vetluga, Sov. Un. (vyĕt-lo͞o′gȧ)	178	57.50 N	45.42 E
Vetluga (R.), Sov. Un.	178	56.50 N	45.50 E
Vetovo, Bul. (vā′tô-vô)	173	43.42 N	26.18 E
Vet R., S. Afr. (vĕt)	223d	28.25 s	26.37 E
Vetren, Bul. (vĕt′rĕn′)	173	42.16 N	24.04 E
Vevay, In. (vē′vā)	110	38.45 N	85.05 W
Veynes, Fr. (vān′′)	169	44.31 N	5.47 E
Vézère (R.), Fr. (vā-zer′)	168	45.01 N	1.00 E
Viacha, Bol. (vēȧ′chȧ)	142	16.43 s	68.16 W
Viadana, It. (vė-ä-dä′nä)	172	44.55 N	10.30 E
Vian, Ok. (vī′ăn)	123	35.30 N	95.00 W
Viana, Braz. (vē-ä′nä)	143	3.09 s	44.44 W
Viana del Bollo, Sp. (vė-ä′nä dĕl bôl′yô)	170	42.10 N	7.07 W
Viana do Alentejo, Port. (vė-ä′nȧ do͞o ä-lĕɴ-tā′ho͞o)	170	38.20 N	8.02 W
Viana do Castelo, Port. (do͞o käs-tā′lo͞o)	170e	41.41 N	8.45 W
Viangchan, Laos	206	18.07 N	102.33 E
Viar (R.), Sp. (vė-ä′rä)	170	38.15 N	6.08 W
Viareggio, It. (vė-ä-rĕd′jô)	172	43.52 N	10.14 E
Viborg, Den. (vē′bôr)	164	56.27 N	9.22 E
Vibo Valentia, It. (vė′bô-vä-lĕ′n-tyä)	172	38.47 N	16.06 E
Vicálvaro, Sp.	171a	40.25 N	3.37 W
Vicente Lòpez, Arg. (vē-sĕ′n-tĕ-lŏ′pĕz)	144a	34.15 s	58.20 W
Vicenza, It. (vė-chĕnt′sä)	172	45.33 N	11.33 E
Vich, Sp. (vēch)	171	41.55 N	2.14 E
Vichuga, Sov. Un. (vē-cho͞o′gȧ)	174	57.13 N	41.58 E
Vichy, Fr. (vė-shē′)	168	46.06 N	3.28 E
Vickersund, Nor.	164	60.00 N	9.59 E
Vicksburg, Mi. (vĭks′bûrg)	110	42.10 N	85.30 W
Vicksburg, Ms.	126	32.20 N	90.50 W
Viçosa, Braz. (vē-sô′sä)	141a	23.46 s	42.51 W
Victoria, Arg. (vēk-tô′rėä)	141c	32.36 s	60.09 W
Victoria, Cam. (vĭk-tō′rĭ-ȧ)	229	4.01 N	9.12 E
Victoria, Can. (vĭk-tō′rĭ-ȧ)	98	48.26 N	123.23 W
Victoria, Chile (vēk-tô-rėä)	144	38.15 s	72.16 W
Victoria, Col. (vēk-tô′rėä)	142a	5.19 N	74.54 W

ăt; finăl; rāte; senåte; ärm; åsk; sofȧ; fâre; ch-choose; dh-as th in other; bē; ėvent; bĕt; recĕnt; cratẽr; g-gō; gh-guttural g; bĭt; ĭ-short neutral; rīde; ĸ-guttural k as ch in German ich;

PLACE (Pronounciation)	PAGE	Lat. °'	Long. °'
Victoria, Phil. (vĕk-tô-ryä)	207a	15.34 N	120.41 E
Victoria, Tx. (vĭk-tō'rĭ-ȧ)	125	28.48 N	97.00 W
Victoria, Va.	127	36.57 N	78.13 W
Victoria (Neigh.), Arg.	60d	34.28 S	58.31 W
Victoria (State), Austl.	215	36.46 S	143.15 E
Victoria I., Nig.	71d	6.26 N	3.26 E
Victoria (L.), Afr.	231	0.50 S	32.50 E
Victoria (R.), Austl.	214	17.25 S	130.50 E
Victoria de las Tunas, Cuba (vĕk-tō'rē-ä dā läs tōō'näs)	134	20.55 N	77.05 W
Victoria Falls, Zambia	231	17.56 S	25.50 E
Victoria Falls, Zimb.	231	17.55 S	25.51 E
Victoria I., Can.	96	70.13 N	107.45 W
Victoria L., Can.	105	48.20 N	57.40 W
Victoria Land, Ant.	232	75.00 S	160.00 E
Victoria Lawn Tennis Association Courts (P. Int.), Austl.	70b	37.51 S	145.02 E
Victoria, Mt., Bur.	198	21.26 N	93.59 E
Victoria, Mt., Pap. N. Gui.	207	9.35 S	147.45 E
Victoria Nile (R.), Ug.	231	2.20 N	31.35 E
Victoria Peak (Mtn.), Hong Kong	68c	22.17 N	114.08 E
Victoria Pk., Belize (vĕk-tōrĭ'ȧ)	132a	16.47 N	88.40 W
Victoria Pk., Can.	98	50.03 N	126.06 W
Victoria River Downs, Austl. (vĭc-tôr'ĭȧ)	214	16.30 S	131.10 E
Victoria Station (P. Int.), Eng.	64b	53.29 N	2.15 W
Victoria Str., Can. (vĭk-tō'rĭ-ȧ)	96	69.10 N	100.58 W
Victoriaville, Can. (vĭk-tō'rĭ-ȧ-vĭl)	103	46.04 N	71.59 W
Victoria West, S. Afr. (wĕst)	226	31.25 S	23.10 E
Vidalia, Ga. (vĭ-dā'lĭ-ȧ)	127	32.10 N	82.26 W
Vidalia, La.	125	31.33 N	91.28 W
Vidin, Bul. (vĭ'dĕn)	173	44.00 N	22.53 E
Vidnoye, Sov. Un.	182b	55.33 N	37.41 E
Vidzy, Sov. Un. (vē'dzĭ)	174	55.23 N	26.46 E
Viedma, Arg. (vyād'mä)	144	40.55 S	63.03 W
Viedma (L.), Arg.	144	49.40 S	72.35 W
Viejo R., Nic. (vyā'hō)	132	12.45 N	86.19 W
Vienna, Ga. (vē-ĕn'ȧ)	126	32.03 N	83.50 W
Vienna, Il.	123	37.24 N	88.50 W
Vienna, Va.	112e	38.54 N	77.16 W
Vienna, see Wien			
Vienne, Fr. (vyĕn')	168	45.31 N	4.54 E
Vienne (R.), Fr.	168	47.06 N	0.20 E
Vieques, P.R. (vyā'kås)	129b	18.09 N	65.27 W
Vieques (I.), P.R. (vyā'kås)	129b	18.05 N	65.28 W
Vierfontien, S. Afr. (vēr'fōn-tān)	223d	27.06 S	26.45 E
Vieringhausen (Neigh.), F.R.G.	63	51.11 N	7.10 E
Viersen, F.R.G. (fēr'zĕn)	169c	51.15 N	6.24 E
Vierwaldstätter See (L.), Switz.	166	46.54 N	8.36 E
Vierzon, Fr. (vyâr-zôN')	168	47.14 N	2.04 E
Viesca, Mex. (vē-ās'kä)	124	25.21 N	102.47 W
Viesca, Laguna de (L.), Mex. (lä-ōō'nä-dĕ)	124	25.30 N	102.40 W
Vieste, It. (vyĕs'tå)	172	41.52 N	16.10 E
Vietnam, Asia (vyĕt'näm')	206	18.00 N	107.00 E
View Park, Ca.	59	34.00 N	118.21 W
Vigan, Phil. (vēgän)	207a	17.36 N	120.22 E
Vigevano, It. (vē-jȧ-vä'nô)	172	45.18 N	8.52 E
Vigentino (Neigh.), It.	65c	45.25 N	9.11 E
Vigny, Fr. (vēn-y'ē')	169b	49.05 N	1.54 E
Vigo, Sp. (vē'gō)	170	42.18 N	8.42 W
Vihti, Fin. (vē'tĭ)	165	60.27 N	24.18 E
Viipuri, see Vyborg			
Vijayawāda, India	197	16.31 N	80.37 E
Vijosë, (R.), Alb.	173	40.15 N	20.30 E
Viksøyri, Nor.	164	61.06 N	6.35 E
Vila, Vanuatu	215	18.00 S	168.30 E
Vila Augusta, Braz.	61d	23.28 S	46.32 W
Vila Boacaya (Neigh.), Braz.	61d	23.29 S	46.44 W
Vila Caldas Xavier, Moz.	231	15.59 S	34.12 E
Vila de Manica, Moz. (vē'lä dā mä-nē'kȧ)	226	18.48 S	32.49 E
Vila de Rei, Port. (vē'lȧ dā rā'ĭ)	170	39.42 N	8.03 W
Vila do Conde, Port. (vē'lȧ dōō kōn'dĕ)	170	41.21 N	8.44 W
Vilafranca de Xira, Port. (fräŋ'kȧ dā shē'rȧ)	170	38.58 N	8.59 W
Vila Guilherme (Neigh.), Braz.	61d	23.30 S	46.36 W
Vilaine (R.), Fr. (vē-lân')	168	47.34 N	0.20 W
Vila Isabel (Neigh.), Braz.	61c	22.55 S	43.15 W
Vila Jaguára (Neigh.), Braz.	61d	23.31 S	46.45 W
Vila Madalena (Neigh.) Braz.	61d	23.33 S	46.42 W
Vila Mariana (Neigh.), Braz.	61d	23.35 S	46.38 W
Vilanculos, Moz. (vē-län-kōō'lōs)	226	22.03 S	35.13 E
Vilāni, Sov. Un. (vē'lȧ-nĭ)	174	56.31 N	27.00 E
Vila Nova de Foz Côa, Port. (nō'vȧ dā fôz-kō'ȧ)	170	41.08 N	7.11 W
Vila Nova de Gaia, Port. (vē'lȧ nō'vȧ dā gä'yä)	170	41.08 N	8.40 W
Vila Nova de Milfontes, Port. (nō'vȧ dā mēl-fôn'tāzh)	170	37.44 N	8.48 W
Vila Progresso, Braz.	61c	22.55 S	43.03 W
Vila Prudente (Neigh.), Braz.	61d	23.35 S	46.33 W
Vila Real, Port. (rā-äl')	170	41.18 N	7.48 W
Vila Real de Santo Antonio, Port. (vē'lä-rē-ä'l-dĕ-sän-tô-än-tô'nyô)	170	37.14 N	7.25 W
Vila Viçosa, Port. (vē-sō'zȧ)	170	38.47 N	7.24 W
Vileyka, Sov. Un. (vē-lā'ē-kȧ)	174	54.19 N	26.58 E
Vilhelmina, Swe.	158	64.37 N	16.30 E
Viljandi, Sov. Un. (vēl'yän-dē)	165	58.24 N	25.34 E
Viljoenskroon, S. Afr.	223d	27.13 S	26.58 E
Vilkaviškis, Sov. Un. (vēl-kȧ-vēsh'kēs)	165	54.40 N	23.08 E
Vilkija, Sov. Un. (vēl-kē'ēȧ)	165	55.04 N	23.30 E
Vil'kitskogo (I.), Sov. Un. (vyl-kēts-kōgō)	180	73.25 N	76.00 E
Vilkovo, Sov. Un. (vĭl-kô-vô)	179	45.24 N	29.36 E
Villa Acuña, Mex. (vēl'yä-kōō'n-yä)	124	29.20 N	100.56 W
Villa Adelina (Neigh.), Arg.	60d	34.31 S	58.32 W
Villa Ahumada, Mex. (ä-ōō-mä'dä)	124	30.43 N	106.30 W
Villa Alta (San Ildefonso), Mex. (äl'tä)(sän ēl-dā-fōn'sō)	131	17.20 N	96.08 W
Villa Angela, Arg. (vē'l-yä à'n-kĕ-lä)	144	27.31 S	60.42 W
Villa Ballester, Arg. (vē'l-yä-bäl-yĕs-tĕr)	144a	34.18 S	58.33 W
Villa Bella, Bol. (bĕ'l-yä)	142	10.25 S	65.22 W
Villablino, Sp. (vēl-yä-blē'nô)	170	42.58 N	6.18 W
Villa Borghese (P. Int.), It.	66c	41.55 N	12.29 E
Villa Bosch (Neigh.), Arg.	60d	34.36 S	58.34 W
Villacañas, Sp. (vēl-yä-kän'yäs)	170	39.39 N	3.20 W
Villacarrillo, Sp. (vēl-yä-kä-rēl'yô)	170	38.09 N	3.07 W
Villach, Aus. (fē'läk)	166	46.38 N	13.50 E
Villacidro, It. (vē-lä-chē'drô)	172	39.28 N	8.41 E
Villa Ciudadela (Neigh.), Arg.	60d	34.38 S	58.34 W
Villa Clara (Prov.), Cuba	134	22.40 N	80.10 W
Villa Constitución, Arg. (kōn-stē-tōō-syōn')	141c	33.15 S	60.19 W
Villa Coronado, Mex. (kō-rō-nä'dhō)	124	26.45 N	105.10 W
Villa Cuauhtémoc, Mex. (vēl'yä-kōō-äōō-tē'mōk)	131	22.11 N	97.50 W
Villa de Allende, Mex. (vēl'yä'dā äl-yĕn'då)	124	25.18 N	100.01 W
Villa de Alvarez, Mex. (vēl'yä-dĕ-ä'l-vä-rĕz)	130	19.17 N	103.44 W
Villa de Cura, Ven. (dĕ-kōō'rä)	143b	10.03 N	67.29 W
Villa de Guadalupe, Mex. (dĕ-gwä-dhä-lōō'på)	130	23.22 N	100.44 W
Villa de Mayo, Arg.	60d	34.31 S	58.41 W
Villa Devoto (Neigh.), Arg.	60d	34.36 S	58.31 W
Villa Diamante (Neigh.), Arg.	60d	34.41 S	58.26 W
Villa Dolores, Arg. (vēl'yä dō-lō'rās)	144	31.50 S	65.05 W
Villa Domínico (Neigh.), Arg.	60d	34.41 S	58.20 W
Villa Escalante, Mex. (vēl'yä-ĕs-kä-län'tĕ)	130	19.24 N	101.36 W
Villa Flores, Mex. (vēl'yä-flō'rās)	131	16.13 N	93.17 W
Villafranca, It. (vēl-lä-fräŋ'kä)	172	45.22 N	10.53 E
Villafranca del Bierzo, Sp. (vēl'yä-fräŋ'kä dĕl byĕr'thō)	170	42.37 N	6.49 W
Villafranca de los Barros, Sp. (vēl-yä-fräŋ'kä dā lōs bär'rōs)	170	38.34 N	6.22 W
Villafranca del Panadés, Sp. (vēl-yäfrän'kä dĕl pä-nä-dās')	171	41.20 N	1.40 E
Villafranche-de-Rouergue, Fr. (dē-rōō-ĕrg')	168	44.21 N	2.02 E
Villa García, Mex. (gär-sē'ä)	130	22.07 N	101.55 W
Villagarcia, Sp. (vēl'yä-gär-thē'ä)	170	42.38 N	8.43 W
Villagram, Mex. (vēl-yä-gräm')	124	24.28 N	99.30 W
Villa Grove, Il. (vĭl'ȧ grōv')	110	39.55 N	88.15 W
Villaguay, Arg. (vē'l-yä-gwī)	144	31.47 S	58.53 W
Villa Hayes, Par. (vēl'yä äyås)(hāz)	144	25.07 S	57.31 W
Villahermosa, Mex. (vēl'yä-ĕr-mō'sä)	131	17.59 N	92.56 W
Villa Hidalgo, Mex. (vēl'yäē-däl'gō)	130	21.39 N	102.41 W
Villa José L. Suárez (Neigh.)	60d	34.32 S	58.34 W
Villajoyosa, Sp. (vēl'yä-hō-yō'sä)	171	38.30 N	0.14 W
Villalba, Sp.	170	43.18 N	7.43 W
Villaldama, Mex. (vēl-yäl-dä'mä)	124	26.30 N	100.26 W
Villa Lopez, Mex. (vēl'yä lō'pĕz)	124	27.00 N	105.02 W
Villalpando, Sp. (vēl-yäl-pän'dō)	170	41.54 N	5.24 W
Villa Lugano (Neigh.), Arg.	60d	34.41 S	58.28 W
Villa Lynch (Neigh.), Arg.	60d	34.36 S	58.32 W
Villa Madero, Arg.	60d	34.41 S	58.30 W
Villa María, Arg. (vē'l-yä-mä-rē'ä)	144	32.17 S	63.08 W
Villamatín, Sp. (vēl-yä-mä-tē'n)	170	36.50 N	5.38 W
Villa Mercedes, Arg. (mĕr-sā'dås)	144	33.38 S	65.16 W
Villa Montes, Bol. (vē'l-yä-mô'n-tĕs)	142	21.13 S	63.26 W
Villa Morelos, Mex. (mō-rĕ'lomcs)	130	20.01 N	101.24 W
Villa Nova, Md.	56c	39.21 N	76.44 W
Villanova, Pa.	56b	40.02 N	75.21 W
Villanueva, Col. (vē'l-yä-nōōĕ'vä)	142	10.44 N	73.08 W
Villanueva, Hond. (vēl'yä-nwā'vä)	132	15.19 N	88.02 W
Villanueva, Mex. (vēl'yä-nōōĕ'vä)	130	22.25 N	102.53 W
Villanueva de Córdoba, Sp. (vēl-yä-nwĕ'vä-dā kôr'dō-bä)	170	38.18 N	4.38 W
Villanueva de la Serena, Sp. (lä sā-rā'nä)	170	38.59 N	5.56 W
Villanueva y Geltrú, Sp. (ē-kĕl-trōō')	171	41.13 N	1.44 E
Villa Obregón, Mex. (vē'l-yä-ô-brĕ-gō'n)	131a	19.21 N	99.11 W
Villa Ocampo, Mex. (ô-käm'pō)	124	26.26 N	105.30 W
Villa Pedro Montoya, Mex. (vēl'yä-pē'drô-môn-tô'yȧ)	130	21.38 N	99.51 W
Villard-Bonnot, Fr. (vēl-yär'bôn-nō')	169	45.15 N	5.53 E
Villa Real (Neigh.), Arg.	60d	34.37 S	58.31 W
Villarreal, Sp. (vēl-yär-rē-äl)	171	39.55 N	0.07 W
Villarrica, Par. (vēl-yä-rē'kä)	144	25.55 S	56.23 W
Villarrobledo, Sp. (vēl-yär-rô-blā'dhō)	170	39.15 N	2.37 W
Villa Sáenz Peña (Neigh.), Arg.	60d	34.46 S	58.31 W
Villa San Andrés (Neigh.), Arg.	60d	34.33 S	58.32 W
Villa Santos Lugares (Neigh.), Arg.	60d	34.36 S	58.32 W
Villa Turdera (Neigh.), Arg.	60d	34.48 S	58.25 W
Villa Union, Mex. (vēl'yä-ōō-nyōn')	130	23.10 N	106.14 W
Villaverde (Neigh.), Sp.	65b	40.21 N	3.42 W
Villavicencio, Col. (vē'l-yä-vē-sē'n-syō)	142a	4.09 N	73.38 W
Villaviciosa de Odón, Sp. (vēl'yä-vē-thē-ō'sä dā ō-dōn')	171a	40.22 N	73.38 W
Villavieja, Col. (vē'l-yä-vē-ĕ'kä)	142a	3.13 N	75.13 W
Villazón, Bol. (vē'l-yä-zō'n)	144	22.02 S	65.42 W
Villecresnes, Fr.	64c	48.43 N	2.32 E
Ville-d'Avray, Fr.	64c	48.50 N	2.11 E
Villefranche, Fr.	168	45.59 N	4.43 E
Villejuif, Fr. (vēl'zhüst')	169b	48.48 N	2.22 E
Ville-Marie, Can.	103	47.18 N	79.22 W
Villemomble, Fr.	64c	48.53 N	2.31 E
Villena, Sp. (vē-lyā'nȧ)	171	38.37 N	0.52 W
Villenbon-sur-Yvette, Fr.	64c	48.42 N	2.15 E
Villeneuve, Can. (vēl'nûv')	95g	53.40 N	113.49 W
Villeneuve-la-Garenne, Fr.	64c	48.56 N	2.20 E
Villeneuve-le-Roi, Fr.	64c	48.44 N	2.25 E
Villeneuve-Saint Georges, Fr. (săN-zhôrzh')	169b	48.43 N	2.27 E
Villeneuve-sur-Lot, Fr. (sür-lō')	168	44.25 N	0.41 E
Villeparisis, Fr.	64c	48.56 N	2.37 E
Ville Platte, La. (vēl plȧt')	125	30.41 N	92.17 W
Villers Cotterêts, Fr. (vē-âr'kô-trā')	168a	49.15 N	3.05 E
Villers-sur-Marne, Fr.	64c	48.50 N	2.33 E
Villerupt, Fr. (vēl'rüp')	169	49.28 N	6.16 E
Ville-Saint Georges, Can. (vĭl-sĕN-zhôrzh')	103	46.07 N	70.40 W
Villeta, Col. (vē'l-yĕ'tá)	142a	5.02 N	74.29 W
Villeurbanne, Fr. (vēl-ûr-bän')	168	45.43 N	4.55 E
Villevaudé, Fr.	64c	48.55 N	2.39 E
Villiers, S. Afr. (vĭl'ĭ-ērs)	223d	27.03 S	28.38 E
Villiers-le-Bâcle, Fr.	64c	48.44 N	2.08 E
Villiers-le-Bel, Fr.	64c	49.00 N	2.23 E
Villingen-Schwenningen, F.R.G.	166	48.04 N	8.33 E
Villisca, Ia. (vĭ-lĭs'kȧ)	115	40.56 N	94.56 W
Villupuram, India	197	11.59 N	79.33 E
Vilnius (Wilno), Sov. Un. (vĭl'nē-ōōs)	165	54.40 N	25.26 E
Vilppula, Fin. (vĭl'pŭ-lȧ)	165	62.01 N	24.24 E
Vilvoorde, Bel.	157a	50.56 N	4.25 E
Vilyuy (R.), Sov. Un. (vēl'yĭ)	181	65.22 N	108.45 E
Vilyuysk, Sov. Un. (vē-lyōō'ĭsk')	181	63.41 N	121.47 E
Vimmerby, Swe. (vĭm'ĕr-bü)	164	57.41 N	15.51 E
Vimperk, Czech. (vĭm-pĕrk')	166	49.04 N	13.41 E
Viña del Mar, Chile (vē'nyä dĕl mär')	141b	33.00 S	71.33 W
Vinalhaven, Me. (vī-nȧl-hā'vĕn)	104	44.03 N	68.49 W
Vinaroz, Sp. (vē-nä'rōth)	171	40.29 N	0.27 E
Vincennes, Fr. (văN-sĕn')	169b	48.51 N	2.27 E
Vincennes, In. (vĭn-zĕnz')	110	38.40 N	87.30 W
Vincennes, Château de (P. Int.), Fr.	64c	48.51 N	2.26 E
Vincent, Al. (vĭn'sĕnt)	126	33.21 N	86.25 W
Vindelälven (R.), Swe.	158	65.02 N	18.30 E
Vindeln, Swe. (vĭn'dĕln)	158	64.10 N	19.52 E
Vindhya Ra., India (vĭnd'yä)	196	22.30 N	75.50 E
Vineland, NJ (vīn'lănd)	111	39.30 N	75.00 W
Vinh, Viet. (vēn'y')	203	18.38 N	105.42 E
Vinhais, Port. (vēn-yä'ēzh)	170	41.51 N	7.00 W
Vinings, Ga. (vī'nĭngz)	112c	33.52 N	84.28 W
Vinita, Ok. (vĭ-nē'tȧ)	123	36.38 N	95.09 W
Vinkovci, Yugo. (vēn'kôv-tsē)	173	45.17 N	18.47 E
Vinnitsa, Sov. Un. (vē'nĕt-sȧ)	175	49.13 N	28.31 E
Vinnitsa (Oblast), Sov. Un.	175	48.45 N	28.01 E
Vinogradovo, Sov. Un. (vĭ-nô-grä'do-vô)	182b	55.25 N	38.33 E
Vinson Massif (Mtn.), Ant.	232	77.40 S	87.00 W
Vinton, Ia. (vĭn'tŭn)	115	42.08 N	92.01 W
Vinton, La.	125	30.12 N	93.35 W
Violet, La. (vī'ō-lĕt)	112d	29.54 N	89.54 W
Virac, Phil. (vē-räk')	203	13.38 N	124.20 E
Virbalis, Sov. Un. (vēr'bȧ-lēs)	165	54.38 N	22.55 E
Virden, Can. (vûr'dĕn)	96	49.51 N	101.55 W
Virden, Il.	123	39.28 N	89.46 W
Virgin (R.), U.S.	121	36.51 N	113.50 W
Virginia, Mn. (vẽr-jĭn'yȧ)	115	47.32 N	92.36 W
Virginia, S. Afr.	223d	28.07 S	26.54 E
Virginia (State), U.S.	109	37.00 N	80.45 W
Virginia Beach, Va.	112g	36.50 N	75.58 W
Virginia City, Nv.	120	39.18 N	119.40 W
Virginia Hills, Va.	56d	38.47 N	77.06 W
Virginia Water, Eng.	62	51.24 N	0.34 W
Virgin Is., N.A. (vûr'jĭn)	129	18.15 N	64.00 W
Viroflay, Fr.	64c	48.48 N	2.10 E
Viroqua, Wi. (vĭ-rō'kwȧ)	115	43.33 N	90.54 W
Virovitica, Yugo. (vē-rō-vē'tē-tsä)	172	45.50 N	17.24 E
Virpazar, Yugo. (vēr'pä-zär')	173	42.16 N	19.06 E
Virrat, Fin. (vĭr'ät)	165	62.15 N	23.45 E
Virserum, Swe. (vĭr'sĕ-rōōm)	164	57.22 N	15.35 E
Vis, Yugo. (vēs)	172	43.03 N	16.11 E
Vis (I.), Yugo.	172	43.00 N	16.10 E
Visalia, Ca. (vĭ-sā'lĭ-ȧ)	120	36.20 N	119.18 W
Visby, Swe. (vĭs'bü)	164	57.39 N	18.19 E
Viscount Mellville Sound, Can.	94	74.80 N	110.00 W
Višegrad, Yugo. (vē'shĕ-gräd)	173	43.45 N	19.19 E
Vishākhapatnam, India	197	17.48 N	83.21 E
Vishera R., Sov. Un. (vĭ'shĕ-rȧ)	182a	60.40 N	58.46 E
Vishnyakovo, Sov. Un.	182b	55.44 N	38.10 E
Vishoek, S. Afr.	226a	34.13 S	18.26 E
Visim, Sov. Un. (vē'sĭm)	182a	57.38 N	59.32 E
Viskan (R.), Swe.	164	57.20 N	12.25 E
Viški, Sov. Un. (vēs'kĭ)	174	56.02 N	26.47 E
Vislinskij Zaliv (B.), Pol.	167	54.22 N	19.39 E
Visoko, Yugo. (vē'sô-kô)	173	43.59 N	18.10 E
Vistula (R.), see Wisla			
Vitacura, Chile	61b	33.24 S	70.36 W
Vitarte, Peru	60c	12.02 S	76.54 W
Vitebsk, Sov. Un. (vē'tyĕpsk)	174	55.12 N	30.16 E
Vitebsk (Oblast), Sov. Un.	174	55.05 N	29.18 E
Viterbo, It. (vē-tĕr'bō)	172	42.24 N	12.08 E
Vitim, Sov. Un. (vē'tĕm)	181	59.22 N	112.43 E
Vitim (R.), Sov. Un. (vē'tĕm)	181	56.12 N	115.30 E
Vitino, Sov. Un. (vē'tĭ-nô)	182c	59.40 N	29.51 E
Vitória, Braz. (vē-tō'rē-ä)	143	20.09 S	40.17 W
Vitoria, Sp. (vē-tô-ryä)	170	42.43 N	2.43 W
Vitória de Conquista, Braz. (vē-tō'rē-ä-dä-kōn-kwē's-tä)	143	14.51 S	40.44 W
Vitré, Fr. (vē-trā')	168	48.09 N	1.15 W
Vitry-le-François, Fr. (vē-trē'lĕ-frăN-swȧ')	168	48.44 N	4.34 E
Vitry-sur-Seine, Fr.	64c	48.48 N	2.24 E
Vittoria, It. (vē-tô'rē-ô)	159	37.01 N	14.31 E
Vittorio, It. (vē-tô'rē-ô)	172	45.59 N	12.17 E
Vivero, Sp. (vē-vā'rō)	170	43.39 N	7.37 W
Vivian, La. (vĭv'ĭ-ăn)	125	32.51 N	93.59 W
Vírgen del San Cristó bal (P. Int.), Chile	61b	33.26 S	70.39 W
Víron, Grc.	66d	37.57 N	23.45 E
Vize, Tur. (vē'zĕ)	173	41.34 N	27.46 E
Vizianagaram, India	197	18.10 N	83.29 E
Vlaardingen, Neth. (vlär'dĭng-ĕn)	157a	51.54 N	4.20 E
Vladimir, Sov. Un. (vlȧ-dyē'mĕr)	174	56.08 N	40.24 E
Vladimir (Oblast), Sov. Un. (vlä-dyē'mĕr)	174	56.08 N	39.53 E

ng-sing; nŋ-baŋk; N-nasalized n; nŏd; cŏmmit; ōld; ôbey; ôrder; oi-boil; fōōd; fŏŏt; ou-out; s-soft; sh-dish; th-thin; pūre; ûnite; ûrn; stŭd; circŭs; ü-as in French tu; '-indeterminate vowel.

PLACE (Pronunciation)	PAGE	Lat. °′	Long. °′
Vladimiro-Aleksandrovskoye, Sov. Un. (vlȧ-dyē'mē-rô ȧ-lěk-sän'drôf-skô-yě)	204	42.50 N	133.00 E
Vladimir-Volynskiy, Sov. Un. (vlȧ-dyē'mēr vô-lēn'skĭ)	167	50.50 N	24.20 E
Vladivostok, Sov. Un. (vlȧ-dē-vôs-tŏk')	181	43.06 N	131.47 E
Vladykino (Neigh.), Sov. Un.	66b	55.52 N	37.36 E
Vlasenica, Yugo. (vlä'sě-nět'sȧ)	173	44.11 N	18.58 E
Vlasotince, Yugo. (vlä'sô-tēn-tsě)	173	42.58 N	22.08 E
Vlieland (I.), Neth. (vlē'länt)	163	53.19 N	4.55 E
Vlissingen, Neth. (vlĭs'sĭng-ěn)	163	51.30 N	3.34 E
Vlorë (Valona), Alb. (vlō'rŭ)	173	40.28 N	19.31 E
Vltava (R.), Czech.	166	49.24 N	14.18 E
Vodl (L.), Sov. Un. (vôd''l)	178	62.20 N	37.20 E
Voël (R.), S. Afr.	226	32.52 S	25.12 E
Voerde, F.R.G.	63	51.35 N	6.41 E
Voesch, F.R.G.	63	51.24 N	6.26 E
Vogelheim (Neigh.), F.R.G.	63	51.29 N	6.59 E
Voghera, It. (vô-gā'rä)	172	44.58 N	9.02 E
Vohwinkel (Neigh.), F.R.G.	63	51.14 N	7.09 E
Voight (R.), Wa.	118a	47.03 N	122.08 W
Voinjama, Lib.	228	8.25 N	9.45 W
Voiron, Fr. (vwȧ-rôɴ')	171	45.23 N	5.48 E
Voisin, Lac (L.), Can. (vwŏ'-zĭn)	100	54.13 N	107.15 W
Voisins-le-Bretonneux, Fr.	64c	48.45 N	2.03 E
Volcán Misti (Vol.), Peru	142	16.04 S	71.20 W
Volchansk, Sov. Un. (vôl-chänsk')	175	50.18 N	36.56 E
Volchonka-Zil (Neigh.), Sov. Un.	66b	55.40 N	37.37 E
Volch'ya (R.), Sov. Un. (vôl-chyä')	175	49.42 N	34.39 E
Volga (R.), Sov. Un. (vôl'gä)	179	47.30 N	46.20 E
Volga, Mouths of the, Sov. Un.	179	46.00 N	49.10 E
Volgograd (Stalingrad), Sov. Un. (vôl-gô-grä't)(stá'lēn-grat)	179	48.40 N	42.20 E
Volgogradskoye (Res.), Sov. Un. (vôl-gô-grad'skô-yě)	179	51.10 N	45.10 E
Volkhov, Sov. Un. (vôl'kôf)	174	59.54 N	32.21 E
Volkhov (R.), Sov. Un.	174	58.45 N	31.40 E
Volkovysk, Sov. Un. (vôl-kô-vēsk')	167	53.11 N	24.29 E
Vollme, F.R.G.	63	51.10 N	7.36 E
Volmarstein, F.R.G.	63	51.22 N	7.23 E
Volmerswerth (Neigh.), F.R.G.	63	51.11 N	6.46 E
Volodarskiy, Sov. Un. (vô-lô-där'skĭ)	182c	59.49 N	30.06 E
Vologda, Sov. Un. (vô'lôg-dȧ)	174	59.12 N	39.52 E
Vologda (Oblast), Sov. Un.	174	59.00 N	37.26 E
Volokolamsk, Sov. Un. (vô-lô-kôlȧmsk)	174	56.02 N	35.58 E
Volokonovka, Sov. Un. (vô-lô-kô'nôf-kȧ)	175	50.28 N	37.52 E
Vólos, Grc. (vô'lôs)	173	39.23 N	22.56 E
Volozhin, Sov. Un. (vô'lô-shēn)	174	54.04 N	26.38 E
Vol'sk, Sov. Un. (vôl'sk)	179	52.10 N	47.00 E
Volta (R.), Ghana	228	6.05 N	0.30 E
Volta Blanche (R.), Burkina	228	11.30 N	0.40 W
Volta, La., Ghana (vôl'tȧ)	228	7.10 N	0.30 W
Volta Noire (Black Volta) (R.), Afr.	228	10.30 N	2.55 W
Volta Redonda, Braz. (vōl'tä-rā-dôn'dä)	141a	22.32 S	44.05 W
Volterra, It. (vôl-těr'rä)	172	43.22 N	10.51 E
Voltri, It. (vōl'trē)	172	44.25 N	8.45 E
Volturno (R.), It. (vôl-tōōr'nô)	172	41.12 N	14.20 E
Vólvi, Límni (L.), Grc.	173	40.41 N	23.23 E
Volzhskoye (L.), Sov. Un. (vôl'sh-skô-yě)	174	56.43 N	36.18 E
Von Ormy, Tx. (vŏn ôr'mē)	119d	29.18 N	98.36 W
Vōōpsu, Sov. Un. (vōōp'sōō)	174	58.06 N	27.30 E
Voorberg, Neth.	157a	52.04 N	4.21 E
Voortrekkerhoogte, S. Afr.	227b	25.48 S	28.10 E
Vop' (R.), Sov. Un. (vôp)	174	55.20 N	32.40 E
Vopnafjördur, Ice.	158	65.43 N	14.58 W
Vorarlberg (Prov.), Aus.	166	47.20 N	9.55 E
Vordingborg, Den. (vôr'dĭng-bôr)	164	55.10 N	11.55 E
Vorhalle (Neigh.), F.R.G.	63	51.23 N	7.28 E
Voríai (Is.), Grc.	173	39.12 N	24.03 E
Vorkuta, Sov. Un. (vôr-kōō'tȧ)	178	67.28 N	63.40 E
Vormholz, F.R.G.	63	51.24 N	7.18 E
Vormsi (I.), Sov. Un. (vôrm'sĭ)	165	59.06 N	23.05 E
Vórois Evvoïkós Kólpos (G.), Grc	173	38.48 N	23.02 E
Vorona (R.), Sov. Un. (vô-rô'na)	179	51.50 N	42.00 E
Voronezh, Sov. Un. (vô-rô'nyězh)	175	51.39 N	39.11 E
Voronezh (Oblast), Sov. Un.	175	51.10 N	39.13 E
Voronezh (R.), Sov. Un.	174	52.17 N	39.32 E
Voronovo, Sov. Un. (vô'rô-nô-vô)	167	54.07 N	25.16 E
Vorontsovka, Sov. Un. (vô-rônt'sôv-kȧ)	182a	59.40 N	60.14 E
Voron'ya (R.), Sov. Un. (vô-rônyȧ)	178	68.20 N	35.20 E
Voroshilovgrad, Sov. Un.	179	48.34 N	39.18 E
Voroshilovgrad (Oblast), Sov. Un.	175	49.08 N	38.37 E
Võrts-Järv (L.), Sov. Un. (vôrts yärv)	174	58.15 N	26.12 E
Võru, Sov. Un. (vô'rû)	174	57.50 N	26.58 E
Vorya R., Sov. Un. (vôr'yȧ)	182b	55.55 N	38.15 E
Vosges (Mts.), Fr. (vōzh)	169	48.09 N	6.57 E
Voskresensk, Sov. Un. (vôs-krě-sěnsk')	182b	55.20 N	38.42 E
Voss, Nor. (vôs)	164	60.40 N	6.24 E
Vostryakovo, Sov. Un.	182b	55.23 N	37.49 E
Votkinsk, Sov. Un. (vôt-kēnsk')	178	57.00 N	54.00 E
Votkinskoye Vdkhr (Res.), Sov. Un.	178	57.30 N	55.00 E
Vouga (R.), Port. (vō'gȧ)	170	40.43 N	7.51 W
Vouziers, Fr. (vōō-zyā')	168	49.25 N	4.40 E
Voxnan (R.), Swe.	164	61.30 N	15.24 E
Voyageurs Natl. Park, Mn.	115	48.30 N	92.40 W
Vozhe (L.), Sov. Un. (vôzh'yě)	178	60.40 N	39.00 E
Voznesensk, Sov. Un. (vôz-nyě-sěnsk')	175	47.34 N	31.22 E
Vrangelya (Wrangel) (I.), Sov. Un.	176	71.25 N	178.30 E
Vranje, Yugo. (vrän'yě)	173	42.33 N	21.55 E
Vratsa, Bul. (vrät'tsȧ)	173	43.12 N	23.31 E
Vrbas, Yugo. (v'r'bäs)	173	45.34 N	19.43 E
Vrbas (R.), Yugo.	172	44.25 N	17.17 E
Vrchlabí, Czech. (v'r'chlä-bē)	168	50.32 N	15.51 E
Vrede, S. Afr. (vrĭ'dě)(vrēd)	223d	27.25 S	29.11 E
Vredefort, S. Afr. (vrĭ'dě-fôrt)(vrēd'fōrt)	223d	27.00 S	27.21 E
Vreeswijk, Neth.	157a	52.00 N	5.06 E
Vršac, Yugo. (v'r'shȧts)	173	45.08 N	21.18 E
Vrutky, Czech. (vrōōt'kē)	167	49.09 N	18.55 E
Vryburg, S. Afr. (vrī'bûrg)	226	26.55 S	29.45 E
Vryheid, S. Afr. (vrī'hīt)	226	27.43 S	30.58 E
Vsetín, Czech. (fsět'yēn)	167	49.21 N	18.01 E
Vsevolozhskiy, Sov. Un. (vsyě'vôlô'zh-skēē)	182c	60.01 N	30.41 E
Vuelta Abajo (Mts.), Cuba (vwěl'tä ä-bä'hō)	134	22.20 N	83.45 W
Vught, Neth.	157a	51.38 N	5.18 E
Vukovar, Yugo. (vōō'kô-vär)	173	45.20 N	19.00 E
Vulcan, Mi. (vŭl'kăn)	110	45.45 N	87.50 W
Vulcano (I.), It. (vōōl-kä'nô)	172	38.23 N	15.00 E
Vŭlchedrŭma, Bul.	173	43.43 N	23.29 E
Vyartsilya, Sov. Un. (vyȧr-tsē'lyȧ)	165	62.10 N	30.40 E
Vyatka (R.), Sov. Un. (vyȧt'kȧ)	178	58.25 N	51.25 E
Vyazemskiy, Sov. Un. (vyȧ-zěm'skĭ)	204	47.29 N	134.39 E
Vyaz'ma, Sov. Un. (vyȧz'mȧ)	174	55.12 N	34.17 E
Vyazniki, Sov. Un. (vyȧz'nē-kē)	178	56.10 N	42.10 E
Vyborg (Viipuri), Sov. Un. (vwē'bôrk)	165	60.43 N	28.46 E
Vychegda (R.), Sov. Un. (vě'chěg-dȧ)	178	61.40 N	48.00 E
Vym (R.), Sov. Un. (vwēm)	178	63.15 N	51.20 E
Vyritsa, Sov. Un. (vē'rĭ-tsȧ)	182c	59.24 N	30.20 E
Vyshnevolotskoye (L.), Sov. Un. (vŭy'sh-ŋě'vôlôt's-kô'yě)	174	57.30 N	34.27 E
Vyshniy Volochëk, Sov. Un. (vēsh'nyĭ vôl-ô-chěk')	174	57.34 N	34.35 E
Vyskov, Czech. (vēsh'kôf)	166	49.17 N	16.58 E
Vysoké Mýto, Czech. (vû'sô-kā mû'tô)	166	49.58 N	16.07 E
Vysokovsk, Sov. Un. (vĭ-sô'kôfsk)	174	56.16 N	36.32 E
Vytegra, Sov. Un. (vû'těg-rȧ)	178	61.00 N	36.20 E
Vyur, Sov. Un.	178	57.55 N	27.00 E

W

PLACE (Pronunciation)	PAGE	Lat. °′	Long. °′
Wa, Ghana	228	10.04 N	2.29 W
Waal (R.), Neth. (väl)	163	51.46 N	5.00 E
Waalwijk, Neth.	157a	51.41 N	5.05 E
Wabamuno, Can. (wŏ'bä-mŭn)	99	53.33 N	114.28 W
Wabasca, Can. (wŏ-bȧs'kă)	99	56.00 N	113.53 W
Wabash, In. (wô'băsh)	110	40.45 N	85.50 W
Wabash (R.), Il.-In.	110	38.00 N	88.00 W
Wabasha, Mn. (wä'bȧ-shô)	115	44.24 N	92.04 W
Wabowden, Can. (wă-bō'd'n)	101	54.55 N	98.38 W
Wabrzeźno, Pol. (vôŋ-bzězh'nô)	167	53.17 N	18.59 E
Wabu Hu (L.), China (wä-bōō hōō)	200	32.25 N	116.35 E
W. A. C. Bennett Dam, Can.	99	56.01 N	122.10 W
Waccamaw (R.), SC (wăk'ȧ-mô)	127	33.47 N	78.55 W
Waccasassa B., Fl. (wă-kȧ-să'sȧ)	126	29.02 N	83.10 W
Wachow, G.D.R. (vä'κōv)	157b	53.32 N	12.46 E
Waco, Tx. (wā'kō)	125	31.35 N	97.06 W
Waconda Lake (Res.), Ks.	122	39.45 N	98.15 W
Wadayama, Jap. (wä'dä'yä-mä)	205	35.19 N	134.49 E
Waddenzee (Sea), Neth.	163	53.00 N	4.50 E
Waddington, Mt., Can. (wŏd'dĭng-tŭn)	98	51.23 N	125.15 W
Wadena, Can.	100	51.57 N	103.50 W
Wadena, Mn. (wŏ-dē'nȧ)	115	46.26 N	95.09 W
Wadesboro, NC (wādz'bŭr-ô)	127	34.57 N	80.05 W
Wadeville, S. Afr.	71b	26.16 S	28.11 E
Wadi Gestro (R.), Eth.	225	6.25 N	41.21 E
Wādī Mūsā, Jordan	191a	30.19 N	35.29 E
Wadley, Ga. (wŭd'lē)	127	32.54 N	82.25 W
Wad Madani, Sud. (wäd mē-dä'nē)	225	14.27 N	33.31 E
Wadowice, Pol. (vȧ-dô'vēt-sě)	167	49.53 N	19.31 E
Wadsworth, Oh. (wŏdz'wûrth)	113d	41.01 N	81.44 W
Wager B., Can. (wā'jēr)	97	65.48 N	88.19 W
Wagga Wagga, Austl. (wôg'ȧ wôg'ȧ)	216	35.10 S	147.30 E
Wagoner, Ok. (wăg'ŭn-ēr)	123	35.58 N	95.22 W
Wagon Mound, NM (wăg'ŭn mound)	122	35.59 N	104.45 W
Wągrowiec, Pol. (vôŋ-grô'vyěts)	167	52.47 N	17.14 E
Waha, Libya	194	28.16 N	19.54 E
Wahiawa, Hi.	106a	21.30 N	158.03 W
Wahoo, Ne (wä-hōō')	114	41.14 N	96.39 W
Wahpeton, ND (wô'pē-tŭn)	114	46.17 N	96.38 W
Währing (Neigh.), Aus.	66e	48.14 N	16.21 E
Wahroonga, Austl.	70a	33.43 S	150.07 E
Waialua, Hi. (wä'ē-ä-lōō'ä)	106a	21.33 N	158.08 W
Waianae, Hi. (wä'ē-ȧ-nä'ä)	106a	21.25 N	158.11 W
Waidhofen, Aus. (vīd'hôf-ěn)	166	47.58 N	14.46 E
Waidmannslust (Neigh.), F.R.G.	65a	52.36 N	13.20 E
Waigeo, Pulau (I.), Indon. (wä-ē-gā'ô)	181	0.07 N	131.00 E
Waikato (R.), N.Z. (wä'ē-kä'to)	217	38.10 S	175.35 E
Waikerie, Austl. (wā'kēr-ē)	216	34.15 S	140.00 E
Wailuku, Hi. (wä'ē-lōō'kōō)	106a	20.55 N	156.30 W
Waimanalo, Hi. (wä-ē-mä'nä-lo)	106a	21.19 N	157.53 W
Waimea, Hi. (wä-ē-mā'ä)	106a	21.56 N	159.38 W
Wainganga (R.), India (wä-ēn-gŭŋ'gä)	196	20.24 N	79.41 E
Waingapu, Indon.	206	9.32 S	120.00 E
Wainwright, Ak. (wān-rīt)	107	74.40 N	159.00 W
Wainwright, Can.	99	52.49 N	110.52 W
Waipahu, Hi. (wä'ē-pä'hōō)	106a	21.20 N	158.02 W
Waiska R., Mi. (wȧ-ĭz-kȧ)	119k	46.20 N	84.38 W
Waitara, Austl.	70a	33.43 S	150.06 E
Waitsburg, Wa. (wāts'bûrg)	116	46.17 N	118.08 W
Wajima, Jap. (wä'jē-mȧ)	205	37.23 N	136.56 E
Wajir, Ken.	231	1.45 N	40.04 E
Wakamatsu, Jap. (wä-kä'mät-sōō)	205	33.54 N	130.44 E
Wakami (R.), Can.	102	47.43 N	82.22 W
Wakasa-Wan (B.), Jap. (wä'kä-sä wän)	205	35.43 N	135.39 E
Wakatipu (L.), N.Z. (wä-kä-tē'pōō)	217	45.04 S	168.30 E
Wakayama, Jap. (wä-kä'yä-mä)	205	34.14 N	135.11 E
Wake (I.), Oceania (wāk)	208	19.25 N	167.00 E
Wa Keeney, Ks. (wô-kē'nē)	122	39.01 N	99.53 W
Wakefield, Can. (wāk-fēld)	95c	45.39 N	75.55 W
Wakefield, Eng.	156	53.41 N	1.25 W
Wakefield, Ma.	105a	42.31 N	71.05 W
Wakefield, Mi.	115	46.28 N	89.55 W
Wakefield, Ne.	114	42.15 N	96.52 W
Wakefield, RI	112b	41.26 N	71.30 W
Wake Forest, NC (wāk fŏr'ěst)	127	35.58 N	78.31 W
Waki, Jap. (wä'kē)	205	34.05 N	134.10 E
Wakkanai, Jap. (wä'kä-nä'ē)	204	45.19 N	141.43 E
Wakkerstroom, S. Afr. (vȧk'ēr-strōm)(wăk'ēr-strōōm)	226	27.19 S	30.04 E
Wakonassin (R.), Can.	102	46.35 N	82.10 W
Walbrzych, Pol. (väl'bzhûk)	166	50.46 N	16.16 E
Waldbauer (Neigh.), F.R.G.	63	51.18 N	7.28 E
Waldoboro, Me. (wôl'dô-bŭr-ô)	104	44.06 N	69.22 W
Waldo L., Or. (wôl'dō)	116	43.46 N	122.10 W
Waldorf, Md. (wăl'dōrf)	112e	38.37 N	76.57 W
Waldron, Mo.	119f	39.14 N	94.47 W
Waldron (I.), Wa.	118d	48.42 N	123.02 W
Wales, Ak. (wālz)	107	65.35 N	168.14 W
Wales, U.K.	162	52.12 N	3.40 W
Walewale, Ghana	228	10.21 N	0.48 W
Walez, Pol. (välch)	166	53.61 N	16.30 E
Walgett, Austl. (wôl'gět)	216	30.00 S	148.10 E
Walgreen Coast, Ant. (wôl'grēn)	232	73.00 N	110.00 W
Walhalla, SC (wŭl-hăl'ȧ)	126	34.45 N	83.04 W
Walikale, Zaire	231	1.25 S	28.03 E
Walkden, Eng.	64b	53.32 N	2.24 W
Walker, Mn. (wôk'ēr)	115	47.06 N	94.37 W
Walker L, Can.	101	54.42 N	96.57 W
Walker L., Nv.	120	38.46 N	118.30 W
Walker (R.), Nv.	120	39.07 N	119.10 W
Walker, Mt., Wa.	118a	47.47 N	122.54 W
Walker River Ind. Res., Nv.	120	39.06 N	118.20 W
Walkerville, Mt. (wôk'ēr-vĭl)	117	46.20 N	112.32 W
Wallace, Id. (wŏl'ȧs)	116	47.27 N	115.55 W
Wallaceburg, Can.	102	42.39 N	82.25 W
Wallach, F.R.G.	63	51.35 N	6.34 E
Wallacia, Austl.	211b	33.52 S	150.40 E
Wallapa B., Wa. (wŏl ȧ pă)	116	46.39 N	124.30 W
Wallaroo, Austl. (wŏl-ȧ-rōō)	216	33.52 S	137.45 E
Wallasey, Eng. (wŏl'ȧ-sē)	156	53.25 N	3.03 W
Walla Walla, Wa. (wŏl'ȧ wŏl'ȧ)	116	46.03 N	118.20 W
Walled Lake, Mi. (wôl'd lāk)	113b	42.32 N	83.29 W
Wallel, Tulu (Mt.), Eth.	225	9.00 N	34.52 E
Wallgrove, Austl.	70a	33.47 S	150.51 E
Wallingford, Eng. (wŏl'ĭng-fērd)	156b	51.34 N	1.08 W
Wallingford, Pa.	56b	39.54 N	75.22 W
Wallingford, Vt.	111	43.30 N	72.55 W
Wallington, NJ	55	40.51 N	74.07 W
Wallington (Neigh.), Eng.	62	51.21 N	0.09 W
Wallis and Funtuna Is., Oceania	208	13.00 S	176.10 E
Wallisville, Tx. (wŏl'ĭs-vĭl)	125a	29.50 N	94.44 W
Wallowa, Or. (wôl'ô-wȧ)	116	45.34 N	117.32 W
Wallowa Mts., Or.	116	45.10 N	117.22 W
Wallowa R., Or.	116	45.28 N	117.28 W
Wallula, Wa.	116	46.08 N	118.55 W
Walmersley, Eng.	64b	53.37 N	2.18 W
Walnut, Ca. (wôl'nŭt)	119a	34.00 N	117.51 W
Walnut (R.), Ks.	123	37.28 N	97.06 W
Walnut Canyon Natl. Mon, Az.	121	35.10 N	111.30 W
Walnut Cr., Tx.	119c	32.37 N	97.03 W
Walnut Creek, Ca.	118b	37.54 N	122.04 W
Walnut Park, Ca.	59	33.58 N	118.13 W
Walnut Ridge, Ar. (rĭj)	123	36.04 N	90.56 W
Walpole, Ma. (wôl'pōl)	105a	42.09 N	71.15 W
Walpole, NH	111	43.05 N	72.25 W
Walsall, Eng. (wôl-sôl)	156	52.35 N	1.58 W
Walsenburg, Co. (wôl'sěn-bûrg)	122	37.38 N	104.46 W
Walsum, F.R.G.	63	51.32 N	6.41 E
Walter F. George Res., Al.-Ga.	126	32.00 N	85.00 W
Walter Reed Army Medical Center (P. Int.), DC	56d	38.58 N	77.02 W
Walters, Ok. (wôl'tērz)	122	34.21 N	98.19 W
Waltersdorf, G.D.R.	65a	52.22 N	13.35 E
Waltham, Ma. (wôl'thȧm)	105a	42.22 N	71.14 W
Waltham Forest (Neigh.), Eng.	62	51.35 N	0.01 W
Walthamstow, Eng. (wôl'tăm-stō)	156b	51.34 N	0.01 W
Walton, Eng.	62	51.24 N	0.25 W
Walton, NY	111	42.10 N	75.05 W
Walton-le-Dale, Eng. (lē-dāl')	156	53.44 N	2.40 W
Walton on the Hill, Eng.	62	51.17 N	0.15 W
Waltrop, F.R.G.	63	51.37 N	7.23 E
Walt Whitman Homes, NJ	56b	39.52 N	75.11 W
Walvis Bay, S. Afr. (wôl'vĭs)	226	22.50 S	14.30 E
Walworth, Wi. (wôl'wûrth)	115	42.33 N	88.39 W
Walze, F.R.G.	63	51.16 N	7.31 E
Wamba (R.), Zaire	230	5.30 N	17.05 E
Wambel (Neigh.), F.R.G.	63	51.32 N	7.32 E
Wamego, Ks. (wŏ-mē'gō)	123	39.13 N	96.17 W
Wami (R.), Tan. (wä'mē)	227	6.31 S	37.17 E
Wanapitei L., Can.	103	46.45 N	80.45 W
Wanaque, NJ (wŏn'ȧ-kū)	112a	41.03 N	74.16 W
Wanaque Res., NJ	112a	41.06 N	74.20 W
Wanda Shan (Mts.), China (wän-dä shän)	199	45.54 N	131.45 E
Wandhofen, F.R.G.	63	51.26 N	7.33 E
Wandoan, Austl.	216	26.09 S	149.51 E

ăt; finăl; rāte; senâte; ärm; ȧsk; sofȧ; fâre; ch-choose; dh-as th in other; bē; ēvent; bĕt; recĕnt; cratēr; g-gō; gh-guttural g; bĭt; ĭ-short neutral; rīde; κ-guttural k as ch in German ich;

PLACE (Pronounciation)	PAGE	Lat. °'	Long. °'
Wandsbek, F.R.G. (vänds'bĕk)	157c	53.34 N	10.07 E
Wandsworth, Eng. (wôndz'wûrth)	156	51.26 N	0.12 W
Wanganui, N.Z. (wôŋ'gȧ-nōō'ē)	217	39.53 N	175.01 E
Wangaratta, Austl. (wŏŋ'gȧ-răt'ȧ)	216	36.23 N	146.18 E
Wangeroog, I., F.R.G. (vän'gĕ-rōg)	166	53.49 N	7.57 E
Wangqing, China (wäŋ-chyĭŋ)	204	43.14 N	129.33 E
Wangqingtuo, China (wäŋ-chyĭŋ-twô)	200	39.14 N	116.56 E
Wangsi, China (wäŋ-sē)	200	37.59 N	116.57 E
Wangsim-ni (Neigh.), Kor.	68b	37.36 N	127.03 E
Wanheimerort (Neigh.), F.R.G.	63	51.24 N	6.46 E
Wanne-Eickel, F.R.G.	63	51.32 N	7.09 E
Wannsee (Neigh.), F.R.G.	65a	52.25 N	13.09 E
Wansdorf, G.D.R.	65a	52.38 N	13.05 E
Wanstead (Neigh.), Eng.	62	51.34 N	0.02 E
Wantage, Eng. (wŏn'tȧj)	156b	51.33 N	1.26 W
Wantagh, NY	112a	40.41 N	73.30 W
Wantirna, Austl.	70b	37.51 S	145.14 E
Wantirna South, Austl.	70b	37.52 S	145.14 E
Wanxian, China (wän shyĕn)	200	38.51 N	115.10 E
Wanxian, China (wän-shyĕn)	203	30.48 N	108.22 E
Wanzai, China (wän-dzī)	203	28.05 N	114.25 E
Wanzhi, China (wän-jr)	200	31.11 N	118.31 E
Waodoan, Austl. (wŏd'ŏn)	216	26.12 S	149.52 E
Wapakoneta, Oh. (wä'pȧ-kô-nĕt'ȧ)	110	40.35 N	84.10 W
Wapawekka Hills, Can. (wŏ'pȧ-wē'kȧ-hĭlz)	100	54.45 N	104.20 W
Wapawekka L., Can.	100	54.55 N	104.40 W
Wapello, Ia. (wŏ-pĕl'ō)	115	41.10 N	91.11 W
Wapesi L., Can. (wŏ-pĕ'zē)	101	50.34 N	92.21 W
Wappapello Res., Mo. (wä'pȧ-pĕl-lō)	123	37.07 N	90.10 W
Wappingers Falls, NY (wŏp'ĭn-jẽrz)	111	41.35 N	73.55 W
Wapsipinicon (R.), Ia. (wŏp'sĭ-pĭn'ĭ-kŏn)	115	42.16 N	91.35 W
Warabi, Jap. (wä'rä-bē)	205a	35.50 N	139.41 E
Warangal, India (wŭ'räŋ-gȧl)	196	18.03 N	79.45 E
Warburton, The (R.), Austl. (wŏr'bûr-tŭn)	214	27.30 S	138.45 E
Ward, Iran	68h	35.48 N	51.10 E
Wardân, Wâdi (R.), Egypt	191a	29.22 N	33.00 E
Ward Cove, Ak.	98	55.24 N	131.43 W
Warden, S. Afr. (wôr'dĕn)	223d	27.52 S	28.59 E
Wardha, India (wŭr'dä)	196	20.46 N	78.42 E
Wardle, Eng.	64b	53.39 N	2.08 W
War Eagle, WV (wôr ē'g'l)	110	37.30 N	81.50 W
Waren, F.R.G. (vä'rĕn)	166	53.32 N	12.43 E
Warendorf, F.R.G. (vä'rĕn-dōrf)	169c	51.57 N	7.59 E
Wargla, Alg.	224	32.00 N	5.18 E
Warialda, Austl.	216	29.32 S	150.34 E
Warley, see Smethwick			
Warlingham, Eng.	62	51.19 N	0.04 W
Warmbad, Namibia (värm'bäd) (wôrm'băd)	226	28.25 S	18.45 E
Warmbad, S. Afr.	223d	24.52 S	28.18 E
Warm Beach, Wa. (wôrm)	118a	48.10 N	122.22 W
War Memorial Stadium (P. Int.), NY	57a	42.54 N	78.52 W
Warm Springs Ind. Res., Or. (wôrm sprĭnz)	116	44.55 N	121.30 W
Warm Springs Res., Or.	116	43.42 N	118.40 W
Warnemünde, G.D.R. (vär'nĕ-mün-dĕ)	164	54.11 N	12.04 E
Warner Ra. (Mts.), Ca.-Or.	116	41.30 N	120.17 W
Warnow R., G.D.R. (vär'nō)	166	53.51 N	11.55 E
Warracknabeal, Austl.	216	36.20 S	142.28 E
Warragamba Res., Austl.	216	33.40 S	150.00 E
Warrandyte, Austl.	70b	37.45 S	145.13 E
Warrandyte South, Austl.	70b	37.46 S	145.14 E
Warrâq al-'Arab, Egypt	71a	30.06 N	31.12 E
Warrâq al-Hadar, Egypt	71a	30.06 N	31.13 E
Warrâq al-Hadar wa Ambūtbah wa Mīt an-Naşârâ, Egypt	71a	30.06 N	31.13 E
Warrawee, Austl.	70a	33.44 S	151.07 E
Warrego (R.), Austl. (wôr'ē-gô)	215	27.13 S	145.58 E
Warren, Ar. (wŏr'ĕn)	123	33.37 N	92.03 W
Warren, Can.	95f	50.08 N	97.32 W
Warren, In.	110	40.40 N	85.25 W
Warren, Mi.	113b	42.33 N	83.03 W
Warren, Mn.	114	48.11 N	96.44 W
Warren, Oh.	110	41.15 N	80.50 W
Warren, Or.	118c	45.49 N	122.51 W
Warren, Pa.	111	41.50 N	79.10 W
Warren, RI	112b	41.44 N	71.14 W
Warrendale, Pa. (wŏr'ĕn-dāl)	113e	40.39 N	80.04 W
Warrensburg, Mo. (wŏr'ĕnz-bûrg)	123	38.45 N	93.42 W
Warrensville Heights, Oh.	56a	41.26 N	81.29 W
Warrenton, Ga. (wŏr'ĕn-tŭn)	127	33.26 N	82.37 W
Warrenton, Or.	118c	46.10 N	123.56 W
Warrenton, Va.	111	38.45 N	77.50 W
Warri, Nig. (wär'ē)	224	5.33 N	5.43 E
Warrington, Eng.	156	53.22 N	2.30 W
Warrington, Fl. (wŏ'ĭng-tŭn)	126	30.21 N	87.15 W
Warrnambool, Austl. (wôr'năm-bōōl)	216	36.20 S	142.28 E
Warroad, Mn. (wôr'rōd)	115	48.55 N	95.20 W
Warrumbungle Ra., Austl. (wôr'ŭm-bŭŋ-g'l)	215	31.18 S	150.00 E
Warsaw, Il. (wôr'sô)	123	40.21 N	91.26 W
Warsaw, In.	110	41.15 N	85.50 W
Warsaw, NY	111	42.45 N	78.10 W
Warsaw, NC	127	35.00 N	78.07 W
Warsaw, see Warszawa			
Warsop, Eng. (wôr'sŭp)	156	53.13 N	1.05 W
Warszawa (Warsaw), Pol. (vár-shä'vá)	167	52.15 N	21.05 E
Warta R., Pol. (vär'tá)	166	52.35 N	15.07 E
Wartburg, S. Afr.	227c	29.26 S	30.39 E
Wartenberg (Neigh.), G.D.R.	65a	52.34 N	13.31 E
Warwick, Austl. (wŏr'ĭk)	216	28.05 S	152.10 E
Warwick, Can.	104	45.58 N	71.57 W
Warwick, Eng.	162	52.19 N	1.46 W
Warwick, NY	112a	41.15 N	74.22 W
Warwick, RI	112b	41.42 N	71.27 W
Warwickshire (Co.), Eng.	156	52.30 N	1.35 W
Wasatch Mts., Ut. (wô'săch)	119b	40.45 N	111.46 W
Wasatch Plat., Ut.	121	38.55 N	111.40 W
Wasatch Ra., U.S.	108	39.10 N	111.30 W
Wasbank, S. Afr.	227c	28.27 S	30.09 E
Wasco, Or. (wäs'kō)	116	45.36 N	120.42 W
Waseca, Mn. (wô-sē'kȧ)	115	44.04 N	93.31 W
Waseda University (P. Int.), Jap.	69a	35.42 N	139.43 E
Washburn, Me. (wŏsh'bŭrn)	104	46.46 N	68.10 W
Washburn, Wi.	115	46.41 N	90.55 W
Washburn, Mt., Wy.	117	44.55 N	110.10 W
Washington, DC (wŏsh'ĭng-tŭn)	112e	38.50 N	77.00 W
Washington, Ga.	126	33.43 N	82.46 W
Washington, In.	110	38.40 N	87.10 W
Washington, Ia.	115	41.17 N	91.42 W
Washington, Ks.	123	39.48 N	97.04 W
Washington, Mo.	123	38.33 N	91.00 W
Washington, NC	127	35.32 N	77.01 W
Washington, Pa.	113e	40.10 N	80.14 W
Washington (State), U.S.	108	47.30 N	121.10 W
Washington (I.), Wi.	115	45.18 N	86.42 W
Washington Court House, Oh.	110	39.30 N	83.25 W
Washington, L., Wa.	118a	47.34 N	122.12 W
Washington Monument (P. Int.), DC	56d	38.53 N	77.03 W
Washington, Mt., NH	111	44.15 N	71.15 W
Washington National Arpt., Va.	56d	38.51 N	77.02 W
Washington Park, Il.	119e	38.38 N	90.06 W
Washita (R.), Ok. (wŏsh'ĭ-tô)	122	35.33 N	99.16 W
Washougal, Wa. (wŏ-shōō'gál)	118c	45.35 N	122.21 W
Washougal (R.), Wa.	118c	45.38 N	122.17 W
Wash, The (Est.), Eng. (wŏsh)	163	53.00 N	0.20 E
Wasilkow, Pol. (vá-sēl'kōōf)	167	53.12 N	23.13 E
Waskaiowaka L., Can. (wŏ'skă-yō'wŏ-kă)	101	56.30 N	96.20 W
Wassenberg, F.R.G. (vä'sĕn-bĕrgh)	169c	51.06 N	6.07 E
Wass L., Can. (wŏs)	101	53.40 N	95.25 W
Wassmannsdorf, G.D.R.	65a	52.22 N	13.28 E
Wassuk Ra., Nv. (wás'sŭk)	120	38.58 N	119.00 W
Waswanipi, Lac (L.), Can.	103	49.35 N	76.15 W
Water (I.), Vir. Is. (U.S.A.) (wô'tẽr)	129c	18.20 N	64.57 W
Waterberge (Mts.), S. Afr. (wôrtẽr'bûrg)	223d	24.25 S	27.53 E
Waterboro, SC (wô'tẽr-bûr-ō)	127	32.50 N	80.40 W
Waterbury, Ct. (wô'tẽr-bĕr-ē)	111	41.30 N	73.00 W
Water Cay (I.), Ba.	135	22.55 N	75.50 W
Waterdown, Can. (wô'tẽr-doun)	95d	43.20 N	79.54 W
Wateree (R.), SC (wô'tẽr-ē)	127	34.40 N	80.48 W
Waterford, Ire. (wô'tẽr-fẽrd)	162	52.20 N	7.03 W
Waterford, Wi.	113a	42.46 N	88.13 W
Waterloo, Bel.	157a	50.44 N	4.24 E
Waterloo, Can. (wô-tẽr-lōō')	103	43.30 N	80.40 W
Waterloo, Can.	103	45.25 N	72.30 W
Waterloo, Eng.	64a	53.28 N	3.02 W
Waterloo, Il.	123	38.19 N	90.08 W
Waterloo, Ia.	113	42.30 N	92.22 W
Waterloo, Md.	112e	39.11 N	76.50 W
Waterloo, NY	111	42.55 N	76.50 W
Waterton-Glacier Intl. Peace Park, Mt.-Can. (wô'ter-tŭn-glā'shûr)	96	48.55 N	114.10 W
Waterton Lakes Nat. Pk., Can.	99	49.05 N	113.50 W
Watertown, Ma. (wô'tẽr-toun)	105a	42.22 N	71.11 W
Watertown, NY	111	44.00 N	75.55 W
Watertown, SD	114	44.53 N	97.07 W
Watertown, Wi.	113	43.13 N	88.40 W
Water Valley, Ms. (văl'ē)	126	34.08 N	89.38 W
Waterville, Me.	104	44.34 N	69.37 W
Waterville, Mn.	113	44.10 N	93.35 W
Waterville, Wa.	116	47.38 N	120.04 W
Watervliet, NY (wô'tẽr-vlēt')	111	42.45 N	73.54 W
Watford, Eng. (wŏt'fŏrd)	156b	51.38 N	0.24 W
Wathaman L., Can.	100	56.55 N	103.43 W
Watling (I.), see San Salvador			
Watlington, Eng. (wŏt'lĭng-tŭn)	156b	51.37 N	1.01 W
Watonga, Ok. (wŏ-tôŋ'gȧ)	122	35.50 N	98.26 W
Watsa, Zaire (wät'sä)	231	3.03 N	29.32 E
Watseka, Il. (wŏt-sē'kȧ)	110	40.45 N	87.45 W
Watson, In. (wŏt'sŭn)	113h	38.21 N	85.42 W
Watsonia, Austl.	70b	37.43 S	145.05 E
Watson Lake, Can.	96	60.18 N	128.50 W
Watsons Bay, Austl.	70a	33.51 S	151.17 E
Watsonville, Ca. (wŏt'sŭn-vĭl)	120	36.55 N	121.46 W
Wattenscheid, F.R.G. (vä'tĕn-shīd)	169c	51.30 N	7.07 E
Watts, Ca. (wŏts)	119a	33.56 N	118.15 W
Watts Bar (R.), Tn. (bär)	126	35.45 N	84.49 W
Wattville, S. Afr.	71b	26.13 S	28.18 E
Waubay, SD (wô'bā)	114	45.19 N	97.18 W
Wauchula, Fl. (wô-chōō'lȧ)	127a	27.32 N	81.48 W
Wauconda, Il. (wô-kŏn'dȧ)	113a	42.15 N	88.08 W
Waukegan, Il. (wŏ-kē'găn)	113a	42.22 N	87.51 W
Waukesha, Wi. (wô'kē-shô)	113a	43.01 N	88.13 W
Waukon, Ia. (wô kŏn)	115	43.15 N	91.30 W
Waupaca, Wi. (wô-păk'ȧ)	115	44.22 N	89.06 W
Waupun, Wi. (wô-pŭn')	115	43.37 N	88.45 W
Waurika, Ok. (wô-rē'kȧ)	122	34.09 N	97.59 W
Wausau, Wi. (wô'sô)	115	44.58 N	89.40 W
Wausaukee, Wi. (wô-sô'kē)	115	45.22 N	87.58 W
Wauseon, Oh. (wô'sē-ŏn)	110	41.30 N	84.10 W
Wautoma, Wi. (wô-tō'mȧ)	115	44.04 N	89.11 W
Wauwatosa, Wi. (wô-wȧ-t'ŏ'sȧ)	113a	43.03 N	88.00 W
Waveland, Ma.	54a	42.17 N	70.53 W
Waveney (R.), Eng. (wāv'nē)	163	52.27 N	1.17 E
Waverley, Austl.	70a	33.54 S	151.16 E
Waverly, Ia. (wā'vẽr-lē)	115	42.43 N	92.29 W
Waverly, Ma.	54a	42.23 N	71.11 W
Waverly, S. Afr.	227c	31.54 S	26.29 E
Waverly, Tn.	126	36.04 N	87.46 W
Wāw, Sud.	225	7.41 N	28.00 E
Wawa, Can.	102	47.59 N	84.47 W
Wāw al-Kabir, Libya	225	25.23 N	16.52 E
Wawanesa, Can. (wŏ'wŏ-nē'sȧ)	101	49.36 N	99.41 W
Wawasee (L.), In. (wô-wô-sē')	110	41.25 N	85.45 W
Waxahachie, Tx. (wăk-sȧ-hăch'ē)	125	32.23 N	96.50 W
Waycross, Ga. (wā'krôs)	127	31.11 N	82.24 W
Wayland, Ky. (wā'lănd)	126	37.25 N	82.47 W
Wayland, Ma.	105a	42.23 N	71.22 W
Wayne, Mi.	113b	42.17 N	83.23 W
Wayne, Ne.	114	42.13 N	97.03 W
Wayne, NJ	112a	40.56 N	74.16 W
Wayne, Pa.	112f	40.03 N	75.22 W
Waynesboro, Ga. (wānz'bŭr-ô)	127	33.05 N	82.02 W
Waynesboro, Pa.	111	39.45 N	77.35 W
Waynesboro, Va.	111	38.05 N	78.50 W
Waynesburg, Pa. (wānz'bûrg)	111	39.55 N	80.10 W
Waynesville, NC (wānz'vĭl)	126	35.28 N	82.58 W
Waynoka, Ok. (wā-nō'kȧ)	122	36.34 N	98.52 W
Wayzata, Mn. (wā-zä-tá)	119g	44.58 N	93.31 W
Wazīrbad, Pak.	196	32.39 N	74.11 E
Wazīrābād (Neigh.), India	67d	28.43 N	77.14 E
Wāzirpur (Neigh.), India	67d	28.41 N	77.10 E
Weagamow L., Can. (wē'ăg-ă-mou)	101	52.53 N	91.22 W
Wealdstone (Neigh.), Eng.	62	51.36 N	0.20 W
Weald, The (Reg.), Eng. (wēld)	162	50.58 N	0.15 W
Weatherford, Ok. (wĕ-dhẽr-fẽrd)	122	85.32 N	98.41 W
Weatherford, Tx.	125	32.45 N	97.46 W
Weaver (R.), Eng. (wē'vẽr)	156	53.09 N	2.31 W
Weaverville, Ca. (wē'vẽr-vĭl)	116	40.44 N	122.55 W
Webb City, Mo.	123	37.10 N	94.26 W
Weber R., Ut.	119b	41.13 N	112.07 W
Webster, Ma.	105a	42.04 N	71.52 W
Webster, SD	114	45.19 N	97.30 W
Webster City, Ia.	115	42.28 N	93.49 W
Webster Groves, Mo. (grōvz)	119e	38.36 N	90.22 W
Webster Springs, WV (sprĭngz)	111	38.30 N	80.20 W
Wedau (Neigh.), F.R.G.	63	51.24 N	6.48 E
Weddell Sea, Ant. (wĕd'ĕl)	232	73.00 S	45.00 W
Wedding (Neigh.), F.R.G.	65a	52.33 N	13.22 E
Weddinghofen, F.R.G.	63	51.36 N	7.37 E
Wedel, F.R.G. (vā'dĕl)	157c	53.35 N	9.42 E
Wedge Mtn., Can. (wĕj)	98	50.10 N	122.50 W
Wedgeport, Can. (wĕj'pōrt)	104	43.44 N	65.59 W
Wednesfield, Eng. (wĕd''nz-fēld)	156	52.36 N	2.04 W
Weed, Ca. (wēd)	116	41.35 N	122.21 W
Weehawken, NJ	55	40.46 N	74.01 W
Weenen, S. Afr. (vā'nĕn)	227c	28.52 S	30.05 E
Weert, Neth.	163	51.16 N	5.39 E
Weesow, G.D.R.	65a	52.39 N	13.43 E
Weesp, Neth.	157a	52.18 N	5.01 E
Wegendorf, G.D.R.	65a	52.36 N	13.45 E
Wegorzewo, Pol. (vôŋ-gô'zhĕ-vô)	167	54.14 N	21.46 E
Wegrow, Pol. (vôŋ'grōōf)	167	52.23 N	22.02 E
Wehofen (Neigh.), F.R.G.	63	51.32 N	6.46 E
Wehringhausen (Neigh.), F.R.G.	63	51.21 N	7.27 E
Wei (R.), China (wā)	200	35.47 N	114.27 E
Wei (R.), China (wā)	202	34.00 N	108.10 E
Weichang, China (wā-chäŋ)	202	41.50 N	118.00 E
Weidling, Aus.	66e	48.17 N	16.19 E
Weidlingau (Neigh.), Aus.	66e	48.13 N	16.13 E
Weidlingbach, Aus.	66e	48.16 N	16.15 E
Weifang, China	200	36.43 N	119.08 E
Weihai, China (wa'hăi')	200	37.30 N	122.05 E
Weilheim, F.R.G. (vīl'hīm')	166	47.50 N	11.06 E
Weimar, G.D.R. (vī'mär)	166	50.59 N	11.20 E
Weinan, China	202	34.32 N	109.40 E
Weipa, Austl.	215	12.25 S	141.54 E
Weir River, Can. (wēr-rĭv-ẽr)	101	56.49 N	94.04 W
Weirton, WV	110	40.25 N	80.35 W
Weiser, Id. (wē'zẽr)	116	44.15 N	116.58 W
Weiser R., Id.	116	44.26 N	116.40 W
Weishi, China (wā-shr)	200	34.23 N	114.12 E
Weissenburg, F.R.G. (vī'sĕn-bōōrgh)	166	49.04 N	11.20 E
Weissenfels, G.D.R. (vī'sĕn-fĕlz)	166	51.13 N	11.58 E
Weitmar (Neigh.), F.R.G.	63	51.27 N	7.12 E
Weixi, China (wā-shyē)	199	27.27 N	99.30 E
Weixian, China (wā shyĕn)	200	36.59 N	115.17 E
Wejherowo, Pol. (vā-hĕ-rô'vô)	167	54.36 N	18.15 E
Welch, WV (wĕlch)	127	37.24 N	81.28 W
Welcome Monument (P. Int.), Indon.	68k	6.11 S	106.49 E
Weldon, NC (wĕl'dŭn)	127	36.24 N	77.36 W
Weldon (R.), Mo.	123	40.22 N	93.39 W
Weleetka, Ok. (wē-lēt'kȧ)	123	35.19 N	96.08 W
Welford, Austl. (wĕl'fẽrd)	216	25.08 S	144.43 E
Welhamgreen, Eng.	62	51.44 N	0.13 W
Welheim (Neigh.), F.R.G.	63	51.32 N	6.59 E
Welhemina, Kanal (Can.), Neth.	157a	51.37 N	4.55 E
Welkom, S. Afr. (wĕl'kŏm)	223d	27.57 S	26.45 E
Welland, Can. (wĕl'ănd)	113c	42.59 N	79.13 W
Wellesley, Ma. (wĕlz'lē)	105a	42.18 N	71.17 W
Wellesley Hills, Ma.	54a	42.19 N	71.17 W
Wellesley Is., Austl.	214	16.15 S	139.25 E
Well Hill, Eng.	62	51.21 N	0.09 E
Wellinghofen (Neigh.), F.R.G.	63	51.28 N	7.29 E
Wellington, Austl. (wĕl'lĭng-tŭn)	216	32.40 S	148.50 E
Wellington, Eng.	156	52.42 N	2.30 W
Wellington, Ks.	123	37.16 N	97.24 W
Wellington, N.Z.	215a	41.15 S	174.45 E
Wellington, Oh.	110	41.10 N	82.10 W
Wellington, Tx.	122	34.51 N	100.12 W
Wellington (I.), Chile (ōōĕ'lĕng-tŏn)	144	49.30 S	76.30 W
Wells, Austl. (wĕlz)	214	26.35 S	123.40 E
Wells, Can.	99	53.06 N	121.34 W
Wells, Mi.	110	45.50 N	87.00 W
Wells, Mn.	115	43.44 N	93.43 W
Wells, Nv.	116	41.07 N	115.04 W
Wellsboro, Pa. (wĕlz'bŭ-rō)	111	41.45 N	77.15 W
Wellsburg, WV (wĕlz'bûrg)	110	40.10 N	80.40 W
Wells Res., Wa.	116	48.05 N	119.45 W
Wellston, Oh. (wĕlz'tŭn)	110	39.05 N	82.30 W
Wellsville, Mo. (wĕlz'vĭl)	123	39.04 N	91.33 W
Wellsville, NY	111	42.10 N	78.00 W
Wellsville, Oh.	110	40.35 N	80.40 W
Wellsville, Ut.	117	41.38 N	111.57 W
Welper, F.R.G.	63	51.25 N	7.12 E

PLACE (Pronounciation)	PAGE	Lat. °′	Long. °′
Wels, Aus. (vĕls)	166	48.10 N	14.01 E
Welshpool, Wales (wĕlsh′pōōl)	162	52.44 N	3.10 W
Welverdiend, S. Afr. (vĕl-vēr-dēnd′)	223d	26.23 S	27.16 E
Welwyn Garden City, Eng. (wĕlĭn)	156b	51.46 N	0.17 W
Wem, Eng. (wĕm)	156	52.51 N	2.44 W
Wembere (R.), Tan.	231	4.35 S	33.55 E
Wembley (Neigh.), Eng.	62	51.33 N	0.18 W
Wen (R.), China (wŭn)	200	36.24 N	119.00 E
Wenan Wa (Swp.), China (wĕn′ăn′ wä)	200	38.56 N	116.29 E
Wenatchee, Wa. (wē-năch′ē)	116	47.24 N	120.18 W
Wenatchee Mts., Wa.	116	47.28 N	121.10 W
Wenchang, China (wŭn-chäŋ)	203	19.32 N	110.42 E
Wenchi, Ghana	228	7.42 N	2.07 W
Wendelville, NY	57a	43.04 N	78.47 W
Wendeng, China (wŭn-dŭŋ)	200	37.14 N	122.03 E
Wendo, Eth.	225	6.37 N	38.29 E
Wendorer, Ut.	117	40.47 N	114.01 W
Wendover, Can. (wĕn-dōv′ēr)	95c	45.34 N	75.07 W
Wendover, Eng.	156b	51.44 N	0.45 W
Wengern, F.R.G.	63	51.24 N	7.21 E
Wenham, Ma. (wĕn′ăm)	105a	42.36 N	70.53 W
Wennington (Neigh.), Eng.	62	51.30 N	0.13 E
Wenonah, NJ (wĕn′ō-nā)	112f	39.48 N	75.08 W
Wenquan, China (wŭn-chyūän)	202	47.10 N	120.00 E
Wenshan, China	203	23.20 N	104.15 E
Wenshang, China (wĕn′shäng)	200	35.43 N	116.31 E
Wensu, China (wĕn-sōō)	198	41.45 N	80.30 E
Wentworth, Austl. (wĕnt′wûrth)	216	24.03 S	141.53 E
Wentworthville South, Austl.	70a	33.49 S	150.58 E
Wenzhou, China (wŭn-jō)	203	28.00 N	120.40 E
Wepener, S. Afr. (wē′pĕn-ēr) (vā′pĕn-ĕr)	226	29.43 S	27.04 E
Werden (Neigh.), F.R.G.	63	51.23 N	7.00 E
Werder, G.D.R. (vĕr′dĕr)	157b	52.23 N	12.56 E
Were Ilu, Eth.	225	10.39 N	39.21 E
Werl, F.R.G. (vĕrl)	169c	51.33 N	7.55 E
Wermelskirchen, F.R.G.	63	51.08 N	7.13 E
Werne (Neigh.), F.R.G.	63	51.29 N	7.18 E
Werneuchen, G.D.R. (vĕr′hoi-ĸĕn)	157b	52.38 N	13.44 E
Wernsdorf, G.D.R.	65a	52.22 N	13.43 E
Werra R., F.R.G. (vĕr′ä)	166	51.16 N	9.54 E
Werribee, Austl.	211a	37.54 S	144.40 E
Werribee (R.), Austl.	211a	37.40 S	144.37 E
Wersten (Neigh.), F.R.G.	63	51.11 N	6.49 E
Wertach R., F.R.G. (vĕr′täk)	166	48.12 N	10.40 E
Weseke, F.R.G. (vĕ′zĕ-kĕ)	169c	51.54 N	6.51 E
Wesel, F.R.G. (vā′zĕl)	169c	51.39 N	6.37 E
Weser R., F.R.G. (vā′zĕr)	166	53.08 N	8.35 E
Weslaco, Tx. (wĕs-lā′kō)	124	26.10 N	97.59 W
Weslemkoon (L.), Can.	103	45.02 N	77.25 W
Wesleyville, Can. (wĕs′lē-vĭl)	105	49.09 N	53.34 W
Wessel (Is.), Austl. (wĕs′ĕl)	214	11.45 S	136.25 E
Wesselsbron, S. Afr. (wĕs′ĕl-brŏn)	223d	27.51 S	26.22 E
Wessington Springs, SD (wĕs′ĭng-tŭn)	114	44.06 N	98.35 W
West Abington, Ma.	54a	42.08 N	70.59 W
West Allis, Wi. (wĕst-ăl′ĭs)	113a	43.01 N	88.01 W
West Alton, Mo. (ôl′tŭn)	119e	38.52 N	90.13 W
West Athens, Ca.	59	33.55 N	118.18 W
West B., Tx.	125a	29.11 N	95.03 W
West Bend, Wi. (wĕst bĕnd)	115	43.25 N	88.13 W
West Bengal (State), India (bĕn-gôl′)	196	23.30 N	87.30 E
West Berlin, F.R.G. (bĕr-lēn′)	157b	52.31 N	13.20 E
West Blocton, Al. (blŏk′tŭn)	126	33.05 N	87.05 W
Westborough, Ma. (wĕst′bŭr-ō)	105a	42.17 N	71.37 W
West Boylston, Ma. (boil′stŭn)	105a	42.22 N	71.46 W
West Branch, Mi. (wĕst branch)	110	44.15 N	84.10 W
West Bridgford, Eng. (brĭj′fērd)	156	52.55 N	1.08 W
West Bromwich, Eng. (wĕst brŭm′ĭj)	156	52.32 N	1.59 W
Westbrook, Me. (wĕst′brōōk)	104	43.41 N	70.23 W
Westbury, NY	55	40.45 N	73.35 W
Westby, Wi. (wĕst′bē)	115	43.40 N	90.52 W
West Caicos (I.), Turks & Caicos (käē′kō) (kī′kōs)	135	21.40 N	72.30 W
West Caldwell, NJ	55	40.51 N	74.17 W
West Cape Howe (C.), Austl.	214	35.15 S	117.30 E
West Carson, Ca.	59	33.50 N	118.18 W
Westchester, Il.	58a	41.51 N	87.53 W
West Chester, Oh. (chĕs′tēr)	113f	39.20 N	84.24 W
West Chester, Pa.	112f	39.57 N	75.36 W
Westchester (Neigh.), Ca.	59	33.55 N	118.25 W
Westchester (Neigh.), NY.	55	40.51 N	73.52 W
West Chicago, Il. (chĭ-kȧ′gō)	113a	41.53 N	88.12 W
West Collingswood, NJ	56b	39.54 N	75.06 W
West Collingswood Heights, NJ.	56b	39.59 N	75.07 W
West Columbia, SC (cŏl′ŭm-bē-ȧ)	127	33.58 N	81.05 W
West Columbia, Tx.	125	29.08 N	95.39 W
West Conshohocken, NJ	56b	40.04 N	75.19 W
West Cote Blanche B., La. (kōt blănch)	125	29.30 N	92.17 W
West Covina, Ca. (wĕst kō-vē′nȧ)	119a	34.04 N	117.55 W
Westdale, Il.	58a	41.56 N	87.55 W
West Derby (Neigh.), Eng.	64a	53.26 N	2.54 W
West Des Moines, Ia. (dē moin′)	115	41.35 N	93.42 W
West Des Moines (R.), Ia.	115	42.52 N	94.32 W
West Drayton (Neigh.), Eng.	62	51.30 N	0.29 W
West Elizabeth, Pa.	57b	40.17 N	79.54 W
West End., Ba.	134	26.40 N	78.55 W
West End, Eng.	62	51.44 N	0.04 W
West End (Neigh.), Eng.	62	51.32 N	0.24 W
West End (Neigh.), Pa.	57b	40.27 N	80.02 W
Westende, F.R.G.	63	51.25 N	7.24 E
Westenfeld (Neigh.), F.R.G.	63	51.28 N	7.09 E
Westerbauer (Neigh.), F.R.G.	63	51.20 N	7.23 E
Westerham, Eng. (wĕ′stēr′ŭm)	156b	51.15 N	0.05 E
Westerholt, F.R.G.	63	51.36 N	7.05 E
Westerhörn, F.R.G. (vĕs′tĕr-hōrn)	157c	53.52 N	9.41 E
Westerlo, Bel.	157a	51.05 N	4.57 E
Westerly, RI (wĕs′tēr-lē)	111	41.25 N	71.50 W

PLACE (Pronounciation)	PAGE	Lat. °′	Long. °′
Western Australia (State), Austl. (ôs-trā′lĭ-ȧ)	214	24.15 S	121.30 E
Western Ghāts (Mts.), India	197	17.35 N	74.00 E
Western Port, Md. (wĕs′tērn pōrt)	111	39.30 N	79.00 W
Western Sahara, Afr. (sȧ-hä′rȧ)	222	23.05 N	15.33 W
Western Samoa, Oceania	208	14.30 S	172.00 W
Western Siberian Lowland, Sov. Un.	176	63.37 N	72.45 E
Western Springs, Il.	58a	41.47 N	87.53 W
Westerville, Oh. (wĕs′tēr-vĭl)	110	40.10 N	83.00 W
Westerwald (For.), F.R.G. (vĕs′tĕr-väld)	166	50.35 N	7.45 E
Westfalenhalle (P. Int.), F.R.G.	63	51.30 N	7.27 E
Westfield, Ma. (wĕst′fēld)	111	42.05 N	72.45 W
Westfield, NJ	112a	40.39 N	74.21 W
Westfield, NY (wĕst′fēld)	112	42.20 N	79.40 W
Westford, Ma. (wĕst′fĕrd)	105a	42.35 N	71.26 W
West Frankfort, Il. (frăŋk′fŭrt)	112	37.55 N	88.55 W
West Ham, Eng.	156b	51.30 N	0.00 W
West Hanover, Ma.	54a	42.07 N	70.53 W
West Hartford, Ct. (härt′fērd)	111	41.45 N	72.45 W
Westhead, Eng.	64a	53.34 N	2.15 W
West Heidelberg, Austl.	70b	37.45 S	145.02 E
West Helena, Ar. (hĕl′ĕn-ȧ)	123	34.32 N	90.39 W
West Hempstead, NY	55	40.42 N	73.39 W
Westhofen, F.R.G.	63	51.25 N	7.31 E
West Hollywood, Ca.	59	34.05 N	118.24 W
West Homestead, Pa.	57b	40.24 N	79.55 W
West Horndon, Eng.	62	51.34 N	0.21 E
West Hoxton, Austl.	70a	33.55 S	150.51 E
West Hyde, Eng.	62	51.37 N	0.30 W
Westick, F.R.G.	63	51.35 N	7.38 E
West Indies (Reg.), N. A. (ĭn′dēz)	129	19.00 N	78.30 W
West Jordon, Ut. (jôr′dăn)	119b	40.37 N	111.56 W
West Kirby, Eng. (kûr′bē)	156	53.22 N	3.11 W
West Lafayette, In. (lä-fā-yĕt′)	110	40.25 N	86.55 W
Westlake, Oh.	113d	41.27 N	81.55 W
Westland, Mi.	57c	42.19 N	83.23 W
West Lawn, Va.	56d	38.52 N	77.11 W
Westleigh, S. Afr. (wĕst-lē)	223d	27.39 S	27.18 E
West Liberty, Ia. (wĕst lĭb′ēr-tĭ)	115	41.34 N	91.15 W
West Liberty (Neigh.), Pa.	57b	40.24 N	80.01 W
West Linn, Or. (lĭn)	118c	45.22 N	122.37 W
Westlock, Can. (wĕst′lŏk)	99	54.09 N	113.52 W
West Los Angeles (Neigh.), Ca.	59	34.03 N	118.28 W
West Malling, Eng.	62	51.18 N	0.25 E
West Manayunk, Pa.	56b	40.01 N	75.14 W
West Medford, Ma.	54a	42.25 N	71.08 W
West Memphis, Ar.	123	35.08 N	90.11 W
West Midlands (Co.), Eng.	156	52.26 N	1.50 W
West Mifflin, Pa.	57b	40.22 N	79.52 W
Westminster, Ca. (wĕst′min-stēr)	119a	33.45 N	117.59 W
Westminster, Md.	111	39.40 N	76.55 W
Westminster, SC	126	34.38 N	83.10 W
Westminster Abbey (P. Int.), Eng.	62	51.30 N	0.07 W
Westmont, Ca.	59	33.56 N	118.18 W
Westmount, Can. (wĕst′mount)	95a	45.29 N	73.36 W
West, Mt., Pan.	128a	9.10 N	79.52 W
West Newbury, Ma. (nū′bĕr-ē)	105a	42.47 N	70.57 W
West Newton, Ma.	54a	42.21 N	71.14 W
West Newton, Pa. (nū′tŭn)	113e	40.12 N	79.45 W
West New York, NJ (nū yŏrk)	112a	40.47 N	74.01 W
West Nishnabotna (R.), Ia. (nĭsh-nȧ-bŏt′nȧ)	123	40.56 N	95.37 W
West Norwood (Neigh.), Eng.	62	51.26 N	0.06 W
Weston, Ma. (wĕs′tŭn)	105a	42.22 N	71.18 W
Weston, WV	110	39.00 N	80.30 W
Westonaria, S. Afr.	223d	26.19 S	27.38 E
Weston-super-Mare, Eng. (wĕs′tŭn sū′pēr-mā′rē)	162	51.23 N	3.00 W
West Orange, NJ (wĕst ŏr′ĕnj)	112a	40.46 N	74.14 W
West Palm Beach, Fl. (päm bēch)	127a	26.44 N	80.04 W
West Peabody, Ma.	54a	42.30 N	70.57 W
West Pensacola, Fl. (pĕn-sȧ-kō′lȧ)	126	30.24 N	87.18 W
West Pittsburg, Ca. (pĭts′bûrg)	118b	38.02 N	121.56 W
Westplains, Mo. (wĕst-plānz′)	123	36.42 N	91.51 W
West Point Ga.	126	32.52 N	85.10 W
West Point, Ms.	126	33.36 N	88.39 W
Westpoint, Ne.	114	41.50 N	96.00 W
West Point, NY	112a	41.23 N	73.58 W
West Point, Ut.	119b	41.07 N	112.05 W
West Point, Va.	111	37.25 N	76.50 W
Westport, Ct. (wĕst′pōrt)	112a	41.07 N	73.22 W
Westport, Ire.	162	53.44 N	9.36 W
Westport, Or. (wĕst′pôrt)	118c	46.08 N	123.22 W
West Puente Valley, Ca.	59	34.04 N	117.59 W
West Pymble, Austl.	70a	33.46 S	151.08 E
Westray (I.), Scot. (wĕs′trā)	162a	59.19 N	3.05 W
West Road (R.), Can. (rōd)	98	53.00 N	124.00 W
West Ryde, Austl.	70a	33.48 S	151.05 E
West Saint Paul, Mn. (sānt pôl′)	119g	44.55 N	93.05 W
West Sand Spit (I.), Ba.	135	21.25 N	72.10 W
West Schelde (R.), Neth.	163	51.25 N	3.30 E
West Seneca, NY	57a	42.50 N	78.45 W
West Slope, Or.	118c	45.30 N	122.46 W
West Somerville, Ma.	54a	42.24 N	71.07 W
West Tavaputs Plat., Ut. (wĕst tăv′ȧ-pōōts)	121	39.45 N	110.35 W
West Terre Haute, In. (tĕr-ē hōt′)	110	39.30 N	87.30 W
West Thurrock, Eng.	62	51.29 N	0.16 E
West Tilbury, Eng.	62	51.29 N	0.24 E
West Turffontein (Neigh.), S. Afr.	71b	26.16 S	28.02 E
West Union, Ia. (ūn′yŭn)	115	42.58 N	91.48 W
West University Place, Tx.	125a	29.43 N	95.26 W
Westview, Oh. (wĕst′vū)	113d	41.21 N	81.54 W
West View, Pa.	113e	40.31 N	80.02 W
Westville, Can. (wĕst′vĭl)	105	45.34 N	62.43 W
Westville, Il.	110	40.00 N	87.40 W
Westville, NJ.	56b	39.52 N	75.08 W
Westville Grove, NJ	56b	39.51 N	75.07 W
West Virginia (State), U.S. (wĕst vēr-jĭn′ĭ-ȧ)	109	39.00 N	80.50 W
West Walker (R.), Ca. (wôk′ēr)	120	38.25 N	119.25 W

PLACE (Pronounciation)	PAGE	Lat. °′	Long. °′
West Warwick, RI (wŏr′ĭk)	112b	41.42 N	71.31 W
Westwego, La. (wĕst-wē′gō)	112d	29.55 N	90.09 W
West Whittier, Ca.	59	33.59 N	118.04 W
West Wickham (Neigh.), Eng.	62	51.22 N	0.01 W
Westwood, Ca. (wĕst′wōōd)	120	40.18 N	121.00 W
Westwood, Ks.	119f	39.03 N	94.37 W
Westwood, Ma.	105a	42.13 N	71.14 W
Westwood, NJ	112a	40.59 N	74.02 W
Westwood (Neigh.), Ca.	59	34.04 N	118.27 W
West Wyalong, Austl. (wī′alông)	216	34.00 S	147.20 E
West Yorkshire (Co.), Eng.	156	53.37 N	1.48 W
Wetar, Pulau (I.), Indon. (wĕt′ȧr)	207	7.34 S	126.00 E
Wetaskiwin, Can. (wĕ-tăs′kē-wŏn)	99	52.58 N	113.22 W
Wetherill Park, Austl.	70a	33.51 S	150.54 E
Wethmar, F.R.G.	63	51.37 N	7.33 E
Wetmore, Tx. (wĕt′mōr)	119d	29.34 N	98.25 W
Wetter, F.R.G.	169c	51.23 N	7.23 E
Wetumpka, Al. (wē-tŭmp′kȧ)	126	32.33 N	86.12 W
Wetzlar, F.R.G. (vets′lär)	169	50.35 N	8.30 E
Wewak, Pap. N. Gui. (wā-wäk′)	207	3.19 S	143.30 E
Wewoka, Ok. (wē-wō′kȧ)	123	35.09 N	96.30 W
Wexford, Ire. (wĕks′fērd)	162	52.20 N	6.30 W
Weybridge, Eng. (wā′brĭj)	156b	51.20 N	0.26 W
Weyburn, Can. (wā′bûrn)	100	49.41 N	103.52 W
Weyer (Neigh.), F.R.G.	63	51.10 N	7.01 E
Weymouth, Eng. (wā′mŭth)	162	50.37 N	2.34 W
Weymouth, Ma.	105a	42.44 N	70.57 W
Weymouth, Oh.	113d	41.11 N	81.48 W
Whalan, Austl.	70a	33.45 S	150.49 E
Whale Cay (I.), Ba.	134	24.50 N	77.45 W
Whale Cay Chans, Ba.	134	26.45 N	77.10 W
Wharton, NJ (hwôr′tŭn)	112a	40.54 N	74.35 W
Wharton, Tx.	125	29.19 N	96.06 W
What Cheer, Ia. (hwŏt chēr)	115	41.23 N	92.24 W
Whatcom, L., Wa. (hwät′kŭm)	118c	48.44 N	123.34 W
Whatshan L., Can. (wŏt′shăn)	99	50.00 N	118.03 W
Wheatland, Wy. (hwēt′lănd)	117	42.04 N	104.52 W
Wheaton, Il. (hwē′tŭn)	113a	41.52 N	88.06 W
Wheaton, Md.	112e	39.05 N	77.05 W
Wheaton, Mn.	114	45.48 N	96.29 W
Wheeler Pk., Nv.	121	38.58 N	114.15 W
Wheeling, Il. (hwēl′ĭng)	113a	42.08 N	87.54 W
Wheeling, WV	110	40.05 N	80.45 W
Wheelwright, Arg. (ōōē′l-rē′gt)	141c	33.46 S	61.14 W
Whelpleyhill, Eng.	62	51.44 N	0.33 W
Whidbey I., Wa. (hwĭd′bē)	118a	48.13 N	122.50 W
Whippany, NJ (hwĭp′ȧ-nē)	112a	40.49 N	74.25 W
Whistler, Al. (hwĭs′lēr)	126	30.46 N	88.07 W
Whiston, Eng.	64a	53.25 N	2.50 W
Whitaker, Pa.	57b	40.24 N	79.53 W
Whitby, Can. (hwĭt′bē)	103	43.50 N	79.00 W
Whitby, Eng.	64a	53.17 N	2.54 W
Whitchurch, Eng. (hwĭt′chûrch)	156	52.58 N	2.49 W
White (L.), Can.	102	48.47 N	85.50 W
White (L.), Can.	103	45.15 N	76.35 W
White (R.), Ar.	123	34.32 N	91.11 W
White (R.), Can.	102	48.34 N	85.46 W
White (R.), Co.	121	40.10 N	108.55 W
White (R.), In.	110	39.15 N	86.45 W
White (R.), SD	114	43.41 N	99.48 W
White (R.), South Fork, SD	114	43.13 N	101.04 W
White (R.), Tx.	122	36.25 N	102.20 W
White (R.), Vt.	111	43.45 N	72.35 W
White B., Can.	105	50.00 N	56.30 W
White Bear Ind. Res., Can.	101	49.15 N	102.15 W
White Bear L., Mn.	119g	45.04 N	92.58 W
White Bear Lake, Mn.	119g	45.05 N	93.01 W
White Castle, La.	125	30.10 N	91.09 W
White Center, Wa.	118a	47.31 N	122.21 W
White Cloud, Mi.	110	43.35 N	85.45 W
Whitecourt, Can. (wīt′côrt)	99	54.09 N	115.41 W
White Earth (R.), ND	114	48.30 N	102.44 W
White Earth Ind. Res., Mn.	114	47.18 N	95.42 W
Whiteface (R.), Mn. (whīt′fās)	115	47.12 N	92.13 W
Whitefield, Eng.	64b	53.33 N	2.18 W
Whitefield, NH (hwīt′fēld)	111	44.20 N	71.35 W
Whitefish (B.), Mi.	115	46.36 N	84.50 W
Whitefish (R.), Mi.	115	46.12 N	86.56 W
Whitefish B., Can.	101	49.26 N	94.14 W
Whitefish Bay, Wi.	113a	43.07 N	77.54 W
Whitefish, Mt. (hwīt′fĭsh)	117	48.24 N	114.25 W
White Hall, Il.	123	39.26 N	90.23 W
Whitehall, Mi. (hwīt′hôl)	110	43.20 N	86.20 W
Whitehall, NY	111	43.30 N	73.25 W
Whitehall, Pa.	57b	40.22 N	79.59 W
Whitehaven, Eng. (hwīt′hā-vĕn)	162	54.35 N	3.30 W
Whitehead, Ma.	54a	42.17 N	70.52 W
Whitehorn, Pt., Wa. (hwīt′hôrn)	118d	48.54 N	122.48 W
Whitehorse, Can. (whīt′hôrs)	96	60.39 N	135.01 W
White House (P. Int.), DC	56d	38.54 N	77.02 W
White L., La.	125	29.40 N	92.35 W
Whiteley Village, Eng.	62	51.21 N	0.26 W
Whiteman, Ma.	54a	42.05 N	70.56 W
Whitemarsh, Pa.	56b	40.07 N	75.13 W
Whitemouth (L.), Can.	114	49.14 N	95.40 W
White, Mt., Ca.	120	37.38 N	118.13 W
White Mts., Me.	104	44.22 N	71.15 W
White Mts., NH	111	42.20 N	71.05 W
White Nile (Abyad, Al-Bahr al-) (R.), Sud.	225	14.00 N	32.35 E
White Oak, Pa.	57b	40.21 N	79.48 W
White Otter (L.), Can.	115	49.15 N	91.48 W
White P., Ak.-Can.	96	59.35 N	135.03 W
White Plains NY	112a	41.02 N	73.47 W
White R., Wa.	116	47.07 N	121.48 W
White R., East Fork, In.	110	38.45 N	86.20 W
White River, Can.	102	48.38 N	85.23 W
White River Plat., Co.	121	39.45 N	107.50 W
White Rock, Can.	118d	49.01 N	122.49 W
Whiterock Res., Tx. (hwīt′rŏk)	119c	32.51 N	96.40 W
Whitesail L., Can. (whīt′sāl)	98	53.30 N	127.00 W
White Sands Natl. Mon., NM	121	32.50 N	106.20 W

ăt; finăl; rāte; senāte; ärm; ȧsk; sofȧ; fâre; ch-choose; dh-as th in other; bē; ēvent; bĕt; recĕnt; cratēr; g-gō; gh-guttural g; bĭt; ĭ-short neutral; rīde; ĸ-guttural k as ch in German ich;

PLACE (Pronounciation)	PAGE	Lat. °′	Long. °′
White Sea, Sov. Un.	178	66.00 N	40.00 E
White Settlement, Tx.	119c	32.45 N	97.28 W
Whitestone (Neigh.), NY	55	40.47 N	73.49 W
White Sulphur Springs, Mt.	117	46.32 N	110.49 W
White Umfolzi (R.), S. Afr. (ŭm-fȯ-lō′zė)	227c	28.12 S	30.55 E
Whiteville, NC (hwīt′vĭl)	127	34.18 N	78.45 W
White Volta (R.), Ghana	228	9.40 N	1.10 W
Whitewater (L.), Can.	114	49.14 N	100.39 W
Whitewater, Wi. (whīt-wŏt′ēr)	115	42.49 N	88.40 W
Whitewater B., Fl.	127a	25.16 N	80.21 W
Whitewater Cr., Mt.	117	48.50 N	107.50 W
Whitewater L., Can.	101	49.15 N	100.20 W
Whitewater R., In.	113f	39.19 N	84.55 W
Whitewell, Tn. (hwĭt′wĕl)	126	35.11 N	85.31 W
Whitewright, Tx. (hwīt′rīt)	123	33.33 N	96.25 W
Whitham (R.), Eng. (wĭth′ŭm)	162	53.08 N	0.15 W
Whiting, In. (hwīt′ĭng)	113a	41.41 N	87.30 W
Whitinsville, Ma. (hwīt′ĕns-vĭl)	105a	42.06 N	71.40 W
Whitman, Ma. (hwĭt′măn)	105a	42.05 N	70.57 W
Whitmire, SC (hwĭt′mīr)	127	34.30 N	81.40 W
Whitney L., Tx. (hwĭt′nė)	125	32.02 N	97.36 W
Whitney, Mt., Ca.	120	36.34 N	118.18 W
Whitstable, Eng. (wĭt′stȧb′l)	156b	51.22 N	1.03 E
Whitsunday (I.), Austl. (hwĭt′s′n-dā)	215	20.16 S	149.00 E
Whittier, Ca. (hwĭt′ĭ-ēr)	119a	33.58 N	118.02 W
Whittier South, Ca.	59	33.57 N	118.01 W
Whittlesea, S. Afr. (wĭt′l′sē)	227c	32.11 S	26.51 E
Whitworth, Eng. (hwĭt′wŭrth)	156	53.40 N	2.10 W
Whyalla, Austl. (hwī-ăl′ȧ)	216	33.00 S	137.32 E
Whymper, Mt., Can. (wĭm′pēr)	98	48.57 N	124.10 W
Wiarton, Can. (wī′ȧr-tŭn)	102	44.45 N	80.45 W
Wichita, Ks. (wĭch′i-tô)	123	37.42 N	97.21 W
Wichita (R.), Tx.	122	33.50 N	99.38 W
Wichita Falls, Tx. (fôls)	122	33.54 N	98.29 W
Wichita Mts., Ok.	162	34.48 N	98.43 W
Wichlinghofen (Neigh.), F.R.G.	63	51.27 N	7.30 E
Wick, Scot. (wĭk)	162	58.25 N	3.05 W
Wickatunk, NJ (wĭk′á-tŭnk)	112a	40.21 N	74.15 W
Wickede (Neigh.), F.R.G.	63	51.32 N	7.37 E
Wickenburg, Az.	121	33.58 N	112.44 W
Wickliffe, Oh. (wĭk′klĭf)	113d	41.37 N	81.29 W
Wicklow, Ire.	162	52.59 N	6.06 W
Wicklow Mts., Ire. (wĭk′lō)	162	52.49 N	6.20 W
Wickup Mtn., Or. (wĭk′ŭp)	118c	46.06 N	123.35 W
Wiconisco, Pa. (wĭ-kȯn′ĭs-kō)	111	43.35 N	76.45 W
Widen, WV (wī′dĕn)	110	38.25 N	80.55 W
Widnes, Eng. (wĭd′nĕs)	156	53.21 N	2.44 W
Wieden, F.R.G. (vē′dĕn)	166	49.41 N	12.09 E
Wiegan, Eng. (wĭg′ăn)	156	53.33 N	2.37 W
Wieliczka, Pol. (vyĕ-lēch′kȧ)	167	49.58 N	20.06 E
Wieluń, Pol. (vyĕ′lo͞on′)	167	51.13 N	18.33 E
Wiemelhausen (Neigh.), F.R.G.	63	51.28 N	7.13 E
Wien (Vienna), Aus. (vēn) (vė-ĕn′ä)	157e	48.13 N	16.22 E
Wien (State), Aus.	157e	48.11 N	16.23 E
Wiener Berg (Hill), Aus.	66e	48.10 N	16.22 E
Wiener Neustadt, Aus. (vē′nĕr noi′shtät)	166	47.48 N	16.15 E
Wiener Wald (For.), Aus.	157e	48.09 N	16.05 E
Wienerwald (Mts.), Aus.	66e	48.16 N	16.12 E
Wieprz, R., Pol (vyĕpzh)	167	51.25 N	22.45 E
Wiergate, Tx. (wēr′gāt)	125	31.00 N	93.42 W
Wiesbaden, F.R.G. (vēs′bä-dĕn)	166	50.05 N	8.15 E
Wiggins, Ms. (wĭg′ĭnz)	126	30.51 N	89.05 W
Wight, Isle of (I.), Eng. (wīt)	162	50.44 N	1.17 W
Wilber, Ne. (wĭl′bēr)	123	40.29 N	96.57 W
Wilburton, Ok. (wĭl′bēr-tŭn)	123	34.54 N	95.18 W
Wilcannia, Austl. (wĭl-cān-ĭȧ)	216	31.30 S	143.30 E
Wildau, G.D.R. (vēl′dou)	157b	52.20 N	13.39 E
Wildberg, G.D.R. (vēl′bĕrgh)	157b	52.52 N	12.39 E
Wildcat Hill, Can. (wīld′kăt)	100	53.17 N	102.30 W
Wildercroft, Md.	56d	38.58 N	76.53 W
Wildhay (R.), Can. (wīld′hā)	99	53.15 N	117.20 W
Wildomar, Ca. (wĭl′dȯ-mär)	119a	33.35 N	117.17 W
Wild Rice (R.), Mn.	114	47.10 N	96.40 W
Wild Rice (R.), ND	114	46.10 N	97.12 W
Wild Rice L., Mn.	119h	46.54 N	92.10 W
Wildspitze (Mtn.), Aus.	166	46.55 N	10.50 E
Wildwood, NJ	111	39.00 N	74.50 W
Wildwood Manor, Md.	56d	39.01 N	77.07 W
Wiley, Co. (wī′lė)	122	38.08 N	102.41 W
Wilge R., S. Afr. (wĭl′jė)	223d	25.38 S	29.09 E
Wilge R., S. Afr.	223d	27.27 S	28.46 E
Wilhelmina Gebergte (Mts.), Sur.	143	4.30 N	57.00 W
Wilhelm, Mt., Pap. N. Gui.	215	5.58 S	144.58 E
Wilhelmshaven, F.R.G. (vėl-hĕlms-hä′fĕn)	166	53.30 N	8.10 E
Wilhelmstadt (Neigh.), F.R.G.	65a	52.31 N	13.11 E
Wilkes-Barre, Pa. (wĭlks′băr-ė)	111	41.15 N	75.50 W
Wilkes Land, Ant.	232	71.00 S	126.00 E
Wilkeson, Wa. (wĭl-kē′sŭn)	118a	47.06 N	122.03 W
Wilkie, Can. (wĭlk′ē)	100	52.25 N	108.43 W
Wilkinsburg, Pa. (wĭl′kĭnz-bûrg)	113e	40.26 N	79.53 W
Wilkins Township, Pa.	57b	40.25 N	79.50 W
Willamette R., Or.	116	44.15 N	123.13 W
Willapa B., Wa.	116	46.37 N	124.00 W
Willard, Oh. (wĭl′ȧrd)	110	41.00 N	82.50 W
Willard, Ut.	119b	41.24 N	112.02 W
Willaston, Eng.	64a	53.18 N	3.00 W
Willcox, Az. (wĭl′kŏks)	121	32.15 N	109.50 W
Willemstad, Neth. Antilles	142	12.12 N	68.58 W
Willesden, Eng. (wĭlz′dĕn)	156b	51.31 N	0.17 W
William Creek, Austl. (wĭl′yăm)	214	28.45 S	136.20 E
Williams, Az. (wĭl′yămz)	121	35.15 N	112.15 W
Williams (I.), Ba.	134	25.30 N	78.30 W
Williamsburg, Ky. (wĭl′yămz-bŭrg)	126	36.42 N	84.09 W
Williamsburg, Oh.	113f	39.04 N	84.02 W
Williamsburg, Va.	127	37.15 N	76.41 W
Williamsburg (Neigh.), NY	55	40.42 N	73.57 W
Williams Lake, Can.	99	52.08 N	122.09 W
Williamson, WV (wĭl′yăm-sŭn)	110	37.40 N	82.15 W
Williamsport, Md.	111	39.35 N	77.45 W
Williamsport, Pa.	111	41.15 N	77.05 W
Williamston, NC (wĭl′yămz-tŭn)	127	35.50 N	77.04 W
Williamston, SC	127	34.36 N	82.30 W
Williamstown, Austl.	70b	37.52 S	144.54 E
Williamstown, WV (wĭl′yămz-toun)	110	39.20 N	81.30 W
Williamsville, NY (wĭl′yăm-vĭl)	113c	42.58 N	78.46 W
Willich, F.R.G.	63	51.16 N	6.33 E
Willimantic, Ct. (wĭl-ĭ-măn′tĭk)	111	41.40 N	72.10 W
Willingale, Eng.	62	51.44 N	0.19 E
Willis, Tx. (wĭl′ĭs)	125	30.24 N	95.29 W
Willis Is., Austl.	215	16.15 S	150.30 E
Williston, ND (wĭl′ĭs-tŭn)	114	48.08 N	103.38 W
Williston, L., Can.	98	55.40 N	123.40 W
Williston Park, NY	55	40.45 N	73.39 W
Willmar, Mn. (wĭl′mär)	99	45.07 N	95.05 W
Willmersdorf, G.D.R.	65a	52.40 N	13.41 E
Willoughby, Austl.	70a	33.48 S	151.12 E
Willoughby, Oh. (wĭl′ȯ-bė)	113d	41.39 N	81.25 W
Willow, Ak.	107	61.50 N	150.00 W
Willow Brook, Ca.	59	33.55 N	118.14 W
Willow Cr., Mt. (wĭl′ȯ)	117	48.45 N	111.34 W
Willow Cr., Or.	116	44.21 N	117.34 W
Willow Grove, Pa.	112f	40.07 N	75.07 W
Willowick, Oh. (wĭl′ȯ-wĭk)	113d	41.39 N	81.28 W
Willowmore, S. Afr. (wĭl′ȯ-môr)	226	33.15 S	23.37 E
Willow Run, Mi. (wĭl′ȯ rūn)	113b	42.16 N	83.34 W
Willow Run, Va.	56d	38.49 N	77.10 W
Willows, Ca. (wĭl′ōz)	120	39.32 N	122.11 W
Willow Springs, Il.	58a	41.44 N	87.52 W
Willow Springs, Mo. (sprĭngz)	123	36.59 N	91.56 W
Willowvale, S. Afr. (wĭ-lȯ′vāl)	227c	32.17 S	28.32 E
Wills Point, Tx. (wĭlz point)	125	32.42 N	96.02 W
Wilmer, Tx. (wĭl′mēr)	119c	32.35 N	96.40 W
Wilmette, Il. (wĭl-mĕt′)	113a	42.04 N	87.42 W
Wilmington, Austl.	216	32.39 S	138.07 E
Wilmington, Ca. (wĭl′mĭng-tŭn)	119a	33.46 N	118.16 W
Wilmington, De.	112f	39.45 N	75.33 W
Wilmington, Eng.	62	51.26 N	0.12 E
Wilmington, Il.	113a	41.19 N	88.09 W
Wilmington, Ma.	105a	42.34 N	71.10 W
Wilmington, NC	127	34.12 N	77.56 W
Wilmington, Oh.	110	39.20 N	83.50 W
Wilmore, Ky. (wĭl′mōr)	110	37.50 N	84.35 W
Wilmslow, Eng. (wĭlmz′lō)	156	53.19 N	2.14 W
Wilno, see Vilnius			
Wilpoort, S. Afr.	223d	26.57 S	26.17 E
Wilson, Ar. (wĭl′sŭn)	123	35.35 N	90.02 W
Wilson, NC	127	35.42 N	77.55 W
Wilson, Ok.	123	34.09 N	97.27 W
Wilson (R.), Al.	126	34.53 N	87.28 W
Wilson, L., Al.	126	34.45 N	86.58 W
Wilson, Mt., Ca.	119a	34.15 N	118.06 W
Wilson Pk., Ut.	117	40.46 N	110.27 W
Wilson, Pt., Austl.	211a	38.05 S	144.31 E
Wilson's Prom., Austl. (wĭl′sŭnz)	216	39.05 S	146.50 E
Wilsonville, Il. (wĭl′sŭn-vĭl)	119e	39.04 N	89.52 W
Wilstedt, F.R.G. (vēl′shtĕt)	157c	53.45 N	10.04 E
Wilster, F.R.G. (vēl′stĕr)	157c	53.55 N	9.23 E
Wilton, Ct. (wĭl′tŭn)	112a	41.11 N	73.25 W
Wilton, ND	114	47.09 N	100.47 W
Wilton Woods, Va.	56d	38.47 N	77.06 W
Wiluna, Austl. (wĭ-lo͞o′nȧ)	214	26.35 S	120.25 E
Wimbledon (Neigh.), Eng.	62	51.25 N	0.12 W
Wimbledon Common (P. Int.), Eng.	62	51.26 N	0.14 W
Winamac, In. (wĭn′ȧ măk)	110	41.05 N	86.40 W
Winburg, S. Afr. (wĭm-bûrg)	223d	28.31 S	27.02 E
Winchester, Ca. (wĭn′chĕs-tēr)	119a	33.41 N	117.06 W
Winchester, Eng.	162	51.04 N	1.20 W
Winchester, Id.	116	46.14 N	116.39 W
Winchester, In.	110	40.10 N	84.50 W
Winchester, Ky.	110	38.00 N	84.15 W
Winchester, Ma.	105a	42.28 N	71.09 W
Winchester, NH	111	42.45 N	72.25 W
Winchester, Tn.	121	35.11 N	86.06 W
Winchester, Va.	111	39.10 N	78.10 W
Windber, Pa. (wĭnd′bēr)	111	40.15 N	78.45 W
Wind Cave Natl. Park, SD	114	43.36 N	103.53 W
Winder, Ga. (wīn′dēr)	121	33.58 N	83.43 W
Windermere, Eng. (wĭn′dēr-mēr)	162	54.25 N	2.59 W
Windfall, Can. (wĭnd′fôl)	99	54.11 N	116.15 W
Windham, Ct. (wĭnd′ăm)	111	41.45 N	72.05 W
Windham, NH	105a	42.49 N	71.21 W
Windhoek, Namibia (vĭnt′ho͝ok)	226	22.05 S	17.10 E
Wind L., Wi.	113a	42.49 N	88.06 W
Wind Mtn., NM	124	32.02 N	105.30 W
Windom, Mn. (wĭn′dŭm)	115	43.50 N	95.04 W
Windora, Austl. (wĭn-dō′rȧ)	216	25.15 S	142.50 E
Wind R., Wy.	117	43.17 N	109.02 W
Wind River Ind. Res., Wy.	117	43.07 N	109.08 W
Wind River Ra., Wy.	117	43.19 N	109.47 W
Windsor, Austl. (wĭn′zēr)	211b	33.37 S	150.49 E
Windsor, Can.	113b	42.19 N	83.00 W
Windsor, Can.	104	44.59 N	64.08 W
Windsor, Can.	105	48.57 N	55.40 W
Windsor, Co.	122	40.27 N	104.51 W
Windsor, Eng.	156b	51.27 N	0.37 W
Windsor, Mo.	123	38.32 N	93.31 W
Windsor, NC	127	35.58 N	76.57 W
Windsor, Vt.	104	43.30 N	72.25 W
Windsor Arpt., (P. Int.), Can.	57c	42.17 N	82.58 W
Windsor Hills, Ca.	59	33.59 N	118.21 W
Windsor, University of (P. Int.), Can.	57c	42.18 N	83.04 W
Windward Is., N. A. (wind′wērd)	129	12.45 N	61.40 W
Windward Pass, N. A.	135	19.30 N	74.20 W
Winefred L., Can.	100	55.30 N	110.35 W
Winfield, Ks.	123	37.14 N	97.00 W
Wing Lake Shores, Mi.	57c	42.33 N	83.17 W
Winifred, Mt. (wĭn ĭ frĕd)	117	47.35 N	109.20 W
Winisk (R.), Can.	97	54.30 N	86.30 W
Wink, Tx. (wĭŋk)	124	31.48 N	103.06 W
Winkler, Can. (wĭnk′lēr)	101	49.11 N	97.56 W
Winneba, Ghana (wĭn′ė-bȧ)	228	5.25 N	0.36 W
Winnebago, Mn. (wĭn′ė-bā′gō)	115	43.45 N	94.08 W
Winnebago Ind. Res., Ne.	114	42.15 N	96.06 W
Winnebago, L., Wi.	115	44.09 N	88.10 W
Winnemucca, Nv. (wĭn-ė-mŭk′ȧ)	116	40.59 N	117.43 W
Winnemucca (L.), Nv.	120	40.06 N	119.07 W
Winner, SD (wĭn′ēr)	114	43.22 N	99.50 W
Winnetka, Il. (wĭ-nĕtkȧ)	113a	42.07 N	87.44 W
Winnett, Mt. (wĭn′ĕt)	117	47.01 N	108.20 W
Winnfield, La. (wĭn′fēld)	125	31.56 N	92.39 W
Winnibigoshish (L.), Mn. (wĭn′ĭ-bĭ-gō′shĭsh)	115	47.30 N	93.45 W
Winnipeg, Can. (wĭn′ĭ-pĕg)	95f	49.53 N	97.09 W
Winnipeg (R.), Can.	96	52.20 N	95.54 W
Winnipeg Beach, Can.	101	50.31 N	96.58 W
Winnipeg, L., Can.	101	52.00 N	97.00 W
Winnipegosis, Can. (wĭn′ĭ-pė-gō′sĭs)	101	51.39 N	99.56 W
Winnipegosis (L.), Can.	101	52.30 N	100.00 W
Winnipesaukee (L.), NH (wĭn′ė-pė-sô′kė)	111	43.40 N	71.20 W
Winnsboro, La. (wĭnz′bŭr′ȯ)	125	32.09 N	91.42 W
Winnsboro, SC	127	34.29 N	81.05 W
Winnsboro, Tx.	123	32.56 N	95.15 W
Winona, Can. (wĭ-nō′nȧ)	95d	43.13 N	79.39 W
Winona, Mn.	115	44.03 N	91.40 W
Winona, Ms.	126	33.29 N	89.43 W
Winooski, Vt. (wĭ′no͞os-kė)	111	44.30 N	73.10 W
Winsen (Luhe), F.R.G. (vēn′zĕn) (lo͞o′hĕ)	157c	53.22 N	10.13 E
Winsford, Eng. (wĭnz′fērd)	156	53.11 N	2.30 W
Winslow, Az. (wĭnz′lō)	121	35.00 N	110.45 W
Winslow, Wa.	118a	47.38 N	122.31 W
Winsted, Ct. (wĭn′stĕd)	111	41.55 N	73.05 W
Winster, Eng. (wĭn′stēr)	156	53.08 N	1.38 W
Winston-Salem, NC (wĭn stŭn-sā′lĕm)	127	36.05 N	80.15 W
Winterberg, F.R.G.	63	51.17 N	7.18 E
Winterberge (Mts.), S. Afr.	227c	32.18 S	26.25 E
Winter Garden, Fl. (wĭn′tēr gär′d′n)	127a	28.32 N	81.35 W
Winter Harbour, Can.	98	50.31 N	128.02 W
Winter Haven, Fl. (hā′vĕn)	127a	28.01 N	81.38 W
Wintering L., Can. (wĭn′tēr-ĭng)	101	55.24 N	97.42 W
Winter Park, Fl. (pärk)	127a	28.35 N	81.21 W
Winters, Tx. (wĭn′tērz)	124	31.59 N	99.58 W
Winterset, Ia. (wĭn′tēr-sĕt)	115	41.19 N	94.03 W
Winterswijk, Neth.	169c	51.58 N	6.44 E
Winterthur, Switz. (vĭn′tĕr-to͞or)	166	47.30 N	8.32 E
Winterton, S. Afr.	227c	28.51 S	29.33 E
Winthrop, Me. (wĭn′thrŭp)	104	44.19 N	70.00 W
Winthrop, Ma.	105a	42.23 N	70.59 W
Winthrop, Mn.	115	44.31 N	94.20 W
Winton, Austl. (wĭn-tŭn)	215	22.17 S	143.08 E
Winz, F.R.G.	63	51.23 N	7.09 E
Wipperfürth, F.R.G. (vĕ′pĕr-fürt)	169c	51.07 N	7.23 E
Wirksworth, Eng. (wûrks′wûrth)	156	53.05 N	1.35 W
Wisconsin (State), U. S. (wĭs-kŏn′sĭn)	109	44.30 N	91.00 W
Wisconsin (R.), Wi.	115	43.14 N	90.34 W
Wisconsin Dells, Wi.	115	43.38 N	89.46 W
Wisconsin Rapids, Wi.	115	44.24 N	89.50 W
Wishek, ND (wĭsh′ĕk)	114	46.15 N	99.34 W
Wisla (Vistula) R., Pol. (vės′wȧ) (vĭs′tu̇-lȧ)	167	52.48 N	19.02 E
Wisloka R., Pol. (vės-wȯ′kȧ)	167	49.55 N	21.26 E
Wismar, G.D.R. (vĭs′mär)	166	53.53 N	11.28 E
Wismar, Guy. (wĭs′mȧr)	143	5.58 N	58.15 W
Wisner, Ne. (wĭz′nĕr)	114	42.00 N	96.55 W
Wissembourg, Fr. (vė-säN-bo͞or′)	169	49.03 N	7.58 E
Wissinoming, (Neigh.), Pa.	56b	40.01 N	75.04 W
Wissous, Fr.	64c	48.44 N	2.20 E
Wister, L., Ok. (vĭs′tēr)	123	35.02 N	94.52 W
Witbank, S. Afr. (wĭt-băŋk)	223d	25.53 S	29.14 E
Witberg (Mtn.), S. Afr.	227c	30.32 S	27.18 E
Witfield, S. Afr.	71b	26.11 S	28.12 E
Witham, Eng. (wĭdh′ăm)	156b	51.48 N	0.37 E
Witham (R.), Eng.	156	53.11 N	0.20 W
Withamsville, Oh. (wĭdh′ămz-vĭl)	113f	39.04 N	84.16 W
Withington (Neigh.), Eng.	64b	53.26 N	2.14 W
Withlacoochee (R.), Fl. (wĭth-lȧ-ko͞o′chė)	127a	28.58 N	82.30 W
Withlacoochee (R.), Ga.	126	31.15 N	83.30 W
Withrow, Mn. (wĭdh′rō)	119g	45.08 N	92.54 W
Witney, Eng. (wĭt′nė)	156b	51.45 N	1.30 W
Witpoortje, S. Afr.	71b	26.08 S	27.50 E
Witt, Il. (vĭt)	110	39.10 N	89.15 W
Witten, F.R.G. (vē′tĕn)	169c	51.26 N	7.19 E
Wittenau (Neigh.), F.R.G.	65a	52.35 N	13.20 E
Wittenberg, G.D.R. (vē′tĕn-bĕrgh)	166	51.53 N	12.40 E
Wittenberge, G.D.R. (vĭt-ĕn-bĕr′gē)	166	52.59 N	11.45 E
Wittlaer, F.R.G.	63	51.19 N	6.44 E
Wittlich, F.R.G. (vĭt′lĭk)	166	49.58 N	6.54 E
Witu, Ken. (wē′to͞o)	227	2.18 S	40.28 E
Witu Is., Pap. N. Gui.	207	4.45 S	149.50 E
Witwatersberg (Mts.), S. Afr. (wĭt-wôr-tērz-bûrg)	227b	25.58 S	27.53 E
Witwatersrand (Ridge), S. Afr. (wĭt-wôr′tērs-rănd)	223d	25.55 S	26.27 E
Witwatersrand, Gold Mine, (P. Int.), S. Afr.	71b	26.12 S	28.15 E
Witwatersrand, University of (P. Int.), S. Afr.	71b	26.12 S	28.02 E
Wkra R., Pol. (f′krȧ)	167	52.40 N	20.35 E
Wloclawek, Pol. (vwô-tswä′vĕk)	167	52.38 N	19.08 E
Wlodawa, Pol. (vwȯ-dä′vä)	167	51.33 N	23.33 E
Wloszczowa, Pol. (vwȯsh-chô′vä)	167	50.51 N	19.58 E
Woburn, Ma. (wo͞o′bŭrn) (wō′bŭrn)	105a	42.29 N	71.10 W
Woburn, (Neigh.), Can.	54c	43.46 N	79.13 W
Woerden, Neth.	157a	52.05 N	4.52 E
Woking, Eng.	156b	51.18 N	0.33 W
Wokingham, Eng. (wȯ′kĭng-hăm)	156b	51.23 N	0.50 W
Wolcott, Ks. (wōl′kŏt)	119f	39.12 N	94.47 W
Woldingham, Eng.	62	51.17 N	0.02 W
Wolf (I.), Can. (wo͝olf)	111	44.10 N	76.25 W

ng-sing; nŋ-banŋk; N-nasalized n; nŏd; cŏmmit; ōld; ȯbey; ŏrder; oi-boil; fo͞od; fo͝ot; ou-out; s-soft; sh-dish; th-thin; pūre; u̇nite; ûrn; stŭd; circŭs; ü-as in French tu; ′-indeterminate vowel.

PLACE (Pronounciation)	PAGE	Lat. °'	Long. °'
Wolf (R.), Ms.	126	30.45 N	89.36 W
Wolf (R.), Wi.	115	45.14 N	88.45 W
Wolfenbüttel, F.R.G. (vôl'fĕn-büt-ĕl)	166	52.10 N	10.32 E
Wolf L., Il.	113a	41.39 N	87.33 W
Wolf Point, Mt. (wo͝olf point)	117	48.07 N	105.40 W
Wolfratshausen, F.R.G. (vôlf'räts-hou-zĕn)	157d	47.55 N	11.25 E
Wolfsburg, F.R.G. (vôlfs'bo͞orgh)	166	52.30 N	10.37 E
Wolfville, Can. (wo͝olf'vĭl)	104	45.05 N	64.22 W
Wolgast, G.D.R. (vôl'gäst)	166	54.04 N	13.46 E
Wolhuterskop, S. Afr.	227b	25.41 S	27.40 E
Wolkersdorf, Aus.	157e	48.24 N	16.31 E
Wollaston, Ma.	54a	42.16 N	71.01 W
Wollaston (L.), Can. (wo͝ol'ȧs-tŭn)	96	58.15 N	103.20 W
Wollaston Pen., Can.	96	70.00 N	115.00 W
Wollongong, Austl. (wo͝ol'ŭn-gông)	216	34.26 S	151.05 E
Wolomin, Pol. (vô-wō'mēn)	167	52.19 N	21.17 E
Wolseley, Can.	100	50.25 N	103.15 W
Wolstanton, Eng. (wo͝ol-stăn'tŭn)	156	53.02 N	2.13 W
Woltersdorf, G.D.R. (vôl'tĕs-dōrf)	157b	52.07 N	13.13 E
Woltersdorf, G.D.R.	65a	52.26 N	13.45 E
Wolverhampton, Eng. (wo͝ol'vĕr-hămp-tŭn)	156	52.35 N	2.07 W
Wolverine, Mi.	57c	42.33 N	83.29 W
Wolwehoek, S. Afr.	223d	26.55 S	27.50 E
Wonga Park, Austl.	70b	37.44 S	145.16 E
Wŏnsan, Kor. (wŭn'sän')	204	39.08 N	127.24 E
Wonthaggi, Austl. (wônt-hăg'ē)	216	38.45 S	145.42 E
Wood, SD (wo͝od)	114	43.26 N	100.25 W
Woodbine, Ia. (wo͝od'bīn)	114	41.44 N	95.42 W
Woodbridge, NJ (wo͝od'brĭj')	112a	40.33 N	74.18 W
Woodbrook, Md.	56c	39.23 N	76.37 W
Wood Buffalo Natl. Park, Can.	96	59.50 N	118.53 W
Woodburn, Il. (wo͝od'bûrn)	119e	39.03 N	90.01 W
Woodburn, Or.	116	45.10 N	122.51 W
Woodbury, NJ (wo͝od'bĕr-ē)	112f	39.50 N	75.14 W
Woodbury, NY	55	40.49 N	73.28 W
Woodbury Terrace, NJ	56b	39.51 N	75.08 W
Woodcrest, Ca. (wo͝od'krĕst)	119a	33.53 N	117.18 W
Woodford, Eng.	64b	53.21 N	2.10 W
Woodford Bridge (Neigh.), Eng.	62	51.36 N	0.04 E
Wood Green (Neigh.), Eng.	62	51.36 N	0.07 W
Woodhaven (Neigh.), NY	55	40.41 N	73.51 W
Woodinville, Wa. (wo͝od'ĭn-vĭl)	118a	47.46 N	122.09 W
Woodland, Ca. (wo͝od'lănd)	120	38.41 N	121.47 W
Woodland, Wa.	118c	45.54 N	122.45 W
Woodland Hills, Ca.	119a	34.10 N	118.36 W
Woodlands, Singapore	67c	1.27 N	103.46 E
Woodlark I., Pap. N. Gui. (wo͝od'lärk)	207	9.07 S	152.00 E
Woodlawn, Md.	56c	39.19 N	76.43 W
Woodlawn, Md.	56d	38.57 N	76.53 W
Woodlawn (Neigh.), Il.	58a	41.47 N	87.36 W
Woodlawn Beach, NY (wo͝od'lôn bēch)	113c	42.48 N	78.51 W
Woodlawn Heights, Md.	56c	39.11 N	76.39 W
Woodlyn, Pa.	56b	39.52 N	75.21 W
Woodlynne, NJ	56b	39.55 N	75.05 W
Woodmansterfe, Eng.	62	51.19 N	0.10 W
Woodmere, NY	55	40.38 N	73.43 W
Woodmoor, Md.	56c	39.20 N	76.44 W
Wood Mountain, Can.	100	49.14 N	106.20 W
Wood Ridge, NJ	55	40.51 N	74.05 W
Wood River, Il.	119e	38.52 N	90.06 W
Woodroffe, Mt., Austl. (wo͝od'rŭf)	214	26.05 S	132.00 E
Woodruff, SC (wo͝od'rŭf)	127	34.43 N	82.03 W
Woods (L.), Austl. (wo͝odz)	214	18.00 S	133.18 E
Woodsburgh, NY	55	40.37 N	73.42 W
Woods Cross, Ut. (krôs)	119b	40.53 N	111.54 W
Woodsfield, Oh. (wo͝odz-fēld)	110	39.45 N	81.10 W
Woodside (Neigh.), NY	55	40.45 N	73.55 W
Woods, L. of the, Can.-Mn.	109	49.25 N	93.25 W
Woodson, Or. (wo͝odsŭn)	118c	46.07 N	123.20 W
Woodstock, Can. (wo͝od'stŏk)	104	43.10 N	80.50 W
Woodstock, Can.	104	46.09 N	67.34 W
Woodstock, Eng.	156b	51.48 N	1.22 W
Woodstock, Il.	115	42.20 N	88.29 W
Woodstock, Va.	111	38.55 N	78.25 W
Woodsville, NH (wo͝odz'vĭl)	111	44.10 N	72.00 W
Woodville, Ms. (wo͝od'vĭl)	126	31.06 N	91.11 W
Woodville, Tx.	125	30.48 N	94.25 W
Woodward, Ok. (wo͝od'wôrd)	122	36.25 N	99.24 W
Woollahra, Austl.	70a	33.53 S	151.15 E
Woolton (Neigh.), Eng.	64a	53.23 N	2.52 W
Woolwich, Eng. (wo͝ol'ĭj)	156b	51.28 N	0.05 E
Woomera, Austl. (wo͞om'ērȧ)	216	31.15 S	136.43 E
Woonsocket, RI (wo͞on-sŏk'ĕt)	112b	42.00 N	71.30 W
Woonsocket, SD	114	44.03 N	98.17 W
Wooster, Oh. (wo͞os'tēr)	110	40.50 N	81.55 W
Worcester, Eng. (wo͞o'stēr)	162	52.09 N	2.14 W
Worcester, Ma. (wo͞os'tēr)	105a	42.16 N	71.49 W
Worcester, S. Afr. (wo͞os'tēr)	226	33.35 S	19.31 E
Worden, Il. (wôr'dĕn)	119e	38.56 N	89.50 W
Workington, Eng. (wûr'kĭng-tŭn)	162	54.40 N	3.30 W
Worksop, Eng. (wûrk'sŏp) (wûr'sŭp)	156	53.18 N	1.07 W
Worland, Wy. (wûr'lănd)	117	44.02 N	107.56 W
Wormley, Eng.	62	51.44 N	0.01 W
Worms, F.R.G. (vôrms)	166	49.37 N	8.22 E
Worona Res., Austl.	211b	34.12 S	150.55 E
Woronora, Austl.	70a	34.01 S	151.03 E
Worsley, Eng.	64b	53.30 N	2.23 W
Worth, Il. (wûrth)	113a	41.42 N	87.47 W
Wortham, Tx. (wûr'dhăm)	125	31.46 N	96.22 W
Worthing, Eng. (wûr'dhĭng)	162	50.48 N	0.29 W
Worthington, In. (wûr'dhĭng-tŭn)	110	39.05 N	87.00 W
Worthington, Md.	56c	39.14 N	76.47 W
Worthington, Mn.	114	43.38 N	95.36 W
Worth L., Tx.	119c	32.48 N	97.32 W
Wowoni, Pulau (I.), Indon. (wō-wō'nē)	207	4.05 S	123.45 E
W, Parcs Nationaux du (Natl. Pk.), Dahomey-Niger	229	12.20 N	2.40 E
Wragby, Eng. (răg'bē)	156	53.17 N	0.19 W
Wrangell, Ak. (răn'gĕl)	107	56.28 N	132.25 W
Wrangell, Mt., Ak.	107	61.58 N	143.50 W
Wrangell Mts., Ak.-Can.	107	62.28 N	142.40 W
Wrath, C., Scot. (răth)	162	58.34 N	5.01 W
Wray, Co. (rā)	122	40.06 N	102.14 W
Wraysbury, Eng.	62	51.27 N	0.33 W
Wreak (R.), Eng. (rēk)	141	52.45 N	0.59 W
Wreck Rfs., Austl. (rĕk)	215	22.00 S	155.52 E
Wrekin, The (Mt.), Eng. (rĕk'ĭn)	156	54.20 N	2.33 W
Wrens, Ga. (rĕnz)	127	33.15 N	82.25 W
Wrentham, Ma.	105a	42.04 N	71.20 W
Wrexham, Wales (rĕk'săm)	156	53.03 N	3.00 W
Wrights Corners, NY (rītz kôr'nērz)	113c	43.14 N	78.42 W
Wrightsville, Ga. (rīts'vĭl)	127	32.44 N	82.44 W
Writtle, Eng.	62	51.44 N	0.26 E
Wroclaw (Breslau), Pol. (vrôtsläv) (brĕs'lou)	167	51.07 N	17.10 E
Wrotham, Eng. (ro͞ot'ŭm)	156b	51.18 N	0.19 E
Wrotham Heath, Eng.	62	51.18 N	0.21 E
Wrzesnia, Pol. (vzhăsh'nyȧ)	167	52.19 N	17.33 E
Wuchang, China	202	44.59 N	127.00 E
Wuchang, China (wo͞o-chäŋ)	203	30.32 N	114.25 E
Wucheng, China (wo͞o-chŭŋ)	200	37.14 N	116.03 E
Wuhan, China	203	30.30 N	114.15 E
Wuhu, China (wo͞o'ho͞o)	200	31.22 N	118.22 E
Wuji, China (wo͞o-jyī)	200	38.12 N	114.57 E
Wujiang, China (wo͞o-jyäŋ)	200	31.10 N	120.38 E
Wulajie, China (wo͞o-lä-jyĕ)	204	44.08 N	126.25 E
Wuleidao Wan (C.), China (wo͞o-lā-dou wän)	200	36.55 N	122.00 E
Wülfrath, F.R.G.	63	51.17 N	7.02 E
Wu Liang Shan (Mts.), China	206	23.07 N	100.45 E
Wulidian, China (wo͞o-lē-dĭĕn)	200	32.09 N	114.17 E
Wünsdorf, G.D.R. (vüns'dorf)	157b	52.10 N	13.29 E
Wupatki Nat'l Mon., Az.	121	35.35 N	111.45 W
Wuping, China (wo͞o-pĭŋ)	203	25.05 N	116.01 E
Wupper (R.), F.R.G.	63	51.05 N	7.00 E
Wuppertal, F.R.G. (vo͞op'ēr-täl)	169c	51.16 N	7.14 E
Wuqiao, China (wo͞o-chyou)	200	37.37 N	116.29 E
Wu R., China (wo͞o')	203	27.30 N	108.00 E
Würm (R.), F.R.G. (Würm)	157d	48.07 N	11.20 E
Würselen, F.R.G. (vür'zē-lĕn)	169d	50.49 N	6.09 E
Würzburg, F.R.G. (vürts'bo͞orgh)	166	49.48 N	9.57 E
Wurzen, G.D.R. (vo͞ort'sĕn)	166	51.22 N	12.45 E
Wushi, China (wo͞o-shr)	198	41.13 N	79.08 E
Wusong, China (wo͞o-sôŋ)	201b	31.23 N	121.29 E
Wusong (R.), China	68a	31.15 N	121.29 E
Wustermark, G.D.R. (vo͞os'tĕr-märk)	157b	52.33 N	12.57 E
Wustrau, G.D.R. (vōost'rou)	157b	52.15 N	12.51 E
Wuustwezel, Bel.	157a	51.23 N	4.36 E
Wuwie, China (wo͞o'wā')	200	31.19 N	117.53 E
Wuxi, China (wo͞o-shyē)	200	31.36 N	120.17 E
Wuxing, China (wo͞o-shyĭŋ)	203	30.38 N	120.10 E
Wuyi Shan (Mts.), China (wo͞o-yē shän)	203	26.38 N	116.35 E
Wuyou, China (wo͞o-yō)	200	33.18 N	120.15 E
Wuzhi Shan (Mtn.), China (wo͞o-jr shän)	203	18.48 N	109.30 E
Wuzhou, China (wo͞o-jō)	203	23.32 N	111.25 E
Wyandotte, Mi. (wī'ăn-dŏt)	113b	42.12 N	83.10 W
Wye, Eng. (wī)	156b	51.12 N	0.57 E
Wye (R.), Eng.	156	53.14 N	1.46 W
Wymore, Ne. (wī'mōr)	123	40.09 N	96.41 W
Wynberg, S. Afr. (wĭn'bĕrg)	226a	34.00 S	18.28 E
Wyncote, Pa.	56b	40.05 N	75.09 W
Wyndham, Austl. (wĭnd'ăm)	214	15.30 S	128.15 E
Wyndmoor, Pa.	56b	40.05 N	75.12 W
Wynne, Ar. (wĭn)	123	35.12 N	90.46 W
Wynnewood, Ok. (wĭn'wo͝od)	123	34.39 N	97.10 W
Wynnewood, Pa.	56b	40.01 N	75.17 W
Wynona, Ok. (wī-nō'nȧ)	123	36.33 N	96.19 W
Wynyard, Can. (wĭn'yērd)	100	51.47 N	104.10 W
Wyoming, Oh. (wī-ō'mĭng)	113f	39.14 N	84.28 W
Wyoming (State), U. S.	108	42.50 N	108.30 W
Wyoming Ra., Wy.	117	42.43 N	110.35 W
Wyre For., Eng. (wīr)	156	52.24 N	2.24 W
Wysokie Mazowieckie, Pol. (vē-sô'kyĕ mä-zô-vyĕts'kyĕ)	166	52.55 N	22.42 E
Wyszkow, Pol. (vĕsh'ko͞of)	166	52.35 N	21.29 E
Wythenshawe (Neigh.), Eng.	64b	53.24 N	2.17 W
Wytheville, Va. (wĭth'vĭl)	127	36.55 N	81.06 W
X			
Xabregas (Neigh.), Port.	65d	38.44 N	9.07 W
Xagua, Banco (Bk.), Cuba (bä'n-kō-sä'gwä)	134	21.35 N	80.50 W
Xai Xai, Moz.	226	25.00 S	33.45 E
Xangongo, Ang.	226	16.50 S	15.05 E
Xanten, F.R.G. (ksän'tĕn)	169c	51.40 N	6.28 E
Xánthi, Grc.	173	41.08 N	24.53 E
Xau, L., Bots.	226	21.15 S	24.38 E
Xcalak, Mex. (sä-lä'k)	132a	18.15 N	87.50 W
Xenia, Oh. (zē'nĭ-ȧ)	110	39.40 N	83.55 W
Xi (R.), China (shyē)	203	23.15 N	112.10 E
Xiajin, China (shyä-jyĭn)	200	36.58 N	115.59 E
Xiamen (Amoy), China	203	24.30 N	118.10 E
Xiamen (I.), China (shyä-mŭn)	203	24.28 N	118.20 E
Xi'an, China (shyē-än)	202	34.20 N	109.00 E
Xiang (R.), China (shyäŋ)	203	26.18 N	112.25 E
Xiangcheng, China (shyäŋ-chŭŋ)	200	33.52 N	113.31 E
Xianghe, China (shyäŋ-hŭ)	202a	39.46 N	116.59 E
Xiangtan, China (shyäŋ-tän)	203	27.55 N	112.45 E
Xianyang, China (shyĕn-yäŋ)	202	34.20 N	108.40 E
Xiao Hinggan Ling (Ra.), see Lesser Khingan			
Xiaohongmen, China	67b	39.49 N	116.26 E
Xiaoxingkai Hu (L.), China (shyou-shyĭŋ-kī ho͞o)	204	42.25 N	132.45 E
Xiaoxintian, China	67b	39.58 N	116.22 E
Xiapu, China (shyä-po͞o)	203	27.00 N	120.00 E
Xiayi, China (shyä-yē)	200	34.15 N	116.07 E
Xicotencatl, Mex. (sē-kō-tĕn-kät''l)	130	32.00 N	98.58 W
Xifeng, China (shyē-fŭŋ)	202	42.40 N	124.40 E
Xigazê, China (shyē-gä-dzŭ)	196	29.22 N	88.57 E
Xiheying, China (shyē-hŭ-yĭŋ)	200	39.58 N	114.50 E
Xiliao (R.), China (shyē-lĭou)	202	41.40 N	122.40 E
Xilitla, Mex. (sē-lē'tlä)	130	21.24 N	98.59 W
Xinchang, China (shyĭn-chäŋ)	201b	31.02 N	121.38 E
Xing'an, China (shyĭŋ-än)	203	25.44 N	110.32 E
Xingcheng, China (shyĭŋ-chŭŋ)	200	40.38 N	120.41 E
Xinghua, China (shyĭŋ-hwä)	200	32.58 N	119.48 E
Xingjiawan, China (shyĭŋ-jyä-wän)	200	37.16 N	114.54 E
Xingtai, China (shyĭŋ-tī)	200	37.04 N	114.33 E
Xingu (R.), Braz. (zhĕŋ-go͞o')	143	6.20 S	52.34 W
Xinhai, China (shyĭn-hī)	200	36.59 N	117.33 E
Xinhua, China (shyĭn-hwä)	203	27.45 N	111.20 E
Xinhuai (R.), China (shyĭn-hwī)	200	33.48 N	119.39 E
Xinhui, China (shyn-hwā)	203	22.40 N	113.08 E
Xining, China (shyē-nĭŋ)	198	36.52 N	101.36 E
Xinjiang Uygur (Sinkiang) (Aut. Reg.), China (shyĭn-jyäŋ)	198	40.15 N	82.15 E
Xinjin, China (shyĭn-jyĭn)	200	39.23 N	121.57 E
Xinmin, China (shyĭn-mĭn)	202	42.00 N	122.42 E
Xintai, China (shyĭn-tī)	200	35.55 N	117.44 E
Xintang, China (shyĭn-täŋ)	201a	23.08 N	113.36 E
Xinxian, China (shyĭn shyĕn)	200	31.47 N	114.50 E
Xinxian, China	202	38.20 N	112.45 E
Xinxiang, China (shyĭn-shyäŋ)	202	35.17 N	113.49 E
Xinyang, China (shyĭn-yäŋ)	200	32.08 N	114.04 E
Xinye, China (shyĭn-yŭ)	202	32.40 N	112.20 E
Xinzao, China (shyĭn-dzou)	201a	23.01 N	113.25 E
Xinzheng, China (shyĭn-jŭŋ)	200	34.24 N	113.43 E
Xinzhuang, China	67b	39.56 N	116.31 E
Xiongyuecheng, China (shyôŋ-yûĕ-chŭŋ)	200	40.10 N	122.08 E
Xiping, China (shyē-pĭŋ)	200	33.21 N	114.01 E
Xishui, China (shyē-shwā)	203	30.30 N	115.10 E
Xixian, China (shyē shyĕn)	200	32.20 N	114.42 E
Xiyang, China (shyē-yäŋ)	200	37.37 N	113.42 E
Xiying, China (shyē-yĭŋ)	200	31.26 N	119.57 E
Xiyou, China (shyē-yō)	200	37.21 N	119.59 E
Xizang (Tibet) (Aut. Reg.), China (shyē-dzäŋ)	198	31.15 N	87.30 E
Xizhong Dao (I.), China (shyē-jôŋ dou)	200	39.27 N	121.06 E
Xochihuehuetlan, Mex. (sô-chē-wĕ-wĕ-tlä'n)	130	17.53 N	98.29 E
Xochimilco, Mex. (sō-chē-mēl'kô)	131a	19.05 N	99.06 W
Xochimilco, Lago de (L.), Mex.	60a	19.16 N	99.06 W
Xuancheng, China (shyůän-chŭŋ)	203	30.52 N	118.48 E
Xuanhua, China (shyůän-hwä)	202	40.35 N	115.05 E
Xuanhuadian, China (shyůän-hwä-dĭĕn)	200	31.42 N	114.29 E
Xuchang, China (shyo͞o-chäŋ)	200	34.02 N	113.49 E
Xuddur, Som.	223a	3.55 N	43.45 E
Xun (R.), China (shyo͞on)	203	23.28 N	110.30 E
Xuyi, China (shyo͞o-yē)	200	31.02 N	113.49 E
Xuzhou, China	200	34.17 N	117.10 E
Y			
Ya'an, China (yä-än)	203	30.00 N	103.20 E
Yablonitskiy Pereval (P.), Sov. Un. (yȧb-lô'nĭt-skĭ pĕ-rĕ-väl')	167	48.20 N	24.25 E
Yablonovyy Khrebet (Mts.), Sov. Un. (yȧ-blô-nô-vē')	181	51.15 N	111.30 E
Yacheng, China (yä-chŭŋ)	203	18.20 N	109.10 E
Yachiyo, Jap.	205a	35.43 N	140.07 E
Yacolt, Wa. (yă'kôlt)	118c	45.52 N	122.24 W
Yacolt (Mt.), Wa.	118c	45.52 N	122.27 W
Yacona (R.), Ms. (yá'cō nă)	126	34.13 N	89.30 W
Yacuiba, Arg. (yȧ-ko͞o-ē'bȧ)	144	22.02 S	63.44 W
Yadkin (R.), NC (yăd'kĭn)	127	36.12 N	80.40 W
Yafran, Libya	225	31.57 N	12.04 E
Yagotin, Sov. Un. (yä'gô-tĕn)	175	50.18 N	31.46 E
Yaguajay, Cuba (yä-guä-hä'ē)	134	22.20 N	79.20 W
Yahagi-Gawa (Strm.), Jap. (yä'hä-gē gä'wä)	205	35.16 N	137.22 E
Yaho, Jap.	69a	35.41 N	139.27 E
Yahongqiao, China (yä-hôŋ-chyou)	200	39.45 N	117.52 E
Yahualica, Mex. (yä-wä-lē'kä)	130	21.08 N	102.53 W
Yajalon, Mex. (yä-hä-lōn')	131	17.16 N	92.20 W
Yakhroma, Sov. Un. (yäl'rô-ma)	182b	56.17 N	37.30 E
Yakhroma R., Sov. Un.	182b	56.15 N	37.38 E
Yakima, Wa. (yăk'ĭmȧ)	116	46.35 N	120.30 W

ăt; finăl; rāte; senåte; ärm; åsk; sofȧ; fâre; ch-choose; dh-as th in other; bē; ēvent; bĕt; recĕnt; cratēr; g-gō; gh-guttural g; bĭt; ĭ-short neutral; rīde; K-guttural k as ch in German ich;

PLACE (Pronounciation)	PAGE	Lat. °′	Long. °′
Yakima R., Wa. (tăk'ĭ-mȧ)	116	46.48 N	120.22 W
Yakoma, Zaire	230	4.05 N	22.27 E
Yakō (Neigh.), Jap.	69a	35.32 N	139.41 E
Yaku (I.), Jap. (yä'kōō)	205	30.15 N	130.41 E
Yakut A.S.S.R., Sov. Un.	181	65.21 N	117.13 E
Yakutat, Ak. (yȧk'ōō-tȧt)	107	59.32 N	139.35 W
Yakutsk, Sov. Un. (yȧ-kōōtsk')	181	62.13 N	129.49 E
Yale, Mi.	110	43.05 N	82.45 W
Yale, Ok.	123	36.07 N	96.42 W
Yale Res., Wa.	116	46.00 N	122.20 W
Yalinga, Cen. Afr. Rep. (yȧ-lĭŋ'gȧ)	225	6.56 N	23.22 E
Yalobusha (R.), Ms. (yȧ-lô-bōōsh'ȧ)	126	33.48 N	90.02 W
Yalong (R.), China (yä-lôŋ)	198	32.29 N	98.41 E
Yalta, Sov. Un. (yäl'tȧ)	179	44.29 N	34.12 E
Yalu (Amnok) (R.), China-Kor.	204	41.20 N	126.35 E
Yalu (R.), China (yä-lōō)	204	48.20 N	122.35 E
Yalutorovsk, Sov. Un. (yä-lōō-tô'rôfsk)	180	56.42 N	66.32 E
Yamada, Jap. (yä'mȧ-dȧ)	205	33.37 N	133.39 E
Yamagata, Jap. (yä-mȧ'gä-tȧ)	204	38.12 N	140.24 E
Yamaguchi, Jap. (yä-mȧ'gōō-chê)	205	34.10 N	131.30 E
Yamaguchi, Jap.	69b	34.50 N	135.15 E
Yamal, P-ov (Pen.), Sov. Un. (yä-mäl')	180	71.15 N	70.00 E
Yamantau, Gora (Mt.), Sov. Un. (gȧ-rä' yä'man-tȧw)	182a	54.16 N	58.08 E
Yamasá, Dom. Rep. (yä-mä'sä)	135	18.50 N	70.00 W
Yamasaki, Jap. (yä'mȧ'sä-kê)	205	35.01 N	134.33 E
Yamasaki, Jap.	205b	34.53 N	135.41 E
Yamashina, Jap. (yä'mä-shê'nä)	205b	34.59 N	135.50 E
Yamashita, Jap. (yä'mä-shê'tä)	205b	34.53 N	135.25 E
Yamato, Jap.	69a	35.44 N	139.26 E
Yamato, Jap.	69a	35.47 N	139.37 E
Yamato, Jap.	205a	35.28 N	139.28 E
Yamato (R.), Jap.	69b	34.36 N	135.26 E
Yamato-Kōriyama, Jap.	205b	34.39 N	135.48 E
Yamato-takada, Jap. (yä'mä-tô tä'kä-dä)	205b	34.31 N	135.45 E
Yambi, Mesa de, Col. (mĕ'sä-dĕ-yȧ'm-bē)	142	1.55 N	71.45 W
Yambol, Bul. (yȧm'bôl)	173	42.28 N	26.31 E
Yamdena (I.), Indon.	207	7.23 S	130.30 E
Yamenkou, China	67b	39.53 N	116.12 E
Yamethin, Bur. (yŭ-mē'thĕn)	198	20.14 N	96.27 E
Yamhill, Or. (yăm'hĭl)	118c	45.20 N	123.11 W
Yamkino, Sov. Un. (yäm'kĭ-nô)	182b	55.56 N	38.25 E
Yamma Yamma, L., Austl. (yăm'ȧ yăm'ȧ)	216	26.15 S	141.30 E
Yamoussoukro, Ivory Coast	228	6.49 N	5.17 W
Yamsk, Sov. Un. (yämsk)	181	59.41 N	154.09 E
Yamuna (R.), India	196	26.50 N	80.10 E
Yamzho Yumco (L.), China (yăm-jwo yōōm-tswo)	203	29.11 N	91.26 E
Yana (R.), Sov. Un. (yä'nȧ)	181	69.42 N	135.45 E
Yanac, Austl. (yăn'ăk)	216	36.10 S	141.30 E
Yanagawa, Jap. (yä-nä'gä-wä)	205	33.11 N	130.24 E
Yanam, India (yŭnŭm')	196	16.48 N	82.15 E
Yan'an, China (yän-än)	198	36.46 N	109.15 E
Yan'an, China	202	36.35 N	109.32 E
Yanbu', Sau. Ar.	192	23.57 N	38.02 E
Yancheng, China (yän-chŭŋ)	200	33.23 N	120.11 E
Yancheng, China	200	33.38 N	113.59 E
Yandongi, Zaire	230	2.51 N	22.16 E
Yangcheng Hu (L.), China (yäŋ-chŭŋ hōō)	200	31.30 N	120.31 E
Yangchun, China (yäŋ-chōōn)	203	22.08 N	111.48 E
Yang'erzhuang, China (yäŋ-är-jûäŋ)	200	38.18 N	117.31 E
Yanggezhuang, China (yäŋ-gŭ-jûäŋ)	202a	40.10 N	116.48 E
Yanggu, China (yäŋ-gōō)	200	36.06 N	115.46 E
Yanghe, China (yäŋ-hŭ)	200	33.48 N	118.23 E
Yangjiang, China (yäŋ-jyäŋ)	203	21.52 N	111.58 E
Yangjiaogou, China (yäŋ-jyou-gō)	200	36.17 N	118.53 E
Yangquan, China (yäŋ-chyûän)	200	37.52 N	113.36 E
Yangtze (Chang) (R.), China (yăng'tse) (chäŋ)	199	30.30 N	117.25 E
Yangxin, China (yäŋ-shyĭn)	200	37.39 N	117.34 E
Yangyang, Kor. (yäng'yäng')	204	38.02 N	128.38 E
Yangzhou, China (yäŋ-jō)	199	32.24 N	119.24 E
Yanji, China (yän-jyē)	202	42.55 N	129.35 E
Yanjiahe, China (yän-jyä-hŭ)	200	31.55 N	114.47 E
Yanjin, China (yän-jyĭn)	200	35.09 N	114.13 E
Yankton, SD (yănk'tŭn)	114	42.51 N	97.24 W
Yanling, China (yän-lĭŋ)	200	34.07 N	114.12 E
Yannina, see Ioánnina			
Yanqi, see Karashahr			
Yanshan, China (yän-shän)	200	38.05 N	117.15 E
Yanshou, China (yän-shō)	202	45.25 N	128.43 E
Yantai, China (yän-tī)	200	37.32 N	121.22 E
Yanychi, Sov. Un. (yä'nĭ-chĭ)	182a	57.42 N	56.24 E
Yanzhou, China (yäŋ-jō)	200	35.35 N	116.50 E
Yanzhuang, China (yän-jûäŋ)	200	36.08 N	117.47 E
Yao, Chad (yä'ō)	215	13.00 N	17.38 E
Yao, Jap.	205b	34.37 N	135.76 E
Yaoundé, Cam. (yȧ-ōōn-dā')	229	3.52 N	11.31 E
Yap (I.), Pac. Is. Trust Ter. (yăp)	208	11.00 N	138.00 E
Yapen, Pulau (I.), Indon.	207	1.30 S	136.15 E
Yaque del Norte (R.), Dom. Rep. (yä'kå dĕl nôr'tå)	135	19.40 N	71.25 W
Yaque del Sur (R.), Dom. Rep. (yä-kĕ-dĕl-sōō'r)	135	18.35 N	71.05 W
Yaqui (R.), Mex. (yä'kē)	128	28.15 N	109.40 W
Yaracuy (State), Ven. (yä-rä-kōō'ē)	143b	10.10 N	68.31 W
Yaraka, Austl. (yȧ-răk'ȧ)	216	24.50 S	144.08 E
Yaransk, Sov. Un. (yä-ränsk')	178	57.18 N	48.05 E
Yarda (Well), Chad (yär'dȧ)	225	18.29 N	19.13 E
Yare (R.), Eng.	163	52.40 N	1.32 E
Yarkand (R.), India (yär-känt')	196	36.11 N	76.10 E
Yarkand, see Shache			
Yarlung Zangbo (R.), see Brahmaputra			
Yarmouth, Can. (yär'mŭth)	104	43.50 N	66.07 W
Yaroslavka, Sov. Un. (yȧ-rô-släv'kȧ)	182a	55.52 N	57.59 E
Yaroslavl', Sov. Un. (yȧ-rô-släv''l)	174	57.57 N	39.54 E
Yaroslavl' (Oblast), Sov. Un.	174	58.05 N	38.05 E
Yarra (R.), Austl.	70b	37.51 S	144.54 E
Yarra Can., Austl.	70b	37.49 S	144.55 E
Yarra-to (L.), Sov. Un. (yȧ'rô-tô')	178	68.30 N	71.30 E
Yarraville, Austl.	70b	37.49 S	144.53 E
Yartsevo, Sov. Un. (yär'tsyĕ-vô)	174	55.04 N	32.38 E
Yartsevo, Sov. Un.	180	60.13 N	89.52 E
Yarumal, Col. (yä-rōō-mäl')	142a	6.57 N	75.24 W
Yasel'da R., Sov. Un. (yä-syŭl'dȧ)	167	53.13 N	25.53 E
Yasinya, Sov. Un.	167	48.17 N	24.21 E
Yateras, Cuba (yä-tā'räs)	135	20.00 N	75.00 W
Yates Center, Ks. (yāts)	123	37.53 N	95.44 W
Yathkyed (L.), Can. (yȧth-kī-ĕd')	96	62.41 N	98.00 W
Yatsuga-take (Mtn.), Jap. (yät'sōō-gä dä'kä)	205	36.01 N	138.21 W
Yatsushiro, Jap. (yät'sōō'shê-rô)	205	32.30 N	130.35 E
Yatta Plat., Ken.	231	1.55 S	38.10 E
Yautepec, Mex. (yä-ōō-tå-pĕk')	130	18.53 N	99.04 W
Yavorov, Sov. Un.	167	49.56 N	23.24 E
Yawata, Jap. (yä'wä-tä)	205b	34.52 N	135.43 E
Yawatahama, Jap. (yä'wä'tä'hä-mä)	205	33.24 N	132.25 E
Yaxian, China (yä shyĕn)	203	18.10 N	109.32 E
Yayama, Zaire	230	1.16 S	23.07 E
Yayao, China (yä-you)	201a	23.10 N	113.40 E
Yazd, Iran	192	31.59 N	54.03 E
Yazoo (R.), Ms. (yă'zōō)	126	32.32 N	90.40 W
Yazoo City, Ms.	126	32.50 N	90.18 W
Ye, Bur. (yā)	206	15.13 N	97.52 E
Yeading (Neigh.), Eng.	62	51.32 N	0.24 W
Yeadon, Pa. (yē'dŭn)	112f	39.56 N	75.16 W
Yecheng, see Karghalik			
Yecla, Sp. (yā'klä)	170	38.35 N	1.09 W
Yedikule (Neigh.), Tur.	66f	40.59 N	28.55 E
Yefremov, Sov. Un. (yĕ-frā'môf)	174	53.08 N	38.04 E
Yegor'yevsk, Sov. Un. (yĕ-gôr'yĕfsk)	174	55.23 N	38.59 E
Yeji, China (yŭ-jyē)	200	31.52 N	115.57 E
Yelabuga, Sov. Un. (yĕ-lä'bōō-gȧ)	178	55.50 N	52.18 E
Yelan, Sov. Un.	179	50.50 N	44.00 E
Yelets, Sov. Un. (yĕ-lyĕts')	174	52.35 N	38.28 E
Yelizavetpol'skiy, Sov. Un. (yĕ'lĭ-za-vĕt-pôl-skĭ)	182a	52.51 N	60.38 E
Yelizavety, Mys (C.), Sov. Un. (yĕ-lyĕ-sȧ-vyĕ'tĭ)	181	54.28 N	142.59 E
Yell (I.), Scot. (yĕl)	162a	60.35 N	1.27 W
Yellow (R.), Fl. (yĕl'ô)	126	30.33 N	86.53 W
Yellowhead Pass, Can. (yĕl'ô-hĕd)	99	52.52 N	118.35 W
Yellowknife, Can. (yĕl'ô-nīf)	96	62.29 N	114.38 W
Yellow R., see Huang			
Yellow Sea, Asia	202	35.20 N	122.15 E
Yellowstone L., Wy.	117	44.27 N	110.03 W
Yellowstone Natl. Park, Wy. (yĕl'ô-stōn)	117	44.45 N	110.35 W
Yellowstone R., Mt.	117	46.28 N	105.39 W
Yellowstone R., Clark Fk., Wy.	117	44.55 N	109.05 W
Yellowtail Res., Mt.-Wy.	117	45.00 N	108.10 W
Yel'nya, Sov. Un. (yĕl'nyȧ)	174	54.34 N	33.12 E
Yemanzhelinsk, Sov. Un. (yĕ-mȧn-zhâ'lĭnsk)	182a	54.47 N	61.24 E
Yemen, Asia (yĕm'ĕn)	190	15.45 N	44.30 E
Yemen, People's Democratic Republic of., Asia	190	14.45 N	46.45 E
Yemetsk, Sov. Un.	178	63.28 N	41.28 E
Yenakiyevo, Sov. Un. (yĕ-nä'kĭ-yĕ-vô)	175	48.14 N	38.12 E
Yenangyaung, Bur. (yā'nän-d oung)	193	20.27 N	94.59 E
Yencheng, China (yŭ-chŭn)	198	37.30 N	79.26 E
Yendi, Ghana (yĕn'dē)	228	9.26 N	0.01 W
Yengisar, China (yŭn-gē-sär)	198	39.01 N	75.29 E
Yenice (R.), Tur.	179	41.10 N	33.00 E
Yenikapi (Neigh.), Tur.	66f	41.00 N	28.57 E
Yeniköy (Neigh.), Tur.	66f	41.07 N	29.04 E
Yenisey (R.), Sov. Un. (yĕ-nē-sĕ'ē)	180	67.48 N	87.15 E
Yeniseysk, Sov. Un. (yĕ-nĭĕsā'ĭsk)	180	58.27 N	90.28 E
Yeo (I.), Austl. (yō)	214	28.15 S	124.00 E
Yerevan, Sov. Un. (yĕ-rĕ-vän')	179	40.10 N	44.30 E
Yerington, Nv. (yē'rĭng-tŭn)	162	39.59 N	119.10 W
Yermak (I.), Sov. Un.	178	66.30 N	71.30 E
Yeste, Sp. (yĕs'tå)	170	38.23 N	2.19 W
Yeu, Île d' (I.), Fr. (ēl dyû)	168	46.43 N	2.45 W
Yevpatoriya, Sov. Un. (yĕf-pä'tô-rĭ-yȧ)	175	45.13 N	33.22 E
Yevrey Aut. Oblast., Sov. Un.	181	48.45 N	132.00 E
Yexian, China (yŭ-shyĕn)	200	37.09 N	119.57 E
Yeya (R.), Sov. Un. (yä'yȧ)	175	46.25 N	39.17 E
Yeysk, Sov. Un. (yĕysk)	175	46.41 N	38.13 E
Yg (R.), see Yug			
Yiannitsá, Grc.	173	40.47 N	22.26 E
Yiaros (I.), Grc.	173	37.52 N	24.42 E
Yibin, China (yē-bĭn)	203	28.50 N	104.40 E
Yichang, China (yē-chäŋ)	203	30.38 N	111.22 E
Yidu, China (yē-dōō)	200	36.42 N	118.30 E
Yiewsley (Neigh.), Eng.	62	51.31 N	0.28 W
Yi He (R.), China (yē hŭ)	200	34.38 N	118.07 E
Yilan, China (yē-län)	202	46.10 N	129.40 E
Yimianpo, China (yē-mĭĕn-pwo)	204	44.59 N	127.56 E
Yinchuan, China (yĭn-chûän)	202	38.22 N	106.22 E
Yingkou, China (yĭŋ-kō)	202	40.35 N	122.10 E
Yining (Gulja), China (yē-nĭŋ)	198	43.58 N	80.40 E
Yin Shan (Mtn.), China (yĭng'shän')	202	40.50 N	110.30 E
Yio Chu Kang, Singapore	67c	1.23 N	103.51 E
Yishan, China (yē-shän)	203	24.32 N	108.42 E
Yishui, China (yē-shwā)	200	35.49 N	118.40 E
Yitong, China (yē-tôŋ)	204	43.15 N	125.10 E
Yíthion, Grc.	173	36.50 N	22.37 E
Yixian, China (yē shyĕn)	202	41.30 N	121.15 E
Yiyang, China (yē-yäŋ)	203	28.52 N	112.12 E
Ymir, Can. (wī'mēr)	99	49.17 N	117.13 W
Yoakum, Tx. (yō'kŭm)	125	29.18 N	97.09 W
Yockanookany, (R.), Ms. (yŏk'ȧ-nōō-kä-nĭ)	126	32.47 N	89.38 W
Yodo-Gawa (Str.), Jap. (yō'dô'gä-wä)	205b	34.46 N	135.35 E
Yog Pt., Phil. (yōg)	203	14.00 N	124.30 E
Yogyakarta, Indon. (yŏg-yȧ-kär'tȧ)	206	7.50 S	110.20 E
Yoho Natl. Park, Can. (yō'hō)	99	51.26 N	116.30 W
Yojoa, Lago de (L.), Hond. (lä'gō dĕ yô-hō'ä)	132	14.49 N	87.53 W
Yokkaichi, Jap. (yô'kä'ê-chê)	205	34.58 N	136.35 E
Yokohama, Jap. (yō'kô-hä'mȧ)	205a	35.37 N	139.40 E
Yokosuka, Jap. (yô-kō'sōō-kä)	205a	35.17 N	139.40 E
Yokota, Jap. (yō-kō'tä)	205a	35.23 N	140.02 E
Yola, Nig. (yō'lä)	224	9.13 N	12.27 E
Yolaina, Cord. de (Mts.), Nic. (kôr-dĕl-yĕ'rä dĕ yō-lä-ē'nä)	133	11.34 N	84.34 W
Yolombó, Col. (yô-lôm-bŏ')	142a	6.37 N	74.59 W
Yomon, Gui.	228	7.34 N	9.16 W
Yonago, Jap. (yō'nä-gō)	205	35.27 N	133.19 E
Yŏnch'on (Neigh.), Kor.	68b	37.38 N	127.04 E
Yonezawa, Jap. (yō'nĕ'zȧ-wä)	204	37.50 N	140.07 E
Yong'an, China (yôŋ-än)	203	26.00 N	117.22 E
Yongding (R.), China (yôŋ-dĭŋ)	202	40.25 N	115.00 E
Yŏngdŏk, Kor. (yŭng'dŭk')	204	36.28 N	129.25 E
Yongdŭngp'o (Neigh.), Kor.	68b	37.32 N	126.54 E
Yŏnghŭng, Kor. (yŭng'hōōng')	204	39.31 N	127.11 E
Yonghŭng Man (B.), Kor.	204	39.10 N	128.00 E
Yongnian, China (yôŋ-nĭĕn)	200	36.47 N	114.32 E
Yongqing, China (yôŋ-chyĭŋ)	202a	39.18 N	116.27 E
Yongshun, China (yôŋ-shōōn)	203	29.05 N	109.58 E
Yonkers, NY (yŏŋ'kĕrz)	112a	40.57 N	73.54 W
Yonne (R.), Fr. (yôn)	168	48.18 N	3.15 E
Yono, Jap. (yō'nō)	205a	35.53 N	139.36 E
Yorba Linda, Ca. (yôr'bă lĭn'dȧ)	119a	33.55 N	117.51 W
York, Al. (yôrk)	126	32.33 N	88.16 W
York, Austl.	214	32.00 S	117.00 E
York, Can.	95d	43.41 N	79.29 W
York, Eng.	162	53.58 N	1.10 W
York, Ne.	123	40.52 N	97.36 W
York, Pa.	111	40.00 N	76.40 W
York, SC	127	34.59 N	81.14 W
York, C., Austl.	215	10.45 S	142.35 E
Yorketown, Austl.	216	35.00 S	137.28 E
York Factory, Can.	101	57.05 N	92.18 W
Yorkfield, Il.	58a	41.52 N	87.56 W
York, Kap (C.), Grnld.	94	75.30 N	73.00 W
York Pen, Austl.	216	34.24 S	137.20 E
Yorkshire Wolds (Hills), Eng. (yôrk'shĭr)	162	54.00 N	0.35 W
Yorkton, Can. (yôrk'tŭn)	100	51.13 N	102.28 W
Yorktown, Tx. (yôrk'toun)	125	28.57 N	97.30 W
Yorktown, Va.	127	37.12 N	76.31 W
Yorkville (Neigh.), Can.	54c	43.40 N	79.24 W
Yoro, Hond. (yō'rô)	132	15.09 N	87.05 W
Yoron (I.), Jap.	208	26.48 N	128.40 E
Yosemite Natl. Park, Ca. (yô-sĕm'ĭ-tê)	120	38.03 N	119.36 W
Yoshida, Jap. (yō'shê-dȧ)	205	34.39 N	132.41 E
Yoshikawa, Jap. (yō-shê'kä'wä')	205a	35.53 N	139.51 E
Yoshino (R.), Jap. (yō'shē-nō)	205	34.04 N	133.57 E
Yoshkar-Ola, Sov. Un. (yôsh-kär'ô-lä')	178	56.35 N	48.05 E
Yosonotú (Santa Catarina), Mex. (yô-sō-nô-tōō') (sän'tä kä-tä-rē'nä)	131	16.51 N	97.37 W
Yos Sudarsa, Pulau (I.), Indon.	207	7.20 S	138.30 E
Yŏsu, Kor. (yŭ'sōō')	204	34.42 N	127.42 W
You (R.), China (yō)	203	23.55 N	106.50 E
Youghal, Ire. (yōō'ôl) (yôl)	162	51.58 N	7.57 E
Youghal B., Ire.	162	51.52 N	7.46 W
Young, Austl. (yŭng)	216	34.15 S	148.18 E
Young, Ur. (yô-ōō'ng)	141c	32.42 S	57.38 W
Youngs (L.), Wa. (yŭngz)	118a	47.25 N	122.08 W
Youngstown, NY	113c	43.15 N	79.02 W
Youngstown, Oh.	110	41.05 N	80.40 W
Yozgat, Tur. (yôz'gȧd)	179	39.50 N	34.50 E
Ypsilanti, Mi. (ĭp-sĭ-lăn'tĭ)	113b	42.15 N	83.37 W
Yreka, Ca. (wī-rē'kȧ)	116	41.43 N	122.36 W
Ysleta, Tx. (ĕz-lĕ'tȧ)	124	31.42 N	106.18 W
Yssingeaux, Fr. (ē-săN-zhō)	168	45.09 N	4.08 E
Ystad, Swe. (ü'städ)	164	55.29 N	13.28 E
Yu'alliq, Jabal (Mts.), Egypt	191a	30.12 N	33.42 E
Yuan (R.), China (yûän)	203	28.50 N	110.50 E
Yuan'an, China (yûän-än)	203	31.08 N	111.28 E
Yuan Huan (P. Int.), Taiwan	68d	25.03 N	121.31 E
Yuanling, China (yûän-lĭŋ)	203	28.30 N	110.18 E
Yuanshi, China (yûän-shr)	200	37.45 N	114.32 E
Yuasa, Jap.	205	34.02 N	135.10 E
Yuba City, Ca. (yōō'bȧ)	120	39.08 N	121.38 W
Yuby, C., Mor. (yōō'bê)	224	28.01 N	13.21 W
Yucaipa, Ca. (yŭ-kȧ-ē'pȧ)	119a	34.02 N	117.02 W
Yucatán (State), Mex. (yōō-kä-tän')	128	20.45 N	89.00 W
Yucatán Chan, Mex.	128	22.30 N	87.00 W
Yucheng, China (yōō-chŭŋ)	200	34.31 N	115.54 E
Yucheng, China	200	36.55 N	116.39 E
Yuci, China (yōō-tsz)	202	37.32 N	112.40 E
Yudoma (R.), Sov. Un. (yōō-dô'mȧ)	181	59.13 N	137.00 E
Yueqing, China (yûĕ-chyĭn)	203	28.02 N	120.40 E
Yueyang, China (yûĕ-yäŋ)	203	92.25 N	113.05 E
Yuezhuang, China (yûĕ-jûäŋ)	200	36.13 N	118.17 E
Yug (R.), Sov. Un. (yōōg)	178	59.50 N	45.55 E
Yugoslavia, Eur. (yōō-gō-slä-vĭ-ȧ)	154	44.48 N	17.29 E
Yukhnov, Sov. Un. (yōōk'nof)	174	54.44 N	35.15 E
Yukon (Ter.), Can. (yōō'kŏn)	96	63.16 N	135.30 W
Yukon R., Ak.-Can.	107	62.10 N	143.00 W
Yukutat B., Ak. (yōō-kū tät')	107	59.34 N	140.50 W
Yuldybayevo, Sov. Un. (yōōld'bä'yĕ-vô)	182a	52.20 N	57.52 E
Yulin, China (yōō-lĭn)	203	22.38 N	110.10 E
Yulin, China	202	38.18 N	109.45 E
Yuma, Az. (yōō'mä)	121	32.40 N	114.40 W
Yuma, Co.	122	40.08 N	102.50 W
Yuma (R.), Dom. Rep.	135	19.05 N	70.05 W
Yuma, Bahia de (B.), Dom. Rep. (bä-ē'ä-dĕ-yōō'mä)	135	18.20 N	68.05 W
Yumbi, Zaire	231	1.14 S	26.14 E
Yumen, China (yōō-mŭn)	198	40.14 N	96.56 E
Yuncheng, China (yōōn-chŭŋ)	202	35.00 N	110.40 E

PLACE (Pronounciation)	PAGE	Lat. °′	Long. °′
Yungho, Taiwan	68d	25.01 N	121.31 E
Yung Shu Wan, Hong Kong	68c	22.14 N	114.06 E
Yunnan (Prov.), China (yun'nän')	198	24.23 N	101.03 E
Yunnan Plat, China (yōō-nän)	198	26.03 N	101.26 E
Yunxian, China (yōōn shyĕn)	202	32.50 N	110.55 E
Yunxiao, China (yōōn-shyou)	203	24.00 N	117.20 E
Yura, Jap. (yōō'rä)	205	34.18 N	134.54 E
Yurécuaro, Mex. (yōō-rā'kwä-rô)	130	20.21 N	102.16 W
Yurimaguas, Peru (yōō-rê-mä'gwäs)	142	5.59 S	76.12 W
Yuriria, Mex. (yōō'rê-rē'ä)	130	20.11 N	101.08 W
Yurovo, Sov. Un.	182b	55.30 N	38.24 E
Yur'yevets, Sov. Un.	178	57.15 N	43.08 E
Yuryuzan', Sov. Un. (yōōr-yōō-zän')	182a	54.47 N	58.45 E
Yuscarán, Hond. (yōōs-kä-rän')	132	13.57 N	86.48 W
Yushan, China (yōō-shän)	203	28.42 N	118.20 E
Yushu, China (yōō-shōō)	202	44.58 N	126.32 E
Yutian, China (yōō-tĭĕn)	200	39.54 N	117.45 E
Yutian (Keriya), China (yōō-tĭĕn) (kĕ-r-yä)	198	36.55 N	81.39 E
Yuty, Par. (yōō-tē')	144	26.45 S	56.13 W
Yuwangcheng, China (yü'wäng'chĕng)	200	31.32 N	114.26 E
Yuxian, China (yōō shyĕn)	202	39.40 N	114.38 E
Yuzha, Sov. Un. (yōō'zhá)	178	56.38 N	42.20 E
Yuzhnny Ural (Mts.) Sov. Un. (yōō'zhnĭ ōō-räl')	182a	52.51 N	57.48 E
Yuzhno-Sakhalinsk, Sov. Un. (yōōzh'nô-sä-кä-lĭnsk')	181	47.11 N	143.04 E
Yuzhnoural'skiy, Sov. Un. (yōōzh-nô-ōō-rál'skĭ)	182a	54.26 N	61.17 E
Yverdon, Switz. (ē-vĕr-dôn)	166	46.46 N	6.35 E
Yvetot, Fr. (ēv-tō')	168	49.39 N	0.45 E

Z

PLACE (Pronounciation)	PAGE	Lat. °′	Long. °′
Zaachila, Mex. (sä-ä-chē'lä)	131	16.56 N	96.45 W
Zaandam, Neth. (zän'dám)	157a	52.25 N	4.49 E
Zabkowice Śląskie, Pol. (zaNb'kô-vē'tsē)	166	50.35 N	16.48 E
Zabrze, Pol. (zäb'zhĕ)	167	50.18 N	18.48 E
Zacapa, Guat. (sä-kä'pä)	132	14.56 N	89.30 W
Zacapoaxtla, Mex. (sä-kä-pō-äs'tlä)	131	19.51 N	97.34 W
Zacatecas, Mex. (sä-kä-tā'käs)	130	22.44 N	102.32 W
Zacatecas (State), Mex.	128	24.00 N	102.45 W
Zacatecoluca, Sal. (sä-kä-tå-kô-lōō'kä)	132	13.31 N	88.50 W
Zacateko, Mex. (zä-kà-tē'kō)	130	19.12 N	98.12 W
Zacatepec (Santiago), Mex. (sä-kä-tå-pĕk') (sän-tē-ä'gô)	131	17.10 N	95.53 W
Zacatlán, Mex. (sä-kä-tlän')	131	19.55 N	97.57 W
Zacoalco de Torres, Mex. (sä-kô-äl'kô dā tōr'rĕs)	130	20.12 N	103.33 W
Zacualpan, Mex. (sä-kōō-äl-pän')	130	18.43 N	99.46 W
Zacualtipan, Mex. (sá-kōō-äl-tē-pän')	130	20.38 N	98.39 W
Zadar, Yugo. (zä'där)	172	44.08 N	15.16 E
Zadonsk, Sov. Un. (zä-dônsk')	174	52.22 N	38.55 E
Żagań, Pol. (zhä'gan')	166	51.34 N	15.32 E
Žagare, Sov. Un. (zhágarē)	165	56.21 N	23.14 E
Zagarolo, It. (tzä-gä-rō'lô)	171d	41.51 N	12.53 E
Zaghouan, Tun. (zá-gwäN')	224	36.30 N	10.04 E
Zagorá, Grc. (zä'gô-rä)	173	39.29 N	23.04 E
Zagorsk, Sov. Un. (zä-gôrsk')	182b	56.18 N	38.08 E
Zagreb, Yugo. (zä'grĕb)	172	45.50 N	15.58 E
Zagro Mts., Iran	192	33.30 N	46.30 E
Zāhedān, Iran (zä'hå-dän)	192	29.37 N	60.31 E
Zahlah, Leb. (zä'lä')	191a	33.50 N	35.54 E
Zahorska-Ves, Czech.	157e	48.24 N	16.51 E
Zahrez Chergui (L.), Alg.	171	35.10 N	2.17 E
Zaire, Afr.	222	1.00 S	22.15 E
Zaire (Congo) (R.), Afr. (kŏn'gō)	230	1.10 N	18.25 E
Zaječar, Yugo. (zä'yĕ-chär')	173	43.54 N	22.16 E
Zákinthos, Grc.	173	37.48 N	20.55 E
Zákinthos (Zante) (I.), Grc.	173	37.45 N	20.32 E
Zakopane, Pol. (zá-kô-pä'nĕ)	167	49.18 N	19.57 E
Zakouma, Parc Natl. de (Natl. Pk.), Chad	229	10.50 N	19.20 E
Zalaegerszeg, Hung. (zŏ'lô-ĕ'gĕr-sĕg)	166	46.50 N	16.50 E
Zalău, Rom. (zá-lŭ'ōō)	167	47.11 N	23.06 E
Zaldívar, Laguna (L.), Cuba	60b	22.58 N	82.26 W
Zaltan, Libya	225	28.20 N	19.40 E
Zaltbommel, Neth.	157a	51.48 N	5.15 E
Zama, Jap.	69a	35.29 N	139.24 E
Zambezi (R.), Afr. (zám-bā'zē)	231	15.45 S	33.15 E
Zambia, Afr. (zăm'bē-á)	222	14.23 S	24.15 E
Zamboanga, Phil. (säm-bô-aŋ'gä)	206	6.58 N	122.02 E
Zambrów, Pol. (zäm'brōōf)	167	52.29 N	22.17 E
Zamora, Mex. (sä-mō'rä)	130	19.59 N	102.16 W
Zamora, Sp. (thä-mō'rä)	170	41.32 N	5.43 W
Zamość, Pol. (zä'môshch)	167	50.42 N	23.17 E
Zanatepec (Santo Domingo), Mex. (sä-nä-tå-pek') (sän-tô dō-miŋ'gô)	131	16.30 N	94.22 W
Zandvoort, Neth.	157a	52.22 N	4.30 E
Zanesville, Oh. (zānz'vĭl)	110	39.55 N	82.00 W
Zangasso, Mali	228	12.09 N	5.37 W
Zanjān, Iran	192	36.26 N	48.24 E
Zansibar, Tan. (zăn'zĭ-bär)	231	6.10 S	39.11 E
Zanzibar (I.), Tan.	231	6.20 S	39.37 E
Zanzibar Chan., Tan.	231	6.05 S	39.00 E
Zaozhuang, China (dzou-jůäŋ)	200	34.51 N	117.34 E
Zapadnaya Dvina (R.), Sov. Un. (zä'pád-ná-yá dvē'ná)	174	55.30 N	28.27 E
Zapala, Arg. (zä-pä'lä)	144	38.53 S	70.02 W
Zapata, Tx. (sä-pä'tä)	124	26.52 N	99.18 W
Zapata, Ciénaga de (Swp.), Cuba (syĕ'nä-gä-dĕ-zä-pá'tä)	134	22.30 N	81.20 W
Zapata, Península de, Cuba (pĕ-nē'n-sōō-lä-dĕ-zä-pá'tä)	134	22.20 N	81.30 W
Zapatera, Isla (I.), Nic. (ē's-lä-sä-pä-tā'rō)	132	11.45 N	85.45 W
Zapopan, Mex. (sä-pō'pän)	130	20.42 N	103.23 W
Zaporoshskoye, Sov. Un. (zá-pô-rôsh'skô-yĕ)	165	60.36 N	30.31 E
Zaporozh'ye, Sov. Un. (zä-pô-rôzh'yĕ)	175	47.53 N	35.25 E
Zaporozh'ye (Oblast), Sov. Un. (zä-pô-rôzh'yĕ ôb'ást)	175	47.20 N	35.05 E
Zapotiltic, Mex. (sä-pô-tēl-tēk')	130	19.37 N	103.25 W
Zapotitlán, Mex. (sä-pô-tē-tlän')	130	17.13 N	98.58 W
Zapotitlán, Mex.	60a	19.18 N	99.02 W
Zapotitlán, Punta (Pt.), Mex.	131	18.34 N	94.48 W
Zapotlanejo, Mex. (sä-pô-tlä-nä'hô)	130	20.38 N	103.05 W
Za R., Mor.	160	34.19 N	2.23 W
Zaragoza, Mex. (sä-rä-gō'sä)	130	23.59 N	99.45 W
Zaragoza, Mex.	130	22.02 N	100.45 W
Zaragoza, Sp. (thä-rä-gō'thä)	171	41.39 N	0.53 W
Zaranda Hill, Nig.	229	10.15 N	9.35 E
Zarand, Munții (Mts.), Rom.	167	46.07 N	22.21 E
Zaranj, Afg.	195	31.06 N	61.53 E
Zarasai, Sov. Un. (zä-rä-sī')	165	55.45 N	26.18 E
Zárate, Arg. (zä-rä'tä)	141c	34.05 S	59.05 W
Zaraysk, Sov. Un. (zä-rä'ēsk)	174	54.46 N	38.53 E
Zarečje, Sov. Un.	66b	55.41 N	37.23 E
Zarga (R.), Jordan	191a	32.13 N	35.43 E
Zaria, Nig. (zä'rē-ä)	229	11.07 N	7.44 E
Zarineh, Rūd-é (R.), Iran	179	36.40 N	46.35 E
Żary, Pol. (zhä'rĕ)	166	51.38 N	15.08 E
Zarzal, Col. (zär-zá'l)	142a	4.23 N	76.04 W
Zashiversk, Sov. Un. (zá'shĭ-vĕrsk')	181	67.08 N	144.02 E
Zastavna, Sov. Un. (zás-táf'ná)	167	48.32 N	25.50 E
Zastron, S. Afr. (zás'trŭn)	227c	30.19 S	27.07 E
Žatec, Czech. (zhä'tĕts)	166	50.19 N	13.32 E
Zavitinsk, Sov. Un.	181	50.12 N	129.44 E
Zawiercie, Pol. (zá-vyĕr'tsyĕ)	167	50.28 N	19.25 E
Zāwiyat Abū Musallam, Egypt	71a	29.56 N	31.10 E
Zāwiyat al-Baydā', Libya	225	32.49 N	21.46 E
Zāwiyat Nābit, Egypt	71a	30.07 N	31.09 E
Zāyandeh (R.), Iran	192	32.15 N	51.00 E
Zaysan (L.), Sov. Un.	180	48.16 N	84.05 E
Zaysan, Sov. Un. (zī'sán)	180	47.43 N	84.44 E
Zaza (R.), Cuba (zá'zá)	134	21.40 N	79.25 W
Zbarazh, Sov. Un. (zbä-räzh')	167	49.39 N	25.48 E
Zbruch R., Sov. Un. (zbrōōch)	167	48.56 N	26.18 E
Zdolbunov, Sov. Un. (zdôl-bōō'nôf)	167	50.31 N	26.17 E
Zdunska Wola, Pol. (zdōōn''skä vō'lä)	167	51.36 N	18.27 E
Zebediela, S. Afr.	223d	24.19 S	29.21 E
Zeeland, Mi. (zē'lănd)	110	42.50 N	86.00 W
Zefat, Isr.	191a	32.58 N	35.30 E
Zehdenick, G.D.R. (tsā'dĕ-nēk)	157b	52.59 N	13.20 E
Zehlendorf, G.D.R. (tsā'lĕn-dôrf)	157b	52.47 N	13.23 E
Zehlendorf (Neigh.), F.R.G.	65a	52.26 N	13.15 E
Zeist, Neth.	157a	52.05 N	5.14 E
Zelaya, Arg.	60d	34.20 S	58.52 W
Želechów, Pol. (zhĕ-lĕ'кōōf)	167	51.48 N	21.55 E
Zelenogorsk, Sov. Un. (zĕ-lă'nô-gôrsk)	165	60.13 N	29.39 E
Zella-Mehlis, G.D.R. (tsāl'á-mā'lĕs)	166	50.40 N	10.38 E
Zémio, Cen. Afr. Rep. (za-myō')	225	5.03 N	25.11 E
Zemlya Frantsa Iosifa (Franz Josef Land) (Is.), Sov. Un.	176	81.32 N	40.00 E
Zempoala, Punta (Pt.), Mex. (pōō'n-tä-sĕm-pô-ä'lä)	131	19.30 N	96.18 W
Zempoatlépetl (Mtn.), Mex. (sĕm-pô-ä-tlā'pĕt'l)	131	17.13 N	95.59 W
Zemun (Semlin), Yugo. (zĕ'mōōn) (sĕm'lĭn)	173	44.50 N	20.25 E
Zengcheng, China (dzŭŋ-chŭŋ)	201a	23.18 N	113.49 E
Zenica, Yugo. (zĕ'nēt-sä)	173	44.10 N	17.54 E
Zeni-Su (Is.), Jap. (zĕ'nē sōō)	205	33.55 N	138.55 E
Zen'kov, Sov. Un. (zĕn-kof')	175	50.13 N	34.23 E
Žepče, Yugo. (zhĕp'chĕ)	175	44.26 N	18.01 E
Zepernick, G.D.R. (tsĕ'pĕr-nēk)	157b	52.39 N	13.32 E
Zeravshan (R.), Sov. Un. (zĕ-räf-shän')	155	40.00 N	65.42 E
Zerbst, G.D.R. (tsĕrbst)	166	51.58 N	12.03 E
Zerpenschleuse, G.D.R. (tsĕr'pĕn-shloi-zĕ)	157b	52.51 N	13.30 E
Zeuthen, G.D.R. (tsoi'tĕn)	157b	52.21 N	13.38 E
Zevenaar, Neth.	169c	51.56 N	6.06 E
Zevenbergen, Neth.	157a	51.38 N	4.36 E
Zeya, Sov. Un. (zâ'yá)	181	53.43 N	127.29 E
Zeya (R.), Sov. Un.	181	52.31 N	128.30 E
Zeytinburnu (Neigh.), Tur.	66f	40.59 N	28.54 E
Zeytun, Tur. (zā-tōōn')	179	38.00 N	36.40 E
Zezere (R.), Port. (zĕ'zå-rĕ)	170	39.54 N	8.12 W
Zghartā, Leb.	191a	34.24 N	35.53 E
Zgierz, Pol. (zgyĕzh)	167	51.51 N	19.26 E
Zgurovka, Sov. Un. (zgōō'rôf-kä)	175	50.31 N	31.43 E
Zhang (R.), China (jäŋ)	200	36.17 N	114.31 E
Zhangbei, China (jäŋ-bā)	202	41.12 N	114.50 E
Zhanggezhuang, China (jäŋ-gŭ-jůäŋ)	202a	40.09 N	116.56 E
Zhang Guangcai Ling (Mts.), China (jäŋ-gůäŋ-tsī lĭŋ)	202	43.50 N	127.55 E
Zhangjiakou, (Kalgan), China (jän-jyä-kō)	202	40.45 N	114.58 E
Zhangqiu, China (jäŋ-chyô)	200	36.50 N	117.29 E
Zhangwu, China (jäŋ-wōō)	204	42.21 N	123.00 E
Zhangye, China (jäŋ-yu)	198	38.46 N	101.00 E
Zhangzhou, China (jäŋ-jō)	203	24.35 N	117.45 E
Zhangzi Dao (I.), China (jäŋ-dz dou)	200	39.02 N	122.44 E
Zhanhua, China (jän-hwä)	200	37.42 N	117.49 E
Zhanjiang, China (jän-jyäŋ)	203	21.20 N	110.28 E
Zhanyu, China (jän-yōō)	202	44.30 N	122.30 E
Zhao'an, China (jou-än)	203	23.48 N	117.10 E
Zhaodong, China (jou-dôŋ)	202	45.58 N	126.00 E
Zhaotong, China (jou-tôŋ)	203	27.18 N	103.50 E
Zhaoxian, China (jou shyĕn)	200	37.46 N	114.48 E
Zhaoyuan, China (jou-yuän)	200	37.22 N	120.23 E
Zhdanov, Sov. Un. (zhdä'nôf)	175	47.07 N	37.32 E
Zhecheng, China (jŭ-chŭŋ)	200	34.05 N	115.19 E
Zhegao, China (jŭ-gou)	200	31.47 N	117.44 E
Zhejiang (Prov.), China (jŭ-jyäŋ)	199	29.30 N	120.00 E
Zhelaniya, Mys (C.), Sov. Un. (zhĕ'lä-nĭ-yá)	180	75.43 N	69.10 E
Zhengding, China (jŭŋ-dĭŋ)	200	38.10 N	114.35 E
Zhen'guosi, China	67b	39.51 N	116.21 E
Zhengyang, China (jŭŋ-yäŋ)	200	32.34 N	114.22 E
Zhengzhou, China (jŭŋ-jō)	200	34.46 N	113.42 E
Zhenjiang, China (jŭn-jyäŋ)	200	32.13 N	119.24 E
Zhenru, China	68a	31.15 N	121.24 E
Zhenyuan, China (jŭn-yůän)	203	27.08 N	108.30 E
Zhigalovo, Sov. Un. (zhē-gä'lô-vô)	181	54.52 N	105.05 E
Zhigansk, Sov. Un. (zhē-gánsk')	181	66.45 N	123.20 E
Zhijiang, China (jr-jyäŋ)	203	27.25 N	109.45 E
Zhitomir, Sov. Un. (zhē'tô'mĕr)	175	50.15 N	28.40 E
Zhitomir (Oblast), Sov. Un.	175	50.40 N	28.07 E
Zhizdra, Sov. Un. (zhēz'drá)	174	53.47 N	34.41 E
Zhizhitskoye (L.), Sov. Un. (zhē-zhēt'skô-yĕ)	174	56.08 N	31.34 E
Zhmerinka, Sov. Un. (zhemyĕ'rĕŋ-ká)	175	49.02 N	28.09 E
Zhongshan Park (P. Int.), China	68a	31.13 N	121.25 E
Zhongwei, China (jôŋ-wā)	202	37.32 N	105.10 E
Zhongxian, China (jôŋ shyĕn)	203	30.20 N	108.00 E
Zhongxin, China (jôŋ-shyĭn)	201a	23.16 N	113.38 E
Zhoucun, China (jō-tsōōn)	200	36.49 N	117.52 E
Zhoukouzhen, China (jō-kō-jŭn)	200	33.39 N	114.40 E
Zhoupu, China (jō-pōō)	201b	31.07 N	121.33 E
Zhoushan Qundao (Is.), China (jō-shän-chyōōn-dou)	203	30.00 N	123.00 E
Zhouxian, China (jō shyĕn)	200	39.30 N	115.59 E
Zhu (R.), China (jōō)	201a	23.48 N	113.36 E
Zhuanghe, China (jůäŋ-hŭ)	202	39.40 N	123.00 E
Zhuanqiao, China (jůäŋ-chyou)	201b	31.02 N	121.24 E
Zhucheng, China (jōō-chŭŋ)	200	36.01 N	119.24 E
Zhuji, China (jōō-jyē)	203	29.58 N	120.10 E
Zhujiang Kou (Can.), China (jōō-jyäŋ kō)	203	22.00 N	114.00 E
Zhukovskiy, Sov. Un. (zhōō-kôf'skĭ)	182b	55.33 N	38.09 E
Zi (R.), China (dzē)	203	26.50 N	111.00 E
Zibo, China (dzē-bwo)	200	36.48 N	118.04 E
Ziel, Mt., Austl. (zēl)	214	23.15 S	132.45 E
Zielona Góra, Pol. (zhyĕ-lô'nä gōō'rä)	166	51.56 N	15.30 E
Zigazinskiy, Sov. Un. (zĭ-gazinskēē)	182a	53.50 N	57.18 E
Ziguinchor, Senegal	228	12.35 N	16.16 W
Zilair, Sov. Un. (zē'lá-ĭr)	182a	52.12 N	57.23 E
Zile, Tur. (zē-lĕ')	179	40.20 N	35.50 E
Žilina, Czech. (zhē'lĭ-nä)	167	49.14 N	18.45 E
Zillah, Libya	225	28.26 N	17.52 E
Zima, Sov. Un. (zē'má)	180	53.58 N	102.08 E
Zimapan, Mex. (sē-mä'pän)	130	20.43 N	99.23 W
Zimatlán de Alvarez, Mex. (sē-mä-tlän' dā äl'vä-rāz)	131	16.52 N	96.47 W
Zimba, Zambia	231	17.19 S	26.13 E
Zimbabwe (Rhodesia), Afr. (rô-dē'zhĭ-á)	222	17.50 S	29.30 E
Zimnicea, Rom. (zēm-nē'chá)	173	43.39 N	25.22 E
Zin (R.), Isr.	191a	30.50 N	35.12 E
Zinacatepec, Mex. (zē-nä-kä-tē'pĕk)	131	18.19 N	97.15 W
Zinapécuaro, Mex. (sē-nä-pā'kwá-rô)	130	19.50 N	100.49 W
Zinder, Niger (zĭn'dĕr)	229	13.48 N	8.59 E
Zion, Il. (zī'ŭn)	113a	42.27 N	87.50 W
Zion Natl. Park, Ut.	121	37.20 N	113.00 W
Zionsville, In. (zīŭnz-vĭl)	113g	39.57 N	86.15 W
Zionz L., Can. (zī'ŏnz)	101	51.25 N	91.52 W
Zipaquirá, Col. (sē-pä-kē-rä')	142a	5.01 N	74.01 W
Zirandaro, Mex. (sē-rän-dä'rō)	130	18.28 N	101.02 W
Zitacuaro, Mex. (sē-tá-kwä'rō)	130	19.25 N	100.22 W
Zitlala, Mex. (sē-tlä'lä)	130	17.38 N	99.09 W
Zittau, G.D.R. (tsē'tou)	166	50.55 N	14.48 E
Ziway (L.), Eth.	225	8.08 N	39.11 E
Ziya (R.), China (dzē-yä)	200	38.38 N	116.31 E
Zlatograd, Bul.	173	41.24 N	25.05 E
Zlatoust, Sov. Un. (zlá-tô-ōōst')	182a	55.13 N	59.39 E
Zlītan, Libya	225	32.27 N	14.33 E
Zloczew, Pol. (zwô'chĕf)	167	51.23 N	18.34 E
Zlynka, Sov. Un. (zlĕŋ'ká)	174	52.28 N	31.39 E
Znamenka, Sov. Un. (znä'mĕn-kä)	175	48.43 N	32.35 E
Znamensk, Sov. Un. (znä'mĕnsk)	165	54.39 N	21.49 E
Znojmo, Czech. (znoi'mô)	166	48.52 N	16.03 E
Zoetermeer, Neth.	157a	52.08 N	4.29 E
Zoeterwoude, Neth.	157a	52.08 N	4.29 E
Zográfos, Grc.	66d	37.59 N	23.46 E
Zolochĕv, Sov. Un. (zô'lô-chĕf)	159	49.48 N	24.55 E
Zolotonosha, Sov. Un. (zô'lô-tô-nô'shá)	175	49.41 N	32.03 E
Zolotoy, Mys (C.), Sov. Un. (mĭs zô-lô-tôy')	204	47.24 N	139.10 E
Zomba, Malawi (zôm'bá)	221	15.23 S	35.18 E
Zongo, Zaire (zôŋ'gō)	225	4.19 N	18.36 E
Zonguldak, Tur. (zôn'gōōl'dák)	179	41.25 N	31.50 E
Zonhoven, Bel.	157a	50.59 N	5.24 E
Zoquitlán, Mex. (sô-kēt-län')	131	18.09 N	97.02 W
Zorita, Sp. (thō-rē'tä)	170	39.18 N	5.41 W
Zossen, G.D.R. (tsō'sĕn)	157b	52.13 N	13.27 E
Zouar, Chad	194	20.27 N	16.32 E
Zouxian, China (dzō shyĕn)	200	35.24 N	116.54 E

ăt; finăl; rāte; senåte; ärm; ásk; sofá; fâre; ch-choose; dh-as th in other; bē; ē̇vent; bĕt; recĕnt; cratēr; g-gō; gh-guttural g; bĭt; ĭ-short neutral; rīde; к-guttural k as ch in German ich;

PLACE (Pronounciation)	PAGE	Lat. °'	Long. °'	PLACE (Pronounciation)	PAGE	Lat. °'	Long. °'	PLACE (Pronounciation)	PAGE	Lat. °'	Long. °'
Zubtsov, Sov. Un. (zoōp-tsôf')	174	56.13 N	34.34 E	Zumbrota, Mn. (zŭm-brō'tá)	115	44.16 N	92.39 W	Zuwayzā, Jordan	191a	31.42 N	35.58 E
Zuera, Sp. (thwā'rä)	171	41.40 N	0.48 W	Zumpango, Mex. (soōm-päŋ-gō)	130	19.48 N	99.06 W	Zvenigorod, Sov. Un. (zvä-nĕ'gô-rôt)	174	55.46 N	36.54 E
Zuger See (L.), Switz. (tsoōg)	166	47.10 N	8.40 E	Zundert, Neth.	157a	51.28 N	4.39 E	Zvenigorodka, Sov. Un.			
Zugló (Neigh.), Hung.	66g	47.31 N	19.08 E	Zungeru, Nig. (zoōŋ-gä'roō)	229	9.48 N	6.09 E	(zvä-nĕ'gô-rôt'kä)	175	49.07 N	30.59 E
Zugspitze Pk., Aus.-F.R.G.	166	47.25 N	11.00 E	Zunhua, China (dzoōn-hwä)	200	40.12 N	117.55 E	Zvolen, Czech. (zvô'lĕn)	167	48.35 N	19.10 E
Zuidelijk Flevoland (Reg.), Neth.	157a	52.22 N	5.20 E	Zuni (R.), Az.-NM	121	34.40 N	109.30 W	Zvornik, Yugo. (zvôr'nĕk)	173	44.24 N	19.08 E
Zuishavane, Zimb.	226	20.15 S	30.28 E	Zuni Ind. Res., NM (zoō'nĕ)	121	35.10 N	108.40 W	Zweckel (Neigh.), F.R.G.	63	51.36 N	6.59 E
Zújar (R.), Sp. (zoō'ĸär)	170	38.55 N	5.05 W	Zuni Mts., NM	121	35.10 N	108.10 W	Zweibrücken, F.R.G. (tsvī-brük'ĕn)	166	49.16 N	7.20 E
Zújar, Embalse del (Res.), Sp.	170	38.50 N	5.20 W	Zunyi, China	198	27.58 N	106.40 E	Zwickau, G.D.R. (tsvīk'ou)	166	50.43 N	12.30 E
Zulueta, Cuba (zoō-loō-ĕ'tä)	134	22.20 N	79.35 W	Zürich, Switz. (tsü'rĭk)	166	47.22 N	8.32 E	Zwolle, Neth. (zvôl'ĕ)	163	52.33 N	6.05 E
Zululand (Reg.), S. Afr.				Zürichsee (L.), Switz.	166	47.18 N	8.47 E	Zyradow, Pol. (zhĕ-rär'doōf)	167	52.04 N	20.28 E
(zoō'loō-lånd)	226	27.45 S	31.29 E	Zushi, Jap. (zoō'shĕ)	205a	35.17 N	139.35 E	Zyryanka, Sov. Un. (zĕ-ryän'kä)	181	65.45 N	151.15 E
Zumbo, Moz. (zoōm'boō)	231	15.36 S	30.25 E	Zuurbekom, S. Afr.	71b	26.19 S	27.49 E	Zyryanovsk, Sov. Un. (zĕ-ryä'nôfsk)	180	49.43 N	83.52 E
Zumbro (R.), Mn. (zŭm'brō)	115	44.18 N	92.14 W	Zuwārah, Libya	225	32.58 N	12.07 E				

ng-sing; nŋ-banŋk; N-nasalized n;   nŏd; cŏmmit; ōld; ôbey; ôrder; oi-boil; foōd; foŏt; ou-out;   s-soft; sh-dish;   th-thin;   pūre; ůnite; ûrn; stŭd; circŭs; ü-as in French tu;   '-indeterminate vowel.